SI Units, Useful Data, and Unit Conversion Factors

The seven base SI units

Unit	Abbreviation	Physical quantity
meter	m	length
kilogram	kg	mass
second	s	time
ampere	A	electric current
kelvin	K	thermodynamic temperature
mole	mol	amount of substance
candela	cd	luminous intensity

Some derived SI units

Unit	Abbreviation	Physical quantity	In terms of base units
newton	N	force	$kg \cdot m/s^2$
joule	J	energy	$kg \cdot m^2/s^2$
watt	W	power	$kg \cdot m^2/s^3$
pascal	Pa	pressure	$kg/m \cdot s^2$
hertz	Hz	frequency	s^{-1}
coulomb	C	electric charge	$A \cdot s$
volt	V	electric potential	$kg \cdot m^2/(A \cdot s^3)$
ohm	Ω	electric resistance	$kg \cdot m^2/(A^2 \cdot s^3)$
farad	F	capacitance	$A^2 \cdot s^4/(kg \cdot m^2)$
tesla	T	magnetic field	$kg/(A \cdot s^2)$
weber	Wb	magnetic flux	$kg \cdot m^2/(A \cdot s^2)$
henry	H	inductance	$kg \cdot m^2/(A^2 \cdot s^2)$

SI Prefixes

10^n	Prefix	Abbreviation	10^n	Prefix	Abbreviation
10^0	—	—			
10^3	kilo-	k	10^{-3}	milli-	m
10^6	mega-	M	10^{-6}	micro-	μ
10^9	giga-	G	10^{-9}	nano-	n
10^{12}	tera-	T	10^{-12}	pico-	p
10^{15}	peta-	P	10^{-15}	femto-	f
10^{18}	exa-	E	10^{-18}	atto-	a
10^{21}	zetta-	Z	10^{-21}	zepto-	z
10^{24}	yotta-	Y	10^{-24}	yocto-	y

Values of fundamental constants

Quantity	Symbol	Value
Speed of light in vacuum	c_0	3.00×10^8 m/s
Gravitational constant	G	6.6738×10^{-11} N · m²/kg²
Avogadro's number	N_A	6.0221413×10^{23}
Boltzmann's constant	k_B	1.381×10^{-23} J/K
Charge on electron	e	1.60×10^{-19} C
Electric constant	ϵ_0	$8.85418782 \times 10^{-12}$ $C^2/(N \cdot m^2)$
Magnetic constant	μ_0	$4\pi \times 10^{-7}$ T · m/A
Planck's constant	h	6.626×10^{-34} J · s
Electron mass	m_e	9.11×10^{-31} kg
Proton mass	m_p	1.6726×10^{-27} kg
Neutron mass	m_n	1.6749×10^{-27} kg
Atomic mass unit	amu	1.6605×10^{-27} kg

Other useful numbers

Number or quantity	Value
π	3.1415927
e	2.7182818
1 radian	57.2957795°
Absolute zero ($T = 0$)	−273.15 °C
Average acceleration g due to gravity near Earth's surface	9.8 m/s²
Speed of sound in air at 20 °C	343 m/s
Density of dry air at atmospheric pressure and 20 °C	1.29 kg/m³
Earth's mass	5.97×10^{24} kg
Earth's radius (mean)	6.38×10^6 m
Earth–Moon distance (mean)	3.84×10^8 m

PRINCIPLES & PRACTICE OF PHYSICS

Eric Mazur
Harvard University

and **Daryl Pedigo**
University of Washington

Additional contributions from

Peter A. Dourmashkin
Massachusetts Institute of Technology

Ronald J. Bieniek
Marshall University

PEARSON

Boston Columbus Indianapolis New York San Francisco Hoboken
Amsterdam Cape Town Dubai London Madrid Milan Munich Paris Montréal Toronto
Delhi Mexico City São Paulo Sydney Hong Kong Seoul Singapore Taipei Tokyo

Executive Editor: Becky Ruden
Publisher: Jim Smith
Project Managers: Beth Collins and Martha Steele
Program Manager: Katie Conley
Managing Development Editor: Cathy Murphy
Senior Development Editor: Margot Otway
Development Editor: Irene Nunes
Editorial Assistant: Sarah Kaubisch
Text Permissions Project Manager: Liz Kincaid
Text Permissions Specialist: Paul Sarkis
Associate Content Producer: Megan Power
Production Management: Rose Kernan
Copyeditor: Carol Reitz
Compositor: Cenveo® Publisher Services
Design Manager: Mark Ong
Interior Designer: Hespenheide Design
Cover Designer: Tandem Creative, Inc.
Illustrators: Rolin Graphics
Photo Permissions Management: Maya Melenchuk
Photo Researcher: Eric Schrader
Manufacturing Buyer: Jeff Sargent
Vice-President of Marketing: Christy Lesko
Marketing Manager: Will Moore
Senior Marketing Development Manager: Michelle Cadden

Cover Photo Credit: Franklin Kappa

Credits and acknowledgments borrowed from other sources and reproduced, with permission, in this textbook appear on the appropriate page within the text or on p. C-1.

Library of Congress Cataloging-in-Publication Data on file.

ISBN 10: 0-321-95777-6; ISBN 13: 978-0-321-95777-1 (Student edition)
ISBN 10: 0-321-95835-7; ISBN 13: 978-0-321-95835-8 (Books a la carte)

2 3 4 5 6 7 8 9 10—DOW—18 17 16 15 14

PEARSON

www.pearsonhighered.com

Brief Contents

Getting the Most Out of *Practice*

The ideas of physics explain phenomena all around you—from static electricity in your laundry to how your smartphone knows your location. Some of these principles are straightforward, while others are not immediately obvious. Understanding physics requires not only understanding the concepts but also being able to *apply* these concepts to new situations. Transferring your knowledge to new situations requires advanced reasoning skills, such as judging which concepts are relevant to the problem at hand and then devising a plan to solve the problem. The *Practice* text puts the ideas you learned in the *Principles* text into practice. It teaches you how to make quantitative assumptions and use reason and strategy to solve problems. After you have read your assigned chapter in the *Principles* text, then turn to the corresponding chapter in your *Practice* text and work your way through the chapter.

Here's how the various parts of each chapter will help you become a competent problem solver:

Begin with the **Chapter Summary,** which highlights the major relationships covered in the chapter. Use it to refresh your understanding before you do your homework or as a quick study tool before class.

The **Review Questions** are designed to make sure you understand the primary points of each section. The answers to these questions are on the last page of the chapter. If you have difficulty answering the Review Questions, go back and re-read the appropriate *Principles* section.

You cannot determine whether the answer you obtain for a problem is reasonable if you have no idea what constitutes a reasonable magnitude for the answer. The **Developing a Feel** exercises help you develop both order-of-magnitude estimation skills as well as a "gut feeling" for the range of values appropriate for the physical quantities introduced in each chapter.

A series of **Worked Problems** provide detailed examples of how to approach, solve, and evaluate problems. Each Worked Problem is followed by a related **Guided Problem,** which guides you to solve a similar problem by yourself. The answers to the Guided Problems are on the last page of the chapter.

The **Questions and Problems** are designed as homework or review for examinations. They are provided in a range of difficulty levels, some with more conceptual emphasis and some with more quantitative emphasis.

Together, the *Principles & Practice of Physics* combine to create a learning tool that was developed with you, the student, at the center. We have worked hard to create accurate, physically plausible scenarios that will help you develop the type of problem-solving skills that will serve you not only in your physics course but also in your future career.

Eric Mazur
Harvard University

Daryl Pedigo
University of Washington

1 PRACTICE Foundations

Organization of this book

The material for this course is presented in two volumes. The first volume (*Principles*) is aimed at guiding you in developing a solid understanding of the principles of physics. The second volume (the one you are reading now, *Practice*) provides a variety of questions and problems that allow you to apply and sharpen your understanding of physics.

Each chapter in the *Practice* volume contains specific aids and exercises targeted to the physics discussed in the corresponding *Principles* chapter. These categories are ordered so that the earlier materials support the later ones:

1. **Chapter summary.** The summary is just what the name implies, a condensed record of the key elements from the corresponding *Principles* chapter.
2. **Review questions.** A set of simple questions probes your understanding of the basic material. You should be able to answer these questions without trouble after having read the corresponding *Principles* chapter.
3. **Developing a feel.** These estimation problems are designed to exercise your ability to grasp the scope of the world around you, following the approach outlined in the section of the same title in the *Principles* volume.
4. **Worked and guided problems.** This section presents a series of paired example problems: a worked example followed by a similar problem presented with only a few guiding hints and questions. The idea is that if you understand the methods of the worked example, then you should be able to adapt those methods (and perhaps add a twist) to solve the guided problem. At the beginning of this section you will find a copy of any **Procedure boxes** from the *Principles* volume.
5. **Questions and problems.** After working your way to this point, you should be ready to solve some problems on your own. These problems are both conceptual and quantitative, organized by chapter section and labeled with a rough "degree of difficulty" scale, indicated by one, two, or three blue dots. One-dot problems are fairly straightforward and usually involve only one major concept. Two-dot problems typically require you to put together two or more ideas from the chapter, or even to combine some element of the current chapter with material from other chapters. Three-dot problems are more challenging, or even a bit tricky. Some of these are designated as "CR" (context-rich), a category that is described later in this chapter of the *Practice* volume. Context-rich problems are in the **Additional Problems** at the end of this section, together with other general problems.
6. **Answers and solutions** to Review Questions and Guided Problems are at the end of the chapter.

Chapter Summary

The scientific method (Section 1.1)

Concepts The **scientific method** is an iterative process for going from observations to a hypothesis to an experimentally validated theory. If the predictions made by a hypothesis prove accurate after repeated experimental tests, the hypothesis is called a **theory** or a **law,** but it always remains subject to additional experimental testing.

Quantitative tools

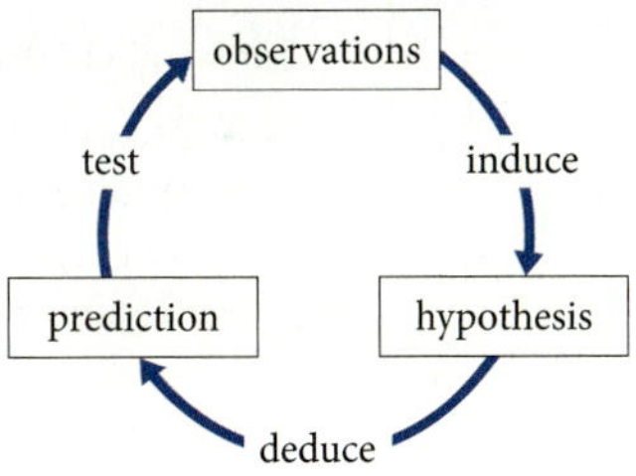

Symmetry (Section 1.2)

Concepts An object exhibits **symmetry** when certain operations can be performed on it without changing its appearance. Important examples are *translational symmetry* (movement from one location to another), *rotational symmetry* (rotation about a fixed axis), and *reflection symmetry* (reflection in a mirror). The concept of symmetry applies both to objects and to physical laws.

Some basic physical quantities and their units (Sections 1.3, 1.4, 1.6)

Concepts **Length** is a distance or extent in space. The SI (International System) base unit of length is the **meter** (m).

Time is a property that allows us to determine the sequence in which related events occur. The SI base unit of time is the **second** (s). The **principle of causality** says that whenever event A causes an event B, all observers see event A happen before event B.

Density is a measure of how much of some substance there is in a given volume.

Quantitative Tools If there are N objects in a volume V, then the *number density* n of these objects is

$$n \equiv \frac{N}{V}. \tag{1.3}$$

If an object of mass m occupies a volume V, then the *mass density* ρ of this object is

$$\rho \equiv \frac{m}{V}. \tag{1.4}$$

To convert one unit to an equivalent unit, multiply the quantity whose unit you want to convert by one or more appropriate *conversion factors.* Each conversion factor must equal one, and any combination of conversion factors used must cancel the original unit and replace it with the desired unit. For example, converting 2.0 hours to seconds, we have

$$2.0\,\cancel{\text{h}} \times \frac{60\,\cancel{\text{min}}}{1\,\cancel{\text{h}}} \times \frac{60\text{ s}}{1\,\cancel{\text{min}}} = 7.2 \times 10^3\text{ s.}$$

Representations (Section 1.5)

Concepts Physicists use many types of representations in making models and solving problems. Rough sketches and detailed diagrams are generally useful, and often crucial, to this process. Graphs are useful for visualizing relationships between physical quantities. Mathematical expressions represent models and problems concisely and permit the use of mathematical techniques.

Quantitative Tools As you construct a model, begin with a simple visual representation (example: represent a cow with a dot) and add details as needed to represent additional features that prove important.

Significant digits (Section 1.7)

Concepts The **significant digits** in a number are the digits that are reliably known.

Quantitative Tools If a number contains no zeros, then all the digits shown are significant: 345 has three significant digits; 6783 has four significant digits.

For numbers that contain zeros:

- Zeros between two nonzero digits are significant: 4.03 has three significant digits.
- Trailing digits to the right of the decimal point are significant: 4.9000 has five significant digits.
- Leading zeros before the first nonzero digit are not significant: 0.000 175 has three significant digits.
- In this book, trailing zeros in numbers without a decimal point are significant: 8500 has four significant digits.

The number of significant digits in a product or quotient is the same as the number of significant digits in the input quantity that has the *fewest significant digits:* $0.10 \times 3.215 = 0.32$.

The number of decimal places in a sum or difference is the same as the number of decimal places in the input quantity that has the *fewest decimal places:* $3.1 + 0.32 = 3.4$.

Solving problems and developing a feel (Sections 1.8, 1.9)

Concepts **Strategy for solving problems:**

1. **Getting started.** Analyze and organize the information and determine what is being asked of you. A sketch or table is often helpful. Decide which physics concepts apply.
2. **Devise plan.** Determine the physical relationships and equations necessary to solve the problem. Then outline the steps you think will lead to the solution.
3. **Execute plan.** Carry out the calculations, and then check your work using the following points:
   Vectors/scalars used correctly?
   Every question answered?
   No unknown quantities in answers?
   Units correct?
   Significant digits justified?
4. **Evaluate result.** Determine whether or not the answer is reasonable.

To develop a feel for the approximate size of a calculated quantity, make an **order-of-magnitude** estimate, which means a calculation rounded to the nearest power of ten.

Quantitative Tools Determining order of magnitude

Example 1:

4200 is 4.200×10^3.

Round the coefficient 4.200 to 10 (because it is greater than 3), so that 4.200×10^3 becomes $10 \times 10^3 = 1 \times 10^4$.

The order of magnitude is 10^4.

Example 2:

0.027 is 2.7×10^{-2}.

Round the coefficient 2.7 to 1 (because it is less than 3), so that 2.7×10^{-2} becomes 1×10^{-2}.

The order of magnitude is 10^{-2}.

Strategy to compute order-of-magnitude estimates:

- Simplify the problem.
- Break it into smaller parts that are easier to estimate.
- Build your estimate from quantities that you know or can easily obtain.

Review Questions

Answers to these questions can be found at the end of this chapter.

1.1 The scientific method

1. What is a common definition of *physics*? That is, what is physics about?
2. Briefly describe the scientific method and what it involves.
3. Name some skills that are useful in doing science.
4. Describe the difference between the two types of reasoning involved in doing science.

1.2 Symmetry

5. What does symmetry mean in physics?
6. What are two types of symmetry that are demonstrated in the reproducibility of experimental results?

1.3 Matter and the universe

7. In physics, what is the definition of *universe*?
8. What does expressing a value to an order of magnitude mean? Why would we express values in this way?
9. To what order of magnitude should you round the numbers 2900 and 3100? Explain why your answers are different for the two numbers.
10. Physicists study phenomena that extend over what range of sizes? Over what range of time intervals?

1.4 Time and change

11. What does the phrase *arrow of time* mean?
12. What principle that relates events depends on the arrow of time? State this principle, and briefly explain what it means.

1.5 Representations

13. When solving physics problems, what are the advantages of making simplified visual representations of the situations?
14. What is the purpose of the *Concepts* part of each chapter in the *Principles* volume of this book? What is the purpose of the *Quantitative Tools* part of each *Principles* chapter?

1.6 Physical quantities and units

15. What two pieces of information are necessary to express any physical quantity?
16. What are the seven SI base units and the physical quantities they represent?
17. What concept does density represent?
18. What is the simplest way to convert a quantity given in one unit to the same quantity given in a different unit?

1.7 Significant digits

19. Explain the difference between number of digits, number of decimal places, and number of significant digits in a numerical value. Illustrate your explanation using the number 0.037 20.
20. What is the difference between leading zeros and trailing zeros? Which ones are considered significant digits?
21. How many significant digits are appropriate in expressing the result of a multiplication or division?
22. How many significant digits are appropriate in expressing the result of an addition or subtraction?

1.8 Solving problems

23. Summarize the four-stage problem-solving procedure used in this book.
24. When checking calculations, what do the letters in the acronym VENUS stand for?

1.9 Developing a feel

25. What are the benefits of making order-of-magnitude estimates?

Developing a Feel

Make an order-of-magnitude estimate of each of the following quantities. Letters in parentheses refer to hints below. Use them as needed to guide your thinking.

(You determine the order of magnitude of any quantity by writing it in scientific notation and rounding the coefficient in front of the power of ten to 1 if it is equal to or less than 3 or to 10 if it is greater than 3. Then write the answer as a power of ten without a coefficient in front. Also remember to express your answer in SI units.)

1. The width of your index finger (C, H)
2. The length of a commercial airliner (E, A)
3. The height of a stack containing 1,000,000 one-dollar bills (G, M)
4. The area of your bedroom floor (J, X)
5. The number of jelly beans needed to fill a 1-gallon jar (F, L)
6. The mass of the air in a typical one-family house (J, D, N)
7. The mass of water needed to fill the passenger compartment of a midsize car (P, I)
8. The mass of a mountain (K, V, S, P)
9. The mass of water in a city swimming pool (T, P)
10. The number of cups of coffee consumed yearly in the United States (R, W)
11. The number of people in the world who are eating at the instant you are reading this question (Q, Z)
12. The number of automobile mechanics in California (B, U, O, Y)

Hints

A. What is the distance between rows?
B. What is the population of California?
C. What is the width of a finger in inches?
D. How many bedroom-size rooms are there in a typical one-family house?
E. How many rows of seats are there in an airliner?
F. What are the dimensions of a jelly bean?
G. How thick is a ream of paper?
H. How many inches make 1 meter?
I. What are the length, width, and height of a car's passenger compartment in meters?
J. What are the length, width, and height of your bedroom in feet?
K. What size and shape could model a mountain?
L. What is the volume of a gallon jar in SI units?
M. How many sheets of paper are there in a ream?
N. What is the mass density of air?
O. How many hours of maintenance does a car need each year?
P. What is the mass density of water?
Q. What is the population of the world?
R. What is the adult population of the United States?
S. How does the mass density of rock compare with that of water?
T. What are the dimensions of a city pool?
U. How many cars are there in California?
V. What volume results from your model?
W. How many cups of coffee does the average American drink daily?
X. How many square feet are there in 1 square meter?
Y. How many hours does an automobile mechanic work each year?
Z. What fraction of your day do you spend eating?

Key (all values approximate)

A. 1 m; **B.** 4×10^7 people; **C.** 0.5 in.; **D.** 8 rooms; **E.** 4×10^1 rows; **F.** $(1 \times 10^{-2}\ \text{m}) \times (1 \times 10^{-2}\ \text{m}) \times (2 \times 10^{-2}\ \text{m})$; **G.** 5×10^{-2} m; **H.** 4×10^1 in./m; **I.** 2 m × 2 m × 1 m; **J.** $(1 \times 10^1\ \text{ft}) \times (2 \times 10^1\ \text{ft}) \times (1 \times 10^1\ \text{ft})$; **K.** a cone 1 mile high with a 1-mile base radius; **L.** 4 quarts $\approx$ 4 L $= 4 \times 10^{-3}\ \text{m}^3$; **M.** 5×10^2 sheets; **N.** $1\ \text{kg/m}^3$; **O.** 6 h; **P.** $1 \times 10^3\ \text{kg/m}^3$; **Q.** 7×10^9 people; **R.** 2×10^8 people; **S.** 5 × larger; **T.** $(7\ \text{m}) \times (2 \times 10^1\ \text{m}) \times (2\ \text{m})$; **U.** 3×10^7 cars; **V.** $4 \times 10^9\ \text{m}^3$; **W.** 1 cup; **X.** $1 \times 10^1\ \text{ft}^2/\text{m}^2$; **Y.** 2×10^3 h; **Z.** 0.1

PRACTICE

Worked and Guided Problems

Procedure: Solving Problems

Although there is no set approach when solving problems, it helps to break things down into several steps whenever you are working a physics problem. Throughout this book, we use the four-step procedure summarized here to solve problems. For a more detailed description of each step, see *Principles* Section 1.8.

1. **Getting started.** Begin by carefully analyzing the information given and determining in your own words what question or task is being asked of you. Organize the information by making a sketch of the situation or putting data in tabular form. Determine which physics concepts apply, and note any assumptions you are making.
2. **Devise plan.** Decide what you must do to solve the problem. First determine which physical relationships or equations you need, and then determine the order in which you will use them. Make sure you have a sufficient number of equations to solve for all unknowns.
3. **Execute plan.** Execute your plan, and then check your work for the following five important points:

   Vectors/scalars used correctly?
   Every question asked in problem statement answered?
   No unknown quantities in answers?
   Units correct?
   Significant digits justified?

   As a reminder to yourself, put a checkmark beside each answer to indicate that you checked these five points.
4. **Evaluate result.** There are several ways to check whether an answer is reasonable. One way is to make sure your answer conforms to what you expect based on your sketch and the information given. If your answer is an algebraic expression, check to be sure the expression gives the correct trend or answer for special (limiting) cases for which you already know the answer. Sometimes there may be an alternative approach to solving the problem; if so, use it to see whether or not you get the same answer. If any of these tests yields an unexpected result, go back and check your math and any assumptions you made. If none of these checks can be applied to your problem, check the algebraic signs and order of magnitude.

These examples involve material from this chapter but are not associated with any particular section. Some examples are worked out in detail; others you should work out by following the guidelines provided.

Worked Problem 1.1 Solar hydrogen

The mass of the Sun is 1.99×10^{30} kg, its radius is 6.96×10^{8} m, and its composition by mass is 71.0% hydrogen (H). The mass of a hydrogen atom is 1.67×10^{-27} kg. Calculate (*a*) the average mass density and (*b*) the average number density of the hydrogen atoms in the Sun.

❶ GETTING STARTED To calculate mass and number densities we need to determine the volume of the Sun. We assume the Sun is perfectly spherical so that we have a formula for its volume. We are given the mass of the Sun and the percentage of hydrogen, so we can determine the mass of hydrogen in the Sun and the number of atoms required to provide this mass.

❷ DEVISE PLAN Mass density is mass per unit volume, $\rho = m/V$, and number density is number per unit volume, $n = N/V$. The (assumed spherical) solar volume is $V = \frac{4}{3}\pi R^3$. The solar radius is given, so we need either the number of hydrogen atoms or the mass of hydrogen in the Sun in order to proceed. The mass of hydrogen is 71.0% of the Sun's mass, so we use that value to compute the mass density first. Then the number N of hydrogen atoms is the mass of all the hydrogen atoms divided by the mass of a single atom. We can use this number to calculate the number density n, or we can simply note that n is equal to the mass density of hydrogen divided by the mass of a single hydrogen atom.

❸ EXECUTE PLAN
(*a*) For the mass density, we have

$$\rho_{\rm H} = \frac{m_{\rm H}}{\frac{4}{3}\pi R_{\rm Sun}^3} = \frac{0.710 m_{\rm Sun}}{\frac{4}{3}\pi R_{\rm Sun}^3} = \frac{(0.710)(1.99 \times 10^{30}\ {\rm kg})}{\frac{4}{3}\pi(6.96 \times 10^{8}\ {\rm m})^3}$$

$$= 1.00 \times 10^{3}\ {\rm kg/m^3}.$$

(*b*) The number density of the hydrogen atoms is

$$n_{\rm H} = \frac{\rho_{\rm H}}{m_{\rm H\,atom}} = \frac{1.00 \times 10^{3}\ {\rm kg/m^3}}{1.67 \times 10^{-27}\ {\rm kg}} = 5.99 \times 10^{29}\ {\rm atoms/m^3}.$$

Using VENUS to check, we have
Vectors/scalars: all quantities are scalars ✔
Every question answered: mass density, ✔ number density ✔
No unknown quantities in answers: none ✔
Units correct: kg/m^3 for mass density, ✔ atoms/m^3 for number density ✔
Significant digits: three in each answer because all given quantities have three ✔

PRACTICE

❹ **EVALUATE RESULT** We calculated a hydrogen mass density equal to the mass density of water. Because hydrogen is a gas, you may think that this mass density is unreasonably large and that the answer should be about equal to the value found for helium gas in *Principles* Exercise 1.6, about 0.2 kg/m^3. However, because the gas in the Sun is highly compressed, a mass density several orders of magnitude larger is not unreasonable. But this value is the mass density of water! Does that make any sense? Well, water vapor certainly has a much smaller mass and number density than liquid water. If the hydrogen atoms in the Sun were squeezed together as closely as the molecules in liquid water, we might expect their mass density to be of the same order of magnitude. We might also compare our answer to the average mass density of the Sun obtained by using the data provided in the problem statement. Assuming a spherical Sun, we obtain

$$\rho_{\text{Sun}} = \frac{m_{\text{Sun}}}{\frac{4}{3}\pi R_{\text{Sun}}^3} = 1.4 \times 10^3 \text{ kg/m}^3.$$

So it seems reasonable that our hydrogen mass density is of the same order of magnitude as the average mass density.

Our result for the number density is also several orders of magnitude larger than the number density of helium found in *Principles* Exercise 1.6, which is what we might expect for a very dense object like the Sun.

Note: When we are dealing with quantities completely outside our everyday experience, a quick check in a reference book or a couple of independent online sources might be needed to remove any lingering doubts. Doing so, we obtain an average solar mass density consistent with the calculation above.

Guided Problem 1.2 Solar oxygen

Oxygen atoms make up 0.970% of the Sun's mass, and each one has a mass of 2.66×10^{-26} kg. Calculate the average mass density of oxygen in the Sun and the average number density of the oxygen atoms. Use information given in Worked Problem 1.1 as needed.

❶ **GETTING STARTED**

1. How much of the plan of Worked Problem 1.1 can be used?

❷ **DEVISE PLAN**

2. What is the definition of mass density? Number density?
3. Do you have enough information to compute these values?

❸ **EXECUTE PLAN**

4. What is the mass of oxygen in the Sun?
5. How is the number density of oxygen related to its mass density and to the mass of an oxygen atom?

❹ **EVALUATE RESULT**

6. Are your answers consistent with the ones in Worked Problem 1.1?

Worked Problem 1.3 Rod volume

A cylindrical rod is 2.58 m long and has a diameter of 3.24 in. Calculate its volume in cubic meters.

❶ **GETTING STARTED** We know that the volume of a cylinder is length times cross-sectional area. We are given the length, and we can use the diameter value given to calculate area. Because the diameter is in inches, however, we must convert to the SI equivalent.

❷ **DEVISE PLAN** First we convert inches to meters via the conversion factors 25.4 mm = 1 in. (Equation 1.5) and 1 m = 1000 mm. Then we use the SI values for length (ℓ) and area (A) in the formula for volume: $V = A\ell = \pi R^2 \ell$.

❸ **EXECUTE PLAN** In meters, the radius, (3.24 in.)/2, is

$$1.62 \text{ in.} \times \frac{25.4 \text{ mm}}{1 \text{ in.}} \times \frac{1 \text{ m}}{1000 \text{ mm}} = 4.115 \times 10^{-2} \text{ m}.$$

Note: We use four significant digits here. Because the values given all have three significant digits, the final answer must have three also. In intermediate steps, though, we carry an extra digit to avoid accumulating rounding errors.

The volume of the rod is thus

$$V = \pi R^2 \ell = \pi (4.115 \times 10^{-2} \text{ m})^2 (2.58 \text{ m}) = 1.37 \times 10^{-2} \text{ m}^3.$$

Using VENUS to check, we have
Vectors/scalars: all quantities are scalars ✔
Every question answered: volume ✔
No unknown quantities in answer: none ✔
Units correct: cubic meters ✔
Significant digits: three in answer because all given quantities have three ✔

❹ **EVALUATE RESULT** Although this rod is about 2.5 m long, its radius is only 1.62 in., which is about 40 mm, or 0.040 m. We can make an order-of-magnitude estimate for comparison by treating the rod as a rectangular block of square cross section 8 cm on a side, with length 3 m. The result is $(8 \times 10^{-2} \text{ m})(8 \times 10^{-2} \text{ m})(3 \text{ m}) \approx 10^{-2} \text{ m}^3$. Therefore a volume of about 10^{-2} m^3 is reasonable.

Guided Problem 1.4 Box volume

A box measures 1420 mm by 2.75 ft by 87.8 cm. Express its volume in cubic meters.

❶ **GETTING STARTED**

1. Is the approach of Worked Problem 1.3 useful?

❷ **DEVISE PLAN**

2. What is the relationship between the given dimensions and the volume of the box?
3. Which of the given quantities do you need to convert to SI units?
4. Can you use any of the values given in SI units in the form given?

❸ **EXECUTE PLAN**

5. What are your conversion factors?

❹ **EVALUATE RESULT**

Worked Problem 1.5 Working with digits

Express the result of each calculation both to the proper number of significant digits and as an order of magnitude:

(*a*) $(42.003)(1.3 \times 10^4)(0.007\,000)$

(*b*) $(42.003)(13{,}000)(0.007\,000)$

(*c*) $\dfrac{170.08\pi}{32.6}$

(*d*) $113.7540 - 0.08$

❶ GETTING STARTED We have two products, a quotient, and a difference involving quantities that have different numbers of significant digits. The number of significant digits in each answer depends on the number of significant digits in the given values.

❷ DEVISE PLAN To express each answer to the proper number of significant digits, we use the rules given in the *Principles* volume. The number of significant digits in a product or quotient is the same as the number of significant digits in the input quantity that has the *fewest* significant digits. The number of decimal places in a sum or difference is the same as the number of decimal places in the input quantity that has the *fewest* decimal places.

To express our answers as orders of magnitude, we write each in scientific notation, round the coefficient either down to 1 (coefficients ≤ 3) or up to 10 (coefficients > 3), and then write the answer as a power of ten without the coefficient.

❸ EXECUTE PLAN
(*a*) In $(42.003)(1.3 \times 10^4)(0.007000)$, the first factor has five significant digits, the second has two significant digits, and the third has four significant digits. Therefore the product can have only two significant digits: 3.8×10^3. The coefficient 3.8 is greater than 3, and so we round it to 10, making the order-of-magnitude answer $10 \times 10^3 = 10^4$.

(*b*) This time the middle factor has five significant digits, so we adjust our calculation to allow four (due to the third factor) significant digits: 3.822×10^3. Of course, the order of magnitude is unchanged.

(*c*) In $170.08\pi/32.6$, the denominator has three significant digits, the first factor in the numerator has five significant digits, and π (=3.14159. . .) has as many significant digits as our calculator shows. So the result can have only three significant digits: 16.4. To express this value as an order of magnitude, we must write it in scientific notation, 1.64×10^1. Because 1.64 is less than 3, we round it to 1, making the order-of-magnitude answer $1 \times 10^1 = 10^1$.

(*d*) The value that has the fewest decimal places is 0.08, meaning the difference must be reported to two decimal places: 113.67. To express this result as an order of magnitude, we write 1.1367×10^2 and round the 1.1367 down to 1, making the order-of-magnitude answer $1 \times 10^2 = 10^2$.

Checking by VENUS gives
Vectors/scalars: all quantities are scalars ✔
Every question answered: all results reported both to the correct number of significant digits and as an order of magnitude ✔
No unknowns in answers: none ✔
Units correct: no units given ✔
Significant digits: all significant digits are correct ✔

❹ EVALUATE RESULT We can check that each answer has the correct order of magnitude.

(*a*) $(42.003)(1.3 \times 10^4)(0.007\,000)$ is about $40 \times 13{,}000 \times 0.01 = 5200$, order of magnitude $5.2 \times 10^3 \approx 10 \times 10^3 = 10^4$, consistent with our answer.

(*b*) The same result holds.

(*c*) $(200\pi)/30 = 600/30 = 20 = 2.0 \times 10^1 \approx 1 \times 10^1 = 10^1$

(*d*) $100 - 0 = 100 = 10^2$

Guided Problem 1.6 Digits on your own

Express the result of each calculation both to the proper number of significant digits and as an order of magnitude:

(*a*) $(205)(0.0041)(489.623)$

(*b*) $\dfrac{(190.8)(0.407\,500)}{\pi}$

(*c*) $6980.035 + 0.2$

❶ GETTING STARTED
1. Are the techniques of Worked Problem 1.5 useful? Sufficient?

❷ DEVISE PLAN
2. For parts *a* and *b*, how many significant digits does each number contain?
3. For part *c*, which value limits the number of decimal places allowed in the answer?

❸ EXECUTE PLAN
4. How do you convert each answer to an order-of-magnitude number?

❹ EVALUATE RESULT

Worked Problem 1.7 Oceans

Make an order-of-magnitude estimate of the percent of Earth's mass that is contained in the oceans.

❶ GETTING STARTED About 70% of Earth's surface is covered by oceans, but the entire volume of Earth contributes to its mass. To obtain a percentage we need to know the mass of the oceans and the mass of Earth. The latter we might look up or recall, but the former requires a computation based on mass density and volume. We must devise a simple model for the volume of the oceans and perhaps also for Earth.

❷ DEVISE PLAN A spherical Earth coated with a thin shell of water covering 70% of the surface seems a reasonable first try. The volume of the oceans is then 70% of the surface area of this sphere multiplied by the ocean depth. The mass of the oceans then involves the mass density of ocean water, the radius of Earth squared, and the average depth of the oceans. We need to estimate the value of each of these and then divide the mass of the oceans by the mass of Earth in order to obtain the desired percentage. That means we must estimate the mass of Earth, too, and this is also related to the radius of Earth. Some factors may cancel out if we express both masses in terms of mass densities.

❸ **EXECUTE PLAN** The mass of Earth, including oceans, is $m_E = \rho_E V_E = \rho_E(\frac{4}{3}\pi R_E^3)$. The area of the oceans is $0.70A_E$. Assuming the oceans have an average depth d, we can approximate their volume as surface area A_o times depth d: $V_o = A_o d = 0.70A_E d$. Their mass is therefore $m_o = \rho_o V_o = \rho_o(0.70A_E d) = \rho_o(0.70)(4\pi R_E^2)d$. The fraction f of Earth's mass contained in the oceans is

$$f = \frac{m_o}{m_E} = \frac{\rho_o(0.70)(4\pi R_E^2)d}{\rho_E(\frac{4}{3}\pi R_E^3)} = 2.1\frac{d}{R_E}\frac{\rho_o}{\rho_E}.$$

There are still four quantities to estimate, but at least all the squaring and cubing of values are eliminated! The ocean's average depth d is about a mile, or 1.6 km. The radius of Earth is about 4000 mi, or 6400 km. The mass density of the ocean is about the same as that of fresh water. The mass density of Earth's solid surface materials (things like rocks) must be a few times greater than the mass density of water because rocks sink readily. Earth's interior must have a considerably larger mass density than this because gravity compresses matter near the center. So we can estimate that the average mass density of Earth is about five times that of water, and therefore the ratio ρ_o/ρ_E is about $1/5$. This makes the fraction f

$$f = (2.1)\left(\frac{1.6\text{ km}}{6400\text{ km}}\right)\frac{1}{5} = 1.1 \times 10^{-4} \approx 10^{-4}.$$

Therefore about $1/100$ of 1% of Earth's mass is contained in the oceans.

Check by VENUS:

Vectors/scalars: all quantities are scalars ✔
Every question answered: the percent is calculated ✔
No unknowns in answers: all quantities known or estimated ✔
Units correct: the answer has no units, it is a percentage ✔
Significant digits: order-of-magnitude estimate ✔

❹ **EVALUATE RESULT** The depth of the oceans is much less than the radius of Earth, and water is considerably less dense than the solid material of Earth. We therefore should expect the oceans to contain a very small percent of Earth's mass. If you look up the actual value, you find that our estimate is within a factor of 2 or so.

Guided Problem 1.8 Roof area

One suggestion for reducing the use of fossil fuels is to cover the roofs of all buildings in the United States with solar collectors. Make an order-of-magnitude estimate of the combined surface area, in square kilometers, of all these solar collectors.

❶ **GETTING STARTED**

1. What simple shape can you use to approximate the United States?
2. Is it reasonable to assume that buildings are primarily in cities?

❷ **DEVISE PLAN**

3. What is the approximate area of the United States?
4. What percent of that area is occupied by cities?

❸ **EXECUTE PLAN**

❹ **EVALUATE RESULT**

Questions and Problems

For instructor-assigned homework, go to MasteringPhysics® MP

Solving context-rich problems

The problems labeled CR are *context-rich* problems—problems that are more like those in the everyday world. These questions are typically embedded in a short narrative and often do not specify what variables you must calculate to answer the question. So, rather than asking What is the mass of …? (telling you that you must calculate the mass of some object), a context-rich problem may ask Do you accept the bet? (leaving it to you to determine what to calculate). The problem typically contains extraneous information, and you may need to supply some missing information, either by estimation or by looking up values.

Like all problems, context-rich problems should be solved using the four-step procedure outlined in the Procedure box in this chapter. Because context-rich problem statements are never broken down into parts, the first two steps ("Getting started" and "Devise plan") are particularly important.

Context-rich problems will sharpen the skills you need to solve everyday problems, where you need to move toward a goal, but the path you must take is not immediately clear (if it were clear, there wouldn't be a problem). The information available to you may be a bit sketchy or contradictory, there may be more than one way to approach a situation, and some ways may be more fruitful than others, but that may not be clear at the outset. So consider context-rich problems as an opportunity to stretch your problem-solving abilities.

Dots indicate difficulty level of problems: • = *easy,* •• = *intermediate,* ••• = *hard;* CR = *context-rich problem.*

1.1 The scientific method

1. In a discussion of what holds airplanes aloft, a classmate offers this hypothesis: "Airplanes are held up by an undetectable force field produced by magnets." Which word in this statement is most likely to keep the statement from satisfying the criteria for a scientific hypothesis? •
2. An advertisement for a food product states that it contains 50% less fat per serving than a competing product. What assumptions are you making if you accept the claim as valid? •
3. You are asked to predict the next item in the following sequence of integers: 1, 2, 3. If your prediction is 4, what assumptions did you make? ••
4. Checkpoint 1.1 of the *Principles* volume states that two coins together have a value of 30 cents but one of them is not a nickel. If the checkpoint said instead that "neither coin is worth 5 cents," what hidden assumptions might prevent you from obtaining a solution? ••
5. In a 4-by-4 Sudoku puzzle with one 2-by-2 subsquare filled in as shown in Figure P1.5, how many ways are there to complete the puzzle? (In Sudoku, the digits 1, 2, 3, 4 must appear only once in each row and once in each column of the 4-by-4 square and only once in each subsquare.) •••

Figure P1.5

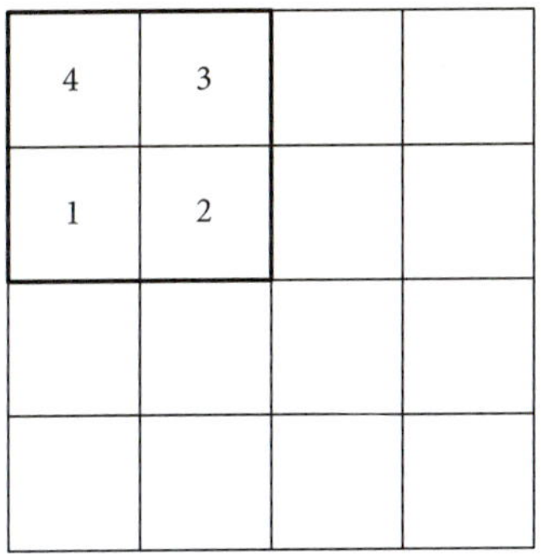

1.2 Symmetry

6. How many axes of reflection symmetry does the triangle in Figure P1.6 have? Restrict your answer to axes that lie in the plane of the triangle. •

Figure P1.6

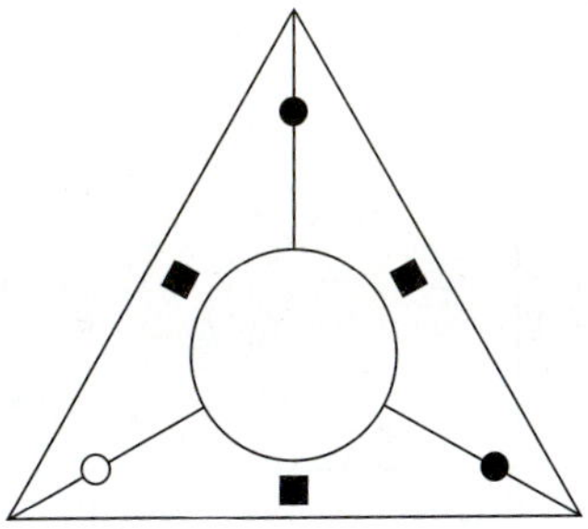

7. How many axes of rotational symmetry does a cone have? •
8. Three identical coins are positioned on a grid as shown in Figure P1.8. Where would you place a fourth coin to form a coin arrangement that has both reflection symmetry and a 90° rotational symmetry? •

Figure P1.8

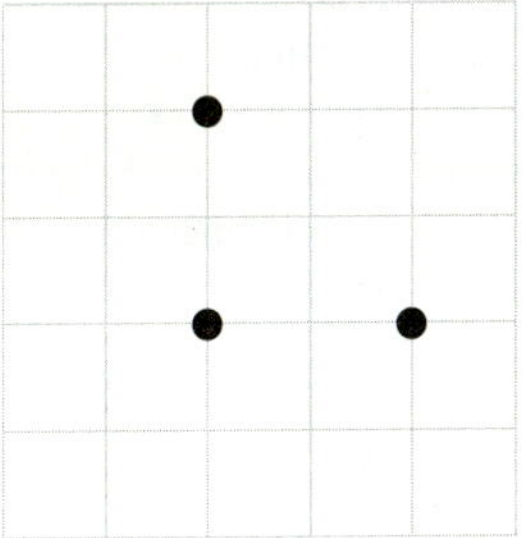

9. Describe the reflection symmetry of each of the letters in the word below: ••

T A B L E S

10. Which types of geometrical symmetry mentioned in the *Principles* volume does a sphere have? ••
11. How many axes of reflection symmetry does a cube have? How many axes of rotational symmetry? ••
12. Suppose you have a square of paper with a single vertical line down the middle and a single horizontal line across the middle. The upper left square is blank. The lower left and upper right squares are blue. The lower right square has a red dot in its center. How many axes of reflection symmetry does the square have? Restrict your answer to axes that lie in the plane of the square. ••
13. A cube is placed on a table with a green side facing up. You know that the side facing down is also green but has a red dot in the middle of the green face. From where you are sitting, you can see that two adjacent vertical sides are one red and the other blue. What is the maximum number of axes of reflection symmetry possible? •••

1.3 Matter and the universe

14. Traveling at 299,792,458 m/s, how far does light travel in 78 years? •
15. The Sun is approximately 93 million miles from Earth. (*a*) What is this distance in millimeters? (*b*) How many Earths could fit side by side in this distance? (See Worked Problem 1.7 for the radius of Earth.) •
16. *Principles* Figure 1.9 tells us that a human contains 10^{29} atoms and a blue whale contains 10^{32} atoms. Use these values to determine the ratio of the length of a blue whale to the height of a human. ••
17. A gastrotrich is a small aquatic organism with a life span of about 3 days, and a giant tortoise has an average life span of 100 years. Make an order-of-magnitude estimate of the number of gastrotrich lifetimes that are equal to one tortoise lifetime. In your calculation, use an order-of-magnitude value for the number of days in 1 year. ••
18. You measure the diameter of a drop of water to be 3 mm. Make an order-of-magnitude estimate of how many such drops are contained in all the water in your body. ••

19. If you could stack copies of your physics textbook until they reached the Moon, what is the order of magnitude of the number of books you would need? ••
20. How many water molecules are there in a swimming pool that is 15 m long, 8.5 m wide, and 1.5 m deep? ••
21. Cube 1 has side ℓ_1 and volume V_1. Cube 2 has side $\ell_2 = 2\ell_1$. (*a*) When making order-of-magnitude estimates, by how many orders of magnitude is the volume of the second cube greater than the volume of the first cube? (*b*) Does the answer depend on the numerical value of ℓ_1? ••
22. Earth requires approximately 365 days to orbit the Sun along a path that can be approximated by a circle with a radius of 1.50×10^8 km. Make an order-of-magnitude estimate of the length of time it would take light to move once around this orbit. ••
23. While admiring a tree, you notice that the leaves form a more or less continuous spherical shell, with relatively few leaves growing in the shell interior. You estimate that the diameter of this shell is about 30 m. Each leaf is about 5 in. long and 3 in. wide. Make an order-of-magnitude estimate of the number of leaves on this tree. •••

1.4 Time and change

24. A human generation is about 30 years, and the age of the universe is 10^{17} s. How many human generations have there been since the beginning of the universe? (Ignore the fact that humans did not exist during most of this time.) •
25. You hear a peal of thunder and go to the window. You then see a flash of lightning. Is it reasonable to assume that the thunder caused the lightning? •
26. A second is defined as the duration of 9.19×10^9 periods of the radiation emitted by a cesium atom. What is the duration in seconds of a single period for this atom? •
27. While watching a railroad crossing, you observe that a crossing barrier is lowered about 30 s before a train passes. This happens every time for a long while, until suddenly after many times the barrier is not lowered but a train passes anyway! Discuss the causal relationship between the passing of a train and the lowering of the barrier. Does the single unusual occurrence make a difference to your answer? ••
28. Assume the radiation from the cesium atom mentioned in Problem 26 moves at the speed of light. How many meters does the radiation travel in the length of time corresponding to the period calculated in Problem 26? ••

1.5 Representations

29. Translate this statement into a mathematical expression, using any symbols you wish, but include a "key" to the meaning of each symbol: A certain type of energy of an object is equal to the object's mass times the speed of light squared. •
30. A planar shape is formed by joining the ends of four straight-line segments, two with length ℓ and two with length 2ℓ. No loose ends are allowed, but crossings are allowed, and only two segment ends may join at any single point. The ends of identical-length segments cannot join each other. What shapes are possible? ••
31. A planar shape is formed from four straight-line segments of length ℓ that do not cross. One end of segment 1 is connected to one end of segment 2 such that they make a 30° angle. The other end of segment 2 is connected to one end of segment 3 such that they also make a 30° angle. Finally, the other end of segment 3 is connected to one end of segment 4, forming another 30° angle. What is the distance between the unconnected ends of segments 1 and 4? ••
32. You are arranging family members for a photograph, and you want them to stand in order of increasing height. Your uncle is half a foot shorter than your aunt, who is taller than your cousin. Your grandmother is 2 in. shorter than your grandfather. Your brother is 1 in. taller than your aunt and 3 in. taller than your cousin. Your grandfather is 1 cm taller than your aunt. List the relatives in order of increasing height. ••
33. The Jupiter–Sun distance is 778 million kilometers, and the Earth–Sun distance is 150 million kilometers. Suppose an imaginary line from Jupiter to the Sun forms a right angle with an imaginary line from Earth to the Sun. How long would it take light to travel from the Sun to a spaceship halfway along the straight-line path between Jupiter and Earth? ••
34. During a physics lab, you and your partner keep track of the position of a small cart while it is moving along a slope. The lab instructions ask you to prepare (*a*) a pictorial representation of the experiment, (*b*) a table recording the position of the cart measured every 2.00 seconds from its initial position, and (*c*) a graph that shows the position of the cart on the vertical axis and time on the horizontal axis. You produce the sketch shown in Figure P1.34. What should your table and your graph look like? ••

Figure P1.34

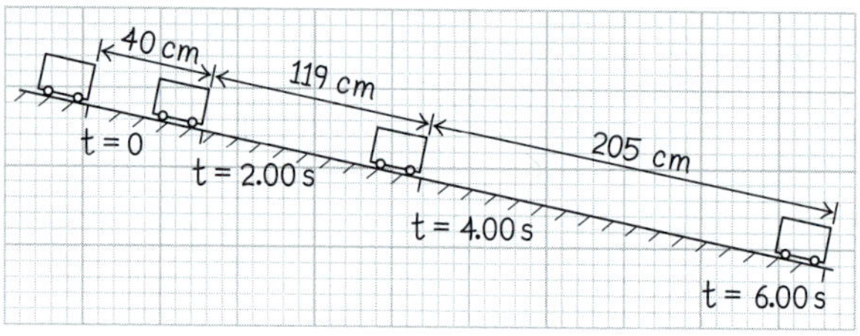

35. The graph in Figure P1.35 shows a relationship between two quantities: position *x*, measured in meters, and time *t*, measured in seconds. Describe the relationship using (*a*) a verbal expression and (*b*) a mathematical expression. •••

Figure P1.35

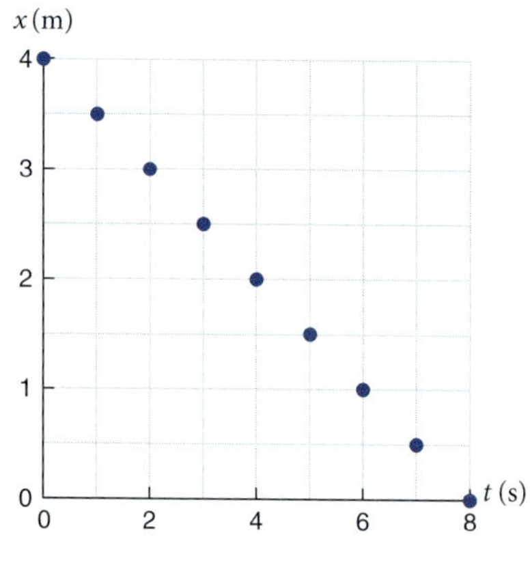

PRACTICE

36. You have four equilateral triangles, two red and two blue. You want to arrange them so that each blue triangle shares a side with the other blue triangle and with both red triangles, and each red triangle shares a side with the other red triangle and with both blue triangles. How can this be done? •••

1.6 Physical quantities and units

37. The world record in the long jump was recently set at 8.95 m. What is this distance in inches? •
38. Planes fly at an altitude of 35,000 ft above sea level. What is this distance in miles? In meters? •
39. A metal block of uniform mass density is cut into two pieces. How does the density of each piece compare with the density of the original block (*a*) if each piece has half the volume of the original block and (*b*) if one piece has one-third of the original volume? •
40. The speed of light is 2.9979×10^8 m/s. Convert this speed to miles per second, inches per nanosecond, and kilometers per hour. ••
41. Suppose you measure the mass and volume of two solid stones. Stone 1 has a mass of 2.90×10^{-2} kg and a volume of 10.0 cm^3. Stone 2 has a mass of 2.50×10^{-2} kg and a volume of 7.50 cm^3. Is it likely that the stones are made from the same material? ••
42. The Kentucky Derby horserace is 1.000 mile and 440 yards long. Express this distance in feet. ••
43. You are doing a calculation in which you must add two quantities A and B. You know that A can be expressed as $A = \frac{1}{2}at^2$, where a has units of meters per second squared and t has units of seconds. No matter what the expression for B is, what must the units of B be? ••
44. Both *mass* and *volume* can be used to describe the amount of matter present in an object. What physical quantity relates these two concepts? ••
45. The average radius of Earth is 6371 km. Give order-of-magnitude estimates of what the mass of Earth would be if the planet has the mass density of (*a*) air (≈ 1.2 kg/m^3), (*b*) 5515 kg/m^3, and (*c*) an atomic nucleus ($\approx 10^{18}$ kg/m^3). ••
46. Suppose $x = ay^{3/2}$, where $a = 7.81\ \mu$g/Tm. Determine the value of y when $x = 61.7$ (Eg · fm^2)/(ms^3). Express the result in scientific notation and simplify the units. (Hint: Refer to *Principles* Table 1.3, and note that SI prefixes are never used to multiply powers of units. For example, the abbreviation cm^2 means $(10^{-2}\text{ m})^2$, not 10^{-2} m^2, and ns^{-1} is 1/ns or 10^9 s^{-1}, not 10^{-9} s^{-1}. Also note that m can stand for meter or for milli, depending on the context.) •••

1.7 Significant digits

47. (*a*) What is the speed of light in vacuum expressed to three significant digits? (*b*) What is the speed of light in vacuum squared expressed to three significant digits? (*c*) Is the numerical value in part *b* the square of the numerical value in part *a*? Why or why not? •
48. Express the distance of the Kentucky Derby in kilometers to the same number of significant digits needed to answer Problem 42. •
49. You have 245.6 g of sugar and wish to divide it evenly among six people. If you calculate how much sugar each person receives, how many significant digits does your answer have? •
50. You are recording your car's gas mileage. Your odometer measures to the tenth of a mile. The gas station pump displays gallons of gasoline dispensed to the thousandth of a gallon. Given these levels of precision, is there any difference in the precision of your calculation when you drive 40.0 miles or 400.0 miles? ••
51. The odometer on your car says 35,987.1 km. To the correct number of significant digits, what should the odometer read after you drive 47.00 m? ••
52. A certain brand of soft drink contains 34 mg of caffeine per 355-mL serving. If one mole of caffeine has a mass of 194.19 g and you drink an average of two servings of this drink a day, how many caffeine molecules do you ingest in one year? ••
53. You work in a hospital and are preparing a saline solution for a patient. This solution must have a concentration of 0.15 mol of NaCl (mass of one mole, 58.44 gram) per liter of solution. You have lots of volume-measuring devices, but the only mass-measuring tool you have is a balance that measures mass to the nearest 0.1 g. What is the minimum amount of solution you should mix? ••
54. You find a container of an unknown clear liquid. You are interested in its contents, but you have no chemical analysis devices at hand. You do have a good electronic scale, so you measure out 25.403 g of the liquid and then pour this liquid into a graduated cylinder, with the level indicated in Figure P1.54. What is the mass density of this liquid? ••

Figure P1.54

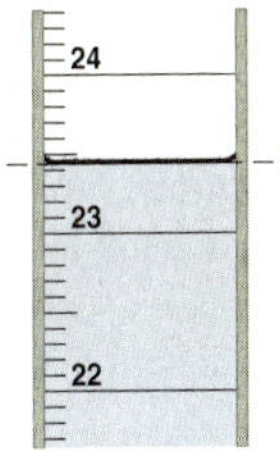

55. Suppose that, in a laboratory exercise, you add 0.335 g of liquid to a 145.67-g ceramic bowl. After you heat the liquid for 25.01 s, you measure the mass of the bowl and liquid together to be 145.82 g. What was the average mass of liquid that evaporated each second? •••

1.8 Solving problems

56. A test question gives the mass density of seawater and asks what volume is occupied by 1.0×10^3 kg of seawater. Someone answers 0.9843 m. Without knowing the mass density value given, explain what is wrong with this answer. •
57. You measure a watch's hour and minute hands to be 8.0 mm and 11.3 mm long, respectively. In one day, by how much does the distance traveled by the tip of the minute hand exceed the distance traveled by the tip of the hour hand? ••
58. An Olympic running track consists of two straight sections, each 84.39 m long, and two semicircular ends, each with a radius of 36.80 m as measured from the inside lane (lane 1). There are eight lanes, each 1.22 m wide. If runners did not start staggered (so that each runner covers the same distance), by how much would the distance traveled by a runner in lane 8 exceed the distance traveled by a runner in lane 1 over one lap? ••

59. You have three coins that are identical in appearance. One is counterfeit, and its mass is different from the mass of the two legitimate coins. You also have an equal-arm balance (a device that compares the masses of two objects and "balances" if they are equal). Describe how you can determine which is the counterfeit coin and whether it is heavier or lighter than the legitimate coins by making only two measurements with the balance. ••

60. A certain type of rice has an average grain length and diameter of 6 mm and 2 mm, respectively. One cup of this rice, after being cooked, contains about 785 food calories. (*a*) How many grains are there in 1 cup of rice? (*b*) How many calories are there in one grain? (*c*) How many cups of uncooked rice are needed to provide 2000 food calories to each of four adults? •••

1.9 Developing a feel

61. What is the order of magnitude of the number of moles of matter in the observable universe? •

62. You add about 10^2 raisins to a loaf of bread you are baking. When fully baked, the loaf is hemispherical with a radius of about 8 in. What is the order of magnitude of the average distance between neighboring raisins? •

63. A tree cut down for lumber has a diameter of 0.80 m over its length of 32 m. About how many 6-ft-long, 2-in. by 2-in. boards can be made from this tree? •

64. Estimate the order of magnitude of the number of times the letter d occurs in this text. ••

65. Estimate the combined length of all the hairs on the head of a person who has a a full head of shoulder-length hair. ••

66. An urban legend making the rounds in quantitative reasoning classes is that a student paid for four years at a private university in the United States exclusively with redeemed deposits on soda cans collected from people's trash. Estimate whether this is possible. ••

67. Computer hard drives have increased dramatically in capacity since their introduction in the 1950s. The first commercial hard drive had a capacity of about 3.8 MB stored on 50 circular platters, each 610 mm in diameter. In the early part of this century, hard drives approached 1.0 TB of storage using just five platters, each with a diameter of about 90 mm. By what order-of-magnitude factor does the storage capacity per unit area of a 21st-century drive exceed that of an original drive? ••

Additional Problems

68. Express the speed 1.08243×10^{19} nm/y in meters per second. •

69. A 200-sheet stack of loose-leaf paper is 2.75 in. thick. What is the thickness in millimeters of one sheet? •

70. A water tank is filled to its 50×10^3-L capacity. (*a*) What is the tank's volume in cubic millimeters? (*b*) What is the mass of the water in milligrams? (*c*) If you drank eight average-sized glasses of water a day, how long would the water in the tank last? ••

71. You are working on an exhibit of the atom at a science museum. You want the exhibit to have a model of the atom in which the nucleus is big enough for visitors to see, about 500 mm in diameter. The model needs to fit inside a square room with walls about 25 m long. Will it fit if you make the nucleus this size? ••

72. Recent experimental values for the universal gravitational constant, the mass and mean radius of Earth, and the standard gravitational acceleration are

$$G = 6.6738 \times 10^{-11}\ \text{m}^3 \cdot \text{kg}^{-1} \cdot \text{s}^{-2}$$
$$M_E = 5.9736 \times 10^{24}\ \text{kg}$$
$$R_E = 6.378\,140 \times 10^{6}\ \text{m}$$
$$g = 9.806\,65\ \text{m} \cdot \text{s}^{-2}$$

Assuming a spherical Earth, these quantities are related by the expression $gR_E^2 = GM_E$. (*a*) To how many significant digits is this relation satisfied using the recent data? (*b*) Can you round off all the data to the same number of significant digits before multiplying and still satisfy this relation to that number of significant digits? If so, what numbers of significant digits work? ••

73. You are in charge of safety at a local park. A tire swing hangs from a tree branch by a 5-m rope, and the bottom of the tire is 1 m from the ground directly beneath it. The land is sloped at a 12° angle toward a pond. From experience, you know that even an energetic user will be unlikely to cause the swing to make a maximum angle exceeding 30° with respect to the vertical. You are certain that parents will want reassurance about the safety of the tire swing. ••• CR

74. While working for a space agency, you are tasked with ensuring that the oxygen needs of human beings on long voyages in outer space are met. Your boss hands you a data table and suggests that you consider the amount of oxygen a person might need in 1 year as well as the storage requirements for this oxygen at room temperature and atmospheric pressure. ••• CR

Volume of one breath	4.5 L
Oxygen content of air, by volume	20.95%
Percent oxygen absorbed per breath	25%
Average breathing rate	15 breaths/min
Mass density of air at room temperature and atmospheric pressure	1.0 kg/m^3

75. Neutron stars can have a mass on the order of 10^{30} kg, but they have relatively small radii, on the order of tens of kilometers. (*a*) What order of magnitude is the mass density of a neutron star? (*b*) How many orders of magnitude larger is this than the mass density of Earth? Of water? (*c*) If water had the mass density of a neutron star, what order of magnitude of mass would be contained in the soda in a full 2-L bottle? •••

PRACTICE

Answers to Review Questions

1. Physics is the study of matter and motion in the universe. It is about understanding the unifying patterns that underlie all phenomena in nature.
2. The scientific method is an iterative process that develops validated theories to explain our observations of nature. It involves observing some phenomenon, formulating a hypothesis from the observations, making predictions based on the hypothesis, and validating the predictions by running experiments to test them.
3. Some useful skills are interpreting observations, recognizing patterns, making and recognizing assumptions, reasoning logically, developing models, and using the models to make predictions.
4. Inductive reasoning is arguing from the specific to the general; deductive reasoning is arguing from the general to the specific.
5. Symmetry means that the appearance of an object, process, or law is not changed by a specific operation, such as rotation or reflection.
6. Translational symmetry in space, in which different observers at different locations get the same value for a given measurement, and translational symmetry in time, in which an observer gets the same value for a given measurement taken at different instants, are two types.
7. The *universe* is the totality of matter and energy plus the space and time in which all events occur.
8. An order of magnitude is a value rounded to the nearest power of ten. Using orders of magnitude gives you a feel for a quantity and is a key skill in any quantitative field.
9. The order of magnitude of 2900 is 10^3, and the order of magnitude appropriate for 3100 is 10^4. This is because the first digit 3 is used as the demarcation between rounding up and rounding down. On a logarithmic scale, the base-10 logarithm of 3 is about halfway between the logarithm of 1 and the logarithm of 10.
10. The size scale ranges from the subatomic (10^{-16} m or smaller) to the size of the universe (10^{26} m or larger). The time scale ranges from a hundredth of an attosecond (10^{-20} s) or smaller to the age of the universe (10^{17} s).
11. Time flows in a single, irreversible direction, from past to present to future.
12. The principle of causality states that if an event A causes an event B, all observers see A happening before B. This means that if event A is observed to occur after event B, then A cannot be the cause of B.
13. Making simplified visual representations such as sketches, graphs, or tables helps you to establish a clear mental image of the situation, relate it to past experience, interpret its meaning and consequences, focus on essential features, and organize more relevant information than you can keep track of in your head.
14. The *Concepts* part develops the conceptual framework of the topics covered in the chapter. The *Quantitative Tools* part develops the mathematical framework for these topics.
15. A numerical value and an appropriate unit of measurement are needed.
16. The SI base units are meter for length, second for time, kilogram for mass, ampere for electric current, kelvin for temperature, mole for quantity of substance, and candela for luminous intensity.
17. Density is the concept of how much there is of some substance in a given volume.
18. Multiply the quantity by a conversion factor, a fraction in which the numerator is a number and the desired unit and the denominator is the equivalent value expressed in the given unit.
19. The number of digits is all the digits written to express a numerical value. The number of decimal places is the number of digits to the right of the decimal point. The number of significant digits is the number of digits that are reliably known. The number 0.037 20 has 6 digits, the last 4 of them significant, and 5 decimal places.
20. Leading zeros are any that come before the first nonzero digit in a number. Trailing zeros are any that come after the last nonzero digit. No leading zero is significant. All trailing zeros to the right of the decimal point are significant. Trailing zeros to the left of the decimal point may or may not be significant.
21. The number of significant digits in the result should be the same as the number of significant digits in the input quantity that has the fewest significant digits.
22. The number of decimal places in the result should be the same as the number of decimal places in the input quantity that has the fewest decimal places.
23. Getting started: Identify problem, visualize situation, organize relevant information, clarify goal.
    Devise plan: Figure out what to do by developing a strategy and identifying physical relationships or equations you can use.
    Execute plan: Proceed stepwise through the plan, performing all the mathematical, algebraic, and computational operations necessary to reach the goal; check calculations.
    Evaluate result: Consider whether the answer is reasonable, makes sense, reproduces known results in limiting or special cases, or can be confirmed by an alternative approach.
24. **V**ectors and scalars used correctly? **E**very question answered? **N**o unknown quantities in answers? **U**nits correct? **S**ignificant digits justified?
25. They allow you to develop a feel for a problem without getting too involved in the details. They help you explore relationships between physical quantities, consider alternative approaches, make simplifying assumptions, and evaluate answers obtained by more rigorous methods.

Answers to Guided Problems

Guided Problem 1.2

$$\rho_{\mathrm{O}} = \frac{0.0097 m_{\mathrm{Sun}}}{\frac{4}{3}\pi R_{\mathrm{Sun}}^3} = 13.7\ \mathrm{kg/m^3};$$

$$n_{\mathrm{O}} = \frac{\rho_{\mathrm{O}}}{m_{\mathrm{O\ atom}}} = 5.14 \times 10^{26}\ \mathrm{atoms/m^3}$$

Guided Problem 1.4 $V = Wh\ell = 1.05\ \mathrm{m^3}$

Guided Problem 1.6 (*a*) 4.1×10^2, 10^3; (*b*) 24.75, 10^1; (*c*) 6980.2, 10^4

Guided Problem 1.8 About $10^5\ \mathrm{km^2}$, assuming that buildings cover about 1%–2% of the land and that the United States is a rectangle with dimensions 1000 mi × 3000 mi (1600 km × 4800 km)

2

PRACTICE

Motion in One Dimension

Chapter Summary

Average speed and average velocity (Sections 2.2–2.4, 2.6, 2.7)

Concepts The **distance traveled** is the accumulated distance covered by an object along the path of its motion, without regard to direction.

The x component of an object's **displacement** is the change in its x coordinate.

The **average speed** of an object is the distance it travels divided by the time interval it takes to travel that distance.

The x component of an object's **average velocity** is the x component of its displacement divided by the time interval taken to travel that displacement. The magnitude of the average velocity is not necessarily equal to the average speed.

Quantitative Tools The **distance** d between two points x_1 and x_2 is

$$d = |x_1 - x_2|. \qquad (2.5)$$

The x component of the **displacement** Δx of an object that moves from a point x_i to a point x_f is

$$\Delta x = x_f - x_i. \qquad (2.4)$$

The x component of the object's **average velocity** is

$$v_{x,\text{av}} = \frac{\Delta x}{\Delta t} = \frac{x_f - x_i}{t_f - t_i}. \qquad (2.14)$$

Vectors and scalars (Sections 2.5, 2.6)

Concepts A **scalar** is a physical quantity that is completely specified by a number and a unit of measure. A **vector** is a physical quantity that is completely specified by a number, a unit of measure, and a direction. The number and unit of measure together are called the **magnitude** of the vector.

A **unit vector** has magnitude one and no units.

To **add** two vectors, place the tail of the second vector in the sum at the tip of the first vector; the vector representing the sum runs from the tail of the first vector to the tip of the second. To **subtract** one vector from another, reverse the direction of the vector being subtracted and add the reversed vector to the vector from which you are subtracting.

Quantitative Tools The unit vector $\hat{\imath}$ has magnitude one and points along the x axis in the direction of increasing x.

A vector $\vec{b}$ that points in the x direction and has an x component b_x can be written in **unit vector notation** as

$$\vec{b} = b_x\,\hat{\imath}. \qquad (2.2)$$

Position, displacement, and velocity as vectors (Sections 2.6, 2.7)

Concepts The **position vector,** or **position,** of a point is drawn from the origin of a coordinate system to the point.

The **displacement vector** of an object is the change in its position vector. It is the vector that points from the tip of the original position vector to the tip of the final position vector.

Quantitative Tools The position $\vec{r}$ of a point that has x coordinate x is

$$\vec{r} = x\,\hat{\imath}. \qquad (2.9)$$

The displacement vector $\Delta\vec{r}$ of an object moving along the x axis is

$$\Delta\vec{r} = \vec{r}_f - \vec{r}_i = (x_f - x_i)\hat{\imath}. \qquad (2.7, 2.8, 2.10)$$

The average velocity of an object moving along the x axis is

$$\vec{v}_{\text{av}} = \frac{\Delta\vec{r}}{\Delta t} = \frac{x_f - x_i}{t_f - t_i}\hat{\imath}. \qquad (2.14, 2.15)$$

Additional properties of velocity (Sections 2.8, 2.9)

When the velocity of an object is constant, its **position-versus-time graph** is a straight line having nonzero slope and its **velocity-versus-time graph** is a horizontal line.

The **instantaneous velocity** of an object is its velocity at any particular instant.

The slope of an object's $x(t)$ curve at a given instant is numerically equal to the x component of the object's velocity at that instant. The area under the object's $v_x(t)$ curve during a time interval is the x component of the object's displacement during that interval.

The x component of an object's instantaneous velocity is the derivative of the object's x coordinate with respect to time:

$$v_x = \frac{dx}{dt}. \tag{2.22}$$

Review Questions

Answers to these questions can be found at the end of this chapter.

2.1 From reality to model

1. A friend constructs a graph of position as a function of frame number for a film clip of a moving object. She then challenges you to construct a graph identical to hers. She tells you that she measured distances in millimeters, but what two additional pieces of information must she give you?
2. How do you determine whether an object is moving or at rest?

2.2 Position and displacement

3. Suppose you have a film clip showing the motion of several objects. If you want to calibrate distances for a graph, what information do you need to know about at least one of the objects?
4. Explain how the information you named in Review Question 3 can be used to calibrate a graph.
5. What is the purpose of using the phrase *x component of* when describing some physical quantities?
6. How do you represent displacement in a drawing or diagram?

2.3 Representing motion

7. What does *interpolation* mean with regard to plotting data points?
8. Describe how to determine the x component of the position of an object at a specific instant, given (*a*) a graph of position x as a function of time t and (*b*) an equation for $x(t)$.

2.4 Average speed and average velocity

9. In an $x(t)$ curve, what is the significance of a steep slope as opposed to a gentle slope? What is the significance of a curve that slopes downward as you move from left to right along the time axis as opposed to a curve that slopes upward as you move from left to right along that axis?
10. What does it signify physically if the x component of an object's average velocity is negative over some time interval?

2.5 Scalars and vectors

11. What are the defining characteristics of a scalar? Of a vector?
12. What is the relationship between the magnitude of a vector and the vector's x component?
13. What is the purpose of the unit vector $\hat{\imath}$?

2.6 Position and displacement vectors

14. What is the mathematical meaning of the symbol Δ, the Greek capital letter delta?
15. Is displacement a scalar or a vector? Is distance a scalar or a vector?
16. Can distance be negative? Can distance traveled be negative?
17. Under what conditions is the x component of the displacement negative?
18. How is distance traveled calculated when motion occurs in three segments: first in one direction along the x axis, then in the opposite direction, and finally in the initial direction?
19. Describe the graphical procedure for adding two vectors and for subtracting one vector from another.
20. If you multiply a vector $\vec{A}$ by a scalar c, is the result a scalar or a vector? If the result is a scalar, what is its magnitude? If the result is a vector, what are its magnitude and direction? What if the scalar $c = 0$?

2.7 Velocity as a vector

21. Is average speed a scalar or a vector? Is average velocity a scalar or a vector?
22. What properties does velocity have that make it a vector?
23. How is an object's average velocity related to its displacement during a given time interval?

2.8 Motion at constant velocity

24. What is the shape of the $x(t)$ curve for an object moving at constant velocity? What is the shape of the $v_x(t)$ curve for this object?
25. An object travels at a constant velocity of 10 m/s north in the time interval from $t = 0$ to $t = 8$ s. What additional information must you know in order to determine the position of the object at $t = 5$ s?
26. In a velocity-versus-time graph, what is the significance of the area under the curve for any time interval $t_f - t_i$?

2.9 Instantaneous velocity

27. What feature of the $x(t)$ curve for a moving object gives the object's x component of velocity at a given instant?
28. Under what conditions is the average velocity over a time interval equal to the instantaneous velocity at every instant in the interval?
29. What mathematical relationship allows you to compute the x component of an object's velocity at some instant, given the object's x component of position as a function of time?

PRACTICE

Developing a Feel

Make an order-of-magnitude estimate of each of the following quantities. Letters in parentheses refer to hints below. Use them as needed to guide your thinking.

1. The height of a 20-story apartment building (D)
2. The distance light travels during a human life span (B, N)
3. The displacement (from your mouth) of an (indigestible) popcorn kernel as it passes through your body, and the distance traveled by the same kernel (F, O)
4. The time interval within which a batter must react to a fast pitch before it reaches home plate in professional baseball (C, H)
5. The time interval needed to drive nonstop from San Francisco to New York City by the most direct route (G, K)
6. The distance traveled when you nod off for 2 s while driving on the freeway (K)
7. The average speed of an airliner on a flight from San Francisco to New York City (G, Q)
8. The average speed of a typical car in the United States in one year (not just while it's running) (E)
9. The time interval for a nonstop flight halfway around the world from Paris, France, to Auckland, New Zealand (J and item 7 above)
10. The number of revolutions made by a typical car's tires in one year (L, E)
11. The maximum speed of your right foot while walking (A, M, P)
12. The thickness of rubber lost during one revolution of a typical car tire (I, R, L, S)

Hints

A. What is your average walking speed?
B. What is the speed of light?
C. What is the speed of a fastball thrown by a professional pitcher?
D. What is the height of each story in an apartment building?
E. What distance does a typical car travel during one year?
F. When you are sitting upright, how far above the chair seat is your mouth?
G. What is the distance between San Francisco and New York City?
H. What is the distance from the pitcher's mound to home plate?
I. What thickness of rubber is lost during the lifetime of a car tire?
J. What is the circumference of Earth?
K. What is a typical freeway speed?
L. What is the circumference of a car tire?
M. For what time interval is your right foot at rest if you walk for 2 min?
N. What is a typical human life span?
O. What is the length of the digestive tract in an adult person?
P. If you walk 10 m in a straight line, what is the displacement of your right foot?
Q. How much elapsed time does a flight from San Francisco to New York City require?
R. How many miles of service does a car tire provide?
S. How many revolutions does a car tire make in traveling 1 m?

Key (all values approximate)

A. 2 m/s; **B.** 3×10^8 m/s; **C.** 4×10^1 m/s; **D.** 4 m; **E.** 2×10^7 m; **F.** 1 m; **G.** 5×10^6 m; **H.** 2×10^1 m; **I.** 1×10^{-2} m; **J.** 4×10^7 m; **K.** 3×10^1 m/s; **L.** 2 m; **M.** 1 min; **N.** 2×10^9 s; **O.** 7 m; **P.** 1×10^1 m; **Q.** 2×10^4 s; **R.** 8×10^7 m; **S.** 0.5 rev/m

Worked and Guided Problems

These examples involve material from this chapter but are not associated with any particular section. Some examples are worked out in detail; others you should work out by following the guidelines provided.

Worked Problem 2.1 Shopping hunt

A frantic shopper performs the following sequence of movements along a supermarket aisle in search of a special item:

(1) He moves eastward at a constant speed of 3.0 m/s for 10 s,
(2) stops for 5.0 s,
(3) walks slowly in the same direction at a constant speed of 0.50 m/s for 20 s, and
(4) immediately turns around and rushes westward at a constant speed of 4.0 m/s for 9.0 s.

(*a*) Plot the shopper's position as a function of time during the 44-s interval. (*b*) What is the x component of his average velocity from $t = 0$ to $t = 35$ s? From $t = 0$ to $t = 44$ s? (*c*) What distance does he travel during the 44-s interval? (*d*) What is his average speed during this interval?

❶ **GETTING STARTED** We know that the shopper first moves in a straight line in one direction, then stops for a while, then moves in the same direction again at a slower speed, and then switches direction. To visualize the motion, we make a sketch that represents the velocity in each of the four segments (Figure WG2.1).

Figure WG2.1

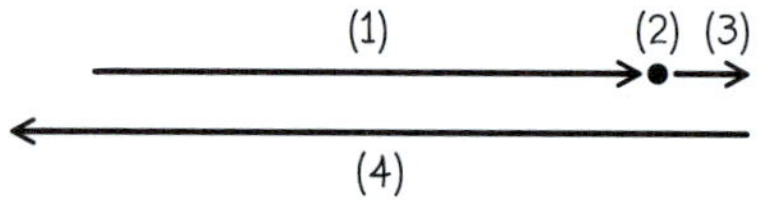

We know that the speed and direction of travel affect the shopper's position at any given instant. Let us say that all the motion is along an x axis. Our first task is to plot the $x(t)$ curve from the starting position, based on the information about his speed and direction of motion from that instant. In addition, we need to determine his average velocity during two time intervals, the distance traveled in 44 s, and the average speed in the 44-s interval.

We summarize the given information to see which quantities we know. We need unambiguous symbols for the quantities in the various segments. We shall use the segment number as a subscript to identify the final instant and final position of each segment; for example, t_3 is the final instant of the third segment, and at this instant the shopper is at position x_3. Choosing the positive x direction to be eastward, we can list this information from the problem statement:

$$v_{x,1} = +3.0 \text{ m/s during interval from } t_0 = 0 \text{ to } t_1 = 10 \text{ s}$$

$$v_{x,2} = 0 \text{ during interval from } t_1 = 10 \text{ s to } t_2 = 15 \text{ s}$$

$$v_{x,3} = +0.50 \text{ m/s during interval from } t_2 = 15 \text{ s to } t_3 = 35 \text{ s}$$

$$v_{x,4} = -4.0 \text{ m/s during interval from } t_3 = 35 \text{ s to } t_4 = 44 \text{ s.}$$

Although it would be tempting to label the initial instant t_i rather than t_0, we recognize that there are several segments to this motion and that the initial instant of motion in one segment is the final instant of motion in the previous segment. Thus t_i in our general kinematic formulas has different values in the different segments and is not always equal to zero. To avoid confusion, therefore, we designate our starting instant by something other than t_i; we choose t_0. Likewise we choose t_4 rather than t_f as the ending instant of the fourth segment to avoid confusion with the symbol t_f used in our general equations as the final instant of each segment.

Because one task is to plot position as a function of time from the starting position, we choose the starting coordinate to be $x_0 = 0$.

❷ **DEVISE PLAN** In order to make our position-versus-time graph for part *a*, we need to determine the shopper's final position for each segment of the motion. The initial position for each successive segment is equal to the final position for the previous segment. We can connect the start and end positions in any segment with a straight line (constant slope) because the velocity is constant in each segment. For motion at constant velocity, we can use Eq. 2.19 to calculate the position x_f at the end of any time interval:

$$x_f = x_i + v_x(t_f - t_i). \quad (1)$$

For part *b*, we can divide the displacement between the two specified instants by the corresponding time interval to get the x component of the average velocity (Eq. 2.14):

$$v_{x,\text{av}} = \frac{x_f - x_i}{t_f - t_i}. \quad (2)$$

For part *c*, we get the distance traveled in 44 s by adding the distances traveled in the four segments, noting that distance traveled is a magnitude. For part *d*, the average speed is the distance traveled in 44 s divided by that time interval. Of our four tasks, the only "hard" part is getting the displacement in each time interval for our position-versus-time graph.

❸ **EXECUTE PLAN** (*a*) To plot position versus time, we need to calculate the position at the end of each segment of the motion. To use Eq. 1, we note that in the first segment the initial position is $x_i = x_0 = 0$, the velocity in the x direction is $v_x = v_{x,1} = +3.0$ m/s, the initial instant is $t_i = t_0 = 0$, and the final instant is $t_f = t_1 = 10$ s. Substituting these values into Eq. 1, we compute the shopper's final position $x_f = x_1$ after 10 s (segment 1)

$$x_1 = x_0 + v_{x,1}(t_1 - t_0) = 0 + (+3.0 \text{ m/s})(10 \text{ s} - 0) = +30 \text{ m.}$$

We repeat this procedure for the other three segments, using the final position of the preceding segment as the initial position of the current segment:

$$x_2 = x_1 + v_{x,2}(t_2 - t_1) = +30 \text{ m} + (0)(15 \text{ s} - 10 \text{ s}) = +30 \text{ m}$$

$$x_3 = +30 \text{ m} + (+0.50 \text{ m/s})(35\text{s} - 15 \text{ s}) = +40 \text{ m}$$

$$x_4 = +40 \text{ m} + (-4.0 \text{ m/s})(44 \text{ s} - 35 \text{ s}) = +4.0 \text{ m.}$$

PRACTICE

Now we plot these positions in Figure WG2.2 and connect them with straight lines. ✔

Figure WG2.2

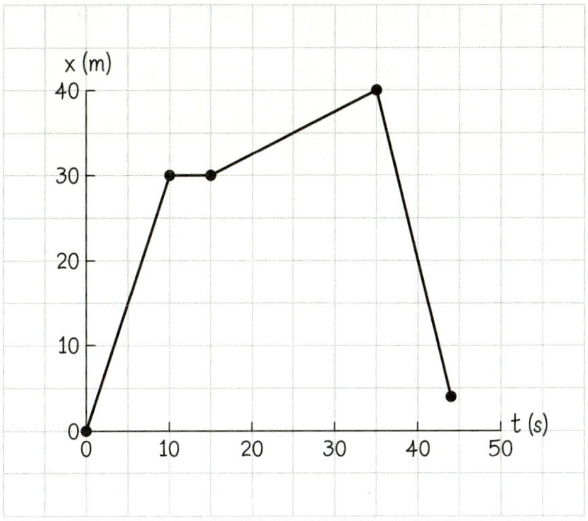

(*b*) From Eq. 2, the *x* component of the average velocity for the first 35 s, which runs to the end of segment 3, is the *x* component of the displacement during that time interval divided by the time interval:

$$v_{x,03} = \frac{x_3 - x_0}{t_3 - t_0} = \frac{+40\text{ m} - 0}{35\text{ s} - 0} = +1.1\text{ m/s}. ✔$$

This result is positive because the overall travel is eastward. The *x* component of the shopper's average velocity over the whole trip (to the end of segment 4) is

$$v_{x,04} = \frac{x_4 - x_0}{t_4 - t_0} = \frac{+4.0\text{ m} - 0}{44\text{ s} - 0} = +0.091\text{ m/s}. ✔ \quad (3)$$

(*c*) The distance traveled in 44 s is the sum of the distances traveled in the various segments. In this case, because each segment involves motion in a single direction, the distance traveled is the same as the distance—that is, the magnitude of the displacement. We can use the symbol *d* with appropriate subscripts to represent the distances traveled in the segments:

$$\begin{aligned} d_{04} &= d_{01} + d_{12} + d_{23} + d_{34} \\ &= |x_1 - x_0| + |x_2 - x_1| + |x_3 - x_2| + |x_4 - x_3| \\ &= |+30\text{ m} - 0| + |+30\text{ m} - (+30\text{ m})| + \\ &\quad |+40\text{ m} - (+30\text{ m})| + |+4.0\text{ m} - (+40\text{ m})| \\ &= 30\text{ m} + 0 + 10\text{ m} + 36\text{ m} = 76\text{ m}. ✔ \end{aligned}$$

(*d*) The average speed is the distance traveled in 44 s divided by that time interval:

$$\begin{aligned} v_{\text{av}} = v_{04} &= \frac{d_{04}}{\Delta t_{04}} = \frac{d_{04}}{t_4 - t_0} = \frac{76\text{ m}}{44\text{ s}} \\ &= 1.7\text{ m/s (between } t_0 \text{ and } t_4). ✔ \end{aligned} \quad (4)$$

Remember that the checkmarks (✔) in our calculations show that VENUS, the mnemonic for checking our work, has been applied.

❹ **EVALUATE RESULT** It is not unreasonable for a frantic shopper to move 76 m in 44 s. This is covering a distance that is a little shorter than the length of a football field in a time interval somewhat less than a minute, which is within the realm of possibility for a person pressed for time.

The signs of our position values agree with the positions we drew in Figure WG2.1: All four *x* values are on the positive side of the *x* axis (because the shopper always stays east of the origin). Notice that the average speed of 1.7 m/s (Eq. 4) is very different from the magnitude of the average velocity, 0.091 m/s (Eq. 3). This is to be expected because average speed is based on distance traveled, which is the sum of the magnitudes of the individual displacements, while average velocity is based on displacement, whose magnitude is much less than the distance traveled because of the shopper's backtracking.

Guided Problem 2.2 City driving

You need to drive to a grocery store that is 1.0 mi west of your house on the same street on which you live. There are five traffic lights between your house and the store, and on your trip you reach all five of them just as they change to red. While you are moving, your average speed is 20 mi/h, but you have to wait 1 min at each light. (*a*) How long does it take you to reach the store? (*b*) What is your average velocity for the trip? (*c*) What is your average speed?

❶ **GETTING STARTED**

1. Draw a diagram that helps you visualize all the driving and stopped segments and your speed in each segment. Does it matter where the traffic lights are located?
2. You start and stop, speed up and slow down. What does the average speed signify in this case, and how is it related to your displacement in each segment?

❷ **DEVISE PLAN**

3. During how long a time interval are you moving? During how long a time interval are you stopped at the lights?
4. What is your displacement for the trip?
5. How can you apply the answers to questions 3 and 4 to obtain your average velocity?
6. What is the distance traveled, and how is it related to your average speed?
7. How are average velocity and average speed related in this case?

❸ **EXECUTE PLAN**

❹ **EVALUATE RESULT**

8. Are your answers plausible, and is your result within the range of your expectations?

Worked Problem 2.3 Head start

Two runners in a 100-m race start from the same place. Runner A starts as soon as the starting gun is fired and runs at a constant speed of 8.00 m/s. Runner B starts 2.00 s later and runs at a constant speed of 9.30 m/s.

(*a*) Who wins the race? (*b*) At the instant she crosses the finish line, how far is the winner ahead of the other runner? (In your calculations, take the race length, 100 m, to be an exact value.)

❶ GETTING STARTED Although runner A has a 2.00-s head start, runner B runs faster than runner A. We want to know who first reaches the finish line, which is at $x_f = +100$ m. We begin by making a position-versus-time graph for both runners. Because both runners have constant speeds, their $x(t)$ curves are straight lines, with both starting at the same position ($x_i = 0$) but at the different initial instants $t_{A,i}$ and $t_{B,i}$ (Figure WG2.3). Note that the faster runner's curve has the steeper slope.

Figure WG2.3

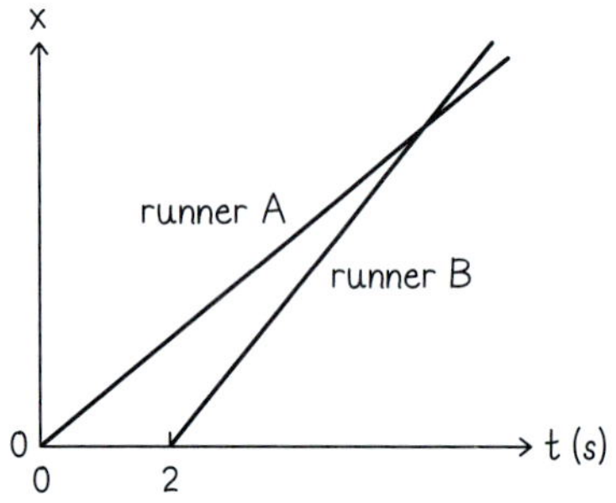

We see from our drawing that at some instant the two $x(t)$ curves intersect, meaning that the runners are at the same position at that instant, but we do not know whether this instant is before or after the slower runner A crosses the 100-m mark on the track.

❷ DEVISE PLAN Because we want to know who crosses the finish line first, we can determine the instant t_f at which each runner reaches the position $x_f = +100$ m using Eq. 2.18: $x_f - x_i = v_x(t_f - t_i)$.

The runner who has the lower value for t_f is the winner. Once we know who wins and at what instant she reaches the finish line, we can find out where the other runner is at that instant and then determine the distance between them. Although both runners start at $x_i = 0$, their start times are not the same, and we must account for this. When runner A leaves the starting position ($x_{A,i} = 0$), the timer's stopwatch reads $t_{A,i} = 0$. When runner B leaves the same starting position ($x_{B,i} = 0$), the stopwatch reads $t_{B,i} = 2.00$ s.

❸ EXECUTE PLAN (*a*) We need to solve for the instant t_f at which each runner reaches the finish line at $x_f = 100$ m. Each runner moves in the direction of the positive x axis, so the x component of the velocity for each of them is positive: $v_x = +v$, where v is the particular runner's speed. Using $\Delta t = t_f - t_i$, we can rearrange Eq. 2.18 to express t_f, the desired quantity, in terms of the other quantities:

$$x_f - x_i = v_x \Delta t = (+v)(t_f - t_i)$$

$$t_f = t_i + \frac{x_f - x_i}{v}.$$

The reading on the timer's stopwatch for runner A as she reaches the 100-m mark is

$$t_{A,f} = t_{A,i} + \frac{x_{A,f} - x_{A,i}}{v_{Ax}} = 0 + \frac{(+100\text{ m}) - 0}{+8.00\text{ m/s}} = 12.5\text{ s}.$$

As runner B crosses the finish line, the stopwatch reads

$$t_{B,f} = t_{B,i} + \frac{x_{B,f} - x_{B,i}}{v_{Bx}} = 2.00\text{ s} + \frac{(+100\text{ m}) - 0}{+9.30\text{ m/s}} = 12.8\text{ s}.$$

Runner A wins because she crosses the finish line first. ✔

(*b*) To determine their distance apart at the instant runner A crosses the finish line, when the stopwatch reads $t_{A,f} = 12.5$ s, we have to compute $x_{B,f}$, the position of runner B at that instant. From Eq. 2.19, we have

$$x_{B,f} = x_{B,i} + v_{Bx}(t_{A,f} - t_{B,i})$$
$$= 0 + (+9.30\text{ m/s})(12.5\text{ s} - 2.00\text{ s}) = +97.6\text{ m}.$$

Their distance apart when runner A crosses the finish line is

$$d = |x_{B,f} - x_{A,f}| = |+97.6\text{ m} - (+100\text{ m})| = 2.4\text{ m}. \checkmark$$

❹ EVALUATE RESULT The values we obtained for $t_{A,f}$ and $t_{B,f}$ are both positive, as they must be because negative values would represent instants before the race started. The time intervals of approximately 12 s to run 100 m are reasonable.

We can also solve the second part of this problem in a different way. Runner B is catching up with runner A at the rate of 9.30 m/s − 8.00 m/s = 1.30 m/s. Runner A has a 2.00-s head start, and so she is (8.00 m/s)(2.00 s) = 16.0 m ahead when runner B starts. Runner A wins the race with a time of 12.5 s; runner B has then been running for 12.5 s − 2.0 s = 10.5 s and has therefore closed the 16.0-m gap by (1.30 m/s)(10.5 s) = 13.6 m; that leaves her 16.0 m − 13.6 m = 2.4 m behind runner A. That result is the same as the one we obtained above.

Guided Problem 2.4 Race rematch

If the two runners in Worked Problem 2.3 want to cross the finish line together in a rematch, and runner A again starts at the instant the starting gun is fired, how many seconds should runner B delay in order to catch runner A right at the finish line?

❶ GETTING STARTED

1. Make a graph that shows the new situation, in which both runners reach 100 m at the same instant t_f.

❷ DEVISE PLAN

2. What type of motion occurs in this race? What equations can you use to describe this motion?
3. What physical quantity must you determine? What algebraic symbol is associated with this variable?

❸ EXECUTE PLAN

❹ EVALUATE RESULT

4. After solving for the desired starting time for runner B, how can you use the result of Worked Problem 2.3 to evaluate your answer?

Worked Problem 2.5 Airplane velocity

An airplane travels in a straight line from one airport to another. It flies at a constant speed of 600 km/h for half the distance and then at a constant speed of 800 km/h for the remainder of the distance in order to reach the destination at the scheduled time. What is its average velocity for the entire trip?

❶ **GETTING STARTED** To picture the situation, we draw a motion diagram. We are not given the distance between the airports, and so we have to use the variable d to represent this distance, as shown in Figure WG2.4.

Figure WG2.4

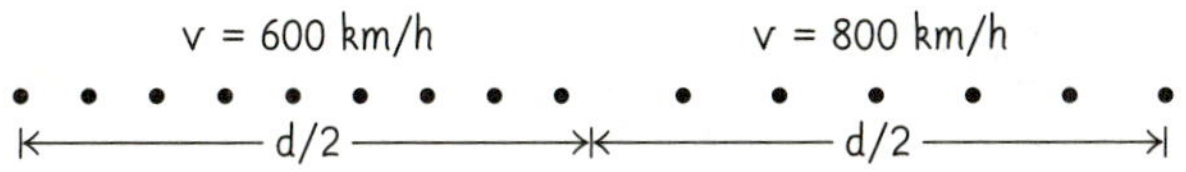

To get the average velocity, we must divide the displacement by the time interval required for the trip, but neither of these values is given! So we have to devise a way to relate these two unknown quantities to the average velocity. The distance traveled in each segment of the trip is the same, but the segment with the slower speed requires a longer time interval. With this insight, we can draw a position-versus-time graph for the plane's motion (Figure WG2.5) that shows the two segments, where we choose the positive x axis to be in the direction of the plane's motion. We include a dashed line to represent a plane that leaves the first airport at the same instant our plane leaves, travels at the average speed of our plane for its whole trip, and arrives at the second airport at the same instant our plane arrives. The slope of this dashed line represents the average velocity that we seek.

Figure WG2.5

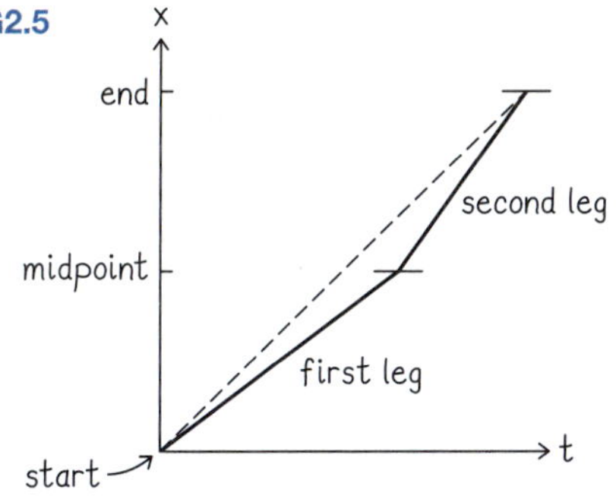

❷ **DEVISE PLAN** If we know the x component of displacement, we can get the x component of the average velocity from Eq. 2.14:

$$v_{x,\text{av}} \equiv \frac{\Delta x}{\Delta t} = \frac{x_f - x_i}{t_f - t_i}.$$

The x component of the displacement is the sum of the x components of the two (equal) displacements during the two segments of the flight. We can use the symbol x_m to represent the x coordinate of the midpoint position:

$$\Delta x = x_f - x_i = (x_f - x_m) + (x_m - x_i) = \Delta x_2 + \Delta x_1 = \Delta x_1 + \Delta x_2.$$

Furthermore, we know that $\Delta x_1 = \Delta x_2 = +\frac{1}{2}d$. The overall time interval is the sum of the two (unequal) time intervals: $\Delta t = \Delta t_1 + \Delta t_2$. The x component of the velocity during each segment is equal to the change in position divided by the time interval for that segment. Knowing this allows us to express the unknown time intervals in terms of the equal (but unknown) distances.

❸ **EXECUTE PLAN** For the entire trip:

$$v_{x,\text{av}} = \frac{\Delta x}{\Delta t} = \frac{\Delta x_1 + \Delta x_2}{\Delta t_1 + \Delta t_2}.$$

Although the time intervals are unknown, we can express them in terms of the two equal x components of the displacements:

$$\Delta t_1 = \frac{\Delta x_1}{v_{x,1}} \quad \text{and} \quad \Delta t_2 = \frac{\Delta x_2}{v_{x,2}}.$$

Substituting these expressions for Δt into the preceding equation gives

$$v_{x,\text{av}} = \frac{\Delta x_1 + \Delta x_2}{\left(\dfrac{\Delta x_1}{v_{x,1}}\right) + \left(\dfrac{\Delta x_2}{v_{x,2}}\right)} = \frac{(+\frac{1}{2}d) + (+\frac{1}{2}d)}{\left(\dfrac{+\frac{1}{2}d}{v_{x,1}}\right) + \left(\dfrac{+\frac{1}{2}d}{v_{x,2}}\right)}$$

$$= \frac{1}{\left(\dfrac{\frac{1}{2}}{v_{x,1}}\right) + \left(\dfrac{\frac{1}{2}}{v_{x,2}}\right)} = \frac{2}{\left(\dfrac{1}{v_{x,1}}\right) + \left(\dfrac{1}{v_{x,2}}\right)}.$$

The x components of the velocities in both segments are positive—that is, equal to the speeds: $v_{x,1} = +v_1$ and $v_{x,2} = +v_2$. Substituting in the numerical values gives us

$$v_{x,\text{av}} = \frac{2}{\left(\dfrac{1}{+600\ \text{km/h}}\right) + \left(\dfrac{1}{+800\ \text{km/h}}\right)} = +686\ \text{km/h}.$$

Because the problem asks for the average velocity, which is a vector, we multiply the x component of the velocity by the unit vector to get the desired result:

$$\vec{v}_{\text{av}} = v_{x,\text{av}}\hat{\imath} = (+686\ \text{km/h})\hat{\imath}. ✔$$

❹ **EVALUATE RESULT** We expect the x component of velocity to be positive because the velocities in both segments are in the positive x direction. The value of the answer is plausible because it lies between the two velocities at which the airplane actually flies.

Using the two constant speeds 600 km/h and 800 km/h means we ignored the short time interval needed to take off and reach cruising speed and the short time interval needed to slow down for landing. These two time intervals are much shorter than the time interval needed for the flight, and so our simplification is a reasonable one.

Guided Problem 2.6 Wrong way

A helicopter pilot at an airport is told to fly a distance d at speed v directly east to pick up a stranded hiker. However, he sees no hiker when he arrives. Radioing the control tower, he learns that the hiker is actually a distance d west of the airport. The pilot turns around and heads straight for the hiker at a speed that is 50% faster than his speed during the initial segment of this wrong-way trip. (*a*) What is the x component of the helicopter's average velocity for the trip from takeoff to rendezvous with the hiker? Assume the x axis points east and has its origin at the airport. (*b*) What is the helicopter's average velocity for the trip?

❶ GETTING STARTED

1. Draw a diagram representing the motion during the trip, indicating the position of the airport, the turning point, and the rendezvous location.
2. Label the eastward and westward segments with symbols you can use to set up appropriate equations. Then indicate how your chosen symbols relate to the given information, d and v.
3. Add labeled vector arrows to your diagram to indicate the velocity in each segment.
4. Would a graph of $x(t)$ be useful?

❷ DEVISE PLAN

5. How does this problem differ from Worked Problem 2.5? How are the two problems similar?
6. Because no numerical values are given, what physical quantities do you expect to be represented by algebraic symbols in your answer?
7. Be careful about the signs of the x component of the displacement and the x component of the velocity in each segment of the trip. Is Δx in the eastward segment positive or negative? Is v_x in this segment positive or negative? What about Δx and v_x in the westward segment? How can these quantities be expressed in terms of v and d?
8. What time interval is needed to fly the eastward segment? What time interval for the westward segment? If you don't get positive values for both intervals, check your signs for Δx and v_x.
9. How can you combine this information to determine the x component of the average velocity and then the average velocity in vector form?

❸ EXECUTE PLAN

❹ EVALUATE RESULT

10. Is the sign on $v_{x,\text{av}}$ what you expect based on the displacement of the helicopter?

Worked Problem 2.7 Uphill putt

The position of a golf ball moving uphill along a gently sloped green is given as a function of time t by $x(t) = p + qt + rt^2$, with the positive direction up the green and with $p = +2.0$ m, $q = +8.0$ m/s, and $r = -3.0$ m/s^2.

(*a*) Calculate the x component of the velocity and the speed of the ball at $t = 1.0$ s and at $t = 2.0$ s.

(*b*) What is the ball's average velocity during the time interval from 1.0 s to 2.0 s?

❶ GETTING STARTED We are asked to calculate velocity, a vector. Equation 2.25 defines velocity as the time derivative of position: $\vec{v} = d\vec{r}/dt$. It is easiest to work with components of vectors and then express the final result as a vector. In this case, the components are x and v_x, which we can use to construct the vectors $\vec{x} = x\hat{\imath}$ and $\vec{v} = v_x\hat{\imath}$. According to Eq. 2.22, the x component of the velocity equals the time derivative of the ball's x coordinate:

$$v_x(t) = \frac{dx}{dt}. \quad (1)$$

The problem statement gives this x coordinate as a function of time, and so we have the needed information.

❷ DEVISE PLAN For part *a*, we need to get v_x through our knowledge of the mathematical expression for the golf ball's position $x(t)$. We can then evaluate v_x at the specified instants to get numerical values. For part *b*, the x component of the average velocity can be determined using Eq. 2.14:

$$v_{x,\text{av}} = \frac{\Delta x}{\Delta t} = \frac{x_f - x_i}{t_f - t_i}. \checkmark \quad (2)$$

All we need to compute in this equation is Δx because we know that the time interval Δt is 1.0 s.

❸ EXECUTE PLAN (*a*) To determine the x component of the velocity as a function of time, we use Eq. 1:

$$v_x(t) = \frac{d}{dt}[p + qt + rt^2] = q + 2rt$$
$$= +8.0\text{ m/s} + 2(-3.0\text{ m/s}^2)t$$
$$= +8.0\text{ m/s} - (6.0\text{ m/s}^2)t. \checkmark$$

Evaluating this at the specified instants yields

$$v_x(1.0\text{ s}) = +8.0\text{ m/s} - (6.0\text{ m/s}^2)(1.0\text{ s}) = +2.0\text{ m/s} \checkmark$$
$$v_x(2.0\text{ s}) = +8.0\text{ m/s} - (6.0\text{ m/s}^2)(2.0\text{ s}) = -4.0\text{ m/s}. \checkmark$$

The desired speeds are the magnitudes of these velocity components, 2.0 m/s and 4.0 m/s. ✔

(*b*) For the average velocity, we need the initial and final coordinates of the motion in the specified time interval for use in Eq. 2:

$$x_i = x(1.0\text{ s}) = 2.0\text{ m} + (8.0\text{ m/s})(1.0\text{ s}) - (3.0\text{ m/s}^2)(1.0\text{ s})^2$$
$$= +7.0\text{ m}$$
$$x_f = x(2.0\text{ s}) = 2.0\text{ m} + (8.0\text{ m/s})(2.0\text{ s}) - (3.0\text{ m/s}^2)(2.0\text{ s})^2$$
$$= +6.0\text{ m}.$$

The average velocity is then

$$\vec{v}_{\text{av}} = v_{x,\text{av}}\hat{\imath} = \left(\frac{x_f - x_i}{t_f - t_i}\right)\hat{\imath} = \frac{(+6.0\text{ m}) - (+7.0\text{ m})}{(2.0\text{ s}) - (1.0\text{ s})}\hat{\imath}$$
$$= (-1.0\text{ m/s})\,\hat{\imath} \quad \text{(between 1.0 s and 2.0 s)}. \checkmark$$

PRACTICE

❹ **EVALUATE RESULT** The negative signs for the x component of the velocity at 2.0 s and the x component of the average velocity mean that the ball, whose initial velocity was positive, changed direction during the motion because of the upward slope of the green. This is consistent with the fact that the position x at 2.0 s is a smaller positive number than the position x at 1.0 s. It is also reassuring that the x component of the average velocity computed from the displacement for the interval from 1.0 s to 2.0 s is between the values we calculated for the instantaneous velocity at 1.0 s and 2.0 s.

Guided Problem 2.8 You're it!

Six children—call them A, B, C, D, E, and F—are running up and down the street playing tag. Their positions as a function of time are plotted in Figure WG2.6. The street runs east-west, and the positive x direction is eastward. Use Figure WG2.6 to answer these questions: (*a*) In which direction is each child moving? (*b*) Which, if any, of the children are running at constant velocity? Of those who are, is the x component of their velocity positive or negative? (*c*) Which, if any, of the children are not moving at constant velocity? Are they speeding up or slowing down? (*d*) Which child has the highest average speed? The lowest average speed? (*e*) Does any child pass another child during the time interval shown in the graph?

Figure WG2.6

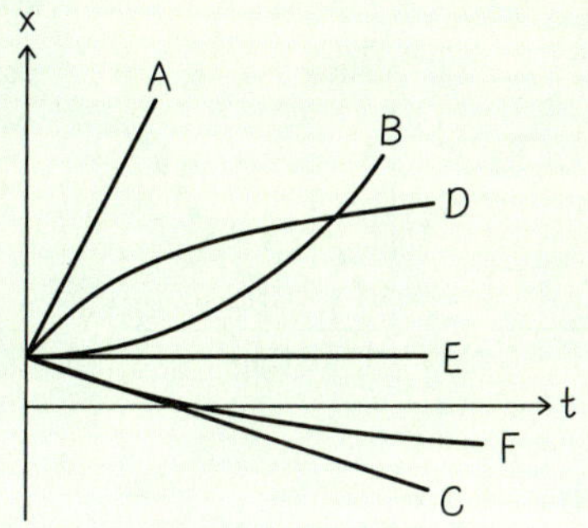

❶ **GETTING STARTED**

1. Use the curves in Figure WG2.6 to describe the motion of each child in words.

❷ **DEVISE PLAN**

2. How can you determine, from an $x(t)$ curve, the direction of a child's motion at any instant, and how is that information related to velocity and to speed?
3. What does motion at constant velocity look like on a position-versus-time graph? What does a changing-velocity situation look like on the graph?
4. How can you tell which child has the highest speed and which the lowest speed?
5. What feature in the graph would indicate that one child has passed another? In other words, what is the relationship of their positions at the instant one passes another?

❸ **EXECUTE PLAN**

❹ **EVALUATE RESULT**

PRACTICE

Questions and Problems

For instructor-assigned homework, go to MasteringPhysics® MP

Dots indicate difficulty level of problems: • = *easy,* •• = *intermediate,* ••• = *hard;* CR = *context-rich problem.*

2.1 From reality to model

1. What minimum information must be extracted from a film clip of a moving object in order to quantify the object's motion? •
2. The sequence in Figure P2.2 represents a ball rolling into a wall and bouncing off of it. The ball is 10 mm in diameter. Make a graph showing the distance from the leading edge of the ball to the closest part of the wall (using the wall as the origin) as it changes from frame to frame. ••

Figure P2.2

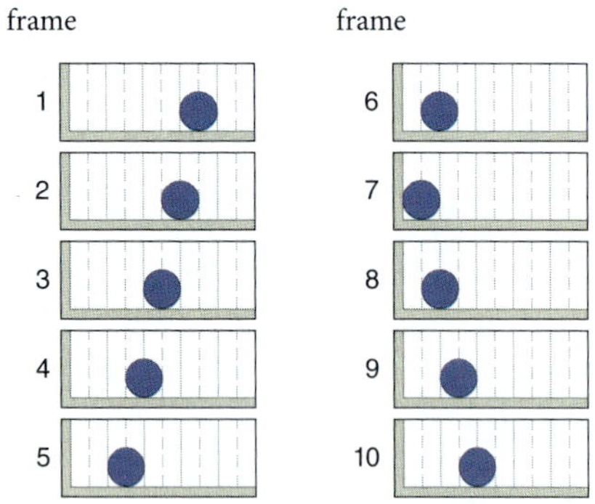

3. The sequence in Figure P2.3 represents a ball that is initially held above the ground. In the first frame the ball is released. In subsequent frames the ball falls, bounces on the ground, rises, and bounces again. The ball is 10 mm in diameter. Make a plot showing the position of this ball relative to the ground. ••

Figure P2.3

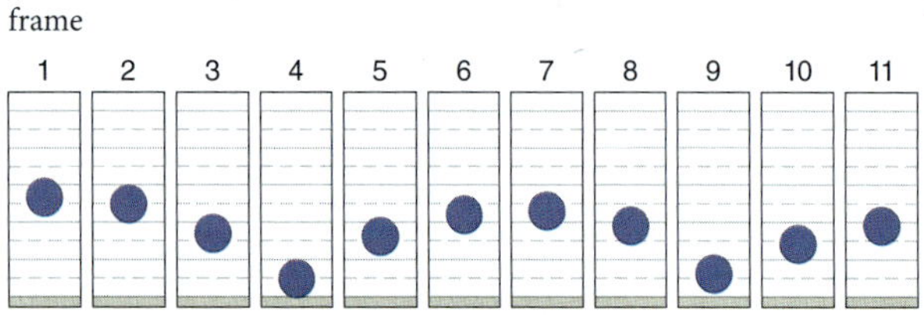

4. Figure P2.4 shows a graph of position versus frame number from a film clip of a moving object. Describe this motion from beginning to end, and state any assumptions you make. ••

Figure P2.4

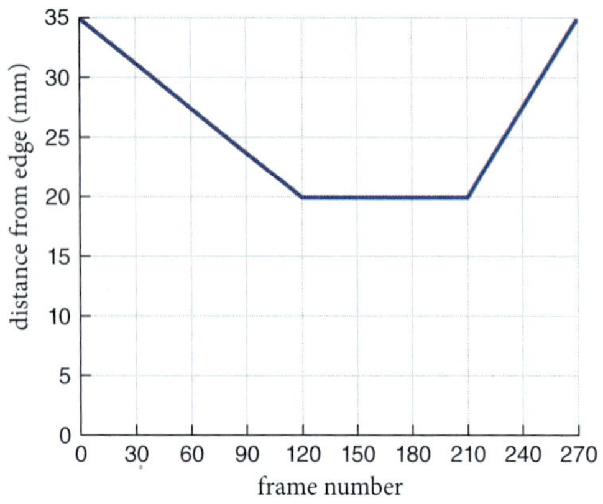

5. Your class observed several different objects in motion along different lines. Figure P2.5 shows some of the graphs other students made of the events. They have labeled the horizontal axis "time" and the vertical axis "position," but they have not marked any points along those axes and have not specified an origin. Which of the graphs could be describing the same motion? ••

Figure P2.5

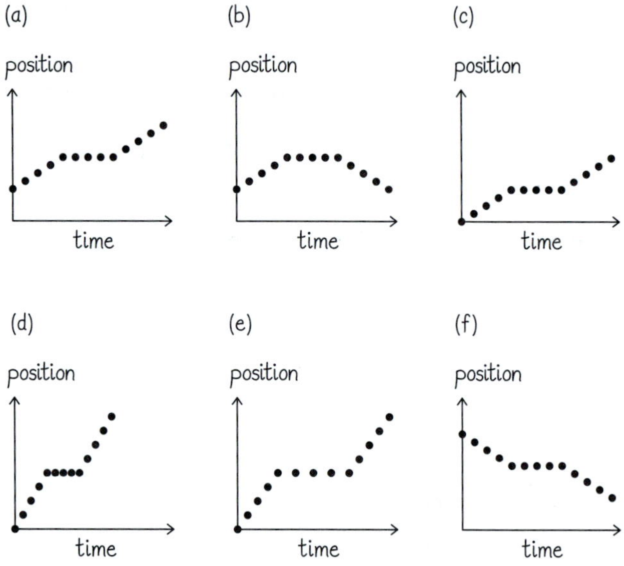

2.2 Position and displacement

6. If an object's initial position is $x_i = +6.5$ m and its final position is $x_f = +0.23$ m, what is the x component of its displacement? •
7. You walk 3.2 km to the supermarket and then back home. What is your distance traveled? What is your displacement? •
8. A 2000-m race is held on a 400-m oval track. From start to finish, what is the displacement of the winner? •
9. You are shown a film clip of a dog running in front of a blank wall. The observations are to be plotted using the horizontal and vertical axes labeled with seconds and meters, respectively. How many different graphs of this motion with respect to time could be produced if: (*a*) No additional information is given? (*b*) An origin is given? (*c*) Both the origin and the length of the dog are given? (*d*) An origin, the length of the dog, and the time interval between frames of the film clip are all given? ••
10. Assume you have a film clip of someone walking from left to right. You draw a position-versus-time graph of the motion and choose your origin to be the left edge of the frame. A friend chooses to take the right edge of the frame as the origin. Both of you choose the positive x direction to be from left to right. (*a*) How would your graphs differ? (*b*) Would the two be equally good representations of reality? ••

11. Suppose the vertical axis in Figure P2.11 was calibrated in inches rather than in meters and the horizontal axis in minutes rather than seconds. How would the shape of the curve change? ••

Figure P2.11

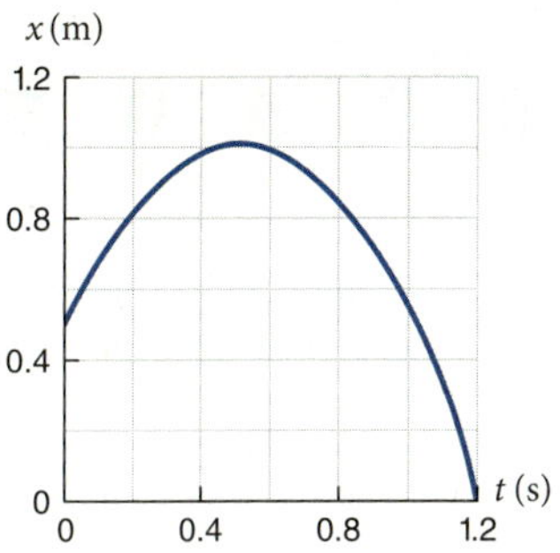

12. In the graph in Figure P2.12, determine (*a*) the displacement of the object and (*b*) the distance the object traveled. ••

Figure P2.12

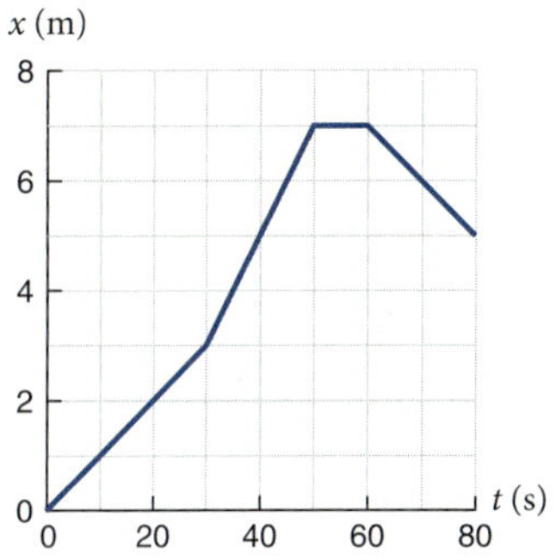

13. You walk four blocks east along 12th Street, then two blocks west, then one block east, then five blocks east, then seven blocks west. Let the x axis point east and have its origin at your starting point. If all blocks are equal in size, what is the x component of your displacement, in blocks? ••

14. In the foreground of a side-view picture of a table, the legs touch the floor at a point that is 12 mm from the bottom of the picture, and the tabletop is 65 mm from the bottom of the picture. One end of the tabletop is 14 mm from the left edge of the picture, and the other end is 99 mm from the left edge. Estimate the actual length of the tabletop. •••

2.3 Representing motion

15. Figure P2.15 shows the position of a swimmer in a race as a function of time. Describe this motion. •

Figure P2.15

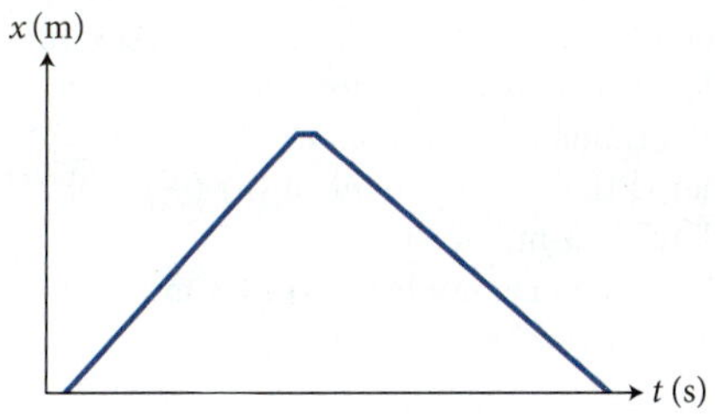

16. In the morning, a hiker at the bottom of a mountain heads up the trail toward the top. At the same instant, another hiker at the top of the mountain heads down the same trail toward the bottom. Each hiker arrives at her destination by the end of the day. Explain why, no matter what happens to either hiker along the way (lunch breaks, turnarounds to fetch dropped pocket knives, or changes of pace), they meet on the trail sometime during the day. •

17. Will interpolation between known data points always give an accurate continuous path? If so, explain why. If not, give a counterexample. •

18. Figure P2.18 shows the motion of an object as a function of time. How long did it take the object to get from the position $x = 2.0$ m to the position $x = 3.0$ m? Is there only one correct answer? ••

Figure P2.18

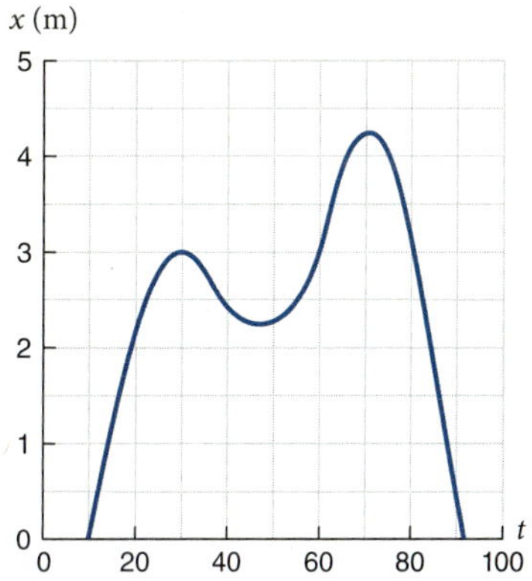

19. Figure P2.19 is based on a multiple-flash photographic sequence of a ball rolling from left to right on a soft surface. Sketch a graph of the ball's position as a function of time. ••

Figure P2.19

20. The position of an object is given by $x(t) = p + qt + rt^2$, with $p = +0.20$ m, $q = -2.0$ m/s, and $r = +2.0$ m/s^2. (*a*) Draw a graph of this motion from $t = 0$ to $t = 1.2$ s. (*b*) What is the displacement of the object in the interval from $t = 0$ to $t = 0.50$ s? (*c*) What maximum distance from the origin does the object reach during the interval in part *a*? ••

21. After a rocket is launched at $t = 0$, its position is given by $x(t) = qt^3$, where q is some positive constant. (*a*) Sketch a graph of the rocket's position as a function of time. (*b*) What is the rocket's displacement during the interval from $t = T$ to $t = 3T$? ••

22. Consider the position function $x(t) = p + qt + rt^2$ for a moving object, with $p = +3.0$ m, $q = +2.0$ m/s, and $r = -5.0$ m/s^2. (*a*) What is the value of $x(t)$ at $t = 0$? (*b*) At what value of t does $x(t)$ have its maximum value? (*c*) What is the value of $x(t)$ at this instant? (*d*) Draw a position-versus-time graph. (*e*) Describe the behavior of an object that is represented by this function. (*f*) How far has the object traveled in these intervals: From $t = 0$ to $t = 0.50$ s? From $t = 0$ to $t = 1.0$ s? From $t = 0.50$ s to $t = 1.0$ s? ••

23. The motion of some object is described by the equation $x(t) = at - b\sin(ct)$, where $a = 1.0\ \text{m/s}$, $b = 2.0\ \text{m}$, and $c = 4\pi\ \text{s}^{-1}$. This motion is being observed by four students, and measurements of the position of this object begin at time $t = 0$. Students A, B, C, and D measure every 1.0 s, 0.5 s, 0.25 s, and 0.1 s, respectively. Draw four graphs of the measurements made by the four different students. Include at least ten data points in each graph. Do the four students agree on the type of motion that is taking place? •••

2.4 Average speed and average velocity

24. In the Midwest, you sometimes see large marks painted on the highway shoulder. How can police patrols flying overhead use these marks to check for speeders? •
25. Calculate the average speed for the runners in the following races: (*a*) 100 m in 9.84 s, (*b*) 200 m in 19.32 s, (*c*) 400 m in 43.29 s, (*d*) 1500 m in 3 min, 27.37 s, (*e*) 10 km in 26 min, 38.08 s, (*f*) marathon (26 mi, 385 yd) in 2 h, 6 min, 50 s. •
26. (*a*) Can two cars traveling in opposite directions on a highway have the same speed? (*b*) Can they have the same velocity? •
27. Figure P2.27 is based on a multiple-flash photographic sequence, taken at equal time intervals, of a ball rolling on a smooth surface from right to left. (*a*) Argue that the ball moves with at least two different speeds during the motion represented in the sequence. (*b*) During which part of the motion does the ball have the larger speed? •

Figure P2.27

28. Can the average speed of an object moving in one direction ever be larger than the object's maximum speed? ••
29. Figure P2.29 shows position as a function of time for two cars traveling along the same highway. (*a*) At what instant(s) are the cars next to each other? (*b*) At what instant(s) are they traveling at the same speed? ••

Figure P2.29

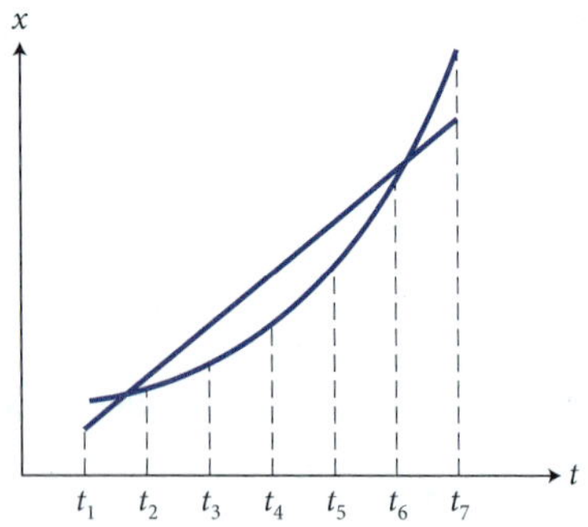

30. Figure P2.30 is based on two multiple-flash photographic sequences of a hockey puck sliding on ice. Sequence *a* was shot at 30 flashes per second, and sequence *b* was shot at 20 flashes per second. Compare the speeds of the puck in the two cases. ••

Figure P2.30

31. A cyclist takes 10 min to ride from point A to point B and then another 10 min to continue on from point B to point C, all along a straight line. If you know that the average speed on the ride from A to B was faster than the average speed on the ride from B to C, what, if anything, can you conclude about the position of point B relative to points A and C? ••
32. In a road rally race, you are told to drive half the trip at 25 m/s and half the trip at 35 m/s. It's not clear from the directions whether this means to drive half the *time* at each speed or drive half the *distance* at each speed. Which would yield the shorter travel time for the entire trip? ••
33. A bicycle racer rides from a starting marker to a turnaround marker at 10 m/s. She then rides back along the same route from the turnaround marker to the starting marker at 16 m/s. (*a*) What is her average speed for the whole race? (*b*) A friend of yours gets an answer of 13 m/s. What is most likely the source of his error? ••
34. You walk 1.25 km from home to a restaurant in 20 min, stay there for 1.0 h, and then take another 20 min to walk back home. (*a*) What is your average speed for the trip? (*b*) What is your average velocity? ••
35. You are going to visit your grandparents, who live 500 km away. As you drive on the freeway, your speed is a constant 100 km/h. Half an hour after you leave home, your brother discovers that you forgot your wallet. He jumps into his car and speeds after you. The two of you arrive at your grandparents' house at the same instant. What is your brother's average speed for the trip? ••
36. You and your brother both leave your house at the same instant and drive in separate cars along a straight highway to a nearby lake. After 10 min, you are both 3.0 km from your house. You are now driving at 100 km/h, and you continue at this constant speed; your brother is going faster than this. After another 20 min, your brother arrives at the lake, but you are still 5.0 km away. (*a*) How far is it from your house to the lake? (*b*) What is your brother's average speed for the trip? (*c*) Your brother beats you to the lake by what time interval? •••

2.5 Scalars and vectors

37. You are standing on a sidewalk that runs east-west. Consider these instructions I might give you: (1) Walk 15 steps along the sidewalk and stop. (2) Walk 15 steps westward on the sidewalk and stop. Do my instructions unambiguously determine your final location in each case? •
38. What is the x component of (*a*) $(+3\ \text{m})\hat{\imath}$, (*b*) $(+3\ \text{m/s})\hat{\imath}$, and (*c*) $(-3\ \text{m/s})\hat{\imath}$? •
39. What is the magnitude of (*a*) $(+3\ \text{m})\hat{\imath}$, (*b*) $(+3\ \text{m/s})\hat{\imath}$, and (*c*) $(-3\ \text{m/s})\hat{\imath}$? •

40. Vectors $\vec{A}$ and $\vec{B}$ each have a magnitude of 5 m and point to the left. Vector $\vec{A}$ begins at the origin, while vector $\vec{B}$ begins at a location 8 m to the right of the origin. (*a*) If the positive x axis is pointed to the right, what is the x component of each vector? (*b*) If the positive x axis is pointed to the left, what is the x component of each vector? ••

41. Vector $\vec{A}$ points to the right, as does the positive x axis. (*a*) Express this vector in unit vector notation. (*b*) Now flip $\vec{A}$ to the opposite direction. Express it in unit vector notation. (*c*) Keep the vector in its new direction and flip the x axis so that the positive direction is to the left. Express the vector in unit vector notation. ••

2.6 Position and displacement vectors

42. Consider two vectors along the x axis, one with x component $A_x = +3$ m and the other with x component $B_x = -5$ m. What are (*a*) $\vec{A} + \vec{B}$ and (*b*) $\vec{A} - \vec{B}$? •

43. You stop to rest while climbing a vertical 10-m pole. With the origin at the level of your head and with the positive x direction upward, as shown in Figure P2.43, what are (*a*) the x coordinate of the pole's tip and (*b*) the tip's position vector? •

Figure P2.43

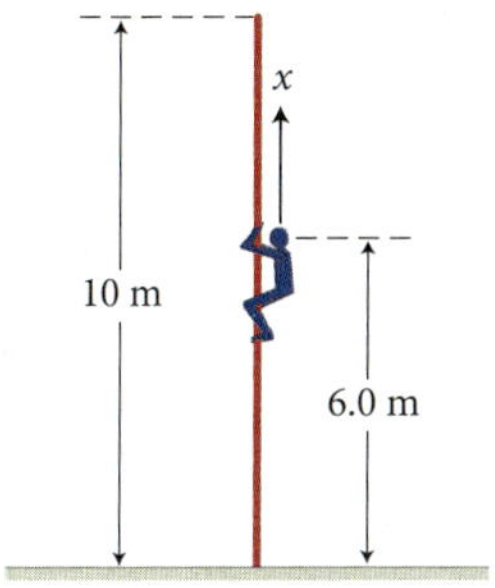

44. The height x above the ground of a vertically launched projectile is given by $x(t) = pt - qt^2$, with $p = 42$ m/s and $q = 4.9$ m/s^2. (*a*) At what instant is the projectile at a height of 20 m? (*b*) What is the meaning of the two solutions obtained in part *a*? (*c*) Sketch a graph of the x component of the projectile's velocity as a function of time. ••

45. Figure P2.45 shows the x coordinate as a function of time for a moving object. What is the object's x coordinate (*a*) at $t = 0$, (*b*) $t = 0.20$ s, and (*c*) $t = 1.2$ s? What is the object's displacement (*d*) between $t = 0$ and $t = 0.20$ s, (*e*) between $t = 0.20$ s and $t = 1.2$ s, and (*f*) between $t = 0$ and $t = 1.2$ s? What is the distance traveled by the object (*g*) between $t = 0$ and $t = 0.80$ s, (*h*) between $t = 0.80$ s and $t = 1.2$ s, and (*i*) between $t = 0$ and $t = 1.2$ s? ••

Figure P2.45

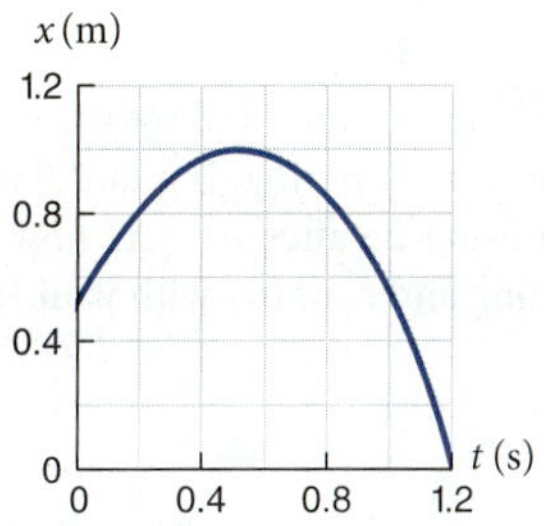

46. Arrange three displacement vectors, of magnitudes 2 m, 5 m, and 7 m, so that their sum is (*a*) $(+10\text{ m})\hat{\imath}$, (*b*) $(-4\text{ m})\hat{\imath}$, and (*c*) 0. ••

47. The direction of vector $\vec{A}$ is opposite the direction of the unit vector $\hat{\imath}$. Vector $\vec{B}$ has half the magnitude of $\vec{A}$, and $\vec{A} - \vec{B}$ is a vector of magnitude $\frac{3}{2}A$. Express $\vec{B}$ in terms of $\vec{A}$. ••

48. You have to deliver some 5.0-kg packages from your home to two locations. You drive for 2.0 h at 25 mi/h due east (call this segment 1 of your trip), then turn around and drive due west for 30 min at 20 mi/h (segment 2). Use a coordinate system with the positive x axis aimed toward the east and the origin at your home. (*a*) What is your position vector at the instant you reach the end of segment 1? (*b*) What is your position vector at the instant you reach the end of segment 2? (*c*) Calculate your displacement during segment 2. (*d*) Calculate your displacement for the whole trip. (*e*) What is the distance traveled? (*f*) Draw to scale the position vectors you found in parts *a* and *b*. (*g*) Use vector addition to determine the displacement vectors asked for in parts *c* and *d*. Do your results in part *g* agree with the values you calculated in parts *c* and *d*? ••

49. (*a*) In Figure P2.49, what vector must you add to $\vec{A}$ to get $\vec{C}$? (*b*) What vector must you subtract from $\vec{A}$ to get $\vec{C}$? Sketch your answers on a copy of the figure to confirm your results. ••

Figure P2.49

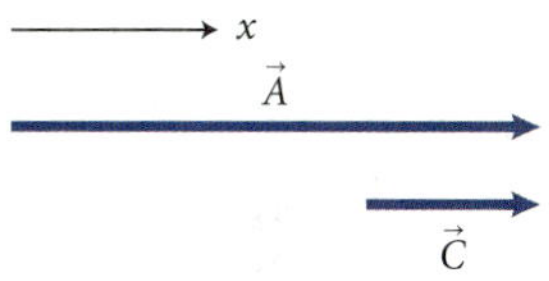

2.7 Velocity as a vector

50. You drive due east at 40 km/h for 2.0 h and then stop. (*a*) What is your speed during the trip? (*b*) Is speed a scalar or a vector? (*c*) How far have you gone? Is distance a scalar or a vector? (*d*) Write a vector expression for your position after you stop (in the form "*N* units of distance in the *Q* direction"). (*e*) Write a vector expression for your velocity during the trip, assuming east is the $+x$ direction. •

51. For the motion represented in Figure P2.45, calculate (*a*) the object's average velocity between $t = 0$ and $t = 1.2$ s, and (*b*) its average speed during this same time interval. (*c*) Why is the answer to part *a* different from the answer to part *b*? ••

52. Figure P2.52 is the position-versus-time graph for a moving object. What is the object's average velocity (*a*) between $t = 0$ and $t = 1.0$ s, (*b*) between $t = 0$ and $t = 4.0$ s, and (*c*) between $t = 3.0$ s and $t = 6.0$ s? (*d*) What is its average speed between $t = 3.0$ s and $t = 6.0$ s? (*e*) Draw to scale the velocity vector for the intervals $t = 3.0$ s to $t = 3.5$ s, $t = 3.5$ s to $t = 4.0$ s, $t = 4.0$ s to $t = 5.0$ s, and $t = 5.0$ s to $t = 6.0$ s. (*f*) What is the sum of all the vectors you drew in part *e*? ••

Figure P2.52

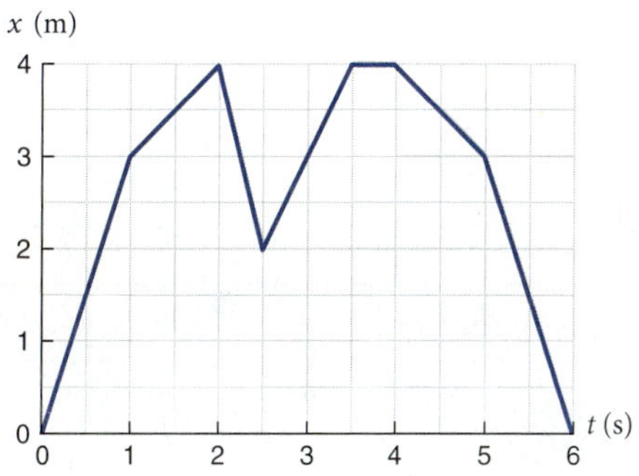

53. You normally drive a 12-h trip at an average speed of 100 km/h. Today you are in a hurry. During the first two-thirds of the distance, you drive at 108 km/h. If the trip still takes 12 h, what is your average speed in the last third of the distance? ●●●

2.8 Motion at constant velocity

54. A cart starts at position $x = -2.073$ m and travels along the x axis with a constant x component of velocity of -4.02 m/s. What is the position of the cart after 0.103 s? ●

55. A bug on a windowsill walks at 10 mm/s from left to right for 120 mm, slows to 6.0 mm/s and continues rightward for another 3.0 s, stops for 4.0 s, and then walks back to its starting position at 8.0 mm/s. Draw a graph (*a*) of the x coordinate of the bug's displacement as a function of time and (*b*) of the x component of its velocity as a function of time. ●

56. You and a friend work in buildings four equal-length blocks apart, and you plan to meet for lunch. Your friend strolls leisurely at 1.2 m/s, while you like a brisker pace of 1.6 m/s. Knowing this, you pick a restaurant between the two buildings at which you and your friend will arrive at the same instant if both of you leave your respective buildings at the same instant. In blocks, how far from your building is the restaurant? ●●

57. Figure P2.57 shows the velocity-versus-time graphs for objects A and B moving along an x axis. Which object has the greater displacement over the time interval shown in the graph? ●●

Figure P2.57

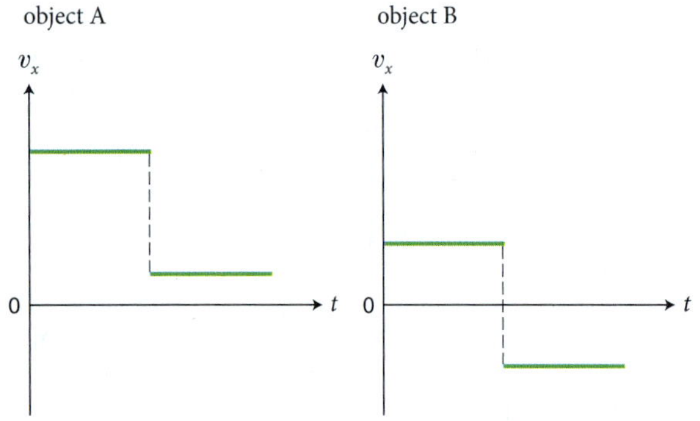

58. Figure P2.58 shows the x component of the velocity as a function of time for objects A and B. Which object has the greater displacement over the time interval shown in the graph? ●●

Figure P2.58

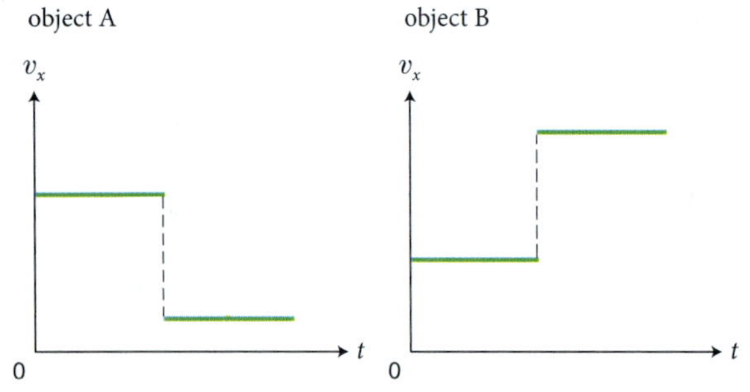

59. An object moving along an x axis starts out at $x = -10$ m. Using its velocity-versus-time graph in Figure P2.59, draw a graph of the object's x coordinate as a function of time. ●●

Figure P2.59

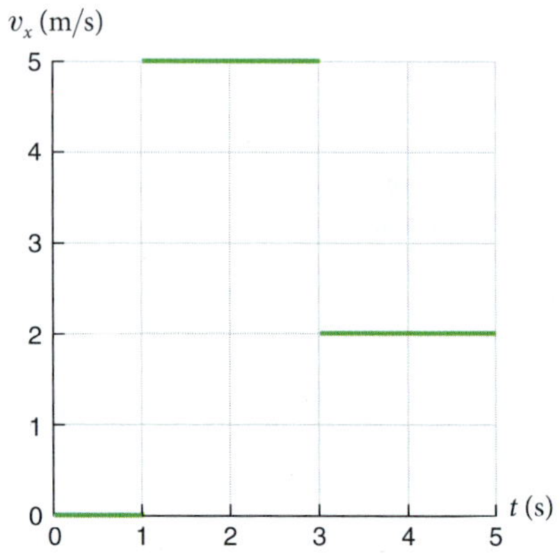

60. You and a friend ride bicycles to school. Both of you start at the same instant from your house, you riding at 10 m/s and your friend riding at 15 m/s. During the trip your friend has a flat tire that takes him 12 min to fix. He then continues the trip at the same speed of 15 m/s. If the distance to school is 15 km, which of you gets to school first? ●●

61. You are going on a bicycle ride with a friend. You start 3.0 min ahead of her from her carport, pedal at 5.0 m/s for 10 min, then stop and chat with a neighbor for 5.0 min. As you chat, your friend pedals by, oblivious to you. You notice that she's forgotten to bring the lunch basket you plan to share, and you immediately start to pedal back to her house to get it, now moving at 10 m/s. When you are halfway back, your friend catches up with you, having herself remembered about the basket. (*a*) What was the magnitude of her average velocity for the trip up to that instant? (*b*) What was the magnitude of her average velocity between the instant she passed you and the neighbor and the instant she caught up with you? ●●●

62. You and your roommate are moving to a city 320 mi away. Your roommate drives a rental truck at a constant 60 mi/h, and you drive your car at 70 mi/h. The two of you begin the trip at the same instant. An hour after leaving, you decide to take a short break at a rest stop. If you are planning to arrive at your destination a half hour before your roommate gets there, how long can you stay at the rest stop before resuming your drive? ●●●

63. You are jogging eastward at an average speed of 2.0 m/s. Once you are 2.0 km from your home, you turn around and begin jogging westward, back to your house. At one point on your return trip, you look to the north and see a friend. You run northward at a greater speed of 3.0 m/s to catch your friend. After jogging next to each other for a time (at 3.0 m/s), you turn around (southward) and return at 3.0 m/s to your original path, and resume jogging at 2.0 m/s westward. If you return home 40 min after you left, how far north did you run while catching and running with your friend? ●●●

2.9 Instantaneous velocity

64. Which of these quantities depend on the choice of origin in a coordinate system: position, displacement, speed, average velocity, instantaneous velocity? •
65. A dragster's position as a function of time is given by $x(t) = bt^{3/2}$, where $b = 30.2\ \text{m/s}^{3/2}$. Calculate the x component of its velocity at 1.0 s and at 4.0 s. •
66. A mouse runs along a baseboard in your house. The mouse's position as a function of time is given by $x(t) = pt^2 + qt$, with $p = 0.40\ \text{m/s}^2$ and $q = -1.20\ \text{m/s}$. Determine the mouse's average velocity and average speed (*a*) between $t = 0$ and $t = 1.0$ s and (*b*) between $t = 1.0$ s and $t = 4.0$ s. ••
67. Car A is spotted passing car B just east of Westerville at exactly 2:00 p.m. The same two cars are then spotted next to each other just west of Easterville at exactly 3:00 p.m. If car B had a constant velocity of 30 m/s eastward for the whole trip, defend the proposition that car A had to have a velocity of 30 m/s eastward at some instant during that hour. ••
68. The motion of an electron is given by $x(t) = pt^3 + qt^2 + r$, with $p = -2.0\ \text{m/s}^3$, $q = +1.0\ \text{m/s}^2$, and $r = +9.0$ m. Determine its velocity at (*a*) $t = 0$, (*b*) $t = 1.0$ s, (*c*) $t = 2.0$ s, and (*d*) $t = 3.0$ s. ••
69. The car in Figure P2.69 passes a bright streetlight at constant speed, casting a shadow on a wall on the other side of the street. For simplicity, assume that car and light are at the same height. (*a*) Which is greater: the average speed of the car or the average speed of the shadow's leading edge? (*b*) Is there any instant at which the speed of the shadow's leading edge is the same as the speed of the car? If so, what is the car's position relative to the streetlight at that instant? If not, why not? ••

Figure P2.69

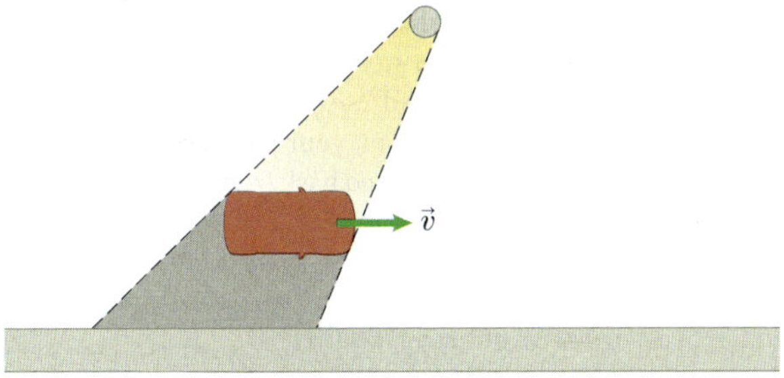

70. The position of a 6.0-kg shopping cart rolling down a ramp is given by $x(t) = p + qt^2$, with $p = +1.50$ m and $q = +2.00\ \text{m/s}^2$. What is the x component of the cart's average velocity (*a*) between $t = 2.00$ s and $t = 3.00$ s, (*b*) between $t = 2.00$ s and $t = 2.10$ s, and (*c*) between $t = 2.00$ s and $t = 2.01$ s? (*d*) Compute the limit of the average velocity between $t_i = 2.00$ s and $t_f = 2.00\ \text{s} + \Delta t$ as Δt approaches zero. (*e*) Show that your result agrees with what is expected by taking the time derivative of position. •••

Additional Problems

71. You leave Fort Worth, Texas, at 2:38 p.m. and arrive in Dallas at 3:23 p.m., covering a distance of 58 km. What is your average speed (*a*) in meters per second and (*b*) in miles per hour? •
72. In a footrace between two runners, is it possible for the second-place finisher to have a greater speed at the finish line than the winner? •
73. You wish to describe the position of the base of the pole in Figure P2.43 using the indicated coordinate system. What are (*a*) the position coordinate of the base, (*b*) the position vector of the base, and (*c*) the magnitude of this position vector? •
74. Runners P, Q, and R run a 5-km race in 15, 20, and 25 min, respectively, each at a constant speed. When runner Q crosses the 1-km mark, what is the distance, to the nearest meter, between runners P and R? Assume that times and distances are correct to at least four significant digits. ••
75. Runners A, B, and C run a 100-m race, each at a constant speed. Runner A takes first place, beating runner B by 10 m. Runner B takes second place, beating runner C by 10 m. By what time interval does runner A beat runner C? ••
76. At $t = 0$, car A passes a milepost at constant speed v_A. Car B passes the same milepost at constant speed $v_B > v_A$ after a time interval Δt has elapsed. (*a*) In terms of v_A, v_B, and Δt, at what instant does car B catch up to car A? (*b*) How far past the milepost does this happen? ••
77. You and your friend are running at a long racetrack. You pass the starting line while running at a constant 4.0 m/s. Fifteen seconds later, your friend passes the starting line while running at 6.0 m/s in the same direction, and at the same instant you increase your speed to 5.0 m/s. (*a*) How long does it take for your friend to catch up with you? (*b*) How far are the two of you from the starting line when your friend catches up with you? ••
78. You drive an old car on a straight, level highway at 45 mi/h for 10 mi, and then the car stalls. You leave the car and, continuing in the direction in which you were driving, walk to a friend's house 2.0 mi away, arriving 40 min after you begin walking. What is your average speed during the whole trip? ••
79. The position of a moving car is given by $x(t) = c\sqrt{t}$. Over the interval $t = 10$ s to $t = 20$ s, is the average speed greater than, equal to, or less than the instantaneous speed (*a*) at $t = 15$ s and (*b*) at $t = 20$ s? ••
80. The following equations give the x component of the position for four objects as functions of time:

object 1: $x(t) = a$, where $a = 5$ m

object 2: $x(t) = bt + c$, where $b = +4$ m/s and $c = -1$ m

object 3: $x(t) = et^2 + ft$, where $e = +5\ \text{m/s}^2$ and $f = -9$ m/s

object 4: $x(t) = gt^2 + h$, where $g = -3\ \text{m/s}^2$ and $h = +12$ m.

(*a*) Which objects have a velocity that changes with time? (*b*) Which object is at the origin at the earliest instant, and what is that instant? (*c*) What is that object's velocity 1 s after the instant you calculated in part *b*? ••

81. A furniture mover is lifting a small safe by pulling on a rope threaded through the pulley system shown in Figure P2.81. (*a*) What is the ratio of the vertical distance the safe moves to the length of the rope pulled by the mover? (*b*) What is the ratio of the speed of the safe to the speed of the segment of rope pulled by the mover? ••

Figure P2.81

PRACTICE

82. Two steamrollers begin 100 m apart and head toward each other, each at a constant speed of 1.00 m/s. At the same instant, a fly that travels at a constant speed of 2.20 m/s starts from the front roller of the southbound steamroller and flies to the front roller of the northbound one, then turns around and flies to the front roller of the southbound once again, and continues in this way until it is crushed between the steamrollers in a collision. What distance does the fly travel? ••

83. Consider a 2.0-kg object that moves along the x axis according to the expression $x(t) = ct^3$, where $c = +0.120\ \text{m/s}^3$. (*a*) Determine the x component of the object's average velocity during the interval from $t_i = 0.500$ s to $t_f = 1.50$ s. (*b*) Repeat for the interval from $t_i = 0.950$ s to $t_f = 1.05$ s. (*c*) Show that your results approach the x component of the velocity at $t = 1.00$ s if you continue to reduce the interval by factors of ten. Use all significant digits provided by your calculator at each step. ••

84. The position of a yo-yo as a function of time is given by $x(t) = A\cos(pt + q)$, where $A = 0.60$ m, $p = \frac{1}{2}\pi\ \text{s}^{-1}$, and $q = \frac{1}{2}\pi$. (*a*) Plot this function at 17 equally spaced instants from $t = 0$ to $t = 8.0$ s. (*b*) At what instants is the velocity zero? (*c*) Plot the x component of the velocity as a function of time over the time interval from $t = 0$ to $t = 8$ s. •••

85. Zeno, a Greek philosopher and mathematician, was famous for his paradoxes, one of which can be paraphrased as follows: A runner has a race of length d to run. At the instant that is a time interval Δt after the start, he is a distance $\frac{1}{2}d$ from the finish line. After an additional time interval of $\frac{1}{2}\Delta t$ (elapsed time is $\Delta t + \frac{1}{2}\Delta t$), he has traveled a distance of $\frac{3}{4}d$. He then is a distance $\frac{1}{4}d$ from the finish line. At elapsed time $\Delta t + \frac{1}{2}\Delta t + \frac{1}{4}\Delta t$, he is a distance $\frac{1}{8}d$ from the finish line, and so on. This description of the motion is an infinite series of smaller and smaller displacements. The paradox is that this analysis suggests that the runner will never make it to the finish line, even though we know he does. (*a*) What is the runner's speed? (*b*) What time interval is needed for the trip? (*c*) Describe the resolution to this seeming paradox. •••

86. Four traffic lights on a stretch of road are spaced 300 m apart. There is a 10-s lag time between successive green lights: The second light turns green 10 s after the first light turns green, the third light turns green 10 s after the second light does (and thus 20 s after the first light turns green), and so on. Each light stays green for 15 s. Having watched this sequence for some time, you understand that there should be one best constant speed to drive to make all four green lights. You do not want to be delayed, but you are a cautious driver and want to drive as slowly as you can but still make it through all the lights on a single cycle. ••• CR

87. Hare and Tortoise of Aesop's fable fame are having a rematch, a mile-long race. Hare has planned more carefully this time. Five minutes into the race, he figures he can take a 40-min nap and still win easily because it takes him only 10 min to cover 1 mi and because he thinks that Tortoise's top speed is 1.0 mi/h. However, Tortoise has been working out, and as he passes napping Hare, he suddenly increases his speed to $\frac{5}{3}$ mi/h. When Hare wakes up, he sees Tortoise way ahead and runs at full speed to try to catch up. ••• CR

88. Two runners are in a 100-m race. Runner A can run this distance in 12.0 s, but runner B takes 13.5 s on a good day. To make the race interesting, runner A starts behind the starting line. If she wants the race to end in a tie, how far behind the starting line should she position herself? •••

89. You are on planet Dither, whose inhabitants often change their minds on how to choose a reference axis. At time $t = 0$, while standing 2.0 m to the left of the origin of a reference axis for which the positive direction points to the left, you launch a toy car that moves with increasing speed to the right. The car's x coordinate (x component of the position) is given by $x(t) = p + qt + rt^2$, where $p = +2.0$ m, $q = -3.0$ m/s, and $r = -4.0\ \text{m/s}^2$. (*a*) What is the equation of the car's x coordinate if the reference axis is flipped so that the positive direction points to the right? (*b*) What is the equation of the car's x coordinate if the axis is kept in its original orientation (leftward is the positive direction) but the origin is moved to where you are standing? (*c*) Draw a position-versus-time graph for each of the three combinations of axis direction and origin location. (*d*) What is the x component of the car's displacement at $t = 4.0$ s in each of these three axis/origin combinations? (*e*) What is the x component of the car's velocity at this instant in each combination? (*f*) Explain why there is no physical difference in the answers to parts *d* and *e* even though some of the mathematical expressions you get look different from one another. •••

90. Your dream job as a 12-year-old was to sit at a computer at NASA mission control and guide the motion of the Mars rover across the Martian surface 2.0×10^8 km away. Communication signals to steer the rover travel at the speed of light between Earth and Mars, and the rover's top speed is 2.0 m/min. In your dream, your job was to make sure, based on television images beamed back from the craft, that the rover does not run off a Martian cliff. The shift supervisor recommended that your first task be to determine how far ahead in the rover's field of view you have to watch out for obstacles in order to avoid a disaster. ••• CR

91. You are a driver for Ace Mining Company. The boss insists that, every hour on the hour, a loaded truck leaves the mine at 90.0 km/h, carrying ore to a mill 630 km away. She also insists that an empty truck traveling at 105 km/h leaves the mill every hour on the half hour to return to the mine. One day you begin to count the empty trucks that you encounter, per hour, on your trip to the mill. The next day you decide that loaded trucks are more important, counted on your return trip. ••• CR

PRACTICE

Answers to Review Questions

1. If your graph is to be identical, she must tell you what she chose as her reference axis and her origin.
2. An object is moving if its position changes with time. It is at rest if its position remains the same as time passes.
3. You need to know the actual size of the object.
4. Use one dimension of the object's actual size to determine what real-world length 1 mm on a frame of the film clip corresponds to. If the object is, for instance, a car 3 m long and the car length on the frame is 2 mm, you know that every 1-mm distance moved by the objects in the film clip represents a real-world distance of 1.5 m. Then use the conversion factor (1.5 m)/(1 mm) to convert any distance each object moves on the film clip to a real-world distance in meters, and plot the distances (or quantities derived from them) on your graph.
5. The phrase reminds you that those quantities are vectors and are measured with respect to some specific x axis.
6. Displacement is a vector, so it is represented by an arrow drawn from the initial position to the final position.
7. *Interpolation* means drawing a smooth curve through a set of data points plotted on a graph. The region of the curve between any two adjacent points tells us, for the infinite number of points between the two plotted points, the numerical value of the quantity being plotted.
8. (*a*) Locate the instant on the time axis and draw a vertical line that passes through that value and intersects the curve. Then draw a horizontal line that passes through the intersection point and extends to the position axis. (*b*) Solve the equation for x, substitute the specific time value wherever the symbol t occurs in the equation, and calculate the numerical value of x.
9. A steep slope indicates a larger speed than that associated with a gentle slope. A downward slope indicates velocity in the negative x direction; an upward slope indicates velocity in the positive x direction.
10. The object moved in the negative x direction during that time interval.
11. A scalar is a mathematical quantity that is completely specified by a number and a unit of measure. A vector is a quantity that must be specified by a direction in addition to a number and a unit of measure.
12. The magnitude of a vector is a number and a unit of measure equal to the absolute value of the x component of the vector.
13. The purpose of $\hat{\imath}$ is to define the direction of the positive x axis.
14. The symbol Δ means "the change in" the variable that immediately follows the symbol Δ. It is the difference between the final value of that variable and its initial value.
15. Displacement is a vector; distance is a scalar.
16. Distance can never be negative because it is defined as the absolute value of the difference between two positions. Distance traveled can never be negative because it is a sum of distances (all positive) between successive positions in the segments of a trip.
17. The x component of the displacement is negative when the direction of the displacement is opposite the direction of the positive x axis.
18. Distance traveled is found by adding the three distances (which are all positive by definition).
19. You add two vectors by placing the tail of the second vector at the tip of the first vector. The sum is the vector that runs from the tail of the first vector to the tip of the second. You subtract one vector from another by reversing the direction of the vector being subtracted and then adding this reversed vector to the other vector.
20. The result is a vector of magnitude $|c\vec{A}| = |c||\vec{A}| = |c|A$. Its direction is the same as the direction of $\vec{A}$ if c is positive and opposite the direction of $\vec{A}$ if c is negative. If c is zero, the result is the *zero vector*, which has no direction.
21. Average speed is a scalar; average velocity is a vector.
22. Velocity has a magnitude (the moving object's speed) and a direction (which way the object is going).
23. The average velocity during some time interval is the displacement divided by the time interval.
24. The $x(t)$ curve is a straight line with a constant slope that is not zero, and the $v_x(t)$ curve is a horizontal line.
25. You need to know its position at some instant during this interval, usually the initial position.
26. The area under the curve gives the x component of the displacement during the time interval.
27. The x component of velocity at a given instant is the slope of the tangent to the $x(t)$ curve at that instant.
28. They are equal when the velocity is constant.
29. The derivative of the position with respect to time $v_x = dx/dt$.

Answers to Guided Problems

Guided Problem 2.2 (*a*) 8 min; (*b*) 7.5 mi/h, west; (*c*) 7.5 mi/h

Guided Problem 2.4 1.8 s

Guided Problem 2.6 (*a*) $-0.43v$; (*b*) $-0.43v\hat{\imath}$, with $\hat{\imath}$ pointing west

Guided Problem 2.8 (*a*) A, B, D east; C, F west; E standing still; (*b*) A, C, E; x component of velocity is positive for A, negative for C, zero for E; (*c*) B speeding up; D, F slowing down; (*d*) A highest average speed, E lowest average speed; (*e*) B passes D

3

PRACTICE

Acceleration

Chapter Summary

Accelerated motion (Sections 3.1, 3.4, 3.5, 3.8)

Concepts If the velocity of an object is changing, the object is **accelerating.** The x component of an object's **average acceleration** is the change in the x component of its velocity divided by the time interval during which this change takes place.

The x component of the object's **instantaneous acceleration** is the x component of its acceleration at any given instant.

A **motion diagram,** which is constructed as described in the Procedure box on page 38, shows the positions of a moving object at equally spaced time intervals.

Quantitative tools The x component of the **average acceleration** is

$$a_{x,\text{av}} \equiv \frac{\Delta v_x}{\Delta t} = \frac{v_{x,\text{f}} - v_{x,\text{i}}}{t_\text{f} - t_\text{i}}. \qquad (3.1)$$

The x component of the **instantaneous acceleration** is

$$a_x = \frac{dv_x}{dt} = \frac{d^2x}{dt^2}. \qquad (3.23)$$

The x component of the change in velocity over a time interval is given by

$$\Delta v_x = \int_{t_\text{i}}^{t_\text{f}} a_x(t)dt. \qquad (3.27)$$

The x component of the displacement over a time interval is given by

$$\Delta x = \int_{t_\text{i}}^{t_\text{f}} v_x(t)dt. \qquad (3.28)$$

Motion with constant acceleration (Section 3.5)

If an object has constant acceleration, the $v_x(t)$ curve is a straight line that has a nonzero slope and the $a_x(t)$ curve is a horizontal line.

If an object moves in the x direction with constant acceleration a_x starting at $t = 0$, with initial velocity $v_{x,\text{i}}$ at initial position x_i, its x coordinate at any instant t is given by

$$x(t) = x_\text{i} + v_{x,\text{i}}t + \tfrac{1}{2}a_x t^2. \qquad (3.11)$$

The x component of its instantaneous velocity is given by

$$v_x(t) = v_{x,\text{i}} + a_x t \qquad (3.12)$$

and the x component of its final velocity is given by

$$v_{x,\text{f}}^2 = v_{x,\text{i}}^2 + 2a_x\Delta x. \qquad (3.13)$$

Free fall and projectile motion (Sections 3.2, 3.3, 3.6)

An object subject only to gravity is in **free fall.** All objects in free fall near the surface of Earth have the same acceleration, which is directed downward. We call this acceleration the **acceleration due to gravity** and denote its magnitude by the letter g.

An object that is launched but not self-propelled is in **projectile motion.** Once it is launched, it is in free fall. The path it follows is called its **trajectory.**

The magnitude g of the downward acceleration due to gravity is

$$g = |\vec{a}_\text{free fall}| = 9.8 \text{ m/s}^2 \quad \text{(near Earth's surface)}. \qquad (3.14)$$

Motion on an inclined plane (Section 3.7)

An object moving up or down an inclined plane on which friction is negligible has a constant acceleration that is directed parallel to the surface of the plane and points downward along the surface.

When friction is negligible, the x component of acceleration a_x for an object moving on an inclined plane that rises at an angle θ above the horizontal is

$$a_x = +g \sin\theta \qquad (3.20)$$

when the x axis is directed downward along the plane.

Review Questions

Answers to these questions can be found at the end of this chapter.

3.1 Changes in velocity

1. What is the difference between velocity and acceleration?
2. Does *nonzero acceleration* mean the same thing as *speeding up*?
3. Does the acceleration vector always point in the direction in which an object is moving? If so, explain why. If not, describe a situation in which the direction of the acceleration is not the same as the direction of motion.
4. How is the curvature of an $x(t)$ curve related to the sign of the x component of acceleration?

3.2 Acceleration due to gravity

5. A cantaloupe and a plum fall from kitchen-counter height at the same instant. Which hits the floor first?
6. Is it correct to say that a stone dropped from a bridge into the water speeds up as it falls because the acceleration due to gravity increases as the stone gets closer to Earth?

3.3 Projectile motion

7. You toss a rock straight up. Compare the acceleration of the rock at the instant just after it leaves your hand with its acceleration at the instant just before it lands back in your hand, which has remained at the point of release.
8. You throw a ball straight up. What is the ball's acceleration at the top of its trajectory?

3.4 Motion diagrams

9. List the information that should be included in a motion diagram.
10. What is the purpose of a motion diagram?

3.5 Motion with constant acceleration

11. What can you say about a train's acceleration if its $v(t)$ curve is (*a*) a straight line that is not parallel to the t axis and (*b*) a horizontal line that is parallel to the t axis?
12. For an object experiencing constant acceleration, the expression for position as a function of time is $x(t) = x_i + v_{x,i}t + \frac{1}{2}a_x t^2$. Explain, in terms of the area under the $v(t)$ curve for the object, why the acceleration term includes the factor $\frac{1}{2}$.
13. For constant acceleration, describe the relationship among displacement, initial and final velocities, and acceleration when the time variable is algebraically eliminated.

3.6 Free-fall equations

14. You throw a ball straight up and then hold your hand at the release position. Compare the time interval between the release of the ball and its arrival at its highest position to the time interval between leaving its highest position and returning to your hand.
15. (*a*) For an object released from rest, describe how the distance the object falls varies with time. (*b*) Describe how the object's speed varies with time.

3.7 Inclined planes

16. How is distance traveled related to the amount of time needed to travel that distance for a ball rolling down an inclined plane?
17. In what way does the motion of an object rolling down an inclined plane resemble that of an object in free fall?
18. On which of the following, if any, does the magnitude of the acceleration of a ball rolling down an inclined plane depend: angle of incline, speed of ball, direction of motion?

3.8 Instantaneous acceleration

19. For what type of motion is it important to distinguish between instantaneous and average acceleration?
20. What does each of the following represent: (*a*) slope of an $x(t)$ curve at a given point on the curve, (*b*) curvature of an $x(t)$ curve at a given point on the curve, (*c*) slope of a $v(t)$ curve at a given point on the curve, (*d*) area under an $a(t)$ curve, (*e*) area under a $v(t)$ curve?

Developing a Feel

Make an order-of-magnitude estimate of each of the following quantities. Letters in parentheses refer to hints below. Use them as needed to guide your thinking.

1. The time interval needed for a hailstone to fall to the ground from the altitude of a cruising airliner (H, F, O, E, G)
2. The speed of a ball released from the top of a 100-story skyscraper just before the ball hits the ground (H, F, R, O, V)
3. The speed at which a hailstone hits the ground after falling from the altitude of a cruising airliner (H, F, R, O, G)
4. The magnitude of the average acceleration of a fast sports car as it accelerates from rest to freeway cruising speed (D, P, O, C)
5. The magnitude of the average acceleration of a passenger car cruising on the freeway when it has to make an emergency stop (D, A, P, K)
6. The magnitude of a car's average acceleration moving at a typical city speed when it crashes into a stalled dump truck (R, M, K, S)
7. The magnitude of your average acceleration while getting up to speed in a sprint run (D, O, Q, T)
8. The magnitude of your average acceleration while getting up to speed on a bicycle (D, I, O, U)
9. The magnitude of your acceleration while landing feet first on the ground after jumping off a wall and falling for 1 s (R, N, J)
10. The magnitude of the average acceleration of an airliner speeding up for takeoff (D, L, B)

Hints

A. How many seconds does it take a car to stop from cruising speed?
B. How many seconds does it take an airliner to lift off after starting from rest?
C. What minimum time interval is needed to reach freeway cruising speed?
D. What expression relates change in velocity, average acceleration, and the time interval over which the velocity change occurs?
E. How are distance traveled, acceleration, and time interval related for this type of motion?
F. What type of motion is this?
G. What is the cruising altitude of an airliner?
H. What must you assume about the effect of air resistance?
I. What is your maximum speed on a bicycle?
J. What is your speed just before your feet hit the ground?
K. What is the final speed?
L. What is an airliner's takeoff speed?
M. What is the typical speed of a car traveling on an uncongested city street?
N. When your feet hit the ground, what maximum vertical displacement could the center of your body travel before stopping?
O. What is the initial speed?
P. What is the cruising speed of a car on a freeway?
Q. What is your sprinting speed?
R. How are initial speed, final speed, acceleration, and displacement related for this type of motion?
S. What distance do you travel while a car accelerates during a crash?
T. How many seconds does it take you to reach sprinting speed?
U. How many seconds does it take you to reach top speed on a bicycle?
V. What is the height of a 100-story skyscraper?

Key (all values approximate)

A. 4 s; **B.** 3×10^1 s; **C.** 4 s; **D.** Eq. 3.1: $a_{x,\text{av}} = \dfrac{\Delta v_x}{\Delta t}$; **E.** for an object starting from rest, (distance traveled) = |displacement| = $|a_x(\Delta t)^2/2|$; **F.** free-fall motion; **G.** 1×10^4 m; **H.** assume that ignoring air resistance does not affect your calculation; **I.** 7 m/s; **J.** 1×10^1 m/s; **K.** 0; **L.** 6×10^1 m/s; **M.** 1×10^1 m/s; **N.** 1 m; **O.** assume $v_\text{i} = 0$; **P.** 3×10^1 m/s; **Q.** 5 m/s; **R.** Eq. 3.13: $v_{x,\text{f}}^2 = v_{x,\text{i}}^2 + 2a_x\Delta x$; **S.** 1 m; **T.** 2 s; **U.** 5 s; **V.** 4×10^2 m

Worked and Guided Problems

Procedure: Analyzing motion using motion diagrams

When you solve motion problems, it is important to begin by making a diagram that summarizes what you know about the motion.

1. Use dots to represent the moving object at equally spaced time intervals. If the object moves at constant speed, the dots are evenly spaced; if the object speeds up, the spacing between the dots increases; if the object slows down, the spacing decreases.
2. Choose an x (position) axis that is convenient for the problem. Most often this is an axis that (a) has its origin at the initial or final position of the object and (b) is oriented in the direction of motion or acceleration.
3. Specify the position and velocity at all relevant instants. In particular, specify the *initial conditions*—position and velocity at the beginning of the time interval of interest—and the *final conditions*—position and velocity at the end of that time interval. Also specify all positions where the velocity reverses direction or the acceleration changes. Label any unknown parameters with a question mark.
4. Indicate the acceleration of the object between all the instants specified in step 3.
5. To consider the motion of more than one object, draw separate diagrams side by side, one for each object, using one common x axis.
6. If the object reverses direction, separate the motion diagram into two parts, one for each direction of travel.

These examples involve material from this chapter but are not associated with any particular section. Some examples are worked out in detail; others you should work out by following the guidelines provided.

Worked Problem 3.1 Speeding up

A woman driving at the speed limit in a 25-mi/h zone enters a zone where the speed limit is 45 mi/h. She accelerates at a constant rate and reaches the new speed limit in 6.00 s. What distance does the car travel during that acceleration?

❶ GETTING STARTED This is a constant-acceleration problem. Let the car's direction of motion be the positive x direction. We sketch a motion diagram (Figure WG3.1) and on it indicate the initial and final velocities v_i and v_f, the time interval $\Delta t = t_f - t_i$, and the unknown distance d the car travels in the time interval Δt.

Figure WG3.1

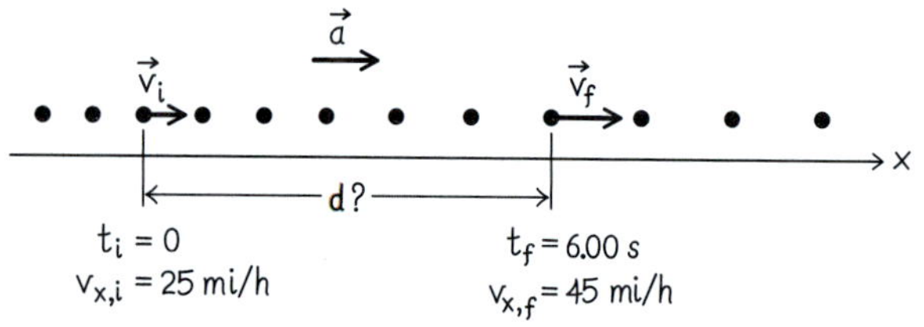

❷ DEVISE PLAN Because the car moves in one direction only, the distance d it travels is equal to the absolute value of its displacement: $d = |\Delta x|$. We must therefore determine Δx. Knowing that displacement is equal to the area under a constant-acceleration $v(t)$ curve, we sketch one that matches *Principles* Figure 3.17b (Figure WG3.2):

Figure WG3.2

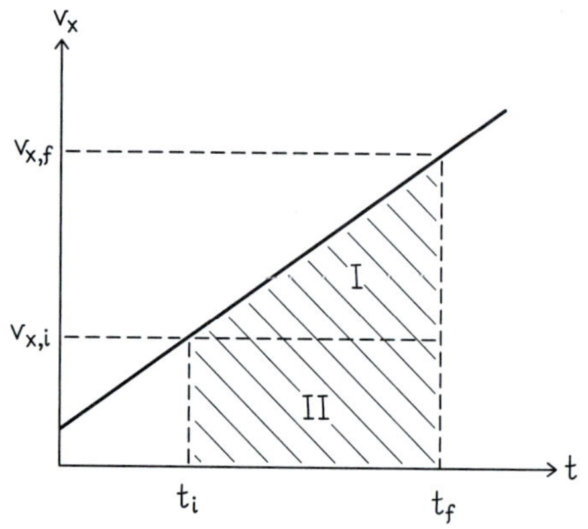

Here the shaded area representing Δx as the car's speed changes from $v_{x,i}$ to $v_{x,f}$ in the time interval Δt.

❸ EXECUTE PLAN The shaded area is most easily analyzed as a triangle (I) plus a rectangle (II). The areas are

$$\text{I} = \tfrac{1}{2}(v_{x,f} - v_{x,i})(t_f - t_i); \qquad \text{II} = v_{x,i}(t_f - t_i).$$

Combining areas I and II, we obtain the car's displacement:

$$\Delta x = \tfrac{1}{2}(v_{x,i} + v_{x,f})\Delta t.$$

After we convert units, this expression allows us to calculate

$$d = |\Delta x|$$

to three significant digits:

$$\frac{25.0 \text{ mi}}{\text{h}} \times \frac{1609 \text{ m}}{1 \text{ mi}} \times \frac{1 \text{ h}}{3600 \text{ s}} = 11.2 \text{ m/s};$$

$$\frac{45.0 \text{ mi}}{\text{h}} \times \frac{1609 \text{ m}}{1 \text{ mi}} \times \frac{1 \text{ h}}{3600 \text{ s}} = 20.1 \text{ m/s}$$

$$d = |\Delta x| = \tfrac{1}{2}(11.2 \text{ m/s} + 20.1 \text{ m/s})(6.00 \text{ s}) = 93.9 \text{ m.} \checkmark$$

❹ **EVALUATE RESULT** Accelerating from 25 mi/h to 45 mi/h in just less than 94 m (a bit more than 300 ft) is about what you might expect based on your experience driving cars.

Guided Problem 3.2 Slowing down

You are driving at 45 mi/h in a 30-mi/h zone. Spotting a police officer ahead, you brake at a constant rate to 27 mi/h, traveling 275 ft in so doing. What time interval do you need to reach your final speed?

❶ **GETTING STARTED**

1. What quantities do you know? What quantity must you compute?
2. Draw a motion diagram. What kind of motion is involved?

❷ **DEVISE PLAN**

3. How is this problem similar to Worked Problem 3.1? How is it different?
4. What are the numerical values of the known quantities in SI units?

❸ **EXECUTE PLAN**

❹ **EVALUATE RESULT**

Worked Problem 3.3 Average and instantaneous

You love projectile motion, and you throw baseballs, rocks, and other small objects almost every day. It occurs to you that, for constant-acceleration motion, there might be a special relationship between average velocity and instantaneous velocity. Standing on a platform with your shoulders at height h_{launch} above the ground, you launch a ball upward at speed v_i and observe that the ball rises to a height h_{max} above the ground and then falls to the ground.

❶ **GETTING STARTED** This is a context-rich problem (see *Practice* Chapter 1) because there is no explicit question. And there are no numbers either! We must therefore generate as much information as we can about average and instantaneous velocities, and hope that a relationship between average velocity and instantaneous velocity reveals itself. We begin with a motion diagram and then write the motion equations.

Figure WG3.3 is the motion diagram for the ball. We separate the motion into upward and downward portions for clarity in the diagram; this separation is not required in the algebraic analysis, however, because the acceleration is the same throughout the motion.

Figure WG3.3

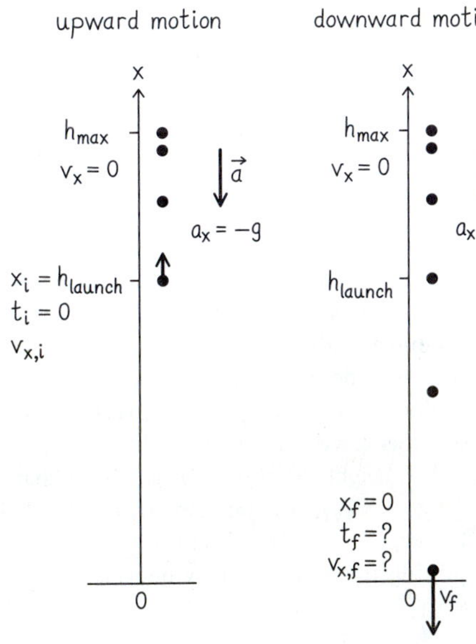

❷ **DEVISE PLAN** The instantaneous velocity values other than $v_{x,i}$ can be obtained from an equation such as Eq. 3.12 with $-g$ in place of a_x:

$$v_x(t) = v_{x,i} - gt. \tag{1}$$

However, we might also use Eq. 3.13, which involves instantaneous velocity and displacement but not a time interval, again with $-g$ in place of a_x:

$$v_{x,f}^2 = v_{x,i}^2 - 2g\Delta x. \tag{2}$$

There is also Eq. 3.11 for position:

$$x(t) = x_i + v_{x,i}t + \tfrac{1}{2}a_x t^2,$$

but this expression does not contain any velocity information other than the initial velocity. We tentatively reject it.

The time interval over which the motion takes place, with t_i set at 0 and the subscript on t_f dropped, is

$$\Delta t = t_f - t_i = t, \tag{3}$$

and t can be obtained from Eq. 1.

Our task is to obtain a relationship between instantaneous velocity v and average velocity v_{av}. Average velocity is defined as the displacement Δx divided by the time interval Δt over which the displacement occurs (see Chapter 2). We should be able to combine the three equations above with our knowledge of the ball's initial and final positions to get an expression for average velocity in terms of instantaneous velocities.

❸ **EXECUTE PLAN** The displacement is the difference in the ball's final and initial positions, both of which are known. We choose the origin at ground level and up as the positive x direction: $x_i = h_{launch}$, $x_f = 0$:

$$\Delta x = x_f - x_i = 0 - h_{launch} = -h_{launch}.$$

We use Eq. 2 to get the ball's final speed at the instant just before it hits the ground:

$$v_{x,f}^2 = v_{x,i}^2 - 2g\Delta x = v_{x,i}^2 + 2gh_{\text{launch}}$$

$$|v_{x,f}| = \sqrt{v_{x,i}^2 + 2gh_{\text{launch}}}. \quad (4)$$

We do not yet know the initial speed needed for Eq. 4, but it must be related to the ball's maximum height $h_{\max}$ because a faster throw should make the ball go higher. Let's use Eq. 2 again to obtain this relationship, evaluating between the initial height h_{launch} and the maximum height $h_{\max}$ (because the ball's speed is zero at $h_{\max}$):

$$0 = v_{x,i}^2 - 2g(h_{\max} - h_{\text{launch}}),$$

so that $$|v_{x,i}| = v_i = \sqrt{2g(h_{\max} - h_{\text{launch}})}.$$

Substituting this expression for $v_{x,i}$ into Eq. 4 gives for the final speed of the ball at the instant before it hits the ground:

$$|v_{x,f}| = \sqrt{v_{x,i}^2 + 2gh_{\text{launch}}} = \sqrt{2g(h_{\max} - h_{\text{launch}}) + 2gh_{\text{launch}}}$$

$$= \sqrt{2gh_{\max} - 2gh_{\text{launch}} + 2gh_{\text{launch}}}$$

$$|v_{x,f}| = \sqrt{2gh_{\max}}.$$

Note that this is a speed, which means we should take the positive square root. We know, though, from our choice of positive x axis upward that the final velocity is directed downward and hence is negative.

We can get the time interval Δt by combining Eqs. 1 and Eq. 3:

$$\Delta t = t = \frac{v_{x,f} - v_{x,i}}{-g}.$$

The average velocity in terms of our expressions for Δx and Δt is

$$v_{\text{av}} = \frac{\Delta x}{\Delta t} = \frac{-h_{\text{launch}}}{\left(\dfrac{v_{x,f} - v_{x,i}}{-g}\right)} = \frac{gh_{\text{launch}}}{v_{x,f} - v_{x,i}}. \quad (5)$$

This is nice, but is there a way to get the right side entirely in terms of instantaneous velocities? Yes, there is. If we substitute $-h_{\text{launch}}$ for Δx in Eq. 2 and rearrange, we have

$$gh_{\text{launch}} = \tfrac{1}{2}(v_{x,f}^2 - v_{x,i}^2).$$

Substituting the term on the right into Eq. 5 gives

$$v_{x,\text{av}} = \frac{\tfrac{1}{2}(v_{x,f}^2 - v_{x,i}^2)}{(v_{x,f} - v_{x,i})} = \tfrac{1}{2}(v_{x,f} + v_{x,i}). \checkmark \quad (6)$$

This expression tells us that the average velocity during a chosen time interval is equal to the numerical average of the initial and final instantaneous velocities for that interval. In this example, because $v_{x,f}$ is negative and of larger magnitude than v_i, which we know from Eq. 4, the average velocity is negative.

This relationship between average and instantaneous velocities seems to be quite general because it does not rely on any values specific to this problem. Of course, it applies only to cases of constant acceleration because Eqs. 1 and 2 are only valid for constant acceleration.

❹ **EVALUATE RESULT** There are no numbers to check, so we seek another way to solve the problem. Perhaps we can visualize this general result graphically. What sort of graph should we draw? A graph of instantaneous velocity versus time comes to mind for several reasons. First, our answer involves instantaneous velocity. Second, from this graph we can obtain displacement (area under the curve) and hence determine average velocity. Third, because velocity is a linear function of time in constant-acceleration problems (Eq. 3.12), this graph is much easier to sketch than the quadratic graph of position versus time (Eq. 3.11). (The acceleration-versus-time graph is even easier to sketch because it is a straight line parallel to the time axis, but it provides less insight.)

Figure WG3.4 shows the velocity-versus-time graph for the ball. Because we chose the positive direction to be upward in our motion diagram, the $v(t)$ curve is a straight line with negative slope (equal to $-g$). The curve extends along the time axis until the ball strikes the ground.

Figure WG3.4

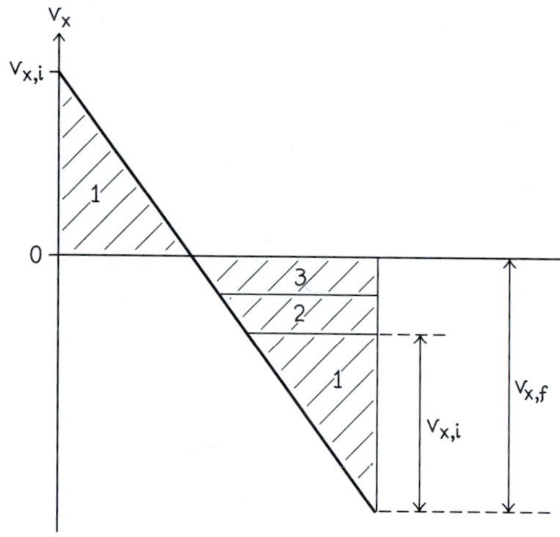

Consider the labeled areas between the $v(t)$ curve and the t axis in Figure WG3.4. Suppose we ask, What (constant) average velocity would produce the same displacement in the same time interval as the varying velocity we had in this problem? As we saw in Chapter 2, at constant velocity the $v(t)$ curve is a straight line parallel to the t axis. In order to produce the same displacement in a given time interval, the area under the constant-velocity curve between any two values t_f and t_i must match the area under the actual $v(t)$ curve for our tossed ball between those same values of t_f and t_i.

Note that the two areas labeled 1 are equal in size and opposite in sign. This means that they cancel when added, and so the net area under the curve is area 2 + area 3. Both these areas are negative in our example, leading to a combined negative area, as we expect for an object with negative average velocity.

Suppose we choose the dividing line between areas 2 and 3 such that these areas have the same height. By construction, area 2 + area 3 has height $-(|v_{x,f}| - |v_{x,i}|)$. Note that $|v_{x,i}| = +v_{x,i}$, while $|v_{x,f}| = -v_{x,f}$, so we can write the height as $-(-v_{x,f} - v_{x,i}) = (v_{x,f} + v_{x,i})$. Note that this is a negative height, as expected. Splitting the height equally between areas 2 and 3 gives each height $\frac{1}{2}(v_{x,f} + v_{x,i})$. Now imagine moving area 2 to the location shown in Figure WG3.5. The result is a rectangle 2 + 3 of height $\frac{1}{2}(v_{x,f} + v_{x,i})$ and length Δt. Thus the area under the $v(t)$ curve, which is the ball's displacement, is equal to the area of rectangle 2 + 3:

$$\Delta x = \tfrac{1}{2}(v_{x,f} + v_{x,i})\Delta t,$$

which means

$$v_{x,av} = \frac{\Delta x}{\Delta t} = \tfrac{1}{2}(v_{x,f} + v_{x,i}), \checkmark \qquad (6)$$

which is the same as Eq. 6. This same geometrical construction works for initial and final velocities that are either negative or positive (try it!), as long as the curve is a line of constant slope (constant acceleration).

Because our graphical and algebraic methods lead to the same results, we have confidence in the answer.

Figure WG3.5

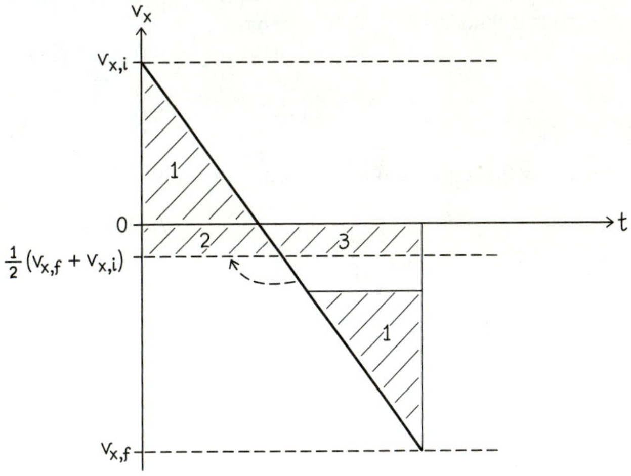

Guided Problem 3.4 Double launch

You throw a ball upward from height h_{launch} as in Worked Problem 3.3 and it rises to height $h_{max} = 2h_{launch}$ before falling to the ground. At the instant you release the ball, a friend standing on a platform at height h_{max} simultaneously throws an identical ball with half the upward velocity you used. Determine (*a*) which ball hits the ground first, (*b*) the final speed of each ball, and (*c*) the time interval between the instant one ball lands and the instant the other ball lands.

❶ **GETTING STARTED**

1. Draw a motion diagram and a velocity-versus-time graph for each ball.
2. Which technique(s) of Worked Problem 3.3 can you use?

❷ **DEVISE PLAN**

3. Where is your friend's ball at the instant your ball reaches its maximum height h_{max}?

❸ **EXECUTE PLAN**

4. Express your answers in terms of the given information.

❹ **EVALUATE RESULT**

Worked Problem 3.5 Inclined track

Your physics instructor prepares a laboratory exercise in which you will use a modern version of Galileo's inclined plane to determine acceleration due to gravity. In the experiment, an electronic timer records the time interval required for a cart initially at rest to descend 1.20 m along a low-friction track inclined at some angle θ with respect to the horizontal.

(*a*) In preparation for the experiment, you must obtain an equation from which you can calculate g on the basis of these measurements. What is that equation?

(*b*) To make it possible to check the students' measurements quickly, the instructor breaks the class into five groups and assigns one value of θ to each group. If no mistakes are made, these five θ values yield time intervals of 0.700, 0.800, 0.900, 1.00, and 1.20 s. What are the five θ values?

❶ **GETTING STARTED** The cart undergoes constant acceleration, from rest, on an inclined plane. We know how to analyze this type of motion, and we know how the acceleration at any given incline angle is related to the acceleration g due to gravity. We sketch a motion diagram (Figure WG3.6), representing a cart moving down an inclined plane, and choose the positive x direction as pointing down the track.

Figure WG3.6

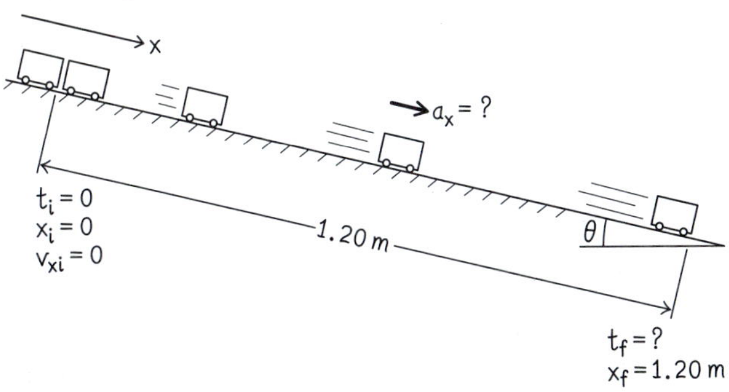

❷ **DEVISE PLAN** The equation asked for in part *a* might be based on Eq. 3.20, $a_x = +g \sin \theta$, but you will not be measuring a_x values directly in this experiment. You will measure displacements Δx and time intervals Δt, which means we need an expression that gives acceleration in terms of these two variables. Equation 3.11 comes to mind, which we can manipulate so that a_x is expressed in terms of Δx and Δt. In part *b*, we can use this result to obtain the five θ values.

PRACTICE

3 EXECUTE PLAN (*a*) Equation 3.11 yields $a_x = 2(x_f - x_i)/t^2 = 2\Delta x/t^2$. Because in the derivation for Eq. 3.11 t_i was taken to be zero, the t^2 is actually $(\Delta t)^2$, so that we have

$$a_x = \frac{2\Delta x}{(\Delta t)^2}.$$

Substituting this expression for a_x in Eq. 3.20 yields

$$\frac{2\Delta x}{(\Delta t)^2} = g \sin\theta,$$

from which we obtain the expression for g to be used in the experiment:

$$g = \frac{2\Delta x}{(\Delta t)^2 \sin\theta}. \checkmark \qquad (1)$$

(*b*) Manipulation of Eq. 1 gives the instructor

$$\sin\theta = \frac{2\Delta x}{g(\Delta t)^2}$$

$$\theta = \sin^{-1}\left(\frac{2\Delta x}{g(\Delta t)^2}\right). \qquad (2)$$

Before evaluating this expression five times, the instructor calculates the constant quantity $2\Delta x/g = 0.2449$ and stores it in her calculator. Substitution of $\Delta t = 0.700$, 0.800, 0.900, 1.00, and 1.20 s into Eq. 2 yields the angles of incline she assigned to the five groups: 30.0°, 22.5°, 17.6°, 14.2°, and 9.79°. ✔

4 EVALUATE RESULT The numerical values for the angles are reasonable: Larger angles are associated with smaller time intervals. Even the shortest interval is considerably longer than the time interval needed for an object to fall freely from a height of 1.2 m, as expected.

Guided Problem 3.6 Another inclined track

At another university, in a laboratory exercise similar to that described in Worked Problem 3.5, students measure the angle of incline θ of a low-friction track, the (nonzero) initial and final speeds of a cart as it descends between two positions on the track, and the distance between those two positions. For an angle of incline of 10.0°, one group obtains the values $v_i = 0.820$ m/s and $v_f = 1.65$ m/s for a distance of 0.608 m. On the basis of these data, what value do these students obtain for g?

1 GETTING STARTED

1. Draw a motion diagram. What kind of motion are we dealing with?
2. Choose an appropriate x direction and origin.

2 DEVISE PLAN

3. How is this problem similar to Worked Problem 3.5? How is it different?

3 EXECUTE PLAN

4 EVALUATE RESULT

4. Consider whether small or large differences in measured data would be needed to produce a result of 9.80 m/s^2.

Questions and Problems

For instructor-assigned homework, go to MasteringPhysics® MP

PRACTICE

Dots indicate difficulty level of problems: • = *easy,* •• = *intermediate,* ••• = *hard;* CR = *context-rich problem.*

3.1 Changes in velocity

1. Figure P3.1 is based on a multiple-flash photographic sequence of an object moving from left to right on a track, as seen from above. The time intervals between successive flashes are all the same. During which portion(s) of the motion is the object (*a*) speeding up and (*b*) slowing down? Explain how you know in each case. (*c*) How would your answers change if the object were moving from right to left? •

Figure P3.1

2. A car is traveling north. What are the direction of its acceleration and the direction of its velocity (*a*) if it is speeding up and (*b*) if it is slowing down? •

3. Figure P3.3 shows a series of photographs of a racehorse taken in 1877 by Eadweard Muybridge (1830–1904). Muybridge used multiple, equally spaced cameras triggered sequentially at equal time intervals. Is the horse accelerating? How can you tell? •

Figure P3.3

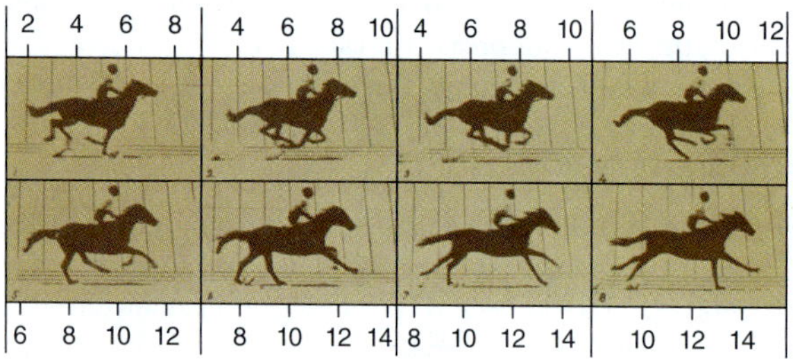

4. Figure P3.4 shows a graph of position as a function of time for an object moving along a horizontal surface. At which of the labeled points is the object speeding up? •

Figure P3.4

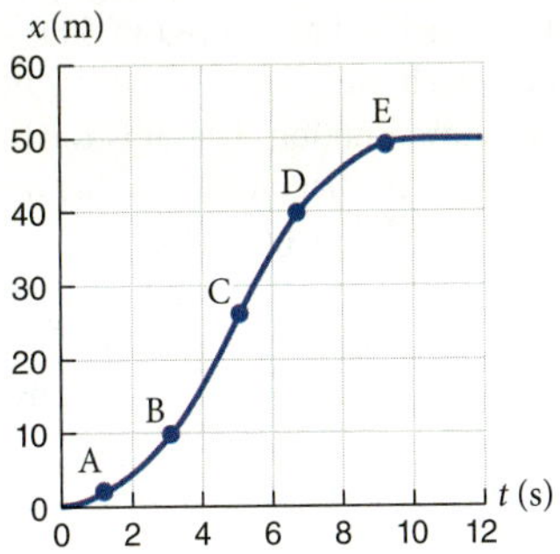

5. While you are driving on a highway, a friend in another car passes you. You accelerate at a constant rate to catch up. When you do catch up, are your two cars going the same speed? Use a graph to support your answer. ••
6. The position of a person pacing in a hall is given by the $x(t)$ curve in Figure P3.6. During which time interval(s) is the acceleration (*a*) positive and (*b*) negative? (*c*) Is the acceleration ever zero during the 4-s interval shown? ••

Figure P3.6

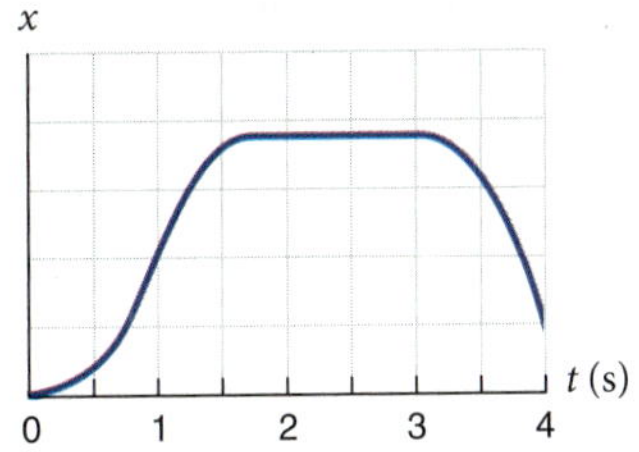

7. You enter an elevator on the ground (first) floor and ride it to the 19th floor. Describe your acceleration at the different stages of this trip. ••
8. Figure P3.8 shows the position curves for two carts, A and B, moving on parallel tracks along a horizontal surface. The instant when the two carts are at the same distance from their starting point is indicated by point P. Which cart has the greater acceleration at that instant? ••

Figure P3.8

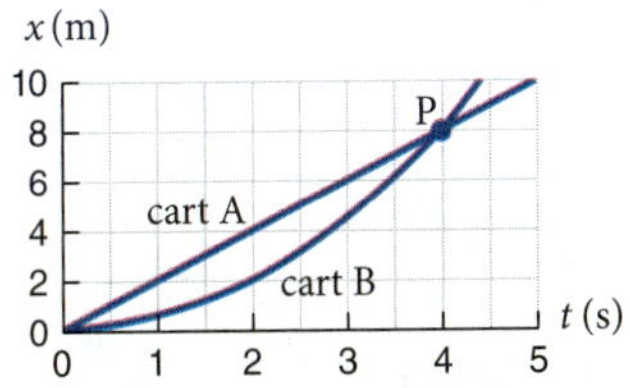

9. Two cars are headed south on the highway at different speeds. Starting when the faster car pulls alongside the slower car, one of the cars accelerates northward for 5.0 s and the other accelerates southward for 5.0 s. At the end of that 5.0-s interval, the two cars have the same speed. Which car is now ahead? •••

3.2 Acceleration due to gravity

10. Is it true that a pebble released from rest off a bridge falls 9.8 m in the first second of its fall? •
11. (*a*) What is the average speed, over the first 1.0 s of its motion, of a pebble released from rest off a bridge? (*b*) What is the pebble's average speed over the second 1.0 s of its motion? (*c*) What is its average speed during these first 2.0 s of its motion? •
12. You toss a (wrapped) sandwich to a friend leaning out of a window 10 m above you, throwing just hard enough for it to reach her. At the same instant, she drops a silver dollar to you. Do the dollar and the sandwich pass each other at a position 5 m above you, more than 5 m above you, or less than 5 m above you? ••
13. Suppose that the acceleration due to gravity near Earth's surface was cut in half (to about 5 m/s^2). How would this affect the graphs shown in *Principles* Figure 3.6, assuming that everything else about the experiment remains the same? Sketch the new curves. ••

3.3 Projectile motion

14. A photographer shows you a multiple-flash photographic sequence of a ball traveling vertically (Figure P3.14). (*a*) If the ball is traveling downward, what is the correct orientation of the picture? (*b*) If the ball is traveling upward, what is the correct orientation of the picture? (*c*) According to the evidence provided by the picture, what is the direction of the ball's acceleration in parts *a* and *b*? •

Figure P3.14

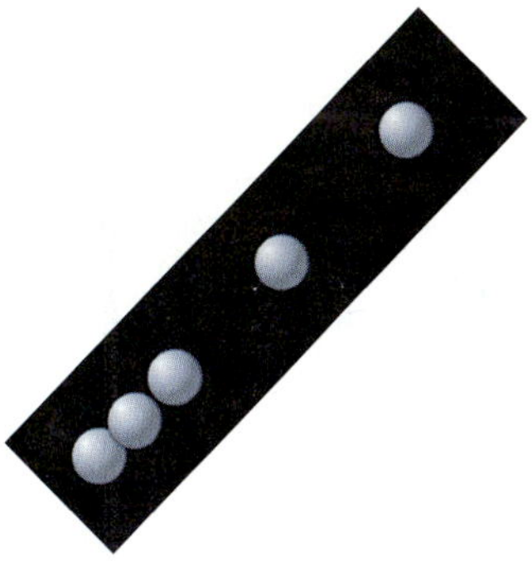

15. A cannonball is shot straight up at an initial speed of 98 m/s. What are its velocity and its speed after (*a*) 5.0 s, (*b*) 10 s, (*c*) 15 s, and (*d*) 20 s? •
16. A coin flipped in the air from elbow height lands on the ground 1.8 s later. Did the coin reach its highest position 0.9 s after it started moving up, earlier than that, or later than that? •
17. Is it possible for an object to have (*a*) zero velocity and nonzero acceleration or (*b*) nonzero velocity and zero acceleration? If you answer yes in either part, give examples to support your answer. ••
18. How would graphs *c* and *d* in *Principles* Figure 3.8 be different if the same experiment was conducted on the surface of the Moon, where the acceleration due to gravity is six times less than it is on Earth? ••

19. You throw snowballs down to the sidewalk from the roof of a building. Which technique, if either, makes the snowballs land with more speed: throwing them straight down as hard as you can or throwing them straight up just as hard? (Ignore air resistance.) ••

20. You are standing by a window and see a ball, thrown from below, moving up past the window. The ball is visible for a time interval Δt_{up}. On its way back down the ball passes the window again, remaining visible for a time interval Δt_{down}. Neglecting the effects of air resistance, is $\Delta t_{\text{up}} > \Delta t_{\text{down}}$, $\Delta t_{\text{up}} = \Delta t_{\text{down}}$, $\Delta t_{\text{up}} < \Delta t_{\text{down}}$, or is it impossible to tell without more information? Briefly explain your reasoning, using graphs. ••

21. For an object in free fall, the curve of its velocity as a function of time is a straight line. How would this curve be different when air resistance is not negligible? •••

22. When air resistance is ignored, it is straightforward to calculate the travel time interval for a Ping-Pong ball tossed up into the air and caught on its way down because the acceleration can be taken to be a constant 9.8 m/s^2 downward. However, a more accurate result is obtained when air resistance is taken into account. When this is done, is the magnitude of the ball's acceleration greater than, less than, or the same as when air resistance is ignored (*a*) as the ball rises and (*b*) as it falls? (*c*) Do you expect the travel time interval obtained in the more accurate analysis to be greater than, less than, or the same as in the simplified case? •••

3.4 Motion diagrams

23. Draw a motion diagram for a car that starts from rest and accelerates at 4.0 m/s^2 for 10 s. •

24. A car accelerating from rest at constant acceleration reaches a speed of 30 km/h in 5.0 s. Draw a motion diagram for the car. •

25. The motion of a cart moving along a horizontal surface is described by the motion diagram shown in Figure P3.25*a*. The position of the cart is measured every 0.5 s. Asked to suggest a qualitative graph of velocity versus time that would correspond to this motion, three of your classmates draw the graphs shown in Figures P3.25*b*–*d*. Which graph is correct? •

Figure P3.25

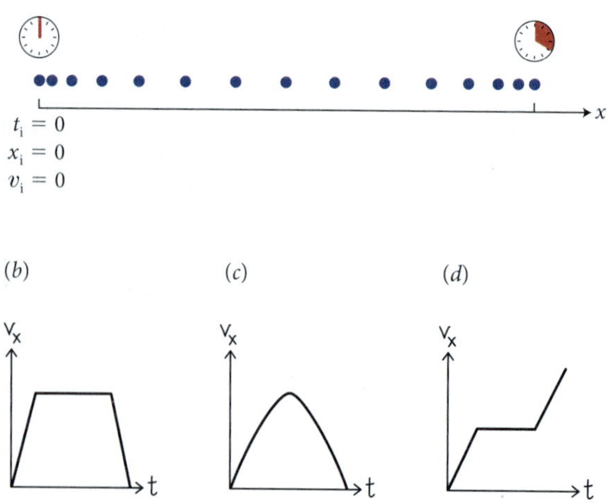

26. Draw a motion diagram for a car that starts from rest and accelerates at 5.0 m/s^2 for 6.0 s, then travels with constant speed for 10 s, and then slows to a stop with constant acceleration in 4.0 s. ••

27. A ball you throw straight up has a speed of 30 m/s when it leaves your hand. Draw a motion diagram for the ball up to the instant at which it has a speed of 30 m/s again. Indicate the instant at which the ball reaches its highest position. ••

28. Figure P3.28 shows motion diagrams for two cars, A and B, beginning a race. The diagrams show the position of each car at instants separated by equal time intervals. Both cars drive up to the starting line and then begin to accelerate. (*a*) Which car has the greater velocity at instant 6? How can you tell? (*b*) Which car has the greater velocity at instant 11? How can you tell? (*c*) Which car has the greater acceleration after instant 6? How can you tell? ••

Figure P3.28

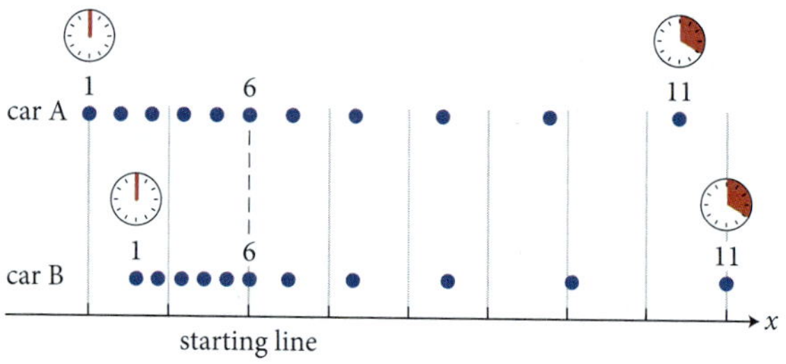

3.5 Motion with constant acceleration

29. You start your car from rest and accelerate at a constant rate along a straight path. Your speed is 20 m/s after 1.0 min. (*a*) What is your acceleration? (*b*) How far do you travel during that 1.0 min? •

30. You and your little brother are rolling toy cars back and forth to each other across the floor. He is sitting at $x = 0$, and you are at $x = 4.0$ m. You roll a car toward him, giving it an initial speed of 2.5 m/s. It stops just as it reaches him in 3.0 s. (*a*) In what direction is the car's acceleration? (*b*) What is the car's average acceleration? •

31. An electron is accelerated from rest to 3.0×10^6 m/s in 5.0×10^{-8} s. (*a*) What distance does the electron travel in this time interval? (*b*) What is its average acceleration? •

32. Figure P3.32 shows a graph of velocity as a function of time for a cart moving along a horizontal surface. When asked to describe the motion that resulted in this graph, a student states, "The cart first moved forward with a constant speed, reached a maximum distance at time 2 seconds, then turned around and came back to its initial position at time 4 seconds." What is your assessment of this comment? •

Figure P3.32

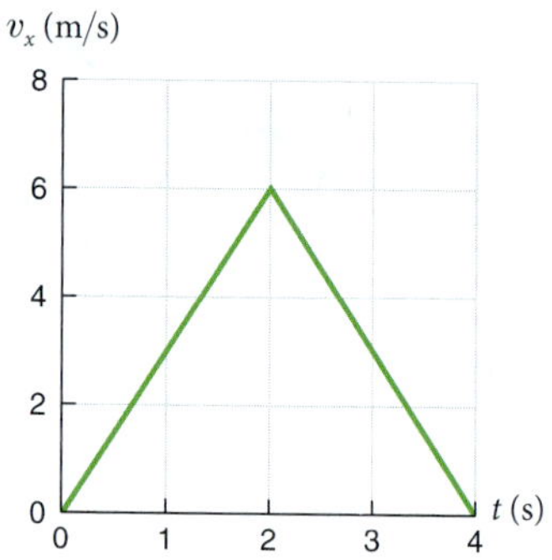

33. (*a*) How do you determine an object's displacement from a velocity-versus-time graph? (*b*) What distance does a car travel as its speed changes from 0 to 20 m/s in 10 s at constant acceleration? (*c*) The *x* component of the average velocity of a particle moving along the *x* axis at constant acceleration is $v_{x,\text{av}} = \frac{1}{2}(v_{x,\text{i}} + v_{x,\text{f}})$ (see Worked Problem 3.3). Is the *x* component of the average velocity also given by this expression when the acceleration is not constant? Use a velocity-versus-time graph to support your answer. ••

34. On a freeway entrance ramp, you accelerate your 1200-kg car from 5 m/s to 20 m/s over 500 m. Having an open lane, you continue to accelerate at the same (constant) rate for another 500 m. Is your final speed 35 m/s, less than 35 m/s, or greater than 35 m/s? ••

35. In an introductory physics laboratory, a student drops a steel ball of radius 15 mm, and a device records its position as a function of time. The clock on the device is set so that $t = 0$ at the instant the ball is dropped. What is the ball's displacement (a) between 0.15 s and 0.25 s and (b) between 0.175 s and 0.275 s? ••

36. Which car has the greater acceleration magnitude: one that accelerates from 0 to 10 m/s in 50 m or one that accelerates from 10 m/s to 20 m/s in 50 m? ••

37. An electron in an old-fashioned television picture tube is accelerated, at a constant rate, from 2.0×10^5 m/s to 1.0×10^7 m/s in a 12-mm-long "electron gun." (*a*) What is the acceleration of the electron? (*b*) What time interval is needed for the electron to travel the length of the gun? ••

38. In a car moving at constant acceleration, you travel 250 m between the instants at which the speedometer reads 40 km/h and 60 km/h. (*a*) How many seconds does it take you to travel the 250 m? (*b*) What is your acceleration? ••

39. Based on the $v(t)$ curve in Figure P3.39, explain whether each of these statements is necessarily true for the time interval shown: (*a*) The acceleration is constant. (*b*) The object passes through the position $x = 0$. (*c*) The object has zero velocity at some instant. (*d*) The object is always moving in the same direction. ••

Figure P3.39

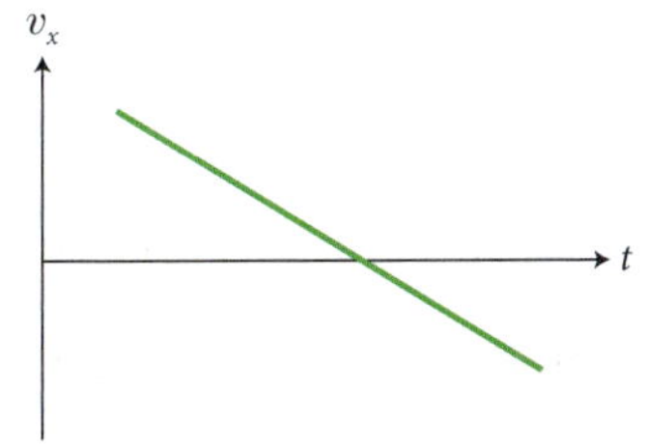

40. In October 1997, Andy Green broke the sound barrier on land in a jet-powered car traveling at 763 mi/h over a 1.0-mi course. As it arrived at the beginning of this measured mile, Green's car had accelerated from rest to 763 mi/h over a 5.0-mi stretch. (*a*) What was Green's average acceleration in that 5.0 mi? (*b*) Calculate the time interval needed for Green to reach his maximum speed. ••

41. You jump on your bicycle, ride at a constant acceleration of 0.60 m/s^2 for 20 s, and then continue riding at a constant velocity for 200 m. You then slow to a stop with a constant acceleration over 10 m. (*a*) What distance do you travel? (*b*) Calculate the time interval needed for your trip. (*c*) What is your average velocity? ••

42. In rush-hour traffic, the car in front of you suddenly puts on the brakes. You apply your brakes 0.50 s later. The accelerations of the two cars are the same. Does the distance between the two cars remain constant, decrease, or increase? ••

43. Two cars are moving at 97 km/h, one behind the other, on a rural road. A deer jumps in front of the lead car, and its driver slams on the brakes and stops. What minimum initial distance between the rear of the lead car and the front of the second car is required if the second car is to stop before hitting the lead car? Assume that the acceleration is the same for both cars and that the driver of the second car begins braking 0.50 s after the lead car begins braking. •••

44. As a physics instructor hurries to the bus stop, her bus passes her, stops ahead, and begins loading passengers. She runs at 6.0 m/s to catch the bus, but the door closes when she's still 8.0 m behind the door, and the bus leaves the stop at a constant acceleration of 2.0 m/s^2. She has missed her bus, but as a physics exercise she keeps running at 6.0 m/s until she draws even with the bus door. (*a*) Calculate Δt from the instant the bus leaves the stop to the instant the instructor draws even with the door. (*b*) At the instant she draws even, how fast is she moving? (*c*) At the instant she draws even, how fast is the bus moving? (*d*) Plot $v(t)$ for the bus and the instructor. (*e*) Plot $x(t)$ for the bus and the instructor. •••

45. The day after the incident described in Problem 44, the instructor finds herself in the same situation. This time, she tries a harder physics exercise. She keeps running at a constant 6.0 m/s after drawing even with the bus door and pulls ahead for a while, but the accelerating bus soon overtakes her. By what maximum distance does she get ahead of the door? •••

3.6 Free-fall equations

46. (*a*) How many seconds does it take a pebble released from rest off a bridge to fall 9.8 m? (*b*) What is the pebble's speed when it has fallen 9.8 m? •

47. Calculated using the value $g = 9.8$ m/s^2, the time interval required for an object released from rest at some arbitrary point A above the ground to reach the ground is Δt. If g were 4.9 m/s^2, by what factor would Δt differ from the value calculated using $g = 9.8$ m/s^2? •

48. A mortar-style fireworks shell is launched upward at 35 m/s. Draw a motion diagram showing the position of the shell and its velocity vector at $t = 0$, 1 s, 2 s, 3 s, and 4 s, and draw a graph of $x(t)$. •

49. The distance a ball thrown upward and released at $t = 0$ travels between $t = 3.0$ s and $t = 4.0$ s is the same as the distance the ball travels between $t = 2.0$ s and $t = 3.0$ s. How is this possible? ••

50. You toss a ball straight up, and it reaches a maximum height h above the launch position. If you want to double the length of the time interval during which the ball stays in the air above the launch position, to what maximum height do you have to throw it? ••

51. (*a*) With what minimum speed must a ball be thrown straight up in order to reach a height of 25 m above the launch position? (*b*) How many seconds does the ball take to reach this height? ••

52. A snowshoer falls off a ridge into a snow bank 3.6 m below and penetrates 0.80 m into the snow before stopping. What is her average acceleration in the snow bank? ••

PRACTICE

53. You are on the second floor of a building under construction, laying bricks of dimensions 63 mm × 89 mm × 170 mm. At your command, a coworker below tosses bricks up to you, and you catch them when they have risen 5.0 m above the launch point. He tosses the bricks consistently so that, if untouched by you, they would rise to a maximum height of 6.0 m above the launch point. (*a*) Soon you both get good at this, and you know exactly how many seconds after you yell "3, 2, 1, throw!" you should reach out and catch the brick on its way up. What is the length of this time interval if your coworker throws without delay at your command? (*b*) If you miss a brick on the way up, during what remaining time interval can you reach out and catch the brick on its way down? ••

54. A rocket ignited on the ground travels vertically upward with an acceleration of magnitude $4g$. A spent rocket stage detaches from the payload after the rocket has accelerated for 5.0 s. With what speed does the spent stage hit the ground? ••

55. Show that the distances traveled by a falling rock in successive 1-s intervals after release are in the ratio 1:3:5:7.... ••

56. A hot-air balloon takes off from the ground traveling vertically with a constant upward acceleration of magnitude $g/4$. After time interval Δt, a crew member releases a ballast sandbag from the basket attached to the balloon. How many seconds does it take the sandbag to reach the ground? •••

57. A rock dropped from the top of a building takes 0.50 s to fall the last 50% of the distance from the top to the ground. How tall is the building? •••

58. A hot-air balloon of diameter 10 m rises vertically at a constant speed of 12 m/s. A passenger accidentally drops his camera from the railing of the basket when it is 18 m above the ground. If the balloon continues to rise at the same speed, how high is the railing when the camera hits the ground? •••

59. A ball tossed vertically upward from the ground next to a building passes the bottom of a window 1.8 s after being tossed and passes the top of the window 0.20 s later. The window is 2.0 m high from top to bottom. (*a*) What was the ball's initial velocity? (*b*) How far is the bottom of the window from the launch position? (*c*) How high does the ball rise above the launch position? •••

3.7 Inclined planes

60. What is the magnitude of the acceleration of a 65-kg skier moving down a hill that makes a 45° angle with the horizontal? Ignore friction. •

61. Starting from rest, a cart takes 1.25 s to slide 1.80 m down an inclined low-friction track. What is the angle of incline of the track with respect to the horizontal? •

62. Imagine that in his experiment with balls rolling down an inclined plane, Galileo had considered balls that were given an initial speed. Would he have reached different conclusions about the ratio of distance and square of time? •

63. A worker releases boxes at the top of a ramp. From the bottom of the ramp the boxes slide 10 m across the floor to a barrier wall. If the ramp is at an elevation angle of 20°, how long must the ramp be if the boxes are to reach the wall 2.0 s after leaving the ramp? Ignore friction. ••

64. A man steps outside one winter day to go to work. His icy driveway is 8.0 m long from top to mailbox, and it slopes downward at 20° from the horizontal. He sets his briefcase on the ice at the top while opening the garage, and the briefcase slides down the driveway. Ignore friction. (*a*) What is its acceleration? (*b*) How many seconds does it take to get halfway to the mailbox? (*c*) How many seconds does it take to reach the mailbox? (*d*) What is its speed at the instant it reaches the mailbox? ••

65. You and a friend ride what are billed as the "world's longest slides" at a county fair. Your slide is 100 m long, and your trip takes 10 s, including any effect of friction. Your friend chooses a taller, 150-m-long slide made from the same material as yours and with the same angle of incline. (*a*) What is the magnitude of your acceleration down the slide? (*b*) What is the magnitude of your friend's acceleration down the slide? (*c*) How many seconds does it take your friend to get to the bottom? (*d*) What is your speed when you hit the bottom? (*e*) What is your friend's speed when she reaches the bottom? ••

66. Two children at a playground slide from rest down slides that are of equal height but are inclined at different angles with respect to the horizontal (Figure P3.66). Ignoring friction, at height h above the ground, which child has (*a*) the greater acceleration and (*b*) the higher speed? ••

Figure P3.66

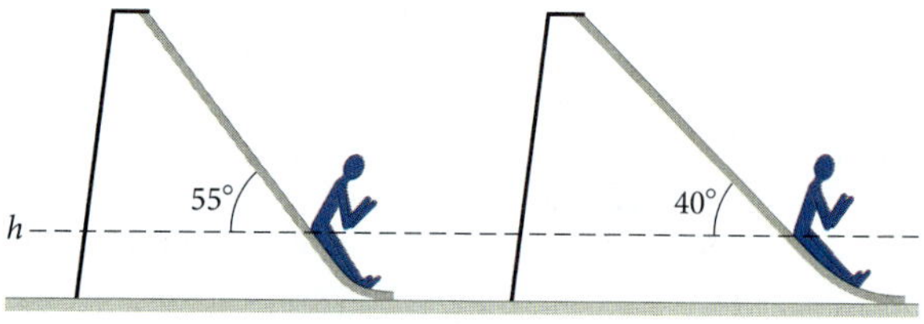

67. You are playing air hockey with a friend. The puck is sitting at rest in his goal when he suddenly lifts his end of the table by 0.50 m. The puck slides down the tilted surface into your goal, 2.4 m away. Ignore friction. (*a*) How many seconds does it take the puck to reach your goal? (*b*) With what speed does the puck hit your goal? ••

68. A block has an initial speed of 6.0 m/s up an inclined plane that makes an angle of 37° with the horizontal. Ignoring friction, what is the block's speed after it has traveled 2.0 m? ••

69. A box is at the lower end of a very slippery ramp of length ℓ that makes a nonzero angle θ with the horizontal. A worker wants to give the box a quick shove so that it reaches the top of the ramp. (*a*) How fast must the box be going after the shove for it to reach its goal? (Ignore the distance traveled while the shove is executed.) (*b*) What is its speed halfway up the ramp? ••

70. A skier is at the top of a run that consists of two slopes having different inclines (Figure P3.70). The skier lets go, beginning the run with essentially zero speed. Ignoring friction, what are (*a*) his speed at the end of the lower slope and (*b*) his average acceleration over the entire run? ••

Figure P3.70

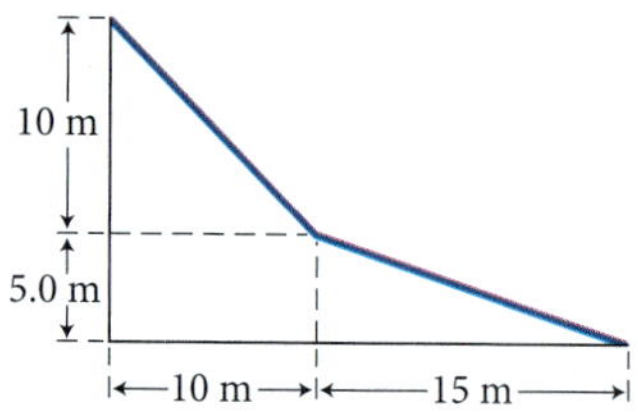

71. A ball is projected vertically upward from an initial position 5.0 m above the ground (Figure P3.71). At the same instant, a cube is released from rest down an ice-covered incline, from a height not necessarily equal to 5.0 m. The two objects reach the ground at the same instant, and both have a final speed of 15 m/s. What is the angle of the incline? •••

Figure P3.71

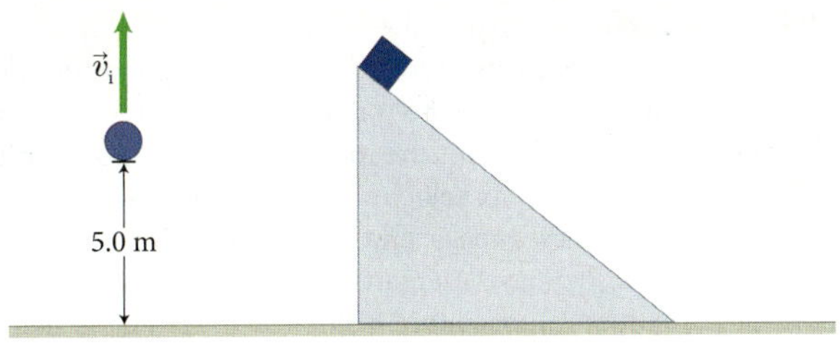

72. You hold a puck at the top of an ice-covered ramp inclined at 60° with respect to the vertical. Your friend stands nearby on level ground and holds a ball at the same height h above ground as the puck. If the puck and the ball are released from rest at the same instant, what is the ratio of the time interval it takes the ball to reach the ground to the time interval it takes the puck to reach the end of the ramp? •••

73. A child on a sled slides down an icy slope, starting at a speed of 2.5 m/s. The slope makes a 15° angle with the horizontal. After sliding 10 m down the slope, the child enters a flat, slushy region, in which she slides for 2.0 s with a constant negative acceleration of $-1.5\ \text{m/s}^2$ with respect to her direction of motion. She then slides up another icy slope that makes a 20° angle with the horizontal. How far up the second slope does she slide? •••

3.8 Instantaneous acceleration

74. You throw a ball straight up with an initial speed of 10 m/s. (*a*) What is the ball's instantaneous acceleration at instant t_1, just after it leaves your hand; at instant t_2, the top of its trajectory; and at instant t_3, just before it hits the ground? (*b*) What is its average acceleration for the upward portion of its journey (t_1 to t_2) and for the entire trip (t_1 to t_3)? •

75. A particle is accelerated such that its position as a function of time is given by $\vec{x} = bt^3\hat{\imath}$, with $b = 1.0\ \text{m/s}^3$. What is the particle's acceleration as a function of time? •

76. Figure P3.76 shows graphs of the x component of acceleration as a function of time for two different carts rolling along a flat horizontal table. In which case is the change in the x component of velocity greater over the time interval shown? •

Figure P3.76

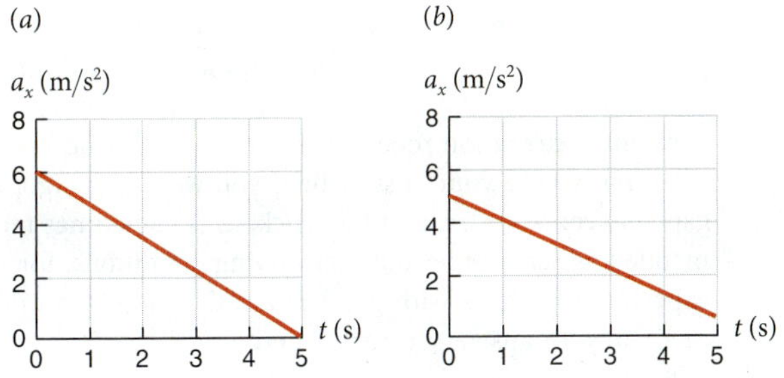

77. The position of a cart on a low-friction track can be represented by the equation $x(t) = b + ct + et^2$, where $b = 4.00$ m, $c = 6.00$ m/s, and $e = 0.200\ \text{m/s}^2$. (*a*) Is the cart accelerating? If so, is the acceleration constant? (*b*) What is the average velocity between $t_i = 0.200$ s and $t_f = 0.400$ s? (*c*) What is the velocity at $t = 0.200$ s and at $t = 0.400$ s? (*d*) What is the average acceleration between $t_i = 0.200$ s and $t_f = 0.400$ s? (*e*) What is the acceleration at $t = 0.200$ s and at $t = 0.400$ s? ••

78. A particle moves in the x direction according to the equation $x(t) = bt^3 + ct^2 + d$, where $b = 4.0\ \text{m/s}^3$, $c = -10\ \text{m/s}^2$, and $d = 20$ m. (*a*) What are its instantaneous velocity and instantaneous acceleration at $t = 2.0$ s? (*b*) What are its average velocity and average acceleration in the interval $t = 2.0$ s to $t = 5.0$ s? ••

79. A rocket's x component of acceleration is given by $a_x = bt$, where $b = 1.00\ \text{m/s}^3$. The rocket begins accelerating from rest at $t = 0$. (*a*) What is its x component of acceleration at $t = 10.0$ s? (*b*) What is its x component of velocity at $t = 10.0$ s? (*c*) What is its x component of average acceleration for the 10.0-s interval? (*d*) How far does it travel in the 10.0-s interval? ••

80. The acceleration of a particular car during braking has magnitude bt, where t is the time in seconds from the instant the car begins braking, and $b = 2.0\ \text{m/s}^3$. If the car has an initial speed of 50 m/s, how far does it travel before it stops? ••

81. A car is 12 m from the bottom of a ramp that is 8.0 m long at its base and 6.0 m high (Figure P3.81). The car moves from rest toward the ramp with an acceleration of magnitude $2.5\ \text{m/s}^2$. At some instant after the car begins moving, a crate is released from rest from some position along the ramp. The crate and car reach the bottom of the ramp at the same instant and at the same speed. (*a*) At what distance d up the ramp was the crate released? (*b*) How many seconds after the car started was the crate released? •••

Figure P3.81

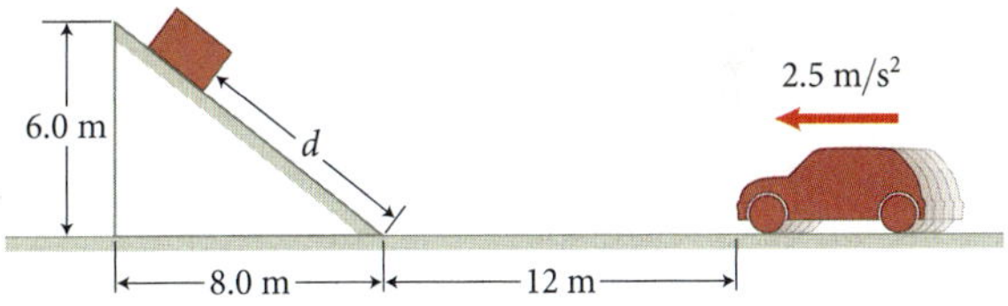

82. In a laboratory experiment, a sphere of diameter 8.0 mm is released from rest at $t = 0$ at the surface of honey in a jar, and the sphere's downward speed v when it travels in the honey is found to be given by $v = v_{max}(1 - e^{-t/\tau})$, where $v_{max} = 0.040$ m/s and $\tau = 0.50$ s. (*a*) Obtain an expression for $a(t)$. (*b*) Draw graphs for $v(t)$ and $a(t)$ for the time interval 0 to 2.0 s. (*c*) Obtain an expression for $x(t)$, choosing the positive x axis as downward, and draw the graph for this function. (*d*) Use your $x(t)$ graph to determine the time interval needed for the sphere to reach the bottom of the container if the surface of the honey is 0.10 m above the bottom of the jar. •••

83. A video recording of a moving object shows the object moving up and down with a velocity given by $v_x(t) = v_{max}\cos(\omega t)$, where $v_{max} = 1.20$ m/s and $\omega = 0.15\ \text{s}^{-1}$ and where the positive x direction is upward. (*a*) Derive an expression for $a(t)$, the object's acceleration as a function of time. (*b*) If the object's position at $t = 0$ is $x(0) = 0$, derive an expression for $x(t)$, its position as a function of time. •••

Additional Problems

84. The motion of a particle in the x direction can be described by the equation $x(t) = bt^2 + ct + d$, where $b = 0.35\ \text{m/s}^2$, $c = 6.0\ \text{m/s}$, and $d = 30\ \text{m}$. (*a*) What is the particle's acceleration at $t = 10$ s? (*b*) What is its velocity at that instant? •

85. It takes you 7.0 m to brake to a panic stop from a speed of 9.0 m/s. Using the same acceleration, how far do you go as you brake to a panic stop from a speed of 27 m/s? •

86. A person standing on a building ledge throws a ball vertically from a launch position 45 m above the ground. If it takes 2.0 s for the ball to hit the ground, (*a*) with what initial speed was the ball thrown and (*b*) in which direction was it thrown? ••

87. A bullet fired straight through a board 0.10 m thick strikes the board with a speed of 480 m/s and emerges with a speed of 320 m/s. (*a*) What is the x component of the average acceleration of the bullet while in the board? (*b*) What is the time interval between the instant the bullet strikes the front face of the board and the instant it exits the back face? (*c*) Assuming the average acceleration you calculated in part *a*, what minimum thickness must the board have in order to stop the bullet? ••

88. During a blackout, you are trapped in a tall building. You want to call rescuers on your cell phone, but you can't remember which floor you're on. You pry open the doors to the elevator shaft, drop your keys down the shaft, and hear them hit bottom at ground level 3.27 s later. (*a*) Making a simple calculation and remembering that the ground floor is numbered floor 1, you determine which floor you're on. What floor is that? (*b*) Before you make the phone call, however, you realize you've forgotten that the sound of the impact at the bottom travels up the shaft at 340 m/s, and so you redo your calculation. What floor number do you tell the rescuers? ••

89. Starting from rest, a motorcycle moves with constant acceleration along a highway entrance ramp 0.22 km long. The motorcycle enters the traffic stream on the highway 14.0 s later at 31 m/s. (*a*) What is the magnitude of the acceleration along the ramp? (*b*) How fast is the motorcycle moving 9.5 s after it begins to accelerate? (*c*) How far along the ramp is the motorcycle 9.5 s after it begins to accelerate? ••

90. Hold a dollar bill with its short sides parallel to the floor, and have a friend hold the thumb and forefinger of one hand on either side of the bottom edge, with the thumb and finger about 20 mm apart. Offer your friend the following deal: He can keep the dollar if he can catch it between his thumb and finger after you release it. Most people fail to catch the bill. Use this information (and your measurement of the length of the long side of a dollar bill) to calculate a typical minimum reaction time. ••

91. A mortar-style fireworks shell must be detonated at a height of 100 m. (*a*) If the shell is to detonate at the top of its trajectory, what must its launch speed be? (*b*) For how many seconds must the detonation fuse burn if it is lit at the instant of launch? ••

92. A rock dropped from the top of a building travels 30 m in the last second before it hits the ground. How high is the building? ••

93. A ball launched directly upward from the ground at an initial speed of 24.5 m/s hits the ground 5.0 s later. What are (*a*) the ball's position 1.0, 2.0, 3.0, and 4.0 s after launch; (*b*) its velocity 1.0, 2.0, 3.0 and 4.0 s after launch; (*c*) its average velocity while it is in the air; and (*d*) its average speed for the entire trip? ••

94. After landing on Mars, you drop a marker from the door of your landing module and observe that it takes 2.1 s to fall to the ground. When you dropped the marker from the module door on Earth, it took 1.3 s to hit the ground. What is the magnitude of the acceleration due to gravity near the surface of Mars? ••

95. A very elastic rubber ball dropped from a height of 2.1 m rebounds to 88% of its original height. If the ball is in contact with the floor for 0.013 s, what is its average acceleration during that interval? ••

96. You are standing on a bridge holding a rock 15.0 m above the water. (*a*) How many seconds after you let go of the rock do you hear it splash into the water? Take the speed of sound to be 340 m/s. (*b*) What is the rock's speed just before it hits the water? (*c*) What is its velocity at that instant? ••

97. An elevator cable breaks, and the elevator car falls four floors (from rest) before the emergency brakes kick in. If the car falls one more floor before it stops, what is its average acceleration during braking? ••

98. A car initially traveling with velocity $\vec{v}_i$ slows down at constant acceleration and stops. (*a*) Sketch a graph of $v_x(x)$, the car's x component of velocity as a function of *position*. (*b*) If the car travels a distance ℓ during this braking, after what displacement does it have half its original speed? ••

99. A theorist has predicted that certain forms of matter exhibit a gravitational *repulsion*. On a planet made of this matter, the "antigravitational acceleration" points upward, away from the planet's surface, and any object released near the ground moves not in free-fall motion but rather in "free-rise motion." Suppose that on this planet, a projectile launched downward from a cliff at an initial speed of 20 m/s is observed 10 s later moving upward at 40 m/s. (*a*) What is the free-rise acceleration on this planet? (*b*) At what instant after launch is the projectile's speed zero? ••

100. A spaceship lifts off vertically with constant acceleration and reaches a speed of 300 km/h in 1.0 min. What are the ship's (*a*) average acceleration, (*b*) velocity at $t = 30$ s, and (*c*) altitude at $t = 60$ s? ••

101. From a promontory overhanging a lake, you throw a stone that enters the water vertically at 15.0 m/s. You hear the splash 2.68 s after you release the stone. Given that the speed of sound in air is 340 m/s: (*a*) What was the stone's initial speed? (*b*) Did you throw the stone down or up? (*c*) From what height above the lake surface did you release the stone? ••

102. Your state's *Driver Handbook* says, "When the vehicle ahead of you passes a certain point such as a sign, count 'one-thousand-one, one-thousand-two, one-thousand-three.' This takes about three seconds. If you pass the same point before you finish counting, you are following too closely." In your car, you are following a truck on the highway, both of you moving at 100 km/h. You are keeping a 3.0-s gap between your front bumper and the rear of the truck. Suddenly a large box appears on the road beneath the rear of the truck. Apparently the truck's axles were tall enough to allow it to pass right over the object, but yours are not! It takes you 0.75 s to react and hit your brakes. (*a*) What is the minimum constant acceleration required if you are not to hit the box? (*b*) What would your answer be if you were keeping a 2.0-s gap between your car and the truck, as is sometimes recommended as safe, under optimal driving conditions, for alert, experienced drivers with good reflexes? Compare and comment on your answers in parts *a* and *b*. ••

PRACTICE

103. A falling rock hits the ground at a speed of 16 m/s. How many seconds were needed for the rock to fall the last 12 m? ••

104. You want to determine whether a tall tree will fit onto your 75-m-long logging trailer after you cut it down. You throw a rock straight up with a speed great enough that the rock just reaches the top of the tree, releasing the rock 2.0 m above the ground. You observe that the time interval from the instant you release the rock to the moment it hits the ground is 5.0 s. ••• CR

105. Your cousin is always bragging about how high his model rockets go, so you go shopping. Unfortunately none of the brands specify altitude, but you do find three models in your price range with comparable technical information. "Cloudscraper" promises a 3.3 s fuel burn time and 2.9g vertical acceleration. "Stratosphere" offers 3.0 s at 3.2g, and "Astronaut" claims 2.7 s at 3.6g. ••• CR

106. You are enjoying a coffee break with your cousin in her highway patrol car when a sports car speeds by at 135 km/h. Your cousin tells you to hold her coffee as she starts the car, and she offers to bet you ten dollars that she can catch the speeder before he reaches the state line. You know that the state line is 2.0 km away along the straight and level highway, and you have read that police cruisers can reach a top speed of 210 km/h within 15 s from a resting start. As the car begins to move, you realize that 5.0 s has already elapsed and that you must decide soon. ••• CR

107. At the drag races, three physics students note that the winning dragster in one category has a speed of 215 mi/h at the end of its quarter-mile run. The run takes 6.30 s, and the car, initially at rest, starts exactly when the timing clock starts. Using these data, and with *Principles* Chapter 3 as their guide, the students calculate the magnitude of the dragster's acceleration. Although their physics instructor verifies that they have made no numerical errors, the students get three different values for the acceleration. (*a*) What are those values? (*b*) One of the students notices an interesting connection among the three values they obtained. What is that connection? (*c*) Is there a reasonable explanation for the discrepancies found in part *a*? •••

108. You are touring a distant planet on which the magnitude of the free-fall acceleration is 65.0% of what it is on Earth. For a little excitement, you jump off a precipice 500 m above the planet's surface. After 5.00 s of free fall, you ignite the jet-pack on your back, changing your acceleration to some new, constant value for the remainder of the fall. You reach the ground 26.0 s after igniting the jet-pack. At what speed do you hit the ground? •••

109. A classmate leaves a message on your voice mail betting that you cannot throw a stone high enough so it lands on the roof of a 20-m-high building. As you stare out of your window pondering whether to accept the challenge, the well in the courtyard suddenly gives you an idea. You drop a stone into the well and note that you hear a splash 4.0 s later. You repeat the experiment with another stone, but this time you throw the stone down as fast as you can. This time the splash comes 3.0 s after the stone leaves your hand. You carry out a quick calculation and then you call back your friend. ••• CR

Answers to Review Questions

1. Velocity measures displacement (change in position) per unit of time; acceleration measures change in velocity per unit of time.
2. No. *Accelerating* means moving with changing velocity. This includes speeding up as well as any other nonconstant velocity, such as slowing down.
3. No. An object that is slowing down along a straight path has an acceleration vector that points in the direction opposite the direction of motion.
4. The x component of acceleration is positive if the curvature is upward and negative if the curvature is downward. No curvature means no acceleration.
5. They hit at the same instant. If we ignore air resistance, all freely falling objects fall with the same constant acceleration.
6. No. While the stone is falling through the air, its acceleration is a constant 9.8 m/s^2 straight down. Its velocity (and, in this case, its speed) increases because of this constant acceleration. (Once in the water, the stone experiences a different acceleration because the water resistance is much greater than the air resistance, which is negligibly small during the stone's fall.)
7. Because air resistance is negligible for a rock tossed in the air, the acceleration is 9.8 m/s^2 downward at both instants. The acceleration due to gravity is constant near Earth's surface, and the rock experiences that acceleration at all instants during its round trip.
8. The acceleration at the top is 9.8 m/s^2 downward, just as it is during the rest of the flight. The fact that $v = 0$ at the top of the trajectory doesn't mean $a = 0$. The ball is headed upward the instant before reaching the top and headed downward an instant later. This change in velocity direction means that the ball must be accelerating at the top, and the only acceleration operating here is that due to gravity.
9. A motion diagram should use dots to represent the position of the moving object at equally spaced time intervals. The spacing of the dots is crucial: Small spacing means low speed, large spacing means high speed. The diagram should include numerical labels (including units) for known quantities as well as information about the direction of travel (represented by an arrow), if known. It should also include a coordinate axis showing a defined positive direction and, for constant-acceleration situations, an arrow showing the acceleration direction.
10. A motion diagram summarizes the information known about a motion. It provides a visual representation that helps with the mathematical solution to a kinematics problem. The diagram organizes your information and helps you break down the problem into parts.
11. (*a*) Its acceleration is constant. (*b*) Its acceleration is zero.
12. The $\frac{1}{2}$ is included because the area of a triangle is one-half base times height, and with a linear $v(t)$ curve the area under any segment involves a triangle and (in most cases) a rectangle. These areas could be combined into a trapezoid, but doing so would obscure the fact that the triangular portion represents the slope of the $v(t)$ curve (and the slope gives us the object's acceleration).
13. For constant acceleration, the difference in the squares of the final and initial x components of velocity is equal to twice the product of the displacement and the acceleration (Eq. 3.13).
14. Both time intervals are the same. The $x(t)$ curve representing the trajectory is symmetrical about the instant at which the ball reaches its highest position.
15. (*a*) Quadratically (Eq. 3.11); (b) linearly (Eq. 3.12).
16. The ratio of the distance traveled to the square of the elapsed time is constant for a ball released from rest rolling down an inclined plane.
17. In both cases, the acceleration is constant and the motion follows a straight path. The motion diagrams are similar, although the numerical values of the acceleration differ.
18. The acceleration magnitude depends on only the angle of incline (Eq. 3.20).
19. Motion with nonconstant acceleration.
20. (*a*) Velocity at that value of t; (*b*) the second time derivative of position, which is the acceleration; (*c*) acceleration at that value of t; (*d*) the integral of a with respect to t, which is the change in velocity during the time interval (Eq. 3.27); (*e*) the integral of v with respect to t, which is the displacement during the time interval (Eq. 3.28).

Answers to Guided Problems

Guided Problem 3.2 5.2 s

Guided Problem 3.4 (*a*) Friend's ball first; (*b*) yours: $|v_f| = \sqrt{4gh_{launch}}$, friend's: $|v_f| = \sqrt{4.5gh_{launch}}$; (*c*) $\Delta t = (2 - \sqrt{2})\sqrt{\frac{h_{launch}}{g}}$

Guided Problem 3.6 9.71 m/s^2

PRACTICE

4 Practice Momentum

Chapter Summary

Inertia (Sections 4.1 – 4.3, 4.5)

Concepts *Friction* is the resistance to motion that one surface encounters when moving over another surface. In the absence of friction, objects moving along a horizontal track keep moving without slowing down.

Inertia is a measure of an object's tendency to resist a change in its velocity. Inertia is determined entirely by the type of material of which the object is made and by the amount of that material contained in the object. Inertia is related to *mass*, and for this reason we use the symbol m to represent it. The SI unit of inertia is the **kilogram** (kg).

Quantitative Tools If an object of unknown inertia m_u collides with an inertial standard of inertia m_s, the ratio of the inertias is related to the changes in the velocities by

$$\frac{m_u}{m_s} \equiv -\frac{\Delta v_{sx}}{\Delta v_{ux}}. \tag{4.1}$$

Systems and momentum (Sections 4.4, 4.6, 4.7, 4.8)

Concepts A **system** is any object or group of objects that can be separated, in our minds, from the surrounding environment. The **environment** is everything that is not part of the system. You can choose the system however you want, but once you decide to include a certain object in the system, that object must remain a part of the system throughout your analysis.

A system for which there are no external interactions is called an **isolated system.**

An **extensive quantity** is one whose value is proportional to the size or "extent" of the system. An **intensive quantity** is one that does not depend on the extent of the system.

A **system diagram** shows the initial and final conditions of a system.

Quantitative Tools The **momentum** $\vec{p}$ of an object is the product of its inertia and velocity:

$$\vec{p} \equiv m\vec{v}. \tag{4.6}$$

The momentum of a system of objects is the sum of the momenta of its constituents:

$$\vec{p} \equiv \vec{p}_1 + \vec{p}_2 + \cdots. \tag{4.11, 4.23}$$

Conservation of momentum (Sections 4.4, 4.8)

Concepts Any extensive quantity that cannot be created or destroyed is said to be **conserved,** and the amount of any *conserved* quantity in an isolated system is *constant*. Momentum is a conserved quantity, and therefore the momentum of an isolated system is constant. The momentum can be transferred from one object to another in the system, but the momentum of the system cannot change.

Quantitative Tools The momentum of an isolated system is constant:

$$\Delta\vec{p} = \vec{0}. \tag{4.17}$$

Another way to say this is that for an isolated system, the initial momentum is equal to the final momentum:

$$\vec{p}_i = \vec{p}_f. \tag{4.22}$$

The **impulse** $\vec{J}$ delivered to a system is equal to the change in momentum of the system:

$$\vec{J} = \Delta\vec{p}. \tag{4.18}$$

For an isolated system, $\vec{J} = \vec{0}$.

Review Questions

Answers to these questions can be found at the end of this chapter.

4.1 Friction

1. Describe several ways of minimizing friction between a surface and an object moving on that surface. Is it possible for a surface to be completely frictionless?

4.2 Inertia

2. Two standard carts collide on a horizontal, low-friction track. How does the change in the velocity of one cart compare with that of the other?
3. Carts A and B collide on a horizontal, low-friction track. Cart A has twice the inertia of cart B, and cart B is initially motionless. How does the change in the velocity of A compare with that of B?

4.3 What determines inertia?

4. An iron cube and an iron sphere contain the same volume of material. How do their inertias compare?
5. Two objects of identical volume and shape are made of different materials: iron and wood. Are their inertias identical?

4.4 Systems

6. What is a system?
7. What is the key difference between an extensive quantity and an intensive quantity?
8. What four processes can change the value of an extensive quantity in a system?
9. What does it mean if an extensive quantity is a conserved quantity?

4.5 Inertial standard

10. Using a pair of standard carts and a baseball, how would you determine the inertia of the baseball?
11. Can the inertia of any object be negative?
12. Which has greater inertia: 1 kg of feathers or 1 kg of lead?

4.6 Momentum

13. Which has greater momentum: a flying bumblebee or a stationary train? Which has greater inertia?
14. A 3-g bullet can knock a wooden block off a fence as easily as a 140-g baseball can. How is this possible?
15. Can the momentum of any object be negative?

4.7 Isolated systems

16. What is the meaning of the word *interaction* in physics?
17. For a given system, what is the distinction between external and internal interactions, and why is the distinction important?
18. What is an isolated system, and of what use is an isolated system?

4.8 Conservation of momentum

19. Are these two statements equivalent? (*a*) The momentum of an isolated system remains constant in time. (*b*) Momentum is conserved.
20. Suppose the 1-kg international inertial standard cylinder were lost or destroyed. How would this affect conservation of momentum?
21. What is impulse, and how is it related to momentum?
22. Compare and contrast the *conservation of momentum* and the *momentum law*.

Developing a Feel

Make an order-of-magnitude estimate of each of the following quantities. Letters in parentheses refer to hints below. Use them as needed to guide your thinking.

1. The inertia of a suitcase filled with physics textbooks (H, L, Q)
2. The ratio of the inertias of an object and a bowling ball if the object, initially at rest on a bowling alley, doesn't move noticeably after being hit by the bowling ball (C, M, B)
3. The magnitude of the momentum of a tennis ball as it crosses the net (F, R)
4. The magnitude of the momentum of a bowling ball moving toward the pins (A, M)
5. The magnitude of the momentum of a baseball pitched by a major-league pitcher (I, S)
6. The magnitude of the momentum of a typical marathon runner (D, O, V)
7. The magnitude of the change in momentum of a baseball bat that reverses the velocity of the baseball of question 5 (G, N)
8. The magnitude of the change in momentum of a stationary bowling ball hit by the tennis ball of question 3 (B, G, N)
9. The magnitude of the change in momentum of a car that leaves the freeway to stop for gas (E, J, T)
10. The magnitude of the change in velocity of a car that hits a stationary deer (E, P, K, U, N)

Hints

A. What is the inertia of a bowling ball?
B. How does the object of less inertia behave after a collision with an object of greater inertia?
C. What is the largest nonzero speed that is too small to be noticed during a few seconds of observation?
D. What is the inertia of a marathon runner?
E. What is the inertia of a typical car?
F. What is the inertia of a tennis ball?
G. What is the magnitude of the change in momentum of the object with less inertia?
H. What is the inertia of a single physics textbook?
I. What is the inertia of a baseball?
J. What is the speed of the car while on the freeway?
K. What is the inertia of a typical deer?
L. What is the volume of a typical suitcase?
M. What is the typical speed of a bowling ball moving toward the pins?
N. What do you know about the momentum of this system of two objects?
O. What time interval is required to run a marathon?
P. What is the likely speed of a car on a road with deer crossings?
Q. What is the volume of a single physics book?
R. What is the speed of a tennis serve?
S. What is the speed of a pitched baseball?
T. What is the speed of a car when fueling?
U. With what speed would the deer rebound? (First consider a moving deer bouncing off a stationary car by analogy to question 8.)
V. What is the length of a marathon?

Key (all values approximate)

A. 7 kg; **B.** it bounces back, approximately reversing its velocity; **C.** 1×10^{-3} m/s; **D.** 6×10^{1} kg; **E.** 2×10^{3} kg; **F.** 6×10^{-2} kg; **G.** because the motion reverses, about twice the magnitude of the object's initial momentum; **H.** 3 kg; **I.** 0.2 kg; **J.** 3×10^{1} m/s; **K.** 5×10^{1} kg; **L.** 0.1 m^3; **M.** 7 m/s; **N.** it remains approximately constant; **O.** 3 h or more; **P.** less than half freeway speed, perhaps 1×10^{1} m/s; **Q.** 3×10^{-3} m^3; **R.** 5×10^{1} m/s; **S.** 4×10^{1} m/s; **T.** 0; **U.** at a speed somewhat slower than twice the initial speed of the car; **V.** 4×10^{1} km

Worked and Guided Problems

Procedure: Choosing an isolated system

When you analyze momentum changes in a problem, it is convenient to choose a system for which no momentum is transferred into or out of the system (an isolated system). To do so, follow these steps:

1. Separate all objects named in the problem from one another.
2. Identify all possible interactions among these objects and between these objects and their environment (the air, Earth, etc.).
3. Consider each interaction individually and determine whether it causes the interacting objects to accelerate. Eliminate any interaction that does not affect (or has only a negligible effect on) the objects' accelerations during the time interval of interest.
4. Choose a system that includes the object or objects that are the subject of the problem (for example, a cart whose momentum you are interested in) in such a way that none of the remaining interactions cross the system boundary. Draw a dashed line around the objects in your choice of system to represent the system boundary. None of the remaining interactions should cross this line.
5. Make a system diagram showing the initial and final states of the system and its environment.

These examples involve material from this chapter but are not associated with any particular section. Some examples are worked out in detail; others you should work out by following the guidelines provided.

Worked Problem 4.1 Jump ship

In a game of canoe-ball on a calm lake, an athlete stands at the front end of a canoe at rest, facing the shore. A player on shore throws a 1.8-kg ball that arrives at the canoe with a speed of 2.5 m/s. The rules of the game demand that the athlete hold on to the ball and immediately dive into the water, which he does, horizontally, off the front of the canoe. His inertia is 60 kg, and the inertia of the canoe is 80 kg. Friends on shore determine that his speed in the dive is 1.2 m/s. How fast is the canoe moving after he jumps off?

❶ GETTING STARTED Because we are given the canoe's inertia, we can determine its speed once we know the magnitude of its momentum ($v = p/m$). The crucial point is that the momentum exchange is both between the canoe and the athlete and between the ball and the athlete. However, some interaction between the water and the canoe is also possible. Because the event we are analyzing happens during a short time interval and because we know that water is "slippery," we choose to ignore any effect that resistance from the water might have on the canoe's motion. With this simplification, the system comprising the ball, canoe, and athlete is isolated.

We draw a system diagram (Figure WG4.1) including the relevant velocity information and using subscripts to keep track of our objects: b for ball, a for athlete, c for canoe. We also use the subscripts i for initial quantities and f for final quantities to keep track of the temporal order of events.

Figure WG4.1

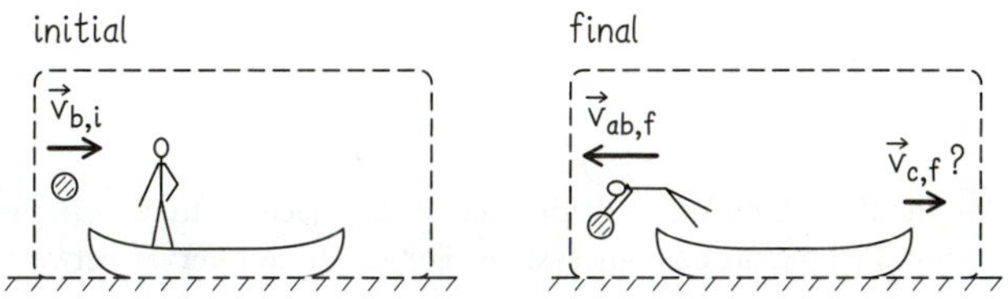

❷ DEVISE PLAN Because momentum is a conserved quantity and because the system is isolated, the system's initial momentum must be equal to the system's final momentum. We notice that the momentum is not zero before the catch because the ball is in motion. We also note that, after the dive begins, the athlete and ball can be treated as a single object because they move with a common velocity. We label this composite object with the subscript ab. We have to account for all the contributions to the system's momentum in the initial state (just before the dive) and in the final state (just after the dive), and set the two equal. It is best to draw initial and final momentum representations to keep track of all the objects in the system and to show the direction we choose for the positive x axis (Figure WG4.2). We draw the final momentum vector for the canoe a bit larger than the vector for the athlete plus ball because the system momentum must be in the same direction and of the same magnitude in the initial and final pictures. Note that we choose the direction of the incoming ball as the positive x direction.

Figure WG4.2

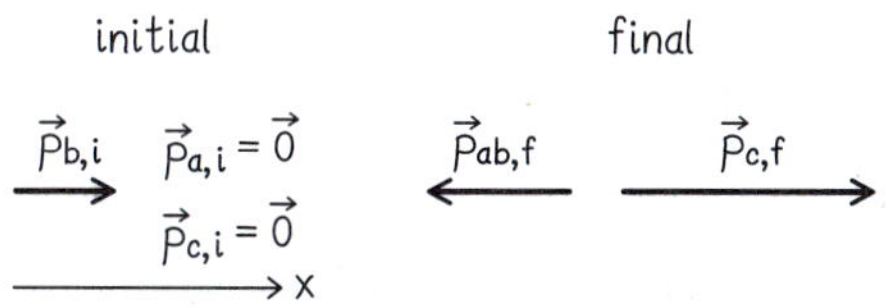

With this figure as a guide, we write an equation setting the initial and final momenta equal to each other:

$$\vec{p}_{a,i} + \vec{p}_{b,i} + \vec{p}_{c,i} = \vec{p}_{ab,f} + \vec{p}_{c,f}$$
$$\vec{0} + m_b\vec{v}_{b,i} + \vec{0} = (m_a + m_b)\vec{v}_{ab,f} + m_c\vec{v}_{c,f}.$$

Because we know all the inertias, the three initial velocities, and the final velocity of the athlete-ball combination, we have all we need to get the final speed of the canoe.

PRACTICE

❸ **EXECUTE PLAN** Recalling that vector components are signed quantities whose signs depend on our choice for the positive x direction, which is in the direction of the incoming ball, we write the equation in component form:

$$m_b v_{bx,i} = (m_a + m_b)v_{abx,f} + m_c v_{cx,f}.$$

In terms of speeds, this becomes

$$m_b v_{b,i} = (m_a + m_b)(-v_{ab,f}) + m_c v_{c,f}.$$

We isolate our unknown, $v_{c,f}$, and then substitute values for the quantities we know:

$$m_c v_{c,f} = m_b v_{b,i} - (m_a + m_b)(-v_{ab,f})$$

$$v_{c,f} = \frac{m_b v_{b,i} + (m_a + m_b)v_{ab,f}}{m_c} \quad (1)$$

$$v_{c,f} = \frac{(1.8 \text{ kg})(2.5 \text{ m/s}) + (60 \text{ kg} + 1.8 \text{ kg})(1.2 \text{ m/s})}{80 \text{ kg}}$$

$$= \frac{78.7 \text{ kg} \cdot \text{m/s}}{80 \text{ kg}} = 0.983 \text{ m/s}.$$

The final speed of the canoe, to two significant digits, is

$$v_{c,f} = 0.98 \text{ m/s}. ✔$$

❹ **EVALUATE RESULT** The numerical value of our result is not unreasonable; that is, it is of the order of magnitude we expect for the speed of a human-powered boat. If there were significant water resistance, it would reduce the canoe's speed, but this reduction would take significantly longer than the jump, as you may know from pushing a boat off. For this reason the assumption that water resistance can be neglected during the time interval of interest is justified.

We should also check to see whether our algebraic answer behaves in the way we expect. Equation 1 shows that the canoe's final speed is a sum of positive terms. If Eq. 1 allowed a negative answer for $v_{c,f}$, we would have to rethink our choice of signs for velocity components. The canoe's final x component of momentum $p_{cx,f}$ must be positive for this reason: Because the initial momentum of the system is positive, the final momentum must also be positive (but the final momentum of the athlete-ball combination is negative). This is consistent with our intuition that the boat moves to the right in Figure WG4.1 as the athlete dives to the left.

Furthermore, we see that Eq. 1 implies that the canoe's final speed would increase if the ball had greater inertia, if it came in at a higher speed, if the athlete had greater inertia, or if he dove at a higher speed. This matches our qualitative understanding that each of these changes would increase either the initial (positive) momentum of the system or the final (negative) momentum of the athlete-ball combination.

Guided Problem 4.2 A pie in the face

At a carnival, a super-sized, 1.0-kg cream pie is thrown with a speed of 5.0 m/s into the face of a 60-kg clown at rest on roller skates. After the pie strikes his face and sticks there, how fast does the clown roll backward?

❶ **GETTING STARTED**

1. Select an isolated system and sketch a system diagram for the pie-clown collision.
2. What object(s) is (are) in motion before the collision? After the collision?

❷ **DEVISE PLAN**

3. What do you know about the momentum of your system?
4. Express your answer to question 3 quantitatively and count the unknowns.

❸ **EXECUTE PLAN**

❹ **EVALUATE RESULT**

5. Is your answer unreasonably large or small?

Worked Problem 4.3 Exploding bicycle pump

You are riding your bike at a steady 4.0 m/s when suddenly you swerve to avoid a pothole. Your bicycle pump falls from its bracket, strikes a rock at the road's edge, and explodes into three pieces. You watch the pump body sail ahead of you, then hit the ground and stop 0.50 s after the explosion. The pump was horizontal when it exploded, and its length was aligned parallel to the road. Retracing your path, you measure the distance from the pump body to the rock as 3.2 m. Just beside the rock is the pump handle. These two pieces were easy to find, but the third piece—a thin metal spring—is going to be hard to spot. If the inertias are 0.40 kg for the pump body, 0.25 kg for the handle, and 0.20 kg for the spring, where should you look for the spring?

❶ **GETTING STARTED** We begin with a sketch of the situation (Figure WG4.3). We are given position information for two of the three pieces, but that alone will not locate the third piece. We also have the inertia of each piece, and we know that the velocity of the pump before the explosion was the same as that of the bike.

Figure WG4.3

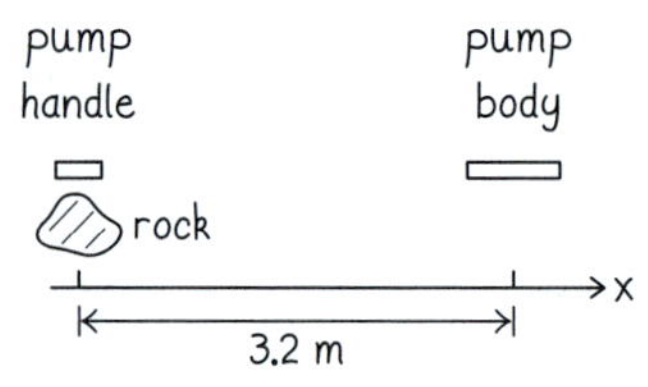

❷ **DEVISE PLAN** We consider the three pieces into which the pump disintegrates as our system. For the time interval between the instant after the pump hits the rock and the instant before the pieces land, the system is isolated and so the momentum of the three-piece system does not change. The best we can do, given the information at hand, is to assume that all three pieces hit the ground 0.50 s after the explosion. This allows us to use Eq. 4.19:

$$\vec{p}_f = \vec{p}_i \quad \text{(isolated system).}$$

There are three objects that move as one (pump) in the initial state but separately (body, handle, spring) in the final state. During the time interval of interest, it is reasonable to assume that all objects move parallel to the road, and so we choose the positive x direction to be the direction of initial travel, from the rock toward the pump body in Figure WG4.3. We arbitrarily locate the origin of the x axis at the rock. The resulting component equation is

$$p_{\text{p}x,\text{i}} = p_{\text{b}x,\text{f}} + p_{\text{h}x,\text{f}} + p_{\text{s}x,\text{f}}$$

$$(m_\text{b} + m_\text{h} + m_\text{s})v_{\text{p}x,\text{i}} = m_\text{b}v_{\text{b}x,\text{f}} + m_\text{h}v_{\text{h}x,\text{f}} + m_\text{s}v_{\text{s}x,\text{f}}. \quad (1)$$

We know the x component of the initial velocity, but we do not know the x components of the final velocities, and so we need more information. Because the pump handle lies beside the rock, we conclude that the x component of the velocity of the pump handle was zero immediately after the explosion. The pump body lies 3.2 m from the rock, and we know that it traveled this far in 0.50 s. We can determine the x component of its final velocity immediately after the explosion from this information. That leaves only the x component of the final velocity of the spring unknown, which we should be able to compute from the momentum equation. With that information we can compute how far the spring traveled in 0.50 s, and hence where to look for it.

❸ **EXECUTE PLAN** The x component of the velocity of the pump body after the explosion is

$$v_{\text{b}x,\text{f}} = \frac{+3.2\text{ m}}{0.50\text{ s}} = +6.4\text{ m/s}.$$

Next we solve Eq. 1 for $v_{\text{s}x,\text{f}}$ and substitute our known values:

$$(m_\text{b} + m_\text{h} + m_\text{s})v_{\text{p}x,\text{i}} = m_\text{b}v_{\text{b}x,\text{f}} + m_\text{h}v_{\text{h}x,\text{f}} + m_\text{s}v_{\text{s}x,\text{f}}$$

$$v_{\text{s}x,\text{f}} = \frac{(m_\text{b} + m_\text{h} + m_\text{s})v_{\text{p}x,\text{i}} - m_\text{b}v_{\text{b}x,\text{f}} - m_\text{h}v_{\text{h}x,\text{f}}}{m_\text{s}}$$

$$= \frac{(0.40\text{ kg} + 0.25\text{ kg} + 0.20\text{ kg})(+4.0\text{ m/s})}{0.20\text{ kg}} - \frac{(0.40\text{ kg})(+6.4\text{ m/s}) + (0.25\text{ kg})(0)}{0.20\text{ kg}}$$

$$= +4.2\text{ m/s}.$$

The spring traveled for 0.50 s at 4.2 m/s, and so we should find it by looking at about

$$x_{\text{s,f}} = 0 + (+4.2\text{ m/s})(0.50\text{ s}) = +2.1\text{ m}$$

from the rock in the initial direction of travel. ✔

❹ **EVALUATE RESULT** The pump was moving in the x direction prior to the explosion, and so the momentum of the pieces should carry at least some of them down the road in the direction of the initial motion. The spring is located at a position between the body and the handle, which is not unreasonable. The value is of the correct order of magnitude.

Guided Problem 4.4 Space maneuvers

The commander of the starship *Enterprise* is stranded in his orbital shuttle craft, which rests a few kilometers from its docking station. Fortunately, he has two cargo pods that can be ejected (in a direction away from the docking station) with an explosive charge, and he hopes that carrying out this maneuver will move the shuttle craft back to the docking station. Pod 1 has inertia m_1, pod 2 has inertia $m_2 < m_1$, and both pods eject with speed v. Which will get him to the docking station more quickly: (*a*) ejecting first pod 1 and then pod 2, (*b*) ejecting first pod 2 and then pod 1, or (*c*) ejecting both at the same instant?

❶ **GETTING STARTED**

1. Choose an isolated system for option *a*, and sketch a system diagram showing the initial and final conditions of the system, building your drawing up as you read each sentence of the problem statement. Do you need a separate diagram for each option?
2. Identify the unknown quantity you are after. What physical principle can be applied to determine this quantity?

❷ **DEVISE PLAN**

3. Do you expect that the order in which the pods are jettisoned makes a difference?
4. How many moving objects are there in choice *a*, choice *b*, and choice *c*?
5. Add a representation of the momentum vectors before and after the explosive charges are fired in each of your system diagrams.
6. Write the appropriate equation(s) for each case and count the unknowns.

❸ **EXECUTE PLAN**

❹ **EVALUATE RESULT**

7. Rank your three answers in order of increasing speed and determine whether or not the order is reasonable based on your conceptual understanding of momentum.

Worked Problem 4.5 Forensic physics

Your friend from law enforcement claims that, in certain cases, a piece of an object hit by gunfire can move toward the shooter rather than away from the shooter. You decide to investigate whether this is possible by firing a target rifle at some melons. Suppose that in one of your tests an 8.0-g bullet is fired at 400 m/s toward a 1.20-kg melon several meters away, splitting the melon into two pieces of unequal size. The bullet lodges in the smaller piece and propels it forward (that is, in the direction the bullet originally traveled) at 9.2 m/s. If the combined inertia of this piece and the lodged bullet is 0.45 kg, determine the final velocity of the larger piece.

❶ GETTING STARTED As usual, we begin by identifying an isolated system. What about one made up of the bullet and melon? There may be some interaction with the ground or the support upon which the melon sits, but if we choose our time interval to start immediately before the bullet strikes the melon and end immediately after the smaller piece breaks loose, we can ignore this interaction. During this very short time interval, we can treat the system as isolated.

Next we sketch a system diagram showing the initial and final conditions of the system (Figure WG4.4). We arbitrarily choose the direction in which the smaller piece moves (to the right in the figure) as our positive x direction. We don't know which way the larger piece moves, and so we draw it as going forward, too. Our calculation will let us know whether this guess is right or wrong. The momentum of the system remains constant during this collision because the system is isolated.

Figure WG4.4

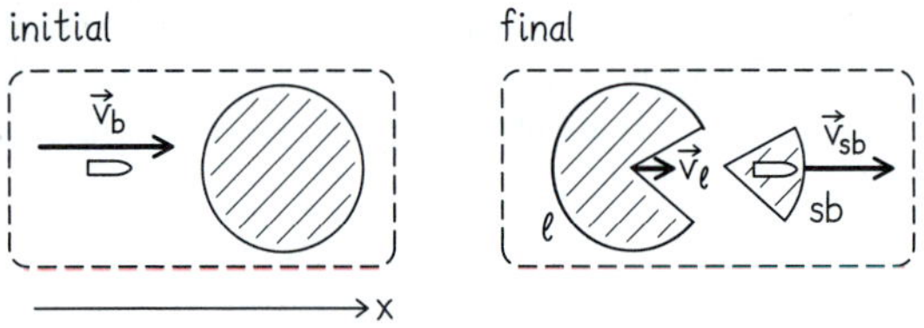

❷ DEVISE PLAN We can translate the information given into an equation that requires no change in the momentum of the system. There are two objects in the system in the final condition, but they are different from the ones in the initial condition. We designate the inertia of the bullet as m_b and the x component of its velocity as v_{bx}, and we note that the intact melon had an initial speed $v_{m,i} = 0$ and inertia m_m. We have

$$\Delta\vec{p} = 0 \Rightarrow \vec{p}_i = \vec{p}_f$$

$$m_b v_{bx,i} + m_m v_{mx,i} = (m_s + m_b) v_{sbx,f} + m_\ell v_{\ell x,f}$$

where the subscript s denotes the smaller piece, the subscript ℓ denotes the larger piece, and the subscript sb denotes the combination of the bullet and the smaller piece. We are looking for $v_{\ell x,f}$, and because all our other variables have known values, the planning is finished.

❸ EXECUTE PLAN We isolate the desired unknown and then insert numerical values. Recall that all of the velocity components in our diagram are in the positive direction.

$$m_\ell v_{\ell x,f} = m_b v_{bx,i} + m_m v_{mx,i} - (m_s + m_b) v_{sbx,f}$$

$$v_{\ell x,f} = \frac{m_b(+|\vec{v}_{b,i}|) - (m_s + m_b)(+|\vec{v}_{sb,f}|)}{m_\ell}$$

$$= \frac{(0.0080\text{ kg})(400\text{ m/s}) - (0.45\text{ kg})(9.2\text{ m/s})}{1.20\text{ kg} - (0.45\text{ kg} - 0.0080\text{ kg})}$$

$$= -1.240\text{ m/s} = -1.2\text{ m/s.} ✔$$

❹ EVALUATE RESULT The negative sign means that the larger piece moves in the negative x direction, which means that our initial guess for the direction of this motion was wrong. Note, however, that the algebra nicely informed us of the incorrect assumption without pain or confusion. The larger piece really does move back toward the rifle. The magnitude of this velocity is fairly small, as we would expect, but it certainly would be noticeable.

PRACTICE

Guided Problem 4.6 Bullet impact

A rifle is fired twice in succession at a target that is free to slide on a frozen pond, and both bullets embed in the target. In terms of the relevant inertias and the rifle's muzzle velocity, compute the velocity of the target after the first impact and after the second impact.

❶ GETTING STARTED

1. Should you choose one system for the entire process or a separate system for each impact?
2. Draw the system diagram(s) you need.
3. What physical principle governs the target's motion?

❷ DEVISE PLAN

4. Carefully consider the time sequence of events when deciding how to apply the labels "initial" and "final."
5. Remember to account for the inertia of the embedded bullets.
6. What equation(s) can you write to describe the physics in each segment of the motion?

❸ EXECUTE PLAN

7. Must you solve each equation separately, or can you combine them into one equation for the target's final speed?

❹ EVALUATE RESULT

8. Are the sign and magnitude of your answer what you expect?

Worked Problem 4.7 Grain dump slows freight

The problem on your new job at the grain elevator is that, as a series of coupled, empty freight cars coast past the grain-loading chute, the grain added to the cars slows the train down. The result is that there is more grain in the rear cars (which pass under the chute when the train is moving slowly) than in the front cars (which pass under the chute when the train is moving quickly). Your boss does not want to incur the expense of a locomotive to move the train at a constant speed. She wants to know how much more grain ends up in the last car than in the first car, and which variables affect the amount of grain in different cars. She hands you a chart of typical coasting speeds, loading rates, empty-car inertias, numbers of cars to be loaded, and so on. You start by assuming that the cars, when empty, are all identical and that all motion occurs along a horizontal straight line (the train tracks).

❶ **GETTING STARTED** We begin as usual with a sketch (Figure WG4.5). Note that the sketch shows the situation at an instant when a car in the middle of the train is being loaded rather than some instant when the first car or last car is taking on grain. Choosing this intermediate instant should make the sketch relevant to our analysis throughout the loading process.

Figure WG4.5

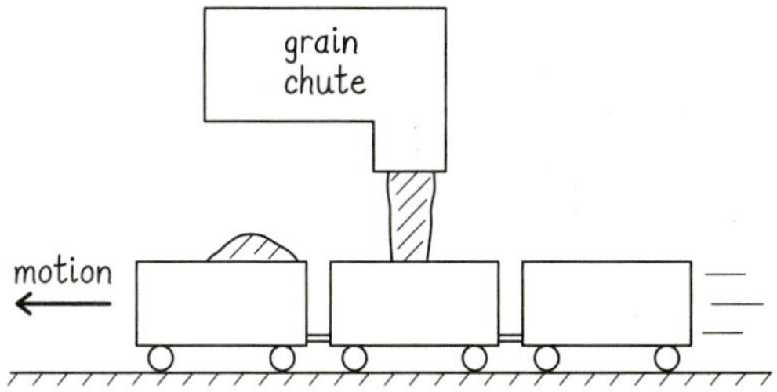

There is a lot going on: Grain is falling into the cars, increasing their inertia; the motion is slowing, allowing more grain into each car as the train moves forward, and the additional grain in the cars changes the train's motion more noticeably with time. We have no numerical values as clues, and so we will have to derive some general expressions. The amount of grain in each car will have some relationship to the speed of that car as it passes under the chute, and so we must obtain a relationship involving speed or velocity. We will also need to know how the time interval a given car spends being loaded depends on how much time has passed since the first car began loading. The problem statement implies that the rate of grain release from the chute is constant. This implication is consistent with the fact that the rear cars end up with more grain, and so we assume a constant loading rate. The final goal is to obtain an expression for how long a time interval each car spends under the chute. Given that and a constant loading rate, we can determine the amount of grain in each car and so compare the amounts in the first and last cars.

❷ **DEVISE PLAN** The system of cars plus grain is isolated if the chute and the track produce no horizontal impulse on the system. We therefore assume that the grain falls vertically into each car and that friction between the track rails and the wheels of the cars is negligible. Under these conditions, the momentum of the system must remain constant, which means that the reduction in velocity exactly balances the increase in the train's inertia. Our analysis begins with N initially empty cars (combined inertia m_i) at the instant $t = 0$ coasting with velocity $\vec{v}_i$.

Equation 4.19 is a good starting point:

$$\vec{p}_i = \vec{p}_f$$

$$m_i\vec{v}_i = m_f\vec{v}_f$$

We seek a general relationship that is valid throughout the loading process, so we represent the final instant by an arbitrary instant t:

$$m_i\vec{v}_i = m(t)\vec{v}(t). \quad (1)$$

Both $m(t)$ and $\vec{v}(t)$ are unknown, which means we need another equation involving either inertia or velocity.

The grain is added in small uniform increments, and the variables that contribute to the momentum of each piece of the system (inertias, velocities) continually change with time. Perhaps we can divide the loading process into very short time intervals, then analyze the inertia change during each interval and integrate over time to obtain an expression for the inertia as a function of time. Substituting the expression we obtain into Eq. 1, we can isolate $v(t)$. Then we must extract information about the time interval each car spends under the chute. This is equivalent to asking, during what time interval does a car move a distance equal to its length ℓ? That suggests we integrate $v(t)$ with respect to time to obtain displacement. We can then define an x axis running along the track and isolate t for the cases $\Delta x = \ell, 2\ell, \ldots, N\ell$. Given these loading time intervals, we can determine the amount of grain in each car, and we will see which variables have an effect on the loading process.

❸ **EXECUTE PLAN** We denote the constant loading rate by $dm/dt = \lambda$ (kg/s). Because we know the initial inertia of the train m_i, we can integrate to obtain an expression for its final inertia at an arbitrary instant t:

$$\int_{m_i}^{m(t)} dm = \int_0^t \lambda dt \Rightarrow m(t) - m_i = \lambda t$$

$$m(t) = m_i + \lambda t.$$

Solving Eq. 1 for $\vec{v}(t)$ and then substituting $m_i + \lambda t$ for $m(t)$, we obtain a general expression for $\vec{v}(t)$:

$$\vec{v}(t) = \frac{m_i\vec{v}_i}{m_i + \lambda t}.$$

Defining the positive x direction to be along the track in the direction of the initial motion allows us to express this as a component equation:

$$v_x(t) = \frac{m_i v_{x,i}}{m_i + \lambda t}.$$

What remains is to extract from this expression the time interval each car spends under the chute. Each car has length ℓ, and so we need an expression for the displacement that can be set equal to an integer number of car lengths. Noting that displacement is the integral of velocity with respect to time, we obtain

$$\Delta x = \int v_x(t)dt = m_i v_{x,i}\int \frac{dt}{(m_i + \lambda t)}.$$

We can either look this integral up or calculate it with a substitution of variables: $u = (m_i + \lambda t)$; $du = \lambda dt$. The result is a natural logarithm:

$$\Delta x = \frac{m_i v_{x,i}}{\lambda}\ln(m_i + \lambda t) + C.$$

To eliminate the constant of integration, we pick specific limits of integration. We start the integral at $t = 0$, as the first car just reaches the loading area, and end it just as each car leaves the loading area. That means we need several upper limits, one for each car.

PRACTICE

For now we use t to represent an arbitrary final instant:

$$\Delta x = \frac{m_i v_{x,i}}{\lambda} \ln(m_i + \lambda t)\Big|_0^t = \frac{m_i v_{x,i}}{\lambda} \ln\left(\frac{m_i + \lambda t}{m_i}\right).$$

We can extract the time variable by isolating the logarithm and then taking an exponential on both sides:

$$\frac{\lambda \Delta x}{m_i v_{x,i}} = \ln\left(\frac{m_i + \lambda t}{m_i}\right)$$

$$e^{\lambda \Delta x / m_i v_{x,i}} = \left(\frac{m_i + \lambda t}{m_i}\right) = 1 + \frac{\lambda t}{m_i}$$

$$\Delta t = t - 0 = t = \frac{m_i}{\lambda}(e^{\lambda \Delta x / m_i v_{x,i}} - 1). \quad (2)$$

Now we can obtain the time interval Δt required to fill one car, two cars, or all the cars in the train by substituting the appropriate length ($\ell, 2\ell, \ldots, N\ell$) for the displacement Δx. Suppose each of the N cars in the train has an inertia m_{car} when empty. Then $Nm_{car} = m_i$. The first car is under the chute for a time interval Δt_1, found with $\Delta x = \ell$:

$$\Delta t_1 = \frac{Nm_{car}}{\lambda}(e^{\lambda \ell / Nm_{car} v_{x,i}} - 1).$$

The amount of grain loaded during an interval Δt is given by

$$\Delta m = \int dm = \int_0^t \lambda\, dt = \lambda \Delta t.$$

The amount loaded into the first car is thus

$$\Delta m_1 = Nm_{car}(e^{\lambda \ell / Nm_{car} v_{x,i}} - 1).$$

For each subsequent car, we obtain the time interval from $t = 0$ until the car leaves the loading area, then subtract the time interval used to fill the previous cars. Thus the second car is under the chute for a time interval $\Delta t_2 - \Delta t_1$, where Δt_2 is the time interval required for the train to travel a distance $\Delta x = 2\ell$:

$$\Delta t_2 = \frac{Nm_{car}}{\lambda}(e^{\lambda 2\ell / Nm_{car} v_{x,i}} - 1)$$

$$\Delta t_2 - \Delta t_1 = \frac{Nm_{car}}{\lambda}(e^{\lambda 2\ell / Nm_{car} v_{x,i}} - e^{\lambda \ell / Nm_{car} v_{x,i}}).$$

The amount of grain added to the second car is therefore

$$\Delta m_2 = \lambda(\Delta t_2 - \Delta t_1) = Nm_{car}(e^{\lambda 2\ell / Nm_{car} v_{x,i}} - e^{\lambda \ell / Nm_{car} v_{x,i}}).$$

For the Nth car, we have

$$\Delta t_N - \Delta t_{N-1} = \frac{Nm_{car}}{\lambda}(e^{\lambda N\ell / Nm_{car} v_{x,i}} - e^{\lambda (N-1)\ell / Nm_{car} v_{x,i}})$$

$$\Delta m_N = \lambda(\Delta t_N - \Delta t_{N-1})$$

$$= Nm_{car}(e^{\lambda N\ell / Nm_{car} v_{x,i}} - e^{\lambda (N-1)\ell / Nm_{car} v_{x,i}}).$$

The ratio of the amount of grain in the last car to the amount in the first car is therefore

$$\frac{\Delta m_N}{\Delta m_1} = \frac{(e^{\lambda N\ell / Nm_{car} v_{x,i}} - e^{\lambda (N-1)\ell / Nm_{car} v_{x,i}})}{e^{\lambda \ell / Nm_{car} v_{x,i}} - 1} = e^{\lambda (N-1)\ell / Nm_{car} v_{x,i}} \checkmark \quad (3)$$

This expression answers both of your boss's questions. It gives the ratio of the amounts of grain in the last and first cars and shows that the variables affecting the amount in each car are the number N of cars in the train, length ℓ of each car, loading rate λ, inertia m_{car} of an empty car, and the initial x component of the train's velocity $v_{x,i}$. ✓

4 EVALUATE RESULT We assumed that the tracks are straight and horizontal, the cars are identical when empty, and the effects of friction are negligibly small. None of these assumptions is unreasonable in this context. We assumed that the grain falls vertically and that it enters the cars at a constant rate. Given that the chute is of a fixed size and shape, it is not unreasonable to assume a constant loading rate, at least over time intervals of a few minutes—more long than enough to get several cars past the chute. This assumption is reasonable but not mandatory. If the loading rate were a controlled variable, however, it could be adjusted to match the speed of the train and your boss would have no problem.

We see from Eq. 2 that the loading time interval increases as expected for cars farther and farther from car 1, as Δx increases. Note also that Δt goes to zero in Eq. 2 as $\Delta x \to 0$ (because it takes no time to move no distance).

The ratio of Eq. 3 grows as the number N of cars increases. This is to be expected because eventually the train slows to a crawl. Let's look at some data. Suppose $N = 4$ cars, $\ell = 15$ m, $m_{car} = 2.7 \times 10^4$ kg, $v_{x,i} = 1.0$ m/s, and $\lambda = 1.5 \times 10^3$ kg/s. Substituting these numbers into Eq. 3 yields a ratio of 1.9; that is, the last car has almost twice the grain of the first car! Even with 3 cars, the third car will contain 50% more grain than the first. It looks like the company should control the loading rate to match the train velocity. You may have a promotion coming when you suggest this and provide the time-distance relationship needed to adjust the loading rate.

PRACTICE

Guided Problem 4.8 Rocket speed

Suppose a rocket that has a combined rocket + fuel inertia m_i starts from rest and then expels fuel at a rate dm/dt. The speed of the fuel as it exits the rocket at any instant t is the difference between the forward speed of the rocket at this instant and the constant nozzle speed of the ejected fuel v_{fuel} (that is, v_{fuel} is the speed with which the fuel is ejected when the rocket is at rest). Use conservation of momentum to show that, once enough fuel has been expelled to reduce the combined rocket + fuel inertia to m_f, the change in the rocket's speed $\Delta v_{rocket} = v_{rocket,f} - v_{rocket,i}$ is

$$v_{rocket,f} - v_{rocket,i} = v_{fuel} \ln\frac{m_i}{m_f}.$$

Ignore any gravity effects. (This classic rocketry formula was first worked out by Russian engineer K. Tsiolkovskii in 1897.)

❶ GETTING STARTED

1. As in Worked Problem 4.7, this is a process with continuous changes in inertia and velocity of parts of a system. How can the approach of Worked Problem 4.7 be modified to suit these circumstances? Consider analyzing a short time interval dt and then integrating.
2. Draw one sketch at arbitrary instant t showing the rocket moving at velocity v_{rocket}. The rocket has inertia $m + dm$, where dm represents a tiny amount of fuel still on board but about to be expelled. This is the initial instant. Then draw a second sketch showing the tiny amount of fuel and the rocket as separate objects at instant $t + dt$, a short time later.
3. The rocket moves at a slightly higher velocity ($v_{\text{rocket}} + dv_{\text{rocket}}$) in the second sketch. What is the velocity of the fuel element dm in the second sketch?

❷ DEVISE PLAN

4. Notice that there are no numbers here but that all of the symbols except v_{rocket} (and dv_{rocket}) can be considered known quantities.
5. Write the equation that compares the momentum at instant t with the momentum at instant $t + dt$.
6. Examine your equation for each situation—with the fuel of inertia dm on board and with it expelled. Can some terms be canceled?
7. Separate variables to get all v terms on the left side of the equation and all m terms on the right side, then integrate. When you integrate, what sign is associated with dm?

❸ EXECUTE PLAN

❹ EVALUATE RESULT

8. Does the expression you obtain behave as you might expect? For example, does the velocity increase with time?
9. Make sure any assumptions you made are not unreasonable. Were any assumptions needed about the mechanism of fuel ejection or about the type of fuel?

Questions and Problems

For instructor-assigned homework, go to MasteringPhysics® MP

Dots indicate difficulty level of problems: • = easy, •• = intermediate, ••• = hard; CR = context-rich problem.

4.1 Friction

1. Two identical hockey pucks slide over the same rough surface. The time interval needed for puck 2 to stop is twice that needed for puck 1 to stop. What explanation can there be for this? •
2. Figure P4.2 shows the velocity of a block of wood as a function of time. The block is sliding over a horizontal surface. Describe the physical processes that led to this graph. •

Figure P4.2

3. The velocity-versus-time graph in Figure P4.3 shows the motion of two different objects sliding across a horizontal surface. Could the change in the x component of velocity with time be attributed to friction in each case? ••

Figure P4.3

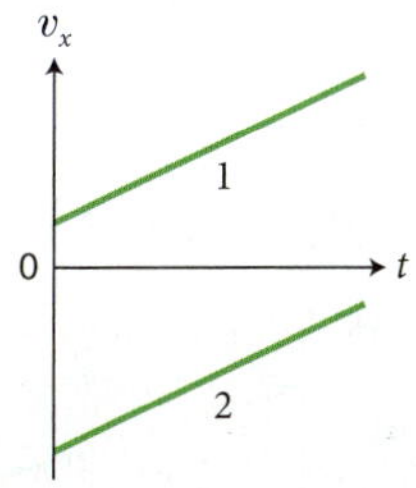

4. Consider the two velocity-versus-time graphs shown in Figure P4.4. Are the motions represented by these curves best described as similar or as different? Is the effect of friction on the motion plausibly more pronounced in one case? ••

Figure P4.4

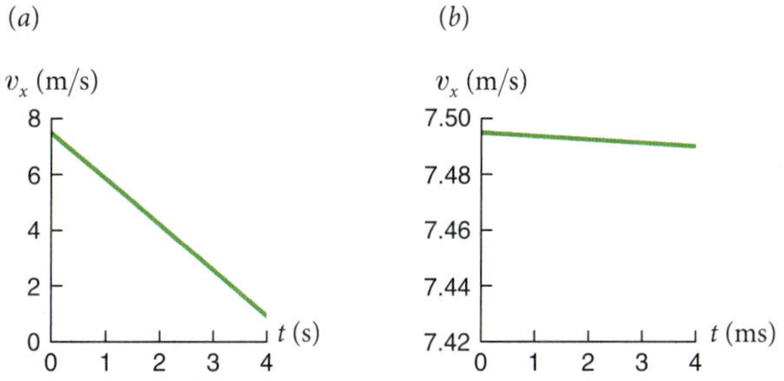

4.2 Inertia

5. Two objects collide on a low-friction track. Object 1 experiences a magnitude of change in velocity $|\Delta\vec{v}_1| = 3$ m/s, while object 2 has $|\Delta\vec{v}_2| = 1$ m/s. How do the inertias of these two objects compare? •
6. In a collision experiment, the ratio of the velocity change between two carts of equal inertia is found to equal 1. What happens to this ratio if the experiment is repeated in the following conditions? (*a*) The inertia of each cart is doubled, and the same initial velocities are used. (*b*) The original value of inertia is used, and the initial velocities of the carts are doubled. •
7. Two carts of equal inertia are moving in opposite directions toward each other. Figure P4.7 represents the positions of the carts until they collide. Sketch the positions of the carts after the collision. •

Figure P4.7

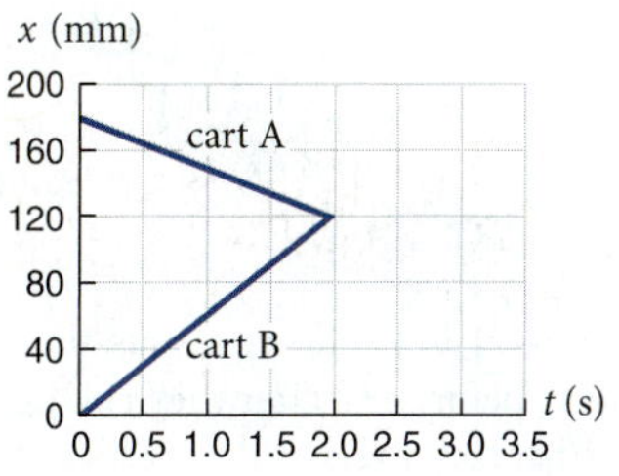

PRACTICE

8. Cart 1 initially at rest is struck by cart 2, which has twice the inertia of cart 1. Figure P4.8 shows the velocity of cart 2 as a function of time. Complete the graph by adding the velocity of cart 1 during the same time. ••

Figure P4.8

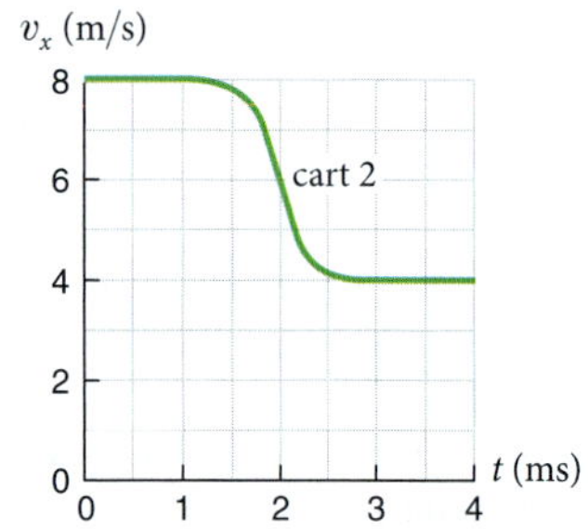

9. Figure P4.9 is the position-versus-time graph for a collision, along a straight line, between two identical amusement-park bumper cars A and B. The inertias of the passengers are different. (*a*) Which post-collision solid line is a continuation of the dotted line for car A? Which is a continuation of the dashed line for car B? (*b*) Which car contains the passenger having the greater inertia? ••

Figure P4.9

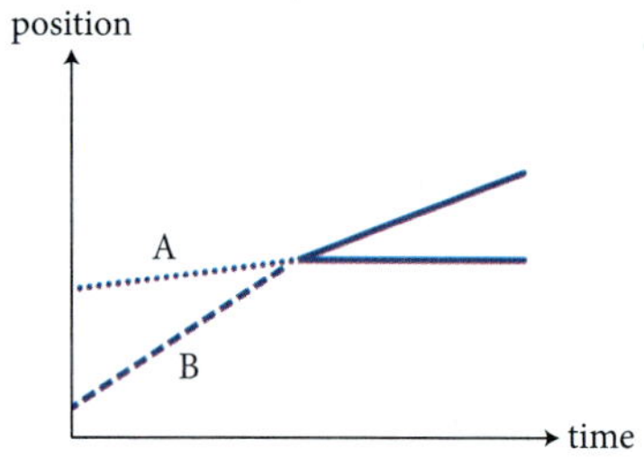

10. Figure P4.10 shows the $v_x(t)$ curves for two carts, A and B, that collide on a low-friction track. What is the ratio of their inertias? ••

Figure P4.10

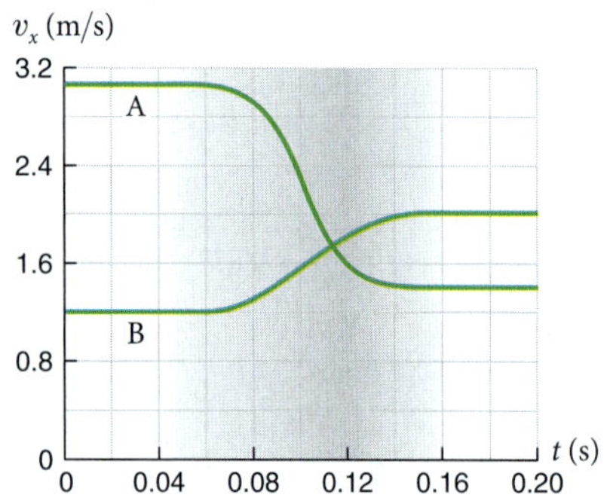

11. Figure P4.11 is a velocity-versus-time graph for two objects, A and B, before and after they collide. Object B is initially at rest. What factor relates the inertias of objects A and B? ••

Figure P4.11

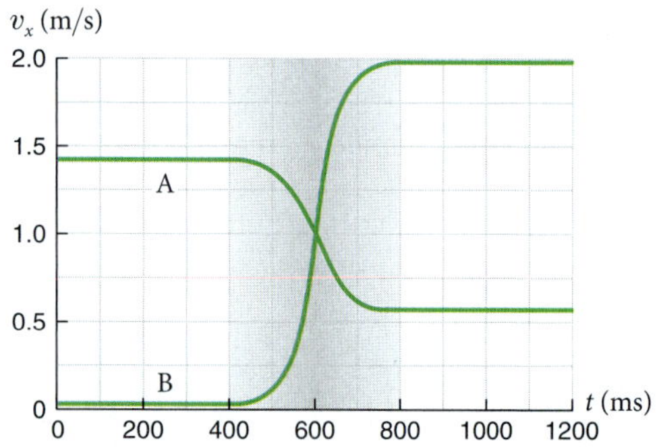

4.3 What determines inertia?

12. Which has greater inertia: a 1-quart milk carton filled with feathers or the same carton filled with buckshot? •

13. A jeweler pounds a small ingot of gold into a thin sheet. What happens to the inertia of the gold? •

14. Five different objects are formed from a constant volume V of different materials, and the objects are placed on various surfaces. Rank the following objects in order of increasing inertia: a cubic lead block on ice, a cubic plastic block on ice, a sphere of lead on ice, a pyramid of plastic on concrete, and a pyramid of lead on concrete. •

15. Which has greater inertia: a bottle full of water or the same bottle after the water has been drunk? Why is this so when the volume of the bottle does not change? ••

16. Does the inertia of a bicycle tire change when you add air to the tire? ••

17. The velocity-versus-time graphs in Figure P4.17 all depict the motion of carts that have the same size and shape. The different graphs show motion on different tracks: a smooth icy track, a dusty unpolished track, and a rough damaged track. In one case wooden carts are used, in one case plastic cars are used, and in one case one cart of each material is used. The carts may initially be moving in opposite directions, in the same direction, or one may be at rest. For each graph, label the track type, cart type, and initial motion. If you cannot determine a property, state why. ••

Figure P4.17

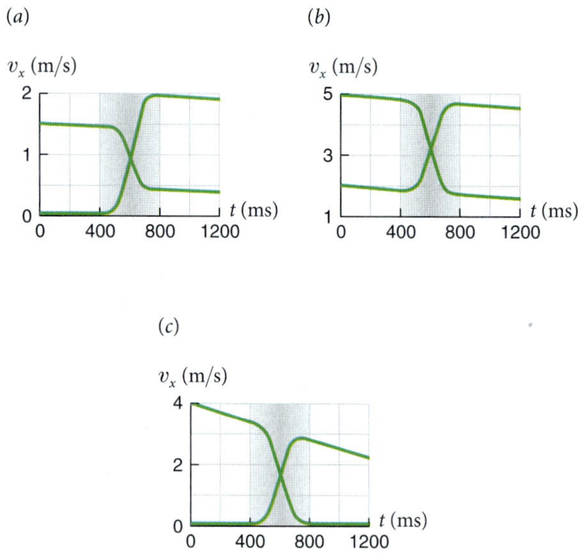

4.4 Systems

18. The label on a bag of cookies lists the number of cookies in the bag, the serving size, and the number of calories per serving. Is each of these quantities intensive or extensive? •

19. You are riding a bus and thinking about the number of passengers on board. (*a*) Is the number of passengers an extensive or intensive quantity? (*b*) Draw a system diagram to help account for the number of passengers. Where is the system boundary? (*c*) Does the number of passengers remain constant? (*d*) Does the number of passengers remain constant as the bus follows its route while its doors stay closed? •

20. A quart is a unit of volume. (*a*) If you have 1 quart of water in one container and 1 quart of water in another container and you pour all the water from both into a larger container, what volume of water do you end up with? (*b*) Suppose you have a 1-quart container filled with marbles and a large pail containing 1 quart of water. When you dump the marbles into the pail, is the final volume the same as in part *a*? Why or why not? (*c*) Compare the inertias in each case before and after mixing. ••

21. Figure P4.21 shows a person on a truck throwing a ball to a friend on the ground. In how many ways can you divide these things into a system and an environment? ••

Figure P4.21

4.5 Inertial standard

22. If two carts collide on a low-friction track, it is possible for both carts to slow down. Yet Eq. 4.1 $\left(\frac{m_u}{m_s} = -\frac{\Delta v_{sx}}{\Delta v_{ux}}\right)$ seems to say that, because inertia is always positive, if one velocity increases, the other must decrease. Explain the apparent discrepancy. •

23. Cart A, of inertia 1.0 kg, is initially at rest on a low-friction track; cart B, of unknown inertia, has an initial velocity of +3.0 m/s in your coordinate system. After the two carts collide, the final velocities are $\vec{v}_A = +2.0$ m/s and $\vec{v}_B = -3.0$ m/s. What is the inertia of cart B? •

24. A 2.0-kg cart collides with a 1.0-kg cart that is initially at rest on a low-friction track. After the collision, the 1.0-kg cart moves to the right at 0.40 m/s and the 2.0-kg cart moves to the right at 0.30 m/s. What was the initial velocity of the 2.0-kg cart? ••

25. A 1-kg standard cart collides with a 5.0-kg cart initially at rest on a low-friction track. After the collision, the standard cart is at rest and the 5.0-kg cart has a velocity of 0.20 m/s to the left. What was the initial velocity of the standard cart? ••

26. Figure P4.26 is the position-versus-time graph for a collision between two carts on a low-friction track. Cart 1 has an inertia of 1.0 kg; cart 2 has an inertia of 4.0 kg. (*a*) What are the initial and final velocities of each cart? (*b*) What is the change in the velocity of each cart? (*c*) Do the values you calculated in part *b* satisfy Eq. 4.1? (d) Draw a velocity-versus-time graph for this collision. (*e*) Does cart 1 have a nonzero acceleration? If so, when, and what is the sign of the acceleration? (*f*) Does cart 2 have a nonzero acceleration? If so, when, and what is the sign of the acceleration? ••

Figure P4.26

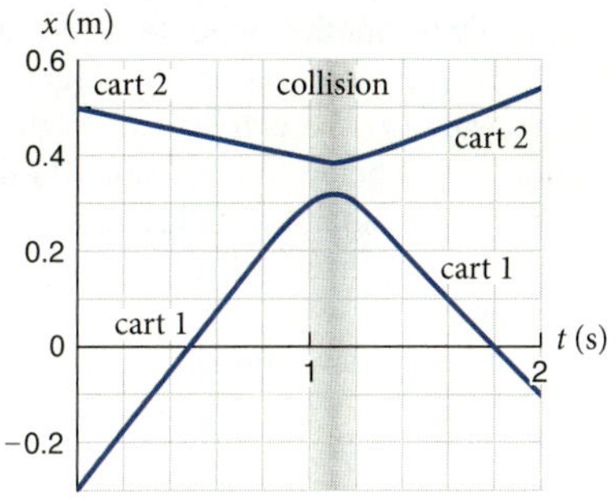

27. The bumper boats at your local theme park each have an inertia of 90 kg. In boat 1 are a man of unknown inertia, a 45-kg woman, and a 3.0-kg dog. In boat 2 are an 80-kg father, a 50-kg mother, and a 30-kg son. Boat 1 collides at 1.5 m/s with boat 2, which is initially at rest. Two seconds after the collision, boat 2 has moved 2.3 m and boat 1 has moved 0.26 m in the opposite direction. (*a*) Taking the initial direction of motion of boat 1 as positive, what is the velocity of each boat after the collision? (*b*) What is the change in velocity of each boat? (*c*) What is the man's inertia? (*d*) If the collision took 0.50 s, what was each boat's average acceleration during the collision? •••

28. A 1-kg standard cart collides with a cart A of unknown inertia. Both carts appear to be rolling with significant wheel friction because their velocities change with time as shown in Figure P4.28. (*a*) What are the carts' velocities at $t = 0$, $t = 5.0$ s, $t = 6.0$ s, and $t = 10$ s? (*b*) When not colliding, are the carts speeding up or slowing down? (*c*) Is the acceleration of each cart the same before and after the collision? (*d*) What is the inertia of cart A? •••

Figure P4.28

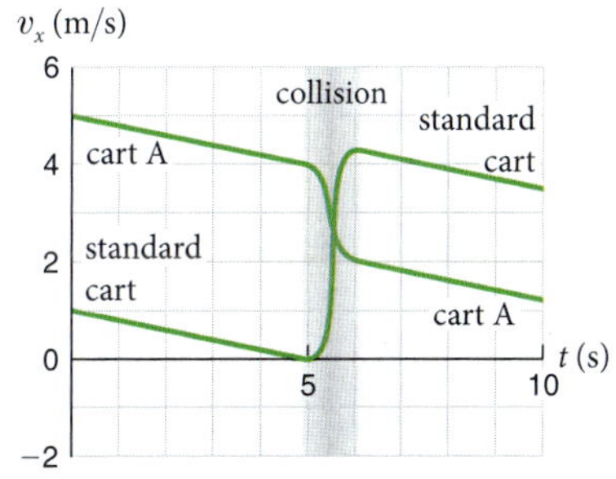

4.6 Momentum

29. Which has greater momentum: a 0.14-kg baseball pitched at 45 m/s or a 0.012-kg bullet fired at 480 m/s? •

30. The student next to you says, "Momentum is inertia times velocity. That means momentum is proportional to inertia, and so things with more inertia have more momentum." What would you say to the student to clarify the matter? •

PRACTICE

31. Two identical cars traveling at 20 m/s both slow to a stop. The driver of car A applies the brakes hard, so that the car comes to a stop in 3.0 s, while the driver of car B brakes gently and comes to a stop in 7.0 s. Which car has the greater change in momentum? •
32. A bicyclist coasting along a road at speed v collides with a grasshopper flying in the opposite direction at the same speed. The grasshopper sticks to the bicyclist's helmet. Make a sketch showing (*a*) the two velocity vectors and the two momentum vectors before the collision, (*b*) the velocity and momentum vectors after the collision, and (*c*) the velocity change and the momentum change for the bicyclist and for the grasshopper. ••
33. Is it possible for the momentum of a system consisting of two carts on a low-friction track to be zero even if both carts are moving? ••
34. A 1.0-kg standard cart A collides with a 0.10-kg cart B. The x component of the velocity of cart A is +0.60 m/s before the collision and +0.50 m/s after the collision. Cart B is initially traveling toward cart A at 0.40 m/s, and after the collision the x component of its velocity is +0.60 m/s. What are (*a*) the x component of the change in the momentum of A, (*b*) the x component of the change in the momentum of B, and (*c*) the sum of these two x components of the changes in momentum? ••
35. You're rolling solid rubber balls on the kitchen floor. Ball 1 has a density of 1.00×10^3 kg/m^3 and a radius of 25.0 mm. Ball 2 has an unknown density and a radius of 40.0 mm and is initially at rest. You roll ball 1 at an initial speed of 3.00 m/s, and the two balls collide head-on. Ball 1 reverses direction and comes back to you at 2.00 m/s, and after the collision, the speed of ball 2 is 1.00 m/s. With the positive x axis in the direction of ball 1's initial motion, what are (*a*) the magnitudes of the initial and final momenta of ball 1, (*b*) the initial and final momenta of ball 2, and (*c*) the density of ball 2? ••
36. What is the magnitude of the momentum change of two gallons of water (inertia about 7.3 kg) as it comes to a stop in a bathtub into which it is poured from a height of 2.0 m? ••
37. From what height would a car have to fall in order for the magnitude of its momentum to equal the magnitude of its momentum when it is moving on a highway at 30 m/s? ••
38. (*a*) Write an expression relating the average acceleration, Δp, and Δt for an object of constant inertia m. (*b*) Given your result in part *a*, what can you say about the magnitude of the acceleration of an object coming to rest after being dropped on a soft bed versus a hard floor? (*c*) Discuss the rationale for airbags in cars. •••
39. You drop a 0.15-kg ball to the floor from a height of 2.0 m, and it bounces to a height of 1.6 m. What is the magnitude of the change in its momentum as a result of the bounce? •••

4.7 Isolated systems

40. When a rifle is fired, it *recoils*, kicking backward into the shooter's shoulder. Why? •
41. A 4.0-kg rifle fires a 10-g bullet at 800 m/s. With what speed does the rifle recoil (move backward toward the shooter's shoulder)? •
42. What is the magnitude of the momentum of the system that consists of all the molecules making up the air in your dorm room? ••
43. A car collides with a telephone pole. (*a*) Does the car alone form an isolated system? (*b*) The car and the pole? (*c*) The car, the pole, and Earth? ••
44. Start walking from a standstill. Can you consider your body an isolated system? ••
45. In a pairs skating competition, a 75-kg male skater moving at 4.0 m/s collides (gently) with his stationary, 50-kg female partner and raises her in a lift. Neither of them makes a horizontal push at the instant of the pickup. What is the speed of the pair after the collision? (Hint: The vertical motion of the female has no bearing on the question.) ••
46. A girl wearing ice skates stands in a skating rink and throws her backpack to a bench just off the ice. (*a*) If her skates are aligned parallel to the direction of the throw, what happens to her as a result? (*b*) When the backpack lands on the bench, it stops. Does the skater stop at the same instant? If not, where does the momentum of the skater-backpack system go? ••
47. A cart moving on a low-friction track has a momentum of 6 kg · m/s to the right. At the end of the track is a wall. (*a*) What is the momentum of the system that consists of the cart and the wall? (*b*) After the cart collides with the wall, the cart's momentum is 6 kg · m/s to the left. What is the wall's momentum after impact? (*c*) Is the system defined in part *a* an isolated system? Why doesn't the wall move? ••

4.8 Conservation of momentum

48. What does conservation of momentum say about the motion of a single cart that doesn't collide with anything as it moves on a low-friction track? •
49. The three carts described in the table collide simultaneously. What is the momentum of the system of three carts (*a*) before the collision and (*b*) after the collision? (*c*) Is the system of three carts isolated during the collision, according to these data? •

Cart	Momentum p_x (kg · m/s) Before collision	After collision
1	+6.0	−4.0
2	−2.0	+2.0
3	−3.0	+3.0

50. Two carts collide on a low-friction track. Cart 1 has an initial momentum of $+10$ kg · m/s $\hat{\imath}$ and a final momentum of -2.0 kg · m/s $\hat{\imath}$. If cart 2 has a final momentum of -6.0 kg · m/s $\hat{\imath}$, what was its initial momentum? •
51. Two carts A and B collide on a low-friction track. Measurements show that their initial and final momenta are $\vec{p}_{A,i} = +10$ kg · m/s $\hat{\imath}$, $\vec{p}_{A,f} = +2.0$ kg · m/s $\hat{\imath}$, $\vec{p}_{B,i} = -4.0$ kg · m/s $\hat{\imath}$, and $\vec{p}_{B,f} = +4.0$ kg · m/s $\hat{\imath}$. (*a*) What is the change in the momentum of each cart during the collision? (*b*) What is the sum of these changes in momenta? (*c*) Is this collision consistent with conservation of momentum? Why or why not? ••

PRACTICE

52. Two carts A and B collide on a low-friction track. Measurements show that their initial and final momenta are $\vec{p}_{A,i} = +3.0\ \text{kg}\cdot\text{m/s}\,\hat{\imath}$, $\vec{p}_{A,f} = +1.0\ \text{kg}\cdot\text{m/s}\,\hat{\imath}$, $\vec{p}_{B,i} = +2.0\ \text{kg}\cdot\text{m/s}\,\hat{\imath}$, and $\vec{p}_{B,f} = -6.0\ \text{kg}\cdot\text{m/s}\,\hat{\imath}$. (*a*) What is the change in the momentum of each cart during the collision? (*b*) What is the sum of these changes in momenta? (*c*) Is this collision consistent with the physics you know? Why or why not? ••

53. A moving object collides with an object at rest. (*a*) Is it possible for both objects to be at rest after the collision? (*b*) Is it possible for just one object to be at rest after the collision? If so, which one? Ignore any effects due to friction. ••

54. Estimate the magnitude of impulse that you impart to a nail (and to whatever the nail is buried in) when you hit it with a hammer. ••

55. A 1200-kg automobile traveling at 15 m/s collides head-on with a 1600-kg automobile traveling at 10 m/s in the opposite direction. (*a*) Is it possible to predict the velocities of the cars after the collision? (*b*) Is it possible to predict the value that any pertinent physical quantity has immediately after the collision? ••

56. A 2.0-kg cart and a 3.0-kg cart collide on a low-friction track. The 3.0-kg cart is initially moving at 1.0 m/s to the right, but after the collision it is moving at 5.0 m/s to the right. After the collision, the 2.0-kg cart is moving to the right at 3.0 m/s. (*a*) What was the 2.0-kg cart's initial velocity? (*b*) What would your answer be if, other quantities being unchanged, the 3.0-kg cart were initially moving to the left at 1.0 m/s? ••

57. Warmly dressed in several layers of clothing, you are standing at the center of a frozen pond. There is not enough friction to permit you to walk to the edge of the pond. How can you save yourself? (Never mind how you got to the center of the pond.) ••

58. Two male moose charge at each other with the same speed and meet on a icy patch of tundra. As they collide, their antlers lock together and they slide together with one-third of their original speed. What is the ratio of their inertias? ••

59. An 80-kg physicist and a friend are ice-skating. The physicist, distracted, collides from behind at 7.0 m/s with his friend, who is skating at 5.0 m/s in the same direction. After the collision, the physicist continues in the same direction at 4.0 m/s, but his friend is now moving (still in the same direction) at 8.0 m/s. What is her inertia? ••

60. You are driving your 1000-kg car at a velocity of $(20\ \text{m/s})\hat{\imath}$ when a 9.0-g bug splatters on your windshield. Before the collision, the bug was traveling at a velocity of $(-2.0\ \text{m/s})\hat{\imath}$. Before the collision, what were (*a*) your car's momentum and (*b*) the bug's momentum? (*c*) What is the change in velocity of the car due to its encounter with the bug? ••

61. Sledding down a hill, you are traveling at 10 m/s when you reach the bottom. You (inertia 70 kg) then move across horizontal snow toward a 200-kg boulder but jump off the sled (inertia 5.0 kg) the instant before it hits the boulder. The boulder is sitting on *very* slick ice and moves freely when the sled hits it. The sled bounces back, moving at 6.0 m/s. (*a*) At what speed does the boulder move after the sled hits it? (*b*) If you stayed on the sled, what would your momentum be just before you hit the boulder? (*c*) Suppose you and the sled hit the boulder and continue forward after the collision at 2.0 m/s. Would the boulder's after-collision speed be higher or lower than the speed you calculated in part *a*? ••

62. A fire hose sprays water against a burning building. The stream of water has cross-sectional area A and density ρ and moves with speed v toward the building. Assume the water splatters against the building without reflecting. What magnitude of impulse does the stream of water deliver during the time interval Δt? ••

63. Playing pool, you send the cue ball head-on (that is, along the line joining the centers of the two balls) into the stationary 8 ball, and the cue ball stops as a result of the collision. (*a*) Describe the momentum of each ball before and after the collision. (*b*) Show that your answer to part *a* is consistent with Eq. 4.18, $\Delta\vec{p} = \vec{J}$. (Note: Pool balls have identical inertias.) ••

64. Three identical carts on a low-friction track have putty on their ends so that they stick together when they collide. In Figure P4.64*a*, two carts already stuck together and moving with speed v are about to collide with the third cart initially at rest. In Figure P4.64*b*, the single cart moving with the same speed v is about to collide with the two carts already stuck together and initially at rest. In which case is the final velocity of the trio of carts greater? ••

Figure P4.64

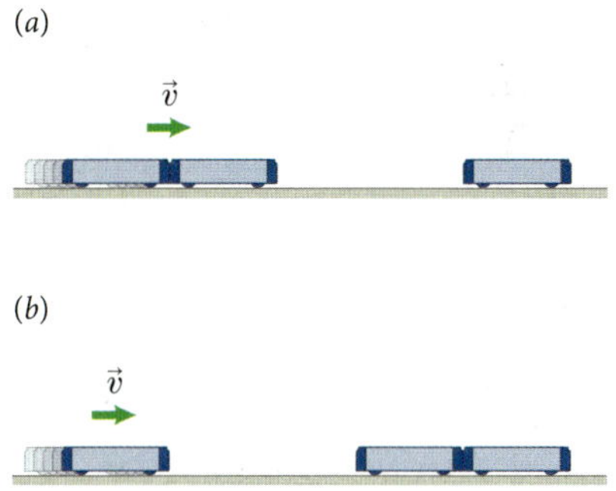

65. A load of coal is dropped from a bunker into a railroad hopper car of inertia 3.0×10^4 kg coasting at 0.50 m/s on a level track. The car's speed is 0.30 m/s after the coal falls. What is the inertia of the load of coal? ••

66. Three identical carts on a low-friction track have putty on their ends so that they stick together when they collide. In Figure P4.66*a*, two carts already stuck together and moving at speed v collide with the single cart initially at rest. In Figure P4.66*b*, there are two collisions: First the center cart, moving at speed v, collides with the cart on the right (and they stick together). Then the left cart, moving at speed v, collides with those two carts. In which case is the final speed of the three carts greater? ••

Figure P4.66

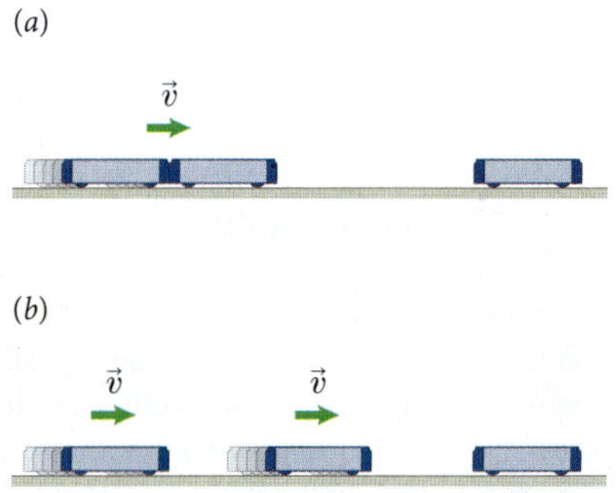

67. Figure P4.67 is a momentum-versus-time graph for a collision between two carts. Carts 1 and 2 have inertias of 1.0 kg and 3.0 kg, respectively. What are the x components of the initial and final velocities of (*a*) cart 1 and (*b*) cart 2? (*c*) What are the momentum changes $\Delta\vec{p}_1$ and $\Delta\vec{p}_2$? (*d*) Do the values you calculated in part *c* satisfy Eq. 4.18, $\Delta\vec{p} = \vec{J}$? (*e*) Draw the velocity-versus-time graph for this collision. (Hint: You can do this by making some simple changes to Figure P4.67.) •••

Figure P4.67

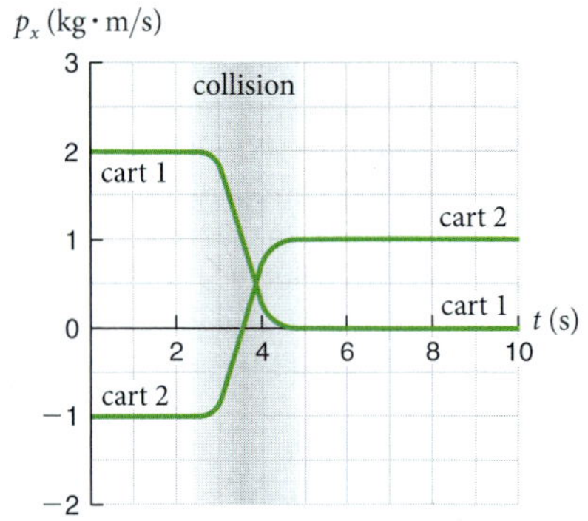

68. Carts A and B collide on a low-friction track. Rank, from largest to smallest, the following four collisions according to the magnitude of the change in the momentum of cart B, which has twice the inertia of cart A. (*a*) A initially moving right at 1.0 m/s, B initially stationary; stick together on impact. (*b*) A initially stationary, B initially moving left at 1.0 m/s; stick together on impact. (*c*) A initially moving right at 1.0 m/s; after impact, A moving left at 0.33 m/s, B moving right at 0.67 m/s. (*d*) A initially moving right at 1.0 m/s, B initially moving left at 1.0 m/s; stick together on impact. •••

69. A red cart and a green cart, both traveling at speed v on a low-friction track, approach each other head-on. The red cart is moving to the right; the green cart, whose inertia is three times that of the red cart, is moving to the left. A black cart that has a spring on its left end and putty on its right end sits on the track between the two moving carts. The moving carts hit the black cart at the same instant. After the collision, the red cart moves left at speed v, and the green and black carts move together at speed $v/5$. What is the inertia of the black cart, expressed as a multiple of the inertia of the red cart? •••

70. A 1.0-kg standard cart collides on a low-friction track with cart A. The standard cart has an initial x component of velocity of +0.40 m/s, and cart A is initially at rest. After the collision the x component of velocity of the standard cart is +0.20 m/s and the x component of velocity of cart A is +0.60 m/s. After the collision, cart A continues to the end of the track and rebounds with its speed unchanged. Before the carts collide again, you drop a lump of putty onto cart A, where it sticks. After the second collision, the x component of velocity of the standard cart is −0.20 m/s and the x component of velocity of cart A is +0.40 m/s. What is the inertia of the putty? •••

71. A 400-kg shipboard cannon fires a 20-kg ball at 60 m/s. The cannon's resulting recoil speed across the deck is regarded as excessive. How much inertia (in the form of sandbags, say) must be added to the cannon if its recoil speed must be reduced to 2.0 m/s? •••

72. You point a tennis-ball serving machine straight up and put a piece of plastic wrap across the top of the barrel, placing a 10-g marble on top of the barrel. When a 58-g tennis ball in the machine is fired, it sends the marble into the air. The marble rises 200 m above the barrel mouth, and the tennis ball rises 54 m. Neglecting the plastic wrap, what is the ball's launch speed? •••

Additional Problems

73. A golf ball has one-tenth the inertia and five times the speed of a baseball. What is the ratio of the magnitudes of their momenta? •

74. A 30,000-kg trailer truck approaches a one-lane bridge at 2.2 m/s; a 2400-kg minivan approaches the bridge from the other direction at 30 m/s. Which vehicle has a momentum of greater magnitude? •

75. You and a friend are bowling. She rolls her 4.5-kg ball at 10 m/s; you roll your ball at 8.0 m/s. What inertia must your ball have if its momentum is to be the same as hers? •

76. Two identical carts collide in three experiments on a low-friction track. In each case, cart A initially has velocity $\vec{v}$ and cart B is at rest. Sketch the velocity-versus-time graph for each cart (*a*) if the carts stick together after the collision, (*b*) if cart A is stationary after the collision, and (*c*) if cart A has velocity $-\vec{v}/10$ after the collision. ••

77. Draw diagrams that show the initial and final velocity vectors and the initial and final momentum vectors when a rapidly moving golf ball hits (*a*) a golf ball at rest and (*b*) a basketball at rest. In each case, assume that the golf ball moves along the line connecting the centers of the two balls. ••

78. The position of a certain airplane during takeoff is given by $x = \frac{1}{2}bt^2$, where $b = 2.0\ \text{m/s}^2$ and $t = 0$ corresponds to the instant at which the airplane's brakes are released at position $x = 0$. The empty but fueled airplane has an inertia of 35,000 kg, and the 150 people on board have an average inertia of 65 kg. What is the magnitude of the airplane's momentum 15 s after the brakes are released? ••

79. A bullet of inertia m_{bullet} is fired horizontally at a speed $v_{\text{bullet,i}}$ into a stationary wooden block of inertia m_{block} lying on a low-friction surface. The bullet passes through the block and emerges with a speed $v_{\text{bullet,f}}$. Determine the final speed of the block in terms of the given quantities. ••

80. The speed of a bullet can be measured by firing it at a wooden cart initially at rest and measuring the speed of the cart with the bullet embedded in it. Figure P4.80 shows a 12-g bullet fired at a 4.0-kg cart. After the collision, the cart rolls at 1.8 m/s. What is the bullet's speed before it strikes the cart? ••

Figure P4.80

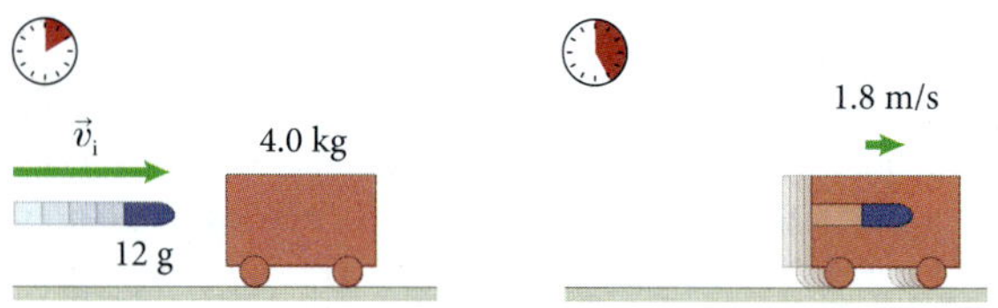

81. The World War II–era rocket launcher called the bazooka was essentially a tube open at both ends. On the basis of momentum considerations, how is the firing of a bazooka different from the firing of a cannon, which is a tube open at one end only? ••

PRACTICE

82. In a football game, a 95-kg player carrying the ball can run the 50-m dash in 5.5 s. Two opponents are available to stop him with a head-on tackle. One opponent has an inertia of 110 kg and a 50-m time of 6.6 s; the other has an inertia of 90 kg and a 50-m time of 5.1 s. Which has the better chance of stopping the 95-kg player, and why? ••

83. In the days before rocketry, some people argued that rocket engines would not work in space because there is no atmosphere for the exhaust to push against. Even today, some people think that a rocket requires a launch pad to push against in order to lift off. Refute such arguments with an argument based on momentum considerations. ••

84. In some collisions, the velocity of one participant changes little while that of the other changes a lot, as Figure P4.84 illustrates. (*a*) In which direction (positive or negative) are the objects moving before the collision? (*b*) After the collision? (*c*) What is the ratio of the inertia of the larger object to the inertia of the smaller object? (*d*) Does friction play an important role in this collision? ••

Figure P4.84

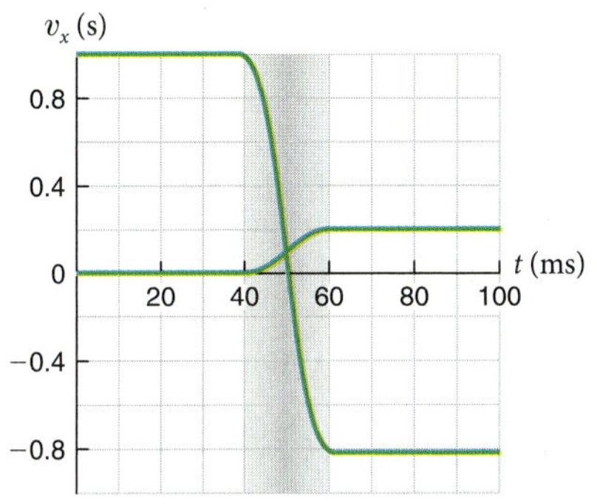

85. In a head-on collision between two cars of different inertias, you might prefer to be the driver of the car that has the greater inertia, at least if you considered momentum only. Why? ••

86. A single-stage rocket is in deep space coasting at $v_{\text{rocket,i}} = 2.0 \times 10^3$ m/s. It fires its engine, which has an exhaust speed of $v_{\text{exhaust}} = 1.0 \times 10^3$ m/s. What is the rocket's speed $v_{\text{rocket,f}}$ after it has lost one-third of its inertia by exhausting burned fuel? Assume that the fuel is ejected all at once. ••

87. In the process of moving out of your house, you are dropping stuff out a second-floor window to a friend 4.0 m below. You are about to drop a 6.0-kg stereo speaker when you begin to worry that catching anything that has a momentum greater than 50 kg · m/s might be harmful. ••• CR

88. You are in mission control in Florida, supervising a probe on its way to Mars. The most recent report indicates that the probe will soon need to fire a quick burst of its booster rocket to increase its speed by 5.2 m/s. You know that the spent fuel is ejected at a speed $v_{\text{fuel}} = 800\ \text{m/s} - v_{\text{i}}$, where v_{i} is the initial speed of the probe before firing, and that 10% of the probe's inertia is currently fuel. Your main worry is whether enough fuel is left for landing maneuvers. ••• CR

89. You have just launched your new hot-air balloon and are hovering 30.0 m above the ground. As you are checking equipment, the burner fails. You know that if you do nothing, the balloon will descend with a constant acceleration of 1.50 m/s^2, and that the balloon's basket will be seriously damaged if it hits the ground with a momentum of 2850 kg · m/s or more. The combined inertia of the balloon, basket, and all equipment and fuel is 195 kg, not counting yourself (85.0 kg) and ten 5.00-kg sandbags carried as ballast. You make some quick calculations and take action to save the day. ••• CR

90. A single gas molecule of inertia m is trapped in a box and travels back and forth with constant speed v between opposite walls A and B a distance ℓ apart. At each collision with a wall, the molecule reverses direction without changing speed. Write algebraic expressions for (*a*) the magnitude of the change in momentum of the molecule as it collides with wall B, (*b*) the amount of time that elapses between collisions with wall B; (*c*) the number of collisions per second the molecule makes with wall B, and (*d*) the change in momentum undergone by wall B, per second, as a result of these collisions. •••

91. Consider a two-stage rocket made up of two engine stages, each of inertia m when empty, and a payload of inertia m. Stages 1 and 2 each contain fuel of inertia m, so that the rocket's inertia before any fuel is spent is $5m$. Each stage exhausts fuel at a speed $v_{\text{fuel}} = v_{\text{ex}} - v_{\text{i}}$, where v_{i} is the speed of the rocket at the instant the fuel is spent. The rocket is initially at rest in deep space. Stage 1 fires, ejects its fuel all at once, and then detaches from the remainder of the rocket. The same process is repeated with stage 2. (*a*) What is the final speed of the payload? (Hint: Determine the speed of the rocket after stage 1 fires. Then, because stage 1 is detached from the rocket, *redefine the system* to include only the payload and stage 2, and determine the speed of the rocket after stage 2 fires.) (*b*) Now consider another rocket of inertia $5m$ but with only a single engine stage, of inertia $2m$, carrying fuel of inertia $2m$. What is the final speed of the payload in this case? (*c*) Which design yields a higher payload speed: two stage or single stage? Why? •••

Answers to Review Questions

1. No one has yet developed a completely frictionless surface, but there are many ways to minimize friction: smooth or polish the surfaces of contact; apply a slippery substance, such as grease or oil; place the object on rollers or mount it on wheels with very good bearings; and float the object on a cushion of air, as is done with low-friction tracks.
2. The changes in velocity are equal in magnitude but of opposite sign.
3. The magnitude of the velocity change of A is half that of B because the ratio of the magnitudes of velocity changes is the inverse of the ratio of the inertias. The two velocity changes are in opposite directions.
4. The inertias are identical because shape has no effect on an object's inertia. The inertia of an object is determined *entirely* by the type of material of which the object is made and by the amount of that material contained in the object.
5. Inertia depends on the material, so they are not identical. Experience suggests that the iron object has greater inertia.
6. A system is an object or group of objects that we can separate in our minds from the surrounding environment.
7. An extensive quantity depends on the extent (size) of the system that you choose; an intensive quantity does not.
8. Input, output, creation, and destruction can change the value.
9. It means that the extensive quantity cannot be created or destroyed. Therefore only two processes can change the value of the quantity in a system: input and output.
10. Fasten the baseball to one standard cart and arrange a collision between this cart and the other standard cart. Measure the change in velocity of each object; then use the fact that the ratio of these changes in velocity is the inverse of the ratio of the inertias of the two objects. Subtract 1 kg from the inertia of the cart with the baseball to obtain the baseball's inertia.
11. No. Inertia is always positive. If one of the objects involved in a collision had negative inertia, *both* objects would have an increase in velocity. Such collisions have never been observed.
12. Their inertias are equal.
13. The bumblebee has greater momentum. The train has zero velocity, and so it has zero momentum. The train has much greater inertia than the bumblebee, however.
14. Even though the inertia of the baseball is greater than the inertia of the bullet, their momenta (and the results of the collisions) can be comparable if the speed of the bullet is proportionately larger than the speed of the baseball.
15. No. Only scalars can be negative, and momentum is a vector. However, the x component of momentum can be negative if the momentum points in the negative x direction.
16. For purposes of this chapter, an interaction is two objects acting on each other such that at least one of them is accelerated.
17. Internal interactions are between two objects in a system, whereas external interactions are between an object inside the system and an object outside the system. The distinction is important because external interactions can change the momentum of a system, while internal interactions cannot.
18. An isolated system is one for which there are no external interactions. Because the momentum of an isolated system does not change with time, we can use information about the momentum at one instant to determine the momentum at a later instant.
19. The statements are not equivalent, but *a* depends on *b*. Statement *b* means that momentum cannot be created or destroyed. Statement *a* applies to only an isolated system, and it applies *because b* is true. By definition, there are no transfers of momentum across the boundary of an isolated system, and so none of the four mechanisms that might change the system's momentum—input, output, creation, and destruction—are available.
20. Conservation of momentum wouldn't be affected in the least. The 1-kg standard is a convention only.
21. *Conservation of momentum* is a verbal statement of the fact that momentum can be neither created nor destroyed. The *momentum law* is a mathematical statement given by Eq. 4.18, $\Delta\vec{p} = \vec{J}$, saying that any change in momentum is due to transfers of momentum. Because it contains no terms for the creation or destruction of momentum, the momentum law embodies the conservation of momentum.
22. Impulse, $\vec{J}$, represents the transfer of momentum between the environment and a system. It is a vector with the same units as momentum, kg · m/s, and, in the nomenclature of Section 4.4, it accounts for the "input" and "output" of the system. Impulse is related to the change in momentum of a system by Eq. 4.18: $\vec{J} = \Delta\vec{p}$.

Answers to Guided Problems

Guided Problem 4.2 8.2×10^{-2} m/s

Guided Problem 4.4 *c*, ejecting both at once to attain the highest speed for the shuttle:

$$v_f = \frac{(m_1 + m_2)}{m_{shuttle}} v$$

Guided Problem 4.6 After the first impact:

$$v_{target} = \frac{m_{bullet}}{(m_{target} + m_{bullet})} v_{muzzle};$$

after the second impact: $v_{target} = \dfrac{2m_{bullet}}{(m_{target} + 2m_{bullet})} v_{muzzle}$

PRACTICE

5

PRACTICE
Energy

Chapter Summary

Kinetic energy (Sections 5.2, 5.5)

Concepts The **kinetic energy** of an object is the energy associated with its motion. Kinetic energy is a positive scalar quantity and is independent of the direction of motion.

Quantitative Tools The **kinetic energy** K of an object of inertia m moving at speed v is

$$K = \tfrac{1}{2}mv^2. \qquad (5.12)$$

The SI unit of kinetic energy is the **joule** (J):

$$1\ \text{J} = 1\ \text{kg} \cdot \text{m}^2/\text{s}^2.$$

Relative velocity, states, and internal energy (Sections 5.1, 5.3, 5.5)

Concepts In a collision between two objects, the velocity of one object relative to the velocity of the other object is the **relative velocity** $\vec{v}_{12}$. The magnitude of the relative velocity is the **relative speed** v_{12}.

The **state** of an object is its condition as specified by some complete set of physical parameters. Energy associated with the object's state but not with its motion is called the **internal energy** of the object.

We can consider a system of two colliding objects to be isolated during the collision. Therefore the momentum of the system remains constant during all the collisions we study.

Quantitative Tools The **relative velocity** $\vec{v}_{12}$ of object 2 relative to object 1 is

$$\vec{v}_{12} \equiv \vec{v}_2 - \vec{v}_1. \qquad (5.1)$$

The **relative speed** v_{12} of object 2 relative to object 1 is the magnitude of $\vec{v}_{12}$:

$$v_{12} = |\vec{v}_2 - \vec{v}_1|.$$

Because momentum is a conserved quantity, the momentum of a system remains constant during a collision:

$$p_{x,\text{i}} = p_{x,\text{f}}.$$

Types of collisions (Sections 5.5, 5.6, 5.8)

Concepts The **coefficient of restitution** e for a collision is a positive, unitless quantity that tells how much of the initial relative speed is restored after the collision.

For an **elastic collision,** the relative speed is the same before and after the collision, and the coefficient of restitution is equal to 1. The collision is **reversible,** and the kinetic energy of the system made up of the colliding objects is constant.

For an **inelastic collision,** the relative speed after the collision is less than it was before the collision. The coefficient of restitution is between 0 and 1, and the collision is **irreversible.** The kinetic energy of the objects changes during the collision, but the energy of the system does not change. If the objects stick together, the final relative speed is zero; the collision is **totally inelastic,** and the coefficient of restitution is 0.

For an **explosive separation,** kinetic energy is gained during the collision and the coefficient of restitution is greater than 1.

Quantitative Tools The **coefficient of restitution** e is

$$e = \frac{v_{12\text{f}}}{v_{12\text{i}}} = -\frac{v_{2x,\text{f}} - v_{1x,\text{f}}}{v_{2x,\text{i}} - v_{1x,\text{i}}}. \qquad (5.18, 5.19)$$

For an **elastic collision,**

$$v_{12\text{i}} = v_{12\text{f}} \qquad (5.3)$$

$$K_\text{i} = K_\text{f} \qquad (5.14)$$

$$e = 1.$$

For an **inelastic collision,**

$$v_{12\text{f}} < v_{12\text{i}}$$

$$K_\text{f} < K_\text{i}$$

$$0 < e < 1.$$

For a **totally inelastic collision,**

$$v_{12\text{f}} = 0 \qquad (5.16)$$

$$e = 0.$$

For an **explosive separation,**

$$v_{12\text{f}} > v_{12\text{i}}$$

$$K_\text{f} > K_\text{i}$$

$$e > 1.$$

Conservation of energy (Sections 5.3, 5.4, 5.7)

Concepts The energy of any system is the sum of the kinetic energies and internal energies of all the objects that make up the system.

The law of **conservation of energy** states that energy can be transferred from one object to another or converted from one form to another, but it cannot be destroyed or created.

A **closed system** is one in which no energy is transferred in or out. The energy of such a system remains constant.

Quantitative Tools The energy of a system is

$$E = K + E_{\text{int}}. \tag{5.21}$$

The law of conservation of energy requires the energy of a **closed system** to be constant:

$$E_{\text{i}} = E_{\text{f}}. \tag{5.22}$$

Review Questions

Answers to these questions can be found at the end of this chapter.

5.1 Classification of collisions

1. What is relative velocity, and how does it differ from relative speed?
2. Explain the order and meaning of the subscripts in the relative velocity symbol $\vec{v}_{12}$.
3. What is the main differentiating characteristic of (*a*) elastic collisions, (*b*) inelastic collisions, and (*c*) totally inelastic collisions?

5.2 Kinetic energy

4. What is kinetic energy?
5. What is the sign of the kinetic energy of an object that is moving in the negative x direction?
6. Is it possible for an object's kinetic energy to be negative or zero?

5.3 Internal energy

7. What is meant by the *state of an object*?
8. What is the difference between a reversible process and an irreversible process?
9. In an inelastic collision, what is the relationship between the system's kinetic energy and internal energy?
10. How do you calculate the change in internal energy in an inelastic collision?

5.4 Closed systems

11. What is a closed system? Is it the same as an isolated system?
12. What is energy conversion, and how is it different from energy transfer?

5.5 Elastic collisions

13. How does the proof that kinetic energy remains constant in an elastic collision (Eqs. 5.4 through 5.13) depend on the elastic nature of the collision?
14. Explain why the relative velocity of two objects changes sign in an elastic collision.

5.6 Inelastic collisions

15. What is the definition of coefficient of restitution?
16. What is the numerical value of the coefficient of restitution for an elastic collision and for a totally inelastic collision?
17. Explain why Eq. 5.19 has a minus sign in front of the fraction.
18. In an elastic collision between a pair of objects where you know the inertias and initial velocities, you can use the fact that the momentum and kinetic energy of the system remain constant to determine the motion of both objects afterward—two equations, two unknowns. In an inelastic collision, however, the kinetic energy does not remain constant. Can you predict the final velocities of both objects in this case, given the inertias and initial velocities?

5.7 Conservation of energy

19. Are you creating energy when you throw a baseball?
20. Can there be a change in the physical state of a system if there is no change in its kinetic energy?
21. Without direct knowledge of how to compute internal energy values, how can we determine the change in the internal energy of a closed system?

5.8 Explosive separations

22. Where does the kinetic energy increase come from in an explosive separation?
23. Is it possible for an explosive separation to be elastic?

Developing a Feel

Make an order-of-magnitude estimate of each of the following quantities. Letters in parentheses refer to hints below. Use them as needed to guide your thinking.

1. The relative velocity of an airliner cruising east seen from a train speeding west (K, R)
2. The relative speed of the Moon in orbit as seen from Earth (E, W)
3. The kinetic energy of a tennis ball as it crosses the net after service (P, I)
4. The kinetic energy of a small car driving along the freeway (G, L)
5. The kinetic energy of an airliner moving at cruising speed (S, K)
6. The speed of the center of a tennis racquet just before the ball is served (P, H, C, X)
7. The change in the kinetic energy of a golf ball hit for a long drive from the tee (A, F, O, T)
8. The chemical energy released during the explosive separation of a professional fireworks shell (N, D, Z)
9. The kinetic energy converted to internal energy when a switching engine couples with a rail car initially at rest (V, J, Y)
10. The amount of useful energy your car can obtain from 1 gallon of gasoline at freeway speed (B, G, M, U, Q)

Hints

A. What distance does the golf ball travel in the air?
B. While cruising on a freeway, how much speed does a car lose in 5 s if it is shifted into neutral?
C. What is the coefficient of restitution for the ball-racquet collision?
D. What is the maximum radius of the exploding sphere?
E. What time interval is needed for one Moon orbit?
F. For how long a time interval is the golf ball in the air?
G. What is the inertia of a typical small car?
H. Considering the inertia of the ball relative to the inertia of the arm plus racquet, how much does the speed of the racquet change during the collision?
I. What is the inertia of a tennis ball?
J. What is the rail car's inertia?
K. What is the speed of a cruising airliner?
L. What is the speed of the car on the freeway?
M. How much kinetic energy is lost by a coasting car in 5 s?
N. What is the inertia of the fireworks payload?
O. What is the speed of a golf ball leaving the tee?
P. What is the speed of a tennis ball after service?
Q. What is the fuel consumption of a typical car on the freeway?
R. What is the speed of a speeding train?
S. What is the inertia of an airliner?
T. What is the inertia of a golf ball?
U. How many kilometers does a car travel in 5 s at freeway speed?
V. What is the switching engine's inertia?
W. What is the radius of the Moon's orbit?
X How does the velocity of the ball relative to that of the racquet compare before and after the collision?
Y. What is the engine's speed before coupling?
Z. How long a time interval is required for the sphere to expand?

Key (all values approximate)

A. 1×10^2 m; **B.** 4 m/s; **C.** $e \approx 1$; **D.** 3×10^1 m; **E.** 1 month, or 3×10^1 days; **F.** 3 s; **G.** 1×10^3 kg; **H.** very little, because the inertia ratio is large; **I.** 6×10^{-2} kg; **J.** 2×10^4 kg; **K.** 2×10^2 m/s; **L.** 3×10^1 m/s; **M.** 1×10^5 J; **N.** 2 kg; **O.** 4×10^1 m/s; **P.** 4×10^1 m/s; **Q.** 0.1 L/km; **R.** 3×10^1 m/s in the United States; much faster in some other countries; **S.** 1×10^5 kg; **T.** 5×10^{-2} kg; **U.** 0.2 km; **V.** 8×10^4 kg; **W.** 4×10^8 m; **X.** relative speed remains roughly the same, but the direction of the velocity reverses; **Y.** 0.4 m/s; **Z.** 1 s

Worked and Guided Problems

Procedure: Choosing a closed system

When we analyze energy changes, it is convenient to choose a system for which no energy is transferred to or from the system (a closed system). To do so, follow this procedure:

1. Make a sketch showing the initial and final conditions of the objects under consideration.
2. Identify all the changes in state or motion that occur during the time interval of interest.
3. Choose a system that includes all the objects undergoing these changes in state or motion. Draw a dashed line around the objects in your chosen system to represent the system boundary. Write "closed" near the system boundary to remind yourself that no energy is transferred to or from the system.
4. Verify that nothing in the surroundings of the system undergoes a change in motion or state that is related to what happens inside the system.

Once you have selected a closed system, you know that its energy remains constant.

These examples involve material from this chapter but are not associated with any particular section. Some examples are worked out in detail; others you should work out by following the guidelines provided.

Worked Problem 5.1 Lofty arrow

You shoot a 0.12-kg arrow vertically upward at 40 m/s. Calculate the arrow's kinetic energy (*a*) at the start of its flight, immediately after it leaves the bow, and (*b*) when it reaches half of its maximum height. (*c*) Use energy arguments to estimate the position of the arrow when it has half its original speed.

1 GETTING STARTED This is a kinematics problem with an energy twist. We can use the kinematics we learned in Chapter 3 first to calculate the velocity (and thus the speed) of the arrow at any position for parts *a* and *b* and then to calculate the position at any speed for part *c*. In addition, because we now know the connection between speed and kinetic energy, we can connect position and kinetic energy. The arrow in motion is not a closed system because of the gravitational interaction, but the arrow + Earth system is closed. A system diagram would include Earth and the arrow but would not provide much additional information. Instead, taking the kinematics approach, we draw a motion diagram (Figure WG5.1).

Figure WG5.1

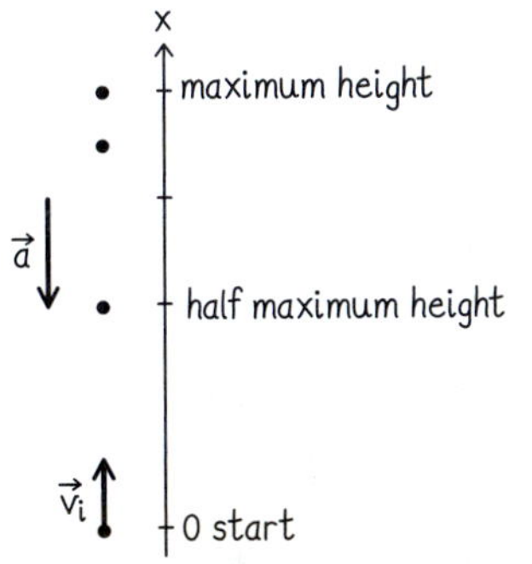

2 DEVISE PLAN The definition of kinetic energy should be sufficient to tackle part *a* because both the inertia and the initial velocity are known. Parts *b* and *c* are more involved. In free fall, acceleration is downward and constant. With our choice in Figure WG5.1 to have the positive *x* axis pointing upward, we have $a_x = -g$. The relationship between the *x* components of velocity and position that does not explicitly involve time is Eq. 3.13:

$$v_{x,\mathrm{f}}^2 = v_{x,\mathrm{i}}^2 + 2a_x(x_\mathrm{f} - x_\mathrm{i}).$$

This equation may be applied between any two points in the motion, and so we can use it to determine either the arrow's height at a specified speed or its speed at a specified height. This plus the definition of kinetic energy should take care of parts *b* and *c*.

3 EXECUTE PLAN

(*a*)

$$K_\mathrm{start} = \tfrac{1}{2}mv_\mathrm{start}^2$$
$$= \tfrac{1}{2}(0.12\ \mathrm{kg})(40\ \mathrm{m/s})^2 = 96\ \mathrm{J}.\ ✔$$

(*b*) Before we can determine the value of *K* at the instant the arrow reaches half its maximum height, we must obtain the distance to the top of the flight. We know the initial position (0) and the *x* components of the initial velocity (+40 m/s), the final velocity (0; why?), and the acceleration (−9.8 m/s²; why minus?), and so we can write

$$v_{x,\mathrm{top}}^2 = v_{x,\mathrm{start}}^2 + 2a_x(x_\mathrm{top} - x_\mathrm{start})$$

$$x_\mathrm{top} = x_\mathrm{start} + \frac{v_{x,\mathrm{top}}^2 - v_{x,\mathrm{start}}^2}{2a_x} = 0 + \frac{(0)^2 - (40\ \mathrm{m/s})^2}{2(-9.8\ \mathrm{m/s^2})}$$
$$= 82\ \mathrm{m}.$$

We now obtain the squared velocity at half this maximum height, $x_\mathrm{half} = x_\mathrm{top}/2$:

$$v_{x,\mathrm{half}}^2 = v_{x,\mathrm{start}}^2 + 2a_x(x_\mathrm{half} - x_\mathrm{start})$$
$$= (+40\ \mathrm{m/s})^2 + 2(-9.8\mathrm{m/s^2})(41\ \mathrm{m} - 0) = 796\ \mathrm{m^2/s^2}.$$

The arrow's speed at half its maximum height is therefore

$$v_{\text{half}} = |\sqrt{v_{x,\text{half}}^2}| = |\sqrt{796\ \text{m}^2/\text{s}^2}| = 28\ \text{m/s}.$$

(Notice that this speed is *not* half the initial speed.) The kinetic energy at this point is thus

$$K_{\text{half}} = \tfrac{1}{2}mv_{\text{half}}^2 = \tfrac{1}{2}(0.12\ \text{kg})(796\ \text{m}^2/\text{s}^2) = 48\ \text{J}. ✔$$

This is half the initial kinetic energy. Having gained half its maximum height, half the kinetic energy has been converted to internal energy of the arrow + Earth system.

(*c*) We know from part *b* that at half its maximum height the arrow's speed is 28 m/s. This means that the position where the speed is 20 m/s, half the initial value, must be above the halfway point. Let's make a guess. Because the velocity in $K = \frac{1}{2}mv^2$ is squared, reducing v to half its initial value reduces K to a quarter of its initial value. We know that $v = 0$ at the top of the arrow's trajectory (see Section 3.3). From part *b* we know that when the arrow is at half its maximum height, half of its kinetic energy has been converted to internal energy. Perhaps at three-quarters of the distance to the top of the flight, three-quarters of the kinetic energy has been converted to internal energy, as shown in the energy bars of Figure WG5.2. Thus, we estimate that the height at which the velocity is +20 m/s, half the original velocity, is about

$$(0.75)(82\ \text{m}) = 61\ \text{m} ✔$$

above the starting position.

Figure WG5.2

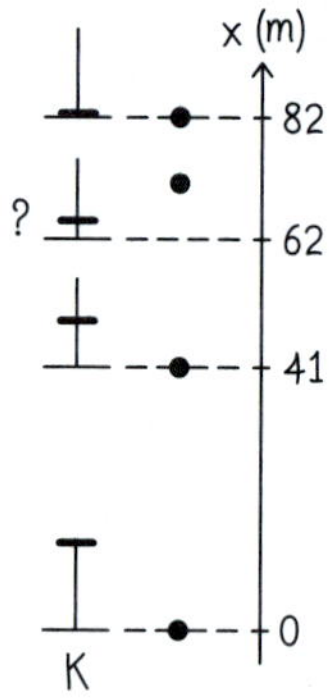

❹ EVALUATE RESULT Comparing the answers to parts *a* and *b* shows that the arrow's speed decreases as the arrow rises, as expected. A maximum distance of 82 m is a reasonable height for an arrow, consistent with the 40-m/s initial speed. We assumed that the arrow was in free fall so that we could use the free-fall value for acceleration, and this is a reasonable assumption for an arrow on its upward flight. The rest of the solution follows from kinematics and the definition of kinetic energy.

In part *c*, we were told to use energy arguments to determine a position. If we had not been restricted that way, we could have used our kinematics equation to obtain the position at which the arrow was moving at +20 m/s, and so let's do that now as a check:

$$v_{x,(c)}^2 = v_{x,\text{start}}^2 + 2a(x_{(c)} - x_{\text{start}})$$

$$x_{(c)} = x_{\text{start}} + \frac{v_{x,(c)}^2 - v_{x,\text{start}}^2}{2a} = 0 + \frac{(20\ \text{m/s})^2 - (40\ \text{m/s})^2}{2(-9.8\ \text{m/s}^2)}$$

$$= 61\ \text{m},$$

in nice agreement with our energy-based guess.

Guided Problem 5.2 Throwing a punch

A boxer delivers a hard blow to the chin of his opponent. The inertia of the boxer's hand (with glove) and forearm is 3.0 kg, and the inertia of the opponent's head is 6.5 kg. You learned in neurobiology class about 10 J of extra internal energy will render an opponent wobbly-kneed, and you guess that about half of the converted energy will end up in the opponent's head. Assuming a coefficient of restitution $e = 0.20$, with what speed does the boxer's fist have to contact the opponent's head in order to deliver the punch?

❶ GETTING STARTED

1. Do the boxer's hand, glove, and forearm form an isolated or closed system? What if the opponent's head is included?
2. What kind of diagram might be useful?

❷ DEVISE PLAN

3. Using your diagram as a guide, write the relevant equation(s).
4. Make sure you have enough information to solve for the requested answer.
5. Does the opponent's head remain stationary as the punch is delivered?

❸ EXECUTE PLAN

6. What value should you use for the converted energy?

❹ EVALUATE RESULT

PRACTICE

Worked Problem 5.3 Poor parking

A car traveling at 3.0 m/s whizzes into an empty parking space. At the same instant, a truck that has an inertia 50% greater than that of the car is using the empty parking space to take a shortcut through the parking lot. Both vehicles are coasting (in other words, both have zero acceleration), and just before they hit head-on, the truck is moving at 4.0 m/s. (*a*) If during the collision 75% of the initial kinetic energy of the car-truck system is converted to internal energy, what are the final velocities of the two vehicles? (*b*) What is the coefficient of restitution for the collision?

❶ **GETTING STARTED** Our first step is to draw a system diagram and then add the information about initial velocities (Figure WG5.3). For the short duration of the collision, the car and truck form an isolated system. Because we are told that a given percentage of kinetic energy is converted, we can also assume that the system is closed. We are not given inertia values but are told only that the truck's inertia is 50% greater than that of the car. We hope we do not need the actual values, but we put the information we have in the diagram to help us think clearly about the situation.

Figure WG5.3

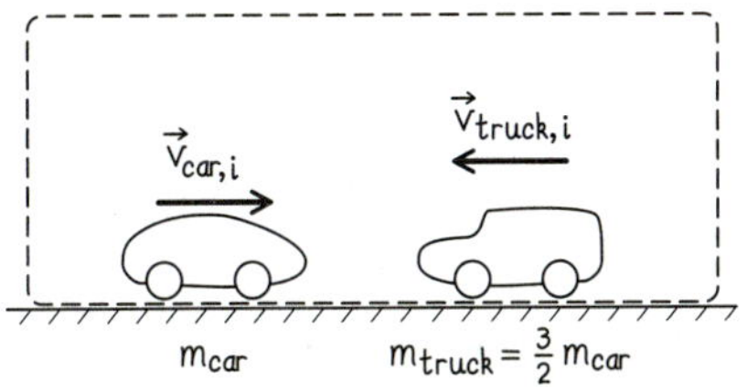

We are asked to determine the two "final velocities," which we assume means "final velocities immediately after the collision" so that any interaction with the environment can be neglected. This information is contained in the momenta of the vehicles. Because kinetic energy is lost, we know that the collision is inelastic.

❷ **DEVISE PLAN** The momentum of the two-vehicle system after the collision is the same as the momentum before the collision. Thus we should draw a diagram representing the initial and final momenta to help plan our approach (Figure WG5.4). To get the directions of the final motion, we shall have to deal with the signs of the momenta with reference to an axis. Let us choose to point our positive x axis toward the left and include it in our diagram. We have drawn both final momenta as being in the positive x direction because the truck has the greater initial momentum.

Figure WG5.4

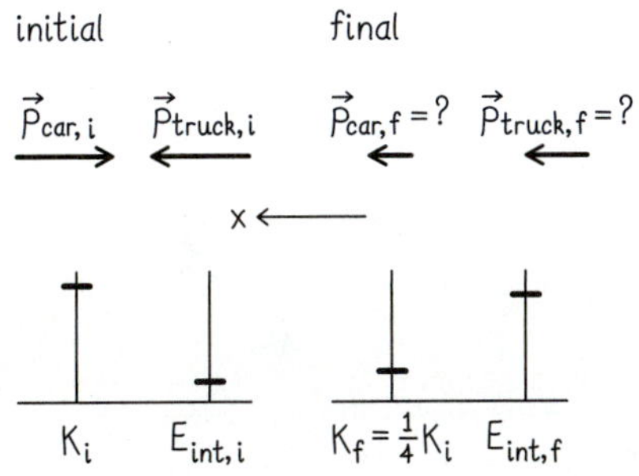

Along the x axis we chose, we have $v_{car\,x,i} = -v_{car,i}$ and $v_{truck\,x,i} = +v_{truck,i}$, where $v_{car,i} = 3.0$ m/s and $v_{truck,i} = 4.0$ m/s. From this, we know that the x components of the initial momenta are $p_{car\,x,i} = m_{car} v_{car\,x,i}$ and $p_{truck\,x,i} = m_{truck} v_{truck\,x,i}$. We also know that, from immediately before to immediately after the collision, the momentum of our system is constant. From this information, we can write

$$p_{car\,x,f} + p_{truck\,x,f} = p_{car\,x,i} + p_{truck\,x,i}.$$

We know only the two quantities on the right, however, and so we need more information. The energy of the system does not change under our assumptions, but the final kinetic energy is reduced substantially as kinetic energy is converted to internal energy. We illustrate this with energy bars sketched on the system diagram, and we write the information in equation form:

$$\Delta E = 0, \quad \text{but} \quad K_f = \tfrac{1}{4} K_i.$$

Using this kinetic energy equation to obtain the final velocities, we can calculate the coefficient of restitution from the expression

$$e = -\frac{v_{car\,x,f} - v_{truck\,x,f}}{v_{car\,x,i} - v_{truck\,x,i}}.$$

❸ **EXECUTE PLAN** (*a*) Conservation of momentum gives us

$$m_{car} v_{car\,x,f} + m_{truck} v_{truck\,x,f} = m_{car} v_{car\,x,i} + m_{truck} v_{truck\,x,i}.$$

That the truck's inertia is given in terms of the car's inertia allows us to get rid of the m_{truck} factors and then simplify further by dividing through by m_{car}:

$$m_{car} v_{car\,x,f} + \tfrac{3}{2} m_{car} v_{truck\,x,f} = m_{car} v_{car\,x,i} + \tfrac{3}{2} m_{car} v_{truck\,x,i}$$

$$v_{car\,x,f} + \tfrac{3}{2} v_{truck\,x,f} = v_{car\,x,i} + \tfrac{3}{2} v_{truck\,x,i}. \quad (1)$$

The final velocities are unknown, and so we have one equation with two unknowns, which means we do not yet have enough information to solve the problem. We need one more equation, so we turn to our energy equation:

$$K_f = \tfrac{1}{4} K_i$$

$$\tfrac{1}{2} m_{car} v_{car\,x,f}^2 + \tfrac{1}{2} m_{truck} v_{truck\,x,f}^2 = \tfrac{1}{4}\left(\tfrac{1}{2} m_{car} v_{car\,x,i}^2 + \tfrac{1}{2} m_{truck} v_{truck\,x,i}^2\right)$$

$$\tfrac{1}{2} m_{car} v_{car\,x,f}^2 + \tfrac{1}{2}\left(\tfrac{3}{2} m_{car}\right) v_{truck\,x,f}^2 = \tfrac{1}{4}\left[\tfrac{1}{2} m_{car} v_{car\,x,i}^2 + \tfrac{1}{2}\left(\tfrac{3}{2} m_{car}\right) v_{truck\,x,i}^2\right].$$

PRACTICE

Multiplying through by 4 and canceling m_{car}, we get

$$2v^2_{car\,x,f} + 3v^2_{truck\,x,f} = \tfrac{1}{2}v^2_{car\,x,i} + \tfrac{3}{4}v^2_{truck\,x,i}. \quad (2)$$

This result combined with Eq. 1 gives us two equations containing two unknowns. To solve them, we express $v_{car\,x,f}$ in Eq. 1 in terms of $v_{truck\,x,f}$:

$$\begin{aligned} v_{car\,x,f} &= v_{car,x,i} + \tfrac{3}{2}v_{truck\,x,i} - \tfrac{3}{2}v_{truck\,x,f} \\ &= (-v_{car,i}) + \tfrac{3}{2}(+v_{truck,i}) - \tfrac{3}{2}v_{truck\,x,f} \\ &= (-3.0\text{ m/s}) + \tfrac{3}{2}(+4.0\text{ m/s}) - \tfrac{3}{2}v_{truck\,x,f} \\ &= +3.0\text{ m/s} - \tfrac{3}{2}v_{truck\,x,f}. \quad (3) \end{aligned}$$

Now we use this result in Eq. 2 and solve for $v_{truck\,x,f}$:

$$2v^2_{car\,x,f} + 3v^2_{truck\,x,f} = \tfrac{1}{2}v^2_{car\,x,i} + \tfrac{3}{4}v^2_{truck\,x,i}$$

$$2(+3.0\text{ m/s} - \tfrac{3}{2}v_{truck\,x,f})^2 + 3v^2_{truck\,x,f} = \tfrac{1}{2}(-3.0\text{ m/s})^2 + \tfrac{3}{4}(+4.0\text{ m/s})^2$$

$$(18\text{ m}^2/\text{s}^2) - (18\text{ m/s})v_{truck\,x,f} + \tfrac{18}{4}v^2_{truck\,x,f} + 3v^2_{truck\,x,f} = \frac{9.0\text{ m}^2/\text{s}^2}{2} + (12\text{ m}^2/\text{s}^2)$$

$$(18\text{ m}^2/\text{s}^2) - (18\text{ m/s})v_{truck\,x,f} + \tfrac{30}{4}v^2_{truck\,x,f} = \frac{33\text{ m}^2/\text{s}^2}{2}$$

$$5.0v^2_{truck\,x,f} - (12\text{ m/s})v_{truck\,x,f} + (1.0\text{ m}^2/\text{s}^2) = 0.$$

Solving this quadratic equation yields

$$v_{truck\,x,f} = +2.3\text{ m/s} \quad \text{or} \quad +0.086\text{ m/s}.$$

Substituting these values into Eq. 3 and solving for $v_{car\,x,f}$ gives

$$v_{truck\,x,f} = +2.3\text{ m/s},\ v_{car\,x,f} = -0.45\text{ m/s}$$

or

$$v_{truck\,x,f} = +0.086\text{ m/s},\ v_{car\,x,f} = +2.9\text{ m/s}.$$

We must choose the result that corresponds to the physical situation. The first result says that the truck keeps moving in the positive x direction and the car keeps moving in the negative x direction, implying that they pass through each other, a physically impossible result. The second solution has the truck continuing but the car switching direction, which is plausible. Consequently, with our having assigned leftward as the positive x direction, the physically correct velocities are

$$v_{truck\,x,f} = +0.086\text{ m/s} \quad (0.086\text{ m/s to the left}) ✔$$

$$v_{car\,x,f} = +2.9\text{ m/s} \quad (2.9\text{ m/s to the left}). ✔$$

(*b*) The coefficient of restitution is

$$e = -\frac{v_{car\,x,f} - v_{truck\,x,f}}{v_{car\,x,i} - v_{truck\,x,i}}$$

$$= -\frac{+2.9\text{ m/s} - (+0.086\text{ m/s})}{-3.0\text{ m/s} - (+4.0\text{ m/s})} = +\frac{2.8}{7.0} = 0.40. ✔$$

❹ **EVALUATE RESULT** The final speeds are reasonable given the initial speeds (which are a bit high for a parking space!). We made sure the velocity directions are realistic when we chose the appropriate root of the quadratic equation. The kinetic energy of the system does decrease substantially, as expected, with the truck moving very slowly after the collision. Because the magnitude of the change in momentum for the two vehicles is equal but the inertias are not, the truck should have the smaller change in velocity. Its velocity change is $(+0.086\text{ m/s}) - (+4.0\text{ m/s}) = -3.9\text{ m/s}$, while the car's is $(+2.9\text{ m/s}) - (-3.0\text{ m/s}) = 5.9\text{ m/s}$, just as we expected. The coefficient of restitution is reassuringly less than 1 for this inelastic collision.

Guided Problem 5.4 Burrowing bullet

A gun that has a muzzle velocity of 600 m/s is used to fire a 12.0-g bullet horizontally into a 4.00-kg block of wood initially at rest. The bullet passes completely through the block, with negligible loss of inertia to either object. After the collision, the block slides at 1.20 m/s in the direction of the bullet's motion. What is the change in internal energy in the bullet-block system? Ignore any effects due to friction between the block and the surface over which it slides.

❶ **GETTING STARTED**

1. Which objects should you include in your system? Draw a system diagram for these objects.
2. Which conservation laws apply here: momentum, energy, or both? How could you represent what happens to these quantities graphically?

❷ **DEVISE PLAN**

3. Write equations relating the initial and final values. Does any equation have a single unknown (and hence can be solved immediately)?
4. What is the relationship between the change in internal energy and the change in kinetic energy?

❸ **EXECUTE PLAN**

❹ **EVALUATE RESULT**

PRACTICE

Worked Problem 5.5 Explosive beat

You decide to build a *ballistocardiograph* that works on the following principle: A patient lies flat on a slab that floats on a cushion of air so that it can move freely in the horizontal direction. When the heart pumps blood horizontally in one direction, the slab and patient move in the opposite direction. For a resting patient, the heart pumps blood preferentially toward the head. The resulting recoil speed can be measured and can be correlated with the medical information you are after, which is the heart's ability to pump blood. You anticipate having patients as large as 1.0×10^2 kg. You know that a normal heart, each time it pumps, converts 2.0 mJ of chemical energy to kinetic energy and moves about 50 g of blood. You also know you can buy velocity sensors that can detect the slab's speed to a sensitivity of 1.0×10^{-5} m/s, and you want the measured speed to be comfortably higher than this—say, by a factor of 10. What is the highest practical value for the slab's inertia if its maximum speed with a patient lying on it is to be 1.0×10^{-4} m/s? Assume that any friction experienced by the slab sliding over the air cushion is negligible and that the slab and patient move as a single unit.

❶ **GETTING STARTED** The heart is converting internal energy to the kinetic energy of the blood moving in one direction and the kinetic energy of the slab and patient moving in the opposite direction. This is an explosive event and a signal that we should probably use conservation of momentum in our analysis, which means our first step is to choose an isolated system and draw a system diagram for it (Figure WG5.5*a*). The "initial" diagram is at an instant between heartbeats, when the patient, the slab, and the small amount of blood about to be pumped can be thought of as motionless. The initial system momentum is therefore zero. We approximate that all the pumped blood moves toward the patient's head. After we add the unknown final velocity information, Figure WG5.5(*b*) shows the notation we shall use. We suspect we may need a coordinate system, and so we arbitrarily choose our positive *x* axis pointing to the left. The "final" diagram shows the small volume of blood moving toward the head and the patient and slab recoiling. We suspect that the amount of internal energy converted to kinetic energy will give us information about the speeds.

Figure WG5.5

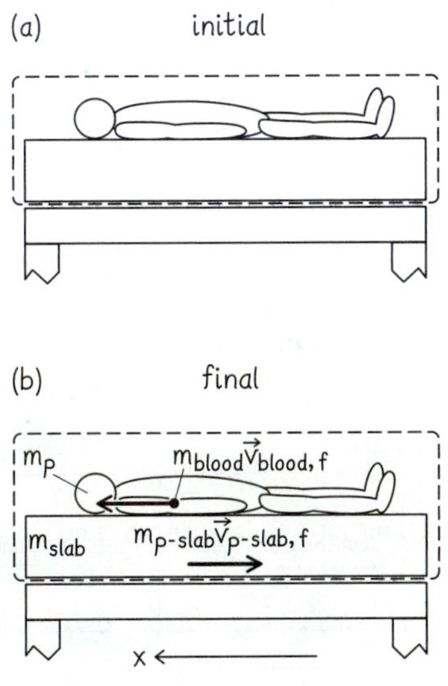

❷ **DEVISE PLAN** Conservation of momentum gives us, for the isolated system of blood, patient, and slab,

$$\vec{p}_{\rm f} = \vec{p}_{\rm i}$$

$$m_{\rm blood}\vec{v}_{\rm blood,f} + (m_{\rm patient} + m_{\rm slab})\vec{v}_{\rm patient+slab,f} = 0. \qquad (1)$$

We want to know the value of $m_{\rm slab}$ that will generate the minimum detectable value for $|\vec{v}_{\rm patient+slab,f}| = 1.0 \times 10^{-4}$m/s. Because we have two unknowns, $m_{\rm slab}$ and $\vec{v}_{\rm blood,f}$, we need another equation. Knowing that the change in the internal energy is $\Delta E_{\rm int} = -2.0$ mJ $= -2.0 \times 10^{-3}$ J, we should be able to use conservation of energy for this closed system to get another equation:

$$\Delta K + \Delta E_{\rm int} = 0$$

$$K_{\rm f} - K_{\rm i} = -\Delta E_{\rm int}$$

$$\left[\tfrac{1}{2}m_{\rm blood}v^2_{\rm blood\,\mathit{x},f} + \tfrac{1}{2}(m_{\rm patient} + m_{\rm slab})v^2_{\rm patient+slab\,\mathit{x},f}\right] - 0 = -\Delta E_{\rm int} \qquad (2)$$

This gives us two equations with everything known except two values: $m_{\rm slab}$ and $v_{\rm blood\,\mathit{x},f}$. We should first use Eq. 1 to express $v_{\rm blood\,\mathit{x},f}$ in terms of $m_{\rm slab}$ and then substitute into Eq. 2.

❸ **EXECUTE PLAN** Notice that the patient and slab move together as one object. It is convenient to use the subscript ps to replace the unwieldy patient+slab. This will require that we solve first for the combined inertia of patient and slab and then subtract the known maximum inertia of the patient to obtain the desired inertia of the slab. With this substitution, Eq. 1 gives

$$m_{\rm blood}v_{\rm blood\,\mathit{x},f} = -m_{\rm ps}v_{\rm ps\,\mathit{x},f}$$

$$v_{\rm blood\,\mathit{x},f} = -\frac{m_{\rm ps}}{m_{\rm blood}}v_{\rm ps\,\mathit{x},f}.$$

Then Eq. 2 gives

$$\tfrac{1}{2}m_{\rm blood}v^2_{\rm blood\,\mathit{x},f} + \tfrac{1}{2}m_{\rm ps}v^2_{\rm ps\,\mathit{x},f} = -\Delta E_{\rm int}$$

$$\tfrac{1}{2}m_{\rm blood}\left(-\frac{m_{\rm ps}}{m_{\rm blood}}v_{\rm ps\,\mathit{x},f}\right)^2 + \tfrac{1}{2}m_{\rm ps}v^2_{\rm ps\,\mathit{x},f} = -\Delta E_{\rm int}$$

$$\frac{1}{2}\frac{m^2_{\rm ps}}{m_{\rm blood}}v^2_{\rm ps\,\mathit{x},f} + \tfrac{1}{2}m_{\rm ps}v^2_{\rm ps\,\mathit{x},f} = -\Delta E_{\rm int}$$

$$\left(\frac{\frac{1}{2}v^2_{\rm ps\,\mathit{x},f}}{m_{\rm blood}}\right)m^2_{\rm ps} + \left(\tfrac{1}{2}v^2_{\rm ps,\mathit{x},f}\right)m_{\rm ps} + \Delta E_{\rm int} = 0. \qquad (3)$$

Because two coefficients involve the same quantity, we divide by that quantity:

$$\frac{1}{m_{\rm blood}}m^2_{\rm ps} + m_{\rm ps} + \frac{2\Delta E_{\rm int}}{v^2_{\rm ps\,\mathit{x},f}} = 0.$$

We solve this quadratic equation for $m_{\rm ps}$ using the quadratic formula:

$$m_{\rm ps} = \frac{-1 \pm \sqrt{(1)^2 - 4\left(\dfrac{1}{m_{\rm blood}}\right)\left(\dfrac{2\Delta E_{\rm int}}{v^2_{\rm ps\,\mathit{x},f}}\right)}}{2\left(\dfrac{1}{m_{\rm blood}}\right)}.$$

Substituting the known numerical values gives

$$m_{ps} = \frac{-1 \pm \sqrt{1 - 4\left[\dfrac{1}{5.0 \times 10^{-2}\text{ kg}}\right]\dfrac{2(-2.0 \times 10^{-3}\text{ J})}{(1.0 \times 10^{-4}\text{ m/s})^2}}}{2\left[\dfrac{1}{5.0 \times 10^{-2}\text{ kg}}\right]},$$

which simplifies to

$$m_{ps} = \frac{-1 \pm \sqrt{1 + 3.2 \times 10^7}}{4.0 \times 10^1\text{ kg}^{-1}}.$$

The positive solution to this equation is $m_{ps} = 1.4 \times 10^2$ kg. We now can obtain the maximum design value for the slab's inertia:

$$m_{slab} = m_{ps} - m_{patient} = 140\text{ kg} - 100\text{ kg} = 40\text{ kg}. ✔$$

❹ EVALUATE RESULT This is not an especially low inertia, and so the answer suggests that such a device might be feasible. Looking at the math confirms that this is a maximum inertia for the slab because a larger slab would require either less patient inertia or a smaller value of v_{ps}. The assumption of an isolated system is not unreasonable, given the air-cushion design. The assumption that all 50 g of blood moves toward the head is an oversimplification, but it is consistent with the problem statement, and in the absence of more accurate blood flow information we have no better alternative.

(Bonus task: You should convince yourself that the slab moves back and forth as the heart beats rather than moving farther and farther in one direction.)

Guided Problem 5.6 Useful approximations

In Worked Problem 5.5, we had to solve a quadratic equation (Eq. 3). Solving such equations can be a bother when you wish to make a quick calculation. The procedure used in Worked Problem 5.5 can be bypassed in explosive separations if the inertia of one object is much greater than that of the other(s). Consider the explosive separation that breaks an object initially at rest into two fragments, one of which has much greater inertia than the other: $m_1 \ll m_2$. In the explosive separation, some of the internal energy of the system is converted to kinetic energy in the fragments. Show that the following are good approximations for the division of energy between the fragments:

$$\tfrac{1}{2}m_2v_2^2 \approx \frac{m_1}{m_2}\Delta K \qquad \text{(A)}$$

$$\tfrac{1}{2}m_1v_1^2 \approx \Delta K, \qquad \text{(B)}$$

where v_1 is the speed of the fragment of inertia m_1 and v_2 is the speed of the fragment of inertia m_2. Equation B tells us that almost all of the internal energy converted to kinetic energy goes to the fragment that has less inertia. Only a small fraction m_1/m_2 of the internal energy goes to the fragment that has greater inertia.

❶ GETTING STARTED

1. Is the approach of Worked Problem 5.5 relevant?
2. Draw a system diagram for the initial and final situations. It may be necessary to use velocities rather than speeds when dealing with momentum.

❷ DEVISE PLAN

3. Is it possible to follow the procedure of Worked Problem 5.5 using the simpler notation m_1, v_1 and m_2, v_2?
4. In your new version of Eq. 3 of Worked Problem 5.5, isolate the kinetic energy of the fragment with greater inertia, $\tfrac{1}{2}m_2v_2^2$.
5. Which is true: $m_1/m_2 \gg 1$ or $m_1/m_2 \ll 1$?

❸ EXECUTE PLAN

6. Remember to approximate, especially if you are adding or subtracting a small number to or from a very large number.
7. You should now be able to do the step that gives Eq. A.
8. To derive Eq. B, repeat the derivation of Worked Problem 5.5 but this time in terms of the speed v_1 of the object with less inertia m_1.

❹ EVALUATE RESULT

9. Use the numerical values given in Worked Problem 5.5 in Eq. A to estimate the maximum practical inertia for the slab. Is the value you calculate consistent with the numerical result obtained in Worked Problem 5.5?

Worked Problem 5.7 Designer bowling

A 7.5-kg bowling ball rolls down the lane toward the 1.5-kg head pin at 5.0 m/s. The bowling alley owner wants to know how fast that pin can go flying, so that the end of the lane can be reinforced properly. You mumble confidently about coefficient of restitution, inertia, and maximum speed, and as the boss leaves she mentions that she wants this information yesterday. Ignore friction between the alley floor and the ball.

❶ GETTING STARTED What have we got to work with? Well, for the short time interval of the collision, the ball and pin form an isolated system whose momentum must remain constant. The system may or may not be closed, but it seems probable that the less energy transferred out of the ball-pin system, the more likely the pin will attain its maximum speed. There is no obvious source of energy to be transferred into the system, so assuming a closed system should be a good approximation. There is also no obvious mechanism for an explosive separation, so the coefficient of restitution must be between 1 and 0. We could simply compute the final velocity in terms of an unknown e and then try different values for the coefficient of restitution to see which yields the highest speed.

We draw a system diagram (Figure WG5.6), as usual, with initial and final pictures to help clarify what is going on and allow us to assign symbols for the variables and establish the direction of a positive x axis.

Figure WG5.6

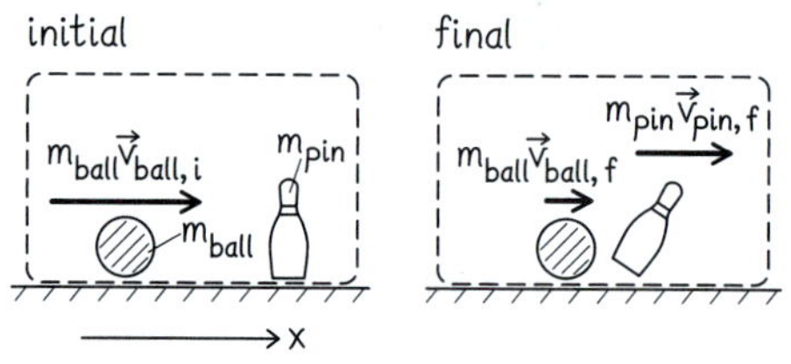

❷ **DEVISE PLAN** Conservation of momentum tells us that

$$\vec{p}_f = \vec{p}_i$$

$$m_{ball} v_{ball\,x,f} + m_{pin} v_{pin\,x,f} = m_{ball} v_{ball\,x,i} + m_{pin} v_{pin\,x,i}, \quad (1)$$

where we assume that the original motion of the ball is in the positive x direction. We know both inertias and both initial velocities, taking $v_{pin\,x,i}$ to be 0. Thus we have two unknowns, $v_{ball\,x,f}$ and $v_{pin\,x,f}$, but we also have a second equation to use:

$$e = \frac{v_{rel,f}}{v_{rel,i}} = -\frac{v_{ball\,x,f} - v_{pin\,x,f}}{v_{ball\,x,i} - v_{pin\,x,i}} = \text{trial value} \quad (2)$$

Thus, assuming a known trial value for e, we have two equations and two unknowns, the x components of the final velocities.

❸ **EXECUTE PLAN** A logical step toward solution is to manipulate Eq. 2 to look more like Eq. 1 (with all the final values on the left and all the initial values on the right) and then look for a way to eliminate an unknown:

$$m_{ball} v_{ball\,x,f} + m_{pin} v_{pin\,x,f} = m_{ball} v_{ball\,x,i} + m_{pin} v_{pin\,x,i} \quad (1)$$

$$v_{ball\,x,f} - v_{pin\,x,f} = -e(v_{ball\,x,i} - v_{pin\,x,i}) \quad (2)$$

Noting that there are different signs on the two final x components of pin velocity, but the same sign on the two final x components of ball velocity, we plan to subtract Eq. 2 from Eq. 1 to eliminate $v_{ball\,x,f}$. To make this work, we multiply Eq. 2 by m_{ball}:

$$m_{ball} v_{ball\,x,f} - m_{ball} v_{pin\,x,f} = -e m_{ball}(v_{ball\,x,i} - v_{pin\,x,i})$$

and subtract this equation from Eq. 1:

$$0 + (m_{ball} + m_{pin}) v_{pin\,x,f}$$
$$= m_{ball}(1 + e) v_{ball\,x,i} + (m_{pin} - e m_{ball}) v_{pin\,x,i}$$
$$v_{pin\,x,f} = \frac{m_{ball}(1 + e) v_{ball\,x,i} + (m_{pin} - e m_{ball}) v_{pin\,x,i}}{(m_{ball} + m_{pin})}.$$

Noting that the initial x component of the pin velocity is zero, we obtain

$$v_{pin\,x,f} = \frac{m_{ball}(1 + e) v_{ball\,x,i} + 0}{(m_{ball} + m_{pin})} = \frac{m_{ball} v_{ball\,x,i}}{(m_{ball} + m_{pin})}(1 + e)$$
$$= \frac{7.5\text{ kg }(5.0\text{ m/s})}{(7.5\text{ kg} + 1.5\text{ kg})}(1 + e).$$

The speed we seek is the magnitude of this x component of velocity.

It is now clear that the larger the value of e, the higher the final speed of the pin. Because the largest reasonable value of e is 1, we compute the maximum speed as

$$v_{pin,f} = |v_{pin\,x,f}| = |(4.17\text{ m/s})(1 + 1)| = 8.34\text{ m/s} = 8.3\text{ m/s}. ✔$$

The owner should design for this speed.

❹ **EVALUATE RESULT** The speed we obtain for the pin is almost 70% faster than the speed of the incoming ball, but that is reasonable given that the ball has greater inertia and keeps rolling in the same direction. We therefore expect the pin to recoil faster than the incoming ball. Because the ball-pin system is closed, we can also check our answer using energy conservation. For an elastic collision, the kinetic energy is constant and so

$$\tfrac{1}{2} m_{ball} v_{ball,f}^2 + \tfrac{1}{2} m_{pin} v_{pin,f}^2 = \tfrac{1}{2} m_{ball} v_{ball,i}^2 + \tfrac{1}{2} m_{pin} v_{pin,i}^2$$

$$\tfrac{1}{2} m_{pin} v_{pin,f}^2 = \tfrac{1}{2} m_{ball} v_{ball,i}^2 - \tfrac{1}{2} m_{ball} v_{ball,f}^2 + \tfrac{1}{2} m_{pin} v_{pin,i}^2.$$

There are still two unknown final speeds, so we compute one of them using Eq. (2).

$$v_{ball\,x,f} = v_{pin\,x,f} - e(v_{ball\,x,i} - v_{pin\,x,i})$$
$$v_{ball\,x,f} = +8.34\text{ m/s} - 1(+5.0\text{ m/s} - 0)$$
$$v_{ball\,x,f} = +3.34\text{ m/s}, \; v_{ball,f} = 3.3\text{ m/s}$$

Using the values computed above for $e = 1$, we have

$$\tfrac{1}{2}(1.5\text{ kg}) v_{pin,f}^2$$
$$= \tfrac{1}{2}(7.5\text{ kg})(5.0\text{ m/s})^2 - \tfrac{1}{2}(7.5\text{ kg})(3.34\text{ m/s})^2 + 0$$
$$v_{pin,f}^2 = 69.2\text{ m}^2/\text{s}^2$$
$$v_{pin,f} = 8.3\text{ m/s},$$

which is the result we obtained.

Guided Problem 5.8 Fast service

Champion table-tennis players can swing the paddle at speeds of 20 m/s. How fast is the ball going after one of these serves?

❶ **GETTING STARTED**

1. Choose a system and draw a system diagram.
2. Is your system isolated? Closed? Which conservation laws are appropriate to describe it?
3. Draw before and after pictures, and label all known and unknown quantities. It may seem at first like you don't have enough information, but plunge ahead anyway.

❷ **DEVISE PLAN**

4. What is the initial velocity of the ball?
5. Based on what you expect the properties of a Ping-Pong ball to be, which type of collision is this likely to be: elastic, inelastic, or totally inelastic?
6. No inertia values are given. Assuming the hand and forearm are part of the paddle, how does the inertia of the ball compare with the inertia of the paddle? How will the paddle's final velocity after the collision compare with its initial velocity before the collision?
7. Write the relative velocity equation. Do you need another equation?

❸ **EXECUTE PLAN**

❹ **EVALUATE RESULT**

8. How does the final speed of the ball compare with the initial speed of the paddle?
9. Which type of collision did you assume? Is that assumption justified (or at least not unreasonable)? How would your result change if you modified the coefficient of restitution a bit?

Questions and Problems

For instructor-assigned homework, go to MasteringPhysics® MP

Dots indicate difficulty level of problems: • = *easy,* •• = *intermediate,* ••• = *hard;* CR = *context-rich problem.*

5.1 Classification of collisions

1. (*a*) While driving a car at 25 m/s, you pass a truck traveling in the same direction at 22 m/s. If you assign the direction in which the two vehicles are moving as the positive *x* direction of a coordinate system, what is the truck's velocity relative to you? (*b*) Now a motorcycle passes you at 29 m/s. What is its velocity relative to you? •
2. Suppose you have an isolated system in which two objects about to collide have equal and opposite momenta. If the collision is totally inelastic, what can you say about the motion after the collision? •
3. Figure P5.3 shows velocity-versus-time graphs for two situations in which a pair of objects collide. For each situation, decide whether the collision is elastic, inelastic, or totally inelastic. ••

Figure P5.3

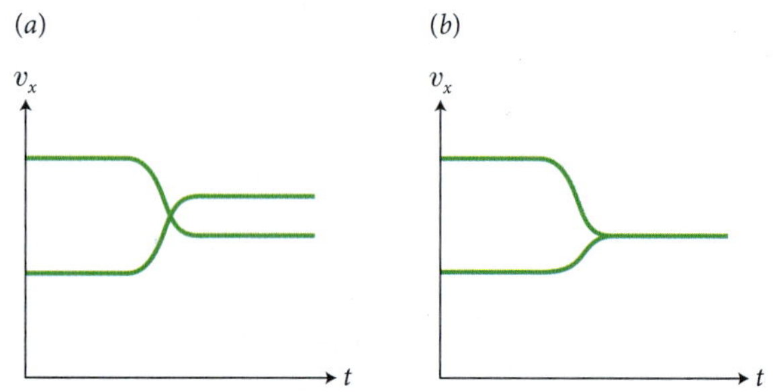

4. When you throw a tennis ball against a wall with some initial speed, is it possible for the ball to bounce back with a higher speed? ••

5.2 Kinetic energy

5. What does doubling an object's velocity do to its momentum and to its kinetic energy? •
6. As a result of an elastic collision between carts 1 and 2, the kinetic energy of cart 1 doubles. Does the kinetic energy of cart 2 change? If so, by what amount? •
7. A common energy unit used in food chemistry is the *food calorie* (1 Cal = 1000 cal = 4186 J). What must be the inertia of a person who is moving at a walking pace of 1.0 m/s and has kinetic energy numerically equal to the food energy in a jelly doughnut (300 Cal)? •
8. (*a*) Write an expression for the kinetic energy of an object in terms of its momentum *p* and inertia *m*. (*b*) If kinetic energy can be written in terms of momentum, how can the kinetic energy of a system change in an inelastic collision even though the law of momentum conservation forces the system's momentum to remain unchanged? ••
9. If two objects A and B have the same momentum but A has four times the kinetic energy of B, what is the ratio of their inertias? ••
10. If two objects A and B have the same kinetic energy but A has four times the momentum of B, what is the ratio of their inertias? ••
11. Object X has great inertia, and object Y has much less inertia. If the objects have the same momentum, which has more kinetic energy? If they have the same kinetic energy, which has greater momentum? ••
12. Draw a graph of kinetic energy versus distance fallen for a brick that is falling vertically from the top of a tall building. ••

5.3 Internal energy

13. You see a book on a table and give the book a push. It slides across the table and then comes to rest. Describe any changes in the physical state of the book-table system. •
14. Which of the following interactions are reversible: (*a*) a collision between two billiard balls, (*b*) a hand tossing a coin in the air, (*c*) a collision between hockey players on ice, (*d*) the firing of a cannon, (*e*) the lighting of a match? •
15. When a loaded cannon is fired, which physical variables are affected? •
16. A small bullet is fired into a large piece of wood. After the bullet penetrates the wood, the assembly moves as one unit along a low-friction track in the direction of travel of the bullet. (*a*) After the bullet is stuck in the piece of wood, is the momentum of the wood (not including the bullet) *greater than, equal to,* or *less than* the initial momentum of the bullet? State any assumptions explicitly. (*b*) Is the combined kinetic energy of the bullet and the wood after the bullet is stuck in the wood *greater than, equal to,* or *less than* the initial kinetic energy of the bullet? ••
17. A block slides with speed v across a low-friction, horizontal surface and collides with and sticks to an identical block at rest. The combination then strikes a spring attached to a fixed wall, bouncing off elastically. (*a*) Choose a system and discuss whether it is isolated. (*b*) Sketch energy bar diagrams for the initial state, the state after the first collision, the state during the collision with the spring, and the state after the final collision. (*c*) Discuss which types of internal energy are involved during this entire sequence of events. (*d*) Determine the final speed of the combined blocks. ••

5.4 Closed systems

18. Is it possible for a change of physical state to occur in an isolated system? In a closed system? •
19. Explain what is going on in terms of energy when your brakes overheat as you use them continuously coasting down a steep hill on a bike or in a car. •
20. Imagine making two springy devices, each made up of a dozen or so metal blocks loosely connected by springs, and then making the two collide head-on. Do you expect the collision to be elastic, inelastic, or totally inelastic? If the collision is not elastic, where does the kinetic energy go? ••
21. Two cars come to a stop from the same initial speed, one braking gently and the other braking hard. Which car converts more kinetic energy to internal energy (for example, thermal energy in the brakes)? ••
22. In the past, cars were built to be fairly rigid in collisions. Now "crumple zones" (areas designed to crumple or deform during a collision) are deliberately engineered. Why do such zones make a car safer in a collision? ••

5.5 Elastic collisions

23. A ball bounces elastically from the floor. It has *x* component of velocity $+v$ just before it hits the floor. What is the magnitude of its change in momentum in the collision? What is the change in its kinetic energy? Are your two answers consistent with each other? •

PRACTICE

24. A 1200-kg car initially at rest undergoes constant acceleration for 8.8 s, reaching a speed of 10 m/s. It then collides with a stationary car that has a perfectly elastic spring bumper. What is the final kinetic energy of the two-car system? •

25. An elastic collision takes place between a 0.080-kg toy car moving at 10×10^2 m/h and a 0.016-kg toy car moving at 20×10^9 mm/yr. What is the kinetic energy of the system in joules? •

26. You want to give a third-grader a common example that illustrates how much energy a joule is. Show that a 0.1-kg ring of keys falling out of your pocket develops about 1 J of kinetic energy before hitting the ground. Can you think of another example? ••

27. You have an inertia of 52 kg and are standing at rest on an iced-over pond in your skates. Suddenly, your 60-kg brother skates in from the right with x component of velocity -5.0 m/s and collides elastically with you. (*a*) What is the siblings' relative speed after the collision? (*b*) If your brother's final x component of velocity is -0.36 m/s, what is your final velocity? (*c*) Is your answer to part *b* consistent with your answer to part *a*? (*d*) What is the change in kinetic energy of the system of you and your brother? ••

28. Two carts, of inertias m_1 and m_2, collide head-on on a low-friction track. Before the collision, which is elastic, cart 1 is moving to the right at 10 m/s and cart 2 is at rest. After the collision, cart 1 is moving to the left at 5 m/s. What are the speed and direction of motion of cart 2 after the collision? If $m_2 = 6$ kg, what is the value of m_1? ••

29. Show that in an elastic collision between two objects of inertias m_1 and m_2, with initial x components of velocity $v_{1i} > 0$ and $v_{2i} = 0$, the final x components of velocity are

$$v_{1x,f} = \left(\frac{m_1 - m_2}{m_1 + m_2}\right)v_{1x,i}$$

$$v_{2x,f} = \left(\frac{2m_1}{m_1 + m_2}\right)v_{1x,i}.$$

Discuss the cases $m_1 \ll m_2$, $m_1 = m_2$, and $m_1 \gg m_2$. Using everyday objects, give an example of each of these three cases. ••

30. Consider two hockey pucks identical in every respect except that one is black and the other is white. The black puck is initially at rest on the ice. A player shoots the white puck directly at the black one with velocity $\vec{v}_{\text{white}}$. The white puck hits the black puck elastically dead center. What are the magnitude and direction of the velocity of each puck after the collision? ••

31. The device shown in Figure P5.31 is called a Newton's cradle. Any collision between the balls in the device in Figure P5.31 is elastic. (*a*) If one end ball is pulled back and let go, as shown, would it be a violation of conservation of momentum if two balls at the other end bounced up at half the first ball's speed? (*b*) Would the result in part *a* be a violation of conservation of energy? (*c*) Show that the *only* result consistent with both conservation laws is that for n balls raised and let go, n balls rise on the other side. ••

Figure P5.31

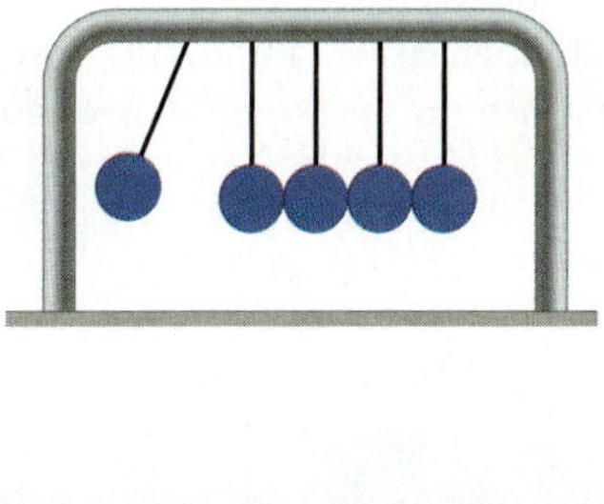

32. Figure P5.32 shows a pattern for the balls in a Newton's cradle just before collision. The arrows indicate the directions of motion of the balls. All the balls have the same size and inertia, and they collide elastically. Assume that all the collisions happen at the same instant. Sketch the pattern of the balls immediately after the collision. ••

Figure P5.32

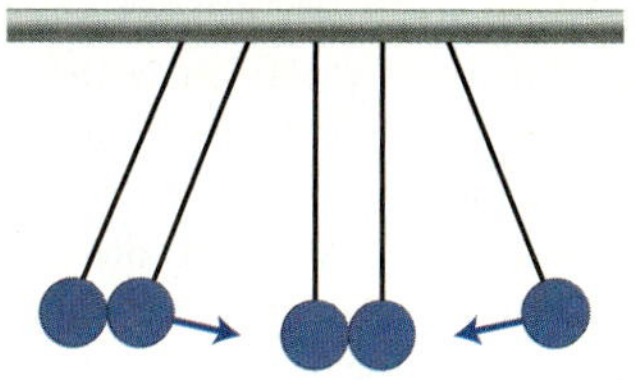

33. A cart of inertia m_1 and velocity $\vec{v}_{1i}$ collides elastically with a cart of inertia m_2 initially moving at velocity $-0.5\vec{v}_{1i}$. What is the speed of each cart after the collision? •••

34. Two carts are initially moving to the right on a low-friction track, with cart 1 behind cart 2. Cart 1 has a speed twice that of cart 2 and so moves up and rear-ends cart 2, which has twice the inertia of cart 1. What is the speed of each cart right after the collision if the collision is elastic? •••

5.6 Inelastic collisions

35. Cart A, with inertia 0.400 kg, is moving on a low-friction track at a speed of 2.2 m/s. It collides with cart B, which is initially at rest. After the collision, cart A continues moving in its original direction at 1.0 m/s, and cart B starts moving in the same direction at 3.0 m/s. Is this collision elastic, inelastic, or totally inelastic? What is the inertia of cart B? •

36. A physics student driving a 1200-kg car runs into the rear of a 2000-kg car stopped at a red light. From the fact that the joined vehicles skidded forward 4.0 m, the investigating police officer calculates that the speed after the collision was 6.6 m/s. Based on this information, calculate the student's speed before impact. •

37. A basketball is thrown horizontally at a heavy door that is free to move. For the two cases in which the ball is (*a*) well inflated and (*b*) flat, sketch a system diagram of the ball and the door, showing momentum vectors and energy bars just before and just after the collision. Make your picture the view from above. •

38. Draw a velocity-versus-time graph for a collision between a 2-kg object moving at an initial speed of 4 m/s and a 6-kg object initially at rest, if the coefficient of restitution is 0.25. ••

39. Consider four identical cars. Two of them collide head-on when both are traveling at 34 m/s. The other two collide head-on when both are traveling at 25 m/s. What is the ratio of the amount of kinetic energy converted to internal energy in the two collisions? ••

40. Take the common case where an object of inertia m_1 collides totally inelastically with a stationary object of inertia m_2. Show that the fraction of kinetic energy converted in the collision is $m_2/(m_1 + m_2)$. Comment on the amount of energy converted for the cases $m_2 \gg m_1$ and $m_2 \ll m_1$. ••

41. Show that when a moving object collides with an identical stationary object, the ratio of the final and initial kinetic energies is related to the coefficient of restitution e by

$$\frac{K_f}{K_i} = \tfrac{1}{2}(1 + e^2). \bullet\bullet$$

42. A 2000-kg truck is sitting at rest (in neutral) when it is rear-ended by a 1000-kg car going 25 m/s. After the collision, the two vehicles stick together. (*a*) What is the final speed of the car-truck combination? (*b*) What is the kinetic energy of the two-vehicle system before the collision? (*c*) What is the kinetic energy of the system after the collision? (*d*) Based on the results of parts *b* and *c*, what can you conclude about which type of collision this is? (*e*) Calculate the coefficient of restitution for this collision. Is this the result you expect for *e*? ••

43. Which head-on collision between a small car and a large truck causes a larger conversion of kinetic energy: one in which their initial momenta are the same magnitude, or one in which their initial kinetic energies are the same? Assume the same kinetic energy for the two-vehicle system in both cases. •••

44. You shoot a 0.0050-kg bullet into a 2.0-kg wooden block at rest on a horizontal surface (Figure P5.44). After hitting dead center on a hard knot that runs through the block horizontally, the bullet pushes out the knot. It takes the bullet 1.0 ms to travel through the block, and as it does so, it experiences an x component of acceleration of -4.9×10^5 m/s^2. After the bullet pushes the knot out, the knot and bullet together have an x component of velocity of +10 m/s. The knot carries 10% of the original inertia of the block. (*a*) What is the initial velocity of the bullet? (*b*) Using conservation of momentum, compute the final velocity of the block after the collision. (*c*) Calculate the initial and final kinetic energies of the block-knot-bullet system. Does the kinetic energy of the system change during the collision? (*d*) Can you calculate the coefficient of restitution for this collision? Which type of collision is it? •••

Figure P5.44

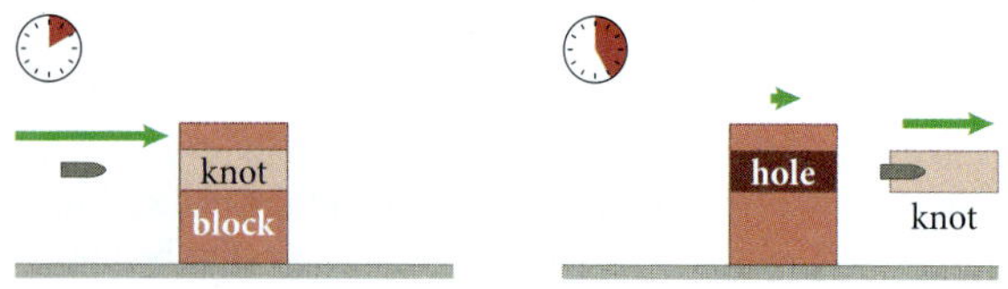

5.7 Conservation of energy

45. An experienced bartender knows just the right initial speed of a glass of beer to get it to come to a stop in front any customer sitting along the bar. Say the initial speed needed to move a glass all the way to the end of the bar is v_{end}. In terms of v_{end}, with what speed should an identical glass of beer be released if it is to stop at a customer sitting three-quarters of the way down the bar? (The kinetic energy converted to thermal energy because of friction is proportional to the distance the glass skids.) •

46. A car goes into a skid and gradually comes to a stop, accelerating at a constant rate. At the midpoint of the skid, how much of its kinetic energy has it lost? •

47. You roll a 0.250-kg wooden croquet ball toward a 0.050-kg golf ball at rest. (*a*) If the wooden ball travels at 5.0 m/s before the impact with the golf ball and then at 4.0 m/s after the impact, what is the speed of the golf ball after impact? (*b*) Is the collision elastic? (*c*) What is the change in internal energy of the two-ball system? ••

48. A 1200-kg car is backing out of a parking space at 5.0 m/s. The unobservant driver of a 1800-kg pickup truck is coasting through the parking lot at a speed of 3.0 m/s and runs straight into the rear bumper of the car. (*a*) What is the change in internal energy of the two-vehicle system if the velocity of the pickup is 1.5 m/s backward after they collide? (*b*) What is the coefficient of restitution for this collision? ••

49. Explain how a police officer at the scene of a car crash can judge whether or not you were speeding when you rear-ended a stopped car, based solely on the length of the skid marks after the collision. Is the speed the officer estimates for your speed just before the collision faster than, equal to, or slower than your actual speed? ••

50. A wagon is coasting along a level sidewalk at 5.00 m/s. Its wheels have very good bearings. You are standing on a low wall, and you drop vertically into the wagon as it passes by. The wagon has an inertia of 100 kg, and your inertia is 50.0 kg. (*a*) Use conservation of momentum to determine the speed of the wagon after you are in it. (*b*) Use conservation of energy to determine that speed. (*c*) After comparing your answers in parts *a* and *b*, explain which method is correct. ••

51. The extinction of the dinosaurs is, according to one theory, attributed to a collision between Earth and an asteroid about 10 km in diameter. Assume that the asteroid had about the same density as Earth. Estimate the energy released by such an impact in megatons of TNT, where 1 megaton = 4.2×10^{15} J. •••

5.8 Explosive separations

52. Can you tell from the coefficient of restitution whether a collision has added kinetic energy to a system, taken some away, or left the system's kinetic energy unchanged? •

53. If the video of an explosive separation (like the firing of a gun) is run backward, the event looks like a totally inelastic collision, with two or more originally separate pieces all sticking together. How are the coefficient of restitution for an explosive separation and that for a totally inelastic collision related to each other? •

54. At the peak of its vertical flight, a fireworks shell explodes into two pieces. Piece 1 has three times the speed of piece 2. What is the ratio of the inertias of the pieces? What is the ratio of their kinetic energies? ••

55. A 52-kg ice skater (this value includes her body, her clothing, and several 1.0-kg snowballs she is carrying) is at rest on the ice. She throws a snowball to the right at 10 m/s. (*a*) What is her speed after the throw? Is her velocity to the left or to the right? (*b*) Calculate the coefficient of restitution for this event. She next throws a second snowball but this time at a speed of 20 m/s to the left. (*c*) What is her speed after this throw? Is her velocity to the left or to the right? (*d*) Calculate the coefficient of restitution for this event. (*e*) Calculate the change in kinetic energy in this second event. Where does the added kinetic energy come from? (*f*) If one food calorie equals 4184 J, how many food calories does the skater burn when she throws the second snowball? ••

56. A mysterious crate has shown up at your place of work, Firecracker Company, and you are told to measure its inertia. It is too heavy to lift, but it rolls smoothly on casters. Getting an inspiration, you lightly tape a 0.60-kg iron block to the side of the crate, slide a firecracker between the crate and the block, and light the fuse. When the firecracker explodes, the block goes one way and the crate rolls the other way. You measure the crate's speed to be 0.055 m/s by timing how long it takes to cross floor tiles. You look up the specifications of the firecracker and find that it releases 9.0 J of energy. That's all you need, and you quickly calculate the inertia of the crate. What is that inertia? ••

57. A two-stage rocket is traveling at 4000 m/s before the stages separate. The 3000-kg first stage is pushed away from the second stage with an explosive charge, after which the first stage continues to travel in the same direction at a speed of 2500 m/s. (*a*) How fast, and in what direction, is the 1500-kg second stage traveling after separation? (*b*) How much energy is released by the explosive separation of the two stages? ••

58. A system consists of a 4.0-kg cart and a 1.0-kg cart attached to each other by a compressed spring. Initially, the system is at rest on a low-friction track. When the spring is released, an explosive separation occurs at the expense of the internal energy of the compressed spring. If the change in the spring's internal energy during the separation is 1.0 kJ, what is the speed of each cart right after the separation? ••

59. A space shuttle of inertia m is attached to a booster rocket that has an inertia nine times greater. This system is moving at a speed of 800 m/s in outer space, as seen by observers in a nearby space station. Then explosive bolts are detonated, separating the shuttle from the rocket and thrusting the shuttle forward at a speed of 100 m/s relative to the rocket. What are the velocities of the rocket and the shuttle right after the explosion? ••

60. A uranium-238 atom can break up into a thorium-234 atom and a particle called an *alpha particle*, α-4. The numbers indicate the inertias of the atoms and the alpha particle in *atomic mass units* (1 amu $= 1.66 \times 10^{-27}$ kg). When a uranium atom initially at rest breaks up, the thorium atom is observed to recoil with an x component of velocity of -2.5×10^5 m/s. How much of the uranium atom's internal energy is released in the breakup? ••

61. A gun with inertia 5.0 kg fires a 10-g bullet at a stationary target located 1.0 km away. After the bullet leaves the gun, its speed decreases (constant x component of acceleration $a = -1.0$ m/s^2) so that the bullet hits the target at 299 m/s. If the direction in which the bullet moves is along a positive x coordinate axis, what is the recoil velocity of the gun? ••

62. An assembled system consists of cart A of inertia m_A, cart B of inertia m_B, and a spring of negligible inertia, clamped together so that the fully compressed spring is aligned between the front end of cart B and the back end of cart A. The internal energy of the system, stored in the compressed spring, is E_{spring}. The system is put on a low-friction track and given a small shove so that it moves to the right at speed v_i, with cart A in front. Once the system is moving, the clamp is released (by remote control, so that the motion of the system as a whole is not affected in any way). As the spring expands, the carts move apart. What are their final speeds? •••

63. Consider the same initial system of spring and carts A and B as in Problem 62. After the system is set in motion with common speed v_i, the clamp is again released. What is the speed of cart A at the instant when the spring is still partially compressed and stores one-fourth of its initial internal energy E_{spring}? •••

64. A toy water-rocket consists of an elongated plastic tank with a nozzle at one end (Figure P5.64). A hand pump is used to get pressurized air into the tank. If there is nothing but air in the tank, the performance is lackluster. If some water is put in the tank before it is pumped up with air, however, the flight is dramatically better. Why? •••

Figure P5.64

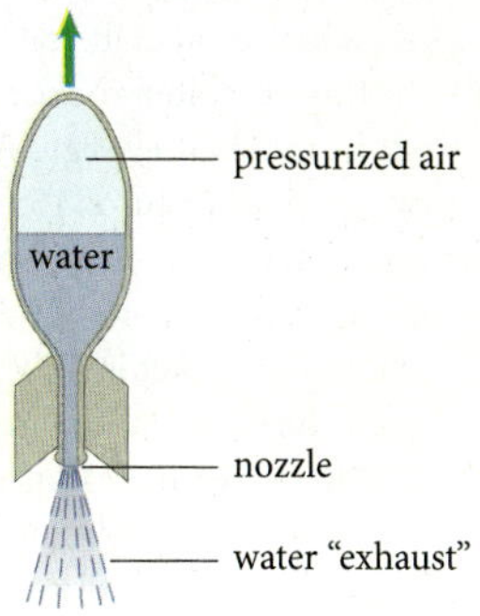

65. A fictional subatomic particle, the solarino, is initially at rest. It then explodes into three particles: two lightons and a heavyon. The inertia of a heavyon is twice the inertia of a lighton. In the explosive separation, the three particles can be kicked out in either direction along a straight line, but the internal energy of the solarino is always entirely converted to the kinetic energy of the three particles. (*a*) Draw the paths of the three particles for the case in which the heavyon has the greatest possible speed. (*b*) Draw the paths of the particles for the case in which one of the lightons has the greatest possible speed. •••

Additional Problems

66. Which has more kinetic energy: a 0.14-kg baseball traveling at 45 m/s or a 0.012-kg bullet traveling at 480 m/s? •

67. Why is it easier to hit a home run from a pitched fastball than from a ball tossed in the air by the batter? •

68. You and a friend are playing catch with a medicine ball. The game has gotten a little unfriendly, and you'd like to knock your friend down with the next throw. To achieve this, should you suggest that your friend catch the ball with his hands or bounce it elastically back to you with his fists? ••

69. Your uncle works at the railroad freight yard, and he has asked you to watch the yard hands couple 20,000-kg boxcars together. As he leaves to get a sandwich, he tells you, "Whatever you do, don't let those cars bang together too hard. The couplings will take only 10,000 J on a hit before they shatter." You ask how hard is too hard, but your uncle has already ducked out. How fast can one moving car bump into a stationary car without the coupling shattering? ••• CR

70. Two solid spheres hung by thin threads from a horizontal support (Figure P5.70) are initially in contact with each other. Sphere 1 has inertia $m_1 = 0.050$ kg, and sphere 2 has inertia $m_2 = 0.10$ kg. When pulled to the left and released, sphere 1 collides elastically with sphere 2. At the instant just before the collision takes place, sphere 1 has kinetic energy $K_1 = 0.098$ J. (*a*) What is the velocity of sphere 1 right before the collision? (*b*) What is the kinetic energy of the system before the collision? (*c*) What is the velocity of each sphere after the collision? (*d*) From part *c*, calculate the kinetic energy after the collision. Does the value you get equal the result of part *b*? Explain why or why not. (*e*) Calculate the coefficient of restitution of the collision. Is this the result you expect? ••

Figure P5.70

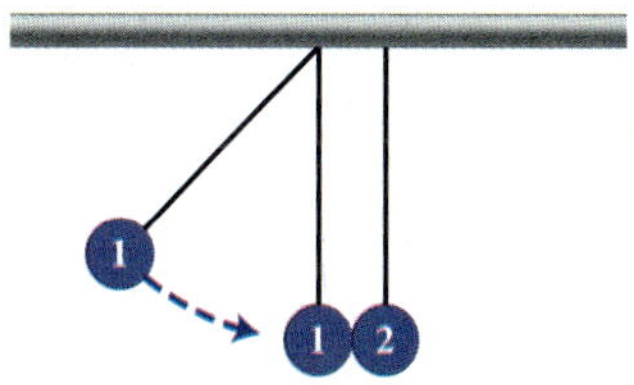

71. Repeat Problem 70 for two spheres made of modeling clay. All the data remain the same, but this time the two spheres stick together upon collision. ••
72. In the toy water-rocket of Problem 64, the pressurized air can store internal energy. Assume you have a rocket that expels water at a speed of 15.0 m/s and the opening through which the water leaves is 10.0 mm in diameter. (*a*) Using Figure P5.72 as a template, sketch energy bar graphs for three instants: when the rocket is fully pressurized but has not been launched, after the launch when half the water has been expelled, and after all the water has been expelled. (*b*) What is the approximate inertia of the water expelled in the first second of flight? (*c*) Does the rocket accelerate at a constant rate? ••

Figure P5.72

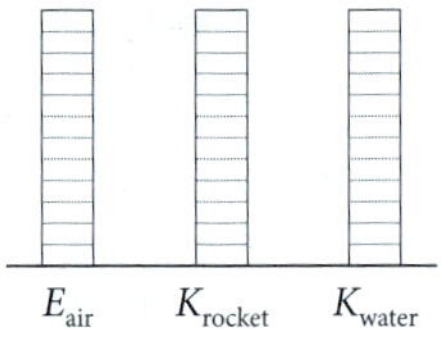

73. Suppose that, as it slides across the floor of a basketball arena, a hockey puck loses kinetic energy because of friction. The amount of energy lost is directly proportional to the distance the puck slides. Sketch a graph of kinetic energy versus time during this slide and then verify with a calculation. •••
74. While bowling one day, you begin to wonder about the inertia of a bowling pin. You know that balls and pins generally make elastic collisions and that your 6.5-kg bowling ball continues to move forward after a collision, even when you hit several pins to make a strike. As it happens, you have just managed to knock down nine of the ten pins, leaving only one pin upright at the end of the lane. You ask your friend to make a video of your next shot so that you can later carefully observe the initial and final velocities of your ball. Sure enough, you hit the remaining pin head-on (make the spare), and after a little video analysis you decide that your ball lost about 40% of its initial speed when it hit the pin. ••• CR
75. For a system of two identical cars, A and B, of the same inertia m but moving at two different velocities, v_A and v_B, show that the kinetic energy of the two-car system can be expressed as the sum of two terms: the kinetic energy of a double car moving with one-half the sum of their velocities, plus the kinetic energy of a double car moving with one-half the difference of their velocities:

$$K_{sum} = \tfrac{1}{2}(2m)\left[\frac{v_A + v_B}{2}\right]^2$$

$$K_{dif} = \tfrac{1}{2}(2m)\left[\frac{v_A - v_B}{2}\right]^2.$$

Interpret the meaning of each of these terms. •••
76. A 1000-kg car traveling with an x component of velocity of $+20$ m/s collides head-on with a 1500-kg light truck traveling with an x component of velocity of -10 m/s. (*a*) If 10% of the system's kinetic energy is converted to internal energy during the collision, what are the final speeds of the car and truck? (*b*) If the car had instead rear-ended the same truck moving with an x component of velocity of $+10$ m/s, how would your answer to part *a* change? •••
77. Your little brother is outside squirting a basketball with the stream of water from a garden hose. As the ball rolls across the yard, you begin to wonder what you would need to know in order to determine the rate at which momentum is transferred from the water to the ball. It should not be hard to measure both the radius r of the hose and the flow rate Q of water out of the hose in cubic meters per second. The density of water is certainly known, but you aren't sure whether the collision is elastic or inelastic. ••• CR
78. Two hockey players push off from a clinch, recoiling from rest. Jean-Claude has an inertia that is 50% greater than Pierre's inertia. After they push off and move across the ice in opposite directions, they lose kinetic energy at the same rate until they come to a stop. (*a*) Who travels farther? (*b*) How much farther? •••

PRACTICE

Answers to Review Questions

1. Relative velocity is the difference between the velocity of a reference object and the velocity of an object being studied. We are free to choose which object is the object of study and which is the reference object, but we must distinguish which is which because relative velocity is a vector. Relative speed is the magnitude of the relative velocity and is the same regardless of which object is the object of study and which is the reference object.
2. The last subscript represents the object whose velocity we are studying. The first subscript represents the object we are measuring relative to (the reference object).
3. (*a*) The relative speed does not change. (*b*) The relative speed changes. (*c*) The final relative speed is zero (the objects stick together).
4. The kinetic energy of an object is the energy associated with the motion of the object. It can be computed as one-half the product of the object's inertia and the square of its speed.
5. The kinetic energy of a moving object is always positive, regardless of the direction in which the object is moving.
6. Kinetic energy can never be negative. It is zero if an object is stationary.
7. The *state* of an object is its condition as specified by the complete set of the physical variables that describe the object, such as shape and temperature.
8. In a reversible process, there is no permanent change in the objects' physical states; in an irreversible process, there is a permanent change in the physical states.
9. The internal energy increases by an amount equal to the decrease in the kinetic energy so that the energy in the system is unchanged.
10. We have no direct way of computing changes in internal energy at this point, but in the absence of energy transfer across the system boundary, the change in internal energy is the negative of the change in kinetic energy that takes place during the collision. Thus determining the change in kinetic energy and taking its negative is one way to determine the internal energy change.
11. A closed system is one in which no energy is transferred across its boundary. This is not the same as an isolated system (one in which no momentum is transferred across its boundary).
12. Energy conversion is energy changing from one form to another, such as from chemical energy to thermal energy; it may, but need not, involve more than one object. Energy transfer is the exchange of energy from one object to another; it may, but need not, involve the energy converting from one form to another.
13. The relative speeds are the same before and after the collision, a fact expressed in Eq. 5.4. This is true only in elastic collisions.
14. Imagine that you are one object in the collision. Before the collision, the distance between you and the other object is decreasing, but after the collision, the distance between you and the other object is increasing. So, the relative velocity between you and the other object changes sign.
15. The coefficient of restitution is the ratio of the relative speed of two objects after their collision to their relative speed before the collision.
16. Elastic: $e = 1$; totally inelastic: $e = 0$.
17. The minus sign is needed to make e positive. Because relative velocity changes sign after a collision, the fraction $v_{12\,x,\mathrm{f}}/v_{12\,x,\mathrm{i}}$ is always negative, and so the minus sign in front of the fraction makes e always positive.
18. No. The final velocities cannot be predicted unless additional information is available—the value of the coefficient of restitution, for instance, or the change in internal energy.
19. No. You are merely converting some of the internal energy of your muscles to the kinetic energy of the ball and your hand.
20. Yes. Internal energy may be transferred from one object in the system to another or may be converted from one form to another (say, chemical to thermal), which means a change in the physical state.
21. Conservation of energy (Eq. 5.23) states that the energy of a closed system remains constant. Thus if we can compute ΔK for the system, ΔE_{int} must be its equal and opposite value, as in Eq. 5.24.
22. Some of the internal energy of the exploding objects is converted to kinetic energy.
23. No. Because the relative speed of the objects increases (from zero before the separation to a nonzero value after), $e = 1$ can never be true. In another approach, you can reason that the kinetic energy of the system changes in an explosive separation. Because the kinetic energy does not change in elastic collisions, no explosive separation can be elastic.

Answers to Guided Problems

Guided Problem 5.2 5.0 m/s
Guided Problem 5.4 1.92×10^3 J
Guided Problem 5.8 40 m/s

6 PRACTICE
Principle of Relativity

Chapter Summary

Inertial reference frames (Sections 6.1–6.4, 6.6)

Concepts A **reference frame** is a combination of a reference axis that defines a direction in space and a reference point that defines the origin from which motion is measured. The **Earth reference frame** is a reference frame at rest relative to Earth.

An **inertial reference frame** is one in which the **law of inertia** holds, which means a reference frame in which an isolated object remains either at rest or in motion at constant velocity.

The **principle of relativity** states that the laws of the universe are the same in all inertial reference frames.

The **zero-momentum reference frame** for a system of objects is the reference frame in which the momentum of the system is zero. The velocity of this reference frame is equal to the velocity of the center of mass of the system.

Quantitative Tools The position $\vec{r}_{cm}$ of the **center of mass** of a system of objects of inertias $m_1, m_2, \ldots$ located at positions $\vec{r}_1, \vec{r}_2, \ldots$ is

$$\vec{r}_{cm} \equiv \frac{m_1\vec{r}_1 + m_2\vec{r}_2 + \cdots}{m_1 + m_2 + \cdots}. \qquad (6.24)$$

The **center-of-mass velocity** of a system of objects is

$$\vec{v}_{cm} \equiv \frac{d\vec{r}_{cm}}{dt} = \frac{m_1\vec{v}_1 + m_2\vec{v}_2 + \cdots}{m_1 + m_2 + \cdots}. \qquad (6.26)$$

This is also the velocity of the **zero-momentum reference frame** for this system.

Relative motion (Section 6.5)

Concepts The **Galilean transformation equations** allow us to transform quantities measured in one inertial reference frame into their values in another inertial reference frame when the two reference frames are moving at constant relative velocity. The transformation equations tell us that *time intervals*, *lengths*, and *accelerations* are the same in any two inertial reference frames moving at constant relative velocity.

Quantitative Tools The **Galilean transformation equations** relate the time t and position $\vec{r}_e$ for an event (e) measured in an inertial reference frame A to these quantities measured for the event in any other inertial reference frame B. If the reference frames have a constant relative velocity $\vec{v}_{AB}$ and have their origins coinciding at $t = 0$, the transformation equations are

$$t_B = t_A = t \qquad (6.4)$$

and

$$\vec{r}_{Be} = \vec{r}_{Ae} - \vec{v}_{AB}t_e. \qquad (6.5)$$

As a consequence of these equations, the velocity $\vec{v}_{Ao}$ of an object (o) measured in an inertial reference frame A is related to the object's velocity measured in any other inertial reference frame B by

$$\vec{v}_{Ao} = \vec{v}_{AB} + \vec{v}_{Bo}. \qquad (6.14)$$

The transformation equations also give the relationship between accelerations measured in any two inertial reference frames A and B:

$$\vec{a}_{Ao} \equiv \vec{a}_{Bo}. \qquad (6.11)$$

Convertible kinetic energy (Section 6.7)

Concepts The **translational kinetic energy** of a system is the kinetic energy associated with the motion of its center of mass. For an isolated system, this kinetic energy is **nonconvertible** because it cannot be converted to internal energy (if it were, the momentum of the system would not be constant).

The **convertible kinetic energy** of an isolated system is the portion of the system's

Quantitative Tools The **translational (nonconvertible) kinetic energy** K_{cm} of a system is

$$K_{cm} \equiv \tfrac{1}{2}mv_{cm}^2, \qquad (6.32)$$

where m is the system's inertia and v_{cm} is the speed of its center of mass.

The **convertible kinetic energy** of a two-particle system is

$$K_{conv} = \tfrac{1}{2}\mu v_{12}^2, \qquad (6.40)$$

kinetic energy that can be converted to internal energy. This energy is the same in all inertial reference frames.

The **kinetic energy** of a system can be split into a convertible part K_{conv} and a nonconvertible part. The nonconvertible part is the system's translational kinetic energy K_{cm}.

where μ is the **reduced inertia** (or *reduced mass*) of the system, given by

$$\mu \equiv \frac{m_1 m_2}{m_1 + m_2}. \tag{6.39}$$

The kinetic energy of a system is

$$K = K_{cm} + K_{conv}. \tag{6.35}$$

Conservation laws and relativity (Section 6.8)

Concepts Changes in the momentum and energy of a system are the same in any two inertial reference frames.

Quantitative Tools If A and B are any two reference frames moving at constant velocity relative to each other, then the changes in the momentum and energy of any system are

$$\Delta \vec{p}_{A\,sys} = \Delta \vec{p}_{B\,sys} \tag{6.47}$$

$$\Delta K_B + \Delta E_{B\,int} = \Delta K_A + \Delta E_{A\,int}. \tag{6.56}$$

Review Questions

Answers to these questions can be found at the end of this chapter.

6.1 Relativity of motion

1. A truck moves at constant velocity on a freeway. Describe how the truck's motion is seen (*a*) by an observer in a car moving with the same constant velocity as the truck and (*b*) by an observer in a car moving at any other constant velocity.
2. On a breezy day, riding a bicycle into the wind can feel like riding into a windstorm. Riding in the direction of the wind on the same breezy day, however, you can sometimes feel no wind at all.

6.2 Inertial reference frames

3. During a given time interval, an observer in inertial reference frame 1 measures an object's change in momentum to be $\Delta\vec{p} = 0$. What is the value of $\Delta\vec{p}$ measured during the same time interval by an observer in inertial reference frame 2, which is moving east at 10 m/s relative to reference frame 1?
4. What is the law of inertia, and of what use is it?
5. An observer sees an isolated object undergo a change in momentum. Is the observer in an inertial reference frame?
6. (*a*) If an object's acceleration is zero in one inertial reference frame, is it zero in all other inertial reference frames? (*b*) If an object is at rest in one inertial reference frame, is it at rest in all other inertial reference frames?

6.3 Principle of relativity

7. State and explain the principle of relativity.
8. Is there any experiment you can do in your own reference frame to determine whether your reference frame is moving at a constant velocity? If yes, can you determine the value of that velocity?
9. If an object is moving forward in one inertial reference frame, it is always possible to find another inertial reference frame in which it is moving backward. If the object is accelerating forward in the first reference frame, which way is it accelerating in the second reference frame?
10. Someone says to you, "Momentum isn't a conserved quantity! All I have to do is change to a different inertial reference frame and the momentum of the system I'm looking at is different from what it was in my first reference frame." How should you respond?
11. Two observers witness an elastic collision from different inertial reference frames. What do they disagree on and what do they agree on regarding kinetic energy? Regarding momentum?

6.4 Zero-momentum reference frame

12. What is the zero-momentum reference frame for a system? How can you use it to solve a problem if the only velocity data you have for the system were measured in a different inertial reference frame?
13. (*a*) Compare the initial and final values of the magnitude of the momentum of a particle involved in an elastic collision when viewed from the zero-momentum reference frame. (*b*) What happens to the direction of the particle's momentum?

6.5 Galilean relativity

14. What are the Galilean transformation equations (Eqs. 6.4 and 6.5) used for?
15. Suppose observers C and D both measure a train's velocity but from different inertial reference frames. C reports velocity $\vec{v}_{Ct}$, and D reports $\vec{v}_{Dt}$. What other information must C have in order to determine whether or not D's measurement is accurate?

6.6 Center of mass

16. How does an object's inertia differ when measured in two different inertial reference frames?
17. How does the position of a system's center of mass measured using one reference point differ from the position measured using some other reference point?
18. In an isolated system that contains moving parts, how does the system's center of mass move?
19. What is the momentum of a system of objects as measured by someone moving along with the center of mass of the system?

6.7 Convertible kinetic energy

20. Is the convertible kinetic energy of a system of objects the same in all inertial reference frames?
21. Which part of a system's kinetic energy changes when an observer switches from one inertial reference frame to another: the convertible part or the nonconvertible part?
22. Can all the initial kinetic energy of two colliding objects be converted to internal energy?
23. (*a*) What is the maximum amount of kinetic energy that can be converted to internal energy in a collision? (*b*) In which type of collision is this maximum conversion possible?

6.8 Conservation laws and relativity

24. (*a*) If the change in momentum of a system is zero in one inertial reference frame, is it zero in all other inertial reference frames? (*b*) If the change in momentum of a system has a specific magnitude and direction in one inertial reference frame, does it have the same magnitude and direction in all other inertial reference frames?
25. (*a*) If the change in energy of a system is zero in one inertial reference frame, is it zero in all inertial reference frames? (*b*) If the change in energy of a system has a specific magnitude in one inertial reference frame, does it have the same magnitude in all other inertial reference frames?

Developing a Feel

Make an order-of-magnitude estimate of each of the following quantities. Letters in parentheses refer to hints below. Use them as needed to guide your thinking.

1. The velocity of the zero-momentum reference frame relative to the Earth reference frame for a head-on collision between a bug and an 18-wheel truck traveling at highway speed (Z, X, R)
2. The velocity of the zero-momentum reference frame relative to the Earth reference frame for a collision between a parked, fully loaded furniture delivery truck and a car traveling on a city street (Z, M, C)
3. The velocity of the zero-momentum reference frame relative to the Earth reference frame for a collision in which a large bird, while flying, is hit from behind by a bullet (E, I, V, P)
4. The reduced inertia of the Earth-Moon system (AA, J, Y)
5. The location of the center of mass of a five-car, one-locomotive train (BB, G, L)
6. The location of the center of mass of your body when you are standing (S, K, T, W)
7. The velocity of the center of mass of a system of 16 billiard balls (including the cue ball) just after the first break shot (A, F, O, U)
8. The kinetic energy converted to internal energy during a head-on collision between a bug and an 18-wheel truck traveling at highway speed (Z, X, D, R)
9. The maximum convertible kinetic energy for a collision between a parked, fully loaded furniture delivery truck and a car traveling on a city street (Z, M, AA, N, C)
10. The maximum convertible kinetic energy for a high-school wrestler slammed to the mat (B, H, Q)

Hints

A. Is the system of balls an isolated system during the break-shot collision?
B. What is an appropriate inertia for the wrestling mat?
C. What is a typical speed of a car driving on a city street?
D. What is the inertia of a bug?
E. What is the inertia of a large bird?
F. What is the speed of the cue ball approaching the 15 other balls?
G. What is the ratio of the inertia of a train car to the inertia of a locomotive?
H. With what speed does the wrestler hit the mat?
I. What is the inertia of a bullet?
J. What is the inertia of Earth?
K. Is your density roughly uniform?
L. How do the lengths of a locomotive and a train car compare?
M. How do the inertias of the two vehicles compare?
N. What is the reduced inertia of the car-truck system?
O. How does the center-of-mass velocity of the billiard balls change during the collision?
P. What is the speed of a bullet in flight?
Q. What is the reduced inertia of the system?
R. What is a typical highway speed of an 18-wheel truck?
S. How tall are you?
T. What is your basic shape when standing?
U. What is the center-of-mass speed of the billiard balls before the collision?
V. What is the speed of a large bird in flight?
W. Where is the center of mass of a uniform cylinder?
X. How do the inertias of the bug and 18-wheel truck compare?
Y. What is the inertia of the Moon?
Z. How is the velocity of the zero-momentum reference frame related to individual velocities and inertias?
AA. How is the reduced inertia related to individual inertias?
BB. How is the center of mass related to individual inertias?

Key (all values approximate)

A. yes, with the cue ball in the system; **B.** the mat is supported by Earth, so the appropriate inertia is huge; **C.** 1×10^1 m/s; **D.** a large bug: 5×10^{-4} kg; **E.** 2 kg; **F.** 1×10^1 m/s; **G.** 1:10; **H.** 4 m/s; **I.** 2×10^{-2} kg; **J.** 6×10^{24} kg; **K.** yes, **L.** they are about equal; **M.** the truck has about five times the inertia of the car; **N.** 5/6 of car inertia, so 1×10^3 kg; **O.** it does not change; **P.** 4×10^2 m/s; **Q.** about the same as the wrestler's inertia—say, 8×10^1 kg; **R.** 3×10^1 m/s; **S.** 2 m; **T.** cylindrical; **U.** from Eq. 6.26, $(10 \text{ m/s})/16 = 0.6$ m/s; **V.** 6 m/s; **W.** halfway along its length; **X.** the bug has almost zero inertia relative to the inertia of the 18-wheel truck; **Y.** 7×10^{22} kg; **Z.** sum of products of individual inertias and velocities divided by sum of inertias, Eq. 6.26; **AA.** product divided by sum, Eq. 6.39; **BB.** sum of products of individual inertias and positions divided by sum of inertias, Eq. 6.24

Worked and Guided Problems

Procedure: Applying Galilean relativity

In problems dealing with more than one reference frame, you need to keep track not only of objects, but also of reference frames. For this reason, each quantity is labeled with two subscripts. The first subscript denotes the observer; the second denotes the object of interest. For example, if we have an observer on a train and also a car somewhere on the ground but in sight of the train, then $\vec{a}_{Tc}$ is the train observer's measurement of the acceleration of the car. Once you understand this notation and a few basic operations, working with relative quantities is easy and straightforward.

observer A's measurement of velocity of car:

$\vec{v}_{Ac}$

observer .... object of interest

1. Begin by listing the quantities given in the problem, using this double-subscript notation.
2. Write the quantities you need to determine in the same notation.
3. Use subscript cancellation (Eq. 6.13) to write an equation for each quantity you need to determine, keeping the first and the last subscripts on each side the same. For example, in a problem where you need to determine $\vec{v}_{Tc}$ involving a moving observer B, write

$$\vec{v}_{Tc} = \vec{v}_{TB} + \vec{v}_{Bc}.$$

4. If needed, use subscript reversal (Eq. 6.15) to eliminate any unknowns.
5. Use the kinematics relationships from Chapters 2 and 3 to solve for any remaining unknowns, making sure you stay in one reference frame.

You can use this procedure and the subscript operations for any of the three basic kinematic quantities (position, velocity, and acceleration).

These examples involve material from this chapter but are not associated with any particular section. Some examples are worked out in detail; others you should work out by following the guidelines provided.

Worked Problem 6.1 Running a train

On a train carrying the university team to a track meet, a sprinter in one of the cars practices his starts by running down the aisle. In the reference frame of the train, the sprinter starts from rest and runs toward the rear of the car. After 2.0 s, he has accelerated to a speed of 10 m/s. If the train is moving at a constant 30 m/s relative to the Earth reference frame, what does an observer standing alongside the tracks measure for the sprinter's initial velocity, final velocity, and acceleration?

❶ **GETTING STARTED** We must translate information from the train reference frame T to the Earth reference frame E, which suggests Galilean transformations for velocity and acceleration. As usual, we begin by making a sketch, paying attention to the directions of the vectors (Figure WG6.1).

Figure WG6.1

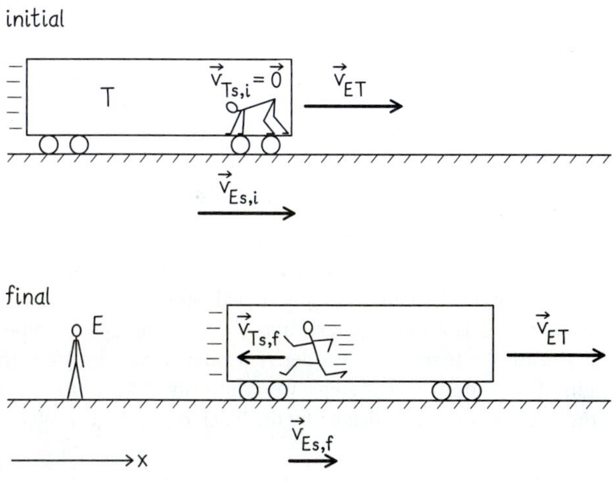

Because the train does not accelerate, T is an inertial reference frame, as is the Earth reference frame E. We are given enough information to calculate the sprinter's initial velocity $\vec{v}_{Ts,i}$, final velocity $\vec{v}_{Ts,f}$, and acceleration $\vec{a}_{Ts}$ measured by an observer at rest in the train reference frame, and we need to determine what the trackside observer measures for these three quantities, which we denote as $\vec{v}_{Es,i}$, $\vec{v}_{Es,f}$, and $\vec{a}_{Es}$ because they are being measured in the Earth reference frame.

❷ **DEVISE PLAN** As Figure WG6.1 shows, we define the positive x direction as the direction in which the train is moving. The train is therefore moving with a velocity that has x component $v_{ETx} = +30\,\text{m/s}$ as measured by the observer in the Earth reference frame. (And to a passenger on the train, the trackside observer moves along the x axis with a velocity that has x component $v_{TEx} = -30\,\text{m/s}$.)

We need to transform velocity information from the T reference frame to the E reference frame, and so we use Eq. 6.14 with the subscripts appropriate to this problem:

$$\vec{v}_{Es} = \vec{v}_{ET} + \vec{v}_{Ts}. \tag{1}$$

For the sprinter's acceleration, we note from Eq. 6.11 that the two inertial reference frames give the same result:

$$\vec{a}_{Es} = \vec{a}_{Ts}.$$

We can use Eq. 1 for both the sprinter's initial velocity and his final velocity measured by the trackside observer. To calculate the acceleration this observer measures, we do not have enough information to take the time derivative of the velocity because we know the sprinter's velocity at only two instants. Thus all we can do is either compute his average acceleration or assume his acceleration is constant. In either case, we have for the acceleration measured by the observer in the Earth reference frame

$$\vec{a}_{\text{Es}} = \frac{\Delta \vec{v}_{\text{Es}}}{\Delta t}.$$

❸ EXECUTE PLAN We first rewrite Eq. 1 in terms of the x components:

$$v_{\text{Es}x} = v_{\text{ET}x} + v_{\text{Ts}x}.$$

For the x component of the initial velocity we have

$$v_{\text{Es}\,x,\text{i}} = (+30\text{ m/s}) + (0) = +30\text{ m/s}, ✔$$

and for the x component of the final velocity we have

$$v_{\text{Es}\,x,\text{f}} = (+30\text{ m/s}) + (-10\text{ m/s}) = +20\text{ m/s}. ✔$$

The x component of the acceleration is then

$$a_{\text{Es}x} = \frac{\Delta v_{\text{Es}x}}{\Delta t} = \frac{(+20\text{ m/s}) - (+30\text{ m/s})}{2.0\text{ s}} = -5.0\text{ m/s}^2. ✔$$

❹ EVALUATE RESULT The positive signs for the x components of the velocities mean that the observer in the Earth reference frame sees the sprinter moving in the positive x direction even though the sprinter is running toward the rear of the car. One way to think about this is to imagine that both the sprinter and the rear wall of the car are headed in the positive x direction but that the speed at which the rear wall moves in this direction is higher than the speed at which the sprinter moves in this direction. The minus sign for acceleration in our coordinate system means that the acceleration is directed toward the rear of the car.

We can check for consistency by calculating the x component of the acceleration with the information measured in the train reference frame:

$$a_{\text{Ts}x} = \frac{\Delta v_{\text{Ts}x}}{\Delta t} = \frac{(-10\text{ m/s}) - (0)}{2.0\text{ s}} = -5.0\text{ m/s}^2.$$

This value agrees with the value obtained using data from the Earth reference frame. The assumption of constant acceleration is not unreasonable, given the limited data at hand. Whether or not the sprinter maintains constant acceleration, the value we obtained is his average acceleration for the 2.0-s interval.

Guided Problem 6.2 Safe passage

You are driving at 35 m/s on the highway when you come up behind a truck traveling at 25 m/s in the same direction. You'd like to have 20 m of space between the front of your car and the back of the truck when you move into the passing lane and 20 m of space between the back of your car and the front of the truck when you switch back into your original lane. If the truck is 10 m long, how many seconds do you need in the passing lane if you keep your speed constant at 35 m/s?

❶ GETTING STARTED

1. Draw a sketch showing the velocities of the truck and car, with arrows to indicate magnitudes and directions. In what reference frame is each velocity in your sketch measured?
2. How does the passing look to the truck's driver? Which is the simpler way to work this problem: from the point of view of the truck's reference frame or from the point of view of the Earth reference frame?
3. Redo your sketch in the appropriate reference frame, if necessary, depending on your answer to question 2.
4. What should you assume for the length of the car?

❷ DEVISE PLAN

5. How is time interval related to displacement for motion at constant speed? In the reference frame you have chosen, which vehicle is undergoing a displacement?
6. Translate your sketch into algebraic equations that contain the desired time interval.

❸ EXECUTE PLAN

❹ EVALUATE RESULT

7. Is the size of your answer reasonable? Consider that most drivers do not allow such margins in actual practice.
8. Does the length of the car matter?

PRACTICE

Worked Problem 6.3 Stacked pennies

You have ten stacks of pennies lined up as in Figure WG6.2—one penny in the first stack, two in the second stack, three in the third, and so on. Where along this row is the center of mass of the system consisting of all the pennies?

Figure WG6.2

❶ GETTING STARTED We suspect that the center of mass of the system is located somewhere in one of the middle stacks, and we know there is a formula to calculate the location involving inertias and positions (Eq. 6.24). We are not told any inertias or dimensions, but we can assume that all the pennies have identical inertias and dimensions. We will use symbols for the inertia and diameter of each penny and answer the question based on that.

❷ DEVISE PLAN Let us call the inertia of each penny m and the diameter of each penny d. (Using a variable to identify an unknown is a better practice than assigning a real number, both because using variables is a more general approach and because numbers can confuse the issue when we derive a final expression.) For the origin of our coordinate system, we arbitrarily choose the center of the leftmost penny, indicated by the black dot in Figure WG6.2.

The lack of numerical values means our answer will be in terms of m and d (unless these values cancel in the algebra). We number the stacks from left to right: $n = 1$ for the leftmost stack, $n = 2$ for the stack to its right, and so on. If we call the inertia of any one stack m_n, the position of the center of mass is

$$x_{cm} = \frac{\sum m_n x_n}{\sum m_n}.$$

We have to figure out the inertia m_n of each stack and its distance x_n from our origin. Let us choose to the right as the positive direction of the x axis. We know that there is one more penny on each stack as we go from left to right and that the position increases by a distance $x = d$ as we move rightward from one stack to the next. We need appropriate equations for m_n and x_n as functions of m, d, and n.

❸ EXECUTE PLAN We note that the number of pennies in a stack equals the stack number n. This means $m_n = nm$. We see that the $n = 1$ stack (containing one penny) is located at $x_1 = 0$ and that the center of each of the other stacks is located a distance $x_n = (n - 1)d$ from the origin. With ten stacks, Eq. 6.24 becomes

$$x_{cm} = \frac{\sum m_n x_n}{\sum m_n} = \frac{\sum_{n=1}^{10} (nm)[(n-1)d]}{\sum_{n=1}^{10} nm} = \frac{md\sum_{n=1}^{10} n(n-1)}{m\sum_{n=1}^{10} n}$$

$$= d\frac{\frac{1}{3}(10-1)(10)(10+1)}{\frac{1}{2}(10)(10+1)} = \tfrac{2}{3}(10-1)d = 6d. ✔$$

This result places the center of mass of the system at the center of the seventh stack, six stacks to the right of the first one. If it is not obvious that the seventh stack is at $x = 6d$, start with your finger on the origin in Figure WG6.2 and count d's to the seventh stack. Note that the center-of-mass location is independent of the inertia m of the pennies.

❹ EVALUATE RESULT The center is somewhere near the middle of this distribution, which is what we expect. Notice that there are $10 + 9 + 8 = 27$ pennies to the right of the seventh stack, but only $1 + 2 + 3 + 4 + 5 + 6 = 21$ pennies to the left of it. However, the pennies to the right of stack 7 are closer to the calculated center of mass, which means this is not an unreasonable result.

Guided Problem 6.4 Balancing a wheel

You have just had a new set of tires put on your car, and now the mechanic has to balance the wheels. For one of the wheels, the center of mass once the tire is installed is located 1.0 mm from the center of the axle. The mechanic corrects for this by crimping a small lead bar on the wheel rim 200 mm away from the axle. With this added inertia, the center of mass is at the center of the axle. If the wheel with the tire installed has an inertia of 10 kg, what is the inertia of the lead bar?

❶ GETTING STARTED

1. Draw a diagram that shows the information given, and add an x axis so that you can specify locations. Where is a convenient place to put the origin of your coordinate system?

❷ DEVISE PLAN

2. The goal is to restore the center of mass to the center of the axle so that $x_{cm} = x_{axle}$. What is the value of the x coordinate of the axle with your chosen origin?
3. Write the equation for the location of the center of mass of the balanced wheel, using the labels you put in your drawing. Convince yourself that you now have everything you need to solve this equation.

❸ EXECUTE PLAN

❹ EVALUATE RESULT

4. Should the numerical value you obtained for the lead bar inertia be negative or positive?
5. Does your calculated inertia value seem reasonable?

Worked Problem 6.5 Fore!

The 0.100-kg head of a golf club is moving at 45 m/s when it strikes a stationary 0.050-kg golf ball. (*a*) What is the kinetic energy of this two-object system in the Earth reference frame? (*b*) In the zero-momentum reference frame, what are the velocities of the club and ball just before they collide? (*c*) What is their relative velocity in the zero-momentum reference frame? (*d*) How much of the kinetic energy of the system can be converted to internal energy? (*e*) What is the translational kinetic energy of the system in the zero-momentum reference frame and in the Earth reference frame?

❶ GETTING STARTED Let us make two drawings, one in each reference frame, partly to establish labels for various quantities and partly to define an x axis (Figure WG6.3). We label the Earth reference frame E, the zero-momentum reference frame Z, and use c for club variables and b for ball variables. Notice that Figure WG6.3 represents the initial situation; it is not necessary to draw the final situation because none of the unknowns requires analysis of the situation after the collision.

Figure WG6.3

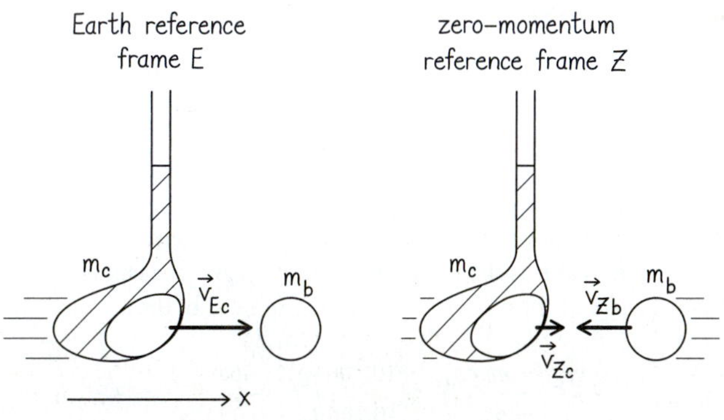

In drawing our diagram for the zero-momentum reference frame, we must be sure to show that the relative velocity measured in this reference frame is the same as the value measured in the Earth reference frame. The momenta of the club and ball should add up to zero in our zero-momentum reference frame, so the club's velocity arrow should be shorter than the ball's velocity arrow because the club's inertia is greater than that of the ball.

2 DEVISE PLAN

(*a*) The kinetic energy of the system is the sum of the kinetic energies of the objects.

(*b*) We first use the fact that v_{EZx}, the value an observer in the Earth reference frame measures for the x component of the velocity of the zero-momentum reference frame, is the same as $v_{Ecm\,x}$, the value an observer in the Earth reference frame measures for the x component of the velocity of the center of mass of the system, which is given by Eq. 6.26:

$$v_{Ecm\,x} = \frac{m_c v_{Ecx} + m_b v_{Ebx}}{m_c + m_b}.$$

We know all the quantities on the right side of this equation, and so we can calculate $v_{Ecm\,x}$. Next we use this Earth-measured center-of-mass velocity in Eq. 6.14 to calculate the x components of the velocities of the club and ball measured in the zero-momentum reference frame, using the equality $v_{ZEx} = -v_{EZx} = -v_{Ecm\,x}$:

$$v_{Zbx} = v_{ZEx} + v_{Ebx} = -v_{Ecm\,x} + v_{Ebx}$$

$$v_{Zcx} = v_{ZEx} + v_{Ecx} = -v_{Ecm\,x} + v_{Ecx}.$$

(*c*) The relative velocity is the same in both reference frames and so can be evaluated in either.

(*d*) This result gives us enough information to compute the kinetic energy in the zero-momentum reference frame as well as the convertible kinetic energy, which is the kinetic energy of the ball and club in the zero-momentum reference frame.

(*e*) We need to measure the translational kinetic energy K_{cm} of the system in both reference frames, using the expression

$$K_{cm} = \tfrac{1}{2}(m_c + m_b)(v_{cm})^2$$

in each one.

3 EXECUTE PLAN

(*a*) The kinetic energy of the club-ball system measured in the Earth reference frame is

$$K_E = \tfrac{1}{2}m_c v_{Ecx}^2 + \tfrac{1}{2}m_b v_{Ebx}^2$$
$$= \tfrac{1}{2}(0.100\,\text{kg})(45\,\text{m/s})^2 + \tfrac{1}{2}(0.050\,\text{kg})(0)^2$$
$$= 1.0 \times 10^2\,\text{J}. \checkmark$$

(*b*) The value an observer in the Earth reference frame measures for the x component of the velocity of the zero-momentum reference frame is the same as the value that Earth observer measures for the x component of the velocity of the center of mass of the system:

$$v_{Ecm\,x} = \frac{m_c v_{Ecx} + m_b v_{Ebx}}{m_c + m_b} = \frac{(0.100\,\text{kg})(+45\,\text{m/s})}{0.100\,\text{kg} + 0.050\,\text{kg}} = +30\,\text{m/s}.$$

The x components of the velocities of club and ball measured by an observer in the zero-momentum reference frame are therefore

$$v_{Zbx} = -v_{Ecm\,x} + v_{Ebx} = -30\,\text{m/s} + 0 = -30\,\text{m/s} \checkmark$$

$$v_{Zcx} = -v_{Ecm\,x} + v_{Ecx} = -30\,\text{m/s} + 45\,\text{m/s} = +15\,\text{m/s}. \checkmark$$

(*c*) We get the x component of relative velocity in the zero-momentum reference frame from our transformed velocities in part *b*:

$$v_{Zbc\,x} = v_{Zcx} - v_{Zbx} = (+15\,\text{m/s}) - (-30\,\text{m/s}) = +45\,\text{m/s}. \checkmark$$

(*d*) The convertible kinetic energy is the kinetic energy of the system measured in the zero-momentum reference frame:

$$K_{conv} = K_Z = \tfrac{1}{2}m_c(v_{Zcx})^2 + \tfrac{1}{2}m_b(v_{Zbx})^2$$
$$= \tfrac{1}{2}(0.100\,\text{kg})(+15\,\text{m/s})^2 + \tfrac{1}{2}(0.050\,\text{kg})(-30\,\text{m/s})^2$$
$$= 34\,\text{J}. \checkmark$$

(*e*) The translational kinetic energy of this system in the zero-momentum reference frame is easy to calculate because the system's center of mass is at rest in this reference frame:

$$K_{Zcm} = \tfrac{1}{2}(m_c + m_b)(v_{Zcm\,x})^2 = \tfrac{1}{2}(0.150\,\text{kg})(0)^2 = 0. \checkmark$$

The system has no translational kinetic energy in the zero-momentum reference frame because the system's center of mass is not translating in that reference frame! In the Earth reference frame, the translational kinetic energy is

$$K_{Ecm} = \tfrac{1}{2}(m_c + m_b)(v_{Ecm\,x})^2$$
$$= \tfrac{1}{2}(0.150\,\text{kg})(30\,\text{m/s})^2 = 68\,\text{J}. \checkmark$$

4 EVALUATE RESULT The signs and magnitudes of the x components of the velocities in the zero-momentum reference frame match our expectations shown in Figure WG6.3. The x component of the relative velocity should be the same in all reference frames. We computed it to be $v_{Zbc\,x} = 45\,\text{m/s}$ in the zero-momentum reference frame. It should be the same in the Earth reference frame:

$$v_{Ebc\,x} = v_{Ecx} - v_{Ebx} = +45\,\text{m/s} - 0 = +45\,\text{m/s}.$$

We can check our calculation of convertible energy by using the definition of convertible kinetic energy with our Earth values:

$$K_{conv} = K_E - K_{Ecm} = 101.3\,\text{J} - 67.5\,\text{J} = 34\,\text{J}.$$

This energy is the amount that could be converted to internal energy in the collision, and it should be (and is) the same in both reference frames. This does not mean that all of it is converted, however. Because of the design and construction of the golf ball, we expect the collision to be nearly elastic, which means that little of the system's kinetic energy is converted to internal energy.

Guided Problem 6.6 Crunch!

Compare the energy lost in a totally inelastic collision between a moving car and a stationary car of the same inertia with the energy lost in a totally inelastic collision between a moving car and a bridge abutment.

1 GETTING STARTED

1. Even if you think they might not be needed, it is good practice to make sketches of the two crashes. What scalar and/or vector variables should you include? It is generally good to include any variables that you use in your equations. (You can add these symbols to your sketch as you go along.)
2. What amount of kinetic energy is convertible (for instance, in deforming a car and making noise)?

2 DEVISE PLAN

3. Because the collision is totally inelastic in both cases, what fraction of the available convertible energy is converted to internal energy?
4. Write the equation for convertible kinetic energy (Eq. 6.40). What quantity do you need to determine in this equation?
5. Which variable in this equation is different in the two cases? What is its value in each case?
6. Suppose in each case the moving car has inertia m_{moving} and what it runs into has inertia m_{rest}. Write an expression for the reduced inertia in this general case.

3 EXECUTE PLAN

7. Are there too many unknowns? Perhaps if you make a ratio of the converted energies in the two cases some variables will cancel.

4 EVALUATE RESULT

8. Based on the result, which would you rather collide with: a parked car or a concrete wall? Do your results agree with your common sense?
9. Were any assumptions needed? If so, check that they are not unreasonable.

Worked Problem 6.7 Hot reactors

Fast-moving neutrons in the core of a nuclear fission reactor are slowed down by collisions with carbon nuclei in the graphite moderator in the core. The ratio of the inertia of a carbon nucleus to the inertia of a neutron is about 12:1. If a neutron moving at 2.0×10^7 m/s strikes a stationary carbon nucleus head-on in an elastic collision, what are the velocities of the two particles after the collision?

1 GETTING STARTED Figure WG6.4 is a drawing that displays the information given. Because we may need either velocity or momentum equations, it is convenient to show the neutron's initial velocity with a labeled vector arrow and to indicate the inertias m and $12m$.

Figure WG6.4

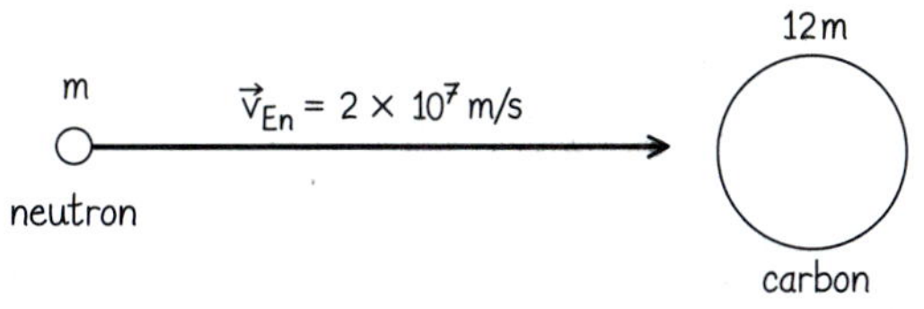

We could answer the question by using conservation of momentum and kinetic energy as we did in Chapter 5, but the algebra might be intimidating. This is because we are looking at the collision from the reference frame in which the carbon nucleus is at rest (the Earth reference frame E), our analysis will be easier if we move to the zero-momentum reference frame Z.

2 DEVISE PLAN We anticipate a Galilean transformation to the zero-momentum reference frame. We can use Eq. 6.26 to get the velocity of the zero-momentum reference frame measured by an observer in the Earth reference frame:

$$\vec{v}_{\text{EZ}} = \vec{v}_{\text{cm}} = \frac{m_{\text{n}}\vec{v}_{\text{n}} + m_{\text{c}}\vec{v}_{\text{c}}}{m_{\text{n}} + m_{\text{c}}}.$$

Because the momenta sum to zero in the zero-momentum reference frame, the collision looks like what is shown in Figure WG6.5, where we have included an x axis so that we can assign signs to our vectors. Because this is the zero-momentum reference frame, the momentum in the positive x direction must cancel the momentum in the negative x direction. Therefore we know that, because of the large differences in inertias, the speed of the carbon nucleus must be much lower than the speed of the neutron in order to have $|m_{\text{n}}\vec{v}_{\text{n}}| = |m_{\text{c}}\vec{v}_{\text{c}}|$.

Figure WG6.5

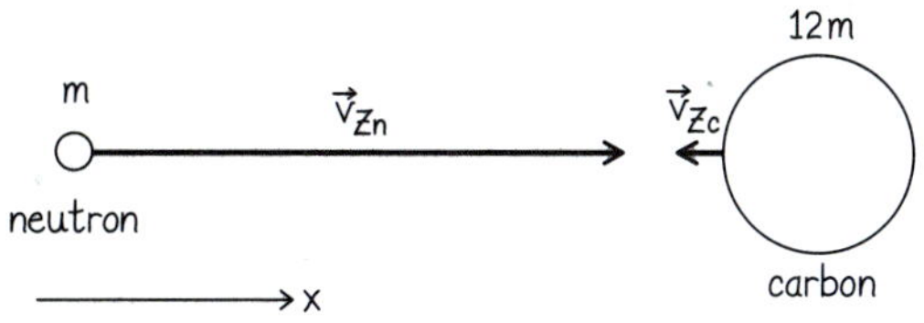

We can compute the initial velocity of each particle in the zero-momentum reference frame using Eq. 6.14 with the appropriate subscripts:

$$\vec{v}_{\text{Zn}} = \vec{v}_{\text{ZE}} + \vec{v}_{\text{En}} = -\vec{v}_{\text{EZ}} + \vec{v}_{\text{En}} = -\vec{v}_{\text{cm}} + \vec{v}_{\text{En}}$$

$$\vec{v}_{\text{Zc}} = \vec{v}_{\text{ZE}} + \vec{v}_{\text{Ec}} = -\vec{v}_{\text{EZ}} + \vec{v}_{\text{Ec}} = -\vec{v}_{\text{cm}} + \vec{v}_{\text{Ec}}.$$

Because this is an elastic collision, the final relative velocity in the x direction is the negative of the initial value. This means that in the zero-momentum reference frame the momentum of each particle changes direction by 180°. We should have enough information to determine the final velocity of each particle after the collision. We then do another transformation using Eq. 6.14 to determine the final velocities measured in the Earth reference frame.

❸ EXECUTE PLAN We first compute the transformation to the zero-momentum reference frame by determining the x component of the velocity of the center of mass measured in the Earth reference frame:

$$v_{\text{cm}\,x} = \frac{m(+v_\text{n}) + 12m(0)}{m + 12m} = +\tfrac{1}{13}v_\text{n}.$$

The x components of the initial velocities of the two particles in the zero-momentum reference frame are then

$$v_{\text{Zn}\,x,\text{i}} = -v_{\text{cm}\,x} + v_{\text{En}\,x,\text{i}} = -\tfrac{1}{13}v_\text{n} + v_\text{n} = +\tfrac{12}{13}v_\text{n}$$

$$v_{\text{Zc}\,x,\text{i}} = -v_{\text{cm}\,x} + v_{\text{Ec}\,x,\text{i}} = -\tfrac{1}{13}v_\text{n} + 0 = -\tfrac{1}{13}v_\text{n}.$$

The negative sign for $v_{\text{Zc}\,x,\text{i}}$ means that the carbon nucleus is moving in the negative x direction. In the zero-momentum reference frame, the initial momenta are equal in magnitude and opposite in direction, and the same is true after the collision, when the momenta have both changed direction by 180° (Figure WG6.6).

Figure WG6.6

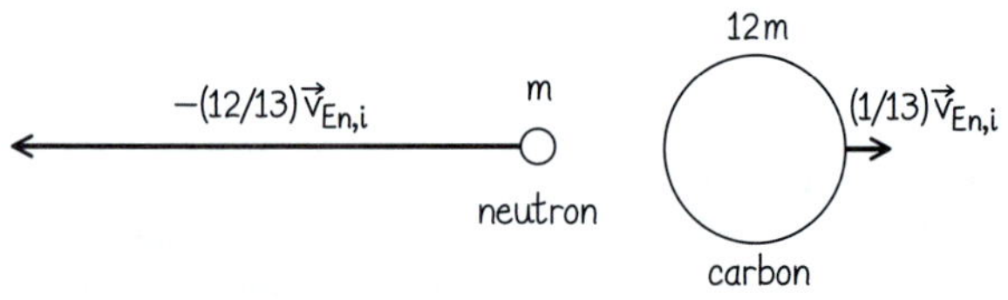

To answer the posed question, we must transform back to the Earth reference frame, again using Eq. 6.14:

$$v_{\text{En}\,x,\text{f}} = v_{\text{EZ}\,x} + v_{\text{Zn}\,x,\text{f}} = +\tfrac{1}{13}v_\text{n} + (-\tfrac{12}{13}v_\text{n}) = -\tfrac{11}{13}v_\text{n}$$

$$v_{\text{Ec}\,x,\text{f}} = v_{\text{EZ}\,x} + v_{\text{Zc}\,x,\text{f}} = +\tfrac{1}{13}v_\text{n} + (+\tfrac{1}{13}v_\text{n}) = +\tfrac{2}{13}v_\text{n}.$$

The neutron reverses direction and speeds away from the carbon nucleus at a velocity of

$$-\tfrac{11}{13}(2.0 \times 10^7\ \text{m/s}) = -1.7 \times 10^7\ \text{m/s}, ✔$$

and the carbon nucleus moves in the positive x direction at a velocity of

$$+\tfrac{2}{13}(2.0 \times 10^7\ \text{m/s}) = +3.1 \times 10^6\ \text{m/s}. ✔$$

❹ EVALUATE RESULT The neutron has lost only 15% of its initial speed, and the post-collision speed of the carbon nucleus is much lower than that of the neutron. This is what we expect for a collision between, say, a golf ball and a basketball, whose inertias differ by a factor of ten or so.

Guided Problem 6.8 Slowing neutrons

In a nuclear reactor, a few uranium nuclei spontaneously split into the nuclei of lighter elements plus several fast neutrons. These neutrons are slowed by the *moderator,* which makes them more likely to be absorbed by other uranium nuclei. That causes them to split and increases the rate of the nuclear reaction. As noted in Worked Problem 6.7, this is usually achieved through elastic collisions between the neutrons and atomic nuclei. The moderator used to slow the neutrons is made of small atoms (like hydrogen and carbon) rather than larger ones (like iron and lead). Why?

❶ GETTING STARTED

1. This collision problem is similar to Worked Problem 6.7, but the important question is: How is it different?
2. What is the desired outcome of the collision between the neutrons and the atoms in the moderator? What physical quantity is associated with this goal?

❷ DEVISE PLAN

3. How can you modify the Worked Problem 6.7 analysis to allow a variable inertia m_T for the target nucleus?
4. Do you need any additional information to do the analysis?
5. Determine the neutron's velocity after the collision in terms of m_n and m_T.

❸ EXECUTE PLAN

6. What is the smallest value possible for the ratio m_T/m_n? (Hint: A hydrogen nucleus "target" is generally a single proton.) What happens to the velocity of the recoiling neutron when this ratio has its smallest value?
7. What is the largest value of m_T one might reasonably have? What happens to the velocity of the recoiling neutron when m_T has this largest value?

❹ EVALUATE RESULT

8. Compare your results with your expectations for a collision between two everyday objects whose inertias are in the same ratio as the inertias of the neutron and target.

Questions and Problems

For instructor-assigned homework, go to MasteringPhysics®

Dots indicate difficulty level of problems: • = easy, •• = intermediate, ••• = hard; CR = context-rich problem.

6.1 Relativity of motion

1. Moving sidewalks are commonplace at large airports, but you must use caution getting on and off them. What should you do to make the transition easy when stepping onto one of these sidewalks? When stepping off? •
2. A flying bug hits the helmet of a coasting bicyclist. (What kind of collision do you expect this to be?) Draw the momentum vectors for the bug and the bicyclist before and after the collision (*a*) in the reference frame in which the bug is initially at rest and (*b*) in the reference frame in which the bicyclist is initially at rest. •
3. The data in the table were recorded for two race cars, A and B, driving down a straight stretch of track. Determine the average velocity of car B as measured by an observer in car A. ••

Time (s)	Car A position (m)	Car B position (m)
1	40	20
2	65	50
3	90	80
4	115	110
5	140	140
6	165	170
7	190	200
8	215	230
9	240	260
10	265	290

4. An observer in the Earth reference frame observes cart A and cart B moving toward each other with the same speed until they collide and come to rest. Consider this event as seen by observer A moving along with cart A. Assume that this observer matches cart A's initial velocity but does not collide with cart B (that is, observer A continues along at the same velocity that cart A had initially). Would the observer in the Earth reference frame and observer A obtain the same value for (*a*) the initial velocity of cart A, (*b*) the final velocity of cart B after the collision, and (*c*) the relative velocity of the two carts after the collision? ••
5. You are sitting, facing rearward, in the bed of a pickup truck and hop off while the truck is moving. When you land, do you move toward or away from the truck (*a*) from the point of view of a person standing alongside the road and (*b*) from the point of view of a person sitting in the truck bed with you? ••
6. Two objects, A and B, of equal inertia approach each other with relative velocity $\vec{v}_{AB}$ and collide elastically. For each object, draw a velocity-versus-time graph for the interval starting a few seconds before the collision and ending a few seconds after the collision (*a*) from the reference frame in which A is initially at rest, (*b*) from the reference frame in which B is initially at rest, and (*c*) from the zero-momentum reference frame. ••

6.2 Inertial reference frames

7. A woman standing beside a road sees a car accelerate from rest to 30 m/s. Describe the car's motion as seen by the driver of a truck traveling in the same direction as the car at a constant 30 m/s. What if the truck is moving in the opposite direction? Is the direction of acceleration of the car affected by the (constant) velocity of the truck driver relative to Earth? •
8. On a long bus ride, you walk from your seat to the back of the bus to use the restroom. If the bus is driving at 100 km/h, and you walk at 2.0 m/s from your seat to the restroom, how quickly are you moving relative to the ground? •
9. A pickup truck has several empty soda cans loose in the bed. Why do the cans roll forward in the bed when the truck slows down? •
10. You drop your keys in a high-speed elevator going up at a constant speed. Do the keys accelerate faster toward the elevator floor than they would (*a*) if the elevator were not moving? (*b*) if the elevator were accelerating downward? ••
11. Train A, m_A = 150,000 kg, is traveling west at 60 km/h. Train B, m_B = 100,000 kg, behind train A on the same track, is traveling west at 88 km/h and so is gaining on train A. Because the engineer driving B fails to slow down, B runs into the back of A. The two trains stick together and then move as a single unit after the collision. What is the momentum of each train before the collision and after the collision according to (*a*) an observer standing alongside the tracks and (*b*) an observer in a westbound automobile traveling at 100 km/h on a road that parallels the tracks? ••
12. A 1000-kg car traveling east at 50 km/h passes over the top of a hill and hits a 3000-kg truck stalled in the middle of the lane. The impact causes the truck to roll eastward at 15 km/h. (*a*) What is the coefficient of restitution for the collision? During the collision, how much kinetic energy is converted to internal energy (*b*) in the Earth reference frame and (*c*) in a reference frame moving at 5 km/h eastward along the road? ••
13. You are riding a 450-kg horse at 14.4 km/h east along a desert road. You have inertia equal to 60.0 kg. A police officer driving past (whom you know and who knows your inertia and the horse's inertia) measures your speed relative to the police car and calculates your kinetic energy to be 16.32 kJ. What possible speed(s) could the police car have been driving at the instant the officer measured your speed? •••

6.3 Principle of relativity

14. Two cars collide head-on on a busy street. An observer standing on the street witnesses the accident and calculates how much of the cars' initial kinetic energy went into deforming the cars upon collision, E_{def}. A police officer was driving next to one of the cars at a matching speed when the cars collided. Would this officer calculate a higher value of E_{def}, a lower value of E_{def}, or the same value of E_{def} if he used the velocities of the cars measured in his reference frame? •
15. At an airport, two business partners both walk at 1.5 m/s from the gate to the main terminal, one on a moving sidewalk and the other on the floor next to it. The partner on the moving sidewalk gets to the end in 60 s, and the partner on the floor reaches the end of the sidewalk in 90 s. What is the speed of the sidewalk in the Earth reference frame? •

16. Do the laws of the universe change if the clocks in two inertial reference frames, A and B, are not synchronized (in other words, if $t_A = t_B + \Delta\tau$, where $\Delta\tau$ is some constant time interval)? ••

17. You place a 0.10-kg sonic ranger on a low-friction track in front of a 0.50-kg cart to measure the cart's velocity in the Earth reference frame, which turns out to be $+(1.0\ \text{m/s})\hat{\imath}$. You are distracted, the cart hits the ranger in a totally inelastic collision, and the two objects then move forward together. A friend is running toward the cart with a velocity of $-(3.0\ \text{m/s})\hat{\imath}$ with her sonic ranger on and pointed at the cart. (*a*) What is the momentum of the cart, with the ranger stuck to it, in your friend's reference frame? (*b*) What velocity does her sonic ranger measure for the cart after the collision? ••

18. At the roller rink, two 20-kg girls accelerate toward each other until they are each moving at 2.0 m/s in the Earth reference frame. They then collide stomach-to-stomach, grab on to each other, and fall to the floor. Calculate the momentum of each girl before the collision and after the collision (*a*) in the Earth reference frame and (*b*) in the reference frame of a mother who started skating with one of the girls and then continued on after the collision without changing speed. (*c*) The fathers decide the collision looks like fun and give it a try. Explain, in terms of energy, why they don't enjoy it nearly as much as their daughters do. ••

19. Carts A and B are identical and are moving toward each other on a track. The speed of cart A is v, while the speed of cart B is $2v$. In the Earth reference frame, the system of the two carts has kinetic energy K. Is there any other reference frame in which the two-cart system has the same kinetic energy K? If so, describe this reference frame. Otherwise, explain why no such reference frame exists. •••

6.4 Zero-momentum reference frame

20. Two identical cars approach each other head-on while traveling at the same speed. What does an observer in the Earth reference frame measure for the speed of the zero-momentum reference frame of this two-car system? Suppose the same cars are traveling in the same direction. Now what does an observer in the Earth reference frame measure for the speed of the zero-momentum reference frame? •

21. Is the kinetic energy of a system zero when measured from the zero-momentum reference frame for the system? •

22. Two identical particles, A and B, collide elastically. In the zero-momentum reference frame, what can you say about the ratios of the final and initial speeds, $v_{A,f}/v_{A,i}$ and $v_{B,f}/v_{B,i}$? •

23. Figure P6.23 shows three identical carts placed on rails (so that they can slide easily left and right) and connected to one another by springs. There are two simple, symmetrical ways for this system to vibrate in the zero-momentum reference frame. One way is the sweeping-X pattern shown in the figure. Draw the other way. ••

Figure P6.23

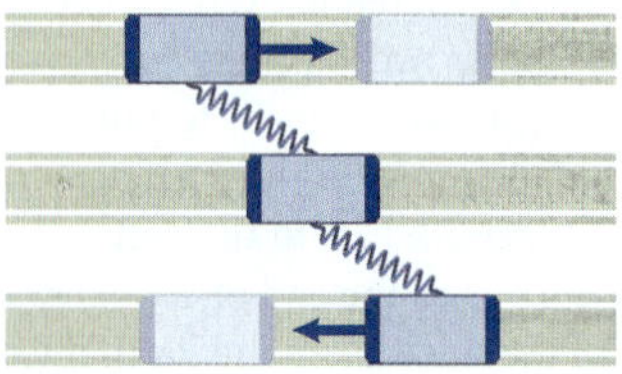

24. Consider two objects, A and B, of inertias m_A and $m_B \gg m_A$. If the two are moving at constant velocities with $\vec{v}_A \neq \vec{v}_B$, is the velocity of the zero-momentum reference frame closer to $\vec{v}_A$ or to $\vec{v}_B$? ••

25. A 4000-kg dump truck is parked on a hill. The parking brake fails, and the truck rolls down the hill. It then coasts briefly along a flat stretch of road at 36 km/h before hitting a stationary 1000-kg car. The car sticks to the grill of the truck, and the two vehicles continue moving forward. (*a*) What is the speed of the combined unit immediately after the collision? (*b*) What is the momentum of the combined unit in the reference frame of a jogger approaching the collision at 2.0 m/s and moving in the direction opposite the direction of the velocity of the moving unit? (*c*) How fast, and in which direction, must the jogger be running in order for the momentum of the combined unit to be zero in his reference frame? ••

26. Object A has ten times the inertia of object B. They approach each other with relative velocity $\vec{v}_{AB}$ and collide elastically. For each object, draw a velocity-versus-time graph for the interval starting a few seconds before the collision and ending a few seconds after the collision (*a*) from the reference frame in which A is initially at rest, (*b*) from the reference frame in which B is initially at rest, and (*c*) from the zero-momentum reference frame. •••

27. In an elastic collision between a lightweight object and a heavy object, which one carries away more of the kinetic energy? Does the answer depend on the initial speeds? (Hint: Begin with the zero-momentum reference frame for clarity.) •••

6.5 Galilean relativity

28. When two identical objects traveling at the same speed collide head-on, an observer standing in the Earth reference frame sees both objects changing direction. Do observers in every inertial reference frame that is moving relative to the Earth reference frame also see both objects changing direction? •

29. You toss a ball into the air and note the time interval between the ball leaving your hand and reaching its highest position. While you are doing this, a construction worker being lifted on a hydraulic platform at constant speed also notes the time interval needed for the ball to reach its highest position. Is the time interval reported by the worker *longer, shorter*, or *the same as* the interval you report? ••

30. A student runs an experiment with two carts on a low-friction track. As measured in the Earth reference frame, cart 1 ($m = 0.36$ kg) moves from left to right at 1.0 m/s as the student walks along next to it at the same velocity. (*a*) What velocity $\vec{v}_{E2,i}$ in the Earth reference frame must cart 2 ($m = 0.12$ kg) have before the collision if, in the student's reference frame, cart 2 comes to rest right after the collision and cart 1 reverses direction and travels from right to left at 0.33 m/s? (*b*) What does the student measure for the momentum of the two-cart system? (*c*) What does a person standing in the Earth reference frame measure for the momentum of each cart before the collision? ••

31. Notice that in *Principles* Figure 6.12 the time intervals of the interaction are all the same, regardless of the reference frame shown. Is this true in all reference frames? Why or why not? ••

PRACTICE

32. In a three-car crash, car A bumps into the back end of car B, which then goes forward and bumps into the back end of car C. Is the distance that car B moves between the collisions the same in all inertial reference frames? ••

33. Riding up an escalator while staying on the same step for the whole ride takes 30 s. Walking up the same escalator takes 20 s. How long does it take to walk down the up escalator? ••

34. A woman is on a train leaving the station at 4.0 m/s, while a friend waving goodbye runs alongside the car she's in. (*a*) If the friend is running at 6.0 m/s and moving in the same direction as the train, how fast must the woman walk, and in which direction, to keep up with him? (*b*) Once the train has reached a speed of 10 m/s, how fast must the woman walk, and in which direction, to keep up with her friend? ••

35. Airline pilots who fly round trips know that their round-trip travel time increases if there is any wind. To see this, suppose that an airliner cruises at speed v relative to the air. (*a*) For a flight whose one-way distance is d, write an expression for the interval Δt_{calm} needed for a round trip on a windless day. Ignore any time spent on the ground, and assume that the airliner flies at cruising speed for essentially the whole trip. (*b*) Now assume there is a wind of speed w. It doesn't matter which way the wind is blowing; all that matters is that it is a head wind in one direction and a tail wind in the opposite direction. Write an expression for the time interval Δt_{wind} needed for a round trip on the day this wind is blowing. Then show that your expression reduces to

$$\Delta t_{\text{wind}} \approx \Delta t_{\text{calm}}\left[1 + \left(\frac{w}{v}\right)^2\right]$$

provided that $w \ll v$. (For the last step, you may need to know that $(1 \pm z)^b \approx 1 \pm bz$ when $z \ll 1$.) •••

6.6 Center of mass

36. The inertia of an object is m measured when the object is at rest in the Earth reference frame. According to Galilean relativity, what is its inertia measured by an observer moving past the object with a constant velocity $\vec{v}$ in the positive x direction? What is the object's momentum according to this observer? •

37. At what distance from the center of Earth is the center of mass of the Earth-Moon system? •

38. (*a*) Determine the location of the center of mass of the system shown in Figure P6.38. All three disks are made of sheet metal of the same material, and the diameters are 1.0 m, 2.0 m, and 3.0 m. (*b*) Repeat the calculation for three solid spheres all made of the same metal and having the same diameters as in part *a*. ••

Figure P6.38

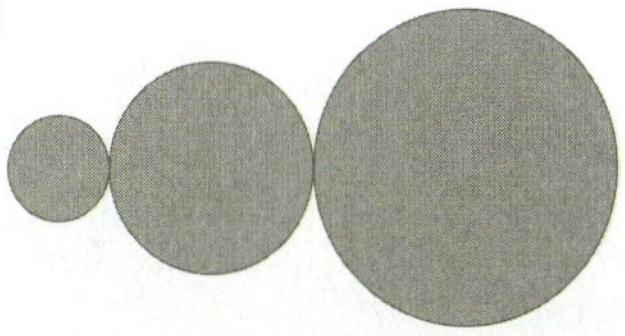

39. A boy and a girl are resting on separate rafts 10 m apart in calm water when the girl notices a small beach toy floating midway between the rafts. The girl and her raft have twice the inertia of the boy and his raft. The rafts are connected by a rope 12 m long, so she decides to pull on the rope, drawing the rafts together until she can reach the toy. Which raft gets to the toy first? How much distance is there between the two rafts when the first one reaches the toy? ••

40. The two cubes in Figure P6.40 have different inertias. The cubes are connected to each other by a spring, and a hammer strikes them in the two ways, (*a*) and (*b*), shown in the figure. Assuming that the same impulse is transferred from the hammer, does the center-of-mass motion after the collision depend on which cube is struck first? ••

Figure P6.40

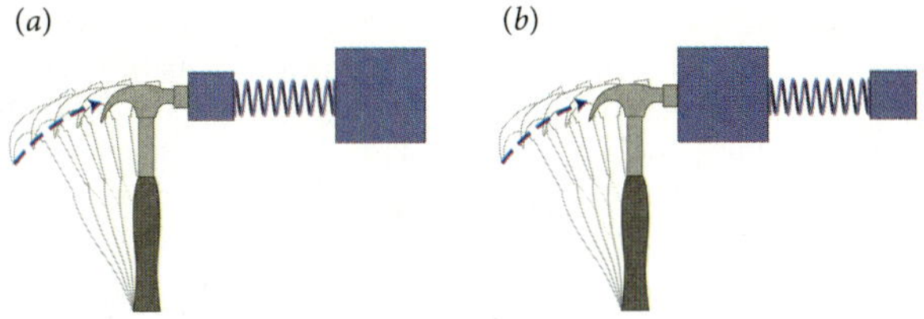

41. Determine the position of the center of mass of the baton shown in Figure P6.41, taking the origin of your coordinate axis to be (*a*) the center of the larger ball, (*b*) the center of the smaller ball, and (*c*) a point 1.0 m to the left of the larger ball. How much calculation was required for each of the three parts of this problem? ••

Figure P6.41

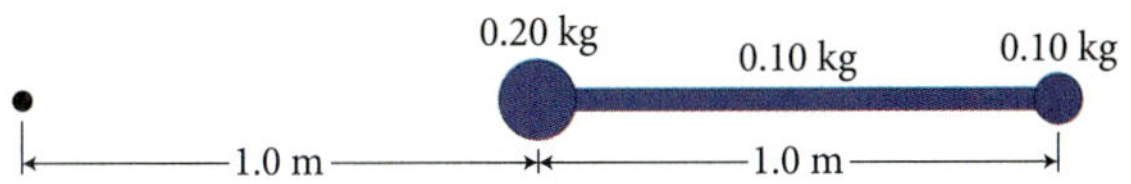

42. The empty cubical box shown in Figure P6.42 has no top face; that is, the box is made up of only five square faces. If all five faces have the same inertia, at what height above the bottom of the box is the center of mass? ••

Figure P6.42

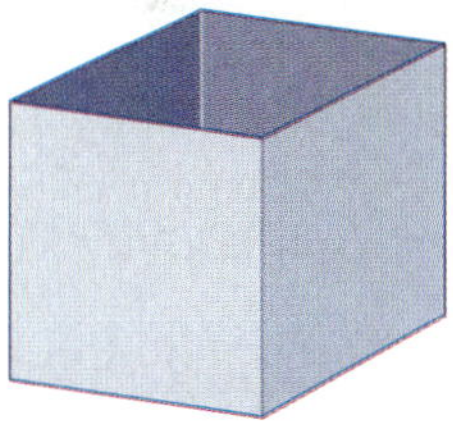

43. How can you tell from the motion of the center of mass of an isolated system whether the reference frame from which the motion is measured is inertial? ••

44. Determine the center of mass of a pool cue whose diameter decreases smoothly from 40 mm to 10 mm over its 1.40-m length (Figure P6.44). Assume that the cue is made from solid wood, with no hidden weights inside. (Hint: See Appendix D for the center-of-mass computation for extended objects. You will find it easier to do the integral for a complete cone. The pool cue is a truncated cone—that is, a cone with its conical tip removed. Slicing off a piece is like adding negative inertia.) •••

Figure P6.44

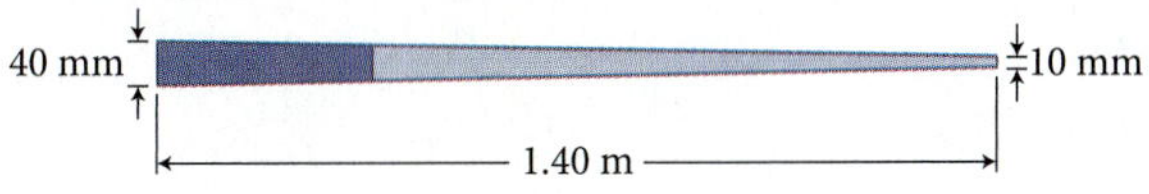

6.7 Convertible kinetic energy

45. An object of inertia m_1 collides totally inelastically with a stationary object of inertia m_2. Plot the fraction of the kinetic energy lost as a function of m_2/m_1 in the range $m_2/m_1 = 0$ to $m_2/m_1 = 4$, and discuss what happens as m_2/m_1 approaches infinity. •

46. A 3.0-g particle is moving toward a stationary 7.0-g particle at 3.0 m/s. What percentage of the original kinetic energy is convertible to internal energy? •

47. Think of a system of two objects of different inertias $m_1 < m_2$. How much larger than m_1 can the reduced inertia μ of the pair be? How much smaller than m_1 can it be? •

48. (*a*) Is there a reference frame in which the kinetic energy of a system is a minimum? If so, what is this reference frame? (*b*) Is there a reference frame in which the kinetic energy of a system is a maximum? If so, what is this reference frame? ••

49. You hit a pitched baseball with a bat. In which reference frame is the translational (nonconvertible) kinetic energy greater: the reference frame in which the bat is at rest before the collision or the reference frame in which the ball is at rest before the collision? ••

50. What is the ratio K_1/K_2 when K_1 is the kinetic energy converted to internal energy when two cars each initially traveling at 88 km/h collide head-on and K_2 is the kinetic energy converted to internal energy when a car moving at 88 km/h hits a stationary car? Assume that both cars have the same inertia and that the collisions are totally inelastic. (Hint: Determine how much of the energy is required to move the center of mass in each case.) ••

51. A 0.075-kg disk initially at rest in the Earth reference frame is free to move parallel to a horizontal bar through a hole at the disk's center. The disk is struck face-on by a 0.050-kg paintball traveling at 11 m/s, as illustrated in Figure P6.51. (*a*) What is the initial relative velocity of the disk and the paintball? (*b*) What is their reduced inertia? (*c*) If all the paint stays on the disk, what percentage of the original kinetic energy is converted to internal energy? (*d*) What is the change in kinetic energy measured by someone riding a bicycle at the velocity of the paintball before the collision? (*e*) Confirm your answer to part *d* by calculating the final and initial kinetic energies in the cyclist's reference frame. ••

Figure P6.51

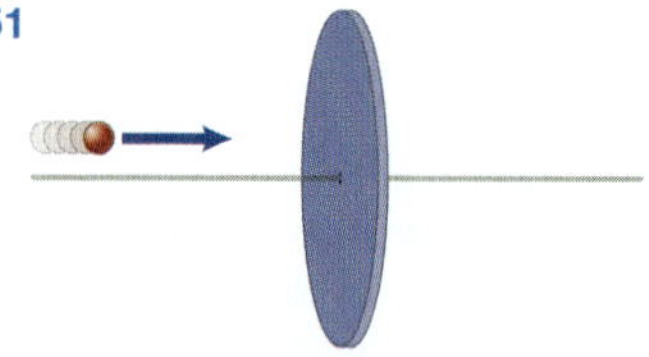

52. Take the common case where a moving object of inertia m_{moving} collides with a stationary object of inertia m_{rest}. (*a*) Show that the fraction of kinetic energy not convertible in the collision is $m_{\text{moving}}/(m_{\text{moving}} + m_{\text{rest}})$. Interpret for the case where $m_{\text{rest}} \gg m_{\text{moving}}$ and for the case where $m_{\text{rest}} \ll m_{\text{moving}}$. (*b*) Does the value of the fraction depend on the elasticity of the collision? (*c*) Why is this energy not convertible? ••

53. Ball 1 is moving toward you at 10 m/s, and you decide to throw ball 2 at it to make it reverse its velocity. The balls collide head-on, and the coefficient of restitution for the collision is 0.90. (*a*) If ball 1 has an inertia of 0.500 kg and ball 2 has an inertia of 0.600 kg, how fast must ball 2 be traveling in order to reverse the velocity of ball 1? (*b*) What is the initial relative velocity of the two balls? (*c*) What is their reduced inertia? (*d*) What percentage of the original kinetic energy is convertible? (*e*) What are the final velocities of the two balls immediately after the collision? ••

54. Ball 1 from Problem 53 is moving away from you at 5.0 m/s, and you decide to throw ball 2 at it to make it go faster. Once again the balls collide head-on, and the coefficient of restitution for the collision is 0.90. (*a*) Given the inertias in Problem 53, how fast must ball 2 be traveling in order to double the velocity of ball 1? (*b*) What is the initial relative velocity of the two balls? (*c*) What is their reduced inertia? (*d*) What percentage of the original kinetic energy is convertible? (*e*) What are the final velocities of the two balls immediately after the collision? ••

55. If the relative velocities are the same in both cases, which has more convertible kinetic energy: a collision between two objects each of inertia m or a collision between an object of inertia m_1 and an object of inertia $m_2 < m_1$ with $m_1 + m_2 = 2m$? ••

56. After coming down a slope, a 60-kg skier is coasting northward on a level, snowy surface at a constant 15 m/s. Her 5.0-kg cat, initially running southward at 3.8 m/s, leaps into her arms, and she catches it. (*a*) Determine the amount of kinetic energy converted to internal energy in the Earth reference frame. (*b*) What is the velocity, measured in the Earth reference frame, of an inertial reference frame in which the cat's kinetic energy does not change? ••

57. You toss a 0.40-kg ball at 9.0 m/s to a 14-kg dog standing on an iced-over pond. The dog catches the ball and begins to slide on the ice. (*a*) Measured from the Earth reference frame, what is the velocity of the dog immediately after he catches the ball? (*b*) Measured from the Earth reference frame, what is the velocity of an inertial reference frame in which the ball's kinetic energy does not change? (*c*) Measured from the Earth reference frame, how much of the original kinetic energy of the system is convertible? (*d*) Measured from the reference frame described in part *b*, how much of the original kinetic energy of the system is convertible? ••

58. Instead of defining a reduced inertia μ to characterize the convertible kinetic energy of a system, we could define a *reduced velocity* v_{red} as follows: For a system of two particles, one of inertia m_1 and velocity v_1 and the other of inertia m_2 and velocity v_2, the kinetic energy is

$$K = K_{\text{cm}} + K_{\text{conv}} = \tfrac{1}{2}(m_1 + m_2)v_{\text{cm}}^2 + \tfrac{1}{2}(m_1 + m_2)v_{\text{red}}^2.$$

Derive an expression for the reduced velocity in terms of the given variables. (Just as the center-of-mass velocity is a weighted mean of the individual velocities, the reduced velocity is a weighted difference between the individual velocities.) •••

PRACTICE

6.8 Conservation laws and relativity

59. In *Principles* you learned about the zero-momentum reference frame. You may be curious whether there is such a thing as a zero-energy reference frame. Does a zero-kinetic energy reference frame always exist, never exist, or sometimes exist? •

60. After a totally inelastic collision, the kinetic energy of an isolated system composed of two objects is zero. What was the momentum of the system in the same reference frame before the collision? •

61. A mother penguin and her chick are on a flat, icy surface. The mother is lying at rest 0.50 m from the edge of the water. The chick, which has one-fourth of its mother's inertia, is sliding, collides with her inelastically, and bounces back at one-eighth of its original speed. The mother wakes up as she hits the water 0.40 s later. (*a*) How fast was the chick going when it hit her? (*b*) To a penguin paddling directly toward them at 1.0 m/s, what is the mother's momentum before and after the collision in terms of m_{mother}? ••

62. A 50-kg ice skater moves across the ice at a constant speed of 2.0 m/s. She is caught by her 70-kg partner, and then the pair continues to glide together. He is at rest when he catches her, and immediately afterward they both coast. (*a*) What is their velocity just after the catch? (*b*) A skater follows the girl at a constant speed of 1.0 m/s. What is the girl's change in momentum in the reference frame of the skater? ••

63. In an inertial reference frame F, an orange of inertia m_{orange} and velocity $\vec{v}_{\text{orange}}$ collides totally inelastically with an apple of inertia m_{apple} initially at rest. (*a*) When this collision is viewed from an inertial reference frame G, the kinetic energy of the orange is unchanged by the collision. What does an observer in the F reference frame measure for the velocity of the G reference frame? (*b*) For the case where $m_{\text{orange}} = m_{\text{apple}}$, sketch the velocity vectors of the two objects in each reference frame before and after the collision. ••

64. A 50-kg meteorite moving at 1000 m/s strikes Earth. Assume the velocity is along the line joining Earth's center of mass and the meteor's center of mass. (*a*) Calculate the amount of kinetic energy converted to internal energy measured from the Earth reference frame. (*b*) What is the gain in Earth's kinetic energy? (*c*) Why does the ground around where the meteor strikes get so hot? ••

65. A 0.20-kg softball is traveling at a velocity of 20 m/s to the east relative to Earth. It collides head-on with a 0.40-kg rubber ball traveling at a velocity of 10 m/s to the west. (*a*) If the system's kinetic energy, as measured from the Earth reference frame, decreases by 20% because of the collision, what are the final velocities of the balls? (*b*) What change in internal energy has occurred? (*c*) An observer watches this collision from a reference frame moving at a velocity of 15 m/s to the east relative to the Earth reference frame. What changes in kinetic and internal energies does this observer measure? (*d*) What changes in kinetic and internal energies would be measured by an observer in a reference frame traveling at 20 m/s east relative to the Earth reference frame? ••

66. Derive an expression showing that when an elastic collision between two objects is viewed from the zero-momentum reference frame, the direction of the momentum of each object is reversed and the magnitude of the change in momentum of each object is twice the magnitude of that object's initial momentum. •••

Additional Problems

67. Just as a car passes a school crossing guard, a child throws a toy from the back seat of the car toward his sister in the front seat. The toy is thrown at a speed of 2.0 m/s relative to the car, and the car is traveling at 10 m/s relative to Earth. Draw the velocity vectors for the toy, the car, and the crossing guard from the reference frame of (*a*) the car, (*b*) the guard, and (*c*) the toy. •

68. A 20-kg child is sliding on an icy surface toward her mother at 3.0 m/s. Her 68-kg mother starts toward her at 2.0 m/s, intending to catch her. What percentage of the original kinetic energy is convertible? •

69. An 80-kg man is walking at 2.0 m/s. A 10-kg dog is running at five times that speed in the same direction. At what speed and in what direction relative to the man would you have to be jogging in order for the dog to have the same momentum as the man in your reference frame? •

70. One rider is in a descending elevator that is accelerating to a stop. Another is in an elevator that is accelerating upward from rest. With their eyes closed, can the riders tell which of the two elevators they are in? ••

71. Suppose you are in a noninertial reference frame observing two isolated objects of inertias m_1 and m_2. What can you say about (*a*) the apparent acceleration of each object and (*b*) the apparent change in momentum of each object? ••

72. A bug of inertia m_B collides with the windshield of a Mack truck of inertia $m_T \gg m_B$ at an instant when the relative speed of the two is v_{BT}. (*a*) Express the system momentum in the truck's reference frame, then transform that expression to the bug's reference frame, and in so doing remove $m_B v_{BT}$ from the expression. (Remember, in the bug's reference frame, the bug is initially at rest and the truck is moving.) (*b*) Now express the system momentum in the bug's reference frame, then transform that expression to the truck's reference frame, and in so doing remove $m_T v_{BT}$ from the expression. (*c*) Is there something wrong here? How can we change the momentum by a small amount $m_B v_{BT}$ doing the transformation one way and by a large amount $m_T v_{BT}$ doing the transformation the other way? ••

73. A 0.045-kg golf ball moving at 50 m/s (measured in the Earth reference frame) collides inelastically with a 1.8-kg, heavy-duty plastic flowerpot sitting on a windowsill. The coefficient of restitution for the collision is 0.50. Calculate the final velocities of the ball and the pot. Do this problem by first transforming to the zero-momentum reference frame, where the collision is much simpler, and then transforming back to the Earth reference frame. (Assume that all the action happens in one dimension and that the friction between pot and sill is insignificant.) ••

74. Asteroid A1, $m_{A1} = 3.60 \times 10^6$ kg, and asteroid A2, $m_{A2} = 1.20 \times 10^6$ kg, collide head-on in space. Approximate (rather poorly) the collision as being elastic. Observers

watch the event from two space platforms. An observer on platform Q measures the speed of A1 to be 528 m/s and the speed of A2 to be 315 m/s, and sees A2 heading directly toward A1. The second platform, platform Z, is at rest in the zero-momentum reference frame of the asteroids. (*a*) What is the combined momentum of the asteroids measured from platform Q? (*b*) What is the velocity of platform Z relative to platform Q? (*c*) Draw velocity, momentum, and kinetic energy graphs for the asteroids as viewed from platform Z, using graphs like those in Figure P6.74. Assume the collision begins at $t = 40$ s and lasts for 20 s. (*d*) Add a curve for the momentum of the system to the momentum graph you constructed in part *c*. (*e*) What happens to the kinetic energy when its curve bends? (*f*) On your kinetic energy graph from part *c*, show what an observer on platform Z sees for the convertible and nonconvertible kinetic energies of the asteroids. (*g*) Repeat parts *c–f* as seen from platform Q. ••

Figure P6.74

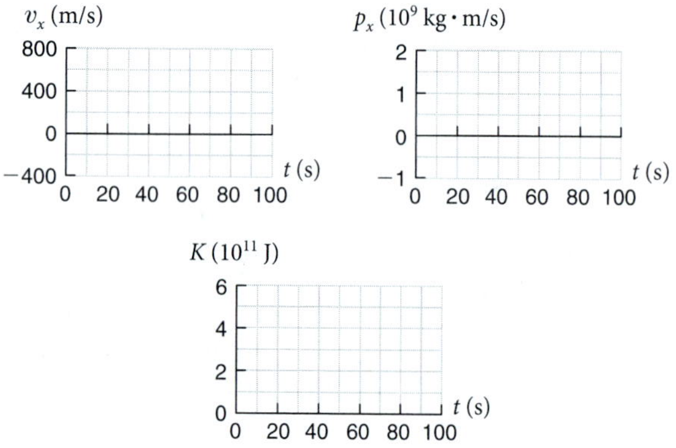

75. Assume that the asteroids in Problem 74 collide totally inelastically. Answer the same questions posed in that problem for this situation. ••

76. A 1500-kg van is coasting to a stoplight at 15 m/s. A 1000-kg car behind the van is doing the same thing at 25 m/s and crashes into the rear of the van. The bumpers collide with a coefficient of restitution of 0.70. (*a*) What are the final velocities of the two vehicles? (*b*) How much kinetic energy is converted to internal energy in this collision? (*c*) How much energy is converted if the bumpers lock together in a totally inelastic collision? ••

77. A 0.30-kg cart traveling along a low-friction track at 2.0 m/s relative to Earth collides with a 0.50-kg cart traveling in the same direction at 1.0 m/s relative to Earth. If the system's kinetic energy measured in the Earth reference frame increases by 30% as a result of the collision, what are the final velocities of the carts in this reference frame? ••

78. The transformation between position and time measurements in an inertial reference frame I and position and time measurements in a constantly accelerating (noninertial) reference frame N is given by

$$t_N = t_I = t$$

$$\vec{r}_N = \vec{r}_I - \vec{v}_{IN}t - \tfrac{1}{2}\vec{a}_{IN}t^2,$$

where $\vec{v}_{IN}$ is the velocity of the noninertial reference frame at $t = 0$ measured from the inertial reference frame and $\vec{a}_{IN}$ is the acceleration of the noninertial reference frame measured from the inertial reference frame. Derive by differentiation the transformation laws, giving v_N and a_N in terms of v_I and a_I. •••

79. The medallion shown in Figure P6.79 has been made by cutting a small circular piece out of a larger circular disk. The diameter of the original disk is twice the diameter of the hole, and the thickness of the disk is uniform. You begin to wonder about the location of the center of mass of this object, but the calculation seems impossibly difficult. Then you visualize two circular pieces coming together in superposition. ••• CR

Figure P6.79

80. As an avid biker, you've come to realize that your top speed is really an air speed, not a ground speed, because air resistance is very noticeable when you ride fast. You like to ride at top speed for exactly an hour every day, and you know that on a calm day, you can ride 20 km before having to turn around and come back the same way. Today, though, you have a 20-km/h head wind for the first leg of the trip (which of course is a tailwind on the way back). You must be back home in an hour, so you look at your map. ••• CR

81. An uncoupled 20,000-kg railroad hopper car coasts along a track at 2.0 m/s. As it passes a grain chute, the chute opens (Figure P6.81), grain fills the car at a rate of 4000 kg/s for 5.0 s, and the chute closes. (*a*) How fast is the car going after the chute closes? (*b*) How far does the car travel during the 5.0 s in which grain is being added? (This distance is the length of the trail of grain in the car.) (*c*) Where is the center of mass of the grain-car system at the end of the 5.0 s? (*d*) Where is the center of mass of the trail of grain at the end of the 5.0 s? (*e*) Why doesn't the center of mass of the trail of grain coincide with the point midway between the two ends of the trail? •••

Figure P6.81

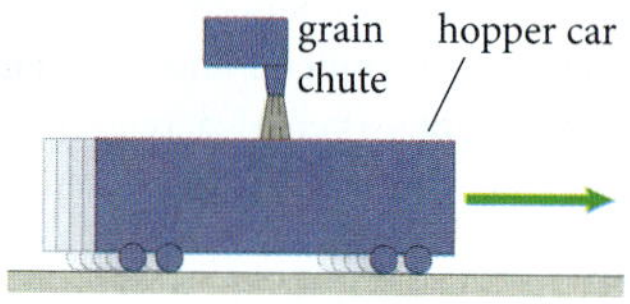

82. A skateboarder coasting at 5.0 m/s decides to coast into a friend going 4.0 m/s on rollerblades in the same direction. Unfortunately, the rollerblader stops right before the collision, too quickly for the skateboarder to react. The rollerblader turns around as he stops and pushes his arms out to ward off the collision. The rollerblader and his gear have a combined inertia of 70 kg, and the skateboarder and his gear have a combined inertia of 79 kg. (*a*) If the skateboarder ends up moving backward at 2.0 m/s, what is the coefficient of restitution for the collision? (*b*) What are the changes in kinetic and internal energies measured by an observer standing alongside the collision? (*c*) What are the changes in kinetic and internal energies measured by an observer in the zero-momentum reference frame for the skateboarder-rollerblader system? (*d*) If the rollerblader had not turned around and stopped, so that the skateboarder was able to grab him and keep coasting, what amount of kinetic energy would have been lost in the collision? ●●●

Answers to Review Questions

1. (*a*) The observer in the car moving with the same velocity as the truck sees the truck as not moving. (*b*) The observer in the car moving at any constant velocity different from the truck velocity sees the truck as moving at some constant velocity that is different from the observer's velocity.
2. In a reference frame attached to the wind, the air is at rest. When you ride into the wind, your velocity measured in this reference frame is higher than your velocity measured in the Earth reference frame. The higher your speed measured in the wind reference frame, the more you feel like you are riding through a storm. When you are moving in the direction of the wind and your speed happens to be the same as the wind speed, you sense the air as being at rest; in other words, you feel no wind at all.
3. The observer in reference frame 2 also measures $\Delta\vec{p} = 0$ because the measured value is zero in *any* inertial reference frame.
4. The law of inertia: In an inertial reference frame, any isolated object at rest remains at rest and any isolated object in motion keeps moving with constant velocity. This law is useful in determining whether a reference frame is inertial: You observe as many isolated objects as possible, and if any of them violates the law, you are observing from a noninertial reference frame. If no objects violate the law, you are observing from an inertial reference frame.
5. The observer is in a noninertial reference frame because the law of inertia does not hold.
6. (*a*) Yes. The acceleration is the same in all inertial reference frames. (*b*) No. An observer in some other inertial reference frame can measure a nonzero velocity for the object. The only thing you can say about this measured nonzero velocity is that it is constant.
7. The principle of relativity: The laws of the universe are the same in all inertial reference frames. This means that it is not necessary to invent different laws to explain results obtained by observers moving at any constant velocity with respect to each other; one set of laws is universally valid.
8. No, because one inertial reference frame is physically indistinguishable from any other inertial reference frame. You can determine whether or not your reference frame is inertial, but you can only measure its velocity relative to the velocity of other inertial reference frames.
9. Because the second reference frame is inertial, the object's acceleration in it is the same as the acceleration in the first reference frame.
10. Conservation of momentum doesn't mean that the momentum of the system must have the same numerical value in all inertial reference frames. What it does mean is that momentum can be neither created nor destroyed, so that any changes in system momentum must be accounted for in terms of impulse (momentum input or output). Because changes in system momentum are identical in all inertial reference frames, momentum conservation is equally valid in all of them.
11. They disagree on the kinetic energy of each object and on the amount of kinetic energy in the system, but they agree that the kinetic energy of the system does not change as a result of the collision. They also disagree about the momentum of each object and the system momentum, but they agree that the momentum of the system does not change.
12. The zero-momentum reference frame is the inertial reference frame in which the momentum of a system is zero. It can be identified by computing the system momentum in some inertial reference frame. If the system momentum is zero in your chosen reference frame, you have the zero-momentum reference frame for the system. If your computed momentum is not zero, compute the velocity of the zero-momentum reference frame by dividing the system momentum you calculated in your chosen reference frame by the system inertia. Subtract this velocity from each object's velocity to obtain the velocity of each object in the zero-momentum reference frame.
13. (*a*) The magnitude does not change. (*b*) The direction reverses.
14. They give us a means to relate measurements made in one inertial reference frame to those made in another.
15. C must know D's velocity $\vec{v}_{CD}$ measured in C's reference frame. If D's measurement is accurate, then the three quantities are related to one another as in Eq. 6.14: $\vec{v}_{Ct} = \vec{v}_{CD} + \vec{v}_{Dt}$.
16. The inertia is the same in *all* inertial reference frames because inertias are determined from Eq. 4.2, $m_o = -(\Delta v_{sx}/\Delta v_{ox})m_s$, and changes in velocity are identical in different inertial reference frames.
17. There is no difference. The numerical value of the x component of position may change with the specific reference point (origin) chosen, but the actual position of the center of mass of a system is a property of the system that is independent of the reference point.
18. The system momentum is constant because the system is isolated. The center of mass moves with the momentum of the system, which means it moves with constant momentum. (Put another way, the center of mass is at rest in the zero-momentum reference frame for the system.) If the inertia of the system is also unchanging, the center of mass moves at constant velocity.
19. The momentum is zero because the center-of-mass velocity is that of the zero-momentum reference frame. (Compare *Principles* Eqs. 6.23 and 6.26.)
20. Yes. This was established for a particular collision in the *Principles* volume, but it is also logically required that energy that appears in the form of thermal energy or crumpled fenders must not depend on the reference frame of the inertial observer.
21. The nonconvertible kinetic energy changes, which is the part associated with the motion of the center of mass.
22. Not in general. The translational kinetic energy of the system's center of mass is nonconvertible energy, and so it cannot be converted to internal energy. If you happen to be using the zero-momentum reference frame, though, this translational kinetic energy is zero, so in this case all of the kinetic energy of the system is convertible and hence can be converted.
23. (*a*) The maximum amount is all of the convertible kinetic energy: $\frac{1}{2}\mu v_{\text{rel,i}}^2$. (*b*) This maximum conversion happens in totally inelastic collisions because $e = 0$.
24. (*a*) Yes, because "zero change in momentum" means the system is isolated, and a system that is isolated in one inertial reference frame is isolated in all inertial reference frames. (*b*) Yes. The change in the momentum of a system is always the same in any inertial reference frame, even though the momentum magnitudes and directions of objects in the system are not always the same, and even though the magnitude and direction of the system momentum may vary from one reference frame to another.
25. (*a*) Yes, because $\Delta E = 0$ means the system is closed, and a system that is closed in one inertial reference frame is closed in all inertial reference frames. (*b*) Yes. The change in energy of a system is the same in all inertial reference frames even though the energy changes of the objects in the system are not always the same, and even though the energy of the system may vary from one reference frame to another.

Answers to Guided Problems

Guided Problem 6.2 5.0 s plus 0.1 s for each meter length of the car

Guided Problem 6.4 5×10^{-2} kg

Guided Problem 6.6 K_{conv} hitting abutment $\approx 2K_{\text{conv}}$ hitting parked car

Guided Problem 6.8 Small nuclei make the best targets because the recoil velocity of the neutron gets lower as the target inertia decreases.

7

PRACTICE
Interactions

PRACTICE

Chapter Summary

The basics of interactions (Sections 7.1, 7.5, 7.6, 7.7)

Concepts An **interaction** is an event that produces either a physical change or a change in motion. A *repulsive interaction* causes the interacting objects to accelerate away from each other, and an *attractive interaction* causes them to accelerate toward each other.

The **interaction range** is the distance over which an interaction is appreciable. A long-range interaction has an infinite range; a short-range interaction has a finite range.

A **field** is a model used to visualize interactions between objects. According to this model, each object that takes part in an interaction produces a field in the space surrounding itself, and the fields mediate the interaction between the objects.

A **fundamental interaction** is one that cannot be explained in terms of other interactions. The four known fundamental interactions are the **gravitational interaction** (a long-range attractive interaction between objects that have *mass*), the **electromagnetic interaction** (a long-range interaction between objects that have *electrical charge;* this interaction can be either attractive or repulsive), the **weak interaction** (a short-range repulsive interaction between subatomic particles), and the **strong interaction** (a short-range interaction between *quarks,* the building blocks of protons, neutrons, and certain other subatomic particles; this interaction can be either attractive or repulsive).

Quantitative Tools If two objects of inertias m_1 and m_2 interact, the ratio of the x components of their accelerations is

$$\frac{a_{1x}}{a_{2x}} = -\frac{m_2}{m_1}. \tag{7.6}$$

Potential energy (Sections 7.2, 7.8, 7.9)

Concepts **Potential energy** is a coherent form of internal energy associated with reversible changes in the *configuration* of an object or system. Potential energy can be converted entirely to kinetic energy.

Gravitational potential energy is the potential energy associated with the relative position of objects that are interacting gravitationally.

Elastic potential energy is the potential energy associated with the reversible deformation of objects.

Changes in potential energy are *independent of path.* This means that the change in an object's potential energy as the object moves from a position x_1 to any other position x_2 depends *only* on x_1 and x_2, and *not* on the path the object takes in moving from x_1 to x_2.

Quantitative Tools The potential energy U of a system of two interacting objects can always be written in the form

$$U = U(x), \tag{7.12}$$

where $U(x)$ is a unique function of a position variable x that quantifies the configuration of the system.

Near Earth's surface, if the vertical coordinate of an object of inertia m changes by Δx, the gravitational potential energy U^G of the Earth-object system changes by

$$\Delta U^G = mg\Delta x. \tag{7.19}$$

Energy dissipation during interactions (Sections 7.3, 7.4, 7.8, 7.10

Concepts All energy can be divided into two fundamental classes: energy associated with motion (kinetic energy) and energy associated with the configuration of interacting objects (potential energy). Each class of energy comes in two forms: *coherent* and *incoherent*. Energy is coherent if it involves ordered motion or configuration; it is incoherent if it involves random motion or configuration. For example, the kinetic energy of a moving object is coherent because all of its atoms move in the same way, whereas the thermal energy of an object is incoherent because the atoms move randomly.

The **mechanical energy** E_{mech} of a system is the sum of the system's coherent energies (kinetic energy K and potential energy U).

The **thermal energy** E_{th} of a system is the incoherent internal energy associated with the random motion of atoms that make up the objects in the system. Thermal energy cannot be entirely converted to coherent energy.

Source energy E_s is incoherent energy (such as chemical, nuclear, solar, and stored solar energy) used to produce other forms of energy.

Dissipative interactions are irreversible interactions that involve changes in thermal energy.

Nondissipative interactions are reversible interactions that convert kinetic energy to potential energy, and vice versa.

Quantitative Tools

$$E_{\text{mech}} = K + U. \quad (7.9)$$

During a dissipative interaction, the sum of the changes in all forms of energy in a closed system is zero:

$$\Delta K + \Delta U + \Delta E_s + \Delta E_{\text{th}} = 0. \quad (7.28)$$

During a nondissipative interaction, the mechanical energy of a closed system does not change:

$$\Delta E_{\text{mech}} = \Delta K + \Delta U = 0. \quad (7.8)$$

Review Questions

Answers to these questions can be found at the end of this chapter.

7.1 The effects of interactions

1. A pool ball collides head-on and elastically with a second pool ball initially at rest. Do any of these properties of the system made up of the two balls change during the interaction: (*a*) momentum, (*b*) kinetic energy, (*c*) the sum of all forms of energy in the system? (Assume no significant interaction between the pool table and the balls.)
2. In an elastic collision between two objects, does their relative speed stay the same during the interaction?
3. Consider a system made up of two objects that collide with each other. Describe the difference between what happens to the system's kinetic energy when the collision is (*a*) totally inelastic, (*b*) inelastic, and (*c*) elastic.
4. Summarize the characteristics of an interaction.

7.2 Potential energy

5. Describe the difference between kinetic and potential energy.

7.3 Energy dissipation

6. Give an example of an interaction that converts kinetic energy to thermal energy.
7. How does energy of motion differ from energy of configuration? How does coherent energy differ from incoherent energy?

7.4 Source energy

8. What is the ultimate source of virtually all the energy we use?
9. What distinguishes dissipative interactions from nondissipative ones?
10. Think of several interactions that occur in everyday life. For each interaction, describe which category of energy is converted and to which category it is converted.

7.5 Interaction range

11. Describe the two models physicists use to represent interactions between objects without requiring direct touching.

7.6 Fundamental interactions

12. Which of the four fundamental interactions do we commonly observe in everyday life? Why not all of them?
13. Which fundamental interaction exerts the most control (*a*) in chemical processes and (*b*) in biological processes?
14. The strength of the gravitational interaction is minuscule compared with the strength of the electromagnetic interaction. Yet we can study the interactions of most ordinary objects without considering electromagnetic interactions, while it is essential that we include gravitational interactions. Give a reason why this is so.

7.7 Interactions and accelerations

15. How are the acceleration and inertia of an object 1 related to the acceleration and inertia of an object 2 when the objects collide (*a*) elastically and (*b*) inelastically?
16. List any assumptions made in deriving the relationship between ratios of acceleration and inertias for two interacting objects.

7.8 Nondissipative interactions

17. Explain why mechanical energy remains constant when nondissipative interactions take place in a closed system.
18. Explain how we know that, in a closed system in which all interactions are nondissipative, potential energy is a function of position only.
19. An object subject to only nondissipative interactions moves from point A to point B and then back to A. How does the object's initial kinetic energy compare with its final kinetic energy?

7.9 Potential energy near Earth's surface

20. In Eq. 7.19, is Δx a horizontal or vertical displacement? Does it matter?
21. For an object placed at a given position relative to the ground, is the value of the object's gravitational potential energy either always positive or always negative?

7.10 Dissipative interactions

22. A car collides totally inelastically with a parked car. In the (isolated) system made up of the two cars, is all the initial kinetic energy dissipated during the collision?
23. In a collision between two objects, how much of the convertible kinetic energy is converted to thermal energy, and how much is temporarily stored as potential energy during the collision (*a*) when $e = 1$ and (*b*) when $e = 0$?

Developing a Feel

Make an order-of-magnitude estimate of each of the following quantities. Letters in parentheses refer to hints below. Use them as needed to guide your thinking.

1. The energy dissipated when you clap your hands once (S, K, A)
2. The energy dissipated when you throw a tennis ball against a wall (E, X, D)
3. The thermal energy released by burning three logs in a fireplace (I, P, AA)
4. The upward acceleration of Earth you cause by jumping off a chair (G, L, U)
5. The acceleration of a rifle when a bullet is fired from it (T, Z, Q)
6. The energy supplied by your muscles when you climb a flight of stairs (H, C, Y, L)
7. The energy supplied by an escalator when it carries 30 people up one flight (L, Y, C, F)
8. The maximum potential energy stored when two protons collide head-on if, before the collision, each is moving at 3×10^7 m/s (J, W)
9. The maximum elastic potential energy stored when you perform a bungee jump (L, R, O, Y, W)
10. The gravitational potential energy stored as a 30-story building is constructed (M, V, N, B, Y)

Hints

A. What is the coefficient of restitution for the collision when you clap your hands?
B. What is the inertia of a 30-story building?
C. Does the speed change on the way up?
D. What is the coefficient of restitution?
E. What is the inertia of a tennis ball?
F. What is the height between floors of a building?
G. What is the inertia of Earth?
H. What is the vertical height of a flight of stairs?
I. How much energy is released by breaking one chemical bond?
J. What is the inertia of a proton?
K. What is the inertia of one hand and forearm?
L. What is the inertia of a typical person?
M. What is the height of a 30-story building?
N. What fraction of the volume of a 30-story building is structural concrete and steel?
O. What is the maximum height difference from bottom to top of one bungee jump?
P. What is the size of an atom?
Q. Over what length does the bullet accelerate along the rifle barrel?
R. Is the inertia of the bungee cord negligible in this situation?
S. What is the speed of each hand just before the two touch each other?
T. What is the ratio $m_{\text{rifle}}/m_{\text{bullet}}$?
U. What is your acceleration in free fall?
V. Where is the vertical location of this building's center of mass?
W. What is the minimum kinetic energy in the zero-momentum reference frame?
X. What is the speed of the ball just before it hits the wall?
Y. How does the gravitational potential energy of the system change?
Z. With what speed does the bullet leave the rifle?
AA. How many atoms are there in a fireplace log?

Key (all values approximate)

A. 0; B. 1×10^7 kg; C. generally no; D. 0.7; E. 0.1 kg; F. 6 m; G. 6×10^{24} kg; H. 3 m; I. 1×10^{-19} J; J. 2×10^{-27} kg; K. 2 kg; L. 7×10^1 kg; M. 1×10^2 m; N. 1/8; O. 1×10^2 m; P. 1×10^{-10} m; Q. 1 m; R. yes; S. 1 m/s; T. 4×10^2, or 400:1; U. 1×10^1 m/s^2; V. less than halfway up—say, 4×10^1 m above ground; W. 0, because in this reference frame there must be at least one instant at which $v_{\text{rel}} = 0$; X. 2×10^1 m/s; Y. increases as object rises, decreases as object falls; Z. 4×10^2 m/s; AA. 1×10^{27} atoms

Worked and Guided Problems

These examples involve material from this chapter but are not associated with any particular section. Some examples are worked out in detail; others you should work out by following the guidelines provided.

Worked Problem 7.1 Watch out below!

A student standing at the top of a wall throws a ball straight down, giving it speed v_i as it leaves her hand. Use energy methods to determine the speed v_f at which the ball strikes the pavement a distance h below her hand. Express your answer in terms of v_i and h.

❶ GETTING STARTED We define our system as being the ball and Earth so that the gravitational interaction can be expressed in terms of potential energy. The initial system diagram displays the given information, and the final system diagram shows the sought quantity, the final speed v_f (Figure WG7.1).

Figure WG7.1

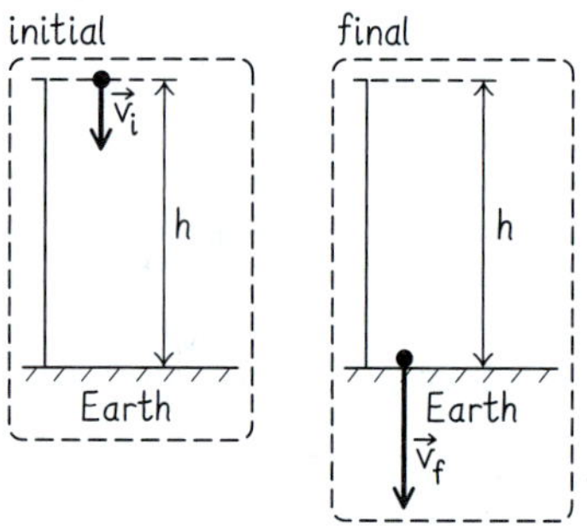

The change in Earth's kinetic energy while the ball is falling is negligible. We know that the ball speeds up because of the acceleration due to gravity, and we are required to use energy methods to determine by how much. If we let the inertia of the ball be m, we know that the ball starts out with initial kinetic energy $\frac{1}{2}mv_i^2$. As the ball travels downward, the system's gravitational potential energy decreases as this energy gets converted to kinetic energy by the gravitational interaction. Ignoring any dissipative interactions (like air resistance), we can assume that the system's mechanical energy (kinetic plus potential) does not change.

❷ DEVISE PLAN Because we have assumed that the mechanical energy of the system is constant, we can set the final mechanical energy equal to the initial value:

$$K_f + U_f = K_i + U_i. \quad (1)$$

We should include the kinetic energy of each object in our system, but we have assumed that Earth's kinetic energy does not change, so the initial and final Earth kinetic energies will simply cancel and need not be explicitly included.

Each gravitational potential energy term depends on the height, and we know neither the initial nor final height. However, if we collect terms, then only the height difference will be needed, and we do know that. We also know the initial kinetic energy term for the ball, which leaves only one unknown: the final kinetic energy of the ball. Because the kinetic energy formula is $\frac{1}{2}mv^2$, we can determine the final speed if we know the final kinetic energy. The ball's inertia m is not given, so we must be sure our answer does not contain this unknown quantity.

❸ EXECUTE PLAN Using the expression for gravitational potential energy near Earth's surface, $U^G = mgx$, we write Eq. 1 in the form

$$\tfrac{1}{2}mv_f^2 + mgx_f = \tfrac{1}{2}mv_i^2 + mgx_i.$$

Isolating the final kinetic energy, we obtain

$$\tfrac{1}{2}mv_f^2 = \tfrac{1}{2}mv_i^2 + mg(x_i - x_f). \quad (2)$$

The difference between the initial and final positions should be the height h, but to ensure that we make no error, we add specific values for x_i and x_f to our drawing (Figure WG7.2). The x axis has to point up because that was an assumption made in the derivation of $U^G = mgx$. We know that the zero level of the potential energy is an arbitrary choice, and so we choose the position at which the ball was released. With this choice, $x_f = -h$ because the ball's final position is a distance h in the negative x direction. We can now solve Eq. 2 for v_f:

$$\tfrac{1}{2}mv_f^2 = \tfrac{1}{2}mv_i^2 + mg[0 - (-h)]$$

$$mv_f^2 = mv_i^2 + 2mgh$$

$$v_f = \sqrt{v_i^2 + 2gh}. \checkmark$$

Figure WG7.2

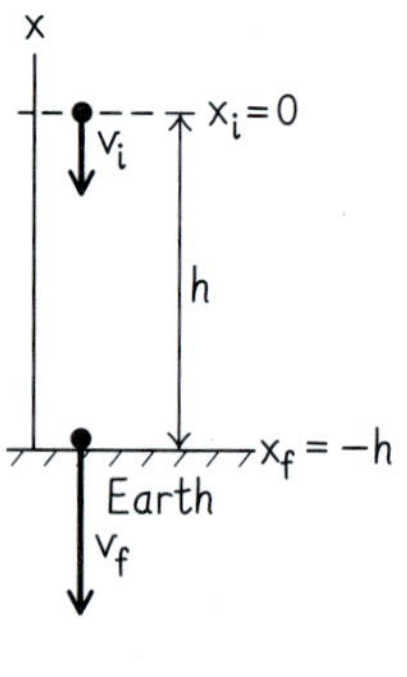

❹ EVALUATE RESULT Because the distance h is a magnitude (as is g) and v_i^2 is always positive, the quantity under the square-root sign is positive. This is reassuring because the final speed must be a real number, not an imaginary one. We expect v_f to increase if either v_i or h increases, and our expression predicts this behavior. We suspect that the actual final speed of a real ball would be lower than this because of air resistance, but our result should be fairly accurate if the ball is more like a baseball than a Ping-Pong ball and if the wall is not too tall.

Guided Problem 7.2 Safe play

A soft rubber ball is held at a height h above the floor and then released. The coefficient of restitution for the ball-floor collision is 0.25. To what height does the ball rise on its first bounce, expressed as a fraction of h?

1 GETTING STARTED

1. Begin by choosing your system and drawing a system diagram that includes the given information and the quantity you seek (labeled with a question mark).

2 DEVISE PLAN

2. What is the numerical value of the ball's speed at the highest point the ball reaches on its first bounce?
3. What kinds of energy conversions take place during the fall, in the ball's collision with the floor, and in the bounce?

3 EXECUTE PLAN

4. With what speed does the ball strike the floor?
5. What is the ball's speed immediately after it bounces off the floor?
6. How much kinetic energy is dissipated in the ball-floor collision?
7. What is the mechanical energy of the system as the ball leaves the floor? What is the mechanical energy at the ball's highest bounce distance above the floor?

4 EVALUATE RESULT

Worked Problem 7.3 Moving explosion

Two 1.0-kg carts coupled together are initially moving to the right at 2.0 m/s on a horizontal, low-friction track. The coupling contains an explosive charge that is ignited remotely, releasing 18 J of energy. Half of the released energy is dissipated into incoherent energy, such as noise, thermal energy, and damage to the carts. (*a*) What are the velocities of the carts just after the explosive separation? (*b*) Draw a bar diagram showing the energy distribution before and after the explosive separation for the system composed of the two carts and the explosive coupling.

1 GETTING STARTED We are told that the carts are coupled together and initially moving to the right at 2.0 m/s. Given that half of the energy released by the explosive charge is dissipated, we conclude that the other half goes into increasing the kinetic energy of the system. We assume that the rear car, which we can call cart 2, is pushed to the left by the collision (slowing it down) and that the leading cart (call it cart 1) is pushed to the right (speeding it up). Figure WG7.3 shows the system diagram of this moving explosive separation based on these assumptions, with the positive x direction chosen to the right. (Although we expect $\vec{v}_{2f}$ to be in the negative x direction, we do not know for sure. The solution will tell us whether our assumption is right.)

Figure WG7.3

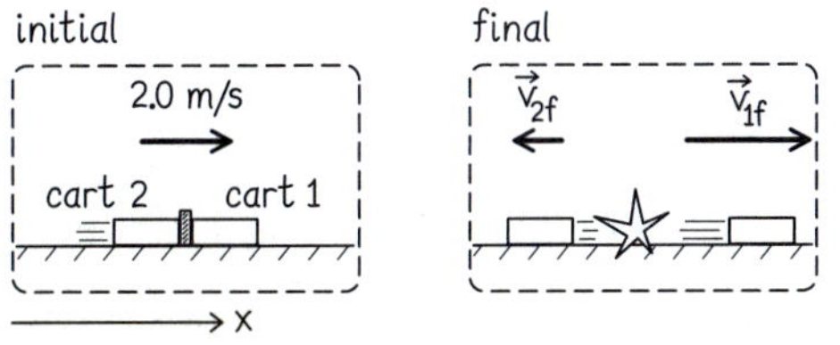

Because this is an explosive separation, we expect to use conservation of momentum. We are also given energy information, which we must incorporate into our analysis.

2 DEVISE PLAN It is often easier to analyze collisions in the zero-momentum reference frame. We are given information in the Earth reference frame, however, so we need to work with Galilean transformations. In the zero-momentum reference frame Z, the system momentum is always zero, and so we know it is zero both before and after the explosive separation:

$$m_1 v_{Z1x,i} + m_2 v_{Z2x,i} = (m_1 + m_2) v_{Zx,i} = 0 \qquad (1)$$

$$m_1 v_{Z1x,f} + m_2 v_{Z2x,f} = 0 \qquad (2)$$

where $v_{Zx,i}$ represents the initial x component of the velocity of the system in the zero-momentum reference frame. Because the inertias are not zero, we conclude from Eq. 1 that

$$v_{Z1x,i} = v_{Z2x,i} = v_{Zx,i} = 0.$$

Because we have two unknowns, $v_{Z1x,f}$ and $v_{Z2x,f}$, we need another independent equation, and so we turn to the energy information. The energy released is energy initially locked up in the chemical bonds of the explosive charge, which means it is a type of source energy. We are given how much of this source energy is released and how much is dissipated to incoherent energy (an amount that is the same in any reference frame). For simplicity, we combine all of the released incoherent energy (noise, deformation, and so on) and label it as thermal energy. Because the sum of all the forms of energy in the system is constant in this explosive separation, the energetics in the Z reference frame are described by

$$\Delta K_Z + \Delta E_{Zs} + \Delta E_{Zth} = 0. \qquad (3)$$

Equations 1–3 should give us all the information we need to calculate the final velocities in the zero-momentum reference frame. Then we do a Galilean transformation to obtain the velocities in the Earth reference frame.

3 EXECUTE PLAN
(*a*) In the Earth reference frame, the x component of the initial velocity of the system's center of mass is given by Eq. 6.26:

$$v_{cm\,x} = \frac{m_1 v_{1x,i} + m_2 v_{2x,i}}{m_1 + m_2}.$$

Because $m_1 = m_2 = m$, this expression simplifies to

$$v_{\text{cm}x} = \frac{mv_{1x,\text{i}} + mv_{2x,\text{i}}}{m + m} = \frac{v_{1x,\text{i}} + v_{2x,\text{i}}}{2}$$

$$= \frac{(+2.0\text{ m/s}) + (+2.0\text{ m/s})}{2} = +2.0\text{ m/s}.$$

In the zero-momentum reference frame the final momentum (like the initial momentum) must be zero, and so from Eq. 2 we have

$$m_1 v_{\text{Z}1x,\text{f}} + m_2 v_{\text{Z}2x,\text{f}} = mv_{\text{Z}1x,\text{f}} + mv_{\text{Z}2x,\text{f}} = 0$$

$$v_{\text{Z}1x,\text{f}} = -v_{\text{Z}2x,\text{f}}. \quad (4)$$

Let us use E to represent the quantity of source energy released, $E = 18$ J. Because the source energy decreases as the chemical bonds in the explosive charge break, the source energy term in Eq. 3 becomes $\Delta E_{\text{Zs}} = -E$. Because half of the released source energy is dissipated to thermal energy, the thermal energy term in Eq. 3 is $\Delta E_{\text{Zth}} = +\frac{1}{2}E$. Equation 3 then becomes

$$\Delta K_{\text{Z}} + \Delta E_{\text{Zs}} + \Delta E_{\text{Zth}} = 0$$

$$\left[\left(\tfrac{1}{2}m_1 v_{\text{Z}1x,\text{f}}^2 + \tfrac{1}{2}m_2 v_{\text{Z}2x,\text{f}}^2\right) - \left(\tfrac{1}{2}m_1 v_{\text{Z}1x,\text{i}}^2 + \tfrac{1}{2}m_2 v_{\text{Z}2x,\text{i}}^2\right)\right]$$

$$+ (-E) + \left(\tfrac{1}{2}E\right) = 0$$

$$\left(\tfrac{1}{2}mv_{\text{Z}1x,\text{f}}^2 + \tfrac{1}{2}mv_{\text{Z}2x,\text{f}}^2\right) - \left(\tfrac{1}{2}m(0)^2 + \tfrac{1}{2}m_2(0)^2\right) = +\tfrac{1}{2}E.$$

Next we substitute from Eq. 4 to get

$$\tfrac{1}{2}m(-v_{\text{Z}2x,\text{f}})^2 + \tfrac{1}{2}mv_{\text{Z}2x,\text{f}}^2 = \tfrac{1}{2}E$$

$$v_{\text{Z}2x,\text{f}} = +\sqrt{\frac{E}{2m}} \quad \text{or} \quad -\sqrt{\frac{E}{2m}}.$$

The positive root implies that cart 2 passes through cart 1 in the zero-momentum reference frame instead of being pushed away, and so we must discard this root as physically impossible. With the negative root, we have

$$v_{\text{Z}2x,\text{f}} = -\sqrt{\frac{E}{2m}}$$

$$v_{\text{Z}1x,\text{f}} = -v_{\text{Z}2x,\text{f}} = -\left(-\sqrt{\frac{E}{2m}}\right) = +\sqrt{\frac{E}{2m}}.$$

In a procedure analogous to that used in Worked Problem 6.5, the Galilean transformation to the Earth reference frame is

$$v_{\text{E}1x,\text{f}} = v_{\text{Z}1x,\text{f}} + v_{\text{cm}x} = +\sqrt{\frac{E}{2m}} + v_{\text{cm}x}$$

$$= +\sqrt{\frac{18\text{ J}}{(2)(1.0\text{ kg})}} + 2.0\text{ m/s} = +3.0\text{ m/s} + 2.0\text{ m/s}$$

$$= +5.0\text{ m/s} ✔$$

and

$$v_{\text{E}2x,\text{f}} = v_{\text{Z}2x,\text{f}} + v_{\text{cm}x} = -\sqrt{\frac{E}{2m}} + v_{\text{cm}x}$$

$$= -3.0\text{ m/s} + 2.0\text{ m/s}$$

$$= -1.0\text{ m/s}. ✔$$

Because to the right is the positive x direction in our coordinate system, cart 1 moves to the right after the explosive separation and cart 2 moves to the left, just as we assumed when we began our solution.

(*b*) The energy diagrams should contain a bar for each energy category: kinetic, potential, source, and thermal (Figure WG7.4). We know that $E_{\text{s,i}} = E = 18$ J, $E_{\text{s,f}} = 0$, $E_{\text{th,i}} = 0$, and $E_{\text{th,f}} = \frac{1}{2}E = 9.0$ J. We leave both U bars empty because there is no interaction in this system to temporarily store potential energy. The initial and final kinetic energies are

$$K_\text{i} = \tfrac{1}{2}m_1(v_{1\text{i}})^2 + \tfrac{1}{2}m_2(v_{2\text{i}})^2$$

$$= \tfrac{1}{2}(1.0\text{ kg})(2.0\text{ m/s})^2 + \tfrac{1}{2}(1.0\text{ kg})(2.0\text{ m/s})^2 = 4.0\text{ J}$$

$$K_\text{f} = \tfrac{1}{2}m_1(v_{1\text{f}})^2 + \tfrac{1}{2}m_2(v_{2\text{f}})^2$$

$$= \tfrac{1}{2}(1.0\text{ kg})(5.0\text{ m/s})^2 + \tfrac{1}{2}(1.0\text{ kg})(1.0\text{ m/s})^2 = 13\text{ J}.$$

These values yield the bar diagram shown in Figure WG7.4. ✔

Figure WG7.4

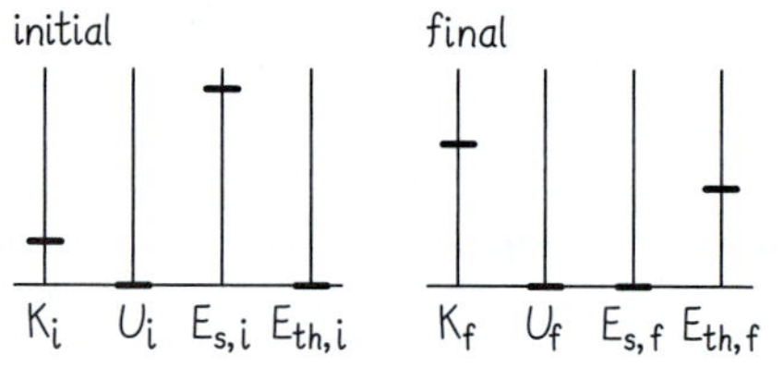

4 EVALUATE RESULT We can check our results in several ways. It is reassuring that we obtained a center-of-mass velocity of $v_{\text{cm}x} = +2.0$ m/s because the two carts are initially locked together and moving at that velocity.

Let us make several other checks, although you normally might not do all of them. We used conservation of momentum in the zero-momentum reference frame. We can verify that this law is satisfied in the Earth reference frame with our calculated numbers:

$$p_{x,\text{i}} = m_1 v_{1x,\text{i}} + m_2 v_{2x,\text{i}}$$

$$= (1.0\text{ kg})(+2.0\text{ m/s}) + (1.0\text{ kg})(+2.0\text{ m/s})$$

$$= +4.0\text{ kg}\cdot\text{m/s}$$

$$p_{x,\text{f}} = m_1 v_{1x,\text{f}} + m_2 v_{2x,\text{f}}$$

$$= (1.0\text{ kg})(+5.0\text{ m/s}) + (1.0\text{ kg})(-1.0\text{ m/s})$$

$$= +4.0\text{ kg}\cdot\text{m/s}.$$

We can verify that the system's energy remains constant by calculating its change in the Earth reference frame:

$$\Delta K + \Delta E_\text{s} + \Delta E_\text{th} = (13\text{ J} - 4.0\text{ J}) + (0 - 18\text{ J}) + (9.0\text{ J} - 0)$$

$$= 0.$$

PRACTICE

We can also check consistency in the kinetic energy:

$$K = \tfrac{1}{2}(m_1 + m_2)(v_{\text{cm}\,x})^2 + K_{\text{conv}}$$

$$= \tfrac{1}{2}(m_1 + m_2)(v_{\text{cm}\,x})^2 + \tfrac{1}{2}\left(\frac{m_1 m_2}{m_1 + m_2}\right)(v_{2x} - v_{1x})^2,$$

where for K_{conv} we have substituted the expression given in Eq. 6.38. Because the inertias are equal, we can simplify to

$$K_{\text{f}} = \tfrac{1}{2}(m + m)(v_{\text{cm}\,x})^2 + \tfrac{1}{2}\frac{m^2}{m + m}(v_{2x,\text{f}} - v_{1x,\text{f}})^2$$

$$= m(v_{\text{cm}})^2 + \tfrac{1}{4}m(v_{2x,\text{f}} - v_{1x,\text{f}})^2$$

$$= (1.0\ \text{kg})(2.0\ \text{m/s})^2 + \tfrac{1}{4}(1.0\ \text{kg})[(-1.0\ \text{m/s}) - (+5.0\ \text{m/s})]^2$$

$$= 4.0\ \text{J} + 9.0\ \text{J} = 13\ \text{J}$$

in agreement with our calculation for the bar diagram in part *b*.

Guided Problem 7.4 An unequal match

On a low-friction track, two carts coupled together are initially moving to the right at 2.0 m/s. The rear cart has an inertia of 2.0 kg, and the lead cart's inertia is one-third of that. An explosive charge attached to the coupling is ignited remotely, releasing 27 J of energy. One-third of that energy is dissipated to incoherent energy, such as noise, thermal energy, and damage to the carts. Use the Earth reference frame for the following tasks. (*a*) Determine the velocities of the carts just after the explosive separation. (*b*) Draw a bar diagram showing the energy distribution before and after the explosive separation.

❶ GETTING STARTED

1. How is this problem similar to Worked Problem 7.3? How does it differ from Worked Problem 7.3?
2. What is a good choice for your system?
3. Draw a system diagram showing all relevant information.
4. Which system quantities remain constant during the explosive separation?

❷ DEVISE PLAN

5. Write the equations describing the conservation laws for the quantities named in question 4, as viewed in the Earth reference frame.
6. How many unknowns do you have? Do you have a sufficient number of equations to solve for them?

❸ EXECUTE PLAN

❹ EVALUATE RESULT

7. Check your numerical answer for consistency in at least two ways.

Worked Problem 7.5 Exploding rocket

A rocket is made up of an unpowered payload of inertia m_{payload} and a powered booster connected to the payload by an explosive coupler. The rocket is fired straight up, uses all its fuel, and reaches the peak of its trajectory at height h_1 above the ground. The coupler is detonated at the peak of the trajectory. The quantity of energy released by the explosion is $E > 0$, one-quarter of which is dissipated to incoherent energy. The explosion separates the booster from the payload, and the latter shoots straight up along its original line of motion. Immediately after the separation, the inertia of the booster is five times that of the payload. What maximum height h_2 above the ground does the payload reach after the explosion? Assume that all the incoherent energy is in the form of thermal energy, and report your answer in terms of h_1, E, and m_{payload}.

❶ GETTING STARTED This problem involves three stages of motion that are best analyzed separately. First there is the trip from ground to h_1, which needs no analysis because h_1 is given information. The remaining two stages are the explosive separation and the post-separation motions of the booster and payload under the influence of Earth's gravitational field.

First we choose an isolated and closed system and draw a system diagram. A good choice is the system composed of booster, explosive coupler, payload, and Earth. In our diagram (Figure WG7.5), we show the initial location of the rocket (the ground), the rocket at height h_1 just before separation, the booster and payload at h_1 just after separation, and the payload at its maximum height h_2. Because we are considering gravitational potential energy, we choose to point the *x* axis vertically upward, with the origin at ground level.

The rocket is at the top of its trajectory when the explosive separation occurs, which means that its velocity at the instant of separation is zero. So, we already have complete information about the momentum and energy of the objects in our system at height h_1, and the initial journey from ground to h_1 need not be analyzed! Because the payload travels straight up after the separation, conservation of momentum tells us that the booster must be thrown downward by the explosion. As the payload moves up, its interaction with Earth's gravitational field causes it to slow down as its kinetic energy gets converted to gravitational potential energy until its velocity is zero at the final maximum height we seek. This last portion of the motion, from h_1 to h_2, is simply projectile motion of the payload, which we can analyze with the techniques of Chapter 3 or with energy methods, as we wish.

Figure WG7.5

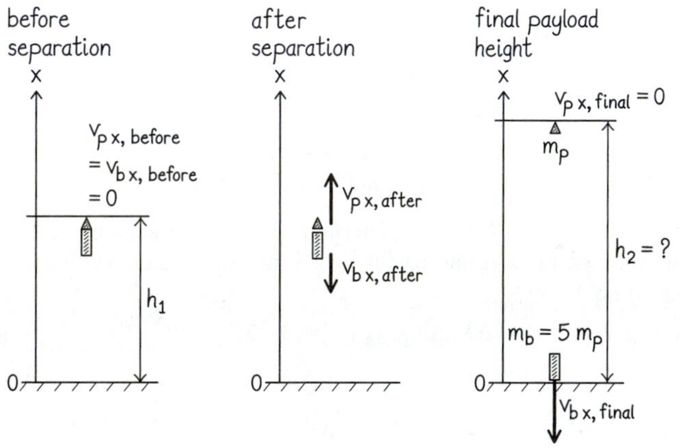

❷ **DEVISE PLAN** Because the height h_2 the payload reaches is determined by the payload velocity right after separation, we first examine the explosion. In the explosion, an amount E of source energy stored in the coupler is converted to other forms ($\Delta E_s = -E$), with one-quarter dissipated as thermal energy ($\Delta E_{th} = +E/4$). Because the booster and payload do not have a chance to move much during the explosion, they are at essentially the same location just before and just after the explosion. Thus we can consider the gravitational potential energy to remain unchanged during the explosion, $\Delta U^G = 0$. Therefore, the expression for the changes in energy for the rocket-Earth system during the explosion can be written as

$$\Delta K_{\text{rocket-Earth}} + \Delta E_s + \Delta E_{th} = 0. \quad (1)$$

Because the rocket has zero speed and consequently zero kinetic energy just before the explosion, we have

$$\Delta K_{\text{rocket-Earth}} = K_{\text{after}} - K_{\text{before}} = K_{\text{after}} - 0.$$

Therefore Eq. 1 gives us an expression for the kinetic energy just after the explosive separation:

$$K_{\text{after}} + \Delta E_s + \Delta E_{th} = 0$$
$$K_{\text{after}} = -\Delta E_s - \Delta E_{th}.$$

We must then determine how much of this kinetic energy is associated with the payload because

$$\Delta K_{\text{rocket-Earth}} = K_{\text{after}} = K_{\text{payload, after}} + K_{\text{booster, after}}. \quad (2)$$

To determine how much kinetic energy is associated with the payload, we consider the explosive separation of the booster and payload separately. During the explosion we can consider the payload-booster system to be isolated and so its momentum remains constant, or $\Delta\vec{p}_{\text{payload}} + \Delta\vec{p}_{\text{booster}} = 0$. We can then use this relation to figure out the relationship between the velocities of the payload and the booster just after the explosive separation. Given the payload velocity just after the separation, we can determine the kinetic energy of the payload. After the separation, the mechanical energy in the payload-Earth system should remain constant because now there is no longer any source energy being dissipated to incoherent forms. For the mechanical energy of the payload-Earth system, we therefore can say

$$\Delta K_{\text{payload-Earth}} + \Delta U^G_{\text{payload-Earth}} = 0. \quad (3)$$

Finally, we realize that Earth's inertia is much greater than that of any rocket. This means that only a vanishingly small fraction of the gravitational potential energy goes into changing Earth's kinetic energy (see Developing a Feel 4), which implies

$$\Delta K_{\text{payload-Earth}} = \Delta K_{\text{payload}} + \Delta K_{\text{Earth}} = \Delta K_{\text{payload}} + 0.$$

Because this is so, the only kinetic energy we need to consider is the payload's. From it we can determine the change in gravitational potential energy and the payload's final height h_2.

❸ **EXECUTE PLAN** We first determine the sum of the kinetic energies of the booster and payload right after separation, beginning with Eq. 1:

$$\Delta K_{\text{rocket-Earth}} + \Delta E_s + \Delta E_{th} = 0$$
$$\Delta K_{\text{rocket-Earth}} + (-E) + (+E/4) = 0$$
$$\Delta K_{\text{rocket-Earth}} = \tfrac{3}{4}E.$$

Substituting from Eq. 2 gives

$$\Delta K_{\text{rocket-Earth}} = K_{\text{payload, after}} + K_{\text{booster, after}} = \tfrac{3}{4}E$$
$$\tfrac{1}{2}m_{\text{payload}}v^2_{\text{payload, after}} + \tfrac{1}{2}m_{\text{booster}}v^2_{\text{booster, after}} = \tfrac{3}{4}E. \quad (4)$$

To determine how this kinetic energy is distributed between payload and booster, we use the fact that the momentum of the payload-booster system is constant during the explosion to determine the relationship of their velocities just after the explosive separation:

$$p_{\text{payload }x\text{, after}} + p_{\text{booster }x\text{, after}} = p_{\text{payload }x\text{, before}} + p_{\text{booster }x\text{, before}}$$
$$m_{\text{payload}}(+v_{\text{payload, after}}) + m_{\text{booster}}(-v_{\text{booster, after}}) = 0 + 0$$
$$v_{\text{booster, after}} = \frac{m_{\text{payload}}}{m_{\text{booster}}}v_{\text{payload, after}},$$

where we have used the velocity directions shown in Figure WG7.5. Substituting this result into Eq. 4 and using the fact that, after separation, $m_{\text{booster}} = 5m_{\text{payload}}$, we obtain

$$\tfrac{1}{2}m_{\text{payload}}v^2_{\text{payload, after}} + \tfrac{1}{2}m_{\text{booster}}\left(\frac{m_{\text{payload}}}{m_{\text{booster}}}v_{\text{payload, after}}\right)^2 = \tfrac{3}{4}E$$
$$\left(\tfrac{1}{2}m_{\text{payload}}v^2_{\text{payload, after}}\right)\left(1 + \frac{m_{\text{payload}}}{m_{\text{booster}}}\right) = \tfrac{3}{4}E$$
$$\left(\tfrac{1}{2}m_{\text{payload}}v^2_{\text{payload, after}}\right)\left(1 + \frac{m_{\text{payload}}}{5m_{\text{payload}}}\right) = \tfrac{3}{4}E$$
$$\left(\tfrac{1}{2}m_{\text{payload}}v^2_{\text{payload, after}}\right)\left(\tfrac{6}{5}\right) = \tfrac{3}{4}E$$
$$\tfrac{1}{2}m_{\text{payload}}v^2_{\text{payload, after}} = \tfrac{15}{24}E = \tfrac{5}{8}E.$$

Now we are ready to determine the quantity we are asked for—h_2, the maximum height reached by the payload after separation. We use Eq. 3 (the mechanical energy for the payload-Earth system remains constant), remembering that the subscript final means values at the maximum payload height h_2 and after means values just after separation (note that, for our choice of origin for the x axis, x_{final} and x_{after} are equivalent to h_2 and h_1, respectively):

$$\Delta K_{\text{payload}} + \Delta U^G_{\text{payload-Earth}} = 0$$
$$\left[\tfrac{1}{2}m_{\text{payload}}v^2_{\text{payload, final}} - \tfrac{1}{2}m_{\text{payload}}v^2_{\text{payload, after}}\right]$$
$$+ \left[m_{\text{payload}}gx_{\text{final}} - m_{\text{payload}}gx_{\text{after}}\right] = 0$$
$$\left[\tfrac{1}{2}m_{\text{payload}}(0)^2 - \tfrac{5}{8}E\right] + \left[m_{\text{payload}}g(+h_2) - m_{\text{payload}}g(+h_1)\right] = 0$$
$$m_{\text{payload}}gh_2 = m_{\text{payload}}gh_1 + \tfrac{5}{8}E$$
$$h_2 = h_1 + \tfrac{5}{8}\frac{E}{m_{\text{payload}}g}. \checkmark$$

PRACTICE

❸ **EVALUATE RESULT** If E is increased, we expect the payload to go higher, which is what our algebraic result predicts. If $m_{payload}$ is increased, we expect the opposite, and this, too, is consistent with our result. Further, the solution suggests that the amount of energy released in the explosive separation, E, appears to be about double the energy required to lift the payload through a height difference $h_2 - h_1$, so the order of magnitude of the result is correct. The assumption $m_{rocket} \ll m_{Earth}$ is reasonable.

One caveat is that we have used an expression for gravitational potential energy that is valid only near Earth's surface; our solution is applicable to only low-flying rockets, a situation we will correct in Chapter 13.

Guided Problem 7.6 Booster impact

A toy rocket comprises an unpowered, 1.0-kg payload and a powered booster connected by an explosive coupler. The rocket is fired straight up and reaches a speed of 90 m/s as the last of its fuel is exhausted 100 m above the ground. At this instant, the coupler is detonated, and the two parts separate from each other. The energy released by the explosive separation is 3000 J, with 1000 J of it converted to incoherent energy. Immediately after the explosive separation, the booster has an inertia of 2.0 kg. Use energy and momentum methods to calculate the speed at which the booster strikes the ground.

❶ **GETTING STARTED**

1. How is this problem similar to Worked Problem 7.5? How does it differ in information and in specific task?
2. Choose your system (or systems) and draw a version of Figure WG7.5 that contains the information supplied in this problem, using a question mark to identify the quantity you need to calculate.

❷ **DEVELOP PLAN**

3. Write an expression for the kinetic energy of the payload-booster system right after the separation.
4. Which law can you use to establish a relationship between $\vec{v}_{payload}$ and $\vec{v}_{booster}$ just after the separation?
5. What is the booster's x coordinate just after the separation, and what is it just as the booster hits the ground?
6. What is the booster's change in potential energy? How is this change related to its change in kinetic energy?

❸ **EXECUTE PLAN**

❹ **EVALUATE RESULT**

Worked Problem 7.7 Somewhat springy potential energy

A 4.0-kg block takes part in only one interaction (with a fixed object) that causes potential energy to be stored in the block-object system as the block moves along an x axis. At $t = 0$, the block is at $x_0 = +2.0$ m and moving in the negative x direction at 2.0 m/s. The amount of potential energy stored depends on the block's position along the axis and is given by $U(x) = ax^2 + bx + c$, where $a = +1.0\ \mathrm{J/m^2}$, $b = -2.0$ J/m, and $c = -1.0$ J. (*a*) Draw a diagram of this potential energy as a function of x, and show the value of the block's mechanical energy on your diagram. (*b*) What is the block's speed after it has traveled 3.0 m from x_0? (*c*) At what value of x is the block's velocity zero? (*d*) Describe what the block does after it passes through that value of x.

❶ **GETTING STARTED** The block and fixed object form a closed, nondissipative system because the only interaction is associated with a potential energy. We can get the potential energy and kinetic energy when the block is at one position and thus determine its mechanical energy at that position. Knowing that the mechanical energy remains constant during the motion allows us to sketch the graph for part *a*. We then need only to determine the potential energy when the block is at any other position in order to obtain the block's kinetic energy and hence its speed there. This covers parts *b* and *c*, and hopefully also provides insight about part *d*.

❷ **DEVISE PLAN** We are given the speed $v_0 = 2.0$ m/s at $x_0 = +2.0$ m, from which we can calculate the kinetic energy $K_0 = K(x_0) = \frac{1}{2}mv_0^2$ and the potential energy $U_0 = U(x_0)$. No sources of energy are involved and no energy is dissipated during the motion, and so the mechanical energy remains constant. Consequently we know that for any position x,

$$E_{mech} = K(x_0) + U(x_0) = K(x) + U(x).$$

Knowing either $K(x)$ or $U(x)$ at any x allows us to calculate the other value:

$$K(x) = E_{mech} - U(x)$$

$$U(x) = E_{mech} - K(x).$$

After the block travels 3.0 m in the negative x direction from $x_0 = +2.0$ m, it is at $x_b = -1.0$ m, where we use the subscript b to remind ourselves that this value is needed to solve part *b*. We can now readily calculate its kinetic energy at that position.

At the instant when the block's velocity is zero at x_c (subscript c because this position is needed to solve part *c*), its kinetic energy is zero: $K(x_c) = 0$. We then get the potential energy from $U(x_c) = E_{mech} - K(x_c) = E_{mech} - 0$, and calculate the value of x_c that gives the block that amount of potential energy.

A similar procedure determines the block's motion thereafter, for part *d*.

❸ **EXECUTE PLAN**
(*a*) We can substitute values of x into the $U(x)$ equation to produce the graph. However, to help us in our thinking (and review some tools for more complex problems), it is good to find out whether there are any extrema (maxima and/or minima) in the potential energy curve by determining the value of x at which the derivative of U with respect to x is zero:

$$\frac{d}{dx}U(x) = \frac{d}{dx}(ax^2 + bx + c) = 2ax + b$$

$$\frac{dU}{dx} = 0 = 2ax + b = 2(+1.0\ \mathrm{J/m^2})x + (-2.0\ \mathrm{J/m}).$$

This equation has a single solution, $x = +1.0$ m, and at that value of x the potential energy is

$$U(+1.0\text{ m}) = (1.0\text{ J/m}^2)(+1.0\text{ m})^2 - (2.0\text{ J/m})(+1.0\text{ m}) - 1.0\text{ J}$$
$$= -2.0\text{ J}.$$

Because the second derivative of the potential energy with respect to x is positive ($+2.0\text{ J/m}^2$) everywhere, the potential energy curve is concave up. The one extremum is therefore a minimum. To pin down the shape of the curve further, we compute the value of U at a few other values of x: $U(-2.0\text{ m}) = +7.0$ J, $U(-1.0\text{ m}) = +2.0$ J, and $U(0) = -1.0$ J. Symmetry gives us the shape on the other side of the minimum, and we end up with the graph shown in Figure WG7.6.

Figure WG7.6

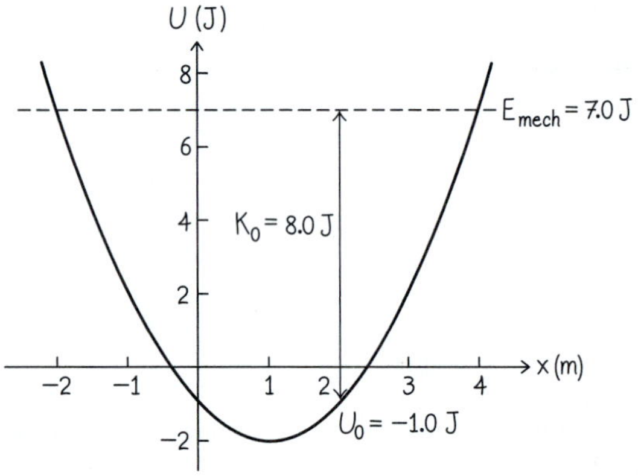

The graph shows that U decreases as the block travels in the negative x direction. Because $E_{mech} = U + K$ stays constant, decreasing U means increasing K, and increasing K means increasing v; in other words, the block speeds up as it moves from $x = +2.0$ m to $x = +1.0$ m. At $x = +1.0$ m, U has its lowest value, and so K must have its highest value. As the block continues to the left of $x = +1.0$ m, it slows down because U increases and so K and v must decrease.

The kinetic energy at $x_0 = +2.0$ m is

$$K_0 = \tfrac{1}{2}mv_0^2 = \tfrac{1}{2}(4.0\text{ kg})(2.0\text{ m/s})^2 = 8.0\text{ J}.$$

The mechanical energy when the block is at $x_0 = +2.0$ m is then

$$E_{mech} = \tfrac{1}{2}mv_0^2 + U_0 = (8.0\text{ J}) + (-1.0\text{ J}) = 7.0\text{ J}.$$

Because the system's mechanical energy is constant, this is also the value of E_{mech} at any other value of x. We include a dashed horizontal line on the graph to illustrate this constant value of E_{mech}. ✔

(*b*) After the block has traveled 3.0 m from x_0, moving in the negative x direction, it is at $x_b = -1.0$ m. We can determine its speed at this position once we get the kinetic energy:

$$K_b = K(x_b) = E_{mech} - U(x_b) = 7.0\text{ J} - (+2.0\text{ J}) = +5.0\text{ J}$$
$$\tfrac{1}{2}mv_b^2 = K_b$$
$$v_b = \sqrt{\frac{2K_b}{m}} = \sqrt{\frac{2(5.0\text{ J})}{4.0\text{ kg}}} = 1.6\text{ m/s.}$$ ✔

(*c*) We determine x_c, the position at which the block's velocity is zero, by using the fact that its kinetic energy is also zero at this position:

$$K_c + U_c = E_{mech}$$
$$0 + (ax^2 + bx + c) = E_{mech}$$
$$(1.0\text{ J/m}^2)x_c^2 + (-2.0\text{ J/m})x_c + (-1.0\text{ J}) = 7.0\text{ J}$$
$$x_c^2 - (2.0\text{ m})x_c - (8.0\text{ m}^2) = 0.$$

This expression can be factored, giving

$$[x_c + (2.0\text{ m})][x_c - (4.0\text{ m})] = 0.$$

The solutions to this equation are $x_c = -2.0$ m and $x_c = +4.0$ m, which agree with the values we read from Figure WG7.6 (the two values of x at which the curve intersects the $E_{mech} = 7.0$ J dashed line). Because the block is moving in the negative x direction, the solution we want here is $x_c = -2.0$ m. ✔

(*d*) At $x_c = -2.0$ m, the block has zero velocity because its kinetic energy is zero. Its acceleration is not zero at this location; indeed, its acceleration is always in the direction of decreasing potential energy. For the block at $x_c = -2.0$ m, this means directed along the positive x axis. Because the direction of motion reverses here, this position is called a *turning point* of the motion.

As the block moves in the positive x direction, it picks up speed as the potential energy decreases along the curve in Figure WG7.6, until it reaches $x = +1.0$ m. After it moves through this position of minimum potential energy, the block slows down as kinetic energy is converted to potential energy. The block eventually again has zero velocity at the other value we obtained in part *c*, $x_c = +4$ m, which is the second turning point of the motion. The block then again moves in the direction of decreasing potential energy, which now is to the left. ✔

4 EVALUATE RESULT We can check whether our calculated answers are consistent with our graph. The kinetic energy K_b at $x_b = -1.0$ m in the graph (the amount of energy that must be added to the potential energy at this point to reach the E_{mech} line) is 5.0 J, which is what we calculated in part *b*. We can see from where the E_{mech} line crosses the potential energy curve that the left turning point is at $x = -2.0$ m as we calculated.

PRACTICE

Guided Problem 7.8 Over the hill

A particle takes part in just one interaction with a fixed object. The interaction causes potential energy to be stored in the particle-object system as the particle moves along an x axis. The particle is released from rest at $x_0 = -3.0$ m, and the amount of potential energy stored (in joules) is given by $U(x) = ax + bx^2 + cx^3$, where $a = +12$ J/m, $b = +3.0$ J/m^2, and $c = -2.0$ J/m^3. (*a*) Make a graph of the potential energy that also displays the particle's mechanical energy. (*b*) In which direction does the particle move initially? (*c*) Describe the particle's motion after it leaves x_0. (*d*) At which positions along the curve you drew in part *a* is the particle speeding up, and at which positions is it slowing down? (*e*) What is the particle's kinetic energy at $x = -1.0$ m, $x = +1.0$ m, and $x = +3.0$ m?

1 GETTING STARTED

1. Which portions of Worked Problem 7.7 are relevant?
2. How can you use calculus to determine the extrema of the potential energy function?
3. What happens to the amount of potential energy stored as x gets larger in the positive direction and as x gets larger in the negative direction?

2 DEVISE PLAN

4. Calculate the potential energy at a few values of x. [Hint: What values are useful for part *e*?] What are the values of the potential energy at the extrema?
5. What is the kinetic energy of the particle at the instant it is released? How can you use this information to determine the (constant) mechanical energy of the system?
6. What determines in which direction the particle tends to move once it is released?

3 EXECUTE PLAN

7. Where is the potential energy increasing, and where is it decreasing?

4 EVALUATE RESULT

Questions and Problems

For instructor-assigned homework, go to MasteringPhysics®

Dots indicate difficulty level of problems: • = *easy*, •• = *intermediate*, ••• = *hard*; CR = *context-rich problem.*

7.1 The effects of interactions

1. A piece of salami is squashed between two pieces of bread. Is there one interaction between the salami and bread or more than one? •
2. Explain why you cannot cause Earth to accelerate very much, even if you jump up and down on it. •
3. Sketch curves, to the same scale, of kinetic energy versus time for an elastic collision between cart A, originally moving with speed v, and cart B, originally at rest, when (*a*) $m_B = m_A$, (*b*) $m_B = 2m_A$, and (*c*) $m_B = m_A/2$. ••
4. Two objects of inertias m_1 and m_2 start from rest and then interact with each other (assume neither is interacting with any other object). (*a*) What is the ratio of their x components of velocity at any instant? (*b*) What is the ratio of their kinetic energies at any instant? ••
5. Two toy cars ($m_1 = 0.200$ kg and $m_2 = 0.250$ kg) are held together rear to rear with a compressed spring between them. When they are released, the cars are free to roll away from the ends of the spring. If you measure the acceleration of the 0.200-kg car to be 2.25 m/s^2 to the right, what is the acceleration of the other car? ••

7.2 Potential Energy

6. You are at the swimming pool and want to make a splash. You climb the ladder to the high diving board, take a big bounce, and produce a prodigious splash. Describe the changes in kinetic and potential energy involved in this motion, beginning when you start to climb and ending when you hit the water. •
7. You throw a stone straight up and then catch it as it falls. Draw the energy bar diagrams for the stone-Earth system (*a*) just after the stone leaves your hand, (*b*) at the top of the stone's path, and (*c*) just before the stone is back in your hand. •
8. A ring is attached at the center of the underside of a trampoline. A sneaky teenager crawls under the trampoline and uses the ring to pull the trampoline slowly down while his 75-kg mother is sleeping on it. When he releases the trampoline, she is launched upward. As she passes through the position at which she was before her son stretched the trampoline, her speed is 3.0 m/s. How much elastic potential energy did the son add to the trampoline by pulling it down? Assume the interaction is nondissipative. ••
9. An elevator might be raised and lowered directly by a winch, as in Figure P7.9*a*, or the mechanism might include a counterweight that moves up when the elevator moves down, as in Figure P7.9*b*. In which case is the change in the gravitational potential energy of the Earth-elevator-winch system lower? ••

Figure P7.9

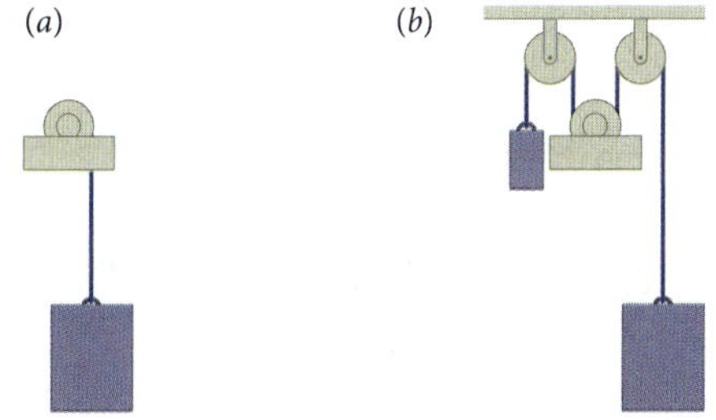

10. *Principles* Figures 7.7 and 7.25 suggest that potential energy in a nondissipative interaction builds up and then diminishes. Is this always the case? ••
11. Two blocks are held together with a compressed spring between them on the surface of a slippery table. One block has three times the inertia of the other. When the blocks are released, the spring pushes them away from each other. What is the ratio of their kinetic energies after the release? •••

PRACTICE

7.3 Energy dissipation

12. A trampoline's springs are what allow you to bounce, and if you bounce long enough, the springs get warm. Using *Principles* Figure 7.10 as a guide, classify the energy in the springs that accounts for (*a*) the bouncing and (*b*) the heating up. (*c*) Where does this energy come from? •

13. You throw a baseball straight up, and because of air resistance some of the ball's energy is converted to thermal energy during the whole trip. Which takes longer: the trip up or the trip down? •

14. An arrow is shot into a hollow pipe resting on a horizontal table and flies out the other end. While the arrow travels in the pipe, its feathers brush against the walls of the pipe. (*a*) Which type of collision is the arrow-pipe interaction: elastic, inelastic, or totally inelastic? (*b*) Is there an instant when the velocity of the arrow relative to the pipe is necessarily zero? (*c*) Describe the energy conversions in the pipe-arrow system. ••

15. (*a*) When you stretch a Slinky spring a moderate amount and then release it, it returns to its original state, and all the potential energy stored by the stretching is converted to another form. If you stretch too much, however, you can permanently bend the spring. Where does the stored potential energy go in this case? (*b*) If you use pliers to carefully straighten the bent spring so that it looks the same as before, do you expect to recover the energy dissipated when you bent it? ••

16. Mattresses are often a linked set of coil springs. Using *Principles* Figure 7.10 as a guide, classify the energy that you give the mattress in each of these cases: (*a*) You slide the mattress from one side of a room to the other side. (*b*) You jump on the mattress several times. (*c*) You run your fingers along the tops of the coils, so that they jiggle around. (*d*) By jumping hard, you manage to snap some of the links between the coils. ••

17. Make a graph of the kinetic energy, potential energy, and incoherent energy versus time for (*a*) a moving billiard ball colliding with a stationary billiard ball, and (*b*) a moving ball of cookie dough colliding with, and sticking to, an identical but stationary ball of cookie dough. ••

18. When a steel ball and a soft rubber ball are dropped from the same height onto a concrete surface, the steel ball bounces higher. When they are dropped onto packed sand, however, the rubber ball bounces higher. Explain the difference. •••

7.4 Source energy

19. Choose an appropriate closed system and draw a bar diagram representing the energy conversions and transfers that occur during each process of *Principles* Checkpoint 7.9: (*a*) a ball launching as the compressed spring it sits on expands, (*b*) a ball released from some height and falling to the ground, (*c*) a coasting bicycle slowing down, (*d*) a car accelerating on a highway. •

20. When an 800-kg compact car accelerates from rest to 27 m/s, it consumes 0.0606 L of gasoline, and 1.0 L of gasoline contains approximately 3.2×10^7 J of energy. What is the efficiency of the car (in other words, what percentage of the energy available from the fuel is delivered to the wheels)? ••

21. (*a*) Figure P7.21 shows initial and final energy bars for a closed system. Adjust the height of any two energy bars in the final version, on the right, so that the diagram does not violate what we know about energy. (There are numerous ways for you to do this.) (*b*) Describe an interaction that would generate an energy bar diagram that matches your version of Figure P7.21. ••

Figure P7.21

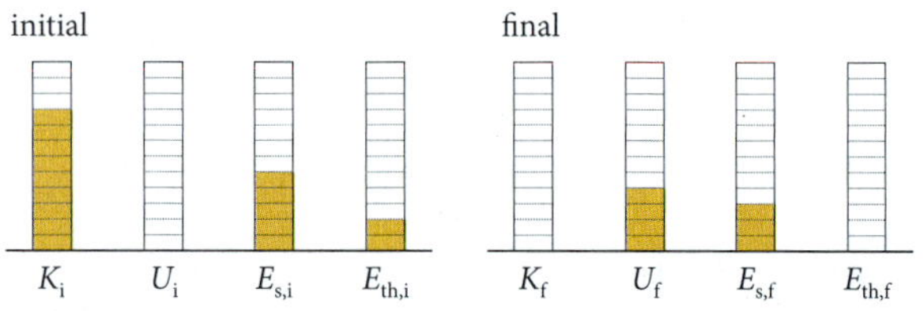

22. Two objects initially moving at velocities that have x components v_{1x} and v_{2x} collide totally inelastically. (*a*) Show that the ratio of the kinetic energy dissipated in the interaction is

$$\frac{\Delta K_1}{\Delta K_2} = -\frac{v_{\text{cm}\,x} + v_{1x,\text{i}}}{v_{\text{cm}\,x} + v_{2x,\text{i}}}.$$

(*b*) What does the minus sign in the expression in part *a* mean? ••

7.5 Interaction range

23. If, on the atomic scale, "contact" between two objects is in fact not *physical* contact, does that have implications for the contact between atoms in a piece of copper? •

24. Look again at *Principles* Checkpoint 7.10. Suppose you and a friend stand within an arm's length of each other and throw a ball back and forth. Describe a method to model an attractive interaction based on throwing the ball. ••

25. Look again at *Principles* Checkpoint 7.10. (*a*) When you throw a ball to a friend, at what instant does your momentum change: at the beginning, middle, or end of the ball's flight? (*b*) At which of these three instants does your friend's momentum change? ••

26. Consider the interactions involved when (*a*) you use a TV remote control to change the channel, and (*b*) you use your cell phone to text your friend. Classify each interaction as long range or short range. ••

7.6 Fundamental interactions

27. Suppose that, instead of two types of electrically charged particles in the universe, there was only one type. What would you expect to happen to the structure of the universe if the particles produced (*a*) an attractive interaction and (*b*) a repulsive interaction? •

28. Explain why friction is not considered a fundamental interaction. •

29. Suppose that the range of the strong interaction were suddenly increased by 20 orders of magnitude, with all other interactions unchanged. Describe the changes that might occur in the structure of our world. ••

30. Picture two objects, A and B, taking part in some interaction involving gauge particles. If object A radiates gauge particles uniformly in all directions, how does the strength of the interaction depend on the distance from A to B? Assume that the gauge particles do not interact with one another and that the strength of the interaction is proportional to the number of gauge particles encountered by B. •••

7.7 Interactions and accelerations

31. On a low-friction track, a 0.66-kg cart initially going at 1.85 m/s to the right collides with a cart of unknown inertia initially going at 2.17 m/s to the left. After the collision, the 0.66-kg cart is going at 1.32 m/s to the left, and the cart of unknown inertia is going at 3.22 m/s to the right. The collision takes 0.010 s. (*a*) What is the unknown inertia? (*b*) What is the average acceleration of each cart? (*c*) Use your answer to part *a* to check your answer to part *b*. •

32. Two children on ice skates pull toward each other on a rope held taut between them. The inertia of one child is 30 kg, and the inertia of the other is 25 kg. (*a*) If at one instant the 30-kg child is accelerating at 1.0 m/s^2 to the left, what is the acceleration of the 25-kg child at that instant? (*b*) What happens to each acceleration if the 25-kg child stops pulling and just hangs on? •

33. A 0.010-kg bullet is fired from a 5.0-kg gun with a muzzle velocity of 250 m/s. (*a*) While the bullet is traveling in the barrel, what is the ratio of the acceleration of the gun to the acceleration of the bullet as a function of time? (*b*) What is the speed of the bullet relative to the ground at the instant the bullet leaves the barrel? (*c*) What is the speed of the gun relative to the ground at that instant? ••

34. A 1500-kg car going at 6.32 m/s collides with a 3000-kg truck at rest. If the collision is totally inelastic and takes place over an interval of 0.203 s, what is the average acceleration of each vehicle? Are the ratio of accelerations and the ratio of inertias related the way you expect them to be? ••

35. A glob of putty thrown to the right bounces off a 0.500-kg cart initially at rest on a low-friction track. The collision takes 0.15 s, and the coefficient of restitution is 0.64. The cart has a final velocity of 1.0 m/s to the right, and the glob has a final velocity of 0.834 m/s to the left. (*a*) What is the inertia of the glob? (*b*) What is the average acceleration of each object during the collision? ••

36. An 8.20-kg object is sliding across the ice at 2.34 m/s. An internal explosion occurs, splitting the object into two equal chunks and adding 16 J of kinetic energy to the system. What is the average acceleration of the two chunks if the explosive separation takes place over a 0.16-s time interval? ••

37. A railroad car that has an inertia of 5.04×10^4 kg is moving to the right at 4.25 m/s when it collides and couples with three identical railroad cars that are already coupled together and moving in the same direction at 2.09 m/s. If the acceleration of the single car is 5.45 m/s^2 to the left while it is changing velocity, how long does the interaction take? ••

38. A 90-kg halfback on a football team runs head-on into a 120-kg opponent at an instant when neither has his feet on the ground. The halfback is initially going west at 10 m/s, and his opponent is initially going east at 4.37 m/s. The collision is totally inelastic. (*a*) If the collision takes 0.207 s, what is the acceleration of each player? (*b*) How much kinetic energy is converted to incoherent energy during the collision? ••

39. You are watching a hockey game on your digital video recorder. Your team's goalie is at rest when he catches a 0.16-kg puck moving straight toward him. The announcer says it was a 40-m/s slap shot, based on radar gun data. Normally the goalie would be braced, but in this case he is resting on parallel skate blades so that there is negligible friction to impede his subsequent motion. The collision is too fast to observe quantitatively, but by running the video in slow motion, you can tell that the goalie's glove is 150 mm from his body when the puck strikes and is right against his chest after the successful catch. It is also clear that the stunned goalie (holding the puck) drifts backward at 71 mm/s for a second or two after the collision is over. (*a*) Compute the average acceleration of the puck and of the goalie during the collision. (*b*) Determine the inertia of the goalie (including his equipment). (*c*) How much kinetic energy is converted to thermal energy in the glove? Check your answers by solving in two ways when possible. •••

40. Two objects, one red and one yellow, start from rest and interact with each other along an *x* axis. (*a*) If $m_{red} < m_{yellow}$, what are the ratios of their changes in momentum, velocity, and kinetic energy? (*b*) Compare these ratios with the ratio of their accelerations. (*c*) What does your answer to part *a* tell you about the relative changes of these quantities for a ball and Earth when you drop the ball? •••

7.8 Nondissipative interactions

41. Draw a bar diagram representing the various kinds of energy for the cart-spring system in *Principles* Figure 7.26*b* when the end of the cart attached to the spring is at locations x_1, x_2, and x_3. •

42. The potential energy of an interaction is given by $U(x) = ax^2$, where $a = +6.4\ J/m^2$. (*a*) If the initial speed of a 0.82-kg object in this system is 2.23 m/s at $x = 0$, how far does the object travel before it reaches a speed of $v = 0$? (*b*) Does your answer in part *a* depend on whether the object is traveling in the positive or negative *x* direction? •

43. Suppose we have a block mounted on a spring and define the zero point for the elastic potential energy of the system to be the relaxed position (meaning the block is positioned such that the spring is neither compressed nor stretched). What is the appropriate sign of the elastic potential energy when the block is repositioned so that the spring is (*a*) stretched and (*b*) compressed? (Hint: Think about what happens to the elastic potential energy when the stretched or compressed spring is released.) ••

44. A 0.36-kg cart and a 0.12-kg cart are held together with a compressed spring between them. When they are released, the 0.36-kg cart moves at 1.1 m/s to the right. How much elastic potential energy was stored in the spring before the release? ••

45. A 0.530-kg cart moving at 0.922 m/s to the right collides elastically with a 0.25-kg cart initially at rest. The 0.25-kg cart then moves off rapidly and compresses a spring before the 0.530-kg cart can catch it again. At the instant the 0.25-kg cart comes to rest, what is the energy stored in the spring? ••

46. A low-friction track is set up with a spring on the right end. In the middle of the track, a 2.0-kg cart moving to the right at 5.0 m/s overtakes a 3.0-kg cart moving to the right at 2.0 m/s. After the collision, the 2.0-kg cart is moving at 1.7 m/s. (*a*) What is the coefficient of restitution of the collision? (*b*) How much energy is stored in the spring when it is at its maximum compression after the collision? ••

47. For a certain interaction, the potential energy in joules is given by $U(x) = ax + bx^2$, where $a = +4.0\ J/m$ and $b = -2.0\ J/m^2$. If, at some instant, a 10-kg object taking part in this interaction has an *x* component of velocity of -3.0 m/s and a position $x = +2.0$ m, what is its speed (*a*) at $x = +1.0$ m and (*b*) at $x = -1.0$ m? ••

48. You release a block from the top of a long, slippery inclined plane of length ℓ that makes an angle θ with the horizontal. The magnitude of the block's acceleration is $g \sin \theta$ (see Section 3.7). (*a*) For an x axis pointing down the incline and having its origin at the release position, derive an expression for the potential energy of the block-Earth system as a function of x. (*b*) How would your expression change if you put the origin of the x axis at the bottom of the incline? (*c*) Does the location of the origin make any difference in the dynamics of the situation? (*d*) Use the expression you derived in part *a* to determine the speed of the block at the bottom of the incline. Does your speed value agree with the result obtained by a kinematic calculation? ●●●

49. On a low-friction track, a 0.36-kg cart initially moving to the right at 2.05 m/s collides elastically with a 0.12-kg cart initially moving to the left at 0.13 m/s. The 0.12-kg cart bounces off the 0.36-kg cart and then compresses a spring attached to the right end of the track. (*a*) At the instant of maximum compression of the spring, how much elastic potential energy is stored in the spring? (*b*) If the spring then returns all of this energy to the cart, and the two carts again collide, what is the final velocity of each cart? ●●●

7.9 Potential energy near Earth's surface

50. A 70-kg woman walks to the top of the Empire State Building, 380 m above street level. What is the change in the gravitational potential energy of the system comprising the woman and Earth? ●

51. At graduation, you toss your mortarboard cap straight up at some initial speed v. How fast is it moving when it comes back down to your hands? How do you know? ●

52. An office worker has his lunch on the 53rd floor of an office building. In which case is the gravitational potential energy of the lunch-Earth system greatest: (*a*) the worker carried the lunch up to the 53rd floor in the elevator, (*b*) he carried it up the stairs to the 53rd floor, or (*c*) he got a ride in a helicopter to the top of the 68-floor building and then carried the lunch down in the elevator to the 53rd floor? ●

53. A 0.0135-kg bullet is fired from ground level directly upward. If its initial speed is 300 m/s, how high does it go? (Neglect air resistance.) ●

54. A typical loaded commercial jet airplane has an inertia of 2.1×10^5 kg. (*a*) Based on the time intervals involved, which do you expect to require more energy: getting the plane up to cruising speed or getting it up to cruising altitude? (*b*) How much energy does it take to get the plane to a cruising speed of 270 m/s? (Ignore wind drag.) (*c*) How much energy does it take to get the plane to a cruising altitude of 10,400 m if it travels to that altitude at its (constant) cruising speed? ●●

55. Two 2.4-kg blocks are connected by a string draped over the edge of a slippery table, so that one block is on the table and the other is just hanging off the edge. A restraint holds the block on the table in place, and the string is 0.50 m long. After the restraint is removed, what speed does the pair of blocks have at the instant the upper one is pulled off the table? ●●

56. A 30-kg child jumps to the ground from the top of a fence that is 2.0 m high. You analyze the problem using upward as the positive x direction. (*a*) Taking $x = 0$ to be at the bottom of the fence, what are the initial potential energy of the child-Earth system and the change in the system kinetic energy during the jump? (*b*) Repeat part *a* for $x = 0$ at the top of the fence. ●●

57. You lean out of your dorm window, which is 12 m above the ground, and toss a 0.12-kg ball up to a friend at a window 11 m above you. (*a*) What is the slowest initial speed at which you can throw the ball so that he just catches it? (*b*) If you throw the ball at this speed and your friend misses it, what is its kinetic energy the instant before it hits the ground? (*c*) Suppose you throw the ball directly downward at the speed calculated in part *a*. What is its kinetic energy just before it hits the ground? ●●

58. Two blocks are hung by a string draped over a pulley, a 1.0-kg block on the left and a 3.0-kg block on the right. The two blocks start out at rest and at the same height. (*a*) What is the change in the gravitational potential energy of the system of blocks and Earth when the 3.0-kg block has dropped 0.53 m? (*b*) What is the change in the kinetic energy of the system between release and this instant? (*c*) What is the velocity of the 1.0-kg block at this instant? ●●

59. You drop a rubber ball from a height of 3.0 m. It bounces off a concrete surface to a height of 2.7 m. (*a*) What is the coefficient of restitution for this collision? (*b*) You want to get the ball to bounce upward to a height of 7.3 m. From the same starting point, how fast must you throw the ball, and in which direction? ●●

60. You throw a 0.52-kg target upward at 15 m/s. When it is at a height of 10 m above the launch position and moving downward, it is struck by a 0.323-kg arrow going 25 m/s upward. Assume the interaction is instantaneous. (*a*) What is the velocity of the target and arrow immediately after the collision? (*b*) What is the speed of the combination right before it strikes the ground? ●●

61. A uniform chain of inertia m and length ℓ is lying on a slippery table. When one quarter of its length hangs over the edge, the chain begins to slip off. How fast is it moving when the last bit of it slips off the table? (Ignore friction.) ●●●

62. A uniform chain of inertia m and length ℓ is lying on a slippery table. When just the tip hangs over the edge, the chain begins to slip off. (Ignore friction.) Calculate the speed of the chain as a function of time. (Hint: $\int \frac{dx}{v} = \int dt$. What's the connection between x and v?) ●●●

63. Two blocks are connected by a string draped over a small pulley. The smaller block has half the inertia of the larger block. For which configuration, (*a*) or (*b*), in Figure P7.63 are the speeds of the blocks greatest after the larger block has descended a distance d? Ignore friction between the table and the sliding block, and check your answer with a computation. ●●●

Figure P7.63

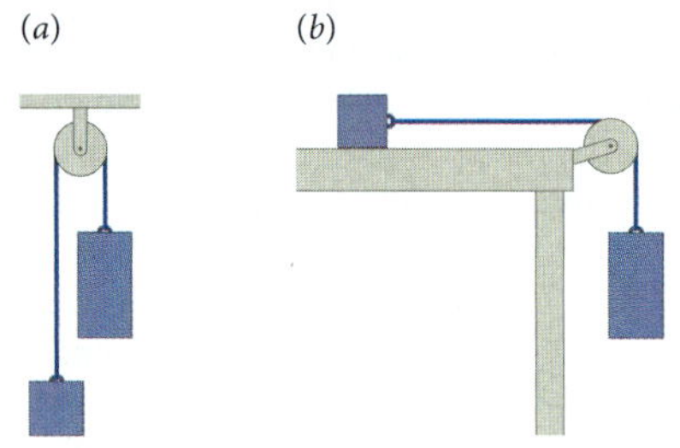

7.10 Dissipative interactions

64. Gravity-powered roller coasters have a motorized chain assembly that hauls the cars up to the top of the first hill. No additional source energy is supplied for the rest of the trip. What is the maximum possible height for all subsequent hills? •

65. You drop a ball from rest from a window 12 m above the ground, and just before it hits the ground its speed is recorded to be 14.6 m/s. What percentage of the ball's kinetic energy is dissipated due to air resistance? •

66. A 5.3-kg steel ball is dropped from a height of 20 m into a box of sand and sinks 0.20 m into the sand before stopping. How much energy is dissipated through the interaction with the sand? ••

67. Two cars collide inelastically on a city street. For the two-car system, which of the following are the same in any inertial reference frame: (*a*) the kinetic energy, (*b*) the momentum, (*c*) the amount of energy dissipated, (*d*) the momentum exchanged? ••

68. A 0.70-kg basketball dropped on a hardwood floor rises back up to 65% of its original height. (*a*) If the basketball is dropped from a height of 1.5 m, how much energy is dissipated in the first bounce? (*b*) How much energy is dissipated in the fourth bounce? (*c*) To which type of incoherent energy is the dissipated energy converted? ••

69. An 80-kg man standing on a frozen lake tosses a 0.500-kg football to his dog. (*a*) If the ball leaves his hands at 15 m/s relative to Earth, what minimum source energy did the man supply? (*b*) His 20-kg dog, standing still, catches the ball and slides with it. How much energy is dissipated in the catch? ••

70. A 2.2-kg measuring instrument is mounted on a balloon by your scientific team for atmospheric studies. At the top of its flight, the instrument is released from the balloon and falls most of the way back to Earth before a parachute opens. You are told that the magnitude of the acceleration at any instant t before the parachute opens is given by $|a| = ge^{-t/\tau}$, where g is the acceleration due to gravity, e is the base of natural logarithms, and τ is a time constant that depends on the shape of the instrument and in this case is 5.68 s. Your primary concern is how much the instrument heats up as it falls, due to air resistance. At what rate, in joules per second, is energy dissipated before the parachute opens? Express your answer as a function of t, where $t = 0$ at release. (Hint: Integrate the acceleration to calculate speed and displacement.) •••

71. A nursery rhyme goes "Humpty Dumpty sat on a wall, Humpty Dumpty had a great fall. All the king's horses and all the king's men couldn't put Humpty Dumpty together again." (*a*) Describe the energy of the Earth-HD system before, during (including the instant just before impact), and after the fall. Use bar diagrams showing K, U, E_s, and E_{th} to illustrate your description. (*b*) In terms of the energy of the Earth-HD system, explain why all the king's horses and all the king's men could not put HD together again. (*c*) Now assume that things had turned out differently for HD. The king's men were able to set up a net so that he fell into the net and bounced back up and once again sat on the wall. Draw energy bar diagrams for this situation, showing the distribution of energy during the fall, at the instant HD arrives at the net (choose the instant at which the net with HD in it is stretched to the lowest position), during the ascent, and when he is back sitting on the wall. •••

72. A small block of wood of inertia m_{block} is released from rest a distance h above the ground, directly above your head. You decide to shoot it with your pellet gun, which fires a pellet of inertia m_{pellet}. After the block has fallen a distance d, the pellet hits it and becomes embedded in it, kicking it upward. At the instant of impact, the pellet is moving at speed v_{pellet}. (*a*) To what maximum height h_{max} does the pellet-block system rise above the ground? Express your answer in terms of the given variables and known values, such as g. (*b*) How much energy is dissipated in the collision? •••

Additional Problems

73. Is the collision between two billiard balls a nondissipative interaction? (Hint: What does the fact that you can hear the collision tell you?) •

74. Draw before and after energy bars for the collision shown in *Principles* Figure 6.8*a* and 6.8*b*. •

75. The observation deck of the Washington Monument is 152 m above the ground. How many king-sized candy bars, each supplying 1.3 MJ of source energy, must an 80-kg man consume to replenish the energy he expends in climbing the 825 stairs up to the observation deck? •

76. You drop a ball from some height. At which position do you expect its speed to be one-half the speed at which it eventually hits the ground: higher than the midpoint of the path, at the midpoint, or lower than the midpoint? Does air resistance change your answer? ••

77. Is it impossible to convert incoherent energy to coherent energy? Can you think of an example where thermal energy can (at least partially) be converted to coherent energy? ••

78. People unenlightened about physics sometimes fire a gun straight up into the air to celebrate big events. By discussing the forms of energy at each stage of the process, explain why this is a bad idea. ••

79. Two 1.20-kg carts on a low-friction track are rigged with magnets so that the carts repel each other when they approach each other. One cart has an initial velocity of $+0.323$ m/s, and the other has an initial velocity of -0.147 m/s. What is the maximum energy stored in the magnetic field during the collision, assuming that the carts never touch each other? ••

80. Wind turns a windmill that stores energy in a battery. Assume that the windmill turns at a constant rate while the battery is charging. The battery is then used to run a toy car that moves at a constant speed until the battery goes dead. Draw bar diagrams representing a sequence of instants that depict the various conversions of energy from one form to another in this situation. For each conversion, name the system you are describing. ••

81. Not looking where you are going, you and your bike collide at 12 m/s into the back of a car stopped at a red light. The car does not have its brakes applied and so is jolted forward. The driver immediately leaps out crying, "Whiplash!" Facing a day in court, you have to determine the acceleration of the car as a result of the collision. You note that you and your bike (combined inertia 80 kg) came to a complete halt in the collision and that the rim of your front wheel was pushed all the way to the center hub. The diameter of the bike wheel before the crash was 0.75 m, and a reference book tells you that the inertia of the car is 1800 kg. ••• CR

82. An amusement park commissions your company to design a roller coaster. Your company specializes in an approach in which the cars are accelerated on a horizontal section of track by magnetic motors rather than being hauled up to the top of a hill and released. The park officials would like the riders to be accelerated via your horizontal design and then sent straight up a vertical length of track 66.4 m tall. (After the cars pass this high point, the ride is the regular ups and downs of a conventional roller coaster.) Your calculations tell you that 212 motors will get the loaded cars up to the necessary speed at an acceleration of $0.85g$, but you wonder whether or not the park has enough horizontal distance available for the acceleration device. ••• CR

83. A 1.00-kg cart has attached to its front end a device that explodes when it hits anything, releasing a quantity of energy E. This cart is moving to the right with speed v when it collides head-on with a 2.00-kg cart traveling to the left at the same speed v. The explosive goes off when the carts hit, causing them to rebound from each other. If one-quarter of the explosive energy is dissipated into the incoherent energy of noise and deformation of the carts, what is the final velocity of each cart? Solve in the zero-momentum reference frame and then check your result by solving in the Earth reference frame. •••

Answers to Review Questions

1. (*a*) The momentum remains constant. (*b*) The kinetic energy dips briefly as some or all of it is converted to internal energy during the collision. (*c*) The sum of all forms of energy in the system remains constant.
2. No. The relative speed must be nonzero before the collision, but it changes to zero at some instant during the interaction.
3. In all cases a portion of the kinetic energy of the system is converted to internal energy. In part *a*, none of this converted energy reappears as kinetic energy after the collision. In part *b*, some of this energy reappears as kinetic. In part *c*, all of it reappears as kinetic energy after the collision.
4. An interaction involves two objects and results in a change of motion, a change of physical state, or both. If a change of motion is involved, the ratio of the x components of the accelerations of the objects is equal to the negative of the inverse ratio of their inertias. Both the momentum and kinetic energy of each object generally change as a result of the interaction, but if the system is isolated, its momentum does not change. If the system is closed, its energy does not change but its kinetic energy changes during the interaction as some portion is converted to internal energy. When the interaction is an elastic collision, all of the converted kinetic energy ultimately reappears as kinetic energy after the interaction.
5. Kinetic energy is the energy any moving object has because of its motion. Potential energy is energy stored in a system due to reversible changes in the configuration state of the system.
6. Many answers are possible. Two possibilities are bending (coherent kinetic energy) a paper clip back and forth, which heats it up (incoherent thermal energy), and rubbing your hands together to warm them.
7. Energy of motion is energy due to the motion of objects or molecules in a system. Energy of configuration is energy associated with the locations of objects or molecules in a system. Coherent energy is associated with either motions or configurations that are organized, so that individual objects or molecules in the system either all move with a common velocity or are all displaced by a small amount along a common direction. Incoherent energy is associated with either motions or configurations that are disorganized, so that objects or molecules in the system move randomly or are displaced randomly.
8. Solar radiation generated by nuclear reactions in the Sun is the ultimate source.
9. Nondissipative interactions cause reversible changes; dissipative interactions cause irreversible changes.
10. Many answers are possible. In the interaction between a car and the gasoline in its fuel tank, source energy (chemical energy of the gasoline) is converted to thermal energy, to the car's kinetic energy, and, if the car is climbing a hill, to gravitational potential energy. When you rub your hands together to warm them, chemical energy in the molecules that make up the muscles you use to move your hands is converted to kinetic energy, which in turn is converted to thermal energy by friction.
11. In the field model, every object is surrounded by a field, and it is with this field that other objects interact. In the gauge-particle model, two objects interact by exchanging fundamental particles called gauge particles.
12. Only the gravitational and electromagnetic interactions have a long enough range to be noticed on the macroscopic scale. The range of the strong and weak interactions is too short to cause changes that we can observe on the macroscopic scale.
13. (*a*) The electromagnetic interaction is most important. (*b*) Again, the electromagnetic interaction is most important.
14. Although the electromagnetic interaction is much stronger, it can be either attractive or repulsive depending on the signs of the electrically charged particles involved in the interaction. Because there are equal numbers of the two types of particles in any macroscopic object, the particles tend to arrange themselves to produce electrical neutrality and to minimize the effect of the interaction. In contrast, the gravitational interaction is always attractive, and no cancellation diminishes its cumulative effect. Because we live on the surface of Earth, the very large effect of the gravitational interaction between macroscopic objects and Earth is generally not negligible.
15. (*a*) $a_{1x}/a_{2x} = -m_2/m_1$. (*b*) Again $a_{1x}/a_{2x} = -m_2/m_1$ because *Principles* Eq. 7.6 holds for all interactions.
16. Two assumptions were made—that the system of interacting objects is isolated, and the inertias of the objects are not changed by the interaction.
17. For a closed system, energy must not change, so the changes in the four categories of energy—kinetic, potential, source, and thermal—must cancel. Both source energy and thermal energy always involve dissipation, so if all interactions are nondissipative, only kinetic and potential energy changes are possible, and they must add to zero. Mechanical energy is the sum of kinetic and potential energies and hence remains constant in such situations.
18. Nondissipative interactions cause only reversible changes. A movie recording the object(s) in such a system must appear the same when run either forward or backward. That means the kinetic energy of each object must have the same value at a given position regardless of whether the object is moving forward or backward at that position (or not moving at all). But mechanical energy remains constant in such systems and is equal to the sum of kinetic and potential energies. If the kinetic energy must be expressible as a function of position, then so must the potential energy.
19. Because of the reversibility of changes due to nondissipative interactions, the initial and final kinetic energies must be equal at the common position (point A).

20. Vertical. Yes, it does matter because changes in gravitational potential energy are zero for horizontal displacements.

21. No, the gravitational potential energy can be either positive or negative, depending on which position you choose for your $U^G = 0$ position.

22. No, only the convertible part of the system's energy is converted. The inconvertible part remains as system kinetic energy. Some final nonzero velocity (and hence final nonzero kinetic energy) is needed to keep the system's momentum constant.

23. (*a*) Equation 7.26, $\Delta E_{th} = -\Delta K = \frac{1}{2}\mu v_{12i}^2(1 - e^2)$, tells us that none of the convertible energy is converted to thermal energy (which means the collision is elastic). All of it is temporarily stored as potential energy. (*b*) Equation 7.26 tells us that all of the convertible kinetic energy is ultimately converted to thermal energy, but all or part of it may still be temporarily stored as potential energy.

Answers to Guided Problems

Guided Problem 7.2 $h/16$

Guided Problem 7.4 (*a*) rear $= -0.12$ m/s, lead $= +8.4$ m/s;

(*b*)

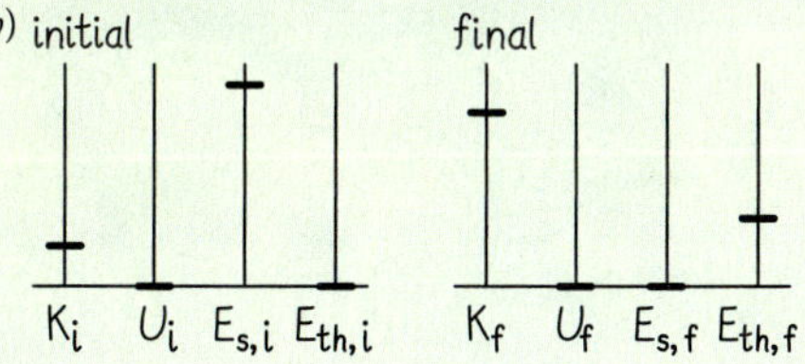

Guided Problem 7.6 $v_f = 78$ m/s

Guided Problem 7.8

(*a*)

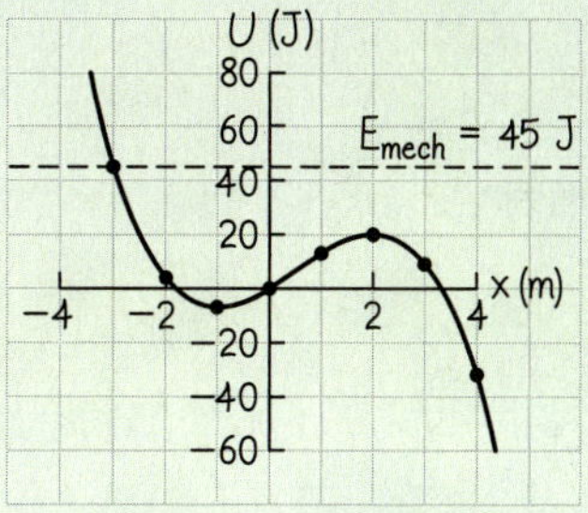

x	U(x)
−3	45
−2	4
−1	−7
0	0
1	13
2	20
3	9
4	−32

(*b*) toward positive *x*; (*c*) accelerates toward positive *x*, then accelerates toward negative *x* between $x = -1.0$ m and $x = +2.0$ m, then accelerates toward positive *x* again; (*d*) speeding up from $x = -3.0$ m to $x = -1.0$ m and from $x = +2.0$ m to large *x* values, slowing down between $x = -1.0$ m and $x = +2.0$ m; (*e*) $K(x = -1.0\text{ m}) = +52$ J, $K(x = +1.0\text{ m}) = +32$ J, $K(x = +3.0\text{ m}) = +36$ J

8

PRACTICE
Force

Chapter Summary

Characteristics of forces (Sections 8.1, 8.2, 8.3, 8.7)

Concepts When an object participates in one interaction only, the **force** exerted on the object is given by the time rate of change in the object's momentum.

A **contact force** is a force that one object exerts on another object only when the two objects are in physical contact.

A **field force** is a force (such as gravity) that one object exerts on another object without the requirement that the two objects be in physical contact.

When two objects interact, the forces they exert on each other form an **interaction pair,** and these forces have equal magnitudes but opposite directions.

Quantitative Tools The SI unit of force is the **newton** (N):

$$1\ \text{N} = 1\ \text{kg}\cdot\text{m/s}^2. \tag{8.9}$$

For an interaction pair of forces,

$$\vec{F}_{12} = -\vec{F}_{21}. \tag{8.15}$$

Some important forces (Sections 8.6, 8.8, 8.9)

Concepts A taut, flexible object (such as a spring, rope, or thread), when subjected to equal and opposite *tensile forces* applied at either end, experiences along its length a *stress* called **tension.** If the object is very light, the tension is the same everywhere in it.

Hooke's law relates the force that a spring exerts on a load to the distance the spring is stretched (or compressed) from its relaxed position.

Quantitative Tools The x component of the force of gravity exerted on an object of inertia m near Earth's surface is

$$F^G_{\text{E}ox} = -mg, \tag{8.17}$$

where the minus sign indicates that the force is directed downward.

Hooke's law: If a spring is stretched (or compressed) by a *small* distance $x - x_0$ from its unstretched length x_0, the x component of the force it exerts on the load is

$$(F_{\text{by spring on load}})_x = -k(x - x_0), \tag{8.20}$$

where k is called the **spring constant** of the spring.

Effects of force (Sections 8.1, 8.4, 8.5, 8.7)

Concepts The vector sum of the forces exerted on an object is equal to the time rate of change of the momentum of the object.

The **equation of motion** for an object relates the object's acceleration to the vector sum of the forces exerted on it.

Newton's laws of motion describe the effects forces have on the motion of objects.

If an object is at rest or moving with constant velocity, it is in **translational equilibrium**. In this case, the vector sum of the forces exerted on it is equal to zero.

A **free-body diagram** for an object is a sketch representing the object by a dot and showing all the forces exerted *on* it.

Quantitative Tools Vector sum of forces exerted on an object:

$$\sum\vec{F} \equiv \frac{d\vec{p}}{dt}. \tag{8.4}$$

Equation of motion:

$$\vec{a} = \frac{\sum\vec{F}}{m}. \tag{8.7}$$

If the inertia m of an object is constant, Newton's second law is usually written as

$$\sum\vec{F} = m\vec{a}. \tag{8.6}$$

For two interacting objects, 1 and 2, Newton's third law of motion states that

$$\vec{F}_{12} = -\vec{F}_{21}. \tag{8.15}$$

Impulse (Section 8.10)

Concepts The **impulse** $\vec{J}$ produced by forces exerted on an object is the product of the vector sum of the forces and the time interval over which the forces are exerted. The impulse delivered to the object is also equal to the change in its momentum.

Quantitative Tools For a constant force,

$$\Delta\vec{p} = \vec{J} = \left(\Sigma\vec{F}\right)\Delta t. \quad (8.24, 8.25)$$

For a time-varying force,

$$\Delta\vec{p} = \vec{J} = \int_{t_i}^{t_f} \Sigma\vec{F}(t)\,dt. \quad (8.26)$$

System of interacting objects (Sections 8.11, 8.12)

Concepts The center of mass of a system of objects accelerates as though all the objects were located at the center of mass and the external force were applied at that location.

Quantitative Tools Acceleration of a system of objects:

$$\vec{a}_{cm} = \frac{\Sigma\vec{F}_{ext}}{m}. \quad (8.45)$$

Review Questions

Answers to these questions can be found at the end of this chapter.

8.1 Momentum and force

1. Does a force exerted on an object always increase the object's speed? If yes, explain why. If no, provide an example in which an exerted force does not increase the object's speed.
2. What are the magnitude and direction of the vector sum of the forces exerted on a car traveling on a straight downward slope of a highway at a constant 100 km/h?
3. What is the relationship between momentum and force?

8.2 The reciprocity of forces

4. Is there any circumstance in which an object 1 may exert a force on an object 2 without an equal, reciprocal force being exerted by object 2 on object 1?
5. A cup filled with coffee sits on a table. Do the downward force the cup exerts on the table and the downward force the coffee exerts on the bottom of the cup form an interaction pair?

8.3 Identifying forces

6. What is the principal difference between a contact force and a field force?
7. Characterize each of the following as a contact force or a field force: (*a*) the force that causes a book sliding across a polished floor to eventually slow down; (*b*) the force that causes a wine glass to fall downward after it has been knocked off a table; (*c*) the force that causes one magnet to repel another; (*d*) the force exerted by the wind on a sailboat; (*e*) the force that causes an object attached to one end of a stretched rubber band to move toward the object attached to the other end.

8.4 Translational equilibrium

8. Can an object that is in translational equilibrium have any forces exerted on it?
9. How can you determine, by observing an object, whether or not it is in translational equilibrium?

8.5 Free-body diagrams

10. Describe the three main elements in a free-body diagram.
11. Give at least two reasons it is important to draw a free-body diagram to analyze physical situations.
12. Why should an arrow representing the vector sum of the forces exerted on an object *not* appear in the free-body diagram for the object?

8.6 Springs and tension

13. How is the change in the length of a spring related (*a*) to the magnitude F_{os} of the force exerted by an object on the spring and (*b*) to the magnitude F_{so} of the force exerted by the spring on the object?
14. What is an elastic force?
15. Under what condition(s) is a pulling force exerted by a hand on one end of a rope, spring, or thread transmitted undiminished to a block attached to the other end?

8.7 Equation of motion

16. Knowing all the forces exerted on an object gives you direct information about which aspect of the object's motion?
17. What condition allows you to convert the relationship $\sum\vec{F} = d\vec{p}/dt$ to the relationship $\sum\vec{F} = m\vec{a}$?
18. State Newton's three laws of motion in your own words.

8.8 Force of gravity

19. (*a*) Which gravitational force exerted by Earth has the larger magnitude: that exerted on an apple or that exerted on a sack of apples? (*b*) How do you reconcile your answer to part *a* with the observation that, when they are in free fall, the apple and the sack of apples accelerate at the same rate?
20. An object at rest has zero acceleration. Does this mean that Eq. 8.17 ($F^G_{\text{Eo}x} = -mg$) does not accurately represent the force of gravity exerted on the object?

8.9 Hooke's law

21. How does the numerical value of the spring constant k for a spring under compression compare with the value of k for the same spring when it is stretched?
22. Equation 8.20 relates the force exerted by a spring to the displacement of the spring's free end: $(F_{\text{by spring on load}\,x}) = -k(x - x_0)$. What is the meaning of the symbol x_0?
23. What is the physical significance of the slope of the curve in *Principles* Figure 8.18, a graph that plots the displacement of the free end of a spring as a function of the x component of the force exerted on the spring?

8.10 Impulse

24. State the impulse equation in words.
25. Suppose that one or more of the forces exerted on an object is not constant, but that you do have information about how each force exerted on the object varies as a function of time during the time interval of interest. How can this information be used to compute the impulse?

8.11 Systems of two interacting objects

26. What distinguishes an internal force from an external force?
27. Explain what is special about the motion of the center of mass of a system made up of two interacting objects when some external force is exerted on the system.

8.12 Systems of many interacting objects

28. What is the numerical value of the vector sum of all internal forces exerted in a system composed of many objects?
29. Explain why the motion of rigid objects is usually easier to analyze than the motion of deformable objects.

Developing a Feel

Make an order-of-magnitude estimate of each of the following quantities. Letters in parentheses refer to hints below. Use them as needed to guide your thinking.

1. The magnitude of the vector sum of forces needed to give a bus the acceleration seen in a sports car that can go from 0 to 60 mi/h in 5 s (K, O)
2. The magnitude of the average force exerted by a bat on a baseball hit straight toward the pitcher (E, W, J, U)
3. The magnitude of the vector sum of forces exerted on an airliner accelerating for takeoff (P, I, G)
4. The magnitude of the gravitational force exerted by Earth on an elephant (S)
5. The magnitude of the upward force exerted by the air on an airliner flying horizontally at constant velocity (A, P, V)
6. Over and above the force required to stand on the floor, the magnitude of the extra force exerted by a professional basketball player on the floor in order to leap for a slam dunk (H, C, X, R, L)
7. The spring constant of the spring in a ballpoint pen (F, T)
8. The spring constant of an automobile spring (D, Z)
9. The magnitude of the impulse required to get a minivan up to freeway speed (N, Y)
10. The magnitude of the impulse required to stop a speeding train in 60 s (B, M, Q)

Hints

A. Is the airliner in translational equilibrium?
B. What is the speed of a speeding train?
C. What has happened to the basketball player's kinetic energy when he is at the top of the jump?
D. By what distance does a car fender drop when an adult of average inertia sits on the car?
E. What is the baseball's incoming velocity?
F. Through what distance is the spring compressed when you click the pen?
G. What is the speed just as the airliner's wheels lift off the ground?
H. How does Newton's third law of motion apply to this situation?
I. How far along the runway does the airliner move before the wheels lift off the ground?
J. What is the baseball's outgoing velocity?
K. What is the magnitude of the acceleration of a sports car?
L. Over what time interval is the force exerted?
M. What is the inertia of a train?
N. What is freeway speed?
O. How does the inertia of a bus compare with the inertia of a sports car?
P. What is the inertia of an airliner?
Q. What portion of the momentum must change in the time interval?
R. What is the inertia of a professional basketball player?
S. What is the inertia of an elephant?
T. What is the magnitude of the force you must exert to click the pen?
U. For what time interval is the ball in contact with the bat?
V. What other force is exerted vertically on the airliner?
W. What is the inertia of a baseball?
X. What is the height of the basketball player's jump?
Y. What is the inertia of a minivan?
Z. What is the inertia of an average adult?

Key (all values approximate)

A. yes; **B.** 3×10^1 m/s; **C.** it has all been converted to gravitational potential energy; **D.** 4×10^1mm; **E.** 4×10^1 m/s toward batter; **F.** 5 mm; **G.** 9×10^1 m/s; **H.** it tells us that $F_{\text{by player on floor}} = F_{\text{by floor on player}}$; **I.** 1 km; **J.** a bit faster than the incoming velocity—say, 5×10^1 m/s away from batter; **K.** 5 m/s^2; **L.** 0.4 s; **M.** 5×10^6 kg; **N.** 3×10^1 m/s; **O.** $m_{\text{bus}} \approx 10m_{\text{car}}$; **P.** 1×10^5 kg; **Q.** the entire momentum, 2×10^8 kg · m/s, must go to zero; **R.** 9×10^1 kg; **S.** 6×10^3 kg; **T.** 3 N; **U.** 2×10^{-2} s; **V.** the gravitational force; **W.** 0.2 kg; **X.** each part of the body rises 0.7 m; **Y.** 2×10^3 kg; **Z.** 8×10^1 kg

PRACTICE

Worked and Guided Problems

Procedure: Drawing free-body diagrams

1. Draw a center-of-mass symbol (a circle with a cross) to indicate the object you wish to consider*—this object is your system. Pretend the object is by itself in empty space (hence the name *free body*). If you need to consider more than one object in order to solve a problem, draw a separate free-body diagram for each.
2. List all the items in the object's environment that are in contact with the object. These are the items that exert *contact forces* on the object. *Do not add these items to your drawing!* If you do, you run the risk of confusing the forces exerted *on* the object with those exerted *by* the object.
3. Identify all the forces exerted *on* the object by objects in its environment. (For now, omit from consideration any force not exerted along the object's line of motion.) In general, you should consider (*a*) the *gravitational field force* exerted by Earth on the object and (*b*) the *contact force* exerted by each item listed in step 2.
4. Draw an arrow to represent each force identified in step 3. Point the arrow in the direction in which the force is exerted and place the tail at the center of mass. If possible, draw the lengths of the arrows so that they reflect the relative magnitudes of the forces. Finally, label each arrow in the form

$$\vec{F}^{\text{type}}_{\text{by on}},$$

where "type" is a single letter identifying the origin of the force (c for contact force, G for gravitational force), "by" is a single letter identifying the object exerting the force, and "on" is a single letter identifying the object subjected to that force (this object is the one represented by the center of mass you drew in step 1).
5. Verify that all forces you have drawn are exerted **on** and not **by** the object under consideration. Because the first letter of the subscript on $\vec{F}$ represents the object exerting the force and the second letter represents the object on which the force is exerted, every force label in your free-body diagram should have the same second letter in its subscript.
6. Draw a vector representing the object's acceleration *next to* the center of mass that represents the object. Check that the vector sum of your force vectors points in the direction of the acceleration. If you cannot make your forces add up to give you an acceleration in the correct direction, verify that you drew the correct forces in step 4. If the object is not accelerating (that is, if it is in translational equilibrium), write $\vec{a} = \vec{0}$ and make sure your force arrows add up to zero. If you do not know the direction of acceleration, choose a tentative direction for the acceleration.
7. Draw a reference axis. If the object is accelerating, it is often convenient to point the positive x axis in the direction of the object's acceleration.

When your diagram is complete it should contain only the center-of-mass symbol, the forces exerted *on* the object (with their tails at the center of mass), an axis, and an indication of the acceleration of the object. Do not add anything else to your diagram.

* Representing, say, a car by a single point might seem like an oversimplification, but because we are interested only in the motion of the car as a whole, any details (like its shape or orientation) do not matter. Any unnecessary details you add to your drawing only distract from the issue at hand.

These examples involve material from this chapter but are not associated with any particular section. Some examples are worked out in detail; others you should work out by following the guidelines provided.

Worked Problem 8.1 Moving a block

A forklift is attempting to pull a 1400-kg block of granite across a warehouse floor with a rope, aided by a push from a worker (Figure WG8.1). The tension in the rope is 2500 N, and the worker exerts a horizontal push of 200 N. The block slides across the floor at a constant speed of 1.5 m/s. What is the magnitude of the frictional force exerted on the block?

Figure WG8.1

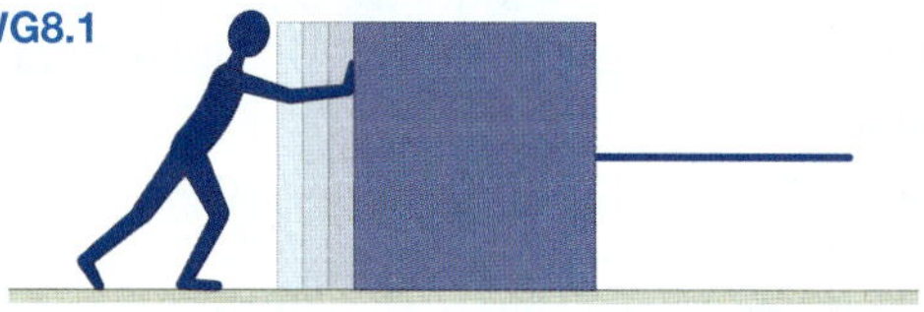

❶ **GETTING STARTED** We are asked to calculate the magnitude of a frictional force. We note that, in addition to the frictional force, there are two other horizontal contact forces exerted on the block: the pulling force exerted by the rope and the pushing force exerted by the worker. A relationship that involves force and motion is needed, so we will likely need *Principles* Eq. 8.6, $\sum \vec{F} = m\vec{a}$, Newton's second law when inertia is constant. A free-body diagram (Figure WG8.2) helps us organize the information. The directions of the pulling and pushing forces must be the same, so we arbitrarily draw those to the right in the figure. The frictional force opposes slipping between the block and the floor surface. If we were to stop pushing and pulling, friction should cause the block to slow and stop, so friction should be directed to the left, opposite the velocity of the block. We note that this velocity is constant, which means the acceleration is zero.

Figure WG8.2

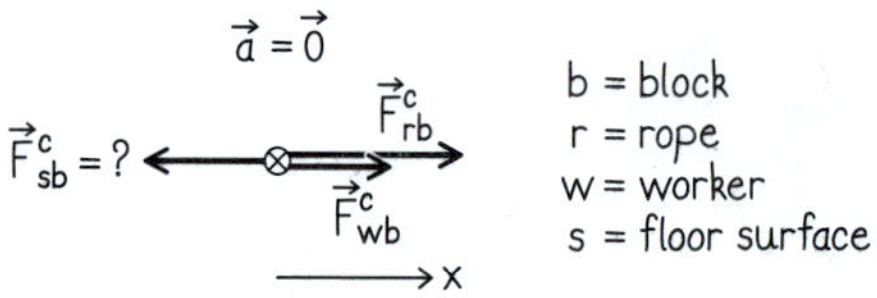

❷ **DEVISE PLAN** We know the tension in the rope and the magnitude of the worker's pushing force. We know that the acceleration is zero, and we know the direction of the frictional force. We arbitrarily choose the positive x direction to be the direction of motion (to the right in Figure WG8.2). The three forces are horizontal, so we need only their x components to relate their values:

$$\sum F_x = 0. \tag{1}$$

One equation is sufficient to solve for the one unknown frictional force.

❸ **EXECUTE PLAN** Using Figure WG8.2 as a guide, we express the left side of Newton's second law as the sum of the x components of the individual forces. By comparing the directions of the forces with the positive x direction, we see that the x components of the pushing and pulling forces are positive and that of the frictional force is negative. If we substitute the magnitude of the forces, Eq. 1 becomes

$$F^c_{\text{rb}\,x} + F^c_{\text{wb}\,x} + F^c_{\text{sb}\,x} = 0$$

$$+F^c_{\text{rb}} + F^c_{\text{wb}} + (-F^c_{\text{sb}}) = 0 \tag{2}$$

$$F^c_{\text{sb}} = F^c_{\text{rb}} + F^c_{\text{wb}} = 2500 \text{ N} + 200 \text{ N} = 2700 \text{ N.} ✔$$

❹ **EVALUATE RESULT** If we substitute this answer into Eq. 2, the signs in the equation are consistent with the force directions shown in Figure WG8.2. No assumptions were required to solve this problem, nor did we require all the numerical values that were given.

Guided Problem 8.2 Car springs

As an automotive engineer, you have been assigned the task of designing a set of springs for a car. If each of the four springs must compress a distance of 30 mm when the 640-kg car body rests on them, what value of the spring constant k should each spring have?

❶ **GETTING STARTED**

1. What interactions does the car body take part in?
2. Draw a free-body diagram of the car body.

❷ **DEVISE PLAN**

3. After the springs stop bouncing, what is the body's acceleration? Add that information to your free-body diagram.
4. Decide on an appropriate direction for the positive x axis and indicate it on the diagram.
5. Using your free-body diagram as a guide, write the component version of the appropriate force equation.

❸ **EXECUTE PLAN**

6. Solve for the force exerted by each spring on the body.
7. How is this force related to the spring constant?

❹ **EVALUATE RESULT**

8. Examine your expression for k. If the inertia of the car were increased, what would happen to k? Is this reasonable?
9. Did you make any assumptions?

Worked Problem 8.3 Truckin' on

A tractor is pulling two trailers. Trailer 1 has an inertia of 4000 kg, and trailer 2 has an inertia of 6000 kg. The tractor pulls its load with a force of 2.5 kN when it starts from rest. (*a*) What is the magnitude of the tractor's acceleration? (*b*) What is the tension in the coupling between the two trailers?

❶ **GETTING STARTED** Figure WG8.3 identifies the objects involved: tractor t, trailer 1, and trailer 2. Because two objects are being pulled, we may need to draw a free-body diagram for each one. What shall we put in our free-body diagrams? The motion is horizontal, so we concern ourselves only with horizontal forces.

Figure WG8.3

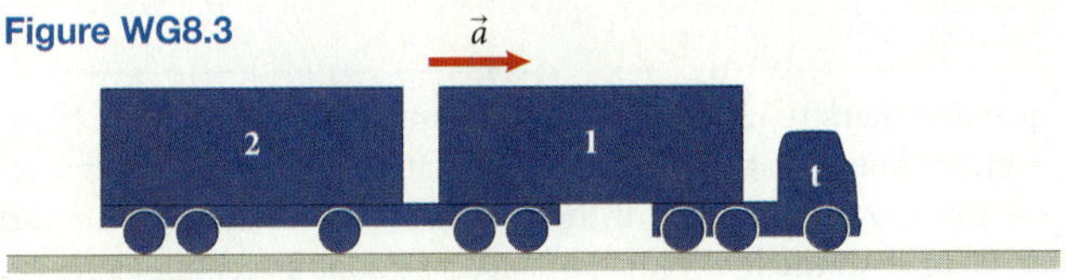

The only force exerted on trailer 2 is the forward pull exerted by the coupling with trailer 1. The forces exerted on trailer 1 are the 2.5-kN force exerted by the tractor pulling forward and the force exerted by the coupling with trailer 2. We ignore air resistance because the truck starts from rest and so is moving at low speed. We also assume the wheels are well greased so that bearing friction does not impede the motion. As long as the tractor and two trailers move together, they must have a common acceleration, and it is in the direction in which the tractor pulls (which we make the positive x direction). We can therefore use the same acceleration symbol a for the tractor and both trailers, and our free-body diagrams are as shown in Figure WG8.4.

Figure WG8.4

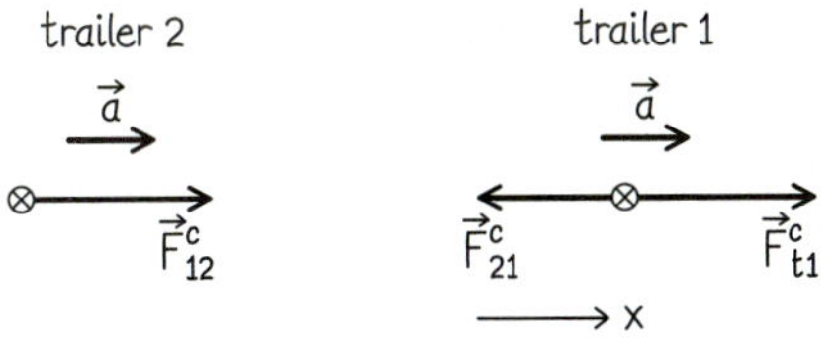

❷ **DEVISE PLAN** Because this problem deals with acceleration and force, we start with Newton's second law. With two free-body diagrams we obtain two equations, one from each diagram:

$$\Sigma F_{1x} = m_1 a_{1x} = m_1 a_x$$

$$\Sigma F_{2x} = m_2 a_{2x} = m_2 a_x.$$

The unknown common acceleration $a = |\vec{a}| = |a_x|$ and the unknown coupling tension $\mathcal{T} = |\vec{F}^{\text{tensile}}| = |\vec{F}^{c}_{12}| = |\vec{F}^{c}_{21}|$ will appear in both equations. We know the magnitude of the tractor's pulling force: $F^{c}_{t1} = 2.5$ kN. Two equations with two unknowns are all we need.

❸ **EXECUTE PLAN**
(a) Our second-law equations give us

$$\Sigma F_{1x} = F^{c}_{21x} + F^{c}_{t1x} = m_1 a_x = -F^{\text{tensile}} + F^{\text{pull}} = m_1(+a)$$

$$\Sigma F_{2x} = F^{c}_{12x} = m_2 a_x = +F^{\text{tensile}} = m_2(+a). \quad (1)$$

Adding these two equations eliminates the tensile force and allows us to solve for the acceleration of each object:

$$m_2 a + m_1 a = (+F^{\text{tensile}}) + (-F^{\text{tensile}}) + (F^{\text{pull}})$$

$$(m_1 + m_2)a = F^{\text{pull}}$$

$$a = \frac{F^{\text{pull}}}{m_1 + m_2} = \frac{2.5 \times 10^3 \text{ N}}{4000 \text{ kg} + 6000 \text{ kg}} = 0.25 \text{ m/s}^2. ✔ \quad (2)$$

(b) We compute the tension $\mathcal{T} = |\vec{F}^{\text{tensile}}|$ in the coupling by substituting the expression we derived for a in Eq. 2 into Eq. 1:

$$\mathcal{T} = m_2\left(\frac{F^{\text{pull}}}{m_1 + m_2}\right) \quad (3)$$

$$\mathcal{T} = \frac{m_2}{m_1 + m_2}F^{\text{pull}} = \frac{6000 \text{ kg}}{4000 \text{ kg} + 6000 \text{ kg}}(2.5 \times 10^3 \text{N})$$

$$= 1.5 \times 10^3 \text{N}. ✔$$

❹ **EVALUATE RESULT** Notice from Eq. 2 that the acceleration is the force exerted by the tractor divided by the inertia of the trailers, which is what we would expect if we had lumped the two trailers together as one object to get the acceleration.

The magnitude of the tension we obtained for the coupling, 1.5×10^3 N, is numerically equal to the magnitude of the tensile force required to accelerate just trailer 2 and should be less than the magnitude of the force exerted by the tractor, 2.5×10^3 N, which has to get both trailers to accelerate at the same rate.

Our algebraic expression for tension in the coupling (Eq. 3) states that the tension is some fraction of the 2.5-kN force exerted by the tractor, as expected. It also predicts that as the inertia of trailer 1 decreases to zero, the tension in the coupling is just the force the tractor pulls with, which is to be expected if trailer 1 becomes just a connector. As m_2 goes to zero, the tension also goes to zero because no force is needed to accelerate a trailer of zero inertia.

We did ignore friction and air resistance, which is reasonable at low speed.

Guided Problem 8.4 Rubber-band leash

A child drags a toy dog around at constant speed, using a rubber band as a leash. If the spring constant of the rubber band is 20 N/m and the frictional force between the toy and the floor is 0.734 N, how much does the rubber band stretch?

❶ **GETTING STARTED**

1. What physical quantity is appropriate to represent the unknown you seek?
2. Which object, the rubber band or the toy, should be the subject of a free-body diagram?
3. Don't forget to include an x axis on your free-body diagram to indicate the positive direction.

❷ **DEVISE PLAN**

4. What relates the tensile force exerted on the object in your free-body diagram to the distance the rubber band stretches?
5. How does the number of equations you have compare with the number of unknowns?

❸ **EXECUTE PLAN**

6. Solve your equations to obtain an algebraic expression for the desired unknown.
7. Substitute the values given.

❹ **EVALUATE RESULT**

8. Does your algebraic expression make sense as you imagine a larger or smaller frictional force? What about a larger or smaller spring constant?
9. Did you make any simplifying assumptions that would significantly affect your answer?

Worked problem 8.5 Retarding a mine cart

In Figure WG8.5, a hanging block suspended by a rope hung over a pulley is used to accelerate a loaded mine cart along rail tracks to the edge of a cliff, where the load is dumped. To help reduce its acceleration as it nears the edge, the cart is attached to a horizontal spring of spring constant k, and the other end of the spring is attached to a wall. Ignoring friction and the small amount of stretch in the rope, determine the acceleration of the cart when the spring is stretched a distance d beyond its relaxed length.

Figure WG8.5

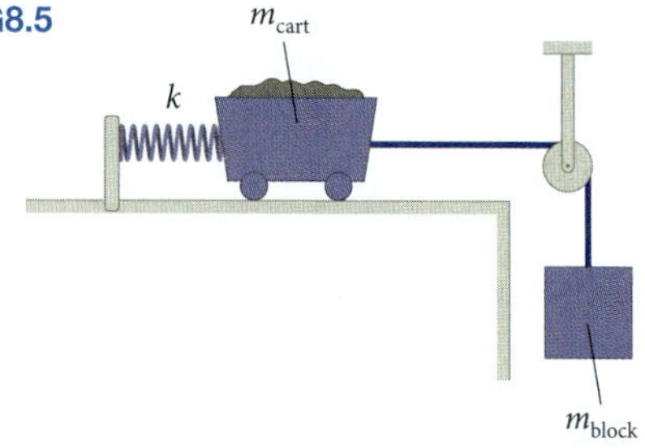

❶ **GETTING STARTED** The rope tends to accelerate the cart to the right in Figure WG8.5, but the stretched spring tends to accelerate it to the left. If the spring is stretched only a little, the force it exerts on the cart is small, and the pull of the rope causes the cart to accelerate to the right. If the spring is stretched a lot, the magnitude of the force it exerts on the cart may be greater than the magnitude of the force exerted by the rope, accelerating the cart to the left.

The block is subject to both the upward tug of the rope and the downward tug of gravity, and so we do not know which way it is accelerating. However, unless the rope goes slack, stretches, or breaks, the magnitude of the acceleration of the cart and the block must be the same. This common magnitude of acceleration is horizontal for the cart and vertical for the block, and the directions of these accelerations must allow the rope to remain taut and of constant length.

Even though the cart moves horizontally and the block moves vertically, each moves in only one dimension, which means this is just two one-dimensional problems coupled by the tension in the rope.

❷ **DEVISE PLAN** We begin with a free-body diagram of the cart because it is the cart's acceleration we are asked to calculate (Figure WG8.6). The cart is subject to two horizontal forces, one exerted by the rope and one by the spring. We know the value of neither, and so, counting the acceleration we seek, there are three unknowns!

The expression we must obtain for the acceleration involves the symbols given in the problem statement. We will be able to substitute for the unknown spring force using $F^{c}_{sc\,x} = -k(x - x_0) = -kd$, where x is the position of the cart end of the spring at any instant when the spring is either stretched or compressed and x_0 is the position of the cart end of the spring when the spring is relaxed. Because we have no obvious substitution for the force exerted by the rope, we need another equation, which suggests that we draw a free-body diagram of the other object, the block [Figure WG8.6]. We show the acceleration in both free-body diagrams but add a question mark to indicate that we are unsure of its direction. However, we know that if the block accelerates downward, the cart accelerates to the right and if the block accelerates upward, the cart accelerates to the left. Thus both accelerations are either along the positive x directions we have chosen (to the right and downward) or along the negative x directions. This allows us to use a single symbol, a_x, for the x component of the acceleration of either object.

Figure WG8.6

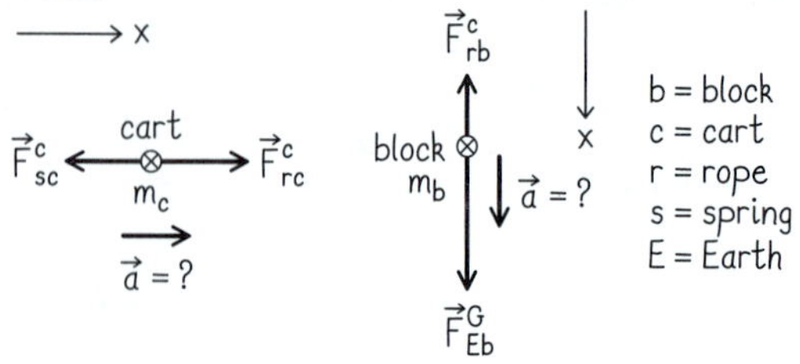

We are now prepared to analyze this problem using forces, generating equations of motion for each free-body diagram. Hooke's law (*Principles* Eq. 8.20) is also involved because it allows us to substitute kd for the unknown force magnitude F^{c}_{sc}. Reciprocity of forces allows us to write $|\vec{F}^{c}_{cr}| = |\vec{F}^{c}_{rc}| = |\vec{F}^{c}_{rb}| = |\vec{F}^{c}_{br}| = \mathcal{T}$, where $\mathcal{T}$ is the tension in the rope (a scalar). Note that the middle equality, $|\vec{F}^{c}_{rc}| = |\vec{F}^{c}_{rb}|$, is due to the ability of a rope to transmit force undiminished from one end to the other and so depends on the rope having a negligibly small inertia.

The free-body diagram for the block allows us to relate the tension (magnitude of the tensile force) in the rope to the known variables m_b and g and to the unknown acceleration $\vec{a}$ or, equivalently, its x component a_x.

❸ **EXECUTE PLAN** The sum of the x components of all forces exerted on the cart is

$$\Sigma F_{cx} = F^{c}_{scx} + F^{c}_{rcx} = m_c a_x.$$

Because we don't know the direction of the acceleration, we choose not to substitute a sign and magnitude for that quantity. However, we can substitute for the force components, using Figure WG8.6 as a guide:

$$-F^{c}_{sc} + F^{c}_{rc} = m_c a_x$$

$$-kd + \mathcal{T} = m_c a_x. \qquad (1)$$

Repeating the process using Figure WG8.6 for the block, we obtain

$$\Sigma F_{bx} = F^{G}_{Ebx} + F^{c}_{rbx} = m_b a_x$$

$$+F^{G}_{Eb} - F^{c}_{rb} = +m_b a_x$$

$$+m_b g - \mathcal{T} = m_b a_x. \qquad (2)$$

We combine Eqs. 1 and 2 to eliminate the unknown tension.

$$+m_b a_x + m_c a_x = +m_b g - \mathcal{T} - kd + \mathcal{T}$$

$$(m_b + m_c) a_x = m_b g - kd$$

$$a_x = \frac{m_b g - kd}{m_b + m_c}. ✔$$

This expression for the x component of acceleration can be either positive or negative, which means that the acceleration of the cart may be either to the right ($a_x > 0$) or to the left ($a_x < 0$).

❸ **EVALUATE RESULT** Our expression for a_x tells us that the acceleration of the cart can be to the left or to the right, depending on the size of kd relative to the magnitude $m_b g$. If either the stretch distance d or the spring constant k is small enough to make $kd < m_b g$, our expression gives a positive value for a_x and the cart accelerates in the positive x direction. If either d or k is large enough to make $kd > m_b g$, we get a negative value for a_x and the cart accelerates in the negative x direction. The acceleration becomes very small if the inertia of the cart is very large, as expected.

Guided Problem 8.6 Atwood machine

A simple device for fully or partially counterbalancing objects, the Atwood machine, consists of two blocks connected by a cable draped across a stationary pulley that rotates freely. The pulley serves only to change the direction of the cable without increasing or decreasing the tension in it. For the simple Atwood machine depicted in Figure WG8.7, what are (*a*) the magnitude of acceleration of each block and (*b*) the tension in the cable after the blocks are released? Assume the blocks are released from rest, and ignore any friction in the pulley.

Figure WG8.7

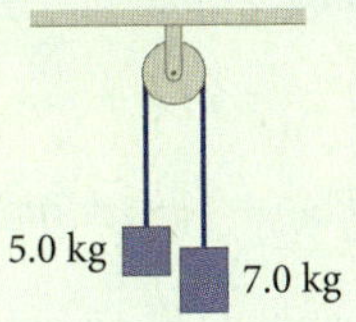

❶ GETTING STARTED

1. Draw a free-body diagram for each block.
2. In which direction should you draw the acceleration vector in each diagram? What is an appropriate direction for the *x* axis in each diagram?
3. Are the accelerations of the two blocks related to each other?

❷ DEVISE PLAN

4. How many equations are needed to solve this problem?
5. For each free-body diagram you can write one equation, paying attention to the signs for each term.
6. Can you use Newton's third law to eliminate any unknowns?

❸ EXECUTE PLAN

7. Isolate the unknowns, and obtain expressions for the acceleration and tension.
8. Substitute the values given, and compute numerical values for the unknowns.

❹ EVALUATE RESULT

9. Do all magnitudes come out positive? If not, determine the source of your error.
10. Examine your expression for a. If the inertia of either block is increased or decreased, what happens to the value of a? Is this reasonable?
11. Examine your expression for $\mathcal{T}$. If the inertia of either block is increased or decreased, what happens to the value of $\mathcal{T}$? Is this reasonable?
12. Compare the numerical values you obtained to known values, such as the acceleration in free fall and the gravitational force on each block. Are the results reasonable?

Worked Problem 8.7 Pulley power

The block-and-tackle system in Figures WG8.8*a* and WG8.8*b* is composed of two pulleys connected by a looped rope, with the upper pulley suspended from a fixed support attached to the ceiling. Starting at the point where the person holds the rope, the rope goes over the upper pulley (rope C), goes under the lower pulley (rope A), is attached to the upper pulley (rope B), which is linked to the ceiling by the support. The object to be lifted from the ground to the platform is hung from the lower pulley. If the pulleys have negligible inertia and good bearings, no energy is lost to turning the pulleys or to friction. If the inertia of the rope is also negligible, the tension is the same everywhere along the rope.

Figure WG8.8

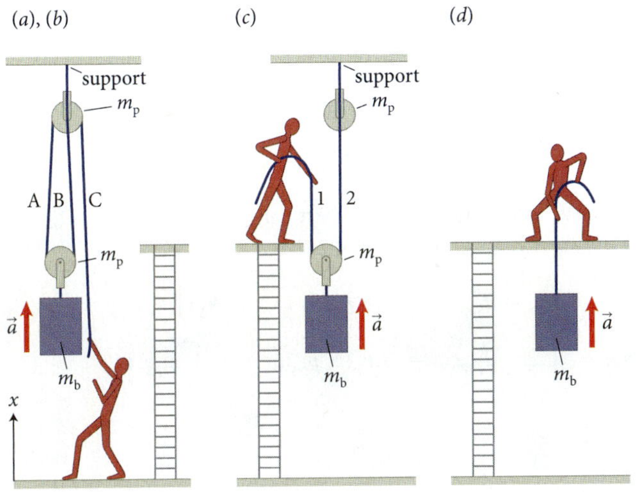

Assume that a block of inertia m_b is the object being lifted and that each pulley has negligible inertia, $m_p \ll m_b$. (*a*) With what force magnitude must a person pull on rope segment C to give the block an upward acceleration of magnitude a? (*b*) As the block moves, what is the tension $\mathcal{T}_{support}$ in the support that attaches the upper pulley to the ceiling? (*c*) Suppose the free end of the rope falls off the upper pulley and the person cannot reach the ceiling to rewrap the rope. He can climb to the platform and use the lower pulley and the rope (with the fixed end of the rope still attached to the ceiling through the support). He positions himself above the block and lower pulley (Figure WG8.8*c*) and lifts the combination by pulling straight up on the free end of the rope. If he wants to give the block an upward acceleration of magnitude a, how does the magnitude of the force he must exert compare with the force magnitude determined in part *a*? (*d*) Now suppose he discards the pulleys, ties the rope around the block (Figure WG8.8*d*), and lifts it with the same acceleration $\vec{a}$ by pulling upward on the rope. Compare the force he must exert in this case with your answers to parts *a* and *c*.

❶ GETTING STARTED (*a*) The lower pulley and the block are raised (as a single unit) by rope segments A and B. The problem statement allows us to assume that the tension $\mathcal{T}$ in the rope is transmitted undiminished throughout the rope, so that this tension equals the magnitude of the pulling force exerted by the worker on segment C, which is what we must calculate in part *a*. Let's call this tension in the three rope segments $\mathcal{T}_{segment}$ to distinguish it from $\mathcal{T}_{support}$, the tension in the ceiling support we need in part *b*.

(*b*) To determine the tension $\mathcal{T}_{support}$ in the support attaching the system to the ceiling, we use the fact that in an object under tension, the opposing forces creating the tension have equal magnitudes. The two tensile forces here are $\vec{F}^c_{cs}$, the upward force exerted by the ceiling on the support, and $\vec{F}^c_{ps}$, the downward force exerted by the upper pulley on the support. If we know either force magnitude, we know $\mathcal{T}_{\text{support}}$. Because we know nothing about the force exerted by the ceiling, we'll have to work with the force exerted by the pulley on the support.

(*c*), (*d*) The free-body diagram for the lower pulley-block system used with Newton's second law gives us what we need to answer part *c*. A similar approach should apply to the block alone in part *d*.

2 DEVISE PLAN (*a*) Let us call the combination of the lower pulley and block our *load* and say that it has an upward acceleration of magnitude a. Rope segments A and B exert on the load upward forces of magnitudes $F^c_{A\ell}$ and $F^c_{B\ell}$, and Earth exerts a gravitational force of magnitude $m_\ell g = (m_p + m_b)g$. We need to draw the free-body diagram for the load and then apply Newton's second law to get the magnitude of the downward pulling force the worker exerts on segment C. This magnitude equals the common tension $\mathcal{T}_{\text{segment}}$ in the rope segments: $\mathcal{T}_{\text{segment}} = F^c_{wC}$. The free-body diagram for the load is shown in Figure WG8.9.

Figure WG8.9

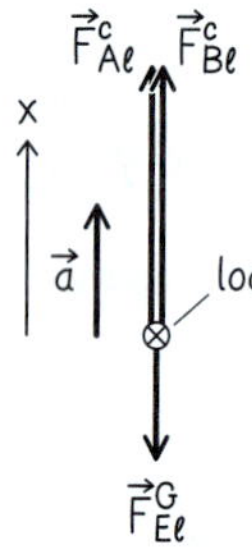

(*b*) We need to determine the force $\vec{F}^c_{ps}$ exerted by the upper pulley on the support because the magnitude of this force equals the tension $\mathcal{T}_{\text{support}}$ in the support. From the reciprocity of forces we know that $\vec{F}^c_{ps}$ has the same magnitude as the force $\vec{F}^c_{sp}$ exerted by the support on the pulley. So, if we calculate the magnitude F^c_{sp}, we have $\mathcal{T}_{\text{support}}$. The support exerts an upward force of magnitude F^c_{sp} on the upper pulley. The three rope segments exert on the upper pulley downward forces of magnitude $F^c_{Ap} = F^c_{Bp} = F^c_{Cp} = \mathcal{T}_{\text{segment}}$. Because this pulley does not rise or fall, its acceleration in the vertical direction is zero, which is information we'll need when we work with the second-law equation.

(*c*) The approach we used in part *a* should work for this part also, but now we need concern ourselves only with the lower pulley plus block. To avoid confusion, we label the two rope segments 1 and 2 for this case (Figure WG8.8*c*). The worker exerts on segment 1 an upward force of magnitude F^c_{w1}, and this magnitude is again equal to the tension in either rope segment.

(*d*) The same approach should apply, this time focusing on only the block. Here we use F^c_{wr} for the magnitude of the force exerted by the worker on the (only) rope.

3 EXECUTE PLAN (*a*) Summing the x components of forces exerted on the load gives us

$$\Sigma F_{\ell x} = m_\ell a_x$$

$$F^c_{A\ell x} + F^c_{B\ell x} + F^G_{E\ell x} = (m_p + m_b)(+a). \quad (1)$$

Because the tensile forces in the three rope segments all have the same magnitude and because this magnitude is equal to the magnitude F^c_{wC} of the pulling force the worker must exert on rope segment C, we have

$$|F^c_{wC\,x}| = |F^c_{A\ell x}| = |F^c_{B\ell x}|.$$

Using Figure WG8.9 as a guide, we can substitute F^c_{wC} for the first two terms in Eq. 1, along with a value for the gravitational force component:

$$F^c_{wC} + F^c_{wC} - m_\ell g = m_\ell a$$

$$2F^c_{wC} = m_\ell a + m_\ell g = (m_\ell)(a + g)$$

$$F^c_{wC} = \tfrac{1}{2}(m_p + m_b)(a + g). \checkmark \quad (2)$$

Remember, this force magnitude F^c_{wC} is equal to the tension $\mathcal{T}_{\text{segment}}$ in the rope segments. We'll need this information in our solution for part *b*.

(*b*) To get the tension in the support, our plan is to calculate F^c_{sp}, the magnitude of the force exerted by the support on the upper pulley, because this magnitude is equal to $\mathcal{T}_{\text{support}}$. The free-body diagram for the upper pulley is shown in Figure WG8.10. Summing force components gives

$$\Sigma F_{px} = m_p a_{p\,x}$$

$$F^c_{spx} + F^c_{Apx} + F^c_{Bpx} + F^c_{Cpx} + F^G_{Epx} = m_p(0).$$

Figure WG8.10

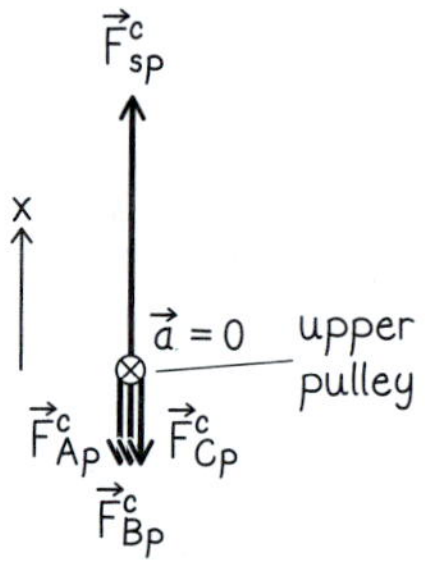

As noted when we devised our plan for part *b*, $F^c_{Ap} = F^c_{Bp} = F^c_{Cp} = \mathcal{T}_{\text{segment}}$, where $\mathcal{T}_{\text{segment}}$ is the tension in any rope segment. Substituting $\mathcal{T}_{\text{segment}}$ for the terms that represent forces exerted by the three rope segments and taking into account the direction in which these forces are exerted give us

$$F^c_{sp} - \mathcal{T}_{\text{segment}} - \mathcal{T}_{\text{segment}} - \mathcal{T}_{\text{segment}} - m_p g = 0$$

$$F^c_{sp} = 3\mathcal{T}_{\text{segment}} + m_p g.$$

Because we know from part *a* that $\mathcal{T}_{\text{segment}} = F^c_{wC} = \frac{1}{2}(m_p + m_b)(a + g)$, we can write

$$F^c_{sp} = \mathcal{T}_{\text{support}} = 3\left[\tfrac{1}{2}(m_p + m_b)(a + g)\right] + m_p g$$

$$\mathcal{T}_{\text{support}} = \tfrac{3}{2}(m_p + m_b)(a + g) + m_p g. \checkmark \quad (3)$$

PRACTICE

(*c*) The physical situation and free-body diagram for the load are illustrated in Figure WG8.11: Rope segments 1 and 2 pull upward on the load with a common tension equal to the force magnitude F^c_{w1} exerted by the worker on rope segment 1: $F^c_{w1} = |F^c_{1\ell x}| = |F^c_{2\ell x}|$. The free-body diagram is just like the diagram for the load in part *a*, and so the mathematical solution is the same here:

$$\sum F_{\ell x} = m_\ell a_x$$

$$F^c_{1\ell x} + F^c_{2\ell x} + F^G_{E\ell x} = m_\ell(+a)$$

$$F^c_{w1} + F^c_{w1} - m_\ell g = m_\ell a$$

$$F^c_{w1} = \tfrac{1}{2}(m_p + m_b)(a + g). \checkmark$$

Figure WG8.11

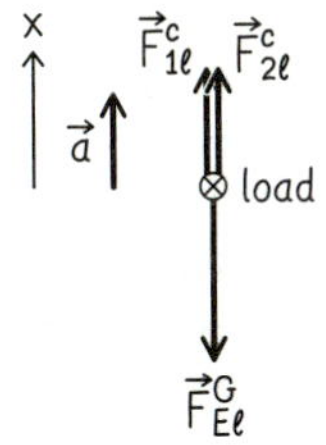

With only one pulley, the person must pull upward with the same magnitude of force he exerts downward on the rope in part *a*.

(*d*) When both pulleys are removed and the person pulls straight up on the load (which now consists of only the block), the free-body diagram has only two forces as shown in Figure WG8.12. The required force magnitude F^c_{wr} is

$$\sum F_{\ell x} = F^c_{r\ell x} + F^G_{E\ell x} = m_b a_x$$

$$F^c_{wr} - m_b g = m_b(+a)$$

$$F^c_{wr} = m_b(a + g).$$

Figure WG8.12

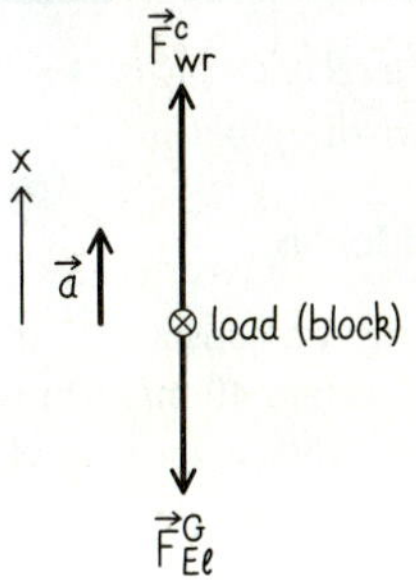

We see that if $m_p \ll m_b$, we have

$$F^c_{wC} = F^c_{w1} = \tfrac{1}{2}F^c_{wr} = \tfrac{1}{2}m_b(a + g). \quad (4)$$

Twice as much force is needed to lift the block without using pulleys. ✓

❶ EVALUATE RESULT Equation 4 shows the mechanical advantage of the block and tackle: This simple system of a rope and two pulleys allows you to raise the load with approximately half the effort of a direct lift! Equation 4 also reveals that the advantage of using two pulleys, with one fixed to the ceiling, must be in something other than the required force. The advantage is one of direction: You should find it easier to pull down (rather than up) to lift a heavy object.

The $+a$ term in Eq. 2 implies that you have to pull harder if you wish the load to have a greater acceleration upward, which is exactly what we expect. Equation 3 implies that the more inertia we have to lift against gravity, the larger the support force has to be, which is reasonable.

We did ignore any effort to turn the pulleys, a topic we will return to in Chapter 11. Real pulleys are often of negligible inertia and nearly frictionless, so the conditions of this problem are reasonable. We also approximated the three rope segments to be vertical even though Figure WG8.8*a* shows segments B and C as slightly angled. Because they are nearly vertical, our answer should be fairly accurate.

Guided Problem 8.8 Support force revisited

Redo part *b* of Worked Problem 8.7. This time, though, calculate $\mathcal{T}_{\text{support}}$ by using *Principles* Eq. 8.44 in the form $\sum F_{\text{ext}\,x} = ma_{\text{cm}\,x}$, where the system comprises the two pulleys and the block.

❶ GETTING STARTED

1. Sketch a system diagram and list the inertias and accelerations of the individual parts of the system.
2. What external forces are exerted on the objects in the system? (Hint: Why is it hard to raise the block?)
3. Are the forces exerted by rope segments A, B, and C internal or external forces? In other words, do they represent interactions between objects in the system or interactions between the system and objects external to the system?

❷ DEVISE PLAN

4. Draw a free-body diagram with an appropriate *x* axis for your system.
5. In the second-law equation, $\sum F_{\text{ext}\,x} = ma_{\text{cm}\,x}$, what is m?
6. What is the acceleration of the system's center of mass, given that two of the objects in the system are accelerating and one is not?
7. Write the sum of the external forces exerted on the system, based on your free-body diagram, and determine the sign and magnitude of each force.

❸ EXECUTE PLAN

8. Solve for the tension in the support $\mathcal{T}_{\text{support}}$.

❹ EVALUATE RESULT

9. Does your expression agree with the one obtained in part *b* of Worked Problem 8.7? If it does not, you might not have correctly identified all the external forces exerted by Earth (an external object) on the system components.

PRACTICE

Questions and Problems

For instructor-assigned homework, go to MasteringPhysics® MP

Dots indicate difficulty level of problems: • = *easy,* •• = *intermediate,* ••• = *hard;* CR = *context-rich problem.*

8.1 Momentum and force

1. A truck is traveling at a constant 25 m/s when a motorcycle speeds past at a constant 40 m/s. On which vehicle, if either, is the magnitude of the vector sum of forces exerted on the vehicle greater? •
2. You wish to move a crate. (*a*) Is there a minimum value for the magnitude of the pushing force you have to exert to set the crate in motion? (*b*) Is there a minimum value for the magnitude of the vector sum of forces that must be exerted on the crate to set it in motion? •
3. Sketch the $\sum F_x(t)$ curve for the vector sum of forces exerted on the object whose x component of momentum is plotted in Figure P8.3. Curve sections are numbered for reference. ••

Figure P8.3

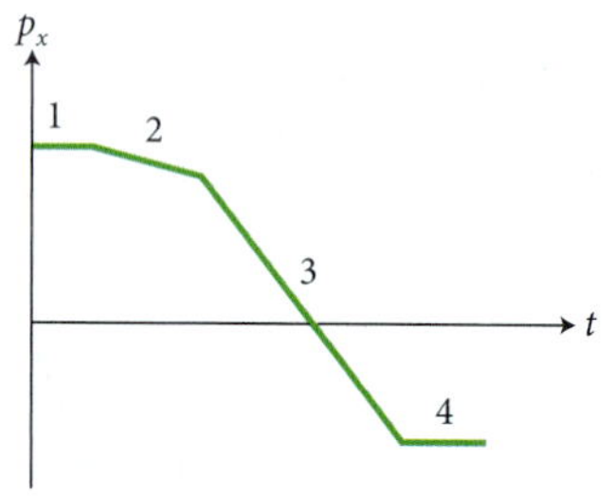

4. The x component of the vector sum of forces exerted on a cart moving on a low-friction track is measured in the laboratory with the aid of a spring-loaded sensor and a monitoring computer. From the data in the table, sketch the $\sum F_x(t)$ curve of the cart and use your graph to estimate the change in the cart's momentum. ••

F (N)	t (s)
0.00	0.00
0.15	0.020
0.32	0.040
0.50	0.060
0.57	0.080
0.37	0.10
0.21	0.12
0.11	0.14
0.070	0.16
0.040	0.18

5. If a single known force is exerted on an object for a certain time interval, you know the change in the object's momentum. However, you don't know its change in kinetic energy. Why not? •••
6. Consider a coal mining cart being loaded with coal as it moves along a horizontal track. Suppose that a tractor exerts a constant horizontal force on this cart. Is there any situation in which the cart-coal system would not accelerate? •••

8.2 The reciprocity of forces

7. A worker pushes a box in a factory. In each case, decide which force has the greater magnitude: the force exerted by the worker on the box or the force exerted by the box on the worker. (*a*) The box is heavy and does not move no matter how hard the worker pushes. (*b*) Some contents are removed, and now when pushed the box slides across the floor at constant speed. (*c*) The worker pushes harder, and the box accelerates. •
8. In many science fiction movies, someone is portrayed moving something with her or his mind—an amazing feat called *telekinesis*. What does your knowledge of forces predict about the effect of a telekinetic event on the gifted person? •
9. Which of the following can exert a force: (*a*) a hammer, (*b*) a nail, (*c*) a person, (*d*) a chair, (*e*) a ship, (*f*) water, (*g*) Earth? ••
10. During a tennis volley, a ball that arrives at a player at 40 m/s is struck by the racquet and returned at 40 m/s. The other player, realizing that the ball is out of bounds, catches it in her hand. Assuming the time interval of contact is the same in both cases, compare the force exerted by the first player's racquet on the ball with the force exerted by the second player's hand on the ball. ••

8.3 Identifying forces

11. A pitcher throws a fastball toward home plate. (*a*) When the ball is halfway to the plate, is the pitcher's push still exerted on the ball? (*b*) What forces, if any, are exerted on the ball at the halfway location? •
12. A car's acceleration forward must be due to a force exerted on the car, and the only thing that can push forward on the car is the road (in contact with the tires). So, what purpose does the engine have? •
13. A baby is bouncing in a seat fastened by an elastic cord to a hook on the ceiling. At the top of his bounce, his velocity is instantaneously zero. Is the vector sum of forces exerted on him at that instant zero? Why or why not? ••
14. (*a*) Can an object ever exert both a contact force and a field force on another object? (*b*) Can an object ever exert a contact force on something without exerting a field force on that same object? ••

8.4 Translational equilibrium

15. You push on a refrigerator, but it doesn't move. Explain why not. •
16. You are discussing physics homework with a friend while the two of you are riding your bikes. Distracted, you collide with a parked car. The car doesn't move. Your friend says, "Of course not! The force of the collision wasn't enough to overcome the inertia of the car." How do you respond? •
17. What interaction does a bathroom (spring) scale actually measure? ••

18. A table sits on the floor, and a vase containing water and flowers sits on top of the table. All objects are at rest. Identify all forces exerted on the table, and describe how these forces are related. ••

8.5 Free-body diagrams

19. You are in a stationary elevator, so that the contact force exerted by the floor on you is equal in magnitude to the force of gravity exerted on you. When the elevator starts downward, which force changes? What happens to its magnitude? •
20. When you are standing motionless on the ground, your feet exert a force on Earth. Why doesn't Earth move away from you? ••
21. You push on a crate, and it starts to move but you don't. Draw a free-body diagram for you and one for the crate. Then use the diagrams your knowledge about forces and interactions to explain why the crate moves but you don't. ••
22. The force of air resistance on any object falling through the air increases with the object's speed. What happens to the acceleration of a raindrop as it falls from a cloud? ••
23. You are carrying your 3-year-old niece on your shoulders in an elevator cabin that is moving upward with velocity 1.5 m/s and constant downward acceleration of $1.0\ \mathrm{m/s^2}$ (Figure P8.23). Your inertia is 50 kg, your niece's inertia is 20 kg, and the cabin's inertia is 100 kg. (*a*) Draw free-body diagrams for the elevator cabin, your niece, and yourself, labeling the forces using the notation introduced in *Principles* Section 8.5. Make sure the lengths of the force vectors are appropriate to the magnitudes of the forces. (*b*) State the magnitudes of as many forces as possible, and identify all the forces that form interaction pairs. Explain briefly how you obtained these magnitudes. •••

Figure P8.23

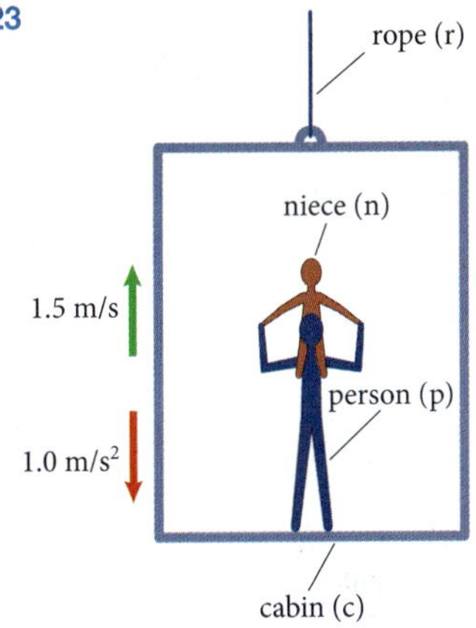

8.6 Springs and tension

24. A delivery person in an elevator is holding a package by an elastic cord. (Don't ask why.) (*a*) What happens to the length of the cord when the elevator accelerates upward? Draw the free-body diagram for the package in this case. (*b*) What happens to the cord length when the elevator slows to a stop after its ascent? Draw the free-body diagram for the package in this case. •
25. Suppose a rope that is hanging by one end from the ceiling has a large inertia. Is the tension in the rope uniform throughout the length? ••
26. Walking beside a pasture, you and a fellow student see a farmer pulling a mule with a rope and getting nowhere. Your friend says, "The force with which the mule is pulling on the rope has the same magnitude as the force with which the farmer is pulling on the rope, but the two forces point in opposite directions. Because the two forces cancel, the tension in the rope is zero." How do you respond? ••
27. In a game of tug of war, the blue team is beating the red team, and the red team is accelerating toward the mud pit between the two teams. Which has the greater magnitude, if either: the force the blue team exerts on the rope or the force the red team exerts on the rope? Assume that the gravitational force exerted on the rope is negligible compared with the forces exerted by the two teams on the rope. ••
28. The standard coupling between railroad cars must be capable of withstanding the maximum tensile force exerted on any coupling in a given train. (*a*) If a locomotive is pulling ten cars and speeding up, on which coupling is the greatest tensile force exerted? (*b*) Is this tensile force due to stretching or compression? (*c*) If the locomotive is slowing the train down, on which coupling is the greatest tensile force exerted? (*d*) Is this tensile force due to stretching or compression? ••

8.7 Equation of motion

29. In an electric breakdown in air (a spark), an electron (inertia 9.11×10^{-31} kg) experiences an electric force of 4.83×10^{-13} N. What is the electron's acceleration? •
30. A 2.3-kg object experiences a single, time-dependent force $F_x(t) = (10\ \mathrm{N/s})t - (20\ \mathrm{N})$. What is the object's acceleration at $t = 0$, 2.0 s, and 4.0 s? •
31. Is it possible to figure out an object's past motion if you know its present position and velocity and the history of all the forces exerted on it? ••
32. The force exerted by expanding gases is what propels a shell out of a gun barrel. Suppose a force that has an average magnitude F propels the shell so that it has a speed v at the instant it reaches the end of the barrel. What magnitude force is required to double the speed of the shell in the same gun? ••
33. A 50-kg pneumatic hammer is fitted with a shock absorber at the top to lessen the impact on the worker. The vertical displacement of the hammer as a function of time is given by $x(t) = at^2 - bt^3$ (during the hammer's bounce), where $a = 15\ \mathrm{m/s^2}$ and $b = 20\ \mathrm{m/s^3}$. The positive x axis is directed upward. (*a*) Write an expression for the x component of the vector sum of forces exerted on the hammer as a function of time. (*b*) At which values of t is the x component of the vector sum of forces on the hammer positive, at which values of t is it negative, and at which values of t is it zero? ••
34. You push with a steady force of 19 N on a 48-kg desk fitted with casters (wheels that swivel) on its four feet. How long does it take you to move the desk 5.9 m across a warehouse floor? ••

35. In Figure P8.35, a 50-kg skier heads down a slope, reaching a speed of 35 km/h. She then slides across a horizontal snow field but hits a rough area. Assume the snow before the rough area is so slippery that you can ignore any friction between the skis and the snow. If the frictional force exerted by the snow in the rough area is 40 N, how far across the rough area does the skier travel before stopping? ••

Figure P8.35

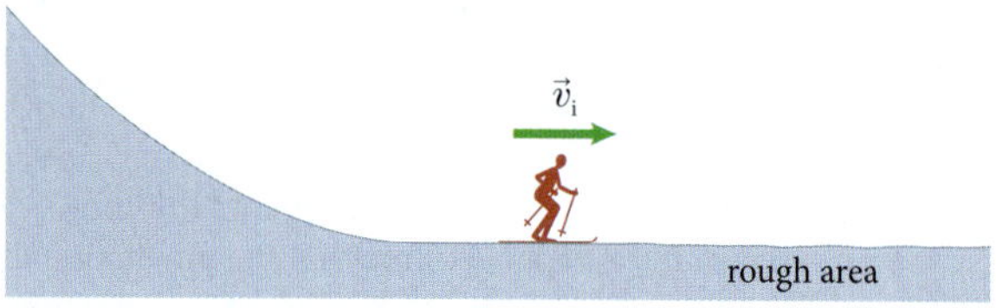

36. A 2.34-kg cart on a long, level, low-friction track is heading for a small electric fan at 0.23 m/s. The fan, which was initially off, is turned on. As the fan speeds up, the magnitude of the force it exerts on the cart is given by at^2, where $a = 0.0200\ \text{N/s}^2$. What is the speed of the cart 3.5 s after the fan is turned on? After how many seconds is the cart's velocity zero? •••

8.8 Force of gravity

37. What is the magnitude of the gravitational force exerted by Earth on a 1.0-kg brick when the brick is (*a*) in free fall and (*b*) resting on a table? •
38. Estimate the magnitude of the force of gravity exerted on (*a*) a packet of sugar, (*b*) a cup of water, (*c*) a packed carry-on suitcase, (*d*) an adult gorilla, and (*e*) a midsize car. •
39. The magnitude of the gravitational force exerted on the piano in Figure P8.39 is 1500 N. With how much force do you have to pull on the rope in order to hold up the piano (*a*) with the single pulley and (*b*) with the double pulley? •

Figure P8.39 (*a*) (*b*)

40. The piano in Figure P8.39 is being lowered with an acceleration of magnitude exactly $g/8$. To maintain this acceleration, with what force magnitude must the person pull on the rope (*a*) with the single pulley and (*b*) with the double pulley? ••
41. If the force of gravity exerted by Earth on a fully suited astronaut at Earth's surface is 1960 N, what is the magnitude of the gravitational force exerted on her (*a*) on Jupiter, where the acceleration due to gravity is $25.9\ \text{m/s}^2$, and (*b*) on the Moon, where the acceleration due to gravity is $1.6\ \text{m/s}^2$? ••
42. You are climbing a rope straight up toward the ceiling. (*a*) What are the magnitude and direction of the force you must exert on the rope in order to accelerate upward at $1.5\ \text{m/s}^2$, assuming your inertia is 60 kg? (*b*) If the maximum tension the rope can support is 1225 N, what is the maximum inertia the rope can support at this acceleration if the inertia of the rope is so small that the gravitational force exerted on the rope can be ignored? ••
43. Two blocks are tied together by a cord draped over a pulley (Figure P8.43). (*a*) At first, the block on the table does not slip. How does the tension in the cord compare with the gravitational force exerted on the hanging block? (*b*) You tip the table a bit, and the block on the table begins to slip. Now how does the tension in the cord compare with the gravitational force exerted on the hanging block? Ignore any friction in the pulley. ••

Figure P8.43

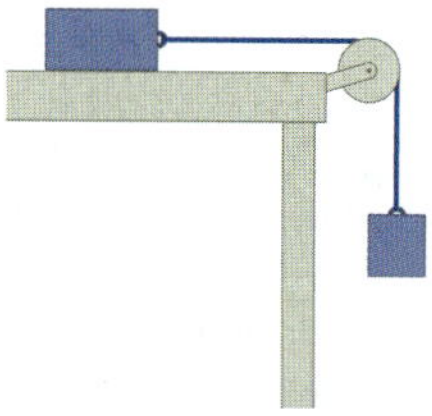

44. Assume that the block on the table in Figure P8.43 has twice the inertia of the hanging block. (*a*) You give the block on the table a push to the right so that it starts to move. If the magnitude of the frictional force exerted by the table on the block is half the magnitude of the gravitational force exerted on the hanging block, what is the acceleration of the hanging block after you have stopped pushing the block on the table? (*b*) What would this hanging-block acceleration be if you had pushed the block on the table to the left instead? Consider only a short time interval after you stop pushing. ••
45. Assume that the block on the table in Figure P8.43 has half the inertia of the hanging block. (*a*) You push the block on the table to the right so that it starts to move. If the magnitude of the frictional force exerted by the table on the table block is half the magnitude of the gravitational force exerted on this block, what is the block's acceleration after you remove your hand? (*b*) What would this acceleration be if you had pushed the block to the left? Consider only a short time interval after you stop pushing. ••
46. A bag of concrete mix is tied to one end of a rope that is looped over a pulley attached to the ceiling, and the other end of the rope is tied to a pallet of lumber (Figure P8.46). The concrete mix has a greater inertia than the lumber. When both loads are released from rest so that the system is free to move, compare the tension in the rope with the magnitudes of the gravitational forces exerted by Earth on the lumber and on the concrete mix. Ignore any friction in the pulley. ••

Figure P8.46

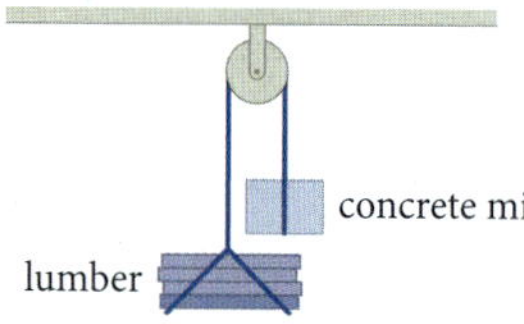

PRACTICE

47. All blocks in Figure P8.47 are identical and you can ignore any friction in the pulleys. Rank the configurations in increasing order of tension in the rope. (Hint: Use free-body diagrams.) ••

Figure P8.47

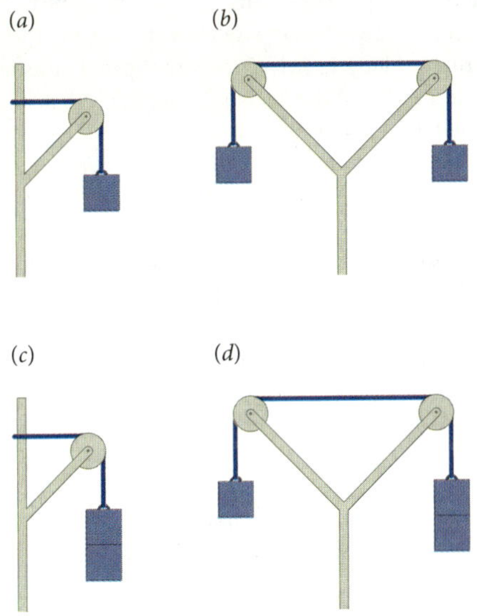

48. Picture an object in free fall. If the leading face of the object (which means the face closest to the ground) has a large surface area, air resistance becomes important. For low speeds, the force due to air resistance may be approximated as proportional to the object's velocity according to the expression $\vec{F}^{a} = -b\vec{v}$, where b is a number that depends on the shape and volume of the object and on the density of the air. (*a*) Show that, for an object of inertia m, there is a limiting speed (called the *terminal speed*) given by $v_t = mg/b$. (*b*) Show that, if the object is released from rest, its speed as a function of time is given by

$$v(t) = v_t\left[1 - e^{-(b/m)t}\right].$$

(*c*) What are the units of m/b? Sketch a graph of v as a function of time, with the horizontal axis in units of multiples of m/b. •••

49. At a munitions factory, chemicals M and P have to be added to a vat containing chemical C. Chemicals M and P have to be added simultaneously to prevent an accidental detonation. Your task, as the chemical engineer in charge, is to come up with a way of doing this, and you devise the pulley scheme shown in Figure P8.49, where block W is a counterweight whose inertia controls the speed at which the buckets containing chemicals M and P move. The idea is that when a strap holding block W at rest is released, the block rises and the buckets containing M and P descend into the vat. In order to have the two buckets have an identical acceleration of magnitude $g/3$, what must be the ratios of the inertias m_W, m_M, and m_P? Ignore any friction in the pulleys. •••

Figure P8.49

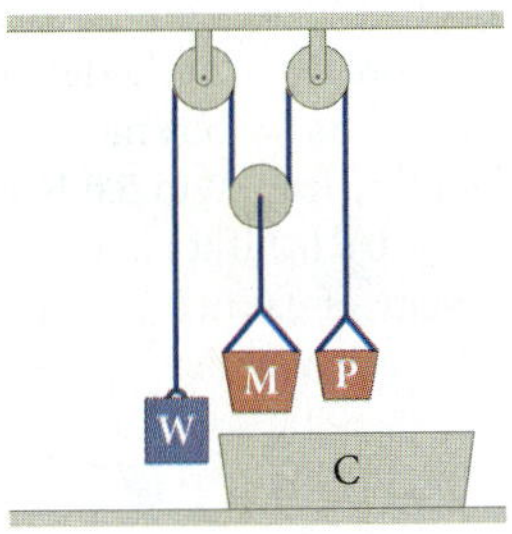

8.9 Hooke's law

50. A 66-kg person experiences a gravitational force of about 660 N. Yet, if this person were to jump onto a spring scale, the scale would briefly read about 2400 N. Why does the scale register a force so much larger than the gravitational force exerted on the person? •

51. A 20-kg child stands in the center of a trampoline. (*a*) If the trampoline center is 0.11 m lower than before she got on, what is the spring constant of the trampoline? (*b*) Assuming the trampoline acts like a spring, how low would her 75-kg father sink if he stood alone in the center? •

52. Two springs have spring constants k_1 and $k_2 > k_1$. Connected as shown in Figure P8.52, they act like one spring. Compute the spring constant of the combination, and determine whether it is smaller than k_1, equal to k_1, between k_1 and k_2, equal to k_2, or greater than k_2. ••

Figure P8.52

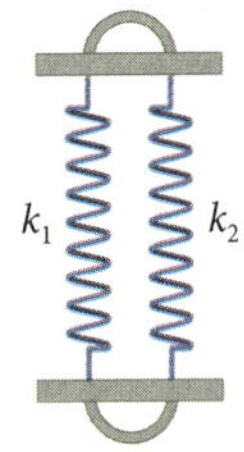

53. Two springs have spring constants k_1 and $k_2 > k_1$. Connected as shown in Figure P8.53, they act like one spring. Compute the spring constant of the combination. Is the combination smaller than k_1, equal to k_1, between k_1 and k_2, equal to k_2, or greater than k_2? ••

Figure P8.53

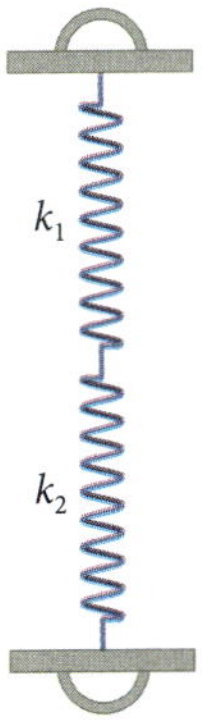

54. Two springs are hooked together end to end. When a 4.0-kg brick is suspended from one end of the combination, the combination stretches 0.15 m beyond its relaxed length. (*a*) What is the spring constant of the combination? (*b*) If the top spring stretches 0.10 m, what is the spring constant of each spring? ••

55. When a 5.0-kg box is hung from a spring, the spring stretches to 50 mm beyond its relaxed length. In an elevator accelerating upward at 2.0 m/s^2, how far does the spring stretch with the same box attached? ••

56. Suppose that when you lie on your bed, your body is supported by 30 of the springs in the mattress. Assuming that all the springs are identical and that your body presses on each spring equally, estimate their spring constant. (Experiment: Lie on your bed and see how far down you sink.) ••

57. In the modified Atwood machine shown in Figure P8.57, each of the three blocks has the same inertia m. One end of the vertical spring, which has spring constant k, is attached to the single block, and the other end of the spring is fixed to the floor. The positions of the blocks are adjusted until the spring is at its relaxed length. The blocks are then released from rest. What is the acceleration of the two blocks on the right after they have dropped a distance d? Ignore any friction in the pulleys. ••

Figure P8.57

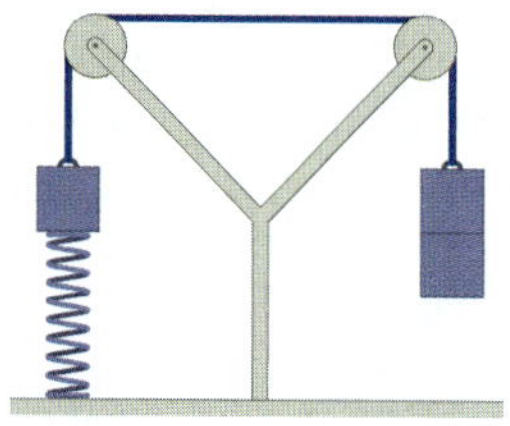

58. Your boss hands you a bag containing four springs, A, B, C, and D, and tells you that they all have the same relaxed length. He wants you to rank them by the values of their spring constants. He locks you in a room with only the springs, a ruler, and a pad and pencil, and tells you to knock when you're done. Each spring has a hook on one end and a handgrip on the other. There is nothing in the room you can use to measure inertia.

After thinking for a few minutes, you hook springs A and B together, stand on one handgrip with your foot, and pull on the other handgrip with your hand until the combination spring has been stretched to double its original length (Figure P8.58). You notice that spring A makes up 65% of the stretched length and spring B makes up the other 35%.

Figure P8.58

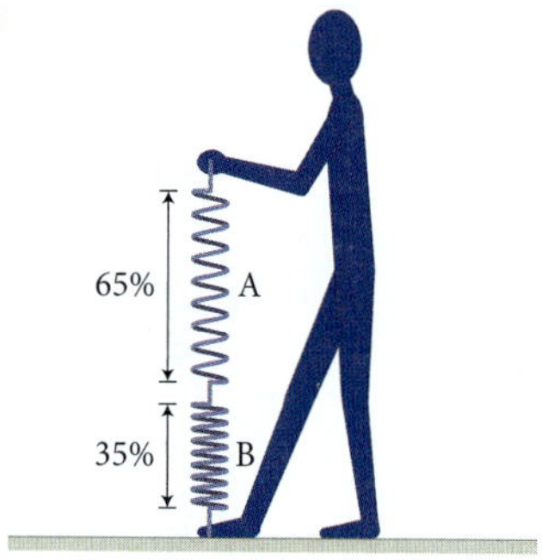

You work your way through the rest of the springs and tabulate the results:

Combination	Percent of stretched length
A/B	A 65, B 35
A/C	A 70, C 30
A/D	A 67, D 33

Based on these results, what are the numerical values in the ratio $k_A : k_B : k_C : k_D$? •••

59. A 5.0-kg red book is suspended from a spring attached to the ceiling of an elevator that is accelerating downward. Attaching the book causes the spring to stretch 71 mm beyond its relaxed length. You also have a yellow book of unknown inertia. When you attach the yellow book and the red one to the spring at the same time, the spring stretches 110 mm beyond its relaxed length. When the elevator is at rest, the combination of the two books stretches the spring 140 mm beyond its relaxed length. (*a*) What is the spring constant? (*b*) What is the inertia of the yellow book? (*c*) What is the elevator's acceleration? •••

8.10 Impulse

60. Why does a dropped dinner plate break when it lands on a tile floor but not when it lands on carpet? •

61. If you try to pound a nail into a board with a 2.5-kg rubber mallet, you will have less luck than if you use a 0.8-kg steel hammer. Why? •

62. In a baseball game, a batter hits the 0.150-kg ball straight back at the pitcher at 180 km/h. If the ball is traveling at 160 km/h just before it reaches the bat, what is the average force exerted by the bat on it if the collision lasts 5.0 ms? •

63. In Figure P8.63, a heavy potted plant hangs by an enveloping hanger made of heavy yarn. (*a*) If you pull slowly on the tassel at the bottom, where is the hanger most likely to break? Why? (*b*) If you yank quickly on the tassel, where is the hanger most likely to break? ••

Figure P8.63

64. Estimate the impulse delivered by a hammer to a nail being driven into a wood plank. ••

65. A 1500-kg car goes from 0 to 100 km/h in 60 s. (*a*) What is the impulse delivered to the car? (*b*) What is the average vector sum of forces exerted on the car? ••

66. A horizontal force F_{slide} is exerted on a 5.0-kg box sliding on a polished floor. As the box moves, the magnitude of F_{slide} increases smoothly from 0 to 5.0 N in 5.0 s. What is the box's speed at $t = 5.0$ s (*a*) if it starts from rest and (*b*) if at $t = 0$ it has a velocity of 3.0 m/s in the direction opposite the direction of F_{slide}? Ignore any friction between the box and the floor. ••

67. Just before hitting the ground, a partially inflated 0.625-kg basketball has a speed of 3.30 m/s. Then it loses half of its kinetic energy as it bounces. (*a*) What is the ball's speed immediately after it bounces? (*b*) If the ball is in contact with the ground for 9.25 ms, what is the magnitude of the average force exerted by the ground on the ball? ••

68. A 1.2-kg ball dropped from a height of 3.0 m onto a steel plate rigidly attached to the ground bounces back up to a height of 2.5 m. (*a*) What is the impulse delivered to the ball by the plate? (*b*) What is the coefficient of restitution of the collision? ••

69. A 0.050-kg egg falls off a table that is 1.0 m high and lands on a tile floor. (*a*) What is the impulse delivered to the egg by the floor? (*b*) The egg lands on its side, and at the instant of impact the part of the shell farthest from the floor is 40 mm above the floor. The collision continues until the center of mass is on the floor. Estimate the time interval over which the collision lasts. (*c*) What is the average force exerted by the floor on the egg? (*d*) If the floor were carpeted, the collision time interval might be extended by as much as a factor of four as the carpet "gives" under the egg. What would the average force exerted on the egg be then? ••

70. When it crashes into a bridge support that does not move, a car goes from 80 km/h to 0 in 1.23 m. (*a*) What is the impulse delivered to the 70-kg driver by the seat belt, assuming the belt makes the driver's motion identical to the car's motion? (*b*) What is the average force exerted by the belt on the driver? (*c*) If the driver were not wearing the seat belt and flew forward until he hit the steering wheel, which stopped him in 0.0145 s, what would be the average force exerted by the steering wheel on him? (*d*) Would he be likely to survive the crash described in part *c*? Justify your answer by comparing the force exerted by the steering wheel on the driver to the gravitational force exerted on him. •••

71. A volleyball player serves the ball. The 0.27-kg ball was moving straight up and is at the high point of its trajectory when she hits it in a purely horizontal direction. The magnitude of the force exerted on the ball while her hand is in contact with it is given by

$$F(t)^{c}_{hb} = at - bt^2,$$

where $a = 3.0 \times 10^5$ N/s and $b = 1.0 \times 10^8$ N/s^2. Her hand is in contact with the ball for 3.0 ms. What is the magnitude of (*a*) the impulse delivered to the ball, (*b*) the average force exerted by her hand on the ball, and (*c*) the maximum force exerted by her hand on the ball? (*d*) What is the velocity of the ball immediately after her hand loses contact with it? •••

8.11 Systems of two interacting objects

72. A 70-kg student is falling toward Earth. (*a*) Draw one free-body diagram for Earth and one for the student. Assume that air resistance can be ignored. (*b*) Calculate the student's acceleration and the vector sum of forces exerted on him. (*c*) Earth's inertia is 5.97×10^{24} kg. What is the magnitude of the planet's acceleration toward the student? •

73. Two 5.00-kg carts, one red and the other green, are 1.00 m apart on a surface where either cart experiences a constant frictional force of 5.00 N when it moves. Throughout the problem, the red cart is pushed with a constant force of 12.0 N toward the green one. What is the acceleration of (*a*) the center of mass before the two carts collide, (*b*) the red cart before they collide, and (*c*) the center of mass after they collide? •

74. Two 0.500-kg carts are 100 mm apart on a low-friction track. You push one of the carts with a constant force of 2.00 N directed so that the cart you push moves away from the other cart. Determine the acceleration of the center of mass of the two-cart system when (*a*) the carts do not interact and (*b*) the carts are connected by a spring of spring constant $k = 300$ N/m. ••

75. A force of magnitude F is exerted on the leftmost face of two blocks sitting next to each other on a slippery surface, with two of their faces touching. The inertia of the block on the right is m, and the inertia of the block on the left is $2m$. (*a*) What is the magnitude of the acceleration of each block? (*b*) What are the magnitude and direction of the contact force the left block exerts on the right block? (*c*) What are the magnitude and direction of the contact force the right block exerts on the left block? (*d*) How do your answers to parts *a*, *b* and *c* change if the positions of the two blocks are interchanged? ••

76. A 2.0-kg cart and an 8.0-kg cart are connected by a relaxed, horizontal spring of spring constant 300 N/m. You pull the 8.0-kg cart with some constant horizontal force. The separation between the carts increases for a short time interval, then remains constant as you continue to pull and the spring is stretched by 0.100 m. (*a*) What pulling force did you exert? (*b*) If you instead pull the 2.0-kg cart, what force must you exert to get the same stretch in the spring? ••

77. A 1500-kg truck and a 1000-kg car are parked with their rear bumpers nearly touching each other in a level parking lot. Both vehicles have their brakes off so that they are free to roll. A man sitting on the rear bumper of the truck exerts a constant horizontal force on the rear bumper of the car with his feet, and the car accelerates at 1.2 m/s^2. (*a*) What are the magnitude and direction of the acceleration of the center of mass of the car-truck system? (*b*) What vector sum of forces (magnitude and direction) is exerted on each vehicle? (*c*) What are the magnitude and direction of the acceleration of the truck? Ignore any friction between the tires and the parking lot surface. ••

78. A 70-kg skier is being towed on a rope behind a 450-kg snowmobile on a smooth, snow-covered surface at 10 m/s when the snowmobile hits a patch of muddy ground that brings it to a halt in 10 m. (*a*) What is the average acceleration of the snowmobile while it is slowing? (*b*) What is the average acceleration of the center of mass of the skier-snowmobile system? ••

79. A 4.0-kg block and a 2.0-kg block are connected to opposite ends of a relaxed spring of spring constant 300 N/m. The blocks are pushed toward each other for 0.50 s. The 4.0-kg block is pushed with a force of 50 N, and the 2.0-kg block is pushed with a force of 20 N. Ignore the inertia of the spring. (*a*) What is the acceleration of the center of mass of the two-block system while this pushing is going on? (*b*) When the blocks are released, what is the velocity of the 2.0-kg block if the 4.0-kg block is moving away from it at 5.0 m/s in the Earth reference frame? ••

8.12 Systems of many interacting objects

80. You push your 0.70-kg pillow across your bed with a constant force of 10 N. The bed provides a frictional force of 6.0 N. What is the acceleration of the center of mass of the pillow? •

81. You and a child are standing on a bathroom scale, which uses compression of a spring to measure the force exerted by your feet on the scale. What happens to the scale reading as you lift the child onto your shoulders? ••

82. You build a 2.0-kg mound of mashed potatoes on a kitchen scale (which is a spring scale). You then use a large spoon to press on the top of the mound at a constant force of 3.0 N. While you are doing this, the scale reading increases by 5.0%. (*a*) What is the acceleration of the center of mass of the potatoes? (*b*) Describe what happens to the shape of the mound and the scale reading as time goes by. ••

83. You use a rope of length ℓ to tie the front of a 1500-kg truck to the rear of a 1000-kg car and then use an identical rope of length ℓ to tie the front of the car to the rear of a 500-kg trailer. Each rope will break if its tension exceeds 2000 N. You attach a strong cable to the rear of the truck and use a winch to pull it with a force of magnitude *F*. (*a*) What is the acceleration of the three-vehicle system? (*b*) What is the maximum pulling force you can exert on the truck before a rope breaks? (*c*) If you now attach the cable to the front of the trailer and again pull the system, what is the maximum force with which you can pull it without snapping a rope? ••

84. A tugboat pulls two barges down the river. The barge connected to the tugboat, carrying coal, has an inertia of 2.0×10^5 kg, and the other barge, carrying pig iron, has an inertia of 3.0×10^5 kg. The resistive force between the coal barge and the water is 8.0×10^3 N, and the resistive force between the pig iron barge and the water is 10×10^3 N. The common acceleration of all three boats is $0.40\ \text{m/s}^2$. Even though the ropes are huge, the gravitational force exerted on them is much smaller than the pulling forces. (*a*) What is the tension in the rope that connects the tugboat to the coal barge? (*b*) What is the tension in the rope that connects the two barges? (*c*) Repeat parts *a* and *b* for the case in which the order of the barges is reversed. ••

85. A farmer is trying to haul three 500-kg trailers connected together with identical ropes that will break if their tension exceeds 2000 N. The first trailer is connected to his tractor with a rigid hitch. (*a*) If the tractor has to overcome a frictional force of 900 N per trailer to start them moving, what is the minimum force the tractor must exert on the first trailer to get them all rolling if the ropes are taut? (*b*) What is the maximum force the tractor can exert without breaking any rope? ••

86. A train engine is pulling four boxcars, each of inertia *m*. The engine can exert a force of magnitude *F* on what it is pulling. Assuming that friction can be ignored, what is the tension in each of the four couplers as the train starts off? ••

87. A red 10-kg cart is connected to a 20-kg cart by a relaxed spring of spring constant 60 N/m. The 20-kg cart is resting against another 10-kg cart, this one blue. All are on a low-friction track. You push the red 10-kg cart to the right, in the direction of the 20-kg cart, with a constant force of 10 N. (*a*) What is the acceleration of the center of mass of the three-cart system? (*b*) What is the acceleration of each cart the instant you begin to push? (*c*) What is the vector sum of the forces on each cart when the spring is compressed 100 mm? •••

PRACTICE

Additional Problems

88. A toy wagon initially at rest is pulled by a child from one end of a driveway to the other end. The magnitude of the force the wagon exerts on the child is the same as the magnitude of the force the child exerts on the wagon. So, how does the child get the wagon moving? •

89. In years past, car frames were built as stiff as possible, but today's cars are built with "crumple zones" in the front and rear portions of the frame. What is the purpose of this design change? •

90. A 60-kg student is in an elevator moving downward with constant velocity. He uses a bathroom scale to measure the upward force exerted on his feet. What force magnitude does the scale read (*a*) when the elevator is traveling at constant velocity, (*b*) when the elevator slows to a stop with an acceleration of magnitude $2.0\ \text{m/s}^2$, and (*c*) when the elevator starts downward again with an acceleration of magnitude $2.0\ \text{m/s}^2$? ••

91. You want to hang an object from the ceiling of an elevator that has a maximum acceleration of $4.0\ \text{m/s}^2$. (*a*) If you hang the object with fishing line that supports 45 N of force, what is the maximum inertia the object can have if the line is not to break? (*b*) What combination of slowing down, speeding up, going up, and going down of the elevator causes the greatest force to be exerted on the fishing line? ••

92. You need to lower a 45-kg safe from a window to the bed of a 1800-kg truck. You have a rope that is just long enough, but it will support no more than 42 kg. What must you be careful to do (or not to do) so that the rope does not break? ••

93. A 10-kg cart is connected to a 20-kg cart by a relaxed spring of spring constant 1000 N/m, and both carts are placed on a low-friction track. You push the 10-kg cart in the direction of the 20-kg cart with a constant force of 10 N. (*a*) What is the acceleration of the center of mass of the two-cart system at any instant? (*b*) What is the acceleration of each cart at the instant you begin to push? (*c*) What is the acceleration of each cart when the spring has its maximum compression? ••

94. A 5.0-kg block suspended from a spring scale is slowly lowered onto a vertical spring (Figure P8.94). (*a*) What does the scale read before the block touches the vertical spring? (*b*) If the scale reads 40 N when the bottom spring is compressed 30 mm, what is *k* for the bottom spring? (*c*) How far does the block compress the bottom spring when the scale reads 0? ••

Figure P8.94

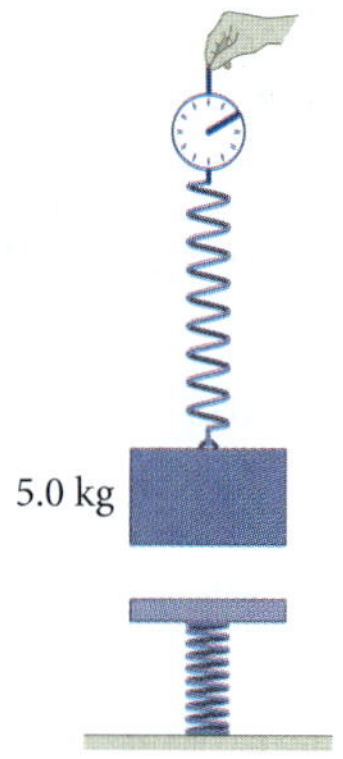

95. You need to lift a heavy load of inertia m_ℓ upward with an acceleration of magnitude $g/8$. You have two pulleys of inertia $m_p \ll m_\ell$, one attached to a beam above the loading dock and another that can be attached to the load. You consider a pulley system similar to that of Worked Problem 8.7, but you realize that these are double pulleys (each has two wheels side by side on a common axle) and you have a long piece of rope. ••• CR

96. You and your uncle are fishing. You are using 22-N fishing line, which means the line can support that much tension without breaking. Your uncle challenges you to catch the biggest fish you can land in the boat with that line, with the provision that you have to hoist the fish out of the water with the line and not with a net. You finally hook a fish that looks to have the right inertia, and you start to reel it in slowly. Just as you get the fish up into the air, though, the line snaps and the fish gets away. You accuse your uncle of having behind your back switched your pole to a line weaker than the 22-N line you thought you were working with, but he denies it. He then points out that you were accelerating the fish upward at $1.0\ \text{m/s}^2$. ••• CR

97. Your 70-kg friend always thinks he can dominate you in contests of strength because, even though you are a very athletic gymnast, your inertia is 63 kg. This time, while the gym class watches, he has attached a pulley to the ceiling of the gym, passed a rope over it, and tied one end of the rope around his waist. He hands you the other end of the rope, which is not quite long enough to reach the floor, and bets you that you cannot lift him off the ground by pulling on the rope. You realize that gravitational forces will favor your friend if the two of you are hanging on opposite sides of the pulley, but then you recall your amazing arm strength gained from years of work on gymnastic apparatus. ••• CR

98. A burst of compressed air pushes a pellet out of a blowpipe. The force exerted by the air on the pellet is given by $F(t) = F_0 e^{-t/\tau}$, where τ is called a *time constant* because it has units of time. (*a*) What does F_0 represent? (*b*) What is the momentum of the pellet after an interval equal to one time constant has elapsed? (*c*) What is the momentum after an interval equal to five time constants has elapsed? (*d*) What is the final momentum of the pellet after a long time interval has elapsed? (*e*) If $\tau = 0.50$ ms, after how long a time interval has the momentum reached 95% of its final value? •••

99. *Thrust* is the force that pushes a rocket forward. It is a force exerted on the rocket as the engine expels hot gases from the rear of the rocket. For most rockets, thrust is variable rather than constant during the "burn time" (the time interval during which fuel is consumed and expelled). However, the thrust of a certain rocket is nearly constant during part of its burn time, beginning when the rocket has consumed 40% of its fuel and continuing until the rocket has consumed about 90% of its fuel. As the rocket consumes and expels its fuel, its inertia decreases. Describe the rocket's acceleration during this interval of constant thrust. •••

Answers to Review Questions

1. No. An opposing force of equal magnitude might also be exerted on the object. For example, a book at rest on a table experiences two forces, the downward gravitational force exerted by Earth and the upward contact force exerted by the table, and yet no change in motion occurs. Also, a force exerted on an object can decrease the object's speed, as when a crate sliding along the floor comes to rest as a result of the frictional force exerted on it.
2. The fact that the velocity is constant tells you that the vector sum of forces is zero. No direction need be specified for a zero vector.
3. The vector sum of all forces exerted on an object equals the time rate of change in the object's momentum.
4. No. Forces always form interaction pairs. Whenever object 1 exerts a force on object 2, object 2 exerts an equal and opposite force on object 1.
5. No. The forces in an interactive pair are exerted on the two objects of the pair. The forces asked about here are $F_{\text{by cup on table}}$ and $F_{\text{by coffee on cup}}$. Because these forces do not involve the same two objects, they do not form an interaction pair. (Each force is one member of an interaction pair, though, and you should be able to name the other member of each pair.)
6. A contact force is one that arises when two objects physically touch each other (which, as seen in Chapter 7, means the surfaces of the two objects must approach within a few atomic diameters of each other in order to create an interaction). A field force is one due to an interaction between two objects that occurs even when the objects are not touching each other. Contact forces require physical contact, while field forces do not.
7. (*a*) Contact (a frictional force); (*b*) field (the gravitational force exerted by Earth); (*c*) field (the magnetic force); (*d*) contact (air touching the sails); (*e*) contact (the pulling force exerted by the rubber band)
8. Yes. The only requirement for translational equilibrium is that the vector sum of the forces being exerted on the object is zero.
9. Watch for changes in its momentum (and use an inertial reference frame to make your observations). An object in translational equilibrium experiences no change in momentum.
10. First, a dot to represent the object that is the focus of the diagram. Second, a vector arrow, with its tail on the dot, for each force exerted on the object. Each arrow is labeled with an **F** carrying a superscript that represents the type of force and a subscript that represents first the object *by* which the force is exerted and then the object *on* which the force is exerted. And third, a separate vector arrow indicating the direction of the acceleration of the object that is the focus of the diagram.
11. Drawing a free-body diagram allows you to separate and focus on a particular object in a system of interacting objects and to account for and keep track of the forces exerted on that object. The goal is to ensure that in analyzing the problem you do not overlook any forces that *are* exerted on the object or include any forces that are *not* exerted on the object.
12. Because all the forces included in the vector sum should already be shown on the diagram. Thus adding an arrow representing the vector sum might lead to double counting of forces.
13. (*a*) As the magnitude of the force exerted on the spring increases, the spring length changes in proportion to the magnitude of the force. If the force is compressing the spring, the length decreases. If the force is stretching the spring, the length increases. (*b*) The magnitude of the force exerted by the spring on the object is identical to that exerted by the object on the spring, so the change in length is still proportional to the magnitude of the force exerted by the spring on the object.
14. An elastic force is a force exerted by an object that is reversibly deformed (either stretched or compressed).
15. The force is undiminished when the gravitational force on the rope, spring, or thread is much less than the pulling force being exerted and much less than the gravitational force on the block—in other words, when the rope, spring, or thread has negligible inertia.
16. Acceleration. There is in general no direct relationship between the vector sum of forces and any other aspect of motion, such as velocity or position.
17. The inertia of the object must be constant.
18. First law: In an inertial reference frame, an isolated object (one on which no forces are exerted) has a constant velocity. Second law: The time rate of change of an object's momentum equals the vector sum of the forces exerted on the object. Third law: When two objects A and B interact, the force exerted by A on B is equal in magnitude to the force exerted by B on A, but the two forces point in opposite directions.
19. (*a*) The force of gravity exerted on an object is proportional to the object's inertia. Because the sack of apples has larger inertia than a single apple, the force of gravity exerted on the sack is larger. (*b*) The free-fall acceleration (g) is the same for both the sack of apples and a single apple because the acceleration of each object is the vector sum of the forces exerted on the object divided by the object's inertia. Thus the effect of larger inertia cancels.
20. No. Equation 8.17 was derived for an object in free fall, but it holds for any object near Earth's surface, even one at rest. Objects subject to multiple forces may have accelerations that differ from g, but they still experience the same gravitational force mg.
21. For a given spring, the numerical value of k is the same for both stretching and compression.
22. The symbol represents the position of the free end when the spring is relaxed (neither stretched nor compressed).
23. The slope represents $1/k$, the inverse of the spring constant k.
24. The impulse delivered to an object equals the product of the vector sum of the forces exerted on the object and the time interval over which the forces are exerted.
25. It is necessary to take into account the time dependence of the variable force (or forces). This can be done by direct integration, as in *Principles* Eq. 8.26, or by determining the average value for each variable force and including that value in *Principles* Eq. 8.25.
26. An internal force is exerted between two objects that are part of the chosen system. An external force is exerted by an object external to the system on an object that is part of the system.
27. The center of mass accelerates as if both objects were located at the system's center of mass and the external force were applied at this location.
28. The vector sum is zero.
29. All parts of a rigid object experience the same acceleration, but for a deformable object different parts of the object have different velocities and different accelerations. For a rigid object, the acceleration of each part is the same as the acceleration of the center of mass, but the same is not true for a deformable object.

Answers to Guided Problems

Guided Problem 8.2 $5.2 \times 10^4\ \text{N/m}$

Guided Problem 8.4 37 mm

Guided Problem 8.6 (*a*) $a = g/6 = 1.6\ \text{m/s}^2$; (*b*) $\mathcal{T} = 57\ \text{N}$

Guided Problem 8.8 $\mathcal{T}_{\text{support}} = \frac{3}{2}(m_p + m_b)(a + g) + m_p g$ reduces to $\mathcal{T}_{\text{support}} = \frac{3}{2} m_b (a + g)$ for $m_p = 0$

PRACTICE

9

PRACTICE
Work

Chapter Summary

Work done by a constant force (Sections 9.1, 9.2, 9.5, 9.6)

Concepts In order for a force to do work on an object, the point of application of the force must undergo a displacement.

The SI unit of work is the **joule** (J).

The work done by a force is positive when the force and the force displacement are in the same direction and negative when they are in opposite directions.

Quantitative Tools When one or more constant forces cause a particle or a rigid object to undergo a displacement Δx in one dimension, the work done by the force or forces on the particle or object is given by the **work equation:**

$$W = (\Sigma F_x)\Delta x_F. \tag{9.9}$$

In one dimension, the work done by a set of constant nondissipative forces on a system of particles or on a deformable object is

$$W = \sum_n (F_{\text{ext}\,nx}\Delta x_{Fn}). \tag{9.18}$$

If an external force does work W on a system, the **energy law** says that the energy of the system changes by an amount

$$\Delta E = W. \tag{9.1}$$

For a closed system, $W = 0$ and so $\Delta E = 0$.

For a particle or rigid object, $\Delta E_{\text{int}} = 0$ and so

$$\Delta E = \Delta K. \tag{9.2}$$

For a system of particles or a deformable object,

$$\Delta K_{\text{cm}} = (\Sigma F_{\text{ext}\,x})\Delta x_{\text{cm}}. \tag{9.14}$$

Energy diagrams (Sections 9.3, 9.4)

Concepts An **energy diagram** shows how the various types of energy in a system change because of work done on the system. (See the Procedure box on page 149.)

In choosing a system for an energy diagram, avoid systems for which friction occurs at the boundary because then you cannot tell how much of the thermal energy generated by friction goes into the system.

Variable and distributed forces (Section 9.7)

Concepts The force exerted by a spring is variable (its magnitude and/or direction changes) but nondissipative (no energy is converted to thermal energy).

The frictional force is dissipative and so causes a change in thermal energy. This force is also a distributed force because there is no single point of application.

Quantitative Tools The work done by a variable nondissipative force on a particle or object is

$$W = \int_{x_i}^{x_f} F_x(x)dx. \tag{9.22}$$

If the free end of a spring is displaced from its relaxed position x_0 to position x, the change in its potential energy is

$$\Delta U_{\text{spring}} = \tfrac{1}{2}k(x - x_0)^2. \tag{9.23}$$

If a block travels a distance d_{path} over a surface for which the magnitude of the force of friction is a constant F^f_{sb}, the energy dissipated by friction (the thermal energy) is

$$\Delta E_{\text{th}} = F^f_{sb}d_{\text{path}}. \tag{9.28}$$

PRACTICE

Power (Section 9.8)

Concepts **Power** is the *rate* at which energy is either converted from one form to another or transferred from one object to another.

The SI unit of power is the **watt** (W), where 1 W = 1 J/s.

Quantitative Tools The **instantaneous power** is

$$P = \frac{dE}{dt}. \tag{9.30}$$

If a constant external force $F_{\text{ext}\,x}$ is exerted on an object and the x component of the velocity at the point where the force is applied is v_x, the power this force delivers to the object is

$$P = F_{\text{ext}\,x} v_x. \tag{9.35}$$

Review Questions

Answers to these questions can be found at the end of this chapter.

9.1 Force displacement

1. What is the meaning of the term *work*?
2. Suppose you exert an external force on a system. Is work necessarily done on the system?

9.2 Positive and negative work

3. (*a*) A headwind pushes on a bicycle coasting eastward, slowing the bicycle down. What is the sign of the work done by the wind on the bicycle? (*b*) If the same wind pushes in the same direction on a bicycle initially at rest and moves the bicycle westward, what is the sign of the work done by the wind on the bicycle?
4. You throw a ball up into the air and then catch it. How much work is done by gravity on the ball while it is in the air?
5. Can the work done by a spring ever be negative?

9.3 Energy diagrams

6. In a system in which all the energy is mechanical, the initial and final energies are $K_i = 10.0$ J, $K_f = 3.0$ J, $U_i = +4.0$ J, $U_f = +6.0$ J. Sketch an energy diagram for the system.
7. A cart is at rest but free to move on a low-friction track. When you push and release the cart, it travels at constant speed to the right until it strikes a spring fixed to the end of the track. After a short time interval in contact with the spring, the cart moves back toward you at the same constant speed it had as it approached the spring. Sketch energy diagrams for the cart during these time intervals: (*a*) from the initial resting state until traveling at constant speed to the right, (*b*) from traveling at constant speed to the right until the spring is fully compressed, (*c*) from spring being fully compressed until traveling to the left at constant speed, (*d*) from the initial resting state until traveling to the left at constant speed.

9.4 Choice of system

8. Why should you avoid choosing a system that has a frictional force exerted across the system boundary?
9. When computing energies, should the gravitational interaction be associated with work, with potential energy, or with both?
10. What is the utility of analyzing an energy problem using more than one choice of system?

9.5 Work done on a single particle

11. State the relationship between work and energy in words.
12. Does the energy law (Eq. 9.1) apply to closed systems? To systems that are not closed?
13. Equations 9.8 and 9.9 are valid only for a particle. Why?
14. Discuss the similarities and differences in the momentum law (Eq. 4.18, $\Delta\vec{p} = \vec{J}$) and the energy law (Eq. 9.1, $\Delta E = W$).
15. In what sense is a crate a particle? Under what circumstances would it be inappropriate to treat a crate as a particle in working a physics problem?

9.6 Work done on a many-particle system

16. How does the energy law (Eq. 9.1) applied to a single particle differ from the energy law applied to a many-particle system? How does the work equation (Eq. 9.9) applied to a single particle differ from the work equation applied to a many-particle system?
17. Why is Eq. 9.18 restricted to nondissipative forces?
18. How does the change in kinetic energy of a many-particle system differ from the work done on the system by its environment?

9.7 Variable and distributed forces

19. When you plot the force exerted on a particle as a function of the particle's position, what feature of the graph represents the work done on the particle?
20. (*a*) In $W_{bs} = \frac{1}{2}k(x - x_0)^2$, the expression obtained in *Principles* Example 9.8 for the work done by a brick in compressing or stretching a spring, where does the factor $\frac{1}{2}$ come from? (*b*) If the force exerted by a load on a spring is $F_{\ell s\,x} = k(x - x_0)$ (Eq. 8.18) and the force displacement is $x - x_0$, why isn't W_{bs} just $F(x - x_0) = k(x - x_0)(x - x_0) = k(x - x_0)^2$?
21. You use Eq. 9.27 or Eq. 9.28 to calculate the thermal energy dissipated by friction as a crate slides across the floor and eventually comes to rest. Could this thermal energy be called the work done on the crate by the frictional force?

9.8 Power

22. How is instantaneous power related to average power?
23. When is the instantaneous power delivered to an object equal to the magnitude of the vector sum of the forces $\sum F_{\text{ext}}$ exerted on the object multiplied by the object's speed?

Developing a Feel

Make an order-of-magnitude estimate of each of the following quantities. Letters in parentheses refer to hints below. Use them as needed to guide your thinking.

1. The minimum work required to lift a large bag of groceries from floor to tabletop (D, J)
2. The energy dissipated when you stand on the top of an empty soda can and flatten the can (B, L, T)
3. The minimum work the engine must do to bring a fully loaded, 18-wheel truck from rest to freeway speed (A, K, Q)
4. The spring constant of a bungee cord (E, H, N, V)
5. The minimum power required to pitch a fastball like a professional baseball player (C, I, S)
6. The power provided to a car by the engine while cruising at freeway speed (F, M, U, Y)
7. The average electrical power used in your home during a typical day (R, G, W)
8. The electrical energy used in a typical U.S. home during a year (R, G, W, O, X)
9. The amount of chemical (source) energy needed to supply electrical power for residential consumption in the United States during one year (R, G, W, O, X, P, Z)

Hints

A. What is the inertia of a loaded 18-wheeler?
B. What is the gravitational force exerted by Earth on you?
C. What is the typical speed of a major league fastball?
D. What is the gravitational force exerted on a large bag of groceries?
E. What is the height of a typical bungee jump?
F. How many kilometers per liter of gasoline do you get cruising at freeway speed?
G. How much power is used during peak consumption hours?
H. What is the unstretched length of a bungee cord?
I. What is the inertia of a baseball?
J. What is the height of a typical table?
K. What is a typical freeway speed?
L. Through what displacement is the force exerted?
M. How much chemical (source) energy is available in 1 L of gasoline?
N. What is the relevant energy change?
O. How many seconds are in 1 year?
P. What is the number of residences in the United States?
Q. Does all the work done by the engine go into changing the truck's kinetic energy?
R. How much power is consumed by a typical appliance?
S. How long a time interval does a pitcher's forward throwing motion require?
T. How does the force you exert on the can relate to the gravitational force exerted by Earth on you?
U. What percentage of the energy in the gasoline is transferred to the drive wheels of the car?
V. What is a typical inertia of a bungee jumper?
W. During what percentage of a full day do you consume electricity at the peak consumption rate?
X. How is the amount of energy consumed related to the average power?
Y. How long a time interval is required to travel 100 km?
Z. What is the efficiency of source energy conversion, including transmission losses?

Key (all values approximate)

A. 3×10^4 kg; **B.** 7×10^2 N; **C.** 4×10^1 m/s; **D.** 1×10^2 N; **E.** 8×10^1 m; **F.** 1×10^1 km/L; **G.** 6×10^3 W; **H.** 3×10^1 m; **I.** 0.2 kg; **J.** 1 m; **K.** 3×10^1 m/s; **L.** 0.1 m; **M.** 4×10^7 J; **N.** gravitational potential energy becomes spring potential energy; **O.** 3×10^7 s; **P.** 90 million; **Q.** we assume it does in order to determine the minimum work; **R.** 100 W for lamps and most small appliances; 1000 W for refrigerators, microwave ovens, irons, toasters, bathroom heaters; 5000 W for central air conditioners; **S.** 0.5 s; **T.** about equal in magnitude; **U.** less than 20%; **V.** 7×10^1 kg; **W.** less than 30%; **X.** $\Delta E = P_{av}\Delta t$; **Y.** 1 h; **Z.** about 10%

Worked and Guided Problems

Procedure: Drawing energy diagrams

1. Specify the **system** under consideration by listing the components inside the system.
2. **Sketch** the system in its initial and final states. (The initial and final states may be defined for you by the problem, or you may have to choose the most helpful states to examine.) Include in your sketch any external forces exerted on the system that undergo a nonzero force displacement, and draw a dot at the point of application of each force.
3. Determine any nonzero **changes in energy** for each of the four categories of energy, taking into account the four basic energy-conversion processes illustrated in Figure 7.13:

   a. Did the speed of any components of the system change? If so, determine whether the system's kinetic energy increased or decreased and draw a bar representing ΔK for the system. For positive ΔK, the bar extends above the baseline; for negative ΔK, it extends below the baseline. (For some problems you may wish to draw separate ΔK bars for different objects in the system; if so, be sure to specify clearly the system component that corresponds to each bar and verify that the entire system is represented by the sum of the components.)

   b. Did the configuration of the system change in a reversible way? If so, draw a bar representing the change in potential energy ΔU for the system. If necessary, draw separate bars for the changes in different types of potential energy, such as changes in elastic and gravitational potential energy.

   c. Was any source energy consumed? If so, draw a bar showing ΔE_s. Source energy usually decreases, making ΔE_s negative, and so the bar extends below the baseline. Keep in mind that conversion of source energy is always accompanied by generation of thermal energy (Figure 7.13*c* and *d*).

   d. Does friction occur within the system, or is any source energy consumed? If so, draw a bar showing ΔE_{th}. In nearly all cases we consider, the amount of thermal energy increases, and so ΔE_{th} is positive.
4. Determine whether or not any **work** W is done by external forces on the system. Determine whether this work is negative or positive. Draw a bar representing this work, making the length of the bar equal to the sum of the lengths of the other bars in the diagram.

   If no work is done by external forces on the system, leave the bar for work blank, then go back and adjust the lengths of the other bars so that their sum is zero.

These examples involve material from this chapter but are not associated with any particular section. Some examples are worked out in detail; others you should work out by following the guidelines provided.

Worked Problem 9.1 Trash that

A janitor starts to push a 75-kg trash can that is initially at rest across a level surface by exerting a constant horizontal force of 50 N. After moving 10 m, the trash can has a speed of 2.0 m/s. (*a*) What are the magnitude and direction of the frictional force exerted by the surface on the can? (*b*) What power does the janitor provide at the 10-m mark?

❶ GETTING STARTED
(*a*) The work done by a force equals the magnitude of the force multiplied by the force displacement. The pushing force and the frictional force are both exerted over a known displacement to change the can's kinetic energy. The can accelerates, so the janitor must provide a force larger than the frictional force. The frictional force opposes the sliding motion, so it is directed in the opposite direction to the janitor's push. We could take the can as our system. However, that would mean the force of friction is exerted at the system boundary (and then we don't know how much of the dissipated energy ends up inside the system). So instead we choose the can and the floor as our system. Figure WG9.1 shows the can and floor system in its initial and final states, the force displacement Δx_F, and the single applied external force (friction is internal!). We need to keep track of components, so we arbitrarily choose the positive x axis along the direction of motion of the can (to the right in Figure WG9.1)

Figure WG9.1

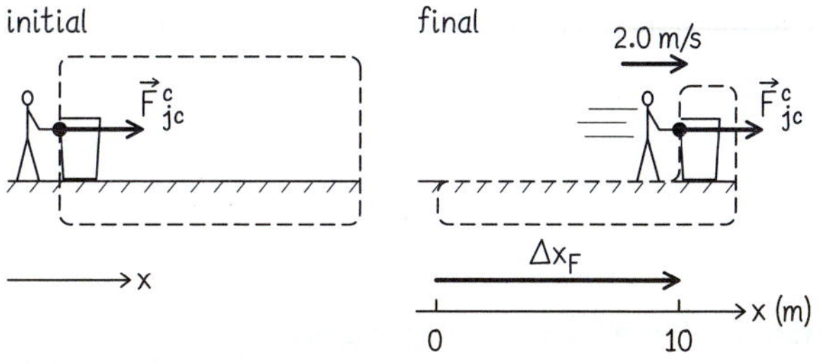

(*b*) Because we know the constant force exerted by the janitor and the can's speed once it has moved 10 m, we can use the product of force and speed to obtain the power delivered at the 10-m position.

2 DEVISE PLAN The surface does not move and so does not contribute to the system kinetic energy. Because the can is rigid, its contribution to the system kinetic energy is computed using the can's center-of-mass motion. The center of mass of the can experiences exactly the same displacement as any other point on the can, which is the force displacement. There is no potential energy to consider (no vertical motion to involve gravity, no springs) and no source energy in our system. The energy law allows us to account for the changes in kinetic energy, thermal energy, and work. We draw an energy diagram (Figure WG9.2) to summarize this information. We have an expression for each of these terms: The change in kinetic energy can be computed from given information, the frictional force is responsible for the change in thermal energy, and the janitor's force is responsible for the work done.

Figure WG9.2

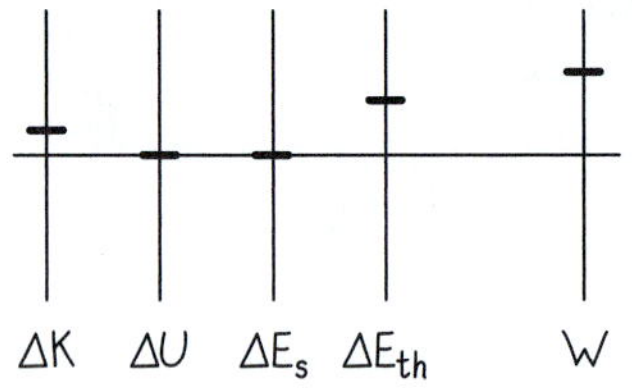

(*a*) We know the change in kinetic energy, the displacement, and the magnitude of the force exerted by the janitor. Thus the only unknown is the one we are asked to calculate: The magnitude of the frictional force. (*b*) Because the only external force that has a force displacement is exerted by the janitor, and that force is constant, the power at any instant is given by Eq. 9.35, $P = F_{\text{ext}\,x}v_x$. We know both the force and the speed at the requested location, so we can obtain the power.

3 EXECUTE PLAN

(*a*) We begin with the energy law, Eq. 9.1:

$$\Delta E = \Delta K + \Delta U + \Delta E_s + \Delta E_{th} = W.$$

The thermal energy change ΔE_{th} is caused by the frictional force, so we can employ Eq. 9.27 to make the relationship explicit:

$$\Delta E_{th} = -F^f_{scx}\Delta x_{cm}.$$

Similarly, we use Eq. 9.9 to express W in terms of the force exerted by the janitor and then substitute both expressions into the energy law:

$$\Delta K + 0 + 0 + (-F^f_{scx}\Delta x_{cm}) = F^c_{jcx}\Delta x. \quad (1)$$

Because the can is rigid, $\Delta x_{cm} = \Delta x$. Substituting this and our usual expression for kinetic energy into Eq. 1 and rearranging terms gives

$$\tfrac{1}{2}mv_f^2 - \tfrac{1}{2}mv_i^2 = F^c_{jcx}\Delta x + F^f_{scx}\Delta x$$

$$\tfrac{1}{2}mv_f^2 - 0 = F^c_{jcx}\Delta x + F^f_{scx}\Delta x$$

$$F^f_{scx} = \frac{\tfrac{1}{2}mv_f^2}{\Delta x} - F^c_{jcx} = \frac{\tfrac{1}{2}(75\text{ kg})(2.0\text{ m/s})^2}{10\text{ m}} - (+50\text{ N}) = -35\text{ N}.$$

Because we chose to the right as the positive x direction in Figure WG9.1, the negative value for F^f_{scx} tells us that the direction of the frictional force is to the left. The magnitude of the frictional force is 35 N. ✔

(*b*) The power delivered by the janitor is

$$P = F_{\text{ext}\,x}v_x = (+50\text{ N})(+2.0\text{ m/s}) = 1.0 \times 10^2\text{ W}. ✔$$

4 EVALUATE RESULT The frictional force is directed to the left and has a magnitude smaller than the force exerted by the janitor, as we expected.

We can also check our answer with kinematics because constant forces imply constant acceleration. The acceleration of the trash can is related to the initial and final speeds and the displacement by (see *Principles* Example 3.4)

$$a_x = \frac{v_{x,f}^2 - v_{x,i}^2}{2\Delta x} = \frac{(2.0\text{ m/s})^2 - 0^2}{2(10\text{ m})} = +0.20\text{ m/s}^2.$$

If we take just the can as our system, the vector sum of forces exerted on the can must therefore be

$$\sum F_{\text{ext}\,x} = ma_x = (75\text{ kg})(+0.20\text{ m/s}) = +15\text{ N}.$$

Knowing this value allows us to solve for the frictional force:

$$\sum F_{\text{ext}\,x} = F^c_{jcx} + F^f_{scx} = +50\text{ N} + F^f_{scx} = +15\text{ N}$$

$$F^f_{scx} = +15\text{ N} - 50\text{ N} = -35\text{ N}$$

in agreement with our previous result.

The power we obtained is that of a 100-W light bulb. The amount of power required to lift a textbook at a constant 0.33 m/s is about 10 W, so this janitor is working about ten times as hard to accelerate the heavy trash can to 2.0 m/s by the end of the 10-m trip. Doing 1 chin-up per second, however, requires an average power of more than 200 W for a 60-kg individual, so the 100 W we obtained is not unreasonable.

PRACTICE

Guided Problem 9.2 Delivering a piano

A moving company decides it's easier to hoist a 150-kg piano up to a second-floor apartment with a pulley rather than negotiate a narrow stairway. The piano is hoisted with a rope to the level of a window 5.3 m above the ground and temporarily brought to rest. How much work is done on the piano (*a*) by the rope and (*b*) by the force of gravity? (*c*) If it takes 1.0 min to hoist the piano, what average power must be supplied by the hoist?

1 GETTING STARTED

1. What is a good choice of system? Should Earth be included in the system? Sketch the system in its initial and final states.
2. Can the piano be treated as a rigid object? How is the motion of its center of mass related to the motion of any other part of it?

3. Draw an energy diagram. Note that the piano is at rest both before and after it is hauled up.
4. Are there external forces exerted on the system? If so, what is the force displacement for each?

❷ DEVISE PLAN

5. How is the change of the system's energy related to the work done on the system by external forces? What formula expresses this relationship?
6. Is it reasonable to ignore any friction in the pulley so you can say that no energy is dissipated?
7. Is there enough information to solve for the unknowns?

❸ EXECUTE PLAN

8. Calculate the requested results.
9. Does the person running the hoist do work on the piano?

❹ EVALUATE RESULT

10. How does your calculated power compare with the power needed to walk up the stairs to the first floor in the same 1-min time interval?
11. Does the power calculated in part *c* seem reasonable for lifting a piano?

Worked Problem 9.3 Human cannonball

A circus performer of inertia m is launched into the air by a "cannon" that contains a spring platform for which the spring constant is k. The performer climbs into the cannon, compressing the spring. Then the spring is additionally compressed (by a winch) so that the initial position of the platform is a distance d below the position of the platform when the spring is relaxed (Figure WG9.3). (*a*) What maximum speed does the performer attain after launch? (*b*) How high above the relaxed position of the spring platform does the performer fly? Ignore any dissipative interactions, and analyze both parts of the problem using two systems: one that allows you to solve the problem using potential energy but not work and one that allows you to solve the problem using work but not potential energy.

Figure WG9.3

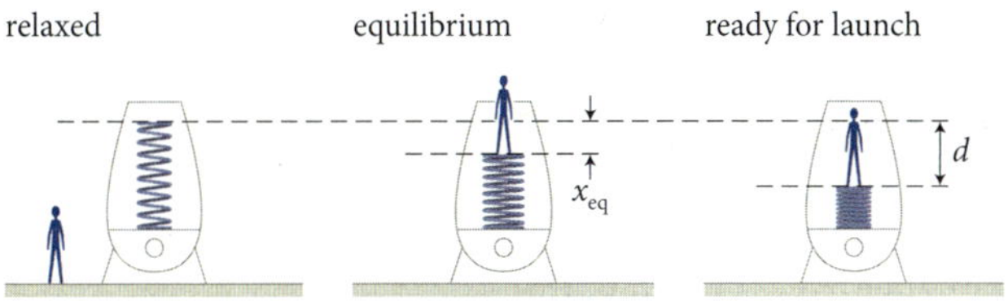

❶ GETTING STARTED For a performer launched from rest by a compressed spring, we must determine the performer's maximum speed and maximum height. We must treat the performer as a particle or rigid object because there is no information that allows us to do otherwise. The release of the spring causes the performer to shoot straight up, and at the highest point of his trajectory he has zero instantaneous velocity as his direction of travel reverses. Because the force exerted by the spring is not constant, using a force approach to solve this problem would give us nonconstant acceleration, which means we cannot use constant-acceleration formulas to get the maximum height.

In choosing our systems, we must consider all the forces that might affect the performer's motion. We are told to ignore dissipative forces, and so it appears that the force exerted by the spring and the gravitational force are the crucial ones. This means we have two interaction pairs: spring-performer and Earth-performer. In order to use potential energy for the gravitational and spring forces, we must include both objects from each pair in our system. We can make this system closed and isolated by including the cannon and the ground underneath it. So system 1 is cannon, spring, performer, and Earth.

To solve the problem by analyzing the work done on the performer, we recall that only forces external to a system can do work on the system. Thus we define system 2 as being only the performer, so that the forces exerted on him are all external forces.

We know that the performer's speed is zero both initially and at his greatest height, and we know the formulas for the elastic and gravitational potential energies and for the work done by each force. The problem requires us to think about two different final instants during the motion: In part *b* we have $t_f =$ the instant the performer reaches his greatest height, but in part *a* we have $t_f =$ the instant he has his highest speed. We therefore analyze parts *a* and *b* separately, using the same initial position but a different final position in each case. But where, exactly, does the performer achieve the maximum speed? There are two forces that affect the speed of the performer: the gravitational force and the spring force. The gravitational force is constant and directed downward. The spring force is not constant and is directed upward. In order for the performer to accelerate upward, the spring force must exceed the gravitational force. As long as this is true, the performer gains speed by accelerating upward. The spring force gets smaller as the performer rises and the spring begins to relax. At some point the spring force must become smaller than the gravitational force so that the performer no longer accelerates upward but begins to accelerate downward, slowing his speed. Thus the maximum speed occurs when the spring force equals the gravitational force so that the performer is instantaneously in equilibrium. This is the position labeled "equilibrium" in Figure WG9.3 (though in that figure the performer is not moving).

Figure WG9.4 shows a time sequence of events, including the instant of launch, the equilibrium position of maximum speed, and the position of maximum height.

Figure WG9.4

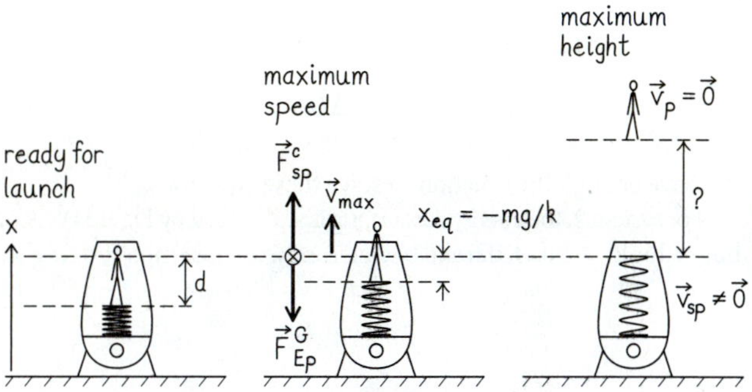

Now we produce an energy diagram for each system, beginning with the performer ready for launch and including the position of maximum speed as well as the position of maximum height (Figure WG9.5). Note that we separate the potential energy into two parts (elastic potential energy U_{sp} in the spring and the performer's gravitational potential energy U^G relative to Earth) and we do the same for work (work W_{sp} done by the spring on the performer and work W_g done by gravity on him).

Figure WG9.5

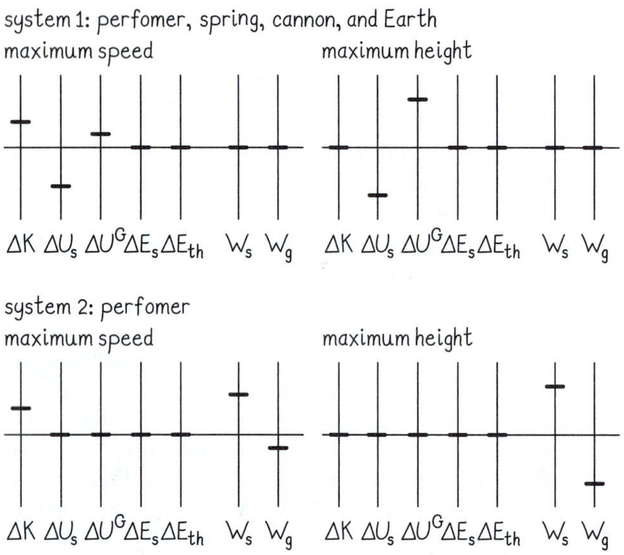

❷ **DEVISE PLAN** Using Figure WG9.5 as a guide, we write for the change in system 1 energy from launch to maximum speed

$$\Delta E_{\text{sys 1}} = \Delta K + \Delta U + \Delta E_s + \Delta E_{th} = 0$$

$$\Delta K + \Delta U_{sp} + \Delta U^G + 0 + 0 = 0$$

$$\Delta K + \Delta U_{sp} + \Delta U^G = 0. \quad (1)$$

For the maximum height computation, both the initial and final kinetic energies of the performer are zero. The spring and platform may continue to move up and down after the performer's feet leave the platform. However, any kinetic energy involved in the final motion of the spring and platform can be expressed as remaining spring potential energy because at the turning points of their motion the energy is entirely potential. This gives

$$\Delta E_{\text{sys 1}} = \Delta K + \Delta U + \Delta E_s + \Delta E_{th} = 0$$

$$\Delta U_{sp} + \Delta U^G = 0. \quad (2)$$

We have enough information to solve these equations.

For system 2, the energy accounting is still guided by Figure WG9.5, but it looks a bit different because now we are not looking at any potential energy changes in the system. For maximum speed we have

$$\Delta E_{\text{sys 2}} = \Delta K + \Delta U + \Delta E_s + \Delta E_{th} = W$$

$$\Delta K + 0 + 0 + 0 = W$$

$$\Delta K = W_g + W_{sp}. \quad (3)$$

For maximum height, we do not have to concern ourselves with any energy remaining in the system due to the motion of the spring because the spring and platform are not part of system 2. This makes the accounting a bit easier:

$$\Delta E_{\text{sys 2}} = \Delta K + \Delta U + \Delta E_s + \Delta E_{th} = W$$

$$0 + 0 + 0 + 0 = W$$

$$W_{sp} + W^G = 0 \quad (4)$$

Because the spring force and the gravitational force are exerted over different force displacements, we track them separately. The gravitational force is exerted during the entire motion, but the spring force is exerted only during the time interval from the last instant at which the spring is in its launch (maximum compression) position to the instant when it reaches equilibrium for Eq. 3, and the position at which performer contact is lost for Eq. 4.

❸ **EXECUTE PLAN**

(*a*) For either system 1 or system 2 maximum speed, the initial position is $x_i = -d$, and the final position is found by imposing the equilibrium condition (that the spring force and gravitational force cancel). The free-body diagram (see Figure WG9.4) can be used to solve for the final position. With the positive x axis directed upward and the origin at the relaxed position, both $\vec{x}_f$ and $\vec{g}$ have negative x components:

$$\Sigma\vec{F} = \vec{0}$$

$$\vec{F}^c_{sp} + \vec{F}^G_{Ep} = \vec{0}$$

$$-k(\vec{x}_f) + m(\vec{g}) = \vec{0}$$

$$-kx_f - mg = 0$$

$$x_f = x_{eq} = -\frac{mg}{k}.$$

The initial speed is zero, so for system 1 we can solve Eq. 1 for the final speed (maximum speed):

$$\Delta K + \Delta U_{sp} + \Delta U^G = 0$$

$$\tfrac{1}{2}mv_{max}^2 - \tfrac{1}{2}mv_i^2 + \tfrac{1}{2}kx_{eq}^2 - \tfrac{1}{2}kx_i^2 + mg(x_{eq}) - mg(x_i) = 0$$

$$\tfrac{1}{2}mv_{max}^2 - 0 + \tfrac{1}{2}k\left[\left(\frac{-mg}{k}\right)^2 - (-d)^2\right]$$

$$+ mg\left[\left(\frac{-mg}{k}\right) - (-d)\right] = 0$$

$$v_{max}^2 = \frac{k}{m}\left[d^2 - \left(\frac{m^2g^2}{k^2}\right)\right] - 2g\left(d - \frac{mg}{k}\right).$$

This expression can be simplified algebraically by combining the second and fourth terms on the right-hand side and then noting that the expression can be factored:

$$v_{max}^2 = \frac{k}{m}\left(d^2 - \frac{2mgd}{k} + \frac{m^2g^2}{k^2}\right)$$

$$v_{max}^2 = \frac{k}{m}\left(d - \frac{mg}{k}\right)^2$$

$$v_{max} = \sqrt{\frac{k}{m}}\left(d - \frac{mg}{k}\right). ✔$$

We now compute the maximum speed for system 2, using Eq. 3:

$$\Delta K = W_g + W_{sp}$$

$$\tfrac{1}{2}mv_{max}^2 - 0 = -mg\left(d - \frac{mg}{k}\right) + \tfrac{1}{2}k\left(d^2 - \frac{m^2g^2}{k^2}\right)$$

$$v_{max}^2 = -2g\left(d - \frac{mg}{k}\right) + \frac{k}{m}\left(d^2 - \frac{m^2g^2}{k^2}\right)$$

$$v_{max} = \sqrt{\frac{k}{m}}\left(d - \frac{mg}{k}\right). ✔$$

(*b*) For the maximum height calculation we must first determine the position at which performer contact is lost. The spring and platform exert a force on the performer given by Hooke's law—that is, a force whose magnitude is proportional to the stretch or compression of the spring, and whose direction is opposite to the displacement of the spring from its relaxed position. However, the performer is not attached to the platform, so the force applied to the performer can be in only the upward direction. That means the performer can experience a force from the spring only when the platform is below the position labeled "relaxed" in Figure WG9.3. We designate the final position of the spring and platform $x_{sp,f}$ and the final position of the performer $x_{p,f}$. The initial position of both objects is still the same, $x_i = -d$. Substituting Eq. 9.23 for the spring potential energy and Eq. 7.19, $\Delta U^G = mg\Delta x$, for the gravitational potential energy in Eq. 2, we have

$$\Delta E_{sys\,1} = \Delta U_{sp} + \Delta U^G = 0$$

$$\tfrac{1}{2}kx_{sp,f}^2 - \tfrac{1}{2}kx_{sp,i}^2 + mgx_{p,f} - mgx_{p,i} = 0$$

$$0 - \tfrac{1}{2}k(-d)^2 + mgh - mg(-d) = 0$$

$$mgh = \tfrac{1}{2}kd^2 - mgd$$

$$h = \frac{kd^2}{2mg} - d. ✔$$

Now we repeat for system 2, noting that the spring force varies with position but the gravitational force does not. Equation 4 gives us

$$W_{sp} + W_g = 0$$

$$\int_{x_{sp,i}}^{x_{sp,f}} F_{sp\,x}^c dx + F_{Ep\,x}^G(x_{p,f} - x_{p,i}) = 0$$

$$+\tfrac{1}{2}k(-d)^2 - mg[+h - (-d)] = 0$$

$$\tfrac{1}{2}kd^2 - mg(h + d) = 0$$

$$h = \frac{kd^2}{2mg} - d. ✔$$

❹ **EVALUATE RESULT** Having obtained the same answers with two systems gives us confidence in the results. As a further check, consider how the height depends on the spring constant: A larger k gives a greater height, as expected. We also expect the performer to rise higher if his inertia is smaller. The only place the performer's inertia appears in our expression for h is in the denominator, which is consistent with our expectation.

Our expression for the maximum speed tells us that d must exceed mg/k in order to get a positive result. This is reasonable because mg/k is the distance by which the spring would compress if the performer were simply standing on the platform; certainly that would not be enough for any launch! Additionally, our expression for h tells us that, to give a sensible result, d must exceed not mg/k but rather $2mg/k$. For small compressions beyond equilibrium, it is reasonable that the performer would not be launched at all—that is, would not lose contact with the platform, but would simply ride up and down with the spring and platform.

Guided Problem 9.4 Thrill seeking

A 50-kg woman goes bungee-jumping off a bridge that is 15 m above the ground. The bungee cords attached to her feet have a relaxed length of 5.5 m, and she is 1.8 m tall. What must the spring constant of the cords be if she is to just miss touching the ground with her head when she jumps?

❶ **GETTING STARTED**

1. What system is appropriate for this problem? Sketch the initial and final situations, showing such details as the relaxed length of the cords, the woman's height, the bridge height, and an x axis.
2. As usual, several approaches are possible, some easier than others. Try energy methods first.
3. Make an energy diagram and a situation diagram for your system.
4. What assumptions do you make?

❷ **DEVISE PLAN**

5. Write a general expression for the changes in energy during an appropriate time interval for the jump.
6. Check that the number of unknowns and the number of equations are the same.

❸ **EXECUTE PLAN**

7. Do the algebra and isolate the spring constant.
8. Substitute your numerical values, including units.

❹ **EVALUATE RESULT**

9. Examine your expression for the spring constant. What happens to k as the woman's inertia increases? As the bridge height increases?
10. Does the numerical answer make sense? Be sure it is the woman's head that just misses the ground and not her feet!
11. Are all assumptions you made reasonable?

Worked Problem 9.5 Working on the railroad

A train engine pulls a boxcar of inertia 12×10^3 kg, which in turn pulls a boxcar of inertia 17×10^3 kg. The train accelerates from rest to 11.1 m/s in 3.0 min. (*a*) How much work is done by the engine on the two-car combination? (*b*) How much work is done on each car individually? Ignore any friction effects.

❶ **GETTING STARTED** The work done by a force equals the magnitude of the force multiplied by the force displacement. We need to determine all forces exerted by any external objects on each car, and how far its point of application moves during the common 3.0-min time interval. The only displacement is horizontal, in the direction of motion of the train, which we will call the positive x direction. Thus only horizontal forces need be considered. Because the train cars are connected and move together, each point on each car has the same displacement as the engine. Therefore each applied force has the same force displacement, $\Delta\vec{x}_F$.

For part *a* we need to calculate the work done by the engine on the two-car combination, and so we take the two cars as our system. If we ignore any dissipative forces, there is one external horizontal force on the system, the pulling contact force $\vec{F}^c_{e1}$ exerted by the engine on the two-car combination. For part *b* we treat each car separately. Figure WG9.6 contains an initial and final sketch of each system, together with an energy diagram for each system.

Figure WG9.6

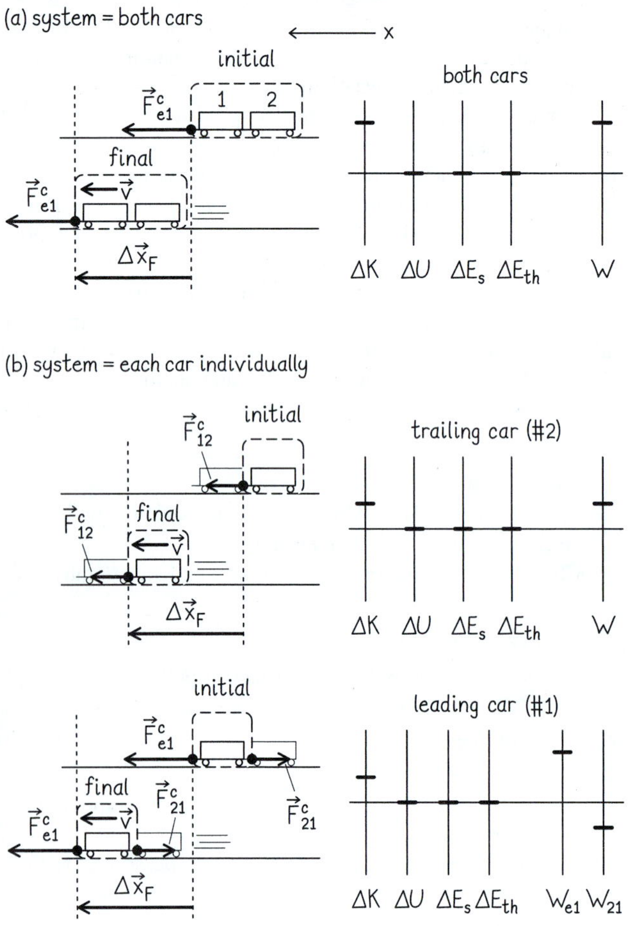

For the system consisting of the trailing car (car 2), there is also one external force that does work: the force exerted by the leading car (car 1). We call this force $\vec{F}^c_{12}$. For the system consisting of the leading car (car 1), there are two external forces that do work: the force exerted by the engine on car 1 ($\vec{F}^c_{e1}$) and the force exerted by car 2 on car 1 ($\vec{F}^c_{21}$). All three systems share some properties: No system has an internal source of energy, each system gains kinetic energy during the 3.0-min time interval of interest, and each experiences work done by external forces. Because we ignore any friction effects, we expect no thermal energy changes in any of the systems.

❷ **DEVISE PLAN** For each of the three systems we begin with the energy law, which in each case can be expressed as

$$\Delta E = \Delta K = W.$$

This expression tells us that the work done on each system depends on *only* the change in the velocity of that system. It does not depend on the time interval over which the force is exerted or on the magnitude of the acceleration. We can compute the change in kinetic energy directly in each case.

❸ **EXECUTE PLAN** Each system has zero initial kinetic energy, and each has a specific final kinetic energy. The difference of these values is the work done by external forces on each system.

(*a*) For the system of two cars, we obtain

$$W = \Delta K = K_f - K_i = \tfrac{1}{2}(m_1 + m_2)v^2 - 0$$

$$W = \tfrac{1}{2}(12 \times 10^3\ \text{kg} + 17 \times 10^3\ \text{kg})(11.1\ \text{m/s})^2$$

$$W = 1.8 \times 10^6\ \text{J}. ✔$$

(*b*) Here we must apply the energy law to each system (car) separately. For the leading car (car 1):

$$W = \Delta K = K_f - K_i = \tfrac{1}{2}(m_1)v^2 - 0$$

$$W = \tfrac{1}{2}(12 \times 10^3\ \text{kg})(11.1\ \text{m/s})^2$$

$$W_1 = 7.4 \times 10^5\ \text{J} ✔$$

For the trailing car (car 2):

$$W = \Delta K = K_f - K_i = \tfrac{1}{2}(m_2)v^2 - 0$$

$$W = \tfrac{1}{2}(17 \times 10^3\ \text{kg})(11.1\ \text{m/s})^2$$

$$W_2 = 1.0 \times 10^6\ \text{J}. ✔$$

❹ **EVALUATE RESULT** These two work values add up (to within rounding error) to the work done on the two-car system by the engine: $W_1 + W_2 = W$. This is reassuring. The only assumption we made is that the force exerted by the engine is the only external force exerted on the two-car system, and that assumption is valid because we were told to ignore friction effects. Based on our knowledge of the energy law, we should have recognized from the beginning that the time interval given was an extraneous piece of information.

Guided Problem 9.6 Fast as a speeding bullet

Because a fired bullet moves so quickly, determining its speed directly is difficult. Here is an indirect way. You fire the bullet (of inertia m_{bullet}) into a block of inertia m_{block} placed against a spring of spring constant k (Figure WG9.7), and the bullet becomes embedded in the block. If the spring compresses to a maximum distance d, what was the speed of the bullet? Ignore friction between the block and the surface on which it rests.

Figure WG9.7

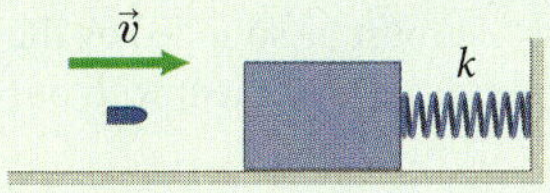

❶ GETTING STARTED

1. How do you expect the compression distance to be related to the speed of the bullet? In other words, what should happen to the compression distance as the speed of the bullet is increased?
2. What can you say about the coefficient of restitution?
3. What kind of energy conversions occur after the collision?
4. Is it reasonable to consider the collision and the compression of the spring separately?

❷ DEVISE PLAN

5. How can you determine the speed of the block with the bullet embedded in it as the spring begins to compress?
6. For what system is the mechanical energy constant from the time immediately after the collision until the spring is fully compressed?

❸ EXECUTE PLAN

❹ EVALUATE RESULT

7. Does your expression for v_{bullet} show that the speed varies as you expect with changes in d, k, m_{bullet}, and m_{block}?

Worked Problem 9.7 Spring forward

One end of a spring of force constant k is attached to a wall, and the other end is attached to a block of inertia m sitting on a horizontal desk (Figure WG9.8). You pull on the block to stretch the spring a distance d past its relaxed position, and then hold the block at that position. A steady wind exerts on the block a constant force directed to the left, opposite the direction in which you moved the block. When you release the block, it moves to the left, experiencing a frictional force of magnitude F^{f}_{sb} until equilibrium is reached with the spring compressed a distance $2d$ from its relaxed position. What is the magnitude of the force exerted by the wind on the block?

Figure WG9.8

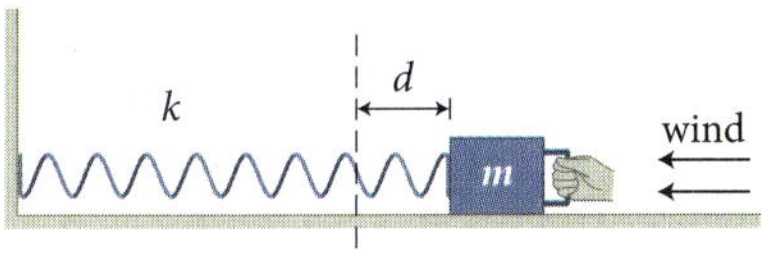

❶ GETTING STARTED Because three horizontal forces are exerted on the block (by the spring, friction, and the wind), we might be tempted to solve this as a force problem. We note, however, that the spring exerts a variable force, which means the acceleration is not constant and we cannot use constant-acceleration kinematics. Because we can calculate the potential energy of the spring and the amount of energy dissipated by the friction interaction, this problem might be solved by energy methods. The force of the wind is constant, and we can readily calculate any work done by this force. Choosing as our system the block, spring, and desk makes both the frictional and spring forces internal forces, so the only work done will be by the wind. Also, at maximum compression, the block's kinetic energy is zero, as it is the instant before you release it. Figure WG9.9 illustrates the initial and final situations and shows an energy diagram.

Figure WG9.9

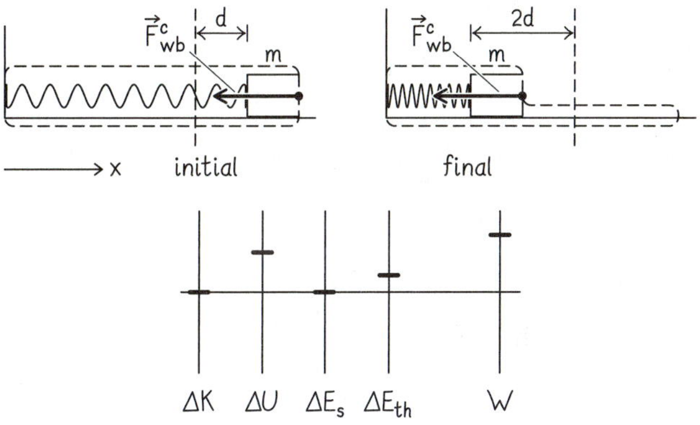

❷ DEVISE PLAN We begin with the energy law, $\Delta E = W$ (Eq. 9.1), with W being the work done on the system by the wind force:

$$\Delta E = W$$

$$\Delta K + \Delta U_{\text{spring}} + \Delta E_s + \Delta E_{\text{th}} = W. \tag{1}$$

Our goal is to determine F^{c}_{wb}, the magnitude of the contact force exerted by the wind on the block, and we know from the definition of work that here $W = F^{c}_{wb}\,\Delta x_F$, where Δx_F is the displacement of the point of application of the force exerted by the wind. Because the wind exerts a force on the right face of the block, Δx_F is equal to the displacement Δx of the block (which, in turn, is equal to the displacement of the end of the spring). Thus, if we know each term on the left in Eq. 1, we can determine F^{c}_{wb}. There is no source energy for this system, and the initial and final speeds of the block are both zero, which makes $\Delta K = 0$. All we need to do is substitute into Eq. 1

the algebraic expressions for the spring's potential energy and the change in the amount of thermal energy dissipated by friction. We choose an x axis along the direction of motion of the block, with the positive direction pointing to the right in Figure WG9.9.

❸ EXECUTE PLAN The potential energy of a spring displaced from its relaxed length is given by Eq. 9.23, $\Delta U_{\text{spring}}(x) = \frac{1}{2}k(x - x_0)^2$, and the energy dissipated by friction (Eq. 9.28) is the magnitude of the frictional force F^{f}_{db} exerted by the desk on the block multiplied by the distance traveled (which in this case is $|\Delta x|$). With x_0 representing the block's position with the spring relaxed, Eq. 1 becomes

$$0 + \tfrac{1}{2}k(x_{\text{f}} - x_0)^2 - \tfrac{1}{2}k(x_{\text{i}} - x_0)^2 + 0 + |F^{\text{f}}_{\text{db}\,x}|\,|\Delta x| = F^{\text{c}}_{\text{wb}\,x}\Delta x$$

$$\tfrac{1}{2}k(x_{\text{f}} - x_0)^2 - \tfrac{1}{2}k(x_{\text{i}} - x_0)^2 + |F^{\text{f}}_{\text{db}\,x}|\,|x_{\text{f}} - x_{\text{i}}| = F^{\text{c}}_{\text{wb}\,x}(x_{\text{f}} - x_{\text{i}}).$$

Now we substitute in values from Figure WG9.9:

$$\tfrac{1}{2}k(-2d - 0)^2 - \tfrac{1}{2}k(+d - 0)^2 + |F^{\text{f}}_{\text{db}\,x}|\,|-2d - (+d)|$$

$$= F^{\text{c}}_{\text{wb}\,x}[-2d - (+d)]$$

$$\tfrac{1}{2}k(4d^2) - \tfrac{1}{2}kd^2 + F^{\text{f}}_{\text{db}}(3d) = -F^{\text{c}}_{\text{wb}}(-3d)$$

$$\tfrac{3}{2}kd^2 + 3F^{\text{f}}_{\text{db}}d = 3F^{\text{c}}_{\text{wb}}d$$

$$F^{\text{c}}_{\text{wb}} = \tfrac{1}{2}kd + F^{\text{f}}_{\text{sb}}. \checkmark$$

❹ EVALUATE RESULT We expect that as F^{f}_{sb} increases, the wind needs to blow harder in order to achieve the same final spring compression. Indeed, if F^{f}_{db} increases, F^{c}_{wb} increases, as predicted by our equation. As k decreases, less wind is needed to achieve the same compression, which is also reflected in our result.

The variation with d involves two opposing effects. As the distance d the spring is stretched increases, more initial elastic potential energy $(\frac{1}{2})(kd^2)$ is stored in the spring. However, an even greater amount $(\frac{1}{2})k(2d)^2 = 2kd^2$ must be stored in the maximally compressed spring. The larger d is, the greater the difference in spring potential energy that must be supplied by the external work done by the wind force. This is in agreement with our result.

Guided Problem 9.8 Darting about

A dart gun uses a compressed spring ($k = 2000$ N/m) to shoot a 0.035-kg dart horizontally at a target 1.0 m away. The spring is originally compressed 25 mm before the dart is released. (*a*) With what speed does the dart leave the gun? (*b*) If the dart penetrates the target to a distance of 10 mm, what average force is exerted on the dart to stop it?

❶ GETTING STARTED

1. How are the two questions related?
2. There are several approaches to solving this problem, some easier than others.
3. Choose an appropriate system and make an energy diagram.
4. Based on your chosen approach, which general equation is appropriate?

❷ DEVISE PLAN

5. Are there external forces exerted on your system? Should you worry about gravity in a horizontal flight over a short distance?
6. Check that you have enough equations for your unknowns.
7. How can you use the dart speed to determine the change in the dart's kinetic energy as it comes to a stop in the target?
8. What causes the dart to slow down? What formula relates the change in kinetic energy to the distance of penetration?

❸ EXECUTE PLAN

❹ EVALUATE RESULT

9. Examine the algebraic expression for the dart's speed. What happens as k gets bigger? Is this what you expect? What about when m (the inertia of the dart) gets bigger?
10. If the frictional force is the same at any depth, does the penetration depth you expect vary properly when making k or m bigger or smaller?
11. Is it reasonable to ignore the effect of gravity on the dart?

Questions and Problems

For instructor-assigned homework, go to MasteringPhysics®

Dots indicate difficulty level of problems: • = *easy,* •• = *intermediate,* ••• = *hard;* CR = *context-rich problem.*

9.1 Force displacement

1. If an impulse is delivered to a system, is work necessarily done on the system? •
2. Hitting a door with your bare fist hurts more than hitting a sofa cushion. In work terms, explain why this is so. •
3. If you drop a brick from a height of 50 mm onto your toe, it probably won't hurt much, but if you drop the brick from a height of 0.5 m, it will hurt. The force of gravity exerted on the brick is the same in both cases. Explain why it hurts more from the increased height. ••
4. An object moves with constant velocity. What can you say about the work done on a system that includes only this object? ••
5. You hold a small steel ball in your hand above a laundry basket. Then you throw it straight up and watch as it rises, falls, and comes to rest in the pile of dirty laundry. Ignoring friction, discuss the forces exerted on the ball, the force displacements associated with those forces, and the work done by each force during this process. ••

9.2 Positive and negative work

6. The x component of velocity of a particle as a function of time is shown in Figure P9.6. Over what intervals is the work done on the particle (*a*) positive, (*b*) negative, (*c*) zero? •

Figure P9.6

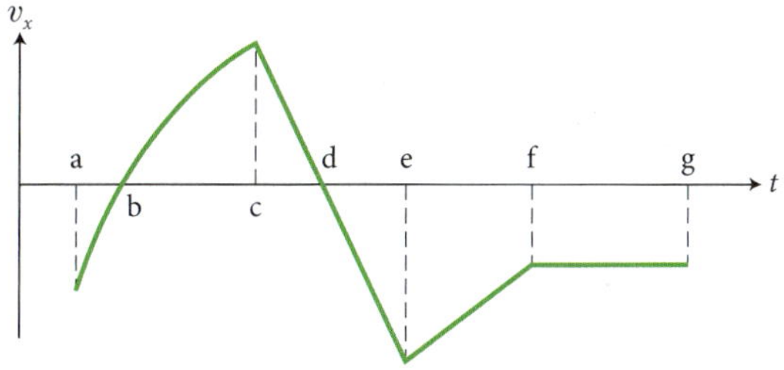

7. When you stand up from a seated position, you push down with your legs. Does this mean you do negative work when you stand up? •
8. Mountain climbers know that it is harder to hike down a hill than to walk on level ground. Why is this so? ••
9. As a car accelerates from rest to highway speed, a pedestrian watching the motion sees positive work done on the car because its kinetic energy increases. However, from the reference frame of someone driving in the same direction at highway speed, the car is initially moving (backward) and then becomes stationary, corresponding to negative work. Which observer is right? ••
10. A system consists of two interacting particles 1 and 2, with particle 1 confined to an x axis and the system in equilibrium when particle 1 is at a given position on that axis. If displacing particle 1 in either direction from this position requires positive work to be done on the system by an external force, what is the shape of the potential energy curve (as a function of position) for the system in the region near equilibrium? •••

9.3 Energy diagrams

11. Does work done on a system necessarily change the system's kinetic energy? •
12. Taking off on a runway, a small jet experiences a forward force of 90,000 N exerted by the engine and a backward force of 16,000 N exerted by the air. Choose a system and draw an energy diagram using the beginning and end of the runway as your initial and final positions. ••
13. A block launched at speed v down an incline slides down the incline (there is friction between the block and incline) and into a spring (Figure P9.13), where it slows to zero speed as the spring compresses. (*a*) Draw an energy diagram for this process using a system consisting of the block, spring, Earth, and incline. If there is more than one object causing energy conversions, use a separate bar for each. (*b*) Repeat part *a* using a system of just the block and incline. (*c*) Why can't you use the block alone as your system? ••

Figure P9.13

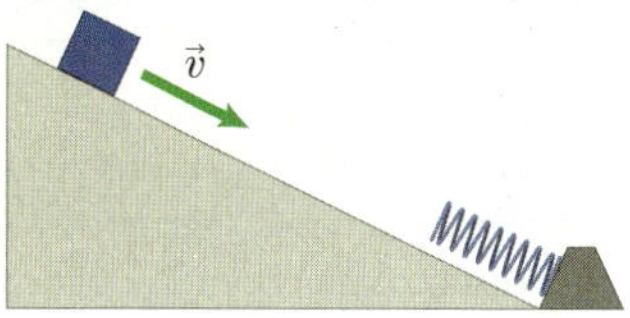

14. What, if anything, is wrong in the energy diagram in Figure P9.14 for a system comprising Earth, an inclined plane, and a block sliding along the incline? The block slides down the incline at constant speed. The only forces exerted on the block are the force of gravity and friction with the incline. ••

Figure P9.14

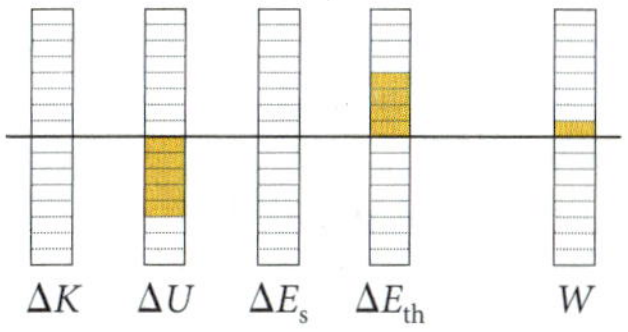

15. What possible scenario is described by the energy diagram in Figure P9.15? •••

Figure P9.15

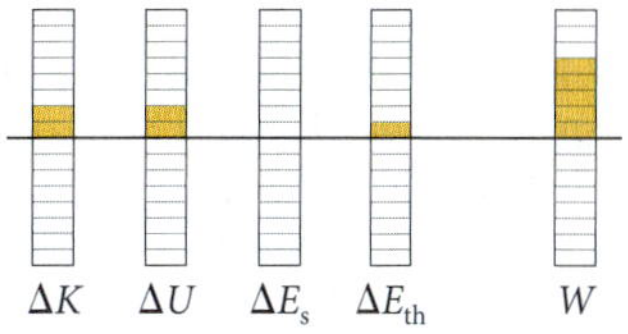

9.4 Choice of system

16. You are lifting a ball at constant velocity. (*a*) When the system is the ball, is work done on the system? If so, by what agent(s)? (*b*) Describe the potential energy of this system during the lift. (*c*) When the system comprises the ball and Earth, is work done on the system? If so, by what agent? (*d*) Describe how the potential energy of the ball-Earth system changes during the lift. •
17. You throw a ball straight up into the air. If air resistance affects the motion of the ball, which takes longer: the upward trip or the downward trip? Analyze using three different systems. •

PRACTICE

18. A tomato is launched vertically from a spring-loaded toy cannon placed on the pavement. The tomato rises to some maximum height and then falls back, but you have removed the cannon so that the tomato splats on the pavement. Discuss the energy conversions during this process using the following systems: (*a*) tomato, cannon, air, Earth, pavement; (*b*) tomato, cannon, air, pavement; (*c*) tomato, air, pavement; and (*d*) tomato. ••

19. Two identical balls collide elastically. If we treat each ball as a separate system, is the work done on each ball the same? ••

9.5 Work done on a single particle

20. How much work does gravity do on a 2.0-mg raindrop as the drop falls to the ground from a cloud 2000 m above the ground? •

21. At the end of a delivery ramp, a skid pad exerts a constant force on a package so that the package comes to rest in a distance *d*. When the pad is replaced by one that requires a distance of 2*d* to stop the same package, what happens to the length of time it takes for the package to stop? •

22. At the end of a delivery ramp, a skid pad exerts a constant force on a package so that the package comes to rest in a distance *d*. The ramp is changed so that the same package arrives at the skid pad at a higher speed and the stopping distance is 2*d*. What happens to the time interval required for the package to stop? •

23. A 55-kg acrobat must jump high and land on his brother's shoulders. To accomplish this, he leaps from a crouched position to a height where his center of mass is 1.20 m above the ground. His center of mass is 400 mm above the ground in the crouch and 900 mm above the ground when his feet leave the ground. (*a*) What is the average force exerted on him by the ground during the jump? (*b*) What is his maximum speed? ••

24. A beetle that has an inertia of 4.0×10^{-6} kg sits on the floor. It jumps by using its muscles to push against the floor and raise its center of mass. (*a*) If its center of mass rises 0.75 mm while it is pushing against the floor and then continues to travel up to a height of 300 mm above the floor, what is the magnitude of the force exerted by the floor on the beetle? (*b*) What is the beetle's acceleration during the motion? ••

25. A bicyclist pedals a distance *d* at constant speed on a level stretch of road. She then pedals up a hill and passes slowly over the top. As she coasts down the other side of the hill, she applies the brakes and comes to a stop when she is a distance *d* past the top (Figure P9.25). Choose an appropriate system and draw an energy diagram from the instant the bicyclist begins her climb until the instant she has stopped on the downslope. ••

Figure P9.25

26. In emergency braking, a certain car requires 7.0 m to come to a stop from an initial speed of 10 m/s. Use an argument based on work done on the car to determine the braking distance required if the car's initial speed is 30 m/s. ••

27. At instant t_0, you are sitting on a dock and you begin using a rope to lower a 4.0-kg lobster trap into the water, 1.4 m below. You lower the trap at a constant speed of 1.0 m/s. At instant t_1 it just reaches the water surface 1.4 m below the dock. You slacken the rope and the trap continues to move downward at a constant speed of 1.0 m/s until at instant t_2 the trap reaches the bottom of the 10-m-deep bay. Choose a system that includes the water, Earth, and the trap. (*a*) Do you do any work on the system in the interval from t_0 to t_2? (*b*) What forces are exerted on the trap during the interval from t_0 to t_2? (*c*) Draw an energy diagram for the interval from t_0 to t_2, showing a correct numerical scale. ••

28. A 1.1-kg lobster climbs into the trap of Problem 27, and at instant t_3 you begin to haul the trap up onto the dock. The trap moves at a constant 0.40 m/s through the water, and it breaks the surface of the water at instant t_4. You adjust your pull so that it continues moving at that speed until it reaches the height of the dock at instant t_5. Use a system of water, Earth, trap, and lobster. (*a*) Do you do any work on the system in the interval from t_3 to t_5? (*b*) What forces are exerted on the trap as it rises? (*c*) Draw an energy diagram for this system from instant t_3 to instant t_5. In your diagram, there are two kinds of energy you have to combine because you have no way to separate them from each other. Indicate this in your labels. ••

29. A 20-kg child runs up the amusement-park wave slide shown in Figure P9.29. When she is nearly at the top of the first hump, which is 0.90 m above the water, she flops down and slides over the top of the hump at 1.5 m/s. She slides down the other side of the hump and then up the slide, until she reverses motion at a height of 0.95 m above the water. What is the increase in thermal energy of the child and the slide due to the sliding from the top of the hump to the top of her motion? ••

Figure P9.29

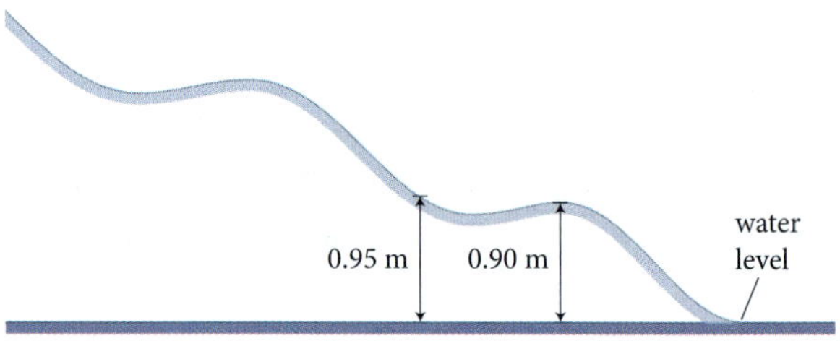

30. In the block-and-tackle arrangement shown in Figure P9.30, three segments of the single rope pull on the block. (*a*) Show that the magnitude F^c_{pr} of the force exerted by a person on the rope to raise the block at constant speed is $mg/3$, where m is the inertia of the block. (*b*) One worker uses this arrangement to lift a heavy block, while another hauls up an identical block with a straight rope. After both blocks have been raised to the same second-floor window, has either worker done more work than the other? If so, which worker has done more work? ••

Figure P9.30

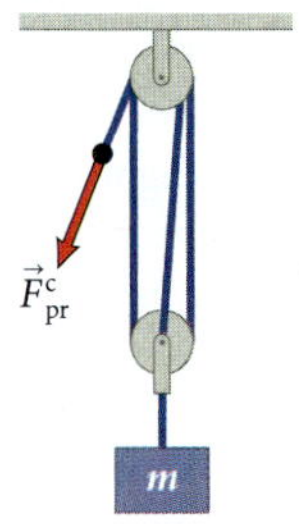

31. The pair of pulleys shown in Figure P9.31 is used to lift a 50-kg block 0.25 m. The constant acceleration of the block during the lift is $+2.5\ \text{m/s}^2$, and the pulleys and rope have negligible inertia and negligible friction. What is the tension (*a*) in the pulling rope and (*b*) in the rope from which the block hangs? (*c*) What force is exerted by the upper mount on the top pulley? (*d*) How much work is done by the person pulling the rope in lifting the block 0.25 m? (*e*) By how much does the kinetic energy of the block change in this process? (*f*) How much work is done on the block by the rope attached to it? (*g*) How much work does the ceiling do in this process? (*h*) How much work does Earth do on the block? (*i*) Draw energy diagrams for three systems during the lifting: block; block and Earth; block, Earth, pulleys, rope, and person. •••

Figure P9.31

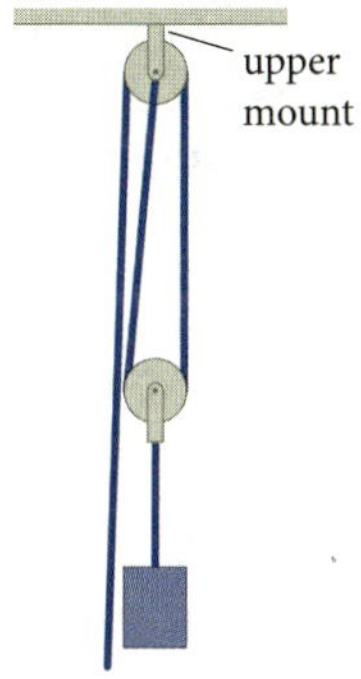

9.6 Work done on a many-particle system

32. You push a blob of gelatin with a constant force of 3.0 N across a wet table on which it slides easily. Because the blob shape distorts, its center of mass moves only 30 mm during the time interval in which the point of application of your force moves 50 mm. (*a*) What is the work done by you on the blob? (*b*) By how much does your force change the kinetic energy of the center of mass? •

33. A 1000-kg car traveling at 5.0 m/s runs into the side of an underpass. The concrete wall is not affected, but the car crumples such that in the time interval from the instant of impact to the instant at which the car comes to rest, its center of mass travels forward 0.50 m. What are (*a*) the magnitude of the average force exerted on the car, (*b*) the work done by the wall on the car, and (*c*) the change in kinetic energy of the car's center of mass? •

34. A 60-kg ice skater stands facing a wall with his arms bent and then pushes away from the wall by straightening his arms. At the instant at which his fingers lose contact with the wall, his center of mass has moved 0.50 m, and at this instant he is traveling at 3.0 m/s. What are (*a*) the average force exerted by the wall on him, (*b*) the work done by the wall on him, and (*c*) the change in the kinetic energy of his center of mass? •

35. Two 0.50-kg carts, one red and one green, sit about half a meter apart on a low-friction track. You push on the red one with a constant force of 2.0 N for 0.15 m and then remove your hand. The cart moves 0.35 m on the track and then strikes the green cart. (*a*) What is the work done by you on the two-cart system? (*b*) How far does the system's center of mass move while you are pushing the red cart? (*c*) By what amount does your force change the kinetic energy of the center of mass of the system? ••

36. Two 0.50-kg carts are pushed toward each other from starting positions at either end of a 6.0-m low-friction track. Each cart is pushed with a force of 3.0 N, and that force is exerted for a distance of 1.0 m. (*a*) What is the work done on the two-cart system? (*b*) What is the change in kinetic energy of the system? (*c*) What is the kinetic energy of the center of mass of the system? ••

37. You have a 2.0-m chain lying on the floor alongside ten 0.10-kg cubical blocks, each 0.20 m on a side. Each block is resting on the floor, and the inertia of the chain is 1.0 kg. Which process requires less work: lifting one end of the chain so that the chain hangs vertically with the bottom link just touching the floor, or stacking the blocks in a column ten blocks tall? ••

38. A 1.0-kg cart and a 0.50-kg cart sit at different positions on a low-friction track. You push on the 1.0-kg cart with a constant 2.0-N force for 0.15 m. You then remove your hand, and the cart slides 0.35 m and strikes the 0.50-kg cart. (*a*) What is the work done by you on the two-cart system? (*b*) How far does the system's center of mass move while you are pushing the 1.0-kg cart? (*c*) By what amount does your force change the kinetic energy of the system's center of mass? ••

39. Two 1.0-kg blocks, one gray and one tan, are lined up along a horizontal x axis. The gray block is at $x = -4.0$ m, and the tan one is at $x = +4.0$ m. A constant force of 1.0 N is exerted on the gray block in the positive x direction through a distance of 2.0 m. Taking the two blocks as the system and ignoring friction, calculate the following over the interval required for the gray block to move from $x = -4.0$ m to $x = -2.0$ m: (*a*) the work done on the system, (*b*) the change in the energy of the system, (*c*) the change in the kinetic energy of the system's center of mass, and (*d*) the value of $F\Delta x_{cm}$, where $F = 1.0$ N and Δx_{cm} is the displacement of the system's center of mass. (*e*) If the blocks collide totally inelastically, what is the energy of the system after the collision? ••

40. Two identical 0.50-kg carts, each 0.10 m long, are at rest on a low-friction track and are connected by a spring that is initially at its relaxed length of 0.50 m and is of negligible inertia. You give the cart on the left a push to the right (that is, toward the other cart), exerting a constant 5.0-N force. You stop pushing at the instant when the cart has moved 0.40 m. At this instant, the relative velocity of the two carts is zero and the spring is compressed to a length of 0.30 m. A locking mechanism keeps the spring compressed, and the two carts continue moving to the right. (*a*) What is the work done by you on the two-cart system? (*b*) How far does the system's center of mass move while you are pushing the left cart? (*c*) By what amount do you change the system's kinetic energy? ••

41. Because the soles of your shoes have cleats, you can exert a forward force of 100 N even on slippery ice. A 10-kg picnic cooler is at rest on a frozen pond, and you want to get it to shore, up the bank, and stuck in the snow. From past experience, you know that, in order to move up the bank and stick, the cooler needs to be moving at 3.0 m/s at the instant it starts up the bank. Standing some distance from the cooler and not wanting to walk to it, you decide to throw 1.0-kg snowballs at it to get it moving. If each snowball smashes into the cooler in a totally inelastic collision, what minimum number of snowballs must you throw? •••

PRACTICE

42. A bullet of inertia m traveling at speed v is fired into a wooden block that has inertia $4m$ and rests on a level surface. The bullet passes through the block and emerges with speed $v/3$, taking a negligible amount of the wood with it. The block moves to the right but comes to rest after traveling a distance d. (*a*) What is the magnitude of the frictional force between the block and the surface while the block is moving? (*b*) What is the ratio of the energy dissipated as the bullet passes through the block to the energy dissipated by friction between the surface and the bottom face of the block? •••

43. You fire a bullet of inertia m into the block shown in Figure P9.43. The bullet is initially traveling at speed v, and the inertia of the block is $4m$. The surface on which the block sits is rough, and the spring has spring constant k. The bullet becomes embedded in the block. If the spring compresses a maximum distance d, what is the magnitude of the frictional force exerted by the surface on the block while the block is moving? •••

Figure P9.43

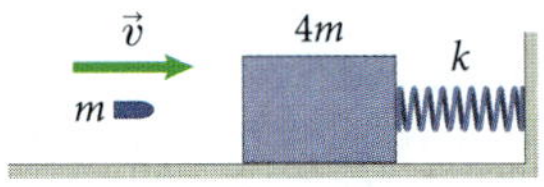

9.7 Variable and distributed forces

44. Spring B is stiffer than spring A. Which one has more energy stored in it if you (*a*) compress both springs with the same force and (*b*) compress both springs the same displacement from their relaxed lengths? •

45. Which arrangement in Figure P9.45 requires more work to give the block a rightward displacement $\vec{d}$? The springs, blocks, and surfaces are identical in the two arrangements and the springs are initially at their relaxed length. •

Figure P9.45

46. Estimate the work done by the force plotted in Figure P9.46 for an object displaced from $x = 1.0$ m to $x = 3.0$ m. •

Figure P9.46

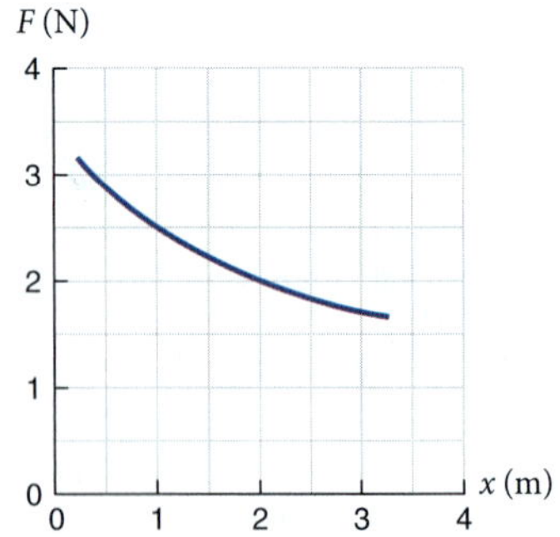

47. Stretching a certain spring 0.10 m from its relaxed length requires 18 J of work. How much more work does it take to stretch this spring an additional 0.10 m? •

48. A force varies with time according to the expression $F = a\Delta t$, where $a = 2.0$ N/s. From this information, can you determine the work done on a particle that experienced this force over a displacement of 0.50 m? ••

49. In pushing a 0.024-kg dart into a toy dart gun, you have to exert an increasing force that tops out at 6.0 N when the spring is compressed to a maximum value of 0.12 m. (*a*) What is the launch speed of the dart when fired horizontally? (*b*) Does your answer change if the dart is fired vertically? ••

50. The work done by a certain force is given by $W(\Delta x) = a\Delta x + b(\Delta x)^3$. Write an expression for the force as a function of Δx. ••

51. A 6.0-kg bowling ball is held 10 mm above a mattress and then released from rest and allowed to fall, sinking into the mattress. Model the mattress as a single spring with spring constant $k = 500$ N/m. (*a*) Calculate the ball's kinetic energy, the gravitational potential energy of the system (ball, spring, and Earth), and the elastic potential energy at the following compressions: 0, 0.050 m, 0.10 m, 0.15 m, 0.20 m. (*b*) What is the maximum compression of the mattress? Ignore the inertia of the spring. ••

52. In a carnival game, the player throws a ball at a haystack. For a typical throw, the ball leaves the hay with a speed exactly one-half of the entry speed. (*a*) If the frictional force exerted by the hay is a constant 6.0 N and the haystack is 1.2 m thick, derive an expression for the typical entry speed as a function of the inertia of the ball. Assume horizontal motion only, and ignore any effects due to gravity. (*b*) What is the typical entry speed if the ball has an inertia of a 0.50 kg? ••

53. The force exerted on a certain object varies with the object's position according to the function $F_x(x) = ax^2 + bx^3$ where $a = 3.0$ N/m^2 and $b = -0.50$ N/m^3. What is the work done on the object by this force as the object moves from $x = -0.40$ m to $x = 2.0$ m? ••

54. You devise a wind-up car powered by a spring for trips to the grocery store. The car has an inertia of 500 kg and is 4.2 m long. It should be able to accelerate from rest to 20 m/s at least 50 times before the spring needs winding. The spring runs the length of the car, and a full winding compresses it to half this length. In order to meet the acceleration requirement, what must the value of the spring constant be? ••

55. A 0.15-kg cart on wheels is at rest at the origin of an x axis between (but not connected to) two relaxed springs aligned along that axis. When the cart is pushed to the left of the origin, the left spring ($k_l = 4.0$ N/m) is compressed and exerts a force on the cart. When the cart is pushed to the right of the origin, the right spring ($k_r = 6.0$ N/m) is compressed and exerts a force on the cart. (*a*) Plot the force exerted on the cart as a function of its displacement. (*b*) If the cart is given an initial speed of 4.0 m/s at the origin $x = 0$, it might be headed to the left or to the right. How far does it go in each case? (*c*) What is the work done on the cart as it moves from $x = 0$ to its extreme right position and from $x = 0$ to its extreme left position? Ignore any friction effects. •••

56. To complement the baseball-pitching machines at the sports complex where you work, you have designed a catching machine using a mitt, a spring, and a latch that locks the spring in place when the ball has stopped moving. Your boss wants to know the speed of the baseballs coming out of a pitching machine that's been breaking down lately, and you figure you can use the compression of the spring in your catching machine to determine this speed. The mitt that catches the balls has three times the inertia of one ball. Derive an expression for the speed of a thrown ball in terms of the ball's inertia, the distance the spring is compressed, and the spring constant. Take the catch to be a totally inelastic collision between mitt and ball. ●●●

9.8 Power

57. Suppose a jogger has to exert a force of 25 N against air resistance to maintain a velocity of $+5.0\ \text{m/s}$. At what rate is the jogger expending energy? ●

58. A 35-kg girl climbs a 10-m rope in 25 s. What is her average power? ●

59. Hiking trails on steep slopes often zigzag back and forth rather than running in a straight path up the slope. What does having a zigzag path accomplish, given that getting to the top of the slope requires the same amount of energy regardless of the path? ●

60. Your 1000-kg car, moving at 7.0 m/s, approaches the bottom of a hill that is 20 m high (Figure P9.60). To save gas, you use on average only 3.3 kW of engine power, realizing that half of the energy delivered by the engine and half of the initial kinetic energy will be dissipated. If you calculated correctly, your car will just barely make it over the hill. What time interval is required for your car to travel from the bottom to the top of the hill? ●●

Figure P9.60

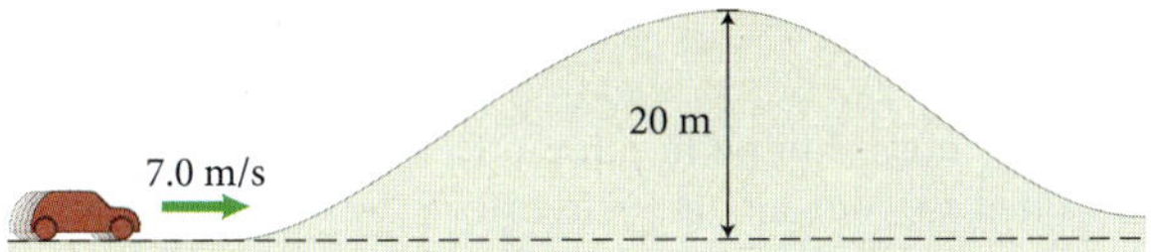

61. A constant, nondissipative external force is exerted on a particle. Is the same work done on the particle each second? ●●

62. A team of dogs accelerates a 200-kg dogsled from 0 to 5.0 m/s in 3.0 s. (*a*) What is the magnitude of the force exerted by the dogs on the sled? (*b*) What is the work done by the dogs on the sled in the 3.0 s? (*c*) What is the instantaneous power of the dogs at the end of the 3.0 s? (*d*) What is their instantaneous power at 1.5 s? Assume that the acceleration is constant. ●●

63. A 20-kg child wants to slide along a horizontal yard toy that consists of a slick plastic sheet covered with a thin layer of water to reduce friction to almost zero. To cause him to slide, you squirt him with a stream of water from a hose. (*a*) If the water from the hose exerts a constant force of 5.0 N on the child, what is the work done by the water in the interval from $t = 0$ to $t = 1.0$ s? (*b*) What is the instantaneous power delivered by the water at $t = 1.0$ s? ●●

64. A cog system on the beginning segment of a roller coaster needs to get 25 occupied cars up a 100-m vertical rise over a time interval of 60 s. Each car experiences a gravitational force of 5670 N. The cars start at rest and end up moving at 0.50 m/s. (*a*) How much work is done by the cog system on the cars? (*b*) What average power must the cog system supply? (*c*) What would happen to the amount of work done by the cog system if the cars had to be lifted the same distance in 30 s? ●●

65. A box slides across a frozen pond toward the left shore as two children standing on opposite shores pull on the box with ropes. The child on the left shore pulls with a force of 3.0 N, and the child on the right shore pulls with a force of 2.0 N. At a certain instant, the speed of the box is 3.0 m/s. (*a*) At that instant, what is the power resulting from each force? (*b*) What is the power resulting from both forces? (*c*) Do your answers to parts *a* and *b* change as the box slides? ●●

66. A motor must lift a 1000-kg elevator cab. The cab's maximum occupant capacity is 400 kg, and its constant "cruising" speed is 1.5 m/s. The design criterion is that the cab must achieve this speed within 2.0 s at constant acceleration, beginning from rest. (*a*) When the cab is carrying its maximum capacity, at what rate must the motor deliver energy to get the cab up to cruising speed? (*b*) At what constant rate must the motor supply energy as the fully loaded cab rises after attaining cruising speed? ●●●

Additional Problems

67. An elevator operated by an electric motor rises at a constant speed. What is the work done on the elevator as it rises a distance *h*? ●

68. Is it possible for a force to be exerted on an object *along the direction of the object's motion* and still produce no change in the object's kinetic energy? If yes, give an example. If no, explain why not. ●

69. A shopping cart that has an inertia of 12 kg when empty is loaded with 38 kg of groceries. A child pushing the loaded cart loses control, and the cart rolls into a concrete lamppost, which sustains no damage. The cart is moving at 2.0 m/s when it strikes the lamppost, and the groceries all crash forward on impact, moving the center of mass forward by 0.10 m before everything comes to a halt. What are (*a*) the average force exerted by the post on the cart-groceries system, (*b*) the work done by the post on the system, and (*c*) the change in kinetic energy of the system's center of mass? ●

70. Is it possible for the kinetic energy of an object to remain constant even when the vector sum of the forces exerted on the object is not zero? If yes, give an example. If no, explain why not. ●●

71. To be rescued from the roof of a burning building, a 70-kg man must be able to jump straight up and catch hold of a rope ladder hanging from a helicopter. He has to raise his center of mass 2.00 m above the roof to do so. (*a*) If he crouches down such that his center of mass is 0.50 m above the roof and his feet leave the roof when his center of mass is 1.05 m above the roof, what minimum force must he exert on the roof to reach the ladder? (*b*) A typical candy bar contains about 850 kJ of food energy. How many candy bars does this jump require? ●●

72. About how much work does a trash collector do in the course of an 8-hour shift? ••

73. A constant, nondissipative external force is applied to a solid block, and it is found that the rate at which energy is delivered by the force is constant as the block moves horizontally. What does this imply for the motion of the block? ••

74. An object is suspended from the ceiling by a spring aligned along a vertical x axis, with upward defined as the positive x direction. When the spring is at its relaxed length, the object is at the origin of the axis. The object is pulled down to position $-x_1$, held at rest, and released. Consider its motion from the instant of release until the instant it returns to $-x_1$. Ignore friction, air drag, and the inertia of the spring. (*a*) What force(s) is exerted on the object during the round trip, and in what direction(s)? (*b*) How much work is done on the object by the spring as the object travels away from $-x_1$ and back to $-x_1$? ••

75. You are midway up hill A in Figure P9.75. Across the valley is hill B, the summit of which is slightly higher than your present spot. You want to roll a ball so that it crests hill B. To get the ball moving, you can roll it either up or down hill A, giving the ball the same initial speed in both cases. (*a*) Which roll direction is more likely to get the ball to crest B, or does it matter? Ignore any energy dissipation. (*b*) In what way would you change your answer if you had to take energy dissipation into account? ••

Figure P9.75

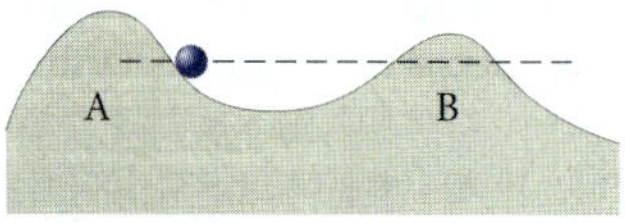

76. A 10-kg dog jumps up in the air to catch a ball. The dog's center of mass is normally 0.20 m above the ground, and he is 0.50 m long. The lowest he can get his center of mass is 0.10 m above the ground, and the highest he can get it before he can no longer push against the ground is 0.30 m. If the maximum force the dog can exert on the ground in pushing off is 2.5 times the gravitational force Earth exerts on him, how high can he jump? ••

77. Assume that when you stretch your torso vertically as much as you can, your center of mass is 1.0 m above the floor. The maximum force you can exert on the floor in pushing off is 2.3 times the gravitational force Earth exerts on you. How low do you have to crouch in order to jump straight up and have your center of mass be 2.0 m above the floor? Is this crouch practical? ••

78. The 2000-kg cab of a freight elevator is rated to carry a maximum load of 1200 kg, but a careless worker fills the cab with freight that has a combined inertia of 1400 kg. The worker then raises the cab 3.1 m at a steady 2.0 m/s. You notice an unfamiliar whine and come over to investigate. As supervisor, you know that the motor has a 10% tolerance in its rated power output, and you must decide whether there's going to be trouble. ••• CR

79. Taking a sip of coffee one day, you start thinking about the effort it takes to do so. Your forearm is a type of lever. As shown in Figure P9.79, the biceps muscle is attached to the forearm bone about 50 mm in front of the elbow joint. The cup of coffee in your hand is 350 mm from the elbow, and you wonder about the work done by your biceps on your forearm as you raise the cup very slowly. You realize that you can use energy principles to estimate the forces involved. ••• CR

Figure P9.79

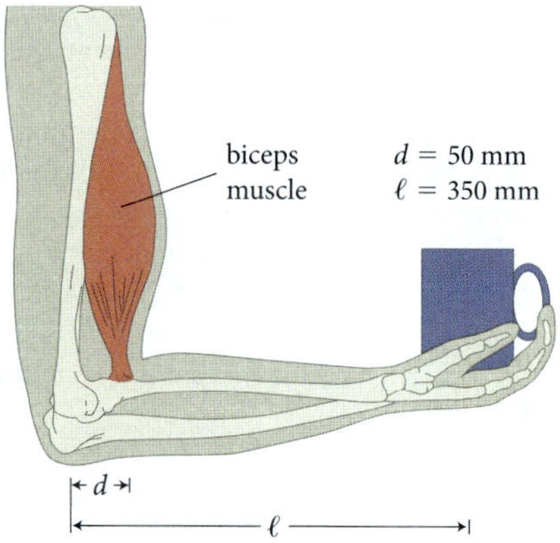

80. You are planning to jump off a bridge with a bungee cord tied to your ankles. The bridge deck is 150 m above the water, and the cord spring constant is 40 N/m. Because you must fall the length of the unstretched cord before it begins to stretch, you realize that the unstretched length of the bungee cord, which is adjustable, has to be adjusted based on your inertia. You enjoy thrills and want to reverse your motion just above the water surface. ••• CR

Answers to Review Questions

1. Work is the change in the energy of a system due to external forces.
2. No. In order for work to be done on a system, an external force must be exerted on the system and *the point of application of that force must move.* If your force is exerted on a concrete wall, for example, there may be no observable displacement, which means you do no work on the wall.
3. (*a*) Negative, because the wind force points in one direction (toward the west) and the force displacement (picture it as the point where the wind "touches" the front of the bicycle) is in the opposite direction. (*b*) Positive, because the direction of the force displacement is the same as the direction of the force.
4. None, because the negative work done by gravity on the ball as it rises is canceled by the positive work done by gravity on the ball as it falls back into your hand.
5. Yes, as when you step on a spring scale. As you compress the spring, it exerts an upward force on you. You are moving downward, though, and so the point of application of the force exerted by the spring on you is displaced downward.
6. Mechanical energy is kinetic and potential energy; there must be no changes in thermal or source energy for this system. $\Delta K = K_f - K_i = +3.0\text{ J} - (+10.0\text{ J}) = -7.0\text{ J}$. $\Delta U = U_f - U_i = +6.0\text{ J} - (+4.0\text{ J}) = +2.0\text{ J}$. The sum of these changes must equal the work done, which allows us to draw the work bar on the system's energy diagram:

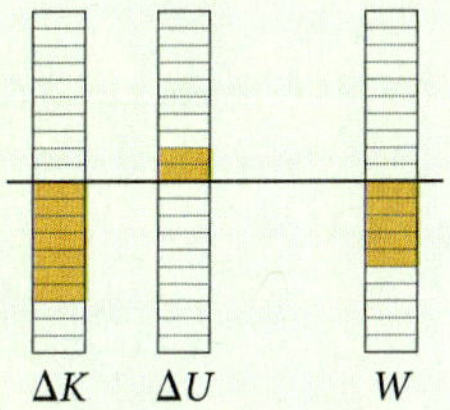

7. With the cart as the system, both your hand and the spring exert external forces during the motion, and both involve nonzero force displacements. Because the cart returns at the same speed, no thermal energy is dissipated along the track or at the spring. Because your hand is outside the system, there is no source energy to consider, and because the spring is outside the system, there is no potential energy to consider. Thus only kinetic energy and work energy bars must be drawn. No numbers are given, so the resulting diagrams cannot be precisely scaled, but they must look like this:

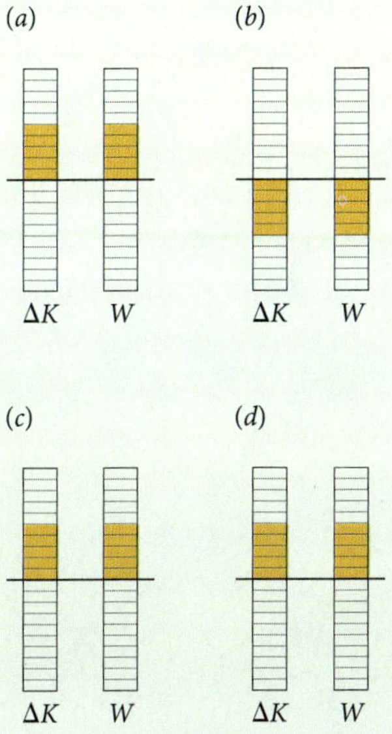

8. First, the point of application of a frictional force is not well defined but involves contact across many points on two surfaces. This makes it impossible to determine the force displacement. Second, the work done by friction changes the thermal energy of not just the system but also the other object in the interaction pair that is outside the system; you do not generally know how to compute the exact split in this thermal energy, so it is not possible to attribute a specific thermal energy change to the system.
9. Never with both. Which form you use depends on your choice of system. If both parts of the interaction pair (Earth and an object) are included in your system, you must use potential energy rather than work. If only half of the interaction pair is in your system, then you must use work rather than potential energy.
10. Using more than one viewpoint gives us a better understanding of what energy transfers and conversions take place. Also, comparing the different results provides a consistency check.
11. The work done on a system, which is the product of the external force exerted on the system and the displacement of its point of application, is equal to the change in the system's energy.
12. The energy law applies to any system. In the case of a closed system, there are no external forces to do work on the system, so the energy of the system remains constant ($\Delta E = 0$). For a system that is not closed, external forces can do work, so the energy of the system may change by the amount of this work ($\Delta E = W$). In either case the energy law ($\Delta E = W$) applies.
13. In deriving this equation, it was necessary to assume that the only possible change in energy was a change in kinetic energy: $\Delta E = \Delta K$. This is not true in general, but it is true for a particle (which has no internal structure and hence cannot have internal energy changes).
14. Both laws express conservation principles. Neither energy nor momentum can be created or destroyed, but either can be transferred into or out of a system. The momentum law states that any change in the momentum of a system must be due to such a transfer, called impulse. The energy law states that any change in the energy of a system must be due to such a transfer, called work. For an isolated system, no momentum transfer is allowed, while for a closed system, no energy transfer is allowed. The laws are thus similar. The momentum law, though, involves vector values. The equation requires careful attention to vector components of momentum and impulse. The energy law involves scalars; there are no components of energy or work to account for, even though computation of work or energy might require attention to components of vectors during some of the intermediate steps.
15. As long as the internal energy changes are negligible, we can think of the crate as a particle. If there is substantial internal energy change (in a collision, for example), the crate cannot be treated as a particle.
16. The energy law has the same form, applied in the same way in both cases: $\Delta E = W$. The work equation has different forms in the two cases. For the single particle, there is only one displacement possible, so all external forces exerted on the particle have the same force displacement, and the work equation is the vector sum of forces multiplied by this common displacement: $W = (\sum F_x)\Delta x$. For a many-particle system, different particles may experience different external forces and different force displacements, so the work equation must keep track of each separate force and displacement:

$$W = \sum_n (F_{\text{ext}\,nx}\Delta x_{Fn}).$$

17. Because dissipative forces generally dissipate energy on both sides of the system boundary in such a way that the precise amount of energy transferred into or out of the system is not calculable.
18. Because energy may appear in forms other than kinetic, the work done on a many-particle system is not necessarily equal to the change in the system's kinetic energy. The work done is the sum of the external forces times the displacement of the point of application of each force (Eq. 9.18), and the change in kinetic energy is the sum of the external forces times the displacement of the center of mass of the system (Eq. 9.14).
19. The area under the curve is the magnitude of the work done on the particle.
20. (*a*) The factor $\frac{1}{2}$ comes from the integration formula $\int x^m\,dx = x^{m+1}/(m+1)$ with $m = 1$. (*b*) Because the force exerted by the spring is a function of how much the spring is stretched or compressed, the same must be true of the force exerted on the spring. Because $F_{\text{on spring}}$ varies, the simple formula $W = F(x - x_0)$ cannot be used. However, the factor $\frac{1}{2}$ in the expression for $W_{\text{on spring}}$ is reasonable in the sense that we expect the average force to be $(\frac{1}{2})k(x - x_0)$, and so $W_{\text{on spring}}$ is $(\frac{1}{2})k(x - x_0)(x - x_0)$.
21. No. The frictional force dissipates energy in both the crate and the floor. Equation 9.28 was derived for a block-surface system, meaning that it contains both the energy change experienced by the block and the energy change experienced by the surface over which the block moves. We do not know how much of this energy to attribute to the block alone, so we cannot in good conscience call this the "work done by the frictional force on the block." We cannot even call it the "work done by the frictional force on the block-surface system" because the frictional force is not external to this system.
22. Instantaneous power is power delivered at any given instant, and average power is power delivered over a time interval Δt. Instantaneous power is average power in the limit that the energy change occurs over a time interval (Δt) that approaches zero. Average power is a ratio of energy change to time interval, while instantaneous power is a derivative of energy with respect to time.
23. When $\sum F_{\text{ext}}$ is constant.

Answers to Guided Problems

Guided Problem 9.2 (*a*) 7.8×10^3 J; (*b*) -7.8×10^3 J; (*c*) 1.3×10^2 W

Guided Problem 9.4 2.5×10^2 N/m

Guided Problem 9.6 $v_{\text{bullet}} = \dfrac{\sqrt{k(m_{\text{block}} + m_{\text{bullet}})}}{m_{\text{bullet}}}d$

Guided Problem 9.8 (*a*) 6.0 m/s; (*b*) 63 N

10

PRACTICE
Motion in a Plane

Chapter Summary

Vectors in two dimensions (Sections 10.1, 10.2, 10.6, 10.9)

Concepts To add two vectors $\vec{A}$ and $\vec{B}$, place the tail of $\vec{B}$ at the head of $\vec{A}$. Their sum is the vector drawn from the tail of $\vec{A}$ to the head of $\vec{B}$.

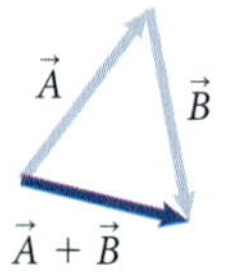

To subtract vector $\vec{B}$ from vector $\vec{A}$, reverse the direction of $\vec{B}$ and then add the reversed $\vec{B}$ to $\vec{A}$.

Any vector $\vec{A}$ can be written as

$$\vec{A} = A_x\hat{\imath} + A_y\hat{\jmath}, \tag{10.5}$$

where A_x and A_y are the *components* of $\vec{A}$ along the x and y axes. The x component of $\vec{A}$ is the projection of $\vec{A}$ on the x axis, and the y component is the projection of $\vec{A}$ on the y axis. The components A_x and A_y are signed numbers and can be negative.

Quantitative Tools The magnitude of any vector $\vec{A}$ is

$$A \equiv |\vec{A}| = +\sqrt{A_x^2 + A_y^2} \tag{10.6}$$

and the angle θ that $\vec{A}$ makes with the positive x axis is given by

$$\tan\theta = \frac{A_y}{A_x}. \tag{10.7}$$

If $\vec{R} = \vec{A} + \vec{B}$ is the vector sum of $\vec{A}$ and $\vec{B}$, the components of $\vec{R}$ are

$$R_x = A_x + B_x$$
$$R_y = A_y + B_y. \tag{10.9}$$

The **scalar product** of two vectors $\vec{A}$ and $\vec{B}$ that make an angle ϕ when placed tail to tail is

$$\vec{A}\cdot\vec{B} \equiv AB\cos\phi. \tag{10.33}$$

Projectile motion in two dimensions (Section 10.7)

Concepts For a projectile that moves near Earth's surface and experiences only the force of gravity, the acceleration has magnitude g and is directed downward. The projectile's horizontal acceleration is zero, and the horizontal component of its velocity remains constant.

At the highest point in the trajectory of a projectile, the vertical velocity component v_y is zero, but the vertical component of the acceleration is g and is directed downward.

Quantitative Tools If a projectile is at a position (x, y), its **position vector** $\vec{r}$ is

$$\vec{r} = x\hat{\imath} + y\hat{\jmath}. \tag{10.10}$$

If a projectile has position components x_i and y_i and velocity components $v_{x,i}$ and $v_{y,i}$ at one instant, then its acceleration, velocity, and position components a time interval Δt later are

$$a_x = 0$$

$$a_y = -g$$

$$v_{x,f} = v_{x,i} \tag{10.17}$$

$$v_{y,f} = v_{y,i} - g\Delta t \tag{10.18}$$

$$x_f = x_i + v_{x,i}\Delta t \tag{10.19}$$

$$y_f = y_i + v_{y,i}\Delta t - \tfrac{1}{2}g(\Delta t)^2 \tag{10.20}$$

Collisions and momentum in two dimensions (Section 10.8)

Concepts Momentum is a vector, so in two dimensions changes in momentum must be accounted for by components. This means two equations, one for x and one for y components of momentum. The coefficient of restitution is a scalar and is accounted for by a single equation.

Quantitative Tools

$$\Delta p_x = \Delta p_{1x} + \Delta p_{2x} = m_1(v_{1x,f} - v_{1x,i}) + m_2(v_{2x,f} - v_{2x,i}) = 0 \tag{10.21}$$

$$\Delta p_y = \Delta p_{1y} + \Delta p_{2y} = m_1(v_{1y,f} - v_{1y,i}) + m_2(v_{2y,f} - v_{2y,i}) = 0. \tag{10.22}$$

PRACTICE

Forces in two dimensions (Sections 10.2, 10.3)

Concepts In two-dimensional motion, the component of the acceleration parallel to the instantaneous velocity changes the speed and the component of the acceleration perpendicular to the instantaneous velocity changes the direction of the instantaneous velocity.

When choosing a coordinate system for a problem dealing with an accelerating object, if possible make one of the axes lie along the direction of the acceleration.

Friction (Sections 10.4, 10.10)

Concepts When two surfaces touch each other, the component of the contact force perpendicular (normal) to the surfaces is called the **normal force** and the component parallel (tangential) to the surfaces is called the **force of friction.**

The direction of the force of friction is such that the force opposes *relative* motion between the two surfaces.

When the surfaces are not moving relative to each other, we have **static friction.** When they are moving relative to each other, we have **kinetic friction.**

The magnitude of the force of kinetic friction is independent of the contact area and independent of the relative speeds of the two surfaces.

Quantitative Tools The maximum magnitude of the force of static friction between any two surfaces 1 and 2 is proportional to the normal force:

$$(F^s_{12})_{\max} = \mu_s F^n_{12}, \tag{10.46}$$

where μ_s is the unitless **coefficient of static friction.** This upper limit means that the magnitude of the frictional force must obey the condition

$$F^s_{12} \leq \mu_s F^n_{12}. \tag{10.54}$$

The magnitude of the force of kinetic friction is also proportional to the normal force:

$$F^k_{12} = \mu_k F^n_{12}, \tag{10.55}$$

where $\mu_k \leq \mu_s$ is the unitless **coefficient of kinetic friction.**

Work (Sections 10.5, 10.9)

Concepts For a sliding object, the normal force does no work because this force is perpendicular to the direction of the object's displacement.

The force of kinetic friction is a nonelastic force and thus causes energy dissipation.

The force of static friction is an elastic force and so causes no energy dissipation.

The work done by gravity is independent of path.

Quantitative Tools The work done by a constant nondissipative force when the point of application of the force undergoes a displacement $\Delta\vec{r}_F$ is

$$W = \vec{F} \cdot \Delta\vec{r}_F. \tag{10.35}$$

The work done by a variable nondissipative force when the point of application of the force undergoes a displacement is

$$W = \int_{\vec{r}_i}^{\vec{r}_f} \vec{F}(\vec{r}) \cdot d\vec{r}. \tag{10.44}$$

This is the line integral of the force over the path traced out by the point of application of the force.

For a variable dissipative force, the change in the thermal energy is

$$\Delta E_{\text{th}} = -\int_{\vec{r}_i}^{\vec{r}_f} \vec{F}(\vec{r}_{\text{cm}}) \cdot d\vec{r}_{\text{cm}}. \tag{10.45}$$

When an object descends a vertical distance h, no matter what path it follows, the work gravity does on it is

$$W = mgh. \tag{10.40}$$

Review Questions

Answers to these questions can be found at the end of this chapter.

10.1 *Straight* is a relative term

1. A plane flying east drops a package (without a parachute) to workers at a logging camp. What does the path of the package look like to a logger standing on the ground? What does the path look like to the pilot? Where is the plane relative to the logger when the package lands at his feet: east of where he stands, west of where he stands, or directly overhead?
2. A passenger in a speeding train drops a peanut. Which is greater: the magnitude of the acceleration of the peanut as measured by the passenger, or the magnitude of the acceleration of the peanut as measured by a person standing next to the track?

10.2 Vectors in a plane

3. Why does describing motion that is not along a straight line require two reference axes?
4. How does adding two vectors that lie in a plane and are neither parallel nor antiparallel to each other differ from adding two vectors that lie along a straight line?
5. Describe how to subtract a vector 1 from a vector 2 when the two do not lie along a straight line.
6. Is vector addition commutative? Is vector subtraction commutative?
7. Describe the procedures for adding and subtracting two vectors.
8. What does it mean when the instantaneous velocity of an object at instant t_1 is not parallel to the average velocity during a short time interval $\Delta t = t_2 - t_1$?
9. Describe the effect of the parallel and perpendicular components of the acceleration of an object on the object's velocity.

10.3 Decomposition of forces

10. What is the meaning of "normal" and "tangential" components of a contact force?
11. Sketch a free-body diagram for a block resting on an inclined surface using (*a*) vector forces and (*b*) normal (*y*) and tangential (*x*) force components.
12. When choosing a rectangular coordinate system for an object moving in two dimensions and being accelerated during that motion, why should you choose a system in which one axis lies along the direction of the acceleration?

10.4 Friction

13. Compare and contrast the normal force with the force of static friction and the force of kinetic friction.
14. You push horizontally on a crate at rest on the floor, gently at first and then with increasing force until you cannot push harder. The crate does not move. What happens to the force of static friction between crate and floor during this process?
15. You are trying to push a heavy desk, and it's not budging. A friend remarks, "You're not pushing it hard enough to overcome its inertia." What's wrong with that statement, and what's really going on?

10.5 Work and friction

16. Why is it all right to choose a system for which static friction occurs at the system boundary but a bad idea to do so for kinetic friction?
17. Describe one case in which a force of static friction does no work and one case in which a force of static friction does work. Make your examples different from the ones given in the *Principles* volume.
18. Explain what is wrong with this statement: The force of friction always opposes motion.

10.6 Vector algebra

19. In polar coordinates, can r be negative? If not, why not?
20. Suppose the angle between a vector $\vec{B}$ and the y axis of a rectangular coordinate system is θ. Write an expression for B_x in terms of the magnitudes of B and θ.
21. How are the component vectors $\vec{A}_x$ and $\vec{A}_y$ of vector $\vec{A}$ and the x and y components A_x and A_y of $\vec{A}$ related?

10.7 Projectile motion in two dimensions

22. A baseball player hits a fly ball that has an initial velocity for which the horizontal component is 30 m/s and the vertical component is 40 m/s. What is the speed of the ball at the highest point of its flight?
23. What is the shape of the path of an object launched at an angle to the vertical, assuming that only the force of gravity is exerted on the object?
24. Does the maximum height achieved by a projectile depend on both the x and y components of its launch velocity? Does the horizontal range depend on both components?

10.8 Collisions and momentum in two dimensions

25. How do the principles and equations describing collisions in two dimensions differ from the principles and equations describing collisions in one dimension?
26. Why is it possible to completely determine the outcome of a one-dimensional collision of two objects given only the inertias and initial velocities of each object and the coefficient of restitution, but it is not possible to do this in two dimensions?

10.9 Work as the product of two vectors

27. Under what circumstances could the scalar product of two vectors be zero?
28. Describe how to calculate the work done by a constant nondissipative force as an object moves along a path from position 1 to position 2, and identify which quantities in your statement are scalars and which are vectors.
29. Describe how to compute the work done by a variable nondissipative force as an object moves from position 1 to position 2.

10.10 Coefficients of friction

30. Discuss the difference between contact area and effective contact area, and explain why this distinction is relevant for frictional forces exerted by two surfaces on each other.
31. A fellow student tells you that, according to a measurement he did, the concrete surface of the road has a coefficient of kinetic friction of 0.77. What's wrong with this statement?
32. Often a wedge-shaped doorstop won't hold a door open unless you kick it until it sits tightly under the door. What does forcing the wedge into a tight fit accomplish?
33. In a panic situation, many drivers make the mistake of locking their brakes and skidding to a stop rather than applying the brakes gently. A skidding car often takes longer to stop. Why?

Developing a Feel

Make an order-of-magnitude estimate of each of the following quantities. Letters in parentheses refer to hints below. Use them as needed to guide your thinking.

1. The sum of the displacement vector from New York to Cheyenne, WY and the displacement vector from Cheyenne, WY to Los Angeles (O, D, I)
2. The work done in one day by a moving sidewalk conveyor in a major airport (AA, H, T, W)
3. The maximum tension you can generate in a rope tied between two trees by pushing steadily against the rope midpoint (CC, Z, E, T, P)
4. The stopping distance for a police car in hot pursuit on the freeway under dry conditions (E, J, L, S)
5. The maximum range of a rifle bullet fired horizontally over level ground from a standing position (G, M, Q)
6. The maximum horizontal range of a thrown baseball (C, R)
7. The average force of static friction exerted on a person by a moving sidewalk conveyor in a major airport (AA, H, T, BB, A)
8. The maximum angle of inclination for which your physics book will not slip down a tilted wooden table (U, Y)
9. The maximum distance a hockey puck can slide on smooth horizontal ice (N, B, F, K, V, X)

Hints

A. How is the work done by constant external forces related to the force displacement?
B. What is the inertia of a hockey puck?
C. What is the average speed of a major league fastball?
D. What does the sum of these displacements represent?
E. What is a reasonable estimate of the coefficient of static friction?
F. What is the inertia of a hockey stick plus the inertia of a player's upper body?
G. What is the initial height of the rifle bullet above the ground?
H. What are the speeds of a person walking and a person walking on a moving sidewalk?
I. What is the displacement vector from Cheyenne to Los Angeles?
J. What is a hot-pursuit freeway speed?
K. At what speed is the hockey stick being swung just before it hits the puck?
L. What is the magnitude of the acceleration produced by the vector sum of the forces exerted on the car when the brakes are applied?
M. For how long is the bullet in the air?
N. How could you determine the launch speed of the puck?
O. How do you apply the graphical method to obtain the sum of two vectors?
P. About how far can you displace the center of the rope by pushing?
Q. What is the bullet's speed as it exits the rifle barrel?
R. How should the x and y components of the launch velocity compare with each other?
S. Given the average (constant) acceleration and the car's initial speed, how can you get the car's displacement from the instant the brakes are applied to the instant the car stops?
T. What is the inertia of a person?
U. What is the coefficient of static friction for a book cover on wood?
V. What is the coefficient of kinetic friction between puck and ice?
W. How many people ride a moving sidewalk in a major airport in one day?
X. How does the puck's displacement relate to the other information you know?
Y. How is the magnitude of the force of static friction related to the magnitude of the normal force?
Z. What is the most useful free-body diagram?
AA. Ignoring dissipation, how is work related to kinetic energy change for an object subject to an external force?
BB. What is the length of a moving sidewalk in an airport?
CC. What is a reasonable length for a rope tied between two trees?

Key (all values approximate)

A. Eq. 9.9, $W = \sum F_x \Delta x_F$; B. 0.2 kg; C. 4×10^1 m/s; D. the displacement from New York to Los Angeles; E. less than 1.0 for most situations, but use 1.0 as a reasonable estimate; F. 2×10^1 kg; G. less than 2 m; H. walking, 1 m/s, walking on moving sidewalk, 2 m/s; I. 2×10^3 km west southwest; J. 5×10^1 m/s; K. 2×10^1 m/s; L. use a free-body diagram to show that $a \approx g$; M. 0.6 s, the time interval it takes to fall from the initial height; N. treat stick-puck hit as an elastic collision; O. place the relevant vectors head to tail on a scale diagram; the vector sum is a vector from the tail of the first vector to the head of the last; P. 1 m; Q. 5×10^2 m/s; R. they should be equal for maximum range; S. Eq. 1 in *Principles* Example 3.4: $\Delta x = (v_{x,f}^2 - v_{x,i}^2)/2a_x$; T. 7×10^1 kg; U. similar to wood on wood, about 0.5; V. 0.1; W. 7×10^3; X. consider the relationship between the initial kinetic energy of the puck and the energy dissipated by friction; Y. Eq. 10.54, $F_{12}^s \leq \mu_s F_{12}^n$; Z. free-body diagram of a small piece of rope at its midpoint; AA. $W = \Delta K$; BB. 4×10^1 m; CC. 3×10^1 m because longer ropes cannot be pulled tight enough that it doesn't sag much under its own weight

Worked and Guided Problems

Procedure: Working with frictional forces

1. Draw a free-body diagram for the object of interest. Choose your x axis parallel to the surface and the y axis perpendicular to it, then decompose your forces along these axes. Indicate the acceleration of the object.
2. The equation of motion in the y direction allows you to determine the sum of the y components of the forces in that direction:

$$\sum F_y = ma_y.$$

Unless the object is accelerating in the normal direction, $a_y = 0$. Substitute the y components of the forces from your free-body diagram. The resulting equation allows you to determine the normal force.
3. The equation of motion in the x direction is

$$\sum F_x = ma_x.$$

If the object is not accelerating along the surface, $a_x = 0$. Substitute the x components of the forces from your free-body diagram. The resulting equation allows you to determine the frictional force.
4. If the object is not slipping, the normal force and the force of static friction should obey Inequality 10.54.

These examples involve material from this chapter but are not associated with any particular section. Some examples are worked out in detail; others you should work out by following the guidelines provided.

Worked Problem 10.1 Mosquito trail

The position of a mosquito along a curved path is given by

$$\vec{r} = (at^3 - bt)\hat{\imath} + (c - dt^4)\hat{\jmath}, \quad (1)$$

where $a = 20.0\ \text{mm/s}^3$, $b = 50.0\ \text{mm/s}$, $c = 60.0\ \text{mm}$, and $d = 70.0\ \text{mm/s}^4$. (*a*) Plot the mosquito's trajectory in the time interval from $t = -2.00$ s to $t = +2.00$ s, and interpret your graph. (*b*) Calculate the mosquito's position, velocity, and acceleration at $t = +2.00$ s. (*c*) What is the orientation of the line tangent to the curved path at this instant?

❶ GETTING STARTED We are given position as a function of time in vector form (Eq. 1). The trajectory we are asked for in part *a* is the curve describing the mosquito's path in two-dimensional space. To obtain the trajectory we must extract the x and y position values from Eq. 1 and plot y versus x. Position, velocity, and acceleration are related by derivatives. We can obtain the position needed for part *b* directly from Eq. 1, and we can take time derivatives of Eq. 1 to obtain the velocity and acceleration at $t = +2.00$ s. We know that the velocity of any object is always tangent to its trajectory, so for part *c*, the orientation of the tangent line should match the direction of the velocity we computed in part *b*.

❷ DEVISE PLAN The trajectory is a plot of the y component of the position versus the x component of the position, and we have the information about each component at any instant in Eq. 1. (*a*) To draw this curve, we need a table of the position components for several values of t. We can choose specific values of t and substitute those values into the expressions for the x and y components of position:

$$x(t) = at^3 - bt \quad (2)$$

$$y(t) = c - dt^4. \quad (3)$$

(*b*) We know that velocity and position are related by $\vec{v} = d\vec{r}/dt$, and acceleration and velocity by $\vec{a} = d\vec{v}/dt$. We need to evaluate these time derivatives at $t = +2.00$ s. (*c*) The tangent to the trajectory at $t = +2.00$ s is in the same direction as the velocity at that instant. We can therefore specify the orientation of the tangent line by computing the angle relative to the x axis that satisfies $\tan\theta = v_y/v_x$.

❸ EXECUTE PLAN
(*a*) We construct a table for the x and y components of the mosquito's position at instants that are close enough so that we can see how to interpolate. To get a rough idea of the shape, we begin with a few equally spaced instants of time: $t = -2.00$ s, -1.00 s, 0, $+1.00$ s, and $+2.00$ s. The results are

t (s)	x (mm)	y (mm)
−2.00	−60.0	−1060
−1.00	+30.0	−10.0
0	0	+60.0
+1.00	−30.0	−10.0
+2.00	+60.0	−1060

This choice of times provides a uniform spread of x values, but the y values are rather widely spread to be useful for interpolation. Now that we know the range of values, we can set the scales of the axes on our graph (which will be quite different for x and y). We also see the need to fill in a few more time values to specify the variation of y, perhaps one extra time between the central table rows and at least two extra values between the outer rows (where y grows

PRACTICE

dramatically). Inserting various values for t into Eqs. 2 and 3, we end up with

t (s)	x (mm)	y (mm)
−2.00	−60.0	−1060
−1.50	+7.50	−294
−1.00	+30.0	−10.0
−0.500	+22.5	+55.6
0	0	+60.0
+0.50	−22.5	+55.6
+1.00	−30.0	−10.0
+1.50	−7.50	−294
+2.00	+60.0	−1060

These data points yield the curve shown in Figure WG10.1.

Figure WG10.1

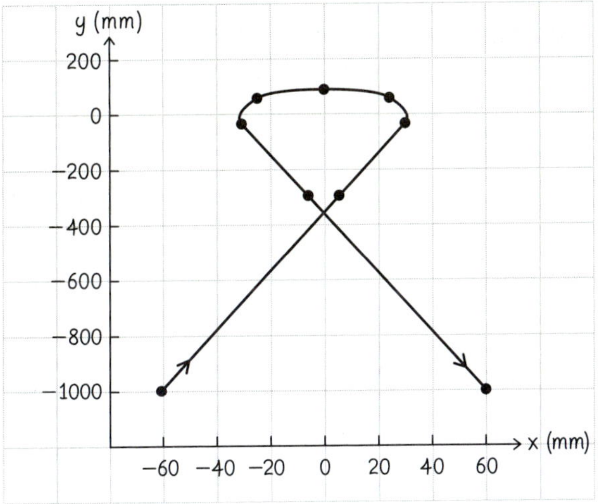

The physical interpretation of Figure WG10.1 is that there are three basic motions. First, the mosquito flies in from the left at high speed, indicated by the large spacing between $t = -2.00$ s and $t = -1.00$ s. That these dots get closer and closer together around $t = -1.00$ s tells us that the mosquito slows down. The more closely spaced horizontal portion indicates a slow speed as the mosquito backtracks around the origin. Then it flies off to the right at increasing speed. ✔

(*b*) Equation 1 gives us the mosquito's position at $t = +2.00$ s. The velocity at that instant is

$$\vec{v} = \frac{d}{dt}[(at^3 - bt)\hat{\imath} + (c - dt^4)\hat{\jmath}]$$
$$= (3at^2 - b)\hat{\imath} - 4dt^3\hat{\jmath}$$

and the acceleration is

$$\vec{a} = \frac{d}{dt}[(3at^2 - b)\hat{\imath} - 4dt^3\hat{\jmath}]$$
$$= 6at\hat{\imath} - 12dt^2\hat{\jmath}.$$

At $t = +2.00$ s, these equations give

$$\vec{r}(+2.00\text{ s}) = [(20.0\text{ mm/s}^3)(2.00\text{ s})^3 - (50.0\text{ m/s})(2.00\text{ s})]\hat{\imath}$$
$$+ [60.0\text{ m} - (70.0\text{ m/s}^4)(2.00\text{ s})^4]\hat{\jmath}$$
$$= +(60.0\text{ mm})\hat{\imath} - (1.06 \times 10^3\text{ mm})\hat{\jmath} \checkmark$$
$$\vec{v}(+2.00\text{ s}) = +(190\text{ mm/s})\hat{\imath} - (2.24 \times 10^3\text{ mm/s})\hat{\jmath} \checkmark$$
$$\vec{a}(+2.00\text{ s}) = (240\text{ mm/s}^2)\hat{\imath} - (3.36 \times 10^3\text{ mm/s}^2)\hat{\jmath}. \checkmark$$

(*c*) The orientation of the line tangent to the trajectory at $t = +2.00$ s is the same as the orientation of the velocity vector at that instant because the velocity always points along the direction of motion. To determine the orientation of a vector in a plane, we use $\theta = \tan^{-1}(v_y/v_x)$. Taking our v_x and v_y values from the velocity expression we derived in part *b*, we have

$$\theta = \tan^{-1}\left(\frac{-2240\text{ mm/s}}{190\text{ mm/s}}\right) = -85.2°.$$

This is the angle between the positive x axis and the line tangent to the trajectory. ✔

❹ **EVALUATE RESULT** Judging from Figure WG10.1, the answers are not unreasonable. The mosquito's speed is fast, mostly in the $\pm y$ direction, and it is accelerating in this general direction. We could have constructed a larger table with more values of t, but the curve we obtained seems to be smooth enough not to hide any surprises.

We can also compare the calculated angle of the tangent line at $t = +2.00$ s with the information in our xy table. At $t = +2.00$ s, the mosquito's horizontal position is $x = 60.0$ mm. We see from Figure WG10.1 that the tangent to the trajectory at that x position does have a negative slope, consistent with our negative angle of −85.2°. However, is the size of the angle consistent with the graph? The angle between the tangent to the curve of Figure WG10.1 at $x = 60.0$ mm and the x axis looks to be approximately −45° rather than −85°. We have to be careful, though! Notice that the scales for the x and y axes are different. If we had used the same scale on both axes, the angle would look like −85°. On the other hand, the resulting graph would contain mostly blank space, with the entire trajectory squeezed into a narrow vertical band along the central portion of the x axis. Having so much blank space in a graph would be a clear sign that some re-scaling is needed.

Guided Problem 10.2 Cannonball trajectory

A cannonball fired from the top of a cliff at instant $t = 0$ has an initial velocity of magnitude v_i and is aimed at an angle θ above the horizontal (Figure WG10.2). (*a*) Someone who wants to know the path of the ball after it leaves the cannon asks you for an equation describing the motion. Using the parameters given in Figure WG10.2, derive the equation

$$y(x) = y_i + (\tan\theta)(x - x_i) - \frac{g}{2(v_i\cos\theta)^2}(x - x_i)^2. \quad (1)$$

(*b*) If the ball lands a distance d from the cliff base, what is the height h from which the cannon ball is fired? Assume the distance between the cliff edge and the cannon's muzzle tip is negligibly small.

Figure WG10.2

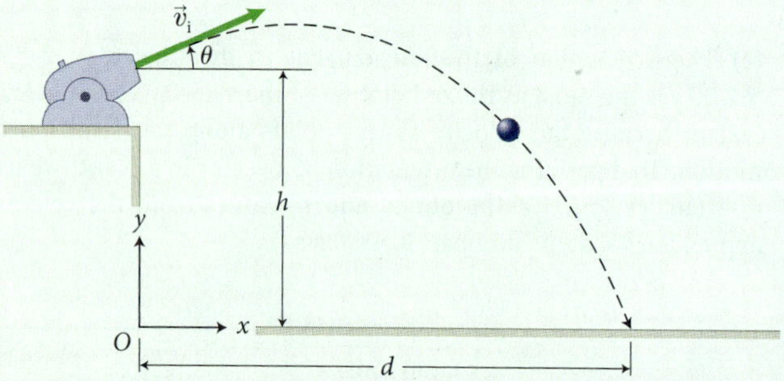

1 GETTING STARTED

1. What type of motion is this?
2. What is the acceleration of the ball after it leaves the cannon? What are the sign and magnitude of a_x and of a_y? If the acceleration is constant, which kinematics equations can you use to derive Eq. 1?

2 DEVISE PLAN

3. Write separate expressions for $x(t)$ and $y(t)$, the ball's position coordinates as a function of time.
4. For Eq. 1, you want the y coordinate as a function of x rather than of t. Can you solve for t in terms of $(x - x_i)$? Make the appropriate replacement of variables in the equation for y.
5. Can the x and y components of the initial velocity be expressed as functions of v_i and θ? Substitute this information as needed.

3 EXECUTE PLAN

6. Do the algebra to finish deriving the trajectory equation.
7. For part *b*, choose a suitable origin for your coordinate system. It should be different from the random origin shown in Figure WG10.2.
8. For your choice of origin, replace the generic symbols x_i, y_i, x, and y with symbols specific to part *b*, such as d and h.

4 EVALUATE RESULT

9. Does Eq. 1 have the expected dependence of y on x?
10. Does the value of h behave as you would expect as v_i, θ, and d change?

Worked Problem 10.3 Moving day

A mover pushes a bench of inertia m up a ramp that extends from the ground to the deck of a moving van and makes an angle θ with the ground (Figure WG10.3). None too smartly, he pushes horizontally with a force that has a magnitude equal to half the magnitude of the gravitational force exerted on the bench. The coefficient of kinetic friction between the ramp and the bench is μ_k. (*a*) Derive an expression for the acceleration of the bench in terms of θ and μ_k. (*b*) What must the coefficient of kinetic friction be (expressed in terms of θ) if the speed of the bench is constant? (*c*) Write an expression for the work done by the mover on the bench as the bench moves a distance d up the ramp.

Figure WG10.3

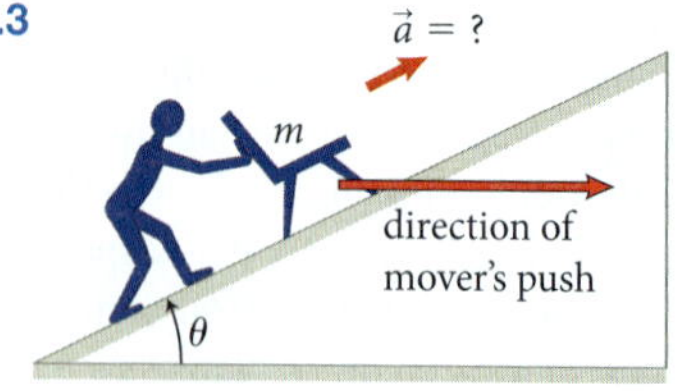

Figure WG10.4

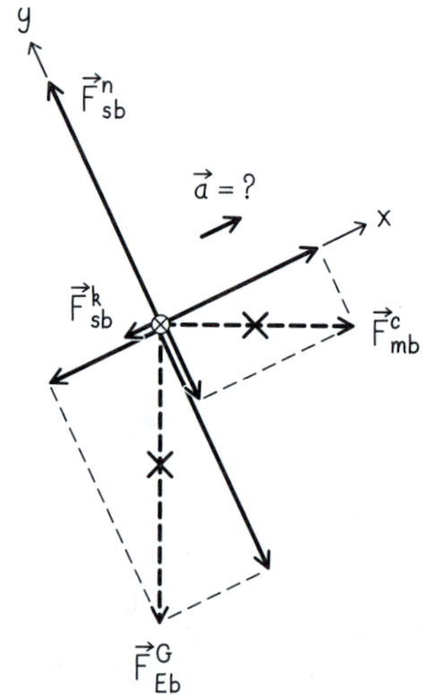

1 GETTING STARTED The bench is the object we must focus on, and several forces are exerted on it: the mover's pushing force, the gravitational force, the frictional force, and the normal force exerted by the ramp surface. We must remember that the pushing force is directed horizontally, not up the ramp. The bench moves only parallel to the ramp, so the component of acceleration perpendicular to the ramp is zero. This information is summarized in the free-body diagram of the bench (Figure WG10.4).

Because the direction of the pushing force (horizontal) is not the same as the direction of the motion, we must take care to get the force components right. We choose a coordinate system tilted like the ramp surface and show components for any vector that is not parallel to an axis. We construct our components by drawing arrows for them along the x and y directions and then crossing out the original vectors. Because the speed is constant up the ramp in part *b*, we know the acceleration is zero in that part, but it is probably not zero in part *a*. However, the acceleration might be directed either up or down the ramp. The question mark at the acceleration in Figure WG10.4 reinforces our uncertainty on this point.

2 DEVISE PLAN

(*a*) We have no numerical values, but using the free-body diagram to construct the vector sum of forces should give us an expression for the acceleration.

Because they each have a component that opposes the x component $F^c_{\text{mb}\,x}$ of the force exerted by the mover, both the frictional force $\vec{F}^k_{\text{sb}}$ and the gravitational force $\vec{F}^G_{\text{Eb}}$ affect the acceleration. Applying some geometry and the information given about some of these forces, we should be able to use $\sum F_{\text{b}y}$ to express the remaining forces in terms of θ and μ_k and then use $\sum F_{\text{b}x}$ to obtain an expression for the acceleration. We can eliminate one unknown because the magnitude of the frictional force depends on the magnitude of the normal force according to the relationship $F^k_{\text{sb}} = \mu_k F^n_{\text{sb}}$.

Because the normal force is in the direction of the y axis, we will employ the vector sum of forces in the y direction to calculate it. There is no acceleration in the y direction, and so $\sum F_{\text{b}y} = ma_y = m(0) = 0$. In addition to the normal force, the gravitational force and the force exerted by the mover have components in the y direction. The only remaining variable is the acceleration, which we symbolize as a_x. We can isolate this variable to obtain the expression we need, and the expression should reveal the correct direction for the acceleration.

(*b*) Constant velocity requires zero acceleration. If we set this expression for acceleration equal to zero, it should be possible to obtain an expression for the coefficient of friction.

(*c*) The work done by a constant external force can be computed as the scalar product of the force and the force displacement. These quantities are not parallel to each other, so we must carefully keep track of components. Because we have information about both the magnitude and direction of each of these quantities, the work done can be computed from Eq. 10.35 regardless of the direction of the acceleration.

3 EXECUTE PLAN (*a*) With our choice of axes orientation, the acceleration is along the x axis, and we start by analyzing the vector sum of the forces in the x direction. Because four forces are exerted on the bench, there should be four terms initially in the sum. We are given that $F^c_{\text{mb}} = \frac{1}{2}F^G_{\text{Eb}} = \frac{1}{2}mg$, and so

$$\sum F_{\text{b}x} = ma_x$$

$$F^k_{\text{sb}x} + F^n_{\text{sb}x} + F^c_{\text{mb}x} + F^G_{\text{Eb}x} = ma_x$$

$$-F^k_{\text{sb}} + 0 + (+F^c_{\text{mb}}\cos\theta) + (-F^G_{\text{Eb}}\sin\theta) = ma_x$$

$$-\mu_k F^n_{\text{sb}} + \tfrac{1}{2}mg\cos\theta - mg\sin\theta = ma_x. \qquad (1)$$

The vector sum of the forces in the y direction gives us

$$\sum F_{\text{b}y} = ma_y$$

$$F^k_{\text{sb}y} + F^n_{\text{sb}y} + F^c_{\text{mb}y} + F^G_{\text{Eb}y} = m(0)$$

$$0 + (+F^n_{\text{sb}}) + (-F^c_{\text{mb}}\sin\theta) + (-F^G_{\text{Eb}}\cos\theta) = 0$$

$$F^n_{\text{sb}} = \tfrac{1}{2}mg\sin\theta + mg\cos\theta.$$

Substituting this value for F^n_{sb} in Eq. 1 yields

$$-\mu_k(\tfrac{1}{2}mg\sin\theta + mg\cos\theta) + \tfrac{1}{2}mg\cos\theta - mg\sin\theta = ma_x$$

$$a_x = \tfrac{1}{2}g\cos\theta - \mu_k g\cos\theta - \tfrac{1}{2}\mu_k g\sin\theta - g\sin\theta$$

$$a_x = g\cos\theta(\tfrac{1}{2} - \mu_k) - g\sin\theta(1 + \tfrac{1}{2}\mu_k). \qquad (2)$$

Thus the acceleration is in either the positive or negative x direction, depending on the relative size of the terms in Eq. 2. Expressing the result in vector form, we have

$$\vec{a} = [g\cos\theta(\tfrac{1}{2} - \mu_k) - g\sin\theta(1 + \tfrac{1}{2}\mu_k)]\hat{\imath}. ✓$$

(*b*) If the bench's speed is constant as it goes up the ramp, a_x must be zero. To determine the value of μ_k for which this is true, we set a_x equal to zero in Eq. 2 and solve for μ_k:

$$0 = g\cos\theta(\tfrac{1}{2} - \mu_k) - g\sin\theta(1 + \tfrac{1}{2}\mu_k)$$

$$= \tfrac{1}{2}g\cos\theta - \mu_k g\cos\theta - \tfrac{1}{2}\mu_k g\sin\theta - g\sin\theta$$

$$\mu_k\cos\theta + \tfrac{1}{2}\mu_k\sin\theta = \tfrac{1}{2}\cos\theta - \sin\theta$$

$$\mu_k(2\cos\theta + \sin\theta) = \cos\theta - 2\sin\theta$$

$$\mu_k = \frac{\cos\theta - 2\sin\theta}{2\cos\theta + \sin\theta}. ✓$$

(*c*) Because the bench is rigid and moves along a straight line, the displacement of the location where the mover exerts his force, the force displacement, is the same as the center-of-mass displacement—namely, a distance d up the ramp. The work done by the mover's force is

$$W = \vec{F}\cdot\Delta\vec{r}_F = \vec{F}^c_{\text{mb}}\cdot\vec{d} = F^c_{\text{mb}}d\cos\theta = \tfrac{1}{2}mgd\cos\theta. ✓$$

4 EVALUATE RESULT Because of the plus and minus signs in Eq. 2, a_x can be positive or negative depending on the relative sizes of μ_k and θ. Because μ_k is always associated with a minus sign in our expression, it tends to make the acceleration negative (down the ramp), as we expect. For small angles, $\cos\theta$ is positive and much larger than $\sin\theta$, making the acceleration positive for small values of μ_k. (If $\mu_k > \frac{1}{2}$, the acceleration must be negative.) As θ increases, $\cos\theta$ decreases, which causes a decrease in $g\cos\theta(\frac{1}{2} - \mu_k)$, the only positive term in 2, relative to the increasing $\sin\theta$ term. Thus increasing θ drives a_x to negative values, which is what we expect: As the slope gets steeper, we expect the bench to slow down rather than speed up. The value of μ_k in part *b* balances these effects to achieve zero acceleration. Note that the work done by the mover is positive because $\cos\theta$ is positive for any inclination between 0 and 90°. This is true regardless of the magnitude or direction of the bench's acceleration, as long as it moves up the ramp.

Guided Problem 10.4 Push that shed

Three winter anglers on an ice-fishing trip push a 120-kg shed out onto the ice. They are somewhat careless and push in different directions. As seen from above, these forces are $\vec{F}^c_{1s} = 32$ N directed 30° east of north, $\vec{F}^c_{2s} = 55$ N directed due north, and $\vec{F}^c_{3s} = 41$ N directed 60° west of north. What are the magnitude and direction of the shed's acceleration?

❶ GETTING STARTED

1. Because this is a force problem involving three vectors, consider which is more appropriate: graphical addition or addition by components.
2. Because forces are involved, a free-body diagram of the shed is useful. Is it possible to draw only the forces in the plane of the ice? If so, why is it a good idea to set things up this way?

❷ DEVISE PLAN

3. Choose two coordinate axes. Does it matter which directions you choose for your axes, given that the direction of the acceleration is unknown? Is one orientation of your coordinate system more appropriate than other orientations, given the information supplied?
4. Write the two components of Newton's second law for forces parallel to the ice.
5. Do you have enough information to compute the value of each component of the three forces in your coordinate system?

❸ EXECUTE PLAN

6. Add components to obtain an x component and y component for the vector sum of the forces.
7. How are the components of the acceleration related to the force components?
8. Can you compute the magnitude and direction of the acceleration (relative to north) given the x and y components of the acceleration?

❹ EVALUATE RESULT

9. Did you make any assumptions? If so, decide whether they are reasonable or should be reconsidered.
10. Is the acceleration direction consistent with what your intuition tells you about the overall effect of the three forces?
11. Is the magnitude of the acceleration reasonable?

Worked Problem 10.5 Spring up that incline

The ramp in Figure WG10.5 has a rough surface and makes an angle θ with the horizontal. The spring attached to the support at the bottom of the ramp has a force constant k. You place a block of inertia m against the free end of the spring and then push the block against the spring until the block has moved a distance d from its position when the spring is at its relaxed length. When you release the block from rest, it slides up the ramp and eventually leaves the spring behind, stopping finally a distance ℓ from its position just before release. Derive an expression for ℓ in terms of k, d, m, θ, and the coefficient of kinetic friction μ_k between block and ramp.

Figure WG10.5

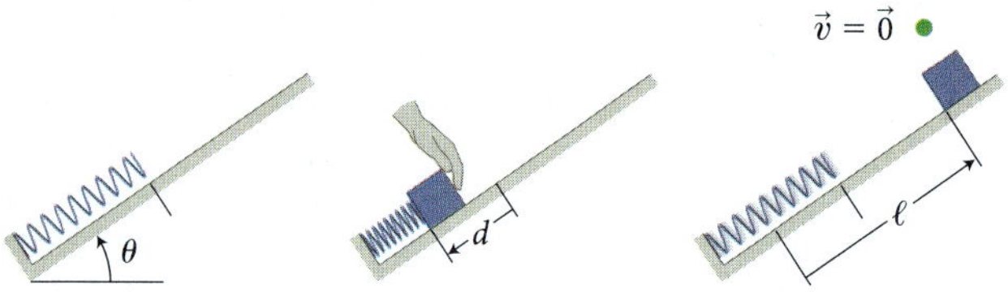

Figure WG10.6

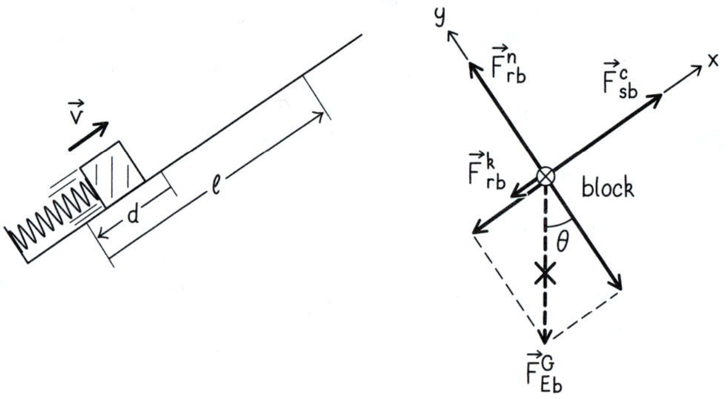

❶ GETTING STARTED Four forces are exerted on the block: the constant force of gravity, the variable spring force, the constant normal force, and the dissipative frictional force. (The phrase *rough surface* in the problem statement is what tells us we must consider friction.) A good first step is to draw a free-body diagram that shows all four forces (Figure WG10.6). To get an expression for the magnitude of the force of kinetic friction, we need to know the magnitude of the normal force. We include in our diagram a tilted coordinate system to help us calculate this force and the components of any vector not parallel to one of our coordinate axes.

Because the spring force varies with position, we should investigate whether we can use work-energy methods, accounting for the action of the spring through the equation for potential energy. Thus a situation diagram is called for, showing the initial compression distance d and the final position of the block a distance ℓ up the ramp (Figure WG10.7). With this approach, the initial elastic potential energy of the compressed spring is converted to gravitational potential energy as the block rises and to thermal energy dissipated through friction. Although the kinetic energy changes during the process, it is the same at start and finish: zero.

Figure WG10.7

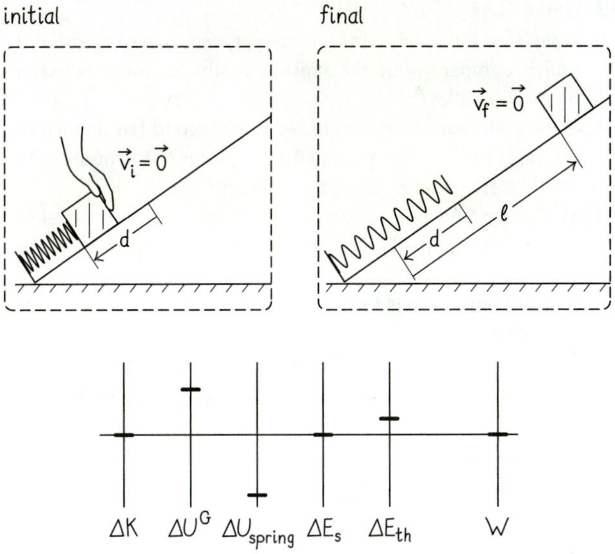

2 DEVISE PLAN If we choose the block, spring, ramp, and Earth as our system, there are no external forces, and therefore no work is done on the system:

$$\Delta E = W = 0$$

$$\Delta K + \Delta U_{\text{spring}} + \Delta U^G + \Delta E_{\text{th}} = 0. \qquad (1)$$

This expression will contain all our variables, and so with a little algebra we should be able to isolate ℓ, the variable we are after.

The thermal energy dissipated is the product of the magnitude of the force of kinetic friction and the distance ℓ over which the block moves:

$$\Delta E_{\text{th}} = F^k_{\text{rb}}\ell = (\mu_k F^n_{\text{rb}})\ell. \qquad (2)$$

To calculate the magnitude F^n_{rb}, we note that the normal force is aligned along the y axis. We employ the vector sum of force components along this axis and the fact that along this axis $a_y = 0$:

$$\Sigma F_{\text{by}} = ma_y = m(0) = 0. \qquad (3)$$

Equations 1–3 should give us all the information we need to derive an expression for ℓ.

3 EXECUTE PLAN Substituting an expression that contains the quantities given in the problem statement for each term in Eq. 1 gives us

$$\left(\tfrac{1}{2}mv_{\text{f}}^2 - \tfrac{1}{2}mv_{\text{i}}^2\right) + \left[\tfrac{1}{2}k(x_{\text{f}} - x_0)^2 - \tfrac{1}{2}k(x_{\text{i}} - x_0)^2\right]$$

$$+ (mgh_{\text{f}} - mgh_{\text{i}}) + F^k_{\text{rb}}\ell = 0$$

$$(0 - 0) + \left[\tfrac{1}{2}k(0)^2 - \tfrac{1}{2}k(-d)^2\right] + mg(h_{\text{f}} - h_{\text{i}}) + \mu_k F^n_{\text{rb}}\ell = 0$$

$$-\tfrac{1}{2}kd^2 + mg(+\ell \sin\theta) + \mu_k F^n_{\text{rb}}\ell = 0$$

$$\ell(mg\sin\theta + \mu_k F^n_{\text{rb}}) = \tfrac{1}{2}kd^2, \qquad (4)$$

where x_0 is the block's position when the spring is at its relaxed length and we have used h to designate vertical height coordinates so as not to mistakenly use the tilted y coordinate. Equation 4 looks pretty close to what we are after (an expression for ℓ in terms of k, d, m, θ, and μ_k). All we need to derive is an expression for F^n_{rb}, which we obtain from Eq. 3, the vector sum of the forces along the y axis. Four forces are exerted on the block, so

$$\Sigma F_{\text{b}y} = F^k_{\text{rb}y} + F^n_{\text{rb}y} + F^c_{\text{sb}y} + F^G_{\text{Eb}y} = 0$$

$$0 + (+F^n_{\text{rb}}) + 0 + (-F^G_{\text{Eb}}\cos\theta) = 0$$

$$F^n_{\text{rb}} = F^G_{\text{Eb}}\cos\theta = mg\cos\theta.$$

Substituting this expression for F^n_{rb} into Eq. 4 gives us what we're after:

$$\ell(mg\sin\theta + \mu_k mg\cos\theta) = \tfrac{1}{2}kd^2$$

$$\ell = \frac{kd^2}{2mg(\sin\theta + \mu_k\cos\theta)}. \checkmark$$

4 EVALUATE RESULT We expect that the greater the force of friction (in other words, the higher the value of μ_k), the shorter the distance ℓ the block travels, as this expression predicts. We also expect that for any fixed value of μ_k, the distance ℓ increases as θ decreases. When $\theta = 0$ (the block sits on a horizontal surface), $\sin\theta = 0$ and ℓ has a large value. Because $\sin\theta$ increases faster than $\cos\theta$ decreases, the $\theta = 0$ value of ℓ is in fact its maximum value (assuming that $\mu_k < 1$).

The larger the spring constant k or the greater the compression distance d, the farther the block should go, which is what our expression predicts. Our result behaves the way we would expect.

Note that the x components of the four forces in this problem contribute to the work done on the system. The two y components, $F^n_{\text{rb}y}$ and $F^G_{\text{Eb}y}$, do not. Their lack of contribution to the system energy is not just because they cancel each other, however. Let us consider the effect of the normal force, which is perpendicular to the direction of motion. The scalar product of two vectors is nonzero only when the vectors have a component in the same direction, so $\vec{F}^n_{\text{rb}} \cdot \Delta\vec{r}_F = 0$ for the normal force as well as for any other force that is always perpendicular to the direction of motion. This means that such forces cannot rearrange energy within the system.

Guided Problem 10.6 Moving a load

A variation of the Atwood machine (see Figure WG8.6) can be used to haul a load up an incline. Using this variation, you must design a coal cart of inertia m_c that moves up an incline set at an angle θ with the horizontal. A rope attached to the cart is thrown over a pulley at the top of the incline, and a metal block of inertia m_b is hung vertically at the other end of the rope as a counterweight. (*a*) In terms of θ and the two inertias, what is the magnitude of the acceleration of the cart if the block alone is used to draw the cart up the incline? (*b*) In terms of θ and m_c, what must the inertia of the block be if the cart is to move at constant speed?

1 GETTING STARTED

1. Sketch the physical situation.
2. What variable must you determine in part *a*? Which approach is more relevant for determining it: force analysis or energy analysis? Can the result of part *a* be adapted to solve part *b*?
3. How many objects are involved in the motion? How are their motions related?
4. When you analyze forces for two or more objects, each must have its own free-body diagram and coordinate system, leading to a set of force-acceleration equations for each object.
5. Put the acceleration of each object in your diagrams, and recall that it is useful to have one coordinate axis parallel to an object's acceleration, with the axes oriented such that the motion of one object along a positive axis in its coordinate system corresponds to the motion of the other object along its corresponding positive axis.

2 DEVISE PLAN

6. How does the tension in the rope segment between cart and pulley compare with the tension in the segment between block and pulley?
7. Which component, *x* or *y*, of Newton's second law applied to the cart contains the requested acceleration? Do you need to consider the other component equation?
8. Make sign and magnitude decisions for the components of vectors where possible (for example, the *x* component of the gravitational force).
9. Repeat your analysis for the block and then count equations and unknowns.
10. If the speed of the cart is to be constant, what is its acceleration? How can this information be used to obtain the value needed for m_b?

3 EXECUTE PLAN

4 EVALUATE RESULT

11. Examine your expression for the required acceleration. Do the magnitude and sign of the acceleration depend as you expect on m_c and m_b? On θ?
12. Do your answers to questions 11 make sense in the limit $\theta = 0$? In the limit $\theta = 90°$?

Worked Problem 10.7 Accident investigation

While on a test flight at an altitude of 2000 m, a 1500-kg unmanned drone moving eastward at 60 m/s exploded into three pieces. Satellite data show that the explosion occurred exactly 50 km east of Reno, Nevada. Beginning directly beneath the explosion site, searchers find a 310-kg piece 1200 m to the south and 600 m to the east. An 830-kg piece is found 400 m to the north and 1500 m to the east. Assume that air resistance is negligible and that all three pieces hit the ground simultaneously. What were the velocities of the three pieces immediately after the explosion, and where should investigators look for the third piece?

1 GETTING STARTED We are seeking the final velocities of three pieces and the final position of one piece. The initial velocity and position of the drone are given, as well as the final positions of two of the three pieces. That still leaves a lot of unknowns! Moreover, this appears to be a three-dimensional problem, something we have not yet encountered. However, each piece is a projectile that moves in a plane (though each moves in a different plane). But it gets better because we have some very useful clues. For example, the assumption that all three pieces hit the ground at the same time will allow us to immediately solve for motion in the vertical direction. Then it will be necessary only to analyze two horizontal components of the motion by using the techniques we already have at our disposal.

Let's organize our thoughts by drawing before and after satellite views (looking down from high above) of the system (Figure WG10.8). The figure shows the drone immediately before the explosion and the known final positions of two of the pieces.

Figure WG10.8

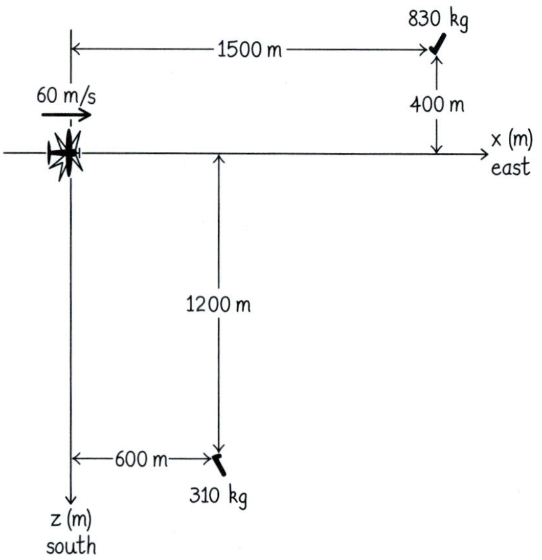

The initial velocity is also indicated, and we set up coordinates with the origin directly under the explosion site, with the positive *x* direction to the east, the positive *y* direction upward (not shown), and the positive *z* direction to the south. We can treat the explosion like an explosive separation, and so the drone is an isolated system. Therefore the momentum of the pieces must be the same before and after the explosion.

❷ **DEVISE PLAN** Because we assume the three pieces hit the ground simultaneously, in the absence of air resistance each must have the same final vertical component of velocity. This is easily seen from the vertical position equation for a projectile, Eq. 10.20:

$$y_f = y_a + v_{y,a}\Delta t - \tfrac{1}{2}g(\Delta t)^2.$$

The subscripts are "a" for immediately after the explosion and "f" for final (just before hitting the ground). Each piece started at the same height y_a, each reached the same final height ($y_f = 0$), and each experienced the same values of g and Δt, so the only unspecified variable is the velocity just after the explosion $v_{y,a}$. The equation thus demands the same value of vertical velocity immediately after the explosion for each piece. Moreover, this vertical velocity must be zero! Prior to the explosion, the system had zero velocity, and thus zero momentum, in the vertical direction. After the explosion, the vertical momentum must still be zero. This might be arranged by having some of the pieces ejected upward and some downward, but then they would not hit the ground at the same time. All three pieces therefore fall from rest as far as the vertical motion is concerned:

$$v_{1y,a} = v_{2y,a} = v_{3y,a} = 0.$$

This allows us to compute the time of fall, which together with the given position information and simple kinematics should give all three x and z components of velocity just after the explosion.

The location of the missing piece can be found using the momentum equation. Alternatively, we might compute it by considering that the center of mass of a system moves with the system momentum.

❸ **EXECUTE PLAN** We carry one extra digit in all of our calculations so as not to accumulate rounding error, but we report the results to two significant digits to match the precision of the given information.

The time of fall from 2000 m for each piece is identical:

$$y_f = y_a + v_{y,a}\Delta t - \tfrac{1}{2}g(\Delta t)^2 = y_a + (0)\Delta t - \tfrac{1}{2}g(\Delta t)^2$$

$$= y_a - \tfrac{1}{2}g(\Delta t)^2$$

$$(\Delta t)^2 = \frac{y_a - y_f}{\tfrac{1}{2}g} = \frac{+2000\text{ m}}{\tfrac{1}{2}(9.8\text{ m/s}^2)}$$

$$\Delta t = 20.2\text{ s}.$$

This leads immediately to the x and z components of velocity after the explosion of the two pieces whose final positions we know:

$$x_{1f} = x_{1a} + v_{1x,a}\Delta t$$

$$v_{1x,a} = \frac{x_{1f} - x_{1a}}{\Delta t} = \frac{+600\text{ m} - 0}{20.2\text{ s}} = +29.7\text{ m/s} = +30\text{ m/s} ✔$$

$$x_{2f} = x_{2a} + v_{2x,a}\Delta t$$

$$v_{2x,a} = \frac{x_{2f} - x_{2a}}{\Delta t} = \frac{+1500\text{ m} - 0}{20.2\text{ s}} = +74.2\text{ m/s} = +74\text{ m/s} ✔$$

$$z_{1f} = z_{1a} + v_{1z,a}\Delta t$$

$$v_{1z,a} = \frac{z_{1f} - z_{1a}}{\Delta t} = \frac{+1200\text{ m} - 0}{20.2\text{ s}} = +59.4\text{ m/s} = +59\text{ m/s} ✔$$

$$z_{2f} = z_{2a} + v_{2z,a}\Delta t$$

$$v_{2z,a} = \frac{z_{2f} - z_{2a}}{\Delta t} = \frac{-400\text{ m} - 0}{20.2\text{ s}} = -19.8\text{ m/s} = -20\text{ m/s}. ✔$$

The velocity of the missing piece can now be obtained from the momentum equation, and its location from the same kinematics employed above. The inertia of the missing piece is 1500 kg − 310 kg − 830 kg = 360 kg. We have

$$\vec{p}_i = \vec{p}_a$$

$$m_{plane}\vec{v}_i = m_1\vec{v}_{1a} + m_2\vec{v}_{2a} + m_3\vec{v}_{3a}.$$

We already know that the y components of velocities are zero immediately after the explosion, so we use the x and z component equations:

$$m_{plane}v_{x,i} = m_1v_{1x,a} + m_2v_{2x,a} + m_3v_{3x,a}$$

$$v_{3x,a} = \frac{m_{plane}v_{x,i} - m_1v_{1x,a} - m_2v_{2x,a}}{m_3}$$

$$= \frac{(1500\text{ kg})(+60\text{ m/s}) - (310\text{ kg})(29.7\text{ m/s})}{360\text{ kg}}$$

$$- \frac{(830\text{ kg})(74.2\text{ m/s})}{360\text{ kg}}$$

$$= +53\text{ m/s} ✔$$

$$m_{plane}v_{z,i} = m_1v_{1z,a} + m_2v_{2z,a} + m_3v_{3z,a}$$

$$v_{3z,a} = \frac{m_{plane}v_{z,i} - m_1v_{1z,a} - m_2v_{2z,a}}{m_3}$$

$$= \frac{(1500\text{ kg})(0) - (310\text{ kg})(59.4\text{ m/s})}{360\text{ kg}}$$

$$- \frac{(830\text{ kg})(-19.8\text{ m/s})}{360\text{ kg}}$$

$$= -5.50\text{ m/s}. ✔$$

The signs in our values for v_3 indicate that piece 3 is moving in the positive x (eastward) and negative z (northward) directions after the explosion. To finish our task—finding the location of piece 3—we apply kinematics. In the 20 s before it struck the ground, piece 3 traveled to this final resting place:

$$x_{3f} = x_{3a} + v_{3x,a}\Delta t$$

$$= 0 + (+53.3\text{ m/s})(20.2\text{ s})$$

$$= +1077\text{ m} = 1.1 \times 10^3\text{ m} ✔$$

$$z_{3f} = z_{3a} + v_{3z,a}\Delta t$$

$$= 0 + (-5.50\text{ m/s})(20.2\text{ s})$$

$$= -111\text{ m} = -1.1 \times 10^2\text{ m}. ✔$$

❹ **EVALUATE RESULT** The calculated velocity components are all comparable in magnitude to the original velocity of the drone. Piece 3 should be found at approximately 1100 m east and 110 m north of the origin (or the point of explosion). The magnitude of the displacement of piece 3 is neither huge nor tiny compared with the displacements of the other two pieces. We can check our result by recalling that the motion of the center of mass of a system is affected only by forces acting from outside the system. Thus the center of mass of the drone follows the parabolic path of a projectile launched at altitude 2000 m with eastward velocity 60 m/s:

$$x_{\text{cm,f}} = x_{\text{cm,i}} + v_{\text{i},x}\Delta t = 0 + (60\text{ m/s})(20.2\text{ s})$$

$$= 1212\text{ m} = 1.2 \times 10^3\text{ m}.$$

We can compute the location of the center of mass of the pieces using the results obtained above:

$$x_{\text{cm}} = \frac{m_1 x_{1\text{f}} + m_2 x_{2\text{f}} + m_3 x_{3\text{f}}}{m_{\text{plane}}}$$

$$= \frac{(310\text{ kg})(+600\text{ m}) + (830\text{ kg})(+1500\text{ m})}{1500\text{ kg}}$$

$$+ \frac{(360\text{ kg})(+1100\text{ m})}{1500\text{ kg}}$$

$$= +1218\text{ m} = 1.2 \times 10^3\text{ m}.$$

This method can also verify that the z component of the center-of-mass position is indeed zero, if we recall that small differences in large numbers cause reduced significant digits:

$$z_{\text{cm}} = \frac{m_1 z_{1\text{f}} + m_2 z_{2\text{f}} + m_3 z_{3\text{f}}}{m_{\text{plane}}}$$

$$= \frac{(310\text{ kg})(+1200\text{ m}) + (830\text{ kg})(-400\text{ m})}{1500\text{ kg}}$$

$$+ \frac{(360\text{ kg})(-111\text{ m})}{1500\text{ kg}}$$

$$= +0.0267\text{ m} = 0.$$

Under the given assumptions about direction of motion and constancy of velocities, the answers we obtain are not unreasonable.

Guided Problem 10.8 Hockey with a bang

Someone puts a firecracker into a hockey puck and slides it onto frictionless ice while you watch. The explosion breaks the puck into exactly two pieces, and you see the two pieces slide across the ice without rising into the air. Piece P (inertia 60 g) moves with speed 4.5 m/s at an angle of 22° south of east. Piece Q (inertia 110 g) moves with speed 1.9 m/s at an angle of 52° north of west. Compute the initial velocity of the hockey puck before the explosion. Ignore the inertia of the firecracker.

❶ **GETTING STARTED**

1. What are you asked to determine?
2. What is an appropriate choice of system?
3. Which fundamental principle(s) would be most useful for this analysis?
4. Make a sketch showing the appropriate initial and final conditions.

❷ **DEVISE PLAN**

5. Write the appropriate equation(s) that express the principle you chose to make the analysis.
6. Are there sufficient equations to compute the unknowns?

❸ **EXECUTE PLAN**

7. Insert known values and evaluate your expression(s).

❹ **EVALUATE RESULT**

8. Is it possible that the hockey puck was at rest before the explosion?
9. Is more than one answer possible? Are your values reasonable?

Questions and Problems

For instructor-assigned homework, go to MasteringPhysics® MP

Dots indicate difficulty level of problems: • = *easy,* •• = *intermediate,* ••• = *hard;* CR = *context-rich problem.*

10.1 *Straight* is a relative term

1. Suppose a missile moving along a trajectory has a constant vertical speed and a constant horizontal acceleration. What is the shape of this trajectory as seen by a stationary observer? •

2. Riding in a train on horizontal tracks, you notice a boy drop a baseball from the roof of his house nearby. (*a*) What is the shape of the trajectory you see for the ball if the train is moving at constant speed? (*b*) Would you see the trajectory as a straight line if the train were accelerating? ••

3. You are performing an experiment similar to the one shown in *Principles* Figure 10.1. The ball is dropped from a height of $y_i = 0.200$ m on the pole above the cart just as the pole and cart pass your origin of coordinates. The ball lands inside the cart at the instant the cart passes the location $x = +0.0600$ m. The lab exercise includes, among other things, that you determine the distance traveled by the ball from when it is released until it lands in the cart. Your lab partner immediately says "0.200 m," but the girl at the next table says "0.0600 m." The lab partners just behind you are arguing about whether it is 0.209 m or 0.214 m. You have not done the calculation, but of these four numbers, which could be correct? ••

10.2 Vectors in a plane

4. Is it possible for the acceleration and velocity vectors of an object to be *always* perpendicular to each other? If no, explain why not. If yes, describe the motion. •

5. A baseball player hits a long fly ball to center field. What is the direction of the ball's acceleration at the highest point of its flight? (Take air resistance into consideration.) •

6. Can an object be accelerated without changing its kinetic energy? •

7. (*a*) Can two vectors of unequal lengths add up to zero? (*b*) What about three vectors of unequal lengths? ••

8. Three swimmers who all swim at the same speed discuss how to cross a river in the shortest amount of time. Swimmer A will swim straight across the river at a right angle to the current. Swimmer B reasons that the current will carry A downstream, meaning that A will cover a greater distance to get across and therefore will take a longer time interval. B says he will aim at an upstream angle such that, allowing for the current, he will reach the other side directly across from where he starts, thus covering the shortest distance and arriving first. Swimmer C, reasoning that the time interval needed for B to cross will be longer than B expects because some of B's effort will be spent battling the current, plans to aim at a downstream angle, so that the current assists rather than opposes him. This way he will be traveling at the highest speed and get across first. Which swimmer gets across first? ••

9. Figure P10.9 shows the position of a regularly flashing light on top of a car (bird's-eye view) as the car moves from (a) to (f). Describe the acceleration of the car at each labeled position based on the information in the figure. ••

Figure P10.9

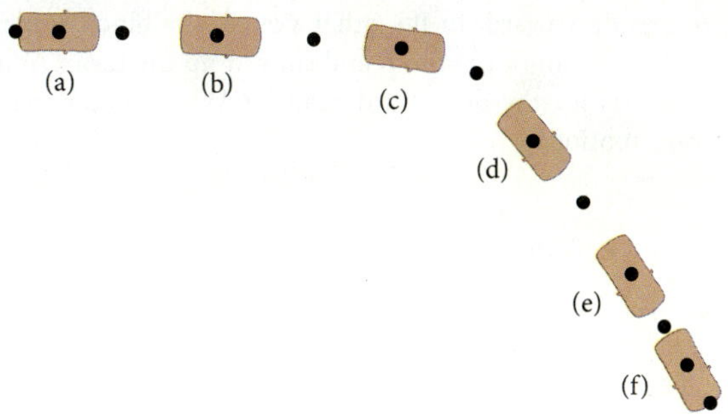

10.3 Decomposition of forces

10. Which is harder to slow down: a car going up a hill or a car going down a hill? Why? •

11. A sweater hanging on a clothesline makes the line sag in the center. Could you tighten the clothesline enough (assuming whatever material for the line you want) to eliminate the sag completely? ••

12. A sign is suspended by two wires as shown in Figure P10.12. Is the tension in each wire *larger than*, *equal to*, or *smaller than* the gravitational force exerted on the sign by Earth? ••

Figure P10.12

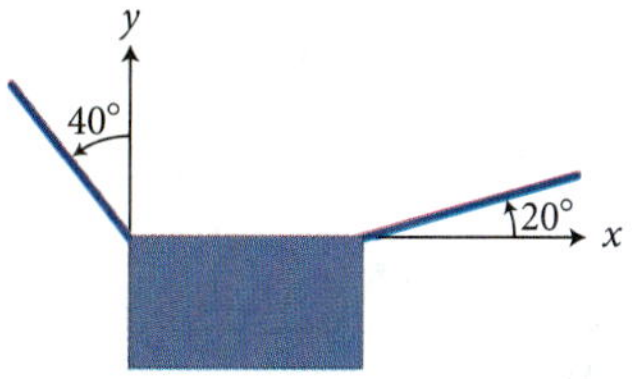

13. A man is crossing a roof that is inclined at an angle of 30° above the horizontal. His path takes him parallel to the roof ridge but 4.0 m (along the roof surface) below the peak. He is supported by two ropes, one attached to an object above each end of the roof. The left rope is attached to a chimney at 1.0 m above the peak of the roof; the right rope is attached to a flagpole at 3.0 m above the peak of the roof. The chimney rope runs parallel to the roof surface, but the flagpole rope does not. Both ropes reach the man at waist level. When the man is halfway across the 10-m-wide roof, describe each force that acts on the man, and identify which have components in each of three perpendicular directions: parallel to the roof ridge, normal to the roof surface, and tangential to the roof surface. •••

10.4 Friction

14. A common parlor trick is to yank a tablecloth hard so that any dishes and glasses on the cloth stay put instead of falling onto the floor. (*a*) Explain how this happens. (*b*) Why, if you pull on the cloth too slowly, do the dishes and glasses get dragged off the table? •

15. When a car accelerates gradually (no squealing tires), is the friction between tires and road kinetic or static? •

PRACTICE

16. Figure P10.16 represents two stroboscopic pictures (taken at the same flash rate) of a block moving along a ramp that exerts a frictional force on the block. In one sketch, the block is released from rest at the top of the ramp and moves downward. In the other sketch, the block is placed at the bottom of the ramp and shoved up the ramp. Which sketch is for the downward motion? Which is for the upward motion? •

Figure P10.16

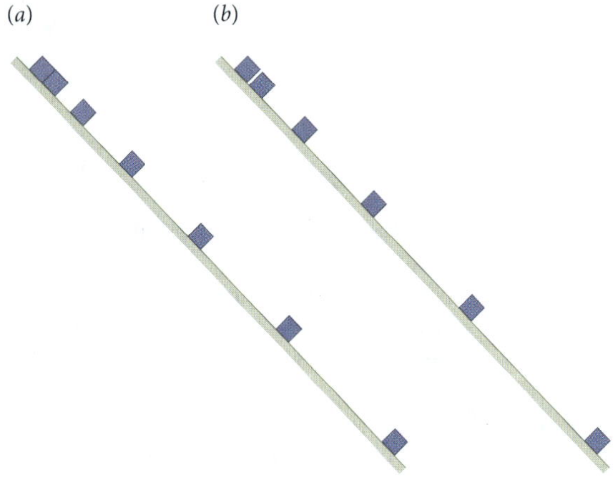

17. You keep a chalkboard eraser pressed against the chalkboard by using your finger to exert a horizontal force on the back of the eraser. (*a*) Which type of force (call it force A) keeps the eraser from falling? (*b*) What is the magnitude of force A? (*c*) Does the magnitude of force A (which keeps the eraser from falling) depend on how hard you press? (*d*) Now release your finger so that the eraser falls. What happens to the magnitude of force A now? ••

18. In Figure P10.18, all surfaces experience friction. Is the magnitude of the horizontal component of the force exerted by A on B greater than, equal to, or less than the magnitude of the horizontal force exerted by A on C if the system of blocks is (*a*) moving at a constant velocity to the right and (*b*) accelerating to the right due to an external force exerted on B? ••

Figure P10.18

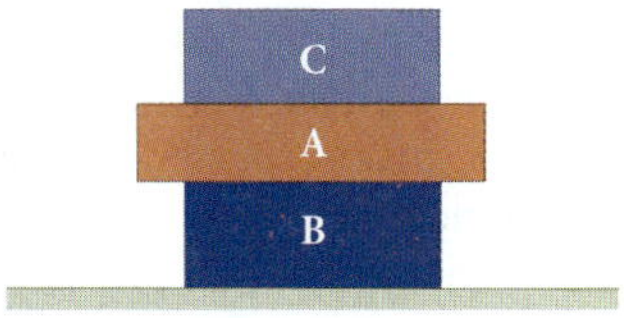

19. A factory worker pulls on a rope attached to a pallet loaded with a crate, dragging the combination across a rough factory floor. Draw a free-body diagram for the pallet and one for the crate (*a*) when the pallet is on level ground and (*b*) when the pallet is being pulled up an incline. The velocity is constant in both situations. ••

10.5 Work and friction

20. What is the direction of the frictional force exerted on a coffee cup (*a*) sitting on a stationary table, (*b*) being pulled to the right across a table, and (*c*) sitting on a table while the table is dragged to the right? •

21. A worker places a circular saw on top of a long board that is lying on the floor. Then she and a coworker lift the ends of the board and carry it across the construction site, placing it across two sawhorses at its destination. Discuss the work done by the normal force and the force of static friction by the board on the saw during this process. •

22. A resort uses a rope to pull a 55-kg skier up a 15° slope at constant speed for 100 m. (*a*) Determine the tension in the rope if the snow is slick enough to allow you to ignore any frictional effects. (*b*) How much work does the rope do on the skier? ••

23. A friend claims that her car can accelerate from a stop to 60 mi/h (26.8 m/s) in 5.1 s, but the speedometer is broken. You decide to test her claim by riding with her, and you bring along a small metal washer, a short length of string, a protractor, and a pen that can write on glass. Sitting in the passenger seat, you tie the washer to one end of the string and then let the string-washer combination hang straight down by rolling up the passenger-door window to pinch the free end of the string. While the car is stationary, you draw a line on the window alongside the vertical string. (*a*) How large is the angle the string makes with the line you drew if the car accelerates at the rate your friend claims? (*b*) If an identical washer does not slide on the horizontal dashboard while this is happening, what is the ratio of the frictional force to the gravitational force exerted on this washer? ••

24. You drive a car onto a 100-vehicle ferry, park, and have a short nap. When the ferry arrives at its destination, you start the car and drive off to begin your vacation. Estimate the magnitude of work done by the forces of static friction between the car tires and either the roadway or the ferry surface during each portion of this journey. ••

25. Two children slide down playground slides of identical heights but different angles, one shallow and one steep. (*a*) Suppose the slides are so slippery that the force of friction is negligibly small. Which child, if either, moves faster at the bottom of the slide? Which one, if either, arrives at the bottom first? (*b*) Now take into account the kinetic friction between the child and the slide. Which child, if either, moves faster at the bottom of the slide? ••

10.6 Vector algebra

26. For the vectors $\vec{A} = 2.0\hat{\imath} + 3.0\hat{\jmath}$ and $\vec{B} = -4.0\hat{\imath} + 5.0\hat{\jmath}$, calculate (*a*) $\vec{A} + \vec{B}$ and (*b*) $\vec{A} - \vec{B}$. (*c*) If the direction (but not the magnitude) of $\vec{B}$ is allowed to change by any amount you like, how large can $|\vec{A} + \vec{B}|$ be? How small? •

27. For the vectors $\vec{A} = 3.0\hat{\imath} + 2.0\hat{\jmath}$ and $\vec{B} = -2.0\hat{\imath} + 2.0\hat{\jmath}$, determine (*a*) $\vec{A} + \vec{B}$ and (*b*) the magnitude of $|\vec{A} + \vec{B}|$. •

28. Determine the polar coordinates of vectors (*a*) $\vec{A} = 3.0\hat{\imath} + 2.0\hat{\jmath}$ and (*b*) $\vec{B} = -2.0\hat{\imath} + 2.0\hat{\jmath}$. •

29. Your directions on a scavenger hunt map say to walk 36 m east, then 42 m south, then 25 m northwest. With the positive *x* direction being east, what is your displacement (*a*) in polar coordinates and (*b*) in Cartesian coordinates? ••

30. In Figure P10.30, if the tension in the cable attaching the platform to the building on the right is 800 N, what are (*a*) the tension in the cable attaching the platform to the building on the left and (*b*) the inertia of the platform? ••

Figure P10.30

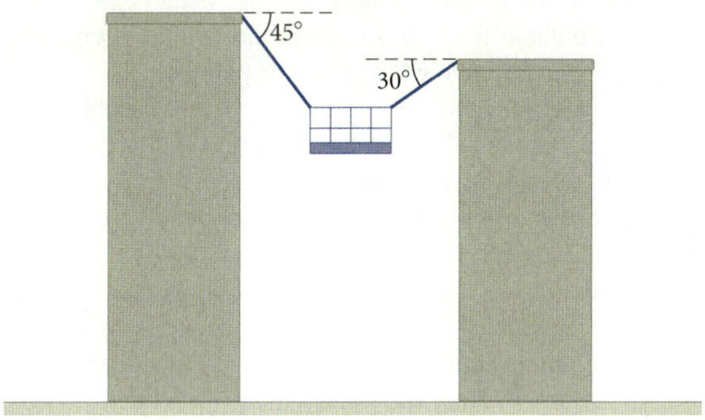

31. You leave your house and walk east for 1.0 h, northeast for 1.5 h, south for 1.0 h, and southwest for 2.5 h, always moving at the same speed. Realizing it is going to get dark soon, you head directly home. How long does it take to walk directly home if your speed stays the same as it was on every leg of the walk? ••

32. An object's displacement is given by $\vec{r}(t) = (At + Bt^3)\hat{\imath} + (C - Dt^2)\hat{\jmath}$. (*a*) Write the expression for $\vec{v}(t)$ for this motion and the expression for $\vec{a}(t)$. (*b*) Using the values $A = 2.0$ m/s, $B = 0.10$ m/s^3, $C = 5.0$ m, and $D = 0.20$ m/s^2, plot the object's position on a graph that has x as the horizontal axis and y as the vertical axis for instants $t = 0$, 1.0 s, 2.0 s, and 3.0 s. At these positions, draw the velocity and acceleration vectors. ••

33. Translate the position function $\vec{r}(t) = A\cos(\omega t)\,\hat{\imath} + A\sin(\omega t)\hat{\jmath}$ into polar coordinates, where A and ω are constants. ••

34. A plane travels in a straight line from position A to position B in 65 min, moving at an average speed of 400 km/h. In a car traveling from A to B, the driver finds that the trip is 600 km long by the route he is forced to take, which goes straight south for a certain distance and then straight west for a longer distance. At what angle south of west does the plane travel? ••

35. A child rides her bike five blocks east and then three blocks north. It takes her 15 min, and each block is 160 m long. What are (*a*) the magnitude of her displacement, (*b*) her average velocity and (*c*) her average speed? ••

36. (*a*) In a Cartesian coordinate system that has axes x and y, the coordinates of a certain point P are (x, y). What are the coordinates of P in a Cartesian coordinate system that has axes x' and y' if the origins coincide but the x' axis is tipped above the x axis by an angle φ? (*b*) If the x and y coordinates of P are (5.0 m, 2.0 m) and $\varphi = 30°$, determine (x', y'). •••

37. (*a*) Suppose you have two arrows of equal length on a tabletop. If you can move them to point in any direction but they must remain on the tabletop, how many distinct patterns are possible such that the arrows, treated as vectors, sum to zero? [Note: If a pattern cannot be rotated on the tabletop to match another pattern in your list, it is a distinct pattern.] (*b*) Repeat part *a* for three arrows, assuming the angle between any adjacent pair must be equal. (*c*) Repeat for four arrows, keeping the angle between neighboring arrows the same throughout the pattern. (*d*) Do you recognize a relationship between the number of arrows (vectors) and the number of distinct patterns? •••

10.7 Projectile motion in two dimensions

38. A ball is hurled horizontally out of a window 10 m off the ground with an initial speed of 15 m/s. How far from the building does the ball hit the ground? •

39. Which is the best representation in Figure P10.39 of the trajectory of a cantaloupe thrown horizontally off a bridge? What is wrong with the other paths? •

Figure P10.39

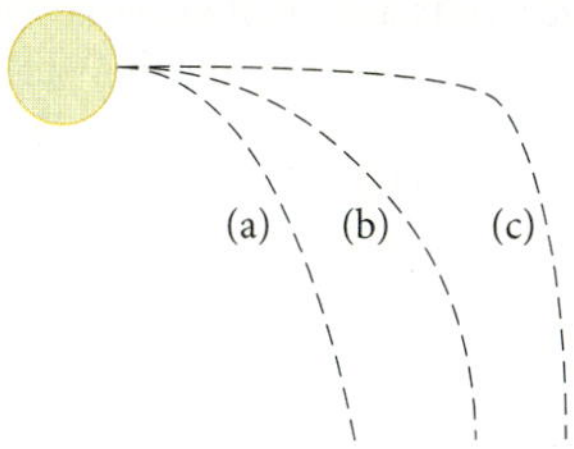

40. A bullet is fired horizontally from a high-powered rifle. At the same instant, a bullet that was resting on top of the rifle falls off. Which bullet hits the ground first? •

41. A rifle is aimed horizontally at a target 100 m away, and the bullet leaves the rifle barrel at 650 m/s. If the gun is aimed right at the bull's-eye, by how much does the bullet miss the center? •

42. On a rifle that has a telescopic sight, the telescope is usually not parallel to the barrel of the rifle. The angle the telescope makes with the barrel has to be adjusted for the distance to the target. Explain why. ••

43. A ball rolls off a table and lands on the floor. The horizontal distance between the position at which the ball lands and the edge of the table is 0.50 m, and the tabletop is 0.80 m above the floor. (*a*) How long does it take the ball to reach the floor? (*b*) What is the ball's speed when it leaves the table? ••

44. A package is dropped from a helicopter traveling at 15 m/s (horizontally) at an altitude of 200 m, but the parachute attached to the package fails to open. (*a*) How long does it take for the package to hit ground? (*b*) How far does the package travel horizontally before it lands? (*c*) What is the speed of the package just before it lands? ••

45. The velocity of an object is given in SI units by $\vec{v} = (at - bt^2)\hat{\imath} + c\hat{\jmath}$, with $a = 14$ m/s^2, $b = 10$ m/s^3, and $c = 22$ m/s. (*a*) If the initial position of the object at $t = 0$ is at the origin ($x_i = y_i = 0$), when, if ever, does the object return to the origin? (*b*) When, if ever, is the velocity zero? (*c*) When, if ever, is the acceleration zero? ••

46. A cannon launches two shells at the same speed, one at 55° above horizontal and one at 35° above horizontal. Which shell, if either, has the longer range? Which shell, if either, is in the air longer? Assume level ground and ignore air resistance. ••

47. A golf ball is hit from the tee and travels above level ground. Accounting for air resistance, where is the horizontal location of the peak of the flight: at a position that is less than half the range, at a position that is half the range, or at a position that is more than half the range? ••

48. A cannon fires a shell at an angle such that the shell's initial velocity has a horizontal component of 20 m/s and a vertical component of 35 m/s. Draw the approximate location of the shell at the instants 0, 1.0 s, 2.0 s, 3.0 s, and 4.0 s. At each location, draw the horizontal and vertical components of the velocity. ••

49. Taking air resistance into account, draw the acceleration vector of a golf ball at five positions along its trajectory from tee to green. Assume for simplicity that the force of air resistance has a constant magnitude. ••

50. How far does a fastball released from the pitcher's hand at a speed of 42 m/s fall as it travels from pitcher to batter, a distance of 18.4 m? (Your answer gives you a good idea of why the pitcher stands on a mound of dirt.) ••

51. The fish in Figure P10.51, peering from just below the water surface, spits a drop of water at the grasshopper and knocks it into the water. The grasshopper's initial position is 0.45 m above the water surface and 0.25 m horizontally away from the fish's mouth. If the launch angle of the drop is 63° with respect to the water surface, how fast is the drop moving when it leaves the fish's mouth? ••

Figure P10.51

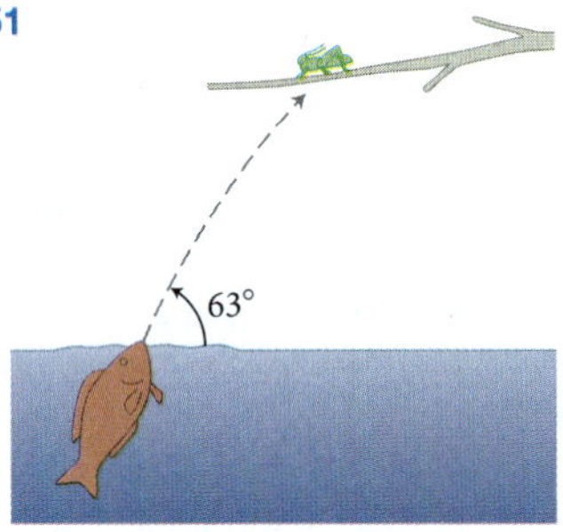

52. A burglar evading the police is running as fast as he can on a building's flat rooftop. At the edge, he sees another flat rooftop across an alley. The horizontal distance across the alley is 8.0 m, the other rooftop is 3.0 m lower than the one on which the burglar is standing, and he can run the 50-m dash in 5.6 s. Can he make the leap when moving at full speed? ••

53. You throw a ball at an angle of 30° above the horizontal at a wall 20 m away. The ball's initial speed is 15 m/s, and it leaves your hand at a height of 1.5 m above the ground. (*a*) How long does the ball take to get to the wall? (*b*) How high up on the wall does it hit? (*c*) What are the horizontal and vertical components of its velocity as it hits the wall? (*d*) When it hits, has it already passed the highest point in its trajectory? ••

54. Figure P10.54 shows a friend standing on the roof of a building that is 51.8 m tall. The roof is square and measures 20 m on a side. You want to shoot a paintball so that it lands on the roof and startles your friend, using a gun that shoots paintballs at a muzzle speed of 42 m/s. The only problem is a slim billboard 67.5 m high between you and the roof, 20 m in front of the building. You position yourself in front of the billboard such that when you hold the gun 1.5 m above the ground and fire, the paintball just barely gets over the billboard at the highest point in its trajectory. (*a*) At what angle θ above the horizontal do you need to shoot the ball to clear the billboard? (*b*) What is your horizontal distance from the billboard? (*c*) How long does the paintball take to move from the highest point in its trajectory to the height of the roof? (*d*) Does the ball strike the roof? (*e*) What is the speed of the ball when it strikes? •••

Figure P10.54

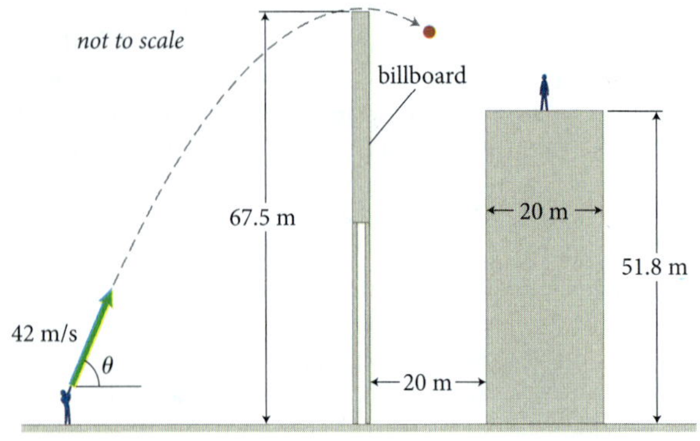

55. A brush fire is burning on a rock ledge on one side of a ravine that is 30 m wide. A fire truck sits on the opposite side of the ravine at an elevation 8.5 m above the burning brush. The firehose nozzle is aimed 35° above horizontal, and the firefighters control the water velocity by adjusting the water pressure. Because the water supply at a wilderness fire is limited, the firefighters want to use as little as possible. At what speed should the stream of water leave the hose so that the water hits the fire on the first shot? •••

56. You are standing on a slope of 20° to the horizontal and are going to throw a ball at 15 m/s up the incline (Figure P10.56). If you throw the ball at 35° with respect to the horizontal, at what distance up the incline from your feet does it land? Assume the ball leaves your hand directly overhead, 2.0 m above the slope. •••

Figure P10.56

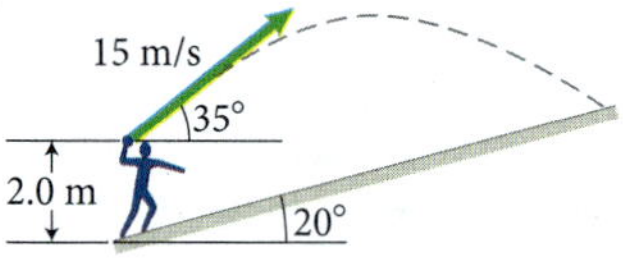

57. A block of inertia m sits at the origin of an xy coordinate system aligned along an incline that makes an angle ϕ with respect to the horizontal (Figure P10.57). You launch the block up the incline, with initial speed v_i directed at an angle θ with respect to the x axis in the plane of the incline. (*a*) What are the magnitude and direction of the block's acceleration expressed in terms of the indicated coordinate system? (*b*) Derive an expression for the block's velocity as a function of time, expressed in unit vector notation for the indicated coordinate system. (*c*) What is the maximum value of the block's displacement Δy along the y axis? (*d*) What is the block's maximum displacement Δx along the x axis? Ignore friction. •••

Figure P10.57

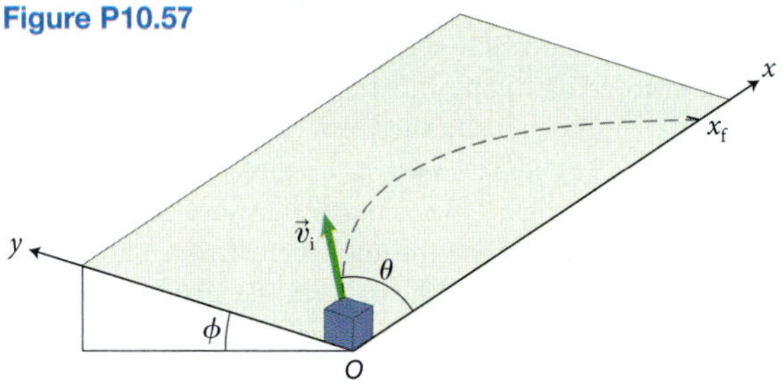

PRACTICE

10.8 Collisions and momentum in two dimensions

58. A shell explodes prematurely in midair. What happens to the center of mass of the shell? •
59. A cue ball of inertia m is given a speed v before it collides elastically with a full rack of 15 stationary balls in a game of pool. If each of the 16 balls has an inertia m, what are (*a*) the *average* speed of each ball after they fly apart and (*b*) the *average* momentum of each ball after they fly apart?" ••
60. Object A, at rest on a low-friction table, is struck a glancing blow by object B. Show that, if the collision is elastic and the two objects have equal inertias, the angle between the final directions of motion of the two objects is 90°. ••
61. Disk 1 (of inertia m) slides with speed 1.0 m/s across a low-friction surface and collides with disk 2 (of inertia $2m$) originally at rest. Disk 1 is observed to bounce off at an angle of 15° to its original line of motion, while disk 2 moves away from the impact at an angle of 55°. (*a*) Calculate the unknown final speed of each disk. (*b*) Is this collision elastic? ••
62. A system of inertia 0.50 kg consists of a spring gun attached to a cart. The system is at rest on a horizontal low-friction track. A 0.050-kg projectile is loaded into the gun, then launched at an angle of 40° with respect to the horizontal plane. With what speed does the cart recoil if the projectile rises 2.0 m at its maximum height? ••
63. A spring (k = 3800 N/m) is compressed between two blocks: block 1 of inertia 1.40 kg and block 2 of inertia 2.00 kg. The combination is held together by a string (not shown in Figure P10.63). The combination slides *without spinning* across low-friction ice at 2.90 m/s when suddenly the string breaks, allowing the spring to expand and the blocks to separate. Afterward, the 2.00-kg block is observed to move at a 34.0° angle to its initial line of motion at a speed of 3.50 m/s, while the smaller block moves off at an unknown speed and angle. Neither block is rotating after the separation, and you can ignore the inertias of the spring and the string relative to those of the blocks. (*a*) Determine the velocity of block 1 after the separation. (*b*) Determine the original compression of the spring, $x - x_0$, from its relaxed length. ••

Figure P10.63

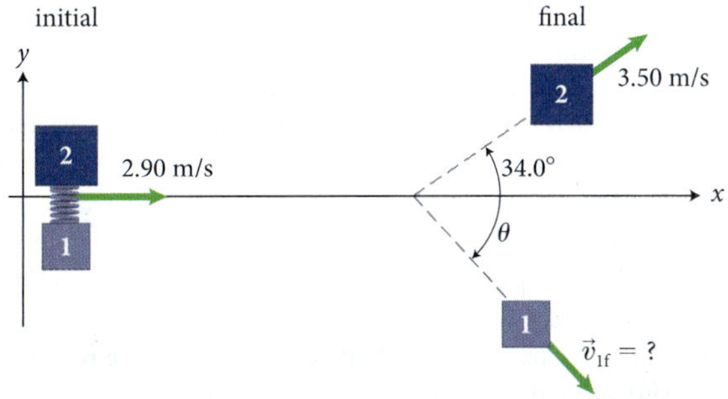

64. Disk P (inertia 0.40 kg) moves at an unknown velocity across a low-friction horizontal surface and collides with disk Q (inertia 0.70 kg), which is initially at rest. After the collision, the two (now slightly dented) disks move apart without spinning. Velocity information is provided in the initial and final top-view diagrams (Figure 10.64). (*a*) What was the initial velocity of disk P? (*b*) What fraction of the initial kinetic energy is converted during the collision? •••

Figure P10.64

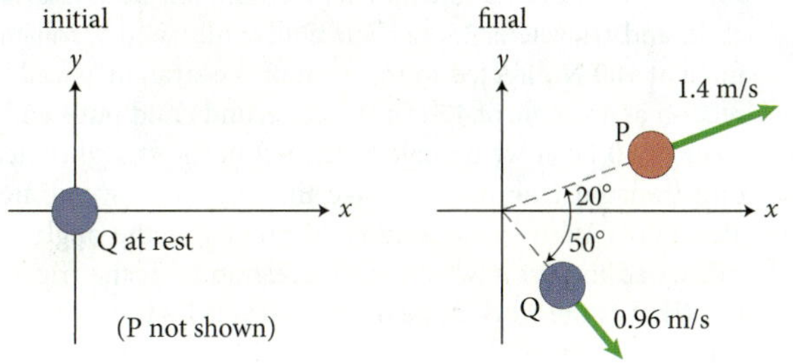

10.9 Work as the product of two vectors

65. If the angle between vectors $\vec{A}$ and $\vec{B}$ is 165° and if A = 3.0 m and B = 2.5 m, what is the value of $\vec{A} \cdot \vec{B}$? •
66. Vector $\vec{A}$ has a magnitude of 3.5 units, and vector $\vec{B}$ has a magnitude of 11 units. If the value of $\vec{A} \cdot \vec{B}$ is 22.4 units squared, what is the angle between $\vec{A}$ and $\vec{B}$? •
67. Vector $\vec{A}$ has a magnitude of 5.0 units in the negative y direction. Vector $\vec{B}$ has a positive x component of 3.0 units and a negative y component of 7.0 units. (*a*) What is the angle between the vectors? (*b*) Determine $\vec{A} \cdot \vec{B}$. •
68. A force $\vec{F} = F_x\hat{\imath} + F_y\hat{\jmath}$ with F_x = 50 N and F_y = 12 N is exerted on a particle as the particle moves along the x axis from x = 1.0 m to x = −5.0 m. (*a*) Determine the work done by the force on the particle. (*b*) What is the angle between the force and the particle's displacement? ••
69. A force $\vec{F} = F_x\hat{\imath} + F_y\hat{\jmath}$ with F_x = 3.0 N and F_y = 2.0 N is exerted on a particle that undergoes a displacement $\vec{D} = D_x\hat{\imath} + D_y\hat{\jmath}$ with D_x = 2.0 m and D_y = −2.0 m. (*a*) Determine the work done by the force on the particle. (*b*) What is the angle between $\vec{F}$ and $\vec{D}$? ••
70. Calculate $\vec{C} \cdot (\vec{B} - \vec{A})$ if $\vec{A} = 3.0\,\hat{\imath} + 2.0\,\hat{\jmath}$, $\vec{B} = 1.0\,\hat{\imath} - 1.0\,\hat{\jmath}$, and $\vec{C} = 2.0\,\hat{\imath} + 2.0\,\hat{\jmath}$. ••
71. You are playing with a toy in which a marble launched by a spring rolls along a track full of loop-the-loops and curves with almost no energy dissipated. You want the marble to have a speed of 0.70 m/s when it arrives at the top of a loop that is 0.30 m higher than the marble's position when you launch it. (*a*) What initial speed must the marble have? (*b*) If the marble has an inertia of 5.0 g and the spring has a spring constant of 13 N/m, how far back do you need to pull the spring on the level launching chute to get the marble to have this initial speed? ••
72. You are unloading a refrigerator from a delivery van. The ramp on the van is 5.0 m long, and its top end is 1.4 m above the ground. As the refrigerator moves down the ramp, you are on the down side of the ramp trying to slow the motion by pushing horizontally against the refrigerator with a force of 300 N. How much work do you do on the refrigerator during its trip down the ramp? ••
73. A 20-kg boy slides down a smooth, snow-covered hill on a plastic disk. The hill is at a 10° angle to the horizontal, and the slope is 50 m long. (*a*) If the boy starts from rest, what is his speed at the bottom of the hill? (*b*) His sister then hauls him and the disk from the bottom to the top by means of a rope attached to the disk. What average force must she exert on the rope if the boy is going 0.50 m/s when he reaches the top? ••

74. Two children pull a third child on a tricycle by means of two ropes tied to the handlebars. The combined inertia of the child and tricycle is 35 kg. One child pulls with a constant force of 100 N directed to the right of the straight-ahead direction at an angle of 45°. (*a*) If the second child pulls with a force of 80 N, at what angle to the left of the straight-ahead direction must he pull to make the tricycle move straight ahead? (*b*) With the second child pulling at the angle you calculated in part *a*, what is the acceleration of the tricycle? (*c*) What is the work done on the tricycle by the two ropes if the children pull constantly like this while the tricycle moves 2.0 m? ••
75. If $\vec{A} = A_x\hat{\imath} + A_y\hat{\jmath}$ and $\vec{B} = B_x\hat{\imath} + B_y\hat{\jmath}$, show that $\vec{A}\cdot\vec{B} = A_xB_x + A_yB_y$. (You may wish to use the fact that the scalar product satisfies the distributive property: $\vec{a}\cdot(\vec{b} + \vec{c}) = \vec{a}\cdot\vec{b} + \vec{a}\cdot\vec{c}$.) •••
76. Starting from rest, an intern pushes a 45-kg gurney 40 m down the hall with a constant force of 80 N directed downward at an angle of 35° with respect to the horizontal. (*a*) What is the work done by the intern on the gurney during the 15-m trip? (*b*) How fast is the gurney going when it has moved 15 m? (*c*) How much time elapses during the 15-m journey? Ignore friction. •••
77. You know you can provide 500 W of power to move large objects. You need to move a 50-kg safe up to a storage loft, 10 m above the floor. (*a*) With what average speed can you pull the safe straight up? (*b*) How much work do you do on the safe in doing this? (*c*) With what average speed can you pull the safe up a 30° incline? (*d*) How much work do you do on the safe moving if you slide it up the incline to the loft? •••

10.10 Coefficients of friction

78. A bartender gives a full mug of beer an initial speed v_{full}, and the mug stops in front of a patron sitting at the end of the bar. This patron later asks for a mug only half full. The bartender stands at the same position as when she sent the full mug to the patron and gives the mug an initial speed v_{half}. If the mug is to again stop in front of the patron, which is true: $v_{\text{half}} < v_{\text{full}}$, $v_{\text{half}} = v_{\text{full}}$, or $v_{\text{half}} > v_{\text{full}}$? •
79. The heavy crate in Figure P10.79 has plastic skid plates on its bottom surface and a tilted handle attached to one side. Which is easier: pushing the crate or pulling it? Assume your force is exerted along the incline of the handle in either case. •

Figure P10.79

80. You want to walk down your icy driveway without sliding. If the incline of the driveway is 15° from the horizontal, what must the coefficient of static friction be between your shoes and the ice? •
81. Moving a 51-kg box across a floor, you discover that it takes 200 N of force to get the box moving, and then 100 N keeps it moving at constant speed. What are the coefficients of static and kinetic friction between box and floor? •
82. Starting from rest, you push your physics book horizontally along a table. Plot the magnitude of the force of friction exerted on the book as a function of the magnitude of the force you exert. Include both static and kinetic cases in the range of force magnitudes you consider. ••
83. A resort uses a rope to pull a 55-kg skier up a 40° slope at constant speed for 100 m. (*a*) Calculate the tension in the rope if the coefficient of kinetic friction between snow and skis is $\mu_k = 0.20$. (*b*) How much work does the rope do on the skier? (If you did Problem 22, you might be interested in comparing your answers here with those in Problem 22.) ••
84. When moving on level ground, cross-country skiers slide their skis along the snow surface to stay moving. The coefficients of friction for a given set of skis and given snow conditions can be modified by various types of waxes. In order to move across the snow as fast as possible, (*a*) should you choose a wax that makes the coefficient of static friction between skis and snow as high as possible or as low as possible? (*b*) Should you choose a wax that makes the coefficient of kinetic friction between these two surfaces as high as possible or as low as possible? ••
85. A janitor is pushing an 11-kg trashcan across a level floor at constant speed. The coefficient of friction between can and floor is 0.10. (*a*) If the janitor is pushing horizontally, what is the magnitude of the force he exerts on the can? (*b*) If he pushes at an angle of 30° down from the horizontal, what must the magnitude of his pushing force be to keep the can moving at constant speed? ••
86. A hockey puck on the ice starts out moving at 10.50 m/s but after 40.00 m has slowed to 10.39 m/s. (*a*) What is the coefficient of kinetic friction between ice and puck? (*b*) On this same ice, what is the speed after 40.00 m when an identical puck is glued on top of the first one and the combination again starts at 10.50 m/s? ••
87. The coefficient of kinetic friction between tires and dry pavement is about 0.80. Assume that while traveling at 27 m/s you lock your brakes and as a result the only horizontal force on the car is the frictional one. (*a*) How many seconds does it take you to bring your car to a stop? (*b*) If the road is wet and the coefficient of kinetic friction between tires and pavement is only 0.25, how long does it take? (*c*) How far do you travel in this time interval? ••
88. A block of inertia m is placed on an inclined plane that makes an angle θ with the horizontal. The block is given a shove directly up the plane so that it has initial speed v, and the coefficient of kinetic friction between the block and the plane surface is μ_k. (*a*) How far up the plane does the block travel before it stops? (*b*) If the coefficient of static friction between block and surface is μ_s, what maximum value of θ allows the block to come to a halt somewhere on the plane and not slide back down? ••
89. A 1.0-kg block on a horizontal tabletop is pushed against the free end of a spring (the other end is attached to a wall) until the spring is compressed 0.20 m from its relaxed length. The spring constant is $k = 100$ N/m, and the coefficient of kinetic friction between block and tabletop is 0.20. When the block is released from being held against the compressed spring, how far does the block travel before coming to rest? ••

90. A man exerts a constant force to pull a 50-kg box across a floor at constant speed. He exerts this force by attaching a rope to the box and pulling so that the rope makes a constant angle of 36.9° above the horizontal. The coefficient of kinetic friction for the box-floor interface is $\mu_k = 0.10$. What is the work done by the man as he moves the box 10 m? ••

91. An inclined plane that makes an angle of 30° with the horizontal has a spring of spring constant 4500 N/m at the bottom (Figure P10.91). A 2.2-kg block released near the top of the plane moves down the plane and compresses the spring a maximum of 0.0240 m from its relaxed length. (*a*) Ignoring any frictional effects, calculate the distance the leading edge of the block travels from the instant the block is released to the instant it briefly stops against the compressed spring. (*b*) Now suppose there is friction between the block and the surface of the plane, with $\mu_k = 0.10$. If the block is again placed somewhere on the plane and allowed to slide down and compress the spring by the same 0.0240 m, how far does the leading edge of the block travel now? ••

Figure P10.91

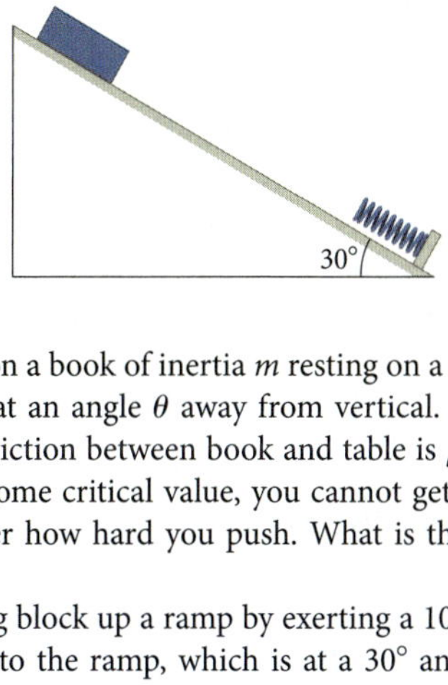

92. You push down on a book of inertia m resting on a table with a force directed at an angle θ away from vertical. The coefficient of static friction between book and table is μ_s. If θ is not larger than some critical value, you cannot get the book to slide no matter how hard you push. What is that critical value? •••

93. You push a 2.0-kg block up a ramp by exerting a 100-N force directed parallel to the ramp, which is at a 30° angle to the horizontal. (*a*) Ignoring any effects due to friction, calculate the block's speed when you have pushed it 2.0 m if its upward speed when you began pushing was 2.0 m/s. (*b*) Now consider friction. If the coefficient of kinetic friction between block and ramp is 0.25, what is the block's speed after you have pushed it 2.0 m? (*c*) With this value of μ_k, how much farther up the ramp does the block move once you stop pushing? •••

94. A platform that rolls on wheels and has inertia m_p is attached to a wall by a horizontal spring of spring constant k. A load of inertia m_ℓ sits on the platform, and the coefficient of static friction between platform and load is μ_s. If you pull the platform away from the wall so that the spring is stretched a distance x from its relaxed length and then let go, the platform-spring combination bounces back and forth. (*a*) At what position(s) in the motion is the load most likely to fall off? (*b*) If you want the load to stay in place held only by friction, what is the maximum distance x_{max} you can stretch the spring from its relaxed length and have the load stay on when you release the platform-spring combination? •••

95. You have to specify the power output of a motor for a ski tow rope that will carry 20 skiers at a time. The grade of the ski slope is 32° above horizontal, and the average coefficient of kinetic friction between skis and snow is 0.12. If the tow speed is to be 3.0 m/s and each skier has an inertia of 60 kg (a reasonable average value), what must the minimum power output of the motor be? •••

96. A spring of spring constant k is attached to a support at the bottom of a ramp that makes an angle θ with the horizontal. A block of inertia m is pressed against the free end of the spring until the spring is compressed a distance d from its relaxed length. Call this position A. The block is then released and moves up the ramp until coming to rest at position B. The surface is rough from position A for a distance $2d$ up the ramp, and over this distance the coefficient of kinetic friction for the two surfaces is μ. Friction is negligible elsewhere. What is the distance from A to B? •••

Additional Problems

97. A sports car skids to a stop, leaving skid marks 290 m long. If the coefficient of kinetic friction between tires and pavement is 0.50, how fast was the car going before the skid? •

98. If you were to throw a penny horizontally as hard as you could from the top floor of the Empire State Building, about how far from the base would it land? •

99. Plot the range of a projectile as a function of the launch angle above horizontal. •

100. Watering the garden, you need to have the water reach farther and instinctively raise the hose nozzle to increase the range of the water stream. You realize that this works because increasing the angle the nozzle makes with the ground increases the time interval during which the water is in flight, thereby letting the horizontal motion continue longer. This maneuver works only up to a point, however. Why? ••

101. A particle initially at the origin of an xy coordinate system and having an initial velocity of $(40\ \mathrm{m/s})\hat{\imath}$ experiences a constant acceleration of $\vec{a} = a_x\hat{\imath} + a_y\hat{\jmath}$, with $a_x = -1.0\ \mathrm{m/s^2}$ and $a_y = -0.50\ \mathrm{m/s^2}$. (*a*) What is the maximum x coordinate of the particle's motion? (*b*) What is its velocity when it reaches this position? (*c*) What is its y coordinate at this instant? ••

102. Describe the properties of two vectors for which (*a*) $\vec{A} + \vec{B} = \vec{A} - \vec{B}$ and (*b*) $|\vec{A}| + |\vec{B}| = |\vec{A} + \vec{B}|$. ••

103. Three forces are exerted on a 2.00-kg block initially at rest on a slippery surface: a 100-N force directed along the positive x axis, a 50.0-N force that makes an angle of 30.0° with the positive x axis, and a 144-N force that makes an angle of 190° with the positive x axis. (*a*) What is the vector sum of the forces exerted on the block? (*b*) What is the work done on the block in 10.0 s? ••

104. An airline pilot begins a trip to Duluth from an airport located 1500 km south of Duluth. Her air speed is 260 m/s, but a wind blows from west to east at 40 m/s that takes her off course if she flies directly north. She has the choice of heading slightly westward so that the wind causes her to end up at Duluth or heading due north until she reaches a position directly east of Duluth and then heading west into the wind to Duluth. Which route takes a shorter time interval? ••

105. The coefficient of static friction between layers of snow is 3.7 under ideal conditions. What is the steepest angle a snow field can form (θ in Figure P10.105) before there is an avalanche? ••

Figure P10.105

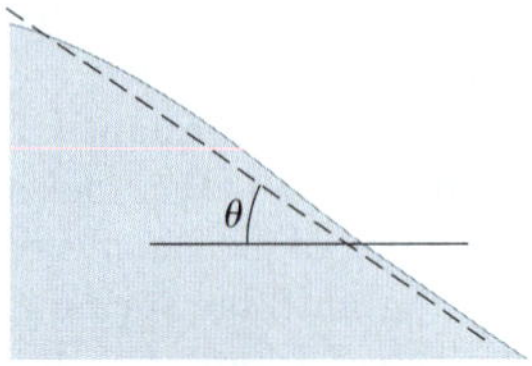

106. Having seen in *Principles* Example 10.6 that there is a simple expression for the horizontal range of a projectile across level ground, you begin to wonder whether there is an expression for the horizontal range of an object that is thrown with initial speed v_i at an angle θ above the horizontal from the edge of a cliff of height h. ••• CR

107. You have inherited property in Vermont that would make an excellent ski resort. One of the slopes has a cliff on the other side of the hill, and this gives you a money-saving idea. Instead of a chair lift or motorized tow rope, you decide to attach a pulley to the top of the cliff and then drape the tow rope over the pulley, with one end of the rope temporarily secured at the base of the ski slope and a counterweight attached to the end that hangs over the pulley at the cliff edge. The plan is to release the rope and pull two skiers (with the inertia for the pair kept between 100 kg and 200 kg) up the 400-m slope, which has an incline angle of 35° and a coefficient of kinetic friction between skis and snow no larger than 0.10. You guess that customers get nervous if they move faster than 5.0 m/s, and you wonder if a single counterweight can satisfy these constraints. ••• CR

108. You are investigating a rural accident. The evidence at the scene suggests that a car was traveling west when struck by a van traveling south. The crushed vehicles stuck together, then came to rest at the end of skid marks of length 14 m along a 76° line as shown in Figure P10.108. (The figure is a top view.) The ground is flat with no curbs, and you estimate a coefficient of kinetic friction $\mu_k = 0.70$ for the crushed vehicles along the path of the skid. You look up the inertias of these model vehicles and find that $m_c = 1400$ kg and $m_v = 6500$ kg. You know that the speed limit is 35 mi/h on both roads, which allows you to decide about driver citations. ••• CR

Figure P10.108

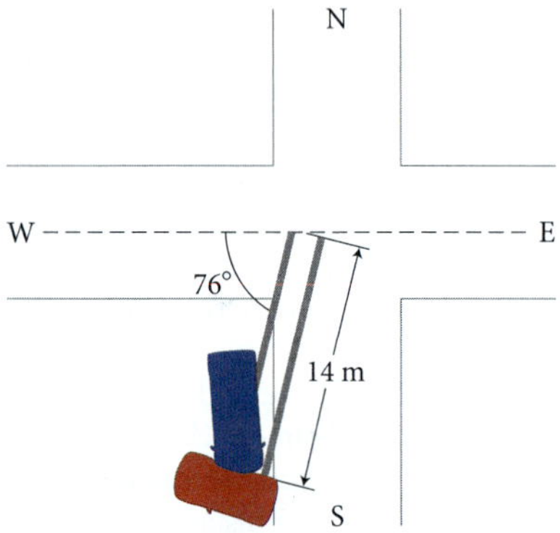

109. A 0.45-kg soccer ball is kicked at an angle θ above the ground with initial speed v_i. (*a*) Determine the height of the ball as a function of the horizontal distance it travels down the field. (*b*) For $\theta = 30°$, what initial speed must the ball have in order to land 48 m from where it is kicked? (*c*) If the foot is in contact with the ball for 0.15 s, what is the average force exerted by the foot on the ball? •••

110. A ballistic pendulum is a device for measuring bullet speeds. One of the simplest versions consists of a block of wood hanging from two long cords. (Two cords are used so that the bottom face of the block remains parallel to the floor as the block swings upward.) A 9.5-g bullet is fired into a ballistic pendulum in which the block has an inertia of 5.0 kg, and the block rises 60 mm above its initial position. (*a*) What is the speed of the bullet just before it hits the block? (*b*) How much energy is dissipated in the collision? What forms does this dissipated energy take? •••

111. A 0.010-kg bullet traveling at 300 m/s hits a 2.0-kg ballistic pendulum like the one described in Problem 110. However, the block is not thick enough for this bullet, and the bullet passes through the block, exiting with one-third of its original speed. How high above its original position does the block rise? •••

Answers to Review Questions

1. The logger sees the package fall in a curved trajectory. The pilot sees it fall in a straight line directly under the plane. The plane is directly above the logger when the package lands at his feet.
2. The accelerations are the same to both observers—namely, g.
3. This type of motion has two vector components, one vertical and one horizontal, and we need a reference axis for each.
4. In both cases, you place the tail of the second vector at the head of the first vector, and their sum is the vector extending from the tail of the first vector to the head of the second one. The difference is that in more than one dimension the magnitude of the sum depends on the angle between the vectors.
5. Subtraction is the same as if the vectors did lie along a straight line: Reverse the direction of vector 1 and then add that reversed vector to vector 2.
6. Yes, $\vec{A} + \vec{B} = \vec{B} + \vec{A}$. No, $\vec{A} - \vec{B} \neq \vec{B} - \vec{A}$.
7. To add two vectors $\vec{A}$ and $\vec{B}$, draw a scale model (magnitude and direction) of vector $\vec{A}$, then draw a scale model of vector $\vec{B}$ such that its tail is placed at the head of vector $\vec{A}$. The sum is a vector drawn from the tail of $\vec{A}$ to the head of $\vec{B}$. To subtract vector $\vec{B}$ from vector $\vec{A}$, reverse the direction of vector $\vec{B}$ and then add it to vector $\vec{A}$ using the addition process. The difference is a vector drawn from the tail of $\vec{A}$ to the head of the reversed $\vec{B}$.
8. The object is not moving in a straight line during the time interval Δt, but it is moving on a curved path.
9. The component of acceleration parallel to an object's velocity changes the magnitude of the velocity (speed) but does not change its direction. The component of acceleration perpendicular to the velocity changes the direction of the velocity but does not change its magnitude.
10. The normal component of this force is perpendicular to the surface of contact, and the tangential component is parallel to this surface.
11. (*a*) (*b*)

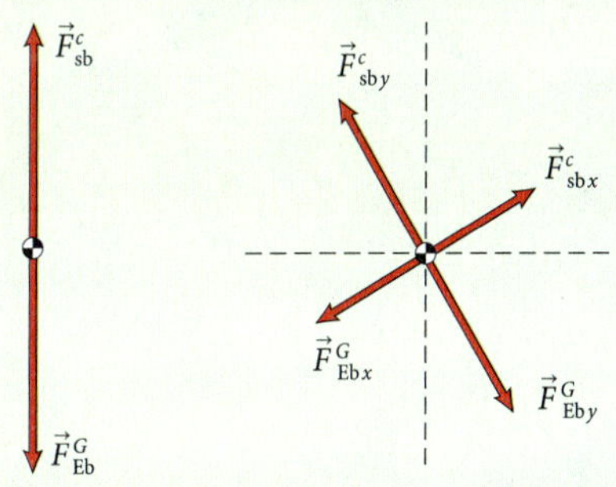

12. With one axis parallel to the acceleration, the components of force along the other axis add to zero, simplifying the algebra.
13. All three forces are components of the contact force experienced by two surfaces in contact with each other. The normal force is the component of the contact force perpendicular to the two surfaces. The force of friction, static or kinetic, is the component of the contact force parallel to the surfaces. The direction of any normal force always opposes interpenetration of the two surfaces; the direction of any frictional force always opposes slipping between the two surfaces. The magnitudes of the normal force and the force of static friction adjust within a range of possible values from zero to some maximum allowed value. Exceeding the maximum allowable normal force results in the failure (breaking) of one or both materials. When this happens, the surface can no longer exert a normal force and so its magnitude becomes zero. Exceeding the maximum allowable magnitude of the force of static friction results in slipping, in which case the force of static friction is replaced by a force of kinetic friction.
14. The force of static friction increases in magnitude as you push harder, so that its magnitude remains equal to the horizontal force you exert on the crate. The direction of the force of static friction opposes the direction of your push at all times.
15. Static friction rather than inertia is what needs to be overcome. The magnitude of your pushing force is smaller than the maximum magnitude of the frictional force the floor can exert on the desk.
16. The force of static friction is an elastic force and hence causes no dissipation of energy. The force of kinetic friction is not elastic and does cause energy dissipation. If this dissipation occurs at the system boundary, we have no means of knowing what fraction of the dissipated energy stays within the system and what fraction is transferred out of the system, so we cannot balance the energy equation.
17. Many answers are possible. The force of static friction between tires and road is responsible for accelerating a car, but it does no work on the car because there is zero force displacement. (Unless there is slipping, which would no longer involve static friction, the point of application of the force does not move.) When you carry a stack of books, the static friction between the top book and the one underneath it is responsible for accelerating the top book whenever you speed up or slow down. Work is done on the top book by the force of static friction because there is a nonzero force displacement.
18. Friction need not oppose motion, as in the case of the books in Review Question 17. What friction does always oppose is slipping, or *relative* motion between the surfaces in contact.
19. No, because in polar coordinates r represents a distance, not a position vector, and distances are always positive.
20. $B \sin\theta$. The sine function is the ratio of the opposite side to the hypotenuse, and the cosine is the ratio of the adjacent side to the hypotenuse. Because angles are generally given between a vector (hypotenuse) and the x axis, the cosine function is usually associated with an x component. Not in this case! (Something helpful for remembering which component is associated with $\sin\theta$ and which is associated with $\cos\theta$: Starting at the vector arrow, draw an arc across θ to the component that forms the other side of the angle. This component is the one associated with $\cos\theta$.)
21. A component vector is one of a set of vectors into which a given vector may be decomposed. Thus the sum of the component vectors equals the given vector. A vector component is the signed scalar that, together with an appropriate unit vector, describes the magnitude and direction of a component vector. The component vectors are related to the x and y components of the same vector by *Principles* Equation 10.5:

$$\vec{A} = \vec{A}_x + \vec{A}_y = A_x\hat{\imath} + A_y\hat{\jmath}.$$

This relationship reflects the option of considering vector addition as (scalar) addition of vector components in a chosen rectangular coordinate system, or (vector) addition of component vectors that lie along the chosen coordinate axes.

22. At the highest point, the vertical component of the velocity is 0, and so the ball's speed is given by the unchanged horizontal component: 30 m/s.
23. The path is parabolic. More specifically, $y(x)$ is a quadratic function.
24. The maximum height depends on only the vertical component of the launch velocity. However, a problem might involve a fixed launch speed with a variable angle of launch, in which case the horizontal and vertical components of the launch velocity are interdependent. The horizontal range of a projectile does depend on both components of launch velocity: the x component in order to move quickly horizontally, and the y component in order to remain in the air long enough to travel far.

25. The principles are the same: The momentum of the system is unchanged by the collision, and the coefficient of restitution determines the relative velocities of the colliding objects after the collision in terms of the relative velocities before the collision. The difference is that, in two dimensions, each momentum vector has two components, giving two equations that must be satisfied rather than one, as in one dimension. The relative velocities also have two components in two dimensions, but their relationship described by the coefficient of restitution still involves a single equation.
26. In one dimension there are two unknown final velocity components and two equations relating initial and final values. Momentum remains unchanged, and the initial and final relative velocities are related by the coefficient of restitution. In two dimensions these same principles provide three equations: two component equations to ensure that the momentum is unchanged, plus the single coefficient of restitution equation relating the initial and final relative velocities. However, in two dimensions there are in general four unknown final velocity components, two for each object. Thus in two dimensions at least one more piece of information is required for a complete solution.
27. The magnitude of one or both of the vectors might be zero, or the vectors might be perpendicular to each other, in which case the factor $\cos\phi$ in Eq. 10.33 is zero because $\phi = 90°$.
28. The work (a scalar) is the scalar product of the constant force (a vector) and the force displacement (a vector) between the two positions. It is equal to the product of the magnitudes (scalars) of these two vectors and the cosine of the angle between them.
29. The force displacement $\Delta\vec{r}_F$ cannot be used. Instead, the path along which the object moves from position 1 to position 2 must be broken up into infinitesimally small force displacements $d\vec{r}$. The work done is computed as a line integral of the scalar product of force and force displacement over the path from position 1 to position 2: $W = \int_1^2 \vec{F} \cdot d\vec{r}$.
30. The contact area is the macroscopic area over which the surfaces touch each other. The effective contact area is the actual area of microscopic contact between the two surfaces. The effective contact area is many thousands of times smaller than the contact area in everyday experience, and it is this effective contact area that increases as the normal force increases. The contact area does not increase with increasing normal force; hence, the force of friction is independent of the contact area. The available frictional force is dependent, as you would expect, on the effective contact area and hence on the normal force exerted by the surfaces on each other.
31. He has to tell you what material he had in contact with the concrete in order for the information to have any value. The coefficients of friction depend on the material of *both* surfaces in contact, not just one.
32. Kicking in the wedge increases the normal force exerted by the floor on the wedge and hence also increases the magnitude of the force of static friction exerted by the floor on the wedge.
33. Skidding involves kinetic friction because the tires and the road are sliding past each other. Rolling involves static friction because the tire and the road do not slip. The magnitude of the force of kinetic friction between any two surfaces is typically smaller than the maximum value of the magnitude of the force of static friction between the surfaces, and so it is the latter you want working for you when you stop a car.

Answers to Guided Problems

Guided Problem 10.2 (*b*) $h = \dfrac{gd^2}{2v_i^2\cos^2\theta} - d\tan\theta$

Guided Problem 10.4 0.88 m/s^2 at 11° W of N

Guided Problem 10.6 (*a*) $a = \dfrac{m_b - m_c\sin\theta}{m_b + m_c}g$; (*b*) $m_b = m_c\sin\theta$

Guided Problem 10.8 $\vec{v}_{p,i} = (0.85\ \text{m/s})\hat{\imath} + (0.37\ \text{m/s})\hat{\jmath}$

11

PRACTICE

Motion in a Circle

Chapter Summary

Rotational kinematics (Sections 11.1, 11.2, 11.4)

Concepts During **rotational motion,** all the particles in an object follow circular paths around the *axis of rotation.*

The **rotational velocity** ω_ϑ of an object is the rate at which the object's rotational coordinate ϑ changes.

The **rotational acceleration** α_ϑ is the rate at which an object's rotational velocity changes.

Quantitative Tools When an object travels a distance s along the circumference of a circle of radius r, the object's **rotational coordinate** ϑ is a unitless quantity defined as s divided by the circle's radius:

$$\vartheta \equiv \frac{s}{r}. \tag{11.1}$$

The arc distance s is measured from the positive x axis. To measure ϑ we need to choose a direction of increasing ϑ and a zero, just as we need to specify a direction of increasing x and an origin to measure position along an axis.

For any rotating object, the rotational velocity and rotational acceleration are

$$\omega_\vartheta = \frac{d\vartheta}{dt} \tag{11.6}$$

$$\alpha_\vartheta = \frac{d\omega_\vartheta}{dt} = \frac{d^2\vartheta}{dt^2}. \tag{11.12}$$

Translational variables for rotating objects (Sections 11.1, 11.4)

Concepts The velocity $\vec{v}$ of an object moving along a circle is always perpendicular to the object's position vector $\vec{r}$ measured from the axis of rotation.

The tangential component v_t of the velocity is tangent to the circle. The radial component v_r of the velocity is zero.

An object moving in a circle has a nonzero acceleration (even if its speed is constant) because the direction of the velocity changes.

An inward force is required to make an object move in a circle, even at constant speed.

Quantitative Tools The tangential and radial components of the velocity of an object moving along a circular path are

$$v_t = r\omega_\vartheta \tag{11.10}$$

$$v_r = 0. \tag{11.18}$$

The radial component of the acceleration is

$$a_r = -\frac{v^2}{r}. \tag{11.16}$$

This radial component is called the **centripetal acceleration** and is directed toward the center of the circle. It can also be written as

$$a_r = -r\omega^2.$$

The tangential component of the acceleration is

$$a_t = r\alpha_\vartheta. \tag{11.23}$$

The magnitude of the acceleration is

$$a = \sqrt{a_r^2 + a_t^2}. \tag{11.21}$$

Constant rotational acceleration (Section 11.4)

Concepts If the tangential acceleration a_t of a rotating object is constant, its rotational acceleration α_ϑ is also constant. In only that case, the rotational kinematics relationships for *constant rotational acceleration* apply.

Quantitative Tools If an object with constant rotational acceleration α_ϑ initially has a rotational coordinate ϑ_i and a rotational velocity $\omega_{\vartheta,i}$, then after a time interval Δt its rotational coordinate and rotational velocity are

$$\vartheta_f = \vartheta_i + \omega_{\vartheta,i}\Delta t + \tfrac{1}{2}\alpha_\vartheta(\Delta t)^2 \tag{11.26}$$

$$\omega_{\vartheta,f} = \omega_{\vartheta,i} + \alpha_\vartheta \Delta t. \tag{11.27}$$

Rotational inertia (Sections 11.3, 11.5, 11.6)

Concepts **Rotational inertia** is a measure of an object's tendency to resist any change in its rotational velocity. The rotational inertia depends on the inertia of the object and on how that inertia is distributed. The SI units of rotational inertia are kilograms-meters-squared ($kg \cdot m^2$).

Quantitative Tools The rotational inertia I of a rotating particle of inertia m is

$$I = mr^2, \tag{11.30}$$

where r is the distance from the particle to the rotation axis. For an extended object, the rotational inertia is

$$I = \int r^2 dm. \tag{11.43}$$

PRACTICE

The **parallel-axis theorem:** If I_{cm} is the rotational inertia of an object of inertia m about an axis A through the object's center of mass, the rotational inertia I of the object about an axis parallel to A and a distance d away from A is

$$I = I_{cm} + md^2. \tag{11.53}$$

Rotational kinetic energy and angular momentum (Section 11.5)

Concepts **Rotational kinetic energy** is the kinetic energy of an object due to its rotational motion.

Angular momentum L_ϑ is the capacity of an object to make other objects rotate.

A particle can have angular momentum even if it is not rotating.

The law of **conservation of angular momentum** says that angular momentum can be transferred from one object to another but cannot be created or destroyed. The angular momentum of an object or system is constant when no tangential forces are exerted on it.

Quantitative Tools The rotational kinetic energy of an object that has rotational inertia I and rotational speed ω is

$$K_{rot} = \tfrac{1}{2}I\omega^2. \tag{11.31}$$

The angular momentum of an object that has rotational inertia I and rotational velocity ω_ϑ is

$$L_\vartheta = I\omega_\vartheta. \tag{11.34}$$

The angular momentum of a particle of inertia m and speed v about an axis of rotation is

$$L = r_\perp mv, \tag{11.36}$$

where $r_\perp$ is the perpendicular distance from the axis to the line of action of the particle's momentum. The distance $r_\perp$ is called the **lever arm distance** of the momentum relative to the axis.

Review Questions

Answers to these questions can be found at the end of this chapter.

11.1 Circular motion at constant speed

1. Give an example of (*a*) an object that has translational motion but no rotational motion, (*b*) an object that has rotational motion but no translational motion, and (*c*) an object that has both rotational motion and translational motion.
2. Is it possible for an object to have a nonzero acceleration if the object is traveling (*a*) at constant velocity and (*b*) at constant speed?
3. For an object moving along a circular path, what is the difference between the object's rotational coordinate ϑ and its polar angle θ?
4. For an object in circular motion at constant speed, describe the directions of the object's position vector (relative to the center of the circular trajectory), velocity vector, and acceleration vector at a given instant.

11.2 Forces and circular motion

5. If you are sitting in the passenger seat of a car that makes a quick left turn, your shoulders seem to lean to the right. What causes this apparent rightward motion?
6. Why shouldn't you use a rotating reference frame when analyzing forces?
7. What can you say about the vector sum of the forces exerted on an object that moves in a circle at constant speed? How does this vector sum of forces vary with speed and radius?

11.3 Rotational inertia

8. Is rotational inertia an intrinsic property of an object? Explain your answer.
9. Why does a tightrope walker carry a long pole?

11.4 Rotational kinematics

10. Does an object moving in a circle always have centripetal acceleration? Does it always have rotational acceleration? Does it always have tangential acceleration?
11. What is the mathematical expression that gives the relationship between rotational coordinate ϑ and polar angle θ?
12. Explain the distinctions among rotational acceleration, tangential acceleration, and centripetal acceleration.
13. For an object moving in circular motion, write an expression showing the relationship between (*a*) its arc length along the circle s and its rotational coordinate ϑ, (*b*) its velocity v_t and rotational velocity ω_ϑ, and (*c*) its tangential acceleration a_t and its rotational acceleration α_ϑ.
14. You are whirling a ball on the end of a string in a horizontal circle above your head. How does the ball's centripetal acceleration change if you increase the speed v so that the time interval needed to complete a revolution is halved?

11.5 Angular momentum

15. Define *rotational inertia* for a particle moving in a circle. Define *lever arm distance* for a particle moving near an axis of rotation.
16. Describe the relationship between the rotational kinetic energy of an object moving in circular motion and the object's rotational inertia.
17. How is angular momentum L related to momentum mv for an object of inertia m moving with constant velocity?
18. If both the rotational inertia I and the rotational speed ω of an object are doubled, what happens to the object's rotational kinetic energy?
19. What is the meaning of the statement: Angular momentum is conserved?

11.6 Rotational inertia of extended objects

20. Your physics book can be rotated around three mutually perpendicular axes passing symmetrically through its center. About which axis is the rotational inertia smallest? About which axis is it largest?
21. A diatomic molecule, which has a dumbbell shape, can rotate about three symmetrical axes that pass through the center of the molecule. Describe them. Rotation at a specific rotational speed about which axis gives the molecule the lowest kinetic energy?
22. State the parallel-axis theorem in words.

Developing a Feel

Make an order-of-magnitude estimate of each of the following quantities. Letters in parentheses refer to hints below. Use them as needed to guide your thinking.

1. The speed v of a point on the equator as Earth rotates (D, P)
2. The rotational inertia of a bowling ball about an axis tangent to its surface (A, R, X)
3. Your rotational inertia as you turn over in your sleep (V, C)
4. The angular momentum around the axle of a wheel/tire combination on your car as you cruise on the freeway (E, I, O, AA, S)
5. The angular momentum of a spinning ice skater with each arm held out to the side and parallel to the ice (G, X, N, U)
6. The speed you would need to orbit Earth in a low orbit (F, P)
7. The magnitude of the force exerted by the Sun on Earth to hold Earth in orbit (B, L, T, Z)
8. The kinetic energy associated with Earth's rotation (Z, P, D)
9. The angular momentum, about a vertical axis through your house, of a large car driving down your street (H, Y, M)
10. The kinetic energy of a spinning yo-yo (K, W, J, Q)

Hints

A. What is the inertia of a bowling ball?
B. How long a time interval is needed for Earth to make one revolution around the Sun?
C. What simple geometric shape is an appropriate model for a sleeping person?
D. What is Earth's rotational speed?
E. What is the combined inertia of the wheel and tire?
F. What is the relationship between force and acceleration for this orbit?
G. How can you model the skater's shape during her spin?
H. What is the inertia of a midsize car?
I. What is the radius of the tire?
J. How many turns are needed to rewind the yo-yo?
K. What is the yo-yo's rotational inertia?
L. What is the radius of Earth's orbit?
M. What is the perpendicular distance from the house to the car's line of motion?
N. What is the skater's rotational inertia with arms held out?
O. How can you model the combined rotational inertia of the wheel and tire?
P. What is Earth's radius?
Q. What is the final rotational speed?
R. What is the radius of a bowling ball?
S. What is the rotational speed of the tire?
T. What is the required centripetal acceleration?
U. What is the skater's initial rotational speed?
V. What is your inertia?
W. When thrown, how long a time interval does the yo-yo take to reach the end of the string?
X. What is needed in addition to the formulas in *Principles* Table 11.3 in order to determine this quantity?
Y. What is a typical speed for a car moving on a city street?
Z. What is Earth's inertia?
AA. What is a typical freeway cruising speed?

Key (all values approximate)

A. 7 kg; **B.** 1 y $= 3 \times 10^7$ s; **C.** solid cylinder of radius 0.2 m; **D.** period = 24 h, so $\omega = 7 \times 10^{-5}\ \text{s}^{-1}$; **E.** 10^1 kg; **F.** from Eqs. 8.6, 8.17, and 11.16, $\sum\vec{F} = m\vec{a}$, so $mg = mv^2/r$; **G.** a solid cylinder with two thin-rod arms of inertia 4 kg held out perpendicularly; **H.** 2×10^3 kg; **I.** 0.3 m; **J.** 2×10^1 turns; **K.** $6 \times 10^{-5}\ \text{kg} \cdot \text{m}^2$ (with yo-yo modeled as solid cylinder); **L.** 2×10^{11} m; **M.** 2×10^1 m; **N.** $4\ \text{kg} \cdot \text{m}^2$; **O.** between MR^2 (cylindrical shell representing tire) and $MR^2/2$ (solid cylinder representing wheel)—say, $3MR^2/4$; **P.** 6×10^6 m; **Q.** about twice the average rotational speed, or $\omega = 5 \times 10^2\ \text{s}^{-1}$; **R.** 0.1 m; **S.** no slipping, so $\omega = v/r \approx 10^2\ \text{s}^{-1}$; **T.** $8 \times 10^{-3}\ \text{m/s}^2$; **U.** $\omega \approx 10\ \text{s}^{-1}$; **V.** 7×10^1 kg; **W.** 0.5 s; **X.** the parallel-axis theorem; **Y.** 3×10^1 mi/h; **Z.** 6×10^{24} kg; **AA.** 3×10^1 m/s

PRACTICE

Worked and Guided Problems

Table 11.3 **Rotational inertia of uniform objects of inertia M about axes through their center of mass**

Rotation axes oriented so that object could roll on surface: For these axes, rotational inertia has the form cMR^2, where $c = I/MR^2$ is called the *shape factor*. The farther the object's material from the rotation axis, the larger the shape factor and hence the rotational inertia.

	thin-walled cylinder or hoop	solid cylinder	hollow-core cylinder	thin-walled hollow sphere	solid sphere
Shape	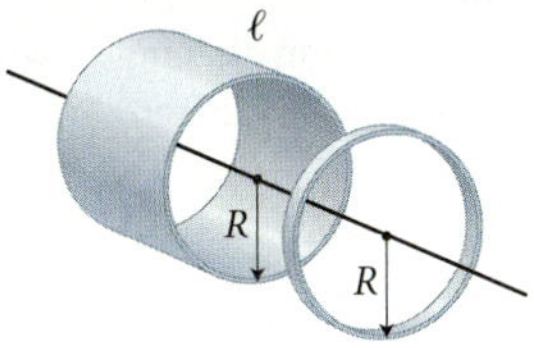	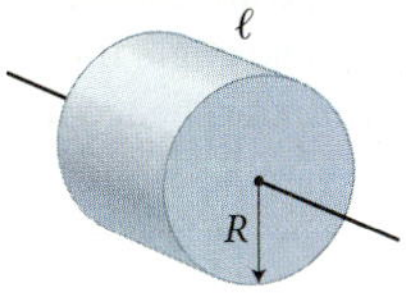	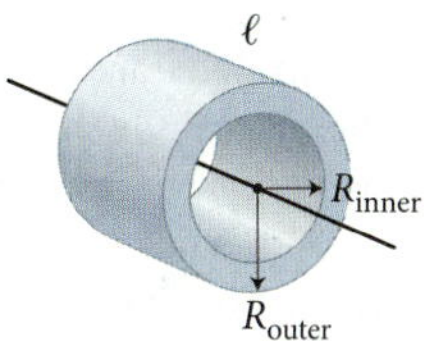	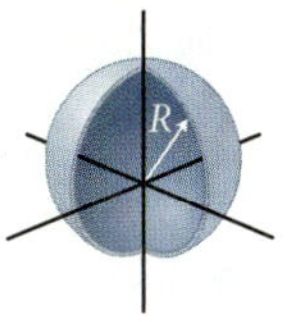	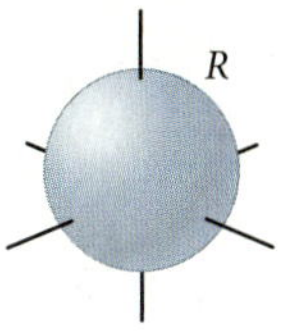
Rotational inertia	MR^2	$\frac{1}{2}MR^2$	$\frac{1}{2}M(R^2_{\text{outer}} + R^2_{\text{inner}})$	$\frac{2}{3}MR^2$	$\frac{2}{5}MR^2$
Shape factor $c = I/MR^2$	1	$\frac{1}{2}$	$\frac{1}{2}\left[1 + \left(\frac{R_{\text{inner}}}{R_{\text{outer}}}\right)^2\right]$	$\frac{2}{3}$	$\frac{2}{5}$

Other axis orientations

	thin-walled hoop	solid cylinder	thin rod	rectangular plate
Shape	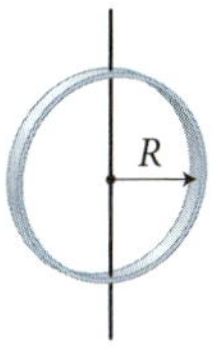	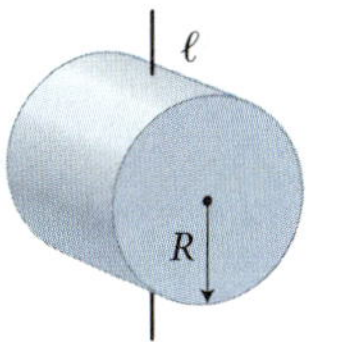	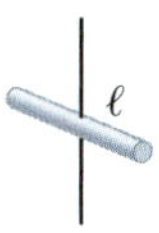	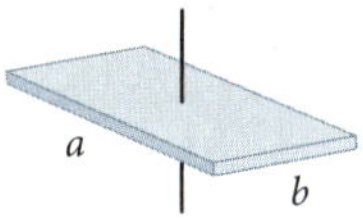
Rotational inertia	$\frac{1}{2}MR^2$	$\frac{1}{4}MR^2 + \frac{1}{12}M\ell^2$	$\frac{1}{12}M\ell^2$	$\frac{1}{12}M(a^2 + b^2)$

These examples involve material from this chapter but are not associated with any particular section. Some examples are worked out in detail; others you should work out by following the guidelines provided.

Worked Problem 11.1 The fan

The ceiling fan in Figure WG11.1 has blades that are 0.60 m long and is spinning at 80 rev/min. It is turned off and comes to rest in 40 s. (*a*) What are the speed v and the magnitude a_c of the centripetal acceleration of the tip of any blade just before the fan is switched off? (*b*) After it is switched off, what is the fan's average rotational acceleration? (*c*) How many revolutions does the fan complete before coming to rest?

Figure WG11.1

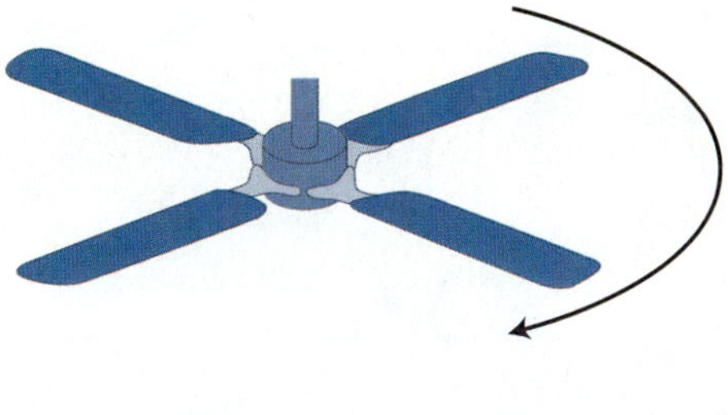

❶ GETTING STARTED We are given information about initial and final rotational speeds, $\omega_i = 80$ rev/min and $\omega_f = 0$. We must obtain kinematic quantities, and this sounds like a straightforward rotational kinematics problem. We approach this problem as we would a kinematics problem involving translational motion. We begin with a motion diagram for the tip of one of the blades (Figure WG11.2). We note that the fan is slowing down, which means that the points

Figure WG11.2

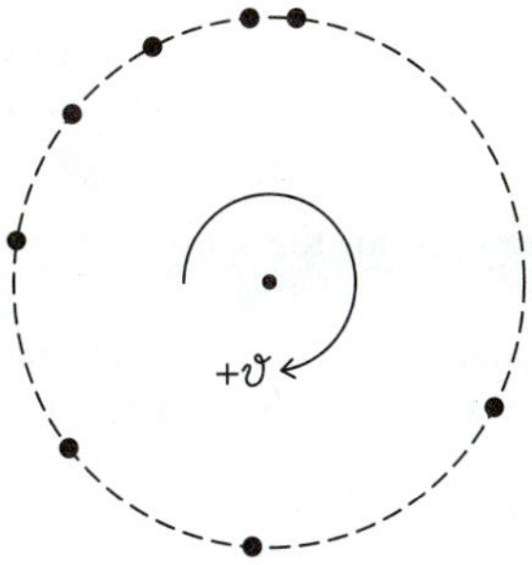

PRACTICE

on the circle representing the blade tip at different instants get closer together as time goes on. We have to pick a direction for the positive sense of the rotation, which we arbitrarily choose to be clockwise as we look up at the fan. This is the equivalent of choosing the direction of the x axis in a translational motion problem. With this choice for direction, the initial rotational velocity is positive. The rotational variables we need should be directly available from the equations given in the *Principles* volume, and the centripetal acceleration can be obtained once we have computed the speed v of the blade tip.

❷ **DEVISE PLAN** The magnitude of the tip's centripetal acceleration is $a_c = v^2/r$, and its speed is $v = \omega r$. The magnitude of the fan's average rotational acceleration after the fan is turned off can be obtained from $\alpha_\vartheta = \Delta\omega_\vartheta/\Delta t$. The number of revolutions can be computed from this rotational motion expression from *Principles* Table 11.2:

$$\Delta\vartheta = \omega_{\vartheta,i}\Delta t + \tfrac{1}{2}\alpha_\vartheta(\Delta t)^2.$$

❸ **EXECUTE PLAN**

(*a*) Before we can calculate the numerical answers, we need to convert the given initial rotational speed from revolutions per minute to inverse seconds. The initial rotational speed is the operating speed, which is constant until the fan turns off. Therefore its initial instantaneous value is equal to the average (operating) value:

$$\omega_i = |\omega_{\vartheta,i}| = \left|\frac{\Delta\vartheta}{\Delta t}\right| = \left(\frac{1}{1\text{ rad}}\right)\frac{\Delta\theta(\text{rad})}{\Delta t}$$

$$= 80\,\frac{\text{rev}}{\text{min}}\left(\frac{2\pi\text{ rad}}{\text{rev}}\right)\left(\frac{1}{1\text{ rad}}\right)\left(\frac{1\text{ min}}{60\text{ s}}\right) = 8.4\text{ s}^{-1}.$$

Before the fan starts to slow down, the speed of the blade tip is

$$v_i = \omega_i r = (8.4\text{ s}^{-1})(0.60\text{ m}) = 5.0\text{ m/s}. ✔$$

The magnitude of the initial centripetal acceleration of the tip is

$$a_c = \frac{v_i^2}{r} = \frac{(5.0\text{ m/s})^2}{0.60\text{ m}} = 42\text{ m/s}^2. ✔$$

(*b*) From our choice of clockwise as the positive rotation sense, the initial rotational velocity is positive: $\omega_{\vartheta,i} = +\omega_i$. The average rotational acceleration during spin-down is

$$\alpha_\vartheta = \frac{\Delta\omega_\vartheta}{\Delta t} = \frac{\omega_{\vartheta,f} - \omega_{\vartheta,i}}{\Delta t} = \frac{0 - (+8.4\text{ s}^{-1})}{40\text{ s}} = -0.21\text{ s}^{-2}, ✔$$

with the minus sign telling us that the direction of this rotational acceleration is counterclockwise, opposite our clockwise choice for the positive sense of rotation.

(*c*) The angle the fan goes through in slowing down can be found from the change in the rotational coordinate:

$$\Delta\vartheta = \omega_{\vartheta,i}\Delta t + \tfrac{1}{2}\alpha_\vartheta(\Delta t)^2$$

$$= (+8.4\text{ s}^{-1})(40\text{ s}) + \tfrac{1}{2}(-0.21\text{ s}^{-2})(40\text{ s})^2$$

$$= 1.7 \times 10^2.$$

Thus the change in angle is equivalent to 170 rad, or

$$(170\text{ rad})\left(\frac{1\text{ rev}}{2\pi\text{ rad}}\right) = 27\text{ rev}. ✔$$

❹ **EVALUATE RESULT** The negative sign in our result for part *b*, -0.21 s^{-2}, indicates that the rotational acceleration is causing the rotational velocity to change in the direction opposite our chosen positive direction. Because the initial rotational velocity is positive, the negative value for rotational acceleration means the rotational velocity is becoming less positive and its magnitude is decreasing; in other words, the fan is slowing down. This is also consistent with a negative tangential acceleration of the tip.

The numerical values do not seem unusually large or small for a ceiling fan. It was necessary to treat the average rotational acceleration as if it were a constant rotational acceleration in order to use the kinematic equation for the angle the blade tip turns through as the fan slows down. This is permissible because, just as with translational motion, an average acceleration produces the same effect as a constant acceleration of the same magnitude.

Guided Problem 11.2 Swift shuttle

A space shuttle follows a circular orbit at an altitude of 300 km above the ground and has a period of 90.5 min. What are the shuttle's (*a*) rotational speed ω, (*b*) speed v, and (*c*) centripetal acceleration magnitude a_c?

❶ **GETTING STARTED**

1. How is rotational speed related to the given information?
2. Are kinematic equations sufficient to provide the relationships you need?
3. Sketch a motion diagram for the shuttle. How should the dots representing its position at various instants be spaced?

❷ **DEVISE PLAN**

4. Write an expression for the speed in terms of the rotational speed.
5. What is the numerical value of the orbit radius?
6. Write an expression for the magnitude of the centripetal acceleration.

❸ **EXECUTE PLAN**

7. Substitute numerical values for the known quantities. Watch out for units!

❹ **EVALUATE RESULT**

8. Is the speed reasonable for a spacecraft? How does the acceleration compare to g?

Worked Problem 11.3 Careful on that curve!

A highway has a flat section with a tight level curve of radius 40 m (Figure WG11.3). If the coefficient of static friction between tires and pavement surface is 0.45, what is the maximum speed v at which a car of inertia m can negotiate the curve safely—in other words, without the tires slipping?

Figure WG11.3

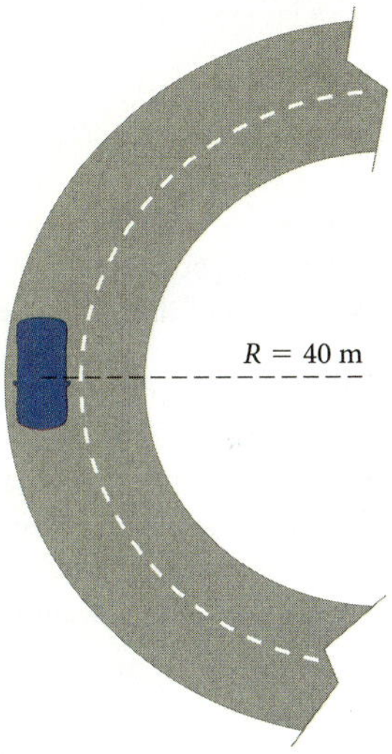

❶ **GETTING STARTED** We know from experience that if it goes too fast in the curve, the car goes off the outer edge of the road. This tells us there must be an inward force exerted on the car to provide centripetal acceleration and thus keep it moving in circular motion. In this case, that force is the frictional force. (Note that even though the tires are moving, the force is the force of *static* friction because the tires are not sliding on the road surface.) Let us use Newton's second law, keeping in mind that there is an acceleration toward the center of the curve. The first step is to produce a free-body diagram for the car and choose our coordinate directions (Figure WG11.4).

Figure WG11.4

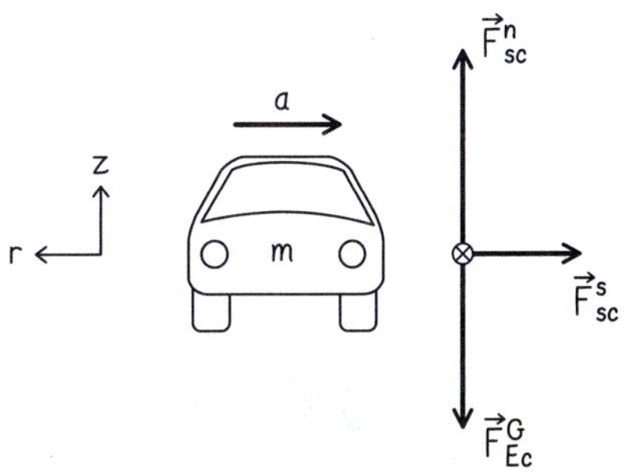

The frictional force is always directed opposite the direction the car would slide if there were no friction, which would be outward in this case. Thus the frictional force is aimed inward, supplying the necessary centripetal component of force directed toward the center of the curve (to the right in Figure WG11.4).

❷ **DEVISE PLAN** Because the acceleration and the frictional force are along our chosen radial r axis, we begin with Newton's second law along that axis:

$$\Sigma F_r = ma_r$$
$$F^n_{sc,r} + F^s_{sc,r} + F^G_{Ec,r} = ma_r$$
$$0 + (-F^s_{sc}) + 0 = m(-a_c)$$
$$F^s_{sc} = ma_c \qquad (1)$$

The centripetal acceleration magnitude is related to the car's speed through $a_c = v^2/R$, where R is the (fixed) radius of the curve. The frictional force is related to the normal force through Eq. 10.54, $F^s_{sc} \leq \mu_s F^n_{sc}$. At the maximum speed, just before slipping, $\leq$ is replaced by $=$ and we have

$$F^s_{sc,max} = \mu_s F^n_{sc}. \qquad (2)$$

This means we have enough equations to solve for the maximum speed v if we know the normal force. Because the normal force is along the z axis, we use Newton's second law along that axis to determine its magnitude.

❸ **EXECUTE PLAN** Starting with Eq. 1 in the form

$$F^s_{sc} = ma_c = m\frac{v^2}{R},$$

we have, at maximum speed,

$$F^s_{sc,max} = m\frac{v^2_{max}}{R}.$$

From Eq. 2 we make the substitution

$$\mu_s F^n_{sc} = m\frac{v^2_{max}}{R}. \qquad (3)$$

To get the magnitude of the normal force, we use Newton's second law in the z direction:

$$\Sigma F_z = ma_z$$
$$F^n_{sc,z} + F^s_{sc,z} + F^G_{Ec,z} = ma_z$$
$$(+F^n_{sc}) + 0 + (-mg) = m(0)$$
$$F^n_{sc} = mg.$$

We substitute this result into Eq. 3 to get

$$\mu_s mg = m\frac{v^2_{max}}{R}$$

$$v_{max} = \sqrt{\mu_s gR}$$
$$= \sqrt{(0.45)(9.8\,\text{m/s}^2)(40\,\text{m})}$$
$$= 13\,\text{m/s} = 30\,\text{mi/h}. ✔$$

❹ **EVALUATE RESULT** The most remarkable feature of the result we obtained for v_{max} is that v_{max} does not depend on the car's inertia. This means that the maximum safe speed is 30 mi/h for both a compact car and a cement truck. Does this make sense? It seems that a truck should go more slowly because more force is required to keep it moving in a circle with the same acceleration as that exerted on a compact car. Although that is true, the frictional force is proportional to the normal force, which in turn is proportional to the inertia. Therefore the inertia cancels out.

A larger coefficient of friction μ_s means you can go faster without slipping, as is also the case for a bigger (straighter) curve with larger radius R. This is exactly what $v_{max} = \sqrt{\mu_s g R}$ says.

No assumptions were made, but we should review our decision to use the maximum available force of static friction. In order for the tires to slip, we must require an inward force greater than friction can provide, and so our use of maximum values is correct. The numerical value for the maximum speed is plausible and raises no red flag to cause us to question our numerical result.

Guided Problem 11.4 It's in the bank

Highway curves are often banked to reduce a vehicle's reliance on friction when negotiating the turn: On a banked curve, there is a centripetal component of normal force acting on the vehicle. When the angle and speed are such that friction plays no role in a vehicle's motion in the curve, the nature of the road surface is immaterial and thus the posted speed limit applies in both wet and dry weather. Suppose the posted speed limit is 100 km/h on a curve of radius 180 m. At what angle θ to the horizontal should the curve be banked so that reliance on friction is not necessary?

❶ **GETTING STARTED**

1. Draw a cutaway view that shows the bank angle θ (Figure WG11.5).

Figure WG11.5

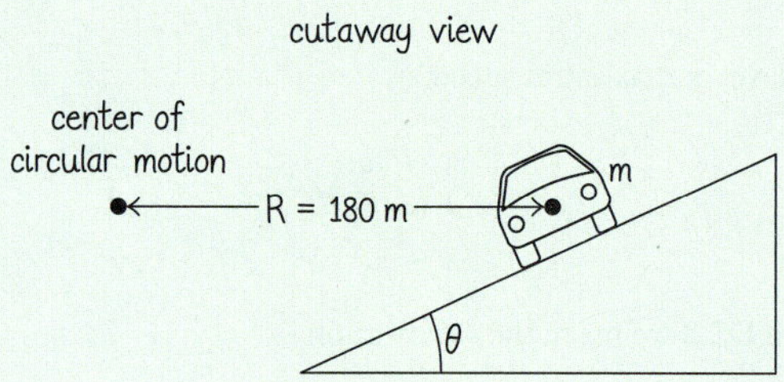

2. Do you notice the similarity to Worked Problem 11.3 and to the roller skater leaning into a curve in *Principles* Example 11.4?

❷ **DEVISE PLAN**

3. What forces are exerted on the car? Remember that you want the force of static friction to be zero.
4. Draw a free-body diagram of the car as seen in the cutaway view.
5. Show the centripetal acceleration that keeps the car moving in a circle in your diagram. Be careful about the direction of this acceleration. Where is the center of the circle?
6. Which directions provide the best choice of an xy coordinate system? Recall that the acceleration should lie along one axis.
7. Count the unknowns. Does the bank angle appear in your equations?

❸ **EXECUTE PLAN**

8. From the component force equations and the relationship of centripetal acceleration magnitude to speed, perform some algebra to solve for the bank angle.
9. Get the numerical value for the angle. Don't forget units.

❹ **EVALUATE RESULT**

10. Examine your algebraic expression for the bank angle. How does the required angle change as the speed increases? As the radius of the curve increases? Are these variations what you expect?
11. Does the angle depend on a vehicle's inertia? Is this reasonable?
12. Consider the numerical value. Is this a reasonable angle? How steep are the angles you usually see on highways?

Worked Problem 11.5 Wind power

The commercial wind turbine in Figure WG11.6 consists of three 6400-kg blades, each 35.0 m long. It generates 1.0 MW of electrical power when it rotates with very little friction at a constant speed in the usually steady wind. However, when the wind suddenly stops, the turbine spins to a stop in 100 s. From this information, estimate the following for the situation when the wind is blowing steadily: (*a*) the rotational kinetic energy of the turbine, (*b*) its rotational speed, and (*c*) the magnitude of its angular momentum.

❶ **GETTING STARTED** When the rotational speed ω is constant, the turbine converts wind energy to electrical energy without changing its own rotational kinetic energy. When the wind stops, the turbine's rotational kinetic energy is converted to electrical energy for as long as that rotational kinetic energy lasts. It is this conversion of energy, not friction, that slows the turbine down when the wind stops. We can gain information about the constant-speed state by backtracking from the spin-down data.

Figure WG11.6

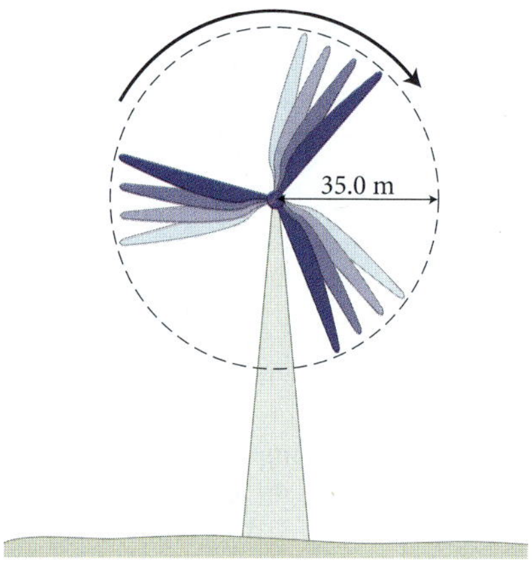

❷ **DEVISE PLAN** When the wind is steady, the turbine rotates with a constant rotational speed and has a certain amount of rotational kinetic energy. Once the wind dies, that kinetic energy is converted to electrical energy as the turbine spins down. During the spinning down, the work done by its environment on the turbine is equal to the change in the rotational kinetic energy:

$$\Delta K_{\text{rot}} = W_{\text{ct}}.$$

In Chapter 9 we saw that the work done by the environment on a system has the same magnitude as the work done by the system on its environment, but the two carry opposite signs. Therefore the work done by the environment on the turbine during the spin-down interval is the negative of the work W_{tc} done by the turbine on the environment during that interval. This work is the average power generated by the turbine multiplied by the time interval the turbine takes to come to rest:

$$\begin{aligned} K_{\text{rot,f}} - K_{\text{rot,i}} &= W_{\text{ct}} \\ &= -W_{\text{tc}} \\ &= -P_{\text{av}}\Delta t. \end{aligned} \qquad (1)$$

Knowing that the final rotational kinetic energy is zero, we can determine the initial rotational kinetic energy if we can reasonably estimate the average power during spin-down. Once we have $K_{\text{rot,i}}$, we can get the initial rotational speed ω_i and the magnitude of the angular momentum from

$$K_{\text{rot,i}} = \tfrac{1}{2} I_{\text{t}}\omega_{\text{i}}^2 \qquad (2)$$

$$L_{\vartheta} = I_{\text{t}}\omega_{\vartheta\text{i}}. \qquad (3)$$

❸ **EXECUTE PLAN** (*a*) We suspect that the rate of power generation decreases as the blades slow down, but we are not given sufficient information to make this statement quantitative. So we need to make a reasonable assumption. Let us say that the average power generated during spin-down is half the constant-speed power of 1.0 MW: $P_{\text{av}} = 500$ kW. Then we can say from Eq. 1 that

$$\begin{aligned} K_{\text{rot,f}} - K_{\text{rot,i}} &= -P_{\text{av}}\Delta t \\ 0 - K_{\text{rot,i}} &= -P_{\text{av}}\Delta t \\ K_{\text{rot, i}} &= P_{\text{av}}\Delta t \\ &= (5.0 \times 10^5\ \text{J/s})(100\ \text{s}) \\ &= 5.0 \times 10^7\ \text{J} \\ &= 50\ \text{MJ}. \checkmark \end{aligned}$$

(*b*) To obtain the rotational speed ω_{i} when the wind is blowing at a constant speed, we solve Eq. 2 for this variable:

$$\omega_{\text{i}}^2 = \frac{2K_{\text{rot,i}}}{I_{\text{t}}}.$$

First we must obtain the rotational inertia for the turbine, which can be modeled as three rods whose ends abut the turbine axle. For a rod of length ℓ and inertia m, the rotational inertia about an axis through one end of the rod is $m\ell^2/3$ (see *Principles* Example 11.11). Thus the rotational inertia for the three-blade turbine is $I_{\text{t}} = 3(m\ell^2/3) = m\ell^2 = (6400\ \text{kg})(35\ \text{m})^2 = 7.84 \times 10^6\ \text{kg}\cdot\text{m}^2$. The steady-state rotational speed of the turbine is then

$$\begin{aligned} \omega_{\text{i}} &= \sqrt{\frac{2K_{\text{rot, i}}}{I_{\text{t}}}} \\ &= \sqrt{\frac{2(5.0 \times 10^7\ \text{J})}{7.84 \times 10^6\ \text{kg}\cdot\text{m}^2}} \\ &= 3.6\ \text{s}^{-1}. \checkmark \end{aligned}$$

(*c*) For the angular momentum, Eq. 3 gives

$$\begin{aligned} |L_{\vartheta,\text{i}}| &= |I_{\text{t}}\omega_{\vartheta,\text{i}}| \\ &= I_{\text{t}}\omega_{\text{i}} \\ &= (7.84 \times 10^6\ \text{kg}\cdot\text{m}^2)(3.6\ \text{s}^{-1}) \\ &= 2.8 \times 10^7\ \text{kg}\cdot\text{m}^2/\text{s}. \checkmark \end{aligned}$$

❹ **EVALUATE RESULT** By being careful in distinguishing between work done *by* the turbine and work done *on* it, we have gotten the signs right: We did not wind up with ω_{i}^2 being negative. The initial rotational speed $\omega_{\text{i}} = 3.6\ \text{s}^{-1}$ corresponds to a rotational period $T_{\text{i}} = 2\pi/\omega_{\text{i}} = 1.7$ s. This seems reasonable for a large commercial wind turbine and is consistent with observations if you have driven by a wind farm: The blades take a couple of seconds to complete each revolution.

We made several approximations: that the turbine blades are rod-shaped, that the rotational inertia of the turbine hub can be ignored, and that the average power during spin-down is half the constant-speed power. This last approximation is the most uncertain, but the average power should be some fraction of the constant-speed power because it must be between the initial and final values. Instead of saying the average power is half the constant-speed value, we might have said one-third or two-thirds. Those choices are both reasonable and would affect the numerical answers but not the spirit of our solution.

The hub's rotational inertia should not be significant because the hub radius is much smaller than the length of the blades. Modeling the blades as rods introduces some error, but the alternative is a very complicated integration procedure requiring specific information about the blades' shape. The error is not greater than the uncertainty introduced by the assumption that $P_{\text{av}} = P_{\text{constant speed}}/2$.

Guided Problem 11.6 Hit that door

You stand in front of a door of inertia m_d and width ℓ_d as it swings toward you with rotational speed ω_i. You throw a ball of inertia m_b and speed v_b toward the door so that it strikes the door perpendicularly at a distance d from the hinged edge, as shown in the overhead view (Figure WG11.7). The ball bounces directly back toward you with one-fourth its original speed. (*a*) What is the final rotational speed ω_f of the door after the collision? (*b*) What must the speed v_b of the ball be at impact if you want the door to swing away from you after the ball hits?

Figure WG11.7

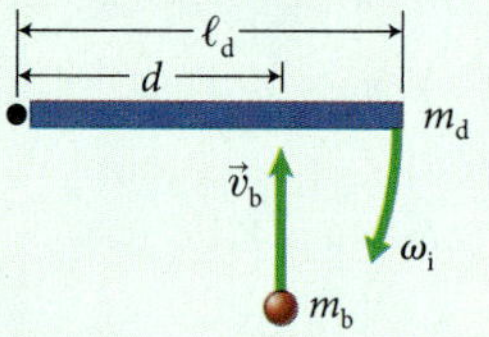

1 GETTING STARTED

1. What is the best choice of system? Is this system isolated? Closed?
2. Modify Figure WG11.7 to obtain a two-part sketch of the system before and after the collision. Because rotational quantities have signs, include a curved arrow about the rotation axis to indicate the direction you choose for the positive sense of rotation.

2 DEVISE PLAN

3. How many unknown quantities do you seek in part *a*? Are there additional unknowns for part *b*?
4. What quantity is constant in this collision? Write the algebraic expression stating the equality of the initial and final values. Make sure to account for all the objects in your system on both sides of the equation.
5. What is the most convenient choice of location for the reference axis? Select the appropriate signs for each term in your equation. Base your decisions about signs on the chosen direction of positive rotation, even for the ball moving in a straight line.

3 EXECUTE PLAN

6. Solve for the door's final rotational speed ω_f.
7. How is ω_f different if the door swings away from you instead of toward you after the ball hits?

4 EVALUATE RESULT

8. Does the equation you get scale as you expect with changes in m_b, m_d, v_i, ℓ_d, and d? For instance, how does ω_f behave as the ball's inertia gets very large or very small?

Worked Problem 11.7 Just unwind

A block of inertia m_b is attached to a very light string wound about a uniform disk of inertia m_d and radius R_d, which rotates on a horizontal axle (Figure WG11.8). If the block is released from rest, what are its speed $v_{b,f}$ and acceleration a_b after it has fallen a distance d? Ignore any friction force exerted on or by the axle.

Figure WG11.8

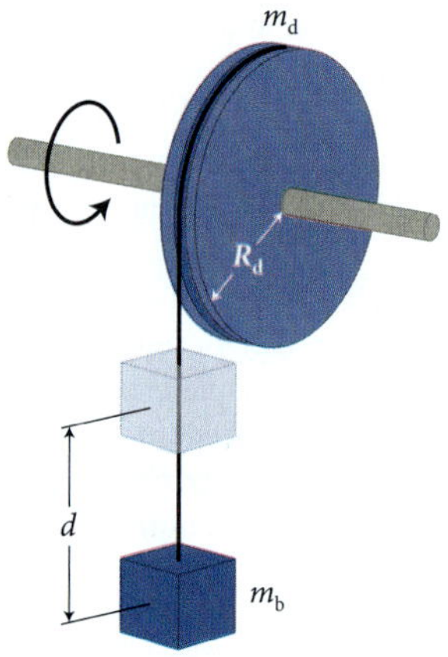

1 GETTING STARTED Here we have two kinds of motion: the rotational motion of the disk about the axle and the translational motion of the block falling under the influence of gravity. We might try applying conservation of energy or angular momentum to determine the block's speed, but we will likely need Newton's second law or kinematic equations to get the block's acceleration. If we choose the disk, block, and string as our system, then the system's angular momentum about the axle does not remain constant—the block and disk both contribute increasing angular momentum in the same direction. We have no experience in dealing with possible changes in Earth's angular momentum, and so perhaps we should try conservation of energy. If we choose the disk, block, string, and Earth as our system, our system is closed.

2 DEVISE PLAN We can determine the speed of the block from its kinetic energy $\frac{1}{2}mv^2$. It gains kinetic energy through the conversion of gravitational potential energy as it falls. Some of the initial potential energy must also go into the kinetic energy of the disk, however, because the rotational and translational motions are connected by the string. Fortunately, we know the relationship: Because of the connecting string, a point on the outer rim of the disk must always have the same speed v as the block. Thus from Eq. 11.10 $v_b = \omega_d R_d$. Because there is no dissipation of energy and no source energy is involved, we know that the mechanical energy $K + U$ of the system is constant:

$$K_f + U_f = K_i + U_i.$$

(Remember that the absence of any subscripts denoting disk or block tells you that these variables are for the system as a whole.)

We can use energy accounting to determine the block's final speed $v_{b,f}$ after it has fallen a distance d. We can then use kinematic equations to get the block's acceleration a_b. The disk can be thought of as a very short solid cylinder, and so we can use the solid cylinder rotational inertia from Table 11.3: $I = mR^2/2$.

Because we want to use the formula for gravitational potential energy (mgy), we choose the positive y axis upward because that direction was assumed in the derivation of this equation (Eq. 7.21).

We also make a diagram to represent all the information given in a convenient way (Figure WG11.9).

Figure WG11.9

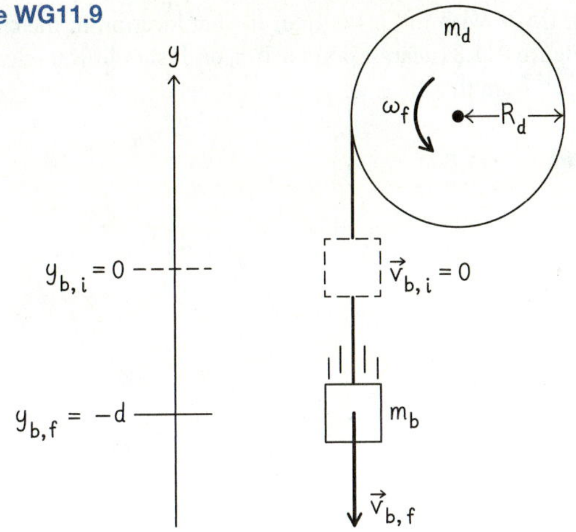

For convenience, we place the origin of our y axis at the initial level of the block, making $y_{b,i} = 0$ (and thus $U_{b,i} = m_b g y_{b,i} = 0$). Because the system starts at rest, $K_i = 0$. After the block has fallen a distance d, it is at $y_{b,f} = -d$, information that we put in our diagram. We can get the block's final speed $v_{b,f}$ by using this final position $-d$ and the relationship between the block's speed and the disk's rotational speed: $v_{b,f} = v_{d,f} = R_d\omega_{d,f}$.

❸ **EXECUTE PLAN** For our system (disk, block, string, Earth), energy conservation tells us that

$$K_f + U_f = K_i + U_i$$

$$\tfrac{1}{2}m_b v_{b,f}^2 + \tfrac{1}{2}I_d\omega_{d,f}^2 + m_b g y_{b,f} + m_d g y_{d,f}$$
$$= 0 + 0 + m_b g y_{b,i} + m_d g y_{d,i}. \qquad (1)$$

Because the vertical position of the disk does not change, $m_d g y_{d,f} = m_d g y_{d,i}$, and so we drop these two terms from the equation. Next, we eliminate the factor containing ω by modifying Eq. 11.10 to $\omega_{d,f} = v_{d,f}/R_d$ and then replacing $v_{d,f}$ with $v_{b,f}$ because any point on the disk rim has the same speed as the block. Then, with I_d replaced by $m_d R_d^2/2$, Eq. 1 becomes

$$\tfrac{1}{2}m_b v_{b,f}^2 + \tfrac{1}{2}\left(\tfrac{1}{2}m_d R_d^2\right)\left(\frac{v_{b,f}}{R_d}\right)^2 + m_b g(-d) = m_b g(0)$$

$$\tfrac{1}{2}m_b v_{b,f}^2 + \tfrac{1}{4}m_d v_{b,f}^2 = m_b g d$$

$$v_{b,f}^2 = \frac{2m_b}{m_b + \frac{1}{2}m_d}gd$$

$$v_{b,f} = \sqrt{\frac{2m_b}{m_b + \frac{1}{2}m_d}gd}. ✔ \qquad (2)$$

Because we do not know the time interval needed for the block to travel the distance d but we do know the initial and final speeds, we can use *Principles* Eq. 3.13, $v_f^2 = v_i^2 + 2a(x_f - x_i)$, for the block's motion along the y axis to get its acceleration:

$$v_{by,f}^2 = v_{by,i}^2 + 2a_{by}(y_f - y_i)$$

$$\frac{2m_b}{m_b + \frac{1}{2}m_d}gd = (0)^2 + 2a_{by}(-d - 0) = -2a_{by}d$$

$$a_{by} = -\frac{m_b}{m_b + \frac{1}{2}m_d}g. ✔$$

❹ **EVALUATE RESULT** If it were not connected to the disk by the string, the block would be in free fall and its speed after it had fallen a distance d would be the familiar free-fall result $v = \sqrt{2gd}$. In our case, the speed is lower because of the presence of the term $\frac{1}{2}m_d$ in the denominator of Eq. 2. We expect this lower speed because some of the gravitational potential energy the system loses as the block falls must go into increasing the rotational kinetic energy of the disk rather than all of it going into increasing the kinetic energy of the block. We also expect that if $m_d \ll m_b$, the disk should have little effect. If we set $m_d = 0$ to get the limiting case, we indeed get the expected free-fall speed.

The negative sign in our acceleration expression indicates that the acceleration is downward because the positive y axis points upward, as we expect for a falling block that starts from rest. Because not all of the system's potential energy goes into translational kinetic energy, the block cannot fall as fast as it would if there were no rotational diversion. Therefore an acceleration magnitude less than g makes sense.

Guided Problem 11.8 Globe pulling

You have a very large globe of Earth that has an inertia of 20 kg and a radius of 0.50 m. It can rotate freely about its polar axis, and you want to start it spinning by wrapping a string around its equator and then pulling on the string. You plan to attach one end of the string to the equator with a bit of museum wax, so that it will not slip until all the string is unwound. If you are restricted to exerting a continuous pulling force of magnitude 2.0 N, how much string do you need to wrap tightly around the globe to make it spin at 0.50 rev/s?

❶ **GETTING STARTED**

1. Draw a sketch of the globe and string showing how the pulling force is exerted.
2. Is your force tangential to the globe surface? Which quantity should you focus on: angular momentum or energy? Can you compute the effect of your force on the quantity you choose?
3. What must you assume about whether the string slips as it is pulled?

❷ **DEVISE PLAN**

4. Write an equation for the quantity you named in step 2. Does the rotational speed appear in this expression?
5. What is the globe's rotational inertia? (Is the globe more like a thin spherical shell or a solid sphere?) How does this variable come into play in this problem?
6. How does the string length come into your calculation? Would a tangential force applied continuously at a single point on the equator (such as a force produced by a small rocket motor attached to the globe) produce the same effect?

❸ **EXECUTE PLAN**

❹ **EVALUATE RESULT**

Questions and Problems

For instructor-assigned homework, go to MasteringPhysics® MP

Dots indicate difficulty level of problems: • = *easy,* •• = *intermediate,* ••• = *hard;* CR = *context-rich problem.*

11.1 Circular motion at constant speed

1. For a given level of technology, there is a maximum density of "bits" of information that can be stored on a computer's hard-drive disk. The data are stored in a tight spiral, so that "tracks" are essentially circles of increasing radius from inner to outer parts of the disk. As the disk spins at a constant rate, data are read at a constant rate regardless of the radius of the track being read. Which determines the disk capacity: the innermost track or the outermost track? •
2. What is the ratio of the rotational speed of Earth's daily rotation to that of its annual revolution? •
3. When one race car passes another during a race, the passing car usually tries to pass on the inner lane of a curve in the track. Why? •
4. The toy race track in Figure P11.4 has three lanes, and cars cannot change lanes. The centerlines of any two adjacent lanes are 100 mm apart, and the innermost lane has a radius of 1.00 m. (*a*) If each car has the same average speed, compare the time intervals needed for the cars to complete 20 laps. (*b*) If all three cars start beside each other and finish the race at the same instant, how do their average speeds compare? ••

Figure P11.4

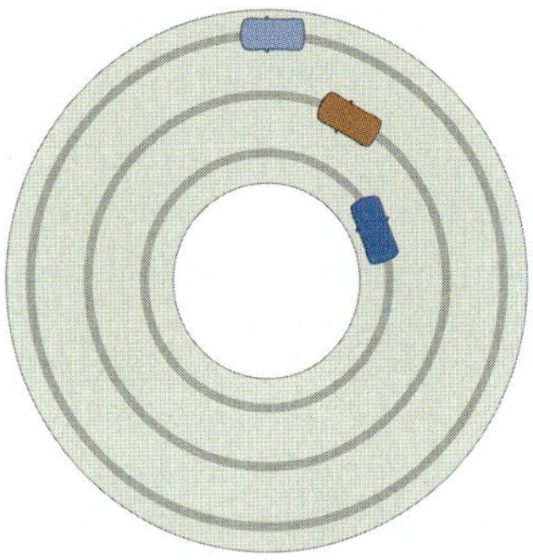

5. Plot, as a function of time, the rotational velocity of your car's wheels as you (*a*) back out of your driveway, (*b*) drive down a residential street, (*c*) turn onto a highway, (*d*) drive on the highway for a while, (*e*) exit the highway and stop at a traffic light, (*f*) drive on a city street, and (*g*) park at your favorite Chinese restaurant. ••
6. Hold a quarter down flat on a table with a finger. Then place a second quarter flat on the table, touching one point on the edge of the first quarter. If you roll the second quarter around the first so that the edges do not slip, describe the revolution and rotation as the second quarter returns to its original location on the table. •••

11.2 Forces and circular motion

7. Suppose the expression for centripetal acceleration is of the form $a_c = v^p r^q$, where p and q are constants. By analyzing the units in this expression, determine the numerical values of p and q. •
8. Standing in front of a tree, you whirl your sling with a rock in it. If you wish to hit the tree, at what location in the circle in Figure P11.8 (nearest point a, b, c, or d) should you release the rock from the sling? •

Figure P11.8

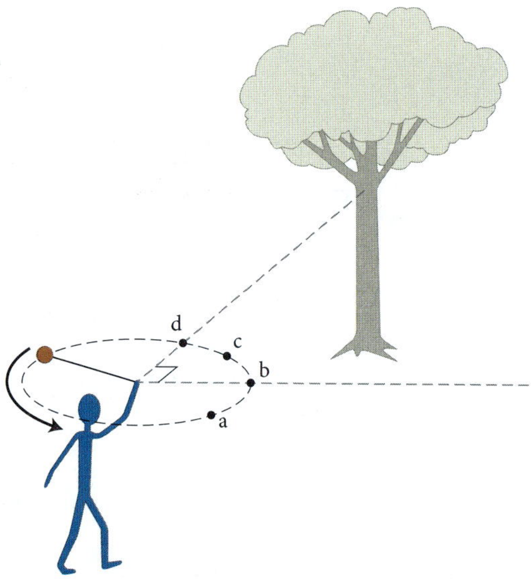

9. The Ferris wheel in Figure P11.9 is turning at constant speed. Draw and label free-body diagrams showing the forces on passengers at the numbered positions. Be careful to show correct relative lengths on your vector arrows. •

Figure P11.9

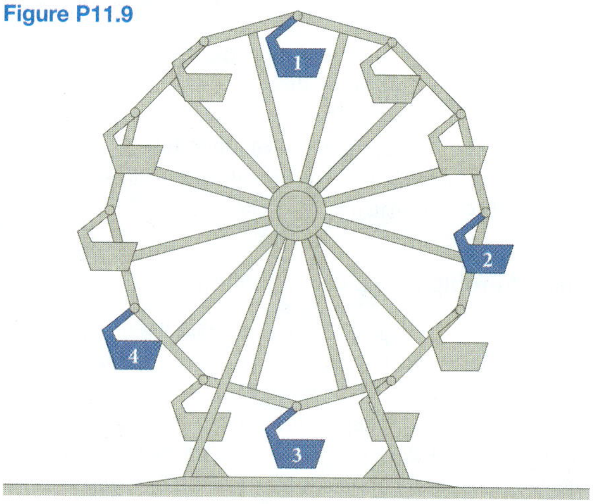

10. To see some of the trouble you can get into with noninertial reference frames, try this experiment. You and a friend stand opposite each other on the edge of a playground merry-go-round and get it rotating. While it is rotating, you attempt to toss a ball to your friend. As seen from above, what does the path of the ball look like (*a*) to an observer standing at the top of a nearby slide, (*b*) to you, and (*c*) to your friend? (*d*) If you did not know you were in a rotating reference frame, how would you explain the path of the ball in part *b*? ••

11. A salad spinner (Figure P11.11) is used to dry lettuce that has been washed. What physics is going on as the spinner does its job? ••

Figure P11.11

12. A race car is negotiating a curve on a banked track. There is a certain speed $v_{critical}$ at which friction is not needed to keep the car on the track in the curve. (This is the speed the car should travel if there is an oil slick on the track, for example.) Draw a free-body diagram showing the forces exerted on the car when it is moving at speed (*a*) $v = v_{critical}$, (*b*) $v > v_{critical}$, and (*c*) $v < v_{critical}$. ••
13. In a certain elaborate roller coaster, the cars are not on tracks but inside a U-shaped track much like a bobsled run. The cars are thus free to swing left and right across the U, climbing the walls as they do so. A student on the ride holds a string with a chunk of metal tied to the free end, with the chunk dangling between his knees as the ride begins. When the car enters a tight left turn, does the chunk swing toward the student's left knee, toward his right knee, or in some other direction? Ignore any friction between cars and track. ••
14. The ball in Figure P11.14 is attached to a vertical rod by two strings of equal strength (able to support much more than one of these balls) and equal length. The strings are light and do not stretch. The rod begins to rotate with its rotational speed increasing slowly, causing the ball to revolve with slowly increasing speed. (*a*) Which string breaks first? (*b*) To justify your answer to part *a*, draw a free-body diagram for the ball, indicating all forces exerted on it and their relative magnitudes. ••

Figure P11.14

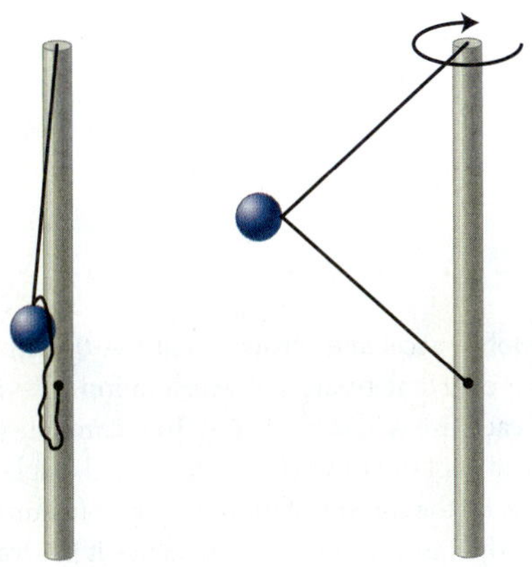

15. Tie a heavy metal washer to one end of a string, hold the string by the other end, and whirl it in a horizontal circle above your head. Pay close attention to where your hand is and to where the washer is as you speed up the rotation. Ignore air resistance. (*a*) Draw the motion of your hand and the motion of the washer. At a given instant, draw the location of the washer and your hand and the string between them. (*b*) As you speed up the rotation, what force is responsible for the acceleration of the washer? Is there a tangential component to this acceleration? A radial component? (*c*) When the washer achieves some given rotational speed, you cease increasing that speed. Describe the motion of your hand now. •••

11.3 Rotational inertia

16. Floor lamps usually have a base with large inertia, while the long body and top have much less inertia. If you want to show off by spinning a floor lamp like a baton, where should you grab the lamp? •
17. A gymnast's backflip is considered more difficult to do in the layout (straight body) position than in the tucked position. Why? •
18. An ice cube and a rubber ball are both placed at one end of a warm cookie sheet, and the sheet is then tipped up. The ice cube slides down with virtually no friction, and the ball rolls down without slipping. If the ball and the ice cube have the same inertia, which one reaches the bottom first? •
19. (*a*) Is there a choice of axes of rotation for a rotating bowling ball and a rotating baseball such that the baseball has a greater rotational inertia? If so, describe the axes. If not, explain why not. (*b*) Repeat for a revolving bowling ball and a revolving baseball. ••
20. You are designing a uniform thin rectangular door to fill a 1 m wide × 2 m tall opening, and you want it to be easy to open. (*a*) Considering only vertical and horizontal axes, what placement of the axis of rotation would result in the smallest rotational inertia? (*b*) Is such an axis practical? ••
21. You stand on the edge of a playground carousel while your friends help you get it going. After they stop pushing, you walk toward the center. (*a*) What happens to the rotational inertia of the carousel-you system as you move inward from the edge? (*b*) How does this change in rotational inertia affect the motion of the carousel? ••

11.4 Rotational kinematics

22. A car's engine is turning the crankshaft at 6000 rev/min. What is the rotational speed ω? •
23. What is the rotational speed of a watch's second hand? Its hour hand? •
24. If your tires are worn, does your odometer (which is keyed to the turns of the axle) underestimate or overestimate the number of miles you drive? •
25. Moving at its maximum safe speed, an amusement park carousel takes 12 s to complete a revolution. At the end of the ride, it slows down smoothly, taking 2.5 rev to come to a stop. What is the magnitude of the rotational acceleration of the carousel while it is slowing down? ••

26. You have a weekend job selecting speed limit signs to put at road curves. The speed limit is determined by the radius of the curve and the bank angle. For a turn of radius 400 m and a 7.0° bank angle, what speed limit should you post so that a car traveling at that speed negotiates the turn successfully even when the road is wet and slick? ••

27. As you drive clockwise around a turn (as viewed from overhead), you see backed-up traffic ahead and so you slow down. Which force diagram in Figure P11.27 best illustrates your acceleration? ••

Figure P11.27

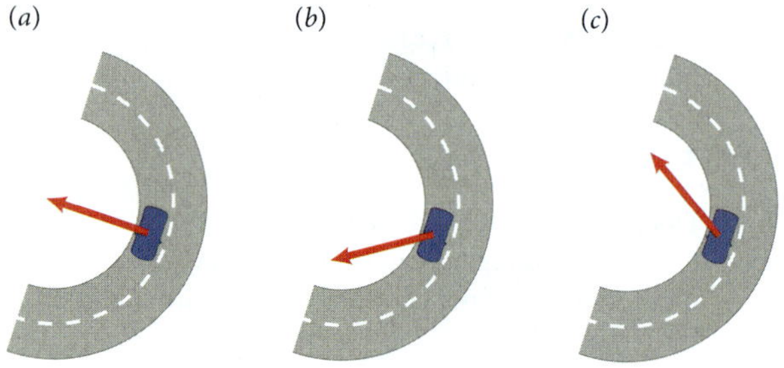

28. At the end of a ride, a carnival carousel decelerates smoothly from some initial rotational speed ω to a stop. (*a*) Plot, as a function of time, the speed v of a carousel horse at radius R and of another horse at radius $2R$. (*b*) Plot the magnitude of the centripetal acceleration of the two horses as a function of time. ••

29. You attach one end of a string of length ℓ to a small ball of inertia m. You attach the string's other end to a pivot that allows free revolution. You hold the ball out to the side with the string taut along a horizontal line, as in Figure P11.29. (*a*) If you release the ball from rest, what is the tension $\mathcal{T}$ in the string as a function of the angle θ swept through? (*b*) What maximum tension should the string be able to sustain if you want it not to break through the ball's entire motion? ••

Figure P11.29

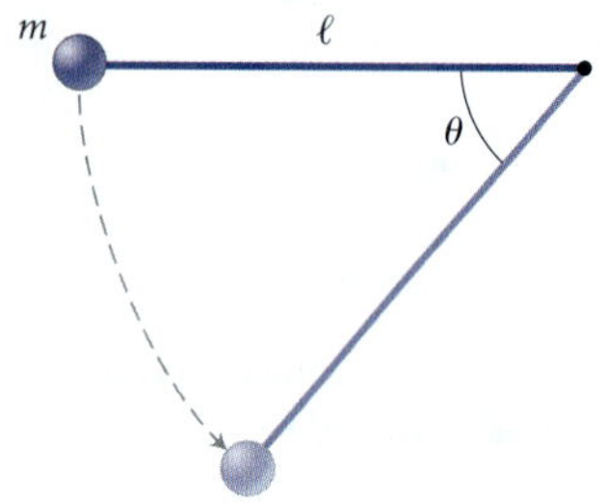

30. A pendulum is made of a bob dangling from a lightweight string of length ℓ. The bob is pulled sideways so that the string makes an angle θ_i with respect to the vertical, then released. As it swings down, what is the rotational speed of the bob as a function of the changing angle θ? ••

31. Assume that Earth's orbit around the Sun is a perfect circle. Earth's inertia is 5.97×10^{24} kg, the radius of its orbit is 1.50×10^{11} m, and its orbital period is 365.26 days. (*a*) What is the magnitude of its centripetal acceleration around the Sun? (*b*) What are the magnitude and direction of the force necessary to cause this acceleration? ••

32. A ball is suspended by a string from the top of a vertical rod as shown in Figure P11.32. The rod starts at rest and then begins to rotate with a small constant rotational acceleration. Qualitatively plot as a function of time the magnitude of (*a*) the vertical component and (*b*) the horizontal component of the tensile force exerted on the ball by the string. ••

Figure P11.32

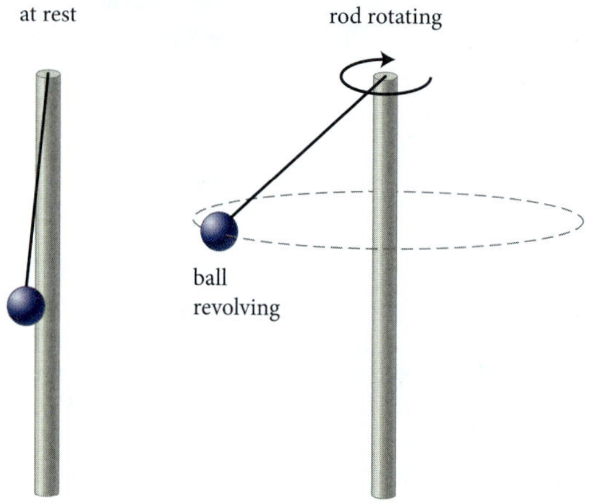

33. You hold a small ice cube near the top edge of a hemispherical bowl of radius 100 mm. When you release the cube from rest, what is the magnitude of its acceleration at the instant it reaches the bottom of the bowl? Ignore friction. ••

34. A 0.100-kg ball attached to a 0.20-m rod of very small inertia moves in a vertical circle in such a way that its speed remains constant. Let $\mathcal{T}_1$, $\mathcal{T}_2$, $\mathcal{T}_3$, and $\mathcal{T}_4$ be the tensions in the rod at positions 1, 2, 3, and 4 in Figure P11.34. (*a*) Rank the tensions in order of magnitude, greatest first. (*b*) What rotational speed is required at position 3 to keep $\mathcal{T}_3$ barely greater than zero? (*c*) At that speed, what is the tension at position 1? ••

Figure P11.34

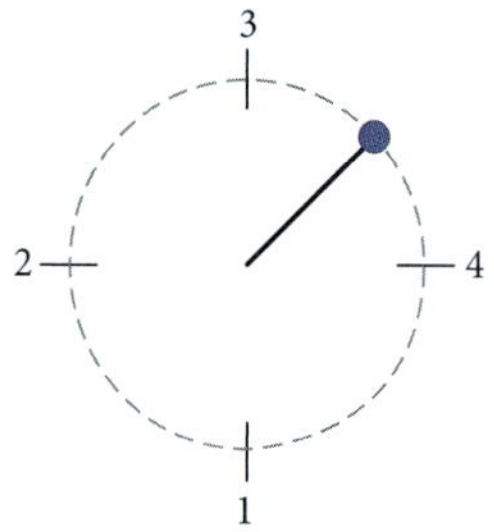

35. An automobile accelerates from rest at $t = 0$ such that its tires undergo a constant rotational acceleration $\alpha = 5.8 \text{ s}^{-2}$. The radius of each tire is 0.33 m. At $t = 10$ s, compute (*a*) the rotational speed ω of the tires, (*b*) the rotational displacement $\Delta\vartheta$ of each tire, (*c*) the speed v of the automobile (assuming the tires stay perfectly round), and (*d*) the distance it has traveled. ••

36. For the tread on your car tires, which is greater: the tangential acceleration when going from rest to highway speed as quickly as possible or the centripetal acceleration at highway speed? ••

37. A roller-coaster car initially at a position on the track a height h above the ground begins a downward run on a long, steeply sloping track and then goes into a circular loop-the-loop of radius R whose bottom is a distance d above the ground (Figure P11.37). Ignore friction. (*a*) What is the car's speed when it reaches the bottom of the loop? (*b*) What is the magnitude of the normal force exerted on the car at that instant? (*c*) What is its speed when its position is one-quarter of the way around the loop? (*d*) What is the magnitude of the normal force exerted on it at the one-quarter position? (*e*) What is the car's acceleration at the one-quarter position? •••

Figure P11.37

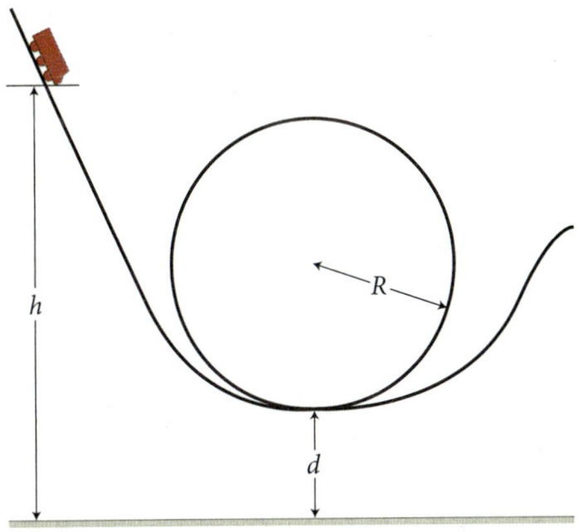

38. (*a*) Consider a circular vertical loop-the-loop on a roller coaster. Show that if a car coasts without power around the loop, the difference between the normal force exerted by the car on a passenger at the top of the loop and the normal force exerted by the car on her at the bottom of the loop is six times the gravitational force exerted on her. (*b*) This difference of $6mg$, referred to as "six gees," is quite a difference for the body to tolerate. To avoid this stress, vertical loops are teardrop-shaped rather than circular, designed so that the centripetal acceleration is constant all around the loop. How must the radius of curvature R change as the car's height h above the ground increases in order to have this constant centripetal acceleration? Express your answer as a function: $R = R(h)$. •••

39. A ball is put into a cone and made to move at a constant speed of 3.00 m/s in a horizontal circle of radius 0.500 m (Figure P11.39). (*a*) What is the centripetal component of the ball's acceleration? (*b*) What is the tangential component of its acceleration? (*c*) What force counteracts the force of gravity to keep the ball moving in a horizontal circle? (*d*) Use these insights to determine the height h at which the ball is circling above the bottom of the cone. [Hint: This is equivalent to determining the angle the cone makes with its vertical axis.] •••

Figure P11.39

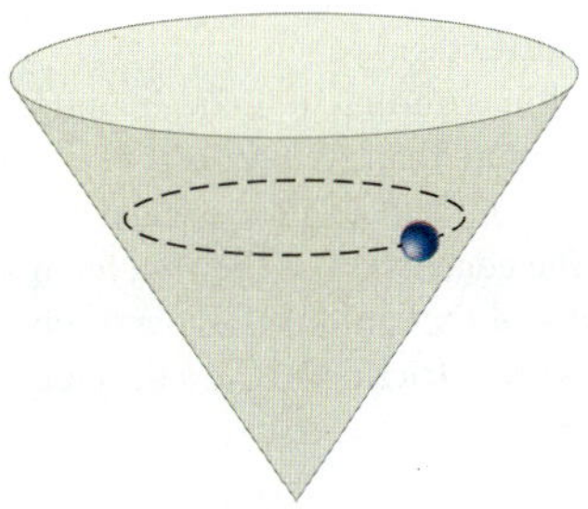

40. A race car driving on a banked track that makes an angle θ with the horizontal rounds a curve for which the radius of curvature is R. (*a*) As described in Problem 12, there is one speed $v_{critical}$ at which friction is not needed to keep the car on the track. What is that speed in terms of θ and R? (*b*) If the coefficient of friction between tires and road is μ, what maximum speed can the car have without going into a skid when taking the curve? •••

11.5 Angular momentum

41. A 0.25-kg ball attached to a string is being spun around on a horizontal surface at a rotational speed of 2.5 rev/s. What is the ball's kinetic energy if the string is 1.0 m long? •

42. Three small, identical 1.0-kg pucks are attached to identical 0.50-m strings, tied together at a common center as shown in Figure P11.42. When whirled in circular motion at angular speed 3.0 s^{-1}, what are (*a*) the rotational kinetic energy and (*b*) the magnitude of the angular momentum about the common center? •

Figure P11.42

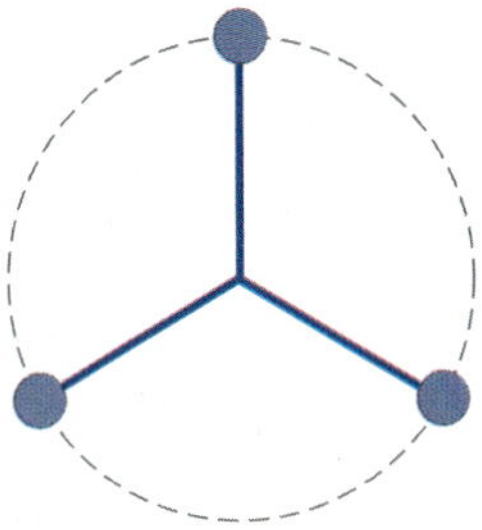

43. As you stand on the sidewalk outside an apartment building, a 2.0-kg bird flies toward you at 2.0 m/s along a straight line that passes 3.0 m above your head and runs parallel to the street. A friend is reclining with his head 4.0 m directly above your head, watching from a balcony. (*a*) What angular momentum do you observe the bird to have, using your head as a reference point? (*b*) What angular momentum does your friend observe the bird to have, using his own head as a reference point? •

44. Puck A, of inertia m, is attached to one end of a string of length ℓ, and the other end of the string is attached to a pivot so that the puck is free to revolve on a smooth horizontal surface. Puck B, of inertia $8m$, is attached to one end of a string of length $\ell/2$, and the other end of the string is attached to a second pivot so that B is also free to revolve. In each case, the puck is held as far as possible from the pivot so that the string is taut and then given an initial velocity $\vec{v}$ perpendicular to the string. (*a*) How does the magnitude of the angular momentum of puck A about its pivot compare with that of puck B about its pivot? (*b*) How does the rotational kinetic energy of A compare with that of B? ••

45. You have a pail of water with a rope tied to the handle. If you whirl the pail in a vertical circle fast enough, none of the water spills out, even when the pail is upside down. Explain why. ••

46. Consider the roller-coaster car in Problem 37. At what minimum value of the starting height h above the ground must the car begin its journey if it is to remain on the track at the top of the loop? ••

47. In Figure P11.47, two identical pucks B and C, each of inertia m, are connected by a rod of length ℓ and negligible inertia that is free to rotate about its center. Then puck A, of inertia $m/2$, comes in and hits B. After the collision, in which no energy is dissipated, what are (a) the rotational speed of the dumbbell and (b) the velocity $\vec{v}$ of A? ••

Figure P11.47

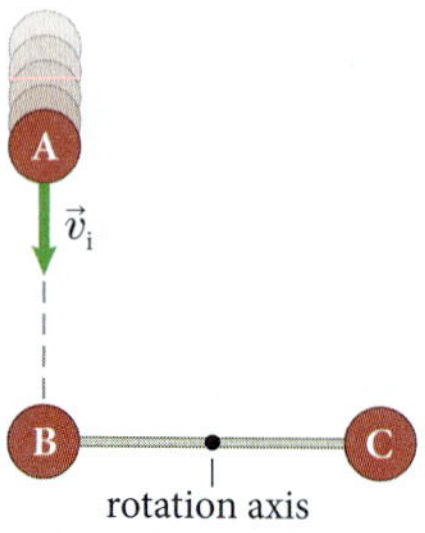

48. A small puck on an air table revolves in a circle with rotational speed ω, held at radius r by a weighted string that passes through a hole in the table. You slowly pull down on the weighted end of the string, decreasing the radius r. Assume that the angular momentum of the puck about the hole remains constant. (a) What is the rotational speed when half the string has been taken up? (b) What has happened to the speed v during this time interval? ••

49. Two skaters skate toward each other, each moving at 3.3 m/s. Their lines of motion are separated by a perpendicular distance of 2.0 m. Just as they pass each other (still 2.0 m apart), they link hands and spin about their common center of mass. What is the rotational speed of the couple about the center of mass? Treat each skater as a particle, one with an inertia of 75 kg and the other with an inertia of 48 kg. ••

50. A record player turntable initially rotating at $33\frac{1}{3}$ rev/min is braked to a stop at a constant rotational acceleration. The turntable has a rotational inertia of 0.020 kg · m². When it is switched off, it slows down to 75% of its initial rotational speed in 5.0 s. (a) How long does it take to come to rest? (b) How much work has to be done on the turntable to bring it to rest? ••

51. A disk of rotational inertia I about the central axis shown in Figure P11.51 is rotating about this axis with initial rotational velocity $\omega_{\vartheta,i}$ on low-friction bearings. A second identical disk is held at rest a few millimeters directly above the first disk and suddenly dropped. After some slipping, the two discs are observed to have a common rotational speed about the original axis of rotation. What is the magnitude of the final rotational velocity of the combined disks? ••

Figure P11.51

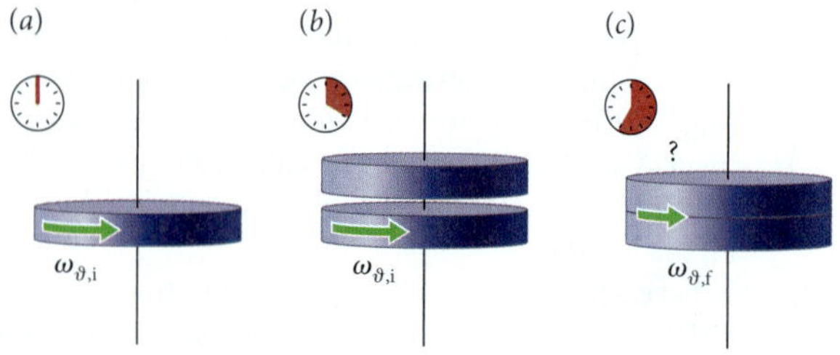

52. A popular ride at some playgrounds consists of two circular disks joined by rungs (Figure P11.52). The center of the unit is attached to a horizontal axle around which the unit rotates. The rotational inertia of the unit is 200 kg · m², and its radius is 1.00 m. A 30.0-kg child runs and grabs the bottom rung of the ride when it is initially at rest. Because the child can pull herself up to meet the rung at waist height, treat her as a particle located on the rung. (a) If the friction between unit and axle is minimal and can be ignored, what is the minimum speed v the child must have when she grabs the bottom rung in order to make the unit rotate about its axle and carry her over the top of the unit? (b) Is this a reasonable speed for a child? •••

Figure P11.52

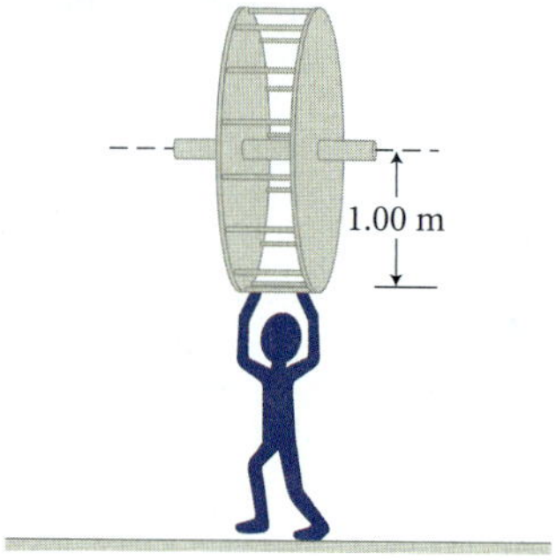

11.6 Rotational inertia of extended objects

53. What is the rotational inertia about the x axis of the rigid object in Figure P11.53? (Treat the balls as particles.) •

Figure P11.53

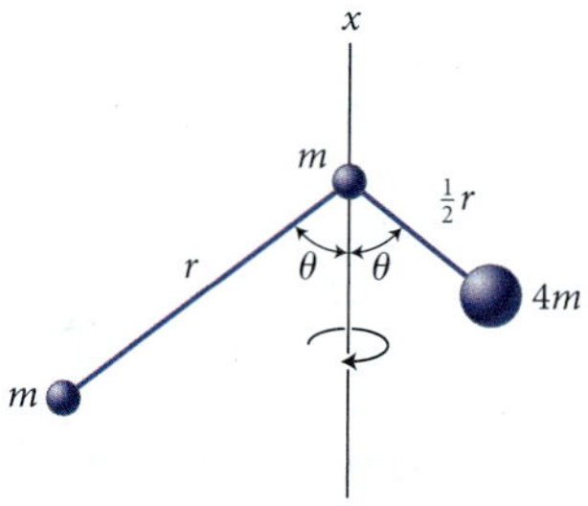

54. A cubical wire framework in which each edge is 0.25 m long has a 0.20-kg steel ball at each of its eight corners. What is the rotational inertia of this framework around an axis along one edge? Ignore the inertias of the wires. •

55. What is the formula for the rotational inertia of a thin spherical shell of inertia m and radius R about an axis tangent to any point on its surface? •

56. A deer's leg is very slender near the hoof, with most of the muscle bunched up near the hip joint. How does this work to the deer's advantage? •

57. A 20-kg child running at 1.4 m/s jumps onto a playground merry-go-round that has inertia 180 kg and radius 1.6 m. She is moving tangent to the platform when she jumps, and she lands right on the edge. What is the rotational speed of the merry-go-round and the child if the merry-go-round started from rest? Ignore any friction in the axle about which the platform rotates. ••

58. Earth has an inertia of 5.97×10^{24} kg and a radius of 6.37×10^{6} m. (*a*) Calculate its rotational inertia about the rotation axis, assuming uniform density. (*b*) The rotational inertia of Earth about its rotation axis has been measured to be $8.01 \times 10^{37}\ \mathrm{kg \cdot m^2}$. What does the difference between this value and the value you calculated in part *a* tell you about the distribution of inertia throughout the planet? ••

59. The rotational inertia of any flat object about an axis perpendicular to the object is equal to the sum of the rotational inertias about two mutually perpendicular axes in the plane of the object, if all three axes pass through a common point. Using this "perpendicular-axis theorem," determine (*a*) the rotational inertia of a uniform hoop of inertia m and radius R about a diameter of the hoop, and (*b*) the rotational inertia of a uniform square sheet of inertia m and side length a about a line drawn from the midpoint of one edge to the midpoint of the opposite edge. ••

60. The structure in Figure P11.60 is made of three identical rods of uniform density. Rank the rotational inertias of the structure, from smallest to largest, about the four rotation axes represented by the dashed lines. ••

Figure P11.60

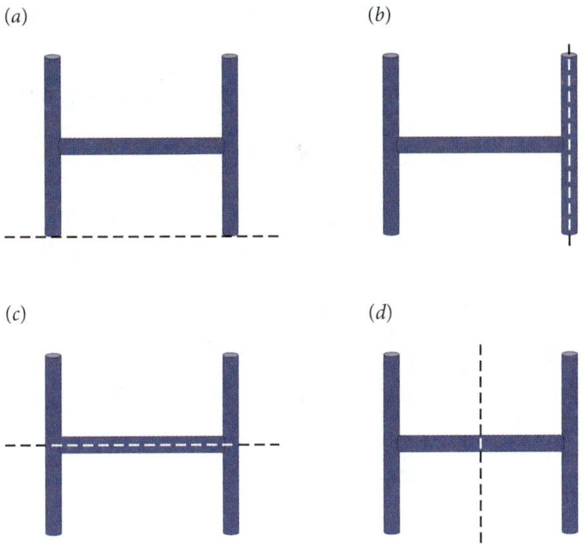

61. Global warming might result in the melting of the polar ice caps. What effect would this melting have on the length of the day? ••

62. A hollow cylinder, a solid cylinder, and a billiard ball are all released at the top of a ramp and roll to the bottom without slipping. (*a*) Rank them, from least to greatest, according to the fraction of the kinetic energy that is rotational as they roll. (*b*) What are the ratios of their speeds when they reach the bottom of the ramp? ••

63. Estimate the rotational inertia of a 70-kg athlete about a horizontal axis passing through her waist from left to right. ••

64. A 0.20-kg block and a 0.25-kg block are connected to each other by a string draped over a pulley that is a solid disk of inertia 0.50 kg and radius 0.10 m. When released, the 0.25-kg block is 0.30 m off the ground. What speed does this block have when it hits the ground? ••

65. You accidentally knock a full bucket of water off the side of the well shown in Figure P11.65. The bucket plunges 15 m to the bottom of the well. Attached to the bucket is a light rope that is wrapped around the crank cylinder. How fast is the handle turning when the bucket hits bottom? The inertia of the bucket plus water is 12 kg. The cylinder has a radius of 0.080 m and inertia of 4.0 kg. ••

Figure P11.65

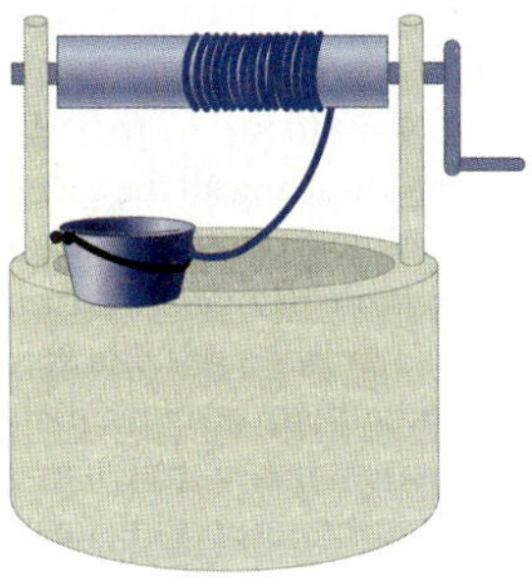

66. A block of inertia m is attached to a block of inertia $2m$ by a light string draped over a uniform disk of inertia $3m$ and radius R that can rotate on a horizontal axle (Figure P11.66). Initially, the block of inertia m is held in place so that the string is taut. When this block is released and so is free to move, what is its speed after it has risen a height h? Ignore friction between disk and axle. ••

Figure P11.66

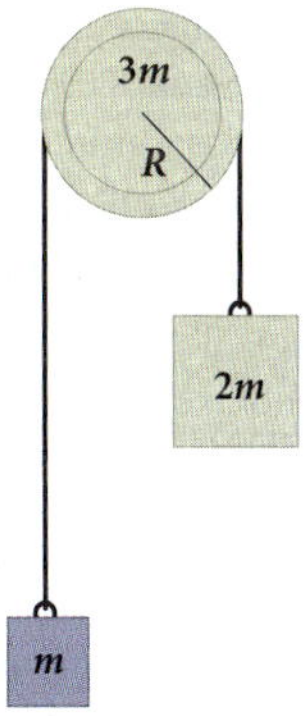

67. A thick-walled cylinder of inertia m has an outer radius R_{outer}, an inner radius $R_{inner} = R_{outer}/2$, and a length ℓ (Figure P11.67). It rotates around an axis attached to its outside along its length. What is its rotational inertia about this axis? ••

Figure P11.67

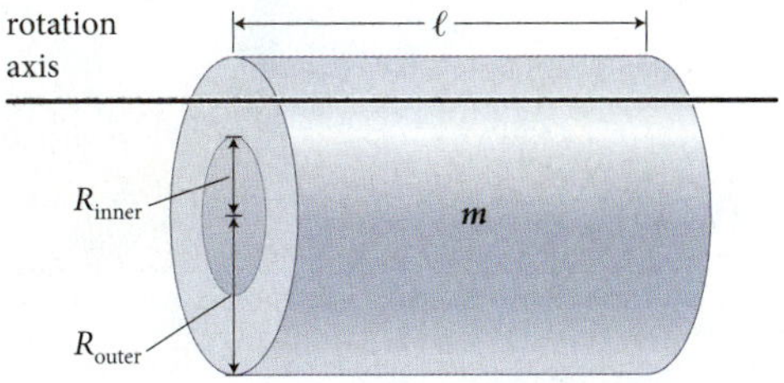

PRACTICE

68. A thin 0.15-kg rectangular sheet has 40-mm short sides and 80-mm long sides. Determine the rotational inertia of the sheet about an axis perpendicular to it and located (*a*) at the center of a long side, (*b*) at the center of a short side, and (*c*) at a corner. ••

69. One type of wagon wheel consists of a 2.0-kg hoop fitted with four 0.80-kg thin rods placed along diameters of the hoop so as to make eight evenly spaced spokes. For a hoop of radius 0.30 m, what is the rotational inertia of the wheel about an axis perpendicular to the plane of the wheel and through the center? ••

70. A thin rod, 0.83 m long, is pivoted such that it hangs vertically from one end. You want to hit the free end of the rod just hard enough to get the rod to swing all the way up and over the pivot. How fast do you have to make the end go? ••

71. Big Ben in London is the most accurate mechanical clock of its size. The 300-kg hour hand is 2.7 m long, and the 100-kg minute hand is 4.2 m long. Calculate the rotational kinetic energy of the two-hand system, treating each hand as if it were a thin rod. ••

72. Consider an object that has rotational inertia I about some arbitrary axis of rotation. The *radius of gyration* of the object is the distance from this axis where all the object's inertia could be concentrated and still produce the same rotational inertia I about the axis. What is the radius of gyration of (*a*) a solid disk of radius R about an axis perpendicular to the plane of the disk and passing through its center, (*b*) a solid sphere of radius R about an axis through its center, and (*c*) a solid sphere of radius R about an axis tangent to the sphere? •••

73. A thin piece of metal in the shape of a right triangle has inertia m. Its perpendicular sides are of lengths ℓ and 2ℓ. Determine the rotational inertia about an axis that runs (*a*) along side ℓ and (*b*) along side 2ℓ. •••

74. A block of inertia m is attached to a light string wound around a uniform disk also of inertia m (Figure P11.74). The disk has radius R and rotates on a fixed horizontal axle through its center. The opposite side of the block is attached to a spring of force constant k and relaxed length ℓ attached at the bottom of an inclined surface that makes an angle θ with the horizontal. The block is at rest with the spring stretched a distance d from its relaxed length, with the block held in this position by a clamp. When the clamp is loosened so that the block is free to move, the block is pulled down the plane by the spring. What is the speed of the block when the spring is at half of its relaxed length? Ignore friction. •••

Figure P11.74

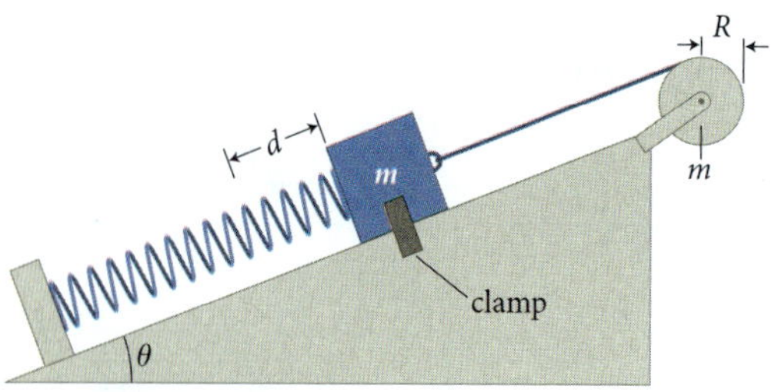

75. A certain baseball bat is a tapered cylinder that increases in diameter from 0.040 m at one end to 0.070 m at the other end and is 0.84 m long. The bat has uniform density and inertia 0.85 kg. What is the rotational inertia of this bat around an axis that passes perpendicularly through the skinny end? •••

Additional Problems

76. In the laboratory, you are trying to put pennies on a rotating platform so that they don't slide off. Your partner tells you, "Pennies on the outside stay on better because $a_c = v^2/r$. For larger r, the centripetal acceleration is less, and so the frictional force has an easier time holding a penny in place out there." Is his reasoning correct? •

77. Solar and lunar eclipses are caused by a fortuitous relationship between the sizes of the Moon and Sun and their distances from Earth. Look up data for the Earth-Moon and Earth-Sun distances and the diameters of the Moon and the Sun. (*a*) Calculate the *angular size* of the Sun's disk as seen by an observer on Earth, where *angular size* is the angle *subtended* by the Sun's disk. (*b*) Calculate the angular size of the Moon's disk. •

78. Show that the centripetal acceleration of an object undergoing circular motion at constant speed can be expressed as

$$a_c = \frac{4\pi^2 r}{T^2},$$

where r is the circle radius and T is the period of the motion. •

79. If you spin a raw egg, stop it momentarily, and then let go, it begins to spin again. You can't do this with a hard-boiled egg. Why? •

80. If you stretch your arm out full length and block the Sun with your thumb, how fast must your thumb move, in millimeters per minute, to track the Sun's motion? ••

81. Out looking for Tarzan, Jane swings on a vine to speed her search. (*a*) During her arc downward, how much work is done on her by the tensile force in the vine? (*b*) At which position along the arc is the force exerted by the vine on Jane greatest? ••

82. The Moon orbits Earth while Earth orbits the Sun, and thus the Moon's motion around the Sun is the combination of those two motions. Is the Moon's motion ever *retrograde* if observed from the Sun, where *retrograde* means that the Moon appears to move in the direction opposite the direction of Earth's motion relative to the distant stars? (You need to look up values for the Earth-Sun distance and the Earth-Moon distance to answer this question.) ••

83. Suppose several particles are in concentric circular orbits under the influence of some centripetal component of force, the magnitude of which depends on distance from the center of the motion. Each particle has a different orbital radius r and a corresponding period T. How does the force depend on r (*a*) if T is proportional to $\sqrt{r}$, (*b*) if T is proportional to $r^{3/2}$, and (*c*) if T is independent of r? ••

84. Approximate the Sun as a uniform sphere of radius 6.96×10^8 m, rotating about its central axis with a period of 25.4 days. If, at the end of its life, the Sun collapses inward to form a uniform dwarf star that is approximately the same size as Earth, what will the period of the dwarf's rotation be? ••

PRACTICE

85. An open door of inertia m_d and width ℓ_d is at rest when it is struck by a thrown ball of clay of inertia m_b that is moving at speed v_b at the instant it strikes the door (Figure P11.85). The impact location is a distance $d = \frac{2}{3}\ell_d$ from the rotation axis through the hinges. The clay ball strikes perpendicular to the door face and sticks after it hits. What is the rotational speed ω of the door-ball system? Do not ignore the inertia m_b. ●●

Figure P11.85

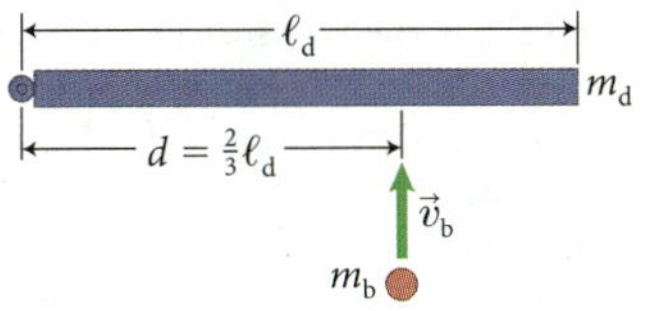

86. Your aunt owns an amusement park, and she wants you to add a circular loop to an existing roller-coaster ride. The first hill for the existing roller coaster is 55 m tall, and your aunt wants you to build, right after this hill, the tallest loop possible without having the cars fall out of the track or the passengers fall out of the cars. You think for a minute and realize what the minimum speed at the top of the loop has to be, and this gives you what you need to design the loop. ●●● CR

87. The spacecraft in the movie *2001: A Space Odyssey* has a rotating cylinder to create the illusion of gravity, inside of which the crew walks and exercises. While watching this old movie, you realize that the radius of the cylinder is roughly three times a crew member's height. You imagine this cylinder rotating sufficiently rapidly to replicate Earth's gravity, but you worry about the difference between the acceleration at the top of the astronaut's head and the acceleration at her feet. Not wanting lightheaded astronauts, you phone NASA with your new design. ●●● CR

88. A turntable of radius 0.320 m is fitted with an electromagnet that causes steel objects to stay in place on the table. A triangular mark on the rim shows the rotational position of the table relative to the surroundings (Figure P11.88). The turntable completes one rotation in 0.360 s, and the rotation is counterclockwise in the view shown in the figure. A 0.125-kg steel rod of length 0.160 m is placed on the table so that one end is at the center and the rod is oriented radially outward, as shown in the figure. The electromagnet is switched on, and the turntable is started. After the table reaches its steady-state rotational speed, the electromagnet is switched off at an instant when the rod lies along the positive x axis. Describe the ensuing motion of the rod. ●●●

Figure P11.88

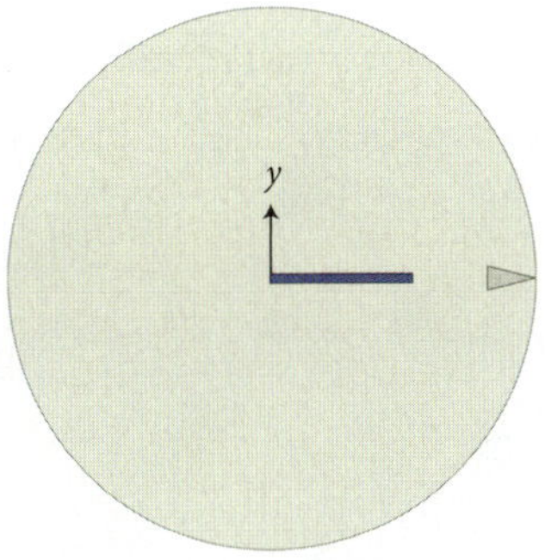

89. You have a toy top that plays music if the rotational speed is at least 1800 rev/min. The way to get this top spinning is to pull on a string wrapped around a spindle of diameter of 6.0 mm. The top has a rotational inertial of about 5.0×10^{-3} kg · m². The string is 1.2 m long. You want to hear the top sing. ●●● CR

90. A dart of inertia m_d is fired such that it strikes with speed v_d, embedding its tip in the rim of a target that is a uniform disk of inertia m_t and radius R_t. The target is initially rotating clockwise in the view shown in Figure P11.90, with rotational speed ω about an axis that runs through its center and is perpendicular to its plane. Assume that the dart's inertia is concentrated at its tip. What is the final rotational speed of the target if the dart strikes (*a*) tangent to the target rim as in Figure P11.90*a* and (*b*) normal to the rim as in Figure P11.90*b*? ●●●

Figure P11.90

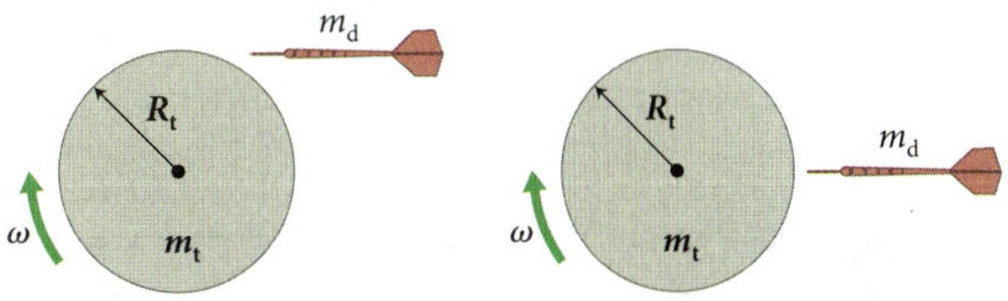

91. A smooth-faced cube of inertia m and side length d sliding along a highly polished floor at speed v strikes a door threshold, and the collision makes the cube tilt as shown in Figure P11.91. As the cube tips over, its center of mass is located at a variable horizontal distance x. What is the rotational speed of the cube as a function of x? The rotational inertia of a cube about one edge is $\frac{2}{3}md^2$. [Hint: Call the vertical distance traveled by the center of mass h.] ●●●

Figure P11.91

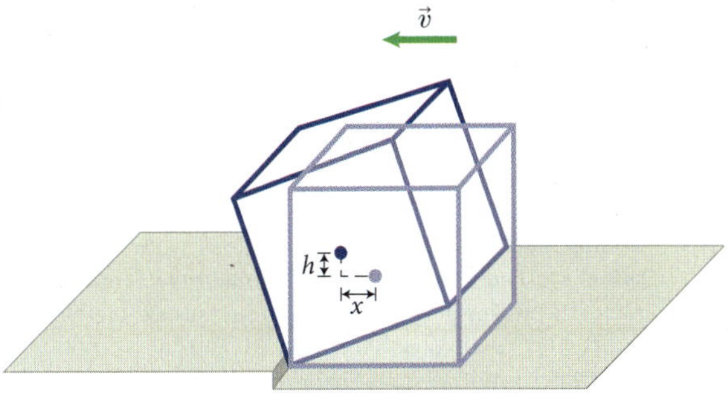

PRACTICE

Answers to Review Questions

1. Many answers possible. Some are: (*a*) falling brick, racehorse on home stretch, cruising airplane; (*b*) spinning compact disc, Ferris wheel, roulette wheel; (*c*) thrown Frisbee, propeller on outboard motor; bowling ball headed toward pins.
2. (*a*) No, because constant velocity means zero acceleration. (*b*) Yes, because a change in direction means nonzero acceleration even if there is no change in speed.
3. The rotational coordinate specifies the location of the object on the circle in terms of a unitless number that increases by 2π for each revolution of the object. The polar angle specifies the location of the object on the circle in units of radians, degrees, or revolutions, typically measured from the positive x axis to the radius vector that locates the object.
4. The position vector points from the center of the circular trajectory to the object at the chosen instant. The velocity vector is perpendicular to the position vector, tangent to the circular trajectory in the direction of the object's motion (along the tangential axis). The acceleration vector points opposite the position vector, toward the center of the circular trajectory.
5. At the beginning of the car's curving motion, your shoulders continue going straight but your legs and lower body are pulled to the left by the frictional force exerted by the car seat. Because the car is accelerating into the curve (leftward) in the Earth reference frame, the car door comes in to meet your right shoulder, an occurrence you mistake for your shoulders traveling out of the curve (rightward) in the car's reference frame.
6. Because a rotating reference frame is accelerating and therefore noninertial. From *Principles* Chapter 6 we know that the methods we use in this text for monitoring energy and momentum changes are not valid in noninertial reference frames.
7. A vector sum of the forces must be directed toward the center of the circle to make the object move at a constant speed in circular motion. The vector sum of the forces provides the required centripetal acceleration, and it increases with increasing speed and decreases with increasing radius.
8. No. An intrinsic property (see *Principles* Section 4.6) is one that we cannot change without changing the object. The value we calculate for a given object's rotational inertia depends on what we choose as the axis of rotation. The rotational inertia of a thin hoop, for instance, is mr^2 for rotation about an axis perpendicular to the hoop face but only $mr^2/2$ for rotation about an axis parallel to the hoop face. Same hoop, different values of I, meaning I is not an intrinsic property.
9. The rotation axis the walker is concerned about is a horizontal axis passing through her feet. Without the pole, all the material in the system (just her) is near the axis. With the pole, some of the material of the walker-pole system is far from the axis, making it more difficult for her to rotate about that axis and fall.
10. Yes. Circular motion always involves centripetal acceleration. The other two forms of acceleration may or may not be involved in the motion. If speeding up or slowing down, the object has both rotational acceleration and tangential acceleration; these are related by a factor of the radius, so they always coexist.
11. The rotational coordinate is the polar angle (expressed in units of radians) divided by one radian:

$$\vartheta = \frac{\theta\,(\text{rad})}{1\,\text{rad}}.$$

12. Rotational acceleration has units of inverse seconds squared and measures the rate at which the rotational speed ω changes with time. Tangential acceleration has units of acceleration (m/s^2) and measures the rate at which the speed v changes with time. They are related in that the magnitude of the tangential acceleration equals the product of the radius and rotational acceleration. Centripetal acceleration has units of acceleration (m/s^2) and measures the rate at which the *direction* of velocity $\vec{v}$ changes with time. Centripetal acceleration is the radial component of acceleration (toward the center of the circle), while tangential acceleration is the component of acceleration tangent to the circle.
13. These relationships are found in *Principles* Table 11.1: (a) $s = r\vartheta$, (b) $v_t = r\omega_\vartheta$, (c) $a_t = r\alpha_\vartheta$.
14. If the time interval is halved, the speed v is doubled. Equation 11.15, $a_c = v^2/r$, tells you that doubling the speed quadruples the centripetal acceleration.
15. The rotational inertia of a particle is defined as the product of the particle's inertia and the square of its radius of circular motion. The lever arm distance (or lever arm) is the perpendicular distance between the line of action of the momentum of the particle and the rotation axis.
16. The rotational kinetic energy of an object is related to its rotational inertia in the same way that the kinetic energy of a particle is related to its inertia, with rotational inertia substituted for inertia and rotational speed substituted for speed:

$$\tfrac{1}{2}mv^2 \leftrightarrow \tfrac{1}{2}I\omega^2.$$

17. The angular momentum of this object is the product of its momentum and the perpendicular distance from the line of action of its momentum to the axis of rotation: $L = I\omega = mvr_\perp$ (Eqs. 11.34 and 11.36).
18. It increases by a factor of 8. The doubling of I in $K_{\text{rot}} = \frac{1}{2}I\omega^2$ causes K_{rot} to increase by a factor of 2, and the doubling of ω causes K_{rot} to increase by a factor of 4.
19. Angular momentum can be neither created nor destroyed (but it can be transferred from one object to another).
20. Smallest rotational inertia: axis running through the center of the book and parallel to its largest dimension. Largest rotational inertia: axis passing through the center of the book and perpendicular to both covers.
21. Two axes pass through the molecule's center perpendicular to the bond connecting the two atoms; the third axis runs parallel to the bond. Rotation about either perpendicular axis involves a sizable rotational inertia. Rotation around the parallel axis involves a smaller rotational inertia and therefore a smaller kinetic energy.
22. The rotational inertia of an object about any axis A is equal to the rotational inertia of the same object about an axis that runs through its center of mass and is parallel to axis A plus a term equal to the product of the object's inertia and the square of the perpendicular distance between the two axes.

Answers to Guided Problems

Guided Problem 11.2 (*a*) $\omega = 1.16 \times 10^{-3}\,\text{s}^{-1}$, (*b*) $v = 7.73 \times 10^3\,\text{m/s}$, (*c*) $a_c = 8.94\,\text{m/s}^2$

Guided Problem 11.4 $\theta_{\text{bank}} = 23.6°$

Guided Problem 11.6 (*a*) $\omega_f = \dfrac{15m_b v_b d}{4m_d \ell_d^2} - \omega_i$, (*b*) $v_b > \dfrac{4m_d \ell_d^2 \omega_i}{15m_b d}$

Guided Problem 11.8 $\ell = 8.2\,\text{m}$

PRACTICE

12 PRACTICE
Torque

Chapter Summary

Torque (Sections 12.1, 12.5)

Concepts The **torque** due to a force exerted on an object is the tendency of the force to give rotational acceleration to the object. The torque about some pivot is the product of the magnitude of the force and the lever arm distance. The SI units for torque are $\text{N}\cdot\text{m} = \text{kg}\cdot\text{m}^2/\text{s}^2$.

An object is in *translational equilibrium* if the vector sum of all the external forces exerted on it is zero. An object is in **rotational equilibrium** if the vector sum of the external torques is zero. If the vector sums of both the forces and the torques are zero, the object is in **mechanical equilibrium.**

Quantitative Tools If $\vec{r}$ is the position vector from a pivot to the location at which a force $\vec{F}$ is exerted on an object and θ is the angle between $\vec{r}$ and $\vec{F}$, the torque τ produced by the force about the pivot is

$$\tau \equiv rF\sin\theta = r_\perp F = rF_\perp, \qquad (12.1)$$

where $r_\perp$ is the component of $\vec{r}$ perpendicular to $\vec{F}$ and $F_\perp$ is the component of $\vec{F}$ perpendicular to $\vec{r}$.

Translational equilibrium: $\sum\vec{F}_{\text{ext}} = \vec{0}$.

Rotational equilibrium: $\sum\tau_{\text{ext}\,\vartheta} = 0$.

Mechanical equilibrium:

$$\sum\tau_{\text{ext}\,\vartheta} = 0 \quad \text{and} \quad \sum\vec{F}_{\text{ext}} = \vec{0}. \qquad (12.14)$$

Rotation of a rigid object (Sections 12.1, 12.2, 12.5–12.7)

Concepts In **free rotation**, an object rotates about its center of mass. The translational and rotational motions are analyzed separately, and the torques and rotational inertia are computed about the center of mass. In *rotation about a fixed axis*, an object is constrained to rotate about a physical axis. Torques and rotational inertia are computed about that axis.

When an object is **rolling without slipping** across a surface, there is no relative motion at the location where the object touches the surface. The object rotates about its geometric center as it translates across the surface. Torques and rotational inertia are computed about the object's center of mass, which for a symmetrical object is the geometric center.

The external force exerted on a rolling object changes the object's center-of-mass kinetic energy. The external torque on a rolling object changes the object's rotational kinetic energy.

Quantitative Tools For both particles and extended bodies, the vector sum of the torques when rotation is about a fixed axis is

$$\sum\tau_{\text{ext}\,\vartheta} = I\alpha_\vartheta. \qquad (12.10)$$

For an object of radius R that is rolling without slipping, the motion of the center of mass is described by

$$v_{\text{cm}\,x} = R\omega_\vartheta \qquad (12.19)$$

$$a_{\text{cm}\,x} = R\alpha_\vartheta \qquad (12.23)$$

$$\sum F_{\text{ext}\,x} = ma_{\text{cm}\,x}$$

$$\sum\tau_{\text{ext}\,\vartheta} = I\alpha_\vartheta. \qquad (12.10)$$

The change in an object's rotational kinetic energy resulting from torques is

$$\Delta K_{\text{rot}} = \left(\sum\tau_{\text{ext}\,\vartheta}\right)\Delta\vartheta \quad \text{(constant torques, rigid object)}. \qquad (12.31)$$

The kinetic energy of a rolling object is

$$K = K_{\text{cm}} + K_{\text{rot}} = \tfrac{1}{2}mv_{\text{cm}}^2 + \tfrac{1}{2}I\omega^2 \qquad (12.33)$$

and the change in the kinetic energy of a rolling object is

$$\Delta K = \Delta K_{\text{cm}} + \Delta K_{\text{rot}}. \qquad (12.34)$$

Angular momentum (Sections 12.1, 12.5)

Concepts A **rotational impulse** J_ϑ is the amount of angular momentum transferred to a system from the environment by external torques.

If the sum of the external torques due to forces exerted on a system is zero, the angular momentum of the system remains constant.

Quantitative Tools External torque caused by forces exerted on an object causes the object's angular momentum L_ϑ to change:

$$\sum\tau_{\text{ext}\,\vartheta} = \frac{dL_\vartheta}{dt}. \qquad (12.12)$$

The **angular momentum law** says that the change in the angular momentum of an object is equal to the **rotational impulse** given to the system:

$$\Delta L_\vartheta = J_\vartheta. \tag{12.15}$$

If the constant external torques on a system last for a time interval Δt, the **rotational impulse equation** says that the rotational impulse is

$$J_\vartheta = (\Sigma \tau_{\text{ext}\,\vartheta})\Delta t. \tag{12.17}$$

The law of conservation of angular momentum states that if $\Sigma \tau_{\text{ext}\,\vartheta} = 0$, then $dL_\vartheta/dt = 0$. This means that

$$\Sigma \tau_{\text{ext}\,\vartheta} = \frac{dL_\vartheta}{dt} = 0 \Rightarrow \Delta L_\vartheta = 0. \tag{12.13}$$

Rotational quantities as vectors (Sections 12.4, 12.8)

Concepts A **polar vector** is a vector associated with a displacement. An **axial vector** is a vector associated with a rotation direction. This vector points along the rotation axis, and its direction is given by the **right-hand rule** for axial vectors: When you curl the fingers of your right hand along the direction of rotation, your outstretched thumb points in the direction of the vector that specifies that rotation.

Right-hand rule for vector products: When you align the fingers of your right hand along the first vector in a vector product and curl them from that vector to the second vector in the product through the smaller angle between the vectors, your outstretched thumb points in the direction of the vector product.

The magnitude of the vector product of two vectors is equal to the area of the parallelogram defined by them.

Quantitative Tools The magnitude of the **vector product** of vectors $\vec{A}$ and $\vec{B}$ that make an angle $\theta \leq 180°$ between them when they are tail to tail is

$$|\vec{A} \times \vec{B}| = AB \sin\theta. \tag{12.35}$$

If $\vec{r}$ is the vector from the origin of a coordinate system to the location where a force $\vec{F}$ is exerted, the torque about the origin due to $\vec{F}$ is

$$\vec{\tau} = \vec{r} \times \vec{F}. \tag{12.38}$$

If $\vec{r}$ is the vector from the origin of a coordinate system to a particle that has momentum $\vec{p}$, the angular momentum of the particle about the origin is

$$\vec{L} = \vec{r} \times \vec{p}. \tag{12.43}$$

Review Questions

Answers to these questions can be found at the end of this chapter.

12.1 Torque and angular momentum

1. Can a small force produce a greater torque than a large force?
2. A friend pushes a doorknob to open the door for you, and the door swings all the way open in 2 s. On the way back, you return the favor but push not on the knob but close to the hinged edge. Although the door again opens all the way in 2 s, your friend notices your exertion and comments, "You had to exert a lot more torque doing it that way." Is he right?
3. What reference point should you choose for computing torques for a stationary object that is not mounted on a pivot, axle, or hinge?
4. Describe a case where the line of action of a force exerted on an object that can rotate either freely or about a fixed axis passes through the pivot even though the point of application of the force is not at the pivot. What is the torque in this case?

12.2 Free rotation

5. Can an object in free rotation rotate or revolve about any point you might choose?
6. Why is the concept of center of mass so useful in analyzing rotational motion?

12.3 Extended free-body diagrams

7. When you hold your left forearm parallel to the floor, what is the direction of the force exerted by the humerus bone on the elbow joint?
8. What is the main difference between a standard free-body diagram and an extended free-body diagram? Why is it necessary to use extended free-body diagrams when we study rotational motion?
9. If what you need in a problem is an extended free-body diagram, why draw a standard free-body diagram first? Isn't it possible to use an extended free-body diagram to compute vector sums of forces as well as vector sums of torques?

12.4 The vectorial nature of rotation

10. Describe the right-hand rule for determining a vector direction for the rotation of an object.
11. What is the direction of the rotational velocity vector for the second hand of a clock hanging on the wall?
12. Why are the words *clockwise* and *counterclockwise* insufficient to describe rotation in three dimensions?

12.5 Conservation of angular momentum

13. Which statement is correct: "In mechanical equilibrium, the vector sum of all the torques and forces is zero" or "In mechanical equilibrium, the vector sum of the torques is zero and the vector sum of the forces is zero."
14. Suppose a single force (one that is not canceled by any other forces) is exerted on an object. Is it possible for this single force to change both the object's momentum and its angular momentum?
15. A baton-twirler tosses her spinning baton up into the air. While it is in the air, is the baton's momentum constant? Is its angular momentum constant?
16. What is rotational impulse, and how is it related to the angular momentum law?
17. Under what circumstances is angular momentum conserved? Under what circumstances does the angular momentum of a system remain constant?

12.6 Rolling motion

18. For a wheel that is rolling without slipping, what is the relationship between the wheel's rotational speed and the speed v of its center of mass?
19. If two gears are in contact, with their teeth meshing, what do they have in common: rotational speed, tangential speed v_t of the teeth, or some other quantity?
20. What is the shape factor for a rolling object, and what does it measure?
21. An object rolls without slipping down a hill. How are the magnitudes of its rotational acceleration α_ϑ and the acceleration of its center of mass a_{cm} related?

12.7 Torque and energy

22. Explain how to compute the work done on a rotating object when you know both the sum of the torques caused by the external forces exerted on the object and the number of rotations the object makes in the time interval of interest.
23. If an object's motion is both translational and rotational, how should its kinetic energy be determined?
24. For an object that rolls without slipping, describe what effect static friction has on the work done on the object and on the object's energy.

12.8 The vector product

25. Draw a vector arrow on a sheet of paper, draw another vector arrow on a second sheet, and then lay the sheets on your desk in any arbitrarily chosen orientations. What angle does the vector representing the vector product of these two vectors make with the desktop? Does your answer depend on the orientation of the two vectors?
26. How is the magnitude of the vector product of two vectors related to the vectors?
27. What is $\vec{A} \cdot (\vec{A} \times \vec{B})$ equal to?
28. If you accidentally compute a torque using $\vec{F} \times \vec{r}$ rather than $\vec{r} \times \vec{F}$, what is wrong with your result?
29. What is the vector relationship between the angular momentum and the momentum for an isolated particle?

PRACTICE

Developing a Feel

Make an order-of-magnitude estimate of each of the following quantities. Letters in parentheses refer to hints below. Use them as needed to guide your thinking.

1. The magnitude of the torque caused by the force you exert to open your bedroom door (C, O)
2. The magnitude of the torque caused by the force required to accelerate a sports car from 0 to 60 mi/h in 4 s (E, R, K)
3. The maximum torque caused by the gravitational force exerted on your bicycle when you lean into a tight turn (A, V)
4. The length of a lever you need to raise the front end of a car in which the engine is in the front (B, H, N, W)
5. The gear ratio (ratio of front gear radius to rear gear radius) for the highest gear of a racing bicycle (D, I, S, Q)
6. The largest feasible gear ratio for a hand-held electric drill (G, L, U)
7. The maximum useful torque that can be delivered to each of a car's two drive wheels (Y, P, K)
8. The work required to remove and replace five lug nuts as you change a flat tire on your car (F, X)
9. The maximum torque caused by the force you exert on a diving board when you dive into a pool (Z, T, J, M)

Hints

A. What is the distance from the pivot to the center of mass?
B. What is the distance from the axis of rotation to the car's center of mass?
C. What is the lever arm distance?
D. What is the diameter of a bicycle wheel?
E. What acceleration is needed?
F. What torque through what angle is needed to "break" each nut loose?
G. What is the minimum number of teeth on a gear to allow smooth turning?
H. What is the distance from the car's axis of rotation to the point where the lever touches the car?
I. At what speed can a strong cyclist move in the highest gear?
J. What is the average force you exert on the diving board?
K. What is the radius of each wheel?
L. If each tooth is 1 mm thick, what minimum radius is needed for the smaller (driveshaft) gear?
M. What distance does the diving board extend beyond any support?
N. What is the ratio of the required lifting force to the gravitational force exerted on you by Earth?
O. What is the force magnitude?
P. What normal force (needed to support the car) is exerted on each drive wheel?
Q. What is the minimum comfortable time interval needed for the cyclist's foot to complete one cycle?
R. What is the vector sum of the forces required?
S. What is the rotational speed of the wheel?
T. What is the time interval between the instant you hit the board on your last bounce and the instant the board is at maximum depression?
U. What maximum gear radius could fit comfortably in the drill casing?
V. What is your maximum angle of lean?
W. What is the minimum distance from the point where you pivot the lever to the location where the lever touches the car?
X. What torque through what angle is needed to unscrew each loosened lug nut?
Y. What coefficient of friction can be used to move the car forward most effectively?
Z. If you jump high on your last bounce, with what speed do you hit the end of the diving board?

Key (all values approximate)

A. 1 m; **B.** axis at rear wheels, center of mass just behind front wheels, so 2 m; **C.** 0.7 m; **D.** 0.7 m; **E.** 7 $\mathrm{m/s^2}$; **F.** 1×10^2 N · m through one-quarter of a turn; **G.** 1×10^1; **H.** about 3 m; **I.** 2×10^1 m/s; **J.** consider both gravitational force and momentum change divided by the time interval, about 2×10^3 N for an 80-kg person; **K.** 0.3 m; **L.** about 3 mm, allowing for spacing between teeth; **M.** less than 3 m; **N.** 14 to 1; **O.** 1×10^1 N; **P.** 4×10^3 N, or one-third of the gravitational force for a front-wheel-drive car; **Q.** 0.4 s; **R.** 0.7 times the gravitational force exerted on the car—say, 7 kN; **S.** $6 \times 10^1\ \mathrm{s^{-1}}$; **T.** 0.3 s; **U.** 3×10^1 mm; **V.** 40° away from vertical; **W.** 0.3 m; **X.** 8 N · m through 5 revolutions; **Y.** to avoid wasteful slipping, use the coefficient of static friction, which may be close to 1; **Z.** 3 m/s

Worked and Guided Problems

Procedure: Extended free-body diagrams

1. Begin by making a standard free-body diagram for the object of interest (the *system*) to determine what forces are exerted on it. Determine the direction of the acceleration of the center of mass of the object, and draw an arrow to represent this acceleration.
2. Draw a cross section of the object in the plane of rotation (that is, a plane perpendicular to the rotation axis) or, if the object is stationary, in the plane in which the forces of interest lie.
3. Choose a reference point. If the object is rotating about a hinge, pivot, or axle, choose that point. If the object is rotating freely, choose the center of mass. If the object is stationary, you can choose any reference point. Because forces exerted at the reference point cause no torque, it is most convenient to choose the point where the largest number of forces is exerted or where an unknown force is exerted. Mark the location of your reference point and choose a positive direction of rotation. Indicate the reference point in your diagram by the symbol ⊙.
4. Draw vectors to represent the forces that are exerted on the object and that lie in the plane of the drawing. Place the tail of each force vector at the point where the force is exerted on the object. Place the tail of the gravitational force exerted by Earth on the object at the object's center of mass.* Label each force.
5. Indicate the object's rotational acceleration in the diagram (for example, if the object accelerates in the positive ϑ direction, write $\alpha_\vartheta > 0$ near the rotation axis). If the rotational acceleration is zero, write $\alpha_\vartheta = 0$.

*Is the gravitational force really exerted at the center of mass? Suppose the gravitational force exerted by Earth were exerted at some other point. The force would then cause a permanent torque about the center of mass, and any object dropped from rest would begin spinning, which is not true.

These examples involve material from this chapter but are not associated with any particular section. Some examples are worked out in detail; others you should work out by following the guidelines provided.

Worked Problem 12.1 Using a wrench

Loosening the rusted lug nuts on a car tire requires 220 N · m of torque. (*a*) A 60-kg mechanic holds a wrench horizontally on one nut. The wrench is 400 mm long, and she holds it at the free end and exerts a force equal to the magnitude of the gravitational force exerted on her. If the direction of the force she exerts is straight downward, how much torque does she cause on the nut? (*b*) Suppose one nut is oriented such that the wrench makes a 37° angle with the horizontal, as in Figure WG12.1. By exerting the identical force she exerted in part *a*, can the mechanic loosen this nut with the 400-mm wrench? If not, how long a wrench must she use to loosen the nut?

Figure WG12.1

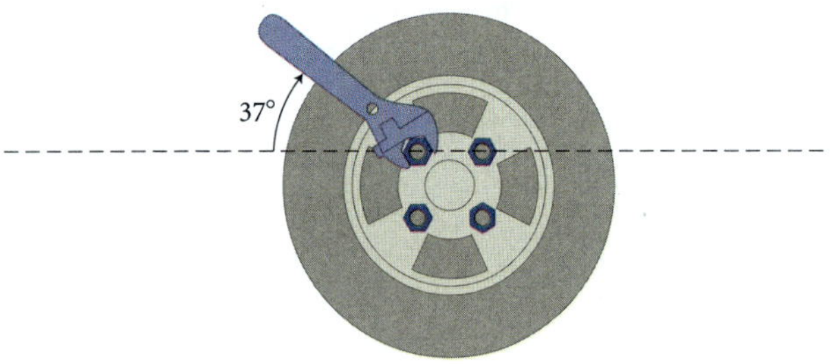

❶ GETTING STARTED Given that this problem involves torques, we follow the procedure for drawing extended free-body diagrams at the top of this page. We begin by making a free-body diagram for the wrench (Figure WG12.2*a*). The wrench is subject to three forces: a downward force exerted by the mechanic on the wrench, an upward contact force exerted by the nut on the wrench, and a downward force of gravitation exerted by Earth on the wrench. Because the gravitational force on the wrench is negligible compared to the other two forces, we ignore this force in this problem. Next we draw extended free-body diagrams for the wrench for both parts of this problem (Figure WG12.2*b* and *c*). In both cases we choose the nut as the reference point. With that choice of reference point, only the force $\vec{F}^c_{mw}$ causes a torque.

Figure WG12.2

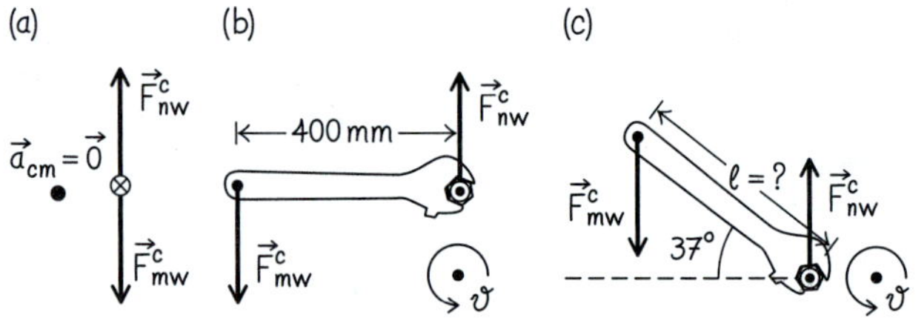

❷ DEVISE PLAN The magnitude of the torque caused by a force exerted on an object is

$$\tau = |\vec{r} \times \vec{F}| = rF \sin \theta, \qquad (1)$$

where θ is the angle between the line of action of the force and the position vector that points from the rotation axis to the point of application of the force. The magnitude of the contact force exerted by the mechanic on the wrench is the magnitude of the gravitational force exerted on her: $F^c_{mw} = F^G_{Em} = m_m g$. The lever arm distance $r_\perp$ is the wrench length ℓ because the point of application of her force is the very end of the wrench. In part *a* the angle between $\vec{r}$ and $\vec{F}^c_{mw}$ is 90°.

The force magnitude and direction remain the same in part *b*, but the angle θ changes. We note that the 37° angle the wrench makes with the horizontal is *not* the angle we use to calculate the torque. We want the angle between the downward force and the wrench, which is $\theta = 90° - 37°$. We can use Eq. 1 for part *b*, with $r = \ell$ in this case, if we solve for the wrench length: $\ell = \tau/(F \sin\theta) = \tau/(F^G_{Em} \sin\theta)$.

❸ **EXECUTE PLAN**
(*a*) The magnitude of the gravitational force exerted on the mechanic is $m_m g = (60\ \text{kg})(9.8\ \text{m/s}^2) = 588\ \text{N}$. The torque caused by the force exerted by the mechanic is then

$$\tau = (0.400\ \text{m})(588\ \text{N})(\sin 90°) = 235\ \text{N}\cdot\text{m}$$
$$= 2.4 \times 10^2\ \text{N}\cdot\text{m}. ✔$$

(*b*) With the wrench making a 37° angle with the horizontal but the force exerted vertically downward, the angle between the line of action of the force and the wrench is $\theta = 90° - 37° = 53°$. The torque her force causes now is

$$\tau = (0.400\ \text{m})(588\ \text{N})(\sin 53°) = 188\ \text{N}\cdot\text{m}.$$

This is insufficient to loosen the rusted nut. She can loosen it with a longer wrench, though. The minimum wrench length ℓ to achieve the needed 220-N · m torque is

$$\ell = \frac{\tau}{F^G_{Em}\sin\theta} = \frac{220\ \text{N}\cdot\text{m}}{(588\ \text{N})(\sin 53°)} = 0.47\ \text{m}. ✔$$

A slightly longer wrench will loosen the nut, or the mechanic can just put a piece of hollow pipe over the end of her 400-mm wrench to increase the lever arm distance a bit.

❹ **EVALUATE RESULT** Our answers are close to the needed torque given in the problem statement, 220 N · m, which gives us confidence in our results, but what other bounds can we establish to test their reasonableness? Consider the force $\vec{F}^c_{wm}$ exerted by the wrench on the mechanic in part *a*. By Newton's third law, this force is equal in magnitude to the force exerted by the mechanic on the wrench, but in the opposite direction. Making full use of the gravitational force exerted on the mechanic in our calculation means we assume that no support force other than $\vec{F}^c_{wm}$ is necessary to keep the mechanic from falling—the wrench provides all the required support. In fact, this is the greatest force she can exert on the wrench without invoking some creative arrangement. In order to exert a downward force greater than the gravitational force, the mechanic would need to be able to push upward against some nearby fixed object, perhaps with her feet. With no mention of such an effort in the problem statement, we assume she did no such contortions.

Exerting a horizontal force requires some frictional force to compensate, or a nearby object on which the mechanic can push horizontally with her feet in order to maintain a zero sum of horizontal forces exerted on herself. Coefficients of friction rarely exceed 1, so again the gravitational force is the upper limit for a typical person to exert on a wrench. In practice, the maximum force possible with a person's hands is likely to be a bit smaller than the gravitation force. Most people must stand on the wrench in order to supply a force as great as the gravitational force exerted on them by Earth.

Guided Problem 12.2 At the grindstone

A circular grindstone, radius 0.17 m, is used to sharpen a knife. The knife is pressed against the grindstone with a normal force of 20 N, and the coefficient of kinetic friction between knife and stone is 0.54. What torque must the motor driving the grindstone maintain in order to keep the stone rotating at constant speed?

❶ **GETTING STARTED**

1. Consider the force exerted by the knife on the grindstone. Does any component of this force cause a torque about the grindstone's axle?

❷ **DEVISE PLAN**

2. To maintain a constant rotational speed, what must be the vector sum of the torques caused by the forces exerted on the grindstone? What two torques are involved?
3. Does the normal force exerted by the knife on the grindstone contribute to the torque equation?

❸ **EXECUTE PLAN**

4. Compute the magnitude of the torque that must be canceled by the motor.

❹ **EVALUATE RESULT**

5. Examine the expression for torque used in step 4. What happens to the torque as the normal force changes? As the coefficient of friction changes? Are these two trends reasonable?
6. Consider your numerical result. Could a motor supply this amount of torque? Could a person supply this amount of torque with a foot pedal? (If you have trouble answering these two questions, review the Developing a Feel questions in this chapter.)

Worked Problem 12.3 Accelerating bicycle

A bicyclist initially traveling at a steady 3.0 m/s accelerates at a constant 1.1 m/s^2. The time interval over which the acceleration takes place is long enough for the wheels to make 20 rotations. If the wheels have a radius of 0.30 m, what is their rotational speed after the acceleration stops?

❶ GETTING STARTED The appropriate diagram for kinematics problems is a motion diagram (Figure WG12.3). The bicyclist moves horizontally while the wheel both rotates and moves horizontally, with increasing rotational speed as the bicyclist accelerates. This is a simple kinematics problem, but the key is to establish a relationship between the given translational quantities and the desired rotational quantities. We use the fact that for rolling without slipping, there is a relationship between the distance the center of each wheel travels and the number of rotations the wheel makes.

Figure WG12.3

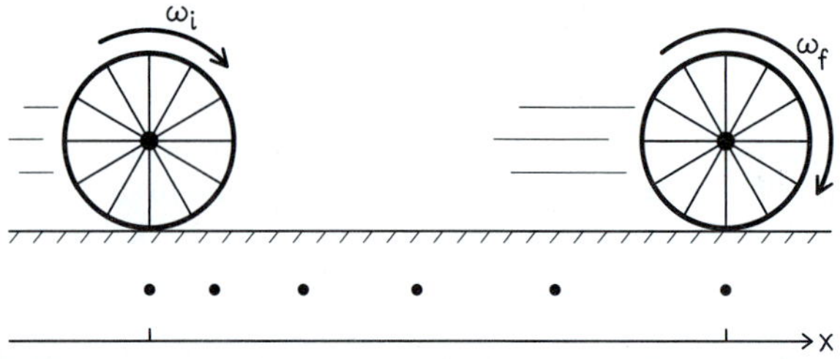

❷ DEVISE PLAN The acceleration of the bicycle is the acceleration of the center of each wheel, which is equal to the tangential acceleration of a point on the rim. The relationships between translational and rotational quantities for rolling without slipping are

$$x = \vartheta R$$
$$v_{\text{cm}\,x} = \omega_\vartheta R$$
$$a_{\text{cm}\,x} = \alpha_\vartheta R.$$

Because the acceleration of the bicycle is constant, the rotational acceleration is also constant. The rotational speed of the wheels is described by the equation

$$\omega^2_{\vartheta,\text{f}} = \omega^2_{\vartheta,\text{i}} + 2\alpha_\vartheta(\vartheta_\text{f} - \vartheta_\text{i}). \quad (1)$$

Thus we have enough information to compute $\omega_{\vartheta,\text{i}}$ and α_ϑ, and $\vartheta_\text{f} - \vartheta_\text{i}$ is the 20 rotations expressed as a change in the rotational coordinate.

❸ EXECUTE PLAN We use Eq. 1 to determine the final rotational speed, substituting translational variables for $\omega_{\vartheta,\text{i}}$ and α_ϑ:

$$\omega_\text{f}^2 = \left(\frac{v_{\text{cm}\,x,\text{i}}}{R}\right)^2 + 2\left(\frac{a_{\text{cm}\,x}}{R}\right)(\vartheta_\text{f} - \vartheta_\text{i}).$$

The final rotational speed is therefore

$$\omega_\text{f} = \left[\left(\frac{3.0\ \text{m/s}}{0.30\ \text{m}}\right)^2 + 2\left(\frac{1.1\ \text{m/s}^2}{0.30\ \text{m}}\right)(20\ \text{rev})(2\pi/\text{rev})\right]^{1/2}$$
$$= 32\ \text{s}^{-1}. ✔$$

❹ EVALUATE RESULT The algebraic equation for ω_f shows that it is greater for larger accelerations and higher initial speeds. Both of these trends are reasonable. The reasonableness of the numerical result can be checked by noting that the final speed is $v = \omega R = (32\ \text{s}^{-1})(0.30\ \text{m}) = 9.6\ \text{m/s} = 34\ \text{km/h} = 21\ \text{mi/h}$, which is a reasonable speed for a cyclist.

Guided Problem 12.4 Inclined race

A solid disk and a hoop, which have different radii and different inertias, are set near the top of a ramp and then released (Figure WG12.4). The ramp is inclined at an angle of 4.0° and is 1.8 m long. (*a*) Which object reaches the bottom first? (*b*) After the first object reaches the bottom, how many seconds pass before the other object reaches the bottom?

Figure WG12.4

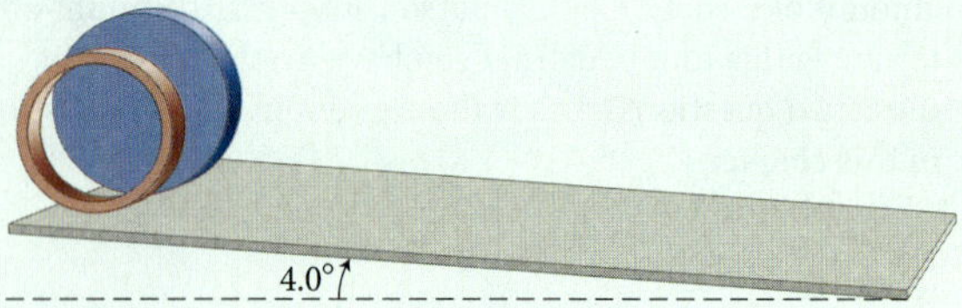

❶ GETTING STARTED

1. What types of motion are involved here?
2. Consider possible approaches to part *a*: conservation laws, other fundamental principles, or kinematics alone. Repeat for part *b*. If more than one approach is feasible, you may be able to use one method to check an answer you obtained using another method.

❷ DEVISE PLAN

3. Draw a diagram showing the physical quantities needed to describe the approach you have decided to use. Write a general equation based on your diagram for the acceleration and rotational acceleration of each object. Consider whether you need separate diagrams for parts *a* and *b*.
4. How does the shape factor for a hoop compare with that for a cylinder (remember that the disk is a very short cylinder)?
5. Which object experiences the greater rotational acceleration: the one with the larger shape factor or the one with the smaller shape factor?
6. For each object, write an expression that relates the acceleration to the time interval the object takes to reach the bottom. Repeat for rotational acceleration. Do you now have enough information to solve the problem?

PRACTICE

3 EXECUTE PLAN

7. Solve the equations you wrote in step 6 for the time interval each object takes to roll down the ramp.
8. Subtract your expression for the time interval for the object that reaches the bottom first from the time interval for the object that reaches the bottom second. How do you know from this difference whether you are wrong about which object reaches the bottom first?

4 EVALUATE RESULT

9. Examine your expression for how the time interval needed to reach the bottom changes as you change the physical conditions. What happens as the length of the ramp increases? As the angle of inclination increases? Are these trends reasonable?
10. Consider your numerical result. Is the order of magnitude about right?

Worked Problem 12.5 Falling yo-yo

A yo-yo is basically a spool consisting of an inner small axle and two outer disks, with a string wrapped around the axle. Calculate the acceleration of a 0.130-kg yo-yo if it's allowed to drop while the free end of the string is held at a fixed distance above the floor. Each disk has a radius of 17.0 mm, which means the yo-yo radius is the same, $R_Y = 17.0$ mm, and the axle radius is $R_a = 5.00$ mm. Ignore the inertia of the axle and assume that the entire 0.130-kg inertia is for the two disks.

1 GETTING STARTED We know that the yo-yo accelerates as it falls because of the gravitational force. At the same time, however, the string tends to pull the yo-yo upward. We also know that the yo-yo increases its spin rate as it falls, an increase that must be due to a vector sum of torques caused by these two opposing forces. This information implies that we have to use force and torque laws to get our acceleration.

2 DEVISE PLAN The torque caused by the force exerted by the string converts gravitational potential energy to kinetic energy. However, energy methods give us the yo-yo's speed after it has dropped a given distance rather than the instantaneous acceleration requested. We can get this acceleration from Newton's second law, except we do not know the value of the tension in the string. Another equation is needed.

If we assume that the string does not slip, we can relate the rotational acceleration to the desired acceleration via $a_{\text{cm}\,x} = R_a\alpha_\vartheta$ and then get the rotational acceleration from the vector sum of the external torques, $\sum\tau_{\text{ext}\,\vartheta} = I\alpha_\vartheta$ (Eq. 12.10).

Although the acceleration of the yo-yo's center of mass does not depend on the locations of the points of application of the forces, its rotational acceleration does. Thus we need both a free-body diagram and an extended free-body diagram for the yo-yo (Figure WG12.5). The only forces exerted are the downward gravitational force exerted by Earth $\vec{F}^G_{\text{EY}}$, the point of application of which is at the yo-yo's center of mass; and the upward force exerted by the string $\vec{F}^c_{\text{sY}}$, which is directed tangent to the axle.

Figure WG12.5

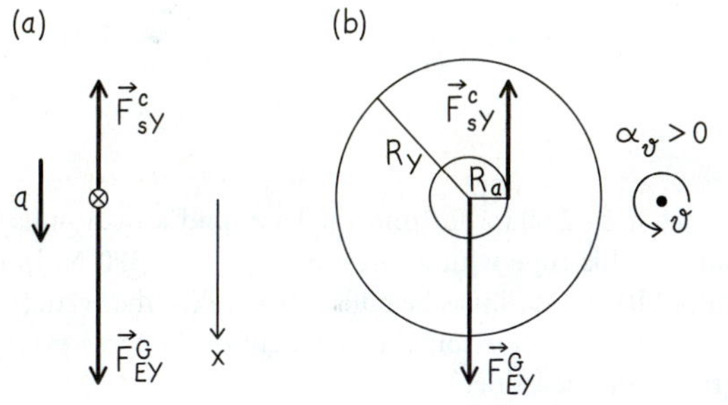

We have to be careful about the signs of our accelerations. The easiest way to do this is to choose directions for our axes such that positive translation corresponds to positive rotation. Because we know that the yo-yo accelerates downward, we choose the positive x axis pointing downward. A positive downward translation corresponds in Figure WG12.5 to a counterclockwise rotation as the string unwinds, so we put a counterclockwise curved arrow labeled ϑ in our diagram. We note that the only force that produces a nonzero torque about the center of mass is the force exerted by the string, because the force of gravity has a zero lever arm distance about this axis.

3 EXECUTE PLAN We begin with the equation of motion based on the vector sum of forces:

$$F^c_{\text{sY}\,x} + F^G_{\text{EY}\,x} = m_Y a_{\text{cm}\,x}.$$

Substituting in the sign and magnitude for each component gives us

$$-F^c_{\text{sY}} + F^G_{\text{EY}} = m_Y a_{\text{cm}\,x}. \quad (1)$$

We suspect that $a_{\text{cm}\,x}$ must be positive, but let us see if the final result bears this out.

The rotational equation of motion for the components along the axis specified by the curved arrow for our rotational coordinate system is

$$\sum\tau_{\text{ext}\,\vartheta} = \tau_{\text{sY}\,\vartheta} + \tau_{\text{EY}\,\vartheta} = I\alpha_\vartheta$$

$$+R_aF^c_{\text{sY}} + 0 = \left(\tfrac{1}{2}m_YR_Y^2\right)\alpha_\vartheta, \quad (2)$$

where we have used the fact that the yo-yo is approximately the shape of a solid cylinder, for which the expression for rotational inertia is $I = mR^2/2$.

The relationship between the rotational acceleration and the acceleration of the center of mass is

$$a_{\text{cm}\,x} = \alpha_\vartheta R_a.$$

Note that the axle radius is the appropriate radius to use here. Solving this equation for α_ϑ, substituting the result into Eq. 2, and dividing through by R_a, we get

$$+R_aF^c_{\text{sY}} + 0 = \left(\tfrac{1}{2}m_YR_Y^2\right)\left(\frac{a_{\text{cm}\,x}}{R_a}\right)$$

$$+F^c_{\text{sY}} = \left(\tfrac{1}{2}m_YR_Y^2\right)\left(\frac{a_{\text{cm}\,x}}{R_a^2}\right). \quad (3)$$

Next we substitute Eq. 3 into Eq. 1, solve the result for $a_{\text{cm}x}$, and insert numerical values:

$$-\left(\tfrac{1}{2}m_{\text{Y}}R_{\text{Y}}^2\right)\left(\frac{a_{\text{cm}x}}{R_{\text{a}}^2}\right) + F_{\text{EY}}^G = m_{\text{Y}}a_{\text{cm}x}$$

$$F_{\text{EY}}^G = m_{\text{Y}}a_{\text{cm}x} + \left(\tfrac{1}{2}m_{\text{Y}}R_{\text{Y}}^2\right)\left(\frac{a_{\text{cm}x}}{R_{\text{a}}^2}\right)$$

$$m_{\text{Y}}g = m_{\text{Y}}\left(1 + \tfrac{1}{2}\frac{R_{\text{Y}}^2}{R_{\text{a}}^2}\right)a_{\text{cm}x}$$

$$a_{\text{cm}x} = \frac{g}{1 + \tfrac{1}{2}\dfrac{R_{\text{Y}}^2}{R_{\text{a}}^2}}$$

$$a_{\text{cm}x} = \frac{9.80\text{ m/s}^2}{1 + \tfrac{1}{2}(0.0170\text{ m})^2/(0.00500\text{ m})^2} = 1.45\text{ m/s}^2. ✔$$

❹ **EVALUATE RESULT** The expression we obtained for $a_{\text{cm}x}$ tells us that the acceleration of the yo-yo depends on the radius R_{a} of the axle and on the shape factor $c = \frac{1}{2}$ (from Table 11.3). If R_{a} decreases so that more of the yo-yo's inertia is concentrated at the end pieces (or if R_{Y} increases), the yo-yo accelerates more slowly. As we expected, our expression shows that $a_{\text{cm}x}$ can only be positive. The numerical value of the acceleration is reasonable: A value quite a bit smaller than the free-fall value makes sense because the force exerted by the string impedes the falling motion.

Guided Problem 12.6 Fickle yo-yo

The yo-yo in Figure WG12.6, which has inertia m_{Y}, outer radius R_{Y}, and axle radius R_{a}, sits on a rough horizontal surface. Depending on the angle ϕ at which the string is pulled with tension $\mathcal{T}$, the yo-yo rolls either to the left or to the right in the drawing. (*a*) For a given angle ϕ, determine expressions for the magnitude and direction of the acceleration. (*b*) What is the critical angle at which the yo-yo changes the direction in which it rolls?

Figure WG12.6

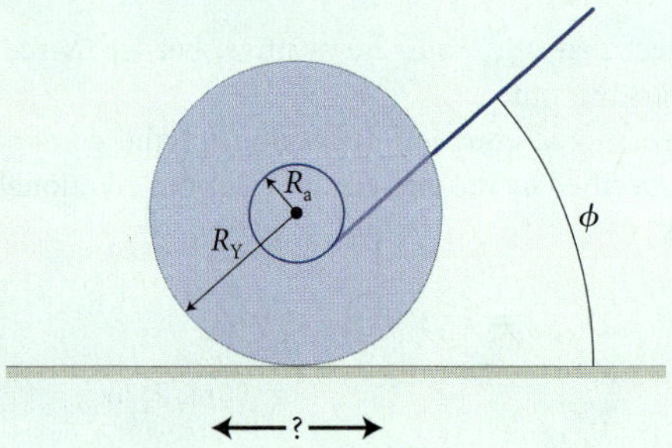

❶ **GETTING STARTED**

1. What sort of motion results when the string is pulled at the critical angle? (Hint: What motion could be intermediate between rolling right and rolling left?)
2. What sort of diagram is appropriate for analyzing torques? Analyzing forces? How many cases must you draw separately?
3. Identify all the forces exerted on the yo-yo. What is the direction of the frictional force? (Hint: In which direction would the yo-yo slide if the surface were ice?)

❷ **DEVISE PLAN**

4. What is a good choice for the axis about which to calculate the torques?
5. Draw both a horizontal x axis and a curved arrow for your selection of a positive sense of rotation about your chosen axis.
6. Write the second-law force and torque equations. Account for all forces and torques. Are any zero? How many unknowns do you have?
7. What is a reasonable shape factor to use for the yo-yo?
8. What condition must be met at the critical angle if the yo-yo rolls neither left nor right?
9. Derive an expression for the critical angle in terms of known quantities.

❸ **EXECUTE PLAN**

10. Make sign and magnitude decisions for each force component and each torque component. Attempt a solution.

❹ **EVALUATE RESULT**

11. Does the coefficient of friction or the magnitude of the frictional force play a role? Is this surprising? Consider possible hidden assumptions.
12. What do your equations tell you about the motion as ϕ approaches zero? As ϕ approaches 90°?
13. Obtain a spool or yo-yo and give this a try. Can you reproduce the behavior exhibited by the equations?

Worked Problem 12.7 Leaning ladder of physics

A ladder of length $\ell = 13.0$ m leans against a smooth vertical wall. The base rests on rough ground at a distance $d_{\text{w}} = 5.00$ m from the wall, and the top is at height $h = 12.0$ m above the ground (Figure WG12.7). The magnitude of the force of gravity exerted on the ladder is 324 N. A rope is attached to the ladder at a distance $d_{\text{r}} = 2.00$ m up from the base, and a man pulls horizontally on this rope with a force of magnitude 390 N. In order for the ladder not to slip as he pulls, what are (*a*) the vertical component and (*b*) the horizontal component of the force exerted by the ground on the ladder?

Figure WG12.7

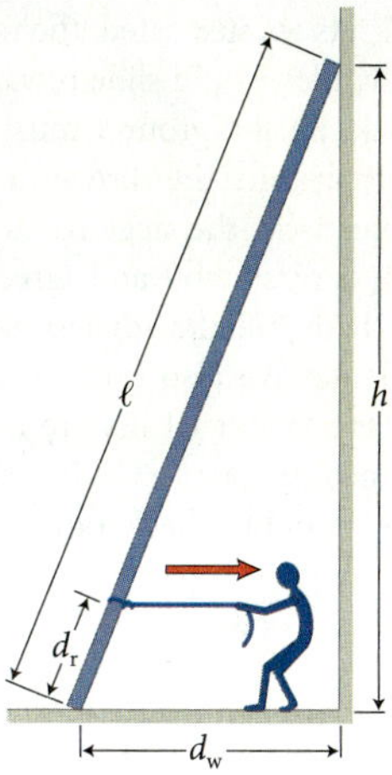

❶ GETTING STARTED A sketch has been provided with the problem, so we can focus on which physical principles elucidate this situation. Because nothing is changing the ladder's state of motion, this is a case of mechanical equilibrium. Therefore the sum of the forces exerted on the ladder must be zero, and the sum of the torques caused by these forces must be zero. Three force components of unknown magnitude are exerted on the ladder, so we should get three component equations from our force and torque analysis.

❷ DEVISE PLAN As usual, we draw a free-body diagram and an extended free-body diagram (Figure WG12.8). Because we need to deal with components of forces and torques, we have to specify axes and a rotational direction. Let us choose the positive x direction to be to the right, the positive y direction to be up, and the pivot about which to calculate the torques to be the base of the ladder, with positive rotation counterclockwise. We put these two sign notations in our diagram.

Figure WG12.8

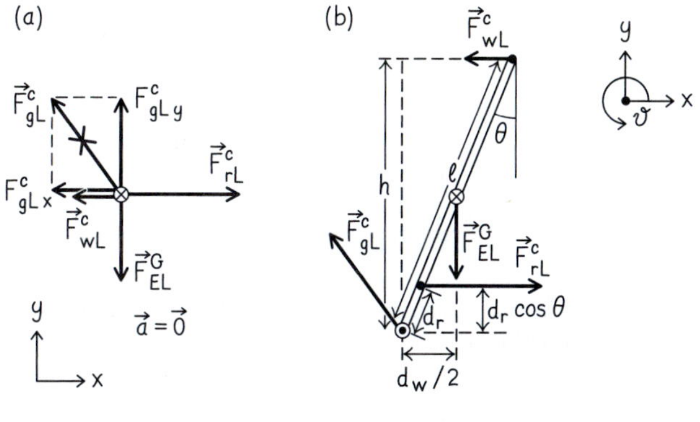

We know the magnitudes and directions of the gravitational force and the force exerted by the man, so we draw those to scale first in our free-body diagram. The man exerts a force to the right, and its magnitude exceeds that of the gravitational force. That means we suspect that in the absence of friction the bottom of the ladder would slide to the right. Thus we draw the contact force exerted by the ground as pointing upward and to the left. If this turns out to be wrong, our equations will provide a correction by virtue of a negative answer.

It is useful to identify a relevant angle for our analysis, and let us select the one between the top of the ladder and the wall, calling it θ. The ladder forms a 5–12–13 right triangle with the wall, and this angle satisfies the relationships $\sin\theta = \frac{5.00}{13.0}$ and $\cos\theta = \frac{12.0}{13.0}$ (making $\theta = 22.6°$).

We want to know the force exerted by the ground on the ladder. We know that because the wall is smooth we can ignore any frictional force exerted by the wall. This means the wall exerts no vertical force, only a horizontal (normal) contact force. We can therefore look at the sum of the forces exerted on the ladder in the vertical direction and not worry about any force in this direction exerted by the wall. The sum of the torques about the base of the ladder must be zero because there is no rotation. We know that the force exerted by the wall is directed to the left in the orientation shown in Figure WG12.7, and we know that the horizontal forces must balance because the ladder isn't accelerating in the x direction. This gives us enough equations to solve for all unknowns.

❸ EXECUTE PLAN
(*a*) Because the sum of the vertical components of the four forces must be zero, we write

$$\Sigma F_y = F^c_{\text{wL}y} + F^G_{\text{EL}y} + F^c_{\text{rL}y} + F^c_{\text{gL}y} = 0.$$

The vertical component of the contact force exerted on the ladder by the ground is the normal force, so we call its magnitude $F^n_{\text{gL}} = |F^c_{\text{gL}y}|$. (The horizontal component is the friction force.) Thus we get

$$\Sigma F_y = 0 + (-F^G_{\text{EL}}) + 0 + F^n_{\text{gL}} = 0$$

$$F^n_{\text{gL}} = |F^c_{\text{gL}y}| = F^G_{\text{EL}} = 324 \text{ N.} ✔$$

Note that the direction of $F^c_{\text{gL}y}$ must be upward because the only other vertical force (the gravitational force) is downward.

(*b*) To determine the horizontal component $F^c_{\text{gL}x}$, we need two equations because there are two unknowns in the equation for the horizontal sum of the forces: $F^c_{\text{gL}x}$ (the one we have to determine) and $F^c_{\text{wL}x}$. Thus we begin with torques. The sum of the ϑ components of the torques caused by the four forces about the rotation axis must be zero because there is no rotation. Using our generic symbol $r_\perp$ for lever arm distances, we write our first torque equation in the general form

$$\Sigma\tau_\vartheta = \pm r_{\text{wL}\perp}F^c_{\text{wL}} \pm r_{\text{EL}\perp}F^G_{\text{EL}} \pm r_{\text{rL}\perp}F^c_{\text{rL}} \pm r_{\text{gL}\perp}F^c_{\text{gL}} = 0.$$

We note that the term $r_{\text{gL}\perp}F^c_{\text{gL}}$, the torque caused by the force exerted by the ground on the ladder, must be zero because the lever arm distance for this torque is zero for a pivot at the base of the ladder.

Our chosen direction for positive rotation determines the sign of each torque. We determine these signs by looking at Figure WG12.8*b* to see which way each force tends to rotate the ladder about the pivot. Remember that counterclockwise in the figure is positive rotation:

$$\Sigma\tau_\vartheta = +hF^c_{wL} + \left(-\tfrac{1}{2}d_w F^G_{EL}\right) + \left[-(d_r\cos\theta)F^c_{rL}\right] + 0 = 0$$

$$(12.0\text{ m})F^c_{wL} - \tfrac{1}{2}(5.00\text{ m})(324\text{ N})$$

$$-\,(2.00\text{ m})\left(\tfrac{12.0}{13.0}\right)(390\text{ N}) = 0.$$

This gives us the magnitude of the force exerted by the wall:

$$F^c_{wL} = \frac{\tfrac{1}{2}(5.00\text{ m})(324\text{ N}) + (2.00\text{ m})\left(\tfrac{12.0}{13.0}\right)(390\text{ N})}{12.0\text{ m}} = 128\text{ N}.$$

The sum of the horizontal forces is

$$\Sigma F_x = F^c_{wLx} + F^G_{ELx} + F^c_{rLx} + F^c_{gLx} = 0$$

$$(-F^c_{wL}) + 0 + (+F^c_{rL}) + F^c_{gLx} = 0,$$

where we have used the known information about the directions of the forces exerted by the wall and the rope. We now solve for the horizontal component of the force exerted on the ladder by the ground:

$$F^c_{gLx} = +F^c_{wL} - F^c_{rL} = 128\text{ N} - 390\text{ N} = -262\text{ N}. ✔$$

❹ **EVALUATE RESULT** As we suspected, the man pulls on the rope hard enough that the ladder would slide toward him if the ground weren't holding it back. So the ground must supply a horizontal force in the direction opposite the direction of the force exerted by the rope, which means in the negative x direction. Thus, the negative value for F^c_{gLx} is reasonable and agrees with our free-body diagram. If the man had pulled with less force, we might have obtained a positive value. We also know that the ground needs to be pushing up on the ladder (if it were not, the ladder would fall through the ground), so our +324 N result in part *a* is reasonable. However, let's double-check our answer by calculating the torque about the ladder's center of mass, which should also be zero:

$$\Sigma\tau_\vartheta = \left[+\left(\tfrac{1}{2}\ell - d_r\right)\cos\theta\right]F^c_{rL} + \left[+\tfrac{1}{2}\ell\cos\theta\right]F^c_{wL}$$

$$+\left[+\tfrac{1}{2}\ell\cos\theta\right]F^c_{gLx} + \left[-\tfrac{1}{2}\ell\sin\theta\right]F^c_{gLy}.$$

Note the absence of any contribution by the gravitational force here. Why is this so?

When we substitute numerical values, we get zero, verifying our earlier torque result. This is one of the nice things about mechanical equilibrium problems. You can pick whichever pivot is easiest to balance around to get an initial answer and then pick a different pivot to check that answer.

Guided Problem 12.8 Moving a refrigerator

Your new refrigerator, of inertia m, has been delivered and left in your garage. As shown in Figure WG12.9, it has length ℓ in vertical dimension and each side of its square base is of length d. You need to slide it across the rough garage surface to get it into your house. The coefficients of static and kinetic friction between base and garage surface are almost equal, so you approximate $\mu = \mu_s = \mu_k$. You push horizontally at a height h above the surface, exerting a force just big enough to keep the refrigerator moving. You dislike bending over, so you push at the highest possible point that will not cause the refrigerator to tip as it slides. Thus the refrigerator is always on the verge of tipping. (*a*) Where along the base of the refrigerator is the effective point of application of the normal force exerted by the garage surface on the refrigerator; that is, at what location can you picture the normal force as being concentrated? (*b*) If the refrigerator is not to tip, and if its center of mass is at its center, what is the maximum value h_{max} at which you can push?

Figure WG12.9

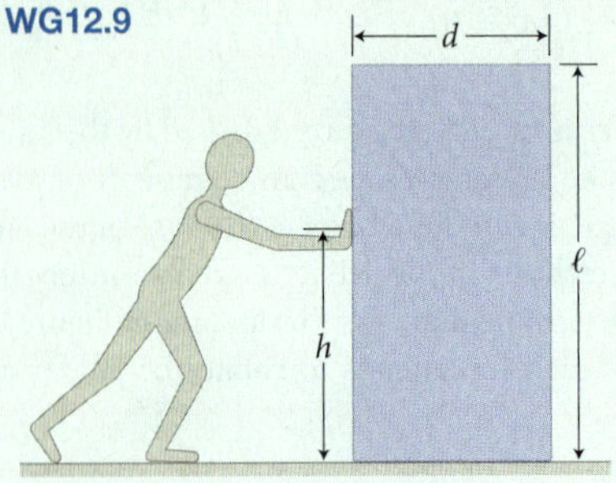

❶ **GETTING STARTED**

1. What condition must be met in order for the refrigerator not to rotate?
2. How can you determine the force you push with to just keep the refrigerator moving?
3. Which force(s) tend to tip the refrigerator, and which tend to prevent it from tipping?

❷ **DEVISE PLAN**

4. Draw a free-body diagram and an extended free-body diagram for the refrigerator. Indicate a sign for each coordinate axis (x, y, and ϑ) so that you can correctly determine the signs of the components.
5. What is the lever arm distance of the normal force $\vec{F}^n_{fr}$ exerted by the floor?
6. How does the height at which you push affect the point of application of $\vec{F}^n_{fr}$?
7. Is there enough information to solve for the value of the lever arm distance of $\vec{F}^n_{fr}$ at which the refrigerator begins to tip?
8. What condition exists just before tipping begins?

❸ **EXECUTE PLAN**

❹ **EVALUATE RESULT**

9. In your expression for the lever arm distance, does each term have a sign that is physically plausible?
10. Does your answer make sense if μ is reduced to zero or increased to 1.0? What if d becomes very large or very small?

Questions and Problems

For instructor-assigned homework, go to MasteringPhysics® MP

Dots indicate difficulty level of problems: • = *easy,* •• = *intermediate,* ••• = *hard;* CR = *context-rich problem.*

12.1 Torque and angular momentum

1. To open a stuck jar lid, wearing rubber gloves sometimes works. Why does that help? •
2. You are using a steel crowbar to lift a big rock, with a smaller stone as a fulcrum at the center of the crowbar, but you are not quite able to lift the rock. What can you change about this setup to lift the rock? •
3. The specifications for tightening the bolts on a car engine's valve cover are given in terms of torque rather than in terms of how much force should be exerted on the tightening wrench. Why is torque a better specification here? •
4. When the wrench you are working with does not loosen a nut, you can sometimes succeed by slipping a length of pipe over the end of the wrench and pushing at the end of the pipe. Why does this work? ••
5. In which cases illustrated in Figure P12.5 does pushing in the way and at the location shown cause a torque about a vertical axis passing through the hinges? The dot shows the point of application of the force in each case, and the dashed lines help indicate the line of action of each force. Forces (*a*), (*b*), and (*f*) are exerted parallel to the gate; forces (*c*), (*d*), and (*e*) are exerted perpendicular to the gate. ••

Figure P12.5

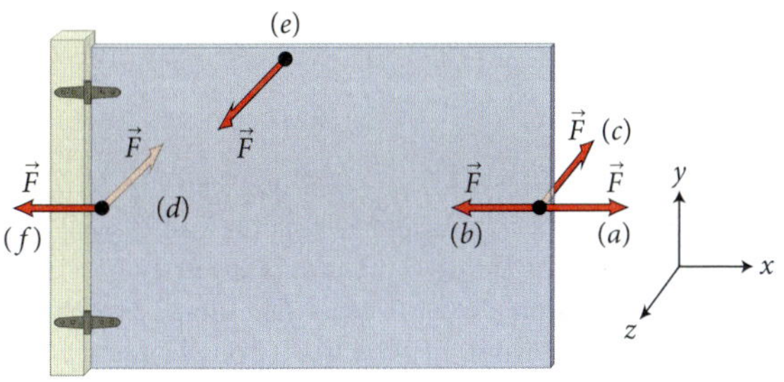

6. Rank, from greatest to smallest, the magnitudes of the torques about the wrench head in Figure P12.6 caused by exerting the same force at the different positions shown. ••

Figure P12.6

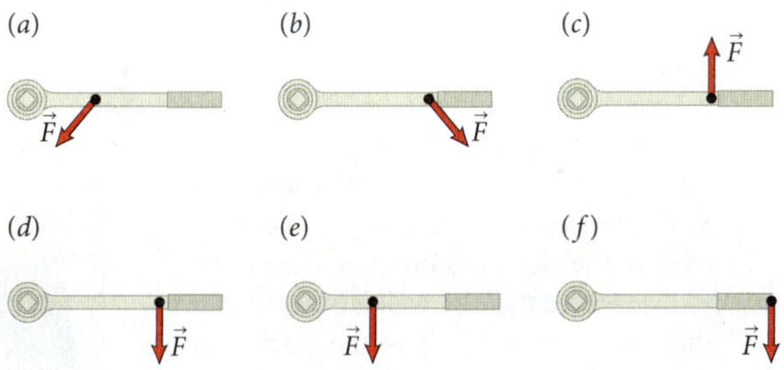

7. Which way is easier to balance the asymmetrical baton of Figure P12.7 on your finger? Explain your choice. ••

Figure P12.7

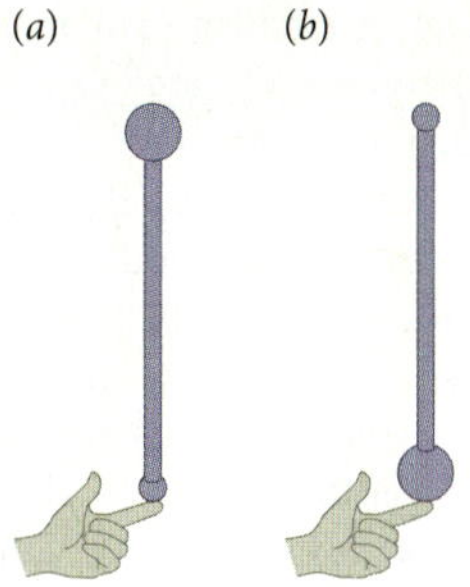

8. Explain why, when a car makes a sharp turn on an unbanked road, the wheels on the inside of the turn tend to come off the ground. ••
9. Figure P12.9 is a top view of a hand-driven carousel in a park. Four parents of the children riding on the device each push on the carousel in different ways. The forces exerted by each of the four parents and the positions at which the forces are exerted are labeled A–D. Rank the parents' pushes in order of increasing torque they cause on the carousel. ••

Figure P12.9

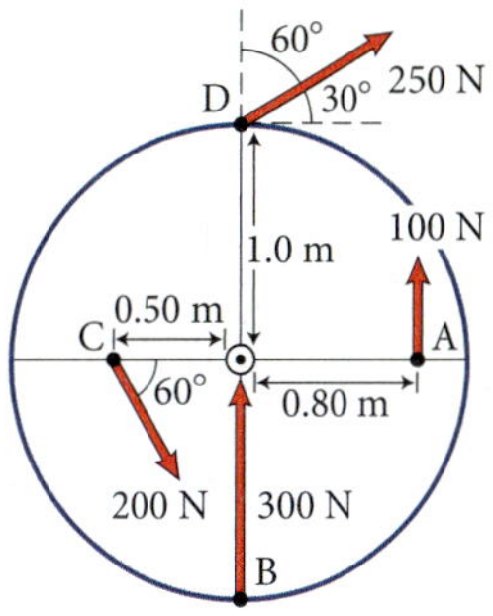

10. The uniform rod shown in Figure P12.10 is fixed to an axis going through its center, so that it is free to rotate clockwise or counterclockwise. It has four hooks: one at each end of the rod and one halfway between the center (axis) and each end. You need to hang four objects from this rod, with one and only one object on each hook, after which the rod must be balanced. The objects have masses M, $3M$, $5M$, and $9M$, respectively. How can this be accomplished? •••

Figure P12.10

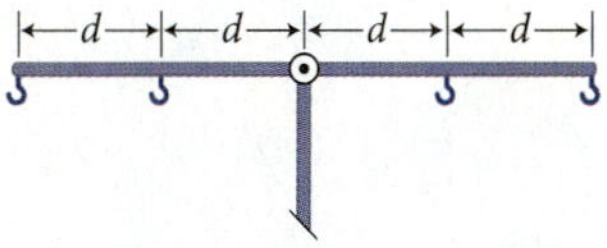

12.2 Free rotation

11. A very thin bar of length ℓ and negligible inertia connects two blocks A and B that have inertias $4m$ and m, respectively (Figure P12.11). When this rod-block system is made to spin with no translational motion and no mechanical pivot, each block moves through a circular path in space, with circumferences C_A and C_B. Determine the ratio C_A/C_B. ••

Figure P12.11

12. The system shown in Figure P12.12 consists of two balls A and B connected by a thin rod of negligible mass. Ball A has three times the inertia of ball B and the distance between the two balls is ℓ. If the system has a translational velocity of v in the x direction and is spinning counterclockwise at an angular speed of $\omega = 2v/\ell$, determine the ratio of the instantaneous speeds of the two balls v_A/v_B at the moment shown. ••

Figure P12.12

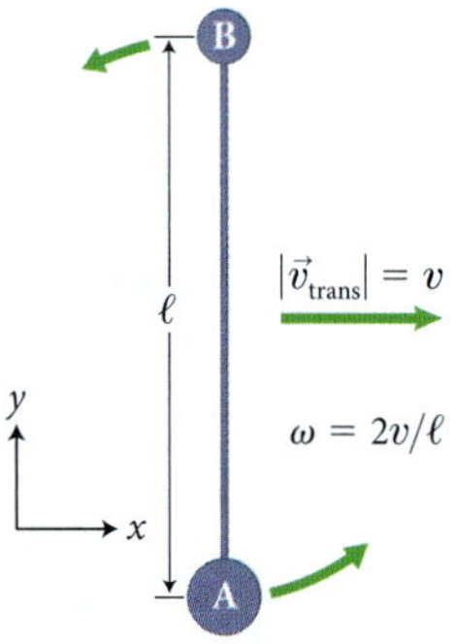

13. Put your index fingers about 1 m apart and rest a meterstick or similar object on top of them. Then, while holding the meterstick parallel to the floor, slowly draw your fingers toward each other. You will find that first one finger slips easily under the stick, then the other finger, then the first one again, then the other one again. No matter how much alternating takes place, however, your fingers *always* meet at the center of the stick. Explain what is happening. •••

12.3 Extended free-body diagrams

14. To change a light bulb, you climb halfway up a stepladder. Draw an extended free-body diagram for the ladder. •
15. Which refrigerator in Figure P12.15 is in the greatest danger of tipping over? Note positions of center of mass. •

Figure P12.15

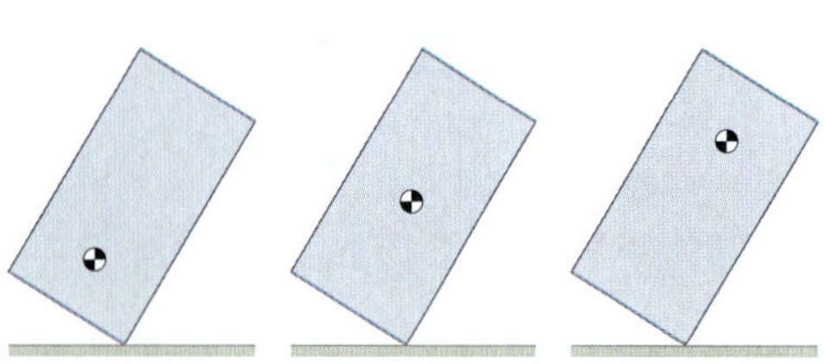

16. Which configuration of the four uniform boxes in Figure P12.16 makes the hand-truck easier to handle? Explain your answer. ••

Figure P12.16

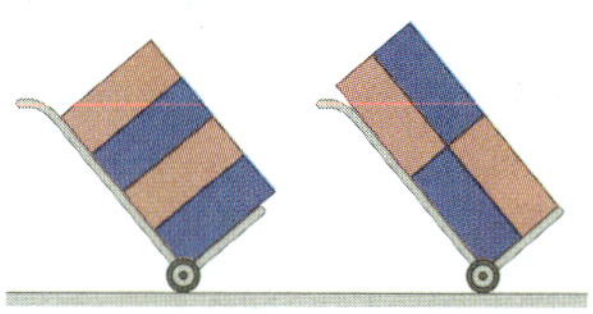

17. A father and son are carrying a sofa down the stairs, with the son leading. Consider the sofa's center of mass to be at the geometric center. (*a*) Draw an extended free-body diagram for the sofa. (*b*) Who carries the greater share of the load? (*c*) Would your answer to part *b* be the same if, instead of the sofa, the men were carrying a sheet of plywood? ••
18. In the mobile in Figure P12.18, what are the inertias of the giraffe and of the elephant in terms of the inertia m_m of the monkey? ••

Figure P12.18

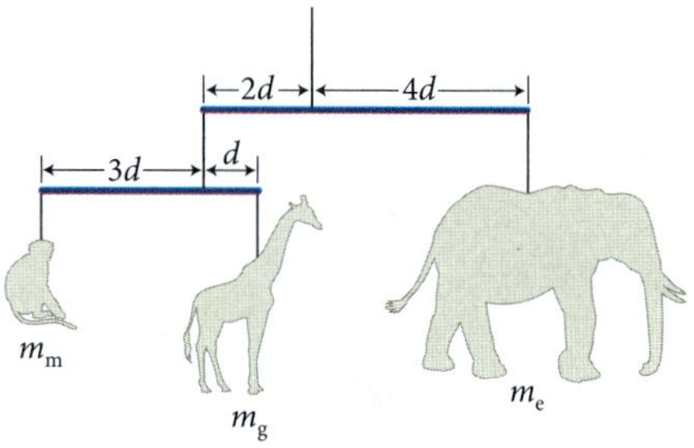

19. A painter leans a ladder at some angle against a smooth wall, with the foot of the ladder resting on wall-to-wall carpeting. Why might the ladder slip as he climbs it? ••
20. You are pushing a cart across the room, and the cart has wheels at the front and the back. Your hands are placed on top of the cart at the center (left to right) of the top edge, pushing horizontally. There is friction between the wheels and the floor. Is the normal force between the floor and the front wheels greater than, smaller than, or equal to the normal force between the floor and the rear wheels? Explain your answer using an extended free-body diagram. ••
21. The top of a ladder of inertia m rests against a smooth wall, and the foot rests on the ground. The coefficient of static friction between ground and ladder is μ_s. What is the smallest angle between the ground and the ladder such that the ladder does not slip? •••
22. A square clock of inertia m is hung on a nail driven into a wall (Figure P12.22). The length of each side of the square is ℓ, the thickness is w, and the top back edge of the clock is a distance d from the wall. Assume that the wall is smooth and that the center of mass of the clock is at the geometric center. Obtain an expression for the magnitude of the normal force exerted by the wall on the clock. •••

Figure P12.22

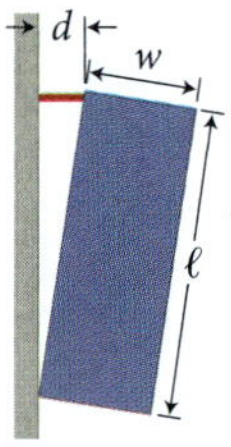

12.4 The vectorial nature of rotation

23. Beginning mechanics sometimes are taught a rule for tightening and untightening bolts: Righty-tighty, lefty-loosey. Explain why this memory device works. •

24. What is the direction of the rotational velocity vector of the jar lid when you open a jar of pickles? •

25. Gear A in Figure P12.25 is spinning such that its rotational velocity vector points in the negative x direction. It is lowered so that its edge comes in contact with the edge of gear B. What is the direction of the rotational velocity caused by the force that A exerts on B? •

Figure P12.25

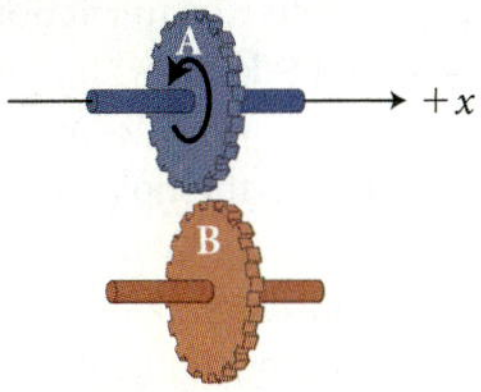

26. An experienced pool player can control the placement of a ball after it hits an edge bumper by putting spin, or "English," on the ball. This is accomplished by aiming the cue stick so that it hits the ball either left or right of the ball's center. Suppose a player gives a ball English by hitting it to the left of center (left from his perspective). Which path in Figure P12.26 does the ball take after it collides with the bumper? Account for this behavior. ••

Figure P12.26

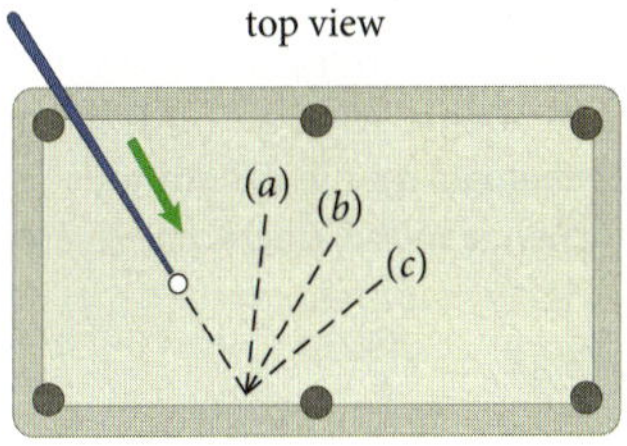

27. The beach ball shown in Figure P12.27 undergoes a rotation of 90° around the x axis and then a rotation of 90° around the y axis. A second, identically colored ball undergoes first the rotation of 90° around the y axis and then the 90° rotation around the x axis. What additional rotations are necessary to put the second ball in exactly the same orientation as the first? ••

Figure P12.27

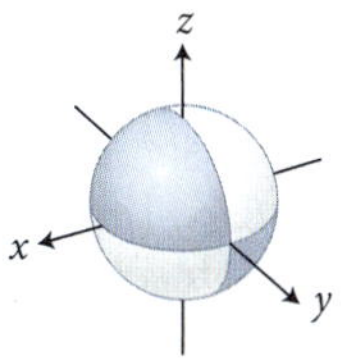

12.5 Conservation of angular momentum

28. Why do quarterbacks throw the football with significant spin about its long axis? •

29. A 1.5-m uniform rod is being used to balance two buckets of paint, each of inertia m, one at each end of the rod. (a) Where is the pivot located? (b) If paint is removed from one bucket until its inertia is $m/4$, where must the pivot now be placed in order to keep the rod balanced? Ignore the inertia of the rod. •

30. A 0.20-kg turntable of radius 0.20 m spins about a vertical axis through its center. A constant rotational acceleration causes the turntable to accelerate from 0 to 28 revolutions per second in 8.0 s. Calculate (a) the rotational acceleration and (b) the torque required to cause this acceleration. •

31. A 44-kg child runs at 3.0 m/s tangent to a stationary 180-kg playground merry-go-round that has a radius of 1.2 m. The child then jumps on and grabs hold, causing the merry-go-round to rotate. Determine the resulting rotational velocity of the merry-go-round. ••

32. Standing on the edge of a rotating playground carousel, you take sight on the center of the carousel and walk directly toward that position. (a) What happens to the rotational speed of the carousel as you walk? (b) In the system consisting of only the carousel (a nonisolated system), any change in angular momentum is due to a torque. Because the hub of the carousel is well lubricated, the only candidate for what causes this torque is the force of friction exerted by your feet on the carousel. "But," you say, "I walked radially inward. How could I possibly cause a torque with my feet?" What's going on? ••

33. Standing with your toes touching the base of a wall, press your nose to the wall and try to stand on tiptoe. What happens and why? ••

34. Draw the angular momentum vector for a tetherball, taking as your origin the center of the pole. Is the angular momentum constant? If not, what force causes the torque that changes the angular momentum? ••

35. Imagine that an asteroid 1 km in diameter collides with Earth. Estimate the maximum fractional change in the length of the day due to this collision. ••

36. You want to hang a 10-kg sign that advertises your new business. To do this, you use a pivot to attach the base of a 5.0-kg beam to a wall (Figure P12.36). You then attach a cable to the beam and to the wall in such a way that the cable and beam are perpendicular to each other. The beam is 2.0 m long and makes an angle of 37° with the vertical. You hang the sign from the end of the beam to which the cable is attached. (a) What must be the minimum tensile strength of the cable (the minimum amount of tension it can sustain) if it is not to snap? (b) Determine the horizontal and vertical components of the force exerted by the pivot on the beam. ••

Figure P12.36

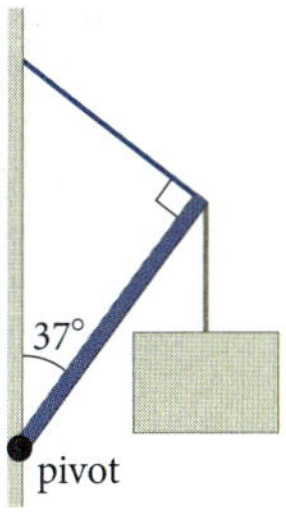

37. The top end of a two-by-four piece of lumber that is 3.0 m long is leaned at a height of 1.8 m against a smooth wall so that the bottom end makes an angle of 37° with the floor. If this board has an inertia of 4.6 kg, what are (a) the normal force exerted by the floor on it and (b) the normal force exerted by the wall on it? ••

38. Your physics instructor calls you up to the front of the class to be a demonstration assistant. She has you stand on a turntable that is free to rotate and hands you a spinning bicycle wheel, as shown in Figure P12.38. Letting go of the top of the wheel's axle, you then stop its spinning with your free hand. What happens when you stop the wheel? ••

Figure P12.38

PRACTICE

39. Helicopters have a small tail rotor as well as the large main rotor. Why is the tail rotor needed? ••

40. A 35-kg child stands on the edge of a 400-kg playground merry-go-round that is turning at the rate of 1 rev every 2.2 s. He then walks to the center of the platform. If the radius of the platform is 1.5 m, what is its rotational speed once he arrives at the center? ••

41. An ice figure skater starts out spinning at 0.85 revolutions per second with her arms outstretched, as shown in Figure P12.41. She wears lightly weighted bracelets to enhance the spin-up effect when she pulls her arms in. (*a*) Calculate her final rotational speed if her rotational inertia is 3.6 kg · m^2 with her arms outstretched and 1.1 kg · m^2 with her arms pulled close to her body. (*b*) Determine the increase in her rotational kinetic energy. (*c*) Where does this added energy come from? ••

Figure P12.41

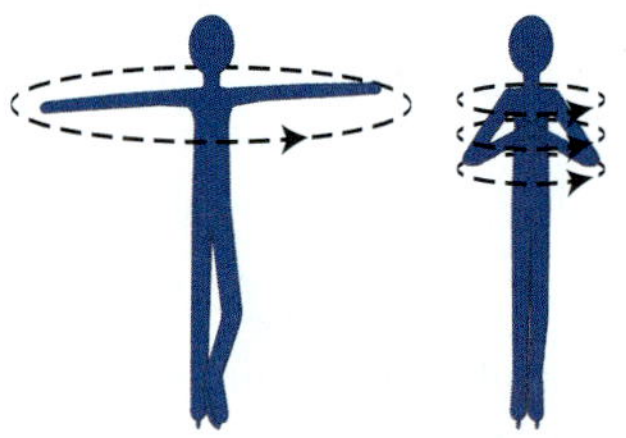

42. A 25-kg child starts at the center of a playground merry-go-round that has a radius of 2.0 m and rotational inertia of 500 kg · m^2 and walks out to the edge. If the merry-go-round has a rotational speed of 0.20 s^{-1} when she is at the center, what is its rotational speed when she gets to the edge? ••

43. In the setup in Figure P12.43, does pulling the string downward while the ball is revolving make the following properties of the ball increase, decrease, or stay the same: (*a*) angular momentum, (*b*) rotational speed, (*c*) rotational kinetic energy? ••

Figure P12.43

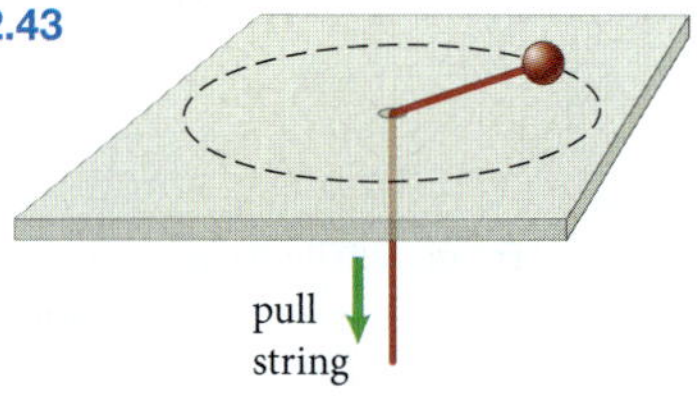

44. Your physics instructor has you sit on a chair that is free to rotate and hands you a spinning bicycle wheel (Figure P12.44). What happens when you flip the wheel over so that the end of the axle that initially pointed up now points down? ••

Figure P12.44

45. A putty ball of inertia m moving at speed v slides on a slick surface along a path that is perpendicular to the long axis of a rod of length ℓ and inertia $2m$ that is at rest on the surface. The ball collides with one end of the rod and sticks to it. (*a*) Just as the ball sticks, where is the center of mass of the ball-rod system? After the collision, (*b*) what are the magnitude and direction of the velocity of the center of mass and (*c*) what is the rotational speed of the system? Ignore any effects due to friction. •••

46. A 4.5-kg bowling ball is perched on a concrete ledge directly below your dorm room window, with the side of the ball opposite the holes touching the wall. Wanting to hold the ball in place so that it doesn't roll off and land on somebody, you manage to hook one of the holes with a wire and exert a purely tangential (and vertical) force on the ball. If the coefficient of static friction between ball and ledge is the same as that between ball and wall, $\mu_s = 0.50$, what is the maximum upward force you can exert so that the ball does not rotate and you lose your hold? Even though the ball has holes drilled in it, assume a uniform distribution of inertia. •••

47. Disk A in Figure P12.47 has radius R_A and thickness h and is initially rotating clockwise, as viewed from above, at $\omega_i/2$. Disk B, made of the same material as A, has radius $R_B = R_A/2$ and thickness h and is initially rotating counterclockwise at ω_i. The two disks are constrained to rotate about the same axis, which runs through their centers. There is friction between the disks, and so once B slides down and touches A, they spin at the same rotational speed. (*a*) What is their common final rotational velocity? (*b*) If the frictional force is the only force that causes the system to lose energy, what is the fractional change in the kinetic energy? •••

Figure P12.47

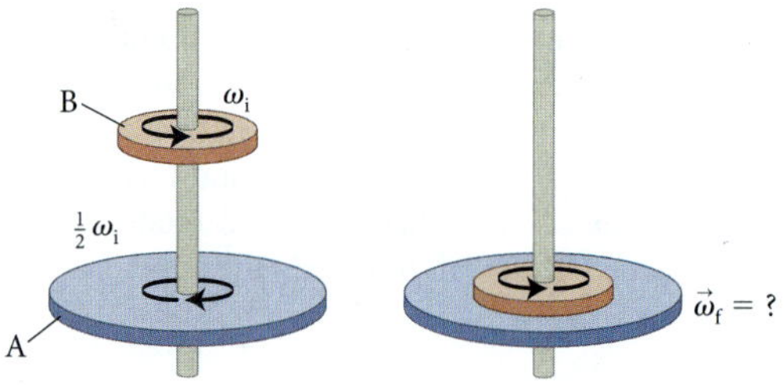

48. A 25-kg ladder of length 5.0 m leans against a smooth wall and makes an angle of 50° with the ground. A 75-kg man starts to climb the ladder. If the coefficient of static friction between ground and ladder is 0.50, what distance along the ladder can the man climb before the ladder starts to slip? •••

12.6 Rolling motion

49. An object rolls without slipping onto a surface where the coefficient of friction between object and surface is twice as great as that needed to prevent slipping. Describe the subsequent motion. •

50. To get better acceleration, you want to reduce the inertia of your bicycle. You have your choice of spending $45 on only one of three light-alloy items, each reducing the inertia of your bicycle by the same amount: a new seat post, a new set of pedals, or a new set of wheel rims. Which is the best buy? •

51. A 3.0-kg solid ball rolls without slipping down a ramp inclined to the horizontal at an angle of 30°. What are (*a*) the acceleration of the ball's center of mass and (*b*) the magnitude of the frictional force exerted on the ball? ••

52. A 5.0-kg solid cylinder of radius 0.25 m is free to rotate about an axle that runs along the cylinder length and passes through its center. A thread wrapped around the cylinder is pulled straight from the cylinder so as to unwrap with a steady tensile force of 20 N. As the thread unwinds, the cylinder rotates and there is no slippage between thread and cylinder. If the cylinder starts from rest at $t_i = 0$, calculate (*a*) its rotational velocity at $t_f = 5.0$ s and (*b*) the angle through which it has turned at $t_f = 5.0$ s. Ignore any friction in the axle. ••

53. A disk and a hoop roll down an inclined plane. If the plane is inclined at an angle of 30° from the horizontal, what is the minimum coefficient of friction required so that neither object slips? ••

54. A 2.0-kg solid cylinder of radius 0.45 m rolls without slipping down a ramp inclined at an angle of 60° to the vertical. Calculate (*a*) the acceleration of the cylinder's center of mass, (*b*) the cylinder's rotational acceleration, and (*c*) the time interval required for it to travel 35 m down the incline if it starts from rest. (*d*) What is the rotational velocity of the cylinder at the end of the time interval found in part *c*? ••

55. Two cans of pumpkin roll down a loading dock ramp. They have identical inertias, but one of them has a larger radius (and a shorter length) than the other. Which one, if either, makes it down the ramp first? ••

56. You deliver a horizontal impulse to a cue ball with a cue stick while playing pool. If the ball is to roll without slipping, at what height h above its center (in terms of its radius R) must you strike it? •••

57. Two balls of the same radius and same inertia roll down an inclined plane, starting from rest. One ball is hollow, and the other is solid. What is the ratio of the time intervals the two balls require to reach the bottom? ••

58. In the Atwood machine shown in Figure P12.58, the pulley radius is 0.10 m, and the rotational inertia of the pulley is 0.15 kg · m². Calculate (*a*) the acceleration of the blocks, (*b*) the tension in the cord on the left, and (*c*) the tension in the cord on the right. Ignore the cord's inertia. •••

Figure P12.58

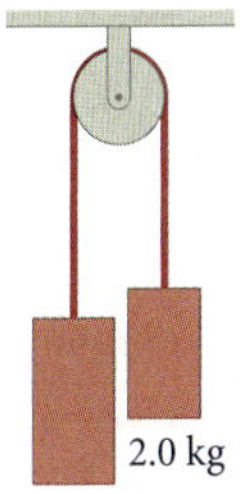

59. A block of inertia m sits on a smooth surface (Figure P12.59). A light string is attached to it and placed over a solid pulley of inertia $3m$ and radius R, and a ball of inertia m is attached to the free end of the string. (*a*) If there is no slippage between string and pulley, determine the magnitude of the block's acceleration. (*b*) If you detach the ball and pull down on the hanging string with a force of magnitude mg, what is the magnitude of the block's acceleration? •••

Figure P12.59

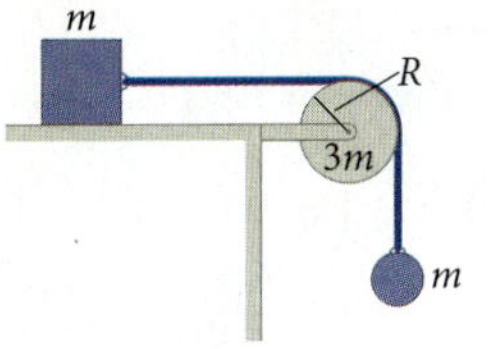

60. A 320-g can of soup is 10.8 cm tall and has a radius of 3.19 cm. (*a*) Calculate the can's rotational inertia about its axis of symmetry, assuming the can to be a solid cylinder. (*b*) When released from rest at the top of a ramp that is 3.00 m long and makes an angle of 25° with the horizontal, the can reaches the bottom in 1.40 s. What is the value of rotational inertia obtained from this experiment? (*c*) Compare the calculated and experimentally determined rotational inertias and suggest possible reasons for the difference. •••

12.7 Torque and energy

61. A 0.20-kg solid cylinder is released from rest at the top of a ramp 1.0 m long. The cylinder has a radius of 0.15 m, and the ramp is at an angle of 15° with the horizontal. What is the rotational kinetic energy of the cylinder when it reaches the bottom of the ramp? •

62. A solid 50-kg cylinder has a radius of 0.10 m. What minimum work is required to get the cylinder rolling without slipping at a rotational speed of 20 s^{-1}? •

63. A 1.0-kg ring with an inner radius of 0.060 m and an outer radius of 0.080 m is sent rolling without slipping up a ramp that makes an angle of 30° with the horizontal. If the initial speed of the ring is 2.8 m/s, how far along the ramp does it travel before it comes to a stop? ••

64. A certain car engine delivers enough force to create 380 N · m of torque when the engine is operating at 3200 revolutions per minute. Calculate the average power delivered by the engine at this rotation rate. ••

65. A 680-kg disk of radius 1.2 m is mounted on a fixed axle. A force exerted on the disk causes a constant torque that gives the disk a rotational acceleration magnitude of 0.30 s^{-2} for 5.0 s. If the disk had an initial rotational speed of 4.5 s^{-1}, how much work was done to provide the torque, assuming no energy is lost to friction? ••

66. A large steel bar of length ℓ is hinged at one end to a wall. A mechanic holds the other end so that the bar is parallel to the ground and places a penny on the bar right at the end he is holding. (*a*) What is the rotational acceleration of the bar when he lets go? (*b*) Does the penny remain in contact with the bar after it is released? ••

67. A light, unstretchable string is wound around the perimeter of a 4.0-kg disk that has a radius of 0.50 m and is free to rotate about an axle that runs perpendicular to the disk face and through the disk center. A 2.0-kg block is connected to the free end of the string and allowed to slide down a ramp that makes an angle of $\theta = 37°$ with the vertical (Figure P12.67). Calculate the magnitude of the disk's rotational acceleration. Ignore friction between block and ramp. ••

Figure P12.67

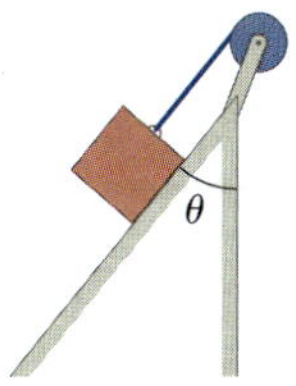

68. A 5.0-kg hollow cylinder of radius 0.25 m rotates freely about an axle that runs through its center and along its long axis. A cord is wrapped around the cylinder and is pulled straight from the cylinder with a steady tensile force of 50 N. As the cord unwinds, the cylinder rotates, with no slippage between cord and cylinder. (*a*) Calculate the work done by the tensile force as the cylinder rotates through 1000 rad. (*b*) If the cylinder starts from rest, calculate its rotational speed after it has rotated through 1000 rad. ••

69. A marble of inertia m is held against the side of a hemispherical bowl as shown in Figure P12.69 and then released. It rolls without slipping. The initial position of the marble is such that an imaginary line drawn from it to the center of curvature of the bowl makes an angle of 30° with the vertical. The marble radius is $R_m = 10$ mm, and the radius of the bowl is $R_b = 100$ mm. Determine the rotational speed of the marble about its center of mass when it reaches the bottom. ••

Figure P12.69

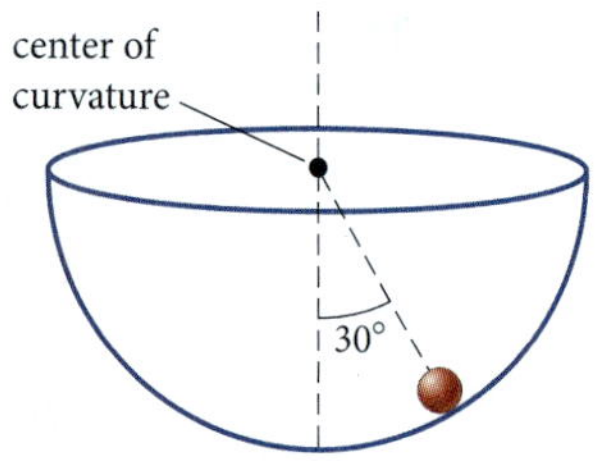

70. A 3.0-kg disk of radius 50 mm rolls down a ramp inclined at an angle of 28° with the vertical. If the disk starts out at rest and the coefficients of static and kinetic friction between the ramp and the disk are both 0.50, what is the rotational speed of the disk after it has traveled 1.5 m? ••

71. An almost-conical toy top (Figure P12.71) that has radius $R = 20$ mm and inertia 0.125 kg is spun up using a force of 5.0 N and a string that is 1.0 m long. What are (*a*) the work done on the top, (*b*) its kinetic energy, and (*c*) its final rotational speed? The shape factor for this top about its axis of symmetry is 0.35. ••

Figure P12.71

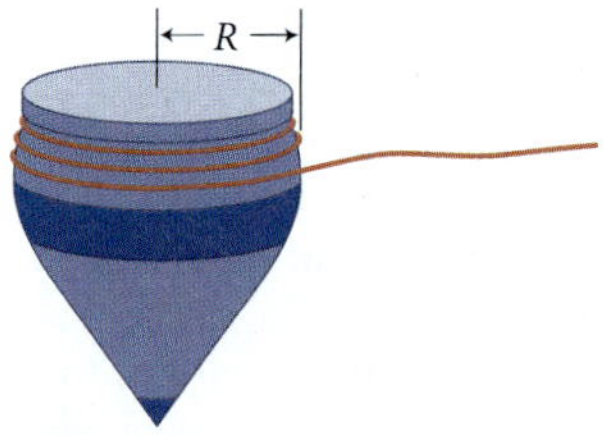

72. Archimedes' screw, one of the first mechanical devices invented for lifting water, is a very large screw fitted tightly inside a shaft (Figure P12.72). The bottom of the device is placed in a pool of water. As someone turns the handle to make the screw turn, water is carried up along the ridges of the screw and comes out the top of the shaft and into a storage tank. As the handle turns, the work done by the force exerted on the handle is converted to gravitational potential energy of the water-Earth system. Let's say you want to take a shower using this device. You figure that your shower will use 44 L of water, and so you have to raise this amount to the storage tank 2.5 m above the pool. Every time you turn the handle, you exert a force that causes a torque of 12 N · m. How many times must you turn the handle? ••

Figure P12.72

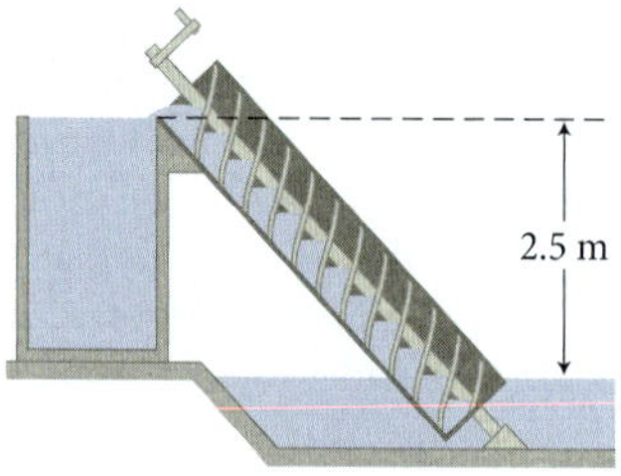

73. You attach a 0.50-m length of string to a 50-g puck and pass the other end of the string through a hole in the center of a table. Grasping the string under the table, you pull just enough string through the hole so that, when your friend gives the puck a sideways push, it moves in a circle of radius $r_i = 0.45$ m at 1.5 m/s. You then slowly pull on the string, decreasing the circle's radius to 0.20 m. (*a*) What is the puck's speed when $r = 0.20$ m? (*b*) What is the tension in the string as a function of r? What is its value when $r = 0.20$ m? (*c*) How much work is done in moving the puck from the 0.45-m circle to the 0.20-m circle? ••

74. A 30-kg solid sphere of radius 0.12 m is rolling without slipping on a horizontal surface at 2.0 m/s. (*a*) What average torque is required to stop the sphere in 5.0 rev without inducing skidding? (*b*) If this torque is caused by a soft braking bumper that is lowered down until it just makes contact with the top of the sphere, what is the magnitude of the frictional force between bumper and sphere? •••

75. A marble that has a radius of 10 mm is placed at the top of a globe of radius 0.80 m. When released, the marble rolls without slipping down the globe. Determine the angle from the top of the globe to the location where the marble flies off the globe. •••

76. A 4.0-kg bowling ball is thrown down the alley with a speed of 10.0 m/s. At first the ball slides with no rotation. The coefficient of friction between ball and alley surface is 0.20. (*a*) How long a time interval does it take for the ball to achieve pure rolling motion? (*b*) What is the ball's translational speed at the end of this time interval? •••

77. You shove a cube of inertia m and side length d so that it slides along a smooth table with speed v_i (Figure P12.77*a*). The cube then hits a raised lip at the end of the table. After it hits the lip, the cube begins to rotate about it (Figure 12.77*b*). (*a*) Show that the magnitude of the cube's angular momentum about the lip before the collision is $L = mdv_i/2$. (*b*) Explain why the angular momentum still has that value at the instant of collision, before the cube has had time to rotate much. (*c*) What is the rotational acceleration of the cube the instant after it hits the lip? (d) What maximum initial speed can the cube have so that it does not topple over the lip? •••

Figure P12.77

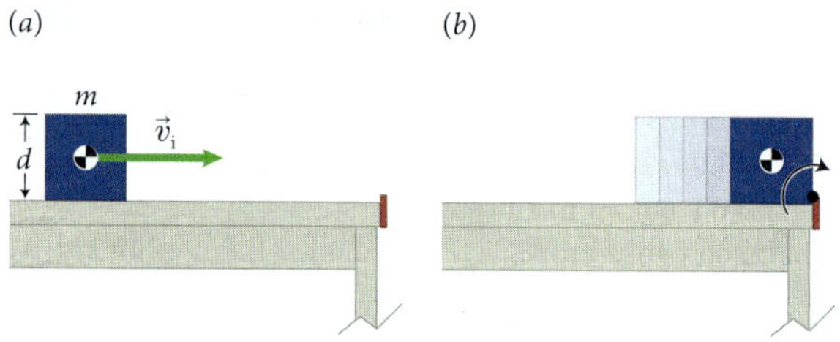

PRACTICE

12.8 The vector product

78. Which of the following expressions make sense: (*a*) $\vec{A} \cdot (\vec{B} \times \vec{C})$, (*b*) $\vec{A} \times (\vec{B} \cdot \vec{C})$, (*c*) $\vec{A} \times (\vec{B} \times \vec{C})$? •

79. When you want to turn a bicycle left, the first thing you do is lean left. Why is it important to do this? •

80. If the magnitude of the vector product of two vectors is the same as the magnitude of the scalar product of the same two vectors, what is the angle between them? •

81. A cyclist exerts a vertical force on a bike pedal. This pedal is at the end of a crank that is 0.20 m long and pivoted to rotate about the axle of the chain wheel. If the cyclist pushes downward with a force of 150 N, determine the magnitude of the torque caused by this force when the crank is (*a*) horizontal, (*b*) 30° from the horizontal, (*c*) 45° from the horizontal, (*d*) 60° from the horizontal, and (*e*) vertical. (*f*) Calculate the average magnitude of this torque exerted by one of the cyclist's feet during one cycle of the pedals, assuming there is no clip holding the cyclist's feet to the pedals. ••

82. The two arms of the L-shaped handle on the spigot of Figure P12.82 have a length ratio of $1:\sqrt{3}$. At what angle θ do you want to pull down on the end of the handle to maximize the torque your force causes? ••

Figure P12.82

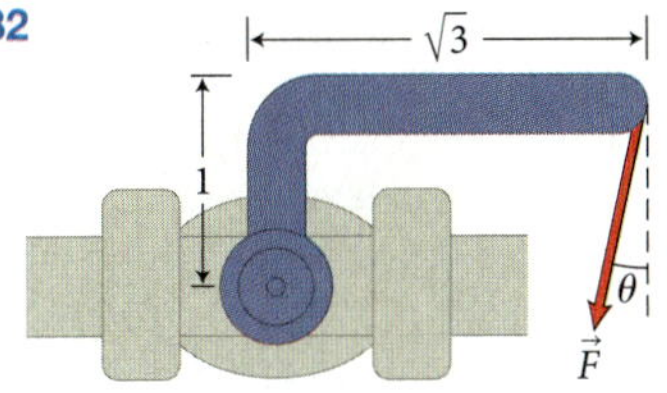

83. Show that, if vectors $\vec{A}$ and $\vec{B}$ are both in an xy plane, $\vec{A} \times \vec{B}$ is a vector that is perpendicular to the xy plane and has magnitude $|\vec{A} \times \vec{B}| = |A_xB_y - A_yB_x|$. ••

84. A 3.0-kg rod that is 1.5 m long is free to rotate in a vertical plane about an axle that runs through the rod's center, is perpendicular to the rod's length, and runs parallel to the floor. A 1.0-kg block is attached to one end of the rod, and a 2.0-kg block is attached to the other end. At some instant, the rod makes an angle of 30° with the horizontal so that the blocks are in the positions shown in Figure P12.84. (*a*) Determine the torque caused by the forces exerted on the system at this instant. (*b*) Determine the rotational acceleration of the system at this instant. Ignore friction and assume the blocks are small enough that any length they add to the rod can be ignored. ••

Figure P12.84

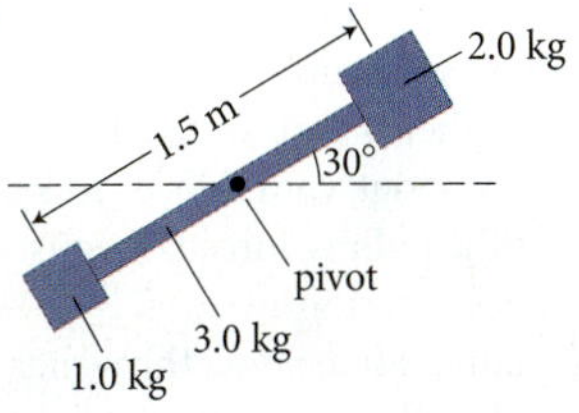

85. A motor drives a disk initially at rest through 23.9 rotations in 5.0 s. Assume the vector sum of the torques caused by the force exerted by the motor and the force of friction is constant. The rotational inertia of the disk is 4.0 kg · m². When the motor is switched off, the disk comes to rest in 12 s. (*a*) What is the torque created by the force of friction? (*b*) What is the torque caused by the force exerted by the motor? ••

86. The angular momentum of the propellers of a small airplane points directly forward from the plane. (*a*) In what direction do the propellers rotate as seen from the rear of the plane? (*b*) If the plane is flying horizontally and suddenly pulls upward, in which direction does the nose of the plane tend to move? Justify your answer. ••

87. A 40-kg sharpening wheel of radius 0.10 m is rotating at 3.3 revolutions per second. A 6.0-kg axe is pressed against the rim with a force of 40 N directed as shown in Figure P12.87. Treat the wheel as a disk, and assume a coefficient of kinetic friction between wheel and axe blade of $\mu_k = 0.35$. (*a*) If there is no power source keeping the wheel rotating, how long does it take to stop? (*b*) How many revolutions does the wheel make while it is slowing down? ••

Figure P12.87

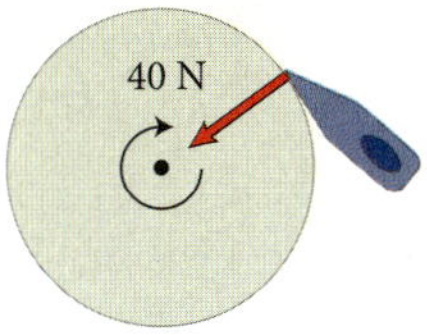

88. A heavy-rimmed bicycle wheel is set spinning in the direction shown in Figure P12.88. A string is tied to one end of the axle, and someone is holding up the string. (*a*) Use torque arguments to explain why the wheel slowly revolves horizontally around the string end of the axle when the free end of the axle is released. (This effect is called *precession*.) (*b*) The precession speed increases as time passes. Explain why. •••

Figure P12.88

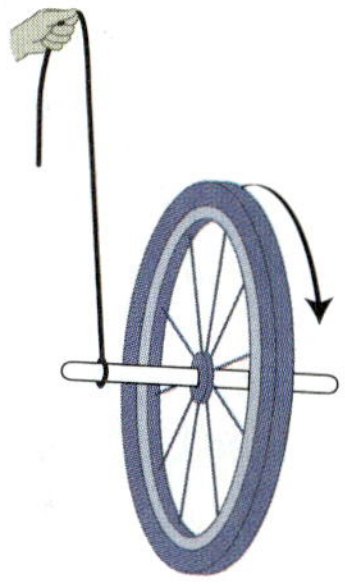

89. A gyroscope consists of a spinning wheel mounted inside a support structure (Figure P12.89). Because of conservation of angular momentum, the gyroscope keeps its orientation in space unless some outside force causes a torque on it. Suppose the 1.0-kg spinning wheel of a certain gyroscope has a radius of 0.10 m and is spinning at 14,200 revolutions per minute. What is the magnitude of the torque required to tilt the gyroscope 90° in 20 s such that the spin speed is still 14,200 revolutions per minute when the gyroscope is in its new orientation? •••

Figure P12.89

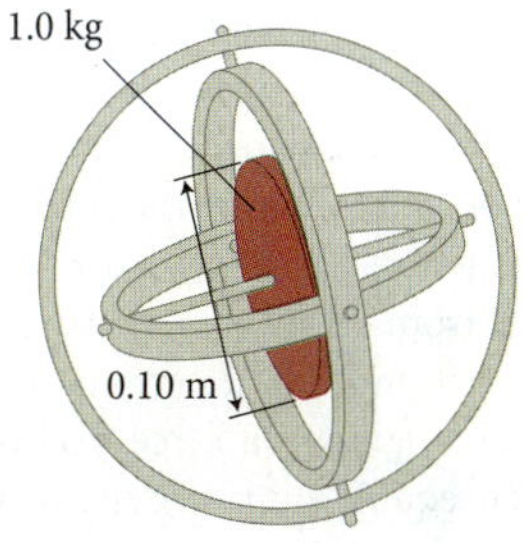

Additional Problems

90. Two identical boxes are placed on opposite ends of the board of a playground seesaw as in Figure P12.90*a*, so that the system is in mechanical equilibrium. (*a*) What happens to that equilibrium if you exert a small, brief force, either upward or downward, on either end of the board? (*b*) With the boxes attached to the underside of the board as in Figure P12.90*b* and the system again in mechanical equilibrium, what happens to the equilibrium if you exert such a force on either end? •

Figure P12.90

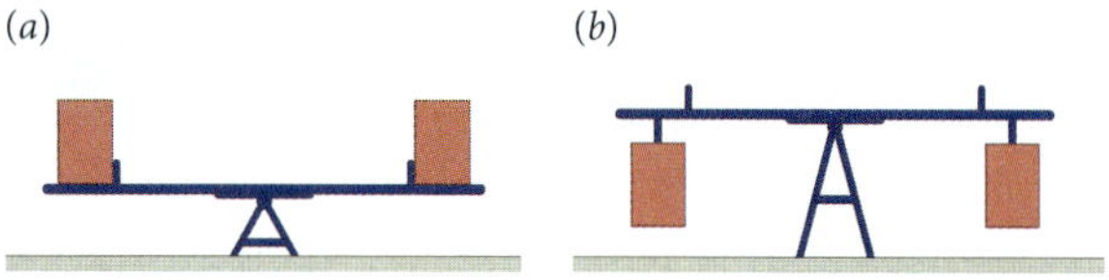

91. For the x and y axes of a right-handed Cartesian coordinate system, what is the direction of $\hat{\imath} \times \{\hat{\imath} \times [\hat{\imath} \times (\hat{\imath} \times \hat{\jmath})]\}$? •
92. Standing on a round raft floating on a pond, how do you turn the raft around 180°? •
93. Dragster drivers have to avoid supplying too much power to the vehicle because too much power causes the front end to rise in a "wheelie," compromising steering control. (*a*) Why does this happen? (*b*) What advantage comes from having front-wheel drive in a dragster? ••
94. If everyone on Earth simultaneously walked from west to east, by what fraction would the length of the day change? Would it lengthen or shorten? ••
95. A 51-kg box is suspended from the right end of a horizontal rod that has very small inertia. The left end of the rod is affixed to a wall by a pin. A wire connects the right end of the rod to the wall directly above the pin, making an angle of 40° with the rod. (*a*) Calculate the tension in the wire. (*b*) Determine the magnitude of the reaction force the pivot exerts on the rod. (*c*) Repeat parts *a* and *b* for a 10.2-kg rod. ••
96. A 35-kg child stands on the edge of a playground merry-go-round that has a radius of 2.0 m and a rotational inertia of 500 kg · m^2. The merry-go-round has a rotational speed of 0.20 s^{-1} when the child is standing still. If the rotational speed increases to 0.25 s^{-1} when the child starts walking along the edge, with what speed is he walking in the reference frame of the merry-go-round, and in which direction? ••
97. A neutron star is the compact remnant of a very large star that has exploded. Suppose that right after one such explosion, when much of the star's inertia has been blasted away, the star's remaining core has an inertia of 4×10^{30} kg, a radius of 13×10^8 m, and completes one revolution every five days. What is the new spin rate once the core gravitationally collapses into a neutron star of radius 20 km? Assume negligible loss of inertia during the collapse. ••
98. A horizontal 2.0-kg rod is 2.0 m long. An 8.0-kg block is suspended from its left end, and a 4.0-kg block is suspended from its right end. (*a*) Determine the magnitude and direction of the single extra force necessary to keep the rod in mechanical equilibrium. (*b*) At what distance from the left end of the rod must the point of application of this force be? ••
99. What maximum torque can a bicyclist deliver to the pedals? ••
100. A solid ball of inertia m rolls without slipping down a ramp that makes an angle θ with the horizontal. (*a*) What frictional force is exerted on the ball? (*b*) As a function of θ, what coefficient of friction is required to prevent slipping? ••
101. You make a lawn roller out of a 125-kg solid cylinder, set to rotate about a central axle. You rig up handles on either side of the axle so that you and a friend can pull on the handles horizontally to pull the roller in a direction perpendicular to its rotation axis (Figure P12.101). (*a*) If each of you pulls with a horizontal force of 500 N, what is the magnitude a of the roller's acceleration? (*b*) What is the minimum coefficient of static friction necessary to keep the roller from slipping? ••

Figure P12.101

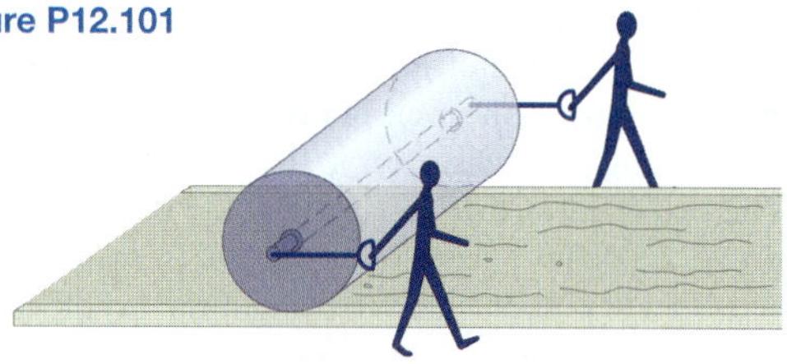

102. A marble is shot across a smooth wooden floor so that the marble both rotates about a horizontal axis and slides. If at a certain instant the marble's rotational kinetic energy equals the translational kinetic energy of its center of mass, what is the ratio of its center-of-mass speed to the speed of a point on its "equator" associated with rotation? ••
103. A 12-kg cylinder of radius 0.10 m starts at rest and rolls without slipping down a ramp that is 6.0 m long and inclined at 30° to the horizontal. When the cylinder leaves the end of the ramp, it drops 5.0 m to the ground. At what horizontal distance from the end of the ramp does it land? ••
104. A child runs in a straight line tangent to a playground carousel, jumps on, and holds tight as the carousel begins to rotate. Which of the following statements is correct for this collision? (*a*) The coefficient of restitution is greater than 1 because there is now rotational energy where there was none before. (*b*) The coefficient of restitution is 1 because the system's translational kinetic energy is completely converted to rotational kinetic energy. (*c*) The coefficient of restitution is less than 1 because the sum of the translational and rotational kinetic energies in the final state is less than the sum in the initial state. (*d*) The coefficient of restitution cannot be defined in a system in which there is both translational motion and rotational motion. (*e*) Explain why all the answers except the one you chose are wrong. ••
105. In a judo hip throw, you pull your 60-kg opponent onto your back to bring her center of mass just above your hip and then rotate her about your hip. Assume that the lever arm distance of your grip on her is 0.30 m from your hip and that her rotational inertia about your hip is 15 kg m^2. (*a*) What is the magnitude of the pulling force you must exert on her to cause a rotational acceleration of 1.0 s^{-1}? (*b*) What is the magnitude of the pulling force if you throw her from a more upright position, so that the gravitational force has a lever arm of 0.12 m about your hip? •••

PRACTICE

106. You've been asked to design a flywheel and the associated emergency friction braking system for an electric vehicle. In order to fit the available space, the flywheel must be cast in the form of a solid steel disk with a thickness of 50 mm and a radius that cannot exceed 0.20 m. For safety purposes, the emergency braking system must slow the flywheel from 6000 revolutions per minute to 0 in 12 revolutions. You know that typical braking systems utilize a pair of "shoes" mounted on calipers to squeeze the thickness of the disc symmetrically near its edge, but you are concerned about how much force the brake shoes might have to exert on the disk. ••• CR

107. A 3.0-kg block is attached to one end of a light, unstretchable string that is wrapped securely around a cylinder that has a 0.30-m radius and a rotational inertia of $0.80\ \text{kg} \cdot \text{m}^2$. The cylinder is free to rotate about an axle aligned along its long axis. The block is held right alongside the cylinder (so there is essentially no unwound string) and then released from rest. As the block falls, it unwinds the string from the cylinder, with no slippage between string and cylinder. (*a*) Calculate the magnitude of the block's acceleration. (*b*) Calculate the rotational speed of the cylinder after the block has dropped 1.5 m. (Hint: First use the acceleration from part *a* to determine the block's speed.) (*c*) Use energy methods to obtain the cylinder's rotational speed after the block has dropped 1.5 m. (*d*) Calculate the tension in the string after the block has dropped this distance. (*e*) Calculate the instantaneous power delivered by the string and block to the cylinder after the block has dropped this distance. •••

108. You are building a pool table and want the design to be such that any ball that rolls into one of the side rails without slipping bounces off the rail and rolls away in another direction, again without slipping. After some experimenting, you decide that you must build the rails to a specific height that is some function of the radius of the balls. (Hint: It seems plausible to assume that the collision is elastic.) ••• CR

109. A yo-yo is composed of two disks of radius a, with many layers of string wrapped around the axle. The radial distance from the center of the axle to the top layer of string at any instant is b. With the end of the string wrapped around your finger and $b/a \approx 1$, you let the yo-yo drop, unwinding string and ultimately spinning pretty fast when it reaches the bottom of the string ($b/a \approx 0$). You begin to wonder how the motion of the yo-yo as the string unwinds depends on the value of b. ••• CR

Answers to Review Questions

1. Yes, because the torque magnitude depends not only on the magnitude of the force but also on the lever arm.
2. Not quite. The fact that the door moves the same distance in 2 s in both cases tells you that the rotational acceleration is the same in both cases, which means that the torque caused by your force must be the same as the torque caused by your friend's force. However, because the rotation axis runs along the hinged edge, the magnitude of your force must be greater than the magnitude of his force because the lever arm of your force is smaller than the lever arm of his force.
3. You may choose any reference point, though it is best to choose a reference point that simplifies the calculation by eliminating one or more unknowns from the torque calculation.
4. There are many examples. The normal force that the ground exerts on the rim of a bicycle tire (when the tire is vertical) is one example. The torque is zero because there is no component of the force perpendicular to the line of action. Similarly, if you pull on a door handle with a force whose line of action passes through the hinged edge, the door will not rotate.
5. No. Objects can be made to rotate or revolve about a specified point only by imposing a constraint, such as a hinge, pivot, or string. Free rotation is the absence of such constraints, so a freely rotating object will rotate about its center of mass.
6. The center of mass of an object or system moves as if all the inertia of the object or system were concentrated at that point. Hence, any free rotation occurs about an axis through the center of mass, allowing complicated motion to be expressed as two independent motions: the translational motion of the center of mass and the rotational motion around that point.
7. Primarily downward, with a small horizontal component toward the hand. One way to see this is to look at the stationary forearm. Being free to choose any pivot around which to sum torques, let's arbitrarily take the pivot to be at the hand. About this point, the torque caused by the force exerted by the biceps muscle on the forearm bone is clockwise from your perspective. To balance this clockwise torque exactly (remember that the arm is not rotating), the torque caused by the force exerted by the humerus on the forearm bone must be counterclockwise. To get this counterclockwise torque, the force causing it must be directed downward. Another viewpoint: If the biceps muscle pulls upward on the forearm, then the humerus must exert a downward force on the elbow-joint end of the forearm in order to prevent upward translation of that end.
8. An extended free-body diagram shows the location of the point of application of each force on the object in question, a necessity for computing torques. Torques are required in order to analyze rotational motion. A standard free-body diagram shows the forces as if the points of application of all of them were at a common point, which is fine for force computations.
9. It is possible to use the extended diagram for both forces and torques, but it is best to draw a standard free-body diagram first until you have gained a lot of experience. You are familiar with free-body diagrams, so just a glance at one will tell you whether the force components are capable of canceling or adding up to the required components of *ma*. The extended free-body diagram is less familiar and has the forces moved to remote locations rather than all tail to tail at one spot. If you accidentally leave one force off the extended free-body diagram, it will be much harder to tell at a glance that anything is wrong. Leaving out a force (or including an inapplicable force) leads to an erroneous result.
10. Curl the fingers of your right hand so that they follow the rotation of the object. Your thumb then points in the direction of the vector that specifies the direction of rotation.
11. The direction is into the wall, by the right-hand rule.
12. In three dimensions, rotations that appear clockwise from one perspective can appear counterclockwise from another.
13. The latter statement is correct. The former cannot be right because the units of force and torque aren't the same and so they can't be added.
14. Yes. As long as the single force is exerted, the momentum changes. As long as that force has a lever arm with respect to some pivot, the force causes a torque, which changes the angular momentum.
15. No. The momentum is not constant because a gravitational force is exerted on the baton. The baton is unconstrained and hence rotates about an axis through its center of mass. Because only a gravitational force is exerted on the baton while it is in the air, and this force is exerted straight downward on the center of mass, it causes no torque about that point. Thus the angular momentum is constant.
16. Rotational impulse represents the transfer of angular momentum between a system and its environment. It can be computed as the product of external torque and the time interval during which the torque is applied, quantified in the rotational impulse equation, $J_\vartheta = (\sum \tau_{\text{ext}\,\vartheta})\Delta t$. The angular momentum law, by analogy to the momentum law from translational motion, states that any change in the angular momentum of a system must be due to the rotational impulse caused by external torque: $\Delta L_\vartheta = J_\vartheta$.
17. Angular momentum is always conserved, which means it cannot be created or destroyed. The angular momentum of a system remains constant if the system is in rotational equilibrium. This occurs when the system is isolated or when the rotational impulse acting on the system is zero.
18. They are related by a factor of the radius of the wheel: $|v_{\text{cm}\,x}| = |R\omega_\vartheta|$.
19. When gears mesh, they turn without slipping, so the tangential speeds of the teeth of the two gears must be identical. The rotational speeds are generally not the same because they depend on the radii of the gears.
20. The shape factor is the ratio of an object's rotational inertia to the rotational inertia of a hoop of the same inertia m and radius R: $c = I/mR^2$. This factor compares the rotational inertia of an object with the rotational inertia if all the object's inertia were concentrated on its rim, so it measures the distribution of inertia in the object. This distribution is loosely referred to as "shape."
21. They are related by a factor of the object's radius: $|a_{\text{cm}\,x}| = |R\alpha_\vartheta|$.
22. The work done is the product of the sum of the torques $\sum\tau$ and the change in the object's rotational coordinate $\Delta\vartheta$. It is necessary to first convert the number of rotations to the change in the rotational coordinate.
23. The kinetic energy of an object or system that is in both translational and rotational motion is equal to the sum of its center-of-mass and rotational kinetic energies.
24. The force of static friction does no work on the object and converts some of the object's translational kinetic energy to rotational kinetic energy.
25. The vector product vector is perpendicular to the desktop, pointing either up or down. Which direction is correct is determined by the right-hand rule. Other than that, the angle is independent of the orientation of the two vectors.

26. The magnitude of the vector product of two vectors is equal to the area of the parallelogram defined by the two vectors. It is also equal to the product of the magnitudes of each vector and the sine of the smaller angle between them when they are placed tail to tail.
27. Zero. The term in parentheses is perpendicular to $\vec{A}$, and so the scalar product is zero.
28. The sign. The magnitude of your answer is correct, but the direction is opposite the correct direction.
29. The angular momentum of an isolated particle about any reference point is equal to the vector product of the position vector that locates the particle relative to the reference point and the momentum of the particle: $\vec{L} = \vec{r} \times \vec{p}$.

Answers to Guided Problems

Guided Problem 12.2 $|\vec{\tau}| = 1.8\ \text{N} \cdot \text{m}$

Guided Problem 12.4 (*a*) The disk wins; (*b*) $\Delta t = 0.4\ \text{s}$

Guided Problem 12.6 (*a*) $a_x = \dfrac{\mathcal{T}}{m_Y(1 + c)}\left(\cos\phi - \dfrac{R_a}{R_Y}\right)$;

(*b*) $\phi_{crit} = \cos^{-1}\left(\dfrac{R_a}{R_Y}\right)$

Guided Problem 12.8 (*a*) beneath the edge of the base opposite you; (*b*) $h_{max} = d/2\mu$

PRACTICE

13 PRACTICE Gravity

Chapter Summary

Universal gravity and the principle of equivalence (Sections 13.1, 13.3–13.5, 13.8)

Concepts The force of gravity is an attraction between all objects that have **mass,** which is a measure of the quantity of material in an object. Mass is the property of an object that determines the strength of its gravitational interaction with other objects.

At everyday speeds, the mass of an object is equal to its inertia.

According to the **principle of equivalence,** one cannot distinguish locally between the effects of a constant gravitational acceleration of magnitude g and the effects of an acceleration of the reference frame of magnitude $a = g$.

Quantitative Tools According to Newton's **law of gravity,** if two objects that have masses m_1 and m_2 are a distance r apart, the magnitude of the gravitational force that each object exerts on the other is

$$F^G_{12} = G\frac{m_1 m_2}{r^2_{12}}, \quad (13.1)$$

where $G = 6.6738 \times 10^{-11}\ \mathrm{N \cdot m^2/kg^2}$ is the **gravitational constant.**

The acceleration due to gravity near Earth's surface is

$$g = \frac{Gm_E}{R^2_E}, \quad (13.4)$$

where m_E is Earth's mass and R_E is its radius.

The gravitational force F^G_{sp} exerted by a uniform solid sphere on a particle of mass m is the same as if all the matter in the sphere were concentrated at its center:

$$F^G_{sp} = G\frac{mM_{sphere}}{r^2}, \quad (13.37)$$

where M_{sphere} is the mass of the sphere and r is the distance from its center to the particle.

Angular momentum and gravitational potential energy (Sections 13.2, 13.6)

Concepts The force of gravity is a **central force,** meaning that its line of action always lies along the line connecting the interacting objects.

In an isolated system of two objects that interact through a central force, each object has a constant angular momentum about the center of mass of the system.

Quantitative Tools The **gravitational potential energy** $U^G(x)$ of a system made up of two objects of masses m_1 and m_2 that are a distance x apart is

$$U^G(x) = -G\frac{m_1 m_2}{x}, \quad (13.11)$$

where we take $U^G(x)$ to be zero at $x = \infty$.

Celestial mechanics (Sections 13.2, 13.7)

Concepts **Kepler's first law of planetary motion:** All planets move in elliptical orbits with the Sun at one focus. This law is a consequence of the fact that the magnitude of the gravitational force has a $1/r^2$ dependence.

Kepler's second law: The straight line from any planet to the Sun sweeps out equal areas in equal time intervals. This law reflects the fact that the angular momentum of a planet is constant because the gravitational force is a central force.

Kepler's third law: The squares of the periods T of the planets are proportional to the cubes of the semimajor axes a of their orbits around the Sun ($T^2 \propto a^3$). This law is a consequence of the fact that the magnitude of the gravitational force has a $1/r^2$ dependence.

Quantitative Tools The energy of a closed ($\Delta E = 0$), isolated ($\Delta L = 0$) system made up of a small object of mass m orbiting a large object of mass $M \gg m$ is

$$E = K + U^G = \tfrac{1}{2}mv^2 - G\frac{Mm}{r}, \quad (13.19)$$

where v is the speed of the small object, r is the distance between the objects, and the large object does not move.

The magnitude of angular momentum of the small object is

$$L = r_\perp mv. \quad (13.20)$$

The value of E in Eq. 13.19 determines the orbit's shape:

$E_{mech} < 0$: elliptical (bound) orbit
$E_{mech} = 0$: parabolic orbit
$E_{mech} > 0$: hyperbolic (unbound) orbit.

Review Questions

Answers to these questions can be found at the end of this chapter.

13.1 Universal gravity

1. Which object exerts a greater pulling force on the other: Earth or the Moon? Which object experiences greater acceleration due to this mutual pull?
2. What is the evidence for Newton's $1/r^2$ law of universal gravitation?
3. What orbital shapes are possible with Newton's $1/r^2$ law of universal gravitation?
4. The length of a year on any planet is defined as the time interval the planet takes to make one revolution around the Sun. What is the length of a year on a planet whose orbital radius is four times Earth's orbital radius?
5. What is the distinction between mass and inertia?

13.2 Gravity and angular momentum

6. Explain how, in an isolated system of two objects interacting through a central force, each object has constant angular momentum about the system's center of mass.
7. State Kepler's three laws of planetary motion.
8. In *Principles* Figure 13.12*a* no force is exerted on the moving object, whereas in Figure 13.12*b* and *c*, there is (the force that keeps the object moving along a curved trajectory). Why is the conclusion about angular momentum the same in all three cases?
9. Which has greater acceleration in its orbit around Earth: the Moon or the International Space Station?

13.3 Weight

10. What is your weight measured by a spring scale as you fly through the air over a trampoline? Assume that you can keep the spring scale beneath your feet.
11. Suppose a balance is loaded with objects of equal mass on each side and then dropped in free fall. Does it remain balanced?
12. You stand on a spring scale placed on the ground and read your weight from the dial. You then take the scale into an elevator. Does the dial reading increase, decrease, or stay the same when the elevator accelerates downward as it moves upward?
13. Explain why astronauts in an orbiting space station are able to float around in the cabin.

13.4 Principle of equivalence

14. State the principle of equivalence, and explain why you must use the word *locally* in your statement.
15. Should we expect light to travel along a curved path when it passes near a massive object?

13.5 Gravitational constant

16. Gravitational forces decrease with a $1/r^2$ dependence, and yet the value of g is constant near Earth's surface. Is this a contradiction?
17. Does a planet that has a greater mass than Earth necessarily have a greater acceleration due to gravity near its surface? (Saturn, for example, has about a hundred times the mass of Earth.)

13.6 Gravitational potential energy

18. What choice causes the gravitational potential energy described by Eq. 13.14, $U(r) = -Gm_1m_2/r$, to be negative for any finite r?
19. What does it mean to say that the work done by the gravitational force exerted on an object is *path independent*?
20. Under what condition is it reasonable to approximate a $1/r$ potential energy curve by a straight line?

13.7 Celestial mechanics

21. When you throw a ball from the roof of a building, is the trajectory a parabola or an ellipse?
22. Where in the orbit of any planet in our solar system is the planet's speed smallest? Where is it greatest?
23. If $E = 0$ for a system that consists of an object orbiting a much more massive object, is the orbit bound or unbound?
24. Describe the orbital shapes available for motion under the gravitational force exerted by the Sun, and relate each to the energy of the system comprising the Sun and the orbiting object.

13.8 Gravitational force exerted by a sphere

25. What approach is used to show that the gravitational force exerted by a solid sphere on an external particle is the same as if all the mass of the sphere were concentrated at its center?
26. Can the process for computing the force exerted by a solid sphere on an external particle be extended to a particle located inside the sphere? To a hollow sphere? To a sphere of nonuniform density?

Developing a Feel

Make an order-of-magnitude estimate of each of the following quantities. Letters in parentheses refer to hints below. Use them as needed to guide your thinking.

1. The magnitude of the gravitational force exerted on you by your partner for a tango (B, N)
2. The magnitude of the gravitational force exerted on you by the population of Earth (B, Q, D, J)
3. The magnitude of the gravitational force exerted on you by a nearby large mountain (S, I, B)
4. The radius of the orbit in which your running speed would be sufficient to keep an object moving in a circular orbit around Earth (A, V)
5. The orbital speed required for a near-surface circular orbit of the Moon (V, C, R)
6. The maximum radius for a planet of Earth's density that you could jump from without falling back (F, K, T)
7. The radius to which Earth must be compressed in order for a light beam to orbit the planet in a circular path (V, G, O)
8. The energy required to remove all the planets from the solar system (E, P, L)
9. The maximum and minimum magnitudes of the vector sum of forces you experience during a bungee jump (H, M, U)
10. The magnitude of Earth's angular momentum as it orbits the Sun (W)

Hints

A. What is a typical human running speed for long distances?
B. What is the mass of a typical human?
C. What is the mass of the Moon?
D. How is the population of Earth distributed?
E. What is the gravitational potential energy of the system after the planets are removed?
F. What is the average density of Earth?
G. What principle provides the key to analyzing the gravitational behavior of light?
H. Where in the jump does the bungee cord begin to stretch?
I. What is the distance to the center of mass of a nearby mountain?
J. What is the radius of Earth?
K. How much can you raise your center of mass on Earth by running and then jumping up?
L. How many terms should you include in computing the initial gravitational potential energy of the solar system?
M. Where in the jump does the bungee cord exert maximum force on you?
N. What typical distance separates your center of mass from that of your partner as you tango?
O. What is the required orbital speed?
P. Do you need to add or remove energy?
Q. What is the population of Earth?
R. What is the radius of the Moon?
S. What is the mass of a large mountain?
T. How can you relate jumping height to vertical speed or planet radius?
U. How is the energy stored in a bungee cord related to the distance through which it has stretched?
V. How is the speed of a small object of mass m_s orbiting a large object of mass m_ℓ related to the radius of the orbit?
W. How is angular momentum related to radius and speed of orbit?

Key (all values approximate)

A. 4 m/s; **B.** 7×10^1 kg; **C.** 7×10^{22} kg; **D.** around Earth's surface—assume a uniform spherical-shell distribution, which is a rough approximation; **E.** zero; **F.** 6×10^3 kg/m^3; **G.** the principle of equivalence; **H.** about one-third of the way down; **I.** 3×10^1 km is a reasonable choice; **J.** 6×10^6 m; **K.** 0.7 m for an average person; **L.** ideally, one term for each pair of objects (Mercury-Sun, Mercury-Venus, Mercury-Earth, and so on), but compare terms for the Sun and the three largest planets to get a sense of scale; **M.** the spring force kx is greatest where the stretch length x is greatest, at the bottom; **N.** 0.5 m; **O.** the speed of light, 3×10^8 m/s; **P.** for each planet in orbit, the gravitational potential energy of the Sun-planet system is negative, so you must add potential energy; **Q.** 7 billion; **R.** 2×10^6 m; **S.** 2×10^{13} kg; **T.** use energy methods: the initial kinetic energy is converted to gravitational potential energy during a jump; **U.** the energy stored is approximately $kx^2/2$, where x is the stretch and k is the cord's spring constant; **V.** the gravitational force is the only force in the vector sum for the small object, and the acceleration is centripetal for circular orbit, so $v_s = (Gm_\ell/r)^{1/2}$; **W.** for circular orbit, $L = rmv$

Worked and Guided Problems

Table 13.1 Solar system data (in SI units and relative to Earth)

	Mass		Equatorial radius		Orbit[†]				
					semimajor axis		eccentricity	period	
	(kg)	(m_E)	(m)	(R_E)	(m)	(a_E)		(s)	(years)
Sun	2.0×10^{30}	3.3×10^5	7×10^8	110	–	–	–	–	–
Mercury	3.30×10^{23}	0.06	2.440×10^6	0.38	5.79×10^{10}	0.39	0.206	7.60×10^6	0.24
Venus	4.87×10^{24}	0.81	6.052×10^6	0.95	1.082×10^{11}	0.72	0.007	1.94×10^7	0.62
Earth	5.97×10^{24}	1	6.378×10^6	1	1.496×10^{11}	1	0.017	3.16×10^7	1
Mars	6.42×10^{23}	0.11	3.396×10^6	0.53	2.279×10^{11}	1.52	0.09	5.94×10^7	1.88
Jupiter	1.90×10^{27}	318	7.149×10^7	11.2	7.783×10^{11}	5.20	0.05	3.74×10^8	11.86
Saturn	5.68×10^{26}	95.2	6.027×10^7	9.45	1.427×10^{12}	9.54	0.05	9.29×10^8	29.45
Uranus	8.68×10^{25}	14.5	2.556×10^7	4.01	2.871×10^{12}	19.2	0.05	2.65×10^9	84.02
Neptune	1.02×10^{26}	17.1	2.476×10^7	3.88	4.498×10^{12}	30.1	0.01	5.20×10^9	164.8
Pluto	1.31×10^{22}	0.002	1.151×10^6	0.18	5.906×10^{12}	39.5	0.25	7.82×10^9	247.9
Moon	7.3×10^{22}	0.012	1.737×10^6	0.27	3.84×10^8	0.0026	0.055	2.36×10^6	0.075

[†]The elliptical orbits of the planets and the Moon are specified by their *semimajor axis a* (half the major axis) and eccentricity *e*; see Figure 13.7. With the exception of Mercury and Pluto, the eccentricity is small and so the orbits are close to being circular.

These examples involve material from this chapter but are not associated with any particular section. Some examples are worked out in detail; others you should work out by following the guidelines provided.

Worked Problem 13.1 Reliable 24/7 communications

In order to supply 24-h reception, a communications satellite is often placed in *geosynchronous orbit,* which means the satellite always appears in the same location relative to the receiver on the ground. This requires, among other things, that the rotational speed at which the satellite orbits Earth is the same as the rotational speed at which Earth spins on its axis. How far above Earth's surface is a satellite in geosynchronous orbit? What else is required?

❶ **GETTING STARTED** We seek an orbit whose period is $T = 24.0\ \text{h} = 8.64 \times 10^4\ \text{s}$. Determining the radius of such an orbit is important, but what else might be needed? Let's consider the goal in detail: In order for the satellite to always appear at the same location relative to a point on the ground, its orbital speed must be constant, matching the rotational speed of the Earth. This means the orbit must be circular. We draw a sketch of the system, labeling both the known mass of Earth m_E and the unknown mass of the satellite m_s (Figure WG13.1).

Figure WG13.1

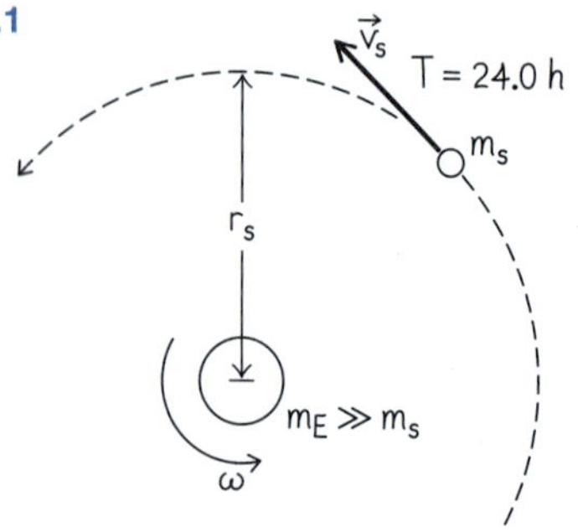

Kepler's third law says the square of the orbital period is proportional to the cube of the distance from the center of the object exerting the gravitational force. Thus a specified period implies a certain orbit radius r. We need to obtain an expression for r in terms of our given parameters. However, does just any orbit of this radius work? The goal is for the satellite to remain fixed relative to a specific point on Earth. Points on the surface of Earth move in circles parallel to the equator as Earth rotates. Thus it seems that our circular orbit must also be parallel to the plane of the equator in order to remain at the same location relative to a point on the ground.

❷ **DEVISE PLAN** As the satellite moves in a circular orbit, it is subject to the gravitational force of Earth only. We draw a free-body diagram for the satellite (Figure WG13.2), choosing the x axis to be in the direction of this force, toward the center of the orbit. Because the orbit is circular, we can use the relationship between radial (centripetal) acceleration and rotational speed ω from *Principles*

Figure WG13.2

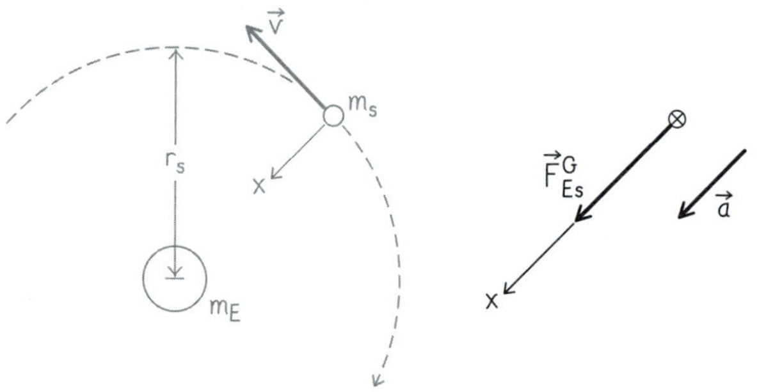

Eq. 11.15: $a_c = \omega^2 r$. The satellite's rotational speed is 2π rad in 24.0 h, making $\omega = 2\pi/T$. The centripetal acceleration is due to the force of gravity exerted by Earth. Because the satellite is not near Earth's surface, we cannot set a_c equal to g. Instead, we can solve for the acceleration by force analysis, using Newton's law of gravity, $F^G_{Es} = Gm_Em_s/r^2$. The only unknown in the equation of motion (*Principles* Eq. 8.8) will be r.

❸ **EXECUTE PLAN** We begin by substituting known formulas into the component form of the equation of motion for the satellite:

$$\Sigma F_x = ma_x$$

$$F^G_{Esx} = m_s a_x$$

$$+F^G_{Es} = m_s(+a_c)$$

$$G\frac{m_E m_s}{r^2} = m_s(\omega^2 r)$$

$$Gm_E = \omega^2 r^3.$$

We want to solve for r in terms of T:

$$Gm_E = \left(\frac{2\pi}{T}\right)^2 r^3$$

$$r^3 = Gm_E\left(\frac{T}{2\pi}\right)^2.$$

This is Kepler's third law in mathematical form for a satellite orbiting Earth. Substituting the values given, we get

$$r^3 = (6.67 \times 10^{-11}\ \text{N}\cdot\text{m}^2/\text{kg}^2)(5.97\ 10^{24}\ \text{kg})\left(\frac{8.64 \times 10^4\ \text{s}}{2\pi}\right)^2$$

$$r = 4.22 \times 10^7\ \text{m}.$$

Thus the satellite must follow a circular orbit whose plane is parallel to Earth's equator, and it must orbit at height

$$h = r - R_E = (4.22 \times 10^7\ \text{m}) - (6.38 \times 10^6\ \text{m})$$
$$= 3.58 \times 10^7\ \text{m} = 3.6 \times 10^4\ \text{km}. ✔$$

❹ **EVALUATE RESULT** This is pretty far up, considering that the International Space Station (ISS) orbits at only a few hundred kilometers above ground. On the other hand, our value for r is an order of magnitude smaller than the distance to the Moon, so the answer is at least plausible. The ISS completes an orbit in a couple of hours, while the Moon requires a month. Our geosynchronous orbit is thus bracketed by these examples in both period and radius—which gives us some confidence in our results.

Note that the mathematical form of Kepler's third law does not depend on the mass of the satellite. (Neither does the version expressed purely in words!) Any geosynchronous satellite must therefore orbit in a circular, equatorial orbit at a common height. This raises a practical issue: If many countries and companies all want geosynchronous satellites, how do we find room up there for them?

Guided Problem 13.2 Disruptive spin

Objects on Earth's surface remain there because of gravitational attraction, despite the fact that objects near the equator move at about 1600 km/h because of Earth's rotation. If the Earth were to spin a lot faster, though, the gravitational force might not be strong enough to prevent objects from flying away from Earth's surface. This effect of rapid spin is especially acute for fluid objects like stars, particularly for the remnant cores of stars that have exploded in a supernova explosion. Some of these, called millisecond pulsars, rotate very rapidly (about once every millisecond) because their angular momentum remained constant as they collapsed. These stars typically have 2 times the mass of our Sun. What is the maximum radius a millisecond pulsar can have in order to avoid losing matter at its surface?

❶ **GETTING STARTED**

1. Describe the problem in your own words. How is the radius involved?
2. What is the shape of the path followed by a small clump of material at the surface of a millisecond pulsar? What force keeps the clump on that path rather than traveling in a straight line?
3. Draw an appropriate diagram.

❷ **DEVISE PLAN**

4. How is the magnitude of the relevant force related to the mass and radius of the pulsar?
5. What physics law allows you to relate this force to the rotational speed of the pulsar? How is the rotational speed related to the pulsar's rotational period?
6. Which unknown quantity do you need to determine?
7. Does your approach allow you to express the unknown quantity in terms of known ones?

❸ **EXECUTE PLAN**

8. Work through the algebra to solve for the unknown quantity.

❹ **EVALUATE RESULT**

9. Did you make any assumptions?
10. Compare your answer with the range of pulsar radii available online.

Worked Problem 13.3 Escape at last

The Mars Colony wants to launch a deep-space probe, but they have no rocket engines. They decide to launch a probe with an electromagnetic cannon, which means they must launch at escape speed. Determine this speed.

❶ **GETTING STARTED** Let us do a quick sketch to help our thinking (Figure WG13.3). We select the Mars-probe system for analysis. In order to reach "deep space," the probe must attain a very great distance from Mars. This will require a significant amount of initial kinetic energy, which the probe must acquire during launch. After launch, the kinetic energy immediately begins to decrease, and the potential energy of the Mars-probe system increases as the separation distance increases. We assume a reference frame where Mars is fixed and only the probe moves. When the probe is far enough away (infinity, really, but practically it doesn't need to go quite this far), the kinetic energy has its minimum value, which we can take to be zero because the colonists presumably do not want to supply any more energy than needed to get the probe out there. The gravitational potential energy has its maximum value, which is also zero. (Remember that universal gravitational potential energy is *negative*.) We also assume that the Sun and other planets have a negligible influence on our system, and we ignore the rotation of Mars.

Figure WG13.3

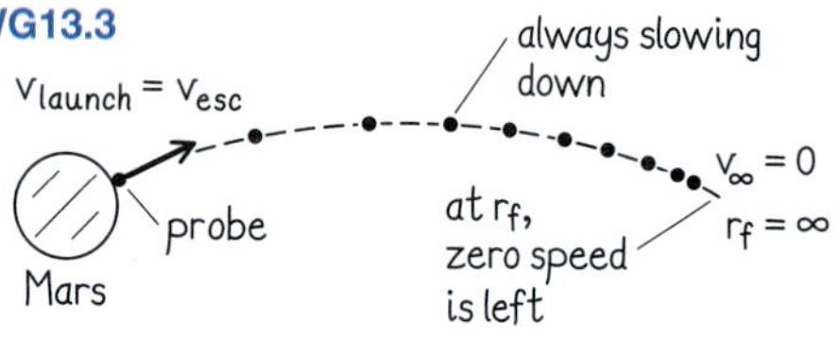

❷ **DEVISE PLAN** We can use conservation of energy because the probe has all of the needed kinetic energy at the beginning, as it is shot from a cannon. As the probe travels, this kinetic energy is converted to gravitational potential energy of the Mars-probe system. We want to know the initial speed of the probe acquired at launch. The initial potential energy is the value when the probe is still near the Martian surface. The final state of the probe is zero speed at an infinite distance from Mars. The *Principles* volume analyzes a similar situation in Section 13.7, leading to Eq. 13.23, so there is no need to derive this result again here. We begin with Eq. 13.23, solving this version of an energy conservation equation for $v_i = v_{esc}$ in terms of the known quantities.

❸ **EXECUTE PLAN** Let us use r_i for the initial Mars-probe radial center-to-center separation distance, $r_f = \infty$ for the final separation distance, R_M for the radius of Mars, and m_M and m_p for the two masses. We begin with Eq. 13.23:

$$E_{mech} = \tfrac{1}{2}m_p v_{esc}^2 - G\frac{m_M m_p}{R_M} = 0$$

$$\tfrac{1}{2}v_{esc}^2 - G\frac{m_M}{R_M} = 0$$

$$\tfrac{1}{2}v_{esc}^2 = G\frac{m_M}{R_M}$$

$$v_{esc} = \sqrt{2G\frac{m_M}{R_M}}$$

$$v_{esc} = \sqrt{2(6.67 \times 10^{-11}\,\text{N}\cdot\text{m}^2/\text{kg}^2)\frac{6.42 \times 10^{23}\,\text{kg}}{3.40 \times 10^6\,\text{m}}}$$
$$= 5.02 \times 10^3\,\text{m/s} = 5.02\,\text{km/s}. ✔$$

Notice that this speed does not depend on the mass of the probe. A probe of any other size shot from the cannon would need the same minimum speed to break free of Mars's gravitational pull.

❹ **EVALUATE RESULT** Our algebraic expression for the escape speed is plausible because it involves the mass of Mars, the initial center-to-center radial separation distance of our two objects (which is Mars's radius), and G. We expect v_{esc} to increase with m_M because the gravitational pull increases with increasing mass. We also expect v_{esc} to decrease as the distance between the launch position and Mars's center increases because the gravitational force exerted by the planet on the probe decreases with increasing separation distance. All this is just what our result predicts.

An escape speed of 18,000 km/h is smaller than (but on the order of) the escape speed from Earth, and so the answer is not unreasonable.

We assumed that the initial Mars-probe separation distance is equal to the planet's radius. Of course, the length of the cannon may be tens of meters, but this tiny difference would have no impact on the numerical answer. We ignored the rotation of Mars, which could supply a small amount of the needed kinetic energy. We also ignored the effect of the Sun, which is fine for getting away from the surface of Mars, but we would need to account for it if the destination was another star.

Guided Problem 13.4 Spring to the stars

Suppose that, instead of using chemical rockets, NASA decided to use a compressed spring to launch a spacecraft. If the spring constant is 100,000 N/m and the mass of the spacecraft is 10,000 kg, how far must the spring be compressed in order to launch the craft to a position outside Earth's gravitational influence?

❶ **GETTING STARTED**

1. Describe the problem in your own words. Are there similarities to Worked Problem 13.3?
2. Draw a diagram showing the initial and final states. What is the spacecraft's situation in the final state?
3. How does the spacecraft gain the necessary escape speed?

❷ **DEVISE PLAN**

4. What law of physics should you invoke?
5. As the spring is compressed, is the gravitational potential energy of the Earth-spacecraft system affected? If so, can you ignore this effect?
6. What equation allows you to relate the initial and final states?

❸ **EXECUTE PLAN**

7. What is your target unknown quantity? Algebraically isolate it on one side of your equation.
8. Substitute the numerical values you know to get a numerical answer.

❹ **EVALUATE RESULT**

9. Is your algebraic expression for the compression plausible for how the compression changes as the spring constant and Earth's mass and radius change?
10. If you were the head of a design team, would you recommend pursuing this launch method?

Worked Problem 13.5 Close encounter

Suppose astronomers discover a large asteroid, still far away, headed for Earth. Calculations indicate that it is traveling at $v_i = 754$ m/s and that a straight-line extension of its velocity would bring it within a distance $d = 3.30 \times 10^8$ m of Earth (which is about the radius of the Moon's orbit around Earth). However, Earth's gravitational attraction will cause its trajectory to be a conic section, as Figure WG13.4 shows. (*a*) What is the value of r_f, the radius of its orbit when the asteroid is closest to Earth? (*b*) What speed v_f does the asteroid have when it gets closest to Earth? Note from Figure WG13.4 that r_f is to be measured from Earth's center, not from Earth's surface.

Figure WG13.4

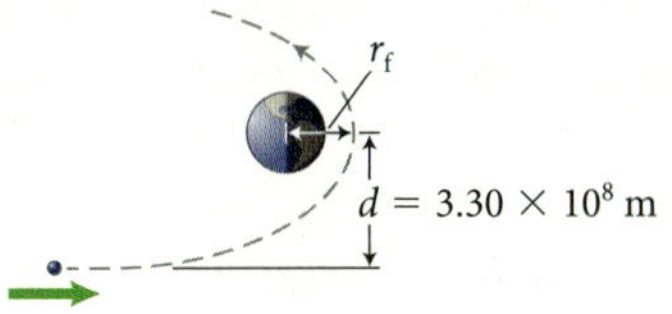

1 GETTING STARTED The problem is one of celestial mechanics. We have an asteroid in orbit (it may be an unbound orbit), and we need to calculate the radius r_f of its orbit when it comes closest to Earth and its speed v_f when it is at that closest-approach position. We know both its speed and direction of motion a long way off, although we don't know its mass. Perhaps we don't need to know this mass. We assume that when the asteroid is first sighted, Earth's gravitational influence on it is negligible.

2 DEVISE PLAN For celestial mechanics problems, we know that both the energy and the angular momentum of a system of objects interacting only gravitationally are constant: $E_i = E_f$ and $\vec{L}_i = \vec{L}_f$. In Earth's reference frame, the angular momentum of the asteroid (of unknown mass m_a) and the energy of the Earth-asteroid system do not change as the asteroid moves from far away to its position of closest approach, where the radius of its orbit is r_f. We can determine the magnitude of its angular momentum at closest approach by looking at its angular-momentum magnitude when it is far from Earth. Its velocity is always tangent to its trajectory, and when it is far away we have information about the perpendicular distance of this tangent line from Earth:

$$L_i = |\vec{r}_i \times \vec{p}_i| = m_a v_i d,$$

where $\vec{p}_i$ is the asteroid's momentum when it is traveling along its straight-line course. At the position of closest approach, the direction of velocity is also perpendicular to its radius of curvature (see *Principles* Example 13.5), so its angular momentum is $L_f = r_f m_a v_f$.

The energy of the Earth-asteroid system at the initial position of sighting, where the influence of Earth's gravitational pull is negligible, is purely kinetic. At the point of closest approach, however, it has both kinetic energy and (negative) gravitational potential energy. All that remains is to do the algebra to solve for r_f and v_f.

3 EXECUTE PLAN
(*a*) Using r_i and r_f for the initial and final Earth-asteroid radial center-to-center distances, we have from conservation of energy:

$$K_i + U_i^G = K_f + U_f^G$$

$$\tfrac{1}{2} m_a v_i^2 + \left(-G\frac{m_E m_a}{r_i}\right) = \tfrac{1}{2} m_a v_f^2 + \left(-G\frac{m_E m_a}{r_f}\right)$$

$$\tfrac{1}{2} v_i^2 + \left(-G\frac{m_E}{\infty}\right) = \tfrac{1}{2} v_f^2 + \left(-G\frac{m_E}{r_f}\right)$$

$$\tfrac{1}{2} v_i^2 = \tfrac{1}{2} v_f^2 - G\frac{m_E}{r_f}.$$

This equation contains the two desired quantities: the orbit radius at closest approach r_f and the speed v_f when the asteroid is at that position. Next we apply conservation of angular momentum:

$$L_i = L_f$$

$$m_a v_i d = r_f m_a v_f$$

$$v_f = \frac{v_i d}{r_f}.$$

We note that the asteroid's mass m_a cancels in all our equations. Substituting this expression for v_f into our energy equation yields

$$\tfrac{1}{2} v_i^2 = \tfrac{1}{2}\left(\frac{v_i d}{r_f}\right)^2 - G\frac{m_E}{r_f} = \frac{1}{2}\frac{(v_i d)^2}{r_f^2} - G\frac{m_E}{r_f}.$$

Multiplying through by r_f^2 and then by $2/v_i^2$, we get a quadratic equation:

$$\tfrac{1}{2} v_i^2 r_f^2 = \tfrac{1}{2}(v_i d)^2 - G m_E r_f$$

$$r_f^2 + 2\frac{G m_E}{v_i^2} r_f - d^2 = 0$$

$$r_f = -\frac{G m_E}{v_i^2} \pm \tfrac{1}{2}\sqrt{\left(2\frac{G m_E}{v_i^2}\right)^2 + 4d^2}$$

$$= -\frac{G m_E}{v_i^2} \pm \sqrt{\left(\frac{G m_E}{v_i^2}\right)^2 + d^2}.$$

The positive result is the physical one we seek, yielding

$$r_f = 7.38 \times 10^7 \text{ m} = 7.38 \times 10^4 \text{ km.} ✔$$

(*b*) The speed at closest approach is

$$v_f = \frac{d v_i}{r_f} = \frac{(3.30 \times 10^8 \text{ m})(754 \text{ m/s})}{7.38 \times 10^7 \text{ m}}$$

$$= 3.37 \times 10^3 \text{ m/s} = 3.37 \text{ km/s.} ✔$$

4 EVALUATE RESULT Earth's radius is 6.38×10^3 km, making $r_f \approx 10 R_E$, which might generate a bit of anxiety among the planet's inhabitants when one considers possible observational errors. The distance of closest approach is about 74,000 km, roughly one-fourth of the Earth-Moon distance. Fortunately, the asteroid does not hit Earth because at closest approach it is moving a lot faster than it was at first sighting ($v_f \approx 5 v_i$). You also might notice that the speed at closest approach is barely greater than the escape speed for an object at this distance r_f from Earth's center, $v_{esc} = \sqrt{2Gm_E/(7.4 \times 10^7 \text{ m})} = 3.3 \times 10^3$ m/s. A near miss indeed!

The expression for r_f shows that a greater straight-path distance d gives a greater r_f value, as we expect. Because we are not given any information about how far away the asteroid is initially, we assumed that Earth has negligible gravitational influence at that instant. Without that assumption, we would not have been able to solve the problem. In any case, if our assumption is false, the decrease in potential energy would have been (somewhat) smaller and therefore the final velocity would have been smaller.

Guided Problem 13.6 More rocket launches

Three rockets are launched from Earth as shown in Figure WG13.5. One rocket is launched vertically (*a*), one horizontally (*b*), and one at 45° with respect to the ground (*c*). All three are launched with a speed $\frac{3}{4}$ of the escape speed from Earth's surface, $v_{esc} = 1.12 \times 10^4$ m/s (from *Principles* Checkpoint 13.22). Calculate the maximum distance from Earth each rocket achieves. Ignore Earth's rotation, and express your answer in terms of Earth's mass and radius.

Figure WG13.5

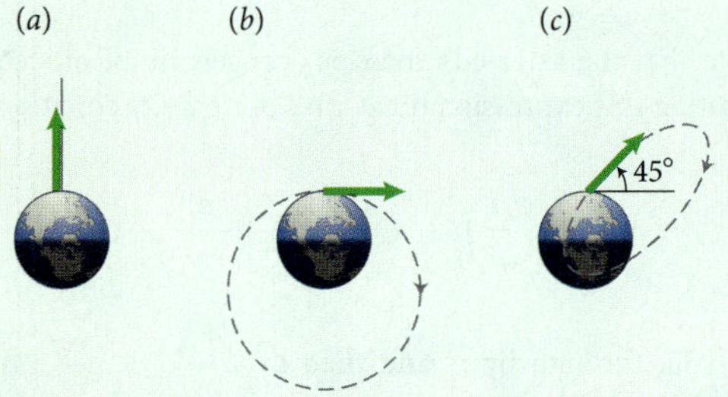

❶ **GETTING STARTED**

1. What are the physical quantities of interest in this problem?
2. Consider the shape of each trajectory. *Principles* Figure 13.37 may aid your thinking.

❷ **DEVISE PLAN**

3. What conservation law(s) should you use? How are the maximum and minimum orbital distances related to other physical quantities?
4. Is the information about the magnitude and direction of the velocities in each of the three cases useful?
5. Which unknown quantities do you need to determine in each case?

❸ **EXECUTE PLAN**

6. Does the same *general* approach work in all three cases?
7. Work through the algebra and obtain an expression for the maximum distance in terms of Earth's mass and radius. Is it possible to use the same expression in all three cases?

❹ **EVALUATE RESULT**

8. Does your expression (or expressions) show plausible algebraic behavior when you vary the launch condition and when you vary Earth's mass and radius?
9. Are your assumptions reasonable?

Worked Problem 13.7 Black hole

A black hole is the remnant of a massive star that, once its nuclear fuel burned out, has collapsed to essentially a point under its own gravitational attraction. The gravitational force exerted by a black hole is so great that not even light can escape from within its interior—hence the name: (black, for the absence of light). Suppose a certain black hole has a mass equal to ten times the mass of the Sun. What is the radius of closest approach for a passing light ray to avoid capture?

❶ **GETTING STARTED** The problem asks about the motion of a light ray in the vicinity of a black hole. We might consider the gravitational force exerted by the black hole on the ray or work from energy or angular momentum conservation. Light has no mass, however, and so we will likely need to invoke the equivalence principle. Conservation principles are usually easier to use than other laws, so let's begin there. It is possible that energy alone can provide the equation we need because only one unknown is sought: a radial distance from the center of the black hole. We know the speed of light, $c = 3.0 \times 10^8$ m/s, and are given the mass of the black hole as 10 solar masses. The mass of the Sun is given in Table 13.1.

❷ **DEVISE PLAN** In any two-object system where one object moves relative to the other, angular momentum, gravitational force, and gravitational potential energy each depend on the masses of the objects. That seems to rule out any of our usual methods for solving this problem because one of our objects has no mass. By the equivalence principle, however, we might be able to treat the light ray as if it were an object subject to the usual laws. Thus we might imagine the ray as having an initial kinetic energy to use in attempting to escape the gravitational pull of the black hole. We used energy methods in Worked Problem 13.3 to derive an expression for the escape speed that depends *not* on the mass of the "escaping" object but only on the mass of the object exerting the gravitational force (which means m_h here) and on the radial distance r separating the objects at the instant of launch: $v_{esc} = \sqrt{2Gm_h/r}$. This expression was derived for an object escaping from a planet's surface, and so we must assume that the gravitational behavior of the black hole is similar enough to that of a planet to allow us to use this relationship. We apply this approach here, with the light ray being the escaping "object" and with r being the "escape radius," the radius at which the light can just barely escape from the black hole, which is the radius of closest approach that we seek. We assume the ray obeys mechanical laws and is launched with speed c, which must be the escape speed at the radius of closest approach.

❸ **EXECUTE PLAN** Squaring our equation for the escape speed from Worked Problem 13.3, substituting $v_{esc} = c$, and solving for r, we get

$$r = 2G\frac{m_h}{c^2}.$$

The mass of the Sun is 2.0×10^{30} kg. Putting in numbers, we arrive at

$$r = 2(6.67 \times 10^{-11}\,\mathrm{N \cdot m^2/kg^2})\frac{10(2.0 \times 10^{30}\,\mathrm{kg})}{(3 \times 10^8\,\mathrm{m/s})^2}$$

$$= 3.0 \times 10^4\,\mathrm{m} = 30\,\mathrm{km}. ✔$$

❹ **EVALUATE RESULT** The gravitational force must be very strong to affect light significantly, and the inverse square dependence of this force (or the inverse first power dependence of the gravitational potential energy) on the radius therefore demands a very small radius. That black holes have much smaller radii than ordinary objects of the same mass is no surprise: Black holes must be very exotic or we would have noticed them in our everyday lives. In addition, light seems unaffected by gravity in ordinary life, so we would expect that a very intense gravitational pull would be required. If the mass is fixed, that leaves only the radius to adjust, and the smaller the radius, the greater the gravitational force.

Note: The assumption we made—that we can ignore the fact that light has no mass and simply apply the escape speed formula—is not technically valid. However, when this calculation is done correctly, using Einstein's general theory of relativity, our expression for the black hole radius of closest approach is correct. The value of this radius is known as the "event horizon" for the black hole because events that take place at radii smaller than this cannot be seen from the outside.

PRACTICE

Guided Problem 13.8 Heavenly rock

A planet that has a mass 25 times that of Earth is orbited by a moon that has a mass eight times that of Earth (Figure WG13.6). The orbital radius is equal to twelve Earth radii. A large rock located near this system is sixteen Earth radii away from the moon, with the line connecting the rock and moon perpendicular to the line connecting the planet and moon. What is the magnitude of the rock's acceleration in terms of the free-fall acceleration (g) it would have on Earth?

Figure WG13.6

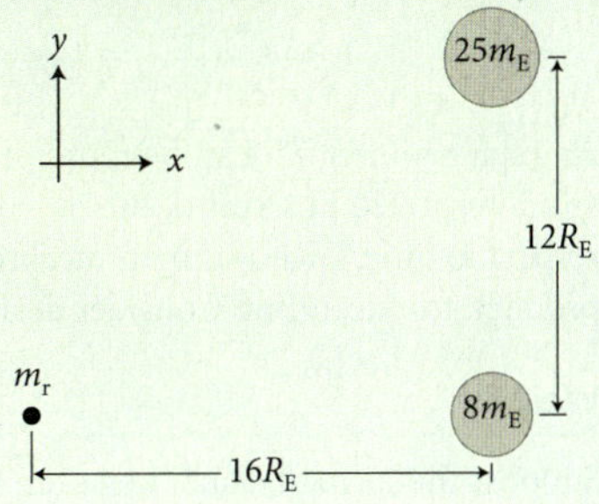

❶ GETTING STARTED

1. Given that the question asks for acceleration, what approach should you take?
2. Does it matter that the rock's mass is not specified? Even though this mass is not given, you should give it a symbolic value m_r in any diagrams you draw and any equations you use to see how it comes in and, perhaps, cancels out.
3. How many forces are exerted on the rock? What is the direction of each force? Draw a free-body diagram for the rock.

❷ DEVISE PLAN

4. What is the center-to-center distance between rock and moon? The center-to-center distance between rock and planet?
5. What is the magnitude of the gravitational force exerted by the moon on the rock? The magnitude of the gravitational force exerted by the planet on the rock?

❸ EXECUTE PLAN

6. Determine the x component of the vector sum of forces exerted on the rock.
7. Determine the y component of the vector sum of forces exerted on the rock.
8. Remember that acceleration is a vector.

❹ EVALUATE RESULT

9. Is your result greater or smaller than g? Given the masses and distances, is this reasonable?

PRACTICE

Questions and Problems

For instructor-assigned homework, go to MasteringPhysics®

Dots indicate difficulty level of problems: • = *easy,* •• = *intermediate,* ••• = *hard;* CR = *context-rich problem.*

[It is convenient for some problems to note that
$G = 6.67 \times 10^{-11}\ \text{N} \cdot \text{m}^2/\text{kg}^2 = 6.67 \times 10^{-11}\ \text{m}^3/(\text{kg} \cdot \text{s}^2)$.]

13.1 Universal gravity

1. If the matter that makes up a planet is distributed uniformly so that the planet has a fixed, uniform density, how does the magnitude of the acceleration due to gravity at the planet surface depend on the planet radius? •
2. In Figure P13.2, suppose the mass of object 1 is three times the mass of object 2. (*a*) At Earth's surface, what ratio r_1/r_2 is needed to have the rod stay horizontal? (*b*) What is this ratio on the Moon, where the magnitude of the gravitational force is only one-sixth of the magnitude of Earth's gravitational force? •

Figure P13.2

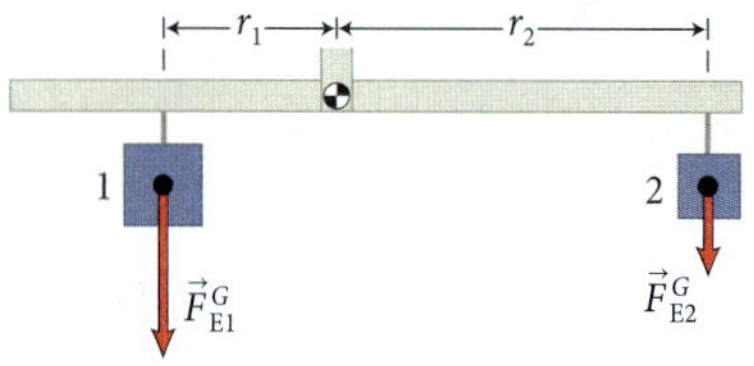

3. Suppose you're making a scale model of the solar system showing the eight planets (not including the dwarf planet Pluto) and having each planet at its farthest position from the Sun. If you use a marble of radius 10 mm for Mercury, how far from the Sun must you place your outermost planet? •
4. Four identical objects are placed at the four corners of a square, far from any star or planet. (*a*) Choose one object and draw to scale the vectors that represent the gravitational forces exerted on it by the other three objects. (*b*) Draw a vector that represents the vector sum of the forces exerted on your chosen object. ••
5. Two basketballs, each of mass 0.60 kg and radius 0.12 m, are placed on a floor so that they touch each other. Two golf balls, each of mass 0.045 kg and radius 22 mm, are placed on a table so that they touch each other. What is the ratio of the gravitational force exerted by one basketball on the other to that exerted by one golf ball on the other? ••

13.2 Gravity and angular momentum

6. An astronaut on the International Space Station gently releases a satellite that has a mass much smaller than the mass of the station. Describe the motion of the satellite after release. •
7. An isolated object of mass m can be split into two parts of masses m_1 and m_2. Suppose the centers of these parts are then separated by a distance r. What ratio of masses m_1/m_2 would produce the largest gravitational force on each part? ••
8. Particles of mass m, $2m$, and $3m$ are arranged as shown in Figure P13.8, far from any other objects. These three particles interact only gravitationally, so that each particle experiences a vector sum of forces due to the other two. Call these $\vec{F}_m$, $\vec{F}_{2m}$, and $\vec{F}_{3m}$. (*a*) Show that the lines of action of $\vec{F}_m$, $\vec{F}_{2m}$, and $\vec{F}_{3m}$ intersect at a common point. (*b*) Is this point of intersection the center of mass of the system? (*c*) Is the analysis of the motion of this system straightforward? ••

Figure P13.8

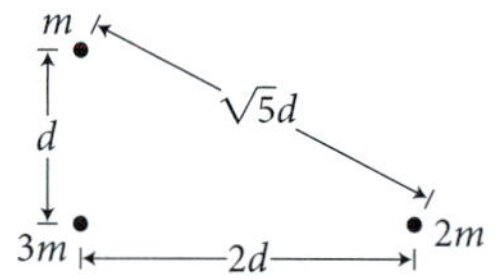

9. Angular momentum can be represented as a vector product and interpreted in terms of the rate of change of an area with respect to time. Give a similar interpretation of another vector product: torque. (Hint: Consider derivatives.) •••

13.3 Weight

10. Suppose the spring/balance device in Figure P13.10 is adjusted so that the spring is slightly stretched and the balance arm is level when the device is in an elevator at rest relative to the ground and a 1.0-kg object is placed as shown. If the elevator accelerates upward, does the balance arm tilt clockwise, tilt counterclockwise, or remain level? •

Figure P13.10

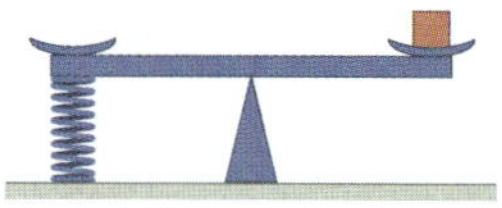

11. Step gently onto a bathroom scale, read the dial, and then jump from a chair onto the same scale. (*a*) Does the dial show different readings in the two cases? (*b*) Has the gravitational force exerted by Earth on you changed? •
12. A balance is purposefully prepared in an unbalanced condition, with too much mass on one side. It is carefully held with two hands, one on the base of the balance and one on the heavier end, so that the balance arm is level. Then both hands release the system from rest at the same instant. While it is in free fall, what happens to the balance arm? ••
13. (*a*) For what downward acceleration does the spring scale in Figure P13.13 read zero? (*b*) What would the answer in part *a* be if the experiment were done on the Moon? (*c*) How would your conclusion about the spring forces change if the brick were hung from the spring scale rather than supported by it? ••

Figure P13.13

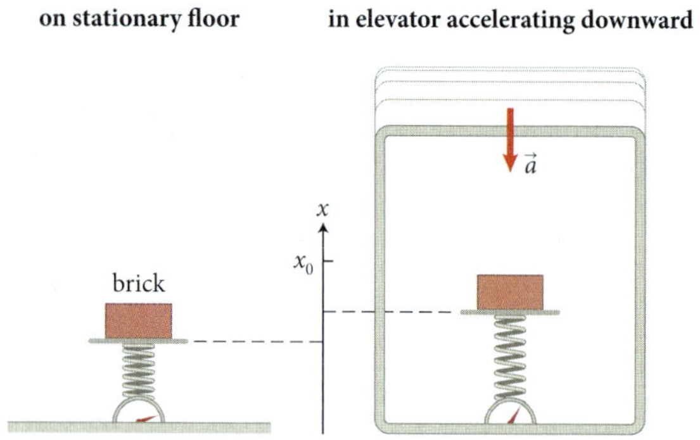

14. You ride your pogo stick (Figure P13.14) across a diving board and into the local swimming pool. Your pogo stick is a special model equipped with a sensor that records the force measured by the spring. Describe the values of force recorded during your ride, using the gravitational force exerted on you by Earth as a benchmark. ••

Figure P13.14

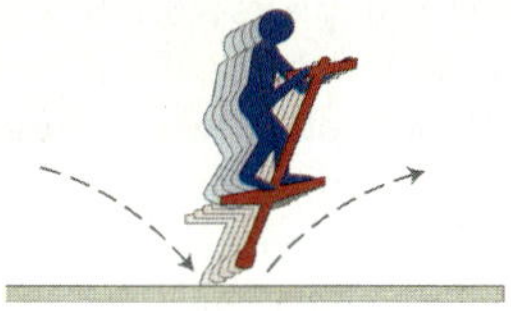

13.4 Principle of equivalence

15. A commercial airliner hits a pocket of turbulence and experiences a downward acceleration of about $2g$. A person who is not fastened into a seat by a safety belt "falls" to the ceiling and suffers a broken neck. Explain how this injury can be so severe. •

16. How should the simulator in Figure P13.16 be tilted to simulate a left turn in a bobsled? Assume that the bobsled run has banked turns and that the sled exerts no tangential force on the ice. ••

Figure P13.16

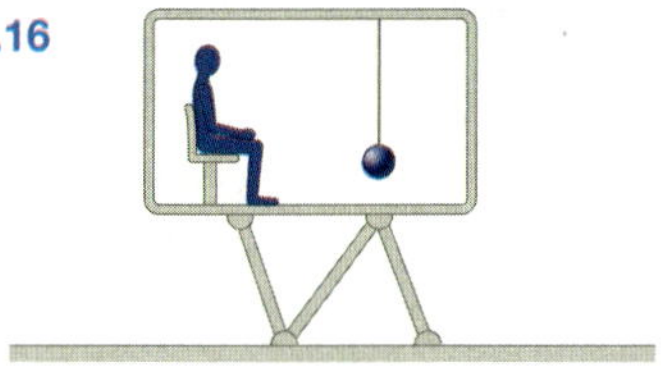

17. A vertical accelerometer for measuring accelerations on a roller coaster can be constructed using a piece of clear plastic pipe, a cork, a rubber band, and a metal bob (Figure P13.17). Where the bob hangs down normally is where you make a mark for an acceleration of g. Without accelerating the pipe, explain how you can calibrate the accelerometer as you assemble it for accelerations of $2g$, $3g$, and so on. ••

Figure P13.17

18. Consider two satellites simultaneously launched 180 km apart at the equator, each placed in a circular orbit that passes above the North Pole and its launch point. (*a*) Describe their relative motion with respect to Earth and with respect to each other. (*b*) Does this motion imply that each satellite exerts a force on the other? ••

19. Let us explore whether there is any way to distinguish acceleration due to rotation from acceleration due to a gravitational force. Imagine a deep bowl with a small volume of milk in it. (*a*) What happens to the milk when you spin the bowl about a perpendicular axis that runs through the center of the bowl bottom? (*b*) What is the shape of an object that exerts a gravitational force that could make the milk behave in a similar fashion? •••

13.5 Gravitational constant

20. What is the magnitude of the gravitational force exerted (*a*) by the Sun on Mars and (*b*) by Mars on the Sun? Approximate Mars's orbit as circular. •

21. What is the magnitude of the gravitational force between two 1.0-g marbles placed 100 mm apart? •

22. The gravitational force between two spherical celestial bodies, one of mass 2×10^{12} kg and the other of mass 5×10^{20} kg, has a magnitude of 3×10^{7} N. How far apart are the two bodies? •

23. Mars has a mass that is about one-ninth of Earth's and a radius that is about half of Earth's. What is the ratio of the acceleration due to gravity on Mars to that on Earth? ••

24. Gravity is the weakest of the fundamental interactions (see *Principles* Section 7.6). (*a*) This being so, what makes it such an important force on Earth? (*b*) What makes it the dominant force in galaxies? ••

25. A neutron star has about two times the mass of our Sun but has collapsed to a radius of 10 km. What is the acceleration due to gravity on the surface of this star in terms of the free-fall acceleration at Earth's surface? ••

26. Which pulls harder on the Moon: Earth or the Sun? ••

27. How far above the surface of Earth do you have to go before the acceleration due to gravity drops by 0.10%, 1.0% and 10%? ••

28. (*a*) As a spacecraft travels along a straight line from Earth to the Moon, at what distance from Earth does the force of gravity exerted by Earth on the coasting spacecraft cancel the force of gravity exerted by the Moon on the spacecraft? (*b*) What do the passengers in the spacecraft notice, if anything, before and after passing this location? ••

29. From the picture of Saturn in Figure P13.29 and known values, estimate the orbital period of particles in Saturn's rings. ••

Figure P13.29

30. The Sun and Moon both exert a gravitational force on Earth. (*a*) Which force has greater magnitude? (*b*) What is the ratio of the two force magnitudes? ••

31. Given that the acceleration due to gravity is 0.0500 m/s^2 at the surface of a spherical asteroid that has a radius of 3.75×10^4 m, determine the asteroid's mass. ••

32. At what height above the surface of Pluto is the acceleration due to gravity half its surface value? ••

33. A test object of mass m_{test} is placed at the origin of a two-dimensional coordinate system (Figure P13.33). An object 1, of the same mass, is at $(d, 0)$, and an object 2, of mass $2m_{test}$, is at $(-d, \ell)$. What is the magnitude of the vector sum of the gravitational forces exerted on the test object by the other two objects? •••

Figure P13.33

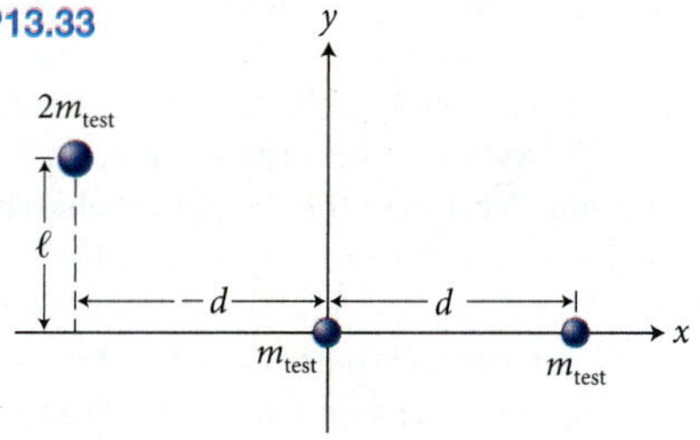

34. Using g for the acceleration due to gravity is valid as long as the height h above Earth's surface is small. Derive an expression for a more accurate value of the acceleration due to gravity as a quadratic function of h. •••

35. Calculate the acceleration due to gravity *inside* Earth as a function of the radial distance r from the planet's center. (Hint: Imagine that a mine shaft has been drilled from the surface to Earth's center and an object of mass m has been dropped down the shaft to some radial position $r < R_E$ from the center, where R_E is the radius of Earth. What is the vector sum of the forces exerted on the object by all of Earth's mass that lies at any distance $d > r$ from the center? $d < r$ from the center?) •••

13.6 Gravitational potential energy

36. What is the gravitational potential energy of the Earth-Sun system? •

37. The asteroid known as Toro has a radius of about 5.0 km and a mass of 2.0×10^{15} kg. Could a 70-kg person standing on its surface jump free of Toro? •

38. (*a*) How much gravitational potential energy does a system comprising a 100-kg object and Earth have if the object is one Earth radius above the ground? (*b*) How fast would a 100-kg object have to be moving at this height to have zero energy? ••

39. An object 1 of mass m_1 is separated by some distance d from an object 2 of mass $2m_1$. An object 3 of mass m_3 is to be placed between them. If the potential energy of the three-object system is to be a maximum (closest to zero), should object 3 be placed closer to object 1, closer to object 2, or halfway between them? ••

40. Two particles, each of mass m, are initially at rest very far apart. Obtain an expression for their relative speed of approach at any instant as a function of their separation distance d if the only interaction is their gravitational attraction to each other. ••

41. Consider an alternate universe in which the magnitude of the attractive force of gravity exerted by Earth on a meteor of mass m_m approaching Earth is given by $F = Cm_m m_E/r^3$, where C is some positive constant and r is the center-to-center distance between Earth and the meteor. (*a*) How much work is done by the gravitational force on the meteor as it falls from very far away (infinite distance) to some height h above Earth's surface? (*b*) If the meteor is moving very slowly when it is very far away, how fast is it moving when it gets to that height? ••

42. Derive expressions for the orbital speed and energy for a satellite of mass m_s traveling in a circular orbit of radius a around a planet of mass $m_p \gg m_s$. ••

43. What maximum height above the surface of Earth does an object attain if it is launched upward at 4.0 km/s from the surface? ••

44. (*a*) Derive an expression for the energy needed to launch an object from the surface of Earth to a height h above the surface. (*b*) Ignoring Earth's rotation, how much energy is needed to get the same object into orbit at height h? ••

45. A spacecraft propelled by a solar sail is pushed directly away from the Sun with a force of magnitude C/r^2, where C is a constant and r is the spacecraft-Sun radial distance. The craft has a mass of 5.0×10^4 kg and starts from rest at a distance $r_i = 1.0 \times 10^8$ km from the Sun. What must the numerical value and units of C be in order for the craft to have a speed of $0.10c$ when it is very far from the Sun? (Hint: $c = 3.00 \times 10^8$ m/s.) ••

46. In 1865, Jules Verne wrote a story in which three men went to the Moon by means of a shell shot from a large cannon sunk in the ground. (*a*) What muzzle speed must the cannon have in order for the shell to reach the Moon? (*b*) If the acceleration was constant throughout the muzzle, how long would the muzzle need to be in order to achieve this speed without exposing the men to an acceleration greater than $6g$? (*c*) Argue whether this launch method is practical or not. ••

47. The center-to-center distance between a 200-g lead sphere and an 800-g lead sphere is 0.120 m. A 1.00-g object is placed 0.0800 m from the center of the 800-g sphere along the line joining the centers of the two spheres. (*a*) Ignoring all sources of gravitational force except the two spheres, calculate the gravitational force exerted on the object. (*b*) Determine the gravitational potential energy per gram at the position of the object. (*c*) How much work is needed to bring the object 0.0400 m closer to the 800-g sphere? ••

48. Derive an expression for the gravitational potential energy of a system consisting of Earth and a brick of mass m placed at Earth's center. Take the potential energy for the system with the brick placed at infinity to be zero. •••

49. Is approximating the gravitational potential energy near the surface of the Sun as $mg_S\Delta x$ accurate over a smaller or larger range of values than approximating the gravitational potential energy near the surface of Earth as $mg_E\Delta x$? •••

50. A uniform rod of mass m_{rod} and length ℓ_{rod} lies along an x axis far from any stars or planets, with the center of the rod at the origin (Figure P13.50). A ball of mass m_{ball} is located at position x_{ball} on the axis. (*a*) Write an expression for the gravitational potential energy of the system made up of the ball and a small element dm_{rod} of the rod located at position x_{dm}. (*b*) Integrate your expression over the length of the rod to determine the potential energy of the system for $x_{ball} > \ell_{rod}/2$. (*c*) It can be shown that for such a system the gravitational force exerted by the rod on an object located a distance x from the origin is $F_x = -dU/dx$. Using this relationship, compute the force exerted by the rod on the ball at any distance x from the rod center. •••

Figure P13.50

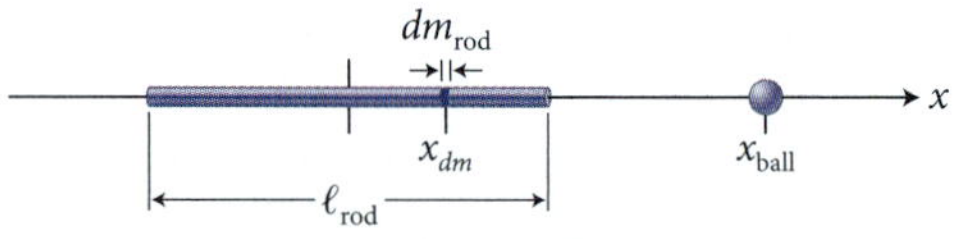

13.7 Celestial mechanics

51. The parabolic orbit of any asteroid around the Sun might be described as a collision between the two objects. Would it be better described as an elastic collision or an inelastic collision? •

52. Assume a particle is located at the surface of the Sun. (*a*) If the particle has mass m, how fast must it be moving away from the Sun's center of mass to escape the gravitational influence of the Sun? (*b*) At what speed must a particle of mass $2m$ move in order to escape the Sun's gravitational influence? •

53. What is the speed of a space probe when it is very far from Earth if it was launched from the surface of Earth at twice its escape speed? •

54. Which trip takes more rocket fuel: from Earth to the Moon or from the Moon to Earth? ••

55. A satellite moves at speed v in very low orbit about a moon that has no atmosphere. You launch a projectile vertically from the same moon's surface at the same speed v. To what height does it rise? ••

56. A satellite in an elliptical orbit around Earth has a speed of 8032 m/s when it is at perigee, the position in the orbit closest to Earth. At this position, the satellite is 112 km above Earth's surface. How far above the ground is the satellite when it is at apogee, the position in its orbit farthest from Earth? ••

57. A certain comet comes in on a parabolic approach around the Sun. Its perihelion is about the same distance from the Sun as the orbit of Mercury. How much faster than Mercury (expressed as a ratio) is the comet traveling at perihelion? ••

58. Show that for circular orbits of two objects about their center of mass, $E = \frac{1}{2}U = -K$. This is a special case of the more general mathematical statement known as the *virial theorem*. ••

59. An attractive central force exerted on a particle of mass m causes the particle to travel in a bound orbit. The orbit is elliptical with semimajor axis a, and the force has magnitude Cm/r^2, where C is a constant and r is the orbit radius. If the particle's speed is $v = \sqrt{C/2a}$ when it is farthest from the source of the force, what is its speed when it is nearest the force source? ••

60. A particle is leaving the Moon in a direction that is radially outward from both the Moon and Earth. What speed must it have to escape the Moon's gravitational influence? ••

61. A meteoroid passes through a position in space where its speed is very small relative to Earth's and it is at a perpendicular distance of 19 Earth radii above Earth's surface. The meteoroid is moving in such a way that Earth captures it. What is the speed of the meteoroid when it is one Earth radius above the ground? ••

62. A space probe can be either launched at escape speed from Earth or transported to a "parking orbit" above Earth and then launched. (*a*) If the parking orbit is 180 km above Earth's surface, what is the escape speed from the orbit? (*b*) What launch speed is required to have the probe escape Earth if it is launched from the ground? ••

63. Two identical stars, each of mass 3.0×10^{30} kg, revolve about a common center of mass that is 1.0×10^{11} m from the center of either star. (*a*) What is the rotational speed of the stars? (*b*) If a meteoroid passes through the center of mass, perpendicular to the orbital plane of the stars, how fast must the meteoroid be going if it is to escape the gravitational attraction of the stars? ••

64. Kepler's third law says that the square of the period of any planet is proportional to the cube of its mean distance from the Sun. Show that this law holds for elliptical orbits if one uses the semimajor axis as the mean distance. (Said another way, orbits that have the same energy but different angular momentum have the same period.) •••

65. Two celestial bodies of masses m_1 and m_2 are orbiting their center of mass at a center-to-center distance of d. Assume each body travels in a circular orbit about the center of mass of the system, and derive the general Newtonian form of Kepler's third law: $T^2 = 4\pi^2 d^3/G(m_1 + m_2)$. •••

66. To travel between Earth and any other planet requires consideration of such things as expenditure of fuel energy and travel time. To simplify the calculations, one chooses a path such that the position in Earth's orbit where the launch occurs and the position in the other planet's orbit when the spacecraft arrives define a line that passes through the Sun, as shown for an Earth-Mars transfer in Figure P13.66. The path the spacecraft travels is an ellipse that has the Sun at one focus. Such a path is called a Hohmann transfer orbit, and the major axis of the ellipse, $2a$, is the sum of the radii of the Earth's and the other planet's orbits around the Sun. Take $m_S = 1.99 \times 10^{30}$ kg, $m_M = 6.42 \times 10^{23}$ kg, $m_E = 5.97 \times 10^{24}$ kg, $a_E = 1.50 \times 10^{11}$ m, and $a_M = 2.28 \times 10^{11}$ m, and assume the planets have circular orbits. (*a*) What is the energy of the system comprising the Sun and a 1000-kg space probe in a Hohmann transfer orbit? (*b*) What is the speed of the probe in this orbit, as a function of r, the probe's radial distance from the Sun? (*c*) What is the probe's speed relative to the Sun as the probe enters the transfer orbit? (*d*) What is its speed relative to the Sun as it approaches Mars? (*e*) Given that the orbital speed of Earth is about 2.98×10^4 m/s, how much additional speed does the probe need to begin the transfer orbit? (*f*) What is the required launch speed from Earth's surface for a probe traveling to Mars in a Hohmann transfer orbit? •••

Figure P13.66

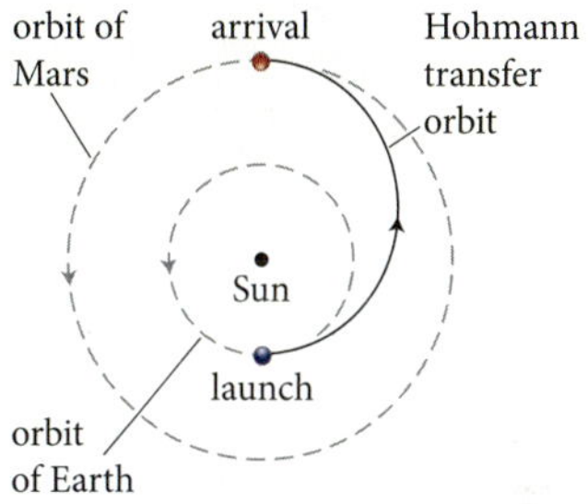

13.8 Gravitational force exerted by a sphere

67. A small disk of mass m is at the center of a larger disk that has an off-center hole drilled in it (Figure P13.67). What is the direction of the gravitational force exerted by the larger disk on the small one? •

Figure P13.67

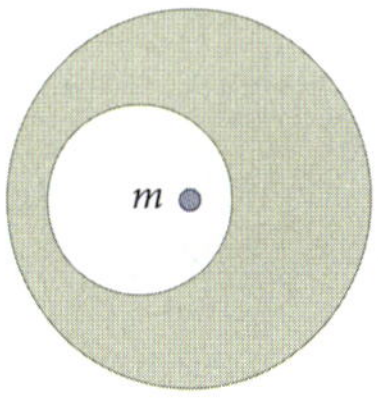

68. Is Eq. 13.37 for the gravitational force exerted by a solid sphere of mass m_s on some object of mass m_o when the two are a radial distance r apart, $F^G_{so} = Gm_o m_s/r^2$, valid for a sphere whose mass is not distributed uniformly? •

69. A uniform ring of mass m_{ring} and radius R_{ring} is shown in Figure P13.69. A small object of mass m_{obj} sits a separation distance s from the ring on the line that is perpendicular to the plane of the ring and passes through the ring's center. Obtain an expression (in terms of the given variables and universal constants) for the magnitude of the gravitational force exerted by the ring on the object. ••

Figure P13.69

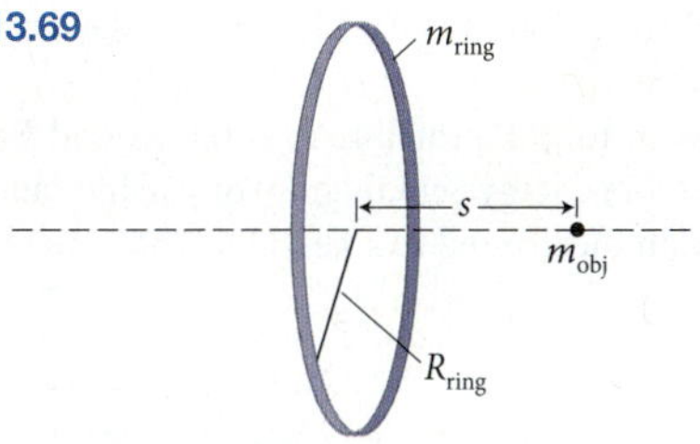

PRACTICE

70. Two uniform spherical shells are located such that their centers are along the x axis in Figure P13.70. The inner shell has mass m_{inner} and radius R, and its center is at $x = 0.80R$. The outer shell has mass $3.0m_{\text{inner}}$ and radius $2.0R$, and its center is at $x = 0$. What is the magnitude of the vector sum of the gravitational forces exerted by these two shells on an object of mass m_{obj} placed (*a*) at $x = 3.0R$, (*b*) at $x = 1.9R$, and (*c*) at $x = 0.90R$? ••

Figure P13.70

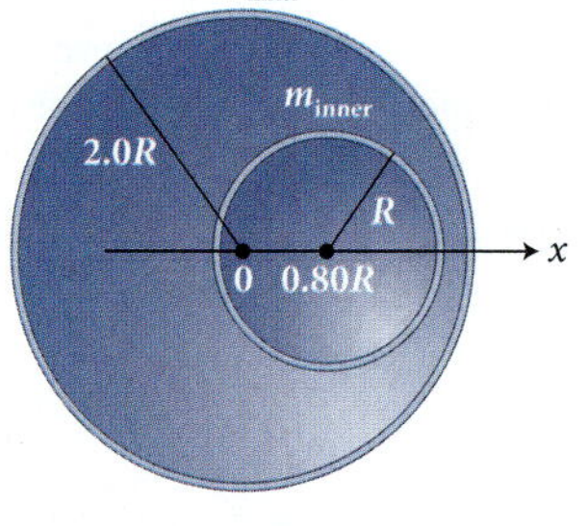

71. A thin disk of radius R has mass m_{disk} uniformly distributed over its area. (*a*) Derive an expression for the magnitude of the gravitational force this disk exerts on a particle of mass m_{part} located a distance y directly above the center of the disk. (*b*) If $y \gg R$, show that this expression reduces to that for two particles. •••

Additional Problems

72. In a system of N particles, how many terms are there in the expression for the gravitational potential energy of the system? •

73. You equip a rocket with enough fuel to reach escape speed from Earth. If you plan to launch the rocket from just above ground level, does it matter whether you launch it vertically, at an angle, or horizontally? •

74. What is the value of the acceleration g_{Venus} due to gravity at the surface of Venus? •

75. Is there any position in the elliptical orbit of a satellite where the tangential component of the acceleration is greater than the component perpendicular to the tangential component? If so, what conditions on the orbit must there be for such a position to exist? ••

76. The *gravitational vector field* $\vec{g}(\vec{r})$ is defined as the gravitational force exerted on a small object located at a particular position $\vec{r}$ divided by that object's mass. (*a*) Sketch the gravitational vector field produced by Earth at a sampling of positions around Earth. Make sure your vector lengths indicate the correct relative sizes. (*b*) Express the gravitational force exerted by Earth on an object of mass m_{obj} located a distance r_{obj} ($> r_E$) from Earth's center in terms of Earth's gravitational vector field. ••

77. Some writers of fiction have placed human beings on asteroids or other "planetoids" whose radius, in the illustrations accompanying the stories, seems not too much greater than the height of the people themselves! What would the density of such a celestial body have to be for the human to feel a gravitational attraction numerically equal to the attraction we feel to Earth? ••

78. You wish to put a satellite in orbit around Earth. (*a*) Which takes more energy per kilogram of satellite: launching the satellite from the ground to a height of 1600 km above the ground or placing the satellite into orbit once it has reached that altitude? (*b*) Repeat for an orbit 3200 km above the ground. (*c*) Repeat for an orbit 4800 km above the ground. ••

79. Unable to sleep, you crawl out of bed one evening and stare out your window at the night sky, finding Jupiter and sitting back to contemplate its grandeur. Remembering your physics, you imagine yourself at some height above the apparent surface of Jupiter, experiencing a gravitational force that has a magnitude equal to the magnitude of the gravitational force you experience at the surface of Earth. ••• CR

80. After seeing an old movie, you become concerned about a large asteroid that could be gravitationally attracted to Earth from very far away. You realize that long ago such an asteroid's speed relative to Earth's might have been very small, and thus you are able to calculate the relative speed it has at any separation distance from Earth. In order to get a baseline, you assume that the only object exerting a gravitational force on the asteroid is Earth, and you ignore the speed of Earth in its path around the Sun. What worries you is that observers might not sight the asteroid until it passes the imaginary line defining the Moon's orbit around Earth, and how little time that would give humanity to react. ••• CR

81. You are working on a project to plot the course of a spy satellite. The satellite has a polar orbit (which means it passes over both of Earth's poles during each orbit), and it is outfitted with a camera carrying a wide-angle lens that can "see" strips of land up to 2500 km wide. The enemy is believed to have chosen an elevation of orbit that just guarantees complete coverage of Earth each day by these surveillance strips. You cannot avoid or block the satellite unless you know where it is. ••• CR

82. While helping an astronomy professor, you discover a binary star system in which the two stars are in circular orbits about the system's center of mass. From their color and brightness, you determine that each star has the same mass as our Sun. The orbital period of the pair is 24.3 days, based on the oscillation of brightness observed as one star occludes (hides) the other. From this information you are able to ascertain the distance between the stars. ••• CR

83. Scientists still are not entirely sure whether the universe is open (which means it will keep expanding forever) or closed (which means it will eventually fall back in on itself in a "Big Crunch"). What determines whether it is open or closed is basically the same thing we calculate to determine escape speeds. Assume that the universe has a uniform density ρ. Then the mass contained in some spherical volume of space of radius R is $\frac{4}{3}\pi R^3\rho$. Model a galaxy located at the edge of this spherical volume as a particle and consider its energy. According to Hubble's law, the speed of this galaxy is HR, where $H = 2.2 \times 10^{-18}\ \text{s}^{-1}$ is called the Hubble constant. (*a*) What is the maximum density of the universe such that it does not close? (*b*) The current estimate of the density of the universe is $10^{-26}\ \text{kg/m}^3$, including about 25% *dark matter,* which is matter we cannot observe directly, and 70% *dark energy*, another constituent that is not directly observable. Both dark matter and dark energy contribute to gravity, though, and so are included in the density estimate. Compare this value with your result and discuss what difference it would make if there were no dark matter in the universe. •••

Answers to Review Questions

1. They exert forces of equal magnitude because the two forces in an interaction pair are always of equal magnitude. However, the Moon has the smaller mass, and so, from $a = F/m$, its acceleration is greater.
2. Several bits of evidence are presented in this section. First, the centripetal acceleration of the Moon (required to produce its known orbital radius and speed) matches the expected $1/r^2$ strength of gravity at the Moon's orbital radius (a distance of 60 Earth radii). Second, the proportionality between period squared and radius cubed for all planets, first identified by Kepler, agrees with a $1/r^2$ force law. Finally, there is the elliptical shape of the planetary orbits, which can be derived from the inverse square law plus conservation of energy.
3. Ellipse, circle, parabola, and hyperbola are possible.
4. Because period squared is proportional to orbital radius cubed, if the radius quadruples, then the period increases by a factor of 8. Thus a "year" on the planet is equivalent to eight years on Earth.
5. Mass is the property of an object that determines the magnitude of the gravitational force it feels due to, or exerts on, another object. Inertia is the property of an object that determines its acceleration under the influence of any nonzero vector sum of forces. These are very different concepts, even though it turns out that mass and inertia have been measured to be identical to great accuracy under ordinary circumstances.
6. The torque about this axis is zero because the lever arm is always zero. This means that the angular momentum about this axis does not change.
7. (1) Planets move in elliptical orbits with the Sun at one focus. (2) As a planet orbits the Sun, a straight line connecting the two bodies sweeps out equal areas in equal time intervals. (3) The period squared for any planet is proportional to its orbital radius cubed.
8. The force exerted in (*b*) and (*c*) is a central force and so causes zero torque. For angular momentum to change, the vector sum of torques must be nonzero.
9. The ISS. The acceleration due to gravity is independent of the orbiting object's mass and is inversely proportional to (the square of) the distance from Earth. Because the station orbits closer to Earth, its acceleration is greater.
10. Zero. During your entire trajectory, the spring scale is pulled toward the trampoline right along with you, so you do not exert any force on it.
11. Yes. The balance compares the normal forces needed to support each mass against their respective gravitational forces, but in free fall no such normal forces are needed. Thus the normal force is zero on each side; that is, it is still balanced.
12. The reading decreases because the supporting force exerted by the scale has a smaller magnitude when you are accelerating downward.
13. While the astronauts are in orbit, the gravitational force exerted on them by Earth is exactly the amount needed to supply the centripetal acceleration that keeps them in orbit. Thus there is no support force required to satisfy Newton's second law.
14. The principle of equivalence states that there is no way to distinguish locally between gravitational effects and those due to acceleration of the reference frame. The qualification *locally* must be used because over large scales the inverse square nature of gravitational forces would become apparent, causing, for example, the gravitational acceleration experienced by an object at two widely separated locations to be different.
15. Yes. According to the principle of equivalence, anything—including light—that moves close to any object that has mass must move in a curved path.
16. The gravitational force exerted by Earth on an object in free fall near the ground does indeed vary as $1/r^2$. However, as the object moves, the change in its distance r from Earth's center is negligible. Therefore the force and hence the acceleration g are constant to a very good approximation.
17. Not necessarily. The larger planet might also have a larger radius, and the acceleration due to gravity decreases inversely with the radius squared. In fact, the acceleration due to gravity on Saturn is very close to that on Earth.
18. The choice that the potential energy is zero when two objects in a system are infinitely far apart makes the potential energy at all finite distances negative.
19. For any choice of initial and final positions, the work done by the gravitational force on an object is the same regardless of the particular path over which the object moves to get from initial to final position.
20. It is reasonable over any distance that is much smaller than the separation distance r.
21. Strictly speaking, the path is an ellipse. You cannot throw an object fast enough so that its kinetic energy exceeds the gravitational potential energy of the Earth-object system. Thus the mechanical energy is negative and the path is elliptical. However, the path is well approximated by a parabola.
22. The speed is smallest when the planet is at aphelion and greatest when the planet is at perihelion.
23. It is just barely unbound; the object can "escape" to an infinite distance from the more massive object.
24. The orbit is an ellipse if the mechanical energy of the object-Sun system is negative (negative potential energy has a greater magnitude than positive kinetic energy). The circle is also possible as a special case of an ellipse with zero eccentricity. The orbit is one branch of a hyperbola if the mechanical energy of the object-Sun system is positive (positive kinetic energy has a greater magnitude than negative potential energy). If the mechanical energy is zero, the orbit is a parabola, the limiting case between an ellipse and a hyperbola.
25. The sphere is divided into concentric thin shells, and then a shell is divided into rings such that each ring lies between two planes perpendicular to the line joining the particle and the center of the sphere. The force exerted by a ring on the particle is computed, and then this is integrated to obtain the force exerted by one spherical shell. The results for each shell are then superposed to obtain the result for the full sphere.
26. The particle may be located inside the sphere; the same process yields a result of zero for the force on a particle inside a spherical shell. The sphere may be hollow because the process involves superposing the results for spherical shells. The density does not have to be uniform across the solid sphere, but it is assumed to be spherically symmetrical for each shell. Hence the density could vary with radius without affecting the result, but the result would change if the density varied with some other component of the position vector.

Answers to Guided Problems

Guided Problem 13.2 $R_{max} = 19$ km

Guided Problem 13.4 $\Delta x = 3.5$ km

Guided Problem 13.6 **vertical launch:** $r_{max} = \frac{16}{7}R_E$ or $h_{max} = \frac{9}{7}R_E$; **horizontal launch:** $r_{max} = \frac{9}{7}R_E$ or $h_{max} = \frac{2}{7}R_E$; **45° launch:** $r_{max} = 1.96R_E$ or $h_{max} = 0.96R_E$

Guided Problem 13.8 $a_{rock} = 0.089g$

14 PRACTICE Special Relativity

Chapter Summary

Time measurements (Sections 14.1, 14.2)

Concepts An **event** is a physical occurrence that takes place at a specific location at a specific instant.

Two events are **simultaneous** when they are observed to occur at the same instant in a reference frame made up of a grid of synchronized clocks. Events that are simultaneous in one reference frame need not be simultaneous in another reference frame moving relative to the first one.

An **invariant** is a quantity whose value does not depend on the choice of reference frame.

The **speed of light** is independent of the motion of the light source relative to any moving observer. Therefore the speed of light is an invariant. It is the limiting speed of any object moving relative to any other object.

Quantitative Tools In SI units, the speed of light in vacuum is $c_0 = 3.00 \times 10^8$ m/s.

Space-time (Sections 14.3, 14.5, 14.6)

Concepts The **proper time interval,** Δt_{proper}, is the time interval between two events that occur at the same position in a particular reference frame but at different instants. An observer measuring the proper time interval between two events records the shortest time interval between those events.

Time dilation: A clock moving relative to an observer is measured to be running more slowly than an identical clock at rest relative to that observer.

The **proper length,** ℓ_{proper}, of an object is the length of that object measured by an observer who is at rest relative to the object.

Length contraction: When an object moves at speed v relative to an observer, the observer measures the length ℓ_v of the object along the direction of its motion to be shorter than the proper length of the object.

Quantitative Tools For an object moving at speed v, the **Lorentz factor** γ is a measure of the extent to which relativity affects our everyday notions of length and time intervals:

$$\gamma \equiv \frac{1}{\sqrt{1 - v^2/c_0^2}}. \tag{14.6}$$

At nonrelativistic speeds ($v \leq 0.1c_0$), $\gamma \approx 1$, but it approaches infinity as v approaches c_0.

Time dilation: If Δt_{proper} is the proper time interval between two events measured by an observer for whom the two events occur at the same position but at different instants, then the time interval Δt_v between those events measured by an observer moving at speed v relative to the observer is

$$\Delta t_v = \gamma \Delta t_{\text{proper}}. \tag{14.13}$$

The **space-time interval** s^2 between two events that are separated by a time interval Δt and a space interval Δx is given by

$$s^2 \equiv (c_0 \Delta t)^2 - (\Delta x)^2. \tag{14.18}$$

If an object that has proper length ℓ_{proper} moves at speed v relative to an observer, that observer measures the length ℓ_v of the object to be

$$\ell_v = \frac{\ell_{\text{proper}}}{\gamma}. \tag{14.28}$$

The **Lorentz transformation equations** are relationships between the coordinates of an event e measured in two reference frames A and B that coincide at $t_A = t_B = 0$ and are moving in the x direction at constant velocity $\vec{v}_{AB}$ relative to each other:

$$t_{Be} = \gamma\left(t_{Ae} - \frac{v_{ABx}}{c_0^2} x_{Ae}\right) \tag{14.29}$$

$$x_{Be} = \gamma(x_{Ae} - v_{ABx} t_{Ae}) \tag{14.30}$$

$$y_{Be} = y_{Ae} \tag{14.31}$$

$$z_{Be} = z_{Ae}. \tag{14.32}$$

Velocity addition: From the Lorentz transformation equations, we find that $v_{\text{Ao}x}$, the x component of the velocity of an object o measured in reference frame A, is related to $v_{\text{Bo}x}$, the x component of its velocity measured in reference frame B, by

$$v_{\text{Bo}x} = \frac{v_{\text{Ao}x} - v_{\text{AB}x}}{1 - \frac{v_{\text{AB}x}}{c_0^2} v_{\text{Ao}x}}. \tag{14.33}$$

Energy and momentum (Sections 14.4, 14.7, 14.8)

Concepts The internal energy E_{int} of an object (energy not associated with the object's motion) is an invariant and is proportional to the object's mass m (the property that determines its gravitational interaction). Mass is also an invariant.

Unlike mass, inertia (a quantitative measure of an object's tendency to resist any change in its velocity) is not an invariant: What an observer measures for an object's inertia depends on the motion of the observer relative to the object.

Quantitative Tools For an object of mass m, its inertia m_v is

$$m_v = \gamma m, \tag{14.41}$$

its momentum $\vec{p}$ is

$$\vec{p} = \gamma m \vec{v}, \tag{14.42}$$

and its kinetic energy K is

$$K = (\gamma - 1) m c_0^2. \tag{14.51}$$

The energy E of an object of mass m and inertia m_v is

$$E = m_v c_0^2, \tag{14.53}$$

and its internal energy E_{int} is

$$E_{\text{int}} = m c_0^2. \tag{14.54}$$

Review Questions

Answers to these questions can be found at the end of this chapter.

14.1 Time measurements

1. What is an event?
2. Name two attributes of clocks that allow us to measure precisely the instants at which various events occur.
3. What must happen in order for an event to be observed?
4. What must you observe about the locations of two events in order to measure the proper time interval between them?
5. Describe what an observer must do to measure the instant at which an event occurs in a reference frame that consists of synchronized clocks placed at various equally spaced positions.

14.2 *Simultaneous* is a relative term

6. Where must a simultaneity detector be placed in order to determine whether two events are simultaneous? When placed at that location, how does the detector operate?
7. How does the speed of light in vacuum depend on the relative velocity of the source and the observer?
8. What can you say about the simultaneity of two events seen by two observers moving relative to each other along the line joining the events?

14.3 Space-time

9. Clock A is moving relative to identical clock B. To an observer at rest relative to B, how does the rate at which A runs compare with the rate at which B runs?
10. Cite two experiments that give direct evidence for time dilation.
11. What is the proper length of an object?
12. What is length contraction?

14.4 Matter and energy

13. What experimental evidence shows that the kinetic energy expression $K = \frac{1}{2}mv^2$ does not apply at relativistic speeds?
14. Which of the variables—inertia, mass, kinetic energy, and internal energy—are invariant, and which depend on the reference frame of the person measuring them?
15. If you change the internal energy of a system, does the system's inertia change, and if so, how?
16. What happens to an object's inertia when you decrease the object's kinetic energy?

14.5 Time dilation

17. What is the definition of the Lorentz factor, and at what speed do its effects on space-time properties become noticeable?
18. What is the relationship between the proper time interval between two events and the time interval between the events measured by an observer for whom the events occur at different locations?
19. What is the difference among *timelike, lightlike,* and *spacelike* values of the space-time interval $s^2 = (c_0\Delta t)^2 - (\Delta x)^2$ between two events?
20. How does the nature of the space-time interval between events (*timelike, lightlike,* or *spacelike*) affect the principle of causality?

14.6 Length contraction

21. What is the relationship between the proper length of an object and the length measured by an observer moving relative to the object?
22. How are time dilation and length contraction related to each other? Consider muons traveling from the top of Earth's atmosphere to the ground to support your answer.
23. What are the requirements for validity of the Lorentz transformation equations? How do they differ from the requirements for the time dilation and length contraction equations (Eqs. 14.13 and 14.28)?

14.7 Conservation of momentum

24. The momentum of a particle was defined in Chapter 4 as the product of its inertia and its velocity. What change, if any, is required so that momentum can be defined for a particle that is traveling at a relativistic speed?
25. Does the momentum of an isolated system remain constant when one or more components travel at a relativistic speed?
26. What is the relationship (*a*) between the mass m of a particle and the inertia m_v we measure as the particle moves at some speed v relative to us, and (*b*) between the particle's inertia and its momentum?

14.8 Conservation of energy

27. How does the mathematical expression for the kinetic energy of a particle moving at relativistic speeds differ from that for a particle moving at nonrelativistic speeds? Are the two expressions compatible?
28. For a system of mass m, what does the quantity mc_0^2 represent?
29. For a system of mass m, what does the quantity γmc_0^2 represent?
30. What is the difference between *conserved* and *invariant,* and how is this difference relevant when we measure energy and momentum?

Developing a Feel

Make an order-of-magnitude estimate of each of the following quantities. Letters in parentheses refer to hints below. Use them as needed to guide your thinking.

1. The difference between 1 and the Lorentz factor for a high-speed rifle bullet (E, T)
2. The difference between the time intervals needed to complete your walking trip, as measured by you and by your friend at rest in the Earth reference frame, beginning when you depart New York City and ending when you reach Los Angeles (Each of you measures only the time intervals you spend *walking*.) (V, J, M, B)
3. The difference between the time intervals, as measured by an astronaut on board the International Space Station (ISS) and by an observer at rest in the Earth reference frame, beginning when the ISS passes directly above Los Angeles and ending when the ISS is directly above New York City (F, J, U, C, P)
4. The length by which the distance from New York City to Los Angeles is contracted when measured by an observer moving east to west relative to Earth at the speed of the ISS (F, J, U, C, P)
5. The distance traveled by a pion during its lifetime, 26 ns in the pion rest reference frame, when the particle is moving at a speed of $0.995c_0$, as measured by an observer at rest in the Earth reference frame (H, Q)
6. The extra inertia in the Earth reference frame of a midsize car traveling at highway speed compared to the same car at rest (R, D, O)
7. The amount of mass converted to energy in the Sun every second (N, A, G)
8. The ratio of the energy of a proton moving at $0.99999c_0$ in the Earth reference frame to the *kinetic* energy of a snail in the same reference frame (S, L, I, K)

Hints

A. What is the distance from the Sun to Earth?
B. What is the Lorentz factor for your walking speed in the Earth reference frame?
C. What fraction of an orbital period does the ISS need to travel from Los Angeles to New York City in the Earth reference frame?
D. What is the Lorentz factor for this speed? (You calculated this in *Principles* Checkpoint 14.14.)
E. What is the speed of a high-speed bullet in the Earth reference frame?
F. At what height does the ISS orbit in the Earth reference frame?
G. How much power does the Sun generate?
H. What length of Earth moves past the pion during its lifetime in the pion reference frame?
I. What is the mass of a snail?
J. What is the distance from New York City to Los Angeles in the Earth reference frame?
K. What is the top speed of a snail in the Earth reference frame?
L. What is the Lorentz factor for this proton in the Earth reference frame?
M. What time interval (in the Earth reference frame) would you need to walk that distance nonstop?
N. What is the amount of average solar power that arrives at each square meter of Earth?
O. What is the mass of a midsize car?
P. What is the Lorentz factor for the ISS in the Earth reference frame?
Q. What is the Lorentz factor for the pion in the Earth reference frame?
R. What is a typical highway speed in the Earth reference frame?
S. What is the mass of a proton?
T. What is the Lorentz factor for this bullet in the Earth reference frame?
U. What is the period of orbit of the ISS in the Earth reference frame?
V. What is your average walking speed in the Earth reference frame?

Key (all values approximate)

A. 2×10^{11} m; **B.** $1 + 2 \times 10^{-17}$; **C.** 1×10^{-1}; **D.** $1 + 5 \times 10^{-15}$; **E.** 1×10^{3} m/s; **F.** 4×10^{2} km; **G.** 5×10^{26} W; **H.** 8 m; **I.** 10^{-2} kg; **J.** 4×10^{6} m; **K.** 10^{-3} m/s; **L.** 2×10^{2}; **M.** 2×10^{6} s; **N.** 1×10^{3} W/m^2; **O.** 1×10^{3} kg; **P.** $1 + 3 \times 10^{-10}$; **Q.** 1×10^{1}; **R.** 3×10^{1} m/s; **S.** 2×10^{-27} kg; **T.** $1 + 6 \times 10^{-12}$; **U.** 9×10^{1} min; **V.** 2×10^{0} m/s

PRACTICE

Worked and Guided Problems

Procedure: Time and length measurements at very high speeds

At very high speeds, measurements of lengths and time intervals depend on the reference frame. Problems involving objects or observers moving at very high speeds therefore require extra care when we consider lengths and time intervals.

1. Identify each observer or reference frame with a letter and determine in which reference frame each numerical quantity given in the problem statement is measured.
2. If the problem involves any time intervals, identify the events that define that time interval. Determine in which observer's reference frame, if any, the two events occur at the same position. This observer measures the proper time interval between the events (Figure 14.26).
3. Identify any distances or lengths mentioned in the problem. Determine for which observer, if any, the object defining that distance or length remains at rest. This observer measures the proper length (Figure 14.29).
4. Use Eqs. 14.13 and 14.28 to determine the time intervals and lengths in reference frames other than the ones in which the intervals and lengths are given.

These examples involve material from this chapter but are not associated with any particular section. Some examples are worked out in detail; others you should work out by following the guidelines provided.

Worked Problem 14.1 Space rescue

You are playing a rescue dispatcher on Earth in a video game involving interstellar travel. In the game, a spaceship that left Earth a few months ago, accelerating toward the star Vega, has suffered an engine failure and is now drifting toward Vega. A distress signal from the ship has been received on Earth, with the signal pulses arriving 2.00 s apart. You know that the distress beacon on the disabled ship emits pulses 1.00 s apart in the ship's reference frame. (*a*) In order to give instructions to a rescue crew being sent out, you must know the speed at which the disabled ship is drifting toward Vega. What is this speed in the Earth reference frame? (*b*) The standard reply signal telling a disabled ship that help is on the way consists of pulses arriving at the ship 1.00 s apart. If the disabled ship is to receive these reply pulses at 1.00-s intervals, what interval between pulses must you use in sending the reply signal?

❶ GETTING STARTED The problem asks us to relate the time difference between the pulses that are emitted in one reference frame and the pulses that are received in another reference frame, so let us consider two pairs of events: Event 1 is the emission of a pulse by the spaceship, and event 2 is the emission of the next pulse by the ship. Event 3 is the reception of the first pulse on Earth, and event 4 is the reception of the next pulse on Earth. Events 1 and 2 occur at the same location relative to the disabled ship, so crewmembers on the ship measure the proper time interval between those two events. Events 3 and 4 occur at the same location relative to Earth, so we measure the proper time interval between them. Because the ship is moving at constant speed with respect to Earth, we can use the formula for time dilation to determine the time interval between events 1 and 2 in the Earth reference frame. We need to remember, though, that we measure the instant at which an event takes place with a clock that is at rest in our reference frame *at the location of the event.* Because events 1 and 2 take place at different locations in the Earth reference frame, the time interval that we measure between them is not the same as the time interval that we measure between events 3 and 4. These two intervals are, however, related by the speed of the ship and the speed of the signal (that is, the speed of light, c_0).

We get oriented with a sketch showing the four events of interest in both the Earth and Ship reference frames (Figure WG14.1).

Figure WG14.1

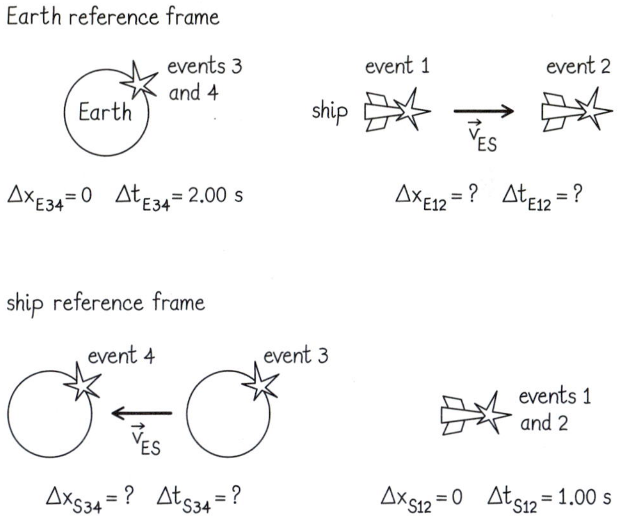

From the point of view of the crew on the disabled ship, they are at rest and Earth is moving away from them at the constant speed that we measure for the ship. Because the respective situations are symmetrical, we should be able to use similar reasoning to solve parts *a* and *b*.

❷ DEVISE PLAN Because the crewmembers on the disabled ship measure the proper time interval between events 1 and 2, we know that the interval as measured in the Earth reference frame is longer by the Lorentz factor, γ:

$$\Delta t_{E12} = \gamma \Delta t_{S12}. \quad (1)$$

PRACTICE

In the Earth reference frame, the time interval it takes for the signals to reach Earth is the distance from the ship to Earth divided by the speed of light, so

$$\begin{aligned}\Delta t_{E34} &= t_{E4} - t_{E3} \\ &= (t_{E2} + x_{E2}/c_0) - (t_{E1} + x_{E1}/c_0) \\ &= \Delta t_{E12} + \Delta x_{E12}/c_0. \qquad (2)\end{aligned}$$

The distance that the ship moves between events 1 and 2 is the ship's speed multiplied by the time interval:

$$\Delta x_{E12} = v_{ES}\Delta t_{E12}. \qquad (3)$$

Substituting first Eq. 3 and then Eq. 1 into Eq. 2 gives

$$\begin{aligned}\Delta t_{E34} &= \Delta t_{E12} + v_{ES}\Delta t_{E12}/c_0 \\ &= \Delta t_{E12}(1 + v_{ES}/c_0) \\ &= \gamma\Delta t_{S12}(1 + v_{ES}/c_0),\end{aligned}$$

which we can simplify by using the definition of the Lorentz factor:

$$\begin{aligned}\Delta t_{E34} &= \frac{\Delta t_{S12}}{\sqrt{1 - (v_{ES}/c_0)^2}}(1 + v_{ES}/c_0) \\ &= \Delta t_{S12}\sqrt{\frac{(1 + v_{ES}/c_0)^2}{1 - (v_{ES}/c_0)^2}} \\ &= \Delta t_{S12}\sqrt{\frac{1 + v_{ES}/c_0}{1 - v_{ES}/c_0}}. \qquad (4)\end{aligned}$$

Finally, we can solve Eq. 4 for v_{ES}, the speed of the ship in the Earth reference frame:

$$\begin{aligned}\Delta t_{E34}^2(1 - v_{ES}/c_0) &= \Delta t_{S12}^2(1 + v_{ES}/c_0) \\ \Delta t_{E34}^2 - \Delta t_{S12}^2 &= \Delta t_{E34}^2 v_{ES}/c_0 + \Delta t_{S12}^2 v_{ES}/c_0 \\ &= v_{ES}(\Delta t_{E34}^2/c_0 + \Delta t_{S12}^2/c_0) \\ v_{ES} &= c_0\frac{\Delta t_{E34}^2 - \Delta t_{S12}^2}{\Delta t_{E34}^2 + \Delta t_{S12}^2}.\end{aligned}$$

❸ **EXECUTE PLAN** (*a*) Substituting the time intervals measured in each reference frame, we obtain

$$v_{ES} = c_0\frac{(2.00\ \text{s})^2 - (1.00\ \text{s})^2}{(2.00\ \text{s})^2 + (1.00\ \text{s})^2} = c_0\frac{3.00}{5.00} = 0.600c_0. ✔$$

(b) Because the relationship between the Earth reference frame and the ship's reference frames is symmetrical, we can use Eq. 4—but this time with E and S exchanged and labeling the two emissions on Earth as 5 and 6 and the two receptions on the ship as 7 and 8—to determine the ratio between the rate of pulses that are sent from Earth and the rate of pulses that are received on the ship:

$$\Delta t_{S78} = \Delta t_{E56}\sqrt{\frac{1 + v_{SE}/c_0}{1 - v_{SE}/c_0}}$$

$$\Delta t_{E56} = \Delta t_{S78}\sqrt{\frac{1 - v_{SE}/c_0}{1 + v_{SE}/c_0}}$$

$$\Delta t_{E56} = (1.00\ \text{s})\sqrt{\frac{1 - 0.600}{1 + 0.600}} = 0.500\ \text{s}. ✔$$

❹ **EVALUATE RESULT** The speed that we calculated in part *a* is substantial. An interstellar ship would have to move at great speed to travel between stars in a reasonable amount of time.

It makes sense that the ship's speed is relativistic because of the large factor by which the received pulse rate differs from the rate at which the pulses were emitted. It also makes sense that we got the same factor for the Earth-to-ship pulses as for the ship-to-Earth pulses because of the symmetry of their situations with respect to each other.

As a check on our math, we can compare the invariant interval between events 1 and 2 using numerical values from each reference frame:

$$s^2 = (c_0\Delta t^2) - \Delta x^2$$

For events 1 and 2 in the Earth frame we have (using Eqs. 1 and 3):

$$\begin{aligned}s_{12}^2 &= (c_0\Delta t_{E12})^2 - \Delta x_{E12}^2 = (c_0\Delta t_{E12})^2 - (v_{ES}\Delta t_{E12})^2 \\ &= (c_0\gamma\Delta t_{S12})^2 - (v_{ES}\gamma\Delta t_{S12})^2 \\ &= [(1.25c_0\ \text{m/s})(1.00\ \text{s})]^2 - [(0.600c_0\ \text{m/s})(1.25)(1.00\ \text{s})]^2 \\ &= c_0^2\ \text{m}^2\end{aligned}$$

In the Ship frame

$$\begin{aligned}s_{12}^2 &= (c_0\Delta t_{S12})^2 - \Delta x_{S12}^2 \\ &= [(c_0\ \text{m/s})(1.00\ \text{s})] - 0 \\ &= c_0^2\ \text{m}^2\end{aligned}$$

This is reassuring.

We are reminded that, when we consider objects that move at relativistic speeds, what we measure for distant events is not what we actually see when we look at them: When an object is moving at a significant fraction of the speed of light, we have to account for the finite time interval that it takes for light to travel from the object to our eyes (or another detector) because we define our measurements as being made locally to the events. In this situation, with the disabled spaceship moving away from Earth, the time interval between the pulses that we receive on Earth is even longer than the time-dilated interval that we measure for the emission of those pulses from the ship. If the ship had been approaching Earth, the time interval between the pulses that we received on Earth would have been shorter than the time interval that we measured for their emission from the ship. (The sign of Δx in Eq. 2 would be opposite, giving us the inverse ratio in Eq. 4.)

Guided Problem 14.2 Relativistic fly-by

Spaceship A makes a fly-by of space station B at very close distance. The duty officer on B determines that, during the fly-by, the length of A was 50.0 m in the reference frame of B. Records show that the measured length of A was 80.0 m when A was in dry-dock on B. (*a*) What does the duty officer on B measure for A's speed during the fly-by? (*b*) The crew on B measures the length of B to be 200 m. What length does an observer on A measure for the length of B during the fly-by?

1 GETTING STARTED

1. Which reference frames should you compare?
2. For each reference frame you use, make a sketch of the objects involved and the information you know about them.

2 DEVISE PLAN

3. How is the speed you must determine related to the two lengths given for the spaceship?
4. Is there any reference frame in which the station length you must determine is a proper length?

3 EXECUTE PLAN

4 EVALUATE RESULT

5. Are your proper lengths greater than their corresponding nonproper lengths?

Worked Problem 14.3 Galactic fireworks

A fast *nova* (from the Latin, *nova stella*, "new star") occurs when a white dwarf star experiences a runaway nuclear reaction, which increases its brightness dramatically during a short interval of time. The enhanced brightness then persists for about a month. Suppose that bright light from "new star" A first appears to observers at MacDonald Observatory on Earth at 11:00 p.m. on July 12. Measurements indicate that star A is moving almost directly away from Earth with a relative speed of 6.0×10^4 m/s and is first observed approximately 9.33×10^{16} m from Earth in the direction of Vega. While still studying star A, observers see another "new star," star B, also in the direction of Vega. Bright light from star B first arrives at the observatory at 2:00 a.m. on July 30, and measurements indicate that star B is moving almost directly away from Earth with a relative speed of 4.0×10^4 m/s and is first observed approximately 6.63×10^{16} m from Earth. (*a*) Determine the space-time interval between these two events: star A goes nova and star B goes nova. (*b*) Describe an inertial reference frame in which these two events are simultaneous, or argue that such a reference frame does not exist.

1 GETTING STARTED The information we have is from the Earth reference frame, so we begin with a picture of the situation in that reference frame (Figure WG14.2). It is convenient to choose an x axis along the straight line that contains both stars and Earth. We arbitrarily choose the positive direction to be toward Vega (toward both new stars). We can compute the light travel time from each star from the given distance. It may be necessary to adjust for the stellar motion, but we have speed and direction information in any case. This should allow us to compute both the x component of displacement between the two events and the time interval between the two events in the Earth reference frame. The value of the space-time interval is the same in all inertial reference frames. It can be computed directly from these Δx and Δt values in the Earth reference frame. Depending on the sign of this result, we should be able to determine whether there is a reference frame in which the events are simultaneous. If there is, such a reference frame could be imagined as moving past Earth at some relative velocity in the x direction—that is, toward one new star and away from the other.

Figure WG14.2

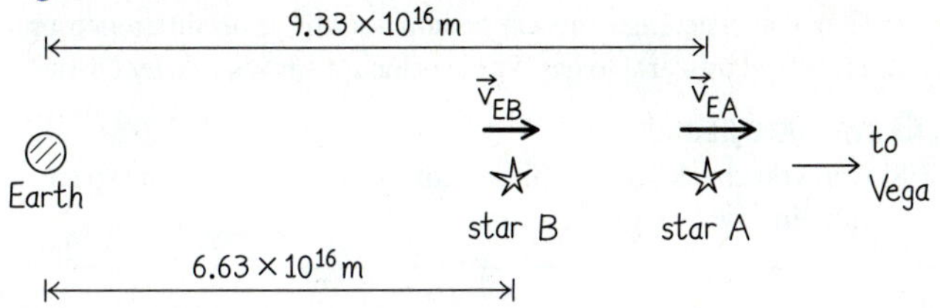

2 DEVISE PLAN For part *a*, the space-time interval between two events can be computed in any reference frame using Eq. 14.18:

$$s^2 = (c_0\Delta t)^2 - (\Delta x)^2.$$

We have enough information to compute the displacement and time interval between the two specified events, but we must decide whether the velocities of the two stars relative to Earth should be taken into account. Both relative velocities are of order of magnitude 10^5 m/s, and the time interval between observations of "first" light from the two stars is of the order 10^6 s. This means that star A might have moved as much as $d = vt = (10^5 \text{ m/s})(10^6 \text{ s}) = 10^{11}$ m before star B was first observed. However, we are given stellar distance information to three significant digits, and both distances are of the order 10^{17} m. Thus any consideration of additional distance due to stellar motion is several digits beyond the precision of our data. In addition, relativistic effects depend on the Lorentz factor:

$$\gamma = \frac{1}{\sqrt{(1 - v^2/c_0^2)}}.$$

For the given relative velocities of these stars, the difference between γ and 1 is on the order of 10^{-8}, which is well beyond the precision of our distance information and, assuming we know the measured times to within 1 minute, also several digits beyond the precision of our time data. Thus a simple calculation of light travel time is appropriate in determining the space-time interval.

For part *b*, the space-time interval can be positive, negative, or zero. If it is positive, the interval is timelike, and it is possible to establish a definite order of events. Thus one of the two events occurs first in all inertial reference frames, and there is no inertial reference frame in which the two events are simultaneous. If the space-time interval is negative, the interval is spacelike. In this case, there is a reference frame in which the events are simultaneous, and we can obtain it by using a simultaneity detector—that is, by devising a reference frame that receives light from each event at an instant when it is equidistant in space between the two events. If the space-time interval is zero, it is lightlike in all inertial reference frames, so a ray of light could travel from one event to the other. Because the speed of light is the same in all reference frames, the events cannot be simultaneous unless they occur at exactly the same place.

❸ **EXECUTE PLAN**

(*a*) The time interval between the two events must be computed using the travel time of light. We observe star A at the location where its light originated—that is, where the star was when it "went nova." Light would require a time interval of

$$\Delta t_{EA} = \frac{\Delta x_{EA}}{c_0}$$

to travel from star A to Earth.

Similarly, the travel time for light from the second event to reach Earth is

$$\Delta t_{EB} = \frac{\Delta x_{EB}}{c_0}.$$

However, these time intervals overlap because star B does not wait for light from star A to reach Earth before "going nova." Thus the time interval between the two events is the difference in the two light travel times plus the delay in reception of the signal from star B compared to star A. The result is a time interval, in the Earth reference frame, between the two events of

$$\Delta t_E = \Delta t_{EA} - \Delta t_{EB} + \Delta t_{E\,\text{detection}}$$

$$= \frac{\Delta x_{EA}}{c_0} - \frac{\Delta x_{EA}}{c_0} + \Delta t_{E\,\text{detection}}$$

$$= \frac{9.33 \times 10^{16}\ \text{m}}{3.00 \times 10^8\ \text{m/s}} - \frac{6.63 \times 10^{16}\ \text{m}}{3.00 \times 10^8\ \text{m/s}}$$

$$+ \left[17\ \text{days}\left(\frac{24\ \text{h}}{1\ \text{day}}\right) + 3\ \text{h}\right]\left(\frac{3600\ \text{s}}{1\ \text{h}}\right)$$

$$= (3.11 \times 10^8\ \text{s}) - (2.21 \times 10^8\ \text{s}) + (1.48 \times 10^6\ \text{s})$$

$$= 9.15 \times 10^7\ \text{s}.$$

The displacement between the two events is, to the precision available, simply the difference in their apparent positions when they went nova:

$$\Delta x_{EA} = 9.33 \times 10^{16}\ \text{m}$$

$$\Delta x_{EB} = 6.63 \times 10^{16}\ \text{m}$$

$$\Delta x_E = \Delta x_{EA} - \Delta x_{EB} = (9.33 \times 10^{16}\ \text{m}) - (6.63 \times 10^{16}\ \text{m})$$

$$= 2.70 \times 10^{16}\ \text{m}.$$

The space-time interval is then

$$s^2 = (c_0 \Delta t_E)^2 - (\Delta x_E)^2$$

$$= [(3.00 \times 10^8\ \text{m/s})(9.15 \times 10^7\ \text{s})]^2 - (2.70 \times 10^{16}\ \text{m})^2$$

$$= 2.4 \times 10^{31}\ \text{m}^2. \checkmark$$

(*b*) The invariant space-time interval is positive, or timelike, so it must be possible to order the events in time. Indeed, star A must go nova first; otherwise, the light from star B, which is closer to Earth, would arrive first. This is true in any inertial reference frame. It is therefore not possible to construct an inertial reference frame in which the events are simultaneous. ✔

❹ **EVALUATE RESULT** Distances between stars are typically very large. The stars in this problem are at distances on the order of 10^{17} m, which is about the distance light travels in 10 years.

For part *a*, the space-time interval is less than $(c_0 \Delta t_E)^2$, which is consistent for events that do not occur at the same location. The time required for light to travel between stars A and B is slightly smaller than the time interval we computed between the events, so in principle a signal from one star could have triggered the other to explode. This is also consistent with a timelike interval between events.

For part *b*, we know that events separated by a timelike space-time interval in one reference frame are also separated by a timelike interval in any other inertial reference frame; hence, they cannot be simultaneous in any reference frame.

Guided Problem 14.4 Lorentz would love it

Observers Carol and Diane move at constant velocity relative to each other along a straight line. They agree to align the positive *x* axis of their respective reference frames along this line. They set their respective clocks to zero just as the origins of the two *x* axes coincide. Diane then observes event 1 at $x_{D1} = +400$ m, $t_{D1} = 1.00 \times 10^{-6}$ s, and event 2 at $x_{D2} = +900$ m, $t_{D2} = 5.00 \times 10^{-7}$ s. Carol observes these two events as occurring simultaneously. (*a*) What is the velocity $\vec{v}_{DC}$ of Carol relative to Diane? (*b*) At what instant does Carol observe the events?

❶ **GETTING STARTED**

1. For each reference frame, make a sketch of the objects involved and the information you know about them.
2. Is any length a proper length in one of the reference frames? Is any time interval a proper time interval in one of the reference frames?

❷ **DEVISE PLAN**

3. What general transformation equation relates time and space coordinates in different reference frames?
4. How can you express Carol's observations of the time coordinates of events 1 and 2 in terms of Diane's observations of the same events?
5. How can you express the difference in time between events 1 and 2 as measured by Carol in terms of Diane's coordinates?
6. Can the Lorentz factor that relates Carol's reference frame to Diane's reference frame be zero?

❸ **EXECUTE PLAN**

7. Can you rearrange the expression for the time difference as measured by Carol to get Carol's velocity as measured by Diane?

❹ **EVALUATE RESULT**

8. Can you check your result for consistency by using the space-time interval between events?

Worked Problem 14.5 To the stars!

The first interstellar exploration spaceship passes remote science post P and has already turned off its engines to coast at a constant cruising speed for its journey beyond the star Alpha Centauri. The scientists on post P measure the ship's speed to be $0.600c_0$. Because Alpha Centauri is known to be 4.00×10^{16} m distant from post P, according to measurements made on post P, the scientists have some time to plan a celebration of humans moving past Alpha Centauri. Cleverly, they schedule the festivities so that astronauts aboard the ship will observe (through their telescopes) the beginning of the scientists' celebration at the same instant the ship speeds past Alpha Centauri. (*a*) What time interval is required for the trip according to spaceship clocks? (*b*) How much time will have elapsed on post P between the instant the ship passes their post and the start of the celebration?

❶ **GETTING STARTED** Because we need to compare information from post P and the ship, we need to analyze the problem from the perspective of both the scientists at post P and the astronauts on the ship. We define two reference frames: reference frame P attached to the post and reference frame S attached to the spaceship. Thus the ship's speed relative to the post is $v_{PS} = 0.600c_0$. We are told that in reference frame P, the distance to Alpha Centauri is 4.00×10^{16} m. We define event 0 to occur when the ship passes the post, event 1 to be when the ship reaches Alpha Centauri, event 2 to occur when the party starts at post P, and event 3 to be when the astronauts on the ship as it passes Alpha Centauri observe the party starting. It is useful to note that, in order for the astronauts to observe the party starting, the light from that event must travel from post P to the ship. We can think of this light representing the start of the party as a signal sent (event 2) and received (event 3). Table WG14.1 organizes the information we know about these events. For convenience, we choose the origin of both time and position in both reference frames at event 0, with the positive x axis pointing toward Alpha Centauri in reference frame P and toward post P in reference frame S. This allows all x components to be positive for each event in each reference frame.

❷ **DEVISE PLAN** We can glean significant information about the trip from the time dilation equation (Eq. 14.13). In order to determine the time interval for the trip according to scientists at post P ($\Delta t_{P01} = t_{P1} - t_{P0}$), we divide the distance traveled by the spaceship as measured in reference frame P by the ship's speed. Because in reference frame S events 0 and 1 both take place at the location of the ship, the time interval between these two events as measured by the ship's clocks ($\Delta t_{S01} = t_{S1} - t_{S0}$) is a proper time interval in reference frame S. Therefore we can use Eq. 14.13 to relate Δt_{S01} and Δt_{P01}, using the appropriate Lorentz factor given by Eq. 14.6. The v in the Lorentz factor is equal to the speed of the ship relative to the monitoring post: $v = v_{PS} = 0.600c_0$.

Because events 1 and 3 are simultaneous in reference frame S, we know that $\Delta t_{S03} = \Delta t_{S01}$. Because event 2 takes place at the post, we know that Δt_{P02} is a proper time interval in reference frame P. Thus we can add some information to Table WG14.1 by using Eq. 14.13. Sorting events 2 and 3 requires something more general, however. We use the invariant (reference-frame-independent) speed of light plus the invariant space-time interval s^2 to compare information between reference frames and then calculate the desired temporal information.

❸ **EXECUTE PLAN** The time interval Δt_{P01} needed for the spaceship to reach Alpha Centauri as measured by clocks at the monitoring post is

$$\Delta t_{P01} = \frac{d_{P01}}{v_{PS}} = \frac{4.00 \times 10^{16}\ \text{m}}{0.600(3.00 \times 10^8\ \text{m/s})} = 2.22 \times 10^8\ \text{s}.$$

We then use Eq. 14.6 to determine the Lorentz factor:

$$\gamma = \frac{1}{\sqrt{1 - v_{PS}^2/c_0^2}} = \frac{1}{\sqrt{1 - (0.600)^2}} = \frac{1}{0.800} = 1.25.$$

(*a*) Now we can use Eq. 14.13 to determine what clocks on the spaceship measure for the proper time interval needed for the ship to travel from the monitoring post to Alpha Centauri:

$$\Delta t_{S01} = \frac{\Delta t_{P01}}{\gamma_{PS}} = \frac{2.22 \times 10^8\ \text{s}}{1.25} = 1.78 \times 10^8\ \text{s}. ✔$$

Both Δt_{S01} and Δt_{P01} begin at $t = 0$, and so we now have full information about events 0 and 1 in Table WG14.1:

$$t_{S1} = 1.78 \times 10^8\ \text{s}, \quad t_{P1} = 2.22 \times 10^8\ \text{s}.$$

Note that we also have most of the information about event 3, missing only a value for t_{P3}. In reference frame S, events 1 and 3 are simultaneous and occur at the same position. This means that in this reference frame the space-time interval s^2 between events 1 and 3 is zero. Thus these two events are separated by a lightlike space-time interval. Events that are simultaneous *and* occur at the same location in one reference frame must also be simultaneous and occur at some common location in *any* inertial reference frame. This is not immediately obvious because it might be possible to calculate a number of different time and space intervals between events 1 and 3 that, when combined, give a space-time interval $s^2 = 0$.

Table WG14.1 Events for Worked Problem 14.5

Event	t_S	x_S	t_P	x_P
0: ship passes post P	$t_{S0} = 0$	$x_{S0} = 0$	$t_{P0} = 0$	$x_{P0} = 0$
1: ship arrives at AC	t_{S1}	$x_{S1} = 0$	t_{P1}	$x_{P1} = +4.00 \times 10^{16}$ m
2: signal that party starts sent from post P	t_{S2}	x_{S2}	t_{P2}	$x_{P2} = 0$
3: signal that party starts received by ship at AC	$t_{S3} = t_{S1}$	$x_{S3} = 0$	t_{P3}	$x_{P3} = x_{P1} = 4.00 \times 10^{16}$ m

Let us try it: Suppose scientists at the monitoring post see the spaceship reach Alpha Centauri (event 1) at some instant and then see the light signal indicating the start of the party received at the star (event 3) at a different instant. Then the signal must be received at a position that makes the space-time interval between events 3 and 1 equal to zero, just as in reference frame S. However, that would mean that the ship travels from the position of event 3 to the position of event 1 at the speed of light because only then does $s^2 = 0 = (c_0\Delta t)^2 - (\Delta x)^2$. This is not possible! The result is that the scientists must also see the signal as being received at Alpha Centauri just as the ship reaches the star. Thus we add to our table of values:

$$t_{P3} = t_{P1} = 2.22 \times 10^8 \text{ s}.$$

(*b*) Now we must determine what scientists at the post measure for the time interval between the instant the ship passes the post (event 0) and the instant the scientists begin their party (event 2). The scientists know that both the ship and the light signal indicating the start of the party must arrive at Alpha Centauri at instant $t_{P3} = t_{P1} = 2.22 \times 10^8$ s. They also know the speed at which that signal travels and the distance it travels. Thus from the instant the signal is sent out (event 2) to the instant it is received at Alpha Centauri (event 3) is a time interval of

$$\Delta t_{P23} = t_{P3} - t_{P2} = \frac{d_{P23}}{c_0} = \frac{d_{P01}}{c_0} = \frac{4.00 \times 10^{16}\text{ m}}{3.00 \times 10^8\text{ m/s}}$$
$$= 1.33 \times 10^8 \text{ s}.$$

We know t_{P3} and so

$$t_{P2} = t_{P3} - \Delta t_{P23} = (2.22 \times 10^8\text{ s}) - (1.33 \times 10^8\text{ s})$$
$$= 0.89 \times 10^8 \text{ s}.$$

We have set $t_{P0} = 0$, so by the clocks at post P the party must start

$$\Delta t_{P02} = t_{P2} - t_{P0} = t_{P2} - 0 = 8.9 \times 10^7 \text{ s} \checkmark$$

after the ship passes.

❹ **EVALUATE RESULT** The light signal indicating the start of the party travels at speed c_0, and the spaceship travels at 60% of that value. If the two must travel the same distance in reference frame P and the signal moves 1.67 times faster than the ship in that reference frame, it seems reasonable that the post scientists should start their party after about 30% to 40% of the ship travel time interval has elapsed. The astronauts, of course, measure a different value for the instant at which the party signal is sent. Because the time interval Δt_{P02} is proper in reference frame P, we can use Eq. 14.13 to calculate the time interval in reference frame S:

$$\Delta t_{S02} = \gamma \Delta t_{P02} = 1.25(8.9 \times 10^7\text{ s}) = 1.1 \times 10^8 \text{ s}.$$

In reference frame P, the space-time interval between events 0 and 2 is

$$s_{02}^2 = (c_0 \Delta t_{P02})^2 - 0 = 7.1 \times 10^{32}\text{ m}^2.$$

The space-time interval must have the same value in reference frame S, allowing us to compute the displacement of post P for the ship when the signal was sent in reference frame S:

$$s_{02}^2 = 7.1 \times 10^{32}\text{ m}^2 = (c_0\Delta t_{S02})^2 - (\Delta x_{S02})^2$$
$$\Delta x_{S02} = \sqrt{[c_0(1.1 \times 10^8\text{ s})]^2 - (7.1 \times 10^{32}\text{ m}^2)} = 1.9 \times 10^{16}\text{ m}.$$

Thus in reference frame S the party signal travels this distance to arrive at the ship (at Alpha Centauri) for event 3. The time interval the astronauts measure for how long the signal takes to travel this distance is

$$\Delta t_{S23} = \frac{1.9 \times 10^{16}\text{ m}}{3.00 \times 10^8\text{ m/s}} = 6.3 \times 10^7 \text{ s},$$

so that the time interval from passing post P to the arrival of the party signal is

$$\Delta t_{S03} = \Delta t_{S02} + \Delta t_{S23} = (1.1 \times 10^8\text{ s}) + (6.3 \times 10^7\text{ s})$$
$$= 1.7 \times 10^8 \text{ s}.$$

The results are all consistent within the two significant digits allowed by the subtraction we used in calculating t_{P2}.

Guided Problem 14.6 Space-time interval

An unstable high-energy particle enters a detector and, before decaying, leaves a track 1.05 mm long. The speed of the particle relative to the detector is $0.992c_0$. Show that the value of the space-time interval s^2 for the interval from the instant the particle enters the detector to the instant the particle decays is the same when computed in a reference frame D at rest relative to the detector and in a reference frame P at rest relative to the particle.

❶ **GETTING STARTED**

1. Identify the two events that bracket the desired space-time interval.
2. Which time or space intervals given in the problem statement are useful in computing the desired space-time interval? In which reference frame(s)?

❷ **DEVISE PLAN**

3. How can you determine the time interval in reference frame D?
4. Is Eq. 14.18 relevant?
5. Is a proper time interval involved in either reference frame? What about a proper length? How might either of these allow you to obtain information in the second reference frame?

❸ **EXECUTE PLAN**

❹ **EVALUATE RESULT**

6. Do your answers for the space-time interval in the two reference frames agree?

Worked Problem 14.7 Pion production

Protons p_1 and p_2, initially moving at the same speed in the Earth reference frame, collide head-on, and the products of the collision are a proton p_3, a neutron n, and a pion π^+ that are at rest in the Earth reference frame. The masses of these particles, in terms of the proton mass m_p, are: neutron mass $m_n = 1.0014\, m_p$ and pion mass $m_{\pi^+} = 0.1488 m_p$. In a reference frame in which proton p_2 is at rest, what is the ratio of the kinetic energy of proton p_1 to its internal energy?

❶ **GETTING STARTED** We are given a description of two protons p_1 and p_2 colliding to create a proton p_3, a neutron, and a pion, and we are told the mass ratios of the products: $m_n/m_p = 1.0014$ and $m_{\pi^+}/m_p = 0.1488$. Our task is to determine the value of the ratio $K_{p1}/E_{int,p1}$ in a reference frame in which p_2 is at rest. We begin by making a sketch of the collision in the Earth reference frame, showing an unknown common speed v for p_1 and p_2 (Figure WG14.3). Note that the Earth reference frame is the zero-momentum reference frame because the protons are moving with opposite velocities and hence the sum of their momenta is zero. We choose to label this reference frame Z because this label will remind us of important momentum information.

Figure WG14.3

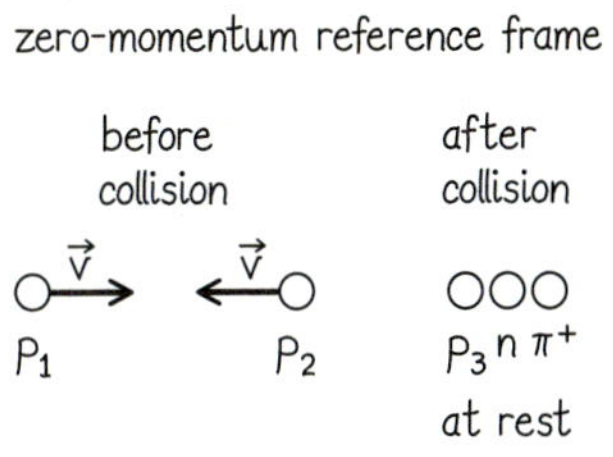

We must also consider the collision from a reference frame in which p_2 is at rest. To keep things simple, let's call this the target reference frame T (because in this reference frame p_2 behaves like a stationary target waiting to be hit by p_1). In reference frame T, the three product particles are all moving to the right at speed v (Figure WG14.4).

Figure WG14.4

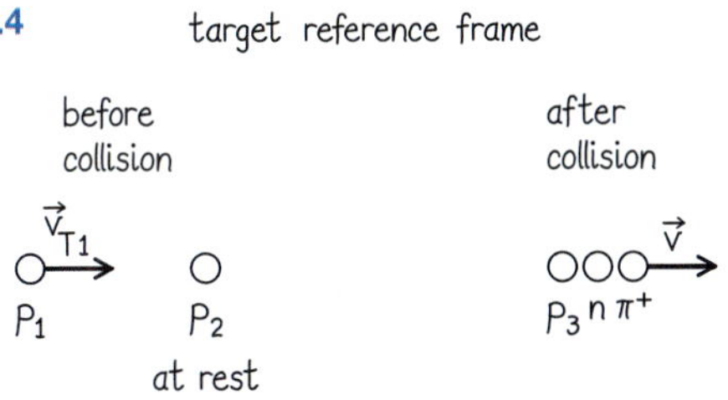

❷ **DEVISE PLAN** We can consider the system (which initially is the protons p_1 and p_2 and finally is the three product particles p_3, n, and π^+) as being both isolated and closed. Therefore the system's initial energy equals its final energy, and its initial momentum equals its final momentum. We know that the energy of a particle is the sum of its kinetic energy and internal energy (Eq. 5.21) and that its internal energy is $E_{int} = mc_0^2$ (Eq. 14.54).

Determining E_{int} for p_1. We can set the initial energy equal to the final energy in both reference frames. This gives us two equations in five quantities: $K_{Z,i}$, $E_{int,i}$, $E_{int,f}$, $K_{T,i}$, and $K_{T,f}$. We can express the internal energies in terms of c_0^2 and the masses m_p, m_n, and m_{π^+}. We can also express the internal energies in terms of the internal energy of a proton, $E_{int,p}$.

Determining K for p_1: We know that in the zero-momentum reference frame Z protons p_1 and p_2 are moving with speed v, and so we can calculate $K_{Z,i}$ using Eq. 14.51 and the Lorentz factor γ_{Zv} (Eq. 14.6). In order to calculate γ_{Zv}, we use Eqs. 14.53 and 14.54 to calculate the initial and final energies of p_1 and p_2 in reference frame Z and then set the initial energy equal to the final energy in order to determine the inertia m_{vp} of p_1 and p_2. We can then use Eq. 14.41 to determine γ_{Zv} for p_1 and p_2. We know that in reference frame T the three product particles are moving with speed v, and so we can calculate $K_{T,f}$ using the same Lorentz factor γ_{Zv}. We can then solve for the kinetic energy $K_{T,i}$ of p_1 in reference frame T.

❸ **EXECUTE PLAN** In the zero-momentum reference frame, the three product particles are created at rest. Therefore none of the energy initially contained in p_1 and p_2 goes into kinetic energy in the product particles. All of the initial energy of the system thus is converted to internal energy in the product particles. Setting the system initial energy (kinetic energy of p_1 and p_2, internal energy in p_1 and p_2) equal to the system final energy (internal energy only, in p_3, n, π^+) yields

$$E_Z = K_{Z,i} + E_{int,i} = E_{int,f},$$

which tells us that the initial kinetic energy is equal to the increase in internal energy:

$$K_{Z,i} = E_{int,f} - E_{int,i}. \quad (1)$$

In reference frame T, the initial momentum is nonzero, which means that the final momentum must also be nonzero. Thus the proton, neutron, and pion are moving at speed v, and the kinetic energy $K_{T,f}$ is also nonzero. Setting the initial energy equal to the final energy yields

$$E_T = K_{T,i} + E_{int,i} = K_{T,f} + E_{int,f},$$

and so we have an expression for the initial kinetic energy in the target reference frame T:

$$K_{T,i} = (E_{int,f} - E_{int,i}) + K_{T,f}. \quad (2)$$

This equation tells us that in reference frame T, the initial kinetic energy is equal to the increase in internal energy plus the final kinetic energy of the three product particles.

Substituting Eq. 1 into Eq. 2 tells us that the initial kinetic energy in reference frame T is

$$K_{T,i} = K_{Z,i} + K_{T,f}. \quad (3)$$

In the zero-momentum reference frame, we set the initial energies of p_1 and p_2 (in the form $m_v c_0^2$ from Eq. 14.53) equal to the final internal energy of the product particles (in the form mc_0^2 from Eq. 14.54) to determine the inertia m_{vp} of p_1 and p_2:

$$2m_{vp}c_0^2 = 2\gamma_{Zv}m_p c_0^2 = (m_p + m_n + m_{\pi^+})c_0^2.$$

Now we use Eq. 14.41 to determine the Lorentz factor γ_{Zv} associated with p_1 and p_2:

$$m_v = \gamma_{Zv} m$$

$$\gamma_{Zv} = \frac{m_v}{m} = \frac{m_p + m_n + m_{\pi^+}}{2m_p} = \frac{1 + (m_n/m_p) + (m_{\pi^+}/m_p)}{2}$$

$$= \frac{1 + 1.0014 + 0.1488}{2} = 1.0751.$$

Because p_1 and p_2 move at speed v in the zero-momentum reference frame, the incoming kinetic energy is (Eq. 14.51)

$$K_{Z,i} = 2(\gamma_{Zv} - 1)m_p c_0^2 = 0.1502 m_p c_0^2.$$

Because the three particles are moving with speed v in reference frame T, we can use the same Lorentz factor to determine the final kinetic energy in this reference frame:

$$\begin{aligned} K_{T,f} &= (\gamma_{Zv} - 1)m_p c_0^2 + (\gamma_{Zv} - 1)m_n c_0^2 + (\gamma_{Zv} - 1)m_{\pi^+} c_0^2 \\ &= (0.0751)(m_p + m_n + m_{\pi^+})c_0^2 \\ &= (0.0751)(1 + 1.0014 + 0.1488)m_p c_0^2 \\ &= 0.162 m_p c_0^2. \end{aligned}$$

We now substitute these values for $K_{Z,i}$ and $K_{T,f}$ into Eq. 3 to determine the initial kinetic energy measured in reference frame T. Because we have specified that p_2 is at rest in this reference frame, this initial kinetic energy all belongs to p_1:

$$\begin{aligned} K_{T,i} = K_{p_1} &= K_{Z,i} + K_{T,f} \\ &= 0.1502 m_p c_0^2 + 0.162 m_p c_0^2 = 0.312 m_p c_0^2. \end{aligned}$$

From Eq. 14.54 we know that $m_p c_0^2$ is the internal energy of p_1. Thus the ratio we are asked for, $K_{p_1}/E_{int,p_1}$ in a reference frame in which p_2 is at rest, is

$$\frac{K_{p_1}}{E_{int,p_1}} = \frac{K_{T,i}}{m_p c_0^2} = 0.312. ✔$$

❹ EVALUATE RESULT We see that $K_{T,i} > 2K_{Zi}$. If we ignore relativistic effects, the speed of p_1 in the target reference frame is $2v$, and so the kinetic energies in the two reference frames are $K_{T,i} = \frac{1}{2}m(2v)^2 = 2mv^2$ and $K_{Z,i} = 2(\frac{1}{2}mv^2) = mv^2$. Thus $K_{T,i} = 2K_{Z,i}$. We would expect that the relativistic increase of inertia with speed should provide extra initial kinetic energy in reference frame T, so our result makes sense.

We can also evaluate our result by using an alternative method to calculate the ratio. First we calculate the speed v of p_1 and p_2 in the zero-momentum reference frame from our calculation for γ_{Zv}:

$$\gamma_{Zv} = \frac{1}{\sqrt{1 - (v/c_0)^2}}$$

$$\gamma_{Zv}^2 = \frac{1}{1 - (v/c_0)^2}$$

$$1 - (v/c_0)^2 = \frac{1}{\gamma_{Zv}^2}$$

$$(v/c_0)^2 = 1 - \frac{1}{\gamma_{Zv}^2}$$

$$v = \left(\sqrt{1 - \frac{1}{\gamma_{Zv}^2}}\right)c_0 = \left(\sqrt{1 - \frac{1}{(1.0751)^2}}\right)c_0 = 0.367 c_0.$$

In order to determine the initial kinetic energy of p_1 in the target reference frame, we need to know the x component of the velocity $v_{Tx,i}$ of p_1 (we choose the positive x direction to be the direction in which p_1 moves). We use Eq. 14.33 with $v_{ZTx} = -v$ and $v_{Zx,i} = v$:

$$v_{Tx,i} = \frac{v_{Zx,i} - v_{ZTx}}{1 - \dfrac{v_{ZTx}}{c_0}\dfrac{v_{Zx,i}}{c_0}} = \frac{v + v}{1 + \dfrac{v^2}{c_0^2}} = \frac{2(0.367)c_0}{1 + (0.367)^2} = 0.647 c_0.$$

Because the kinetic energy of p_1 in reference frame T depends on the Lorentz factor associated with its motion (Eq. 14.51), we first calculate that factor:

$$\gamma_{Tv} = \frac{1}{\sqrt{1 - \left(\dfrac{v_{Tx,i}}{c_0}\right)^2}} = \frac{1}{\sqrt{1 - (0.647)^2}} = 1.311.$$

The kinetic energy of p_1 in the target reference frame is thus

$$K_{T,i} = (\gamma_{Tv} - 1)m_p c_0^2 = 0.311 m_p c_0^2$$

$$\frac{K_{T,i}}{m_p c_0^2} = 0.311,$$

in agreement with our result above.

Guided Problem 14.8 Particle production

A pion π^- of mass m_{π^-} collides with a proton p of mass m_p that is at rest relative to an inertial reference frame R. The pion has the minimum kinetic energy necessary such that the collision destroys the proton and pion and produces two particles: a neutral kaon K of mass m_K and a lambda particle Λ of mass m_Λ. Derive an expression that gives, in reference frame R, the kinetic energy of the pion in terms of c_0 and the masses of the four particles.

❶ GETTING STARTED

1. If possible, choose an isolated and closed system.
2. Decide how many reference frames you must analyze, and sketch the initial and final states in each reference frame.
3. In the zero-momentum reference frame, at the minimum kinetic energy necessary to produce the kaon and lambda particle, are these two particles at rest or moving? Is the reference frame R the zero-momentum reference frame?
4. Assign symbols for the velocity of the kaon and lambda particle in the reference frame R in which the proton is at rest. It is generally good to include symbols in your sketches for any quantities that you may need for the energy equations and the momentum equations.

❷ DEVISE PLAN

5. Can you write invariant expressions for the energy and momentum for the pion and proton in reference frame R?
6. Is there a reference frame in which the magnitude of the momentum of the kaon equals that of the lambda particle? What is the invariant expression for the energy and momentum of the kaon-lambda particle combination?

❸ EXECUTE PLAN

7. Determine the kinetic energy of the pion in the reference frame R in which the proton is at rest.

❹ EVALUATE RESULT

8. In the reference frame in which the proton is at rest, do you expect the sum of the energy of the pion and the internal energy of the proton to be greater than, equal to, or less than the sum of the internal energies of the kaon and lambda particle?

Questions and Problems

For instructor-assigned homework, go to MasteringPhysics® MP

Dots indicate difficulty level of problems: • *= easy,* •• *= intermediate,* ••• *= hard;* CR *= context-rich problem.*

14.1 Time measurements

1. Which of the following are events? (*a*) The local television station's newscast runs from 11:00 to 11:30 p.m. (*b*) The ceremonial first pitch is thrown at a baseball game in Omaha, Nebraska. (*c*) The Perseid meteor shower is seen across the eastern coast of North America. (*d*) A rainstorm lasts all day in Kyoto, Japan. (*e*) Two cars crash in front of your home. (*f*) An all-night concert starts in a local park. (*g*) Light emitted by a supernova reaches a spherical shell of radius 40,000 light years relative to its source. (One light year is the distance light travels in one year.) •

2. You are in a rocket moving away from Earth at one-third the speed of light relative to Earth. A friend is on Earth, and an astronaut in another rocket is moving toward Earth at one-third the speed of light (in the Earth reference frame), on a path collinear with your path. If each of you records the duration of your journey in your three respective reference frames, which of you records the proper time interval? •

3. A set of atomic clocks is placed on a square grid as shown in Figure P14.3. In order to synchronize these clocks, you set the time on each to a certain reading before they are allowed to run. Clock *O* starts first, and at precisely 12:00 noon, it sends out a light pulse in all directions. Each of the other clocks starts running as soon as the pulse reaches it. What initial time should you use for clocks A, B, C, and D to synchronize them with clock *O*? Express your answer to the nearest microsecond before or after 12:00 noon. ••

Figure P14.3

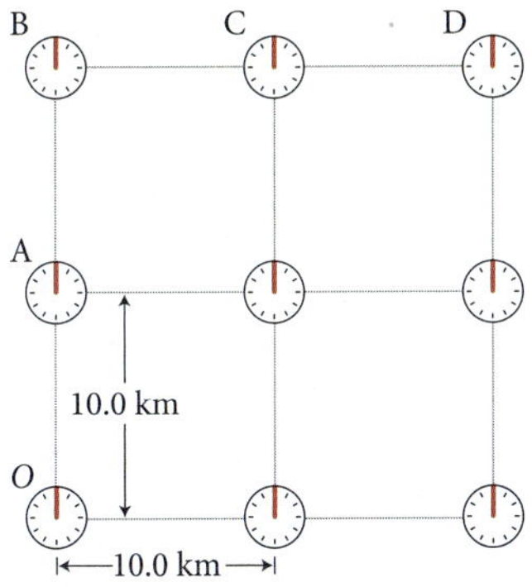

4. Events 1 and 2 are exploding firecrackers that each emit light pulses. In the reference frame of the detector, event 1 leaves a char mark at a distance 3.40 m from the detector, and event 2 leaves a similar mark at a distance 2.10 m from the detector. If the two events are simultaneous in the reference frame of the detector and occur at instant $t = 0$, at what instant of time will each light pulse be detected? ••

5. Consider the grid of clocks in *Principles* Figure 14.6. Do observers stationed at clocks far from the reference clock read earlier, later, or the same time as the time on the reference clock (*a*) if the clocks are to be synchronized after a pulse is sent out activating them but this pulse has not yet been sent, and (*b*) if the pulse has been sent out and all clocks are running? (*c*) Suppose the pulse has been sent and all clocks are running. If you stand at the reference clock and use a telescope to read the time on distant clocks, do you read a time earlier, later, or the same as the time on the reference clock? ••

6. Observers A and B are both at rest in the Earth reference frame, in different parts of a large city, awaiting the start of a fireworks show. They want to synchronize their atomic clocks for some experiments to be conducted later that evening. A and B plan to start their clock displays at an agreed signal, so each clock display is preset to exactly 10:00 p.m., but they will not record time until the "start" buttons are pressed. Observer A suggests that each of them start upon *seeing* the first firework, and observer B suggests that each of them start upon *hearing* the first firework. (*a*) Which plan leads to the clocks being more closely synchronized, and why? (*b*) Is it possible for the two methods to give the same agreement between clocks? •••

14.2 *Simultaneous* is a relative term

7. Observer A is stationary in the Earth reference frame, and pilot B is flying toward pilot A at relative speed v_{AB}. What speed does observer A measure for the speed of the light emitted by a signal light on pilot B's ship? •

8. Alarm clock 1 is positioned at $x = -d$ and alarm clock 2 at $x = +d$ in reference frame A. According to a clock in reference frame A, both go off at $t = 0$. An observer in reference frame B, which is moving relative to A, measures alarm clock 2 as going off first. In what direction is B moving relative to A? •

9. You are traveling toward a large fixed mirror at a constant relative speed $0.20c_0$. At $t = 0$, when the mirror is a distance d from you (measured in your reference frame), you emit a light pulse from a lantern and then detect the reflected light pulse 0.80 μs later. What is the value of d? ••

10. You are in a jet helicopter traveling horizontally at 180 m/s relative to Earth. At one instant you observe the light pulses from two lightning strikes, one directly ahead of the helicopter and one directly behind it. (*a*) Can you say that the strikes occurred simultaneously in your reference frame? (*b*) How would your answer change if you were instead hovering at rest relative to the ground when you observed the two pulses? (*c*) How would your answer change if the pilot told you that the two strikes occurred at equal distances from the helicopter in the helicopter's reference frame? (*d*) Would an observer on the ground agree with your answers to parts *a*, *b*, and *c*? ••

11. Consider a lightweight, straight, rigid rod that has a proper length of 1×10^6 m. If you rotate the rod at 100 turns/s about a perpendicular axis through its center, at what speed do the ends of the rod move? What prevents such a case from occurring? ••

12. Observer A on Earth sees spaceship B moving at speed $v = 0.600c_0$ away from Earth and spaceship C moving at the same speed in the opposite direction. Observer A determines that both ships simultaneously sent out a radio signal at 12:00:00 noon and another signal at 12:05:00 p.m., making the time interval A measures between the emission of the signals from each ship $\Delta t_A = 5.00$ min. Let Δt_{BB} denote the time interval measured on ship B between the emission of signals on ship B, Δt_{BC} denote the time interval measured on ship B between the emission of signals on ship C, and Δt_{CB} denote the time interval measured on ship C between emission of signals on ship B. (a) Is Δt_{BB} greater than, less than, or equal to Δt_A? (b) Is Δt_{BC} greater than, less than, or equal to Δt_{CB}? ••

PRACTICE

14.3 Space-time

13. An astronaut takes what he measures to be a 10-min nap in a space station orbiting Earth at 8000 m/s. A signal is sent from the station to Earth at the instant he falls asleep, and a second signal is sent to Earth the instant he wakes. Does an observer on Earth measure the astronaut's nap as being shorter than, longer than, or equal to 10 min? •
14. Suppose you could move at nearly the speed of light. If you were to move at this speed for a large portion of your life, would it be possible for you to live long enough to see a later calendar year on Earth than you otherwise would have? Compare your answer with that for Checkpoint 14.8. •
15. Standing somewhere between two vertical mirrors, you hold a lantern and at $t = 0$ emit a light pulse that travels in all directions. You observe the pulse reflected from the mirror on your right at $t = 2.5\ \mu s$ and from the mirror on your left at $t = 6.5\ \mu s$. What is the distance between the two mirrors in your reference frame? •
16. A spaceship of proper length $\ell = 100$ m travels in the positive x direction at a speed of $0.800c_0$ relative to Earth. An identical spaceship travels in the negative x direction along a parallel course at the same speed relative to Earth. At $t = 0$, an observer on Earth measures a distance $d = 50{,}000$ km separating the two ships. At what instant does this observer see the leading edges of the two ships pass each other? ••
17. A spacecraft traveling away from Earth at relative speed $0.850c_0$ sends a radio message when it is 65,000,000 km away from Earth in the Earth reference frame. Earth-based engineers immediately send a reply to the spacecraft. What do these engineers measure for the time interval from the instant the spacecraft sends the original message to the instant the spacecraft receives the reply? ••
18. Spaceships A, B, and C in Figure P14.18 all have the same proper length and all fly with the same speed according to an observer on Earth. Rank the lengths of the three ships as measured by an observer in ship A, longest first. ••

Figure P14.18

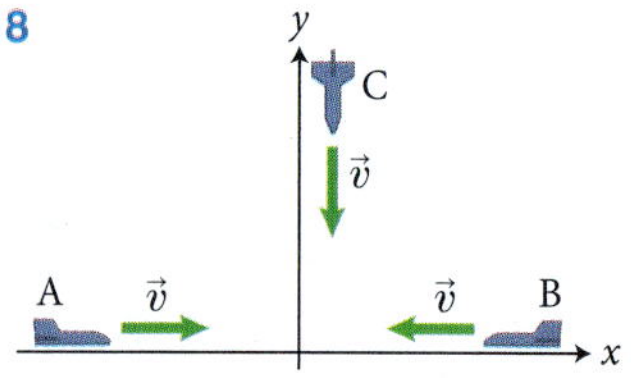

19. The boundary of a lunar base is a square 1 km wide and 1 km long in the Moon reference frame. Spaceship A flies at high relative speed close to the Moon parallel to the edge that we shall call the length of the field. Crew A measures the length and width, and reports that the area of the field is 0.5 km^2 in reference frame A. Spaceship B flies with the same relative speed as spaceship A, but parallel to one diagonal of the field. Crew B measures both diagonals. What surface area does crew B calculate in reference frame B? •••

14.4 Matter and energy

20. How fast must a pin move relative to your reference frame so that you measure its inertia to be three times its mass? •
21. A golf ball hit from a tee accelerates from rest to a speed of 40.0 m/s relative to the Earth reference frame. By what percent does the mass of the ball increase as it is hit? •
22. One end of a vertical spring of spring constant $k = 1500$ N/m is attached to the floor. You compress the spring so that it is 2.40 m shorter than its relaxed length, place a 1.00-kg ball on top of the free end, and then release the system at $t = 0$. (All values are measured in the Earth reference frame.) (*a*) By how much does the mass of the spring change during the time interval from $t = 0$ to the instant the ball leaves the spring? (*b*) By how much does the mass of the Earth-ball-spring system change during the time interval from $t = 0$ to the instant the ball reaches its maximum height? ••
23. You pick up your physics book from the floor and put it on your desk. In the Earth reference frame, which of the following quantities have changed for the system made up of Earth and the book: mass, energy, inertia, kinetic energy? ••
24. Observer A is on Earth looking at the Moon, and observer B is on the Moon looking at Earth. Which of the following quantities do the observers agree on for the Earth-Moon system: inertia, energy, mass, kinetic energy? ••
25. How far above Earth's surface must a 10,000-kg boulder be moved to increase the mass of the Earth-boulder system by 2.50 mg? Assume the same ratio of energy change to mass change as in *Principles* Exercise 14.5(*b*): 8.98×10^{16} J/kg. ••

14.5 Time dilation

26. A bullet is fired from a rifle (event 1) and then strikes a soda bottle, shattering it (event 2). Is there some inertial reference frame in which event 2 precedes event 1? If so, does the existence of this reference frame violate causality? •
27. Classify the space-time interval between each pair of events as timelike, spacelike, or lightlike: (*a*) A sunspot erupts on the surface of the Sun and is seen on Earth 500 s later. (*b*) A supernova explodes and is noticed 8.00×10^{20} m away after 8.45×10^4 y by an observer at rest relative to the supernova. (*c*) You receive light in the Earth reference frame emitted by a satellite 60,000 km away at $t = 0$, and 233 ms later receive light emitted by a spaceship 180,000 km away in the same direction as the satellite. (*d*) At $t = 0$, a pilot traveling at $0.75c_0$ relative to a star system receives signals from two planets A and B in that system. She then passes planet A (event 1) at $t = 450$ s and 90 s after that passes planet B (event 2). •
28. Calculate the Lorentz factor for an object moving relative to Earth at (*a*) 60 mi/h, (*b*) 0.34 km/s (speed of sound in air), (*c*) 28×10^3 km/h (orbital speed of the International Space Station), (*d*) $0.1c_0$, (*e*) $0.3c_0$, and (*f*) $0.995c_0$. Express your answers as "1 + correction." ••
29. You measure the period of light clock A to be T as it moves relative to you with a speed $0 < v_A < 0.5c_0$. You measure the period of an identical light clock (clock B) to be $3T$ as it moves relative to you with speed $v_B = 2v_A$. Determine numerical values for the speeds of each clock in your reference frame. ••
30. A space station sounds an alert signal at time intervals of 1.00 h. Spaceships A and B pass the station, both moving at $0.400c_0$ relative to the station but in opposite directions. How long is the time interval between signals (*a*) according to an observer on A and (*b*) according to an observer on B? (*c*) At what speed must A move relative to the station in order to measure a time interval of 2.00 h between signals? ••

PRACTICE

31. A certain muon detector counts 600 muons per hour at an altitude of 1900 m and 380 muons per hour at sea level. Given that the muon half-life at rest is 1.5×10^{-6} s, determine the speed of the muons relative to Earth, assuming they all have the same speed. ••

32. Planets A and B are 10 light years apart in the reference frame of planet A. (One light year is the distance light travels in one year.) A deep-space probe is launched from A, and 5 y later (in reference frame A) a similar probe is launched from B. Does a reference frame exist in which these two events (*a*) are simultaneous and (*b*) occur at the same position? (*c*) Compute, if possible, the proper time interval between the events? (*d*) How do your answers to parts *a*–*c* change if the planets are (in reference frame A) 5 light years apart and the time interval between launch from A and launch from B is 10 y? ••

33. *Principles* Section 14.3 describes how the number of muons reaching Earth's surface is greater than the number expected based on the muon half-life of 1.5×10^{-6} s. How fast, relative to Earth, must muons be moving in order for one of every million muons to pass through a distance equal to Earth's diameter without decaying? ••

34. One cosmonaut orbited Earth for 437 days, as measured by Earth clocks. His speed of orbit was 7700 m/s relative to Earth during this time interval. Assume two clocks were synchronized on Earth, and one went into space with the cosmonaut while the other remained on Earth. You are interested in knowing by how much the clock readings disagree at the end of the 437 days. What are some problems with applying Eq. 14.13 to this situation? What information other than the cosmonaut's speed relative to Earth might you need to know? If you used Eq. 14.13, would you expect the clock readings to be very different from each other? •••

14.6 Length contraction

35. A cosmic ray traveling at $0.400c_0$ relative to Earth passes observer A (event 1) and then a short time interval later passes observer B (event 2). The observers are at rest, 8.00 km apart in the Earth reference frame. What are (*a*) the proper length and (*b*) the proper time interval between these events? •

36. An elementary particle is launched from Earth toward the Regulus system, 77.5 light years distant. At what speed relative to Earth must this particle travel to make this trip in 10 y in the reference frame of the particle? •

37. Spaceships A and B pass a space station at the same instant, the two ships moving in opposite directions at the same speed of $0.600c_0$ relative to the station. What is the Lorentz factor associated with the relative motion of the ships? •

38. Two elementary particles pass each other moving in opposite directions, each moving at speed $0.800c_0$ relative to Earth. What is the speed of one particle relative to the other? •

39. The radius of Earth is 6370 km in the Earth reference frame. In the reference frame of a cosmic ray moving at $0.800c_0$ relative to Earth, how wide does Earth seem (*a*) along the flight direction and (*b*) perpendicular to the flight direction? •

40. Show that the Lorentz transformation equations (Eqs. 14.29–14.32) reduce to the Galilean transformation equations in the limit $v_{AB} \ll c_0$. ••

41. An elementary particle moving away from Earth reaches its destination after two weeks (in the reference frame of the particle) traveling at $0.9990c_0$ relative to Earth. How far has it traveled in (*a*) its reference frame and (*b*) the Earth reference frame? ••

42. Describe the shape of the Moon as measured by an observer in a reference frame traveling past the Moon at a relative speed of (*a*) 1000 m/s, (*b*) $0.50c_0$, and (*c*) $0.95c_0$. ••

43. When at rest in the Earth reference frame, the delta-wing spaceship in Figure P14.43 is 7.00 m long and has a wingspan of 8.00 m. (*a*) What is the opening angle α of its wings? (*b*) If the same ship is moving forward at $0.700c_0$ relative to Earth, what does an observer on Earth measure for the plane length, wingspan, and opening angle α? ••

Figure P14.43

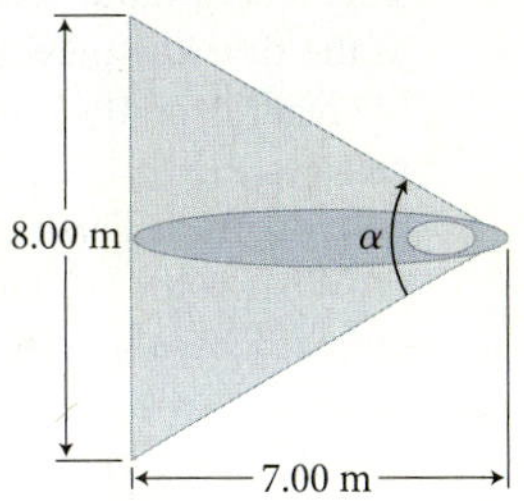

44. Standing at rest in the Earth reference frame, you observe two events, also at rest in that reference frame, occurring at these coordinates: event 1: $x_1 = 10$ km, $y_1 = 5.0$ km, $z_1 = 0$, $t_1 = 20\ \mu$s; event 2: $x_2 = 30$ km, $y_2 = 5.0$ km, $z_2 = 0$, $t_2 = 30\ \mu$s. At what speed and in what direction must your friend travel relative to Earth so as to observe these events as being simultaneous? ••

45. Use the Lorentz transformation equations (Eq. 14.29–14.32) to prove that the space-time interval s^2 between two events is *Lorentz-invariant*, which means it has the same value for all possible inertial reference frames. ••

46. An elementary particle travels at $0.840c_0$ across a solar system that has a diameter of 8.14×10^{12} m (both measurements in the reference frame S of the solar system). (*a*) What value does an observer in reference frame S measure for the time interval needed for the particle to cross the solar system? (*b*) What time interval is needed in the reference frame P of the particle? (*c*) What is the proper length of the diameter? (*d*) What is the proper time interval for the particle's trip across the system? (*e*) What is the diameter of the solar system in reference frame P? ••

47. A space colony defines the origin of a coordinate system in reference frame C, and you are at rest in this reference frame at position $x = +3.000 \times 10^5$ km. A ship passes the colony moving in the positive x direction at $0.482c_0$ in reference frame C. By prearrangement, observers on the ship (reference frame S) and on the colony use this event (event 0) to define $x = 0$ and $t = 0$ in both reference frames. Just as the ship passes, the colonists send out a light pulse toward you (event 1), and you transmit a reply pulse (event 2) immediately upon receipt. (*a*) At what position in reference frame S do observers see the colonists' pulse originate? (*b*) At what instant does the pulse originate according to these observers? (*c*) At what position in reference frame S do the observers see your reply pulse originate? (*d*) At what instant does the reply pulse originate according to observers on the ship? ••

48. Observer O at the origin of a coordinate system is at rest relative to two equidistant space stations located at $x = +3.00 \times 10^6$ km (station A) and $x = -3.00 \times 10^6$ km (station B) on the x axis. In reference frame O, station A sends out a light pulse at $t = 0$ (event 1) and station B also sends out a light pulse at $t = 0$ (event 2). Observer C moves relative to O with velocity $0.600c_0$ in the positive x direction, and observer D moves relative to O with velocity $0.600c_0$ in the negative x direction. What are the displacement from event 1 to event 2, and the time interval between events 1 and 2, according to (*a*) observer C and (*b*) observer D? ••

49. A spaceship travels at $0.610c_0$ away from Earth. When the ship is 3.47×10^{11} m away in the Earth reference frame, the ship clock is set to $t = 0$ and a message (light signal) is sent to its ground crew on Earth. When this message is received, the ground crew immediately sends a reply (light signal) to the ship. The ground crew adjust their clocks to specify $t = 0$ as the time the message was sent from the ship. (*a*) What is the reading on the ground crew's clock at the instant the ship receives the reply signal? (*b*) According to the ground crew, how far from Earth is the ship when it receives the reply? (*c*) What is the reading on the ship's clock at the instant the reply reaches the ship? •••

50. According to an observer at rest in the Earth reference frame, ship A travels in one direction at speed $0.862c_0$ while ship B moves in the opposite direction at $0.717c_0$. Ship A sends out a shuttle module M that travels to ship B at speed $0.525c_0$ relative to A. For every 1.00 s that passes on M, how many seconds pass according to (*a*) a clock on A, (*b*) a clock on B, and (*c*) a clock held by the observer on Earth? •••

51. Two asteroid clusters at rest with respect to each other are 3.00×10^9 m apart, and both measure 6.00×10^8 m across in the reference frame of the clusters. A pilot in a spaceship moving at $0.900c_0$ relative to the cluster reference frame is trying to pass between the two clusters. To an observer who is stationary in the reference frame of the clusters, the ship just barely misses the corners of the clusters as shown in Figure P14.51. If a line were drawn between the centers of the two clusters, what would be the angle between that line and the ship's path in (*a*) the reference frame of the clusters and (*b*) the reference frame of the ship? •••

Figure P14.51

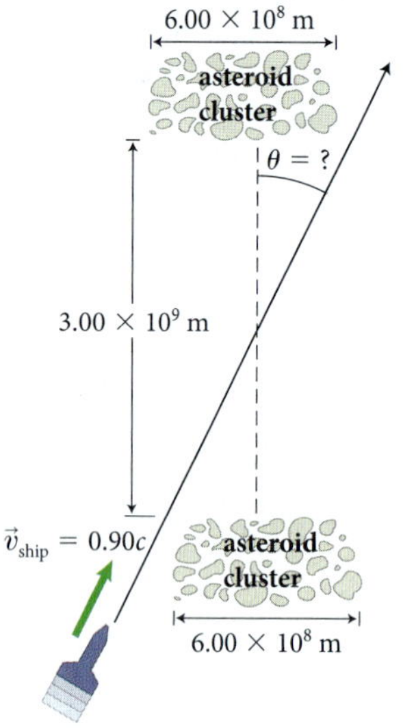

14.7 Conservation of momentum

52. Determine the magnitude of the momentum of a muon in a reference frame in which the muon moves with speed $0.500c_0$. The mass of a muon is 207 times the mass of an electron. •

53. An electron accelerates from $0.700c_0$ to $0.900c_0$ in the Earth reference frame. In this reference frame, by what factor do (*a*) its mass and (*b*) its inertia increase? •

54. (*a*) What is the magnitude of the momentum of an electron in a reference frame in which it is moving at $0.500c_0$? (*b*) At what speed must the electron move in a reference frame in which it has twice the momentum you calculated in part *a*? ••

55. Object A, mass 4.24×10^5 kg, is at rest in reference frame A, and object B, mass 7.71×10^4 kg, moves at $0.875c_0$ in this reference frame. (*a*) What does an observer at rest in A measure for the momentum of B? (*b*) What does an observer at rest with respect to object B measure for the momentum of A? (*c*) A reference frame C moves at $0.300c_0$ relative to reference frame A and moves in the same direction as object B. What are the momenta of objects A and B as measured by an observer at rest in reference frame C? ••

56. A uniform 200-kg cube that has a volume of $8.00\ m^3$ (measured when the cube is at rest in the Earth reference frame) travels perpendicular to a pair of its faces at $0.672c_0$ relative to Earth. (*a*) What is the mass density of the cube according to an observer at rest on Earth? (*b*) How fast (in the Earth reference frame) must a 100-kg object travel in the opposite direction to stop this cube in a collision? ••

57. Muons are formed 10.0 km above Earth's surface. What magnitude of momentum (in the Earth reference frame) must they have immediately after formation in order for only one of every 10,000 of them to reach the ground? The mass of a muon is 207 times the mass of an electron. ••

58. Two chunks of rock, each having a mass of 1.00 kg, collide in space. Just before the collision, an observer at rest in the reference frame of a nearby star determines that rock A is moving toward the star at $0.500c_0$ and rock B is moving away from the star at $0.300c_0$. If the rocks stick together after the collision, what are the direction and magnitude of their velocity (in the reference frame of the star) immediately after the collision? ••

59. In the Earth reference frame, a 150-kg probe travels at $0.860c_0$ while a 250-kg probe travels at $0.355c_0$ in the opposite direction. What are the velocities of the probes in the zero-momentum reference frame? •••

14.8 Conservation of energy

60. At what speed must a particle move in your reference frame so that its kinetic energy is equal to its internal energy? •

61. Particles A, B, and C each have mass m, and their energies are $E_A = E$, $E_B = 2E$, and $E_C = 3E$. Rank the particles, largest first, in order of (*a*) Lorentz factor, (*b*) kinetic energy, (*c*) speed, and (*d*) magnitude of momentum.

62. What is the internal energy of an electron moving at $0.750c_0$ in the Earth reference frame? •

63. Uranium-238 decays to thorium and helium according to the reaction $^{238}U \rightarrow {}^{234}Th + {}^{4}He$. How much energy is released when 1.00 kg of uranium-238 decays? Compare this amount with the energy released when 1.00 kg of coal is burned (approximately 30 MJ). The atomic masses are $m_U = 395.292599 \times 10^{-27}$ kg, $m_{Th} = 388.638509 \times 10^{-27}$ kg, and $m_{He} = 6.646478 \times 10^{-27}$ kg. ••

64. Assume that 437 days is a reasonable limit for how long a human can endure constant-velocity space travel. Proxima Centauri, the star closest to our Sun, is 4.24 light years away from Earth. If you wanted to fly to Proxima Centauri within the 437-day limit in a rocket of mass 2.00×10^6 kg, how much energy would be required to accelerate the rocket to the necessary speed in the Earth reference frame? For this rough estimate, ignore the energy required to stop, and disregard the hundreds of days required at each end of the journey for acceleration. Compare your answer with 0.6×10^{21} J, the yearly worldwide energy consumption predicted for 2015. ••

PRACTICE

65. A particle of mass m_{orig}, initially at rest in the Earth reference frame, decays into two particles 1 and 2 that have masses m_1 and m_2, respectively. Use conservation of energy, conservation of momentum, and Eq. 14.57, $E^2 - (c_0 p)^2 = (mc_0^2)^2$, to calculate the energy and momentum magnitude of particle 1 in the Earth reference frame in terms of m_{orig}, m_1, m_2, and c_0. ••

66. Which of the following forms of energy contribute to the mass of a gas molecule: (*a*) energy due to the molecule rotating about its center of mass, (*b*) energy due to compression of atoms in the molecule, (*c*) energy due to the molecule's translational motion relative to Earth? ••

67. At the Large Hadron Collider in Switzerland, two high-energy protons collide to create new particles. Prior to collision, each proton is accelerated to an energy of 7000 GeV in the Earth reference frame. (*a*) What is the speed of each proton? (*b*) What is the maximum mass possible for any particle created in the collision? The proton mass is 938 MeV/c_0^2; 1 GeV = 1000 MeV. ••

68. An electron e^- and positron e^+ moving at the same speed in the Earth reference frame collide head-on and produce a proton p and an antiproton $\bar{p}$. The electron and positron have the same mass. The proton and antiproton also have the same mass. The mass of the proton is 1836.15 times the mass of the electron. Calculate, in the Earth reference frame, the minimum value possible for the ratio of the electron's kinetic energy to its internal energy in order to have the reaction $e^- + e^+ \rightarrow p + \bar{p}$ take place. ••

69. Antihydrogen is the only antimatter element that has been produced in the laboratory, albeit just a few atoms at a time. Each antihydrogen atom consists of a positron in orbit around an antiproton and has the same atomic mass as hydrogen. If an antihydrogen atom collides with a hydrogen atom, they annihilate each other and create gamma radiation. (*a*) What minimum amount of energy is released in this process? (*b*) If this energy could be harnessed in a matter-antimatter automobile engine, how far could a car travel on 10 mg each of antihydrogen and hydrogen? At highway speeds, a typical automobile expends about 2.5×10^3 J per meter. •••

Additional Problems

70. Galaxy A moves away from galaxy B at $0.600c_0$ relative to B. A spaceship leaves a planet in galaxy A traveling at $0.500c_0$ relative to galaxy A. If the direction in which the ship travels is the same as the direction in which A is moving away from B, what do observers in B measure for the ship's speed? •

71. A tree that is 32.6 m tall leans 26.0° from the vertical in the Earth reference frame. How tall is the tree, and at what angle does it lean, in the reference frame of a cosmic ray muon moving parallel to the tree at a speed of $0.382c_0$ relative to Earth? •

72. Consider a searchlight on the ground that casts a spot on a cloud 1000 m overhead. If the searchlight is rotated rapidly—say, 30° in 1 μs—how fast does the spot move in the Earth reference frame? Is this a violation of special relativity? ••

73. Two events occur at different locations on Earth and are simultaneous in the reference frame of an observer standing on Earth halfway between the events. Is there any other inertial reference frame in which the two events are simultaneous? ••

74. Pilot A is seated in the middle of a ship that has a proper length of 250 m, and pilot B is seated in the middle of an identical ship. Pilot B passes A at a speed that A measures to be $0.580c_0$. How long does it take B's ship to pass pilot A (*a*) according to A and (*b*) according to B? How long does it take A's ship to pass pilot B (*c*) according to A and (*d*) according to B? ••

75. Relative to Earth, spaceship A travels at $0.732c_0$ away from Earth, and spaceship B travels at $0.914c_0$ toward Earth along the same straight line. (*a*) How fast does A move according to an observer aboard B? (*b*) At $t = 0$ the two ships are separated by 4.5×10^{10} m in the Earth reference frame. At what instant t do they pass each other according to an observer at rest on Earth? ••

76. A proton p_1 moving in the Earth reference frame collides with a proton p_2 that is at rest in that reference frame. The collision creates a particle that has mass m and an internal energy 40 times the internal energy of a proton: $mc_0^2 = 40m_p c_0^2$. The velocity of this new particle in the Earth reference frame is not given. What is the ratio of the energy of p_1 to its internal energy in the Earth reference frame? (Hint: First analyze the collision in the zero-momentum reference frame in which p_1 and p_2 are both in motion, moving in opposite directions at the same initial speed.) ••

77. You are consulting for an episode of *Stars Wars, Part XVI*. As this episode opens, starship Orion zooms past a space station at $t = 0$ ship's time, traveling at a constant $0.6000c_0$ relative to the station. When the Orion's clock reads $t = 1000$ s, her sensors detect a hostile battle cruiser 8.00×10^7 km dead ahead and closing in, traveling on a direct line toward the Orion and the space station at a speed of $0.8000c_0$ relative to the Orion. The Orion immediately sends a light signal to the station warning the crew to evacuate. Your boss says to assume that evacuating the station requires 45.0 min measured in the reference frame of the station, and wants to know if a rewrite is required. ••• CR

78. Your boss wants you to construct a spring that, when compressed, experiences a mass increase of 1/10,000 of 1%. He has no idea whether this is possible, but you decide to write a report listing desirable parameters (spring mass, spring constant, load mass), discussing problems you might encounter in attempting to make such a spring, and considering whether or not the conventional spring equations apply. ••• CR

79. The Lorentz Cup spaceship race is won by the pilot who can travel 1.00×10^9 m in the shortest time interval. The rules state that the start and finish lines must be 10^9 m apart in the ships' reference frame, but the time interval is measured by an observer at rest in the Earth reference frame. There are many racing speeds you might try, such as $0.420c_0$ and $0.980c_0$ relative to the Earth reference frame, but trying a few combinations randomly makes you wonder if there is a better way than trial and error to decide on a strategy for this race. ••• CR

Answers to Review Questions

1. An event is something that happens at a specific location at a specific instant.
2. Clocks measure equal known time intervals, and they can be synchronized so that their readings agree.
3. A signal of some sort must travel from the event to the observer.
4. You must see the two events as occurring at the same location. If you see them taking place at different locations, you cannot measure the proper time interval.
5. The observer must note, at the instant the event occurs, the reading on the clock nearest the event location.
6. The detector must be placed equidistant from the two locations at which the events take place. If the signals from the two events reach it at the same instant, the detector activates; if the signals arrive at different instants, the detector stays unchanged.
7. The speed is always $c_0 = 3.00 \times 10^8$ m/s, independent of the relative velocity of the source and the observer.
8. If the relative velocity of the observers is sufficiently large, they do not both report the two events as being simultaneous.
9. The observer sees time passing more slowly (time *dilates*) on clock A.
10. Time dilation has been confirmed by measurements on atomic clocks flown in airplanes around the world and by observations of cosmic-ray muons.
11. An object's proper length is its length measured by an observer who is at rest relative to the object.
12. Length contraction is the phenomenon whereby an observer moving relative to an object measures the object's length in the direction of motion as being shorter than the object's proper length.
13. This expression solved for v says that quadrupling K doubles v, but experiments on objects initially moving at relativistic speeds measure an increase in speed much less than the predicted doubling.
14. Mass and internal energy are invariant; inertia and kinetic energy depend on the measurer's reference frame.
15. The inertia changes in the same direction as the internal energy: Increasing the internal energy increases the inertia, and decreasing the internal energy decreases the inertia.
16. The inertia decreases.
17. The Lorentz factor is $\gamma = 1/\sqrt{1-(v^2/c_0^2)}$ (Eq. 14.6). Its effects become noticeable at speeds greater than $0.1c_0$.
18. The time interval the observer measures is equal to the product of the Lorentz factor and the proper time interval (Eq. 14.13.)
19. The space-time interval is spacelike if less than zero, timelike if greater than zero, and lightlike if zero. When the interval between the events is timelike, there is an inertial reference frame in which the events occur at the same location but at different instants and are hence separated by only a time interval. When the interval is spacelike, there is an inertial reference frame in which the events occur at different locations but at the same instant and hence are separated by only a distance in space. When the interval is lightlike, the two events are separated spatially by exactly the distance light travels in the time interval between the events.
20. To distinguish cause and effect, it is necessary to determine the sequence of events. For a pair of events that have a timelike space-time interval ($s^2 > 0$), we can establish a reference frame in which we can study both events at the same position, and so we can determine their sequence with certainty and establish their causal relationship. For a pair of events that have a spacelike space-time interval ($s^2 < 0$), we cannot uniquely determine the time order of events and therefore cannot determine any causal relationship. However, for two events to be causally related, they must be able to interact physically. When $s^2 < 0$, the events occur in such rapid succession that a light signal cannot travel from one event to the other in the time interval between them. Because no information can travel faster than the speed of light, such events cannot interact and so cannot be causally related. Only events that have a timelike space-time interval can be causally related, and for such events the time sequence can be uniquely determined.
21. The length the observer measures is equal to the proper length divided by the Lorentz factor (Eq. 14.28).
22. Time dilation and length contraction are the same effect seen by different observers. Muons can travel the proper distance through the atmosphere to reach Earth's surface because according to an observer at the surface their lifetime is lengthened by time dilation and according to an observer traveling with the muons their proper lifetime is sufficient for them cover the contracted length of the atmosphere.
23. The Lorentz transformation equations allow observers in any two inertial reference frames to compare measurements, whereas the length contraction and time dilation equations allow comparisons only between specific reference frames in which a proper time interval or proper length cannot be measured.
24. The momentum for a particle traveling at a relativistic speed is still defined as the product of its inertia and its velocity.
25. Yes. The system momentum remains constant because even with components moving at relativistic speeds, the definition of momentum is still the product of each component's inertia and its velocity.
26. (*a*) The inertia m_v is equal to the product of the particle's mass and the particle's Lorentz factor: $m_v = \gamma m$ (Eq. 14.41). (*b*) The momentum is the product of the particle's inertia and its velocity: $\vec{p} = \gamma m\vec{v} = m_v\vec{v}$.
27. The nonrelativistic form of kinetic energy is $K = \frac{1}{2}mv^2$. The relativistic expression is $K = (\gamma-1)mc_0^2 = m_v c_0^2 - mc_0^2$ (Eq. 14.51). The two expressions are compatible; the latter reduces to the former at speeds much smaller than the speed of light in vacuum.
28. The quantity mc_0^2 represents the internal energy of the system (Eq. 14.54).
29. The quantity γmc_0^2 represents the energy of the system (Eq. 14.53), which equals the sum of the kinetic and internal energies (Eq. 14.52).
30. A conserved quantity is one that cannot be created or destroyed, but observers in different reference frames can measure different values for a given conserved quantity. An invariant quantity is one that has the same value for all observers, regardless of any difference in the reference frames of the observers. Because they are conserved quantities, the energy and momentum of an isolated, closed system have constant values for a given observer but can have a different set of values for an observer measuring from a different reference frame. In order to obtain, for a given system, a parameter value that is the same for all observers in all reference frames, the invariant combination $E^2 - (c_0p)^2 = (mc_0^2)^2$ must be used.

Answers to Guided Problems

Guided Problem 14.2 (*a*) $0.781c_0$; (*b*) 125 m

Guided Problem 14.4 (*a*) $\vec{v}_{DC} = -0.300c_0\hat{\imath}$; (*b*) $t_{C1} = t_{C2} = 1.47 \times 10^{-6}$ s

Guided Problem 14.6 $s^2 = 1.79 \times 10^{-8}$ m^2

Guided Problem 14.8 $K_{\pi^-} = \dfrac{(m_K + m_\Lambda)^2c_0^4 - m_{\pi^-}^2c_0^4 - m_p^2c_0^4}{2m_pc_0^2} - m_{\pi^-}c_0^2$

15 PRACTICE Periodic Motion

Chapter Summary

Fundamental characteristics of periodic motion (Sections 15.1, 15.5)

Concepts **Periodic motion** is any motion that repeats itself at regular time intervals. **Oscillation** (or **vibration**) is back-and-forth periodic motion.

The *period* T is the minimum time interval in which periodic motion repeats, and the **amplitude** A of the motion is the magnitude of the maximum displacement of the moving object from its equilibrium position.

Quantitative Tools The **frequency** f of periodic motion is the number of cycles per second and is defined as

$$f \equiv \frac{1}{T}. \tag{15.2}$$

The SI unit of frequency is the **hertz** (Hz):

$$1\ \text{Hz} \equiv 1\ \text{s}^{-1}. \tag{15.3}$$

Simple harmonic motion (Sections 15.2, 15.4, 15.5)

Concepts **Simple harmonic motion** is periodic motion in which the displacement of a system from its equilibrium position varies sinusoidally with time. A system moving in this way is called a *simple harmonic oscillator*.

A restoring force that is linearly proportional to displacement tends to return a simple harmonic oscillator to its equilibrium position. For small displacements, restoring forces are generally proportional to the displacement and therefore cause objects to execute simple harmonic motion about any stable equilibrium position.

A **phasor** is a rotating arrow whose component on a vertical axis traces out simple harmonic motion. The **reference circle** is the circle traced out by the tip of the phasor, and the length of the phasor is equal to the amplitude A of the simple harmonic motion.

Quantitative Tools The **angular frequency** ω of oscillation is equal to the rotational speed of a rotating phasor whose vertical component oscillates with a frequency f. Angular frequency is measured in s^{-1} and is related to the frequency (measured in Hz) by

$$\omega = 2\pi f. \tag{15.4}$$

For a simple harmonic oscillator of amplitude A, the displacement x as a function of time is

$$x(t) = A \sin(\omega t + \phi_\text{i}), \tag{15.6}$$

where the sine argument is the **phase** $\phi(t)$ of the periodic motion,

$$\phi(t) = \omega t + \phi_\text{i}, \tag{15.5}$$

and ϕ_i is the *initial phase* at $t = 0$.

The x components of the velocity and acceleration of a simple harmonic oscillator are

$$v_x \equiv \frac{dx}{dt} = \omega A \cos(\omega t + \phi_\text{i}) \tag{15.7}$$

$$a_x \equiv \frac{d^2x}{dt^2} = -\omega^2 A \sin(\omega t + \phi_\text{i}). \tag{15.8}$$

Any object that undergoes simple harmonic motion obeys the **simple harmonic oscillator equation:**

$$\frac{d^2x}{dt^2} = -\omega^2 x, \tag{15.10}$$

where x is the object's displacement from its equilibrium position.

The mechanical energy E of an object of mass m undergoing simple harmonic motion is

$$E = \tfrac{1}{2} m\omega^2 A^2. \tag{15.17}$$

Fourier series (Section 15.3)

Concepts **Fourier's theorem** says that any periodic function with period T can be written as a sum of sinusoidal simple harmonic functions of frequency $f_n = n/T$, where n is an integer. The $n = 1$ term is the **fundamental frequency** or **first harmonic,** and the other components are **higher harmonics.**

Oscillating springs (Section 15.6)

Quantitative Tools For an object attached to a light spring of spring constant k, the simple harmonic oscillator equation takes the form

$$\frac{d^2x}{dt^2} = -\frac{k}{m}x, \tag{15.21}$$

and the angular frequency of the oscillation is

$$\omega = +\sqrt{\frac{k}{m}}. \tag{15.22}$$

The motion of the object is described by

$$x(t) = A\sin\left(\sqrt{\frac{k}{m}}t + \phi_i\right). \tag{15.23}$$

Rotational oscillations (Section 15.7)

Concepts A horizontal disk suspended at its center by a thin fiber forms a type of *torsional oscillator.*

A pendulum is any object that swings about a pivot. A *simple pendulum* consists of a small object (the bob) attached to a very light wire or rod.

Quantitative Tools If a torsional oscillator of rotational inertia I is twisted through a small angle from its equilibrium position ϑ_0 to position ϑ, the restoring torque τ_ϑ is

$$\tau_\vartheta = -\kappa(\vartheta - \vartheta_0), \tag{15.25}$$

where κ is the *torsional constant.* When $\vartheta_0 = 0$, the simple harmonic oscillator equation for the torsional oscillator is

$$\frac{d^2\vartheta}{dt^2} = -\frac{\kappa}{I}\vartheta. \tag{15.27}$$

The rotational position ϑ of the torsional oscillator at instant t is given by

$$\vartheta = \vartheta_{max}\sin(\omega t + \phi_i), \tag{15.28}$$

where ϑ_{max} is the maximum rotational displacement and

$$\omega = \sqrt{\frac{\kappa}{I}}. \tag{15.29}$$

For small rotational displacements, the simple harmonic oscillator equation of a pendulum is

$$\frac{d^2\vartheta}{dt^2} = -\frac{m\ell_{cm}g}{I}\vartheta \tag{15.32}$$

and its angular frequency is

$$\omega = \sqrt{\frac{m\ell_{cm}g}{I}}, \tag{15.33}$$

where ℓ_{cm} is the distance from the center of mass of the pendulum to the pivot.

The period of a simple pendulum is $T = 2\pi\sqrt{\frac{\ell}{g}}$.

Damped oscillations (Section 15.8)

Concepts In **damped oscillation,** the amplitude decreases over time due to energy dissipation. The cause of the dissipation is a *damping force* due to friction, air drag, or water drag.

A damped oscillator that has a large *quality factor* Q keeps oscillating for many periods.

Quantitative Tools At low speeds, the damping force $\vec{F}^{d}_{ao}$ tends to be proportional to the velocity of the object:

$$\vec{F}^{d}_{ao} = -b\vec{v}, \qquad (15.34)$$

where b, the *damping coefficient,* has units of kilograms per second.

For small damping, the position $x(t)$ of a damped spring is

$$x(t) = Ae^{-bt/2m}\sin(\omega_d t + \phi_i), \qquad (15.37)$$

and its angular frequency ω_d is

$$\omega_d = \sqrt{\frac{k}{m} - \frac{b^2}{4m^2}} = \sqrt{\omega^2 - \left(\frac{b}{2m}\right)^2}. \qquad (15.38)$$

The **time constant** τ for a damped system is $\tau = m/b$. In one time constant, the energy of a damped simple harmonic oscillator is reduced by a factor of $1/e$.

The amplitude $x_{max}(t)$ and energy $E(t)$ of a damped oscillation of initial amplitude A and initial energy E_0 decrease exponentially with time:

$$x_{max}(t) = Ae^{-t/2\tau} \qquad (15.39)$$

$$E(t) = E_0 e^{-t/\tau}. \qquad (15.40)$$

The *quality factor* Q of a damped system is

$$Q = 2\pi\frac{\tau}{T}. \qquad (15.41)$$

PRACTICE

Review Questions

Answers to these questions can be found at the end of this chapter.

15.1 Periodic motion and energy

1. What is required in order that the motion of an object be called periodic?

2. The terms *amplitude* and *frequency* are often applied to periodic motion. What is the meaning of each?

3. It requires 5.00 s for an oscillator to complete four cycles. What is the period T? What is the frequency f?

4. In periodic motion, where is the kinetic energy of the moving object greatest? Where is the magnitude of its potential energy greatest? Where is each of these variables zero?

15.2 Simple harmonic motion

5. A playground swing moves in simple harmonic motion. If you don't pump your legs on the swing, the amplitude of your motion decreases. What happens to the period?

6. Explain why the restoring force exerted on an object in simple harmonic motion must be a linear function of the object's displacement.

7. What is a turning point in simple harmonic motion?

8. How is simple harmonic motion related to circular motion at constant speed?

15.3 Fourier's theorem

9. State Fourier's theorem and explain why it is important in the study of periodic motion.

10. How can the fundamental frequency of a Fourier series be determined from the time dependence of the original periodic function?

11. What is meant by the *spectrum* of a periodic function?

12. What is Fourier analysis, and what is Fourier synthesis?

15.4 Restoring forces in simple harmonic motion

13. Which of the three types of equilibrium—stable, unstable, neutral—allow periodic motion?

14. Two pendulums have identical shape and length, but one of them has twice the mass of the other. Which has the greater period, if either?

15. What common feature of all restoring forces is crucial for ensuring simple harmonic motion for small displacements from equilibrium?

16. A child and an adult are on adjacent identical swings at the playground. Is the adult able to swing in synchrony with the child?

15.5 Energy of a simple harmonic oscillator

17. Is there anything actually going around in a circle as a spring oscillates? If not, what purpose does the reference circle serve?

18. Describe the simple harmonic oscillator equation in words.

19. If you know the initial position of an oscillator, what else do you need to know in order to determine the initial phase of the oscillation?

20. How do we distinguish frequency f from angular frequency ω if both have units of $(\text{time})^{-1}$?

15.6 Simple harmonic motion and springs

21. If you know the mass of an object hanging from a spring in an oscillating system, what else do you need to know to determine the period of the motion?

22. You stop your car to pick up a member of your car pool. After she gets in, does the angular frequency ω of oscillation due to the car's suspension increase, decrease, or stay the same?

23. Given an object suspended by a spring, which of these variables of the motion can you control by varying the initial conditions: period, amplitude, energy of the system, frequency, phase, maximum velocity, maximum acceleration?

24. How does the frequency of a vertically oscillating block-spring system compare with the frequency of an identical block-spring system oscillating horizontally?

15.7 Restoring torques

25. Two pendulums have identical shape and mass, but pendulum B is twice as long as pendulum A. Which has the greater period, if either?

26. The pendulum on a grandfather clock consists of a heavy disk fastened to a rod in such a way that the position of the disk along the rod is adjustable. If the clock runs slow, how should you adjust the pendulum?

27. What approximation is necessary in order for a pendulum to execute simple harmonic motion?

28. What are the units of the torsional constant in Eq. 15.25, $\tau_\vartheta = -\kappa(\vartheta - \vartheta_0)$?

15.8 Damped oscillations

29. Does an overdamped oscillator oscillate?

30. Describe the changes in the periodic motion of an oscillator as the damping coefficient is gradually increased from $b = 0$ to $b = 0.5m\omega_0$.

31. During a time interval of one time constant, by what factor does the mechanical energy of an oscillating system decrease?

Developing a Feel

Make an order-of-magnitude estimate of each of the following quantities. Letters in parentheses refer to hints below. Use them as needed to guide your thinking.

1. The energy involved in the oscillation of water sloshing in a bathtub (E, J, P, Z)
2. The energy involved in the oscillation of a child on a playground swing (O, A, F, U)
3. The maximum frequency at which you can continuously shake a bowling ball horizontally at chest height for 1 minute, fully extending your arms during each cycle (N, G, C, K, Q)
4. The length of a grandfather-clock pendulum for which the period of oscillation is 2 s (O, W)
5. The angular frequency ω of your leg oscillating as a pendulum (D, I, M)
6. The angular frequency ω of each piston in a four-cylinder gasoline engine as you drive your car, and the initial phase difference $\Delta\phi_i$ between each of the four oscillating pistons (R, X, L, T)
7. The maximum restoring torque caused by the forces exerted on a child on a playground swing (J, A, F, U)
8. The damping coefficient for a shock absorber on a midsize car (S, Y, B, H, V)

Hints

A. What is the maximum angle of oscillation?
B. What spring constant is needed for each wheel?
C. How many times during each cycle must you provide the full oscillation energy to move or stop the bowling ball?
D. What are the mass and length of your leg?
E. What maximum height above the equilibrium level does the sloshing water reach?
F. What is the mass of the child plus the swing seat? (You can ignore the mass of the chains supporting the swing.)
G. What energy is required for these pushups?
H. What is the frequency of the vertical oscillation of your car?
I. What is the rotational inertia of your leg pivoted at your hip?
J. What type of restoring force is involved?
K. What is the mass of a bowling ball?
L. Does each piston fire simultaneously?
M. What is the length from the pivot to your leg's center of mass?
N. How many pushups can you do in 1 minute?
O. Is it reasonable to approximate this as a simple pendulum?
P. How is the water's energy related to the maximum height the water reaches?
Q. What is the amplitude of oscillation?
R. What is a typical cruising-speed angular frequency ω, in revolutions per minute, for the crankshaft (the shaft to which the pistons are attached)?
S. What is the mass of a midsize car?
T. What is the initial phase between two pistons adjacent in the firing order?
U. What is the length of the pendulum?
V. How many oscillations occur before the shock absorber damps out the motion?
W. How is period related to length for a simple pendulum?
X. What is the angular frequency ω of each piston?
Y. Through what distance does a fender deflect when you sit on it?
Z. At maximum height, where is the center of mass of the volume of water above the equilibrium level?

Key (all values approximate)

A. 45°; **B.** 2×10^4 N/m; **C.** four; **D.** 1×10^1 kg, 1 m; **E.** 0.2 m; **F.** 3×10^1 kg; **G.** $30mgh$, where $h \approx 0.3$ m, $m \approx 7 \times 10^1$ kg, gives 6×10^3 J; **H.** 1 Hz; **I.** 3 kg · m^2 because it is roughly a uniform rod; **J.** the gravitational force exerted by Earth; **K.** 7 kg; **L.** no, they fire one at a time; **M.** 0.4 m; **N.** if you are fit, 3×10^1; **O.** yes; **P.** at maximum height, there is no kinetic energy; **Q.** 0.3 m; **R.** 2×10^3 rev/min; **S.** 1×10^3 kg; **T.** π rad; **U.** 3 m; **V.** a well-adjusted system allows less than one full oscillation; **W.** $T = 2\pi\sqrt{\ell/g}$; **X.** the same as for the crankshaft, 2×10^2 s^{-1}; **Y.** 5×10^1 mm; **Z.** this volume has a triangular shape, so its center of mass is at about one-third the maximum height

Worked and Guided Problems

These examples involve material from this chapter but are not associated with any particular section. Some examples are worked out in detail; others you should work out by following the guidelines provided.

Worked Problem 15.1 Swayin' in the breeze

A treetop sways back and forth with a period of 12 s, and you estimate the amplitude of the motion to be 1.2 m (Figure WG15.1). You begin timing at some instant after the treetop passes through the upright position, and after you have been watching this motion for 36 s, the treetop is 0.60 m to the left of the upright position. (*a*) Write the equation for the position of the treetop as a function of time. (*b*) What is the maximum speed of the treetop? (*c*) At what instants does the treetop have this speed? (*d*) What is the maximum magnitude of the treetop's acceleration? (*e*) What is the magnitude of its acceleration at the instant $t = 36$ s?

Figure WG15.1

❶ **GETTING STARTED** This treetop is executing periodic motion, and we assume the motion can be described with a sine function. We are given several bits of information from which to construct the position as a function of time. Two of these bits are the period $T = 12$ s and the amplitude $A = 1.2$ m. We also know that the treetop is 0.60 m to the left of vertical at $t = 36$ s. Parts *b–e* all require the general equation of motion, and so once we have that, we're set.

❷ **DEVISE PLAN** We begin with the general equation for position in simple harmonic motion, Eq. 15.6:

$$x(t) = A \sin(\omega t + \phi_i).$$

With the data we have, we can determine the amplitude A, angular frequency ω, and initial phase ϕ_i. Then we can obtain the maximum speed and the acceleration magnitude from $v_x = dx/dt$ and $a_x = dv_x/dt$.

❸ **EXECUTE PLAN** (*a*) The angular frequency is $\omega = 2\pi/T = 2\pi/(12\text{ s}) = (\pi/6)\text{ s}^{-1}$. (Generally you should leave π in expressions because it often either cancels or produces an easily evaluated trig function.) The initial phase ϕ_i can be found by using the information we have about the position at 36 s:

$$x(t = 36\text{ s}) = -0.60\text{ m} = (1.2\text{ m}) \sin\left[(\tfrac{1}{6}\pi\text{ s}^{-1})(36\text{ s}) + \phi_i\right]$$

$$-0.50 = \sin(6\pi + \phi_i) = \sin(\phi_i)$$

$$\phi_i = \sin^{-1}(-0.50) = -\tfrac{1}{6}\pi.$$

With this value for ϕ_i, $x(t) = A \sin(\omega t + \phi_i)$ for this particular motion becomes

$$x(t) = (1.2\text{ m}) \sin\left[(\tfrac{1}{6}\pi\text{ s}^{-1})t - \tfrac{1}{6}\pi\right]. ✔$$

(*b*) The velocity is given by Eq. 15.7:

$$v_x(t) = \frac{dx}{dt} = \frac{d}{dt}A \sin(\omega t + \phi_i) = \omega A \cos(\omega t + \phi_i)$$

$$= (\tfrac{1}{6}\pi\text{ s}^{-1})(1.2\text{ m}) \cos\left[(\tfrac{1}{6}\pi\text{ s}^{-1})t - \tfrac{1}{6}\pi\right]$$

$$= (0.20\pi\text{ m/s}) \cos\left[(\tfrac{1}{6}\pi\text{ s}^{-1})t - \tfrac{1}{6}\pi\right].$$

The maximum speed occurs when the cosine function is 1, which means that $v_{max} = 0.20\pi\text{ m/s} = 0.63\text{ m/s}$. ✔

(*c*) The tree has this maximum speed whenever it passes through the position $x = 0$, which is when the tree is vertical. This occurs when the cosine function is ± 1. Solving first for the positive values, we have

$$1 = \cos\left[(\tfrac{1}{6}\pi\text{ s}^{-1})t - \tfrac{1}{6}\pi\right]$$

$$\Rightarrow (\tfrac{1}{6}\pi\text{ s}^{-1})t_n - \tfrac{1}{6}\pi = 2n\pi, \qquad n = 0,1,2,\ldots$$

$$t_n - \tfrac{1}{6}\pi\left(\frac{6}{\pi}\text{ s}\right) = 2n\pi\left(\frac{6}{\pi}\text{ s}\right), \quad n = 0,1,2,\ldots$$

$$t_n = (1 + 12n)\text{ s}, \quad n = 0,1,2,\ldots$$

$$t = 1\text{ s}, 13\text{ s}, 25\text{ s}, \ldots. ✔$$

We repeat the calculation for the negative values:

$$-1 = \cos\left[(\tfrac{1}{6}\pi\text{ s}^{-1})t - \tfrac{1}{6}\pi\right]$$

$$\Rightarrow (\tfrac{1}{6}\pi\text{ s}^{-1})t_n - \tfrac{1}{6}\pi = n\pi, \qquad n = 1,3,5,\ldots$$

$$t_n - \tfrac{1}{6}\pi\left(\frac{6}{\pi}\text{ s}\right) = n\pi\left(\frac{6}{\pi}\text{ s}\right), \quad n = 1,3,5,\ldots$$

$$t_n = (1 + 6n)\text{ s}, \quad n = 1,3,5,\ldots$$

$$t = 7\text{ s}, 19\text{ s}, 31\text{ s}, \ldots. ✔$$

PRACTICE

(*d*) The acceleration is given by Eq. 15.8:

$$a_x(t) = \frac{dv_x}{dt} = \frac{d}{dt}[\omega A \cos(\omega t + \phi_i)] = -\omega^2 A \sin(\omega t + \phi_i)$$

$$= -(0.33\ \mathrm{m/s^2}) \sin\left[\left(\frac{\pi}{6}\,\mathrm{s^{-1}}\right)t - \frac{\pi}{6}\right].$$

The maximum acceleration occurs when the sine function is 1, which makes $a_{max} = 0.33\ \mathrm{m/s^2}$. ✔

(*e*) At $t = 36$ s, the acceleration magnitude is $a_x(36\ \mathrm{s}) = 0.16\ \mathrm{m/s^2}$. ✔

❹ EVALUATE RESULT Given that the amplitude is not very large relative to the tree height, the acceleration maximum indicates gentle swaying in the breeze rather than a hurricane. The value we obtained for the maximum speed confirms this. The answers are the right order of magnitude for a swaying tree.

Guided Problem 15.2 Archaic music medium

A long-playing phonograph record is 12.0 in. (305 mm) in diameter and rotates at $33\frac{1}{3}$ rev/min. Suppose a bug is at the edge of one such record, as in Figure WG15.2, at instant $t = 0$. Imagine that a distant light source casts a shadow of the bug along an x axis that runs tangent to the turntable at the rim position opposite the bug's initial position. (*a*) Write an equation that describes the motion of the shadow as a function of time. (*b*) What is the shadow's maximum speed along the x axis? (*c*) What is the maximum magnitude of its acceleration along the x axis?

Figure WG15.2

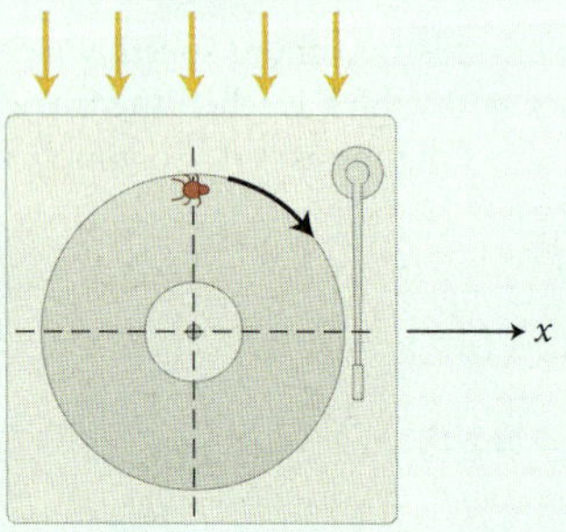

❶ GETTING STARTED

1. What does it mean to have the bug's motion projected onto the x axis? Make sketches showing the shadow's location at several instants as the turntable and bug rotate.
2. How can the properties of a right triangle and the sine and cosine functions help you in this problem?
3. Describe the relationship between circular motion and oscillation.

❷ DEVISE PLAN

4. What unknown quantities do you need to determine?
5. What equations allow you to express the unknown quantities in terms of known ones?
6. Write the generic equation for part *a*. Do you have to take derivatives of an expression?

❸ EXECUTE PLAN

7. Manipulate your equations to obtain an expression for the position of the shadow along the x axis as a function of time.
8. How do you get the shadow's speed and the magnitude of its acceleration from the expression you found in step 7?
9. Which trigonometric function must be a maximum when the speed is a maximum, and what is that function's maximum value?
10. Which trigonometric function must be a maximum when the acceleration magnitude is a maximum, and what is that function's maximum value?

❹ EVALUATE RESULT

11. Are the maximum speed and acceleration of the shadow of the right order of magnitude? Compare these values with the speed and maximum acceleration of the bug.

Worked Problem 15.3 Keeping lunar time

(*a*) What is the period of a simple pendulum of length 0.50 m on the Moon? (*b*) How does this period compare with the period of the same pendulum on Earth?

❶ GETTING STARTED We have to think about the factors that affect the period and about how these factors change when we move from Earth to the Moon. From videos of astronauts on the Moon, we are aware that things drop more slowly there, which implies that the free-fall acceleration is smaller there than on Earth.

❷ DEVISE PLAN From *Principles* Example 15.6, we know that the angular frequency of a simple pendulum is $\omega = \sqrt{g/\ell}$ and its period of oscillation is

$$T = \frac{2\pi}{\omega} = 2\pi\sqrt{\frac{\ell}{g}}.$$

The derivation of this relationship in the *Principles* volume does not require that the pendulum be oscillating on Earth, and so the result is general. Because Equation 13.4 in the generic form $g = Gm/R^2$ tells us the free-fall acceleration g at the surface of *any* celestial body of radius R, we can apply it to the Moon:

$$g_M = G\frac{m_M}{R_M^2}.$$

We get the mass and radius of the Moon from *Principles* Table 13.1.

❸ EXECUTE PLAN (*a*) The magnitude of G is the same no matter where we are (that's why Newton's gravitational law is called the law of *universal* gravitation), so Eq. 13.4 gives

$$g_M = (6.674 \times 10^{-11}\ \mathrm{N\cdot m^2/kg^2})\frac{7.3 \times 10^{22}\ \mathrm{kg}}{(1.74 \times 10^6\ \mathrm{m})^2} = 1.6\ \mathrm{m/s^2}.$$

PRACTICE

The period of a 0.50-m lunar pendulum is therefore

$$T_M = 2\pi\sqrt{\frac{0.50\text{ m}}{1.6\text{ m/s}^2}} = 3.5\text{ s.}\ ✔$$

(*b*) We can use the general expression for period and our knowledge of the lunar and earthly free-fall accelerations to get the desired ratio of periods without having to calculate the pendulum's period on Earth:

$$\frac{T_M}{T_E} = \sqrt{\frac{g_E}{g_M}} = \sqrt{\frac{9.8\text{ m/s}^2}{1.6\text{ m/s}^2}} = 2.5.\ ✔$$

❹ **EVALUATE RESULT** The longer period on the Moon makes sense because, as we found in part *a*, the gravitational acceleration on the Moon, 1.6 m/s^2, is about one-sixth that on Earth.

Guided Problem 15.4 In sync

A block of mass m is hung from a vertical spring, stretching the spring a distance h beyond its relaxed length. The block is pulled down a bit and released, resulting in a vertical oscillation. The block is then removed from the spring and used as the bob on a simple pendulum. If the period of the oscillating pendulum is the same as the period of the oscillating block-spring system, what is the length of the pendulum?

❶ **GETTING STARTED**

1. How are the motions of the spring and pendulum analogous to each other?
2. Sketch both oscillating systems at an arbitrary instant, labeling key variables.
3. What assumptions do you need to make in order to solve this problem?

❷ **DEVISE PLAN**

4. What general expressions give you the periods of the two systems?
5. What unknown quantities must you determine before setting the two periods equal? What information can help you determine these quantities? For example, how can you calculate the spring constant k? Does calculating this constant help?

❸ **EXECUTE PLAN**

6. Work through the algebra and solve for the pendulum length.

❹ **EVALUATE RESULT**

7. Is the answer plausible, that is, does your expression behave as you expect it to with variations in m and h?

Worked Problem 15.5 A very tall grandfather clock

Suppose you could construct a pendulum consisting of a very long string (nearly infinitely long) and a bob that swings just above Earth's surface with an amplitude that is small compared to Earth's diameter. What would the period of its oscillation be?

❶ **GETTING STARTED** The problem statement describes a simple pendulum. From Worked Problem 15.3, we know that the period of a pendulum increases with the square root of its length: $T = 2\pi\sqrt{\ell/g}$. This relationship implies that the period of our very long pendulum should be really long, increasing without limit to infinity as the length increases. So, what is at issue? Why do we bother with this problem if the solution is that easy? To answer this question, we need to derive an expression for the period. Let us start with a sketch showing how this infinite pendulum might differ from a normal pendulum (Figure WG15.3).

Figure WG15.3

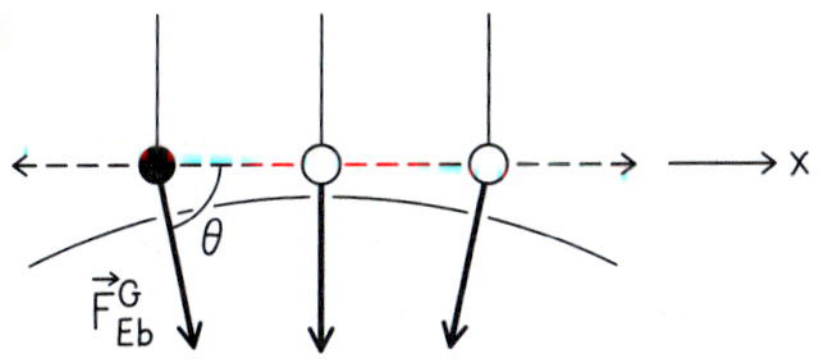

We note that an infinite string length means that the string is always vertical and the arc described by the bob is very nearly a straight line. We choose this line of motion as the x axis, with the origin at the equilibrium point and the positive direction to the right in the figure. Next we notice that the angle of the gravitational force exerted on the pendulum bob changes direction, always pointing toward Earth's center rather than straight down in the figure. From this changing direction, we conclude that although gravity provides a restoring force that pulls the bob toward the center of the motion, it is not the same as the constant gravitational force used in the analysis of a normal pendulum.

Because this is a hypothetical ("Suppose you could…") problem, we assume that practical considerations of pendulum construction and air drag should be ignored.

❷ **DEVISE PLAN** Because the pendulum's motion is nearly linear, we will use an analysis similar to that in *Principles* Example 15.8 to derive the angular frequency, beginning with Newton's second law, $\Sigma\vec{F} = m\vec{a}$, and casting it in a form that looks like a harmonic oscillator equation (Eq. 15.9):

$$a_x = \frac{d^2x}{dt^2} = -\omega^2 x. \tag{1}$$

We use a linear variable x to describe the position of the bob along its essentially straight-line horizontal path (straight and horizontal because we are taking our infinitely long string to be always vertical).

❸ **EXECUTE PLAN** From the free-body diagram (Figure WG15.4), we see that two forces are exerted on the bob: the tensile force exerted by the string and the force of gravity exerted by Earth. Because the pendulum is near Earth's surface at all times, we can use g for the acceleration magnitude.

Figure WG15.4

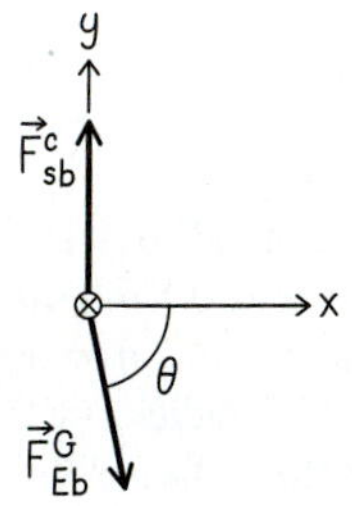

PRACTICE

The horizontal component of the gravitational force, which points to the right in Figure WG15.4, is unbalanced and so produces an acceleration, causing the oscillations. The positive x direction is, for consistency with our earlier choice, to the right in Figure WG15.4. Thus the x component of force is

$$F^G_{\text{Eb}x} = ma_x = mg\cos\theta. \qquad (2)$$

The gravitational-force vector in Figure WG15.4 is directed from the pendulum bob to the center of Earth. We can construct a right triangle (Figure WG15.5) that contains this same angle θ using the distance from the bob to Earth's center, the displacement x, and the radius of Earth. Note that the height above Earth's surface of the pendulum bob at the midpoint of its motion is negligible compared to the radius of Earth. Using this triangle, we can rewrite $\cos\theta$ in terms of the bob's displacement x and Earth's radius:

$$\cos\theta = \frac{-x}{\sqrt{R_E^2 + x^2}} \approx \frac{-x}{R_E}.$$

Using Eq. 2 in the form $a_x = g\cos\theta$ and then writing the acceleration a_x as the second derivative of position with respect to time give

Figure WG15.5

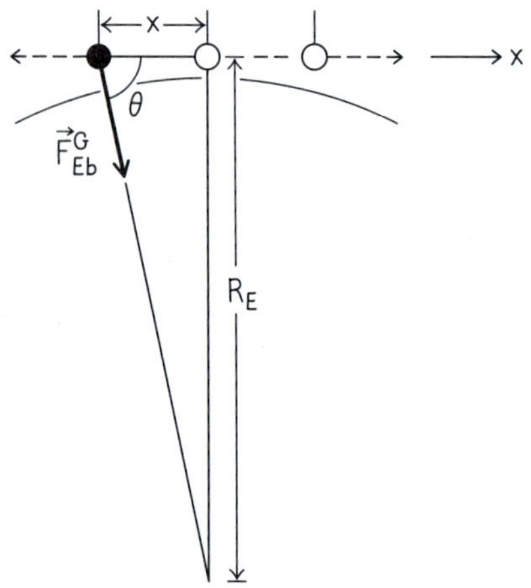

$$\frac{d^2x}{dt^2} = g\cos\theta = -\frac{g}{R_E}x, \qquad (3)$$

our desired equation of motion for the oscillator.

We obtain the period of oscillation by comparing Eqs. 1 and 3:

$$a_x = -\omega^2 x$$

$$\omega^2 = -\frac{a_x}{x} = -\left(\frac{-gx}{R_E}\right)\left(\frac{1}{x}\right) = \frac{g}{R_E}.$$

Equation 15.1, $\omega = 2\pi/T$, gives us

$$\omega^2 = \frac{g}{R_E} = \left(\frac{2\pi}{T}\right)^2, \quad \text{and so} \quad T = 2\pi\sqrt{\frac{R_E}{g}}.$$

Notice that the period does not depend on the mass of the bob. Putting in numbers, we get

$$T = 2\pi\sqrt{\frac{6.38 \times 10^6 \text{ m}}{9.8 \text{ m/s}^2}} = 5070 \text{ s} = 84 \text{ min.} ✓$$

❹ **EVALUATE RESULT** This is a large oscillation period, but long pendulums have large periods. Even if we didn't work through the calculation, it would be surprising that the period is not infinite, as the result of *Principles* Example 15.6, $T = 2\pi(\ell/g)^{1/2}$, implies it should be. The derivation of that equation assumed that the gravitational force always points vertically downward, whereas in this case we used the fact that the gravitational force is directed radially toward the center of Earth.

We assumed that the magnitude of the gravitational acceleration and the string direction do not change over the path of the swing, which is consistent with the requirement that the amplitude of the motion be small compared to the diameter of Earth. These assumptions do not undermine the main element of the derivation: The direction of the gravitational force changes even though we have assumed its magnitude does not.

Guided Problem 15.6 One deep hole

In another hypothetical exercise, suppose you could dig a tunnel that begins where you are standing now, passes through Earth's center, and comes out on the other side of the globe. What would happen to a rock you drop into this tunnel? How long would it take the rock to return to you? (For simplicity, assume Earth does not rotate and ignore air drag.)

❶ **GETTING STARTED**

1. Describe the physical situation and posed task in your own words. Draw a sketch consistent with your description.
2. What do you expect the rock to do after you release it?

❷ **DEVISE PLAN**

3. Recall from *Principles* Section 13.8 that a solid sphere exerts a gravitational force as if all the mass of the sphere were concentrated at its center.
4. To determine the magnitude of the gravitational force exerted by Earth on the rock after it has been dropped into the tunnel and is a radial distance $r < R_E$ from Earth's center, imagine the portion of Earth that has radius r (at the instant you are analyzing, your rock is on the surface of this imaginary sphere).
5. Refer to Checkpoint 13.23 if necessary.
6. What is the rock's acceleration as it passes through Earth's center?
7. Write the equation of motion for the rock as it passes a specific position x in its motion through the tunnel. Can you make this look like a simple harmonic oscillator equation?
8. What is the average density of Earth? Add information to your sketch as needed to help you visualize your approach.

❸ **EXECUTE PLAN**

9. Write an equation for the position of the rock as a function of time.
10. What is the angular frequency ω of the oscillation? What is the period T?

❹ **EVALUATE RESULT**

11. Compare your period with that of the "infinite" pendulum of Worked Problem 15.5. What insight do you gain from this comparison?

PRACTICE

Worked Problem 15.7 A damping influence

You decide to test the effect of a viscous liquid on the motion of a simple pendulum consisting of a thin rod 9.0 m long, a 2.0-kg spherical bob, and pivot bearings at the end of the rod opposite the bob. You place the pendulum in a huge vat of maple syrup. The rod is so thin that it experiences very little drag, so essentially the entire drag force is exerted on the bob. You start the pendulum swinging with a small amplitude, and 10 s later the motion is indiscernible. (*a*) Derive an equation that shows how the angle the pendulum makes with the vertical depends on time. (*b*) What is the approximate period of oscillation of this pendulum? Ignore any friction in the bearings.

❶ GETTING STARTED This problem involves damped oscillations but for a pendulum rather than the block-spring system examined in *Principles* Section 15.8. A drag force exerted by the syrup opposes the motion of the pendulum. We do not know anything about the amplitude of the motion except that after 10 s the motion is undetectable. So we have to use our judgment here. Damped oscillations die out exponentially, which means that they never truly reach zero amplitude (the motion just becomes too small to notice). A reasonable guess is that the final amplitude is 1% of the initial value.

❷ DEVISE PLAN To make use of the solution worked out in *Principles* Section 15.8, we need to derive an equation in the form of Eq. 15.36,

$$m\frac{d^2x}{dt^2} + b\frac{dx}{dt} + kx = 0,$$

and make the appropriate mathematical correspondence with our rotational quantities (for instance, x becomes ϑ). As with the block-spring system of *Principles* Section 15.8, we assume that the drag force exerted by the syrup on the pendulum is proportional to the pendulum's velocity: $\vec{F}^{d}_{sp} = -b\vec{v}_p$ (Eq. 15.34). This force produces a torque on the pendulum in addition to the gravitational torque produced by Earth. Therefore we can use Eq. 15.24, $\Sigma\tau_\vartheta = I\alpha_\vartheta$, in the form

$$I\frac{d^2\vartheta}{dt^2} = \tau_{\text{Ep}\,\vartheta} + \tau_{\text{sp}\,\vartheta}. \quad (1)$$

We use Eq. 15.31, $\tau_\vartheta = -(m\ell_{cm}g)\vartheta$, to simplify the $\tau_{\text{Ep}\,\vartheta}$ term. The torque $\tau_{\text{sp}\,\vartheta}$ is proportional to the pendulum's translational speed dx/dt and therefore to its rotational speed $d\vartheta/dt$. This information should give us the derivatives we need in the equation of motion for the damped oscillator in part *a*.

In order to get the period of the motion, we need to know the number of oscillations in a given time interval, which means we need to know the angular frequency ω_d of the damped motion. Because damping is present, the angular frequency ω_d is given by Eq. 15.38. Once we have ω_d, we obtain the period of the motion from the relationship $T_d \approx 2\pi/\omega_d$.

❸ EXECUTE PLAN
(*a*) Let ℓ be the length of the rod and m the mass of the pendulum. The torque caused by the gravitational force is given by Eq. 15.31, as noted above. The torque caused by the drag force exerted by the syrup is

$$\tau_{\text{sp}\,\vartheta} = F^{d}_{\text{sp}\perp}\ell = -(bv_{\text{p}\perp})\ell = -[b(\ell\omega_\vartheta)]\ell$$

$$= -b\ell^2\frac{d\vartheta}{dt},$$

where we have used Eq. 15.34 to substitute for the factor $F^{d}_{\text{sp}\perp}$ and the relationship between speed and rotational speed for motion along a circular arc, $v_{\text{p}\perp} = \ell\omega_\vartheta$, to substitute for the factor $v_{\text{p}\perp}$. Inserting these values into Eq. 1 yields

$$I\frac{d^2\vartheta}{dt^2} = [-(m\ell g)\vartheta] + \left[-b\ell^2\frac{d\vartheta}{dt}\right]$$

$$I\frac{d^2\vartheta}{dt^2} + (b\ell^2)\frac{d\vartheta}{dt} + (m\ell g)\vartheta = 0.$$

This result has the same form as Eq. 15.36,

$$m\frac{d^2x}{dt^2} + b\frac{dx}{dt} + kx = 0,$$

with the substitutions I for m, ϑ for x, $b\ell^2$ for b, and $m\ell g$ for k. We infer from Eq. 15.37 that the equation for the rotational position as a function of time for the damped pendulum is

$$\vartheta(t) = Ae^{-b\ell^2 t/2I}\sin(\omega_d t + \phi_i).$$

(Recall from *Principles* Section 15.5 that ϕ_i is the initial phase of the motion.) The rotational inertia for a simple pendulum is $I = m\ell^2$. Substituting this rotational inertia into our rotational position equation yields

$$\vartheta(t) = Ae^{-b\ell^2 t/2(m\ell^2)}\sin(\omega_d t + \phi_i),$$

where $$\omega_d = \sqrt{\frac{m\ell g}{m\ell^2} - \left(\frac{b\ell^2}{2m\ell^2}\right)^2}$$

$$\vartheta(t) = Ae^{-bt/2m}\sin(\omega_d t + \phi_i),$$

where $$\omega_d = \sqrt{\frac{g}{\ell} - \left(\frac{b}{2m}\right)^2}. ✔ \quad (2)$$

As with the block-spring case, the angular frequency ω is modified by a term, $(b/2m)^2$, that depends on the damping, telling us that the oscillations decrease exponentially. The ratio $b/2m$ determines the damping.

(*b*) We assumed that the oscillation amplitude decreases to 1% of its initial value in 10 s: $(0.010)A = Ae^{-b(10\text{ s})/2m}$. Solving for $b/2m$ yields

$$\ln 0.010 = -\frac{b}{2m}(10\text{ s})$$

$$\frac{b}{2m} = \frac{4.61}{10\text{ s}} = 0.46\text{ s}^{-1}.$$

The estimated angular frequency and period are therefore

$$\omega_d = \sqrt{\frac{9.8\text{ m/s}^2}{9.0\text{ m}} - (0.46\text{ s}^{-1})^2}$$

$$= \sqrt{(1.09 - 0.21)\text{ s}^{-2}} = 0.94\text{ s}^{-1}$$

$$T_d \approx \frac{2\pi}{0.94\text{ s}^{-1}} = 6.7\text{ s. ✔}$$

❹ EVALUATE RESULT If we remove the pendulum from the syrup, we have an undamped simple pendulum, for which the angular frequency is $\omega = \sqrt{g/\ell}$, which is what our expression for ω_d reduces to for $b = 0$.

We can gain further confidence by seeing whether our algebraic expression for ω_d behaves the way we expect as we change the value of the damping coefficient b. If b increases, we expect ω_d to decrease because the pendulum must overcome a greater resistive force as it swings. We see that the term $b/2m$ is subtracted in the square-root term in Eq. 2, causing ω_d to decrease with increasing b.

Note that the pendulum's angular frequency without syrup would be $\omega = 1.04\ \text{s}^{-1}$, so under our assumption the syrup has a 10% effect on the angular frequency and period. Our decision to make 1% of the original amplitude the state of undetectable motion is of course arbitrary. What if we chose 0.10% instead? The value of $b/2m$ becomes $0.69\ \text{s}^{-1}$, which makes $\omega_d = 0.78\ \text{s}^{-1}$, and now we are closer to a 25% effect of damping on the angular frequency. The size of the effect clearly depends on our assumption. However, under this revised assumption, the period would be about 8 s, so the sensitivity is not dramatic.

One last thing to consider is why we must say that the period is only approximately equal to $2\pi/\omega_d$ instead of using the equality $T = 2\pi/\omega$ (from Eq. 15.1, $\omega = 2\pi/T$). The reason we must use the approximation is that the motion is not strictly periodic because of the exponential time dependence of the amplitude. The motion does not simply repeat itself, which makes the definition of *period* a bit ambiguous. Thus $T_d \approx 2\pi/\omega_d$ is the best estimate we can make.

Guided Problem 15.8 Prevent oscillation

A typical engineering design element in systems susceptible to unwanted oscillation is *critical damping*. The idea is that a disturbance displaces some moving part, but rather than oscillating around its equilibrium position, the part returns as quickly as possible to its equilibrium position without overshooting it. This requires that the damped angular frequency be zero: $\omega_d = 0$. (*a*) For the pendulum in Worked Problem 15.7, what must be the value of the damping coefficient b if critical damping is desired? (*b*) When the system is critically damped, how long does it take for the amplitude to decrease to 1% of its initial value?

❶ GETTING STARTED

1. What is the physical significance of the damping coefficient b?
2. Should the value of $b/2m$ be greater or smaller than it is in Worked Problem 15.7?

❷ DEVISE PLAN

3. Is the condition for critical damping given in the problem statement, $\omega_d = 0$, useful in determining the desired value for part *a*?
4. What equation or expression can be used to solve part *b*? Can you save a bit of derivation by using results from Worked Problem 15.7?

❸ EXECUTE PLAN

5. Solve algebraically for the desired quantities, doing part *a* first and then part *b*. Are there any other unknown quantities in your expression that must be eliminated?
6. Substitute known values and compute your answers.

❹ EVALUATE RESULT

7. How does your algebraic expression for part *b* behave if the value of b is twice the critical value? If it is half the critical value?

PRACTICE

Questions and Problems

For instructor-assigned homework, go to MasteringPhysics® MP

Dots indicate difficulty level of problems: • = easy, •• = intermediate, ••• = hard; CR = context-rich problem.

15.1 Periodic motion and energy

1. If you photograph a flock of birds taking off from ground level, some of the wings will be blurred in the photograph even though the bodies are in focus. In which wing positions are the wings least blurry? •
2. Plot kinetic energy and potential energy as a function of time for the cart in *Principles* Figure 15.2. •
3. Based on the energy diagrams in *Principles* Figure 15.2, sketch a graph showing velocity as a function of position for the cart represented in the figure. ••
4. (*a*) At what displacement (expressed as a fraction of the amplitude of the motion) is the kinetic energy of the cart in *Principles* Figure 15.2 half its maximum value? (*b*) What is the velocity (expressed as a fraction of the maximum velocity) at this displacement? ••
5. Figure P15.5 shows a graph of the potential energy U of a moving object as a function of its position x. What is the maximum range of x values possible for periodic motion in this system? ••

Figure P15.5

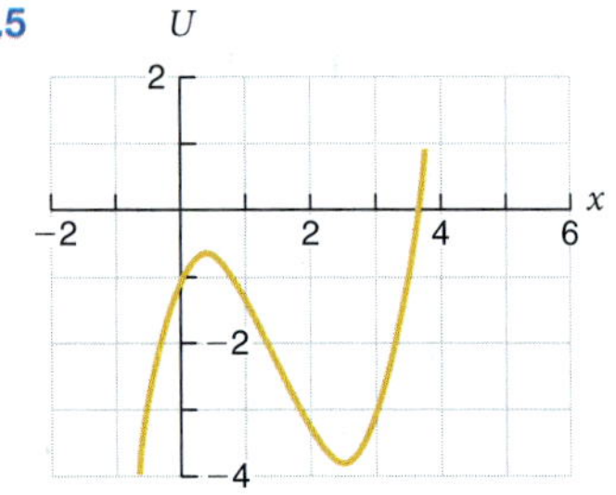

15.2 Simple harmonic motion

6. What distance does an oscillator of amplitude A travel in 2.5 periods? •

7. What is the period of the motion represented by the curve in Figure P15.7? •

Figure P15.7

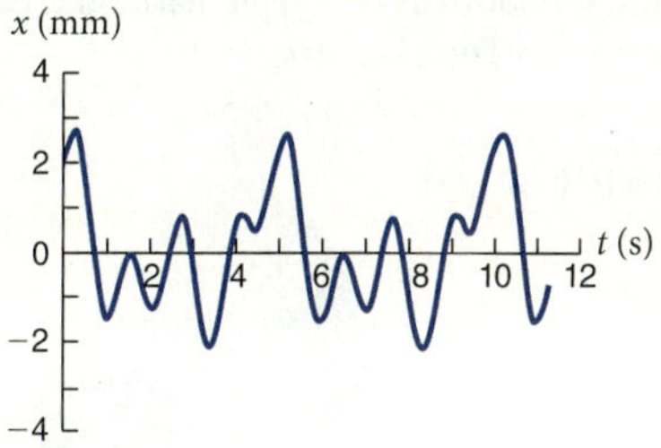

8. (*a*) Explain why the motion of the engine piston in Figure P15.8 is only approximately simple harmonic motion. (*b*) What must you do to the length of the connecting rod if you want to make the motion more nearly simple harmonic motion? ••

Figure P15.8

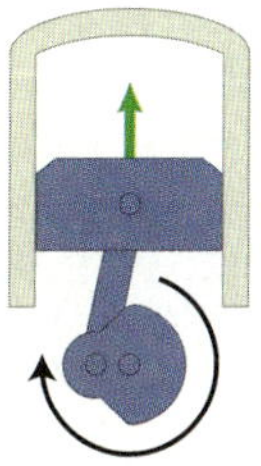

9. Is the typical up-and-down motion of a yo-yo periodic motion, assuming no energy is dissipated? Is it simple harmonic motion? ••

10. A highly elastic ball is dropped from a height of 2.0 m onto a hard surface. Assume the collision is elastic and no energy is lost to air friction. (*a*) Show that the ball's motion after it hits the surface is periodic. (*b*) Determine the period of the motion. (*c*) Is it simple harmonic motion? Why or why not? ••

15.3 Fourier's theorem

11. Fourier analysis of a particular spectrum includes the harmonic frequencies 889 Hz, 1143 Hz, and 1270 Hz. What is the fundamental frequency f_1, assuming that $f_1 > 100$ Hz? •

12. Even when a piano and a trumpet play the same note (which means the sounds have the same frequency f), the two instruments sound completely different. What is it about the sound from the instruments that accounts for this difference? ••

13. Estimate the number of harmonics (counting the fundamental frequency) that contribute significantly in the Fourier analysis of the spectrum in Figure P15.7. ••

14. Suppose you create a periodic function by adding together only sine functions whose amplitudes decrease like $1/n^2$, where n is any odd integer multiple of the fundamental frequency, and where every other term is subtracted rather than added. (*a*) What general properties would this periodic function exhibit? (*b*) Describe the shape of the function obtained by adding only the four terms of frequencies f, $3f$, $5f$, and $7f$. (Hint: Construct the graph using superposition.) •••

15. What harmonic series is required to produce a "square wave," as illustrated in Figure P15.15? •••

Figure P15.15

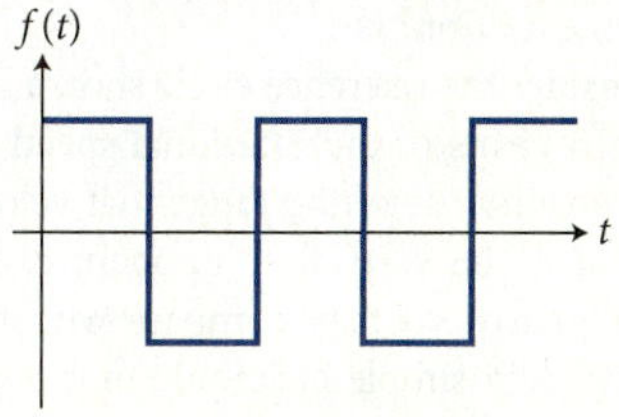

15.4 Restoring forces in simple harmonic motion

16. Which of these forces could result in simple harmonic motion: (*a*) $F(x) = 2x$, (*b*) $F(x) = -2x$, (*c*) $F(x) = -2x^2$, (*d*) $F(x) = 2x^2$, (*e*) $F(x) = -2x + 2$, (*f*) $F(x) = -2(x - 2)^2$? •

17. When you dive off a diving board, the board oscillates while you are flying toward the swimming pool. (These oscillations are significantly damped for a good diving board.) Identify the restoring force (or torque) responsible for these oscillations as well as the relevant mass. ••

18. A spring-cart system and a simple pendulum both have the same period near Earth's surface. What happens to the period of each motion when both systems are in orbit inside the International Space Station? ••

19. *Principles* Figure 15.12 illustrates the x component of the vector sum of forces on an object for conditions of stable, unstable and neutral equilibrium. (*a*) Examine this graph carefully. What visible feature differs in the three types of equilibrium? (*b*) Express your result as a set of mathematical relationships that can be used to discriminate stable from unstable or neutral equilibrium. (*c*) Are these relationships general? That is, can you construct a graph showing the x component of the vector sum of forces versus position that meets the requirements for stable equilibrium but violates your mathematical expression? ••

20. (*a*) When air resistance is ignored, does a pendulum clock run faster or slower at higher altitude? (*b*) Does your answer change if you don't ignore the effects of air resistance? •••

15.5 Energy of a simple harmonic oscillator

21. Write Eqs. 15.6, 15.7, and 15.8 in terms of the period T of the motion. •

22. Is the initial phase ϕ_i positive, zero, or negative for each oscillation graphed in Figure P15.22? •

Figure P15.22

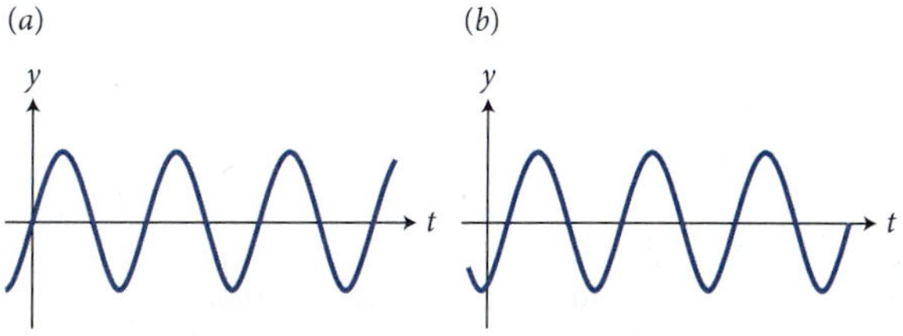

23. In *Principles* Figure 15.22, the vertical component of the phasor moves in simple harmonic motion. (*a*) Does the horizontal component also move in simple harmonic motion? (*b*) What is the phase difference $\Delta\phi = \phi_v - \phi_h$ between the vertical and horizontal components? ••

24. Consider the nearly circular orbit of Earth around the Sun as seen by a distant observer standing in the plane of the orbit. What is the effective "spring constant" of this simple harmonic motion? ••

25. Consider the reference circle shown in *Principles* Figure 15.22. (*a*) In terms of the rotational speed ω of the phasor, what is the magnitude of the tangential velocity $\vec{v}$ of the phasor tip? What is the vertical component of this velocity? How does this phasor velocity compare with the velocity of an object moving in simple harmonic motion? (*b*) In terms of the rotational speed ω of the phasor, what is the magnitude of the centripetal acceleration of the phasor tip? What is the vertical component of this acceleration? How does this phasor acceleration compare with the acceleration of an object moving in simple harmonic motion? ••

26. The position of a particle undergoing simple harmonic motion is given by $x(t) = 20\cos(8\pi t)$, where x is in millimeters and t is in seconds. For this motion, what are the (*a*) amplitude, (*b*) frequency f, and (*c*) period? (*d*) What are the first three instants at which the particle is at $x = 0$? (*e*) Determine the x components of position, velocity, and acceleration of the particle at $t = 0.75$ s. ••

27. An object undergoes simple harmonic motion along an x axis with a period of 0.50 s and amplitude of 25 mm. Its position is $x = 14$ mm when $t = 0$. (*a*) Write an equation of motion with all variables identified. (*b*) Draw a position-versus-time graph for this motion. ••

28. You are standing next to a table and looking down on a record player sitting on the table. Take the spindle (axis of rotation) to be the center of your coordinate system and the y axis to be perpendicular to the side of the player you are standing next to. Long-playing records revolve $33\frac{1}{3}$ times per minute. You put a small blob of clay at the edge of a record that has a radius of 0.15 m, positioning the clay such that it is at its greatest value of y at $t = 0$. (*a*) What is the rotational speed of the clay? (*b*) Write the equation of motion for the y component of the clay's position. ••

29. A 1.0-kg object undergoes simple harmonic motion with an amplitude of 0.12 m and a maximum acceleration of 5.0 m/s^2. What is its energy? ••

30. The position of a particle undergoing simple harmonic motion is given by $x(t) = a\cos(bt + \pi/3)$, where $a = 8.00$ m and $b = 2.00\ \text{s}^{-1}$. What are the (*a*) amplitude, (*b*) frequency f, and (*c*) period? (*d*) What are the speed and acceleration magnitude of the particle at $t = \pi/2$ s? (*e*) What is its maximum acceleration magnitude, and at what instant after $t = 0$ does the particle first have this acceleration? (*f*) What is its maximum speed, and at what instant after $t = 0$ does it first have this speed? ••

31. For any simple harmonic motion, the position, velocity, and acceleration can all be written as the same type of trigonometric function (sine or cosine) by correctly adding a *relative phase factor*. (*a*) Show that an x component of the position function given by $x(t) = \beta\cos(\omega t + \delta)$ is also a valid general solution for simple harmonic motion. (*b*) Write the x components of the velocity and acceleration associated with this position function. (*c*) Draw the reference circles for the x components of position, velocity, and acceleration, with the phasors correctly drawn for $t = 0$ and the amplitude clearly indicated. •••

32. You get a crazy idea to dig a tunnel through Earth from Boston to Paris, a surface distance of 5850 km, and run a passenger train between the two cities (Figure P15.32). The train would move down the first part of the tunnel under the pull of gravity and then coast upward against gravity. If you assume that the motion will be simple harmonic motion, how long will a one-way trip take? •••

Figure P15.32

33. You have developed a method in which a paint shaker is used to measure the coefficient of static friction between various objects and a known surface. The shaker oscillates with a fixed amplitude of 50 mm, but you can adjust the frequency of the motion. You have affixed a horizontal tabletop (the known surface) to the shaker so that the tabletop oscillates with it. Then you put an object on the tabletop and increase the frequency until the object begins to slip on the surface. If a frequency $f = 1.85$ Hz is required before a penny positioned on the tabletop starts to slide, what is the coefficient of static friction between penny and tabletop? •••

15.6 Simple harmonic motion and springs

34. Even a spring without a block hanging on the end of it has an oscillation period. Why isn't the period zero? •

35. A vertical spring on which is hung a block of mass m_1 oscillates with frequency f. With an additional block of mass $m_2 \neq m_1$ added to the spring, the frequency is $f/2$. What is the ratio m_1/m_2? •

36. Two vertical springs have identical spring constants, but one has a ball of mass m hanging from it and the other has a ball of mass $2m$ hanging from it. If the energies of the two systems are the same, what is the ratio of the oscillation amplitudes? •

37. A horizontal spring-block system made up of one block and one spring has oscillation frequency f. A second spring, identical to the first, is to be added to the system. (*a*) Does f increase, decrease, or stay the same when the two springs are connected as shown in Figure P15.37*a*? (*b*) What happens to f when the springs are arranged as in Figure P15.37*b*? ••

Figure P15.37

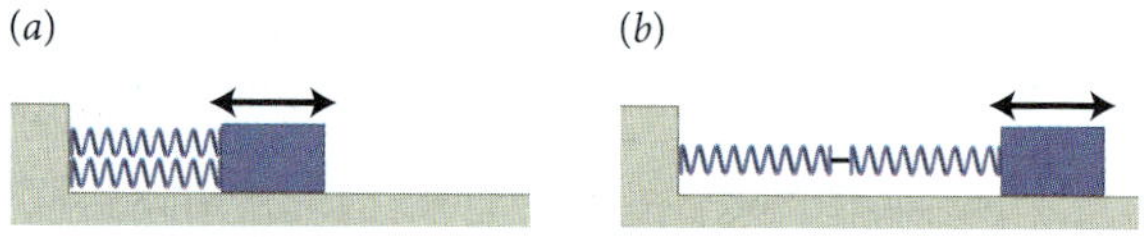

38. Two balls of unequal mass are hung from two springs that are not identical. The springs stretch the same distance as the two systems reach equilibrium. Then both springs are compressed and released. Which one oscillates faster? ••

PRACTICE

39. A table outfitted with springs on its feet bounces vertically in simple harmonic motion. A cup of coffee is sitting on the table. Discuss whether any of the following changes to this system could cause the cup to lose contact with the table: (*a*) increase the amplitude, (*b*) increase the period, (*c*) decrease the period, (*d*) decrease the mass of the table, (*e*) increase the mass of the table, (*f*) change the phase of the motion. (*g*) Would your answers be different if you considered not the cup bottom losing contact with the table but rather the coffee flying out of the cup? ••

40. A 2.0-kg cart is attached to a horizontal spring for which the spring constant is 50 N/m. The system is set in motion when the cart is 0.24 m from its equilibrium position, and the initial velocity is 2.0 m/s directed away from the equilibrium position. (*a*) What is the amplitude of the oscillation? (*b*) What is the speed of the cart at its equilibrium position? (*c*) How would the answers to parts *a* and *b* change if the initial direction of motion were toward the cart's equilibrium position? ••

41. A vertical spring-block system with a period of 2.3 s and a mass of 0.35 kg is released 40 mm below its equilibrium position with an initial upward velocity of 0.12 m/s. For this system, determine the (*a*) amplitude, (*b*) angular frequency ω, (*c*) energy, (*d*) spring constant, (*e*) initial phase angle, and (*f*) equation of motion. ••

42. A 5.0-kg object is suspended from the ceiling by a strong spring, which stretches 0.10 m when the object is attached. The object is lifted 0.050 m from this equilibrium position and released. Determine the amplitude and period of the resulting simple harmonic motion. ••

43. A 5.0-kg block is suspended from the ceiling by a strong spring and released to perform simple harmonic motion with a period of 0.50 s. The block is brought to rest, and the length of the spring with the block attached is measured. By how much is this length reduced when the block is removed? ••

44. A 4.0-kg object is suspended from the ceiling by a spring and undergoes simple harmonic motion with an amplitude of 0.50 m. At the highest position in the motion, the spring is at the length that would be its relaxed length if no object were attached. (*a*) Calculate the energy of the system. For the object at its lowest position, its equilibrium position, and its highest position, calculate (*b*) the elastic potential energy of the spring, (*c*) the kinetic energy of the object, and (*d*) the gravitational potential energy of the Earth-object system. ••

45. A 6.0-kg block free to slide on a horizontal surface is anchored to two facing walls by springs (Figure P15.45). Both springs are initially at their relaxed length. Then the block is displaced 20 mm to the right and released. (*a*) What is the effective spring constant of the system? (*b*) What is the equation for the position of the block as a function of time, assuming $+x$ to be to the right? Ignore friction. ••

Figure P15.45

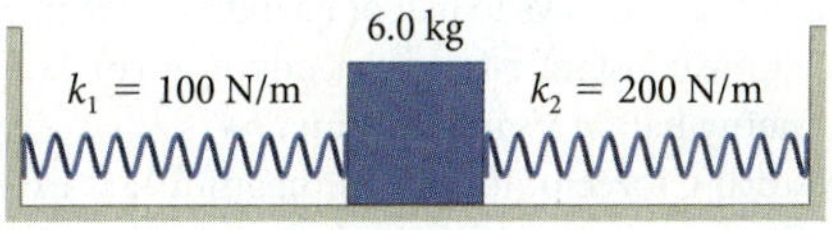

46. Block B in Figure P15.46 is free to slide on the horizontal surface. With block C placed on top of B, the system undergoes simple harmonic motion with an amplitude of 0.10 m. Block B has a speed of 0.24 m/s at a displacement of 0.060 m from its equilibrium position. (*a*) Determine the period of the motion. (*b*) What minimum value for the coefficient of static friction μ_s between B and C is needed if C is never to slip? Ignore any friction between B and the horizontal surface. •••

Figure P15.46

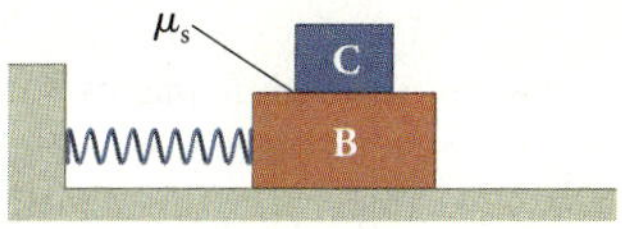

47. After gluing two 0.50-kg blocks together, you determine that you can pull the blocks apart with a force of 20 N. You attach the top block to a vertical spring for which the spring constant is 500 N/m. What is the maximum possible amplitude of oscillation for which the glue can keep the blocks together? •••

48. Two blocks, of masses m_1 and m_2, are placed on a horizontal surface and attached to opposite ends of a spring as in Figure P15.48. The blocks are then pushed toward each other to compress the spring. When the blocks are released, (*a*) describe the motion of the center of mass of the system and (*b*) derive an expression for the angular frequency ω of the motion. (*c*) What is ω in the limit $m_2 \gg m_1$? (*d*) What is ω when $m_1 = m_2$? Ignore friction and the mass of the spring. •••

Figure P15.48

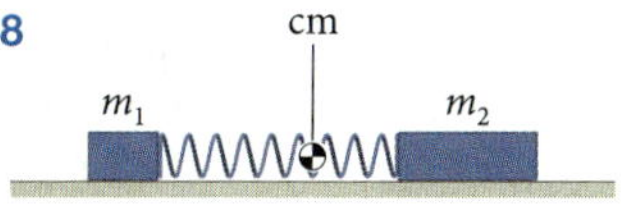

15.7 Restoring torques

49. You want to build a pendulum clock in which the time interval during which the "tick" sound is made (pendulum swinging one way) and the time interval during which the "tock" sound is made (pendulum swinging the other way) are each 0.50 s. If we assume the pendulum is a simple one, what should its length be? •

50. What happens to the period of the pendulum shown in Figure P15.50*a* when the stand supporting the pendulum is tipped backward as shown in Figure P15.50*b*? •

Figure P15.50

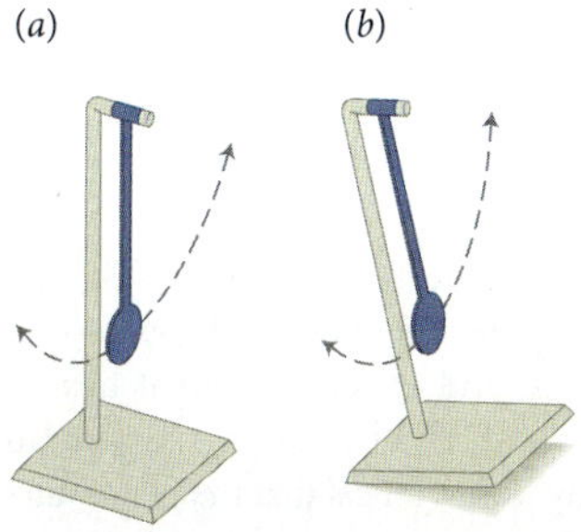

PRACTICE

51. Which pendulum in Figure P15.51 has the greater period? ••

Figure P15.51

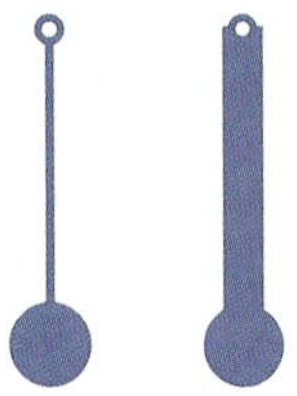

52. A small-angle approximation was used to derive Eq. 15.31, $\tau = -(m\ell g)\vartheta$. (*a*) What constitutes *small* in this context? In other words, how large can ϑ be before it can no longer be called small? (*b*) As a quantitative benchmark, how large does ϑ have to be before $(m\ell g)\vartheta$ deviates by more than 1% from the true value of τ? ••

53. The maximum angle from the vertical reached by a simple pendulum of length ℓ is ϑ_{max}. What is the linear speed v of the bob for any angle ϑ from the vertical? ••

54. The 800-mg balance wheel of a certain clock is made up of a thin metal ring of radius 15 mm connected by spokes of negligible mass to a fine suspension fiber as in *Principles* Figure 15.31. The back-and-forth twisting of the fiber causes the wheel to move in simple harmonic motion with period T. The clock ticks four times each second, with the interval between ticks equal to $T/2$. (*a*) Determine the rotational inertia I of the balance wheel. (*b*) What is the torsional constant of the fiber that drives the balance wheel? ••

55. A thin 0.100-kg rod that is 250 mm long has a small hole drilled through it 62.5 mm from one end. A metal wire is strung through the hole, and the rod is free to rotate about the wire. (*a*) Determine the rod's rotational inertia I about this axis. (*b*) Determine the period of the rod's oscillation. ••

56. A rod of mass m and length ℓ is rigidly connected at a right angle to the midpoint of one face of a uniform cube of mass m and side length ℓ (Figure P15.56). The other end of the rod is connected to a pivot so that the system can oscillate freely. What is the period of small oscillations about the pivot? ••

Figure P15.56

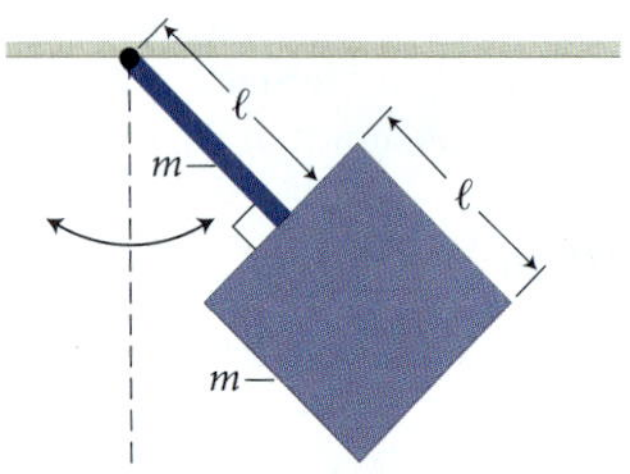

57. A simple pendulum of length 0.30 m has a 0.30-kg bob. At $t = 0$, the bob passes through the lowest position in its motion, and at this instant it has a horizontal speed of 0.25 m/s. (*a*) What is the maximum angular displacement ϑ_{max} away from vertical that the pendulum reaches? (*b*) What is the bob's linear speed v when it has angular displacement $\vartheta_{max}/2$? ••

58. A uniform disk of mass m and radius R lies in a vertical plane and is pivoted about a point a distance ℓ_{cm} from its center of mass (Figure P15.58). When given a small rotational displacement about the pivot, the disk undergoes simple harmonic motion. Determine the period of this motion. ••

Figure P15.58

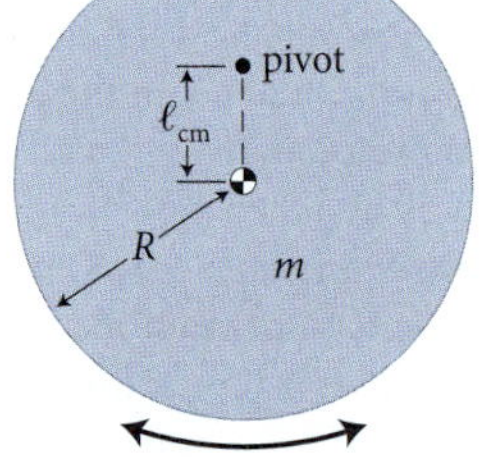

59. A thin 0.50-kg ring of radius $R = 0.10$ m hangs vertically from a horizontal knife-edge pivot about which the ring can oscillate freely. If the amplitude of the motion is kept small, what is the period? ••

60. If a person is 20% shorter than average, what is the ratio of his walking pace (that is, the frequency f of his motion) to the walking pace of a person of average height? Assume that a person's leg swings like a pendulum and that the angular amplitude of everybody's stride is about the same. •••

61. A pendulum consists of a bob of mass m_{bob} hanging at the end of a light rod of mass m_{rod} and length ℓ. If you ignore the mass of the rod, the period is T_0, and if you use m_{rod} in your calculation, the period is T. How far from the true value T is T_0? Express the error $\Delta T = T - T_0$ in terms of some power of the ratio m_{rod}/m_{bob}. (*Hint:* Some sort of series expansion is useful here.) •••

15.8 Damped oscillations

62. Verify that the time constant $\tau = m/b$ has units of time for damped oscillations. •

63. As the quality factor Q for a damped oscillation increases but the period T of undamped motion is held constant, what happens to the angular frequency ω_d of the damped motion? •

64. Express, as a function of τ, the time interval needed for the amplitude of an oscillation to reduce to half of its initial value. •

65. A 0.400-kg object is oscillating on a spring for which the force constant is 300 N/m. A damping force that is linearly proportional to the object's velocity is exerted on the system, and the damping coefficient is $b = 5.00$ kg/s. (*a*) Verify that the units given for b are correct. (*b*) What is the frequency f of the oscillation? (*c*) What is the time constant τ? (*d*) What is the quality factor Q? ••

66. A simple pendulum consists of a 1.00-kg bob on a string 1.00 m long. During a time interval of 27.0 s, the maximum angle this pendulum makes with the vertical is found to decrease from 6.00° to 5.40°. Determine the numerical values of the damping coefficient b and the time constant τ. ••

67. A 0.25-kg bob is suspended from a string that is 0.60 m long. When the pendulum is set into small-amplitude oscillation, the amplitude decays to half of its initial value in 35 s. (*a*) What is the time constant τ for the pendulum? (*b*) At what instant is the energy half of its initial value? ••

68. A restoring force of unknown magnitude is exerted on an object that oscillates with a period of 0.50 s. When the object is in an evacuated container, the motion is simple harmonic motion, with an amplitude of 0.10 m. When air is allowed into the container, the amplitude decreases by 2.0% with each cycle of the oscillation. (*a*) What is the amplitude after 25 cycles? (*b*) What fraction of the initial energy is left 6.3 s after air is admitted? ••

69. A 0.500-kg block oscillates up and down on a vertical spring for which $k = 12.5$ N/m. The initial amplitude of the motion is 0.100 m. (*a*) What is the natural angular frequency ω? (*b*) If the observed angular frequency is $\omega_d = 4.58\ s^{-1}$, what is b? (*c*) Write an equation for the position as a function of time. ••

70. A damped oscillator has a quality factor of 20. (*a*) By what fraction does the energy decrease during each cycle? (*b*) By what percentage does the damped angular frequency ω_d differ from the undamped angular frequency? ••

71. One reference book states that, after a large earthquake, Earth can be treated as an oscillator that has a period of 54 min and a quality factor of 400. (*a*) What percentage of the energy of oscillation is lost to damping forces during each cycle? (*b*) What fraction of the original energy is left after 2.0 days? ••

72. A gong makes a loud noise when struck. The noise gradually gets less and less loud until it fades below the sensitivity of the human ear. The simplest model of how the gong produces the sound we hear treats the gong as a damped harmonic oscillator. The tone we hear is related to the frequency f of the oscillation, and its loudness is proportional to the energy of the oscillation. (*a*) If the loudness drops to 85% of its original value in 4.0 s, what is the time constant of the damped oscillation? (*b*) How long does it take for the sound to be 25% as loud as it was at the start? (*c*) What fraction of the original loudness remains after 1.0 min? ••

73. *Critical damping* is a term used to describe a situation where the damping coefficient b is just great enough that no oscillation occurs (See Guided Problem 15.8. This is how you want the springs in your car to behave, so that when they flex to take you smoothly over a bump, they don't cause the car to jump up and down, reducing contact with the road.) (*a*) For an object of mass m attached to a spring of spring constant k, what is the value b_{crit} needed for critical damping? (*b*) Describe the motion if $b > b_{crit}$. ••

74. A small 3.0-kg object dropped from the roof of a tall building acquires a terminal speed of 25 m/s. Assume the drag force exerted on the object has the same form as the damping force exerted on a damped oscillator; that is, the force is opposed to the motion, and its magnitude is linearly proportional to the object's speed. An object identical to the dropped one is attached to a vertical spring ($k = 230$ N/m) and set into oscillation in the air with an initial amplitude of 0.20 m. (*a*) What is the quality factor for this oscillation? (*b*) How long does it take for the amplitude to drop to half its initial value? (*c*) How much energy is lost in this time interval? •••

75. An object resting on a table oscillates on the end of a horizontal spring. Because the table is covered with a viscous substance, the motion is damped and the amplitude gets smaller with each cycle. At $t = 1.5$ s, the object is 60 mm from its equilibrium position, and this is the farthest from equilibrium it reaches. The amplitude of the next cycle of the motion is 56 mm, and the object reaches this maximum x value at $t = 2.5$ s. Write the equation for the object's x component of position as a function of time, using numerical values for all constants. •••

Additional Problems

76. Do the turning points in simple harmonic motion have to be equidistant from the equilibrium position? •

77. If the amplitude of a simple harmonic motion doubles, what happens to (*a*) the energy of the system, (*b*) the maximum speed of the moving object, and (*c*) the period of the motion? •

78. A pendulum is swinging in a stationary elevator. What happens to the period when the elevator (*a*) accelerates upward, (*b*) travels downward at constant speed, and (*c*) travels downward and gradually slows to a stop? •

79. You measure the oscillation frequency f_{whole} of a vertical block-spring system. You then cut the spring in half, hang the same block from one of the halves, and measure the frequency f_{half}. What is the ratio f_{half}/f_{whole}? ••

80. The hand in Figure P15.80*a* holds a vertical block-spring system so that the spring is compressed. When the hand lets go, the block, of mass m, descends a distance d in a time interval Δt before reversing direction (Figure P15.80*b*). Once the system comes to rest, the block is removed, a block of mass $2m$ is hung in its place, and the experiment is repeated. To what maximum distance does the block descend? ••

Figure P15.80

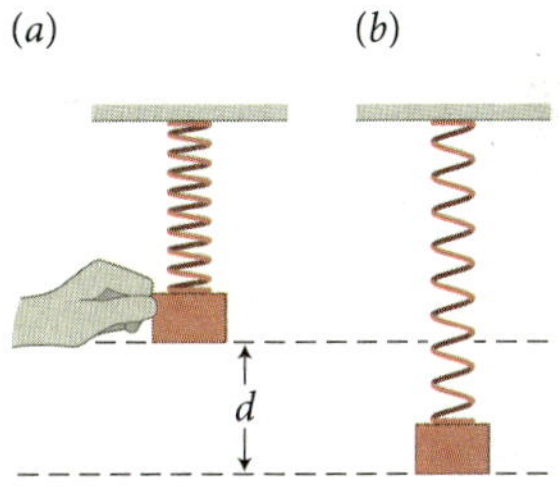

81. Two oscillatory motions are given by $x(t) = A\sin(m\omega t)$ and $y(t) = A\sin(n\omega t + \phi)$, where m and n are positive integers. Consider displaying these motions on a single graph with x and y axes oriented perpendicular to each other. What restrictions are necessary on m, n, and ϕ if the trajectory is to be a closed curve? These curves are called *Lissajous figures*. Plot these curves for (*a*) $m = n = 1$, $\phi = 0$; (*b*) $m = n = 1$, $\phi = \pi/4$; and (*c*) $m = 2$, $n = 3$, $\phi = 0$. ••

82. What would be the period of oscillation of this book if you held it at one corner between index finger and thumb and allowed it to swing slightly? To first order, ignore any effect on the oscillation by friction between your fingers and the book. ••

83. You have a teardrop-shaped 2.00-kg object that has a hook at one end and is 0.28 m long along its longest axis (Figure P15.83). When you try to balance the object on your fingers, it balances when your fingers are 0.20 m from the hook end. When you hang the object by the hook and set it into simple harmonic motion, it completes 10 cycles in 11 s. What is its rotational inertia I? ••

Figure P15.83

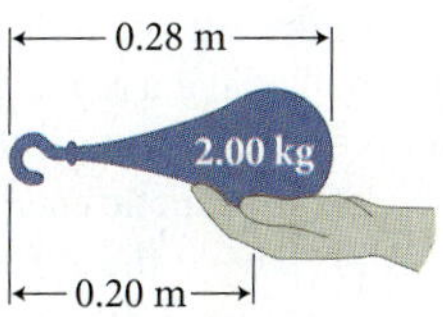

PRACTICE

84. A 2.00-kg object is free to slide on a horizontal surface. The object is attached to a spring of spring constant 200 N/m, and the other end of the spring is attached to a wall. The object is pulled in the direction away from the wall until the spring is stretched 50.0 mm from its relaxed position. The object is not released from rest, but is instead given an initial velocity of 2.00 m/s away from the wall. (*a*) Determine the energy of the oscillating system. (*b*) Write the equation for the object's position as a function of time. Ignore friction. ••

85. A hole is drilled through the narrow end of a 0.960-kg baseball bat, and the bat is hung on a nail so that it can swing freely (Figure P15.85). The bat is 0.860 m long, the hole is drilled 0.0300 m from the end, and the center of mass is located 0.670 m from the end. If the period of oscillation is 1.85 s, what is the bat's rotational inertia (*a*) about the pivot and (*b*) about the center of mass? (*c*) If the hole had been drilled 0.200 m from the end, what would the period be? ••

Figure P15.85

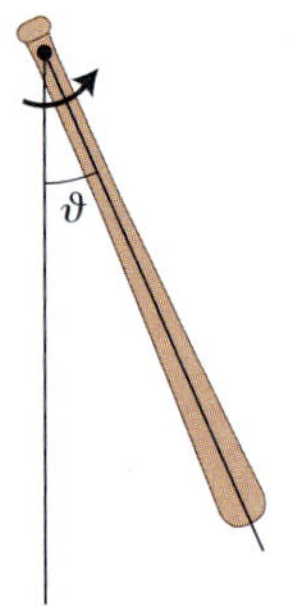

86. A meter stick is free to pivot around a position located a distance x below its top end, where $0 < x < 0.50$ m (Figure P15.86). (*a*) What is the frequency f of its oscillation if it moves as a pendulum? (*b*) To what position should you move the pivot if you want to minimize the period? ••

Figure P15.86

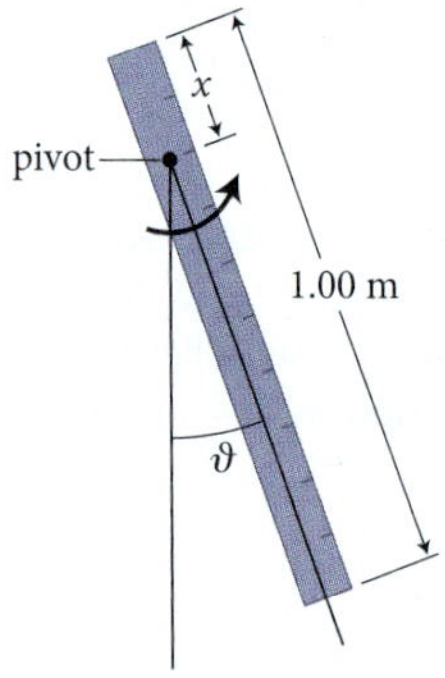

87. To determine what effect a spring's mass has on simple harmonic motion, consider a spring of mass m and relaxed length ℓ_{spring}. The spring is oriented horizontally, and one end is attached to a vertical surface. When the spring is stretched a distance x, the potential energy of the system is $\frac{1}{2}kx^2$. If the free end of the spring is moving with speed v when the free end is at x, calculate the kinetic energy of the spring in terms of m and v. (Hint: Divide the spring into many infinitesimal elements each of length $d\ell_{segment}$ and located at position $\ell_{segment}$; then determine the speed of each piece in terms of $\ell_{segment}$, $d\ell_{segment}$, m, v, and x and integrate from $\ell_{segment} = 0$ to $\ell_{segment} = \ell_{spring} + x$.) •••

88. (*a*) Show that for an object moving in simple harmonic motion, the speed of the object as a function of position is given by $v(x) = \omega\sqrt{A^2 - x^2}$. (*b*) Noting that $v_x = dx/dt$, isolate dt and integrate to determine how long it takes for an oscillator to move from its equilibrium position to some arbitrary position $x < A$. Compare this result with the value of $\Delta t = t_{x<A} - t_{x=A}$ calculated from Eq. 15.6, $x(t) = A \sin(\omega t + \phi_i)$. •••

89. The King's clock fails to keep time, and because you designed it, he's holding you responsible. Examining the spring-ball system you used as the central timekeeping oscillator, you realize that a simple pendulum might be more reliable, and there happens to be a bit of thin, strong wire handy. Unfortunately, you don't have any way of timing the oscillations, nor can you remember what the period is supposed to be. You don't even have a ruler to measure the wire for the pendulum, and there is not enough wire on hand to rely on trial and error. You suddenly realize that all you need to do is observe how far the ball stretches the spring when the spring is held vertically! You calm the King's wrath by putting your new design for the pendulum timekeeping mechanism in operation. ••• CR

90. In physics lab, you are measuring the period of a vertically hung spring-ball system in which the mass of the ball is 0.50 kg. As the system oscillates up and down, it also swings from side to side, a motion that interferes with your measurements of the vertical motion. After running several trials and calculating the period for the system set up this way, you decide to eliminate the side-to-side motion by rigging up the spring horizontally with a string draped over a pulley of radius 0.035 m, as in Figure P15.90. With this arrangement, your measured period is 10% greater than the value you measured for the vertically hung system. Realizing an opportunity for extra credit, you wonder if the rotational inertia of the pulley is buried in your data. ••• CR

Figure P15.90

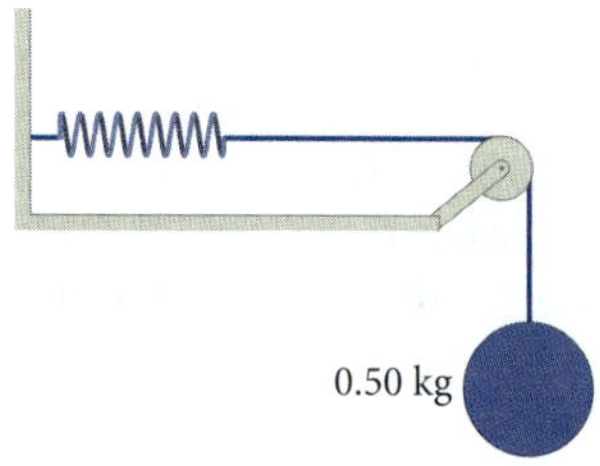

91. You are aboard the International Space Station and are required to keep track of your mass because of your long stay in the free-fall conditions of deep space. To carry out this task, you hook a 215-kg cargo box to one end of a stiff spring and hook yourself to the spring's other end. With the spring and box initially at rest relative to you, you push off from the cargo box. Floating inside the cabin, you and the cargo box oscillate with a period of 2.21 s. You then unhook yourself from the spring and attach in your place a cargo box identical to the one at the other end of the spring. The oscillation period for this two-box system is 3.13 s. Amazingly, even with squeeze-tube food, you seem to be gaining mass. ••• CR

Answers to Review Questions

1. Motion is periodic if the motion repeats itself at regular time intervals.
2. The amplitude is the magnitude of the moving object's maximum displacement from the equilibrium position. The frequency is the number of cycles of the repetitive motion completed during each second.
3. The period is the time interval needed to complete one cycle: $(5.00 \text{ s})/(4 \text{ cycles}) = 1.25 \text{ s/cycle}$; $T = 1.25$ s. The frequency is the reciprocal of the period, $f = 1/T = 0.800$ Hz.
4. The kinetic energy is greatest at the equilibrium position and zero at the extremes of the motion. The magnitude of the potential energy is greatest at the extremes of the motion and zero at the equilibrium position.
5. As long as the amplitude is not too great, the period does not change because simple harmonic motion is isochronous.
6. All simple harmonic motion is isochronous. The acceleration for isochronous motion is directly proportional to the object's displacement from its equilibrium position. The restoring force is proportional to the object's acceleration by Newton's second law and hence directly proportional to the object's displacement. Direct proportionality guarantees a linear relationship.
7. A turning point is a point at which the object turns around—that is, changes its direction of motion. These points are the extrema of the motion, the points farthest from the equilibrium position.
8. Circular motion is two dimensional, and hence the position of an object in circular motion can be described using two orthogonal components. Either component may be expressed as a sinusoidal function of time. Any motion that can be expressed as a sinusoidal function of time is simple harmonic motion. Thus simple harmonic motion has the same functional behavior as one component of constant-speed circular motion.
9. Any periodic function, no matter how complex, can be written as a sum of sinusoidal simple harmonic functions of frequency $f_n = n/T$, where $n \geq 1$ is an integer and T is the period of the motion. This means that any periodic function can be treated as a superposition of simple harmonic motions, and so we need to understand only simple harmonic motion in order to deal with any periodic motion.
10. The fundamental frequency is the same as the frequency of the original periodic function.
11. The spectrum of a periodic function is a plot of the square of the amplitudes of each harmonic frequency in the Fourier series versus frequency.
12. Fourier analysis is the breaking down of a function into a Fourier series (a sum of sinusoidal functions with frequencies that are integer multiples of the fundamental frequency). Fourier synthesis is the inverse of Fourier analysis: the construction of periodic functions by adding together sinusoidal functions with frequencies that are integer multiples of some fundamental frequency.
13. Stable equilibrium allows periodic motion.
14. They have identical periods. Both the restoring force and the rotational inertia are proportional to m, and so the dependence on m cancels.
15. For sufficiently small displacements away from the equilibrium position, restoring forces are always linearly proportional to the displacement.
16. The period of the swing does not depend on the mass of the pendulum bob—in this case, the rider. Thus the two stay in synchrony, as your common experience tells you.
17. No, even the angular frequency ω associated with simple harmonic motion is merely a convenience that exploits the mathematical similarity between simple harmonic motion and circular motion at constant speed. (That is why we don't call it *rotational velocity* here, although it is mathematically the same.) The reference circle helps you relate simple harmonic motion to circular motion, providing a visual interpretation for angular frequency, phase, and amplitude.
18. The variable x describes simple harmonic motion if (and only if) the second derivative of x with respect to time is equal to minus a constant (the square of the angular frequency) times the variable x.
19. You need to know the amplitude A because $\sin \phi_i = x_i/A$ (from Eq. 15.6, with $t = 0$).
20. Angular frequency is given in units of s^{-1}, just as for circular motion, while frequency is given in units of Hz (Hertz).
21. You need to know the spring constant k because $T = 2\pi\sqrt{m/k}$ (from Eqs. 15.1 and Eq. 15.22).
22. It decreases. After another person gets into the car, the mass of the load compressing the springs increases, and angular frequency ω is inversely proportional to the square root of that mass (Eq. 15.22).
23. You can control all except period and frequency, which are determined by the design (mass and spring constant) of the oscillating system.
24. When the friction in the horizontal system is negligibly small, the frequencies are identical.
25. B. Equation 15.33 shows the ratio ℓ/I in the expression for the angular frequency: $\omega = \sqrt{m\ell g/I}$. Length ℓ is double for B, but I for this pendulum is greater by a factor of 4 because it is proportional to the length squared (Equation 11.30; $I = mr^2$). Hence ω is smaller for B. Because period is inversely proportional to angular frequency ($\omega = 2\pi/T$), T is greater for this pendulum.
26. Because the clock is losing time, you need to increase the angular frequency ω of the oscillation. You should therefore shorten the length of the pendulum by moving the disk higher up on the rod to decrease the rotational inertia.
27. The small-angle approximation is required. The equation of motion for a pendulum equates the gravitational torque, which is proportional to $\sin \vartheta$, to the inertial term (which is proportional to the second derivative with respect to time of the angular position ϑ). The simple harmonic oscillator equation requires that the variable involved in the second derivative also be present as a linear term (first power only) in the restoring term. This is possible only if we replace $\sin \vartheta$ with ϑ. This is called the "small-angle approximation" because it is valid for only angular positions much less than 1, or angles much less than 1 radian.
28. In Eq. 15.25, the rotational displacement is unitless, so the torsional constant has same units as torque, newton-meters.
29. No. The overdamped condition occurs when the damping is so great that the system returns to equilibrium without oscillating.
30. The amplitude of the oscillations dies out more and more rapidly as the damping coefficient increases. When b reaches its greatest value, the system makes only a few complete oscillations before the motion becomes too small to measure. Also the angular frequency ω decreases as the damping increases, but this effect amounts to no more than a 5% change.
31. The energy decreases by a factor of e, or 2.718, so that approximately 37% of the energy at the beginning of the time interval remains at the end.

Answers to Guided Problems

Guided Problem 15.2 (*a*) $x(t) = (152 \text{ mm})\sin[(3.49 \text{ s}^{-1})t]$; (b) $v_{max} = 532 \text{ mm/s}$; (c) $a_{max} = 1.86 \text{ m/s}^2$

Guided Problem 15.4 $\ell = h$

Guided Problem 15.6 The rock begins to oscillate and it falls all the way through Earth, then returns. The time interval needed for the rock to return to you is one period, $T = 84$ min.

Guided Problem 15.8 (*a*) $b = 2m\omega$; (*b*) $t = 0.73T = 4.4$ s

16 PRACTICE Waves in One Dimension

Chapter Summary

Representing waves (Sections 16.1, 16.2, 16.5)

Concepts A **wave** is a *disturbance* that propagates through material (the medium) or through empty space.

A **wave pulse** is a single isolated propagating disturbance.

The **wave function** represents the shape of a wave at any given instant and changes with time as the wave travels.

The **wave speed** c is the speed at which a wave propagates. For a mechanical wave, c is different from the speed v of the particles of the medium and is determined by the properties of the medium.

The **displacement** $\vec{D}$ of any particle of a medium through which a mechanical wave travels is a vector that points from the equilibrium position of the particle to its actual position.

In a **transverse** mechanical wave, the particles of the medium move perpendicular to the direction of the pulse movement. In a **longitudinal** mechanical wave, these particles move parallel to the direction of the pulse movement.

In a **periodic wave,** the displacement at any location in the medium is a periodic function of time. A periodic wave is **harmonic** when the particle displacement can be represented by a sinusoidally varying function of space and time.

Quantitative Tools If a wave travels in the x direction with speed c and $f(x)$ describes the form (shape) of the wave, then the y component D_y of the displacement of a particle of the medium is

$$D_y = f(x - ct) \qquad (16.3)$$

if the wave travels in the positive x direction and

$$D_y = f(x + ct) \qquad (16.4)$$

if the wave travels in the negative x direction.

The **wavelength** λ of a periodic wave is the minimum distance over which the wave repeats itself.

For a periodic wave of period T, frequency f, and speed c, the **wave number** k is

$$k = \frac{2\pi}{\lambda}. \qquad (16.7)$$

The wavelength λ is

$$\lambda = cT, \qquad (16.9)$$

the angular frequency ω is

$$\omega = \frac{2\pi}{T}, \qquad (16.11)$$

and the wave speed is

$$c = \lambda f. \qquad (16.10)$$

For a transverse harmonic wave of amplitude A and initial phase ϕ_i traveling in the positive x direction, the y component D_y of the displacement of a particle of the medium is

$$D_y = f(x, t) = A \sin(kx - \omega t + \phi_i). \qquad (16.16)$$

Combining waves (Sections 16.3, 16.4, 16.6)

Concepts **Superposition of waves:** The resultant displacement of two or more overlapping waves is the algebraic sum of the displacements of the individual waves.

Interference occurs when two waves overlap. The interference is *constructive* when the displacements due to the two waves are in the same direction and *destructive* when the displacements are in opposite directions.

If the displacement at a point in space remains zero as a wave travels through, that point is a **node.** The displacement at other points typically varies with time. If the displacement at a point in space varies over the greatest range as a wave travels through, that point is an **antinode.**

Quantitative Tools If two harmonic waves of equal wavelength λ and equal amplitude A travel in opposite directions on a string, they produce a standing wave. The y component D_y of the string displacement at any position x along the string is given by

$$D_y = 2A \sin kx \cos \omega t. \qquad (16.20)$$

The nodes occur at

$$x = 0, \pm\frac{\lambda}{2}, \pm\lambda, \pm\frac{3\lambda}{2}, \ldots \qquad (16.22)$$

and the antinodes occur at

$$x = \pm\frac{\lambda}{4}, \pm\frac{3\lambda}{4}, \pm\frac{5\lambda}{4}, \ldots . \qquad (16.24)$$

When a wave pulse (the *incident* wave) reaches a boundary where the transmitting medium ends, the pulse is *reflected,* which means it reverses its direction.

When a wave pulse is reflected from a fixed boundary, the reflected pulse is *inverted* relative to the incident pulse. When the reflection is from a boundary that is free to move, the reflected pulse is not inverted.

A **standing wave** is a pulsating stationary pattern caused by the interference of harmonic waves of equal amplitude and wavelength traveling in opposite directions.

Waves on a string (Sections 16.7—16.9)

Quantitative Tools For a uniform string of mass m and length ℓ, the **linear mass density** μ (mass per unit length) is

$$\mu = \frac{m}{\ell}. \tag{16.25}$$

The speed of a wave on a string under tension $\mathcal{T}$ is

$$c = \sqrt{\frac{\mathcal{T}}{\mu}}. \tag{16.30}$$

The average power P_{av} that must be supplied to generate a wave of period T is

$$P_{av} = \tfrac{1}{2}\mu\lambda A^2\omega^2/T = \tfrac{1}{2}\mu A^2\omega^2 c. \tag{16.42}$$

Any function f of the form $f(x - ct)$ or $f(x + ct)$ that represents a wave traveling with speed c is a solution of the **wave equation:**

$$\frac{\partial^2 f}{\partial x^2} = \frac{1}{c^2}\frac{\partial^2 f}{\partial t^2}. \tag{16.51}$$

Review Questions

Answers to these questions can be found at the end of this chapter.

16.1 Representing waves graphically

1. What physical quantities are transported by a wave?
2. Classify each wave as longitudinal or transverse: the wave created when a whip is snapped, the wave represented by cars slowing down and speeding up in a traffic jam on a highway, water waves spreading out from the location where a stone is thrown into a pond, the wave created when a guitar string is plucked.
3. What is the difference between the wave speed c of a wave traveling along a rope and the speed v of a small segment of that rope?
4. For a given wave pulse, is it true that the wave function (a function of time) always looks the same as the displacement curve (a function of space)?

16.2 Wave propagation

5. You are sitting at the beach watching the waves. What is the difference between their frequency and their speed?
6. If the hand in *Principles* Figure 16.5 initially stretches the spring leftward rather than compresses it as shown, what happens to the wave speed?
7. Are waves always periodic? Are they always harmonic?
8. If you shake a rope at one end, slowly at first and then faster and faster, what changes about the wave you create in the rope? What remains the same?

16.3 Superposition of waves

9. In what sense is the constructive or destructive interference caused by two wave pulses a temporary phenomenon?
10. How are the values of kinetic energy and potential energy carried by any wave pulse related to each other?
11. When superposing waves, how are the wave functions combined?

16.4 Boundary effects

12. (*a*) How does a pulse reflected from a fixed boundary differ from the incident pulse? (*b*) How does a pulse reflected from a free boundary differ from the incident pulse?
13. Describe the graphical method for determining the shape of the reflected pulse when a wave pulse traveling along a string arrives at a boundary.

16.5 Wave functions

14. List all the variables required to describe a traveling harmonic wave.
15. What is the definition of *wave number,* and what is its purpose?
16. What is the direction of travel of the wave represented by the time-dependent wave function $D(x, t) = 3 \sin(5x - 2t)$?

16.6 Standing waves

17. What is an *antinode*?
18. What is the distance between a node and an adjacent antinode in a standing wave of wavelength λ?
19. Is the displacement of the medium in which a standing wave exists ever zero at an antinode?

16.7 Wave speed

20. An astronaut takes his ukulele out on a space walk. When he strums the strings in space, is the wave speed on each string higher than, lower than, or the same as on Earth?
21. A vibrating string is clamped at both ends, with one of the clamps being a tension-adjustment screw. By what factor must you change the tension in the string to double its frequency of vibration without changing the wavelength?
22. What is the *linear mass density* of a string or rope?

16.8 Energy transport in waves

23. Describe in words the relationship between power and wave properties expressed in Eq. 16.42.
24. When you shake the end of a string to produce a wave, what fraction of the energy you transfer to the string becomes kinetic energy associated with the motion of the string? What fraction becomes potential energy associated with the stretching of the string?

16.9 The wave equation

25. How does a partial derivative differ from an ordinary derivative?
26. A wave pulse moves along a stretched string. Describe the relationship among the speed at which the pulse moves, the pulse curvature, and the acceleration of small segments of the string.

Developing a Feel

Make an order-of-magnitude estimate of each of the following quantities. Letters in parentheses refer to hints below. Use them as needed to guide your thinking.

1. The longest wavelength possible for a standing wave on a guitar string (B, N)
2. The speed of transverse waves on a guitar string (A, R)
3. The speed of transverse vibrations in a telephone wire strung between two poles (C, I, L, T)
4. The frequency of a radio wave whose wavelength equals your height (D, J)
5. The longest wavelength possible for a standing wave around the circumference of a helium atom (O, S)
6. The wave number for a wave whose wavelength equals the circumference of Earth's orbit about the Sun (F, P)
7. The power involved in the vibration of a guitar string (A, H, M, R)
8. The ratio of the linear mass density of the thickest string on a guitar to the linear mass density of the thinnest string (K, Q, U, E, G)

Hints

A. What is the linear mass density of a typical guitar string?
B. What is a typical length for a guitar string?
C. What is the distance between the telephone poles?
D. At what speed do radio waves travel?
E. How does the linear mass density vary with wave speed?
F. What is the radius of Earth's orbit?
G. How do the two wave speeds compare?
H. What is the amplitude of the vibration?
I. What is the maximum vertical sag in the wire?
J. What is the relationship among wavelength, frequency, and speed?
K. What is the fundamental frequency played on each string?
L. What angle does the tensile force exerted on the wire make with the horizontal?
M. What is a typical frequency for a vibrating guitar string?
N. What is the node/antinode pattern on the string when it is vibrating?
O. What is the radius of a helium atom?
P. What is the relationship between wave number and wavelength?
Q. Do the two strings have equal tension?
R. What is a typical guitar string tension?
S. What is the node/antinode pattern in a standing wave that has the longest wavelength possible?
T. Is it possible to compute the vibration speed without knowing the mass of the wire?
U. How do the wavelengths of the fundamental (single-antinode) vibrations compare on the two strings?

Key (all values approximate)

A. 2×10^{-3} kg/m; **B.** 0.7 m; **C.** 2×10^{1} m; **D.** the speed of light, 3×10^{8} m/s; **E.** $\mu = \mathcal{T}/c^2$; **F.** 2×10^{11} m; **G.** because the wavelengths are equal, c is proportional to f; **H.** 3 mm; **I.** 0.5 m; **J.** $\lambda f = c$; **K.** 1×10^{2} Hz on the thickest string, 4×10^{2} Hz on the thinnest string; **L.** 5×10^{-2} rad (sag height divided by half the wire length); **M.** 3×10^{2} Hz; **N.** for the fundamental vibration, one antinode at the center and a node at each end; **O.** 1×10^{-10} m; **P.** $k = 2\pi/\lambda$; **Q.** yes, to a first approximation; **R.** 7×10^{1} N; **S.** two nodes and two antinodes; **T.** yes, to a first approximation, mass appears in both numerator and denominator and so cancels; **U.** two strings of the same length, with the same fundamental node/antinode pattern, have identical wavelengths;

PRACTICE

Worked and Guided Problems

These examples involve material from this chapter but are not associated with any particular section. Some examples are worked out in detail; others you should work out by following the guidelines provided.

Worked Problem 16.1 Bobbing up and down

A passing speedboat sends out a wake that rocks a rowboat in which a physics student calmly fishes. She notices that the wake has a trough-to-peak height of 0.80 m and that the wave rocks the rowboat with a period of 1.5 s. The distance between crests is 1.7 m. What are (*a*) the wave speed, (*b*) the wave function, and (*c*) the maximum vertical speed of the rowboat?

❶ **GETTING STARTED** Our physics student has measured several parameters of the wave, and we need to calculate others. We begin with a sketch to help us visualize our ideas and approach (Figure WG16.1). We need to calculate three things: the wave speed, which is the speed at which the wave moves across the water surface, the wave function that describes the wave, and the speed at which the rowboat bobs up and down. In calculating this last value, we assume the boat rides lightly on the surface of the waves as opposed to riding low in the water; with this assumption the amplitude and speed of the boat's motion will match those of the water beneath the boat. For simplicity, we assume that the wave approximates a sine wave in determining the wave function.

Figure WG16.1

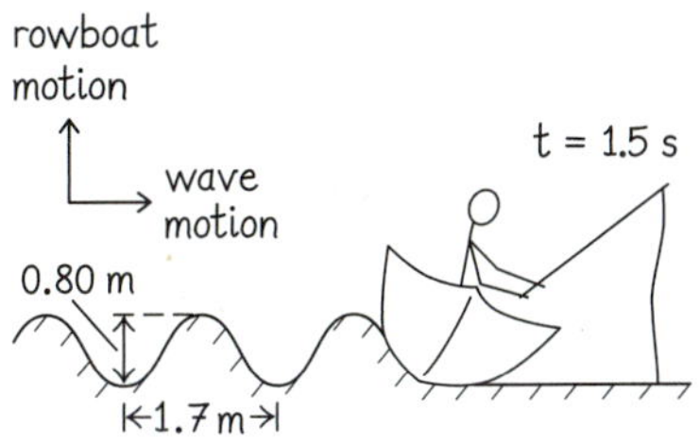

❷ **DEVISE PLAN** The wave speed can be found from the period and wavelength, $c = \lambda/T$ (Eq. 16.9). The rowboat's vertical speed is the speed of a water particle at the boat's location moving up and down in simple harmonic motion as the wave passes the location. Because the boat follows the vertical displacement of the water, the displacement curve for the boat should match that of the water. Because the motion of the water at a particular value of x along the wave is perpendicular to the direction along which the wave propagates (which we take to be the x axis), we take the displacement of the water surface (and the rowboat) to be along a y axis, making the wave function

$$y(x, t) = D(x, t) = A \sin(kx - \omega t).$$

Because the boat motion is up and down along the y axis, we can obtain the y component of the boat's velocity by taking the partial derivative of the boat's y coordinate with respect to time:

$$v_y = \frac{\partial y}{\partial t}.$$

We determine the maximum value this function can have to obtain the boat's maximum bobbing speed.

❸ **EXECUTE PLAN** (*a*) The wave speed is

$$c = \frac{\lambda}{T} = \frac{1.7 \text{ m}}{1.5 \text{ s}} = 1.1 \text{ m/s.} \checkmark$$

(*b*) The peak-to-trough height is twice the wave amplitude, which gives $A = \frac{1}{2}(0.80 \text{ m}) = 0.40$ m. We know from Eqs. 16.7 and Eq. 16.11 that $k = 2\pi/\lambda$ and $\omega = 2\pi f = 2\pi/T$. Consequently, the wave function is

$$y(x, t) = A \sin\left(\frac{2\pi}{\lambda}x - \frac{2\pi}{T}t\right)$$

$$= (0.40 \text{ m}) \sin\left(\frac{2\pi}{1.7 \text{ m}}x - \frac{2\pi}{1.5 \text{ s}}t\right)$$

$$= (0.40 \text{ m}) \sin[(3.7 \text{ m}^{-1})x - (4.2 \text{ s}^{-1})t]. \checkmark$$

(*c*) Because the wave is sinusoidal, the x component of the boat's vertical velocity is

$$v_y(x, t) = \frac{\partial}{\partial t}A \sin(kx - \omega t) = -\omega A \cos(kx - \omega t).$$

No matter where the boat is located along the x axis, there is some instant t_{max} at which the bobbing speed reaches a maximum. This instant occurs when $|\cos(kx - \omega t_{max})| = 1$, and at that instant the bobbing speed is ωA:

$$v_{max} = \omega A(1) = \frac{2\pi}{1.5 \text{ s}}(0.40 \text{ m}) = 1.7 \text{ m/s.} \checkmark$$

❹ **EVALUATE RESULT** If you think about water waves moving across the surface of a lake, a wave speed of 1.1 m/s and a bobbing speed of 1.7 m/s both seem reasonable. We assumed that the boat moves with the water, so our results for the boat are based on the wave function, which describes how a water particle at position x moves along the y axis as the wave passes. The assumption seems reasonable for a small boat.

We also assumed that the wave caused by the wake of the boat is sinusoidal. The greatest possible bobbing speed for waves of any shape is given by assuming the boat is in free fall as it moves from a crest to a trough, which means that

$$v_{max}^2 < 2gh = 2(9.8 \text{ m/s}^2)(0.80 \text{ m}) = 16 \text{ m}^2/\text{s}^2$$

$$v_{max} < 4.0 \text{ m/s}.$$

The value we obtained, 1.7 m/s, appears to be in the right ballpark.

PRACTICE

Guided Problem 16.2 Human wave

A "people wave" is created by the crowd in a stadium when each person stands up just as one neighbor sits down and then sits down just as the other neighbor stands. A sophisticated crowd produces a "people wave" with each person approximately executing simple harmonic motion as they repeatedly stand and sit. (*a*) Estimate the frequency, wavelength, wave speed, and amplitude of such a wave, and use these values to construct a wave function that describes the wave. (*b*) What is the maximum speed of each person in the wave as she or he stands up and then sits down?

1 GETTING STARTED

1. Describe the problem in your own words.
2. Assuming a sinusoidal wave, what is a generic expression for the wave function?

2 DEVISE PLAN

3. Which of the asked-for values can you confidently estimate? Which ones do you have more uncertainty about? You might want to start with amplitude and wavelength.
4. In addition to amplitude and wavelength, what other quantities do you need in order to specify the wave function?
5. How can you determine the stand–sit speed of the wave "particles" (the people)?
6. How can you determine the maximum speed of each person?

3 EXECUTE PLAN

4 EVALUATE RESULT

7. Are your assumptions and estimates plausible? What errors are introduced by the uncertainty of your estimates?

Worked Problem 16.3 Musical wire

One end of a wire is attached to a wall, and the other end is strung over a pulley and attached to a block (Figure WG16.2). The distance from wall to pulley is 2.30 m, and the wire has a linear mass density of 1.3×10^{-3} kg/m. Plucking the horizontal section of the wire in specific ways can produce standing waves that contain specific numbers of antinodes: The first harmonic has one antinode, the second harmonic has two antinodes, and so on. What should the block's mass be in order that the third-harmonic standing wave (containing three antinodes) vibrates at frequency $f = 550$ Hz?

Figure WG16.2

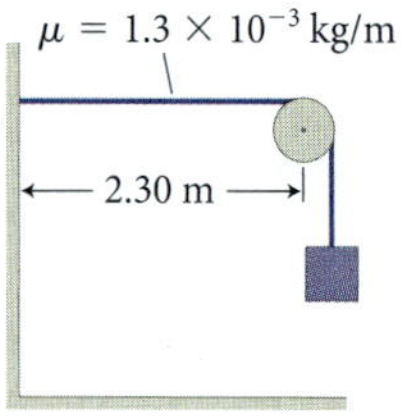

1 GETTING STARTED The tensile force exerted by the block on the wire provides the tension in the wire, and so we need to determine this force and then use the relationship between the tensile force and the gravitational force on the block to obtain the block mass needed to create the standing wave asked for. The number of antinodes is related to how many wavelengths of the traveling waves fit into the horizontal section of the wire. The third harmonic has three antinodes and is illustrated in Figure WG16.3. Thus we want to calculate what tension is required to create, along the horizontal section of the wire, a three-antinode standing wave vibrating at 550 Hz. We assume that the block moves negligibly when the wire is vibrating.

Figure WG16.3

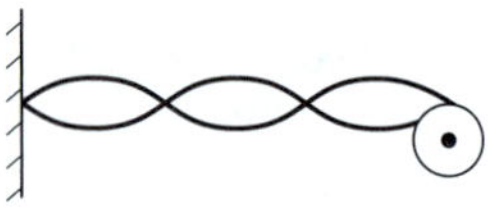

2 DEVISE PLAN We need to relate the frequency f, wavelength λ, and tensile force. Because the block is supported in equilibrium by the string, the tension (magnitude of tensile force) is $\mathcal{T} = |\vec{F}^c_{sb}| = |\vec{F}^G_{Eb}| = m_b g$. Equations 16.10 and 16.30 permit us to relate the tension to wavelength and frequency, and we can determine λ from Eq. 16.21. For the third harmonic, there are three antinodes and four nodes. The first node is at the wall; the fourth node (the one for which $n = 3$ in Eq. 16.21) occurs at $x = \ell$, where ℓ is the length of wire between the wall and the pulley. Knowing λ, we can solve Eq. 16.30 for the tension $\mathcal{T}$ and then equate $\mathcal{T}$ with the tensile force F exerted by the block to determine m_b.

3 EXECUTE PLAN Substituting ℓ for x and 3 for n in Eq. 16.21, we get $\ell = \frac{3}{2}\lambda$. This tells us that the third harmonic has wavelength $\lambda = 2\ell/3$. Solving Eq. 16.30 for the tension gives us

$$c = \sqrt{\frac{\mathcal{T}}{\mu}}$$

$$\mathcal{T} = \mu c^2,$$

and from Eq. 16.10 we can rewrite this as $\mathcal{T} = \mu(\lambda f)^2$. Because the tension is created by the tensile force exerted by (or on) the block, we have

$$m_b g = \mathcal{T} = \mu(\lambda f)^2 = \mu(\tfrac{2}{3}\ell f)^2$$

$$m_b = \frac{4\mu(\ell f)^2}{9g}$$

$$= \frac{4(0.00130\ \text{kg/m})[(2.30\ \text{m})(550\ \text{Hz})]^2}{9(9.8\ \text{m/s}^2)} = 94\ \text{kg}. ✔$$

4 EVALUATE RESULT Our result shows that we need quite a massive block to obtain the desired third harmonic. We know one has to increase the tension in a string to obtain a higher pitch (higher frequency) from it. Our algebraic expression indeed shows that the block's mass must be increased to increase the frequency f. We would also expect the required mass to be inversely proportional to g because if the gravitational pull were stronger, a block of smaller mass would be sufficient to create the required tension.

Our assumption that the block does not move is likely to be accurate given the mass of the block. We ignored the mass of the hanging portion of the wire in our calculation, but that seems reasonable considering the very small value for μ. The mass of the 2.30-m horizontal section is only 0.003 kg, so even a relatively long section of string has negligible mass relative to that of the block.

Guided Problem 16.4 Pitch-perfect guitar

A guitarist breaks the highest string on her guitar. If a new string is a steel wire of mass density $7.8 \times 10^3\ \text{kg/m}^3$ and radius 0.120 mm, what tension must the string be under if it is to produce the frequency 330 Hz as its fundamental (first harmonic, one antinode) frequency? The distance between the wire's two attachment points on the guitar is 640 mm.

❶ GETTING STARTED

1. Sketch the shape of the string oscillating at its fundamental frequency.
2. What variables affect the frequency?

❷ DEVISE PLAN

3. What equation relates the wave's frequency and wavelength to the tension?
4. How can you use the information that there is only one antinode in the standing wave to determine the wavelength of the traveling waves that interfere to produce this standing wave?
5. How can you determine the mass of the wire from the mass density of steel? How can you determine the wire's linear mass density from this?

❸ EXECUTE PLAN

❹ EVALUATE RESULT

6. Is your computed value of tension the right order of magnitude for the tension in a guitar string?

Worked Problem 16.5 Basic telephone service

Two children playing telephone use some string to connect two paper cups. To make the separation large enough, they use two strings of different linear mass densities connected at the center. String A has a linear mass density of $8.20 \times 10^{-3}\ \text{kg/m}$, and string B has a linear mass density of $5.90 \times 10^{-3}\ \text{kg/m}$. Consider a traveling wave that originates on string A, passes the junction at the center, and continues along string B. What is the ratio of the wavelength of this wave on string B to its wavelength on string A?

❶ GETTING STARTED We start with a sketch (Figure WG16.4), labeling the junction at the center by the letter J. We are asked to determine how the wavelength changes as a wave traveling from A to B passes the junction. The wavelength is related to the frequency and speed of the wave. Because the two strings have different linear mass densities, waves travel at different speeds in the two strings. We need to determine out how this change in speed affects the wavelength. We might also have to consider the tension in the strings because the tension affects the wave speed.

Figure WG16.4

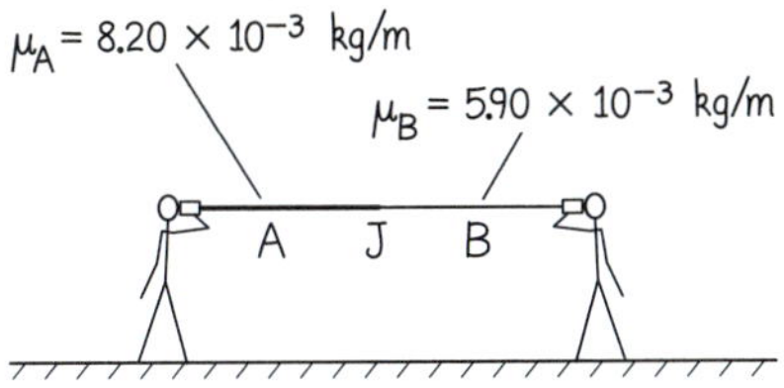

❷ DEVISE PLAN The wave speed along a taut string is given by Eqs. 16.10 and 16.30, $\lambda f = c = \sqrt{\mathcal{T}/\mu}$, where $\mathcal{T}$ is the tension in the strings and μ is its linear mass density. Neither the tension nor the frequency f in the two strings is specified. However, we can reasonably argue that the tension is the same in the two strings by considering what would happen if it were not. If the tension on the left were greater, then a free-body diagram of the junction would show a greater tensile force to the left than to the right, causing the junction to accelerate to the left. This would reduce the tension on the left and increase it on the right, ultimately leading to equilibrium at a new junction position.

To determine the frequency, we consider the vertical motion of the junction. The frequency at which the junction moves up and down is equal to the frequency of the incoming wave from A, which means that the junction end of string A produces the wave that goes into B with the same frequency. Therefore the frequency of the wave *must* be constant throughout the joined strings. However, the wavelength does change because the wave speed changes due to the difference in linear mass densities.

We can solve Eq. 16.30 for the tension $\mathcal{T}$ in each segment, set the two tensions equal to each other, and use Eq. 16.10 to replace each c by its equivalent λf. The f values cancel, leaving us with the ratio of the wavelengths.

❸ EXECUTE PLAN Solving Eq. 16.30 for the tension and then substituting λf for c from Eq. 16.10 give

$$\mathcal{T} = \mu(\lambda f)^2.$$

Setting the tensions equal in the two strings, we have

$$\mathcal{T}_A = \mathcal{T}_B$$

$$\mu_A \lambda_A^2 f_A^2 = \mu_B \lambda_B^2 f_B^2.$$

Canceling the frequencies because they are the same in both segments gives us

$$\frac{\lambda_B}{\lambda_A} = \sqrt{\frac{\mu_A}{\mu_B}} = \sqrt{\frac{8.20 \times 10^{-3}\ \text{kg/m}}{5.90 \times 10^{-3}\ \text{kg/m}}} = 1.18. ✔$$

❹ EVALUATE RESULT The relationship $c = \sqrt{\mathcal{T}/\mu}$ tells us that the string that has the smaller linear mass density generates the greater wave speed c. Thus in one period of the motion the leading edge of the traveling wave moves a greater horizontal distance in the thinner string, which is B. This means that the distance between two adjacent crests is greater in B than in A; in other words, the wavelength is longer in B, which is consistent with our calculation. The 18% difference we obtained is reasonable: The mass densities differ by more than 30%, and we need to take the square root of these mass densities to obtain the wavelength.

Our assumption that the tension is the same in the two strings would be strictly valid only if no gravity were present. The gravitational force exerted by Earth causes both strings to sag, and the tension in the two strings must adjust differently to this sagging because the strings have different masses. However, the gravitational forces exerted on the strings are much smaller than the typical tension in a string telephone, and so our assumption should have a negligible effect on our answer.

Guided Problem 16.6 At the junction

In Figure WG16.5, string B has twice the linear mass density of string A. When an incident wave described by the function $y_I(x, t) = A_I \sin(k_A x - \omega t)$ initially traveling left to right through string A hits the junction, some of the wave is reflected and the rest is transmitted into string B. What fraction of the incident wave power is reflected and what fraction is transmitted? (For simplicity, Figure WG16.5 does not show the reflected wave.)

Figure WG16.5

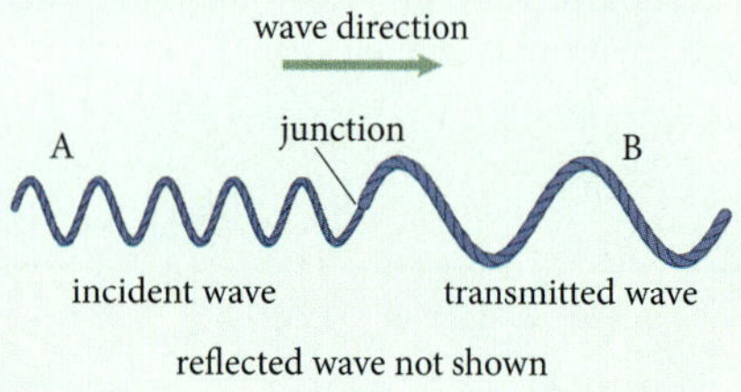

❶ GETTING STARTED

1. Does the boundary at the junction behave as fixed or free?
2. The incident wave $y_I(x, t)$ is given. The reflected wave $y_R(x, t)$ must have an amplitude $A_R \neq A_I$, but what is the expression for its wave function? In writing your expression, consider direction of travel, inverted or upright amplitude, and so on.
3. The transmitted wave $y_T(x, t)$ has an amplitude $A_T \neq A_I$. What is an appropriate form for its wave function? Remember that the wave number k_B, the number of wavelengths in 2π m of string B, may not equal k_A.)

❷ DEVISE PLAN

4. Wave power is proportional to the square of the wave amplitude by Eq. 16.42, $P_{av} = \frac{1}{2}\mu A^2\omega^2 c$.
5. Where do the waves have the greater speed; in A or in B? Why?
6. Based on what you learned from the solution to Worked Problem 16.5, what is the relationship between the frequencies f_A and f_B (and thus the relationship between ω_A and ω_B)? What is the relationship between the tensions $\mathcal{T}_A$ and $\mathcal{T}_B$?
7. What is the relationship between the wavelengths λ_A and λ_B? Between the wave numbers k_A and k_B?
8. The wave function and its slope (derivative) must be continuous everywhere, including at the junction, where superposition gives $y_I(x_J, t) + y_R(x_J, t) = y_T(x_J, t)$ and $\frac{\partial}{\partial x}[y_I(x, t) + y_R(x, t)]_{x=x_J} = \frac{\partial}{\partial x}[y_T(x, t)]_{x=x_J}$.

❸ EXECUTE PLAN

9. Take these derivatives to infer what the ratios A_R/A_I and A_T/A_I must be in order to ensure continuity.
10. The algebra is simplified if you choose the origin at the junction so that $x_J = 0$.

❹ EVALUATE RESULT

11. Does the sum of the transmitted and reflected power equal the incident power? If not, why not?

Worked Problem 16.7 A pulse on a rope

A certain transverse wave pulse traveling along a rope is described by the time-dependent wave function $f(x, t) = Ae^{-(kx-\omega t)^2}$, with wave number $k = 2\pi \text{ m}^{-1}$ and angular frequency $\omega = 2\pi \text{ s}^{-1}$. (*a*) Sketch the time-independent wave function at $t = 0$ and $t = 5.00$ s. (*b*) Sketch the pulse as a function of time (the displacement curve) at $x = 0$ and $x = 5.00$ m. (*c*) Show that the function given above satisfies the wave equation. (*d*) What is the wave speed of the pulse?

❶ **GETTING STARTED** We are given an equation for a particular wave pulse. We need to sketch the pulse at various positions and instants and then show that the given expression is a solution to the wave equation. Then we need to determine the wave speed of the pulse.

❷ **DEVISE PLAN** To make the sketches, we can make tables of values at various positions for the wave function of part *a* and various instants for the displacement curve of part *b*, and then plot the data. A graphing calculator would make this task easier, but we shall make one table just to get the idea.

Then we need to show that the given expression satisfies the wave equation

$$\frac{\partial^2 f}{\partial x^2} = \frac{1}{c^2}\frac{\partial^2 f}{\partial t^2}.$$

To do that, we can take appropriate derivatives of the given function, insert calculated values on both sides of the wave equation, and check that the values we get for the two sides are equal to each other.

The wave speed required for part *d* is given by the value of c in the wave equation.

❸ **EXECUTE PLAN** (*a*) First let us make a table of the wave function for the $t = 0$ case. Because the value of the amplitude A is not given, we divide $f(x)$ by A and compute only the exponential function.

x (m)	f(x)/A
−0.500	5.17×10^{-5}
−0.400	1.81×10^{-3}
−0.300	2.86×10^{-2}
−0.200	2.06×10^{-1}
−0.100	6.74×10^{-1}
0	1.00×10^{0}
0.100	6.74×10^{-1}
0.200	2.06×10^{-1}
0.300	2.86×10^{-2}
0.400	1.81×10^{-3}
0.500	5.17×10^{-5}

A similar calculation can be done for $t = 5.00$ s. The resulting plots for the pulse positions at these two instants are shown in Figure WG16.6. This exponential pulse is just a bump that travels to the right. In part *a*, $t = 0$, the peak is at $x = 0$, and in part *b*, $t = 5.00$ s, the peak has moved on to $x = 5.00$ m.

Figure WG16.6

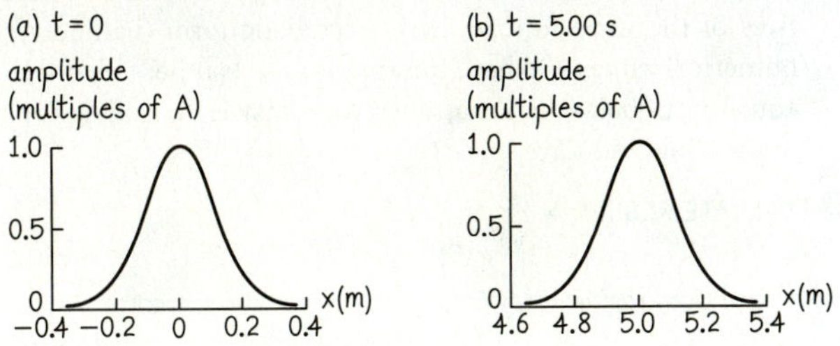

(*b*) The displacement curves $f(x = 0, t)$ and $f(x = 5.00\text{ m}, t)$ at the two positions given in the problem statement yield the graphs of Figure WG16.7*a* and *b*, where we have plotted $f(t)/A$ as a function of t. ✔

Figure WG16.7

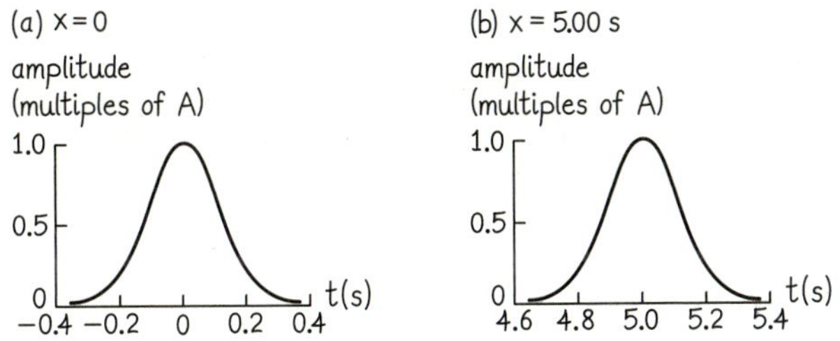

(*c*) Now, to confirm that the expression given for the pulse is a solution to the wave equation, we have

$$\frac{\partial^2}{\partial x^2}Ae^{-(kx-\omega t)^2} \stackrel{?}{=} \frac{1}{c^2}\frac{\partial^2}{\partial t^2}Ae^{-(kx-\omega t)^2}$$

$$-\frac{\partial}{\partial x}2k(kx-\omega t)Ae^{-(kx-\omega t)^2}$$

$$\stackrel{?}{=} \frac{1}{c^2}\frac{\partial}{\partial t}2\omega(kx-\omega t)Ae^{-(kx-\omega t)^2}$$

$$[-2k(kx-\omega t)]^2Ae^{-(kx-\omega t)^2} - 2k^2Ae^{-(kx-\omega t)^2}$$

$$\stackrel{?}{=} \frac{1}{c^2}\{[2\omega(kx-\omega t)]^2Ae^{-(kx-\omega t)^2} - 2\omega^2Ae^{-(kx-\omega t)^2}\}.$$

Eliminating the exponential factor gives

$$[-2k(kx-\omega t)]^2 - 2k^2 \stackrel{?}{=} \frac{1}{c^2}\{[2\omega(kx-\omega t)]^2 - 2\omega^2\}$$

$$2k^2[2(kx-\omega t)^2 - 1] \stackrel{?}{=} \frac{1}{c^2}2\omega^2[2(kx-\omega t)^2 - 1]$$

$$2k^2 \stackrel{?}{=} \frac{1}{c^2}2\omega^2.$$

This equation is true only if

$$c = \frac{\omega}{k},$$

which we know to be true from Eq. 16.11, $kc = \omega$. Our pulse function is indeed a solution to the wave equation. ✔

(*d*) The wave speed of the pulse is

$$c = \frac{\omega}{k} = \frac{2\pi\text{ s}^{-1}}{2\pi\text{ m}^{-1}} = 1.00\text{ m/s}. ✔$$

The values of ω and k are known to many significant digits, but we choose to report three because the other data are known to three significant digits.

❹ **EVALUATE RESULT** We've demonstrated that this type of pulse is a solution to the wave equation. The speed is reasonable, if a bit slow. Also, the shape looks reasonable for a pulse on a rope.

Guided Problem 16.8 Superposed waves

Most of the waves in our everyday world, such as radio waves from a station's transmitter or sound waves from a plucked or bowed violin string, are not simple sine or cosine waves but rather a superposition of many different harmonic waves, as shown in Figure WG16.8 As an example, consider the wave function $f(x, t) = \sin(kx - \omega t) + (1.5)\sin(2kx - 2\omega t)$. You are informed that $k = 8.00\text{ m}^{-1}$ and that the frequency at which the pattern repeats is $f = 440$ Hz. (*a*) Sketch the wave as a function of time at $x = 0$ for three cycles on a suitable graph. (*b*) Show that this wave function is a solution to the wave equation, $(\partial^2 f/\partial x^2) = (1/c^2)(\partial^2 f/\partial t^2)$. (c) What is the speed of this wave?

Figure WG16.8

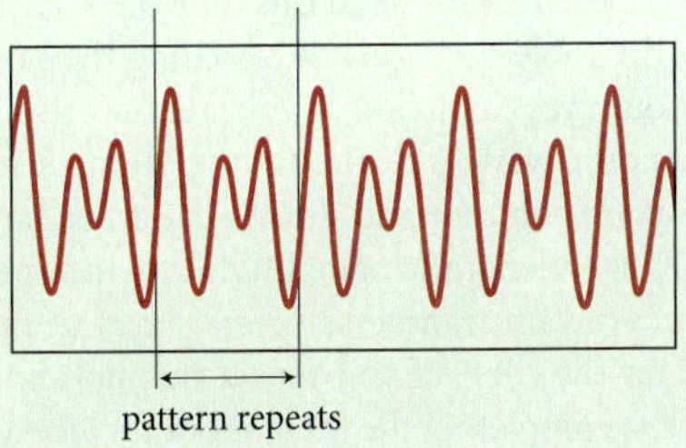

❶ **GETTING STARTED**

1. You'll need numerical values in order to complete parts *a* and *c*. List the values you know and those you need to determine.
2. What must be the value of ω to get the interference pattern to repeat at the specified frequency? What time interval elapses before the pattern starts to repeat itself?
3. For a fixed value of x, how many seconds would it take for the first term in the wave function to go through one cycle? How many seconds for the second term to go through one cycle?

❷ **DEVISE PLAN**

4. Think through a simple consistent procedure to determine the displacement curve at the specified value of x for three cycles.

How do you determine how closely spaced the time values along your horizontal axis should be?

5. The procedure in Worked Problem 16.7 can be used to see whether the function satisfies the wave equation, but how can the wave speed be related to the quantities you know?

3 EXECUTE PLAN

6. Plot your data.

7. Write the wave equation and take the required partial derivatives of the wave function in its symbolic form (without the numerical values you have inferred for ω). Is it possible for the equation to balance? What does your answer to this question imply about the wave speed?

4 EVALUATE RESULT

Questions and Problems

For instructor-assigned homework, go to MasteringPhysics®

Dots indicate difficulty level of problems: • = easy, •• = intermediate, ••• = hard; CR = context-rich problem.

16.1 Representing waves graphically

1. Is it possible for the same medium to carry both a longitudinal and a transverse wave? If so, give an example. If not, explain why not. •

2. Suppose you have a light spring stretched out and one end is attached to a wall. With this setup, you can move the free end in any of three directions (x, y, z). If the spring lies along, say, the z axis, which type of wave—transverse or longitudinal—do you create when you move the free end along the z axis? Along the x axis? Along the y axis? •

3. Figure P16.3 is a snapshot at $t = 0.80$ s of a wave pulse traveling on a string. Construct (a) the wave function at $t = 1.1$ s and (b) the displacement curve for the position $x = 3.0$ m. Assume that the wave pulse was created at the origin at $t = 0$. ••

Figure P16.3

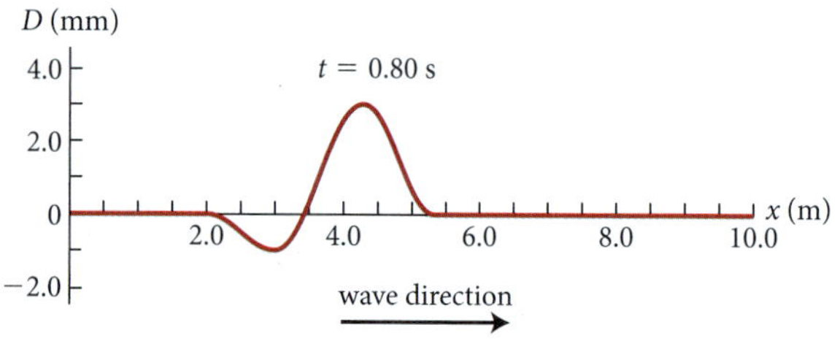

4. The graphs in Figure P16.4 show the displacement caused by a wave moving along a string at two instants, (a) t_1 and (b) t_2. Let v_{av} denote the average speed of a piece of string during the time interval between t_1 and t_2. Compare the wave speed c to v_{av} of a piece of the string at the position $x = a$. ••

Figure P16.4

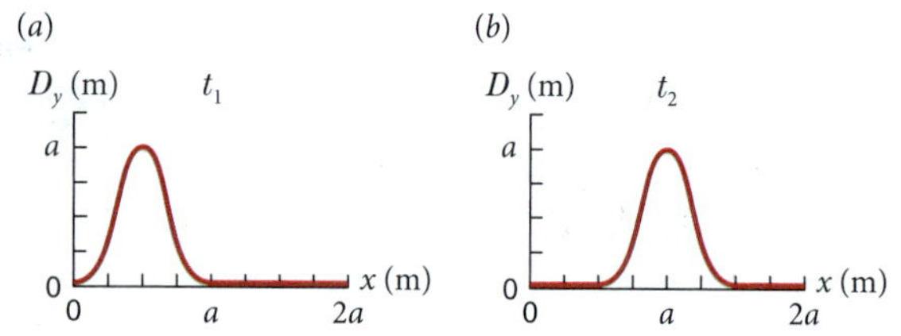

5. Figure P16.5 shows the displacement curve for the particle located at $x = a$ as a wave moves to the right along a string. If the wave advances a distance a each second, draw the wave function at the instant $t = 0$. •••

Figure P16.5

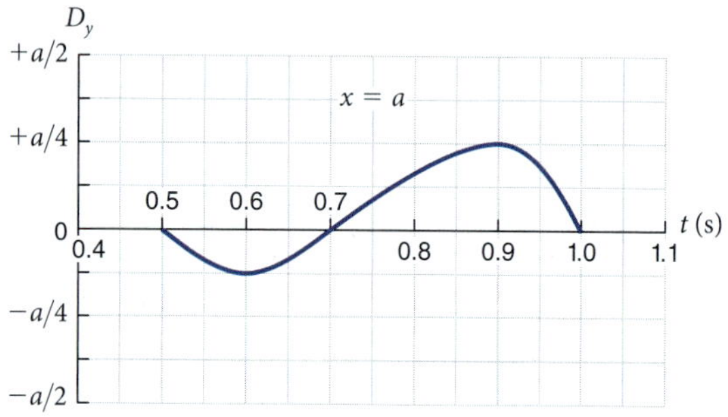

16.2 Wave propagation

6. Identical ropes were tied to two trees, and two men, A and B, started shaking the free ends at the same instant a short while ago (Figure P16.6). Which rope has the greater tension? Which man is shaking with the greater frequency? •

Figure P16.6

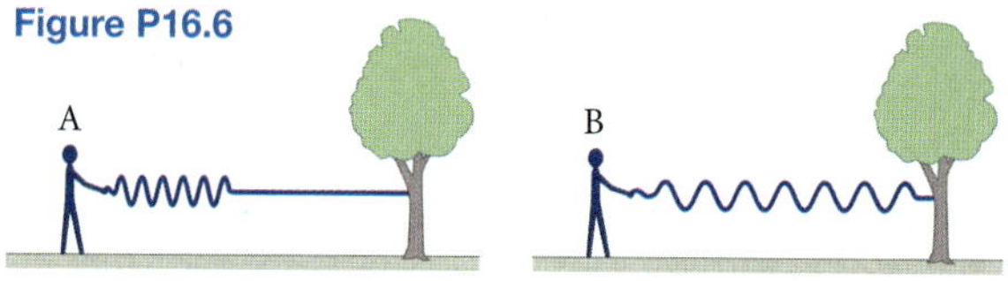

7. What is the definition of *frequency* for a nonharmonic periodic wave? •

8. You and a friend each have one rope. You tie the two ropes together and stand as far apart as possible, each holding one end of the new longer rope and pulling to put it under tension. You then begin moving your arm in such a way as to produce a harmonic wave with a wavelength of 1.0 m. Your friend looks at the waves as they reach her arm. Is it possible that she measures a wavelength of (a) 0.8 m, (b) 1.0 m, or (c) 1.2 m? ••

9. You are watching a ship being loaded with large crates. The ship is held in place by several long steel cables attached to the dock. At one point, a crate bumps one of the cables and sends a wave pulse along the cable. The pulse moves rather slowly up to the bow of the ship. A few minutes later another crate strikes the same cable, and this time the wave pulse shoots up along the cable very quickly, reaching the bow almost faster than your eyes can follow it. Explain how this is possible. ••

10. A harmonic wave is made to travel along a string when you move your hand up and down. The wave has a specific period T_1, wavelength λ_1, amplitude A_1, and speed c_1, and also causes a certain transverse speed $v(x, t)$ of the particles that make up the rope. If you repeat this up-and-down motion, this time completing the same motion twice as fast as before, what happens to the (a) period, (b) wavelength, (c) amplitude, (d) speed, and (e) transverse speed? •••

PRACTICE

16.3 Superposition of waves

11. Water parks often have a pool with a wave-making machine at one end, consisting of a piston that pushes water back and forth. There are some places in the pool where the waves make inner-tube riders bounce up and down wildly, but other places where the water hardly moves. Explain what is happening. •

12. Suppose wave pulses in an aquarium are produced by a mechanical motor that moves a bob up and down at the surface. If the setup uses a 10-W motor and has a period of 1.5 s between bobs, how much kinetic energy is in each outgoing pulse? •

13. Figure P16.13 shows two waves in a rope approaching each other at instant $t = 0$. For any instant after $t = 0$, determine the maximum displacement that occurs (*a*) at $x = 0$, (*b*) at $x = 0.90$ m, and (*c*) anywhere along the rope. ••

Figure P16.13

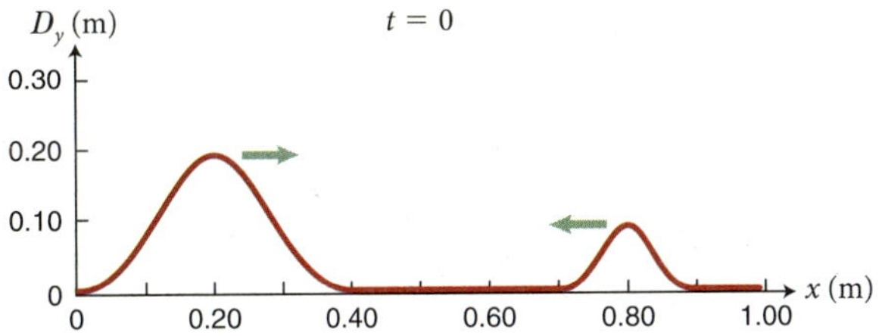

14. The two wave pulses in Figure P16.14 are traveling on the same string at $t = 1.0$ s. Sketch the shape of the string at this instant. ••

Figure P16.14

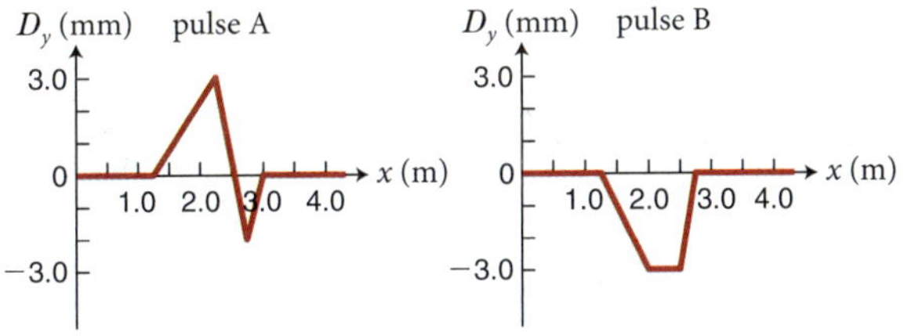

15. Suppose two waves, identical except for the direction of travel, approach each other in a medium that obeys Hooke's law. At certain instants, the waves interfere constructively at all positions. At one such instant, when their peaks align, determine the kinetic energy of the wave function that results from the superposition of both waves. •••

16.4 Boundary effects

16. A harmonic wave traveling along a light string approaches a splice to a heavier string, as shown in Figure P16.16. Which changes as the wave crosses the boundary: wavelength, frequency, both, or neither? •

Figure P16.16

17. A transverse wave in a swimming pool reaches the concrete side and is reflected. Determine whether the reflected wave is inverted. •

18. A rope is attached to a tree trunk and made taut, and then a pulse traveling rightward is sent along the rope. For each case depicted in Figure P16.18, determine whether or not the reflected pulse is depicted correctly. ••

Figure P16.18

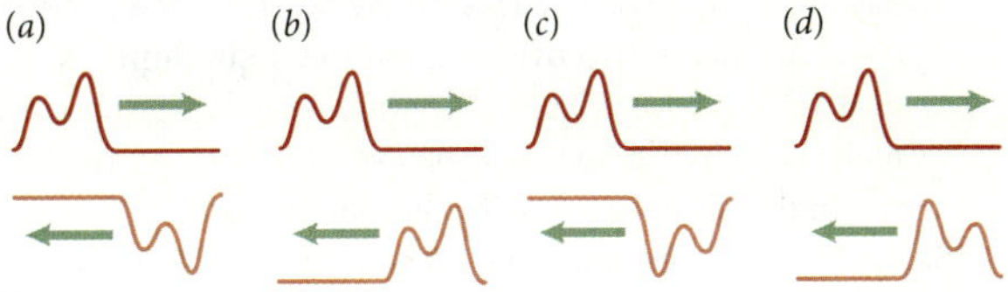

19. Figure P16.19 shows two strings of different linear mass densities at some instant. At some earlier instant, only one pulse existed on one of the strings. (*a*) Determine which string carried the initial pulse, and (*b*) sketch the approximate shape of the strings at the instant the initial pulse was created. ••

Figure P16.19

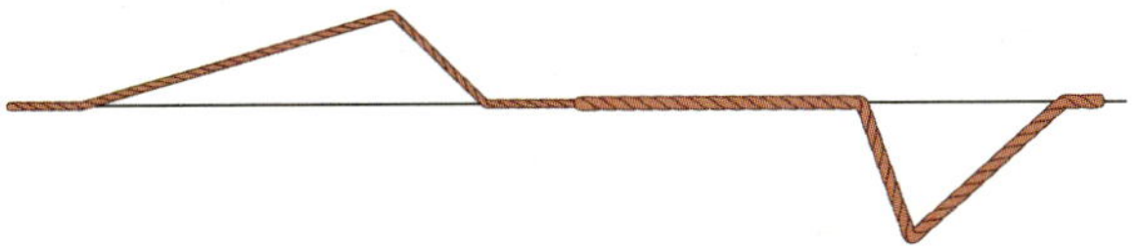

20. You shake the end of a taut string, creating two periods of a traveling sinusoidal wave, as shown in Figure P16.20. The string you are shaking (string 1) is connected to a second, much more massive, string (string 2). The wave speeds on the two strings differ by a factor of 2. (*a*) On the template, sketch the shape of the two strings a time interval $4T$ after the instant represented in Figure P16.20, with T the period of the original wave on string 1. Briefly explain how you determined the shape of the strings. (*b*) How do the periods of the waves on string 1 and string 2 compare? ••

Figure P16.20

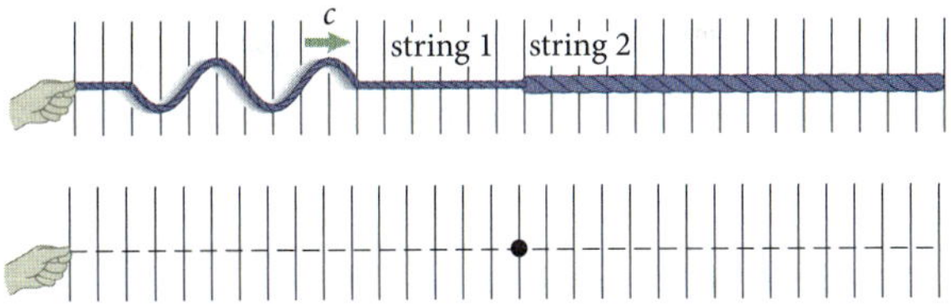

21. Figure P16.21 shows a pulse as it approaches a fixed end of a rope. Draw the shape of the rope halfway through the reflection (that is, when half of the pulse length is still moving to the right and the other half of the pulse has already been reflected). •••

Figure P16.21

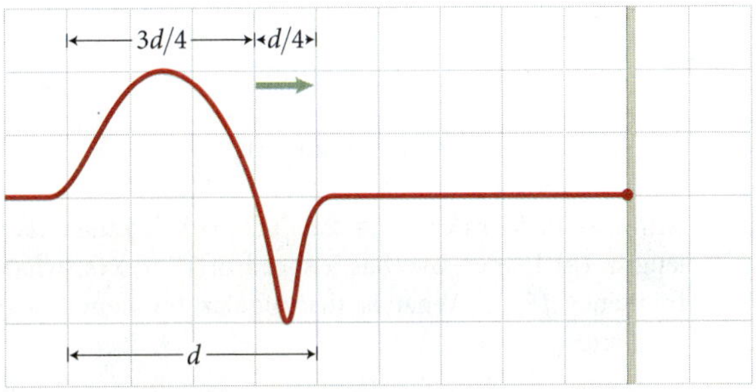

PRACTICE

16.5 Wave functions

22. Walking along the beach, you notice that a new wave reaches the shore every 4.0 s, and you estimate the wave crests to be 2.5 m apart. At what wave speed c are the waves moving? •

23. While on a sailboat at anchor, you notice that 12 waves pass its bow every minute. If the waves have a speed of 6.0 m/s, what is the distance between two adjacent wave crests? •

24. Participating in a human rally wave at a football game, you have to stand up every 15 s. (*a*) What is the wave frequency? (*b*) If the stadium is oval and the inner circumference of the oval is 0.56 km, what is the wave speed? Assume that the main wave pulse spans 30 people and that the distance between the heads of any two adjacent people is 1.0 m. ••

25. (*a*) Plot the time-independent wave function for the traveling pulse described by the time-dependent wave function

$$D_y(x, t) = \frac{a}{b^2 + (x - ct)^2},$$

with $a = 5.0\ \text{m}^3$, $b = 1.0$ m, and $c = 2.0$ m/s for $t = 0$, 1.0 s, 2.0 s, and 3.0 s. (*b*) What is the wave speed c of this pulse? ••

26. What is wrong with each displacement curve in Figure P16.26 ••?

Figure P16.26

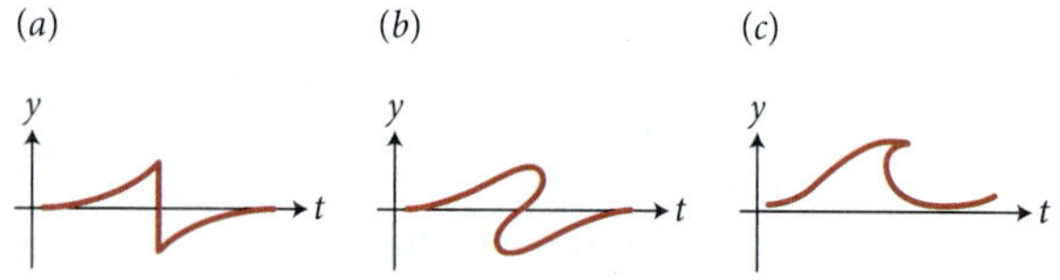

27. At $t = 0$, a wave pulse has a shape given by the time-independent wave function

$$f(x) = \frac{a}{b^2 + x^2},$$

where $a = 0.030\ \text{m}^3$ and $b = 2.0$ m. (*a*) If the pulse travels in the positive x direction at a wave speed of 1.75 m/s, write the time-dependent wave function $f(x, t)$ for this transverse wave. (*b*) Plot the time-dependent wave function $f(x, t)$ at $t = -0.50$ s and at $t = +0.50$ s over the range of x in which $f(x, t)$ is substantially changing. (*c*) Plot the displacement curve at $x = 2.0$ m. ••

28. A wave traveling along a string is described by

$$f(x, t) = a \sin(\pi bx + qt),$$

with $a = 30$ mm, $b = 0.33\ \text{m}^{-1}$, and $q = 10.47\ \text{s}^{-1}$. (*a*) Calculate the amplitude, wavelength, period, and speed of the wave. (*b*) Compute the y component of the displacement of the string at $x = 0.500$ m and $t = 1.60$ s. ••

29. A wave is described by the equation

$$f(x) = a \sin(bx),$$

with $a = 0.095$ m and $b = 2.25\ \text{m}^{-1}$. (*a*) Calculate its wavelength. (*b*) If the wave has a speed of 17.0 m/s, what is its frequency f? (*c*) What is the angular frequency ω of the oscillation? ••

30. As an earthquake starts, you are standing 150 km (as the wave travels) from the epicenter. A geophysicist near the epicenter immediately telephones you to let you know that the transverse wave from the earthquake is on its way to you and that it is described by the equation

$$f(x, t) = a \sin(bx - \omega t),$$

where $a = 0.560$ m, $b = 0.0157\ \text{m}^{-1}$, and a full wavelength passes any given location every 0.500 s. How long will it be before the ground you are standing on starts to shake? ••

31. The motion of a wave traveling along an x axis is given by

$$f(x, t) = a \sin[bx + qt],$$

with $a = 6.00$ m, $b = \pi\ \text{cm}^{-1}$, and $q = 12.0\ \text{s}^{-1}$. Determine the direction of travel and the wave speed. ••

32. A plucked violin string carries a traveling wave given by the equation

$$f(x, t) = a \sin[b(x - ct) + \phi_i],$$

with $a = 0.00580$ m, $b = 33.05\ \text{m}^{-1}$, and $c = 245$ m/s. (*a*) If $f(0, 0) = 0$, what is ϕ_i? (*b*) Determine the simple harmonic period of a point on the string. ••

33. A wave that was produced by a harmonic oscillator and is traveling along a string is described by the equation

$$f(x, t) = a \sin[b(x - ct)],$$

with $a = 46$ mm, $b = 4\pi\ \text{m}^{-1}$, and $c = 45$ m/s. Calculate the (*a*) wavelength, (*b*) angular frequency ω, (*c*) frequency f, and (*d*) period. ••

34. The amplitude of a wave traveling on a string is 0.250 m. The 80.0-Hz wave is traveling in the positive x direction at a wave speed of 17.5 m/s. (*a*) Determine its wavelength, and write the equation for its time-independent wave function. (*b*) For $t = 3.00$ s, compute the displacement and transverse velocity of the point on the string at $x = 1.25$ m, assuming an initial phase ϕ_i of zero. (*c*) Write the time-dependent wave function for the wave. (*d*) If the string displacement at $x = 1.25$ m is 0.210 m at $t = 3.00$ s, write the time-dependent wave function that uses the smallest possible value of ϕ_i. •••

16.6 Standing waves

35. Watching your fish swim in their tank, you notice that when one fish repeatedly jumps, it causes a standing wave given by the time-independent function

$$f(x) = a \sin(bx),$$

with $a = 0.015$ m and $b = 19.6\ \text{m}^{-1}$. If the tank is 0.96 m long, determine the positions of the first three nodes, beginning with the node at one end of the tank. •

36. After tying one end of a rope to a stationary object, you flick the free end so as to cause a sinusoidal standing wave that has a maximum displacement of 0.50 m and a wavelength of 1.33 m. Write the time-dependent wave function in terms of the wave speed. •

37. When one end of a string is tied to a pole and the other end is moved with frequency f, the standing wave pattern shown

PRACTICE

in Figure P16.37 is created. What is the smallest frequency at which the string can be moved to produce any standing wave? ••

Figure P16.37

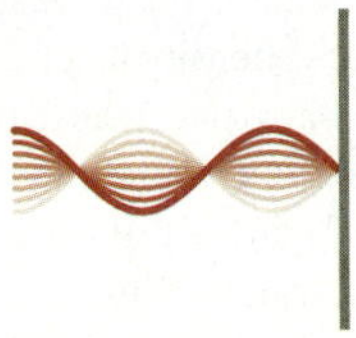

38. You have two string segments of equal length, segment 1 of linear mass density μ_1 and segment 2 of linear mass density $\mu_2 > \mu_1$. You splice the two together and then tie the combination tautly between two posts. You splice in such a way that, once attached to the posts, the length of segment 1 to the left of the splice is the same as the length of segment 2 to the right of the splice. When you pluck at a particular frequency, you set up a standing wave that has this pattern: nodes at the splice and where each segment is attached to its pole plus two more nodes in one of the segments and three more nodes in the other segment (eight nodes in all). What is the numerical value of the ratio μ_1/μ_2 ••?

39. A guitar string has a length of 0.650 m and a mass of 4.00×10^{-3} kg. (*a*) If it is kept under a tension of 126 N, what is the fundamental (smallest harmonic) frequency at which it vibrates? (*b*) At what other frequencies (higher harmonics) could it vibrate at this fixed length? ••

40. The equations for two waves traveling along the same string are

$$f_1(x, t) = a \sin(bx - qt)$$

and

$$f_2(x, t) = a \sin\left(bx + qt + \tfrac{1}{3}\pi\right),$$

with $a = 3.00 \times 10^{-2}$ m, $b = 4\pi$ m^{-1}, and $q = 500$ s^{-1}. (*a*) Calculate the amplitude and wavelength of the resultant displacement of the string at $t = 3.00$ s. (*b*) At $t = 1.70$ s, what is the displacement of the point on the string located at $x = 2.00$ m? ••

41. A string vibrates in a standing wave according to the function

$$f(x, t) = a \sin(bx)\cos(qt),$$

with $a = 6.00 \times 10^{-2}$ m, $b = \tfrac{1}{3}\pi$ cm^{-1}, and $q = 40\pi$ s^{-1}. What are the amplitude and wave speed of each of the component waves that form this standing wave? ••

42. A traveling wave on a long string is described by the time-dependent wave function

$$f(x, t) = a \sin(bx - qt),$$

with $a = 6.00 \times 10^{-2}$ m, $b = 5\pi$ m^{-1}, and $q = 314$ s^{-1}. You want a traveling wave of this frequency and wavelength but with amplitude 0.0400 m. Write the time-dependent wave function for a second traveling wave that could be added to the same string in order to achieve this. ••

43. You have a trough 3.60 m long. It is filled with water, and you want to create a standing wave such that a node occurs every 0.30 m. (*a*) What is the wavelength of this wave? (*b*) A leaf floating on the water 0.60 m from the one end of the trough is displaced a vertical distance $D_y = 10$ mm at $t = 3.2$ s, and the leaf's displacement has a period of 0.60 s. What is the resultant displacement of the standing wave? (*c*) Write the time-dependent wave function for the standing wave. ••

44. Two sinusoidal waves travel along the same string. Their time-dependent wave functions are

$$f_1(x, t) = a \sin\left(bx - qt - \tfrac{1}{4}\pi\right)$$

$$f_2(x, t) = a \sin\left(bx - qt - \tfrac{1}{3}\pi\right),$$

with $a = 5.00 \times 10^{-2}$ m, $b = 0.120$ m^{-1}, and $q = 180$ s^{-1}. (*a*) What is the phase difference between these two waves? (*b*) Write the time-dependent wave function for the wave created by the superposition of these two waves. (*c*) What is the displacement of the string at $x = 2.00$ m at $t = 1.70$ s? •••

45. Two sinusoidal waves travel in opposite directions along the same string. The wavelength and frequency are the same in both waves, and each has amplitude 0.0289 m. If one wave has a phase difference $\Delta\phi$ with respect to the other wave, what is the maximum displacement of the wave created by the superposition? •••

16.7 Wave speed

46. A piano wire has a linear mass density of 5.00×10^{-3} kg/m and is under 1.35 kN of tension. At what speed does a wave travel along this wire? •

47. Your professor uses a plastic chain 10 m long to demonstrate transverse waves in class. If you measure the speed of a traveling wave to be 15 m/s, and the professor measures the tension in the chain to be 100 N, what is the chain's mass? •

48. A large crane is being used to lower a 10,000-kg storage unit into place on a barge. If the cable that supports the unit from the end of the crane is 12 m long, and the linear mass density of the cable is 1.78 kg/m, how long does it take a wave to travel the length of the cable? •

49. A violinist is bowing one string to produce a certain note. List three ways in which she can produce a note of higher frequency, either while playing or by preparing the violin differently before she begins to play. ••

50. How long after the propellers at the back of an oil tanker start turning does the front of the ship start to move? ••

51. A wave traveling along a string has a speed of 24 m/s when the tension in the string is 120 N. What is the speed of the same wave if the tension is reduced to 100 N? ••

52. Two wires that have different linear mass densities, 0.45 kg/m and 0.29 kg/m, are spliced together. They are then used as a guy line to secure a telephone pole. If the tension is 300 N, what is the difference in the speed of a wave traveling from one wire to the other? ••

53. A string of linear mass density μ_1 fixed at both ends is replaced by a string of linear mass density $16\mu_1$. By what factor does the frequency of the fundamental standing wave change if the tension and wavelength remain what they were in the original string? ••

54. A 25.0-m steel wire and a 50.0-m copper wire are attached end to end and stretched to a tension of 145 N. Both wires have a radius of 0.450 mm, and the densities are $7.86 \times 10^3\ \text{kg/m}^3$ for the steel and $8.92 \times 10^3\ \text{kg/m}^3$ for the copper. (Note that these are mass densities, mass per unit volume, not linear mass densities, mass per unit length.) How long does a wave take to travel from one end to the other end of the combination wire? ••

55. A 100-m steel cable that helps support the Golden Gate Bridge is 72.0 mm in diameter and composed of 100 steel wires twisted together. Approximate this as a single uniform steel cable that has a mass density of $7.86 \times 10^3\ \text{kg/m}^3$. The wind generates in the cable a vibration that creates a wave that travels down the cable at 380 m/s. What is the tension in the cable? ••

56. One end of the wire in Figure P16.56 is anchored to the side of a building, and the other end is attached at an angle of 27° to a light horizontal bar from which a 75-kg sign hangs. The linear mass density of the wire is 0.067 kg/m. If the wind causes the sign to vibrate so that a wave travels along the wire, at what speed does the wave travel? •••

Figure P16.56

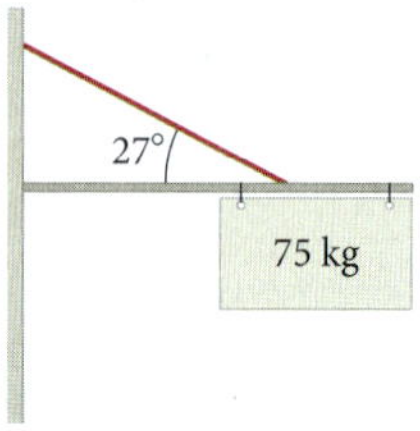

16.8 Energy transport in waves

57. A taut rope has a mass of 0.128 kg and a length of 3.60 m. What average power must be supplied to the rope to generate sinusoidal waves that have amplitude 0.200 m and wavelength 0.600 m if the waves are to travel at 25.0 m/s? •

58. Consider two waves X and Y traveling in the same medium. The two carry the same amount of energy per unit time, but X has half the amplitude of Y. What is the ratio of their wavelengths? Which wave has the longer wavelength? •

59. Transverse waves are being generated on a rope being held under constant tension. By what factor is the power required to generate the wave increased or decreased (*a*) if the length of the rope is halved, (*b*) if the amplitude and angular frequency are doubled, and (*c*) if the wavelength and rope length are doubled? ••

60. You hold one end of a string that is attached to a wall by its other end. The string has a linear mass density of 0.067 kg/m. You raise your end briskly at 12 m/s for 0.016 s, creating a transverse wave that moves at 31 m/s. (*a*) How much work did you do on the string? What are the wave's (*b*) energy, (*c*) potential energy, and (*d*) kinetic energy? ••

61. One end of a horizontal string that has a linear mass density of 3.5 kg/m is displaced vertically at a speed of 45 m/s for 6.7 ms. The pulse created by this motion travels down the string at 78 m/s. How much kinetic energy travels along the string? ••

62. A wave traveling along a string is described by the time-dependent wave function $f(x, t) = a \sin(bx + qt)$, with $a = 0.0268$ m, $b = 5.85\ \text{m}^{-1}$, and $q = 76.3\ \text{s}^{-1}$. The linear mass density of the string is 0.0456 kg/m. Calculate (*a*) the wave speed c, (*b*) the wave frequency f, and (*c*) the power P supplied by the wave. ••

63. An oscillator attached to a string transmits 350 mW of power down the string. The wave created by this motion has amplitude 0.0165 m and wavelength 1.80 m. If the string is under 14.8 N of tension, what is the wave speed? ••

64. A cord of linear mass density 0.360 kg/m is attached to a harmonic oscillator that has a maximum output of 200 W. (*a*) With the oscillator operating at this maximum power and the tension in the cord set at 30.0 N, a wave of amplitude 8.00×10^{-3} m is created. What is the minimum wavelength possible for a wave of this amplitude? (*b*) What is the power output of the oscillator if the wave generated has the same amplitude but double the wavelength you calculated in part *a*, and the tension is 15.0 N? •••

65. One end of a 9.00-m wire vibrates sinusoidally, creating a wave that travels in the positive x direction. The wave has a frequency of 60.0 Hz, a wavelength of 3.00 m, and an amplitude of 0.0725 m. (*a*) Write the time-dependent wave function that describes this wave. (*b*) If the mass of the wire is 1.20×10^{-2} kg, what is the power supplied to the wire to create this wave? •••

16.9 The wave equation

66. Show that $f(x, t) = e^{b(x-vt)}$, where b and v are constants, is a solution to Eq. 16.51, the wave equation. •

67. What keeps a surfer riding the crest of a wave from dropping down to the wave's base? ••

68. A string initially hanging vertically is displaced to the right with a speed of 25 m/s for 0.040 s, then returned to its original position in 0.010 s. This motion is repeated, with no delays, numerous times. The wave created by this motion travels down the string at 67 m/s and has a period of 0.050 s. (*a*) Write the time-dependent wave function for this pulse, and (*b*) show that this function is a solution to the wave equation (Eq. 16.51). ••

69. Show that if $f_1(x, t) = A_1 \sin(k_1 x - \omega_1 t)$ and $f_2(x, t) = A_2 \sin(k_2 x - \omega_2 t)$ are both solutions to the wave equation (Eq. 16.51), then $f(x, t) = f_1(x, t) + f_2(x, t)$ is also a solution. ••

70. (*a*) Show that the equations (*i*) $A \cos(kx + \omega t)$, (*ii*) $e^{-b|x-qt|^2}$, and (*iii*) $-(b^2 t - x)^2$ all satisfy the wave equation (Eq. 16.51) provided that A, k, ω, b, and q are constants. (*b*) Calculate the speed of each wave of part *a*. •••

Additional Problems

71. Two children are holding a rope taut between them when one suddenly yanks the rope. (*a*) Does the child at the other end instantly get pulled? (*b*) Answer the same question for two children holding a rigid steel bar between them. •

72. A heavy rope is hanging by one end from the ceiling with a block hanging from the other end. Is the speed of a pulse in the rope greater at the top or the bottom of the rope? •

73. First you stretch a spring to twice its initial length and send pulse A from one end to the other. Then you stretch the spring to three times its initial length and send pulse B from one end to the other. How does the time interval needed for A to travel through the spring compare with the time interval needed for B to do so? ••

74. You pluck a guitar string so as to produce a standing wave for which $\lambda = 1.3$ m. What is the maximum value of the string's displacement at a position 0.500 m from the lower end of the string if the maximum resultant displacement of the wave is 0.75 mm? ••

PRACTICE

75. Tossing rocks into the center of a pond, you notice that the ripples are evenly spaced 170 mm apart. If it takes 5.0 s for 15 ripples to pass a log sticking up out of the water, (*a*) what is the wave speed? (*b*) How long does it take a ripple to reach shore if the pond is 12 m in diameter? ••

76. When a person sings in the shower, certain notes seem louder than others. What's going on? ••

77. A standing wave is created on a string that is 1.75 m long. The wave has eight nodes counting the nodes at the two ends. (*a*) What is the wavelength? (*b*) What is the frequency if the wave speed is 130 m/s? (*c*) If the resultant displacement is 20.0 mm, write the time-dependent wave function that describes the standing wave, including units where appropriate. ••

78. Would water waves traveling along a trough on the surface of Mars travel faster than, slower than, or at the same speed as water waves traveling along a similar trough on the surface of Earth? (Hint: You'll need data from Table 13.1 on page 236 of the *Practice* volume.) ••

79. You hold one end of a horizontal string and raise your hand during a time interval of 0.18 s, doing 1.2 J of work on the string in the process. You then allow your hand to return to its original position. If the wave pulse you create travels along the string at 67 m/s and the linear mass density of the string is 0.0282 kg/m, what was the vertical speed of your hand? ••

80. Your friend wants to test your understanding of waves. She weaves together one end of two different ropes (one with greater mass density than the other, but each with the same radius and length) to make a single rope. Then she attaches one end of the combination to a pole. You are blindfolded and asked to hold the other end of the stretched rope. Your friend expects you to determine not only which end you are holding (the heavier or lighter rope), but also whether your friend used a fixed or free method of attachment to the pole. You think for a minute, then laugh and declare that you can even estimate the ratio of the linear mass densities! While she is speechless, you create a single wave pulse with your hand. ••• CR

81. Your job as assistant coach is to attach one end of several heavy, 10-m ropes to the trusses that support the gym ceiling, leaving the other end of each hanging free. The team is going to spend the afternoon climbing these ropes, but you begin to wonder about wave pulses traveling on such a rope. You could shake the free end of a rope back and forth once and measure how long it takes the pulse created by this motion to arrive at the top of the rope, but you are more of a calculation person. ••• CR

Answers to Review Questions

1. A wave transports energy and momentum but no matter, which means that for mechanical waves, each portion of the medium is at its original location after the wave passes through.
2. The traffic jam is longitudinal, and the other three are transverse.
3. The wave speed is the speed at which the wave moves along the rope. The speed of any small segment of the rope is the magnitude of the velocity at which that segment gets displaced from its equilibrium position as the wave passes through.
4. No, unless the pulse is symmetrical. In general, the displacement curve is the mirror image of the wave function.
5. The frequency is the number of wave crests that arrive each second, in units of hertz (Hz). The wave speed is how fast a wave travels in meters per second (m/s).
6. It remains the same. See Checkpoint 16.5.
7. Waves are not always periodic. A periodic wave is created only when the motion that causes the wave is repeated at regular intervals. A wave pulse is generally not periodic. Neither are waves always harmonic. A harmonic wave is created only when the motion that causes the wave is harmonic (that is, the motion is the particular type of periodic motion that yields a sine curve).
8. Assuming that you move your hand only vertically, the horizontal component of force you exert on the rope as you shake it remains constant and equal to the tension. The wave speed is therefore unaffected by whether you move your hand rapidly or slowly. Assuming that you move your hand up and down by the same distance each time, the amplitude of each pulse you create remains the same. Thus only the period, frequency, and wavelength of the wave change.
9. The interference is temporary in the sense that it occurs at only those instants and places where the pulses overlap. After the pulses move apart, they again have their original size and shape, and the interference no longer exists.
10. Wave pulses always carry equal amounts of kinetic and potential energy.
11. The wave functions are added algebraically at each point of overlap.
12. (*a*) The reflected pulse is inverted and left–right reversed. (*b*) The reflected pulse is left–right reversed but not inverted.
13. At each instant that the shape is desired, sketch a scale diagram of the wave pulse approaching the boundary and a reversed pulse (traveling in the opposite direction at the same speed) designed to arrive at the boundary at the same instant as the actual pulse. If the string beyond the boundary has a greater linear mass density (or if the boundary is a fixed end), the reversed pulse is drawn inverted. If the string beyond the boundary has a smaller linear mass density (or the boundary is a free end), the reversed pulse is drawn upright. Now superimpose the two pulses where they overlap by adding the displacements of each pulse at common positions. The result is an outline of the shape of the pulse at the chosen instant.
14. A complete description requires amplitude A; plus period T, frequency f, or angular frequency ω; plus wavelength λ, wave number k, or wave speed c; plus direction of motion.
15. The wave number of a harmonic wave is the number of wavelengths of the wave that fit in a length of 2π meters. The wave number is a conversion constant that is used to change distances in meters into unitless angles in the arguments of the sinusoidal functions that are used to describe harmonic waves.
16. The wave travels in the positive x direction. The relative sign of the position and time terms gives you this information.
17. An antinode is any point in a standing wave where the amplitude of the displacement attains its greatest value. These points occur halfway between nodes (positions of zero amplitude).
18. They are separated by a distance $\lambda/4$.
19. Yes. The antinodes cycle through all values of medium displacement, including zero.
20. The same. The wave speed depends on the tension and linear mass density of the strings, neither of which has changed.
21. You need to double the wave speed. This means quadrupling the tension, assuming that the string does not stretch (change its linear mass density).
22. Linear mass density is the mass per unit length of a string or rope, measured in units of kg/m.
23. The average power required to generate a wave is directly proportional to the linear mass density of the string and the wave speed and to the square of the amplitude and angular frequency of the wave.
24. Half of the energy transferred becomes kinetic energy and half potential energy.
25. A partial derivative is used for functions that contain more than one variable and is evaluated as an ordinary derivative with respect to one variable while all other variables are held constant.
26. The curvature of any location on the pulse increases as the acceleration of the string segments in the vicinity increases and decreases as the wave speed increases.

Answers to Guided Problems

Guided Problem 16.2 (*a*) A range of values is possible; for example, $f = 1/3$ Hz, $\lambda = 12$ m, $c = 4$ m/s, and $A = 1$ m give $f(x, t) = (1\text{ m})\sin(\pi x/6 - 2\pi t/3 + \phi)$. (*b*) These values result in a vertical speed of 2 m/s for each participant.

Guided Problem 16.4 $\mathcal{T} = 63$ N

Guided Problem 16.6 $\dfrac{A_R}{A_I} = \dfrac{k_A - k_B}{k_A + k_B}$ and $\dfrac{A_T}{A_I} = \dfrac{2k_A}{k_A + k_B}$, so 97.1% of the incident power is transmitted and 2.9% is reflected.

Guided Problem 16.8 (*a*) Figure GPS16.8

Figure GPS16.8

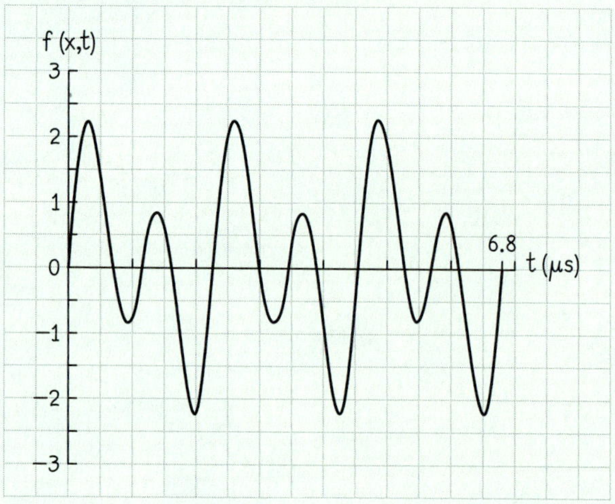

(*c*) $c = \dfrac{\omega}{k} = \dfrac{2\omega}{2k} = \dfrac{2\pi(440\text{ Hz})}{8.00\text{ m}^{-1}} = 346$ m/s

17

PRACTICE

Waves in Two and Three Dimensions

Chapter Summary

Characteristics of waves in two and three dimensions (Sections 17.1, 17.4, 17.5)

Concepts A **wavefront** is a curve or surface in a medium on which all points of a propagating wave have the same phase.

A **planar wavefront** is a flat wavefront that is either a plane or a straight line.

A **surface wave** is a wave that propagates in two dimensions and has circular wavefronts. A **spherical wave** is a wave that propagates in three dimensions and has spherical wavefronts.

According to **Huygens' principle,** any wavefront may be regarded as a collection of many closely spaced, coherent point sources.

Diffraction is the spreading out of waves either around an obstacle or beyond the edges of an aperture. The effect is more pronounced when the size of the obstacle or aperture is about equal to or smaller than the wavelength of the wave.

Quantitative Tools If no energy is dissipated, the amplitude A of a wave originating at a point source decreases with increasing distance r from the source as

$$A \propto \frac{1}{\sqrt{r}} \quad \text{(surface wave)}$$

or

$$A \propto \frac{1}{r} \quad \text{(spherical wave).}$$

The **intensity** I (in W/m^2) of a spherical wave that delivers power P to an area A oriented normal to the direction of propagation is

$$I \equiv \frac{P}{A}. \tag{17.1}$$

If a point source emits waves uniformly in all directions at a power P_s and no energy is dissipated, the intensity a distance r from the source is

$$I = \frac{P_s}{4\pi r^2}. \tag{17.2}$$

The intensity I_{surf} (in W/m) of a surface wave that delivers power P to a length L oriented normal to the direction of propagation is

$$I_{surf} \equiv \frac{P}{L}. \tag{17.3}$$

Sound waves (Sections 17.2, 17.5)

Concepts **Sound** is a longitudinal *compressional* wave propagating through a solid, liquid, or gas. The wave consists of an alternating series of *compressions* (where the molecules of the medium are crowded together) and *rarefactions* (where the molecules are spaced far apart). The frequency range of *audible* sound is 20 Hz to 20 kHz.

The speed of sound c depends on the density and elastic properties of the medium. In dry air at 20 °C, the speed of sound is 343 m/s.

Quantitative Tools The *threshold of hearing* I_{th} is the minimum sound intensity audible to humans. For a 1.0-kHz sound,

$$I_{th} \approx 10^{-12}\ \text{W/m}^2.$$

For a sound of intensity I, the **intensity level** β in decibels is

$$\beta \equiv (10\ \text{dB}) \log\left(\frac{I}{I_{th}}\right). \tag{17.5}$$

Interference effects (Sections 17.3, 17.6)

Concepts Two or more sources emitting waves that have a constant phase difference are called **coherent sources.** If that constant phase difference is zero, the sources are said to be *in phase*.

Along **nodal lines,** waves cancel each other, and so the displacement of the medium is zero. Along **antinodal lines,** the displacement of the medium is a maximum.

The superposition of two waves of equal amplitude but slightly different frequencies results in a wave of oscillating amplitude. This effect is called **beating.**

Quantitative Tools When two waves of frequencies f_1 and f_2 result in **beating,** the **beat frequency** is

$$f_{beat} \equiv |f_1 - f_2|, \tag{17.8}$$

and the displacement D_x of the particles of the medium is

$$D_x = 2A \cos\left[2\pi(\tfrac{1}{2}\Delta f)\,t\right] \sin(2\pi f_{av} t), \tag{17.12}$$

where $\Delta f = |f_1 - f_2|$ and $f_{av} = \frac{1}{2}(f_1 + f_2)$.

PRACTICE

The effects of motion on sound (Sections 17.7, 17.8)

Concepts The **Doppler effect** is a change in the observed wave frequency caused by the relative motion of a wave source and an observer.

A **shock wave** is a conical (wedge-shaped) disturbance caused by the piling up of wavefronts from a source moving at a speed greater than or equal to the wave speed in the medium.

Quantitative Tools If a source moving with speed v_s relative to the medium produces sound of frequency f_s, the **Doppler effect** causes an observer moving with speed v_o relative to the medium to observe the sound as having a frequency f_o given by

$$\frac{f_o}{f_s} = \frac{c \pm v_o}{c \pm v_s}. \tag{17.21}$$

The $\pm$ signs are chosen so that $f_o > f_s$ when the source and observer approach each other and $f_o < f_s$ when they move apart.

As a shock wave propagates at speed c, the angle θ it makes with the direction in which the source moves is given by

$$\sin\theta = \frac{c}{v_s} \quad (v_s > c), \tag{17.22}$$

where v_s is the speed of the source relative to the medium. The ratio v_s/c is the *Mach number.*

Review Questions

Answers to these questions can be found at the end of this chapter.

17.1 Wavefronts

1. Name two ways in which two- and three-dimensional waves differ from one-dimensional waves.
2. Which of the following factors plays a role in how much a wave's amplitude decreases as the wave travels away from its source: dissipation of the wave's energy, dimensionality of the wave, destructive interference by waves created by other sources?
3. Consider a sound wave, created at one end of a hollow pipe, that moves through the medium filling the pipe. How does the amplitude change as the wave travels away from the sound source inside the pipe? Ignore energy dissipation.

17.2 Sound

4. Are sound waves in air longitudinal or transverse?
5. What is the range of frequencies audible to humans who have normal hearing?
6. Describe a demonstration that shows that air is elastic.
7. In a sound wave, how do the locations of maximum and minimum medium displacement compare with the locations of maximum and minimum medium density?

17.3 Interference

8. Is the sound created by two sound waves passing a given position P always louder than the sound at P created by either wave alone?
9. Suppose your seat at a poorly designed concert hall is at a *dead spot,* which is a position where destructive interference destroys the sound coming from the stage. Is it a dead spot for all musical notes?
10. Picture two identical coherent wave sources placed side by side and sending out waves that interfere with each other, creating a moiré pattern. If the distance between the two sources is increased, does the number of nodal lines in the pattern increase, decrease, or remain the same?
11. Can destructive interference occur when waves emanating from three or more sources overlap?

17.4 Diffraction

12. What is Huygens' principle?
13. Why is it important that a bat use high-frequency waves to locate insects sonically?
14. Describe the relative extent of spreading of sound waves after they pass through a gap in a barrier. Consider three possibilities: The wavelength is (*a*) much smaller than the gap width, (*b*) comparable to the gap width, and (*c*) much greater than the gap width.

17.5 Intensity

15. A point source emits sound waves uniformly in all directions. How does the sound intensity I vary with distance from the source?
16. Increasing your distance from a point source of spherical waves by a factor of 10 reduces the intensity level β by how many decibels?
17. Explain why the units of intensity I differ for a ripple on the surface of a pond and for a sound wave from an emergency alert siren.

17.6 Beats

18. How is the beat frequency created by two interfering waves related to the frequencies of the waves?
19. One way to tune a piano is to strike a tuning fork (which emits only one specific frequency), then immediately strike the piano key for the frequency being sounded by the fork, and listen for beats. In making an adjustment, a piano tuner working this way causes the beat frequency to increase slightly. Is she going in the right direction with that adjustment?

17.7 Doppler effect

20. A train approaches as you wait at a crossing. Is the whistle frequency you hear higher than, lower than, or the same as the frequency you would hear if the train were stationary?
21. Which produces a greater frequency ratio f_o/f_s: a wave source approaching a stationary observer at a speed of $0.250c$ or an observer approaching a stationary source at a speed of $0.250c$?

17.8 Shock waves

22. Does the angle of a shock wave depend on the frequency of the sound emitted?
23. A boat travels through the water. If its speed increases, what happens to the angle of the bow wave it creates in the water?

Developing a Feel

Make an order-of-magnitude estimate of each of the following quantities. Letters in parentheses refer to hints below. Use them as needed to guide your thinking.

1. The wavelength of the sound wave traveling in air when you whistle (M, T)
2. The number of wavelengths of the musical tone A above middle C (440 Hz) in a standing wave that fills an auditorium (H, M, Q)
3. The width of the smallest object that can be located using sound in the range of human hearing (P, B, F)
4. The greatest distance at which you can just hear a large fireworks shell explode (A, C, I, R, S, U)
5. The power output of the warning horn on a freight train (G, J, N, R, E)
6. The maximum distance over which you can hear a train horn (E, R, L)
7. The ratio of the wavelength of a sound on your vocal cords to the wavelength of the same sound in air (D, K, O)

Hints

A. How much energy is released by a commercial fireworks shell?
B. Which end of the range of human hearing is more useful for detecting a very small object?
C. During what time interval is the energy released?
D. What is the length of a human vocal cord?
E. What is the intensity level β near the horn?
F. What is the frequency range of human hearing?
G. At what distance must the horn be heard?
H. What is the greatest dimension of an auditorium?
I. What fraction of the energy released goes into sound?
J. What must the intensity level β be inside an automobile approaching the tracks in order for the driver to hear the horn?
K. What is a typical frequency for the human voice?
L. What is the minimum intensity level β needed to hear this sound in an open field?
M. What is the speed of sound in air?
N. What must the intensity level β be outside the car?
O. What is the wavelength in air for this typical voice frequency?
P. What is the relationship between the width of the object and the wavelength of the sound wave being used to detect it?
Q. What is the wavelength for this tone?
R. How does the intensity I drop off with distance?
S. What fraction of the sound energy is absorbed or dissipated over great distances?
T. What is the frequency of sound emitted when you whistle?
U. What background noise level is appropriate?

Key (all values approximate)

A. 2 J; **B.** the smallest object requires the smallest possible wavelength for the sound wave, which means the highest possible frequency in the human-hearing range; **C.** 5 ms; **D.** 2×10^1 mm; **E.** 120 dB 1 m from horn; **F.** 2×10^1 Hz to 2×10^4 Hz; **G.** 1×10^2 m for a fast train, which may travel this distance in a few seconds; **H.** 6×10^1 m; **I.** taking into account energy to create light and kinetic energy of fragments—say, 1/2; **J.** above the intensity level of conversation or radio loudness—say, 65 dB; **K.** 2×10^2 Hz; **L.** 30 dB; **M.** 3×10^2 m/s; **N.** because the windows may be closed, allow a good margin—say, 80 dB; **O.** 2 m; **P.** wavelengths longer than the object's width diffract around the object instead of being reflected back to the detector; **Q.** 0.7 m; **R.** as $1/r^2$, because the wavefronts are spherical; **S.** say, another 1/2; **T.** 1 kHz; **U.** for a best case, 30 dB

PRACTICE

Worked and Guided Problems

These examples involve material from this chapter but are not associated with any particular section. Some examples are worked out in detail; others you should work out by following the guidelines provided.

Worked Problem 17.1 Minimal sound

Two small, spherical speakers simultaneously emit a note of wavelength λ. The speakers are a distance $10\lambda/3$ apart. If a microphone is moved along the line between their centers, at what positions does it detect (*a*) an unusually loud sound and (*b*) an unusually faint sound?

1 GETTING STARTED We know that the closer the microphone is to a speaker, the louder the sound it detects because the intensity I of the sound waves is greatest near the source. However, the question says *unusually loud,* which hints that we are being asked about the effects of constructive and destructive interference. We are asked for the positions where the microphone records very loud and very faint sounds, and so we draw a diagram that shows what we know and specifies a suitable reference position against which to measure distances. We choose this reference position to be the center of the left speaker, which we call speaker 1 (Figure WG17.1).

Figure WG17.1

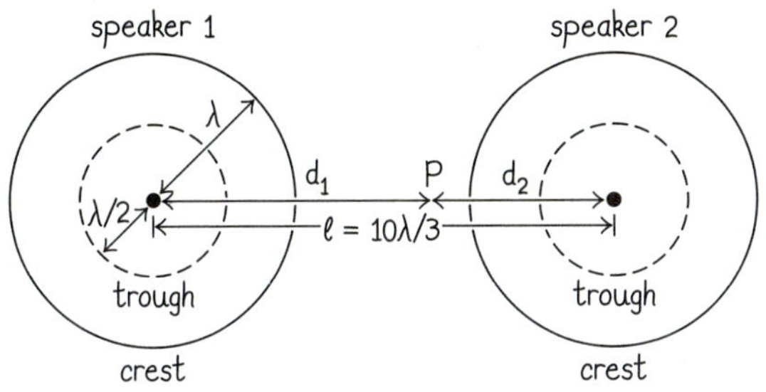

2 DEVISE PLAN Consider the arbitrary position labeled P in Figure WG17.1, which is on the line that connects the speaker centers. Constructive interference occurs at P when waves from the two speakers arrive at P in phase. To achieve this, the phase difference at P must be a multiple of one cycle: $0, \pm 2\pi, \pm 4\pi, \ldots$. Because there is one wavelength in each cycle, the number of wavelengths in distances d_1 and d_2 must differ by an integral number of wavelengths: $0, \pm\lambda, \pm 2\lambda, \ldots$. So, for constructive interference,

$$\text{constructive interference:} \quad \frac{d_1 - d_2}{\lambda} = n, \quad n = 0, \pm 1, \pm 2, \ldots$$

$$d_1 - d_2 = n\lambda.$$

Destructive interference occurs in locations where the two waves are out of phase by $180° = \pi$ rad. Using the same argument as above, we can say

$$\text{destructive interference:} \quad \frac{d_1 - d_2}{\lambda} = n + \tfrac{1}{2}, \quad n = 0, \pm 1, \pm 2, \ldots$$

$$d_1 - d_2 = (n + \tfrac{1}{2})\lambda.$$

We have to make sure that our values for d_1 and d_2 remain between the two speakers, which requires that $d_1 + d_2 = \ell$ and that $0 < d_1 < \ell$ and $0 < d_2 < \ell$.

3 EXECUTE PLAN
(*a*) Because $d_2 = \ell - d_1$, we have for constructive interference

$$d_1 - d_2 = d_1 - (\ell - d_1) = 2d_1 - \ell = 2d_1 - \tfrac{10}{3}\lambda = n\lambda$$

$$d_{1,n}^{\text{con}} = \tfrac{1}{2}(n + \tfrac{10}{3})\lambda, \quad n = 0, \pm 1, \pm 2, \ldots$$

Now we can substitute the first few values of n to obtain all the constructive-interference positions between the speakers:

$$d_{1,0} = \tfrac{1}{2}(0 + \tfrac{10}{3})\lambda = \tfrac{5}{3}\lambda$$

$$d_{1,-1} = \tfrac{1}{2}(-1 + \tfrac{10}{3})\lambda = \tfrac{7}{6}\lambda$$

$$d_{1,+1} = \tfrac{1}{2}(+1 + \tfrac{10}{3})\lambda = \tfrac{13}{6}\lambda$$

$$d_{1,-2} = \tfrac{1}{2}(-2 + \tfrac{10}{3})\lambda = \tfrac{2}{3}\lambda$$

$$d_{1,+2} = \tfrac{1}{2}(+2 + \tfrac{10}{3})\lambda = \tfrac{8}{3}\lambda$$

$$d_{1,-3} = \tfrac{1}{2}(-3 + \tfrac{10}{3})\lambda = \tfrac{1}{6}\lambda$$

$$d_{1,+3} = \tfrac{1}{2}(+3 + \tfrac{10}{3})\lambda = \tfrac{19}{6}\lambda$$

$$d_{1,-4} = \tfrac{1}{2}(-4 + \tfrac{10}{3})\lambda = -\tfrac{1}{3}\lambda$$

$$d_{1,+4} = \tfrac{1}{2}(+4 + \tfrac{10}{3})\lambda = \tfrac{11}{3}\lambda.$$

These last two distances are not between the speakers, which are a distance $10\lambda/3 = 20\lambda/6$ apart, and so we discard them. Thus the positions between the speakers where the microphone detects unusually loud sounds are at these distances from speaker 1:

$$d_1^{\text{con}} = \tfrac{1}{6}\lambda, \tfrac{2}{3}\lambda, \tfrac{7}{6}\lambda, \tfrac{5}{3}\lambda, \tfrac{13}{6}\lambda, \tfrac{8}{3}\lambda, \tfrac{19}{6}\lambda. ✔$$

PRACTICE

(*b*) Using the same procedure, we discover that the distances from speaker 1 that produce destructive interference satisfy the expression

$$2d_1 - \tfrac{10}{3}\lambda = (n + \tfrac{1}{2})\lambda$$

$$d_{1,n}^{\text{des}} = \tfrac{1}{2}(n + \tfrac{23}{6})\lambda, \quad n = 0, \pm 1, \pm 2, \ldots$$

$$d_{1,0} = \tfrac{1}{2}(0 + \tfrac{23}{6})\lambda = \tfrac{23}{12}\lambda$$

$$d_{1,-1} = \tfrac{1}{2}(-1 + \tfrac{23}{6})\lambda = \tfrac{17}{12}\lambda$$

$$d_{1,+1} = \tfrac{1}{2}(+1 + \tfrac{23}{6})\lambda = \tfrac{29}{12}\lambda$$

$$d_{1,-2} = \tfrac{1}{2}(-2 + \tfrac{23}{6})\lambda = \tfrac{11}{12}\lambda$$

$$d_{1,+2} = \tfrac{1}{2}(+2 + \tfrac{23}{6})\lambda = \tfrac{35}{12}\lambda$$

$$d_{1,-3} = \tfrac{1}{2}(-3 + \tfrac{23}{6})\lambda = \tfrac{5}{12}\lambda$$

$$d_{1,+3} = \tfrac{1}{2}(+3 + \tfrac{23}{6})\lambda = \tfrac{41}{12}\lambda$$

$$d_{1,-4} = \tfrac{1}{2}(-4 + \tfrac{23}{6})\lambda = -\tfrac{1}{12}\lambda$$

$$d_{1,+4} = \tfrac{1}{2}(+4 + \tfrac{23}{6})\lambda = \tfrac{47}{12}\lambda.$$

Again we want only positions that lie between the speakers, which are $10\lambda/3 = 40\lambda/12$ apart. The last three values we just calculated are not on this center-to-center line, and so our destructive-interference positions are

$$d_1^{\text{des}} = \tfrac{5}{12}\lambda, \tfrac{11}{12}\lambda, \tfrac{17}{12}\lambda, \tfrac{23}{12}\lambda, \tfrac{29}{12}\lambda, \tfrac{35}{12}\lambda. ✔$$

4 EVALUATE RESULT We expect constructive interference halfway between the speakers because the waves from the two speakers travel the same distance to reach this position. This distance is $\tfrac{1}{2}(\tfrac{10}{3}\lambda) = \tfrac{5}{3}\lambda = d_{1,0}^{\text{con}}$, and we see that this value does appear in our constructive-interference list.

We expect the spacings between constructive and destructive positions to be related to the wavelength in some simple way. In other words, the same type of interference should occur as the difference $d_1 - d_2$ changes by one wavelength. This is easiest to see with the constructive-interference positions. The midpoint between the speakers is a position of constructive interference. As we move from this midpoint toward speaker 2, d_1 increases and d_2 decreases. If d_1 increases by $\lambda/2$, d_2 decreases by $\lambda/2$, and the difference $d_1 - d_2$ changes by one wavelength. Thus positions of constructive interference should be a distance $\lambda/2$ apart, positions of destructive interference should be a distance $\lambda/2$ apart, and this is just what we see.

We expect destructive interference halfway between each pair of constructive-interference positions, which is just what we see—for example,

$$\tfrac{1}{2}[d_{1,+1}^{\text{con}} + d_{1,0}^{\text{con}}] = \tfrac{1}{2}\left[\tfrac{13}{6}\lambda + \tfrac{5}{3}\lambda\right] = \tfrac{23}{12}\lambda = d_{1,0}^{\text{des}}.$$

We made one assumption that can affect the accuracy of our answers. We assumed that the amplitude of the waves is constant along the line that joins the speakers, and this is not true. The closer you are to one speaker, the higher the amplitude of the wave coming from it and the lower the amplitude of the wave coming from the other speaker. Thus, positions where the phase difference is $\lambda/2$ are not positions where the crest of one wave cancels the trough of the other. This deviation from the ideal case causes both the constructive and the destructive interference to be less than complete. Nevertheless these are positions of unusually loud or faint sound.

Guided Problem 17.2 Dripping disturbance

A dripping faucet creates waves on the surface of a still pool of water in a stoppered sink. The drops enter the water at position P, and the crest-to-trough height of the waves 10 mm from P is 7.0 mm. (*a*) What is the amplitude of the waves 150 mm from P? (*b*) By what factor does the wave intensity 150 mm from P differ from the wave intensity 10 mm from P?

1 GETTING STARTED

1. Describe what happens to the waves as they spread out.
2. What is the difference between a water wave spreading out in two dimensions and a sound wave spreading out in three dimensions?
3. Equation 17.1, $I = P/A$, is for three-dimensional waves. How does the denominator of the fraction change when you write the intensity equation for a two-dimensional wave?

2 DEVISE PLAN

4. What unknown quantities do you need to determine?
5. What principles or methods can help you obtain these quantities?
6. How is energy related to a quantity you've studied in this chapter?
7. Which equations allow you to express the unknown quantities in terms of known quantities?

3 EXECUTE PLAN

4 EVALUATE RESULT

8. Are these results consistent with your experience with such water waves?

PRACTICE

Worked Problem 17.3 Bottle music

When you blow across the mouth of a bottle, you can cause a standing wave in the air in the bottle, which makes a musical sound. Blowing harder can give a higher musical pitch, but that takes practice. Assume for any liquid height in the bottle that you can reliably obtain only the fundamental (first harmonic) and the next higher harmonic frequency by blowing. You have a beverage bottle 0.23 m in length, with an original liquid height of 0.20 m (before you drink any of the beverage). Given that the speed of sound in air is 343 m/s, what range of frequencies can you obtain as you slowly sip the liquid in the bottle?

❶ GETTING STARTED Sound waves are longitudinal waves, but standing waves in the bottle should form only for certain wavelengths, as for transverse standing waves on a string (see *Principles* Section 16.6). We must determine what standing wave patterns form in the air above the liquid in the bottle. The top surface of the liquid in the bottle (or the bottom of the bottle when the contents are consumed) acts as a fixed end because sound waves are longitudinal, and the displacement of air molecules is greatly reduced at the liquid or glass surface. Therefore we expect a node at this location. The top end of the bottle is open, and displacement of air molecules is not constrained at this end of the bottle. This corresponds to a free end for reflection, resulting in a displacement antinode near the top of the bottle. Now we just need to figure out how many wavelengths fit in the bottle to match these boundary conditions. The smallest number we obtain corresponds to the fundamental frequency.

❷ DEVISE PLAN We need to determine what fraction of a wavelength satisfies our boundary conditions. From the allowed wavelengths and the known speed of sound in air, we can then use the relationship $c = \lambda f$ to compute the frequencies.

One node in a standing wave pattern is separated from the next node by half a wavelength, so to get from one node to an adjacent antinode is a quarter of a wavelength. The fundamental pattern requires one-quarter wavelength to fit into the open space in the bottle. For each shorter wavelength that satisfies the same conditions, we need to add another half wavelength, adding an additional node and antinode so that there is still a node at the bottom and an antinode at the top of each pattern. Like the standing waves on a string, the patterns differ from each other by one-half wavelength. Unlike the standing waves on strings, the higher harmonics do not simply occur for every integer multiple of the half wavelength. Instead, the harmonics occur for odd integer multiples of one-quarter wavelength:

$$\frac{\lambda}{4}, \frac{3\lambda}{4}, \frac{5\lambda}{4}, \ldots .$$

Only the first two patterns are relevant for this problem. If the length of air in the bottle is ℓ, each pattern must fit into that length. The first two patterns must satisfy

$$\ell = \frac{\lambda}{4} \quad \text{and} \quad \ell = \frac{3\lambda}{4}$$

$$\lambda = 4\ell \quad \text{and} \quad \lambda = \frac{4\ell}{3}.$$

The resulting frequencies are

$$f = \frac{c}{\lambda} = \frac{c}{4\ell} \quad \text{and} \quad \frac{3c}{4\ell}.$$

We must determine these frequencies for the range of lengths available.

❸ EXECUTE PLAN The minimum length of air in the bottle occurs before we take the first sip: It is the difference between the height of the bottle and the original height of the liquid. For this case we obtain frequencies

$$f_1 = \frac{c}{4\ell} = \frac{343\ \text{m/s}}{4(3.0 \times 10^{-2}\ \text{m})} = 2.9 \times 10^3\ \text{Hz}$$

$$f_3 = \frac{3c}{4\ell} = 3f_1 = 8.6 \times 10^3\ \text{Hz}.$$

Any longer length ℓ will result in smaller frequencies, so the maximum frequency we can attain is just above 8500 Hz. The lower frequency limit will occur for the greatest value of the air column—that is, when the bottle is empty:

$$f_1 = \frac{c}{4\ell} = \frac{343\ \text{m/s}}{4(0.23\ \text{m})} = 3.7 \times 10^2\ \text{Hz}$$

$$f_3 = 3f_1 = 1.1 \times 10^3\ \text{Hz}.$$

The lowest possible frequency for these conditions is thus just over 370 Hz, giving a range of

$$370\ \text{Hz} < f < 8600\ \text{Hz}. ✔$$

❹ EVALUATE RESULT Many of us have produced tones by blowing across the mouth of a bottle, so it is reasonable that we obtain frequencies that can be heard. Both ends of this frequency range are well within the range of human hearing, although the upper limit is a pretty high note, perhaps reminiscent of a piccolo. Experience also tells us that longer bottles produce deeper notes, in agreement with our results.

Guided Problem 17.4 Bottle orchestra

Preparing to watch a ballgame on television, you raid the refrigerator for two 0.23-m-tall bottles of your favorite beverage for yourself and your roommate. After a few minutes the game is boring, so your roommate begins blowing across the top of his bottle. That looks like fun, so you decide to try it, too. Each of you has a bottle with a slightly different level of liquid, but the depth of liquid in each bottle is roughly 10^2 mm. What is the minimum difference in the heights of the liquid in the two bottles that will allow you to hear two different musical notes when you and your roommate "play" your bottles simultaneously at their fundamental frequencies?

❶ GETTING STARTED

1. If the two bottles produce notes whose frequencies differ by just a few Hz, what pattern of sound do you expect to hear?
2. What is the lowest frequency note that humans can hear?
3. How is the fundamental frequency related to the depth of the liquid in the bottle?

2 DEVISE PLAN

4. Given the height of the bottle and the depth of the liquid, can you determine the frequency of the sound that forms a fundamental standing wave in the air in the bottle?
5. Examine Eq. 17.11, the immediate precursor to the beat equation (Eq. 17.12). Is there any difference in principle between the sine and cosine terms? Figure 17.27, the superposed displacement curves of two waves of slightly different frequencies, may help you answer.
6. What minimum difference in frequencies is needed so that either the sine or cosine term in Eq. 17.11 might represent a note that can be detected by the human ear?
7. Relate this minimum frequency difference to the minimum difference in the depths of liquid in the two bottles.

3 EXECUTE PLAN

4 EVALUATE RESULT

8. Is your result plausible? What are the two frequencies that can be heard if the average depth of liquid is 100 mm and the difference in the depths is your computed value?
9. You might try this experimentally, but realize that you may not have perfect hearing.

Worked Problem 17.5 Sharp cruising

Driving down a quiet street on a summer day with the car windows down, you see a convertible approaching from the opposite direction, with the driver playing her car stereo loudly. Having a well-trained musician's ear, you notice that the song you hear is in a key that is one semitone (the interval between adjacent notes on a piano) above the key in which the song is typically played. You also know that to shift any note by one semitone (from C to C-sharp, for instance, or from E-flat to E), the frequencies must be related by a factor of about 1.06. Assuming that both drivers are traveling at about the same speed, what is this speed?

1 GETTING STARTED You know that if you are moving toward a stationary sound source, the frequency you hear is higher than the frequency you would hear if you were standing still. The same is true if a moving source approaches you, so both motion effects should contribute to a higher frequency. Thus we need to determine the common speed that gives us $f_o/f_s = 1.06$. The use of the word *about* in the problem statement should cause us to reduce the number of significant digits in our answer from three to two.

2 DEVISE PLAN For a moving observer who is approaching a moving source, the change in frequency is given by Eq. 17.21:

$$\frac{f_o}{f_s} = \frac{c \pm v_o}{c \pm v_s}.$$

Under the assumption that the speeds of the two cars are equal, we can substitute $v = v_o = v_s$. We also must decide which signs to use, so we will pick the signs that produce a higher observed frequency due to motion of both the source and observer. Then, using the known speed of sound in air, we can solve for the single unknown v.

3 EXECUTE PLAN

$$\frac{f_o}{f_s} = 1.06 = \frac{c + v}{c - v}$$

$$1.06(c - v) = c + v$$

$$0.06c = 2.06v$$

$$v = \frac{0.06c}{2.06} = \frac{0.06(343\ \text{m/s})}{2.06} = 10\ \text{m/s}. ✔$$

4 EVALUATE RESULT The positive sign for v is consistent with our choices for signs in the numerator and denominator; a negative value for v would indicate some error in our thinking. This speed is reasonable for cars that are approaching each other on a quiet, therefore likely suburban, street ($10\ \text{m/s} = 22\ \text{mi/h}$).

Guided Problem 17.6 Cut to the chase

A motorist driving at 100 km/h is overtaken by a police car, siren blaring, chasing down a speeder (Figure WG17.2). The police car is moving at 136 km/h. What frequency does the motorist hear for the siren (*a*) before and (*b*) after he is passed if the frequency in the police car's reference frame is 1526 Hz?

Figure WG17.2

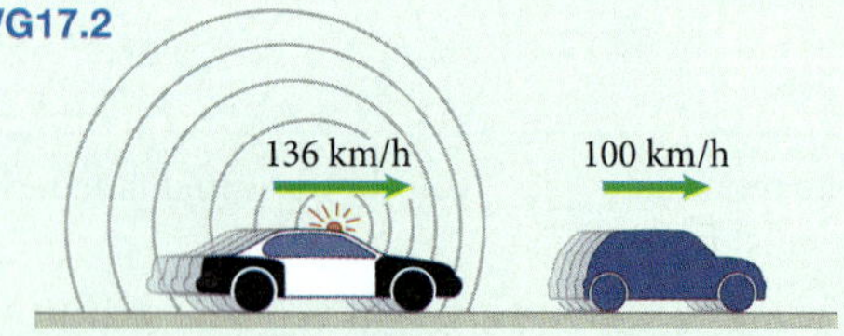

1 GETTING STARTED

1. You have a sketch of the situation before the police car overtakes the motorist, so draw a sketch showing the situation after the police car has passed the motorist.
2. Can part *a* and part *b* be solved separately?
3. Keep in mind that both cars are moving relative to the air.

2 DEVISE PLAN

4. What is the motional relationship between source and observer before the police car passes the motorist? After the police car passes?
5. Which Doppler equation is appropriate for each part of the motion?

3 EXECUTE PLAN

4 EVALUATE RESULT

6. Are your answers plausible? Does the frequency change the way you expect it to (that is, compare your answers with the general trend of frequency shifts when the source is approaching or receding)?

Worked Problem 17.7 Leaving a wake

A speedboat travels across the water of a shallow lake at 55 km/h, creating behind it a wake that spreads out from the line that bisects the boat along the boat's direction of travel. You estimate that the wake moves 1.0 m perpendicular to the bisector for every 3.0 m of forward motion of the boat. (*a*) How fast do the surface waves travel on the water? (*b*) At what water equivalent of a Mach number is the boat traveling?

❶ **GETTING STARTED** A wake is a shock wave that forms because the speed of the boat on the water surface is greater than the speed of the waves on the water surface. We're asked to determine (*a*) what this wave speed is and (*b*) how it compares with the speed of the boat.

❷ **DEVISE PLAN** Equation 17.22 relates the angle of a shock wave to the speed of the waves that create the shock wave and to the source speed:

$$\sin\theta = \frac{c}{v_s}.$$

We should be able to calculate the angle θ of the shock wave from the given distance information, and we know the boat speed v_s, so we can determine the wave speed c.

Mach numbers relate object speed to wave speed in a given medium. Once we have the wave speed, therefore, we can determine the "water Mach number" for the boat.

❸ **EXECUTE PLAN** (*a*) The wake moves 1 m sideways for each 3-m forward motion of the boat, so the angle of the wake to the bisector of the boat should be given by

$$\tan\theta = \frac{1.0\text{ m}}{3.0\text{ m}} = 0.33 \qquad \theta = 18.4^\circ.$$

Solving Eq. 17.22 for the wave speed gives

$$c = v_s \sin\theta = (55\text{ km/h})\sin 18.4^\circ = 17.4\text{ km/h} = 4.8\text{ m/s. ✔}$$

(*b*) Mach number is defined as the ratio of the speed of an object in a given medium to the speed of waves in that medium. The water Mach number is therefore

$$\frac{v_s}{c} = \frac{55\text{ km/h}}{17.4\text{ km/h}} = 3.2. ✔$$

❹ **EVALUATE RESULT** The answer to part *a* indicates that water waves spread across the surface at about 15 ft/s, a value that is not unreasonable. Part *b* shows that it is much easier to break the "water barrier" with a speedboat than to break the "sound barrier" with a jet airplane!

Guided Problem 17.8 Shocked, I say—shocked

A high-speed jet is flying across the Atlantic Ocean at an altitude of 15 km. It passes over a ship, and 34 s after it passes directly overhead, a sonic boom is heard by the ship's passengers. At what Mach number and speed is the jet flying?

❶ **GETTING STARTED**

1. Start with a diagram of the situation showing the relevant distances and the shock wave angle θ.
2. Do you need to make any assumptions?

❷ **DEVISE PLAN**

3. What information can help you determine the required unknowns?
4. How is the angle of the shock wave related to the speed of the jet?
5. Which equations allow you to express the unknown quantities in terms of known ones?

❸ **EXECUTE PLAN**

❹ **EVALUATE RESULT**

6. Can a jet travel this fast? If not, go back and check your work.

Questions and Problems

For instructor-assigned homework, go to MasteringPhysics® MP

Dots indicate difficulty level of problems: • = *easy*, •• = *intermediate*, ••• = *hard*; CR = *context-rich problem.*

17.1 Wavefronts

1. A neat trick for determining whether or not a train is coming is to press your ear to a railroad track. Why is this much more effective than listening for the train's sound carried by air? •
2. Suppose a material is stiffer in the x direction than in the y direction. Draw the wavefronts emanating from a point source embedded in this material and radiating in these two directions. ••
3. Your professor delivers a lecture. Does the amplitude of sound waves in the classroom decrease like $1/r$, where r is the distance from the professor to you? ••
4. A cannon is fired some distance away from you, and you wish to estimate that distance by determining how much sound energy enters your ear. (*a*) How does the sound energy depend on the distance between the cannon and your ear? (*b*) Now you use the dependence you described in part *a* to judge how far away the cannon is. First you estimate the distance assuming that none of the energy in the sound waves is dissipated (into, say, random motion of the molecules that make up the air), and then you repeat the estimate assuming that some of the sound energy is dissipated. Is your first estimate higher or lower than your second estimate? ••
5. One form of whispering gallery is an elliptical room where a person standing at one focus can hear quite clearly someone speaking very quietly at the other focus. Use your knowledge of ellipses to explain how this works. •••

17.2 Sound

6. How many octaves are there in the human audible-frequency range? •
7. Because the audible range in bats is about 10 kHz to more than 120 kHz, these animals are oblivious to normal human conversation, which is at frequencies of typically several hundred hertz. If you shout, though, you may in fact startle a bat. Why? ••
8. Standing waves (see Section 16.6) can form when the sound traveling in air inside a tube reflects from each end. Just as for waves on strings, the wavelength and tube length must satisfy some relationship in order for the standing wave to persist. Apply the arguments of Worked Problem 17.3 to determine the relationship between wavelength and tube length for the fundamental and the next two harmonics for standing waves in a tube that is open at both ends. ••
9. Sketch the three lowest-frequency harmonic wave function patterns for standing waves in the air in a tube that is open at both ends, (*a*) representing *displacement* nodes and antinodes and (*b*) representing *pressure* nodes and antinodes. Your sketches should be similar to *Principles* Figure 17.9*c*. ••

17.3 Interference

10. If the frequency of the sources in Figure P17.10 is increased, do the nodal lines get farther apart, get closer together, or remain unchanged? •

Figure P17.10

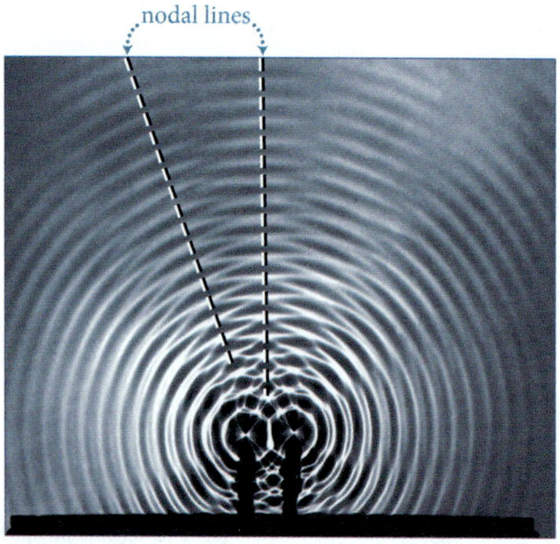

11. What happens to the nodal lines in Figure P17.10 if the phase of one of the sources is shifted by 180°? •
12. Are stable nodal lines formed by two sources that emit waves that have the same amplitude but different frequencies? ••
13. Speaker manufacturers often discourage placing speakers in front of curtains or drapes because having an uncovered wall behind the speakers often alleviates dead listening spots in the room. Explain why a wall helps. ••
14. How many nodal lines are created by two point sources that are separated by a distance equal to 2.5λ? ••
15. Vibration in a car can create concentric ripples on the surface of a cup of coffee sitting on the dashboard. What kind of waves are the ripples, and why are they circular? ••
16. Two sound sources emitting at the same wavelength λ are placed a distance d_s apart and a perpendicular distance d_m away from a row of microphones. Show that the distances Δx between those microphones that experience maximum variations in loudness are given by $\Delta x = d_m \lambda / d_s$ in the limit $d_m \gg d_s$. •••
17. Two coherent sources of water waves of frequency f are a distance d apart. (*a*) Far away from the sources, what are the angles between the nodal lines in the water and the perpendicular to the line joining the sources? (*b*) If you introduce a phase difference ϕ between the sources, how do the directions of the nodal lines shift? (Hint: For nodal destructive interference far from the sources, assume that the wavefronts from each source are parallel to one another and that their amplitudes are equal. Also see Worked Problem 17.1) •••
18. Three equally spaced, coherent sources of water waves of frequency f are in a line with a distance d separating each adjacent pair. Far away from the sources, what are the angles between the nodal lines in the water and the perpendicular to the line joining the sources? (Hint: For nodal destructive interference far from the sources, assume that the wavefronts from each source are parallel to one another and that their amplitudes are equal. Also see Worked Problem 17.1.) •••

17.4 Diffraction

19. When your mother shouted at you to come inside when you were a kid, how could you hear her when you were around a corner? •
20. The speaker in Figure P17.20 faces a narrow obstructing panel made of sound-absorbing material. A microphone is placed dead center behind the panel. Does the microphone pick up sound or not? ••

Figure P17.20

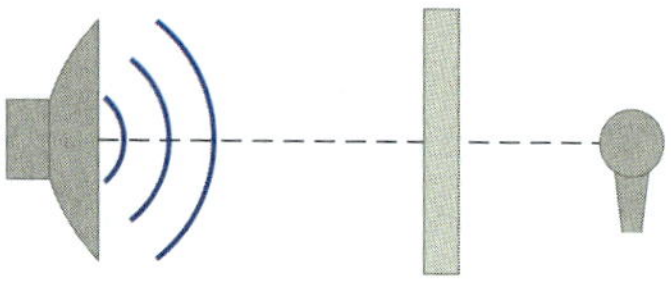

21. Two very small, coherent sources are separated by $d = 2\lambda$, where λ is the wavelength of the circular waves created by each source. (*a*) Use Huygens' principle to construct a dozen wavefronts from each source, six troughs and six crests. Mark antinodes with blue lines and mark nodes with red lines, starting each line at least two wavelengths from either source. (*b*) Repeat for the case when the two sources are not coherent, so that waves from one source are exactly one-half wavelength out of phase with waves from the other. (*c*) Compare your diagrams. Are the original antinodes still antinodes? Are the original nodes still nodes? ••
22. Phasors (see *Principles* Section 15.5) are useful for adding waves that are out of phase. For example, assume you have two sources, 1 and 2, that emit sound waves of the same frequency f. At your detector, the waves from source 1 have an amplitude of 1.00×10^{-8} m, and those from source 2 have an amplitude of 0.600×10^{-8} m and a phase of $+\pi/3$ relative to the phase of the source 1 waves. If the phase of the waves from source 1 is arbitrarily assigned to be $\phi_1 = 0$, what are the amplitude and phase of the combined waves? (Hint: It will help to draw the two waves as phasors.) •••

PRACTICE

17.5 Intensity

23. A radio station has a power output of 140 W and is located 1.5 km from your house. The radio signal is emitted uniformly in all directions. What is the intensity I of the signal at your house? •

24. You measure the intensity of a sound wave to be 5.70 W/m². If the power output of the signal is 90 W and the signal is emitted in all directions, how far away from the source are you? •

25. One mosquito positioned 0.50 m from a decibel meter emits a sound that has an intensity level of 15 dB. What is the intensity level of the sound emitted by 100 mosquitoes at the same distance? •

26. If ten screaming children on the playground produce a sound for which the intensity level is 80 dB, how many children do you need to produce an 82-dB sound? •

27. A sound source at the center of a cubical room radiates uniformly in all directions. What is the difference in decibels between the intensity level at a ceiling corner of the room and the intensity level at the center of one of the walls? Ignore reflections. ••

28. At a distance of 3.0 m from your stereo system with two speakers, what power output must your stereo amplifier have in order for the intensity level to be 80 dB? Assume that all the energy from the amplifier goes into producing sound. ••

29. A satellite orbiting Earth at an altitude of 450 km emits a radio signal that has a power level of 12 W when it reaches Earth. The signal is beamed in such a way that it covers an area of 8.0 m² on Earth's surface. What power is received by a ground-based antenna if the surface area of the antenna is 400 mm²? ••

30. At a basketball game in an enclosed arena, you happen to sit next to a screaming baby. If the baby's yell arrives at your ear with an intensity level of 75 dB, and the music that reaches your ear from the loudspeakers during the teams' warm-up is at 80 dB, (*a*) what is the intensity I of the overall sound you hear and (*b*) what is the intensity level of the sound you hear? ••

31. The intensity level from a directional loudspeaker at your position at a political rally is 95 dB. (*a*) What is the intensity I of the sound in watts per square meter? (*b*) What is the power output of the loudspeaker if you are 20 m from the speaker and it emits sound into one hemisphere only? ••

32. You are on the design team for a new airport. The developer wants to build a hotel as close to the airport as possible. The intensity level of a large jet during takeoff is 140 dB at 50 m from the jet. The developer wants to build the hotel such that the intensity level heard by guests is not higher than 50 dB inside the hotel rooms and not higher than 125 dB in the parking lot of the hotel. (*a*) How far from the airport would you suggest the developer build the hotel? (*b*) What is the maximum allowable intensity I of the sound in the hotel rooms? ••

33. The intensity level at the front of a library reading room is 70 dB when 120 students are in the room and 20 dB when the room is empty. What do you expect the intensity level to be when 60 students are in the room? ••

34. A typical car horn has an intensity level of 90 dB at a distance of 1.0 m. (*a*) What is the intensity level of 16 cars all honking their horns at an intersection on a city street? (*b*) What is the power output of the combined horns at a distance of 5.0 m? (*c*) What is the intensity level three city blocks away? Assume 100 m for the length of each block. ••

35. On a whale-watching expedition, your underwater sound detector picks up a whale sound that has an intensity of 9.0 μW/m². (*a*) What is the intensity level β of this sound? (*b*) If your detector tells you that you are 2.3 km from the whale, what is the power of the emitted signal? (*c*) How many whales, emitting sound at the same intensity $I = 9.0\ \mu\text{W/m}^2$, are needed to produce an intensity level of 100 dB at your location? ••

36. A frequency generator (a device that produces sinusoidal signals whose frequency and amplitude can be independently set) is used to power a horn. The frequency is set to 2000 Hz, and for a particular amplitude the sound intensity is measured to be 0.050 W/m² at a distance of 12 m. (*a*) What is the power output of the horn in this case? (*b*) If the power output is increased to 92 W, what is the new intensity reading? ••

37. Suppose that two coherent, spherical sound sources, 1 and 2, each generate the same amount of power P. The distance between the sources is 2λ. Point R is on a line of maximum destructive interference, and the distance between R and source 1 is equal to 9λ. Point Q is on a line of maximum constructive interference, and the distance between Q and source 1 is 6λ. Obtain expressions for the intensity at points R and Q. •••

38. Your bedroom is 8.0 m away from the living room. When requested by your parents to turn down your stereo, you do, and the intensity level where they are sitting in the living room drops from 50 dB to 45 dB. What is the change in the power of the sound emitted by your stereo? •••

17.6 Beats

39. If two superimposed frequencies differ by more than about 20 Hz, what do you hear? •

40. Two oboe players are next to each other on the stage. One is playing a 350-Hz note, and the other is playing a 355-Hz note. What is the beat frequency heard by the audience? •

41. Two tuba players in a marching band appear to your trained ear to be playing the correct note, 196 Hz, but there is an annoying warble that you interpret as being four beats per second. What are the frequencies of the notes played by the two tubas? •

42. The lowest frequency a certain sound receiver can detect is 760 Hz. If the receiver detects a frequency of 762 Hz that is then mixed with an unknown frequency, also detectable by the receiver, and you hear four beats per second, what is the unknown frequency? ••

43. You have four electronic audio generators, A, B, C, and D, all producing tones near 1200 Hz that are easily audible but not distinguishable by ear. When you increase the frequency of generator A a little, the beat frequencies between A and B, A and C, and A and D all increase. When you increase the frequency of generator B a little, the B-C beat frequency increases and the B-A and B-D beat frequencies decrease. Rank the generators by frequency, from lowest to highest. ••

44. One tuning fork vibrates at a frequency of 528 Hz, and a second one vibrates at 524 Hz, but you don't know which is which. After applying a small piece of modeling clay to the end of one fork, you notice that the beat frequency has increased. On which fork did you put the clay? ••

45. Three tenors are giving a concert at an outdoor amphitheater. What are the possible beat frequencies if tenor 1 holds a 262-Hz note while tenor 2 holds a 264.3-Hz note and tenor 3 holds a 258-Hz note? ••

46. When two frequencies are added together, the beat frequency and the average frequency are an octave apart. What is the ratio of the original frequencies? ••

47. Two violin strings, each having a linear mass density of 0.0014 kg/m and under the same 100-N tension, have the same fundamental frequency of 660 Hz. If the tension in one of the strings is changed to 102 N, what is the beat frequency? ••

48. During a fire drill in your dormitory, you notice that the sound waves from the two alarms on your floor interfere with each other, and you hear five beats every two seconds. (*a*) If the average of the two frequencies is 3500 Hz, what are the frequencies of the two alarms? (*b*) If your room is 15 m from each alarm, what is the intensity I of the sound if the power output is 60 W for each alarm? ••

17.7 Doppler effect

49. What happens to the magnitude of the Doppler shift you hear in the whistle of a passing train if you increase the distance between you and the tracks? •

50. While driving down the road, you spot a friend standing on the sidewalk. You honk your horn at him while driving 70 km/h. Your horn emits a frequency of 360 Hz. What frequency does your friend hear (*a*) as you approach and (*b*) after you pass by? •

51. The electric bells at your school buzz with a frequency of 400 Hz. If you are late for class and riding your bike down a hill toward the school at a constant speed of 4.47 m/s, what is the frequency of the sound you hear? •

52. At the racetrack, you estimate that the whine of the cars changes by one octave as the cars pass. About how fast are the cars going? ••

53. How fast do you have to travel away from a stationary sound source in order for the frequency to be shifted by (*a*) 1%, (*b*) 10%, and (*c*) a factor of 2? ••

54. While you watch a parade, a band on a float passes you. You detect the frequency of a note played on a flute to be 352 Hz when the float is coming toward you and 347 Hz after the float passes you. At what speed is the float traveling? ••

55. You and a friend are riding bikes, you moving at 9.72 km/h and she moving at 7.20 km/h. She is behind you and turns on her electric horn, which has a frequency of 300 Hz. (*a*) What frequency do you hear? (*b*) What frequency is heard by a person who is standing alongside your route after you both have passed him? ••

56. While you are driving on a straight road at 97 km/h, a police car traveling in the opposite direction comes toward you with the siren blaring, and the frequency you hear is 310 Hz. Starting when the two of you are 200 m apart, it takes you 3.00 s to pass the police car. What is the frequency of the siren? ••

57. A car traveling west at 90 km/h along a road running parallel to a railroad track approaches a train traveling east at 65 km/h. If the train's whistle emits a frequency of 400 Hz, what is the frequency heard by the driver of the car (*a*) as the car approaches the train and (*b*) after the two vehicles have passed each other? ••

58. A foghorn that emits a frequency of 150 Hz is mounted on a buoy in the bay. If a ship approaches the buoy at 21.2 km/h, (*a*) what frequency does the captain of the ship hear? (*b*) Hearing the foghorn is a signal for the captain to slow his ship. After passing the buoy, the captain hears the horn again, but the frequency he detects is now 149 Hz. What is the new speed of the ship? ••

59. Two airplanes simulating a dogfight are headed right for each other, plane A moving at 285 km/h and plane B moving at 295 km/h. The electronic machine gun on A can emit 300 rounds per minute, with each round accompanied by a sound pulse. (*a*) How many pulses does the pilot in B hear during a burst that lasts 10 s according to observer A? (*b*) How long does the burst last for the pilot in B? ••

60. You stand in your yard and hold a battery-powered buzzer that is emitting a frequency of 560 Hz as a friend stands next to you. (*a*) What frequency does your friend hear if you throw the buzzer away from you with a speed of 18.0 m/s? (*b*) You and your friend now get on a flat railroad car that begins to travel at 12.0 m/s, and you throw the buzzer in the direction opposite the direction of the car's velocity. What frequency does your friend hear? (*c*) What frequency would a person standing alongside the tracks hear? ••

61. A dog whistle has a frequency of 21 kHz, which is above the high end of the audible range for humans. At what minimum speed and in what direction must you travel in order to just hear the whistle? ••

62. During trials of a new submarine, its speed is measured with an underwater sonar gun anchored to the ocean floor. The gun emits sound waves at a frequency f, and these waves reflect off the surface of the submarine and return to the source at a frequency $f' \neq f$. If the submarine is receding from the sonar gun at speed v, derive an expression for f' in terms of f, v, and c (the speed of the waves through water). •••

63. A device that both emits and receives sound waves is traveling at 80 km/h. The emitted waves have a frequency of 700 Hz. If the waves are reflected off a stationary flat surface in front of the device, what frequency is detected by the device? •••

64. Two students standing 54.9 m apart are tossing around footballs designed to whistle while they are airborne. (*a*) When student A throws her football toward student B at 16.0 m/s, it emits a frequency of 680 Hz. What frequency is heard by student B? (*b*) When student B throws his football toward student A at 15.0 m/s, it emits a frequency of 670 Hz. What frequency is heard by student A? (*c*) If the two footballs are thrown simultaneously, what is the beat frequency? •••

17.8 Shock waves

65. A supersonic jet airplane passing directly overhead creates a shock wave that makes an angle of 47° with the horizontal. What is the speed of the airplane? •

66. As a boat travels at 48.0 km/h across the surface of a still lake, the waves it creates in the water have a speed of 20.1 km/h. What is the angle of the shock wave created by the waves? •

67. A speedboat traveling at 73.0 km/h causes a shock wave that makes an angle of 14.3° with the path of the boat. At what speed are the waves moving through the water? •

68. Two jets flying at the same altitude pass over your head simultaneously, one traveling at Mach 1.5 and the other at Mach 2.5. Which plane's sonic boom do you hear first? ••

69. While attending an air show, you observe a fighter jet traveling horizontally at a speed of Mach 1.30. At the instant you hear the sonic boom, what is the angle between your line of sight to the jet and the horizontal? ••

70. Many years ago, test pilots accelerating through Mach 1 reported that the ride was pretty rough just before Mach 1 but smoothed out suddenly as Mach 1 was breached. How can you account for this? ••

71. Concerned about being disturbed by sonic booms, residents near an Air Force base located along a seacoast submit a petition asking that all jet aircraft from the base head out to sea before attaining Mach 1 and proceed inland only after they have reached supersonic speed. What do you think of the physics reasoning behind this idea? ••

72. A woman standing on the ground observes a jet directly overhead flying at an altitude of 20,000 m. If the jet has a speed of Mach 2 and its shock wave makes an angle of 30° with the horizontal, how long will it be until she hears the sonic boom? ••

73. At a pistol range, a microphone is placed between a shooter and the target so that when a bullet is fired we can hear its sonic boom. A bullet passes by the microphone at a speed of Mach 2.1. The microphone picks up the sonic boom 0.0021 s after the bullet passes above the microphone. (*a*) What is the angle of the shock wave? (*b*) What is the vertical distance between bullet and microphone? ••

74. A jet flying directly over you at an altitude of 3000 m produces a shock wave. If the angle of the shock wave is 42°, (*a*) how long will it be until the sonic boom reaches you, and (*b*) how far does the jet travel during this time interval? ••

75. At White Sands, New Mexico, a car powered by a rocket engine passes you while you are standing still. If you hear the sonic boom 0.045 s after the car passes and the angle of the shock wave is 37.0°, what is your perpendicular distance from the path of the car? •••

Additional Problems

76. What does an observer hear on the ground before and after a sonic boom caused by a jet passing overhead? •

77. Is a second sonic boom generated when a plane reaches a speed of Mach 2? •

78. Two test pilots are flying in a jet trainer going faster than Mach 1. Can the pilot in the front of the cockpit hear the pilot in back? ••

79. Two guitar strings, 1 and 2, plucked simultaneously produce standing waves described by ••

$$D_1 = A\sin(ax)\cos(bt)$$

$$D_2 = A\sin(qx)\cos(dt),$$

with $a = 14.5\ \text{m}^{-1}$, $b = 2512\ \text{s}^{-1}$, $q = 19.3\ \text{m}^{-1}$, and $d = 2575\ \text{s}^{-1}$. (*a*) What is the frequency of each wave? (*b*) What is the beat frequency of the combined wave?

80. A race car traveling at 350 km/h passes a spectator in the stands. If the spectator has an air horn that emits a sound of frequency 400 Hz, what is the range of frequencies of the sound heard by the driver of the car? ••

81. Which type of conic section (circle, ellipse, parabola, or hyperbola) is formed by the nodal-line pattern produced by two coherent wave sources? (Hint: For a given nodal line, the difference in distance between any point on it and the two sources is the same for all points.) ••

82. Why is the high-frequency "tweeter" on a stereo speaker usually much smaller than the low-frequency "woofer"? ••

83. You are standing beneath a Ferris wheel when two children riding in cars on opposite sides of the wheel both scream at 600 Hz. Your well-trained ears notice a beat frequency that is maximum when one child is moving directly toward you and the other is moving directly away from you. The Ferris wheel takes 24.0 s to complete one rotation, and its diameter is 27.0 m. You begin to wonder whether a Doppler shift could produce observable beats under these circumstances. ••• CR

84. You have tickets for an outdoor rock concert, fourth row from the stage. However, at that distance the intensity level is 100 dB, too loud to be enjoyable. You decide to move to a row where the intensity level is a more moderate 80 dB. Fortunately, turning around and counting the right number of rows back (assuming that the distance between rows is uniform), you see that the seats you want are available. ••• CR

85. You want to build a portable device that can detect pirate radio stations broadcasting at about 50 W of power a few miles from your beachfront home. You have a 0.60-m diameter bowl you might use as an antenna dish, but you are worried that your amplifier input will require a signal of at least 0.10 μW. ••• CR

86. Your car is third in line at a railroad crossing as a train moving at a constant speed approaches, with its whistle blowing constantly. To keep yourself from going crazy with the noise, you begin thinking about the relative difference between the frequency you hear and the frequency the engineer hears. Surely this must depend on the angle that your line of sight to the engine of the train makes with the perpendicular to the track. ••• CR

Answers to Review Questions

1. (1) The amplitude of two- and three-dimensional waves decreases as they propagate, even in the absence of energy dissipation. (2) Some interference effects that are not observed in one-dimensional waves occur in two- and three-dimensional waves.
2. Dissipation of the wave's energy leads to a decrease in amplitude as the wave travels, but even without dissipation, the dimensionality of the wave is important. Amplitude decreases as $1/\sqrt{r}$ in a two-dimensional wave and as $1/r$ in a three-dimensional wave.
3. The pipe circumference and thus its cross-sectional area are unchanged all along the pipe. Therefore the wave's amplitude remains constant because there is no change in the area over which the wave's energy is spread as the wave propagates from one end of the pipe to the other.
4. Sound waves in air are longitudinal.
5. The range is 20 Hz to 20 kHz.
6. Squeeze a plastic soda bottle that contains only air and has its cap screwed on tightly. You can decrease the volume only slightly because the compressional force you exert on the walls is transmitted to the air molecules inside. The air compresses elastically, exerting a force on the walls in the opposite direction.
7. Maximum and minimum medium densities occur at locations where the medium displacement is zero. Therefore the locations of maximum and minimum medium density are one-quarter wavelength away from (90° out of phase with) the locations of maximum and minimum displacement.
8. No. The sound is louder only if at P the interference between the two waves is constructive. If it is destructive, the sound when the two waves pass P is softer than the sound of either wave passing P alone.
9. No. A given position in the hall is dead for only certain frequencies because the relative phase of two waves coming to that position is determined by the ratio $\Delta r/\lambda$. Thus destructive interference occurs for only certain frequencies.
10. The number of nodal lines increases.
11. Yes. Any number of sources can be arranged such that wave maxima and minima overlap at certain locations. For example, a set of closely spaced collinear point sources creates constructive interference along a line perpendicular to the sources and destructive interference in other directions.
12. Huygens' principle is the model that considers wavefronts as a collection of closely spaced, coherent point sources, each of which creates new coherent waves that travel in all directions but, when superposed, cancel in all directions other than forward. The result can be used to sketch the shapes of additional forward-propagating wavefronts.
13. High frequencies correspond to short wavelengths, and wavelengths comparable to the size of the insect are needed for reliable location by reflected waves.
14. The amount of spreading depends on the size of the wavelength relative to the gap width: The longer the wavelength, the greater the extent to which the waves spread out. Thus in (*a*) very little spreading occurs, in (*b*) the spreading is quite noticeable, and in (*c*) the waves spread out in all directions, producing a pattern similar to that of a point source.
15. If we ignore dissipation, the intensity varies inversely with the square of distance from the source: $I \propto 1/r^2$ (Eq. 17.2). This is because the energy of the waves is constant regardless of the distance from the source, but the area over which this energy is distributed increases as the distance from the source increases.
16. The intensity I decreases by a factor of $(10)^2 = 100$ because of its $1/r^2$ dependence: $I = P/4\pi r^2$ (Eq. 17.2). Equation 17.5 for intensity level, $\beta = (10\text{ dB})\log(I/I_{\text{th}})$, tells you that there is a 10-dB drop in intensity level β for each power-of-ten reduction in intensity I, and so the drop in intensity level is 20 dB.
17. In the case of ripples on a pond, as each ripple expands, the energy is spread over the circumference of a circle (formula $2\pi r$). This gives intensity units of W/m. An emergency warning siren is typically mounted on a tall pole, which allows the sound energy to spread out in all directions. In this case the energy carried by each wavefront is spread across the surface of a sphere (formula $4\pi r^2$). The intensity units are therefore W/m^2.
18. The beat frequency is the difference between the two wave frequencies.
19. No. As the tuning fork frequency and the piano key frequency approach equality, which is the tuner's aim, the beat frequency decreases.
20. The frequency is higher because of the Doppler effect for a moving source.
21. The ratio is greater for source approaching observer. Here's why. The source moving toward the stationary observer means that the observed frequency is higher than the emitted frequency and thus $f_o/f_s > 1$. Because $v_o = 0$, Eq. 17.21 becomes $f_o/f_s = c/(c \pm v_s)$. In order to have the fraction be greater than 1, you use a minus sign in the denominator: $f_o/f_s = c/(c - 0.250c) = 1.33$.
   The observer moving toward the stationary source means again $f_o > f_s$ and thus again $f_o/f_s > 1$. Because in this case $v_s = 0$, Eq. 17.21 becomes $f_o/f_s = (c \pm v_o)/c$. In order to have the fraction be greater than 1, you use a plus sign in the numerator: $f_o/f_s = (c + 0.250c)/c = 1.25$.
22. No. Equation 17.22, $\sin\theta = c/v_s$, contains no information about frequency.
23. As v_s in Eq. 17.22, $\sin\theta = c/v_s$, increases, $\sin\theta$ decreases, which means that θ decreases and the bow wave narrows.

Answers to Guided Problems

Guided Problem 17.2 (*a*) 0.90 mm; (*b*) $\frac{1}{15}$
Guided Problem 17.4 about 4 mm
Guided Problem 17.6 (*a*) 1.58×10^3 Hz; (*b*) 1.49×10^3 Hz
Guided Problem 17.8 Mach number 1.6 or 5.5×10^2 m/s

PRACTICE

18 PRACTICE Fluids

Chapter Summary

Pressure due to a fluid (Sections 18.1, 18.5, 18.6)

Concepts A **fluid** is a substance that has no fixed shape and the ability to flow. A *nonviscous* fluid is one that has no resistance to deformation by shear stress.

Pascal's principle states that a pressure change applied to an enclosed liquid is transmitted undiminished to every part of the liquid and to the walls of the container.

Quantitative Tools If a fluid exerts a force $\vec{F}^c_{fs}$ perpendicular to a surface of area A, the **pressure** P on this area is a scalar defined by

$$P \equiv \frac{F^c_{fs}}{A}. \tag{18.1}$$

The SI unit of pressure is the **pascal** (Pa):

$$1 \text{ Pa} \equiv 1 \text{ N/m}^2. \tag{18.2}$$

The atmospheric pressure at sea level is 1.01325×10^5 Pa.

The pressure P at a depth d below the surface of a liquid at rest is independent of the shape of the container and is

$$P = P_{surface} + \rho g d, \tag{18.8}$$

where $P_{surface}$ is the pressure at the surface of the liquid, g is the acceleration due to gravity, and ρ is the mass density of the liquid.

When pressure is measured, the actual pressure P is the sum of *gauge pressure* (pressure in excess of atmospheric pressure) and atmospheric pressure:

$$P = P_{gauge} + P_{atm}. \tag{18.16}$$

Buoyancy (Sections 18.2, 18.5)

Concepts If an object is fully or partially submerged in a fluid, the fluid exerts an upward **buoyant force** on the object. **Archimedes' principle** states that the buoyant force is equal in magnitude to the force of gravity exerted on the fluid displaced by the object. The volume of the displaced fluid is equal to the volume of the submerged part of the object.

Quantitative Tools The **buoyant force** $\vec{F}^b_{fo}$ that a fluid of mass density ρ_f exerts on an object that displaces a volume V_{disp} of fluid has magnitude

$$F^b_{fo} = \rho_f V_{disp} g. \tag{18.12}$$

Laminar flow of nonviscous fluids (Sections 18.3, 18.7)

Concepts In **laminar flow,** the velocity of the fluid at any given location is constant. Chaotically changing flow is called **turbulent flow.**

The mass density of an incompressible fluid is the same at all locations in the fluid.

Quantitative Tools The **continuity equation** for laminar flow of a nonviscous fluid through a tube is

$$\rho_1 A_1 v_1 = \rho_2 A_2 v_2, \tag{18.23}$$

where ρ, A, and v are the fluid mass density, tube cross-sectional area, and fluid speed, respectively, at any given location.

The **volume flow rate** Q (m^3/s) of a volume V of the fluid flowing past a given location in the tube in a time interval Δt is

$$Q \equiv \frac{V}{\Delta t}. \tag{18.25}$$

The volume flow rate can also be expressed as

$$Q = Av, \tag{18.26}$$

where A is the cross-sectional area of the tube and v is the fluid speed.

Bernoulli's equation describing laminar flow in an incompressible, nonviscous fluid is

$$P_1 + \rho g y_1 + \tfrac{1}{2}\rho v_1^2 = P_2 + \rho g y_2 + \tfrac{1}{2}\rho v_2^2, \quad (18.36)$$

where y is the vertical distance above an arbitrarily chosen reference location.

Viscosity and surface tension (Sections 18.4, 18.8)

Concepts **Viscosity** is a scalar measure of a fluid's resistance to shear deformation.

Surface tension is a scalar that gives the magnitude of the force per unit length exerted by a liquid surface on the perimeter of the surface.

Quantitative Tools The **viscosity** η (Pa · s) of a fluid confined between a lower fixed plate and an upper plate that is free to move is defined by

$$F^c_{\text{fp}\,x} \equiv -\eta A \frac{v_x}{d}, \quad (18.38)$$

where $F^c_{\text{fp}\,x}$ is the x component of the force $\vec{F}^c_{\text{fp}}$ exerted by the fluid on the upper plate when it moves in the plane of the plate with speed v_x, A is the plate surface area, and d is the vertical distance between the plates. More generally, we can write

$$F_{\text{fp}\,x} = -\eta A \frac{dv_x}{dy}, \quad (18.39)$$

where dv_x/dy is the rate at which one infinitesimally thin fluid layer moves past an adjacent layer.

Poiseuille's law: If P_1 and P_2 are the pressures at opposite faces of a cylindrical tube of radius R and length ℓ, the flow rate through the tube is

$$Q = \frac{\pi R^4}{8\eta\ell}(P_1 - P_2). \quad (18.47)$$

If a liquid exerts a force $\vec{F}_{\text{fw}}$ on a length ℓ of wire, the **surface tension** γ (N/m) of the liquid is

$$\gamma \equiv \frac{F_{\text{fw}}}{2\ell}. \quad (18.48)$$

Laplace's law states that the pressure difference $P_{\text{in}} - P_{\text{out}}$ across a curved liquid surface of radius of curvature R is

$$P_{\text{in}} - P_{\text{out}} = \begin{cases} \dfrac{2\gamma}{R} \text{ (spherical surface)} & (18.51) \\[2ex] \dfrac{\gamma}{R} \text{ (cylindrical surface).} & (18.52) \end{cases}$$

Review Questions

Answers to these questions can be found at the end of this chapter.

18.1 Forces in a fluid

1. What are the three basic types of stress? Describe the forces involved in each type.
2. What is the difference in how nonviscous liquids and viscous liquids react to shear stress? Give an example of each type of liquid.
3. Describe the difference in how gases and liquids respond to bulk stress.
4. What is the relationship between force and pressure? How are the two different from each other?
5. What effect does Earth's gravitational force have on the pressure in a fluid at rest in a container?
6. How does a pressure change applied to the top of a column of liquid held in a closed container affect the pressure throughout the liquid?

18.2 Buoyancy

7. What is the relationship between Earth's gravitational force and the buoyant force exerted by a fluid on a fully or partially submerged object?
8. What determines whether an object sinks or floats in a liquid?
9. How can an object composed of a material that typically sinks in water be made to float on water?

18.3 Fluid flow

10. How do the properties of streamlines differ for laminar and turbulent flow?
11. What is *viscosity*?
12. What factors determine whether the flow of fluid past an object is laminar or turbulent?
13. What does it mean to streamline an object, and what benefit is there to doing so?
14. What does it tell you if the streamlines for a fluid in laminar flow are closer together in one part of the flow and farther apart in another part of the flow?
15. What is the connection between flow speed and pressure in a moving fluid when the flow is laminar?

18.4 Surface effects

16. Describe the interaction between two particles of fluid as a function of their separation distance.
17. Describe the difference between the forces experienced by particles in the interior of a liquid and the forces experienced by particles at the liquid surface that creates the effect called surface tension.
18. How does the relationship between surface tension in a liquid surface and surface shape differ from the relationship between tension in an elastic membrane enclosing a fluid and membrane shape?
19. What factor determines whether or not a liquid wets a solid surface with which it is in contact? (Ignore the presence of any surrounding gas.)
20. What determines whether the meniscus formed by a liquid in a capillary tube is concave or convex?

18.5 Pressure and gravity

21. What are three effects that contribute to the pressure in all fluids? What is a fourth effect that contributes to the pressure only in liquids?
22. Approximately what is the difference in air pressure between your feet and your head when you're standing at sea level?
23. What is hydrostatic pressure, and how does it vary in a liquid at rest?
24. How does an object's average mass density determine whether the object floats, sinks, or hangs motionless when placed in a fluid?

18.6 Working with pressure

25. What is *gauge pressure*, and what is its relationship to atmospheric pressure?
26. Describe the main components of a hydraulic system and how the system can multiply a force magnitude.

18.7 Bernoulli's equation

27. For laminar flow of a nonviscous liquid through a tube in which the cross-sectional area at point 1 is different from the cross-sectional area at point 2, how does the mass of liquid flowing past point 1 at a given instant differ from the mass of liquid flowing past point 2 at that instant?
28. An aqueduct of constant diameter is at some points along its length very close to the ground and at other points far above the ground. If the flow of water in the duct is laminar, how does the water pressure at some location 1 along the duct length compare with the water pressure at some other location 2 along the length?
29. A horizontal aqueduct is constructed of pipes that have different diameters. If the water flow in the duct is laminar, how does the water pressure in a small-diameter portion compare with the water pressure in a large-diameter portion?

18.8 Viscosity and surface tension

30. What is a velocity gradient in a fluid?
31. How does the temperature dependence of viscosity in liquids compare with the temperature dependence of viscosity in gases?
32. For any fluid moving through a tube, what does Poiseuille's law tell us about the relationship among viscosity, tube size, and volume flow rate?
33. How is surface tension related to the energy associated with the surface of a liquid?
34. How does pressure differ across a curved fluid surface that is under surface tension?

Developing a Feel

Make an order-of-magnitude estimate of each of the following quantities. Letters in parentheses refer to hints below. Use them as needed to guide your thinking.

1. The mass of the atmosphere [C, N, X]
2. The difference between your mass density and the mass density of water [A, G, Y]
3. The pressure at the lowest point in the ocean [U, F, Y]
4. The decrease in air pressure as you move from ground level to the top of a skyscraper [J, V]
5. The magnitude of the force required to separate two 0.50-m-diameter rigid hemispheres when the air between them has been pumped out [T, I, O]
6. The magnitude of the force required to open a passenger airplane emergency door at cruising altitude [D, Q]
7. The upward force exerted on the roof of a single-family house by a hurricane-force wind blowing over it [S, E, L]
8. The magnitude of the horizontal force exerted on a passenger car traveling at highway speed when a truck traveling in the opposite direction passes close by [P, B]
9. The volume flow rate of water moving through a garden hose 30 m long [W, Z, K, H]
10. The maximum mass of a 70-mm wire that can be supported by a soap film [R, M]

Hints

A. When you float vertically in a pool with only your head above water, what fraction of your body volume remains unsubmerged?
B. What is the area of the side of the car?
C. What is the surface area of Earth?
D. What is the pressure difference between the air inside and outside the airplane?
E. What is the difference between the air pressure just inside and just outside the roof?
F. How does pressure vary with depth?
G. What is the relationship between the mass of your whole body (submerged portion plus above-water portion) and the mass of the water displaced by the submerged portion?
H. What is the hose radius?
I. What is the relationship between the magnitude of the force exerted on the sphere surface and the pressure difference from Hint T?
J. What is the height of a skyscraper?
K. What pressure difference (inside versus outside the hose) is needed to squirt the water to the appropriate height?
L. What is the area of the roof?
M. What fraction of the surface tension of water is appropriate for soap film?
N. What is atmospheric pressure at sea level?
O. What is the equatorial cross-sectional area of the sphere?
P. What is the difference between the speed of the air passing the driver's side and the speed of the air passing the passenger side?
Q. What is the area of the door?
R. What forces must cancel?
S. What is the wind speed?
T. What is the pressure difference between the inside and outside of the sphere?
U. How deep below sea level is the bottom of the Mariana Trench, which is the deepest recorded part of the ocean?
V. What is the mass density of air?
W. What water viscosity value is appropriate in this situation?
X. How is the force exerted by the atmosphere on all of Earth's surface related to the atmosphere's mass?
Y. What is the mass density of water?
Z. To what height will the water rise if the hose end is held vertically?

Key (all values approximate)

A. 8×10^{-2}; **B.** 3 m^2; **C.** 5×10^{14} m^2; **D.** 5×10^4 Pa; **E.** 8×10^2 Pa; **F.** Eq. 18.17: $P = P_{atm} + \rho gh$; **G.** these two masses are equal; **H.** 1×10^1 mm; **I.** $F = (P_{in} - P_{out})\pi R^2$, where R is the sphere radius; **J.** 3×10^2 m; **K.** 0.1 atm or 1×10^4 Pa; **L.** 2×10^2 m^2; **M.** $\frac{1}{3}$ of 7×10^{-2} N/m; **N.** 1×10^5 Pa; **O.** 2×10^{-1} m^2; **P.** 3×10^1 m/s; **Q.** 1 m^2; **R.** gravitational and surface tension forces; **S.** 4×10^1 m/s; **T.** 1×10^5 Pa; **U.** 1×10^1 km; **V.** 1 kg/m^3; **W.** 1×10^{-3} Pa·s, the value at 20°C; **X.** that force is the atmosphere's mass times the acceleration due to gravity; **Y.** 1×10^3 kg/m^3; **Z.** 1 m or less without a nozzle

Worked and Guided Problems

Procedure: Working with pressure in liquids at rest

The branch of physics that deals with pressure in a liquid at rest is called *hydrostatics*. The pressure in a liquid at rest is determined by gravity and by what happens at the boundary of the liquid. To determine the pressure in such liquids:

1. Begin by making a sketch showing all the **boundaries** and identifying all the factors that affect pressure: pistons, gases at surfaces open to the atmosphere, and so on. Note the known vertical heights of liquid surfaces, the areas of these surfaces, the surface areas of pistons, and the liquid mass densities.
2. Determine the **pressure at each surface.** The pressure at a liquid surface open to the air is equal to atmospheric pressure P_{atm}. The pressure at a liquid surface bordering a vacuum is zero: $P = 0$. The pressure at a liquid surface open to a gas other than the atmosphere is equal to the pressure in the gas: $P = P_{gas}$. The pressure at a liquid surface that is in contact with a solid, such as a piston, is $P = F^c_{sl}/A$, where F^c_{sl} is the magnitude of the force exerted by the solid on the liquid and A is the area over which that force is exerted.
3. Use **horizontal planes.** The pressure is the same at all points on a horizontal plane in a connected liquid. The pressure difference between two horizontal planes 1 and 2 is given by $P_1 = P_2 + \rho g d$ (Eq. 18.7), where d is the vertical distance between the horizontal planes and 1 is below 2.

These examples involve material from this chapter but are not associated with any particular section. Some examples are worked out in detail; others you should work out by following the guidelines provided.

Worked Problem 18.1 Mars balloon

It has been suggested that we could explore the surface of Mars by sending an inflated balloon fitted with an instrument package to hover above the surface. To see if this suggestion is feasible, calculate the radius needed in order for such a balloon (supporting only itself and the gas filling it—no instruments) to hover just above the Martian surface, where the mass density of the atmosphere is 0.020 kg/m³. Assume the balloon is filled with hydrogen gas (at Martian atmospheric pressure, $\rho_{hy} = 9.0 \times 10^{-4}\ \text{kg/m}^3$) and is made of plastic film that has a mass density of $\rho_{film} = 1.2 \times 10^3\ \text{kg/m}^3$ and is 0.30 mm thick.

❶ **GETTING STARTED** We can think of the Martian atmosphere as a fluid that supports the gas-filled balloon by exerting a buoyant force on it. For the balloon to hover, the forces exerted on it must balance, which means that the magnitude of the buoyant force must be equal to the magnitude of the gravitational force exerted by Mars on the balloon and on the hydrogen gas.

❷ **DEVISE PLAN** The magnitude of the buoyant force exerted by the atmosphere on the balloon is equal to the magnitude of the gravitational force exerted by Mars on a volume of its atmosphere that is equal to the volume of the balloon. This buoyant force magnitude is given by Eq. 18.12: $F^b_{atm,bal} = \rho_{atm} V_{disp} g = \rho_{atm} V_{bal} g$, where g is the acceleration due to gravity on Mars. This force magnitude must be equal to the magnitude of the gravitational force exerted on the hydrogen-filled balloon, which is

$$F^G_{planet,bal} = m_{bal} g + \rho_{hy} V_{bal} g = (\rho_{film} V_{film} + \rho_{hy} V_{bal}) g.$$

Note the different subscripts on V: V_{film} is the volume not of the inflated balloon but rather of the plastic film of which the balloon is made. We assume that the balloon is a sphere of radius R that has walls of thickness $t \ll R$. The volume of the film is therefore the surface area of the sphere times the film thickness: $V_{film} = 4\pi R^2 t$. The volume of the atmosphere displaced by the balloon is equal to the balloon volume, $V_{bal} = \frac{4}{3}\pi R^3$.

❸ **EXECUTE PLAN** Equating the buoyant and gravitational forces exerted on the balloon gives

$$F^b_{atm,bal} = F^G_{planet,bal}$$

$$\rho_{atm} V_{bal} g = (\rho_{film} V_{film} + \rho_{hy} V_{bal}) g$$

$$(\rho_{atm} - \rho_{hy})\left(\tfrac{4}{3}\pi R^3\right) = \rho_{film}(4\pi R^2 t).$$

Solving for R gives

$$R = \frac{3\rho_{film} t}{\rho_{atm} - \rho_{hy}}$$

$$= \frac{3(1.2 \times 10^3\ \text{kg/m}^3)(0.00030\ \text{m})}{(0.020\ \text{kg/m}^3) - (9.0 \times 10^{-4}\ \text{kg/m}^3)} = 57\ \text{m.}\ ✔$$

❹ **EVALUATE RESULT** A radius of 57 m means that the balloon diameter is about 110 m, 10% longer than a football field. This is big, but given the low mass density of the Martian atmosphere not unreasonable. In addition, the surface of Mars is mostly flat, so a large balloon may be practical for such a project. Of course, to carry an instrument package the balloon would have to be somewhat larger, depending on the mass of the instruments.

Note that we do not need to know the value of g because this variable cancels out in our algebra.

Guided Problem 18.2 Trial balloon

Before sending the balloon discussed in Worked Problem 18.1 to Mars, it would be necessary to test it on Earth. At sea level, the mass density of air is $1.286\ \text{kg/m}^3$ and that of hydrogen gas is $0.090\ \text{kg/m}^3$. (The testers might need to use helium, however, because of the danger posed by the oxygen in our atmosphere; at sea level the mass density of helium is $0.179\ \text{kg/m}^3$.) What must the radius of such a test balloon be if it is to be able to hover above Earth's surface? Use information as needed from Worked Problem 18.1.

1 GETTING STARTED

1. What forces must balance in order for the balloon to hover?
2. How can you determine each of these forces?

2 DEVISE PLAN

3. Which parts of the approach used in Worked Problem 18.1 are applicable?
4. Which values require replacement?

3 EXECUTE PLAN

5. Repeat the calculation used in Worked Problem 18.1 for the balloon on Earth, using hydrogen as the inflating gas.
6. Using helium for safety, repeat the calculation.

4 EVALUATE RESULT

7. Is your answer consistent with the value in Worked Problem 18.1 for the balloon's radius?
8. Is your result surprising? Is the use of helium feasible for the Earth test?

Worked Problem 18.3 Dam the canyon

You wish to design a dam that remains upright and in place when holding back a 30-m depth of water. The opening is a canyon with a rectangular cross section that is 50 m across and 30 m top to bottom. You do not want to rely on braces or connections with the canyon walls to support the dam, and so that leaves only normal and frictional forces to keep the dam in place. The normal and frictional forces exerted on the dam base will greatly exceed those exerted on the dam sides, so ignore these forces on the dam sides. The most straightforward solution seems to be a rectangular concrete block of height $h = 30$ m, horizontal length $\ell = 50$ m, and thickness t (Figure WG18.1). What minimum thickness of high-density concrete (mass density $5200\ \text{kg/m}^3$) is required for this design? Assume a coefficient of static friction of $\mu_s = 0.60$ between ground and concrete.

Figure WG18.1

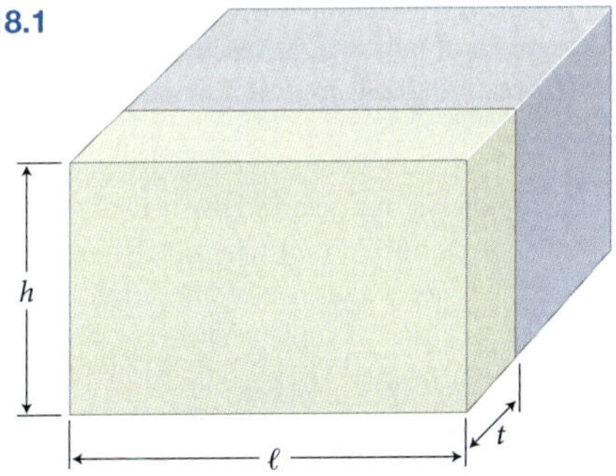

1 GETTING STARTED *Principles* Example 18.6 obtained an expression for the magnitude of the force exerted by water on a dam. The difference is that this time we need the vector sum of all forces exerted on the dam, which means we must include the force exerted by the air on the front of the dam. The mass of the dam determines the normal force, and the normal force determines the frictional force, which must balance the vector sum of the horizontal forces exerted on the dam by the water and air. Once we have an expression involving the dam mass, we can use it in combination with the concrete density to determine the volume of the dam. Because we know height and length, we can use the volume expression to calculate the required minimum thickness.

There is a catch, however: The dam might not simply be pushed horizontally by the vector sum of the forces; it could tip over instead! Thus we need to consider torques as well as forces. The side-view extended free-body diagram in Figure WG18.2 shows the forces exerted on the dam by the air and water as "distributed loads." That is, these forces are represented not by single arrows, but by a distribution of arrows intended to illustrate that they are applied across entire dam surfaces. In order to sum such forces (or the torques they cause) it will be necessary to mentally divide the dam into a large number of thin horizontal strips, each small enough that these pressure forces do not vary appreciably across its (infinitesimal) height. Two such strips are illustrated in Figure WG18.2, but our calculations will rely on many (an infinite number of) strips that span the dam from bottom to top. Note that the magnitude of the force exerted by the air is the same for every strip but the magnitude of the force exerted by the water increases with depth.

Figure WG18.2

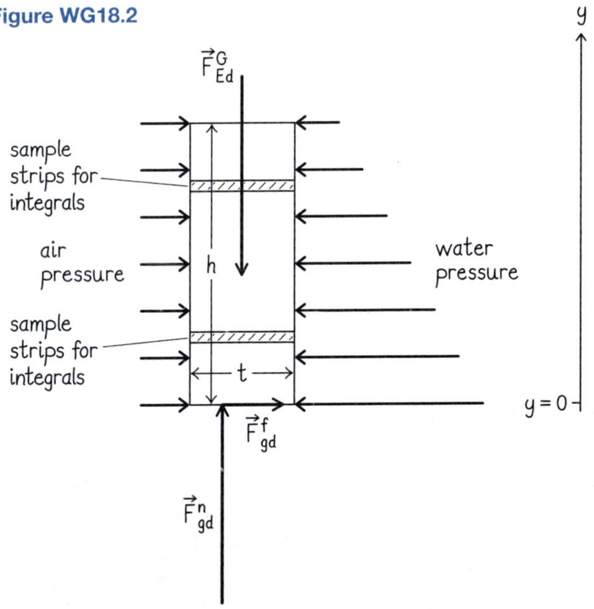

PRACTICE

❷ **DEVISE PLAN** The contact force exerted by the water on each horizontal strip is

$$dF^c_{ws} = P(y)dA = P(y)\ell dy,$$

where $P(y)$ is the pressure at height y and $dA = \ell dy$ is the area of a horizontal strip of length ℓ and height dy. We calculate the force exerted by the water on the dam by integrating this expression from height 0 at the base to height h at the top (*Principles* Example 18.6):

$$F^c_{wd} = \ell h\left(P_{atm} + \tfrac{1}{2}\rho_w gh\right).$$

The force exerted by the air on the dam is easier to compute because atmospheric pressure does not vary noticeably over the 30-m height:

$$F^c_{ad} = P_{atm}A = P_{atm}\ell h.$$

The forces exerted by the water and air oppose each other, and so their vector sum is

$$F^c_{wd} - F^c_{ad} = \ell h(P_{atm} + \tfrac{1}{2}\rho_w gh) - \ell h P_{atm} = \tfrac{1}{2}\rho_w \ell g h^2. \quad (1)$$

This horizontal force must be balanced by the frictional force exerted by the ground on the dam, which is

$$F^f_{gd} = \mu_s F^n_{gd} = \mu_s mg = \mu_s \rho_{concrete} V_d g.$$

We now have an expression that contains $\rho_{concrete}$ and V_d, so we can compute the minimum volume of the dam, which will lead to a minimum thickness.

The thickness we obtain via force analysis may not be sufficient to prevent rotation, though, so we must check the torques caused by the forces. Suppose the dam were to tip over. If it were to rotate, it would rotate about the bottom edge of the side opposite the water, and so we choose that edge as our axis of rotation. If the dam were just about to rotate, the normal force exerted by the ground, which is usually distributed uniformly across the bottom face, would concentrate at the rotation edge, the last line of contact with the ground. In this just-about-to-rotate case, the line of action of both the normal force and the frictional force would pass through the rotation axis and thus contribute zero torque. Thus, to keep the dam from rotating, the torque caused by the gravitational force exerted on the just-about-to-rotate dam would have to cancel the torque caused by the forces exerted by the water and the air.

To compute the contribution the gravitational force makes to the torque, we must calculate the distance from the dam's center of mass, which is the point of application of this force, to the rotation axis, so that we know the lever arm for the gravitational force. To compute the contribution the forces exerted by the air and water make to the torque, we must integrate to sum the torque contributions from all horizontal strips:

$$d\vec{\tau} = \vec{r} \times d\vec{F}.$$

Whichever computation—force or torque—yields the greater minimum thickness value is our desired result because both translational equilibrium and rotational equilibrium are required.

❸ **EXECUTE PLAN** The gravitational force exerted on the dam is

$$F^G_{Ed} = mg = \rho_{concrete} V_d g = \rho_{concrete}\ell thg. \quad (2)$$

The magnitude of the normal force equals this gravitational force, so the frictional force is

$$F^f_{gd} = \mu_s F^n_{gd} = \mu_s \rho_{concrete}\ell thg.$$

For stability against translational motion, this frictional force must balance the two contact forces due to the water pressure and air pressure:

$$F^f_{gd} = F^c_{wd} - F^c_{ad}$$

$$\mu_s \rho_{concrete}\ell thg = \tfrac{1}{2}\rho_w \ell g h^2,$$

where the term on the right is from Eq. 1. Solving for the dam thickness, we get

$$t = \frac{\rho_w h}{2\mu_s \rho_{concrete}}. \quad (3)$$

Now consider torques about our chosen rotation axis, the bottom edge on the air side of the dam. At the instant the dam is about to rotate, the torque caused by the gravitational force tends to rotate the dam clockwise in Figure WG18.2, and the force exerted by the water on the base of the dam tends to rotate the dam counterclockwise. These two terms must cancel to prevent rotation. Beginning with the gravitational force, notice that the lever arm for this vertical force is horizontal and is just one-half the thickness of the dam. Using our Eq. 2 expression for F^G_{Ed} thus yields

$$\tau_{Ed} = F^G_{Ed}(\tfrac{1}{2}t) = \tfrac{1}{2}\rho_{concrete} t^2 \ell hg.$$

The lever arm for the force exerted by the water is vertical, but its length varies from one horizontal strip to the next. At any height y, the force exerted by the water is the vector sum of the force exerted by the water and the opposing force exerted by the air at that height. The combined pressure at y is $P_{atm} + \rho_w gy - P_{atm} = \rho_w gy$. The force exerted by the water at y is thus $dF^c_{wd} = PA = (\rho_w gy)(\ell\, dy)$. For a strip at any height y, the torque is thus

$$d\tau_{wd} = y dF^c_{wd} = y(\rho_w gy)(\ell\, dy) = \rho_w g y^2 \ell\, dy.$$

Performing the integration from bottom to top gives

$$\tau_{wd} = \int_0^h \rho_w g y^2 \ell\, dy = \rho_w g \ell \int_0^h y^2 dy$$

$$= \tfrac{1}{3}\rho_w g \ell h^3.$$

PRACTICE

Setting these two torque magnitudes equal allows us to solve for the minimum thickness needed to prevent rotation:

$$\tau_{Ed} = \tau_{wd}$$

$$\tfrac{1}{2}\rho_{concrete}t^2\ell hg = \tfrac{1}{3}\rho_w g\ell h^3$$

$$t^2 = \frac{2\rho_w h^2}{3\rho_{concrete}}$$

$$t = h\sqrt{\frac{2\rho_w}{3\rho_{concrete}}}. \quad (4)$$

Determining which thickness value is greater requires a numerical comparison. Equation 3 gives

$$t_{translation} = \frac{h}{2\mu_s}\frac{\rho_w}{\rho_{concrete}} = \frac{30\text{ m}}{2(0.60)}\frac{1000\text{ kg/m}^3}{5200\text{ kg/m}^3} = 4.8\text{ m},$$

and from Eq. 4 we get

$$t_{rotation} = h\sqrt{\frac{2\rho_w}{3\rho_{concrete}}} = (30\text{ m})\sqrt{\frac{2(1000\text{ kg/m}^3)}{3(5200\text{ kg/m}^3)}} = 11\text{ m.} \checkmark$$

The minimum thickness needed to keep the dam in place—neither translating nor rotating—is 11 m.

❹ **EVALUATE RESULT** The required minimum thickness is less than half the height, so the dam really would have the shape of a rectangular block. We know from experience that tipping over a tall, thin object is easier than tipping over a short, thick one, however, and so it is reasonable that the minimum thickness, though small enough to give us confidence in modeling the dam as having a rectangular cross section, is a good fraction of the height.

Most dams are not shaped like rectangular blocks because other shapes are more efficient (require less concrete). Shapes that are thicker at the base and narrower at the top, and arched shapes that allow significant support from surrounding materials (so that the dam itself need not bear the entire effort of holding back the water) are typically used. The wider base makes a greater lever arm for the gravitational force, enhancing the torque this force causes without much effect on the torque due to pressure.

Guided Problem 18.4 Under pressure

Show, by integration, that the force due to the pressure difference $P_{in} - P_{out}$ across the hemispherical surface of a liquid drop (Figure WG18.3) is equal to the pressure difference times the equatorial cross-sectional area.

Figure WG18.3

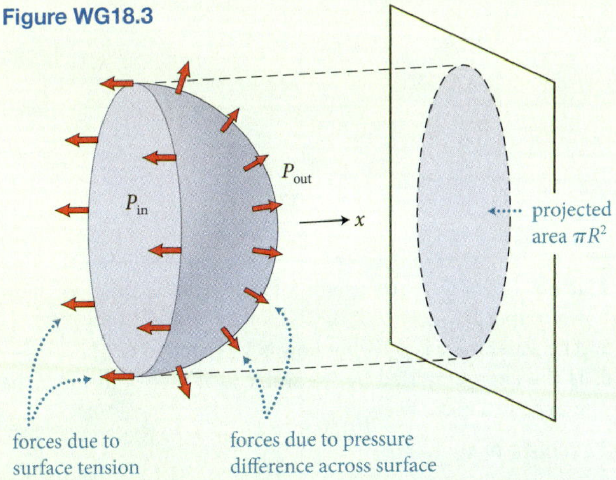

❶ **GETTING STARTED**

1. Examine the arrows illustrating the magnitude and direction of the forces exerted on the hemisphere at representative locations.
2. Why isn't the difference $P_{in} - P_{out}$ a function of location on the hemispheric surface? Have you had to make an assumption?
3. Consider symmetry in establishing whether certain force components cancel.

❷ **DEVISE PLAN**

4. Which choice of area elements is best? Hint: Consider slicing the hemisphere into thin vertical rings, each centered on the central horizontal axis of the hemisphere. Each ring has radius $R\sin\theta$ and width (tangent to the hemisphere) $Rd\theta$, where R is the hemisphere radius and θ is the angle from the central axis to the ring. (This angle varies from 0 for the tiny ring closest to the central axis to 90° for the ring with the maximum circular cross section.)
5. Consider the horizontal and vertical components of the forces due to air pressure on one such ring. Which of these components cancel?
6. Express the force component along the horizontal symmetry axis as a function of the variables P_{in}, P_{out}, R, and θ. Call this the x component of the force due to the air pressure.

❸ **EXECUTE PLAN**

7. Have you found that the only remaining force component exerted on a ring is $dF_x = (P_{in} - P_{out})\cos\theta\, dA = (P_{in} - P_{out})\cos\theta(2\pi R\sin\theta R\, d\theta)$?
8. Integrate over the hemisphere, from $\theta = 0$ to $\theta = \pi/2$. Why isn't this integration from $\theta = 0$ to $\theta = \pi$?

❹ **EVALUATE RESULT**

9. Is the force you computed consistent with the Laplace equation for a sphere and with what you know about surface tension for water?

Worked Problem 18.5 Plumber's dream

In a household water line, the pipes typically have an inside diameter of 15 mm. With the cold water tap turned on, it takes 11 s to fill a 1.0-L jar. The viscosity of water at 10°C is 1.307×10^{-3} Pa · s. What is the change in water pressure as water at this temperature flows through a 2.5-m length of pipe? What is the greatest speed attained by the water?

❶ GETTING STARTED We are given the flow rate for water at 10 °C moving through a certain length of pipe, the water's viscosity, and the pipe diameter and length. We must use this information to determine how much the pressure in the water changes along the given pipe length and what maximum speed the water has. We begin with a sketch showing this information (Figure WG18.4).

The speed of a viscous fluid is not the same everywhere in a pipe, but depends on the distance from the center and is a maximum at the center (see *Principles* Figure 18.57).

Figure WG18.4

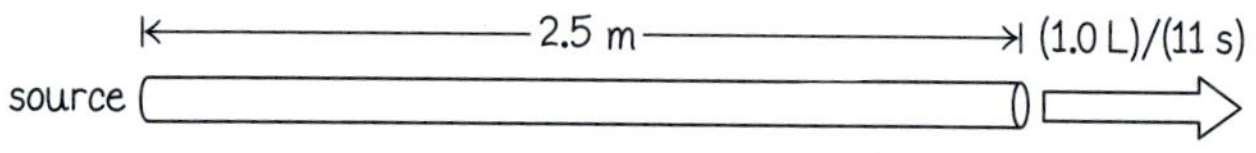

❷ DEVISE PLAN. The time interval given for filling the 1.0-L jar tells us the flow rate Q of the water. Once we have Q, we can use Poiseuille's law, Eq. 18.47, to calculate the pressure difference $P_1 - P_2$ along the 2.5-m length of the pipe. From Eq. 18.44 we know that the speed of the water any radial distance r from the center of a pipe of radius R is $v_x = [(P_1 - P_2)/4\eta\ell](R^2 - r^2)$ and that the speed has its maximum when $r = 0$ (that is, the speed is greatest at the center of the pipe).

❸ EXECUTE PLAN. Our first task is to convert the non-SI unit liters to the SI volume unit meters^3:

$$1.0\text{ L} \times \frac{1 \times 10^{-3}\text{ m}^3}{1\text{ L}} = 1.0 \times 10^{-3}\text{ m}^3.$$

The water flow rate is

$$Q = \frac{V}{\Delta t} = \frac{1.0 \times 10^{-3}\text{ m}^3}{11\text{ s}} = 9.09 \times 10^{-5}\text{ m}^3/\text{s}.$$

Solving Poiseuille's law (Eq. 18.47) for the pressure difference gives

$$P_1 - P_2 = \frac{8\eta\ell Q}{\pi R^4}$$

$$= \frac{8(1.307 \times 10^{-3}\text{ Pa}\cdot\text{s})(2.5\text{ m})(9.09 \times 10^{-5}\text{ m}^3/\text{s})}{\pi(7.5 \times 10^{-3}\text{ m})^4}$$

$$= 0.24 \times 10^3\text{ Pa.}\ ✔$$

To calculate the maximum speed, we set r equal to 0 in Eq. 18.44:

$$v_{\max} = \frac{P_1 - P_2}{4\eta\ell}(R^2 - 0^2)$$

$$= \frac{240\text{ Pa}}{4(1.307 \times 10^{-3}\text{ Pa}\cdot\text{s})(2.5\text{ m})}(7.5 \times 10^{-3}\text{ m})^2$$

$$= 1.0\text{ m/s.}\ ✔$$

❹ EVALUATE RESULT A pressure difference of 240 Pa is about 0.0024 atm, which is quite small and not significant in typical household pipes. A maximum water speed of 1.0 m/s seems reasonable as we observe water coming out of a home faucet.

Guided Problem 18.6 Devastating flood

The 1889 Johnstown Flood in Pennsylvania was one of the most devastating in American history. Heavy rains caused a breach in a dam holding back a reservoir, releasing a wall of water that killed more than 2200 people. Researchers have calculated that the breach measured 13 m high by 90 m across and that the peak water discharge rate was greater than 8500 m^3/s. Determine the maximum speed of the water as it burst out of the breach and the maximum rate at which mass and energy gushed from the reservoir, with the given quantities accurate to two significant digits.

❶ GETTING STARTED

1. How are the maximum *speed*, maximum *mass* flow rate, and maximum *energy* flow rate related to the known maximum *volume* flow rate at which water left the reservoir?
2. Can the water be treated as incompressible? Nonviscous?

❷ DEVISE PLAN

3. There are lots of flow rates. Label them Q_{vol} for volume flow rate, Q_{mass} for mass flow rate, and Q_{energy} for energy flow rate.
4. Is Eq. 18.26, $Q = Av$, useful for determining the maximum water speed?
5. The water mass is $\rho_w V$, but how is V related to Q_{vol}?
6. Is the energy carried by the water as it moves through the breach its kinetic energy?

❸ EXECUTE PLAN

❹ EVALUATE RESULT

7. Is your maximum water speed reasonable? Remember that a large volume of water can pass through a huge opening in a short time interval, even at a relatively slow speed.
8. Compare the mass and energy flow rates with similar rates for something more familiar, such as the motion of cars on a freeway.

Worked Problem 18.7 Tapered flow

The inside diameter of a horizontal pipe narrows from 15 mm to 10 mm, and the pipe carries water that moves at 750 mm/s in the wide part of the pipe. Ignoring the very small viscosity of water, what is the difference between the water pressure at a position in the wide part and the water pressure at a position in the narrow part if the two positions are 280 mm apart? At which position is the water pressure higher?

❶ **GETTING STARTED** Figure WG18.5 shows the horizontal pipe with our two positions of interest marked x_1 in the narrow part and x_2 in the wide part, with the two separated by 280 mm. For fluid-flow problems, the first thing to consider is whether or not the flow is laminar because knowing this lets us know whether or not Bernoulli's equation and/or one of the continuity equations can be used. Because this is a nonviscous, incompressible fluid, laminar flow is likely at low speeds, so we can use these equations. Given that we are seeking a pressure difference and have diameter and speed information, using Bernoulli's equation looks like a good approach. Because our fluid is nonviscous and incompressible, we can use the Eq. 18.24 version of the continuity equation.

Figure WG18.5

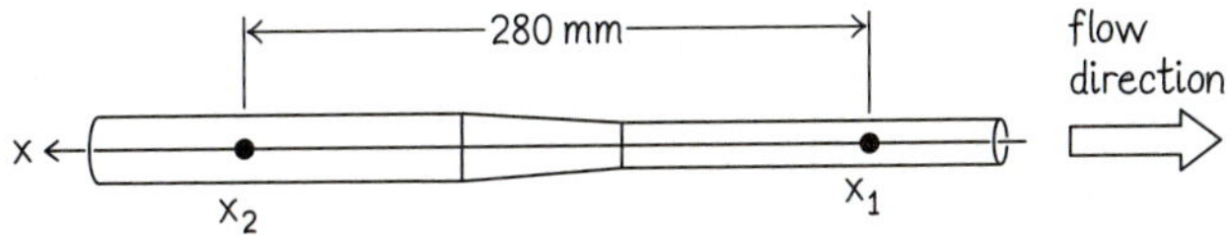

❷ **DEVISE PLAN** The Eq. 18.24 version of the continuity equation relates the speeds at the two positions. Using d for the diameters, we have

$$A_1 v_1 = A_2 v_2$$

$$\pi\left(\frac{d_1}{2}\right)^2 v_1 = \pi\left(\frac{d_2}{2}\right)^2 v_2$$

$$v_1 d_1^2 = v_2 d_2^2. \quad (1)$$

The heights of these two positions are identical because the tube is horizontal, so Bernoulli's equation with $y_1 = y_2$ becomes

$$P_1 + \tfrac{1}{2}\rho v_1^2 = P_2 + \tfrac{1}{2}\rho v_2^2$$

$$P_2 - P_1 = \tfrac{1}{2}\rho(v_1^2 - v_2^2). \quad (2)$$

We need to determine only the pressure difference $\Delta P = P_2 - P_1$ between the two positions, not the absolute pressure at each position. Thus we have two equations with two unknowns, ΔP and v_1, and so we can determine ΔP.

❸ **EXECUTE PLAN** Equation 1 solved for our unknown v_1 gives

$$v_1 = v_2 \frac{d_2^2}{d_1^2}$$

$$v_1^2 = v_2^2\left(\frac{d_2}{d_1}\right)^4.$$

Next we use this expression for v_1^2 in Eq. 2 to get the pressure difference:

$$\Delta P = P_2 - P_1 = \tfrac{1}{2}\rho(v_1^2 - v_2^2) = \tfrac{1}{2}\rho\left[v_2^2\left(\frac{d_2}{d_1}\right)^4 - v_2^2\right]$$

$$= \tfrac{1}{2}\rho v_2^2\left[\left(\frac{d_2}{d_1}\right)^4 - 1\right]$$

$$= \tfrac{1}{2}(1000\ \text{kg/m}^3)(7.50 \times 10^{-1}\ \text{m/s})^2\left[\left(\frac{15\ \text{mm}}{10\ \text{mm}}\right)^4 - 1\right]$$

$$= 1.1 \times 10^3\ \text{Pa.}$$ ✔

That this result is positive means $P_2 > P_1$; that is, the pressure is greater in the wide part of the pipe. ✔

❹ **EVALUATE RESULT** The pressure difference is about 1% of atmospheric pressure, great enough to measure with either a water or mercury manometer but not great enough to deform the pipe walls or to make us question our assumption of incompressibility.

Equation 1 tells us that v_1 is 1.7 m/s. Thus the speeds in both parts of the pipe are on the order of 1 m/s and thus not fast enough to cause concern about laminar flow. We expect the speed to increase and the pressure to be reduced in the narrow part, and this is what we obtain. This is reasonable because to speed up the flow in the narrow portion, we need a force in the same direction as the motion, which is consistent with greater pressure in the wide portion.

Note that we had no reason to use the given information about the distance separating positions 1 and 2. Laminar flow is the same at all positions that have a common pipe diameter, so as long as each point is well away from the transition from one diameter to the next, the precise positions are not relevant.

Guided Problem 18.8 Reoriented flow

The pipe in Figure WG18.5 is rotated 90° counterclockwise so that it is vertical, with the wide part above the narrow part. Assuming that the speed in the wide part remains the same as in Worked Problem 18.7, what is the pressure difference between positions in the two parts now, and which position is at the greater pressure?

❶ **GETTING STARTED**

1. Sketch the situation.
2. Will the approach of Worked Problem 18.7 work in this case?

❷ **DEVISE PLAN**

3. Are there differences between Worked Problem 18.7 and this problem other than $y_1 \neq y_2$?
4. Write Bernoulli's equation and the appropriate form of the continuity equation.
5. Do you have sufficient information to solve the problem?

❸ **EXECUTE PLAN**

6. Insert the given numerical values and obtain a result.

❹ **EVALUATE RESULT**

7. Is your result reasonable? Is it unexpected?

Questions and Problems

For instructor-assigned homework, go to MasteringPhysics® (MP)

Dots indicate difficulty level of problems: • = *easy,* •• = *intermediate,* ••• = *hard;* CR = *context-rich problem.*

Unless told otherwise, use 1000 kg/m^3 for the mass density of water.

18.1 Forces in a fluid

1. The liquid-filled cylinder in Figure P18.1 is clamped in place and has a piston on either end. The piston on the right is cylindrical and has a radius of 30.0 mm. The piston on the left is also cylindrical and has a radius of 10.0 mm. If the right cylinder is pushed leftward with a force of 30.0 N, what force must be exerted on the left cylinder to keep it from moving? •

Figure P18.1

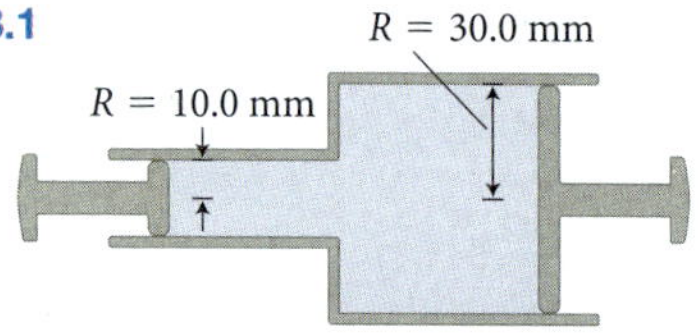

2. On Earth, a cylindrical container of water open to the atmosphere experiences atmospheric pressure at the top surface and a greater pressure at the bottom of the container. How do these pressures change when the container is being carried on the orbiting International Space Station? •
3. A box has six faces with three distinct areas $A < B < C$. Assume that A and B represent the four vertical surfaces, and the two horizontal surfaces have area C. When the box is submerged, rank the faces in order of (*a*) increasing water pressure and (*b*) increasing force exerted by the water. ••
4. You are designing a wedge-shaped container as illustrated in Figure P18.4. You must choose a value for the angle θ, which then determines the other two equal angles in this isosceles wedge. (*a*) When the container is filled with a fluid, what must the value of θ be if F/A, the ratio of the magnitude of the force exerted by the fluid on a side to the area of that side, is the same for all three sides? (*b*) What must θ be in order to have the magnitude of the force exerted by the fluid be the same on all three sides? ••

Figure P18.4

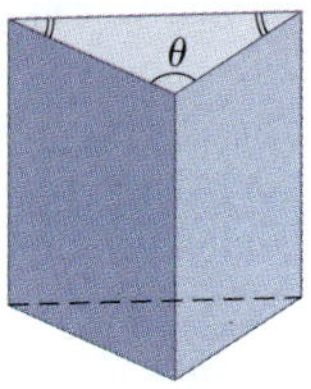

5. The fixed container in Figure P18.5 is filled with a liquid and fitted with a piston at the bottom. Give the direction (if any) of the following: (*a*) the force $\vec{F}^c_{\ell w}$ exerted by the liquid on the wall at location A, (*b*) the pressure P in the liquid at A, (*c*) the force $\vec{F}^c_{w\ell}$ exerted by the wall on the liquid at location B, (*d*) the force $\vec{F}^c_{\ell p}$ exerted by the liquid on the piston if the piston is pushed, and (*e*) the force $\vec{F}^c_{\ell p}$ exerted by the liquid on the piston if the piston is pulled. (*f*) Which answers would change if the container were filled with a gas rather than a liquid? ••

Figure P18.5

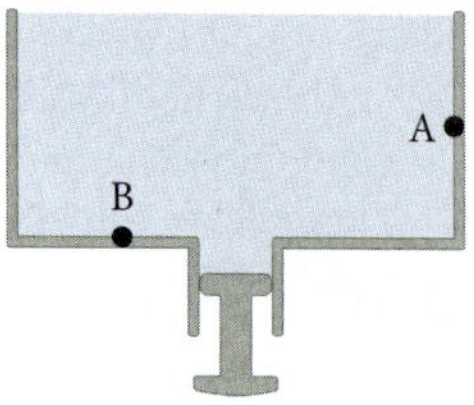

6. You and your snowboard, with a combined mass of 70 kg, ride a half-pipe that has a radius of 5.0 m. As you pass the bottom, you create a pressure of 57 kPa on the half-pipe while moving at 8.2 m/s. If your snowboard is 1.3 m long, what is the average width of the part of your snowboard that is in contact with the half-pipe? ••
7. For the floor in any room, the *floor loading* is the maximum safe *average* pressure on the floor (the gravitational force exerted by Earth on all objects resting on the floor divided by the floor area), and the floor's *point loading* is the maximum safe *actual* pressure (the gravitational force exerted by Earth on all objects resting on the floor divided by the floor area covered by those objects). A particular room has a floor loading of 3 kPa and a point loading of 60 kPa. What fraction of the floor area can be subjected to the point loading without exceeding the floor loading? ••
8. Three jars each have volume V and height h, but they have different shapes as shown in Figure P18.8. Water is to be added to each jar and the pressure is to be measured right at the bottom of each jar. Rank the jars in order of increasing pressure if the volume of water is (*a*) V and (*b*) $V/2$. ••

Figure P18.8

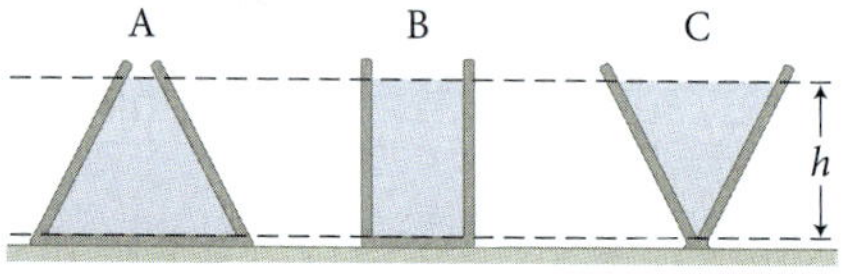

9. In a galaxy far, far away, a planet composed of an incompressible liquid of uniform mass density ρ has mass m_{planet} and radius R. Determine the pressure midway between the surface and the center of the planet. •••

18.2 Buoyancy

10. A cube measuring 100 mm on a side floats upright in water with 70.0 mm submerged. What is the mass of the cube? •
11. A scuba diving weight has a mass of 5.0 kg and is made from a material that has a mass density of 2000 kg/m^3. How much force is required to lift it from the bottom of a shallow pool? •
12. You have three bricks made of lead, stone, and plastic. The bricks have identical dimensions. When completely submerged (*a*) which brick feels the greatest buoyant force, and (*b*) which is most likely to float when released? •
13. A ship constructed of 2.50×10^6 kg of steel is roughly shaped like a box of length 50.0 m, width 20.0 m, and height 20.0 m. (*a*) What is the mass density of the ship? (*b*) Does the ship float? (*c*) If it floats, what is the maximum cargo mass it can carry without sinking? ••
14. A wooden block of height h is pushed from the air into a bucket of water that has a depth equal to $2h$. Make a graph showing how the buoyant force exerted on the block changes as its bottom moves from the surface to the bottom of the bucket. You do not need to specify the size of the buoyant force, only how it changes with depth. ••
15. Glass A contains 250 g of water, and an identical glass B contains 220 g of water with a 30-g cube of ice floating in it. How do the water levels in the two glasses compare? ••
16. A rowboat floating in a small swimming pool has a large concrete block in it. If the block is thrown overboard into the pool, does the water level in the pool rise, fall, or stay the same? ••

17. You have constructed a raft that is 2.00 m long, 2.00 m wide, and 0.100 m thick. If the mass of the raft is 40.0 kg and your mass is 55.0 kg, how many 65.0-kg friends can cross a river with you during one trip? ••

18. A spherical balloon filled with helium gas must lift a 1.50-kg scientific payload off the ground, and the mass of the empty balloon is 0.500 kg. (*a*) What is the minimum diameter of the balloon? (*b*) A helium shortage forces the scientists to consider using nitrogen gas in the balloon. What minimum balloon diameter is needed if nitrogen gas is used? The mass densities are $1.286\ \mathrm{kg/m^3}$ for air, $0.179\ \mathrm{kg/m^3}$ for helium gas, and $1.251\ \mathrm{kg/m^3}$ for nitrogen gas. ••

19. Two same-sized blocks of wood float in a tank as shown in Figure P18.19. Block 1 has two-thirds of its volume submerged, and block 2 has one-third of its volume submerged. Determine the ratio ρ_1/ρ_2 of the mass densities of the blocks. ••

Figure P18.19

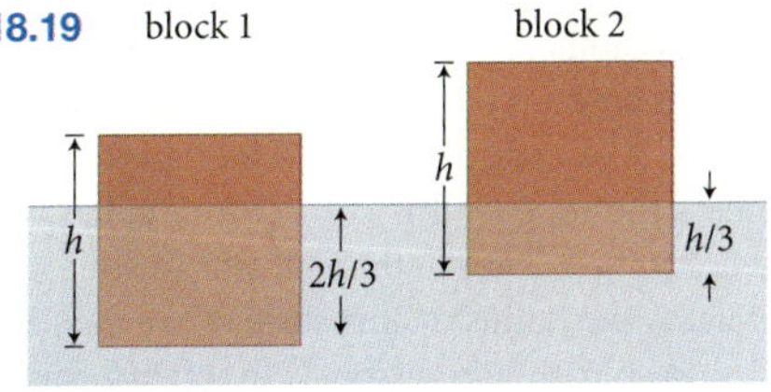

20. A 5.00-kg air-filled, sealed, rigid float tank that has a volume of $1.00\ \mathrm{m^3}$ is pulled 50.4 m down to the seafloor in order to assist in lifting a sunken object. A diver standing on the seafloor cranks a winch to pull the tank down (Figure P18.20). (*a*) How much work is required to pull the tank down? (Ignore the mass of the air in the tank and the mass of the winch rope. Assume that the water mass density does not change with depth.) (*b*) What is the average power required if it takes 10 min to winch down the tank? ••

Figure P18.20

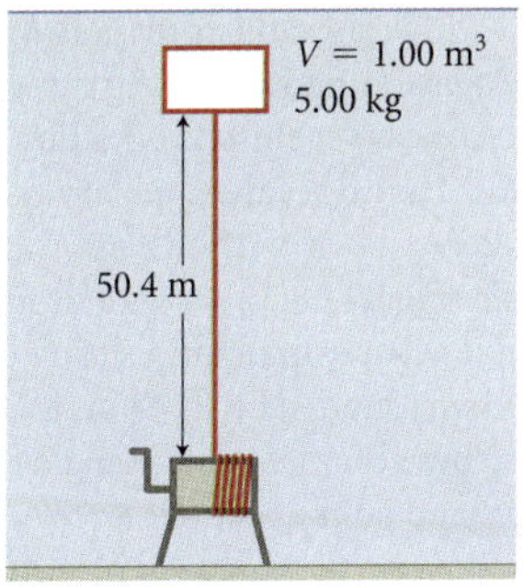

21. You want to determine the lifting force of a helium balloon. When you tie a long cord to the balloon and then release the balloon, it floats up until it supports a 63.2-mm length of cord and then it remains stationary, as shown in Figure P18.21. A 1.00-m length of the cord has a mass of 0.0160 kg, and the mass of the uninflated balloon is 2300 mg. What is the volume of the inflated balloon? The mass densities are $1.286\ \mathrm{kg/m^3}$ for air and $0.179\ \mathrm{kg/m^3}$ for helium. ••

Figure P18.21

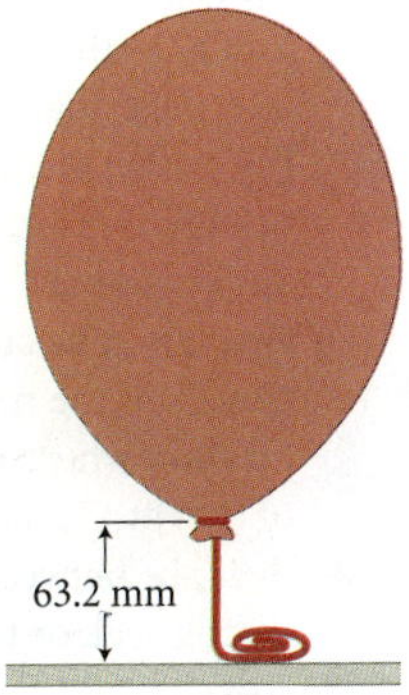

22. A cylindrical water tank that has a diameter of 2.50 m contains water to a depth of 3.75 m. A 40.0-kg object placed in the water floats with 75% of its volume submerged. By how much does the addition of the object increase the pressure in the water at the bottom of the tank? •••

23. An uninflated balloon of mass 6.00×10^{-3} kg has a volume of $6.90 \times 10^{-2}\ \mathrm{m^3}$ when fully inflated with a mixture of helium and hydrogen gas. You tie a long, heavy cord to the balloon and allow the balloon to float above a table. The length of cord lifted off the table is 283 mm, and the linear mass density of the cord is 0.260 kg/m. (*a*) What is the mass density of the gas mixture in the balloon? (*b*) What is the ratio of helium to hydrogen in the mixture? The mass densities are $1.286\ \mathrm{kg/m^3}$ for air, $0.179\ \mathrm{kg/m^3}$ for helium gas, and $0.090\ \mathrm{kg/m^3}$ for hydrogen gas. •••

18.3 Fluid flow

24. The pipe in Figure P18.24 shrinks from a diameter of 100 mm in the wide section to a diameter of 10.0 mm in the narrow section. If the water's speed is 100 mm/s at location A, what is its speed at location B? •

Figure P18.24

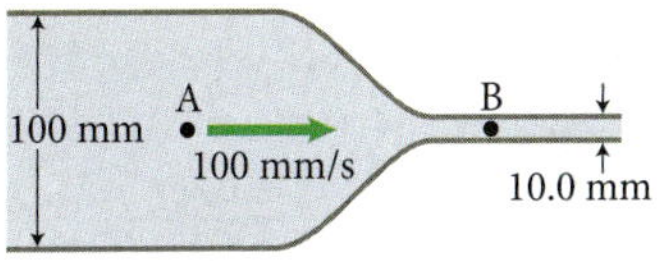

25. In an air duct running along the outside of a building, air flowing through the duct has a mass density of $1.20\ \mathrm{kg/m^3}$ and is moving at 5.38 m/s. The duct passes through a wall into an air-conditioned room. If the mass density of the air in the duct rises to $1.24\ \mathrm{kg/m^3}$ once the air reaches the air-conditioned region, what is the air's new speed? (Ignore the small dimensional change of the duct material in the colder room.) •

26. A viscous liquid is flowing through the pipe in Figure P18.26. If the flow is laminar, rank the speed of the liquid at points 1–4 in order of increasing speed. •

Figure P18.26

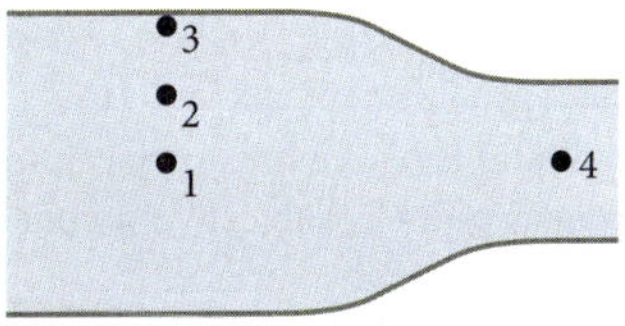

27. Figure P18.27 shows streamlines of water flowing in two regions A and B of the same pipe (neither of the two regions shown spans the entire diameter of the pipe). Between these two regions no other pipes are connected to this one. Compare the speed, pressure, and pipe diameter in the two regions A and B. ••

Figure P18.27

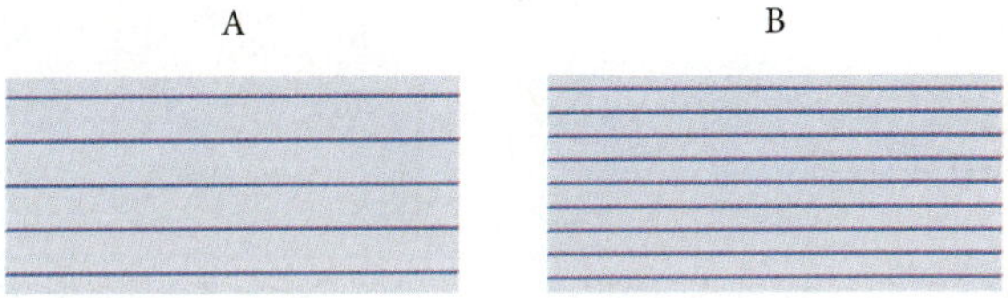

PRACTICE

28. The water in a river flows gently in a continuous, straight channel of uniform width. Over a certain distance downstream, the water's speed decreases. What is most likely happening? State your reasons. ••

29. You are traveling in a car when the driver lights a cigarette. Why is it that when you open a window slightly the smoky air blows out of the car? Why doesn't air from the outside flow in through the opening instead? ••

30. The capped end of a pipe in your basement springs a leak. The pipe has a diameter of 50.0 mm and is attached to a joist so that it is 2.00 m above the basement floor. The water squirts out horizontally through a hole that has a diameter of 3.00 mm and hits the floor 6.00 m from the leak. What is the speed of the water inside the pipe as it moves toward the leak? Ignore air resistance. ••

31. A garden hose 30.0 m long and 40.0 mm in diameter attached to a faucet carries water that enters the hose at 2.00 m/s. The hose was previously cut at its center and has been repaired by splicing a length of hose that is 5.00 m long and 30.0 mm in diameter into the break (Figure P18.31). (*a*) What is the water speed in the small middle section of the repaired hose? (*b*) How long does the water take to flow the length of the repaired hose? ••

Figure P18.31

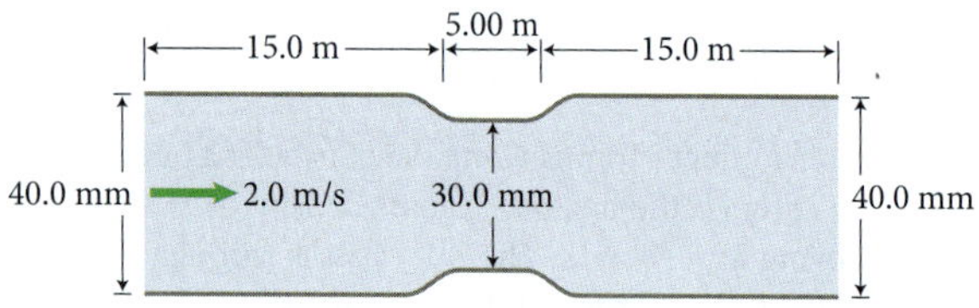

32. Consider a nonviscous fluid undergoing laminar flow in an open, horizontal channel. The Bernoulli effect says that where the flow speed is greater, the pressure is smaller, but the pressure at the surface, in contact with the surrounding air, is atmospheric pressure everywhere. How is that possible? •••

18.4 Surface effects

33. A drop of liquid is placed on a surface. A particle of the liquid at the contact point is subject to a cohesive force of 4.00 N directed 52.0° above the surface. If the contact angle is 104°, what is the magnitude of the adhesive force between the particle and the surface? •

34. Three water droplets are shown in Figure P18.34. All three are in the same room with the same atmospheric pressure. In which of the three droplets is the pressure greatest and why? •

Figure P18.34

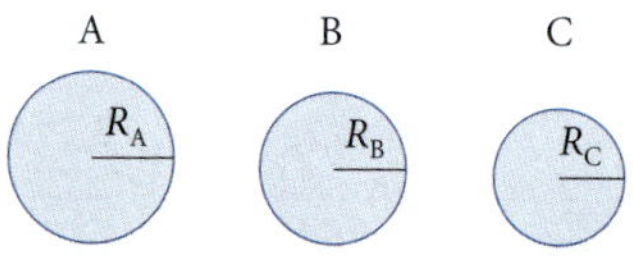

35. A partially inflated and irregularly shaped balloon is shown in Figure P18.35. Rank the points on the balloon's surface in order of (*a*) increasing tension in the membrane and (*b*) increasing pressure on the inside. •

Figure P18.35

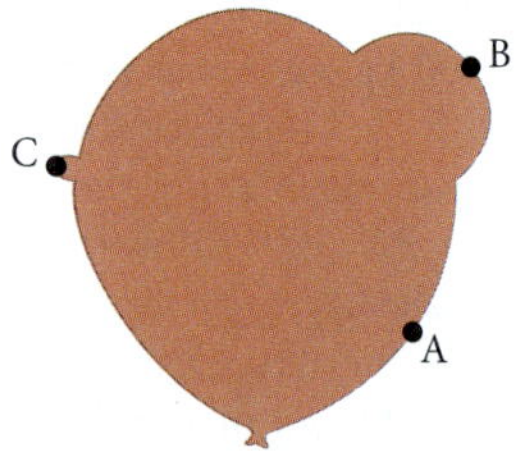

36. Suppose a certain liquid in contact with a surface has cohesive and adhesive forces such that its behavior is exactly between wetting and not wetting a surface. How do the magnitudes of the adhesive and cohesive forces compare? ••

37. A glass capillary tube has a diameter of 2.00 mm and contains a small amount of liquid that forms a concave spherical meniscus. A particle of the liquid located where the liquid surface meets the tube wall is subject to a cohesive force of 4.00 N at an angle of 35.0° to the wall and an adhesive force of 1.00 N. What is the radius of curvature of the meniscus? ••

38. Dishwashing liquid dissolved in water forms an aqueous solution containing bubbles (the "suds") that are soap-film spheres filled with air. How does the pressure difference across the surface of one of these bubbles in the solution compare with the pressure difference across the surface of a bubble of the same size that escapes from the solution and floats in the air? ••

39. What is the relationship between the radius of a capillary tube R_{tube} and the radius of curvature R_{men} of the spherical meniscus a liquid forms in the tube? Answer for both a wetting liquid and a nonwetting liquid. (Hint: See *Principles* Figure 18.36.) ••

40. Liquid A forms a concave meniscus of radius R in a capillary tube in which its capillary rise is h_A. Liquid B has twice the surface tension and twice the mass density of liquid A and forms a concave meniscus of radius $R/2$ in an identical capillary tube. How does the capillary rise h_B of liquid B compare with h_A? ••

41. *Principles* Figure 18.32 shows a drop of a wetting liquid and a drop of a nonwetting liquid sitting on a horizontal solid surface and surrounded by air. Show that, for both drops, the relationship between the contact angle and the magnitudes of the cohesive and adhesive forces exerted on a particle of liquid at the gas-liquid-solid junction is $2\sin(\theta_c/2) = F_{cohesive}/F_{adhesive}$. Assume that the surface is smooth and clean, the liquid contains no impurities, and the contact angle is not influenced by the gas. •••

42. You have three capillary tubes that are made of paraffin wax and have diameters of 1.00 mm, 2.00 mm, and 3.00 mm. (*a*) Is the meniscus that water forms in each tube convex or concave? (*b*) How might you change the water so that the answer to part *a* changes? (*c*) Because any liquid surface in a capillary tube curves either concavely or convexly, the peak or trough of the meniscus is vertically higher or lower than the location where the liquid surface meets the tube wall. Which of the three capillary tubes has the greatest vertical separation distance between the liquid-wall contact point and the meniscus peak or trough? •••

43. Figure P18.43 shows the capillary rise h for the liquid in a capillary tube sitting in a dish of liquid. Suppose you insert an identical capillary tube into the liquid but push this tube deep enough into the liquid to make the top of the tube be a distance $h/2$ above the surface of the liquid in the dish. How far do you expect the liquid to rise in this tube? •••

Figure P18.43

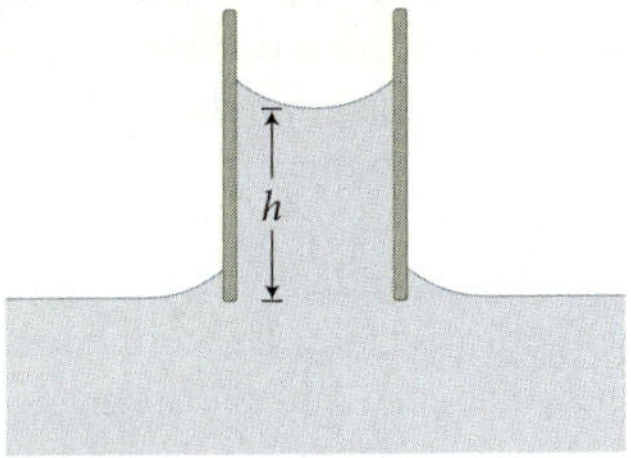

18.5 Pressure and gravity

44. A certain class of submarines can dive to 730 m below sea level. What is the pressure at this depth? •

45. The thresher shark has large eyes, about 0.10 m in diameter. Calculate the force exerted on a thresher shark's eye by the hydrostatic pressure in ocean water at a depth of 400 m. (Assume the water's mass density at this depth is $1000\ \text{kg/m}^3$.) •

46. Timbers used in building construction can withstand a pressure of 1.4×10^7 Pa before being crushed. If the mass density of wood is $\rho = 960\ \text{kg/m}^3$, calculate the height h a pile of timbers would have to be in order for the ones at the bottom to be crushed. Assume that all the timbers have the same size and shape and that they are piled one on top of the other. ••

47. A cylindrical space capsule lands in the ocean. This capsule is 2.34 m long, 1.10 m in diameter, and weighted at one end so that it floats with its long central axis vertical and 0.820 m of its length above the water surface. The mass density of sea water is $1025\ \text{kg/m}^3$. (*a*) What is the magnitude of the buoyant force exerted on the capsule? (*b*) Suppose the capsule springs a leak and sinks. What is the magnitude of the buoyant force exerted on it once it sinks? (*c*) Why does the capsule sink if the magnitude of the buoyant force is greater after it has sunk than when it was floating? ••

48. A certain diving bell for use in the ocean has a square window measuring 0.250 m on each side. The inside of the bell is pressurized and maintained at a pressure of 2.00 atm. How deep can this bell be lowered before the vector sum of forces exerted by the seawater on the window exceeds 195 kN? The mass density of seawater is $1025\ \text{kg/m}^3$. ••

49. Pascal demonstrated his principle by causing a wooden barrel full of water to burst when a small amount of additional water was poured into a long, thin tube extending vertically upward from the top of the barrel. Explain why this worked and estimate the magnitude of the force that burst the barrel's top (diameter 0.42 m) and the length of the tube (diameter 6.0×10^{-3} m) if $3.39 \times 10^{-4}\ \text{m}^3$ of water (less than 12 fluid ounces) was added. ••

50. When a garden hose with an output diameter of 20 mm is directed straight upward, the stream of water rises to a height of 0.15 m. You then use your thumb to partially cover the output opening so that its diameter is reduced to 10 mm. How high does the water rise now? Ignore drag and assume that the smaller opening you create with your thumb is circular. ••

51. (*a*) For the garden hose of Problem 51, calculate how high the water would rise if you constricted the opening to make its diameter 1.0 mm rather than 10 mm. (*b*) Based on your experience, would you expect to see such a height from the stream? If not, what physical effects do you think are responsible? ••

52. (*a*) Consider a fluid whose mass density ρ varies with height y above sea level. Use Eq. 18.6, $P_1 + \rho g y_1 = P_2 + \rho g y_2$, to obtain an expression that shows how dP, the change in pressure along a column of the fluid of infinitesimal height dy, varies with y. (*b*) Using the simplification that the mass density of air at any given height y above sea level is proportional to atmospheric pressure at that height, integrate the differential equation you found in part *a* to obtain an expression that shows how atmospheric pressure varies with height y above sea level. •••

53. A river valley is in the shape of a V. A dam is built in this valley, so it also has a V shape, of height h and width w at the top and essentially zero at the bottom. Write an expression for the magnitude of the force that the water exerts against this dam? •••

18.6 Working with pressure

54. If the outside air pressure changes from 1.0 atm to 1.1 atm, by how much does mercury in a barometer rise? The mass density of mercury is $13{,}534\ \text{kg/m}^3$. •

55. A small block of mass m sits atop a piston that seals a volume of air in a flask in which the radius of the neck is R (Figure P18.55). Obtain an equation for the pressure in the bottle as a function of atmospheric pressure. •

Figure P18.55

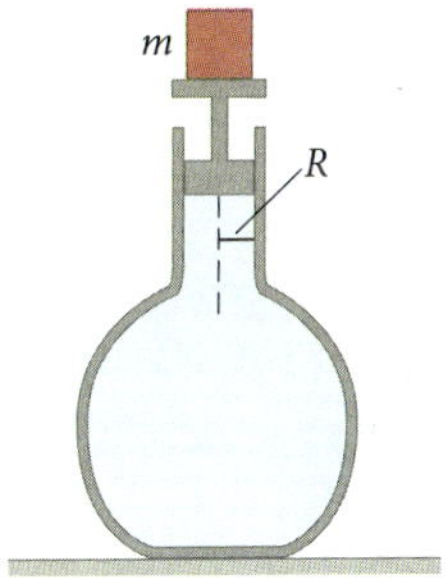

56. The two pistons in the hydraulic system shown in Figure P18.56 are coupled through a reservoir of water. The pistons are at the same height above ground. The piston on the right has a radius of 1.6 m, and the mass of the car sitting on the piston is 1000 kg. You are standing on the left piston, and neither you nor the car is moving. If your mass is 65 kg, what is the radius of the left piston? •

Figure P18.56

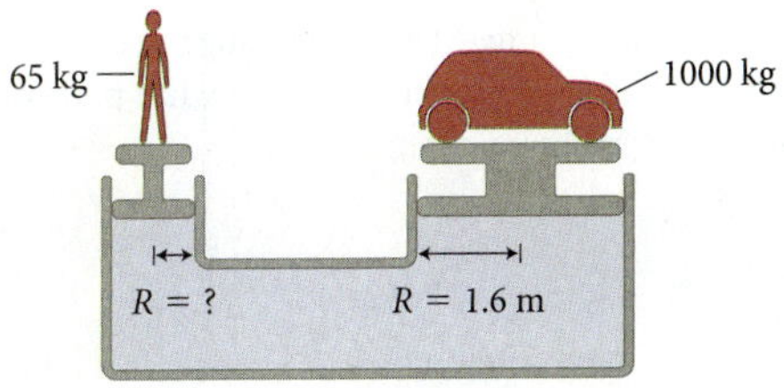

57. The container on the left in Figure P18.57 is a cube of side length h. The dimensions of the container on the right are height h, width $h/2$, and length $h/2$. Points A and A′ are at height $h/2$, and points B and B′ are at the bottoms of the containers. Calculate the ratio of gauge pressures $(P_A/P_B)/(P_{A'}/P_{B'})$ if the left container is filled with water and the right container is filled with glycerol. The mass density of glycerol is $1261\ \text{kg/m}^3$. ••

Figure P18.57

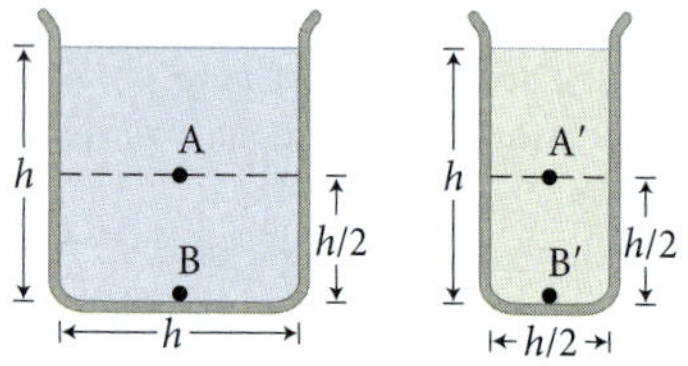

58. After pouring some water into the U-tube of Figure P18.58, you pour a volume V_1 of oil of mass density $\rho_1 = 800\ \text{kg/m}^3$ into the left side of the tube and a volume V_2 of oil of mass density $\rho_2 = 700\ \text{kg/m}^3$ into the right side. Once the two oils have been added, the levels on the left and right sides are the same, and the water level on the right side is a height $h_2 = 20$ mm higher than the water level on the left side. What is the height h_1 of the oil on the left side? ••

Figure P18.58

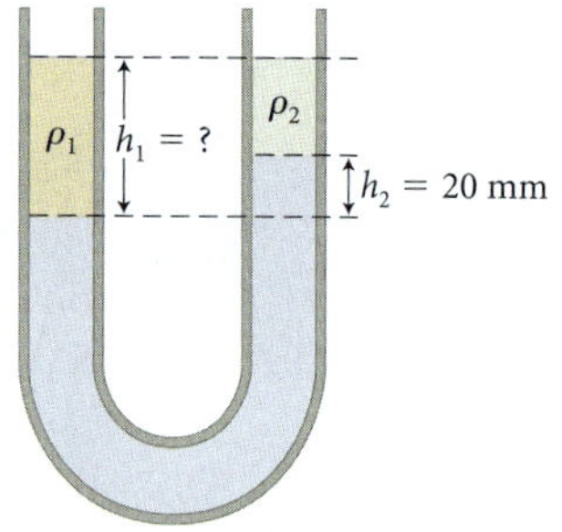

59. Initially, both legs of a mercury manometer are open to the atmosphere, and the mercury height in the left leg is 40.0 mm. You inflate a balloon until it has a surface area of $0.300\ \text{m}^2$ and affix its open end to the opening of the manometer's right leg. When you do this, the mercury level in the left leg changes to 65 mm. What is the magnitude of the inward force exerted by the balloon's elasticity on the air in the balloon? The mass density of mercury is $13.5 \times 10^3\ \text{kg/m}^3$. ••

60. Suppose you increase the gauge pressure in the tires of your car by 10%. (*a*) How does the area of the tires in contact with a level road change? (*b*) If the gauge pressure in the tires is 2.0 atm before you increase it, by what percentage does the actual tire pressure change? ••

61. In a service station's hydraulic lift, the diameter of the large piston is 200 mm and the diameter of the small piston is 30 mm. Force is exerted on the small piston by an air compressor. (*a*) How much gauge pressure must the compressor supply to lift a 1500-kg car? (*b*) If the car must be raised 1.8 m off the floor, through what distance must the small piston travel? ••

62. A hydrogen-filled balloon is used to lift a 125-kg stone off the ground. The basket holding the stone has a mass of 15.0 kg. What must the minimum radius R of the balloon be in order to lift the stone off the ground? Use $1.29\ \text{kg/m}^3$ for the mass density of air, and ignore the mass of the hydrogen and the mass of the balloon. ••

63. In a large vat that is initially empty, a solid aluminum cylinder hangs by an ideal spring. The cylinder is 52.5 mm long and 30.0 mm in diameter, and the spring is stretched 42.0 mm. The vat is then filled with a liquid, submerging the cylinder and causing it to rise 11.8 mm. What is the mass density of the liquid? The mass density of aluminum is $2700\ \text{kg/m}^3$. ••

64. A 15.0-kg block measures 0.750 m top to bottom, and each horizontal face has an area of $0.0125\ \text{m}^2$. The block hangs, with its long central axis vertical, from a wire that can support a maximum tension of 135 N. The block is initially submerged in water, but then the water level is gradually lowered. What is the greatest distance the surface of the water can be below the top of the block without breaking the wire? ••

65. At an atmospheric pressure of 1.00 atm, the height of the liquid in the tube of a mercury barometer is 760 mm *only if* you ignore capillary rise in the tube. Obtain an expression that shows how h, the number of millimeters the mercury height differs from 760 mm, depends on the diameter d of the tube, and then calculate the value of h for $d = 7.0$ mm. The contact angle for mercury on this glass tube is 137°, and its mass density is $13.5 \times 10^3\ \text{kg/m}^3$. •••

66. A small, smooth cube made of wood that has a mass density of $850\ \text{kg/m}^3$ is dropped from rest 5.00 m above the surface of a lake. Determine (*a*) the maximum depth the cube reaches and (*b*) the time interval the wood is under water before it returns to the surface. Assume that viscous drag is negligible so that the only force the water exerts on the cube is the buoyant force. •••

67. A right circular cone that has altitude h and a base of radius R is submerged in a liquid of mass density ρ. The cone's vertex points directly downward, so that the circular bottom face of the cone is horizontal. The volume of a right circular cone is $\pi R^2 h/3$. (*a*) By direct integration of the pressure over the surface of the cone, calculate the magnitude of the upward force exerted by the liquid on the cone. (*b*) Show that your answer in part *a* is consistent with Archimedes' principle. •••

18.7 Bernoulli's Equation

68. Water from a faucet can fill a 4.00-L bucket in 1 min. If the diameter of the water pipe feeding the faucet is 12.5 mm, what is the speed of the water in the pipe? •

69. The water behind a dam built across one end of a large lake is 25.2 m deep. If the dam springs a leak 1.40 m above the lakebed, at what speed does water exit the hole? •

PRACTICE

70. Two tractor trailers, each 16 m long and 4.0 m tall, are parked next to each other as shown in Figure P18.70. A light wind that is blowing at 5.0 m/s in the parking lot but at 20 m/s between the trailers causes the air pressure between them to drop. What is the magnitude of the force exerted by the air on each trailer? (Use 1.0 kg/m^3 for the air mass density.) •

Figure P18.70

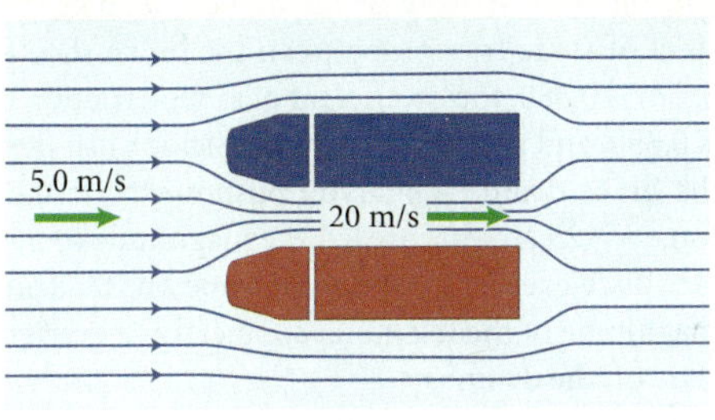

71. Water leaks out of a small hole in the side of a bucket. The hole is a distance d below the surface of the water, and the diameter of the hole is much smaller than the diameter of the bucket. *Principles* Example 18.9 derived an expression for the speed v_2 at which water exits the hole by assuming that $v_1 \approx 0$ for the speed at which the water surface moves downward. Derive an expression for v_2 when v_1 cannot be ignored. ••

72. You carry a fire hose up a ladder to a height of 10.0 m above ground level and aim the nozzle at a burning roof that is 9.00 m high. You hold the hose horizontally and notice that the water strikes the roof at a horizontal distance of 7.0 m from where it exits the nozzle. The hose is connected to a large pressurized chamber in the fire truck 0.500 m above ground level. What is the pressure in the chamber? Ignore air resistance. ••

73. In an aorta that has a radius of 11 mm and a transmural pressure (pressure difference across the aorta wall) of 12 kPa, blood is moving in laminar flow at 350 mm/s. What percentage of the cross-sectional area of this aorta must be blocked in order for the transmural pressure in the blocked part to fall to zero? Assume that the blood has a mass density of 1060 kg/m^3 and is nonviscous, incompressible, and undergoing laminar flow at a speed of 350 mm/s in the unobstructed part. Ignore any pressure variation with height. ••

74. Does the laminar flow of a viscous fluid exhibit the Bernoulli effect? Does Bernoulli's equation (Eq. 18.36) apply to such a liquid? ••

75. A cylindrical tube that is 2.20 m long and has a radius of 150 mm is filled with water. It is oriented with its long central axis vertical, and it is open to the air at the upper end. A hole 80.0 mm in radius is drilled in the bottom, and the water is allowed to drain out. When the water level is half the height of the tube, (*a*) what is the speed of the water exiting though the hole, (*b*) at what rate (in meters cubed per second) is the water leaving the tube, and (*c*) how fast is the top of the water column falling? ••

76. Use integration to obtain an expression for the time interval needed for the water surface in the bucket in Problem 72 (or *Principles* Example 18.9) to drain down to the level of the hole. You can't ignore v_1 anymore, but you can use either the expression for v_2 obtained in Problem 71 or an approximate expression for v_2 that is valid during most of the time interval in which the water is draining. •••

18.8 Viscosity and surface tension

77. A hollow stirrer that has a diameter of 1.0 mm is inserted into a cup of water at 20 °C. The surface tension of water at that temperature is $\gamma = 7.28 \times 10^{-2}$ N/m. What is the mass of the water supported by the surface tension in the stirrer? •

78. You insert a pipette of diameter 0.700 mm into a liquid that is at 20.0 °C and has a mass density of 1261 kg/m^3. If the liquid rises 29.0 mm up the pipette due to surface tension, what is the surface tension of the liquid? •

79. The volume flow rate of water at 20.0 °C through a cylindrical pipe is 2.00×10^{-4} m^3/s. What is the volume flow rate of castor oil moving through this pipe under the same conditions? At 20.0 °C, $\eta_{\text{castor oil}} = 0.986$ Pa · s. •

80. In a low-flow showerhead that contains 18 nozzle holes, the volume flow rate of the water is 4.00 L/min and the water speed is 4.30 m/s. What is the diameter of each hole? ••

81. In the device for measuring surface tension shown in *Principles* Figure 18.58, the length of the movable wire is ℓ. When the film holding the wire in place is water at 20 °C, you must do 1.46 μJ of work on the wire to move it a distance Δx downward. If the film were instead mercury at the same temperature, how much work would be required to move the wire a distance $\Delta x/2$? The surface tensions at 20 °C are 7.28×10^{-2} N/m for water and 0.465 N/m for mercury. ••

82. A horizontal pipeline is 500 mm in diameter and carries oil at a rate of 150 kg/s. This oil has a mass density of 850 kg/m^3 and a viscosity of 0.224 Pa·s at the temperature of the pipeline. If the pressure in the oil is 3.75 atm at the front end, how long can the pipeline be so that the pressure at the far end is no less than 2.50 atm? ••

83. Water from a faucet fills a bathtub with 100 L of water in 5.00 min. That water travels through a cylindrical pipe that has a diameter of 12.5 mm. What is the maximum speed of the water? ••

84. The archerfish can form a tube by curling its tongue against a groove in the top of its mouth and then snapping shut its gills. The fish can then spit a stream of water at its prey (Figure P18.84). One archerfish was observed shooting a stream of water to a height of 1.86 m, and his tongue tube was measured to be 1.60 mm in diameter. What is the minimum volume flow rate of the spit water? ••

Figure P18.84

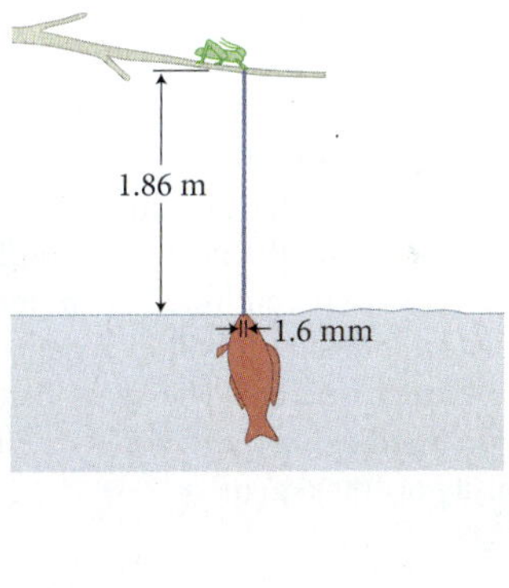

PRACTICE

85. Two horizontal cylindrical pipes are connected together, and a viscous liquid undergoes laminar flow through them. The first pipe has radius R_1 and length ℓ_1, and the second has radius R_2 and length $2\ell_1$. If the pressure where the pipes connect is midway between the pressures at the other ends of the pipes, how does R_2 compare with R_1? ••

86. A liquid of viscosity 0.456 Pa • s and mass density 882 kg/m^3 flows through a pipe at a volume flow rate of 2.00 $\text{m}^3\text{/s}$. You need to increase this rate to 8.50 $\text{m}^3\text{/s}$ by adding to the liquid a substance that will change its viscosity but not appreciably affect its mass density. (*a*) If nothing else (including the pressure difference) changes, what new viscosity value do you need in order to achieve the desired volume flow rate? What is the *mass* flow rate, in kilograms per second, (*b*) before you change the viscosity and (*c*) after you make the change? ••

87. Drops of an oil that has a mass density of 700 kg/m^3 are released from a broken undersea oil pipe that is 1000 m below the ocean surface. (*a*) If the drops have an average diameter of 100 μm, how long do they take to rise to the surface? Hint: The drops quickly reach terminal speed and experience a viscous drag force of magnitude $F^{d}_{wo} = (0.0200 \text{ Pa} \cdot \text{s})Rv$, where R is the radius of the drops and v is their speed. (*b*) After a chemical dispersant is applied to the oil to reduce the average drop diameter to 2.0 μm, how long do the drops take to rise to the surface? Use 1000 kg/m^3 for the mass density of ocean water. •••

88. Consider the cylindrical outer surface of the column of liquid in a tube of length ℓ and radius R. Imagine slicing this surface into two half cylinders along the long central axis of the pipe. Show, by integration, that Eq. 18.52 is valid—that is, (*a*) that the magnitude of the force due to the pressure difference $P_{in} - P_{out}$ across the right semi-cylindrical surface (balanced by the force due to the surface tension due to the left half) is equal to the pressure difference $(P_{in} - P_{out})$ times $2\ell R$, and (*b*) that the direction of this force is perpendicular to the pipe length and bisects the semi-cylindrical surface. •••

Additional Problems

89. A liquid moves through a pipe of diameter d at volume flow rate Q_1. When the pipe diameter is reduced to $d/4$ while the pressure is held constant, what is the new volume flow rate Q_2 in terms of Q_1? •

90. A blood vessel has a diameter of 3.20 mm because it is partially clogged by cholesterol. You want to remove enough cholesterol to double the volume flow rate of the blood through the vessel without changing its speed. What should be the new vessel diameter? Assume the blood is nonviscous and the flow is laminar. •

91. Europa, a satellite of Jupiter, appears to have a liquid ocean of water below an ice layer on its surface. The acceleration due to gravity at the surface is 1.3 m/s^2, and there is no atmosphere. You are designing a probe to descend into Europa's ocean, and it must withstand the pressure 125 m deep in that ocean. When you are testing the probe here on Earth, how deep in Earth's ocean should you lower the probe to have it experience the same pressure it will experience when it is 125 m down in Europa's ocean? The mass density of seawater is 1025 kg/m^3, and assume the water in Europa's ocean has a mass density of 1000 kg/m^3. •

92. Estimate how much the air surrounding your body affects the scale reading when you stand on a spring scale. ••

93. In an automobile braking system, the brake pedal pushes on one end of a column of liquid (the *brake fluid*) in a rigid tube. At the other end of the tube, the liquid presses on a piston attached to a brake shoe that pushes against the brake drum and slows the car's wheel by friction. In one such system, the diameter of the tube at which the brake pedal pushes is 12.0 mm, the diameter of the piston at the brake drum is 44.0 mm, and the mass density of the liquid is 850 kg/m^3. The coefficient of static friction between the brake shoe and the brake drum is 0.880, the coefficient of kinetic friction between them is 0.650, and the piston and brake shoe push perpendicular to the brake drum. When you push on the brake pedal with a force of 125 N, what are (*a*) the magnitude of the normal contact force exerted by the brake shoe on the drum and (*b*) the magnitude of the frictional contact force exerted by the brake shoe on the drum? ••

94. A thick layer of oil of mass density 800 kg/m^3 floats atop (but does not mix with) water in a deep container. You gently place a sphere of uniform mass density in the container so that it floats with 65.0% of its volume in the water and the remaining 35.0% in the oil. What is the mass density of the material of which the sphere is made? ••

95. In bubble tea with pearls, a popular drink from Taiwan, balls of tapioca are put into cold tea mixed with sugar and milk. Some of the balls fall to the bottom of the cup, others rise to the surface, and a few hang motionless in the liquid. (*a*) If the tea mixture has a mass density of 1350 kg/m^3, what is the approximate mass of a ball that neither rises nor falls and just fits into a straw that has a diameter of 10 mm? (*b*) Do you expect the ball to continue to hang motionless if the temperature of the mixture changes? ••

96. A cubical box measures 1.50 m on each side and has a mass of 3000 kg. Its walls are made of a dense but very thin metal, and the box is placed upright in a lake. (*a*) Once equilibrium is achieved, how far below the lake surface is the bottom of the box? (*b*) If you slowly add water to the box, how deep can the water level in the box be before the box sinks? Assume that the box always remains level. ••

97. On a planet the same size as Earth, ocean water has a mass density of 1000 kg/m^3. A space probe measures the atmospheric pressure at the surface of this planet to be 2.40×10^5 Pa. At a depth of 150 m in the ocean, the probe reports a pressure of 14.4×10^5 Pa. What is the mass of the planet? ••

98. A fire hose shoots water from ground level at an angle of 60.0° above the horizontal, with negligible air resistance. The initial speed of the water is such that the water strikes a building horizontally at a height of 25.0 m above the ground. The diameter of the cylindrical hose is 0.120 m at the location where the water exits. What are (*a*) the volume flow rate of water leaving the hose and (*b*) the mass flow rate of that water in kilograms per second? ••

99. A spherical measuring device of radius 250 mm and mass density 1500 kg/m^3 is suspended under water by two wires. Wire A pulls horizontally to the left on the sphere, and wire B pulls upward and to the right at an angle of 50.0° above the horizontal. Calculate the tension in each wire. ••

100. A long *evacuated* tube has a cross-sectional area of 1.50×10^{-3} m^2 and is permanently sealed at one end but can be opened at the other. When the tube is opened while oriented vertically with its open end just below the surface of the liquid in a large open beaker, the liquid rises to a height of 1.28 m in the tube. If the air pressure in the room is 1.00 atm, what is the mass density of the liquid? ••

101. A large iceberg in the shape of a cube has a mass density of 917 kg/m^3 and floats upright in seawater that has a mass density of 1024 kg/m^3. (*a*) If the sides of the cube measure 75.0 m, what is the iceberg's frequency of oscillation? Hint: First show that the motion is simple harmonic. (*b*) What would be the frequency of a cube-shaped iceberg that was twice as massive? Solve this part by proportional reasoning. ••

102. A cylindrical log of length ℓ and radius R floats horizontally half submerged in a liquid of mass density ρ. (*a*) By direct integration of the pressure over the surface of the log, calculate the vector sum of the upward forces exerted on the log by the liquid. (*b*) Show that your answer in part *a* is consistent with Archimedes' principle. •••

103. Working on a team designing a new cargo ship, you have been charged with investigating what dimensions enable a steel ship to carry as much cargo as possible. Certainly the larger the ship, the more cargo it can carry, but you are given a fixed amount of steel with which to work. Assume the ship can be modeled as a box of any dimensions. You realize at once that you cannot use the design with the smallest mass density. ••• CR

104. Watching a parent and child balancing on a seesaw, you begin to wonder what effect the buoyant force exerted by the surrounding air might have on the distance each of them must be from the pivot to achieve balance. ••• CR

105. You have been given the task of determining, for a redwood tree 100 m tall, the mechanisms that allow the tree to grow to such a height and the mechanisms that prevent it from growing any taller. Using your knowledge of fluid dynamics, you determine that capillary rise causes water to rise a height h through a tree's xylem (the hollow tubelike cells in trees that carry water), and for a xylem radius r, this height is approximately given by $h = (0.137\ \text{J/m}^2)/(\rho_{\text{water}} g r)$. Using a microscope, you observe that the xylem has a diameter of about 5 μm. You are convinced that a mechanism other than capillary rise is needed to enable the water to rise to the top leaves. ••• CR

Answers to Review Questions

1. The three types are tensile/compressive stress, bulk stress, and shear stress. Tensile stress is caused by equal-magnitude forces exerted in opposite directions on an object in such a way as to elongate the object along the line of action of the forces; compressive stress is caused by equal-magnitude forces exerted in opposite directions in such a way as to shorten the object along the line of action of the forces. Bulk stress is the result of forces that are exerted equally on all surfaces of an object and cause the object's volume to decrease. Shear stress is caused by forces exerted in opposite directions on opposite surfaces of an object, causing the object's shape to "shear" along the line of action of the forces.
2. Nonviscous liquids cannot support shear stress and so remain unchanged when such stress is exerted; examples include water, gasoline, ethanol, and mercury. Viscous liquids can sustain shear stress, which means that the shape of a given volume of such a liquid changes when subject to shear stress; examples include jelly, tar, molasses, and honey.
3. A gas that is experiencing bulk stress compresses, which means the volume of the sample decreases and its mass density increases. A liquid is essentially incompressible and so does not undergo any change in volume or mass density when subject to bulk stress.
4. For a given force magnitude, pressure is defined as the ratio of the magnitude of the force exerted by the fluid on a surface to the area of that surface, $P = F/A$. Two principal differences are: (1) Force is a vector and pressure is a scalar, and (2) because pressure depends on the surface area over which a force is exerted, two forces of the same magnitude can cause very different pressures if those forces are exerted over different surface areas.
5. The gravitational force exerted by Earth on the fluid causes the pressure in the fluid to be greatest at the bottom of the container and to decrease with height in the container.
6. The pressure change is transmitted equally to all locations throughout the liquid. This is Pascal's principle.
7. The magnitude of the buoyant force on the object is equal to the magnitude of the gravitational force exerted by Earth on the volume of fluid displaced by the object.
8. If the magnitude of the force of gravity exerted on the object is greater than the buoyant force exerted on it, the object sinks. Otherwise, it floats.
9. The object must be designed in such a way that the magnitude of the gravitational force exerted on the object is smaller than the magnitude of the gravitational force exerted on the volume of water displaced by the object. Such a design is usually achieved by making all or part of the object hollow.
10. In laminar flow, streamlines maintain their shape and relative positions; in turbulent flow, they change erratically.
11. Viscosity is the property of a fluid that measures the fluid's resistance to shear stress. Viscous fluids have high viscosity and tend not to flow easily even when experiencing shear stress. Nonviscous fluids have low or zero viscosity and flow easily.
12. The factors are the flow speed, the shape of the object, and the viscosity of the fluid.
13. Streamlining an object means adjusting its shape to maintain streamline flow around the object. This minimizes energy dissipation when the object moves at high speeds relative to the fluid.
14. The different spacings tell you that the fluid's speed is different in the two parts. The speed is greatest where the streamlines are closest together and smallest where they are farthest apart.
15. The pressure in the fluid is greatest where the speed is smallest and smallest where the speed is greatest.
16. When the particles are far apart, as in a gas, they exert no appreciable force on each other. When the separation distance is equal to a few particle diameters, which is typical of particles in a liquid, the particles exert cohesive forces on each other. At separation distances smaller than one particle diameter, as happens when gas particles collide with each other, the particles exert repulsive forces on each other.
17. Each interior particle has neighbors in all directions, which means that the vector sum of the cohesive forces exerted by neighbors on the particle in question is zero. Each surface particle has no liquid particles above it, so the vector sum of the cohesive forces exerted on it by all its neighbors is nonzero. The resultant force on the surface particle is directed inward and causes the surface particles to act like a membrane that is under tension.
18. The tension in the elastic membrane increases as the radius of curvature increases, whereas the surface tension in a liquid surface is independent of the radius of curvature of the surface.
19. The determining factor is the contact angle between liquid and surface. If the contact angle is smaller than 90°, the liquid wets the solid surface; if the contact angle is greater than 90°, the liquid does not wet the surface.
20. If the liquid is able to wet the tube walls (water in a glass tube, say), the meniscus is concave as viewed from above. If the liquid does not wet the walls (mercury in a glass tube, say), the meniscus is convex as viewed from above.
21. The gravitational force exerted on the fluid, the motion of the fluid, and collisions between fluid particles (or between particles and container walls) contribute to the pressure in all fluids. Surface tension contributes to the pressure only in liquids.
22. At sea level, the change in atmospheric pressure with height is 12 Pa/m, which means the difference for a person 2 m tall is about 24 Pa.
23. Hydrostatic pressure is that part of the pressure at any location in a liquid that results from the gravitational force. In a stationary liquid, with constant mass density, hydrostatic pressure decreases linearly with height in the liquid.
24. The object floats if its average mass density ρ_{av} is smaller than the mass density ρ_f of the fluid, hangs motionless if ρ_{av} is the same as ρ_f, and sinks if ρ_{av} is greater than ρ_f.
25. Gauge pressure is the pressure shown on the indicator of a pressure gauge. When the gauge is used to measure the pressure inside any container, the gauge pressure tells you the pressure in excess of atmospheric pressure. The gauge is itself under atmospheric pressure, and so the pressure it records is any pressure above atmospheric pressure. The true pressure in the fluid is thus the recorded value plus 1×10^5 Pa of atmospheric pressure.
26. A hydraulic system consists of two or more liquid-filled cylinders connected to one another, each cylinder fitted with a piston. The pressure created in the liquid when a force is exerted on one piston is transmitted equally to all parts of the liquid, which means that a force is exerted on all the other pistons. Force is multiplied in the system if the surface area of the piston on which the initial force is exerted is smaller than the surface area of the other pistons. Because $F = PA$ and P is the same everywhere in the liquid, the magnitude of the force exerted by the larger-surface-area pistons is greater than the magnitude of the initial force exerted.
27. There is no difference in the masses because the mass of liquid passing *any* point along the tube length is the same as the mass passing all other points, as expressed by the continuity equation (Eq. 18.23).
28. The pressure is lower at whichever location is higher (Eq. 18.36).

29. The pressure is lower in the small-diameter portion because the flow speed here is higher than the flow speed in the large-diameter portion (Eqs. 18.24 and 18.36).
30. A velocity gradient is a measure of the rate at which one fluid layer moves relative to an adjacent layer or, expressed another way, a measure of how quickly the fluid velocity changes with distance perpendicular to the flow direction.
31. In general, the viscosity of liquids decreases as temperature increases, and the viscosity of gases increases as temperature increases.
32. The law says that the volume flow rate is directly proportional to the fourth power of the tube radius and inversely proportional to the viscosity of the fluid: $Q = (\pi R^4/8\eta\ell)(P_1 - P_2)$.
33. Increasing the surface area means that work is done by surface tension forces. Increasing the surface area also means bringing more particles from the interior of the liquid to its surface, which reduces the number of bonds between particles. The work done by the surface tension forces equals the energy required to break these bonds.
34. The pressure is greater inside (on the concave side of the surface); the difference is proportional to the surface tension and inversely proportional to the radius of curvature. Quantitatively, this is given by Laplace's law: $P_{in} = (\gamma/R) + P_{out}$ for a cylindrical surface, and $P_{in} = (2\gamma/R) + P_{out}$ for a spherical surface, where γ is the surface tension of the liquid and R is the radius of curvature of the surface.

Answers to Guided Problems

Guided Problem 18.2 $R = 0.98$ m for helium

Guided Problem 18.4 This is a proof that $F = (P_{in} - P_{out})\pi R^2$.

Guided Problem 18.6
$v_{max} = 7.3$ m/s, $Q_{mass} = 8.5 \times 10^6$ kg/s, $Q_{energy} = 2.3 \times 10^8$ J/s

Guided Problem 18.8 $P_2 - P_1 = -1.6 \times 10^3$ Pa, greater pressure at bottom (narrow) end

PRACTICE

19 PRACTICE Entropy

PRACTICE

Chapter Summary

Entropy of a closed system (Sections 19.1, 19.2, 19.3, 19.5)

Concepts The **probability** of an event is the fraction of times it occurs in a large number of repetitions.

The **macrostate** of a system is that state described by its large-scale properties (on a scale much larger than molecular size), such as volume, pressure, and temperature. The **basic state** of a system is that state described in terms of the properties of the particles that make up the system, such as their position and velocity.

If the interaction between different parts of a system randomizes the distribution of energy in the system, then each particle in the system tends to have an equal share of that energy (**equipartition of energy**), and the particles tend to distribute themselves uniformly in the available volume (**equipartition of space**).

Quantitative Tools If a closed volume of space containing N distinguishable particles is divided into M distinguishable equal-sized compartments, the number of basic states Ω in the system is

$$\Omega = M^N. \qquad (19.1)$$

The **entropy** S of a system is a unitless quantity that is a measure of the number of basic states in the system and is defined as

$$S \equiv \ln \Omega. \qquad (19.4)$$

For a gas that contains N particles confined to a closed system, if the volume of the gas changes from V_i to V_f, the entropy change of the gas is

$$\Delta S = N \ln\left(\frac{V_f}{V_i}\right). \qquad (19.8)$$

The second law of thermodynamics (Sections 19.4, 19.5)

Concepts The **equilibrium state** of a system is the macrostate that has the greatest number of basic states and is therefore the most probable macrostate. At equilibrium, the number of basic states reaches its maximum value Ω_{max}, and the entropy of the system is a maximum.

Second law of thermodynamics (entropy law): A closed system always evolves so as to maximize the number of basic states Ω. When this number has reached a maximum, the system is in equilibrium.

For a system that is not closed, the entropy can increase, decrease, or stay the same.

An **ideal gas** consists of a very large number of particles that occupy a very small fraction of the volume of their container and interact with one another only during collisions that randomize the energy distribution and the spatial distribution of the particles.

Quantitative Tools For a closed system evolving toward equilibrium, the entropy increases:

$$\Delta S > 0. \qquad (19.5)$$

For a closed system at equilibrium, $\Omega = \Omega_{max}$ and the entropy does not change:

$$\Delta S = 0. \qquad (19.6)$$

These two equations, collectively called the **entropy law,** are a mathematical expression of the second law of thermodynamics.

If a system consists of two subsystems, A and B, the number of basic states for the system is

$$\Omega = \Omega_A \Omega_B \qquad (19.9)$$

and the entropy of the system is

$$S = S_A + S_B. \qquad (19.10)$$

Entropy and energy (Section 19.6)

Concepts In a monatomic ideal gas, the internal structure of the atoms can be ignored. For this reason, the thermal energy E_{th} of the gas is the incoherent kinetic energy of all the atoms.

If two gases are in **thermal equilibrium,** their absolute temperatures are the same. In this condition, thermal energy is equipartitioned over the system and the entropy of the system is a maximum.

Quantitative Tools The **root-mean-square speed** v_{rms} of a gas is the square root of the average of the squares of the speeds of all the atoms of the gas:

$$v_{rms} \equiv \sqrt{(v^2)_{av}}. \qquad (19.21)$$

If a monatomic ideal gas contains N atoms, each of mass m, the average kinetic energy of an atom is

$$K_{av} \equiv \tfrac{1}{2}m(v^2)_{av} = \tfrac{1}{2}mv_{rms}^2 = \frac{E_{th}}{N}. \qquad (19.27)$$

If the thermal energy of a monatomic ideal gas changes from $E_{th,i}$ to $E_{th,f}$, the resulting entropy change is

$$\Delta S = \tfrac{3}{2} N \ln\left(\frac{E_{th,f}}{E_{th,i}}\right). \tag{19.33}$$

The **absolute temperature** T of a gas, measured in **kelvins,** is related to the rate at which the entropy of the gas changes with respect to its thermal energy:

$$\frac{1}{k_B T} \equiv \frac{dS}{dE_{th}}, \tag{19.38}$$

where k_B is the **Boltzmann constant:**

$$k_B = 1.381 \times 10^{-23}\ \mathrm{J/K}. \tag{19.39}$$

Properties of a monatomic ideal gas (Sections 19.7, 19.8)

Quantitative Tools The pressure in a monatomic ideal gas containing N atoms at an absolute temperature T and occupying a volume V is

$$P = \tfrac{2}{3}\frac{E_{th}}{V}, \tag{19.48}$$

and the thermal energy of the gas is

$$E_{th} = \tfrac{3}{2} N k_B T. \tag{19.50}$$

The **ideal gas law** applied to the gas is

$$P = \frac{N}{V} k_B T. \tag{19.51}$$

The average kinetic energy of its atoms is

$$K_{av} = \tfrac{1}{2} m v_{rms}^2 = \tfrac{3}{2} k_B T, \tag{19.52}$$

where m is the mass of each atom, and their root-mean-square speed is

$$v_{rms} = \sqrt{\frac{3 k_B T}{m}}. \tag{19.53}$$

If the gas is in equilibrium, its entropy is

$$S = N \ln(T^{3/2} V) + \text{constant}. \tag{19.60}$$

If the gas changes from an equilibrium state having T_i and V_i to one having T_f and V_f, its entropy change is

$$\Delta S = \tfrac{3}{2} N \ln\left(\frac{T_f}{T_i}\right) + N \ln\left(\frac{V_f}{V_i}\right). \tag{19.61}$$

PRACTICE

Review Questions

Answers to these questions can be found at the end of this chapter.

19.1 States

1. What is the distinction between the kinetic energy of a swinging pendulum and the kinetic energy of all the molecules in the air surrounding the pendulum?
2. What is Brownian motion?
3. For a system consisting of a large number of objects, what is the difference between the system's macrostates and its basic states?
4. What does it mean to say that energy is quantized?
5. What is the recurrence time of a system?

19.2 Equipartition of energy

6. How is the energy of a system shared among the system's randomly interacting parts?
7. In a system made up of N particles, how is the average energy of a given particle related to the thermal energy E_{th} of the system?

19.3 Equipartition of space

8. With a container divided by porous walls into five equal-sized compartments, how many basic states are possible in a three-particle system if the system's macrostate is two particles confined to compartment 1?
9. How do the particles in a sample of gas distribute themselves in the volume occupied by the sample, and what is this phenomenon called?

19.4 Evolution toward the most probable macrostate

10. For a given system, what distinguishes the equilibrium state from all other possible macrostates for the system?
11. What is the underlying reason for irreversibility?
12. What tendency of natural systems gives us our sense of time moving in one direction only?
13. State the second law of thermodynamics.
14. Is the entropy of Earth necessarily increasing?

19.5 Dependence of entropy on volume

15. What are the conditions that define an ideal gas?
16. What is the statistical definition of entropy?
17. What is the entropy law?
18. Does the second law of thermodynamics apply to all systems in the universe?
19. How does a change in the volume of a closed system containing an ideal gas initially at equilibrium affect the entropy of the gas?
20. What is the relationship between the individual entropies of two systems and the entropy of the system formed by the combination of the two original systems?

19.6 Dependence of entropy on energy

21. What is the root-mean-square speed of the particles in a sample of gas?
22. How does the entropy of a sample of a monatomic ideal gas containing N particles change as the thermal energy of the gas changes?
23. Define the absolute temperature of an ideal gas in terms of its entropy and thermal energy.
24. If two ideal gases, A and B, are in thermal equilibrium, what is the relationship between their absolute temperatures?

19.7 Properties of a monatomic ideal gas

25. What two atomic parameters determine the pressure in a monatomic ideal gas?
26. State the ideal gas law in words.
27. Under what conditions is the ideal gas law a good description of the behavior of real gases?
28. Which two parameters of a monatomic ideal gas at equilibrium determine the root-mean-square speed of the gas atoms, and what is the equation expressing this speed?

19.8 Entropy of a monatomic ideal gas

29. For a monatomic ideal gas, which three macroscopic parameters determine how the entropy of the system changes as the gas changes from one equilibrium state to a different equilibrium state?
30. How does the change in entropy as a gas changes from one equilibrium state to another depend on how that change takes place?

Developing a Feel

Make an order-of-magnitude estimate of each of the following quantities. Letters in parentheses refer to hints below. Use them as needed to guide your thinking. For simplicity, you can treat the air as a monatomic ideal gas in any situations involving air.

1. The number of basic states of one page of text in this book [C, Q]
2. The time interval needed for one person typing letters randomly to produce the first ten letters of Shakespeare's *Hamlet* [E, W]
3. The population of Manhattan, New York, if Earth's population were equipartitioned by land area [F, T, X, I]
4. The entropy change if all the gas particles in the air in your bedroom moved so as to occupy only the top half of the room [M, S]
5. The entropy change when a helium balloon deflates in your bedroom overnight [B, H, M, Y]
6. The entropy increase of the gas particles in the air in your car tire as it heats up while you drive (assume that air is a monatomic ideal gas) [A, G, O, Z]
7. Root-mean-square speed of the gas particles in air at room temperature [K, V]
8. Root-mean-square speed of atoms in a sample of helium gas at a temperature just above the boiling point of helium [J, P]
9. The thermal energy of the atmosphere [N, V, D, R]
10. The entropy change of the atmosphere over the United States from 2:00 p.m. to 2:00 a.m. [L, N, V, D, R, U, Z]

Hints

A. What is the temperature change?
B. What is the volume of a balloon?
C. How many characters are on a page?
D. How many gas particles are there in the atmosphere?
E. What is the probability of having a random ten-letter sequence match a specific ten-letter sequence?
F. What is Earth's population?
G. What is the volume of the air in your car tires?
H. How many helium atoms are in the balloon?
I. What is the area of Manhattan?
J. What is the boiling temperature of helium?
K. What is an average room temperature?
L. What is the temperature change?
M. What is the volume of a typical bedroom?
N. What is the mass of Earth's atmosphere?
O. How many gas particles are in your tires?
P. What is the mass of a helium atom?
Q. How many basic states does one character have?
R. What is the average temperature of the atmosphere?
S. How many gas particles are contained in the volume of air in the room?
T. What is the surface area of Earth?
U. What fraction of Earth's atmosphere is over the United States?
V. What is the mass of one gas particle?
W. How many letters per second do you type?
X. What fraction of Earth's surface is land?
Y. What is the change in temperature?
Z. What is the change in volume of air?

Key (all values approximate)

A. 1×10^1 K; **B.** 3×10^{-3} m^3; **C.** 4×10^3 characters/page (each position on a page is one possible "compartment" for each character); **D.** 1×10^{44} particles; **E.** 1 in $26^{10} = 7 \times 10^{-15}$; **F.** 7×10^9 people; **G.** 2×10^{-2} m^3; **H.** 7×10^{22} atoms; **I.** 6×10^7 m^2; **J.** 4 K; **K.** 3×10^2 K; **L.** decrease of 1×10^1 K; **M.** 3×10^1 m^3; **N.** 5×10^{18} kg; **O.** 1×10^{24}; **P.** 7×10^{-27} kg; **Q.** 1×10^2 basic states (each basic state possible is one of the 26 letters of the alphabet, upper and lower case, plus numerals, symbols, and punctuation); **R.** lower than 3×10^2 K; **S.** 7×10^{26} particles; **T.** 5×10^{14} m^2; **U.** 2×10^{-2}; **V.** air is mainly nitrogen gas (N_2) of molecular mass 5×10^{-26} kg; **W.** 4 letters/s; **X.** 0.3; **Y.** assume no change in temperature. **Z.** assume no change in volume

PRACTICE

Worked and Guided Problems

These examples involve material from this chapter but are not associated with any particular section. Some examples are worked out in detail; others you should work out by following the guidelines provided.

Worked Problem 19.1 Counting basic states

A closed wooden box has three identical holes—1, 2, and 3—of diameter d_{hole} cut into one side. Five indistinguishable balls, each of diameter $d_{ball} < d_{hole}$, are placed inside the box, and the box is shaken until all five have fallen out through one of the holes. What is the probability of two of the balls (and only two) falling through hole 1?

❶ **GETTING STARTED** We are told that a box containing five balls is shaken until all the balls fall out through one of three holes—1, 2, and 3—and we are asked to determine the probability of two of the balls exiting through hole 1. Thus we imagine gathering up the balls each time the box empties, placing them back in the box, shaking until the box is again empty, and repeating this action many times. Each emptying of the box is one *event*, and our task is to determine the fraction of this large number of repetitions that has two of the balls falling through hole 1.

Let N_1 be the number of balls that fall through hole 1 in any given event, N_2 be the number that fall through hole 2 in that event, and N_3 be the number that fall through hole 3. We identify a macrostate of the system as being the number of balls that fall through hole 1, and there are six possible macrostates: $N_1 = 0, 1, 2, 3, 4, 5$. In order to determine the probability of the macrostate $N_1 = 2$, we need to count the basic states possible for each of the six macrostates.

❷ **DEVISE PLAN** We can count the number of basic states associated with each of the six macrostates $N_1 = 0$, $N_1 = 1$, $N_1 = 2$, $N_1 = 3$, $N_1 = 4$, $N_1 = 5$. We can then count the number of basic states Ω_{tot} associated with the system and the number of basic states $\Omega(N_1 = 2)$ associated with the macrostate $N_1 = 2$ (two balls falling through hole 1). The probability of two balls falling through hole 1 is then the fraction $\Omega(N_1 = 2)/\Omega_{tot}$.

❸ **EXECUTE PLAN** The macrostate $N_1 = 0$ (no balls through hole 1) has six basic states, $\Omega(N_1 = 0) = 6$:

$$(0, 5, 0),\ (0, 4, 1),\ (0, 3, 2),\ (0, 2, 3),\ (0, 1, 4),\ (0, 0, 5),$$

where each triplet representing a basic state is of the form (N_1, N_2, N_3). The macrostate $N_1 = 1$ has five basic states, $\Omega(N_1 = 1) = 5$:

$$(1, 4, 0),\ (1, 3, 1),\ (1, 2, 2),\ (1, 1, 3),\ (1, 0, 4),$$

the macrostate $N_1 = 2$ has four, $\Omega(N_1 = 2) = 4$:

$$(2, 3, 0),\ (2, 2, 1),\ (2, 1, 2),\ (2, 0, 3),$$

the macrostate $N_1 = 3$ has three, $\Omega(N_1 = 3) = 3$:

$$(3, 2, 0),\ (3, 1, 1),\ (3, 0, 2),$$

the macrostate $N_1 = 4$ has two, $\Omega(N_1 = 4) = 2$:

$$(4, 1, 0),\ (4, 0, 1),$$

and the macrostate $N_1 = 5$ has one, $\Omega(N_1 = 5) = 1$:

$$(5, 0, 0).$$

The number of basic states available to the system is then

$$\Omega_{tot} = \sum_{i=0}^{i=5} \Omega(i) = 6 + 5 + 4 + 3 + 2 + 1 = 21.$$

The probability of two balls exiting through hole 1 is the fraction

$$\frac{\Omega(N_1 = 2)}{\Omega_{tot}} = \tfrac{4}{21}. \checkmark$$

❹ **EVALUATE RESULT** We assumed that there is an equal probability for each of the five balls to pass through each of the three holes, which is the only sensible assumption based on the information given. We do not know the size of the holes compared to the size of the balls, except that the holes must be large enough for a ball to pass through. Depending on the hole size, each hole is at least partially blocked for a short time interval as a ball passes through it, but we have no way to take this into account without further information.

Our numerical result indicates a probability just over 19% that two balls will pass through hole 1. There are six different numbers of balls that might fall through hole 1 (0, 1, 2, 3, 4, or 5), so we might naively expect the probability that exactly two balls will pass through is one out of six, or just under 17%. However, our analysis shows that each of these six outcomes is not equally probable, so we should not expect this to exactly match our computed result. Our list of macrostates also allows us to compute the average number of balls falling through hole 1 by summing the product of the number of balls through hole 1 and the probability of the corresponding macrostate:

$$0\left(\tfrac{6}{21}\right) + 1\left(\tfrac{5}{21}\right) + 2\left(\tfrac{4}{21}\right) + 3\left(\tfrac{3}{21}\right) + 4\left(\tfrac{2}{21}\right) + 5\left(\tfrac{1}{21}\right) = \left(\tfrac{35}{21}\right) = \tfrac{5}{3}.$$

This makes sense because there are five balls that can fall through any one of three holes, and so the average number of balls falling through any hole should be 5/3. Two balls falling through hole 1 is thus more than we would expect on average, and so the probability of this happening should be smaller than average. As a rough upper bound, consider that roughly one-third of the balls should pass through each hole. Because 2 is greater than 5/3, we expect the probability for two balls to pass through hole 1 to be smaller than 33%. Because our result lies between the lower bound of 17% and the upper bound of 33%, it is not unreasonable.

As a final check, we could sum the probabilities for all possible outcomes ($N_1 = 0$ through 5) to check that they add to unity, as all five balls must pass through one of the holes (you may want to verify this yourself).

Guided Problem 19.2 Shared energy

Consider a system consisting of three particles—1, 2, and 3—that share six units of energy. What is the probability that particle 3 has two units of energy?

1 GETTING STARTED

1. Are the particles distinguishable or indistinguishable?
2. Is each energy unit distinguishable or indistinguishable?
3. How should you define your basic states?
4. How might you define your macrostates?

2 DEVISE PLAN

5. How many basic states do you have for each macrostate?
6. How do you calculate the probability that particle 3 has two units of energy?

3 EXECUTE PLAN

7. Describe the basic states associated with each macrostate.

4 EVALUATE RESULT

8. On average, how many energy units do you expect each particle to have?
9. Does your counting of basic states agree with what you expect?

Worked Problem 19.3 Volume and entropy changes

Figure WG19.1 shows a closed system consisting of two monatomic ideal gases that are in thermal equilibrium. A partition that is free to move horizontally keeps the gases separated in compartments X and Y but lets them exchange energy through collisions with the partition. Compartment X has four times as many atoms as compartment Y. The initial number of atoms per unit volume in compartment X is twice the number of atoms per unit volume in compartment Y. The change in entropy of the system as it evolves from this initial macrostate to the equilibrium state is 2.631×10^{23}. Determine the number of gas atoms in compartments X and Y.

Figure WG19.1

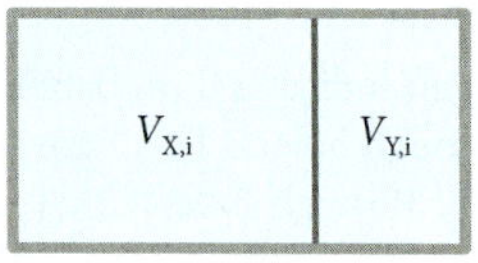

1 GETTING STARTED We are trying to determine the number of gas atoms N_X in compartment X and the number of gas atoms N_Y in compartment Y. We are not given the initial volumes, $V_{X,i}$ and $V_{Y,i}$, or the final volumes, $V_{X,f}$ and $V_{Y,f}$. We know that the volume V of the system is fixed; $V = V_{X,i} + V_{Y,i} = V_{X,f} + V_{Y,f}$. From the initial information given in the problem statement, we know that $N_X = 4N_Y$. Because the gas atoms do not cross through the partition, this relationship holds while the partition moves. We also know that the initial gas atoms per unit volume (number density) in the two compartments are related by $N_X/V_{X,i} = 2N_Y/V_{Y,i}$ of each compartment.

2 DEVISE PLAN Because the gases are in thermal equilibrium and the system is closed, we know that the entropy changes in each compartment are given by Eq. 19.8, $\Delta S = N \ln(V_f/V_i)$. Because entropy is an extensive quantity, the change in entropy of the system is the sum of the changes in the two compartments: $\Delta S = \Delta S_X + \Delta S_Y$ (Eq. 19.10). We know that when the new equilibrium state is reached, the number density of the gas atoms is equal on the two sides of the partition, $N_X/V_{X,f} = N_Y/V_{Y,f}$ (Eq. 19.20). We can use this condition along with the given information relating the number of atoms in each compartment and the number density in each compartment to calculate the volume ratios $V_{X,f}/V_{X,i}$ and $V_{Y,f}/V_{Y,i}$. This allows us to solve Eq. 19.10 for the number of gas atoms in compartment Y. We can then use the given information that $N_X = 4N_Y$ to obtain N_X.

3 EXECUTE PLAN We can combine the given information that $N_X = 4N_Y$ and $N_X/V_{X,i} = 2N_Y/V_{Y,i}$ in order to determine a relationship between the initial volume $V_{Y,i}$ of compartment Y and the initial volume $V_{X,i}$ of compartment X:

$$V_{Y,i} = 2V_{X,i}\frac{N_Y}{N_X} = \frac{V_{X,i}}{2}. \quad (1)$$

We can substitute Eq. 1 into $V = V_{X,i} + V_{Y,i}$ to obtain

$$V = \tfrac{3}{2}V_{X,i}. \quad (2)$$

When the new equilibrium state is reached, the number of gas atoms per volume is the same in compartments X and Y (Eq. 19.20):

$$\frac{N_X}{V_{X,f}} = \frac{N_Y}{V_{Y,f}}. \quad (3)$$

We can combine $N_X = 4N_Y$ and Eq. 3, to obtain a relationship between the final volume $V_{Y,f}$ of compartment Y and the final volume $V_{X,f}$ of compartment X:

$$V_{Y,f} = V_{X,f}\frac{N_Y}{N_X} = \frac{V_{X,f}}{4}. \quad (4)$$

We can substitute Eq. 4 into $V = V_{X,f} + V_{Y,f}$ to obtain

$$V = \tfrac{5}{4}V_{X,f}. \quad (5)$$

Next we combine Eqs. 5 and 2 to determine the ratio of the final and initial volumes of compartment X:

$$\tfrac{5}{4}V_{X,f} = \tfrac{3}{2}V_{X,i} \Rightarrow \frac{V_{X,f}}{V_{X,i}} = \tfrac{6}{5}. \quad (6)$$

We now divide Eq. 4 by Eq. 1 and then use Eq. 6 to determine the ratio of the final and initial volumes of compartment Y:

$$\frac{V_{Y,f}}{V_{Y,i}} = \tfrac{1}{2}\frac{V_{X,f}}{V_{X,i}} = \tfrac{3}{5}. \quad (7)$$

Equations 19.10 and 19.8 provide the change in entropy of the system:

$$\Delta S = \Delta S_X + \Delta S_Y = N_Y\left(4\ln\left(\frac{V_{X,f}}{V_{X,i}}\right) + \ln\left(\frac{V_{Y,f}}{V_{Y,i}}\right)\right). \quad (8)$$

We now use Eqs. 6 and 7 and our given value for the change in entropy in Eq. 8 to solve for the number of particles in compartment Y:

$$N_Y = \frac{\Delta S}{\left(4\ln\left(\frac{V_{X,f}}{V_{X,i}}\right) + \ln\left(\frac{V_{Y,f}}{V_{Y,i}}\right)\right)} = \frac{2.631 \times 10^{23}}{(4\ln\left(\frac{6}{5}\right) + \ln\left(\frac{3}{5}\right))}$$

$$= 1.204 \times 10^{24}. \checkmark$$

The number of particles in compartment X is then $N_X = 4N_Y = 4.817 \times 10^{24}$. ✔

❹ **EVALUATE RESULT** We know that 1 mole corresponds to 6.022×10^{23} gas atoms, so in compartment Y we have 2 moles of gas and in compartment X we have 8 moles of gas. We are not given the initial temperature, pressure, and volume in either compartment, but we know that these quantities must be related by the ideal gas law: $P = Nk_BT/V$ (Eq. 19.51). There is no mention in the problem statement of special heating or cooling apparatus or of a container able to tolerate multiple atmospheres of pressure. At room temperature and 1 atm, 1 mole occupies a volume just exceeding 24 L, which would require a container volume in the range of 250 L, or about one-quarter m^3. Such an apparatus would fit easily on a laboratory table. This lends some credence to our numerical result.

Guided Problem 19.4 Thermal equilibrium

Figure WG19.2 shows a closed system consisting of two monatomic ideal gases separated by a fixed partition that keeps the gases apart but lets them exchange thermal energy. Compartment X contains 6.0×10^{23} atoms, and compartment Y contains 1.5×10^{24} atoms. Initially, the absolute temperature of the gas in compartment X is three times the absolute temperature of the gas in compartment Y. What is the change in entropy of the system as it evolves from this initial macrostate to the equilibrium state?

Figure WG19.2

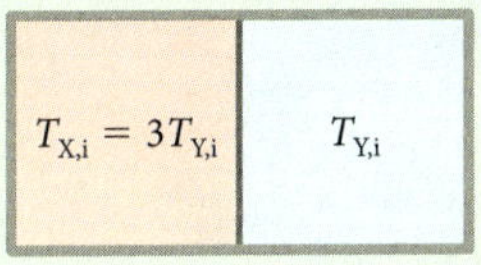

❶ **GETTING STARTED**

1. What changes and what remains the same as the system evolves from the initial state to the equilibrium state?
2. How is the change in entropy of the system related to the changes in entropy of the two gases?

❷ **DEVISE PLAN**

3. How is temperature related to the thermal energy per particle?
4. What fraction of thermal energy resides in each compartment at equilibrium?
5. How is the thermal energy per particle related to the entropy changes in each compartment?

❸ **EXECUTE PLAN**

❹ **EVALUATE RESULT**

6. Which compartment experiences a decrease in temperature, and which an increase?
7. Is the entropy change of the system positive or negative?

Worked Problem 19.5 Cooling an ideal gas

A sample of a monatomic ideal gas containing 6.02×10^{23} atoms occupies a volume of 2.24×10^{-2} m^3 at a pressure of 1.01×10^5 N/m^2. With the volume held constant, the gas is cooled until the atoms are moving at a root-mean-square speed of 4.02×10^2 m/s. If the mass of each atom is 6.646×10^{-27} kg, what is the change in entropy of the gas?

❶ **GETTING STARTED** We are given the number of gas atoms in a sample and their mass, and we are told that the sample is cooled at constant volume. We are also given the value of this volume, the initial pressure, and the final speed of the atoms. Our task is to determine the entropy change for this cooling, but we know from Eq. 19.56, $\Delta S = \frac{3}{2}N\ln(T_f/T_i)$, that in order to do that we need to determine the initial and final temperatures, which are not given.

❷ **DEVISE PLAN** We can use the ideal gas law, Eq. 19.51, to determine the initial temperature of the gas and Eq. 19.53 to determine its final temperature. We then can use Eq. 19.56 to determine the entropy change the gas undergoes as it cools.

❸ **EXECUTE PLAN** For the initial temperature, we write Eq. 19.51 in the form

$$T_i = \frac{P_iV_i}{Nk_B} = \frac{(1.01 \times 10^5 \text{ N/m}^2)(2.24 \times 10^{-2} \text{ m}^3)}{(6.02 \times 10^{23})(1.38 \times 10^{-23} \text{ J/K})} = 272 \text{ K}.$$

For the final temperature, we write Eq. 19.53 in the form

$$T_f = \frac{m(v_{rms,f})^2}{3k_B}$$

$$= \frac{(6.646 \times 10^{-27} \text{ kg})(4.02 \times 10^2 \text{ m/s})^2}{(3)(1.38 \times 10^{-23} \text{ J/K})} = 25.9 \text{ K}.$$

Now Eq. 19.56 gives us the change in entropy of the gas:

$$\Delta S = \frac{3}{2}N\ln\left(\frac{T_f}{T_i}\right)$$

$$= \frac{3}{2}(6.02 \times 10^{23})\ln\left(\frac{25.9}{272}\right) = -2.12 \times 10^{24}. \checkmark$$

❹ **EVALUATE RESULT** A negative entropy change means that the number of basic states available to the atoms in the final macrostate is smaller than the number of basic states available in the initial macrostate. As the gas cools, the root-mean-square speed of the atoms decreases, and so the number of basic states decreases, in agreement with our answer.

Guided Problem 19.6 Heating an ideal gas

A sample of a monatomic ideal gas containing 9.03×10^{23} atoms occupies a constant volume of 4.48×10^{-2} m^3 and is initially at a pressure of 1.01×10^5 N/m^2. The mass of each atom is 6.646×10^{-27} kg. If the gas is heated until the change in entropy is 1.415×10^{23}, what is the final root-mean-square speed of the atoms?

1 GETTING STARTED

1. What quantities do you need to know in order to calculate $v_{\text{rms,f}}$?
2. What quantities are you given?

2 DEVISE PLAN

3. How can you determine the initial temperature of the gas?
4. How can you determine its final temperature?
5. How can you use this information to determine $v_{\text{rms,f}}$?

3 EXECUTE PLAN

6. Calculate the initial absolute temperature.
7. Determine the final absolute temperature using the fact that $e^{\ln(T_f/T_i)} = T_f/T_i$.
8. Calculate the value of $v_{\text{rms,f}}$.

4 EVALUATE RESULT

9. How does this speed compare with the escape speed, 1.1×10^4 m/s, from Earth?
10. Do you expect the number of basic states to increase or decrease?

Worked Problem 19.7 Expansion and entropy change

A sample of a monatomic ideal gas containing 6.00×10^{23} atoms in a volume of 8.00×10^{-3} m^3 is initially in thermal equilibrium with its surroundings at 300 K. The gas is made to expand until the final volume is 6.40×10^{-2} m^3 and the final temperature is 50 K. What is the change in entropy of the gas?

1 GETTING STARTED We are given the number of gas atoms in a sample, the initial and final volumes, and the initial and final absolute temperatures. Our task is to determine the change in entropy of the gas as its volume and temperature change.

2 DEVISE PLAN Both the volume and the temperature of this gas change during the expansion process. We have all the information we need in order to use Eq. 19.61 to calculate the entropy change.

3 EXECUTE PLAN

$$\Delta S = \tfrac{3}{2}N\ln\left(\frac{T_f}{T_i}\right) + N\ln\left(\frac{V_f}{V_i}\right)$$

$$= \tfrac{3}{2}N\ln\left(\frac{50\text{ K}}{300\text{ K}}\right) + N\ln\left(\frac{6.40 \times 10^{-2}\text{ m}^3}{8.00 \times 10^{-3}\text{ m}^3}\right) = -3.6 \times 10^{23}. \checkmark$$

4 EVALUATE RESULT The negative value for ΔS means that the entropy of the system decreases as the system goes from its initial macrostate to its final macrostate. This makes sense because the system is not closed so entropy does not have to increase. The negative change in entropy results from the greater decrease in entropy due to the energy leaving the system compared to the positive increase in entropy due to the volume expansion.

Guided Problem 19.8 Cooling and entropy change

What is the entropy change for a sample of a monatomic ideal gas that contains 1.20×10^{24} atoms when the sample is cooled at constant pressure from 400 K to 300 K?

1 GETTING STARTED

1. What quantities do you need to know in order to calculate the entropy change?
2. What quantities are you given?

2 DEVISE PLAN

3. Does the volume of the gas increase, decrease, or remain the same?
4. You know neither V_f nor V_i, and so how can you use the ideal gas law to remove these variables from your calculation?
5. How can you then calculate the change in entropy?

3 EXECUTE PLAN

6. Determine the relationship between the temperature change and the volume change.
7. Compute the entropy change.

4 EVALUATE RESULT

8. Does a negative entropy change make sense for this situation?

Questions and Problems

For instructor-assigned homework, go to MasteringPhysics® MP

Dots indicate difficulty level of problems: • *= easy,* •• *= intermediate,* ••• *= hard;* CR *= context-rich problem.*

Unless told otherwise, assume all gas particles in these problems behave like the particles of a monatomic ideal gas.

19.1 States

1. With a standard deck of 52 playing cards, what is the probability of randomly picking (*a*) any 8 card and (*b*) any king, queen, jack, or ace? •

2. When two standard dice are thrown, what is the probability that the sum of the dots on the two top faces will be 7? •

3. Particles in a closed container move around and collide with one another and with the walls of the container. There are 5.00×10^{13} basic states possible for this system, and the recurrence time is 365 days. How long is the average time interval between collisions? •

4. A bag contains 10 black jellybeans, 12 green ones, 3 orange ones, and 20 blue ones. If you reach in and grab one randomly, what is the probability of picking (*a*) a black one, (*b*) an orange one, and (*c*) a blue one? ••

5. A manufacturer sells three types of motorcycles—call them types A, B, and C—each available in yellow, red, glossy black, or matte black and each offered with either a 600-cc motor or an 850-cc motor. (*a*) How many configurations are available? (*b*) If each motorcycle is available with 26 different options packages, how many configurations are available? ••

6. When three standard dice are thrown, what is the probability that the sum of the dots on the three top faces will be 4? ••

7. A pendulum is in a container that has been evacuated so that there are only two atoms A and B in the container with the pendulum. If the pendulum initially has six units of energy and the two atoms have none, what is the probability that all six energy units will leave the pendulum and be absorbed by the atoms? ••

8. A pendulum is released from an elevation of 1.15 m and allowed to swing in a room filled with 1.50×10^{21} nitrogen molecules having an average speed of 550 m/s. If the energy of the pendulum is equal to the energy distributed over all the nitrogen molecules, what is the pendulum's mass? The mass of a nitrogen molecule (N_2) is 4.65×10^{-26} kg. ••

9. (*a*) When a coin is tossed five times, which sequence of outcomes is more likely: HHHHH or HTHTH? (*b*) Without regard to order, which is more likely: that in five tosses the coin lands heads-up five times or lands heads-up three times? ••

10. Some musical instruments have valves that can be either opened or closed to produce different tones. How many tones can be produced by a horn that has (*a*) two valves, (*b*) three valves, and (*c*) six valves? (*d*) Some trumpet players do something called *half-valve work*, where they play a valve that is neither fully open nor fully closed. If this technique adds a third possible valve setting, how many tones can be produced with a trumpet that has three valves by a player doing half-valve work? ••

11. Six particles in a container can move in only one of six directions: up, down, left, right, forward, and backward. If they move randomly such that all six collide and change direction every 1.0×10^{-6} s, for how many seconds during a 24-h day are all six particles moving in the same direction? •••

12. An adsorbing filter allows gas particles to stick to locations on the filter surface. Once a particle sticks to a location, that location is filled. The filter can no longer remove gas particles when all locations are filled. Each 1.0 nm^2 of the filter surface has six adsorbing locations, each capable of adsorbing one gas particle. In the volume just adjacent to one 1.0-nm^2 area, there are 100 gas particles. Each of these particles has a slightly different energy, making each particle unique. In how many ways can these 100 particles adsorb onto the six locations? •••

19.2 Equipartition of energy

13. A system contains three particles—A, B, and C—and three units of thermal energy. Determine the probability of one particle having all the energy. •

14. In a system of three particles—A, B, and C—that share nine units of energy, which energy distribution is more likely at a given instant: particle A has two units of energy or particle A has three units of energy? •

15. The air in a room held at a steady temperature T is made up largely of nitrogen molecules ($m_{N_2} = 4.652 \times 10^{-26}$ kg) and oxygen molecules ($m_{O_2} = 5.3135 \times 10^{-26}$ kg). At equilibrium, what is the ratio of the average speed of the nitrogen molecules to the average speed of the oxygen molecules? Even though both gases are diatomic, assume they behave as monatomic gases. ••

16. A closed container initially holds 50 monatomic A particles that have a combined energy of 120 units. After 100 monatomic B particles with a combined energy of 180 units are added to the container, the system is allowed to come to thermal equilibrium. (*a*) At equilibrium, how many energy units does each A particle have? (*b*) How many does each B particle have? ••

17. In a system that contains four distinguishable particles and five units of energy, what is the probability that one particle has all the energy? ••

18. A 0.10-kg pendulum swings inside a box that contains 1.0×10^{23} nitrogen molecules. The initial speed of the pendulum is 0.80 m/s, and it comes to rest in 5.0 min. When the number of nitrogen molecules in the box is increased to 2.5×10^{23} and the experiment is repeated, how many seconds does it take for the pendulum to come to rest? ••

19. If the thermal (incoherent kinetic) energy of a system made up of 1.00 mol of argon atoms (6.02×10^{23} atoms) is 498 J, what is the average speed of each atom? The mass of an argon atom is 6.63×10^{-26} kg. ••

20. To a vessel that contains 1.00 mol of monatomic ideal gas A is added 0.100 mol of monatomic ideal gas B. The mass of each atom of gas A is 3.35×10^{-26} kg, and the mass of each atom of gas B is 1.39×10^{-25} kg. What is the final average speed of the A atoms if the final average speed of the B atoms is 123 m/s? ••

21. Inside a box, a 1.00-kg ball is gently launched from a height of 1.00 m (Figure P19.21). The box contains 1.00 mol of argon atoms, each having a mass of 6.63×10^{-26} kg and moving at an average speed of 100 m/s before the ball is dropped. The ball rebounds elastically against the floor of the box, and so its energy is transferred only to the argon atoms. (*a*) What is the average energy of each argon atom before the ball is dropped? (*b*) After a long time interval has passed, the ball stops bouncing and rests on the box floor. What is the average speed of the argon atoms now? •••

Figure P19.21

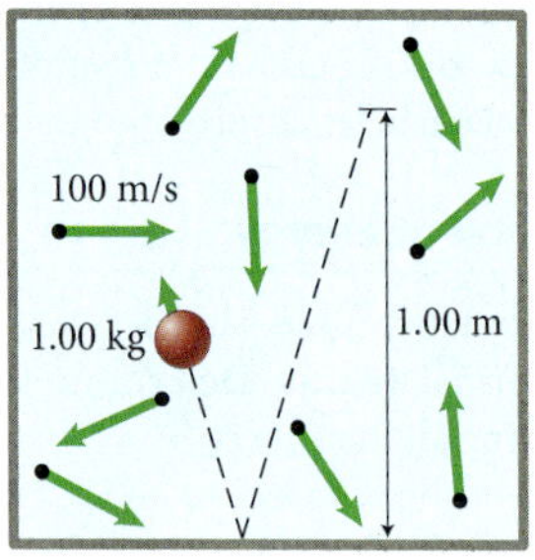

22. A spherical balloon that has a diameter of 0.500 m and contains 1.00 mol of helium gas is left in the Sun for 10.0 min. During that interval, the Sun irradiates the balloon with an average intensity of 1120 W/m², all of which is absorbed. Before being warmed by the Sun, the average speed of the helium atoms is 367 m/s. What is their average speed after being warmed? Assume the balloon diameter remains constant. The mass of a helium atom is 6.646×10^{-27} kg. •••

19.3 Equipartition of space

23. A cube can be envisioned as an assembly of identical octants (numbered 1–8 in no particular order). The cube contains three identical particles. How many basic states in this system yield a macrostate (*a*) in which all three particles are in octant 1 and (*b*) in which two particles are in octant 8? •

24. A box sitting in a room occupies 1/64 of the room volume. When the box is opened, two identical particles are released into the room. What is the probability that at any instant after they are released, the two particles (*a*) return to the box simultaneously and (*b*) occupy the same 1/64 of the room? •

25. Three particles are released into a box that can be thought of as a set of four identical quadrants. How many basic states are possible if the particles are (*a*) indistinguishable from one another and (*b*) distinguishable from one another? ••

26. Four distinguishable particles move freely in a room divided into octants (there are no actual partitions). Let the basic states be given by specifying the octant in which each particle is located. (*a*) Give an example of a macrostate for this system. (*b*) How many basic states are there? (*c*) The door to this room is opened, allowing the particles to move into an adjacent, identical room, also divided into octants. Now that the amount of space that can be occupied has been doubled, by what factor has the number of basic states increased? ••

27. You have six identical particles in a box divided into four quadrants. For a certain experiment, you need to have a certain number of particles in the upper left quadrant. You observe that in a given day, the distribution of particles you need occurs for 51.43 min. How many particles do you need to be in the upper left quadrant in your experiment? ••

28. A cube that has a volume of 1.00 m³ contains N distinguishable particles. Determine the probability that all the particles are in a smaller volume V of the cube if (*a*) $N = 1$, $V = 0.500$ m³; (*b*) $N = 1$, $V = 0.250$ m³; (*c*) $N = 1$, $V = 0.0100$ m³, (*d*) $N = 2$, $V = 0.500$ m³; and (*e*) $N = 4$, $V = 0.500$ m³. ••

29. A space probe measures the number density of particles of interstellar gas by enclosing 1.00 m³ of space and measuring the number of atoms that pass from that volume through a detector in the shape of a cylinder 15.0 mm in diameter and 5.00 mm long. In one area of space, the number density of particles of interstellar gas is assumed to be 1 atom/1.00×10^{-6} m³. Out of a hundred tests, how many times does the detector register the presence of a particle in the cylindrical volume? •••

30. A box divided into four quadrants can hold a maximum of 30 particles in each quadrant. (*a*) If 114 particles are placed in the box, how many basic states and macrostates are possible, if the macrostates are defined as the number of particles in the upper left quadrant? (*b*) What is the most probable number of particles in the upper left quadrant? (*c*) What is the average number of particles in the upper left quadrant? (Hint: Instead of considering where the particles are located, consider where they are not located.) •••

19.4 Evolution toward the most probable macrostate

31. A box divided into compartments A and B contains 14 particles in A and 6 in B. The separating partition allows energy exchange between compartments as the particles collide with the partition. Table P19.31 lists the numbers of basic states possible when 10 energy units are distributed in various combinations over the 20 particles. How much more likely is it for compartment A to contain 7 energy units (macrostate $E_A = 7$, $E_B = 3$) than for this compartment to contain 3 energy units (macrostate $E_A = 3$, $E_B = 7$)? •

32. In how many ways can you distribute 10 indistinguishable energy units over 14 distinguishable particles? (Hint: Use Table P19.31.) •

33. A system has the numbers of macrostates and basic states shown in Table P19.33. (*a*) In which macrostate is the system in equilibrium? (*b*) Which macrostates are least likely? (*c*) How many basic states are possible for the system? (*d*) What is the probability that the system occupies macrostate B? •

34. A box divided into identical compartments A and B contains 25 distinguishable particles in A and 20 distinguishable particles in B. There are nine energy units in the box, initially distributed only among the particles in B. The system is closed, but the energy units can move from one compartment to the other as the particles collide with the separating partition. If one energy unit is exchanged during each partition-particle collision, what is the smallest number of collisions between the particles in B and the partition that must occur before the system reaches equilibrium? ••

35. A box divided into identical compartments A and B contains two distinguishable particles in A and three distinguishable particles in B. There are five energy units in the box, initially shared by the two particles in A. The system is closed, but particles can exchange energy through collisions with the partition. Calculate the number of basic states (*a*) initially and (*b*) once the system has reached equilibrium. ••

PRACTICE

Table P19.31 Number of basic states Ω associated with macrostates having 10 energy units distributed over 20 particles. (This table duplicates Table 19.2 in the *Principles* volume.)

E_A	E_B	Ω_A	Ω_B	$\Omega = \Omega_A\Omega_B$	$\ln \Omega$
Energy units in A	**Energy units in B**	**Corresponding number of basic states for A**	**Corresponding number of basic states for B**	**Corresponding number of basic states for macrostate**	
0	10	1	3003	3.00×10^3	8.01
1	9	14	2002	2.80×10^4	10.2
2	8	105	1287	1.35×10^5	11.8
3	7	560	792	4.44×10^5	13.0
4	6	2380	462	1.10×10^6	13.9
5	5	8568	252	2.16×10^6	14.6
6	4	27,132	126	3.42×10^6	15.0
7	3	77,520	56	4.34×10^6	15.3
8	2	203,490	21	4.27×10^6	15.3
9	1	497,420	6	2.98×10^6	14.9
10	0	1,144,066	1	1.14×10^6	14.0
Total		1,961,256	8008	$\Omega_{tot} = 2.00 \times 10^7$	

Table P19.33

Macrostate	Associated number of basic states
A	1
B	4
C	6
D	4
E	1

36. A box like the one in Problem 31 has two particles in compartment A, two particles in compartment B, and four energy units to be distributed. (*a*) Construct a table like Table P19.31 for this setup. (*b*) Does equipartition of energy take place even with such a small number of particles? ••

37. System 1 is in equilibrium, and a separate system 2 is also in equilibrium. The systems are independent of each other but have an equal probability of being in equilibrium. The number of basic states possible in system 1 is 3422 times greater than the number possible in system 2. In system 2, the equilibrium state has 489 possible basic states. How many possible basic states does the equilibrium state of system 1 have? ••

38. A system has three macrostates. Macrostates 1 and 3 are least likely and have one basic state each. Macrostate 2 is the equilibrium state and is six times more likely to occur than either of the other two macrostates. (*a*) What is the probability that the equilibrium state 2 occurs? (*b*) What is the probability that macrostate 1 or 3 occurs? (*c*) What is the sum of the probabilities for all macrostates? ••

39. A cylindrical box is divided into three equal-volume, pie-shaped regions—A, B, and C—by vertical partitions that allow the transfer of energy but not of particles from one region to another. Each region shares a partition with the other two. Each region contains 13 particles, and the system contains 39 energy units, initially all located in region A. If each particle-partition collision transfers one energy unit, is it possible for the system to evolve to its most probable state in (*a*) 18 collisions, (*b*) 27 collisions, (*c*) 29 collisions? •••

19.5 Dependence of entropy on volume

40. What is the entropy of a closed system in which 25 distinguishable grains of sand are distributed among 1000 distinguishable equal-sized compartments? •

41. A number of distinguishable spherical beads, each having a radius of 15.0 mm, are placed into individual compartments in a 1.00-m^3 container. The same number of beads, each having a radius of 20.0 mm, are placed into similar compartments in a container of the same volume. Which system has the greater entropy, and by what factor? Assume that each compartment is a cube, with each side equal to the diameter of the bead. •

42. You have 80 particles moving randomly in a closed container, and the system contains 80 energy units. Which is less likely: that a single particle has all 80 energy units, or that each particle has one energy unit? •

43. The volume of a cylindrical chamber is controlled by a movable piston. A sample of gas is placed in the chamber, and the volume is allowed to change from 0.0100 m^3 to 0.100 m^3 at a constant temperature. If the entropy of the system increases by 6.91×10^{18} during the volume change, how many gas particles are there in the chamber? ••

44. A closed box contains 20 particles, 10 on each side of a movable partition. The particles in the left compartment are small and occupy a volume δV_{left}. Those in the right compartment are larger and occupy a volume $\delta V_{right} = 8\delta V_{left}$. (*a*) If the box dimension along which the partition moves is 1.00 m long and the partition starts out pushed far to the right, what is the position of the partition when the system reaches equilibrium? (*b*) Does it matter what volume the particles occupy? ••

PRACTICE

45. Rank the following systems according to their entropy, lowest first:
A. 1,000,000 different colors that can be assigned to each of the 70×10^{21} stars in the observable universe
B. The particles in 1 mol of an ideal gas that can be adsorbed (one particle per site) at any of 83 sites on an adsorbent material
C. The particles in 0.8 mol of an ideal gas that can be adsorbed (one per site) at any of 106 sites on an adsorbent material
D. The 100 trillion cells in the human body when each is to be classified as having one of three levels of relative cellular health
E. The 1×10^{14} microbes in the average human body when each is to be classified as either alive or dead ••

46. Figure P19.46 shows a device consisting of two units, A and B. Each unit has a volume V, and at one end a partition separates off a small compartment that has volume $V/3$, as shown in part *a*. Initially, unit A has 3 mol of a gas in its smaller compartment, and unit B has 2 mol of the same gas in its smaller compartment. When the partitions are removed and the gas in each unit is allowed to expand into the volume V as shown in part *b*, what is the change in the entropy of the two-unit system? ••

Figure P19.46

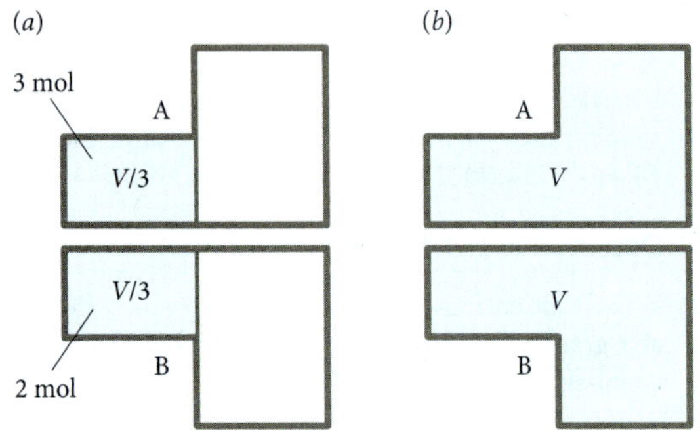

47. Suppose 50 distinguishable objects have a volume of $1.00 \times 10^{-9}\ \text{m}^3$ and are initially in a box that has a volume of $1.00 \times 10^{-6}\ \text{m}^3$. If the volume of the box is doubled, (*a*) by what factor does the number of basic states change and (*b*) by what factor does the entropy increase? ••

48. A box of volume V has a movable partition separating it into two compartments. The left compartment contains 3000 particles, the right one contains 1000 particles, and initially the partition is in the middle so that the compartments are of equal volume. The partition is released and slides horizontally until the system is in a new equilibrium state. (*a*) In terms of V, what is the volume of each compartment once the new equilibrium state is reached? (*b*) What is the change in the system's entropy during this process? ••

49. A change in the volume occupied by a set of distinguishable particles increases the number of basic states by a factor of 6633 and increases the entropy by a factor of 1.10. How many distinguishable particles are there in the system? •••

50. A box that is 1.00 m long measured from left to right has a sliding partition that separates it into two compartments. The left compartment contains 10 particles, the right one contains 60 particles, and initially the partition is 0.750 m from the left wall of the box. If the partition is allowed to move freely, what is the change in entropy after the system reaches equilibrium? •••

19.6 Dependence of entropy on energy

51. A container holds 1.0 mol of an ideal monatomic gas at 72 K, and then 0.50 mol of another monatomic ideal gas at 126 K is added. What is the equilibrium temperature? •

52. Initially, 1.00 mol of an ideal monatomic gas has 75.0 J of thermal energy. If this energy is increased by 25.0 J, what is the change in entropy? •

53. A theory predicts a reaction that produces ideal monatomic gas particles that have the following speeds: 6.2 m/s, 7.4 m/s, 7.4 m/s, 7.8 m/s, 8.3 m/s, 12.6 m/s, 20.1 m/s, 20.1 m/s. What are (*a*) the average speed of the particles and (*b*) their root-mean-square speed? •

54. What is the root-mean-square speed of four monatomic ideal gas particles that have the following velocities (written in component form): (4.0, 6.0, 2.0) m/s, (8.0, −3.0, 8.0) m/s, (7.0, 1.0, 6.0) m/s, (8.0, 9.0, 5.0) m/s? ••

55. An ideal monatomic gas is at 125 °C. If you increase the thermal energy of the gas and the root-mean-square speed of the gas particles triples, by what factor does the absolute temperature change? ••

56. The rate of change of entropy with respect to thermal energy is 1.81×10^{20} in a system at 400 K. At what absolute temperature is the rate of change twice this value? ••

57. The entropy for a certain monatomic gas has been empirically determined to be given by the expression $S = \frac{7}{2}N \ln E_{\text{th}} + NE_{\text{th}}^{2/15}$. Express the factor $1/k_{\text{B}}T$ for this gas in terms of N and E_{th}. ••

58. In (x, y, z) notation, four ideal monatomic gas particles have the velocities $\vec{v}_1 = (-6.0, 5.0, 1.0)$ m/s, $\vec{v}_2 = (4.0, 5.0, -2.0)$ m/s, $\vec{v}_3 = (7.0, 0, 8.0)$ m/s, and $\vec{v}_4 = (-4.0, -9.0, -6.0)$ m/s. (*a*) What is the average velocity of the particles? (*b*) What is the root-mean-square speed of the particles? (*c*) Why is Eq. 19.25, $v_{\text{rms}}^2 = 3(v_x^2)_{\text{av}}$, unlikely to give the correct answer here? ••

59. A box is divided into four equal-sized quadrants. Each quadrant contains gaseous hexane (C_6H_{14}), which we treat as monatomic. The partition that separates the quadrants allows energy to be exchanged, but not particles. However, there is a tiny hole in the partition between quadrants 1 and 2 that allows gas particles to be exchanged. The initial values for the mass of gas in each quadrant and the root-mean-square speed of the particles are Q_1: 3.00 g, 400 m/s; Q_2: 5.50 g, 500 m/s; Q_3: 2.00 g, 420 m/s; Q_4: 6.75 g, 445 m/s. After the system sits for a long time interval, what is the root-mean-square speed for the particles in quadrant 2? •••

19.7 Properties of a monatomic ideal gas

60. At 24.0 °C, what is the average speed of atoms of helium gas? The mass of each atom is 6.646×10^{-27} kg. •

61. What is the root-mean-square speed of helium atoms (mass 6.646×10^{-27} kg) in a star where the temperature is 1.8×10^4 K? •

62. A cubical box measuring 1.25 m on each side contains a monatomic ideal gas at a pressure of 2.0 atm. (*a*) How much thermal energy do the particles of this gas contain? (*b*) If half the thermal energy of the particles were converted to the kinetic energy of a 3.0-kg cat, how fast would the cat be moving? •

63. An empty 2.00-L soft drink bottle is filled with 0.0100 mol of a monatomic ideal gas at atmospheric pressure (1.01×10^5 N/m^2). (*a*) What is the average kinetic energy of each gas particle in the bottle? (*b*) Compare the value you obtained in part *a* with the kinetic energy of a bacterium of mass 1.0×10^{-14} kg moving at 1.0×10^{-7} m/s and with the kinetic energy of a 0.0010-kg garden slug moving at 0.0100 m/s. ••

64. A particle accelerator exerts a force on particles that are initially at rest. Each of the particles has a mass of 1.6726×10^{-27} kg, and the point of application of the force is along the entire 100-m length of the accelerator. The particles traverse this distance in 0.0179 s and then collide with a target that is in thermal contact with a monatomic ideal gas. If the particles distribute their kinetic energy elastically, what is the temperature of the gas after the accelerator has been running for a long time interval? ••

65. Very dilute, monatomic cool gases A and B are separated by a partition but allowed to exchange energy through the partition. After a long time interval, $v_{\text{rms,A}} = 6v_{\text{rms,B}}$. What is the relationship between the mass of a particle of gas A and the mass of a particle of gas B? ••

66. A thermally insulated 3.00-L flask contains monatomic xenon gas at an initial temperature of 50.0 °C and pressure of 2.50 atm. You now add enough energy to double the thermal energy of the gas. The mass of a xenon atom is 2.18×10^{-25} kg. (*a*) How many atoms does the flask contain? (*b*) How much energy did you add to the flask? (*c*) By what factor did you change the root-mean-square speed of the atoms? ••

67. In a sample of a monatomic ideal gas that has a number density of 3.61×10^{24} particles/m^3, the average kinetic energy of the gas particles is 7.50×10^{-21} J. If the particles are colliding with a wall that has an area of 1.00×10^{-2} m^2, what is the average change in momentum per unit of time for the gas? ••

68. Chamber X contains monatomic ideal gas X. The gas particles have a root-mean-square speed of 42 m/s. Chamber Y, identical to chamber X, contains a different monatomic ideal gas with the same mass as the gas in chamber X but with twice the number of gas particles as the gas in chamber X. If the absolute temperatures in the chambers are T_X and $T_Y = 1.2T_X$, what is the root-mean-square speed of the particles in Y? ••

69. A jar contains a mixture of helium gas and krypton gas, with the sample containing equal masses of the two gases, $m_{\text{sample,He}} = m_{\text{sample,Kr}}$. Both gases are monatomic, they behave ideally, and the system is in equilibrium. (*a*) What percentage of the pressure in the mixture is due to the helium? What percentage is due to the krypton? (*b*) Explain why your answer in part *a* is reasonable. The atom masses are $m_{\text{He}} = 6.646 \times 10^{-27}$ kg and $m_{\text{Kr}} = 1.391 \times 10^{-25}$ kg. ••

70. Neon atoms at 260 K pass through a fan that gives each mole of neon gas an additional kinetic energy of 16.0 J. (*a*) What is the average temperature of the neon atoms immediately after coming through the fan? (*b*) If you found an increase in temperature in part *a*, how do you explain the fact that fans are usually used to make people cooler rather than hotter? ••

71. A pollution-control device installed in the smokestack of equipment used to run an industrial process measures the root-mean-square speed of pollutant particles given off by the process. If v_{rms} exceeds a given limit, the process is shut down to prevent the release of pollutants into the air. (Consider the particles to be ideal and monatomic.) The safety operator knows that the average mass density of the particles involved in this process is 5600 kg/m^3. (*a*) At what threshold should he set the device if the process is running at 936 °C and the particle diameter is 10 nm? (*b*) As the particles rise and exit the smokestack, the 10-nm particles coalesce to an average diameter of 1.0 μm and cool to 190 °C. What is the root-mean-square speed of the particles as they exit the smokestack? (Ignore viscosity and drag.) •••

72. You are constructing an improvised detector for radon gas, using the cooling core from an old refrigerator capable of cooling air to 255 K, a detector tube 50 mm long, a vacuum pump to evacuate the tube, and an electric circuit that can measure the time interval needed for gas particles to travel a given distance. To determine if there is radon in the air in your room, you intend to inject samples of the air into the evacuated tube and measure the time interval needed for particles in the sample to travel from one end of the tube to the other and their root-mean-square speed for the trip. (*a*) To what scale of measurement should you set the time-interval sensor if you want to detect the monatomic radon atoms? (Ignore any collisions between these atoms and other particles in the sample.) (*b*) Can you suggest any modifications to this device to improve accuracy? (*c*) Do you think you will need to calibrate your system if you have to make the more realistic assumption that the collisions between radon atoms and other particles in the sample cannot be ignored? If so, why? •••

19.8 Entropy of a monatomic ideal gas

73. What is the change in entropy per particle of a monatomic ideal gas heated from 300 K to 400 K? Assume constant volume, and thermal equilibrium in both the initial and final states. •

74. If 1.85×10^5 atoms of a monatomic ideal gas are heated from 300 K to 500 K in a sealed container that has a fixed volume of 0.0560 m^3, what is the change in entropy of the gas? •

75. A monatomic ideal gas in a container of fixed volume contains 4.20×10^{24} atoms. If you add enough thermal energy to double the root-mean-square speed of the gas atoms, by how much have you changed the entropy of the gas? •

76. A container of fixed volume contains 8.72×10^{23} helium atoms, each of mass 6.646×10^{-27} kg. You put the container in a freezer and decrease its temperature from 25.0 °C to −135 °C. What are (*a*) the change in the thermal energy of the gas and (*b*) the change in its entropy? ••

77. A 3.50-L expandable chamber contains monatomic neon gas at 2.00 atm and 30.0 °C. Thermal energy is slowly added to the gas until its volume is 8.00 L while its pressure remains constant. What is the entropy change during this expansion? ••

78. A monatomic ideal gas has its volume halved while its pressure is held constant. What is the change in entropy per atom? ••

79. As a sample of argon gas is heated in a sealed container, its root-mean-square speed changes from 350 m/s to 540 m/s. By how much has the entropy been increased per argon atom? The mass of an argon atom is 6.63×10^{-26} kg. ••

80. A monatomic ideal gas is enclosed in a cubic box of side length ℓ. While preserving the cubic shape, the container volume is decreased until the side length is halved, and this change causes the pressure in the box to triple. (*a*) What is the change in entropy per particle of gas in the box? (*b*) Is this system closed? ••

81. A sample containing 3.65 mol of a monatomic ideal gas is heated from 289 K to 458 K, and the entropy remains constant. If the initial volume of the sample was 0.0980 m^3, by what factor did the pressure increase or decrease during this process? ••

82. A constant-volume encasement vessel surrounds a liquid-nitrogen bath that has cooled 1.00 mol of a monatomic ideal gas to 77.2 K. This closed system is initially in thermal equilibrium at this temperature, but over time the liquid nitrogen boils away, and then the ideal gas and the nitrogen gas are in equilibrium in the encasement vessel at room temperature, 297 K. (*a*) What is the change in entropy of the ideal gas as it undergoes this temperature change? (*b*) The nitrogen gas is then condensed and again cools the ideal gas. What is the entropy change for the ideal gas as it returns to 77.2 K? (*c*) Where in this process did entropy increase, as required by the second law of thermodynamics for an irreversible process? ••

83. Ten particles of a monatomic ideal gas are initially at thermal equilibrium with their surroundings. When the sample is then heated to 634 K while the volume is held constant, the entropy doubles. What was the initial temperature of the sample? ••

84. In a cylindrical chamber that initially has a volume of 2.25 L, a sample of helium gas is at equilibrium at 3.20 atm and 85.0 °C. The gas is slowly compressed to a new equilibrium state at a volume of 1.10 L and pressure of 4.40 atm. What is the entropy change during this compression? ••

85. A thermally insulated chamber is divided by a partition into two compartments of equal volume. The left side contains 9.00×10^{23} helium atoms, and the right side contains 2.70×10^{24} argon atoms. The gases in both compartments are in equilibrium and at the same temperature. A small hole develops in the partition so that after a long time interval both gases leak through the hole and eventually the system comes to a new equilibrium state. (*a*) What is the difference in entropy between the two equilibrium states? Which state, if either, has the greater entropy? (*b*) What is the change in the thermal energy of the gases during this process? Assume ideal behavior for all atoms. ••

86. A rigid 1.20-L bottle contains helium gas at 150 °C and 2.75 atm. If you slowly add 755 J of thermal energy to the gas, what is the entropy change for the gas? Assume the helium gas is ideal. ••

Additional Problems

87. Suppose you are dropping five small pieces of clay randomly onto a chessboard (eight squares by eight squares). If basic states are determined by the squares on which each piece of clay lands, how many basic states are possible? Assume a square can be occupied by multiple pieces. •

88. Consider two egg cartons, one with spaces for a dozen eggs and one with spaces for a half-dozen eggs. If each carton contains six eggs, all of different colors, what is the ratio of the number of possible basic states in the one-dozen carton to the number of possible basic states in the half-dozen carton? •

89. Two boxes each have a volume of 1.50 m^3. Box A contains 1000 helium atoms, and box B contains 2000 neon atoms. When the boxes are connected together by a very small tube, the atoms redistribute themselves throughout both boxes. What is the entropy change of the two-box system during the redistribution? •

90. A sample of neon gas is at 100 °C. The mass of a neon atom is 3.35×10^{-26} kg. (*a*) What is the average kinetic energy of a neon atom? (*b*) If the thermal energy of the sample is 175 J, how many neon atoms does it contain? •

91. At 35 °C, the root-mean-square speed of a certain monatomic ideal gas is 186 m/s. (*a*) What is the mass of each atom? (*b*) What is the average kinetic energy of a typical atom at that temperature? •

92. A 0.0423-kg sample of an ideal gas in a fixed-volume, 0.750-L container at 50.0 °C exerts a pressure of 2.24 atm. What is the mass of one particle of this gas? ••

93. The atoms of an element can come in different forms, depending on the number of neutrons in the nucleus. These different forms are called *isotopes* of the element. The two most common isotopes of uranium are uranium-235 (143 neutrons) and uranium-238 (146 neutrons), having masses of 3.90×10^{-25} kg and 3.95×10^{-25} kg, respectively. In a sample of uranium gas, these isotopes have slightly different root-mean-square speeds, and this difference can be used to separate the isotopes for use in nuclear reactors or nuclear weapons. When both gases are at the same temperature, what is the percent difference in the root-mean-square speeds of the atoms of each isotope? Which isotope has the greater root-mean-square speed? ••

94. A sealed 1.50-L chamber filled with helium gas initially at 20 °C and 1.00 atm is heated until the gas temperature is 232 °C. (*a*) How much thermal energy is added to the gas during this process? (*b*) What is the entropy change of the gas during this process? (*c*) What was the final pressure inside the container? Ignore any thermal expansion of the container; the mass of a helium atom is 6.646×10^{-27} kg. ••

95. (*a*) At what temperature is the root-mean-square speed of neon atoms (mass 3.35×10^{-26} kg) equal to the speed of sound in a typical room, 344 m/s? (*b*) At the temperature you found in part *a*, how much thermal energy do 6.02×10^{23} neon atoms have? ••

96. A monatomic ideal gas is in a fixed-volume flask. (*a*) By what factor must you increase the root-mean-square speed of the gas particles to double the gas pressure? (*b*) By what factor does the thermal energy of the gas change when you increase v_{rms} by this factor? ••

97. A sample of a monatomic ideal gas contains *N* atoms. You want to compress the gas slowly to one-fourth of its original volume. (*a*) By what factor must you change the absolute temperature of the sample in order to increase its entropy by $3N$? (*b*) For the process in part *a*, by what factor does the root-mean-square speed of the gas particles change? ••

98. The temperature of the Sun's corona (the outermost gas layer) is 1.0×10^6 K, and this layer is just above the photosphere layer, which has a radius of 6.96×10^8 m. The mass of the Sun is 1.99×10^{30} kg. Is the root-mean-square speed of helium atoms in the corona great enough to allow the atoms to escape from the Sun's gravitational pull? The mass of a helium atom is 6.646×10^{-27} kg. ••

99. Consider a helium atom that is part of Earth's atmosphere and is initially at the planet's surface, where the temperature is 20 °C. To what maximum altitude can this atom rise if its speed is equal to the root-mean-square speed of the helium in the atmosphere? The mass of a helium atom is 6.646×10^{-27} kg, the mass of Earth is 5.97×10^{24} kg, and Earth's radius is 6.38×10^6 m. (Careful! The value of *g* varies with altitude.) ••

100. A box initially divided into two equal halves by a partition contains some number of particles. When the partition is removed, the particles are free to move throughout the volume of the box. Assume that all the particles have an average speed that allows them to cross from one side of the box to the other every 2.50 s, on average. Note that this does not mean that they uniformly switch sides; it means that they move randomly in such a way that they enter a new random distribution every 2.50 s. Determine the probability of all particles being in the left half of the box and the average time interval required for this to happen for (*a*) two particles and (*b*) ten particles. ••

101. A cylindrical chamber is oriented with its long central axis along the vertical *y* axis of an *xyz* coordinate system. The top face of the chamber is a piston that can slide up and down to change the chamber volume. The chamber is initially filled with a monatomic ideal gas. When the chamber temperature is lowered, the piston slides downward very slowly at constant velocity until the chamber volume is one-fifth of its original value. At this instant, the contraction stops with the gas in an equilibrium state. (*a*) By what factor does the root-mean-square speed of the gas particles change during this contraction? Does this speed increase or decrease? (*b*) By what factor does the thermal energy of the gas change during this contraction? Does the energy increase or decrease? •••

102. A cylindrical canister fitted with a piston at one end contains an ideal gas and floats at the surface of a freshwater lake, where the temperature is 300 K. The gas pressure inside the canister is just enough to balance atmospheric pressure, and so the piston does not slide downward. Initially the canister volume is 3.64 L. The canister is lowered into the lake until it is 12.0 m below the surface, where the temperature is 280 K. (*a*) What is the canister volume once equilibrium is reached at this depth? (*b*) What is the change in entropy of the gas during this process? Ignore friction and ignore the effect of gravity on the piston. •••

103. Your work in a laboratory requires a certain dangerous ideal gas, which you will be using for the next three weeks. You know that the gas is corrosive and that gas particles are constantly colliding with one another and, more worrisome, with the walls of the container. Thus there is some finite probability that a gas particle will react with a particle of the container and weaken the container wall. You have 4.00×10^{-3} kg of this gas in a spherical 6.45-L container in which the walls are 10.0 mm thick. The mass of each gas particle is 6.054×10^{-26} kg. The temperature of the gas is always close to room temperature and certainly never rises above 30 °C. After a little on-line search, you realize that each time a gas particle hits the container wall there is a one in 3 million chance of a corrosive reaction. That causes you to wonder about safety issues. ••• CR

104. A tank filled with helium gas has been left in a hot car for hours. The mass of the filled tank is 21.2 kg, and after you use all the helium to fill 100 balloons for a child's birthday party, the tank mass is 20.8 kg. You notice that the filled balloons are shrinking over time. Each filled balloon is roughly spherical and started out with a radius of 200 mm, but now each radius has shrunk to 100 mm. Some of the children are afraid the balloons will deflate completely. You estimate that the gauge pressure inside the balloon was initially 50.0 kPa and that this pressure must increase linearly with balloon surface area. You are puzzled by the shrinking because the air temperature at the party is 35.0 °C. That causes you to wonder whether the balloons have an equilibrium radius or you should prepare the children for complete deflation. ••• CR

Answers to Review Questions

1. The pendulum's kinetic energy is coherent mechanical energy because all the particles of the pendulum swing together. The kinetic energy of the molecules in the air is incoherent thermal energy because the motion of these molecules is random.
2. Brownian motion is the zigzag motion of a small particle suspended in a fluid. The particle is bombarded by the surrounding molecules of the fluid. Because the motion of the fluid molecules is random, the bombardment is usually not equal on opposite sides of the particle, which causes the particle to move randomly in the fluid.
3. The system's macrostates are specified by the large-scale properties of the system, such as pressure, volume, and temperature. The system's basic states are specified by descriptions of the individual objects that make up the system, such as the position and velocity of each particle in a sample of gas.
4. That energy is quantized means that it comes in very small, discrete, indivisible units. Energy transfers take place through exchanges of these units rather than in a continuous stream.
5. The recurrence time is the average time interval needed to cycle randomly through all the possible basic states of the system.
6. Each part tends to have an equal share of the system's energy. This is called the equipartition of energy.
7. The average energy of each particle is E_{th}/N.
8. Four basic states are possible, with the third particle in any one of compartments 2 through 5: 2, 1, 0, 0, 0; 2, 0, 1, 0, 0; 2, 0, 0, 1, 0; 2, 0, 0, 0, 1.
9. The particles tend to be distributed uniformly throughout the volume. This is called the equipartition of space.
10. It is the most probable macrostate.
11. Over time, a system tends to evolve from less probable macrostates to the most probable macrostate. Once the most probable macrostate is attained, if the system is disturbed into any subsequent less probable macrostate, it will tend to move back toward the most probable macrostate.
12. Our sense of the direction of time comes from the tendency of all naturally occurring processes to evolve irreversibly toward equilibrium.
13. A closed system always evolves toward the macrostate that has the maximum number of basic states and at this point is in equilibrium.
14. Because Earth is not a closed system, Earth's entropy is not necessarily increasing.
15. The conditions are a large number of particles that occupy a negligible fraction of the volume of the container holding the gas and interact with one another and with the container walls only during collisions that randomize both their energy distribution and their spatial distribution.
16. The entropy of any system is the natural logarithm of the number of basic states available to the system.
17. The entropy law is the mathematical version of the second law of thermodynamics, describing how a closed system not in equilibrium always evolves in the direction of increasing entropy ($\Delta S > 0$) until it reaches equilibrium and its entropy no longer changes ($\Delta S = 0$).
18. No. It applies only to closed systems (energy is constant). The law says that a closed system's entropy either increases ($\Delta S > 0$) or stays unchanged ($\Delta S = 0$), but if the system is not closed, the entropy of the system can increase, decrease, or stay the same.
19. The entropy change is proportional to the natural logarithm of the ratio of the final and initial volumes, with the proportionality constant being N, the number of gas particles: $\Delta S = N \ln(V_f/V_i)$ (Eq. 19.8).
20. The entropy of the combined system equals the sum of the entropies of the two initial systems.
21. The root-mean-square speed is the square root of the average of the squares of the speeds of all the particles: $v_{rms} = \sqrt{(v^2)_{av}}$ (Eq. 19.21).
22. The entropy change is proportional to the natural logarithm of the ratio of the final and initial thermal energies, with the proportionality constant being $3N/2$: $\Delta S = \frac{3}{2}N \ln(E_{th,f}/E_{th,i})$ (Eq. 19.33).
23. The absolute temperature equals the inverse of the product of the Boltzmann constant and the derivative of the entropy of the gas with respect to its thermal energy: $1/T = k_B(dS/dE_{th})$ (Eq. 19.38).
24. Being in thermal equilibrium means that the two gases have the same absolute temperature.
25. The atomic parameters number density N/V of the atoms and their average kinetic energy $\frac{1}{2}mv_{rms}^2$ determine the pressure in the gas.
26. For an ideal gas in equilibrium, the pressure P in the gas equals the number density N/V of the gas particles times the absolute temperature T times the Boltzmann constant k_B.
27. The ideal gas law describes the behavior of real gases when the pressure in the gas is low and the gas temperature is high.
28. The parameters are the absolute temperature of the gas and the mass of one gas atom. The equation is $v_{rms} = \sqrt{3k_BT/m}$ (Eq. 19.53).
29. The entropy change depends on the number of atoms in the gas, on any change in absolute temperature, and on any change in volume.
30. The entropy is a function of the equilibrium state only, so changes in it are independent of the process involved.

Answers to Guided Problems

Guided Problem 19.2 $\frac{\Omega(2)}{\Omega_{tot}} = \frac{5}{28}$

Guided Problem 19.4 $\Delta S = +4.4 \times 10^{23}$

Guided Problem 19.6 $v_{rms,f} = 1.58 \times 10^3$ m/s

Guided Problem 19.8 $\Delta S = -8.6 \times 10^{23}$

PRACTICE

20 PRACTICE Energy Transferred Thermally

Chapter Summary

Thermal interactions and temperature (Sections 20.1, 20.2, 20.5)

Concepts During a **thermal interaction,** thermal energy is transferred from an object at a higher temperature to an object at a lower temperature. The energy Q transferred is called **energy transferred thermally.**

During an **adiabatic process,** only mechanical energy is transferred (work is done on the system); no energy is transferred thermally, so $Q = 0$.

When a gas volume decreases, positive work is done on the gas ($W > 0$); when the volume increases, negative work is done on the gas ($W < 0$).

During a **quasistatic process,** the system always remains close to equilibrium. If a quasistatic process is carried out adiabatically ($Q = 0$), the entropy of the system does not change ($\Delta S = 0$).

At the **triple point of water,** the solid, liquid, and gas phases coexist in thermal equilibrium. This point occurs at 273.16 K and 610 Pa.

Quantitative Tools When the kinetic, potential, and source energies of an ideal gas are constant, only a change in the thermal energy can change the energy of the gas, and this change is given by

$$\Delta E_{\text{th}} = W + Q. \tag{20.2}$$

The work done on a gas during a quasistatic process is

$$W = -\int_{V_i}^{V_f} P\,dV. \tag{20.8}$$

Conversions between the Celsius, Kelvin, and Fahrenheit temperature scales:

$$T_C = \frac{1\,^\circ\text{C}}{1\,\text{K}}T - 273.15\,^\circ\text{C}$$

$$T_C = \frac{5\,^\circ\text{C}}{9\,^\circ\text{F}}(T_F - 32\,^\circ\text{F})$$

Thermodynamic processes (Sections 20.3–20.7)

Concepts The **heat capacity** (J/K) of an *object* is a scalar defined as the amount of energy transferred thermally to an object divided by the resulting change in temperature of the object.

The **specific heat capacity** (J/K · kg) is a scalar equal to the heat capacity of an object divided by the mass of the object.

A **degree of freedom** is any independent way of storing energy in a particle.

In an ideal gas in thermal equilibrium, each particle's **equipartition energy share** of the energy of the gas is $dk_BT/2$, where d is the number of degrees of freedom available to the particles.

A *PV* diagram is a graph of the pressure in a gas as a function of the gas volume. Any point on a *PV* diagram represents an equilibrium state in which the gas has a well-defined temperature, thermal energy, and entropy. Any continuous path on a *PV* diagram represents a quasistatic process.

A **thermal reservoir** is a body of material large enough that its temperature does not change in a thermal interaction.

An **isothermal process** is one that occurs at constant temperature. An **isobaric process** is one that occurs at constant pressure. An **isochoric process** is one that occurs at constant volume. An **isentropic process** is one in which the entropy does not change.

Quantitative Tools At temperature T, the thermal energy of a sample of an ideal gas that contains N particles, each having d degrees of freedom, is

$$E_{\text{th}} = \frac{d}{2}Nk_BT, \tag{20.4}$$

where $k_B = 1.381 \times 10^{-23}$ J/K is the Boltzmann constant.

At constant volume, the **heat capacity per particle** of a gas that contains N particles, each having d degrees of freedom, is

$$C_V \equiv \frac{Q}{N\Delta T} = \frac{d}{2}k_B. \quad (20.13)\ (20.14)$$

At constant pressure, the **heat capacity per particle** is

$$C_P \equiv \frac{Q}{N\Delta T} = C_V + k_B = \left(\frac{d}{2} + 1\right)k_B. \quad (20.20)\ (20.24)\ (20.25)$$

For any ideal gas process,

$$\Delta E_{\text{th}} = NC_V\Delta T. \tag{20.15}$$

The unitless **heat capacity ratio** γ is

$$\gamma \equiv \frac{C_P}{C_V} = 1 + \frac{2}{d}. \tag{20.26}$$

Table 20.4 Phase transition temperatures and specific transformation energies for melting (m) and vaporization (v)

Substance	T_m (K)	L_m (10^3 J/kg)	T_v (K)	L_v (10^3 J/kg)
Helium	–	–	4.230	20.8
Hydrogen	13.84	58.6	20.37	449
Nitrogen	63.18	25.5	77.36	199
Oxygen	54.36	13.8	90.19	213
Ammonia	195	331	239.8	1369
Carbon tetrachloride	250.3	16	349.8	194
Ethanol	159	100.7	351	837
Water	273.15	334	373.12	2256
Mercury	234	11.8	630	272
Aluminum	933.6	395	2740	10,500
Lead	600.5	24.5	2023	871
Sulfur	392	38.1	717.75	326
Gold	1336.15	64.5	2933	1578
Copper	1356	134	2840	5069

Entropy in ideal gas processes (Sections 20.2, 20.8)

Concepts At **absolute zero** ($T = 0$), the thermal energy of a system is a minimum and its entropy is zero because it has only one basic state available to it.

Quantitative Tools The entropy of an ideal gas that has d degrees of freedom is

$$S = N \ln V + \frac{d}{2} N \ln T + \text{ constant}, \tag{20.33}$$

and the change in its entropy during a process is

$$\Delta S = N \ln\left(\frac{V_f}{V_i}\right) + \frac{d}{2} N \ln\left(\frac{T_f}{T_i}\right). \tag{20.34}$$

Table 20.6 Energy law for an ideal gas and constrained ideal gas processes

Process	Constraint	W	Q	ΔE_{th}	Energy law for ideal gas
isochoric	V fixed	0	$NC_V \Delta T$		$\Delta E_{th} = Q$
isentropic	S fixed		0	$NC_V \Delta T$	$W = \Delta E_{th}$
isobaric	P fixed	$-Nk_B \Delta T$	$NC_P \Delta T$	$NC_V \Delta T$	$\Delta E_{th} = W + Q$
isothermal	T fixed	$-Nk_B T \ln\left(\frac{V_f}{V_i}\right)$		0	$Q = -W$

For any isentropic process:

$$T_i V_i^{\gamma-1} = T_f V_f^{\gamma-1} \tag{20.44}$$

$$P_i V_i^{\gamma} = P_f V_f^{\gamma} \tag{20.46}$$

$$P_i^{\frac{1}{\gamma}-1} T_i = P_f^{\frac{1}{\gamma}-1} T_f. \tag{20.47}$$

PRACTICE

Entropy in nonideal gas processes (Section 20.9)

Quantitative Tools For a solid or liquid that has a specific heat capacity c_V, the entropy change when a sample of mass m undergoes a temperature change is

$$\Delta S = \frac{mc_V}{k_B}\ln\left(\frac{T_f}{T_i}\right). \tag{20.53}$$

The entropy change during a melting or vaporization phase transition at temperature T is

$$\Delta S = \frac{mL}{k_B T}. \tag{20.57}$$

The entropy change during a solidification or condensation phase transition at temperature T is

$$\Delta S = -\frac{mL}{k_B T}. \tag{20.58}$$

Review Questions

Answers to these questions can be found at the end of this chapter.

20.1 Thermal interactions

1. What is the symbol for energy transferred thermally into or out of a system, and when is this quantity positive?
2. What are the two ways to transfer energy to a system, and what is the distinction between them?
3. What is an adiabatic process?
4. What is a quasistatic process?
5. How does the entropy of a system change when the only energy transferred to the system is transferred thermally?
6. How does the entropy of a system change when it undergoes a quasistatic adiabatic process?

20.2 Temperature measurement

7. What is the basis of most methods used to measure temperature?
8. What is the definition of the triple point of water? What is its value on the Kelvin temperature scale?
9. How is the triple point of water used in calibrating an ideal gas thermometer? How is the absolute temperature of a gas determined by an ideal gas thermometer?
10. What happens to the thermal energy and entropy of a system at absolute zero?

20.3 Heat capacity

11. What is the heat capacity of a system?
12. What is a degree of freedom? What determines how many degrees of freedom a gas particle has?
13. How many degrees of freedom does a monatomic gas atom have? How many does a diatomic gas molecule have?
14. How is thermal energy distributed among the degrees of freedom of a gas particle in thermal equilibrium?
15. How can you determine whether a particular degree of freedom contributes to the heat capacity per particle in a gas sample?

20.4 *PV* diagrams and processes

16. For a sample of an ideal gas that contains a fixed number of particles, what does a point on the *PV* diagram for the gas represent?
17. Define the terms *isotherm* and *isentrope*.
18. How is a quasistatic process represented on a *PV* diagram?
19. When an ideal gas is transformed from one equilibrium state to another, which of the following quantities are independent of the path taken from the initial state to the final state: (*a*) change in entropy, (*b*) change in thermal energy, (*c*) work done on the gas, (*d*) quantity of energy transferred thermally?

20.5 Change in energy and work

20. Under what conditions does the energy law, $\Delta E = W + Q$, reduce to an expression that deals with only ΔE_{th}?
21. On which variables does the work done on an ideal gas depend?
22. What does the minus sign in Eq. 20.8 indicate?

20.6 Isochoric and isentropic ideal gas processes

23. According to the $\Delta E_{th} = W + Q$ form of the energy law (Eq. 20.2), what is the change in the thermal energy of an ideal gas equal to in an isochoric process and in an isentropic process?
24. Which three macroscopic properties of an ideal gas must you know in order to calculate the change in the thermal energy of the gas for any process the gas might undergo?

20.7 Isobaric and isothermal ideal gas processes

25. What is the relationship between the heat capacities per particle for an ideal gas at constant volume and at constant pressure?
26. For an isothermal process carried out on an ideal gas, what is the relationship between the quantity of energy transferred thermally and the work done on the gas?

20.8 Entropy change in ideal gas processes

27. For an isentropic process carried out on an ideal gas, what is the relationship between the gas pressure and volume? Between the gas pressure and temperature? Between the gas volume and temperature?

20.9 Entropy change in nonideal gas processes

28. What is the intensive quantity related to heat capacity, and how is it defined?
29. What are the units of heat capacity? Of specific heat capacity?

Developing a Feel

Make an order-of-magnitude estimate of each of the following quantities. Letters in parentheses refer to hints below. Use them as needed to guide your thinking.

1. Work done quasistatically to inflate all four flat tires on your car [C, O, G]
2. The number of strokes of a bicycle pump required to fully inflate two high-pressure bicycle tires that are initially completely deflated [K, T, X]
3. The time interval needed for a microwave oven to bring 0.3 L of water from room temperature to the boiling point [S, A, V, BB]
4. Of the energy used to heat an aluminum teakettle full of water on the stove, the fraction of the energy used to raise the temperature of the kettle [H, P]
5. The temperature of an empty iron pot after being left on a hot stove for 2 min (ignoring energy transferred thermally from the pot to the surroundings and the mass of the heating element) [E, M, Z]
6. The volume of a container that holds 4 moles of an ideal gas at standard temperature and pressure (STP), defined as $T = 0\,^{\circ}\mathrm{C} = 273.15$ K and $P = 1$ atm $= 1.013 \times 10^5$ Pa [AA]
7. The work done adiabatically in compressing a tennis ball to 80% of its original volume [W, Q, Y, F]
8. The temperature increase in the fuel-air mixture in a car engine cylinder when 10^3 J are added isochorically as the fuel ignites (ignoring the mass of the gasoline burned and assuming all the energy is transferred to the air in the cylinder) [Q, Y, L]
9. The entropy change in the air inside a fully inflated 4-L Mylar balloon taken from indoors to outdoors on a very hot day, assuming the balloon does not change its volume [Y, B, R]
10. The entropy change in the air inside a floating, fully inflated 4-L Mylar balloon when it is pushed 2 m under the surface of a swimming pool [U, B, I]
11. The energy needed to heat the air in a hot-air balloon so that it can lift an additional two people (ignoring any energy transferred from the air in the balloon to the outside air) [D, J, N, Q, Y]

Hints

A. What is the temperature change?
B. How many gas particles are there in the balloon?
C. Which macroscopic properties of the air inside the tires change as you inflate the tires?
D. What is the volume of a hot-air balloon?
E. What is the mass of the pot?
F. What is the change in the temperature of the tennis ball?
G. What is the pressure in a properly inflated car tire?
H. What are the masses of the water and the kettle?
I. What is the change in the pressure?
J. What additional buoyant force is needed to lift the payload?
K. What is the volume of an inflated bicycle tire?
L. What is the maximum volume of the cylinder?
M. What is the power delivered by a stovetop heating element?
N. What temperature change is required?
O. What are the volumes of an inflated and a flat car tire?
P. What are the specific heat capacities of the water and the teakettle?
Q. How many moles are in 2 cubic meters of air at 1 atm and 20 °C?
R. What are the initial and final temperatures, T_i and T_f?
S. What is the mass of this volume of water?
T. What is the pressure in an inflated high-pressure bicycle tire?
U. Which type of process is this: isothermal, isochoric, isobaric, or isentropic?
V. What is the power delivered by the oven?
W. What is the diameter of a tennis ball?
X. What volume of air does a typical bicycle pump deliver on each stroke?
Y. How many degrees of freedom does an air particle have?
Z. What is the specific heat capacity of iron?
AA. How many particles are there in one mole?
BB. What is the specific heat capacity of water?

Key (all values are approximate.)

A. 8×10^1 K; **B.** at STP about 1/6 mol, or 1×10^{23}; **C.** volume (thus not isochoric), pressure (thus not isobaric), number of gas particles, temperature (thus not isothermal); **D.** 2×10^3 m^3; **E.** 1 kg; **F.** 3×10^1 K; **G.** gauge pressure 2 atm, absolute pressure 3 atm $= 3 \times 10^5$ Pa; **H.** 4 kg for the water, 0.2 kg for the kettle; **I.** 2×10^4 Pa; **J.** 1×10^3 N; **K.** 2×10^{-3} m^3; **L.** 5×10^{-4} m^3; **M.** 2 kW; **N.** about 3% per person, or 2×10^1 K for two people; **O.** inflated 2×10^{-2} m^3, flat 20% smaller; **P.** 4×10^3 J/K · kg for the water, 9×10^2 J/K · kg for the kettle; **Q.** 8×10^1 mol; **R.** $T_i = 2 \times 10^1$ °C, $T_f = 4 \times 10^1$ °C; **S.** 0.3 kg; **T.** gauge pressure 6 atm, absolute pressure 7 atm $= 7 \times 10^5$ Pa; **U.** isothermal; **V.** 1×10^3 W; **W.** 0.06 m; **X.** 2×10^{-4} m^3; **Y.** air is essentially all diatomic N_2 and O_2 particles, each of which has five degrees of freedom, $d = 5$; **Z.** 4×10^2 J/K · kg; **AA.** 6.02×10^{23} particles/mole; **BB.** 4181 J/(K · kg)

Worked and Guided Problems

These examples involve material from this chapter but are not associated with any particular section. Some examples are worked out in detail; others you should work out by following the guidelines provided.

Worked Problem 20.1 Compressed gas

A sample of a monatomic ideal gas is in a thermally insulated cylinder fitted with a piston that can change the cylinder volume. Initially, the cylinder volume is $V_i = 2.00 \times 10^{-3}$ m^3, the gas pressure is 1.01×10^5 Pa, and the temperature is 290 K. The piston then moves until the cylinder volume is $0.200V_i$. If the compression is quasistatic and isentropic, how much work is done on the gas?

1 GETTING STARTED We begin by making a *PV* diagram for the process (Figure WG20.1). The process is a quasistatic isentropic compression, so in our diagram we draw the path going upward (from lower pressure to higher pressure) and leftward (from greater volume to smaller volume) along an isentrope.

Figure WG20.1

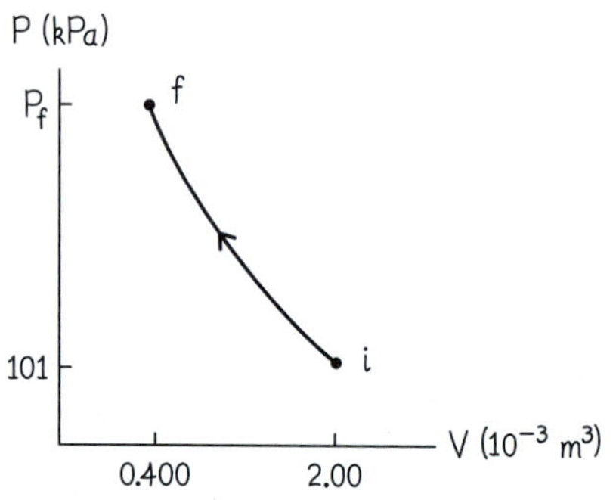

2 DEVISE PLAN We know there is no energy transferred thermally in an isentropic process (Eq. 20.17: $Q = 0$). Therefore the work done on the gas during the compression increases the thermal energy (Eq. 20.18; $\Delta E_{th} = W$). The change in the thermal energy for any ideal gas process is independent of the path taken from initial state to final state and is proportional to the change in temperature (Eq. 20.15). Thus we need to determine the initial and final temperatures of the gas, the number of gas particles in the sample, and the heat capacity per particle C_V. (Remember that even though Eq. 20.15 is written in terms of C_V, it applies to all processes involving ideal gases, not just isochoric ones.) We know the initial temperature, pressure, and volume, and therefore we can use Eq. 19.51, the ideal gas law, $P = (N/V)k_BT$, to determine the number of particles. We know the initial and final volumes, so we can use Eq. 20.46 for an isentropic process to obtain the final pressure. Because the gas is monatomic, we know the number of degrees of freedom and can calculate C_V with Eq. 20.14. We then use the ideal gas law to calculate T_f and Eq. 20.19, $\Delta E_{th} = W = NC_V\Delta T$, to calculate the work done on the gas.

3 EXECUTE PLAN From Eq. 19.51, the number of gas particles in the sample is

$$N = \frac{P_iV_i}{k_BT_i} = \frac{(1.01 \times 10^5 \text{ N/m}^2)(2.00 \times 10^{-3} \text{ m}^3)}{(1.38 \times 10^{-23} \text{ J/K})(290 \text{ K})} = 5.05 \times 10^{22}.$$

We now apply Eq. 20.46 to calculate the final pressure. Because the gas is monatomic and so has three degrees of freedom, the exponent in this equation is $\gamma = 1 + \frac{2}{d} = \frac{5}{3}$. The final volume is $0.200(2.00 \times 10^{-3} \text{ m}^3) = 0.400 \times 10^{-3} \text{ m}^3$, making the final pressure

$$P_f = P_i\left(\frac{V_i}{V_f}\right)^{5/3} = (1.01 \times 10^5 \text{ N/m}^2)\left(\frac{2.00 \times 10^{-3} \text{ m}^3}{0.400 \times 10^{-3} \text{ m}^3}\right)^{5/3}$$
$$= 1.48 \times 10^6 \text{ N/m}^2.$$

We then apply the ideal gas law to obtain the final temperature:

$$T_f = \frac{P_fV_f}{k_BN} = \frac{(1.48 \times 10^6 \text{ N/m}^2)(0.400 \times 10^{-3} \text{ m}^3)}{(1.38 \times 10^{-23} \text{ J/K})(5.05 \times 10^{22})} = 849 \text{ K}.$$

Being monatomic, each gas particle has three degrees of freedom and so $d = 3$. Therefore $C_V = (\frac{3}{2})k_B = 2.07 \times 10^{-23}$ J/K (Eq. 20.14), and the work done on the gas is, from Eq. 20.19,

$$W = E_{th} = NC_V\Delta T$$
$$= (5.05 \times 10^{22})(2.07 \times 10^{-23} \text{ J/K})(849 \text{ K} - 290 \text{ K})$$
$$= 584 \text{ J.} ✔$$

4 EVALUATE RESULT From our *PV* diagram, we can place upper and lower limits on the work done on the gas. The work done on the gas for an isobaric process is $W = -P\Delta V$. The change in volume is $\Delta V = -1.60 \times 10^{-3}$ m^3. If the compression were isobaric at the final pressure, $P_f = 1.48 \times 10^6$ N/m^2, then the work done on the gas would be

$$W_1 = -P_f\Delta V = -(1.48 \times 10^6 \text{ N/m}^2)(-1.60 \times 10^{-3} \text{ m}^3)$$
$$= 2.37 \times 10^3 \text{ J}.$$

If the compression were isobaric at the initial pressure, $P_i = 1.01 \times 10^5$ N/m^2 = 101 kPa, then the work done on the gas would be

$$W_2 = -P_i\Delta V = -(1.01 \times 10^5 \text{ N/m}^2)(-1.60 \times 10^{-3} \text{ m}^3)$$
$$= 1.62 \times 10^2 \text{ J}.$$

If the path were a diagonal straight line, then the work done would be one-half the sum of these two, $(\frac{1}{2})(W_1 + W_2) = 1.27 \times 10^3$ J. We expect the area under the isentrope to be smaller than the area under a straight line, so our answer is in the right range. The sign of the work should be positive because during compression work is done on the gas, in agreement with our answer.

Guided Problem 20.2 Work during compression

A cylinder that contains a sample of a monatomic ideal gas is fitted with a piston that can change the cylinder volume. Initially the volume is 6.00×10^{-3} m^3, the gas pressure is 1.01×10^5 Pa, and the temperature is 250 K. The gas undergoes a quasistatic isentropic compression until the cylinder volume is 3.00×10^{-3} m^3 and the gas pressure is 3.21×10^5 Pa. How much work is done on the gas sample during the compression?

1 GETTING STARTED

1. Which type of process is this: isobaric, isothermal, isentropic, or isochoric? What characterizes that process?
2. Make a *PV* diagram.
3. Which quantities for your initial and final states are known, and which are unknown?

2 DEVISE PLAN

4. For an isentropic process, what quantities do you need in order to determine the work done on the gas sample?
5. How does the fact that the gas is monatomic help you?
6. How can you use the ideal gas law to determine the relevant unknown quantities?

3 EXECUTE PLAN

7. Solve for the final temperature.
8. Solve for number of particles in the sample.
9. Solve for the work done on the gas.

4 EVALUATE RESULT

10. Does your value for the amount of work done agree with your expectation for an isentropic compression?
11. Does the sign of the work agree with what you expect for a compression?

Worked Problem 20.3 Two expansions

Consider two processes for taking a 0.500-mol sample of hydrogen gas (H_2, diatomic particles) from an initial state i to a final state f. The gas behaves ideally, and in both processes the initial volume and pressure are 4.00×10^{-3} m^3 and 3.03×10^5 N/m^2 = 303 kPa. In process A, the sample undergoes a quasistatic isothermal expansion to a volume of 1.60×10^{-2} m^3 and pressure P_f. In process B, the gas undergoes an isobaric expansion to a volume of 1.60×10^{-2} m^3 followed by an isochoric pressure decrease to P_f, with both processes quasistatic. What is the difference in the quantities of energy transferred thermally to the gas in the two processes?

1 GETTING STARTED We begin by making a *PV* diagram showing both processes (Figure WG20.2). Process A is an isothermal expansion, and so we draw its path from initial state i to final state f downward (decreasing pressure) along an isotherm from P_i to P_f and curving to the right (increasing volume) from V_i to V_f. The path for process B has two legs. We represent the isobaric expansion by a horizontal line from initial state i rightward to intermediate state 1 at $V_1 = V_f$. The isochoric pressure decrease we represent by a vertical line from state 1 downward to final state f.

Figure WG20.2

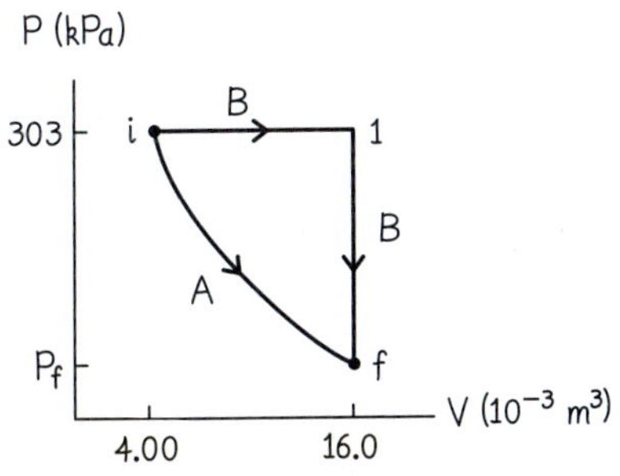

2 DEVISE PLAN We need to determine Q for two processes, one isothermal and the other an isobaric change followed by an isochoric change. Equation 20.31, $Q = Nk_BT\ln(V_f/V_i)$, is for isothermal changes; Eq. 20.21, $Q = NC_P(T_f - T_i)$, is for isobaric changes; and Eq. 20.12, $Q = (d/2)Nk_B(T_f - T_i)$, is for isochoric changes. We can use Avogadro's number to get N from the known number of moles of gas. For the heat capacities, we know that diatomic particles have five degrees of freedom. Therefore we know $C_V = \frac{5}{2}k_B$ (Eq. 20.14) and $C_P = \frac{5}{2}k_B + k_B = \frac{7}{2}k_B$ (Eq. 20.25).

For process A we know the initial and final volumes we need for Eq. 20.31, and we can calculate the constant temperature T by using initial values in the ideal gas law (Eq. 19.51). This gives us what we need to use Eq. 20.31 to calculate the energy Q_A transferred thermally to the gas.

For the isobaric expansion leg of process B, we know C_P and can use the ideal gas law to calculate the temperature at intermediate state 1. Using $T_1 - T_i$ for the temperature factor in Eq. 20.21, we get $Q_{B,\text{isobaric}}$. For the isochoric pressure decrease, we know that $T_f = T_i$ because process A is isothermal and the two processes have the same initial and final states. Thus we know the temperature difference $T_f - T_1$ needed in Eq. 20.12 and can determine $Q_{B,\text{isochoric}}$.

Our final step is to determine the difference in the quantities of energy transferred thermally to the gas in the two processes.

3 EXECUTE PLAN We use the ideal gas law to calculate the initial temperature after we calculate the number of particles in our sample:

$$0.500 \text{ mol} \times \frac{6.02 \times 10^{23} \text{ particles}}{1 \text{ mol}} = 3.01 \times 10^{23} \text{ particles}$$

$$T_i = \frac{P_iV_i}{Nk_B} = \frac{(3.03 \times 10^5 \text{ N/m}^2)(4.00 \times 10^{-3} \text{ m}^3)}{(3.01 \times 10^{23})(1.38 \times 10^{-23} \text{ J/K})} = 292 \text{ K}.$$

We next use Eq. 20.31 for process A:

$$Q_A = Nk_BT_i\ln\left(\frac{V_f}{V_i}\right)$$
$$= (3.01 \times 10^{23})(1.38 \times 10^{-23})(292 \text{ K})\ln\left(\frac{1.60 \times 10^{-2} \text{ m}^3}{4.00 \times 10^{-3} \text{ m}^3}\right)$$
$$= 1.68 \times 10^3 \text{ J}.$$

For the isobaric leg of process B, we know that $P_1 = P_i$ and thus we can get T_1 from the ideal gas law in the form

$$T_1 = \frac{P_iV_1}{Nk_B} = \frac{(3.03 \times 10^5 \text{ N/m}^2)(1.60 \times 10^{-2} \text{ m}^3)}{(3.01 \times 10^{23})(1.38 \times 10^{-23} \text{ J/K})}$$
$$= 1.17 \times 10^3 \text{ K}.$$

PRACTICE

Using this temperature in Eq. 20.21 and remembering that for our diatomic H_2 particles $C_P = 7k_B/2$, we get Q for this leg of process B:

$$\begin{aligned} Q_{B,\text{isobaric}} &= NC_P(T_1 - T_i) \\ &= (3.01 \times 10^{23})[\tfrac{7}{2}(1.38 \times 10^{-23}\ \text{J/K})] \\ &\quad \times (1.17 \times 10^3\ \text{K} - 292\ \text{K}) \\ &= 1.28 \times 10^4\ \text{J}. \end{aligned}$$

For the isochoric compression in process B, Eq. 20.12 is $Q_{B,\text{isochoric}} = (\frac{d}{2})Nk_B(T_f - T_1)$. Because $T_f = T_i$, we can rewrite this as

$$\begin{aligned} Q_{B,\text{isochoric}} &= \tfrac{5}{2}(3.01 \times 10^{23})(1.38 \times 10^{-23}\ \text{J/K}) \\ &\quad \times (292\ \text{K} - 1170\ \text{K}) \\ &= -9.12 \times 10^3\ \text{J}. \end{aligned}$$

The algebraic sum of $Q_{B,\text{isobaric}}$ and $Q_{B,\text{isochoric}}$ gives us the quantity of energy added thermally to the sample in process B:

$$Q_B = 1.28 \times 10^4\ \text{J} + (-9.12 \times 10^3\ \text{J}) = 3.68 \times 10^3\ \text{J}.$$

The difference in the energies transferred thermally to the gas in the two processes is

$$Q_B - Q_A = (3.68 \times 10^3\ \text{J}) - (1.68 \times 10^3\ \text{J}) = 2.00 \times 10^3\ \text{J}. ✔$$

❹ **EVALUATE RESULT** From our PV diagram, the area under the curve for process B is larger than the area under the curve for process A. Because $V_f > V_i$, the work done on the gas is negative, so we expect that $W_B - W_A < 0$. Therefore $Q_B - Q_A > 0$, in agreement with our calculation. The work done on the gas for the isobaric leg in process B is

$$\begin{aligned} W_B &= -P_i\Delta V = -(3.03 \times 10^5\ \text{N/m}^2)(12.0 \times 10^{-3}\ \text{m}^3) \\ &= -3.64 \times 10^3\ \text{J}. \end{aligned}$$

The initial and final states are at the same temperature, so $P_f = P_iV_i/V_f = P_i/4$. Therefore the work done on the gas during an isobaric expansion at the final pressure would be

$$W_1 = -P_f\Delta V = -P_i\Delta V/4 = -9.1 \times 10^2\ \text{J}.$$

The difference in the energies transferred thermally to the gas in the two processes should have a magnitude near the average of these; $\frac{1}{2}(W_B + W_1) = -2270$ J. A difference of 2000 J for these two processes is therefore reasonable.

Guided Problem 20.4 Two more expansions

Consider two processes for taking a 0.200-mol sample of helium gas (He, monatomic particles) from an initial state i to a final state f. The gas behaves ideally, and in both processes the initial volume and pressure are $8.00 \times 10^{-3}\ \text{m}^3$ and $9.00 \times 10^4\ \text{N/m}^2$. In process A, the gas undergoes a quasistatic isentropic expansion to a volume of $1.20 \times 10^{-2}\ \text{m}^3$. In process B, the gas undergoes an isochoric pressure decrease followed by an isobaric expansion to a volume of $1.20 \times 10^{-2}\ \text{m}^3$, both quasistatically. What is the difference in the amounts of work done on the gas during the two processes?

❶ **GETTING STARTED**

1. Draw a PV diagram showing both processes. Are there any intermediate states you can identify in process B?
2. What are your target quantities, and what principles can you use to determine them?
3. What is the heat capacity ratio for a sample of helium gas?
4. Which quantities do you know? Which quantities are unknown for the initial and final states in both processes? Which are unknown for the intermediate state in process B?

❷ **DEVISE PLAN**

5. Which quantities must you know to determine the work done in process A? Which must you know to determine the work done in each part of process B?
6. How can you use the fact that process A is isentropic to determine some of your target quantities?

❸ **EXECUTE PLAN**

7. Determine the number of gas particles in the sample and then the initial temperature.
8. Use the fact that process A is isentropic to determine the final temperature and pressure.
9. Determine the remaining quantities you seek.

❹ **EVALUATE RESULT**

10. Based on your PV diagram, do you expect the difference in work done to be positive, zero, or negative? Does your result agree with your expectation?

Worked Problem 20.5 Two-step versus one-step compression

Consider two processes for taking a 0.200-mol sample of helium gas (He, monatomic particles) from an initial state i to a final state f. The gas behaves ideally, and in both processes the initial temperature and pressure are 150 K and $1.01 \times 10^5\ \text{N/m}^2 = 101$ kPa. In process A, the gas undergoes a quasistatic isothermal compression to a volume of $2.00 \times 10^{-3}\ \text{m}^3$. In process B, the gas undergoes a quasistatic isentropic compression followed by a quasistatic isobaric compression to $V_f = 2.00 \times 10^{-3}\ \text{m}^3$. What are (*a*) the difference $|Q_A - Q_B|$ in the quantity of energy transferred thermally to the gas in the two processes, (*b*) the difference $|W_A - W_B|$ in the amount of work done on the gas in the two processes, and (*c*) the entropy change resulting from either process?

❶ **GETTING STARTED** We begin by drawing a PV diagram showing both processes (Figure WG20.3). Process A is an isothermal compression, so we show its path running along an isotherm leftward

PRACTICE

(decreasing volume) and upward (increasing pressure) from initial state i to final state f. The path for process B has two legs. The isentropic compression we represent by a curve running leftward along an isentrope from initial state i to intermediate state 1 at volume V_1 and pressure $P_1 = P_f$. The isobaric compression we represent by a horizontal line running leftward from intermediate state 1 to final state f.

Figure WG20.3

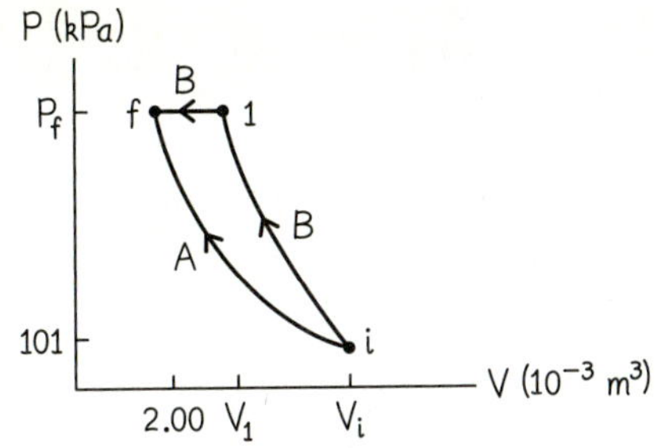

❷ **DEVISE PLAN** We need to (*a*) compare the energy transferred thermally, Q, for two processes that take a gas sample from an initial state to a final state, (*b*) compare the work done on the sample in the two cases, and (*c*) determine how the entropy of the sample changes in going from the initial to final state. For parts *a* and *b*, we know that, in a system going from one macrostate to another, the change in the system's thermal energy, ΔE_{th}, is independent of path and so is the same for the two processes. Process A is isothermal, so $T_f = T_i = 150$ K. Hence Eq. 20.15 tells us that $\Delta E_{th} = NC_V\Delta T = 0$ for both processes. Therefore the Eq. 20.2 form of the energy law requires that $\Delta E_{th} = 0 = W_A + Q_A = W_B + Q_B$. From this we conclude that $|Q_A - Q_B| = |W_A - W_B|$; that is, our answer to part *b* is going to be identical to our answer to part *a*.

We can use Eq. 20.31, $Q = -W = Nk_BT\ln(V_f/V_i)$, to calculate Q_A because we can obtain V_i from the ideal gas law. For the isentropic leg of process B, we know that the energy transferred thermally to get to intermediate state 1 is $Q = 0$. Thus the only quantity we need to calculate in order to know Q_B is the value of Q for the isobaric leg, and for this we can use Eq. 20.21, $Q = NC_P\Delta T$. We know C_P from Eq. 20.25, but we need to calculate T_1 in order to know ΔT. For T_1, we can use Eq. 20.47, $P_i^{\frac{1}{\gamma}-1}T_i = P_f^{\frac{1}{\gamma}-1}T_f$, but to do so we need a value for P_f, and for that we turn to the ideal gas law once again.

The last step in solving part *a* is to determine the difference $|Q_A - Q_B|$. For part *b*, $|Q_A - Q_B| = |W_A - W_B|$, as noted above. In part *c*, we can use Eq. 20.35, $\Delta S = N\ln(V_f/V_i)$, to obtain the entropy change, which is the same for the two processes because both are changes from the same macrostate i to the same macrostate f.

❸ **EXECUTE PLAN** (*a*) We begin with the ideal gas law (Eq. 19.51) to determine the volume V_i. Avogadro's number tells us that for this sample of helium particles, $N = (0.200 \text{ mol})(6.02 \times 10^{23} \text{ particles/mol}) = 1.20 \times 10^{23}$ particles. Thus

$$V_i = \frac{Nk_BT_i}{P_i}$$

$$= \frac{(1.20 \times 10^{23})(1.38 \times 10^{-23} \text{ J/K})(150 \text{ K})}{1.01 \times 10^5 \text{ N/m}^2}$$

$$= 2.46 \times 10^{-3} \text{ m}^3.$$

We then use Eq. 20.31 to determine the quantity of energy transferred thermally in process A:

$$Q_A = Nk_BT_i\ln\left(\frac{V_f}{V_i}\right)$$

$$= (1.20 \times 10^{23})(1.38 \times 10^{-23} \text{ J/K})$$

$$\times (150 \text{ K})\ln\left(\frac{2.00 \times 10^{-3} \text{ m}^3}{2.46 \times 10^{-3} \text{ m}^3}\right)$$

$$= -51.4 \text{ J}.$$

The plan for Q_B is to apply Eq. 20.21, $Q = NC_P\Delta T$, to the isobar from intermediate state 1 to final state f. We know that $T_f = 150$ K, but we don't know T_1, which is the value of T_i we need in $\Delta T = T_f - T_i$ along the isobar. To calculate T_1, we begin by solving Eq. 19.51 for P_f, remembering that $T_f = T_i = 150$ K for both processes:

$$P_f = \frac{Nk_BT_f}{V_f}$$

$$= \frac{(1.20 \times 10^{23})(1.38 \times 10^{-23} \text{ J/K})(150 \text{ K})}{2.00 \times 10^{-3} \text{ m}^3}$$

$$= 1.24 \times 10^5 \text{ N/m}^2 = 124 \text{ kPa}.$$

Because this leg of process B is isobaric, we know that $P_f = P_1$.

Now we turn to the isentropic leg of process B. Here the quantity we are after, T_1, is what we must use for T_f in any equations we use, and P_1 is what we must use for P_f. We begin by solving Eq. 20.47 for T_f, which is now our T_1:

$$T_1 = \left(\frac{P_i}{P_1}\right)^{(\frac{1}{\gamma}-1)}T_i.$$

Because $\gamma = \frac{5}{3}$, the exponent $(1/\gamma) - 1$ is $-\frac{2}{5}$, and so

$$T_1 = \left(\frac{P_i}{P_1}\right)^{-2/5}(T_i) = \left(\frac{1.01 \times 10^5 \text{ N/m}^2}{1.24 \times 10^5 \text{ N/m}^2}\right)^{-2/5}(150 \text{ K}) = 163 \text{ K}.$$

Now we are ready for Eq. 20.21. For monatomic helium particles with their three degrees of freedom, $C_P = (\frac{5}{2})k_B$, and thus Eq. 20.21 is

$$Q_B = (1.20 \times 10^{23})(\tfrac{5}{2})(1.38 \times 10^{-23} \text{ J/K})(150 \text{ K} - 163 \text{ K})$$

$$= -53.8 \text{ J}.$$

Therefore the difference in the quantities of energy transferred thermally to the gas in the two processes is

$$|Q_A - Q_B| = |(-51.4 \text{ J}) - (-53.8 \text{ J})| = 2.4 \text{ J}. ✔$$

(*b*) As noted in Devise Plan, the quantity $|Q_A - Q_B|$ is equal to the difference in the work done on the gas for the two processes, $|W_A - W_B| = 2.4$ J. ✔

(*c*) Equation 20.35 gives us the change in entropy as the gas goes from state i to state f via either process:

$$\Delta S = N\ln\left(\frac{V_f}{V_i}\right)$$

$$= (1.20 \times 10^{23})\ln\left(\frac{2.00 \times 10^{-3} \text{ m}^3}{2.46 \times 10^{-3} \text{ m}^3}\right) = -2.48 \times 10^{22}. ✔$$

❹ **EVALUATE RESULT** By comparing the areas under the paths in the PV diagram, we expect that the difference in the work done on the gas in the two processes is approximately $W_B - W_A = -(\frac{1}{3})(P_f - P_i)\Delta V$. From our calculations, the change in volume is $\Delta V = V_f - V_i = -0.46 \times 10^{-3}$ m, and the change in pressure is $P_f - P_i = 0.23 \times 10^5$ N/m^2. Therefore the difference in the work done on the gas is approximately

$$W_B - W_A = -(\tfrac{1}{3})(0.23 \times 10^5 \text{ N/m}^2)(-0.46 \times 10^{-3} \text{ m})$$
$$= 3.5 \text{ J},$$

which is in reasonable agreement with our calculation in part *a*. That our calculated entropy change in part *c* is negative makes sense because the gas volume decreases and the particles have fewer basic states available in the smaller volume. This same entropy change must occur in process B, and so calculating that entropy change is a further check on our result in part *c*. Here we need to calculate only the change for the isobaric leg, which is given by Eq. 20.41:

$$\Delta S = \frac{NC_P}{k_B}\ln\left(\frac{T_f}{T_i}\right)$$
$$= \frac{(1.20 \times 10^{23})(\frac{5}{2}k_B)}{k_B}\ln\left(\frac{150 \text{ K}}{163 \text{ K}}\right) = -2.49 \times 10^{22},$$

in agreement with the ΔS value we calculated with Eq. 20.35.

Guided Problem 20.6 Two-step versus one-step entropy change

Consider two processes for taking a 0.600-mol sample of hydrogen gas (H_2, diatomic particles) from an initial state i to a final state f. The gas behaves ideally, and in both processes the initial volume and pressure are 6.00×10^{-3} m^3 and 2.00×10^5 N/m^2. In process A, the gas undergoes a quasistatic isentropic expansion to a final volume of 2.00×10^{-2} m^3. In process B, the gas undergoes a quasistatic isothermal expansion followed by a quasistatic isochoric pressure decrease. What is the entropy change for process A and for each leg of process B?

❶ **GETTING STARTED**

1. Make a PV diagram showing both processes. Are there any intermediate states that you can identify in process B?
2. What is the heat capacity ratio for H_2?

❷ **DEVISE PLAN**

3. In both legs of process B, on what quantities does the change in entropy depend?
4. Which quantities do you know and which are unknown for the initial, intermediate, and final states of process B? Which of these are your target quantities?
5. How can you use the fact that process A is isentropic to determine some of your target quantities?
6. How can the ideal gas law help you determine some of your target quantities?

❸ **EXECUTE PLAN**

7. Determine the number of gas particles in the sample and then ΔS for process A.
8. Determine the initial temperature of the gas and then the final temperature and pressure.
9. Determine ΔS for each leg of process B.

❹ **EVALUATE RESULT**

10. Do you expect a positive, zero, or negative value of ΔS for the isothermal leg of process B? For the isochoric leg?
11. Does your result for process B agree with your expectation?
12. Does the algebraic sum of your entropy changes for process B match your result for process A?

Worked Problem 20.7 Cool drink of water

Three 0.0100-kg ice cubes initially at -10.0 °C are placed in 0.250 kg of water initially at 25.0 °C. Once all the ice melts, what is the temperature of the liquid in the glass? The specific heat capacity for ice is 2.090×10^3 J/K·kg, that for liquid water is 4.181×10^3 J/K·kg, and for ice the specific transformation energy for melting is 3.34×10^5 J/kg.

❶ **GETTING STARTED** We must determine the final temperature T_f for a system that starts out as 0.250 kg of liquid water plus 0.0300 kg of ice and ends up as 0.280 kg of liquid water. We assume that the water and ice form a closed system, which means no energy is thermally transferred either to or from the mixture in the glass. Because the temperatures are given in degrees Celsius, we note that -10 °C = 263 K, 0 °C = 273 K, and 25 °C = 298 K.

To melt the ice, energy is thermally transferred out of the 0.250 kg of water, lowering the temperature of the water to T_f. This energy lost by the water is thermally transferred to the ice, first raising its temperature to 0 °C, then melting the cubes while their temperature stays at 0 °C, and then raising the temperature of the 0.0300 kg of liquid water formed from the cubes to T_f.

We draw two energy diagrams. One for the 0.250 kg that is liquid water throughout the process and one for the 0.0300 kg that is initially ice (Figure WG20.4). In the water diagram, $Q_{water} < 0$ because energy is thermally transferred out of the water. In the ice diagram, $Q_{ice} > 0$ because energy is thermally transferred to the cubes.

Figure WG20.4

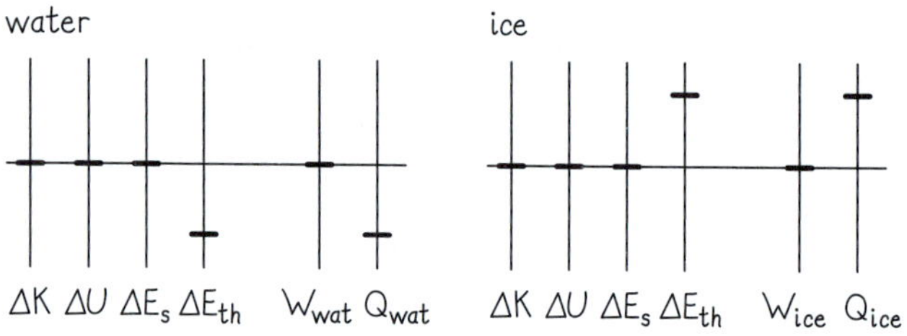

❷ **DEVISE PLAN** The change in temperature for the 0.250 kg of water is $\Delta T_{water} = T_f - T_{water,i} = T_f - 298$ K. We know the specific heat capacity of water, $c_{water} = 4.181 \times 10^3$ J/K · kg, and we know the mass of the water, which means we can use Eq. 20.49 to calculate Q_{water}, the quantity of energy transferred thermally out of the water to cause this temperature change ΔT_{water}. The quantity Q_{ice} of energy thermally transferred to the ice cubes to increase their temperature to T_f has three components. First the temperature of the cubes is raised from 263 K to 273 K, so that for this increase we can say $\Delta T_{ice,1} = 10.0$ K. Knowing the specific heat capacity of ice, $c_{ice} = 2.090 \times 10^3$ J/K · kg, and the mass of the ice, we can use Eq. 20.49 to calculate the first component of Q_{ice}. Next the cubes melt to 0.0300 kg of liquid water while the temperature remains constant at 273 K. Knowing the specific transformation energy needed to melt ice to liquid water, $L_m = 3.34 \times 10^5$ J/kg, and the mass of the ice, we can use Eq. 20.55 to calculate the second component of Q_{ice}. Finally the temperature of the 0.0300 kg of liquid water formed from the cubes is raised to T_f, and we express this temperature change as $\Delta T_{ice,2} = T_f - 273$ K. To determine this third component of Q_{ice}, we use Eq. 20.49 again with the specific heat capacity of water, but this time with a mass of 0.0300 kg, to calculate the thermal energy transferred for this temperature change. Because the system is closed, $Q_{ice} = -Q_{water}$, and we use this condition to obtain T_f.

❸ **EXECUTE PLAN** Equation 20.49 gives an expression for the energy thermally transferred out of the water:

$$Q_{water} = m_{water} c_{water} \Delta T_{water}.$$

Next we use Eqs. 20.49 and 20.55 to write an expression for the three components of Q_{ice}:

$$Q_{ice} = m_{ice} c_{ice} \Delta T_{ice,1} + m_{ice} L_m + m_{ice} c_{water} \Delta T_{ice,2}.$$

Note that in the final term we must use the specific heat capacity for liquid water because now the 0.0300 kg of ice is liquid. Setting $Q_{ice} = -Q_{water}$ yields

$$m_{ice} c_{ice} \Delta T_{ice,1} + m_{ice} L_m + m_{ice} c_{water} \Delta T_{ice,2} = -m_{water} c_{water} \Delta T_{water}.$$

To have this equation contain our target quantity, T_f, we substitute for the delta factors:

$$m_{ice} c_{ice}(\Delta T_{ice,1}) + m_{ice} L_m + m_{ice} c_{water}(T_f - T_{melt})$$
$$= -m_{water} c_{water}(T_f - T_{water,i})$$

$$T_f = \frac{m_{water} c_{water} T_{water,i} + m_{ice} c_{water} T_{melt}}{(m_{water} + m_{ice}) c_{water}} - \frac{m_{ice} c_{ice}(\Delta T_{ice,1}) + m_{ice} L_m}{(m_{water} + m_{ice}) c_{water}}$$

$$= \frac{(0.250 \text{ kg})(4.181 \times 10^3 \text{ J/K} \cdot \text{kg})(298 \text{ K})}{(0.280 \text{ kg})(4.181 \times 10^3 \text{ J/K} \cdot \text{kg})} + \frac{(0.0300 \text{ kg})(4.181 \times 10^3 \text{ J/K} \cdot \text{kg})(273 \text{ K})}{(0.280 \text{ kg})(4.181 \times 10^3 \text{ J/K} \cdot \text{kg})}$$
$$- \frac{(0.0300 \text{ kg})(2.090 \times 10^3 \text{ J/K} \cdot \text{kg})(10.0 \text{ K})}{(0.280 \text{ kg})(4.181 \times 10^3 \text{ J/K} \cdot \text{kg})} - \frac{(0.0300 \text{ kg})(3.34 \times 10^5 \text{ J/kg})}{(0.280 \text{ kg})(4.181 \times 10^3 \text{ J/K} \cdot \text{kg})}$$

$T_{sys,f} = 286 \text{ K} = 13.0$ °C. ✔

❹ **EVALUATE RESULT** Our result is lower than the initial temperature of the water and higher than the initial temperature of the ice, in line with our expectations. Because the mass of the water is about eight times the mass of the ice, we would expect T_f to be close to the initial water temperature—say, about 20 °C. However, once we take into account the specific transformation energy for melting the ice, we expect T_f to be lower than this, and so our 13 °C result is reasonable.

Guided Problem 20.8 Hot and cool water

Sample A is 1.50 kg of water initially at 100 °C. Sample B is 2.00 kg of water initially at 20.0 °C. When the two samples are brought into thermal contact with each other and allowed to reach equilibrium, what is the change in entropy $\Delta S_A + \Delta S_B$?

❶ **GETTING STARTED**

1. Define a closed system.
2. List the unknown quantities and decide which are your target variables.
3. Are there any quantities you may need to look up?

❷ **DEVISE PLAN**

4. Draw any relevant energy diagrams.
5. Which quantities do you need to know in order to determine the entropy change?
6. What principle do you need to use to determine the quantity of energy transferred thermally from one sample to the other?
7. Write an expression that contains the final equilibrium temperature as one term.

❸ **EXECUTE PLAN**

8. Calculate the final equilibrium temperature.
9. Use this temperature to determine the entropy changes for the two samples.

❹ **EVALUATE RESULT**

10. Do you expect the entropy to increase, stay the same, or decrease?
11. Does your result agree with your expectation?

Questions and Problems

For instructor-assigned homework, go to MasteringPhysics® MP

Dots indicate difficulty level of problems: • = *easy*, •• = *intermediate*, ••• = *hard*; CR = *context-rich problem.*

Unless you are told otherwise, assume that all processes in these problems are quasistatic and that all gases are monatomic and ideal.

20.1 Thermal interactions

1. When the volume of a gas increases, is the work done by the gas on its surroundings positive, negative, or zero? •
2. A thermally insulated chamber fitted with a piston as its bottom surface contains an ideal gas. The piston slowly moves upward and compresses the gas into a smaller volume. Draw an energy diagram for this process, taking the gas as your system. •
3. State whether each process is quasistatic, adiabatic, both, or neither for the defined system: (*a*) Water boils in a pot. System: water. (*b*) A balloon filled with air is slowly compressed and cooled. System: balloon and air. (*c*) An initially sealed vial of air is opened in an air-filled room that is isolated from its outside environment, where the temperature and number density of air particles are the same inside and outside the vial. System: vial, room, and air. •
4. A sample that contains 5.60×10^{21} particles of a monatomic ideal gas expands adiabatically and quasistatically from 1.00 L to 2.00 L. If the initial gas pressure is 30.5 kPa, what is the final temperature of the gas? ••
5. You are designing an engine that contains several pistons that each move 150 mm per stroke. You believe the engine may consume less energy than a traditional engine if many of the processes in the engine are reversible. The gas is a mixture of several substances, but the particles have an average mass of 7.548×10^{-26} kg per particle, and the gas temperature can reach 300 °F. Determine an upper limit on the number of cycles a piston can go through each second, and satisfy the reversibility constraint. How could this upper limit be increased? Is the reversibility constraint sensible? •••

20.2 Temperature measurement

6. While converting a list of Kelvin temperatures to degrees Fahrenheit and degrees Celsius, you notice that one temperature on the Kelvin scale has the same numerical value on both the Fahrenheit and Celsius scales. What is this Kelvin temperature? •
7. Express the difference between the boiling and freezing points of water in (*a*) kelvins, (*b*) degrees Celsius, and (*c*) degrees Fahrenheit. •
8. Liquid nitrogen at atmospheric pressure boils at −196 °C. What is this temperature on the Kelvin scale? •
9. Describe how an ideal gas thermometer is constructed and how it measures temperature. ••
10. When a certain ideal gas thermometer is placed in water at the triple point, the mercury level in the right arm is 986 mm above the reference mark. How far is the mercury level above the reference mark when this thermometer is placed in boiling water at a location where the atmospheric pressure is 1.00 atm? ••
11. When a certain ideal gas thermometer is dipped in water boiling at atmospheric pressure, the mercury level in the right arm is 1279 mm above the reference mark. When the thermometer is removed from the water and allowed to reach room temperature, the mercury level drops by 267 mm. (*a*) What is the room temperature in degrees Celsius? (*b*) Is your answer to part *a* a reasonable temperature for a room? ••
12. When a certain ideal gas thermometer is immersed in a water-ice mixture at 273.15 K, the mercury level in the right arm is 102 mm above the reference mark. When this thermometer is then immersed in a liquid of unknown temperature, the mercury level is 29 mm above the reference mark. (*a*) What is the temperature of the liquid? (*b*) What is a potential source of error in this measurement? ••
13. An engineer planning a weld from manufacturer specifications realizes that the units for temperature have been accidentally omitted. The specifications say, "The temperature of the weld should be no lower than 95% of 1960 but can be safely welded at a much higher temperature." The engineer is not sure whether the 1960 is 1960 K or 1960 °C. To what temperature (in degrees Celsius) should she specify the weld to be sure it is not done at too low a temperature? ••
14. For an environmental study, you need to collect temperature data for a year in a North American desert, where the temperature ranges from 255 K in winter to 320 K in summer. You have a single thermal sensor that can be calibrated in degrees Celsius or degrees Fahrenheit, but the readout is fixed to one decimal place. (*a*) Which scale, Fahrenheit or Celsius, will give you greater precision? (*b*) Your research group doubts your choice, so you must provide numerical evidence to support it. What is the ratio of the number of readings possible on the scale you chose to the number of readings possible on the scale you didn't choose? •••

20.3 Heat capacity

15. How much energy is required to heat 100 L of water from 20 °C to 55 °C? •
16. To make yourself some coffee, you put one cup of water (236 g) in a small pot on the stove. What quantity of energy must be transferred thermally to the water to raise its temperature from 20 °C to 100 °C? (Ignore the mass of the pot.) •
17. According to the Can Manufacturers Institute, the energy used to make an aluminum can from recycled aluminum is 5% of the energy used to make an aluminum can from virgin ore. In a typical year, 1.7 billion pounds of aluminum cans are recycled. How much energy is thermally transferred to get this mass of aluminum from 20 °C to its melting point, 660 °C? ••
18. Three diatomic molecules from different gas samples—one at 3 K, one at 298 K, and one at 1000 K—are in thermal equilibrium with their respective surroundings. (a) Rank the molecules according to heat capacity per molecule at constant volume, highest first. (b) What is the thermal energy of each molecule, expressed in terms of T and k_B? ••
19. A swimming pool has a length of 50.0 m, a width of 35.0 m, and an average depth of 2.00 m. (*a*) How much energy is required to raise the temperature of the water in this pool by 1.00 °C? (*b*) If this energy were used to lift a truck, to what height could a 1.0×10^4-kg truck be lifted? ••
20. A 3.50-kg block of iron initially at 8.00×10^2 K is placed on top of a 6.25-kg block of copper initially at 4.00×10^2 K. How much energy is transferred thermally from the iron to the copper as the two blocks come to thermal equilibrium? Assume the

blocks are thermally insulated from their surroundings but not from each other and that they constitute a closed system. ••

21. Devil's Throat, the longest drop in Iguazu Falls on the Brazil-Argentina border, has a height of 82 m. If all the kinetic energy a given volume of water acquires in dropping through Devil's Throat goes into heating the water, by how much does the water temperature rise? ••

22. You pour 5.0 L of water at 20 °C into a large pot to make spaghetti. If the heating element on your stove is rated at 1250 W, how many minutes does it take for the water to start boiling? Ignore any energy thermally transferred to the environment. ••

23. A helium atom at 77 K is in thermal equilibrium in a nanowire (a wire with a diameter on the scale of molecules). (*a*) The atom is constrained in the nanowire and so can move in only one dimension, along the wire length. What is the atom's thermal energy? (*b*) The atom is boiled off the nanowire and allowed to float free at 295 K. What is its thermal energy now? •••

24. A diatomic molecule in thermal equilibrium at 120 K is constrained to move freely only on a two-dimensional surface. (*a*) What is the molecule's thermal energy? (*b*) The molecule is boiled off the surface and allowed to float freely in a gas at thermal equilibrium at 298 K. What is the molecule's thermal energy now? (*c*) What is its thermal energy if it is heated to 3000 K? ••

25. A cryogenic substance is found to have a specific heat capacity c that varies with temperature according to $c = \beta T^2$, where β is an empirically derived constant with units $\mathrm{J/K^3 \cdot kg}$. If 231 J of energy must be transferred thermally to an 8000-mg sample of this substance to raise the temperature of the sample from 1.00 to 6.00 K, what is the value of β? •••

20.4 *PV* diagrams and processes

26. An ideal gas expands adiabatically and quasistatically in a chamber fitted with a piston. Is this process isothermal, isentropic, isobaric, isochoric, or none of these? •

27. Figure P20.27 shows two processes, A and B, carried out on an ideal gas. In which process was the amount of work done by the gas greater? •

Figure P20.27

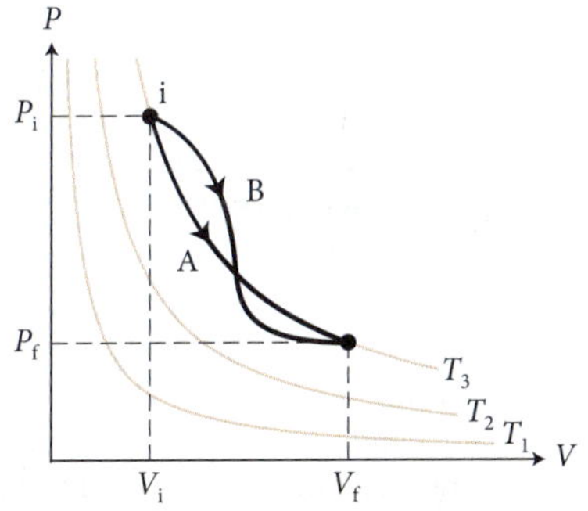

28. Figure P20.28 is the *PV* diagram for a process carried out on 10 mol of an ideal gas in thermal equilibrium that begins and ends on the same state (the initial state i and the final state f for the gas are at 1). (*a*) Characterize each leg of the process—$1 \rightarrow 2$, $2 \rightarrow 3$, $3 \rightarrow 4$, $4 \rightarrow 1$—as being isothermal, isobaric, isochoric, or isentropic. (*b*) Determine the temperature at state 1 and at state 3. ••

Figure P20.28

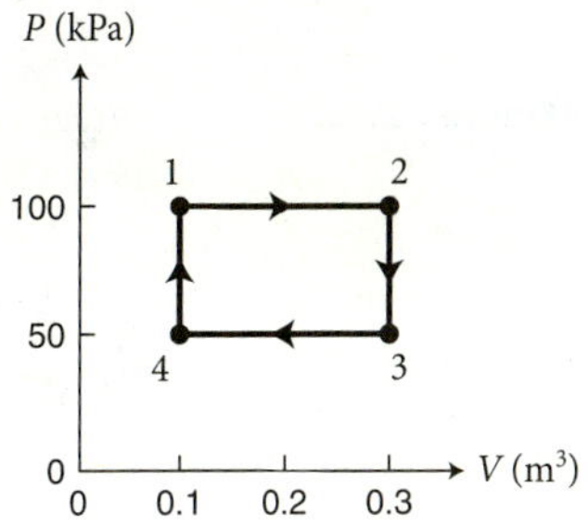

29. The curves in Figure P20.29 are isochors, isobars, isotherms, or isentropes. If a system is taken from initial state i to final state f, with $V_i = 0.15\ \mathrm{m^3}$ and $P_f = 1.00$ atm, what is the change in the entropy of the system? ••

Figure P20.29

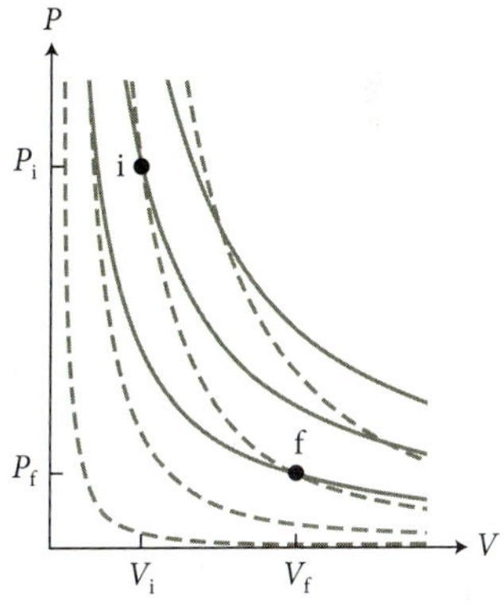

30. A 0.300-kg sample of nitrogen gas (diatomic molecules, $m_{N_2} = 4.652 \times 10^{-26}$ kg) in a chamber fitted with a piston undergoes an isothermal expansion from $0.0500\ \mathrm{m^3}$ to $0.150\ \mathrm{m^3}$. If the final pressure is 150 kPa, what is the final temperature? ••

31. Figure P20.31 shows four isotherms on the *PV* diagram for an ideal gas. What are the temperatures of isotherms A, B, and C? ••

Figure P20.31

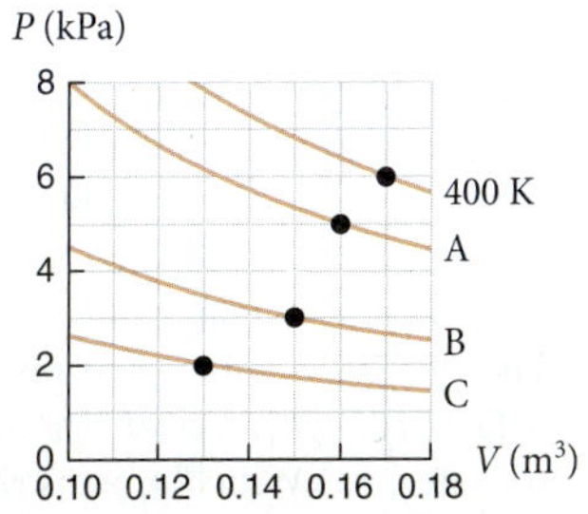

20.5 Change in energy and work

32. An ideal gas undergoes the process represented in Figure P20.32, where the gas is in state 1 when the process begins and again in state 1 at the finish. (*a*) Determine the work done by the gas during each of the four legs—$1 \rightarrow 2$, $2 \rightarrow 3$, $3 \rightarrow 4$, $4 \rightarrow 1$. (*b*) Determine the work done by the gas for the process. •

Figure P20.32

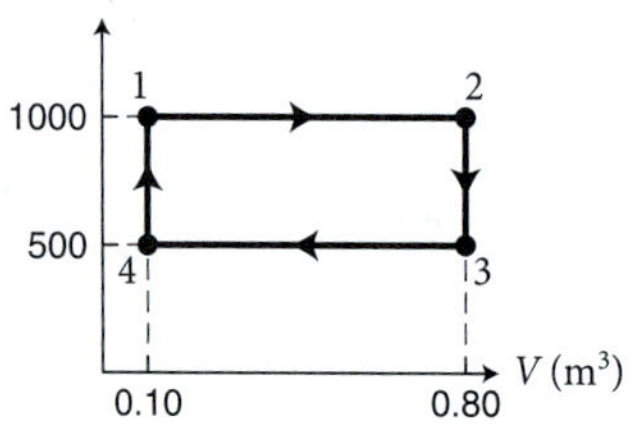

33. An ideal gas undergoes the process represented by the *PV* diagram of Figure P20.33, where the gas is in state 1 when the process begins and again in state 1 at the end of the process. Calculate the work done on the gas as a function of the initial pressure and volume. •

Figure P20.33

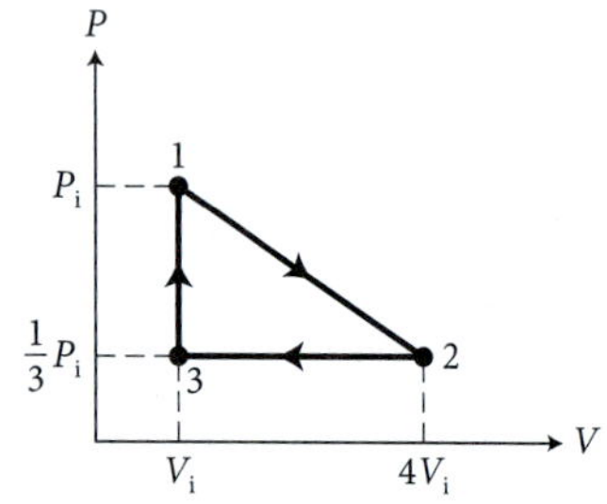

34. If 1.00 mol of an ideal monatomic gas initially at 72 K absorbs 100 J of thermal energy, what is the final temperature? Assume the volume does not change. •

35. An ideal gas is inside a cylinder fitted with a piston of cross-sectional area $0.10\ \text{m}^2$, and initially the gas pressure is 5.0×10^4 Pa. A quantity $Q = 5.0$ kJ of thermal energy is transferred slowly to the gas while the piston moves 0.10 m and the gas expands. If the expansion is isobaric, how much work is done on the gas? ••

36. What is the thermal energy associated with 5.6×10^{18} nitrogen molecules, N_2, at 100 ° F? Assume the nitrogen can be treated as an ideal gas. ••

37. In a cylindrical chamber fitted with a piston, the piston compresses 10.0 mol of ideal gas from $1.00\ \text{m}^3$ to $0.100\ \text{m}^3$ at a constant temperature of 300 K. Suppose this compression was done by placing a 100-kg block on top of the piston. What is the piston radius? Assume the air pressure outside the piston is 1.00 atm, and ignore the piston mass. ••

38. Figure P20.38 shows two processes, A and B, for moving 3.45×10^{22} particles of a monatomic ideal gas from state i to state f. (*a*) Which process requires less work done on the gas? (*b*) Which process requires a smaller quantity *Q* of energy transferred thermally to the gas? (*c*) By how much does the work done on the gas in process A differ from the work done on the gas in process B? ••

Figure P20.38

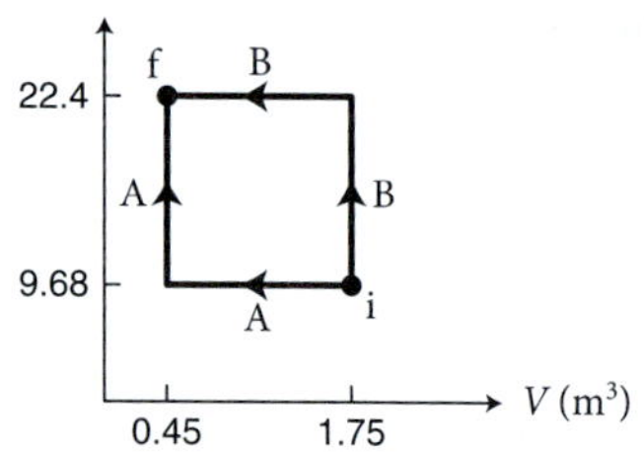

39. A 1.00-mol sample of an ideal diatomic gas in which the gas particles both translate and rotate is initially at 600 K. Energy is then added thermally to the sample until its temperature is 1000 K. At this temperature, the particles also vibrate. The sample is then heated to 1200 K. How much thermal energy does the sample absorb? ••

40. You have a sample that contains 9.70×10^{21} particles of an unknown gas in a chamber that has a volume of $0.0100\ \text{m}^3$. The initial pressure in the chamber is 1.84×10^4 Pa, and you determine that 378 J of energy must be added to the sample to increase the pressure to 2.68×10^4 Pa. (*a*) What can you say about the structure of the particles? (*b*) If your choices for the identity of the gas are helium, hydrogen, ammonia, and nitrogen, which do you choose, and why? •••

20.6 Isochoric and isentropic ideal gas processes

41. The *PV* diagram in Figure P20.41 shows two processes for taking an ideal gas from an initial state i to a final state f. How much work is done on the gas in the isochoric leg labeled A? •

Figure P20.41

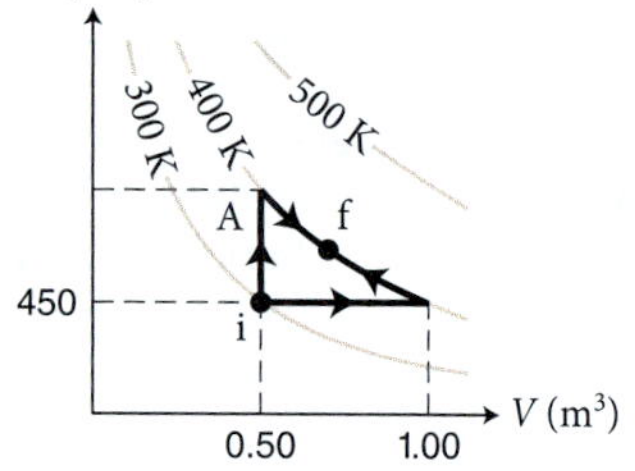

42. You park your car in the sun with the windows rolled up, and the interior temperature rises from 35 °C at 100 kPa to 48 °C. The interior volume of your car is roughly $1.5\ \text{m} \times 2.0\ \text{m} \times 1.0\ \text{m}$. (*a*) What is the mass of the air in the car, assuming a mass density of $1.13\ \text{kg/m}^3$ for air at 35 °C? (*b*) How much energy was delivered from the Sun to the interior to raise the temperature as indicated if all the energy went into the air? Use $720\ \text{J/K} \cdot \text{kg}$ for the specific heat capacity of air. ••

43. Your one-story house has a floor area of $2.0 \times 10^2\ \text{m}^2$ and 3.0-m-high ceilings. (*a*) On a hot day, you leave home with all the windows closed and the air-conditioning on. A power failure causes the air-conditioning to stop, and by the time you return home, the quantity of thermal energy you calculated in Problem 42 has been added to the inside air. By how many kelvins has the inside air temperature increased? (*b*) How much thermal energy from the Sun would be required to raise the temperature in your house from 24 °C to 25 °C? ••

44. Steam at 120 °C and 101.3 kPa is added to a hollow steel can that is then sealed and allowed to cool. (*a*) What is the pressure inside the can at 101 °C? (*b*) The can is 0.20 m tall and 0.10 m in diameter. What is the magnitude of the force exerted by the atmosphere on the curved and flat portions of the can exterior? (*c*) Once the steam cools to 100 °C, it begins to condense into liquid water and the can collapses inward. Why did the can retain its shape down to 101 °C but not below 100 °C? (Hint: Search "collapsing soda can" on your favorite Internet video site.)

45. A sample of helium gas is allowed to expand in a process that is adiabatic and quasistatic. As the gas cools from 105 °C to 101 °C, it does 9.05 J of work on a piston. How many helium atoms are there in the sample? ••

20.7 Isobaric and isothermal ideal gas processes

46. A 2.00-L sample of an ideal gas initially at 1.00 atm and 273 K undergoes an isobaric process that cools the sample to 265 K. (*a*) What is the final pressure in the gas? (*b*) What is the final volume of the gas? •

47. A cylinder fitted with a piston contains 1.00 mol of air at room temperature, 20.0 °C. The air is slowly compressed by the piston while the temperature is kept constant. What is the work done on the air if the final volume is one-third the initial volume? •

48. A chamber fitted with a piston can be controlled to keep the pressure in the chamber constant as the piston moves up and down to increase or decrease the chamber volume. If the chamber contains an ideal gas at 296 K and 1.00 atm, what is the work done on the gas as the piston compresses it from 1.00 L to 0.333 L? •

49. Your lab mate is measuring the heat capacity ratio of an unknown diatomic gas at room temperature and standard atmospheric pressure. She obtains values for C_P and C_V and tells you the ratio is 6/9. Give at least two reasons you need to check your lab mate's work. ••

50. A spherical air bubble in a lake expands as it rises slowly to the surface. At the point it starts to rise, the pressure is 2.00 atm, the temperature of the water is 10.0 °C, and the radius of the bubble is 5.00×10^{-3} m. At the surface, the pressure is 1.00 atm and the temperature of the water is 20.0 °C. (*a*) What is the final-to-initial volume ratio for the expanding bubble? (*b*) What is the change in thermal energy of the bubble? ••

51. A chamber fitted with a piston contains 1.00 mol of an ideal gas. (*a*) The piston is slowly moved to decrease the chamber volume while the gas temperature is held constant at 296 K. How much work is done *by* the gas if the final chamber volume is one-third the initial volume? (*b*) If, instead of moving in the direction that decreases the chamber volume, the piston slowly moves in the direction that increases that volume, how much work is done *by* the gas if the final chamber volume is three times the initial volume? ••

52. To change the volume of a gas isothermally by a factor f_1 of its initial value, it is necessary to do work W_1 on the gas. What work W_2 is needed to change the volume by a factor f_2 of the initial gas volume at the same temperature? Express your answer in terms of f_1, f_2, and W_1. ••

53. An ideal gas initially at volume V_1, pressure P_1, and temperature T_1 undergoes an isobaric process that changes its temperature to T_2. The gas immediately undergoes an isothermal process that changes its volume to V_3. What is the final pressure in the gas in terms of these variables? ••

54. At temperature T, a balloon is partly inflated with an ideal gas to a volume of 1.0 L. The balloon is then put in a low-pressure container at the same temperature T and its volume is increased to 2.0 L. If 26 J of work was done by the gas to accomplish this expansion, what is the final pressure inside the balloon in the low-pressure container? ••

55. A 1.00-mol sample of an ideal gas expands such that its entropy doubles to 1.345×10^{24}. The temperature is held constant at 100 K during the expansion. (*a*) How much work is done by the gas on its surroundings? (*b*) What quantity Q of energy is transferred thermally to the gas? ••

56. A 0.320-kg piston seals a chamber that contains helium atoms initially at 2.00 °C. The piston is free to move vertically, but it is originally held fixed in place with the chamber volume at 0.250 m³. When the piston is released, the chamber volume immediately increases as the piston moves upward. At the instant when the piston has moved 0.320 m from its initial position, its velocity is 43.5 mm/s upward. The air pressure in the room is 1.00 atm, and the piston has a circular cross-section and a radius of 0.200 m. What is the final temperature of the gas if the expansion is (*a*) isentropic and (*b*) isothermal? •••

57. The ideal gas law is valid for a gas when, among other things, any interactions between particles are ignored. A more realistic model was proposed by Johannes Diderik van der Waals in 1873, for which he received a Nobel Prize in 1910. The van der Waals equation of state is

$$\left(P + \frac{an^2}{V^2}\right)(V - nb) = Nk_BT,$$

where a and b are constants, and n is the number density of the gas particles. Use this equation to determine the work done on a gas undergoing an isothermal process. Verify that your result reduces to the ideal gas case when $a = b = 0$. •••

58. A sample of diatomic ideal gas ($\gamma = 1.4$) initially has a volume of 20.0 L and is at 5.00 atm and 320 K. The gas undergoes the process shown in Figure P20.58. First it expands isothermally ($1 \rightarrow 2$) until the pressure is 2.00 atm, and then it is compressed isentropically ($2 \rightarrow 3$) until the pressure is 5.00 atm again. (*a*) Determine the volume of the gas after the isothermal expansion and the work done by the gas during the expansion. (*b*) Determine the volume and temperature of the gas after the isentropic compression, and the work done on the gas during the compression. (*c*) Determine the change in entropy of the gas by determining ΔS for $1 \rightarrow 2$ plus ΔS for $2 \rightarrow 3$. (*d*) Show that the entropy change is the same when the gas undergoes the isobaric process $1 \rightarrow 3$. •••

Figure P20.58

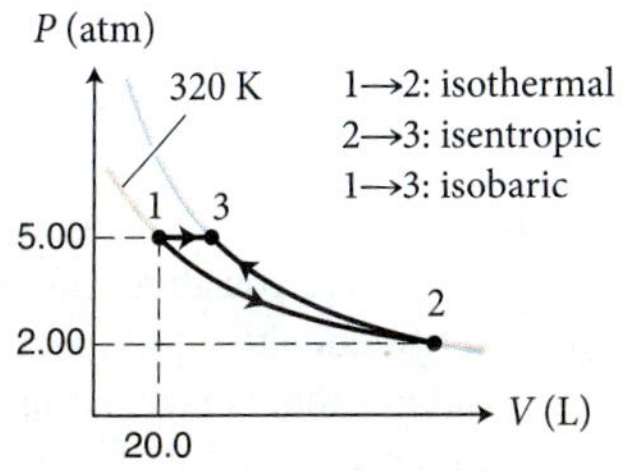

PRACTICE

20.8 Entropy change in ideal gas processes

59. A sample of nitrogen gas ($\gamma = 1.4$) initially has a volume of $0.61\ m^3$ and a pressure of 1.00 atm. If the sample expands isentropically to a volume of $1.00\ m^3$, what is the final pressure? •

60. A sample of an ideal gas for which $\gamma = \frac{7}{5}$ initially has a volume of 1.00 L and a pressure of 100 Pa. If the gas expands isentropically to 1.20 L, what is the final pressure? •

61. Figure P20.61 shows the PV diagram for a monatomic ideal gas undergoing an isobaric expansion $1 \rightarrow 2$ followed by an isochoric pressure increase $2 \rightarrow 3$. If the sample contains N gas particles, what is the change in entropy of the gas expressed in terms of nothing more than the initial and final pressures and volumes, and N. ••

Figure P20.61

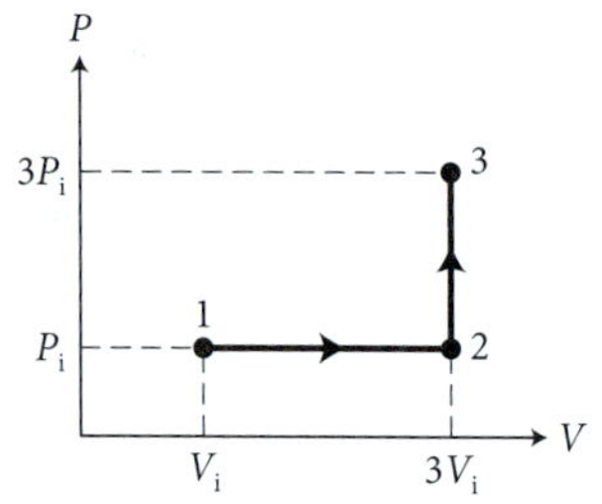

62. An ideal gas for which $\gamma = 1.4$ initially has a volume of $1.5\ m^3$ and a pressure of 15 MPa. The gas is then slowly compressed isentropically to a volume of $0.50\ m^3$. (*a*) What is the final pressure in the gas? (*b*) By how much did the entropy of the gas change? ••

63. A $\frac{1}{3}$-mol sample of an ideal gas is sealed in a container and heated from 273 K to 500 K. For this gas, what is the value of C_P in units of k_B if the temperature increase causes an entropy change of 1.8215×10^{23}? ••

64. Two identical thermally insulated spherical tanks, A and B, are connected by a valve. Initially tank A contains 10 mol of an ideal diatomic gas, tank B is evacuated, and the valve is closed. If the valve is opened and the gas expands isothermally from A to B, what is the change in the entropy of the gas? ••

65. As part of a physics experiment, air under high pressure is allowed to expand isentropically out of a metal can and into an empty plastic bag. When the expansion is complete, the bag and contents are at atmospheric pressure. The air inside the can is initially at 5.0 atm and 25 °C. What is the air's temperature once it is in the plastic bag? ••

66. A gas is inside a cylinder fitted with a piston. The gas and its surroundings are both at 20 °C, and the gas is compressed as the piston moves and decreases the cylinder volume. The compression takes place slowly enough to allow the gas temperature to stay at 20 °C, and the work done on the gas by the compression is 2.0×10^3 J. What is the change in entropy of the gas? ••

67. An ideal gas that initially has a volume of 1.00 mL and is at 1.00 atm expands isentropically to 10.0 mL and 0.0215 atm. (*a*) How many degrees of freedom do the gas particles have? (*b*) What does this tell you about the structure of the particles? ••

68. A chamber fitted with a piston contains 1.00 mol of a monatomic ideal gas that is taken from an initial state i to a final state f via states 1 and 2. The chamber volume is initially $V_i = 0.100\ m^3$, and the temperature is $T_i = 273$ °C. To take the gas to state 1, it is heated isochorically to $T_1 = 373$ °C. To take it to state 2, it is heated isobarically to $T_2 = 473$ °C. Finally, the gas is allowed to expand isothermally until its volume is $V_f = 2V_2$. What is the change in entropy of the gas? ••

69. An ideal monatomic gas expands isentropically from an initial pressure P_i and initial volume V_i to a final pressure $P_f = P_i/20$ and final volume $V_f = 6V_i$. What is the work done by the gas, expressed in terms of P_i and V_i? [Hint: Use Eq. 20.8 (but remember that you want work done *by* the gas, so watch your signs) and the fact that PV^γ = constant for an isentropic expansion (Eq. 20.46), with $\gamma = \frac{5}{3}$ for a monatomic ideal gas.] •••

20.9 Entropy change in nonideal gas processes

70. A thermodynamic process raises the temperature of 1.00 mol of water from 59.0 °C to 61.0 °C. What is the change in thermal energy of the water? •

71. An ice cream maker is in the form of a soccer ball (Figure P20.71). You fill the inner container with a mixture of cream and sugar at 32.0 °C and add rock salt and ice to the sleeve encircling the inner container. You then put both lids on and kick the ice cream maker around like a regular soccer ball until the internal temperature is low enough (−3.00 °C) to freeze the cream-sugar mixture into ice cream. (*a*) If the specific heat capacity of the mixture is 2900 J/K · kg, what quantity of thermal energy must be removed from the inner container to bring 0.500 kg of the mixture to the temperature required for freezing? (*b*) If the mass of the maker plus its contents is 3.80 kg, how high above ground level would you need to lift the unit in order for the gravitational potential energy of the ice cream maker-Earth system to be equal to the quantity of energy you found in part *a*? ••

Figure P20.71

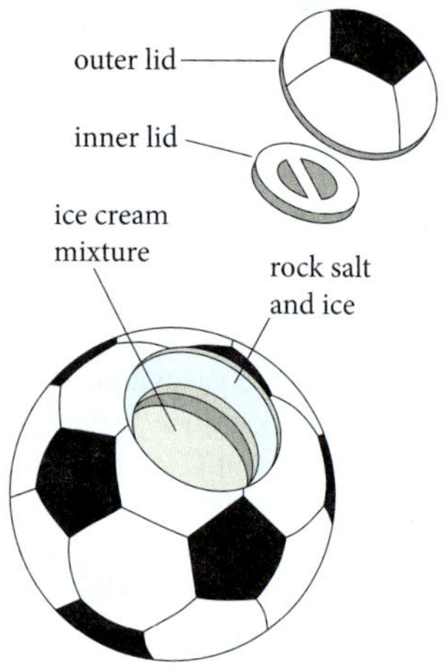

72. 2.00×10^4 J of energy is transferred thermally into a huge tank filled with liquid water. The water temperature remains constant at 10.0 °C during the process. By how much does the entropy of the water change? ••

73. An iceberg initially at 273 K is stopped in its motion by a small island. During the first few seconds of contact, 10 kJ of energy is transferred thermally from the island to the iceberg without the temperature of either object changing significantly. If the island temperature before the collision is 300 K, what is the change in entropy of the iceberg-island system as a result of the energy transfer? ••

PRACTICE

Additional problems

74. The average normal temperature of the human body is 98.6 °F. What is this temperature on the Celsius scale? •

75. Which are the most likely units for a measured temperature with a numerical value of (*a*) −322 and (*b*) 0? •

76. An ideal gas undergoes an isentropic process that changes its pressure from P_i to P_f and its volume from V_i to V_f. What is the work done on the gas? ••

77. A 22.7-g sample of diatomic oxygen gas molecules is in a sealed rigid container that has a volume of 0.0240 m^3. If the gas is initially at −1.50 °C, by how much does the pressure in the container change when the gas is cooled to −23.00 °C? ••

78. It is sometimes said, erroneously, that biological organisms violate the second law of thermodynamics because the biochemical reactions they carry out reduce their entropy by converting incoherent raw materials to coherent substances. To show that this is not so, consider your body at 37.0 °C transferring energy thermally into its immediate environment, where the temperature is 20 °C. For the system made up of your body and its environment, determine whether the entropy of the system increases or decreases over time, and at what rate. Assume your body transfers energy thermally at a rate of 100 W. ••

79. Two identical samples of a monatomic ideal gas start out at the triple point of water. Sample A is heated isochorically to five times its original temperature. Sample B is compressed isentropically and quasistatically to one-fifth of its original volume. In which process is the quantity of energy transferred thermally to the sample greater, and by how much? •••

80. You are working in a factory that uses water in its cooling systems and consequently has a lot of steam reservoirs. Due to carelessness, a 70.0-kg metal plate has been left on top of the only steam vent for a certain steam reservoir, and as a result the pressure in the reservoir builds up sufficiently to lift the plate a small distance. With the plate raised, the reservoir pressure drops slightly, and the plate lowers slowly back down and gently comes to rest on top of the vent. The vent is circular and has a diameter of 100 mm, and the plate is a square, 450 mm on a side. No steam is seen seeping out after this incident, and so you assume the plate has made a good seal such that only the circular section of plate directly above the vent is in contact with the steam. A flow meter attached to the reservoir tells you that 85.0 kg of liquid water was piped into that reservoir, and you know that this reservoir has a volume of 100 m^3. A coworker sees a few drops of water that have condensed on a glass portal located in the reservoir wall and thinks that the steam in the reservoir must have cooled enough to begin condensing to water (most of what's in the reservoir is still steam, though). Your coworker is about to grab the plate with his hands in order to uncover the vent and allow the steam to escape as it is designed to do when you suddenly realize that touching the plate might not be a good idea. ••• CR

81. You are the founder of a start-up company that extracts electrical energy from ocean waves, a process called WaveGen. Your basic technology is a tube anchored vertically to the ocean floor. The unit is installed close to shore so that the bottom is anchored to the seabed and the top is above the water surface. At the top of the unit is a turbine generator for creating electricity. Waves rise and fall in the tube like a piston going up and down. As a wave rises in the tube, it pushes the air above it up into the generator. As the wave falls, air from the atmosphere flows into the tube through holes drilled in the part of the tube that is not under water. The average change in vertical wave height is 2.00 m, and the waves repeat on average every 5.00 s. A nearby seaside town requires 0.500 MW, and your goal is to supply all this electrical power. You know that the WaveGen tubes can be made economically up to a diameter of 2.00 m and that the efficiency of the generator in converting wave power to electricity is 68.0%, but your production is limited to a few tubes per day. ••• CR

Answers to Review Questions

1. The symbol is Q, and it is positive when energy is transferred into the system.
2. Energy can be transferred to a system by heating it or by doing work on it. Heating transfers energy by means of a thermal interaction between system and surroundings, as when a flame (surroundings) transfers some of its thermal energy to a volume of water (system). Doing work on the system transfers energy by means of a mechanical interaction, as when a system's gravitational potential energy is increased by moving a boulder up a hill.
3. An adiabatic process is one in which no energy is transferred thermally.
4. A quasistatic process is one carried out in such a way that the system remains close to equilibrium at every instant during the process.
5. The entropy increases because thermally transferring energy to the system increases the system's temperature, and entropy increases as temperature increases.
6. The entropy does not change.
7. Some physical properties of matter change as the temperature changes.
8. The triple point of water is the unique pressure-temperature combination (610 Pa, 0.01 °C) at which ice, liquid water, and water vapor coexist in equilibrium. The temperature at which this occurs is defined as 273.16 K on the Kelvin scale.
9. The vessel holding the gas is put into water that is at the triple-point temperature, $T_{tp} = 273.16$ K, and the height h_{tp} above the reference level is noted for the mercury level in the unattached arm. You then draw a straight line on a plot of height measured vs. temperature that passes through the origin (0, 0) and (h_{tp}, T_{tp}). For any other absolute temperature, measure the height h and then determine the corresponding absolute temperature T, such that the point (h, T) lies on the straight line.
10. At absolute zero, the system has only one basic state available, which means its entropy is zero, and its thermal energy is a minimum, which means $T = 0$ is the lowest possible temperature for anything.
11. The heat capacity of a system is the ratio of the quantity of energy transferred thermally into the system to the change in the absolute temperature caused by the added energy.
12. A degree of freedom is an independent way a particle can store thermal energy. The number of degrees of freedom for a particle is equal to the number of ways the particle can translate, rotate, and vibrate.
13. An atom has three degrees of freedom, one for each direction (x, y, z) in which it translates in space. At moderate temperatures, a diatomic molecule has five, three associated with the x, y, z directions in which it translates and two associated with its rotation about the two axes that do not run through the centers of both atoms.
14. The energy is distributed such that each degree of freedom has a portion of the particle's thermal energy equal to the *equipartition energy share*, $k_B T/2$.
15. The number of degrees of freedom a particle has is equal to the number of ways the particle can translate, rotate, and vibrate. Each motion requires a specific quantum (amount) of energy added to the particle. Thus you can compare the equipartition share of energy at a particular temperature, $k_B T/2$, with the quantum of energy required for a given motion. If $k_B T/2$ is less than the required quantum of energy, the motion cannot take place and that degree of freedom does not contribute to the heat capacity per particle of gas.
16. Each point represents an equilibrium state that has a definite temperature, thermal energy, and entropy (as well as a definite pressure and volume).
17. An isotherm is a curve in a PV diagram whose points represent, for a fixed amount of ideal gas, all the equilibrium states that have the same temperature. An isentrope is a curve on the diagram whose points represent all the equilibrium states that have the same entropy.
18. Because a quasistatic process is carried out in such a way that the system passes from one equilibrium state to another, it is represented by a continuous path that runs from the point representing the initial state on the diagram to a second point representing the final state.
19. (a) and (b), because both depend on only the equilibrium state, which means changes in these quantities depend on only the initial and final states, not on the path taken. (c) is path-dependent because it equals an area under a curve in the PV diagram for the process and that area depends on the path taken from initial to final state. (d) is path-dependent because it is the difference between ΔE_{th} (path-independent) and W (path-dependent).
20. In a system in which there are no changes in kinetic, potential, and source energies, $\Delta K = \Delta U = \Delta E_s = 0$, and the energy law, $\Delta E = W + Q$, reduces to $\Delta E_{th} = W + Q$ (Eq. 20.2).
21. The work done depends on the gas pressure and on the change in the gas volume: $W = -\int_{V_i}^{V_f} P\,dV$ (Eq. 20.8).
22. The minus sign indicates that if the gas volume increases, the work done on the gas by its surroundings is negative. If the volume decreases, the work done on the gas is positive.
23. In an isochoric process, the work done on the gas is zero, so the change in thermal energy equals the quantity of energy thermally transferred to the gas ($\Delta E_{th} = Q$; Eq. 20.11). In an isentropic process, no energy is transferred thermally ($Q = 0$), so the change in thermal energy equals the work done on the gas ($\Delta E_{th} = W$; Eq. 20.18).
24. You must know the number of gas particles N, the constant-volume heat capacity per particle C_V of the gas, and the change in temperature resulting from the process: $\Delta E_{th} = NC_V \Delta T$ (Eq. 20.15).
25. The heat capacity per particle at constant pressure is greater than that at constant volume by an amount equal to Boltzmann's constant: $C_P = C_V + k_B$ (Eq. 20.24).
26. Because the change in the thermal energy of the gas is zero for an isothermal process, the Eq. 20.2 form of the energy law, $\Delta E_{th} = W + Q$, requires that the quantity of energy transferred thermally equal the negative of the work done on the gas: $Q = -W$ (Eq. 20.28).
27. The pressure-volume relationship is that the product of the pressure and the volume raised to the power $\gamma = C_P/C_V$ is constant, which means $P_i V_i^\gamma = P_f V_f^\gamma$ (Eq. 20.46). The pressure-temperature relationship is $(P_i^{\frac{1}{\gamma}-1})T_i = (P_f^{\frac{1}{\gamma}-1})T_f$ (Eq. 20.47). The volume-temperature relationship is $T_i V_i^{\gamma-1} = T_f V_f^{\gamma-1}$ (Eq. 20.44).
28. The related intensive quantity is specific heat capacity. For any given substance, the specific heat capacity is the quantity of energy transferred thermally divided by the mass of the system and by the temperature change.
29. The units of heat capacity are joules per kelvin; those of specific heat capacity are joules per kelvin per kilogram.

Answers to Guided Problems

Guided problem 20.2 536 J

Guided problem 20.4 $W_A - W_B = -73$ J

Guided problem 20.6 $\Delta S_A = 0$, $\Delta S_{B,\text{isothermal}} = +4.35 \times 10^{23}$, $\Delta S_{B,\text{isochoric}} = -4.35 \times 10^{23}$

Guided problem 20.8 $\Delta S_A + \Delta S_B = +6.7 \times 10^{24}$

21

PRACTICE

Degradation of Energy

Chapter Summary

Converting energy (Sections 21.1, 21.5)

Concepts A system's **energy input** is the sum of the mechanical input of energy W_{in} and the thermal input of energy Q_{in}. The **energy output** is the sum of the mechanical output of energy W_{out} and the thermal output of energy Q_{out}.

The work done on a system is

$$W = W_{in} - W_{out},$$

and the energy transferred thermally to the system is

$$Q = Q_{in} - Q_{out}.$$

A **steady device** converts energy in such a way that the energy changes and entropy changes of the device are zero either continuously or over some repeating time interval (a *cycle*).

Quantitative Tools For a steady device over one cycle:

$$\Delta E = 0 \quad (21.1)$$

$$W = Q_{out} - Q_{in} \quad (21.2)$$

$$\Delta S_{dev} = 0 \quad (21.3)$$

$$\Delta S_{env} \geq 0. \quad (21.5)$$

Figure SUM21.1

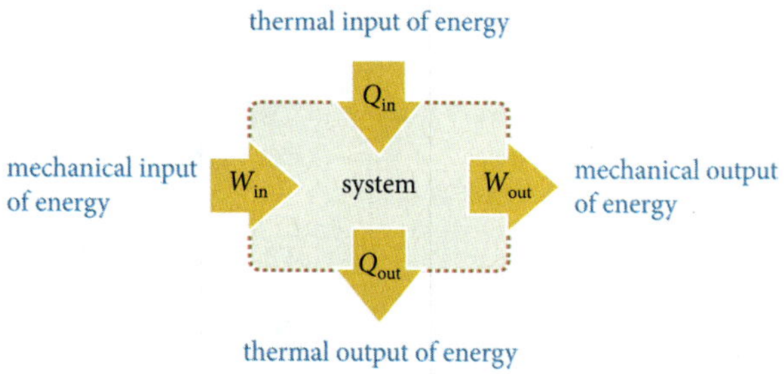

Entropy and energy quality (Sections 21.2, 21.5)

Concepts An **entropy diagram for a steady device** consists of an entropy gradient axis, one or more rectangles representing energy transfers from input to output, and downward- or upward-pointing arrows representing thermal or mechanical inputs or outputs of energy. Each rectangle has an arrowhead to indicate the direction of energy transfer. Thermal energy transferred into the device causes the entropy of the environment to decrease; thermal energy transferred out of the device causes the entropy of the environment to increase. (See the Procedure box "Drawing entropy diagrams for a steady device.")

A *degradation* in an environment's **energy quality** is associated with an increase in the environment's entropy; an *upgrading* in an environment's energy quality is associated with a decrease in the environment's entropy. The higher the quality of energy transferred, the smaller the associated entropy change. The amount of useful work obtainable from a quantity of energy decreases as the quality of the energy decreases.

Quantitative Tools The **entropy gradient** dS/dE of a system is the rate at which the entropy of the system changes with a change in thermal energy:

$$\frac{dS}{dE} \equiv \frac{1}{k_B T}.$$

See the Procedure box "Computing entropy changes from entropy diagrams" for how to use an entropy diagram to compute an entropy change.

PRACTICE

Heat engines and heat pumps (Sections 21.3, 21.6)

Concepts A **heat engine** does work on its environment by thermally taking in energy Q_{in} at a high temperature and thermally expelling energy Q_{out} at a lower temperature.

A **heat pump** uses mechanical energy to take in energy thermally at a low temperature and transfer out energy thermally at a higher temperature.

Quantitative Tools For a reversible heat engine in which Q_{in} enters at temperature T_{in} and Q_{out} leaves at T_{out},

$$\frac{Q_{out}}{Q_{in}} = \frac{T_{out}}{T_{in}}. \tag{21.20}$$

The **efficiency** η of a heat engine is

$$\eta \equiv -\frac{W}{Q_{in}} = 1 - \frac{Q_{out}}{Q_{in}}, \tag{21.21, 21.22}$$

where W is the work done on the steady device during one cycle. The maximum efficiency is achieved by a reversible heat engine and is

$$\eta_{max} = 1 - \frac{T_{out}}{T_{in}}. \tag{21.23}$$

The **coefficient of performance of heating** for a heat pump is

$$\text{COP}_{heating} \equiv \frac{Q_{out}}{W}. \tag{21.24}$$

The **coefficient of performance of cooling** for a heat pump is

$$\text{COP}_{cooling} \equiv \frac{Q_{in}}{W} = \text{COP}_{heating} - 1. \tag{21.27, 21.28}$$

Thermodynamic cycles (Sections 21.4, 21.7, 21.8)

Concepts The magnitude of the work done on a system during one thermodynamic cycle is equal to the area enclosed by the path that represents the cycle in a *PV* diagram. The work done on the system is negative for a clockwise cycle and positive for a counterclockwise cycle.

The **Carnot cycle** consists of two isothermal processes and two isentropic processes. It operates at the maximum possible efficiency between two temperature reservoirs.

Quantitative Tools

Figure SUM21.2

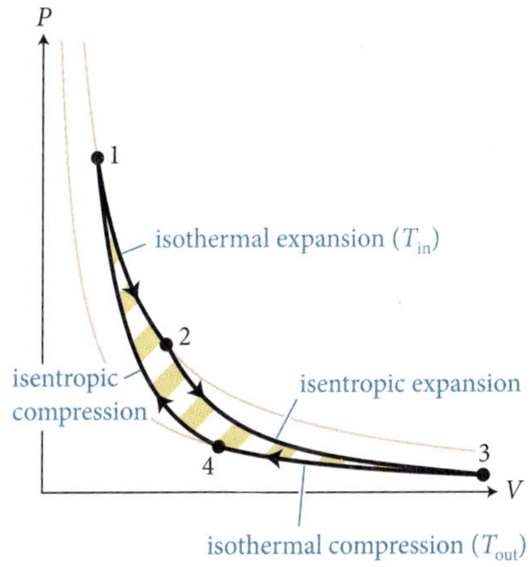

PRACTICE

Concepts The **Brayton cycle** consists of two isobaric processes and two isentropic processes.

Quantitative Tools The efficiency of a Carnot engine is

$$\eta = \frac{T_{\text{in}} - T_{\text{out}}}{T_{\text{in}}}. \qquad (21.36)$$

Figure SUM21.3

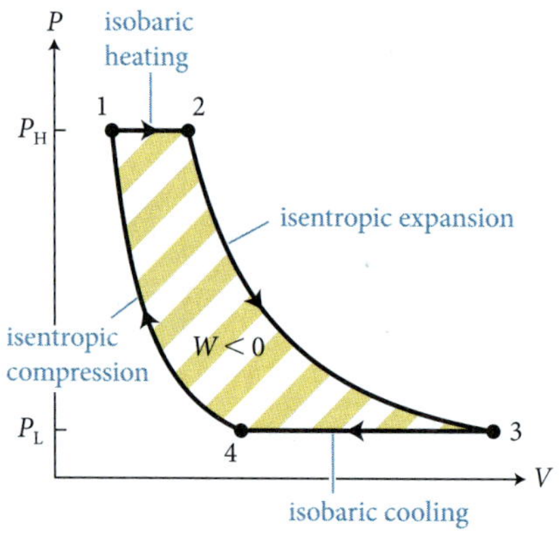

The efficiency of a Brayton cycle that operates between pressures P_H and P_L is

$$\eta = 1 - \frac{T_4}{T_1} = 1 - \left(\frac{P_H}{P_L}\right)^{\frac{1}{\gamma}-1}, \qquad (21.44, 21.47)$$

where T_1 is the temperature of the working substance when it exits the compressor, T_4 is the lowest temperature in the cycle, and γ is C_P/C_V. The quantity P_H/P_L is the *pressure ratio* of the cycle.

Summary of *Principles* Tables 20.6 and 20.7

Process	W	Q	ΔE_{th}	ΔS
isochoric	0	$NC_V\Delta T$	Q	$\frac{NC_V}{k_B}\ln\left(\frac{T_f}{T_i}\right)$
isothermal	$-Nk_BT\ln\left(\frac{V_f}{V_i}\right)$	$-W$	0	$N\ln\left(\frac{V_f}{V_i}\right) = \frac{Q}{k_BT}$
isobaric	$-Nk_B\Delta T$	$NC_P\Delta T$	$NC_V\Delta T$	$\frac{NC_P}{k_B}\ln\left(\frac{T_f}{T_i}\right)$
isentropic	ΔE_{th}	0	$NC_V\Delta T$	0

PRACTICE

Review Questions

Answers to these questions can be found at the end of this chapter.

21.1 Converting energy

1. Which type of energy is associated with the complementary state changes that occur (*a*) when a gas burns and (*b*) when a ball drops from a rooftop to ground level?
2. How is the work done on a system defined?
3. Describe the energy transfers associated with the operations of a car engine and a refrigerator.
4. What is a steady device, and why is such a device the best choice for any everyday situation where energy must be continuously converted from one form to another?
5. What constraints are imposed by the entropy law (Eq. 19.5, $\Delta S > 0$ for a closed system moving toward equilibrium) in (*a*) a steady device designed to convert mechanical energy to thermal energy, as in *Principles* Figure 21.8*a*, and (*b*) a steady device designed to convert thermal energy to mechanical energy, as in *Principles* Figure 21.8*b*?

21.2 Quality of energy

6. What is the entropy gradient dS/dE equal to? What does it tell you about the relationship between a thermal reservoir's entropy and temperature when energy is added to or taken from the reservoir?
7. What is the entropy cost of an energy change?
8. Describe the energy transfer that takes place when two thermal reservoirs at different temperatures (the environment) are connected by a copper rod (the system). Is the energy transfer reversible or irreversible?
9. For a given amount of energy change, what is the relationship between energy quality and dS/dE? What is energy quality a measure of?
10. What is the energy quality associated with a mechanical input of energy?

21.3 Heat engines and heat pumps

11. What is a heat engine? Describe how a car engine operates as a heat engine.
12. Describe how entropy changes and energy transfers are illustrated in an entropy diagram.
13. How is the efficiency of a heat engine defined?
14. What is a heat pump?
15. Describe the difference in how a heat pump operates as an air-conditioner and as a heating unit for a building.
16. Define the terms *coefficient of performance of cooling* and *coefficient of performance of heating.*

21.4 Thermodynamic cycles

17. On the *PV* diagram that represents the working substance in a heat engine or heat pump, why is the cycle direction clockwise for a heat engine and counterclockwise for a heat pump?
18. Describe the steps of a Carnot cycle.
19. What properties of the Carnot cycle make it unsuitable for operating everyday devices?
20. Describe the steps of a Brayton cycle.
21. What everyday devices run on Brayton cycles?

21.5 Entropy constraints on energy transfers

22. Describe how Eq. 21.5, $\Delta S_{\text{env}} \geq 0$, restricts cyclic devices designed to transfer energy thermally from one thermal reservoir to another.
23. How can an entropy diagram be used to compute the change in entropy associated with an energy transfer for a steady process?

21.6 Heat engine performance

24. For a reversible heat engine, what is the relationship between Q_{in}, the thermal energy taken in from the higher-temperature reservoir, and Q_{out}, the thermal energy discarded to the lower-temperature reservoir, and the temperatures of the reservoirs?
25. What restrictions does the entropy law impose on the efficiency of heat engines? Consider both reversible and irreversible engines in answering.
26. In the energy diagram that represents a heat pump used as a heater, do the variables Q_{in} and T_{in} belong to the higher-temperature reservoir or the lower-temperature reservoir? What about in the energy diagram for a heat pump used as an air-conditioner?
27. How is the coefficient of performance of heating for a reversible heat pump related to the thermal energy output to the higher-temperature reservoir and the thermal energy input from the lower-temperature reservoir? How is its maximum $\text{COP}_{\text{heating}}$ defined?
28. What is the relationship between the coefficient of performance of heating for a heat pump and its coefficient of performance of cooling?
29. Does the maximum efficiency of any heat engine depend on what is used as the working substance?

21.7 Carnot cycle

30. When determining the efficiency $-W/Q_{\text{in}}$ of a heat engine running a Carnot cycle, why must you be concerned only with the work done during the two isothermal steps? Why doesn't the work done during the isentropic steps factor into the efficiency calculation?
31. How does the efficiency of an engine that operates according to a Carnot cycle compare to the maximum efficiency of any heat engine?

21.8 Brayton cycle

32. What are two advantages of the Brayton cycle over the Carnot cycle?
33. What is the relationship between the efficiency of a Brayton cycle for a jet engine and the various temperatures in the cycle?

Developing a Feel

Make an order-of-magnitude estimate of each of the following quantities. Letters in parentheses refer to hints below. Use them as needed to guide your thinking.

1. The change in entropy for system plus environment when 1 GJ of thermal energy leaks out of a house on a cold winter day [G, O]
2. The change in entropy per second for a 1-kW baseboard heater that uses hot water as its working substance [G, K]
3. The maximum efficiency for a heat engine that converts the thermal energy of ocean water to usable energy by using warm surface water as the higher-temperature reservoir and cold deep water as the lower-temperature reservoir [I, D, N]
4. The input water flow (in kilograms per second) needed to generate 1 GW of power from the heat engine of Developing a Feel 3 [I, D, M, U, H]
5. The maximum coefficient of performance of cooling for a heat pump used to cool a house on a hot summer day [G, D, T, R]
6. The volume of outside air needed per day by a heat pump to heat a house on a cold winter day, assuming the maximum amount by which the outside air can be cooled is 7 K [G, O,V, F, A, E, J]
7. The volume of groundwater needed per month by a heat pump to heat a house in winter when the groundwater is the lower-temperature reservoir for the pump, assuming the maximum amount by which the water can be cooled is 10 K [G, C, V, F, A, H, M, Q]
8. The maximum coefficient of performance of cooling for a refrigerator that maintains helium in the liquid state [G, P, R]
9. The combustion pressure required to obtain an efficiency of 0.67 in a jet engine on a commercial airliner at cruising altitude [B, L, S]

Hints

A. How much energy is needed to heat a house on a cold winter day?
B. Which thermodynamic cycle is involved?
C. What is the temperature difference?
D. What is the temperature difference?
E. What is the specific heat capacity of air?
F. On a cold day, for what fraction of the day is the heating system in operation?
G. What is the indoor temperature?
H. What is the specific heat capacity of water?
I. What is the temperature of the surface water?
J. What is the mass density of air under these conditions?
K. What is the temperature difference?
L. What is the input pressure at cruising altitude?
M. How is Q_{in} related to the mass of water needed?
N. How are Q_{in} and Q_{out} related to the temperatures of the two reservoirs?
O. What is the temperature difference?
P. What is the highest temperature at which helium remains liquid?
Q. What is the mass density of water?
R. How is the maximum coefficient of performance of cooling related to cycle temperatures?
S. What is the heat capacity ratio for the working substance?
T. With a heat pump, T_{in} is for which reservoir?
U. How is maximum efficiency (from Developing a Feel 3) related to Q_{in} and Q_{out}?
V. What power is supplied by a typical home's central heating system?

Key (all values approximate)

A. 1 GJ; **B.** the Brayton cycle; **C.** 1×10^1 K; **D.** 2×10^1 K; **E.** 1 kJ/K · kg; **F.** as much as 1/3 of the day; **G.** 3×10^2 K; **H.** 4 kJ/K · kg; **I.** 3×10^2 K; **J.** 1 kg/m^3; **K.** 6×10^1 K; **L.** about 30% of the pressure at sea level and so, say, 3×10^4 Pa; **M.** $Q_{in} = m_{water}c_{water}\Delta T$; **N.** for an ideal engine, $Q_{out}/Q_{in} = T_{out}/T_{in}$; **O.** 3×10^1 K; **P.** 4 K; **Q.** 1×10^3 kg/m^3; **R.** $COP_{cooling,\ max} = Q_{in}/W = T_{in}/(T_{out} - T_{in})$; **S.** air, so $\gamma = \frac{7}{5}$; **T.** the lower-temperature reservoir; **U.** $Q_{in} = -W/\eta$ and $W = Q_{out} - Q_{in}$; **V.** 3×10^4 J/s

PRACTICE

Worked and Guided Problems

Procedure: Drawing entropy diagrams for a steady device

1. Draw an entropy gradient axis pointing right. Add a short vertical axis to indicate the origin of the axis. Label the axis $1/k_B T$ to remind yourself of the relationship between entropy gradient and temperature.
2. Mark the positions along the axis of the thermal inputs and outputs of energy of the device. Transfers at higher temperature are on the left, transfers at lower temperature on the right. Use downward pointing arrows for inputs, upward pointing arrows for outputs, and label these Q_{in} and Q_{out}.
3. Mechanical transfers of energy are placed at the origin of the axis. Use downward pointing arrow when the work done on the system is positive and an upward pointing arrow when the work done on the system is negative. Label this arrow by W and indicate whether $W > 0$ or $W < 0$.
4. Draw rectangles to represent each energy transfer. Make the height of each rectangle proportional to the amount of energy transferred (but see point 5 below). Use an arrowhead to indicate the direction of each transfer.
5. For the operation of the device to be permitted by the entropy law, the combined area of the rectangles in which the arrows point right must be larger than the combined area of the rectangles in which the arrows point left.

Procedure: Computing entropy changes from entropy diagrams

To determine the entropy change in the environment from an entropy diagram, compute the area of the rectangles representing the energy transfers as follows.

1. Determine the length of the horizontal part of each rectangle by subtracting the position of the left end of the rectangle on the $1/k_B T$ scale from the position of the right end on the scale. The position of mechanical energy is always at the zero point on this scale. Verify that the result is a positive quantity. (If it isn't, you made a mistake somewhere.)
2. Express the height of each rectangle in terms of Q_{in}, Q_{out}, and W. Remember that the height must be a positive quantity; Q_{in} and Q_{out} are always positive, but W can be positive or negative. Avoid using the input or output where two rectangles meet; if necessary you can use Eq. 21.2, $W = Q_{out} - Q_{in}$, to express the height in terms of the quantities that are given in the problem.
3. Determine the sign of the entropy change. If the rectangle points left (energy upgrade), the entropy change is negative. If the rectangle points right (energy degradation), the entropy change is positive.
4. The entropy change for each rectangle is given by the area of the rectangle (the length multiplied by the height computed in steps 1 and 2), preceded by the algebraic sign determined in step 3.

$$\Delta S = (\text{sign}) \times (\text{length}) \times (\text{width}).$$

5. The entropy change for the process is the sum of the individual entropy changes you have calculated.

These examples involve material from this chapter but are not associated with any particular section. Some examples are worked out in detail; others you should work out by following the guidelines provided.

Worked Problem 21.1 Auto energy conversion

In an automobile moving at 95 km/h, the engine burns gasoline and delivers mechanical energy at a rate of 2.7×10^4 J/s with an efficiency of 0.30. What volume of gasoline is burned per second? For gasoline, the specific transformation energy for combustion is 4.4×10^7 J/kg and the mass density is 7.2×10^2 kg/m^3.

❶ **GETTING STARTED** We have an automobile engine burning gasoline, which means releasing the chemical energy of the gasoline, and this energy is converted to the mechanical energy that moves the vehicle. We are told the rate at which the mechanical energy is delivered and the engine efficiency, and we must determine how much gasoline is burned each second to sustain that rate of energy delivery.

This is a problem in which a quantity Q_{in} of thermal energy is transferred from the gasoline into the engine. The mechanical output of energy W_{out} of the engine is 30% of Q_{in} and the remaining 70% goes to the environment as Q_{out}. We know that the device is a steady device, so the change in energy of the device is zero. Figure WG 21.1 is an energy input-output diagram with $W_{out} = 0.30\ Q_{in}$ and $Q_{out} = 0.70\ Q_{in}$.

Figure WG21.1

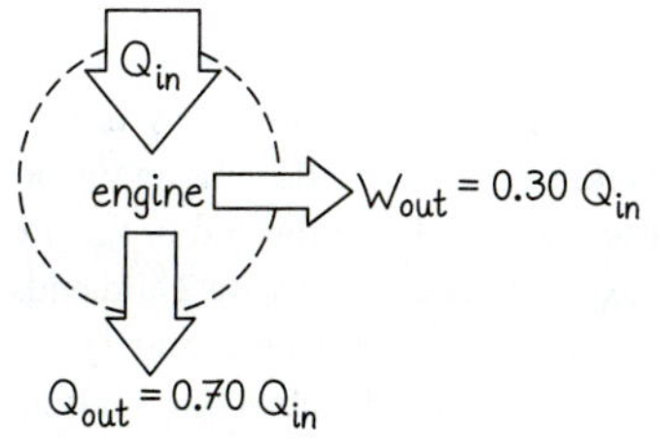

PRACTICE

❷ **DEVISE PLAN** We know that the rate at which mechanical energy is delivered, 2.7×10^4 J/s, is only 30% of the rate of energy Q_{in} released from the burning gasoline. We can use this information in Eq. 21.21 to determine Q_{in}. By differentiating Eq. 21.21 with respect to time, we get the thermal energy input per second from the burning gasoline. Next we can determine the mass of gasoline burned per second by dividing the thermal energy input per second by the specific transformation energy for combustion. Dividing the mass of gasoline burned per second by the mass density of the gasoline gives us the volume burned per second.

❸ **EXECUTE PLAN** Because the engine does work on the environment, the work done on the engine is negative, which makes the rate at which work is done $dW/dt = -2.7 \times 10^4$ J/s. Differentiating Eq. 21.21 gives us the thermal energy input per second. Thus we have

$$\frac{dQ_{in}}{dt} = -\frac{1}{\eta}\frac{dW}{dt} = -\frac{1}{0.30}(-2.7 \times 10^4\ \text{J/s}) = 9.0 \times 10^4\ \text{J/s}.$$

We now divide this rate of energy input by the specific transformation energy for combustion to determine the mass of gasoline burned per second:

$$\frac{dm_{gas}}{dt} = \frac{1}{L}\frac{dQ_{in}}{dt} = \frac{9.0 \times 10^4\ \text{J/s}}{4.4 \times 10^7\ \text{J/kg}} = 2.0 \times 10^{-3}\ \text{kg/s}.$$

We now convert this to the volume of gasoline burned per second:

$$\frac{dV_{gas}}{dt} = \frac{1}{\rho}\frac{dm_{gas}}{dt} = \frac{2.0 \times 10^{-3}\ \text{kg/s}}{7.2 \times 10^2\ \text{kg/m}^3} = 2.8 \times 10^{-6}\ \text{m}^3/\text{s}. ✔$$

❹ **EVALUATE RESULT** We can check the reasonableness of our result by converting the volume of gasoline burned per second to what is colloquially called *mileage*, the number of miles a vehicle travels per gallon of gasoline burned. The volume of gasoline burned each hour is

$$(2.8 \times 10^{-6}\ \text{m}^3/\text{s})\left(\frac{3600\ \text{s}}{1\ \text{h}}\right) = 1.0 \times 10^{-2}\ \text{m}^3/\text{h}.$$

To convert to gallons per hour, we reason that 1 gal is 4 qt and 1 qt is about the same volume as 1 L, which is equal to 1×10^{-3} m³. Thus

$$(1.0 \times 10^{-2}\ \text{m}^3/\text{h})\left(\frac{1\ \text{L}}{1 \times 10^{-3}\ \text{m}^3}\right)\left(\frac{1\ \text{gal}}{4\ \text{L}}\right) = 2.5\ \text{gal/h}.$$

The automobile is moving at 95 km/h, which is 60 mi/h, so the "mileage" is

$$\frac{60\ \text{mi/h}}{2.5\ \text{gal/h}} = 24\ \text{mi/gal},$$

which is a reasonable miles-per-gallon figure for automobiles.

Guided Problem 21.2 Geothermal power

A geothermal power plant that has a power output of 10 MW extracts thermal energy from Earth's interior via a shaft drilled to a depth where the temperature is 600 °C and discards thermal energy at Earth's surface into a large mass of ice at −5 °C. What is the minimum possible value for the rate of thermal energy output?

GETTING STARTED

1. What assumptions do you need to make about the power plant?

DEVISE PLAN

2. How can you use the temperature difference between the two reservoirs to determine the plant's maximum efficiency?
3. For a power output of 10 MW, what is the minimum rate of thermal energy input?
4. How can you apply the energy law, $\Delta E = W + Q$, to this steady device to determine the rate of thermal energy output?

EXECUTE PLAN

5. Calculate the maximum efficiency.
6. Calculate the minimum thermal energy input rate.
7. Calculate the minimal possible rate of thermal energy output.

EVALUATE RESULT

8. Is the thermal output of energy greater or smaller than the thermal input of energy?

Worked Problem 21.3 Carnot cycle

Consider a reversible heat engine that operates on the Carnot cycle. The working substance is air, which consists primarily of diatomic nitrogen molecules. During the isothermal expansion, the pressure of the air decreases by a factor of 5. During the isentropic expansion, the work done by the engine on the environment is 3.50×10^2 J. How much work does the engine do on the environment during one cycle?

❶ **GETTING STARTED** We assume that the working substance is an ideal gas. Because the molecules are diatomic, they have $d = 5$ degrees of freedom. We begin by drawing a *PV* diagram for this cycle (Figure WG21.2), identifying the beginning of the isothermal expansion as state 1 and the end of the process as state 2. The isentropic expansion begins at state 2 and ends at state 3. The isothermal compression begins at state 3 and ends at state 4. The isentropic compression begins at state 4 and ends at state 1. We are given that $P_1/P_2 = 5$, and we show this information on our diagram. We are also given that for the isentropic expansion (process $2 \rightarrow 3$), $W = -3.50 \times 10^2$ J.

❷ **DEVISE PLAN** We can use Eq. 21.34 to determine the work done W_{cycle} by the environment on the engine. We need to know

Figure WG21.2

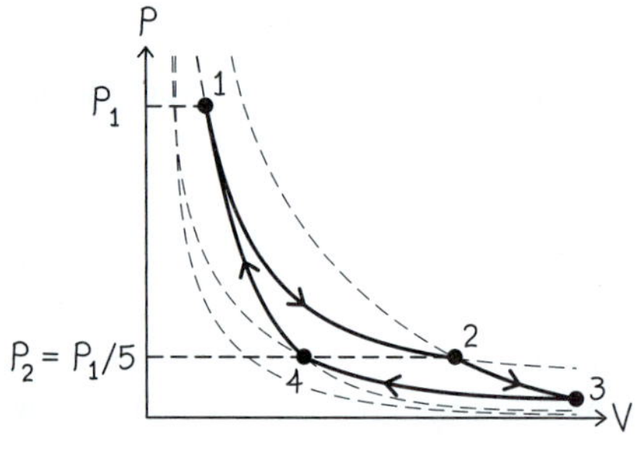

the number of molecules N, the temperature difference between the two reservoirs $T_{in} - T_{out}$, and the volume ratio V_2/V_1. We are given W for the isentropic expansion and we know from Eq. 20.19 that $W = NC_V(T_{out} - T_{in})$. We also know the number of degrees of freedom of these molecules so we can calculate $C_V = (\frac{d}{2})k_B$. Therefore we can use Eq. 20.19 to determine the product $Nk_B(T_{out} - T_{in})$. For the isothermal expansion (process $1 \rightarrow 2$), we can use the ideal gas law, $P = Nk_BT/V$, to determine the ratio V_2/V_1. We can now determine W_{cycle}. The work done by the engine on the environment is then $-W_{cycle}$.

❸ **EXECUTE PLAN** Because $d = 5$, the heat capacity per particle at constant volume is $C_V = (\frac{d}{2})k_B = (\frac{5}{2})k_B$. To determine the product of the number of molecules and the temperature difference between the two reservoirs, we rewrite Eq. 20.19 as

$$Nk_B(T_{in} - T_{out}) = -\frac{W}{(d/2)} = -\frac{-3.50 \times 10^2 \text{ J}}{(5/2)}$$
$$= 1.40 \times 10^2 \text{ J}.$$

We now apply the ideal gas law to states 1 and 2. Because process $1 \rightarrow 2$ is an isothermal expansion, $P_1V_1 = P_2V_2$. Therefore the volume ratio is $V_2/V_1 = P_1/P_2 = 5$. We now use Eq. 21.34 to determine the work done W_{cycle} by the environment on the engine:

$$W_{cycle} = -Nk_B(T_{in} - T_{out})\ln\left(\frac{V_2}{V_1}\right)$$
$$= -(1.40 \times 10^2 \text{ J})\ln(5) = -2.25 \times 10^2 \text{ J.} ✔$$

❹ **EVALUATE RESULT** The cycle is clockwise, so the work done on the system is negative, in agreement with our result. The work done by the engine on the environment is smaller in magnitude than the the work done on the engine during the isothermal expansion because the area inside the cycle on the PV diagram is smaller than the area under the PV curve corresponding to the isothermal expansion.

Guided Problem 21.4 Brayton cycle

Consider a jet engine operating on the Brayton cycle. The working substance is air, which consists primarily of diatomic nitrogen molecules. The air is drawn in at atmospheric pressure, 1.01×10^5 Pa, at 250 K. During compression this pressure is increased to 28.3×10^5 Pa, and the combustion raises the temperature to 1500 K. How much work per mole of air does the engine do on the environment during one cycle?

❶ **GETTING STARTED**

1. Draw a PV diagram for this cycle. (Hint: See *Principles* Figure 21.30.)
2. Label your PV diagram with known values of pressure and temperature.

❷ **DEVISE PLAN**

3. What quantities do you need to know in order to determine the work done by the engine?
4. How can you obtain the efficiency from the given information?
5. How can you determine Q_{in} per mole?
6. How is the number of particles related to the number of moles?
7. How can you determine the work done per mole by the engine on the environment from knowledge of the efficiency and the given information about the isentropic compression?

❸ **EXECUTE PLAN**

8. Calculate the pressure ratio.
9. How many degrees of freedom do the gas particles in air have at these temperatures?
10. Calculate the efficiency of the engine.
11. How much thermal energy per mole is transferred during the isobaric expansion?
12. How much work per mole does the engine do on the environment?

❹ **EVALUATE RESULT**

13. Does your answer agree with Eq. 21.37?

Worked Problem 21.5 Otto Cycle

In a model gasoline engine, the working substance, which is the air-gasoline mixture, can be treated approximately with the thermodynamic cycle known as the Otto cycle. In the first process ($1 \rightarrow 2$), the gas, initially at 300 K, undergoes an isentropic compression (the engine's compression stroke) during which its temperature rises to 671 K. The next process ($2 \rightarrow 3$) is an isochoric pressure increase, and the gas temperature reaches 1574 K as the gasoline burns. Next ($3 \rightarrow 4$), the gas undergoes an isentropic expansion (the engine's power stroke) during which its temperature drops to 809 K. Finally ($4 \rightarrow 1$), the gas experiences an isochoric pressure decrease during which its temperature drops to its initial value. What is the efficiency of this model engine?

❶ **GETTING STARTED** We assume that the working substance is an ideal gas. We begin by drawing a PV diagram for this cycle (Figure WG21.3), identifying the beginning of each process as states 1, 2, 3 and 4. We are given that $T_1 = 300$ K, $T_2 = 671$ K, $T_3 = 1574$ K, and $T_4 = 809$ K.

Figure WG21.3

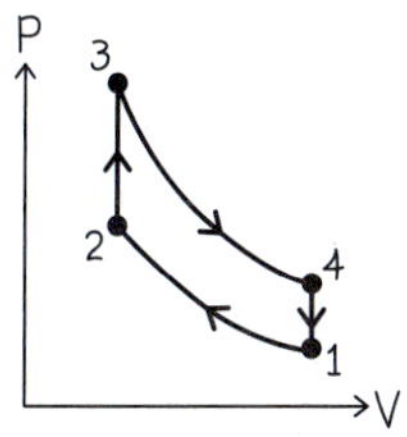

No energy is transferred thermally during the isentropic processes ($1 \rightarrow 2$ and $3 \rightarrow 4$). We denote the energy transferred thermally during the isochoric pressure increase ($2 \rightarrow 3$) by $Q_{2\rightarrow 3} = Q_{in} > 0$ and the energy transferred thermally during the isochoric pressure decrease ($4 \rightarrow 1$) by $Q_{4\rightarrow 1} = -Q_{out} < 0$.

❷ **DEVISE PLAN** We can use either Eq. 20.12, $Q = \frac{d}{2}Nk_B\,\Delta T$, or Eq. 20.13, $C_V = Q/N\,\Delta T$, to calculate the quantity of energy transferred thermally during each isochoric process. The energy transferred

PRACTICE

thermally during the cycle is the sum $Q_{2\to3} + Q_{4\to1} = Q_{in} - Q_{out}$. We can then use Eq. 21.22 to calculate the efficiency.

3 EXECUTE PLAN We choose to use Eq. 20.13. For the first isochoric process $(2 \to 3)$ we have $Q_{2\to3} = NC_V(T_3 - T_2)$, and for the second $(4 \to 1)$ we have $Q_{4\to1} = NC_V(T_1 - T_4) < 0$.

So the thermal efficiency is, from Eq. 21.22,

$$\eta = 1 - \left(\frac{Q_{out}}{Q_{in}}\right) = 1 - \left(\frac{-Q_{4\to1}}{Q_{2\to3}}\right) = 1 - \left(\frac{-NC_V(T_1 - T_4)}{NC_V(T_3 - T_2)}\right)$$

$$= 1 + \left(\frac{(T_1 - T_4)}{(T_3 - T_2)}\right) = 1 + \frac{300\text{ K} - 809\text{ K}}{1574\text{ K} - 671\text{ K}} = 0.436. ✔$$

4 EVALUATE RESULT We expect the efficiency to be less than 1 for any heat engine. The only other familiar cycle is the Carnot cycle, which produces the maximum efficiency for a given temperature range. This cycle requires two constant-temperature processes, which we do not have as part of the Otto cycle. However, if we average the temperatures for the thermal input of energy for process $(2 \to 3)$ as $T_{in} = (T_3 + T_2)/2 = 1123$ K and the thermal output of energy for process $(4 \to 1)$ as $T_{out} = (T_4 + T_1)/2 = 555$ K, then we can compare our result to the maximum efficiency of an engine undergoing a Carnot cycle between these average temperatures. This is given by Eq. 21.23:

$$\eta_{max} = 1 - \left(\frac{T_{out}}{T_{in}}\right) = 1 - \left(\tfrac{555}{1123}\right) = 0.506.$$

This efficiency is slightly greater than our calculated efficiency for the Otto process, which gives us confidence that our calculation for the Otto cycle is reasonable.

Guided Problem 21.6 Diesel Cycle

In a diesel engine, the working substance is mostly air, a mixture of oxygen (O_2) and nitrogen gas (N_2). The air is compressed, and only then is a small amount of fuel injected at the "top" of the compression stroke. The high pressure and temperature ignite the fuel and cause rapid combustion, creating various by-products that we will ignore. The mostly diatomic working substance undergoes the following cycle: $(1 \to 2)$ The gas, initially at 300 K, experiences an isentropic compression during which its temperature rises to 889 K. $(2 \to 3)$ This process is an isobaric expansion during which the fuel is injected. The gas reaches 1778 K as the fuel rapidly burns. $(3 \to 4)$ The gas then undergoes an isentropic expansion during which its temperature drops to 884 K. $(4 \to 1)$ The final step is an isochoric pressure decrease during which the gas temperature drops to its initial value. What is the efficiency of this diesel engine?

1 GETTING STARTED

1. Make a *PV* diagram for the diesel cycle.
2. During which processes is energy transferred thermally either into or out of the working substance?

2 DEVISE PLAN

3. Which equations describe the thermal energy transfers made during the cycle? Which table in the *Principles* volume might come in handy?
4. How many degrees of freedom do the molecules of the working substance have?
5. What are the heat capacities per particle at constant volume and constant pressure?
6. Which quantity is Q_{out} for the cycle? Which quantity is Q_{in}?
7. How do you determine the work for the cycle?
8. How do you determine the engine's efficiency?

3 EXECUTE PLAN

9. How much energy is transferred thermally into the gas?
10. How much energy is transferred thermally out of the gas?
11. Calculate the engine's efficiency.

4 EVALUATE RESULT

12. Compare your calculated efficiency with that of an engine operating on the Carnot cycle between 300 K and 1778 K. Are the relative efficiencies what you expect?

PRACTICE

Worked Problem 21.7 Cyclic Process I

The working substance in an engine is 0.300 mol of nitrogen gas. Initially, in state 1, the gas volume is $V_1 = 8.00 \times 10^{-4}\text{ m}^3$, and the pressure is $P_1 = 900\text{ kPa} = 9.00 \times 10^5\text{ N/m}^2$. The gas undergoes a cycle that consists of four processes: $(1 \to 2)$ an isobaric expansion until the volume doubles, $(2 \to 3)$ an isochoric pressure decrease until the temperature is the same as the initial temperature, $(3 \to 4)$ an isobaric compression until the volume is back at its initial value, and $(4 \to 1)$ an isochoric pressure increase until the pressure is what it was in state 1. Calculate Q, $W_{on\ gas}$, ΔE_{th}, and ΔS for each process and for the cycle.

1 GETTING STARTED We are told that the working substance is 0.300 mol of nitrogen molecules. Because the molecules are diatomic, they have $d = 5$ degrees of freedom at typical engine temperatures. We draw a *PV* diagram for the cycle (Figure WG21.4) and add our labels, showing state 1 as the initial state positioned at $P_1 = 9.00 \times 10^5\text{ N/m}^2$, $V_1 = 8.00 \times 10^{-4}\text{ m}^3$. We are told that $V_2 = 2V_1$, $T_3 = T_1$, and $V_4 = V_1$. We know that $V_2 = V_3$ and $V_4 = V_1$ because processes $2 \to 3$ and $4 \to 1$ are isochoric. We know that $P_1 = P_2$ and $P_3 = P_4$ because processes $1 \to 2$ and $3 \to 4$ are isobaric. Thus the only quantities in the ideal gas law we must determine are P_3, T_1, T_2, and T_4.

Figure WG21.4

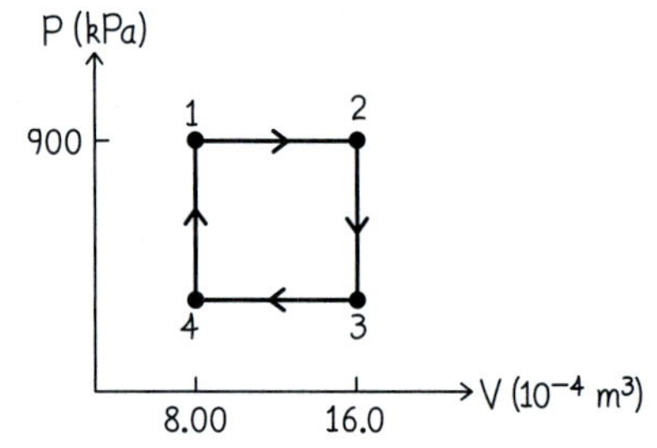

2 DEVISE PLAN We know the number of moles of the working substance and so can determine the number of molecules N. We know the number of degrees of freedom of these molecules and so can calculate C_V and C_P. We can use the ideal gas law, $P = Nk_BT/V$, to calculate the values of T_1, T_2, T_4, and P_3. We then can use the summary table on page 376 to determine Q, W, ΔE_{th}, and ΔS for each process. We know that $\Delta E_{th} = 0$ for a cycle, and therefore by the energy law, $W_{cycle} = -Q_{cycle}$. We can sum the four W values to determine W_{cycle}.

3 EXECUTE PLAN From Avogadro's constant, we know that the number of molecules is

$$N = (0.300 \text{ mol})\left(\frac{6.022 \times 10^{23}}{1 \text{ mol}}\right) = 1.81 \times 10^{23}.$$

Because $d = 5$, we have $C_V = (\frac{5}{2})k_B$ (Eq. 20.14) and $C_P = (\frac{7}{2})k_B$ (Eq. 20.25). We now apply the ideal gas law to the various states to determine T_1, T_2, T_4, and P_3:

State 1: $T_1 = \dfrac{P_1V_1}{Nk_B} = \dfrac{(9.00 \times 10^5 \text{ N/m}^2)(8.00 \times 10^{-4} \text{ m}^3)}{(1.81 \times 10^{23})(1.38 \times 10^{-23} \text{ J/K})} = 288 \text{ K}.$

State 2: We know that $V_2 = 2V_1$. Therefore

$$T_2 = \frac{P_2V_2}{Nk_B} = \frac{P_12V_1}{Nk_B} = 2T_1 = 576 \text{ K}.$$

State 3: We know that $V_3 = V_2 = 2V_1$ and $T_3 = T_1$. Therefore

$$P_3 = \frac{Nk_BT_3}{V_3} = \frac{Nk_BT_1}{2V_1} = \frac{P_1}{2} = 4.50 \times 10^5 \text{ N/m}^2.$$

State 4: We know that $V_4 = V_1$ and $P_4 = P_3 = P_1/2$. Therefore

$$T_4 = \frac{P_4V_4}{Nk_B} = \frac{P_3V_1}{Nk_B} = \frac{P_1V_1}{2Nk_B} = \frac{T_1}{2} = 144 \text{ K}.$$

We now use the results from the summary table on page 376 to calculate Q, W, ΔE_{th}, and ΔS for each process:

Isobaric process $1 \to 2$: We know that $\Delta T_{12} = T_2 - T_1 = 2T_1 - T_1 = T_1$, and so

$$W_{1\to2} = -Nk_B\Delta T_{12} = -Nk_BT_1 = -719 \text{ J}$$

$$Q_{1\to2} = NC_P\Delta T_{12} = NC_PT_1 = 2.52 \times 10^3 \text{ J}$$

$$\Delta E_{th,1\to2} = NC_V\Delta T_{12} = NC_VT_1 = 1.80 \times 10^3 \text{ J}$$

$$\Delta S_{1\to2} = \frac{NC_P}{k_B}\ln\left(\frac{T_2}{T_1}\right) = (1.81 \times 10^{23})(\tfrac{7}{2})(\ln 2) = 4.39 \times 10^{23}.$$

Isochoric process $2 \to 3$: We know that $\Delta T_{23} = T_3 - T_2 = T_1 - 2T_1 = -T_1$, so

$$W_{2\to3} = 0$$

$$Q_{2\to3} = NC_V\Delta T_{23} = -NC_VT_1 = -1.80 \times 10^3 \text{ J}$$

$$\Delta E_{th,2\to3} = NC_V\Delta T_{23} = -NC_VT_1 = -1.80 \times 10^3 \text{ J}$$

$$\Delta S_{2\to3} = \frac{NC_V}{k_B}\ln\left(\frac{T_3}{T_2}\right) = (1.81 \times 10^{23})(\tfrac{5}{2})(\ln 0.5) = -3.14 \times 10^{23}.$$

Isobaric process $3 \to 4$: With $\Delta T_{34} = T_4 - T_3 = \frac{T_1}{2} - T_1 = -\frac{T_1}{2}$, we have

$$W_{3\to4} = -Nk_B\Delta T_{34} = Nk_B\frac{T_1}{2} = 360 \text{ J}$$

$$Q_{3\to4} = NC_P\Delta T_{34} = -NC_P\left(\frac{T_1}{2}\right) = -1.26 \times 10^3 \text{ J}$$

$$\Delta E_{th,3\to4} = NC_V\Delta T_{34} = -NC_V\left(\frac{T_1}{2}\right) = -899 \text{ J}$$

$$\Delta S_{3\to4} = \frac{NC_P}{k_B}\ln\left(\frac{T_4}{T_3}\right) = -\Delta S_{12} = -4.39 \times 10^{23}.$$

Isochoric process $4 \to 1$: With $\Delta T_{41} = T_1 - T_4 = T_1 - \frac{T_1}{2} = \frac{T_1}{2}$, we have

$$W_{4\to1} = 0$$

$$Q_{4\to1} = NC_V\Delta T_{41} = NC_V\left(\frac{T_1}{2}\right) = 899 \text{ J}$$

$$\Delta E_{th,4\to1} = NC_V\Delta T_{41} = NC_V\left(\frac{T_1}{2}\right) = 899 \text{ J}$$

$$\Delta S_{4\to1} = \frac{NC_V}{k_B}\ln\left(\frac{T_4}{T_1}\right) = -\Delta S_{23} = 3.14 \times 10^{23}.$$

The cycle: The work done by the environment on the gas during the cycle is

$$W_{cycle} = W_{1\to2} + W_{2\to3} + W_{3\to4} + W_{4\to1} = -360 \text{ J}.$$

The energy change over the cycle must be zero, and that is just what we obtain:

$$\Delta E_{th,cycle} = \Delta E_{th,1\to2} + \Delta E_{th,2\to3} + \Delta E_{th,3\to4} + \Delta E_{th,4\to1} = 0.$$

Because $\Delta E_{th,cycle} = 0$, the energy transferred thermally from the environment to the gas during the cycle is $Q_{cycle} = -W_{cycle} = 360$ J. Finally, the entropy change over the cycle is zero:

$$\Delta S_{cycle} = \Delta S_{1\to2} + \Delta S_{2\to3} + \Delta S_{3\to4} + \Delta S_{4\to1} = 0. ✔$$

4 EVALUATE RESULT We assumed that nitrogen has five degrees of freedom at typical engine temperatures, but 144 K is low enough to call that assumption into question. We can check this using the values given in *Principles* Example 20.3, which show that nitrogen molecules rotate even at temperatures of this magnitude.

The fact that the cycle direction is clockwise in Figure WG21.4 means that the work done on the gas is negative. We know that the magnitude of the work done per cycle is the area enclosed by the curves for the four processes. The negative of that area is

$$W_{cycle, on engine} = -(P_1 - P_4)(V_2 - V_1)$$

$$= -\left(P_1 - \frac{P_1}{2}\right)(2V_1 - V_1) = -\frac{P_1V_1}{2}$$

$$= -\frac{(9.0 \times 10^5 \text{ N/m}^2)(8.0 \times 10^{-4} \text{ m}^3)}{2} = -360 \text{ J},$$

in agreement with our result.

The work done during the cycle by the engine on the environment is positive:

$$W_{cycle, on envir} = -(W_{1\to2} + W_{2\to3} + W_{3\to4} + W_{4\to1}) = 360 \text{ J},$$

which is what we expect for a clockwise cycle.

Guided Problem 21.8 Cyclic Process II

The working substance in an engine is 3.00×10^{23} helium atoms. Initially, in state 1, the gas volume is $V_1 = 1.50 \times 10^{-3}\ \text{m}^3$ and the pressure is $P_1 = 1.00 \times 10^6\ \text{N/m}^2$. The gas undergoes a cycle that consists of four processes: $(1 \rightarrow 2)$ an isothermal expansion, $(2 \rightarrow 3)$ an isobaric compression until the volume is $V_3 = 2.00 \times 10^{-3}\ \text{m}^3$ and the pressure is $2.00 \times 10^5\ \text{N/m}^2$, $(3 \rightarrow 4)$ an isothermal compression until the volume is $V_4 = V_1$, and $(4 \rightarrow 1)$ an isochoric pressure increase until it returns to its initial state. Calculate $W_{\text{on gas}}$, Q, ΔE_{th}, and ΔS for each process and for the cycle.

1 GETTING STARTED

1. How many degrees of freedom do the gas particles have?
2. Draw a *PV* diagram for the cycle and label the four states 1, 2, 3, and 4, including all known *P* and *V* values.
3. List the information you know about the relationships between the various *P* values, between the various *T* values, and between the various *V* values.

2 DEVISE PLAN

4. What are C_V and C_P for helium atoms?
5. What information do you need to determine in order to calculate Q, W, ΔE_{th}, and ΔS for each process? Is there a useful table?
6. How can you use the ideal gas law to determine that information?
7. Which of the quantities W, Q, ΔE_{th}, and ΔS is zero for the cycle?

3 EXECUTE PLAN

8. Calculate C_V and C_P.
9. Calculate the temperatures $T_1 = T_2$ and $T_3 = T_4$ during the isothermal expansion and compression and the volume V_2 after the expansion.
10. From the summary table on page 376, calculate W, Q, ΔE_{th}, and ΔS for each process.
11. Calculate W, Q, ΔE_{th}, and ΔS for the cycle.

4 EVALUATE RESULT

12. Do you expect W_{cycle} to be positive or negative?

Questions and Problems

For instructor-assigned homework, go to MasteringPhysics® (MP)

Dots indicate difficulty level of problems: ● = *easy,* ●● = *intermediate,* ●●● = *hard;* CR = *context-rich problem.*

Unless stated otherwise, take the working substance in all heat engines, heat pumps, and thermodynamic cycles to be an ideal gas.

21.1 Converting energy

1. Figure P21.1 shows a gas confined to a cylinder fitted with a movable piston. The cylinder is immersed in a tank of water that acts as a thermal reservoir, so that the temperature of the gas never changes. (*a*) With the system defined as the gas, draw an energy input-output diagram for the system as sand grains are slowly removed from the top of the piston and the piston rises. (*b*) Does the system's energy change? Does its entropy change? (*c*) Is this a steady device? ●

Figure P21.1

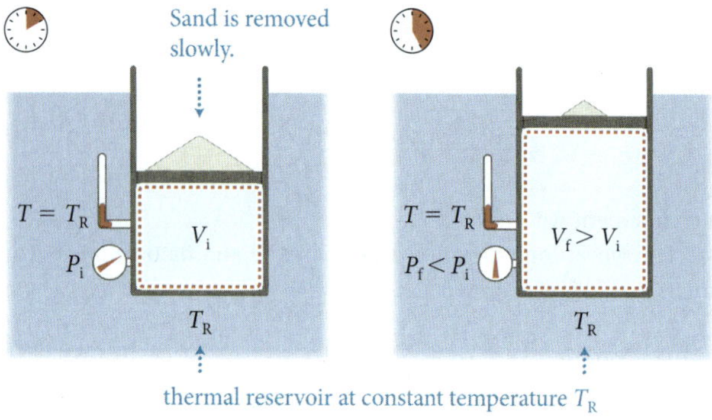

2. Draw an energy input-output diagram for a steady device that partially converts thermal energy to work, drawing your input and output arrows such that their relative sizes indicate the relative amounts of the quantities being represented. Label changes in the energy and entropy of the device. ●
3. The snowboarder in Figure P21.3 starts at the top of a snow-covered hill and boards down the hill, which produces a change in entropy ΔS_1. At the bottom, she slides over a patch of grass, which quickly slows her down and produces a change in entropy ΔS_2. She then climbs back up and slides down the other side of the hill, which is covered in ice rather than snow, producing a change in entropy ΔS_3. Rank the entropy changes by magnitude, smallest first. ●

Figure P21.3

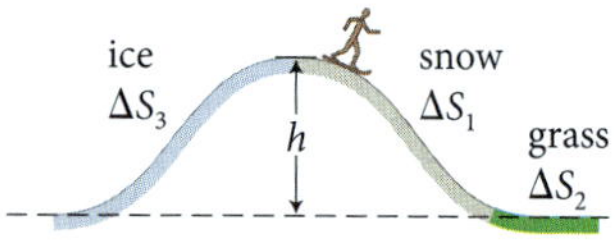

4. For the steady device shown in Figure P21.4, determine the values of W_{in} and Q_{in}. ●●

Figure P21.4

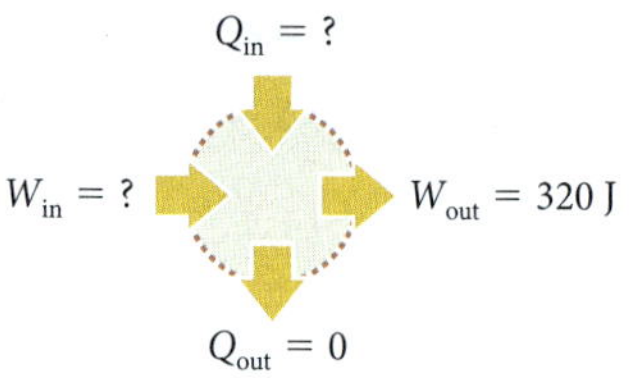

5. A source adds 150 J of thermal energy to a steady device while 275 J of work is done on the device. The device is in contact with its environment. Without specifying anything about the way the entropy of the device, source, or environment responds to changes in energy, what is the maximum amount of work W_{out} the device can do? ••

6. A 5.3-kg ball is dropped from a height of 2.0 m into a vat of water. The impact produces 0.80 J of sound energy, the ball gains 4.50 J of thermal energy from the impact, and 21 J of thermal energy escapes from the vat after the impact. (*a*) How much energy does the water absorb? (*b*) If the vat is thermally insulated and the process repeated, how much energy does the water absorb? ••

7. A steady device operates on the 600-W output of a motor. The device runs at 20 Hz and can convert 68% of its input to usable power to pump water. (*a*) How much thermal energy does the device output per cycle? (*b*) How much thermal energy does the device output in 8.0 h? (*c*) If 50% of the output thermal energy of part *b* were captured and recycled, how many kilograms of water could it raise from ground level to a height of 10 m? ••

21.2 Quality of energy

8. Three reservoirs of heated water are represented on the entropy diagram in Figure P21.8. All three reservoirs contain equal amounts of energy, so that $E_1 = E_2 = E_3$. (*a*) For which reservoir would you be least concerned about burning yourself if you dunked your hand into the water? (*b*) Which reservoir is most useful for converting thermal energy to mechanical energy? •

Figure P21.8

9. The entropy of material 1 varies as $S_1 = 2\gamma E^2$, where γ is a constant, and the entropy of material 2 varies as $S_2 = \gamma E^3/9$. With $E = 4$ units of energy, which material is better suited to converting lower-quality thermal energy to useful higher-quality mechanical energy? •

10. A reversible steady device operates between two thermal reservoirs, one at 390 K and one at 250 K. If no work is done on the device, what is the maximum value for the percentage of thermal energy input Q_{in} converted to mechanical energy W_{out}? (Hint: Consider the entropy diagram of a reversible process and the change in entropy.) ••

11. A thermal reservoir has entropy gradient $dS/dE = bE^3$, where $b = 2.00\ \mathrm{J}^{-4}$. At $E = 3.00$ MJ, what is the temperature of the reservoir? ••

12. Consider two reservoirs at unknown temperatures. The entropy of reservoir 1 is defined by the function $S_1 = aE^2$, where $a = 1.00\ \mathrm{J}^{-3}$, and that of reservoir 2 is defined by the function $S_2 = bEe^{-cE}$, where $b = 3.00\ \mathrm{J}^{-1}$ and $c = 1.00\ \mathrm{J}^{-1}$. (*a*) What is the entropy gradient of S_1 when $E = 1.00$ MJ? (*b*) What is the entropy gradient of S_2 for all values of E? (*c*) What is the entropy gradient of S_2 for $E = 1.00$ J? •••

21.3 Heat engines and heat pumps

13. Draw an entropy diagram for a reversible steady device that takes seawater at 29 °C and upgrades as much energy as possible to a reservoir filled with water at 100 °C and on the verge of boiling. The rest of the energy is deposited at 14 °C, the temperature of deeper seawater. •

14. A composite of several processes that take place in a steady device is represented by the entropy diagram in Figure P21.14. What is ΔS for the composite? •

Figure P21.14

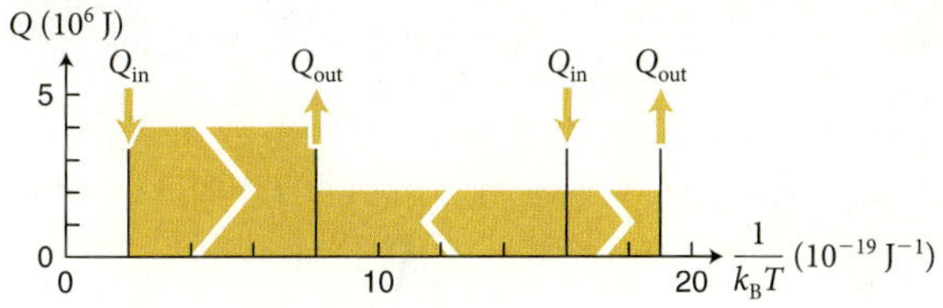

15. A reversible steady device puts out $W_{out} = 750$ J of mechanical energy. The only input energy is the quantity Q_{in} transferred thermally from a thermal reservoir at 355 K. If the temperature of the environment (which serves as low-temperature reservoir) is 300 K, what quantity of energy Q_{out} is transferred thermally out of the device? ••

16. The energy input-output diagram for a heat pump is shown in Figure P21.16. What are (*a*) the value of Q_{in}, (*b*) the coefficient of performance of heating, and (*c*) the coefficient of performance of cooling? ••

Figure P21.16

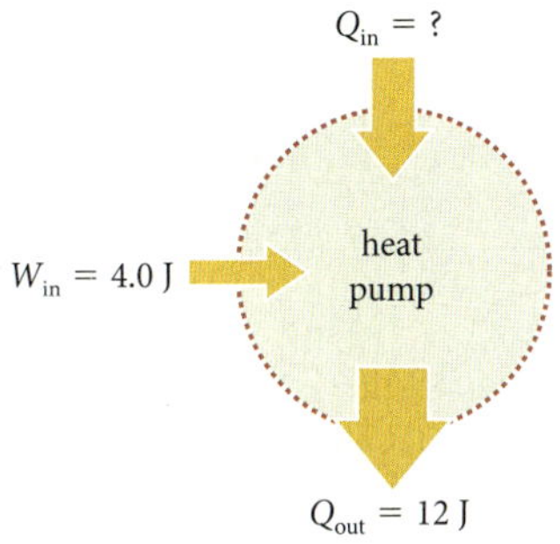

17. Three identical steady devices, A, B, and C, operate between three thermal reservoirs, 1, 2, and 3, as shown in Figure P21.17. Each device takes thermal energy from the warmer of its two reservoirs, and each upgrades to mechanical energy as much of that thermal energy as possible without lowering the entropy of the three-device, three-reservoir system. (*a*) Which reservoir has the highest-quality energy? (*b*) Is enough information provided to determine which device can upgrade the highest percentage of its input thermal energy to mechanical energy? If so, which is the most efficient of the three devices? If not, what information is lacking? •••

Figure P21.17

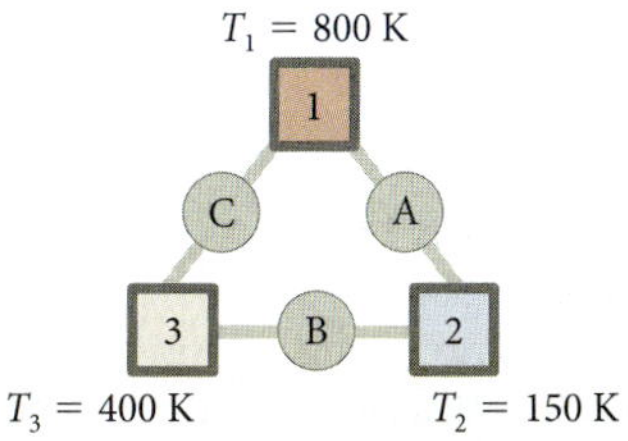

21.4 Thermodynamic cycles

18. Figure P21.18 shows PV diagrams for four thermodynamic cycles. In each case, the cycle consists of three or four processes carried out on identical working substances, and each process is isothermal, isobaric, isochoric, or isentropic. The pressures P_H and P_L have the same values in all four cycles. For which single cycle is the most work done on the gas? •

Figure P21.18

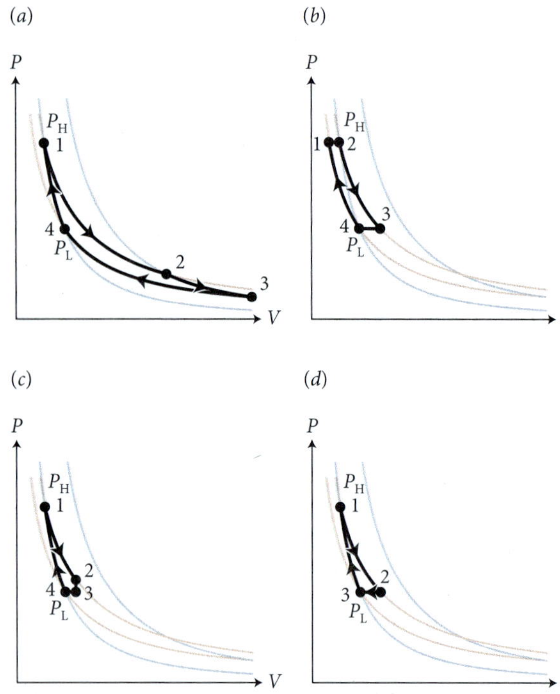

19. Which of the four thermodynamic cycles illustrated in Figure P21.18 has the greatest efficiency? ••

20. Two thermodynamic processes, each involving the same type and amount of monatomic gas as a working substance and each working as a heat engine, begin and end their cycles from a common state: $P_1 = 1.00 \times 10^5$ Pa, $V_1 = 2.50 \times 10^{-2}$ m^3, and $T_1 = 300$ K. The first is a Carnot cycle, the second is a Brayton cycle, and each does 200 J of work on the environment during each cycle. (*a*) Draw an entropy diagram for each process. (*b*) Which process causes the greater change in entropy of the environment? ••

21.5 Entropy constraints on energy transfers

21. The working substance in a steady device is a gas that undergoes expansion followed by compression. The negative work done on the gas during expansion is -6.4 J, and the positive work done on it during compression is 8.2 J. What is the work done on the gas during the cycle? •

22. What is the entropy change in the environment when 5.0 MJ of energy is transferred thermally from a reservoir at 1000 K to one at 500 K? •

23. In one cycle, a steady device transfers 1.55×10^6 J of thermal energy from a reservoir at 450 K to a reservoir at 300 K. Calculate the entropy change for the device and for the environment. •

24. Draw an entropy diagram for a steady device that in each cycle converts 135 J of work to thermal energy that is released into a reservoir at 340 K. Calculate numerical values for the length and height of the entropy bar and for the change in entropy that results from this transfer. ••

25. An ideal gas is held at 70 K in a cylinder fitted with a movable piston. When a 5.0-kg cube is placed on the piston, the piston slides down a distance of 200 mm. What is the entropy change in the environment that results from the change in the gas volume? ••

26. Processes A and B in Figure P21.26 each transfer energy thermally. If the energies transferred thermally by the two processes are related by $Q_A = \sqrt{2} \times Q_B$, and process A causes $\Delta S_{env} = 2.6 \times 10^{24}$, what is ΔS_{env} for process B? ••

Figure P21.26

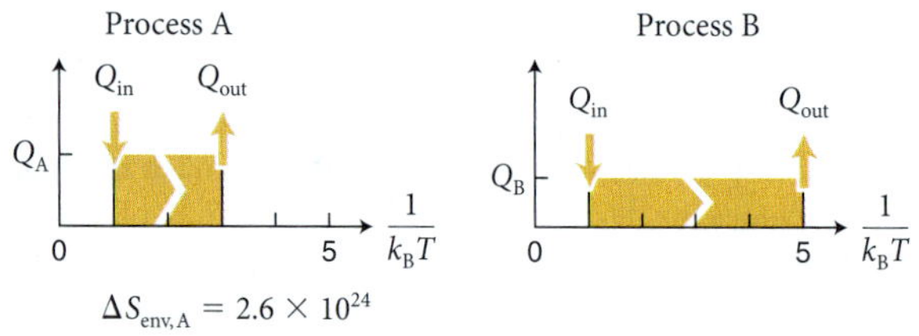

21.6 Heat engine performance

27. What is the maximum efficiency of a reversible heat engine that transfers energy from a 373 K reservoir to a 273 K reservoir? •

28. A heat engine takes in 6.45×10^3 J of thermal energy from a reservoir at 500 K and returns some of this energy to a reservoir at $T_L < 500$ K. If this engine operates at an efficiency of 0.450, what is the maximum value possible for T_L? •

29. A reversible heat pump takes in thermal energy from a reservoir at 273 K and expels thermal energy to a reservoir at 320 K. How much energy does the pump expel for every 16.0 MJ of energy taken in? •

30. A heat pump used to heat a house has a coefficient of performance of heating of 5.4. Over 24 h, the house needs to receive 2.4 GJ of thermal energy from the pump to keep the occupants comfortable. How many kilowatts of power is required to drive the heat pump? •

31. A heat engine does 85 J of work per cycle while expelling 110 J of waste thermal energy. How much energy is transferred thermally to this engine each cycle, and what is the efficiency of the engine? ••

32. Energy input-output diagrams for two heat pumps are shown in Figure P21.32. What are (*a*) Q_{out} for pump 1 and (*b*) W_{in} for pump 2? ••

Figure P21.32

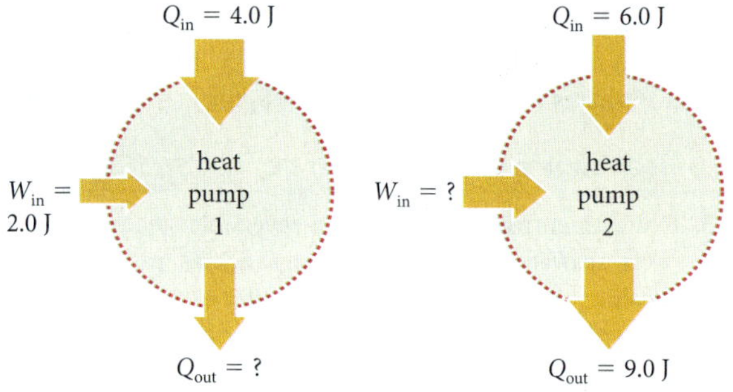

PRACTICE

33. The heat engine represented by the *PV* diagram in Figure P21.33 exhausts 43.5 kJ of thermal energy per cycle. What is the engine's efficiency? ••

Figure P21.33

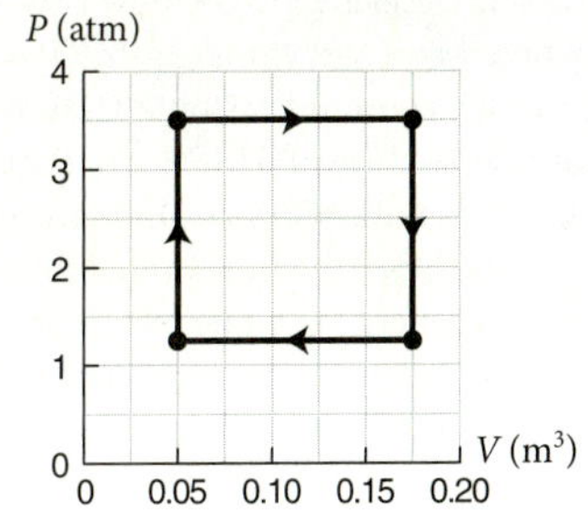

34. During each cycle, a heat engine ejects 75 J of thermal energy for every 115 J of input thermal energy. This engine is used to lift a 375-kg load a vertical distance of 27.0 m at a steady rate of 52.5 mm/s. How many cycles of the engine are needed to accomplish this task? ••

35. In winter, you like to keep your house interior at 21.0 °C. Your geothermal heating system, which was advertised as being reversible, draws thermal energy from an underground reservoir at 347 K. In a cold winter, with the average outdoor temperature being 0.0 °C, thermal energy escapes from the house at a rate of 1000 W ±5%. Distributing the thermal energy supplied by the heating system throughout the house requires 180 W (provided by the heating system). Is your heating system reversible within your 5% margin of error, or was the advertisement false? Ignore any inefficiency in converting electrical energy to mechanical energy. ••

36. An engine has a rated maximum efficiency of 0.22 when burning a certain fuel, but the manufacturer claims that burning a new type of fuel will increase the maximum efficiency. In testing this claim, you determine that, with an identical energy input, the ratio of the work done on the environment using the new fuel to the work done on the environment using the old fuel is 1.14. What is the efficiency using the new fuel? ••

37. For a heat pump that operates on a Carnot cycle, calculate (*a*) the coefficient of performance of cooling when the pump is used to cool a house to 72 °F on a day when the outside air is at 105 °F and (*b*) the coefficient of performance of heating when the pump is used to heat a house to 72 °F on a day when the outside air is at −15 °F. ••

38. Reversible heat engines 1 and 2 are connected to each other in such a way that the output temperature of engine 1 is the input temperature of engine 2, $T_{1out} = T_{2in}$, and the quantity of energy transferred thermally out of engine 1 is the quantity transferred into engine 2, $Q_{1out} = Q_{2in}$. Calculate Q_{2out} if $T_{1in} = 270\,K$, $T_{2out} = 422\,K$, and $Q_{1in} = 3.70 \times 10^{11}$ J. ••

39. On a day when the outdoor temperature is 35 °C, a walk-in freezer in a butcher shop where there is no air-conditioning must remove 3000 J of thermal energy from its interior each second to maintain an interior temperature of −4 °C. (*a*) What is the maximum coefficient of performance of cooling of the heat pump in the freezer? (*b*) What would this maximum coefficient be if the freezer were installed in the shop's basement, where the air temperature is 19 °C? (*c*) How much energy could the owner save in a day by installing the freezer in the basement? •••

40. The internal temperature of a freezer is 269 K, and the temperature of the cooling coils on the back of the freezer is 325 K. (*a*) What is the maximum coefficient of performance of cooling of the freezer? (*b*) You measure the time interval it takes to freeze a sample of water and estimate that, during each cycle, the freezer absorbs 118 J from its interior. How much thermal energy does the freezer transfer to the environment during each cycle? (*c*) How much work is done on the freezer each cycle? (*d*) You notice that the room in which the freezer is located is warmer than nearby rooms, and you wonder how efficient the freezer is at warming the room compared with the efficiency of a small electric space heater. Estimate the relative heating efficiencies of these two devices. •••

21.7 Carnot cycle

41. How much work is done by a Carnot cycle that doubles the volume of 1.00 mol of a monatomic ideal gas during isothermal expansion and triples the initial temperature of 0.0 °C during isentropic compression? •

42. An automobile manufacturer determines that, on a summer day when the ambient temperature is 311 K, the temperature inside their new, ready-to-deliver cars reaches 339 K when parked with the windows rolled up, a temperature that causes minor damage to the interiors. An engineer suggests a small in-window ventilation system. What is the maximum efficiency of an engine that operates between these two temperatures? •

43. A heat engine that operates on a Carnot cycle has an efficiency of 0.480 when its low-temperature reservoir is at 10 °C. By how many degrees Celsius must you increase the temperature of the high-temperature reservoir to increase the efficiency to 0.600 if you continue to use the same low-temperature reservoir? •

44. A heat engine operates on a Carnot cycle that runs clockwise between a reservoir at 340 K and a reservoir at 280 K. One cycle moves enough energy from the high-temperature reservoir to raise the temperature of 1.0 kg of water by 1.0 K. How much work is done by the engine in one cycle? ••

45. The Carnot cycle shown in Figure P21.45 uses 1.00 mol of a monatomic ideal gas as its working substance. From the information given in the graph, determine the values of P_1, P_2, P_3, P_4, V_3, and V_4. ••

Figure P21.45

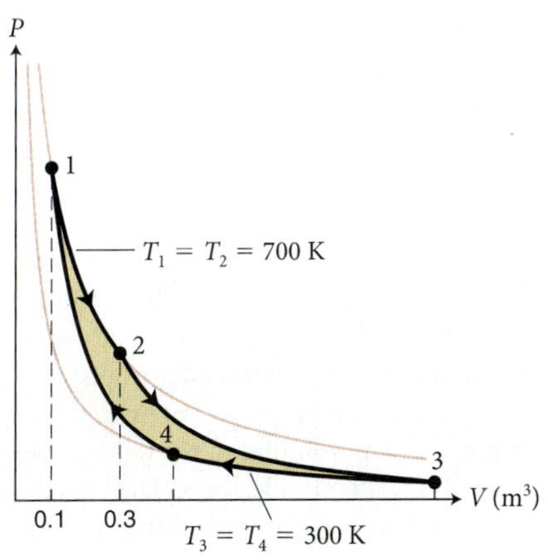

PRACTICE

46. Carnot cycles A and B run on the same amount of the same working substance and draw their thermal energy from the same high-temperature reservoir. The two cycles start with their working substances occupying different volumes. During the isothermal expansion, cycle A doubles its volume and cycle B triples its volume. If cycle A does twice as much work as cycle B, which cycle is more efficient and by how much? ••

47. Heat engines 1 and 2 operate on Carnot cycles, and the two have the same efficiency. Engine 1 takes in boiling water at 373 K and outputs water that is twice as hot as the output water from engine 2. What is the temperature of the input water for engine 2? ••

48. A heat pump that operates on a Carnot cycle cools a house in a very hot climate. During the hottest part of the day, the outside temperature is 45 °C, and you want to keep the inside temperature at 20 °C. The heat pump operates on electricity. (*a*) What is the coefficient of performance of cooling during the hottest part of the day? (*b*) At what maximum rate does the pump use electrical energy if it removes thermal energy from the house at a rate of 1.50 kW? ••

49. A heat pump that operates on a Carnot cycle uses N_2 gas and operates on electricity. (*a*) At what rate is it using electrical energy when it adds thermal energy at a rate of 1.35 kW to a room that is at 22 °C when the outside temperature is −25 °C? (*b*) What is the pump's coefficient of performance of heating? ••

50. To meet energy regulations, the coefficient of performance of cooling of a refrigerator that operates on a Carnot cycle must be 4.00. At what rate is this refrigerator expelling thermal energy into the kitchen if it consumes electrical energy at a rate of 225 W? ••

51. A heat engine that operates on a Carnot cycle uses a low-temperature reservoir at 25 °C and runs at an efficiency of 0.350. The working substance is nitrogen gas, and the gas chamber contains 7.50×10^{23} N_2 molecules. What is the change in the thermal energy of the N_2 gas between its lowest and highest temperatures? ••

52. An electric heat pump used as a heater operates on a Carnot cycle. The low-temperature reservoir consists of a pipe driven 10 m into the ground to a region where the temperature is always 10 °C. The high-temperature reservoir is the interior of a house, kept at 20 °C. (*a*) For every 1.0 J of electrical energy used to run the heat pump, what quantity of thermal energy is delivered to the house? (*b*) If the low-temperature reservoir were the air outside the house at −23 °C rather than underground, what quantity of thermal energy would 1.0 J of electrical energy deliver to the house? Does it seem to be worth the added expense of drilling to tap the underground reservoir? (*c*) What is the coefficient of performance of heating of the heat pump in part *a* and in part *b*? ••

53. The temperature of Earth's oceans at a depth of 2500 m is about 4 °C. Suppose you want to use this water as the low-temperature thermal reservoir for an electric heat pump to heat the cabin of a boat to 20 °C. If the pump operates on a Carnot cycle and uses electrical energy at a rate of 75 W, at what rate are you changing the entropy of the deep ocean and the entropy of the air in the cabin? ••

54. An experimental six-cylinder engine that operates on a Carnot cycle has been proposed for a car. Each cylinder is fitted with a movable piston that allows the cylinder to fill with 1.00 mol of a monatomic ideal gas. During isothermal expansion at 700 K, the length of each cylinder increases from 100 mm to 200 mm as the piston moves. The isothermal compression occurs at 400 K. Each isothermal process takes 9.00 s, and each isentropic process takes 2.00 s. If the mass of the car is 750 kg, how long a time interval is required for this car and its 70.0-kg driver to accelerate from rest to 50.0 km/h? Ignore drag and friction. •••

55. A freezer that operates on a Carnot cycle maintains an interior temperature of –18 °C and exhausts thermal energy into a kitchen at 22 °C. You place a tray containing 0.500 kg of water at 0 °C in the freezer and observe that the freezer draws electrical energy at a rate of 115 W. (*a*) How long does it take to transform all the water to ice? (*b*) What is the freezer's coefficient of performance of cooling? (*c*) How much thermal energy is exhausted into the kitchen during the time interval it takes to freeze the water? (*d*) What is the change in entropy of the water as it freezes? (*e*) What is the change in entropy of the system that consists of the water plus the kitchen? For water, the specific transformation energy for melting is $L_{\text{melting}} = 334$ kJ/kg. •••

21.8 Brayton cycle

56. Determine T_4 for the Brayton cycle represented in Figure P21.56. •

Figure P21.56

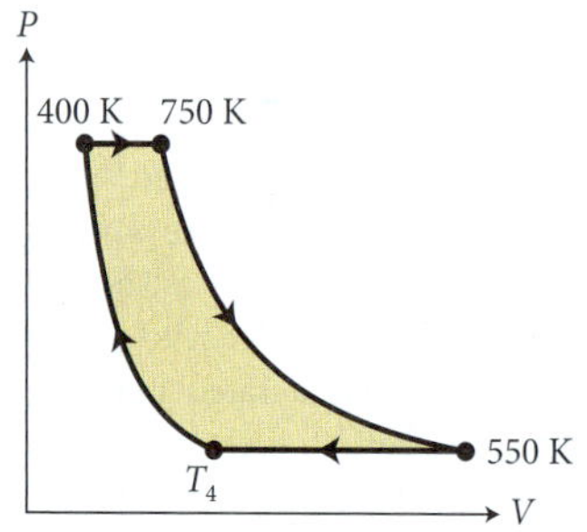

57. An engine that operates on a Brayton cycle uses oxygen gas (diatomic molecules, O_2) as the working substance. During the isobaric cooling, the temperature decreases by 85 °C. During the isobaric heating, the temperature increases by 100 °C. What is the maximum efficiency of this cycle? •

58. A gas engine that operates on a Brayton cycle has an efficiency of 0.22. On a cold day, the temperature of the air drawn into the engine is 267 K. What is the temperature of the air exhausted from the engine? •

59. An experimental car engine operates on a Brayton cycle and uses a monatomic ideal gas as the working substance. If the pressure in front of the moving car is 103,500 Pa and the pressure behind the moving car is 99,700 Pa, what is the maximum efficiency possible for the engine? ••

60. An engine that operates on a Brayton cycle uses air as its working substance, compressing ambient air initially at a pressure of 1.0 atm to 6.0 atm. (*a*) What is the engine's pressure ratio? (*b*) If the heat capacity ratio $\gamma = C_P/C_V$ is 1.40 for air, what is the engine's efficiency? (*c*) At high altitudes, $\gamma = 1.44$ and the ambient air pressure is 0.40 atm. If the engine compresses this air to 4.8 atm, what is its efficiency now? ••

61. A heat engine that operates on a Brayton cycle has a pressure ratio of 5 and uses as its working substance a gas for which the heat capacity ratio C_P/C_V is 1.333. You wish to replace this engine with one that operates on a Carnot cycle and has the

PRACTICE

same efficiency as the Brayton engine. If the low-temperature reservoir for the Carnot engine is to be 15 °C, what must the temperature of the high-temperature reservoir be? ••

62. You need to replace a heat engine that operates on a Carnot cycle with one that has the same efficiency but operates on a Brayton cycle. The Carnot engine low and high temperatures are −10 °C and 225 °C. If the working substance in your replacement engine has a C_P/C_V ratio of 1.667, what must the engine's pressure ratio be? ••

63. A heat engine that operates on a Brayton cycle uses N_2 gas and has a pressure ratio of 10. It is being used to lift a 535-kg pallet of bricks vertically at a steady rate of 100 mm/s. At what rate must thermal energy be supplied to this engine to accomplish this task? ••

64. You need to design a heat engine that operates on a Brayton cycle and, during each cycle, does 175 J of work while exhausting 65 J of energy. (*a*) If the working substance is helium gas, what should the pressure ratio be? (*b*) If the working substance is carbon dioxide gas, CO_2, is the pressure ratio the same as with helium gas? If so, prove it; if not, determine the new pressure ratio. ••

65. If the Brayton cycle represented in Figure P21.65 operates on 4.0 mol of an ideal gas, how many degrees of freedom do the particles of the gas have? •••

Figure P21.65

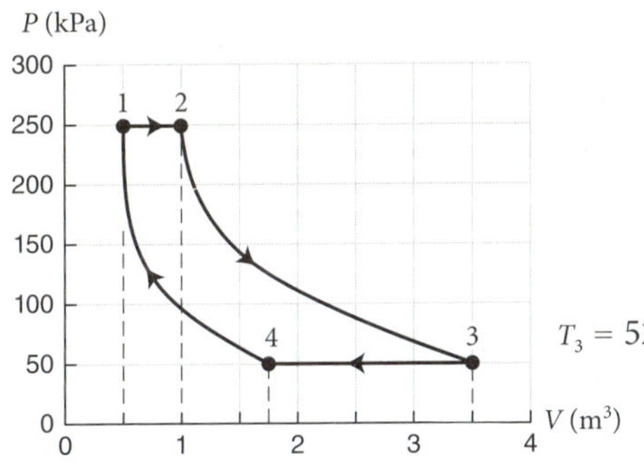

66. You are designing a gas engine that operates on a Brayton cycle and uses air ($\gamma = 1.4$) as its working substance. By making the engine larger and larger, you can have the pressure ratio be 16, 17, 18, 19, or 20. At the higher pressure ratios, however, the efficiency is a smaller fraction of the ideal Brayton cycle efficiency. You determine that, over this range of ratios, the factor relating the efficiency of the real engine to that of the ideal cycle, $\eta_{\text{real}} = f\eta_{\text{ideal}}$, can be described by the formula $f = (1.45)(1 - \eta_{\text{ideal}})^{0.8}$. (*a*) Which pressure ratio do you choose to maximize efficiency? (*b*) This is a simplified problem. Other than increasing mass, what other reasons can you think of for why engine designers don't have the pressure ratio as great as possible? •••

Additional problems

67. A thermal reservoir is held at 265 K. If 4180 J of energy is transferred thermally to it, what is the change in entropy of the reservoir? •

68. The entropy of a system is increased by 3.8×10^{21} for every 10 J of energy added to it. What is the temperature of this system? •

69. In the past 40 years, the average power a refrigerator requires to provide a given amount of cooling has dropped from 160 W to 40 W. By what factor has the COP of cooling for refrigerators changed during this time interval? •

70. A 1000-kg iceberg at 0 °C falls into the ocean at a location where the water temperature is 2 °C, and all the ice melts by absorbing thermal energy from the water. What is the entropy change for the system comprising the water and the iceberg? For ice, the specific transformation energy for melting is 334 kJ/kg. ••

71. The low-temperature reservoir for a heat engine that operates on a Carnot cycle is at −5 °C. Using only 1.00 MJ of thermal energy, this engine needs to pull a 1200-kg boulder at a steady rate 65.0 m up a ramp inclined at 35.0° above the horizontal. (*a*) What must the temperature of the high-temperature reservoir be? (*b*) How much of the 1.00 MJ of input energy is wasted as the boulder travels this distance? Ignore any friction between the boulder and the ramp surface. ••

72. An electric heat pump that operates on a Carnot cycle is used to cool a house interior to 20 °C on a day when the outside temperature is 38 °C. (*a*) For every 1.0 J of electrical energy used, what quantity of thermal energy is removed from the house? (*b*) What is the pump's coefficient of performance of cooling? ••

73. A Carnot heat engine in a factory operates at an efficiency of 0.33 when it takes in thermal energy from a reservoir of heated water and releases thermal energy into the 28 °C surface water of an outdoor pool. By how much could the efficiency be improved if the thermal energy were released into the pool at a depth where the water temperature is 18 °C? ••

74. A heat engine that operates on a Carnot cycle is used to pump water out of a well that is 45.0 m deep. The high-temperature reservoir for the heat engine is at 215 °C, and the low-temperature reservoir is at −10 °C. The engine must move water from the bottom of the well to the surface at a rate of 6600 L/min, and the speed of the water when it reaches the surface is negligible. At what rate must thermal energy be supplied to the engine? ••

75. An electric heat pump that operates on a Carnot cycle is used to keep the air in a laboratory chamber at a constant 35 °C by extracting energy from outside air that is at 5 °C. Due to conduction and small leaks, the chamber loses thermal energy at a rate of 12.0 W. (a) At what rate must the pump extract energy from the outside air? (b) At what rate is the pump using electrical energy? ••

76. A heat pump that operates on a Carnot cycle must deliver thermal energy to your house at a rate of 12.5 kW to keep the rooms at 22 °C. The pump uses outside air at −10 °C as its low-temperature reservoir and runs on electricity that costs 2.69¢/MJ. How much does it cost to keep your house at 22 °C from 8 a.m. to 10 p.m.? ••

77. The thermal gradient of Earth's crust is approximately 25 K/km at locations away from tectonic plate boundaries. Suppose you want to use this thermal gradient to run a heat engine that operates on a Carnot cycle at a location where the base of the crust is 30 km below Earth's surface and the surface temperature is 28 °C. (*a*) What is the maximum efficiency the engine can achieve at this location? (*b*) Because drilling 30 km into the crust presents great technological problems, you will settle for an efficiency of 0.50. How deep into the crust must your high-temperature reservoir be in order for the engine to have an efficiency of 0.50? ••

78. The average daytime temperature at the surface of the Moon is 380 K, and the temperature of the lunar core is estimated at 1000 K. Suppose you want to run a heat engine that operates on a Carnot cycle to use this temperature difference to run a 2.50-MW power station at some future lunar colony. (*a*) At what rate does this engine extract thermal energy from the lunar core? (*b*) At what rate does the process change the entropy of the core system? (*c*) What is the thermal efficiency of this engine? ••

79. A heat engine that operates on a Carnot cycle has efficiency η. When the engine is run in reverse as a heat pump, what are, in terms of η, (*a*) the coefficient of performance of cooling when the pump is used for cooling and (*b*) the coefficient of performance of heating when the pump is used for heating? (*c*) For each case, check your answer to see whether the range of the coefficients of performance is physically reasonable. ••

80. A heat engine that operates on a Carnot cycle is used to pump crude oil at a rate of 25,000 barrels/day from a well that is 1.70 km deep. The mass density of the oil is 850 kg/m^3, the oil is under minimal pressure and so has no initial speed, and it has negligible speed as it reaches the surface. The engine operates between 50 °F and 250 °F, and each barrel has a volume of 0.159 m^3. At what rate must thermal energy be supplied to this heat engine? ••

81. A heat engine that operates on a Carnot cycle between 150 °C and 10 °C is used to accelerate a flywheel from rest to a rotational speed of 8.50 s^{-1}. The 1500-kg flywheel is a solid uniform cylinder that rotates about its long central axis without appreciable friction. Its diameter is 1.00 m, and it is 750 mm long. How much thermal energy must be transferred into this engine to accelerate the flywheel to the desired rotational speed, and how much of this thermal energy is wasted in the process? ••

82. A 950-kg car uses an engine that operates on a Brayton cycle for which the pressure ratio is 8 and the working substance is helium (He) gas. During each cycle, 25% of the work done by the engine is used to overcome friction. If the engine must accelerate the car from rest to 30 m/s, how much energy must be transferred thermally to the engine? ••

83. The Brayton cycle represented in Figure P21.83 operates with 2.00 mol of working substance. How many degrees of freedom does each particle of the working substance have? •••

Figure P21.83

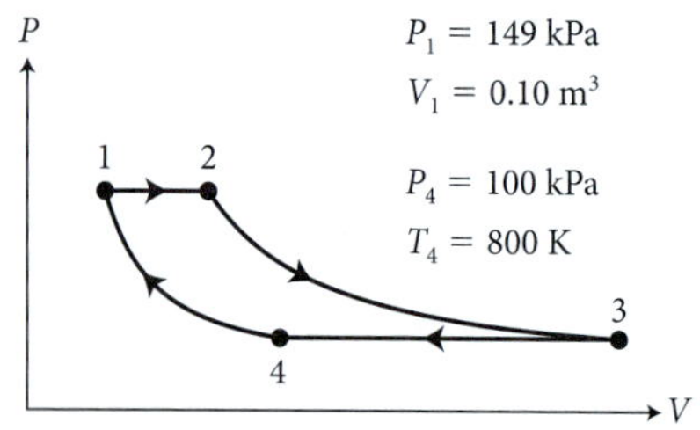

84. You have taken a job as a patent examiner, and your first assignment is to evaluate a "zero-point energy perpetual motion machine." You are skeptical, but after the applicant gives it an initial energy of 1000 J, the machine starts operating and does not immediately run down. Hours later, tired of waiting for the machine to stop, you use an infrared sensor and determine that the machine is losing thermal energy at an average rate of 200 μJ/s. You would like to examine other devices while waiting for the machine to stop, but you do not want to miss its final few minutes of operation, and you are also concerned about its effect on the entropy of the environment. ••• CR

85. Working for an automotive journal, you are reviewing two proposed new models that have identical frame shapes and identical masses. Car 1 runs on a Brayton cycle that does enough work to accelerate the car from 0 to 100 km/h in 11.5 s when internal friction, air resistance, and other retarding factors are left out of the equations. When air resistance is taken into account, the car's top speed is 105 km/h. In the cycle, the isobaric cooling is accomplished by exposing the working substance to normal atmospheric pressure and 350 K, the temperature under the car's hood. When the working substance is compressed, the pressure increases by a factor of 5.00, and the temperature of the working substance after the isobaric combustion is 700 K. At the compressor, the engine takes in 1.00 mol of the working substance (which the designer has modeled as having four degrees of freedom) and the operating speed is 8.00 cycles/s. Car 2 runs on a Carnot cycle that has the same minimum and maximum temperatures of 350 K and 700 K, the same fuel intake, and the same piston volume. The frame shapes and masses of the cars are nearly identical. The only difference (other than the cycle itself) is that car 2 runs at only 1.00 cycle per second. ••• CR

86. You work for a toy company that wants to produce a bathtub toy boat that operates on a Carnot cycle and slowly putts around the bathtub. It is assumed that the temperature of the bathwater will be about 100 °F and the air temperature will be about 70 °F. After some experimenting, you determine that your prototype model operates at about 40% of the efficiency of an ideal Carnot cycle between these two temperatures. Your engineer tells you that the boat needs to have an efficiency of 0.045 in order to move around well in the tub. You begin to consider simple design modifications in an attempt to reach this goal. ••• CR

PRACTICE

Answers to Review Questions

1. (*a*) When a gas burns, one state change involves the chemical bonds in the gas particles, associated with the chemical potential energy locked in the bonds, and the complementary state change is in the gas temperature, associated with the particles' thermal energy. (*b*) When a ball drops to the ground, one state change is the ball's speed, associated with its kinetic energy, and the complementary state change is in the configuration of the ball-Earth system, associated with the system's gravitational potential energy.
2. The work done on a system is the difference between the mechanical input of energy and the mechanical output of energy.
3. In a car engine, chemical energy from burned fuel is thermally transferred into the engine. Energy is mechanically transferred out of the engine as the motion of the engine does work through the linkage to produce circular motion in the wheels. Energy is also transferred thermally out of the engine via the exhaust and as the temperature of the air around the engine increases. In a refrigerator, energy is transferred mechanically into the system in the form of work done on the refrigerator by its compressor. Energy is also transferred thermally into the refrigerator from room-temperature items placed inside the refrigerator. Energy is thermally transferred out of the refrigerator as the thermal energy of the air surrounding the refrigerator increases.
4. A steady device is a device that converts energy from one form to another in such a way that either the initial state of the device never changes as the energy conversion takes place or, if the initial state does change, the change is cyclic and the steady device periodically returns to its initial state. In a nonsteady device, some property of the device such as temperature or pressure continues to change to the point where the device no longer operates.
5. (*a*) No restrictions are imposed when the device converts mechanical energy to thermal energy because the conversion to thermal energy increases the entropy of the environment, obeying the entropy law. (*b*) Converting thermal energy to mechanical energy decreases the entropy of the environment and so violates the entropy law; such a device does not exist.
6. The entropy gradient is $dS/dE = 1/(k_B T)$. It says that the change in a reservoir's entropy dS when a given quantity of thermal energy dE is transferred to or from the reservoir is inversely proportional to the reservoir temperature. For a given quantity of energy, the magnitude of the entropy change when that quantity is removed from a higher-temperature reservoir is smaller than the entropy change when that quantity is added to a lower-temperature reservoir.
7. The entropy cost is a measure of the change in entropy caused by a given change in energy; hence it is determined by the entropy gradient at the temperature at which the energy change takes place, i.e., energy is transferred into or out of the system.
8. The rod thermally transfers energy from the higher-temperature reservoir to the lower-temperature one. The entropy of the system (rod) may increase or decrease for a short time interval while the system reaches a steady state; this depends on the initial state (temperature) of the rod. However, after a steady state is reached, the entropy of the rod will neither increase nor decrease, and the rod acts as a steady device to transfer energy. The transfer is irreversible because the ΔS for a given ΔE is inversely proportional to temperature. The amount by which the transferred energy increases the entropy, ΔS_L, of the lower-temperature reservoir is greater than the amount by which it decreases the entropy, ΔS_H, of the higher-temperature reservoir; thus the entropy change for the environment is positive, making the conversion irreversible.
9. Energy quality is a measure of how much useful work can be obtained from a given form of energy. Energy change is generally associated with an entropy change, and the entropy change of the environment for a steady device must be positive. The quality of the energy is inversely proportional to the energy gradient. High-quality energy has a small energy gradient. High-quality energy input has a small associated entropy change and so will require a small corresponding thermal energy output to the environment in order for the entropy of the environment to increase. Hence, most of the energy input will result in a mechanical output of energy. Low-quality energy input requires a greater thermal energy output to ensure that the entropy of the environment increases; hence it will have a smaller associated mechanical output of energy. Therefore the energy quality is a measure of how much useful work can be obtained from a given amount of energy change.
10. The entropy gradient associated with mechanical energy input is zero; therefore a mechanical input of energy is the highest-quality energy input.
11. A heat engine is a steady device that takes in thermal energy from a higher-temperature reservoir, converts part of this energy to mechanical energy, and transfers the rest to a lower-temperature reservoir. A car engine takes in thermal energy from burning fuel, converts part of that energy to the mechanical energy that moves the car, and transfers the remainder to the environment.
12. An entropy diagram consists of a horizontal axis representing the entropy gradient, $dS/dE = 1/k_B T$, and a vertical axis representing energy. Rectangles drawn in this coordinate system represent entropy changes, with the product of the two axes giving the magnitude of the entropy change for a given rectangle. Vertical arrows represent energy transfers into (downward arrows) and out of (upward arrows) the system. The locations of these arrows along the horizontal axis indicate at what entropy gradient in a process the energy transfers occur. A left-pointing arrowhead within an entropy-change rectangle indicates that entropy in the environment decreases; hence the energy is upgraded in that process. A right-pointing arrowhead within an entropy-change rectangle indicates that entropy in the environment increases; hence the energy is downgraded in that process.
13. The efficiency of a heat engine is the ratio of the quantity of work done by the engine on its environment $(-W)$ to the quantity of energy Q_{in} transferred thermally to the engine: $-W/Q_{in}$.
14. A heat pump is a steady device that degrades mechanical energy in order to thermally transfer energy from a lower-temperature reservoir to a higher-temperature reservoir.
15. There is no difference. In both cases, the pump transfers thermal energy from a lower-temperature reservoir to a higher-temperature reservoir. In summer, the lower-temperature reservoir is a room and the higher-temperature reservoir is the outdoors. In winter, the lower-temperature reservoir is the outdoors and the higher-temperature reservoir is the room being heated.
16. The coefficient of performance of cooling, a measure of how efficient a heat pump is when used for cooling, is the ratio of the quantity of energy transferred thermally into the pump to the quantity of work done on the pump: Q_{in}/W. The coefficient of performance of heating, a measure of how efficient a heat pump is when used for heating, is the ratio of the quantity of energy transferred thermally out of the pump to the quantity of work done on the pump. Q_{out}/W.
17. A heat engine does positive work on the environment; hence the work done on the working substance (system) must be negative. An expansion process on a *PV* diagram represents negative work done on the system, and a compression process represents positive work done on the system. In order for a cyclic process to result in negative work done on the system, the expansion curve must be above the compression curve corresponding to a clockwise cycle. Therefore the path on a *PV* diagram for a heat engine must be clockwise. A heat pump does positive work on the system, so the expansion curve must lie below the compression curve, corresponding to a counterclockwise cycle.

18. A working substance sequentially undergoes an isothermal expansion (energy transferred to substance from reservoir at T_{in}), an isentropic expansion (substance temperature drops to that of reservoir at T_{out}), an isothermal compression (energy transferred from substance to reservoir at T_{out}), and an isentropic compression back to its initial state (substance temperature rises to T_{in}).
19. The engine does only a small amount of work on the environment in each cycle, which means little mechanical energy is produced, and the two isothermal steps take place very slowly, which makes the engine's power (energy delivered per unit of time) too small to be practicable.
20. A working substance sequentially undergoes an isobaric expansion, an isentropic expansion, an isobaric compression, and an isentropic compression back to the initial state.
21. Gas turbines and jet engines run on cycles that are a good approximation of a forward Brayton cycle. Refrigerators and air-conditioners run on cycles that are a good approximation of a reverse Brayton cycle.
22. It is impossible to construct a cyclic device whose only interaction with its environment is to transfer energy thermally from a lower-temperature reservoir to a higher-temperature reservoir.
23. An entropy diagram is a rectangle drawn so that the height of the rectangle represents the amount of energy transferred and the length of the rectangle represents the difference in values of $(1/k_B T)$ for the process. The product (area) thus gives the magnitude of the entropy change of the environment for the process, by Eq. 21.10. The sign of the entropy change is given by the direction of the process: If the rectangle points to the right, energy is degraded and the entropy change of the environment is positive. If the rectangle points to the left, energy is upgraded and the entropy change is negative.
24. Q_{out} is directly proportional to the temperature of the lower-temperature reservoir and inversely proportional to the temperature of the higher-temperature reservoir: $Q_{out} = Q_{in}(T_{out}/T_{in})$ (from Eq. 21.20).
25. A heat engine upgrades some portion of Q_{in} to mechanical energy in the form of work done by the engine on the environment. This upgrading means the environment's entropy decreases. The entropy law, $\Delta S \geq 0$, requires that some Q_{in} must be degraded to compensate for this decrease in S_{env}. The degraded portion is Q_{out}. Because $Q_{out} < Q_{in}$, the efficiency $\eta = 1 - (Q_{out}/Q_{in})$ of any heat engine, reversible or irreversible, is always less than 1. Because the efficiency of irreversible heat engines is always less than that of reversible engines, the maximum efficiency, $\eta_{max} = (T_{in} - T_{out})/T_{in}$ (Eq. 21.23), is applicable to reversible engines only. In practice, no heat engine can operate at maximum efficiency because it is impossible to eliminate all dissipation of energy in the engine.
26. In both a heat pump and an air-conditioner, the thermal energy input comes from the lower-temperature reservoir; therefore Q_{in} and T_{in} belong to the lower-temperature reservoir.
27. The coefficient of performance is the quantity Q_{out} of energy transferred thermally to a higher-temperature reservoir divided by the work done on the heat pump. Because the work done on the heat pump is equal to the difference between Q_{out} and the quantity Q_{in} of energy transferred thermally from a lower-temperature reservoir, Eq. 21.25, $COP_{heating} = Q_{out}/(Q_{out} - Q_{in})$. The maximum value is the temperature T_{out} of the higher-temperature reservoir divided by the difference between T_{out} and the absolute temperature T_{in} of the lower-temperature reservoir: Eq. 21.26, $COP_{heating,\,max} = T_{out}/(T_{out} - T_{in})$.
28. The coefficient of performance of cooling equals the coefficient of performance of heating minus 1 (Eq. 21.28).
29. No. The maximum efficiency of a heat engine is independent of the working substance.
30. The isentropic work does not contribute to W because one isentropic work value contains the difference $(T_{out} - T_{in})$ and the other contains the difference $(T_{in} - T_{out})$, causing these two terms to cancel each other. The work done during the isothermal steps does not cancel.
31. The efficiency of an engine that operates on a Carnot cycle is equal to the maximum efficiency of any heat engine.
32. The Brayton cycle produces more mechanical energy than the Carnot cycle, and because the Brayton cycle involves no isothermal steps, the rate at which it produces that energy—the power output—is greater than the rate at which mechanical energy is produced in the Carnot cycle.
33. The cycle efficiency equals 1 minus the ratio of the absolute temperature T_4 of the gas just as it begins isentropic compression to the absolute temperature T_1 of the gas at the end of the compression (Eq. 21.44).

Answers to Guided Problems

Guided Problem 21.2 $Q_{out,min} = 4.4$ MW

Guided Problem 21.4 $W_{environment} = 1.52 \times 10^4$ J/mol

Guided Problem 21.6 $\eta = 0.605$

Guided Problem 21.8

$W_{12} = -2.41 \times 10^3$ J, $Q_{12} = +2.41 \times 10^3$ J,
$\Delta E_{th,12} = 0$, $\Delta S_{12} = +4.82 \times 10^{23}$

$W_{23} = +1.10 \times 10^3$ J, $Q_{23} = -2.75 \times 10^3$ J,
$\Delta E_{th,23} = -1.65 \times 10^3$ J, $\Delta S_{23} = -9.91 \times 10^{23}$

$W_{34} = +115$ J, $Q_{34} = -115$ J,
$\Delta E_{th,34} = 0$, $\Delta S_{34} = -8.63 \times 10^{22}$

$W_{41} = 0$, $Q_{41} = +1.65 \times 10^3$ J,
$\Delta E_{th,41} = +1.65 \times 10^3$ J, $\Delta S_{41} = +5.94 \times 10^{23}$

$W_{cycle} = -1.20 \times 10^3$ J, $Q_{cycle} = +1.20 \times 10^3$ J,
$\Delta E_{cycle} = 0$, $\Delta S_{cycle} = 0$

22 PRACTICE Electric Interactions

Chapter Summary

Electric interactions (Sections 22.1, 22.2, 22.5)

Concepts An **electric interaction** is a long-range interaction between objects that carry a surplus **electrical charge.** The electric force is sometimes called the *electrostatic* force because interactions between charged objects become more complicated for objects that are not at rest (see Chapter 27).

There are only two types of charge: **positive charge** and **negative charge.** Objects that carry like charges repel each other; objects that carry opposite charges attract each other. Any microscopic object that carries electrical charge, such as an electron or ion, is called a **charge carrier.**

The SI unit of charge is the **coulomb** (C), which is the magnitude of the charge carried by about 6.24×10^{18} electrons. It is also equal to the amount of charge transported in 1 s by a steady current of 1 ampere (see Chapter 27).

Quantitative Tools **Coulomb's law** states that if particle 1 carrying charge q_1 and particle 2 carrying charge q_2 are a distance r_{12} apart, the **electric force** $\vec{F}^E_{12}$ exerted by particle 1 on particle 2 is

$$\vec{F}^E_{12} = k\frac{q_1 q_2}{r^2_{12}}\hat{r}_{12}, \tag{22.7}$$

where the unit vector $\hat{r}_{12}$ points from particle 1 to particle 2 and the constant k is

$$k = 9.0 \times 10^9\ \mathrm{N \cdot m^2/C^2}. \tag{22.5}$$

The **elementary charge** e is the smallest observed amount of charge and is equal to the magnitude of the charge carried by one electron:

$$e = 1.60 \times 10^{-19}\ \mathrm{C}. \tag{22.3}$$

The charge q carried by any object comes in whole-number multiples of e:

$$q = ne \quad (n = 0, \pm 1, \pm 2, \pm 3, \ldots). \tag{22.4}$$

Movement of charge carriers (Sections 22.3, 22.4)

Concepts Charge carriers can flow through an **electrical conductor** but cannot readily flow through an **electrical insulator.** Charge carriers can be transferred from one nonconductor to another only by bringing the nonconductors into contact with each other, and the carriers remain near the spot at which they were deposited.

We **ground** an object by connecting it electrically to Earth. Grounding permits the exchange of charge carriers with Earth, a huge reservoir of charge carriers. A charged, conducting object that is grounded will retain no surplus of either type of charge, assuming no other nearby electrical influences.

An **ion** is an atom or molecule that has lost or gained one or more electrons.

According to the principle of **conservation of charge,** electrical charge can be created or destroyed only in identical positive-negative pairs, with the result that the charge of a closed system always remains constant.

Polarization, which is the separation of charge carriers in an object, allows neutral objects to interact electrically.

Charging by induction is a method of using a charged object to charge a neutral object without the two objects touching each other.

Forces due to multiple charges (Section 22.6)

Quantitative Tools The electric force exerted on a charged particle 1 by any number of other charged particles 2, 3, ... is

$$\sum\vec{F}^E_1 = k\frac{q_2 q_1}{r^2_{21}}\hat{r}_{21} + k\frac{q_3 q_1}{r^2_{31}}\hat{r}_{31} + \ldots. \tag{22.10}$$

Review Questions

Answers to these questions can be found at the end of this chapter.

22.1 Static electricity

1. Blow up a balloon, tie it closed, hold it next to your head, and let go. What is the interaction responsible for the balloon's fall? This interaction is between which two objects? Now rub the balloon against your hair until it sticks against your head when you let go. What is the interaction responsible for the balloon's behavior? This interaction is between which two objects?
2. Name two differences between the gravitational interaction and the electric interaction.

22.2 Electrical charge

3. What experimental evidence tells us there is more than one type of electrical charge?
4. You rub a balloon on a friend's hair, and the balloon clings to her head. You say her hair put charge on the balloon, and she says the balloon put charge on her hair. Which of you is right?

22.3 Mobility of charge carriers

5. How much charge can you produce *within* any closed system by any process?
6. You scuff your feet on the carpet and then a spark leaps from your fingertip when you touch a metal doorknob. What does this observation tell you about whether your body is an electrical conductor or an electrical insulator?
7. Classify each of the following as an electrical insulator or conductor: paper, paper clip, seawater, car tire, air.
8. Breaking a piece of wood involves breaking chemical bonds. Why doesn't this usually leave the resultant pieces charged?

22.4 Charge polarization

9. Describe the process by which an electrically neutral object can be attracted by an electrically charged rod.
10. Suppose early researchers in electricity had assigned electrons a positive charge and protons a negative charge. What would be different in the electric phenomena you have studied up to this point?
11. How is charge polarization similar in electrical insulators and conductors? How is it different?
12. Negatively charged object A attracts object B. (*a*) Which state or states are possible for object B: positively charged, neutral, negatively charged? (*b*) Negatively charged object C repels object D. Which state or states are possible for object D: positively charged, neutral, negatively charged?

22.5 Coulomb's law

13. Use Newton's third law and the experimental observation that the magnitude F^E_{AB} of the electric force exerted by a charged object A on a charged object B is proportional to the charge on B to argue that the magnitude of the electric force between the two *must* be proportional to the *product* of the charges (as opposed to, say, proportional to the *sum* of the charges or to one of the charges only).
14. If you double the charge on *each* of two objects, how much must you increase the distance between the objects to restore the force exerted on them to its original value?
15. In a carbon atom, where six electrons are located around a nucleus that contains six protons (and usually six neutrons), which force magnitude is larger, if either: that of the force exerted by an electron on the nucleus or that of the force exerted by the nucleus on an electron?

22.6 Force exerted by distributions of charge carriers

16. Consider some arrangement of charge carriers 1, 2, and 3. What is wrong with the expression

$$\Sigma \vec{F}_1 = k\frac{q_2 q_1}{r_{21}^2}\hat{r}_{21} + k\frac{q_3 q_1}{r_{31}^2}\hat{r}_{31} + k\frac{q_3 q_2}{r_{32}^2}\hat{r}_{32}$$

for the force exerted on carrier 1 by carriers 2 and 3?
17. Charged particle 1, carrying charge $+q$, is fixed at the origin of an x axis. Charged particle 2, carrying charge $-2q$, is fixed at $x = +2.0$ m. Where on the x axis should charged particle 3, carrying charge $+3q$, be placed so that the vector sum of forces exerted on particle 3 is zero: (*a*) $0 < x < 2.0$ m, (*b*) $2.0 \text{ m} < x < +\infty$, (*c*) $-\infty < x < 0$?

PRACTICE

Developing a Feel

Make an order-of-magnitude estimate of each of the following quantities. Letters in parentheses refer to hints below. Use them as needed to guide your thinking.

1. The minimum magnitude for the electric force exerted on a tiny bit of paper lifted by attraction to a charged comb (C, O)
2. The magnitude of the electric force between a proton and an electron in an atom (R, S)
3. The magnitude of the electric force between a sodium ion and a neighboring chloride ion in a sodium chloride molecule (D, V, S)
4. The number of protons in a 1-liter bottle of cola (E, N, H, W)
5. The number of electrons in Earth (Y, T, M, J)
6. The magnitude of the electric force between you and a friend standing 10 m apart if each of you had 1% more electrons than protons (Z, H, K, W, A)
7. The percentage of Earth's electrons that, if transferred to the Moon, would create an electrical attraction equal to the gravitational attraction of these bodies (G, L, Y, U, results of number 5 above)
8. The amount of like charge on each of two identical pith balls hung by two 80-mm strings from a common point, if the two balls are at their equilibrium positions when the angle formed by the two strings is 40° (X, Q, I)
9. The maximum amount of like charge you can put equally on two pith balls you are holding without feeling their force of repulsion (B, F, P)
10. The charge-to-mass ratio q/m for two identical, isolated particles that would remain at rest if released from rest at any separation (X, G, U)

Hints

A. What is the magnitude of charge carried by 1% of a person's electrons?
B. What minimum gravitational force can you detect with your fingers?
C. To lift any object, what force must be overcome?
D. What is the separation distance between two neighboring ions in the crystal?
E. What is the main ingredient in cola?
F. How can you minimize the magnitude of the electric force between the pith balls?
G. If you equate the gravitational force and electric force expressions, what cancels?
H. What is the mass of a molecule of water?
I. What must the magnitude of the electric force be?
J. How many electrons are there for each proton in Earth?
K. What is the mass of a person?
L. What is the mass of the Moon?
M. What is the mass of a proton?
N. What is the mass of 1 liter of cola?
O. What is the mass of a tiny bit of paper?
P. What maximum distance can you create between your hands?
Q. What is the mass of a pith ball?
R. What is a typical separation distance between a proton and an electron in an atom?
S. What is the magnitude of the charge carried by an electron or a proton?
T. What fraction of this mass is due to protons?
U. What is the ratio of gravitational to electrical constants in the force expressions?
V. What charge does each ion carry?
W. How many protons are there in one molecule of water?
X. What is the vector sum of the forces acting on each object?
Y. What is the mass of Earth?
Z. What is the main ingredient in the human body?

Key (all values approximate)

A. 4×10^7 C; **B.** about $1/10$ of the gravitational force exerted by Earth on a penny, which has a mass of 2×10^{-3} kg—thus 2×10^{-3} N; **C.** gravitational force; **D.** 2×10^{-10} m; **E.** water; **F.** hold them as far apart as possible; **G.** the separation distance; **H.** two H atoms plus one O atom, 3×10^{-26} kg; **I.** 4×10^{-4} N; **J.** one; **K.** 70 kg; **L.** 7×10^{22} kg; **M.** 2×10^{-27} kg; **N.** 1 kg; **O.** 10^{-5} kg; **P.** 2 m; **Q.** 1×10^{-4} kg; **R.** 5×10^{-11} m; **S.** 1.6×10^{-19} C, the elementary charge; **T.** half, because atoms have about equal numbers of protons and neutrons, and these two particles have nearly identical masses; **U.** with both constants in SI units, $G/k = 7 \times 10^{-21}\ C^2/kg^2$; **V.** Na^+ and Cl^-, each with an elementary charge; **W.** ten; **X.** zero; **Y.** 6×10^{24} kg; **Z.** water

PRACTICE

Worked and Guided Problems

These examples involve material from this chapter but are not associated with any particular section. Some examples are worked out in detail; others you should work out by following the guidelines provided.

Worked Problem 22.1 Mutual attraction

We often feel what is called a "physical attraction" to other people. If this were literally true and due to the electric force between two persons, one of them would have to carry surplus positive charge and the other would have to carry surplus negative charge. Suppose you and a friend stand 1 m apart and feel an attractive electric force of 10 N between you. Estimate the fraction q/q_{body} for each of you, where q is the surplus charge of a given type in either body and q_{body} is all the charge of that type in the body.

❶ **GETTING STARTED** We begin with a sketch of the physical situation (Figure WG22.1).

Figure WG22.1

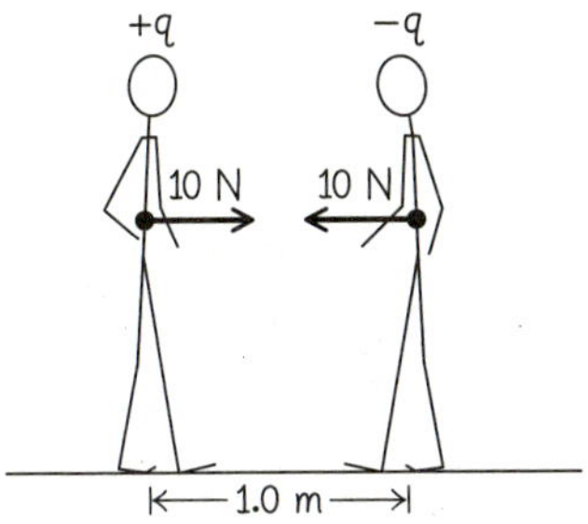

We first need to determine the amount of surplus charge q on each body that produces 10 N of force between the bodies, and to do this we must make some assumptions about where on each body that charge is located. We then need to estimate the number of charged particles of a given type in each body. These particles are the protons and electrons in the molecules of the body. Multiplying the number of particles by the elementary charge gives the charge q_{body} of that type in each body, and so we have the fraction we are asked to calculate. This solution will require many estimates.

❷ **DEVISE PLAN** We know the force magnitude and the separation distance between you and your friend. Let's assume you both have the same mass and equal amounts of surplus charge (though of opposite signs). Because it would be difficult to calculate the force if the charge were uniformly distributed throughout each body, we assume that all the charge in each body is concentrated at the body's center, with a center-to-center distance of 1 m. The human body is mostly water, H_2O (see Developing a Feel 6), and so dividing body mass by the mass of a water molecule gives us the number of water molecules in each body. Multiplying that number by the number of protons or electrons in each molecule gives us the charge of each type in the body.

❸ **EXECUTE PLAN** We use Coulomb's law to solve for the magnitude of the surplus charge q needed to produce the 10-N force:

$$F = k\frac{|(+q)(-q)|}{r^2}$$

$$q = \sqrt{\frac{Fr^2}{k}} = \sqrt{\frac{(10\ \text{N})(1\ \text{m})^2}{9.0 \times 10^9\ \text{N}\cdot\text{m}^2/\text{C}^2}} = 3.3 \times 10^{-5}\ \text{C}.$$

To determine the change q_{body} of a given type in each body, let's use 60 kg as a reasonable value for your mass. Each H_2O molecule contains ten protons and eight neutrons, for a mass of 3×10^{-26} kg, making the number of water molecules in your body

$$\frac{60\ \text{kg}}{3 \times 10^{-26}\ \text{kg}/\text{H}_2\text{O molecule}} = 2 \times 10^{27}\ \text{H}_2\text{O molecules in body.}$$

Each of these molecules contains ten protons (and ten electrons), so the charge q_{body} of a given type (positive or negative) in the body is

$$q_{body} \approx (2 \times 10^{27}\ \text{molecules})(10\ \text{elementary charges/molecule}) \times (1.6 \times 10^{-19}\ \text{C/elementary charge}) \approx 3 \times 10^9\ \text{C}.$$

Thus the fraction of surplus charge is

$$\frac{q}{q_{body}} \approx \frac{3.3 \times 10^{-5}\ \text{C}}{3 \times 10^9\ \text{C}} \approx 1 \times 10^{-14}. ✔$$

This is approximately one surplus electron (or proton) for every 10 trillion (10^{13}) water molecules!

❹ **EVALUATE RESULT** It is hard to estimate whether or not this answer is reasonable because most people do not have a good feel for the magnitudes of various electric forces in our world. In reality, of course, attractive electric forces are not felt between humans. The actual fraction of surplus charge in your body is essentially zero under normal conditions. However, you can observe some consequences of surplus body charge when you rub your feet on a carpet, transferring charge to your body. You might get a trillion or so surplus elementary charges in this case, for a surplus charge fraction of about 10^{-16}. What gives you a shock when you then touch a metal doorknob is this surplus charge leaving your body.

Guided Problem 22.2 Electroscope

In Figure WG22.2, two identical 0.017-kg spheres are attached to nonconducting threads affixed to the ceiling. Initially, the spheres touch each other (a), but then an equal amount of charge is put on each (by touching them, for instance, with a charged rod not shown in the drawing) (b). If each thread is 120 mm long and the spheres come to rest at a separation d = 93 mm, what is the electrical charge on each sphere?

Figure WG22.2

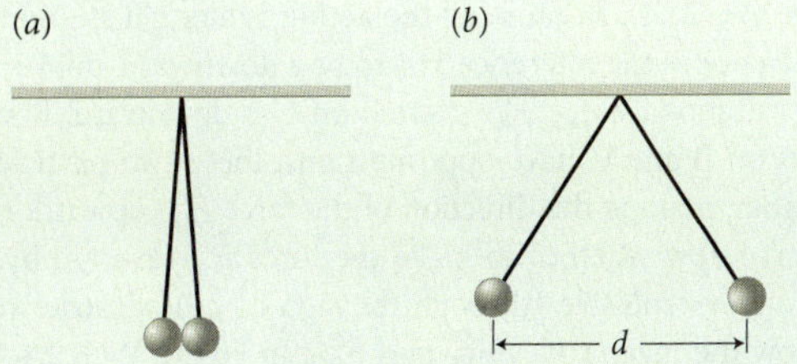

PRACTICE

❶ GETTING STARTED

1. In what sense is this problem similar to Worked Problem 22.1? In what sense is it different?
2. Why do the spheres push apart but then come to an equilibrium configuration? What forces produce this motion?

❷ DEVISE PLAN

3. Draw the free-body diagram for each sphere. List any assumptions you make.
4. What quantity do you need to know to decompose the forces into components?
5. Choose a coordinate system, and then decompose the forces into x and y components.

❸ EXECUTE PLAN

6. Solve for the desired electrical charge q. Avoid solving for intermediate quantities if possible.

❹ EVALUATE RESULT

7. Think about how q should depend on the separation distance d. Does your algebraic answer reflect this expectation?

Worked Problem 22.3 Levitation

One possible way of levitating an object might be to use the forces associated with charged objects. For example, suppose you have two charged spheres fixed 0.50 m apart on a vertical pole. The lower sphere carries a fixed charge of $-3.0\ \mu C$, and the upper one carries a charge that can be adjusted. A 30-g sphere carrying a charge of $+8.0\ \mu C$ can move freely on the pole below the other two. You want this sphere to levitate (float) 1.0 m below the $-3.0\text{-}\mu C$ sphere. What should the charge on the upper sphere be adjusted to in order to achieve this feat?

❶ GETTING STARTED As usual, we begin with a sketch of the situation (Figure WG22.3). Let's label the upper fixed-position sphere A, the other fixed-position sphere B, and the movable sphere C. Let's use q_A for the unknown adjustable charge on sphere A. In order for sphere C to float at the specified position, we need to balance the electric and gravitational forces exerted on this sphere so that their vector sum is zero. We assume we're near Earth, so that g is a constant $9.8\ m/s^2$. The gravitational forces between C and B and between C and A are much smaller than the electric force between the pairs (you should verify this), and so the only forces we need to consider are the gravitational force exerted by Earth on C, the attractive upward electric force exerted by B on C, and the electric force exerted by A on C.

Figure WG22.3

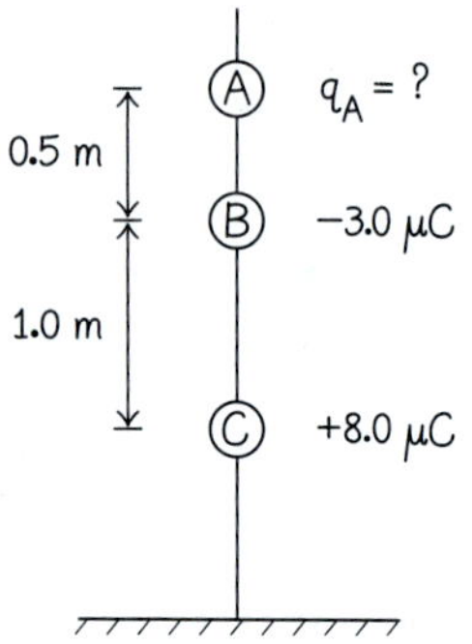

❷ DEVISE PLAN We want the vector sum of forces exerted on C to be zero. A free-body diagram is always helpful in force problems (Figure WG22.4). Because all the action is along a straight vertical line, we choose the reference axis to be a downward-pointing y axis. The gravitational force $\vec{F}^G_{EC}$ exerted on C is downward. Because the charges on B and C have opposite signs, these two particles attract each other, making the direction of the force $\vec{F}^E_{BC}$ upward. However, we don't know whether to make the force $\vec{F}^E_{AC}$ exerted by A on C attractive or repulsive (through the sign of q_A) because we do not yet know the magnitudes F^G_{EC} and F^E_{BC}. In Figure WG22.4, we draw the vector arrow for $\vec{F}^E_{AC}$ in the direction of our y axis, but we don't assume that its component along that axis is positive. It may point in the opposite direction, depending on the sign we calculate for q_A.

Figure WG22.4

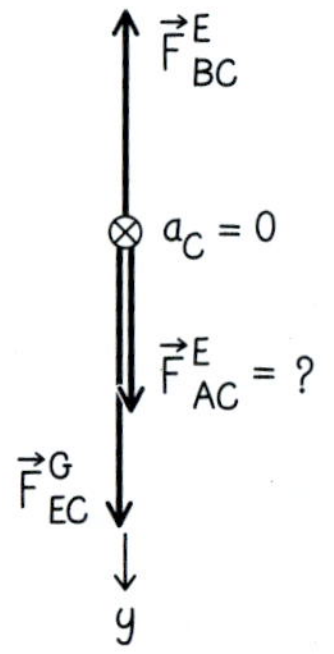

❸ EXECUTE PLAN For stable levitation ($a_C = 0$), we must have

$$\Sigma F_y = F^G_{ECy} + F^E_{BCy} + F^E_{ACy} = +F^G_{EC} + (-F^E_{BC}) \pm F^E_{AC} = 0.$$

We allow the final term to be either positive or negative because these are the only two options for the direction of $\vec{F}^E_{ACy}$. We can verify this by using the mathematical expression for the electric force (Eq. 22.7):

$$\vec{F}^E_{ACy} = k\frac{q_A q_C}{r^2_{AC}}(\hat{r}_{AC})_y.$$

Remembering that $\hat{r}_{AC}$ is the unit vector pointing from sphere A to sphere C, we see that $(\hat{r}_{AC})_y = +1$ in this coordinate system. The sign of the final term is thus determined by the sign of the unknown charge q_A. Thus

$$\Sigma F_y = +m_C g + \left[-k\frac{|q_B q_C|}{r^2_{BC}}\right] + \left[k\frac{q_A q_C}{r^2_{AC}}\right] = 0.$$

Solving for q_A and then substituting numerical values, we find

$$q_A = \frac{r^2_{AC}}{kq_C}\left(k\frac{|q_B q_C|}{r^2_{BC}} - m_C g\right) = \frac{r^2_{AC}}{r^2_{BC}}|q_B| - \frac{m_C g r^2_{AC}}{kq_C}$$

$$= \frac{(1.5\ m)^2}{(1.0\ m)^2}|-3.0 \times 10^{-6}\ C|$$

$$- \frac{(0.030\ kg)(9.8\ m/s^2)(1.5\ m)^2}{(9.0 \times 10^9\ N \cdot m^2/C^2)(8.0 \times 10^{-6}\ C)}$$

$$= -2.4 \times 10^{-6}\ C. ✔$$

This result shows us that we must put a negative charge on sphere A. This charge produces a force that is directed upward (attracting positively charged sphere C) and helps sphere B counteract the downward gravitational force exerted by Earth on C.

❹ EVALUATE RESULT Do we expect q_A to be negative, which makes $\vec{F}^E_{AC}$ attractive (aimed upward)? If we make rough estimates of our known force magnitudes, we see that $F^G_{EC} \approx 3 \times 10^{-1}$ N and $F^E_{BC} \approx 2 \times 10^{-1}$ N. Thus Earth pulls C down more than sphere B pulls it up, which means sphere A needs to supply an upward force to make the vector sum of the forces exerted on C be zero. With its negative $m_C g$ term, our expression for q_A correctly predicts the negative sign for q_A.

Is this system in stable or unstable equilibrium (see Section 15.4)? Does your answer to that question depend on the sign of q_A? As a further check of your understanding of the problem, re-derive the expression for q_A for the case where the charges on B and C have the same sign.

Guided Problem 22.4 Electron orbit

In the classical model of the hydrogen atom, a single electron orbits the single proton of the hydrogen's nucleus at a radius of 0.053 nm. *(a)* How fast is the electron moving? *(b)* How long does it take to complete one orbit?

❶ GETTING STARTED

1. Make a sketch showing the electron going around a circle and a proton fixed at the center of the circle.
2. Is the assumption that the proton is fixed justified?
3. What force or forces are exerted on the electron?

❷ DEVISE PLAN

4. Draw a free-body diagram for the electron.
5. Do you see any analogy between this problem and the topics discussed in Chapter 13?
6. What is the relationship between the electron's speed and the period of the orbit?

❸ EXECUTE PLAN

❹ EVALUATE RESULT

7. How does the electron's speed compare with the speed of light?

Worked Problem 22.5 Charge square

Four charged particles are arranged in a square as shown in Figure WG22.5. If $q = +3.9 \times 10^{-6}$ C and $a = 6.9$ mm, what is the vector sum of the forces exerted on particle D by the other three particles?

Figure WG22.5

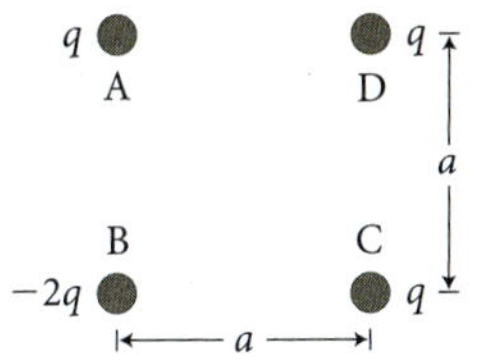

❶ GETTING STARTED This is an application of Coulomb's law, Eq. 22.7. We know all the charge magnitudes and the distances r_{AD} and r_{CD}, and we can use trigonometry to obtain the distance r_{BD}.

❷ DEVISE PLAN The first step is to draw Figure WG22.6, a free-body diagram of particle D. We can simplify the problem by choosing our axes to exploit symmetry, as shown. With the axes aligned this way, the force $\vec{F}^E_{BD}$ has no y component and the components F^E_{CDy} and F^E_{ADy} cancel each other. Thus all we need to calculate are the x components of the forces, which we get from Eq. 22.7.

Figure WG22.6

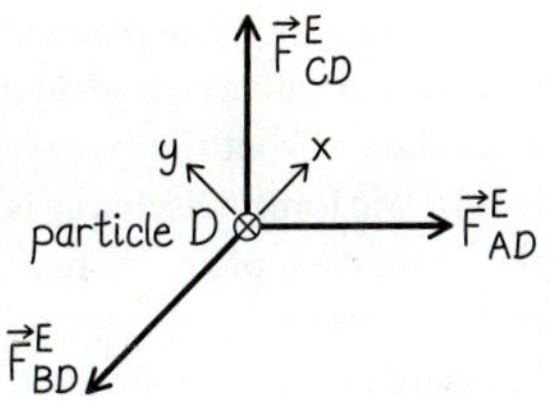

❸ EXECUTE PLAN The expression for the vector sum of the x components is

$$\begin{aligned}\Sigma F_{Dx} &= F^E_{ADx} + F^E_{BDx} + F^E_{CDx}\\ &= F^E_{AD}\cos 45° + (-F^E_{BD}) + F^E_{CD}\cos 45°\\ &= 2F^E_{AD}\cos 45° + (-F^E_{BD})\\ &= 2\left(k\frac{qq}{a^2}\right)\frac{\sqrt{2}}{2} - k\frac{(2q)q}{(\sqrt{2}a)^2}\\ &= k\frac{q^2}{a^2}(\sqrt{2} - 1)\\ &= (9.0 \times 10^9\ \mathrm{N \cdot m^2/C^2})\frac{(3.9 \times 10^{-6}\ \mathrm{C})^2}{(0.0069\ \mathrm{m})^2}(\sqrt{2} - 1)\\ &= 1.19 \times 10^3\ \mathrm{N} = 1.2\ \mathrm{kN},\end{aligned}$$

which means the vector sum of the forces exerted on D is a force of magnitude 1.2 kN directed along the positive x axis of our coordinate system. ✔

❹ EVALUATE RESULT Because two of the forces are repulsive and one is attractive, we expect to see terms of different signs in the algebraic answer. Reassuringly, we see that a *difference* of two terms is computed: the first term due to the two repulsive forces $\vec{F}^E_{AD}$ and $\vec{F}^E_{CD}$ and the second term due to the attractive force $\vec{F}^E_{BD}$. The computed force magnitude does seem large. However, the particles carry a sizable charge (remember, 1 C is a lot of charge) and they are close to one another.

Symmetry is a very powerful tool in approaching physics problems, and you should take advantage of it whenever possible.

Guided Problem 22.6 Charge pyramid

Six ions are locked in a square pyramidal structure as shown in Figure WG22.7. The length of each side of the pyramid is $a = 0.13$ nm, and the sixth (shown in green) ion is at the center of the base of the pyramid. Calculate the vector sum of the electric forces exerted on the top ion if each of the six ions is missing one electron.

Figure WG22.7

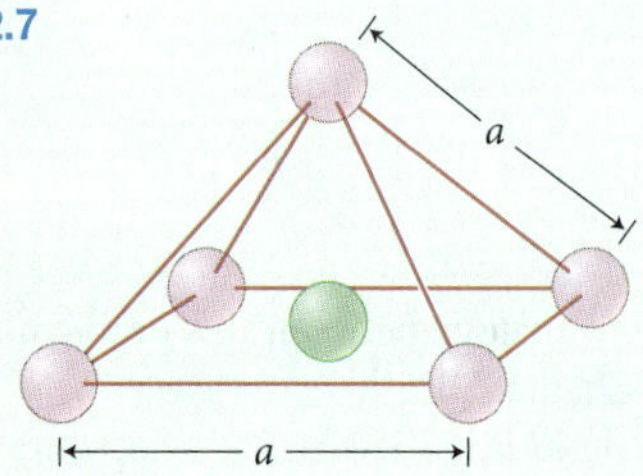

1 GETTING STARTED

1. What causes the electric force experienced by the top ion?
2. Look for any symmetry you can exploit to make the problem simpler. Remember that this is a three-dimensional situation.
3. What is the amount of surplus charge on each ion?

2 DEVISE PLAN

4. Which equations allow you to express the electric force experienced by the top ion in terms of known quantities?
5. Can the problem be reduced from three dimensions to two by an appropriate choice of coordinate axes?

3 EXECUTE PLAN

6. Write an algebraic expression for the electric force you are seeking, and then substitute known values to get a numerical result.

4 EVALUATE RESULT

7. Compare your numerical answer to the electric force between two protons a distance *a* apart.

Questions and Problems

For instructor-assigned homework, go to MasteringPhysics® MP

Dots indicate difficulty level of problems: • = easy, •• = intermediate, ••• = hard; CR = context-rich problem.

22.1 Static electricity

1. A piece of tape is pulled from a spool and lowered toward a 100-mg scrap of paper. Only when the tape comes within 8.0 mm is the electric force magnitude great enough to overcome the gravitational force exerted by Earth on the scrap and lift it. Determine the magnitude and direction of the electric force exerted by the tape on the paper at this distance. •
2. A baseball bat is placed on a table such that the narrow end of the bat hangs over the edge. Two freshly pulled strips of tape are hung from opposite sides of the overhanging end of the bat. The strips repel each other so that they hang in the air in an inverted V shape, with an angle of about 50° between the strips. Describe at least three things you could do to reduce the angle between the hanging strips. •
3. A plastic spring with spring constant $k = 450$ N/m has a relaxed length of 0.100 m. The spring is positioned vertically on a table, and a charged plastic 1.00-kg sphere is placed on the top end of the spring. Another charged object is suspended above the sphere without making contact. If the length of the spring is now 0.0950 m, what are the magnitude and direction of the electric force exerted on the sphere? ••

PRACTICE

22.2 Electrical charge

4. Two small objects carry the same amount of charge, and the magnitude of the electric force exerted by one object on the other is 0.10 N when they are held 30 mm apart. If the force magnitude increases when the objects are released and free to move, are the objects of the same charge or opposite charge? •
5. How might the results from electrostatic experiments with tape strips described in *Principles* Section 22.2 differ from those actually observed if there were three types of electrical charges in the universe? ••
6. If you must do positive work to bring a charged balloon toward a negatively charged sphere, is the charge on the balloon positive or negative? ••
7. Suppose you have three identical, electrically neutral pieces of tape, A, B, and C. (*a*) Describe how you could make two of them repel each other. (*b*) Is it possible for all three to repel one another? ••
8. Suppose that in Figure P22.8, $|q_2| > |q_1| > 0$ but these particles may carry charges of the same or opposite type. A third particle carrying charge q_3 is to be placed in this system along the axis such that the vector sum of electric forces on the third particle is zero. In which region—I, II, or III—might this be possible if (*a*) q_1 and q_2 have the same sign and (*b*) q_1 and q_2 have opposite signs? (*c*) Under what circumstances can the third particle be placed in region I and have the vector sum of electric forces exerted on it be zero? ••

Figure P22.8

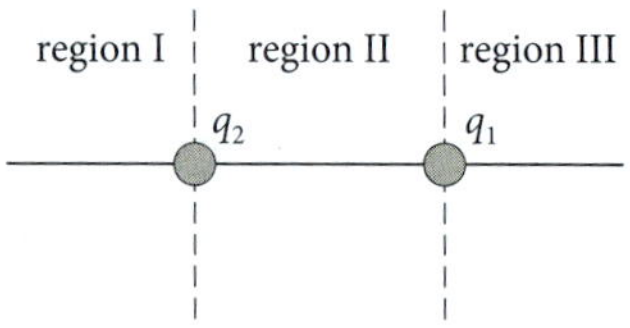

9. A salvage yard operator wants to make an electric force linkage for his wrecker crane as a safety device, so that when a vehicle being lifted is too massive, it will break the linkage before the force exerted by the vehicle topples the crane. His plan is to attach two metal plates to the crane cable as shown in Figure P22.9 and connect the plates to the crane's power system. There is to be a positive charge on one plate and a negative charge on the other, so that the two stick together because of the attractive electric force. Discharge is prevented by spraying a layer of plastic on each plate. He needs to know what diameter to make the plates so that they come apart when the vehicle being lifted has a mass greater than 2000 kg. On the micro level, the electric force is between a surface atom carrying surplus

positive charge on one plate and a surface atom carrying surplus negative charge on the other plate. The electric force for each atom pair has a magnitude of 2.3×10^{-12} N, and each atom occupies an area of 3×10^{-21} m^2. (*a*) Before doing any calculations, estimate the necessary plate surface area. Which is this surface area comparable to: that of a pinhead, a fingernail, a music compact disc, a dinner plate, or a manhole cover? (*b*) Calculate the necessary area. How accurate was your estimate as to which object the plate area is comparable to? •••

Figure P22.9

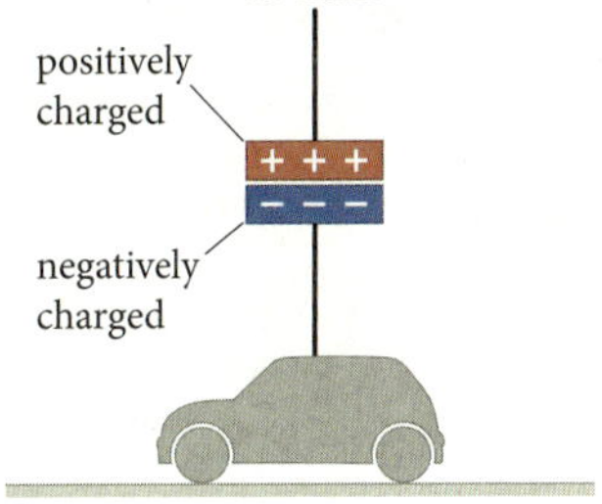

22.3 Mobility of charge carriers

10. Which of the following phenomena are due to the electric interaction: (*a*) dissolution of salt in water, (*b*) surface tension in water, (*c*) the elliptical orbit of comets, (*d*) the binding of protons in an atomic nucleus, (*e*) "traction" between tires and pavement. •

11. Technicians who repair electronic devices know that a spark can damage electronic chips. They therefore wear a wriststrap connected by a metal wire to the metal leg of a worktable that is electrically "grounded" to Earth. How does wearing such a strap help prevent damage? •

12. You have two rods A and B, both made of a nonconducting material. Initially, neither rod is charged. A sphere carrying 100 units of surplus positive charge is placed close to the left end of rod A. One end of rod B is touched to the right end of rod A for some time interval and then removed. What is the final charge on rod B? •

13. Some survivors of lightning strikes have reported feeling their hair standing on end shortly before the strike. What causes the hair to behave in this way? •

14. A closed system consists of a neutron and a positron. The neutron eventually decays. After decay, what are the most likely particles in the system, and what is the charge in the system? (Use the principle of conservation of charge.) ••

15. Two identical 500-mg paper clips, 1 and 2, dangle from two strings, the top ends of which are tied to the same nail. The clips are charged in such a way that the two strings hang with an angle of 32.0° between them. (*a*) Draw a free-body diagram for clip 1, which is to the left of clip 2. (*b*) What are the magnitude and direction of the electric force exerted by one clip on the other? (*c*) If the two clips were brought in contact with each other for an instant and then released, might they discharge into each other and no longer repel? ••

16. A pith ball is suspended from a string, and when a rubber rod is brought close to the ball at $t = 0$, the ball is not noticeably affected by the rod. At $t = 5.00$ s the rod is turned around such that the opposite end is nearest the ball. Now the ball is attracted to the rod. At $t = 10.0$ s the rod and ball are brought into contact. Draw a charge-versus-time graph showing a plausible charge magnitude on the rod in the time interval from $t = 0$ to $t = 15$ s. ••

17. At separation distance r_1, charged Ping-Pong balls A and B repel each other with an electric force of magnitude 0.40 N. At separation distance r_2, charged Ping-Pong balls A and C repel each other with a force of magnitude 1.4 N. Maintaining the separation distances r_1 and r_2, how should you arrange B and C around A (*a*) to create the maximum electric force exerted on A and (*b*) to create the minimum electric force exerted on A? ••

18. A metal sphere is grounded via a single wire. One end of a plastic rod is given a positive charge and held near the sphere. (*a*) If the ground wire is removed while the rod and sphere are near each other but have not touched, is there an electric force between the two? Why or why not? (*b*) If the rod end is brought in contact with the sphere and then the ground wire is removed, is there an electric force between rod and sphere after they are separated? Why or why not? •••

22.4 Charge polarization

19. A rubber rod exerts no electric force on a small scrap of paper. After it is rubbed on cat fur for several seconds, the rod exerts an attractive force on the scrap. Is the force exerted by the fur on the same scrap attractive or repulsive? •

20. Three small pieces of electrically neutral paper are placed far apart from one another on a table. One piece is given a negative electric charge, one is given a positive charge, and one is left neutral. They all look identical, and in order to tell which is which, a student runs a comb through her hair and waves the comb over each piece. She observes that one is strongly attracted to the comb; she labels this A. She observes that another is weakly attracted to the comb; she labels this B. The last piece, which is repelled by the comb; she labels C. Which piece is positive, which is negative, and which is neutral? •

21. The electrically neutral metal rod in Figure P22.21 stands between two charged pith balls, and then a negatively charged rubber rod is scraped along the center of the metal rod. Draw the free-body diagram for each ball after the rubber rod is taken away. •

Figure P22.21

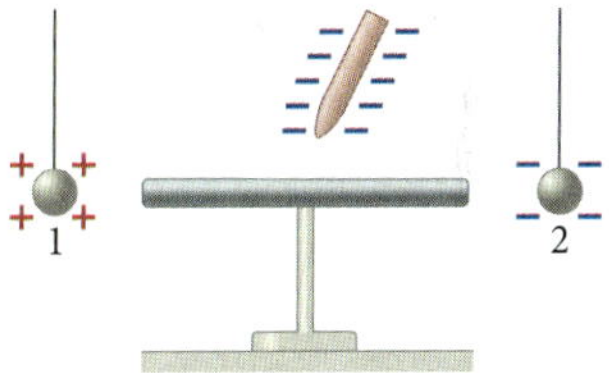

22. A charged sphere with 1×10^8 units of negative charge is brought near a neutral metal rod. The half of the rod closer to the sphere has a surplus charge of 1×10^4 units. What is the magnitude of the charge on the half of the rod farther from the sphere? Is this charge positive or negative? •

23. Near one end of an electrically neutral aluminum rod lying on a table made of nonconducting material, you hold a comb that is also made of a nonconducting material but carries a positive charge (Figure P22.23). Does a small steel sphere located near the other end of the rod roll toward the rod, roll away from the rod, or stay where it is if the sphere is (*a*) electrically neutral and (*b*) positively charged? ••

Figure P22.23

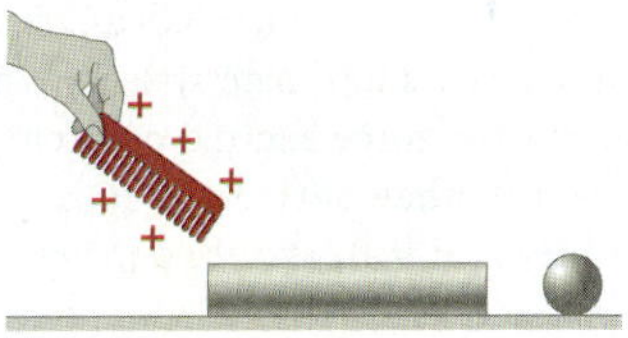

PRACTICE

24. Two metal rods A and B are initially lying end to end on a wooden table and are touching each other. A sphere carrying surplus positive charge is brought close to the middle of rod A. While the sphere is still in place, the rods are pulled apart by someone wearing gloves made of a fabric that is an electrical insulator. Then the sphere is moved far away. (*a*) Do the two rods attract each other, do they repel each other, or is there no electric force between them? (*b*) Describe the surplus charge on each rod as positive, zero, or negative. ••

25. You have three pairs of spheres. Pair A consists of two conducting spheres, pair B of two nonconducting spheres, and pair C of one nonconducting sphere and one conducting sphere. If all spheres have the same charge q added to them and in each pair the two spheres are separated by the same distance d, rate the magnitude of the electric force between the two spheres of each pair when q is (*a*) positive on both spheres, (*b*) negative on both, and (*c*) positive on one sphere in the pair and negative on the other. ••

26. Metal sphere A is hung from the ceiling by a long, thin string and given a positive charge. An identical sphere B is suspended nearby with an identical string and given a *negative* charge that has the same magnitude as the charge on A. The two spheres are 50 mm apart when in equilibrium. If an identical sphere C carrying no surplus charge is placed between them, does the distance between A and B increase, decrease, or remain the same? ••

27. You are an astrophysicist working on a problem involving Saturn's rings and trying to figure out why the larger ice chunks in the rings stick to smaller chunks. You hypothesize that as the chunks come out of the shadow of Saturn into the sunlight, the outside of the larger chunks heats up sooner than the center and this temperature difference creates a nonuniform distribution of the charged particles in the larger chunks. (Charge polarization due to temperature differences is known as the "thermoelectric effect.") Then, even though the chunk is electrically neutral, it has a charge separation. The small ice chunks presumably heat up uniformly all the way through and hence are not affected. Explain why small chunks gradually stick to larger ones. •••

22.5 Coulomb's law

28. Suppose you have three identical metal spheres, A, B, and C. Initially sphere A carries a charge q and the others are uncharged. Sphere A is brought in contact with sphere B, and then the two are separated. Spheres C and B are then brought in contact and separated. Finally spheres A and C are brought in contact and then separated. What is the final charge on each sphere, in terms of q? •

29. Two electrons are separated by 1.50 nm. What is the magnitude of the electric force each electron exerts on the other? Is this force attractive or repulsive? •

30. Two particles carrying charges q_1 and q_2 are separated by a distance r and exert an electric force $\vec{F}^E$ on each other. If q_1 is doubled, what change must you make to one of the other variables in order to keep the magnitude F^E constant? There is more than one answer. •

31. A particle carrying a -4.0-μC charge is located at the origin of an xy coordinate system. What are the components of the electric force exerted on a particle carrying a $+1.0$-μC charge if that particle is located (*a*) at $x = 10$ m, $y = 0$ and (*b*) at $x = 0$, $y = -6.0$ m? •

32. (*a*) By what distance do two objects carrying 1.0 C of charge each have to be separated before the electric force exerted on each object is 1.0 N? (*b*) How much charge should be placed on each of two small objects separated by 1.0 m so that the electric force exerted on each is 1.0 N? •

33. In a chamber 0.300 m high, sphere 1 carrying charge $q_1 = 1.00\ \mu$C is suspended by a spring above a sphere 2 that carries charge q_2 and sits on the floor of the chamber (Figure P22.33). The relaxed length of the suspended spring is 70.0 mm, its spring constant is 30.0 N/m, and the mass of sphere 1 is 5.00 g. If sphere 1 comes to rest 0.200 m above the floor (and above sphere 2), what is the value of q_2? ••

Figure P22.33

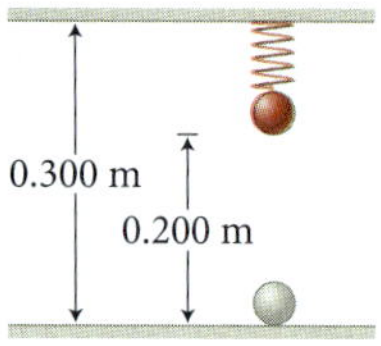

34. Two identical 9.60-g metal spheres (small enough to be treated as particles) are hung from separate 300-mm strings attached to the same nail in a ceiling. Surplus electrons are added to each sphere, and then the spheres are brought in contact with each other and released. Their equilibrium position is such that each string makes a 13.0° angle with the vertical. How many surplus electrons are on each sphere? ••

35. Suppose two particles carry a positive charge of 1.00 C for every kilogram of their mass. Compare the gravitational force and the electric force they exert on each other at a given separation. ••

36. Two metal spheres, one carrying a 6.0-μC charge and the other carrying a -24-μC charge, are initially 100 mm apart. They are brought in contact with each other and then moved back to their original positions. What is the numerical value of the ratio F_i^E/F_f^E, where F_i^E is the magnitude of the electric force between the spheres before they are brought in contact and F_f^E is the magnitude of that force after they are brought together and then moved back to their initial positions? ••

37. The device in Figure P22.37 is a so-called Newton's cradle. When you raise steel sphere 1 and then release it, its momentum is transferred to the other four steel spheres, and this momentum transfer causes sphere 5 to rise. When it falls, momentum is again transferred through the row of spheres, and sphere 1 rises and falls, and so on. Imagine modifying the device by positioning a charged wire in such a way that every time each end steel sphere rises, it touches the wire and acquires 10 units of charge. You lift sphere 1 and allow it to touch the wire for the first time and acquire 10 units of charge. You release the sphere and it hits the others, transferring its

Figure P22.37

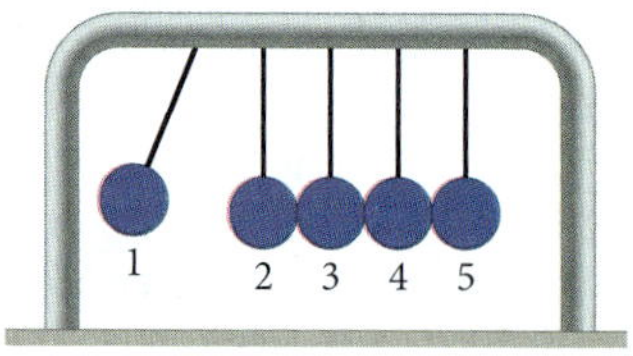

momentum and causing sphere 5 to rise. Sphere 5 touches the charged wire, descends, hits the row of spheres, and transfers its momentum so that sphere 1 rises again and touches the wire for the second time. How many units of charge does sphere 1 carry (*a*) just before it touches the wire this second time and (*b*) just before it touches the wire after one more round of this momentum-transfer motion? ••

38. Two 1.00-kg spheres carry identical charges and are placed a distance d from each other. (*a*) How large should the charge on each sphere be so that the repulsive electric force between them balances the attractive gravitational force between them? (*b*) What is the smallest mass that can balance in this way, given that the smallest possible charge is $e = 1.602 \times 10^{-19}$ C? (*c*) Why doesn't the distance between the balls affect this calculation? ••

39. A charged oil drop that has a mass of 5.00×10^{-12} kg and carries 10 elementary charges is centered 50 mm below the center of an oppositely charged sphere that has a radius of 5.0 mm. What charge should the sphere be given so that the electric force it exerts on the drop causes the drop to float in the air for an instant? Treat the drop as a particle. ••

40. In the Bohr model, a hydrogen atom consists of an electron orbiting a one-proton nucleus. (*a*) Derive an algebraic expression for the relationship between the electron's speed v and the radius R_{orbit} of its orbit. (*b*) Review the derivation of Kepler's third law in *Principles* Chapter 13 (page 310), and derive a corollary that relates the period T of the electron's orbital motion and the orbit radius R_{orbit}. ••

41. You scrunch up three same-size sheets of aluminum foil to form three balls 1, 2, and 3, and stick each one onto the end of a wooden stake (which allows you to transport the balls without touching them). You place the stakes holding balls 1 and 2 an arm's length apart and then give each ball charge q. Call the electric force between them $\vec{F}^E_{12}$. You then place charge $-2q$ on ball 3 and bring it first in contact with ball 1. Then you move it away from ball 1 and bring it in contact with ball 2. (*a*) Once you have moved ball 3 far away from balls 1 and 2, what is the magnitude, in terms of F^E_{12}, of the electric force between balls 1 and 2? (*b*) Has the direction of $\vec{F}^E_{12}$ changed? ••

42. (*a*) Draw and label the electric force exerted on each of the charged spheres in Figure P22.42 and compute their magnitudes. The centers of the spheres are separated by 0.11 m. (*b*) Repeat the problems, drawing to the same scale, if the charge on the left sphere is $-6.30\ \mu$C. ••

Figure P22.42

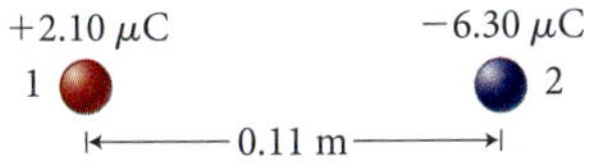

43. Sphere A carries 6.0 nC of charge. It is placed 100 mm from sphere B, which carries 3.0 nC of charge. Assume the spheres are much smaller than their separation distance. (*a*) What is the magnitude of the electric force exerted on A? (*b*) Draw a figure showing the charges and the electric force vectors on each sphere. (*c*) Draw and label $\vec{r}_{AB}$ on your diagram. ••

44. You have two marbles, one carrying a uniformly distributed charge $q_p = +1.0\ \mu$C and the other carrying a uniformly distributed charge $q_n = -0.50\ \mu$C. (*a*) What is the magnitude of the electric force between them when they are held 100 mm apart? (*b*) What happens when the marbles are released and so are free to move? (*c*) If the marbles are metallic and share charge when they come in contact with each other, what is the magnitude of the electric force between them when they are again moved 100 mm apart, assuming no charge is transferred either to or from the surroundings of the two-marble system? ••

45. Two charged particles 3.0 m apart exert on each other an attractive electric force of magnitude 8.0×10^{-3} N. If the charge on the two particles sums to 6.0 μC, what is the charge on each particle? ••

46. Determine the magnitude and direction of the electric force exerted by a 25-nC charged particle located at the origin of a Cartesian coordinate system on a 20-nC charged particle located at (2.0 m, 2.0 m). Draw a diagram illustrating the various quantities in your calculation. ••

47. The electric force between two identical positively charged ions is 3.7×10^{-9} N when they are 0.50 nm apart. How many electrons are missing from each of the original atoms? ••

48. Two particles 1 and 2, each carrying 71 pC of charge, are released from rest on a nonconducting, low-friction track. Particle 1 accelerates initially at 7.0 m/s^2. Particle 2, which has a mass of 0.49 mg, accelerates initially at 9.0 m/s^2. (*a*) What is the mass of particle 1? (*b*) What is the separation distance between the particles at the instant they are released? ••

49. Two identical lightweight conducting balls are suspended by thin strings of identical length from a common point. One of the balls is given a charge q, and both are constrained in their motion by only the tension in the strings, gravity, and air resistance. (*a*) Describe the behavior of the balls from the instant the first one is charged. (*b*) Determine q in terms of m, the mass of the balls, ℓ, the length of the strings, d, the final distance between the balls, and any necessary constants. •••

50. Suppose you want to use a repulsive electric force to launch a rocket. (*a*) How much charge do you need to create enough repulsion to bring a 100,000-kg rocket to escape speed (11,200 m/s) while the rocket travels 100 mm? Assume that two identical charged objects, one mounted on the rocket, are separated by an average distance of 1.0 m for the whole launch. (*b*) If each elementary charge requires adding mass equivalent to the mass of one hydrogen atom to the rocket, how much additional mass would be required? •••

51. Two metal spheres carry a charge and exert an electric force on each other. Sphere A carries $2n$ more surplus electrons than sphere B, where n is a positive integer. The two spheres are brought into electrical contact and then returned to their initial separation. Is the electric force between them increased, decreased, or unaffected? •••

52. (*a*) Prove that the repulsive electric force between two charged particles is a maximum when each particle carries charge $q/2$, where q is the sum of the charges carried by the two particles. (*b*) Explain why this is *not* true for the attractive electric force between charged particles. •••

22.6 Force exerted by distributions of charge carriers

53. Particle 1 carrying charge $+4q$ is fixed at the origin of a rectangular coordinate system, particle 2 carrying charge $-q$ is fixed 15.0° above the positive horizontal axis, and particle 3 carrying charge $-q$ is fixed 15.0° below the positive horizontal axis (Figure P22.53). Particles 2 and 3 are both 2.00 m from the origin. You must add two charged particles to the system in such a way that the vector sum of the electric forces exerted on particle 1 is zero. What quantity of which type of charge must each added particle carry, and at what locations must you place the particles? •

Figure P22.53

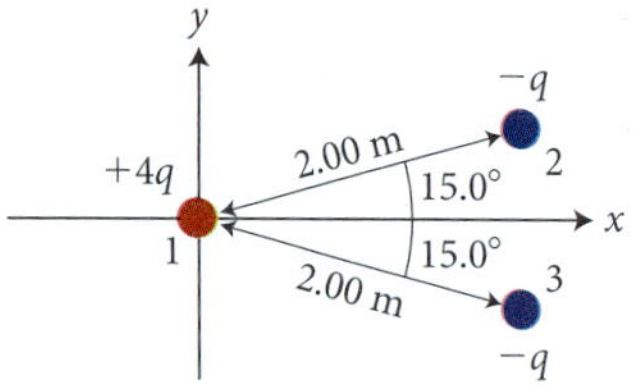

54. Particle 1 carrying $-4.0\ \mu C$ of charge is fixed at the origin of an xy coordinate system, particle 2 carrying $+6.0\ \mu C$ of charge is located on the x axis at $x = 3.0$ m, and particle 3, identical to particle 2, is located on the x axis at $x = -3.0$ m. What is the vector sum of the electric forces exerted on particle 3? •

55. Cesium chloride (CsCl) is a crystalline salt that forms in a cubic lattice structure, which you can imagine as a cube with Cs^+ ions at the eight corners and a Cl^- ion at the center. The edge length of the cube is 412 pm. Suppose that at the edge of a crystal, two cesium atoms have been stripped from adjacent corners of a cube, as shown in Figure P22.55. What is the vector sum of the electric forces exerted on the chloride ion by the six Cs^+ ions remaining in the cube? •

Figure P22.55

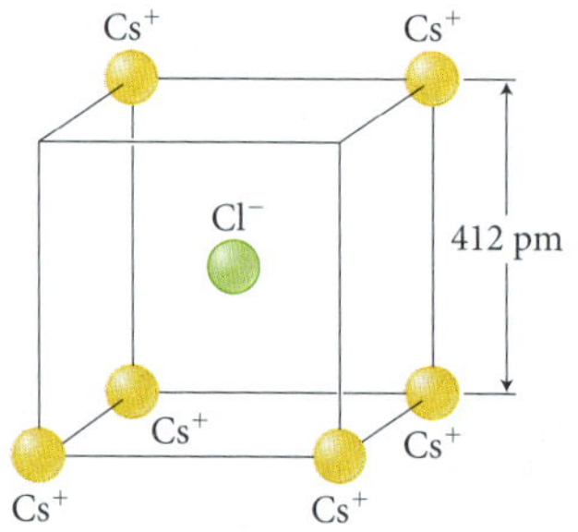

56. An xyz coordinate system contains three charged particles: particle 1, $q_1 = -5.0\ \mu C$, at (4.0 m, −2.0 m, 0); particle 2, $q_2 = 12\ \mu C$, at (1.0 m, 2.0 m, 0); and an electron at (−1.0 m, 0, 0). (*a*) Draw a diagram showing the vectors you need in order to determine the direction of the separate electric forces exerted on the electron by particles 1 and 2. (*b*) Calculate the vector sum of these two forces. ••

57. Particle 1 carrying charge q is at the origin of an xy coordinate system, particle 2 carrying charge $-2q$ is at (1, 0), and particle 3 carrying charge $3q$ is at (0, 1). What is the angle with respect to the x axis of the electric force exerted on a particle 4 carrying charge q and located at (2, 0)? (Hint: Use simple geometry and ratios.) ••

58. Charged particles 1, 2, and 3 ($q_1 = 10.0\ \mu C$, $q_2 = -5.00\ \mu C$, and $q_3 = -3.00\ \mu C$) are arranged in an equilateral triangle in an xy coordinate system. Particle 1 is at (0, 0), particle 2 at (1.0 m, 0), and particle 3 at (0.50 m, $\sqrt{3}/2$ m). Determine the magnitude and direction of the electric force exerted on particle 3. ••

59. Four negatively charged particles each carry a charge q_n and form a square of side length d. A positively charged particle carrying a charge q_p is at the square's center. If the arrangement is in equilibrium (the vector sum of the electric forces on each particle is zero), what is the numerical value of the ratio q_p/q_n? ••

60. Particle 1 carrying 2.0 μC of charge is fixed at the origin of a rectangular coordinate system, particle 2 carrying $-1.0\ \mu C$ is fixed 45° above the positive horizontal axis 2.0 mm from the origin, and particle 3 carrying $-1.0\ \mu C$ is fixed 45° below the horizontal axis 2.0 mm from the origin. Where in the system should you place a particle 4 carrying $-2.0\ \mu C$ so that the vector sum of the electric forces exerted on particle 1 is zero? ••

61. For the charge distribution in Figure P22.61, what is the ratio of the magnitude of the electric force exerted by particle 2 on particle 1 to the magnitude of the electric force exerted by particle 3 on particle 1? ••

Figure P22.61

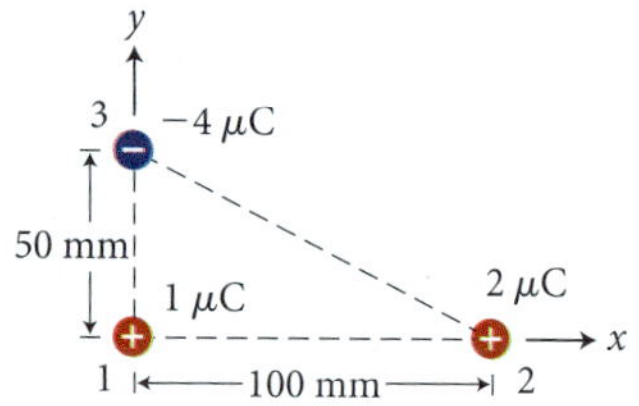

62. For the charge configuration shown in Figure P22.62, what is the vector sum of the electric forces exerted on particle 3? ••

Figure P22.62

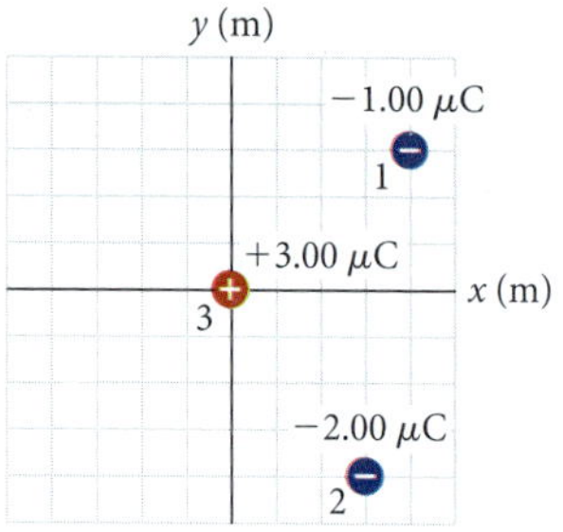

63. Two particles, each carrying charge $-q$, are fixed at opposite corners of a square, and a third particle, carrying charge $+q$, is fixed at a third corner (Figure P22.63). (*a*) Draw an arrow representing the vector sum of the forces exerted on a particle carrying charge $+q$ as it is placed first at position A, then at position B, and then at position C. (*b*) Sketch the trajectory of this particle if it is released at each of these three positions. ••

PRACTICE

Figure P22.63

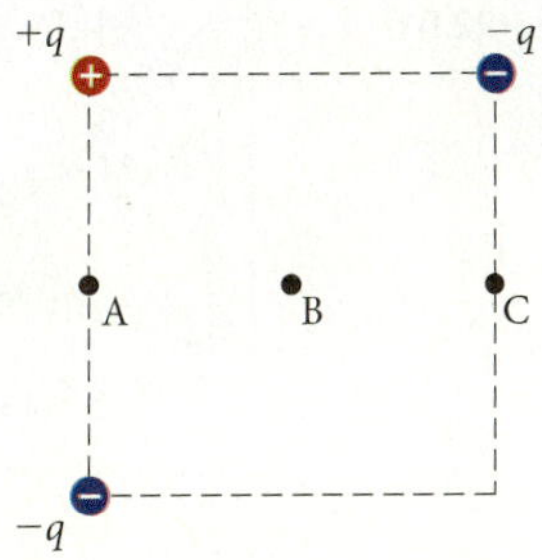

64. Two particles are located on the x axis of a Cartesian coordinate system. Particle 1 carries a charge of $+2.0$ nC and is at $x = -30$ mm, and particle 2 carries a charge of -2.0 nC and is at $x = 30$ mm. What are the magnitude and direction of the vector sum of the electric forces exerted by these two particles on particle 3, which carries a charge of $+5.0\ \mu$C and is located on the positive y axis 80 mm from the origin? ••

65. Particle 1 carrying charge $4q$ is fixed at the origin of an xy coordinate system, and particle 2 carrying charge q is fixed at (0, 0.12 m). Particle 3 carrying 2.0 μC of charge can move along the y axis. This particle experiences zero electric force when at $y = 0.080$ m and an electric force of 126.4 N $\hat{\jmath}$ when at $y = 0.040$ m. What is the value of q? ••

66. Conducting spheres 1, 2, and 3 are placed at three corners of a square. Spheres 1 and 2 at opposing corners are very small and oppositely charged, and the magnitude of the charge on negatively charged sphere 1 is twice the magnitude of the charge on positively charged sphere 2. Sphere 3 is much larger than the other two and electrically neutral. (*a*) Draw the three spheres, showing the approximate distribution of charge on sphere 3. (*b*) Sketch a free-body diagram for sphere 2. ••

67. You are working as an engineer designing ink-jet printers. Your boss has come across a printer design that involves a charged drop of ink experiencing a force exerted by 100 small, fixed charged particles. As shown in Figure P22.67, the particles are arranged in a ring of radius 6.00 mm, and each carries a charge of 1.00 nC. The ink drop is released at a point 6.00 mm away from the plane of the ring and along the central axis running perpendicular to the plane of the ring. Your boss gives up on calculating the initial force exerted on the charged drop, but you take one look at the setup and realize you can do the calculation in less than a minute. (*a*) Explain how you can do the calculation so quickly, even though it involves 100 separate forces. (*b*) Determine the magnitude and direction of the initial force exerted on a drop that carries a charge of 8.00 nC. (*c*) If the printer adds to each drop of ink a charge equal to 1.00 C per kilogram of ink mass, what is the initial acceleration of each drop? •••

Figure P22.67

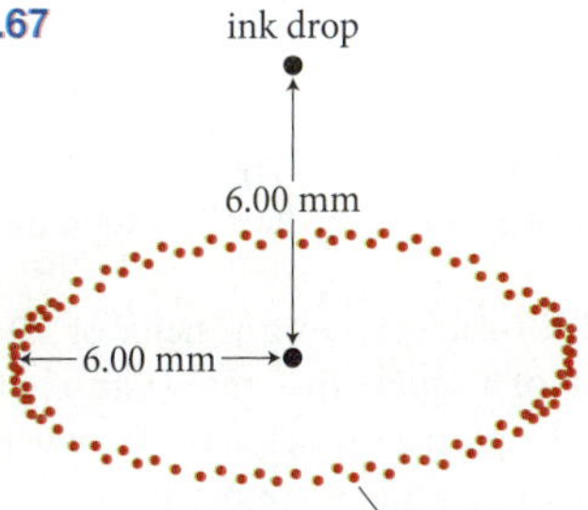

68. A 0.160-kg hockey puck modified to hold $+50\ \mu$C of charge is placed at one end of an ice hockey rink that is 61 m long. At the other end of the rink is a device capable of generating a charge of -0.10 C, but only for a short time interval. The coefficient of kinetic friction between ice and puck is $\mu_k = 0.015$. The puck is given a tiny nudge (just enough to get it moving but at a speed of nearly 0, which means you can ignore static friction), and then the charge generator is turned on for 100 ms. (*a*) Is the puck able to reach the generator? (*b*) If so, what is the puck's speed when it arrives at the generator? (For both parts, assume the 100-ms time interval is short enough to allow you to assume that the distance between the puck and the charge generator is constant.) •••

69. Two particles 1 and 2, each carrying 6.0 nC of charge, are located along an x axis, one particle at $x = -30$ mm and the other at $x = 30$ mm. Where along the y axis is a particle 3 carrying a charge of $+2.0$ nC if it experiences an electric force of 6.9×10^{-5} N $\hat{\jmath}$? •••

70. Figure P22.70 shows strips of transparent tape repelling each other. Use information given on the packaging of a roll of transparent tape to estimate what fraction of the atoms in either strip lose an electron in order to produce the repulsive effect. (Assume that the material of the tape is mostly carbon and hydrogen atoms present in a 1:2 ratio.) •••

Figure P22.70

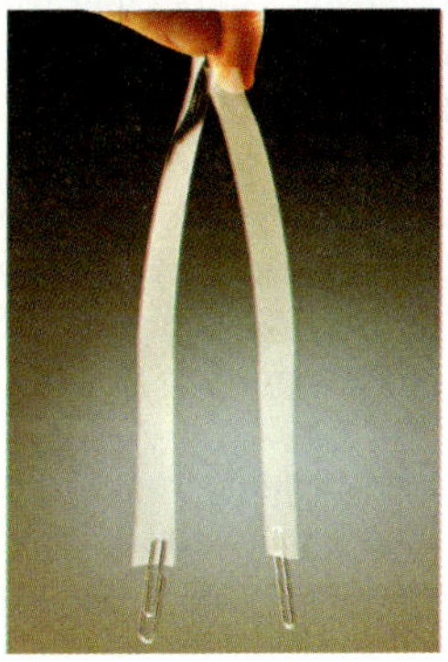

Additional problems

71. If electrons move easily in electrical conductors, why aren't pieces of metal usually negatively charged on the bottom and positively charged on top, due to gravitational settling of the electrons? •

72. Metals are often good thermal conductors as well as good electrical conductors. In fact, usually the better a metal is as a thermal conductor, the better it is as an electrical conductor. Give a physical explanation for this. •

73. Suppose a glass rod is rubbed on wool. When held 35.0 mm above a 0.20-g scrap of paper, the rod lifts the paper with an initial acceleration of 0.14 m/s^2. Calculate the magnitude and direction of the electric force exerted by the rod on the scraps. •

74. Three identical conducting spheres, A, B, and C, are given different initial charges. Sphere A, which initially carries 12 units of negative charge, is brought in contact with sphere B, which initially has 4 units of negative charge. Then sphere B is brought into contact with sphere C, which is initially neutral. What is the final charge ratio A:C? •

75. Particle A carrying a 4.0-μC charge is located at $y = 3.0$ m on the y axis of an xy coordinate system, and particle B carrying a 6.0-μC charge is located at the origin. What are the magnitude and direction of the electric force exerted (*a*) on A and (*b*) on B? •

76. Protons and neutrons are made up of particles called quarks. The particles known as up quarks carry a charge of $2e/3$, and those known as down quarks carry a charge of $-e/3$. How could you assemble a proton from up and down quarks to account for its charge? How could you assemble a neutron? ••

77. Three charged particles are arranged along a line as in Figure P22.77. If particle 2 experiences zero electric force, what is the charge on particle 3? ••

Figure P22.77

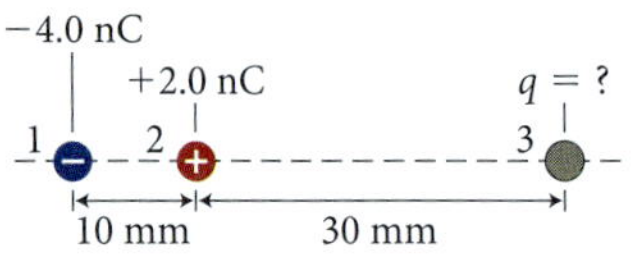

78. Four identical charged particles are constrained along an x axis. Identify one possible configuration of the particles that would leave one of them at rest at the origin when the others are fixed in place. No two charged particles can be at the same location. ••

79. (*a*) A particle carrying charge $+q$ is located at the center of a square with sides of length ℓ. Given four particles, two carrying charge $+q$ and two carrying charge $-q$, how should you place them at the four corners of the square, with one particle at each corner, such that the vector sum of the electric forces exerted on the center particle is zero? (*b*) If you leave the corner particles in the arrangement determined in part *a* but move the center particle to the midpoint of one side of the square, what are the magnitude and direction of the vector sum of the forces exerted on this particle? ••

80. A small charged sphere hanging from a thin string next to an oppositely charged plate experiences a 2.3-N attractive electric force (Figure P22.80). If the string makes an angle of 3.6° with the vertical, what is the mass of the sphere? ••

Figure P22.80

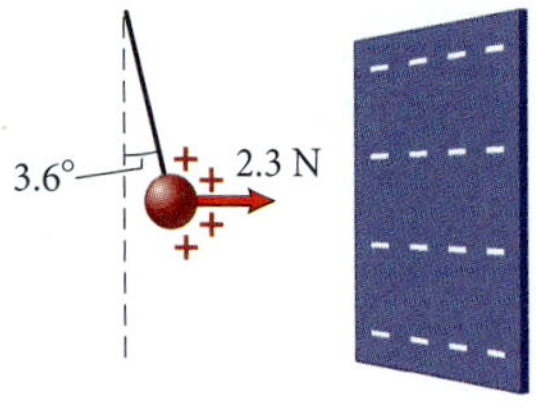

81. The accelerometer in a certain video game controller is constructed as shown in Figure P22.81. A block made of material that is an electrical conductor is grounded by a small stretched spring and is constrained to sliding along a rail. A nonconducting, positively charged block is fixed in position on the rail. When the magnitude of the electric force between the blocks is 0.100 N, the spring makes a 45.0° angle with the wall and is stretched 3.00 mm from its equilibrium position. What is the spring constant? Ignore friction. ••

Figure P22.81

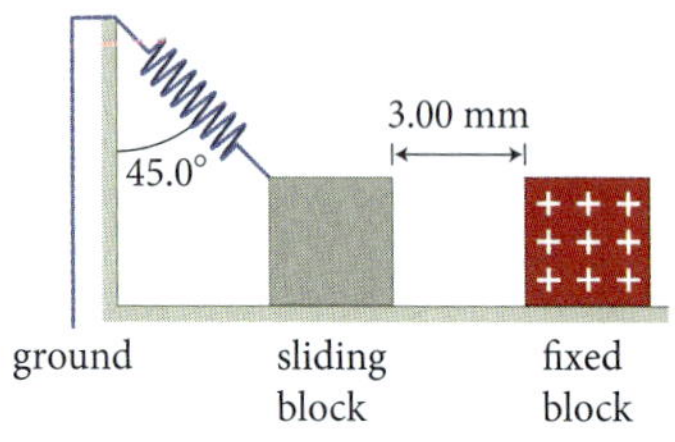

82. An anti-hydrogen atom, A, is composed of one positron orbiting one antiproton just as a regular hydrogen atom is composed of one electron orbiting one proton. The difference is that each antiparticle has the usual mass but an opposite charge of its regular counterpart. Atom A is placed in a closed container with a neutron. What is the most likely charge of the system after the neutron decays? (Hint: Use charge conservation.) ••

83. All life on Earth is based on one of many two-polymer systems, each made up of a protein and a nucleic acid. In a cell, these polymers are, for the most part, charge-balanced, with the nucleic acid in any pair carrying a negative charge and the protein carrying an equal amount of positive charge. Consider a distribution of eight of these polymers, where the eight proteins sit together near the center of the cell and the nucleic acids are spread out along the circumference of a circle with the radius equal to one-quarter of the cell diameter, centered on the proteins. If seven of the eight nucleic acids are at $\pi/4$, $\pi/2$, $3\pi/4$, π, $3\pi/2$, $7\pi/4$, and 2π rad, where on the circle must you place the eighth acid to give the system a balanced charge distribution? (Hint: Begin by making a sketch.) ••

84. In a simplistic model of the hydrogen atom, the electron orbits the proton in a circle of radius 53 pm. What is the orbital period of the electron, in seconds, if the force responsible for the proton-electron attraction is (*a*) gravitational and (*b*) electric? ••

85. (*a*) About how many electrons are there in a copper penny, which has a mass of about 0.003 kg? (*b*) If you could isolate these electrons, how much charge would you have? (*c*) Estimate the magnitude of the electric force it would require to bring one more electron to within 1.0 nm of these electrons, assuming they are combined to form one small charged object. (*d*) Based on this force magnitude, do you think it would be possible to combine this amount of negative charge? ••

86. Earth exerts an electric force on small charged objects located near its surface. The effect can be modeled by assuming Earth is a particle at the center of Earth carrying a charge of -6.76×10^5 C. (*a*) What is the magnitude of the electric force exerted by Earth on an electron at its surface? Is this force attractive or repulsive? (*b*) How does this force magnitude compare with the magnitude of the gravitational force exerted by Earth on the electron? (*c*) How much negative charge would you have to put on a penny in order for the repulsive electric force exerted by Earth on the penny to cancel the attractive gravitational force exerted by Earth on the penny? (*d*) How many electrons would you have to add to the penny to achieve this? ••

87. Four particles, each carrying a charge of 3.0 nC, are located at the corners of a square that has a side length of 50 mm. The charge on the particle at the lower left corner is positive, and the other three particles are negatively charged. (*a*) Draw a free-body diagram showing the electric forces exerted on the particle at the upper right corner. (*b*) Determine the magnitude and direction of the vector sum of the electric forces exerted on this particle. ••

88. A small sphere 1 carrying charge q is fixed a few meters above the Moon's surface next to a spaceship. An astronaut holds a charged sphere 2 a couple of meters above sphere 1, almost but not quite directly over sphere 1. Sketch the trajectory for sphere 2 when the astronaut drops it if the charge on sphere 2 is (*a*) q, (*b*) $9q$, and (*c*) $-q$. •••

89. Someone has challenged you in a friendly bet that, given a set of six charged spheres with three carrying positive charge and three carrying negative charge, you can't place any three of them in a line (a board with a groove in it serves the purpose) and have them be in translational equilibrium. You determine which of the three spheres are the positively charged ones and call them 1, 2, and 3. By comparing the electric force exerted by sphere 1 on sphere 3 with the electric force exerted by sphere 2 on sphere 3, you rank 1 as smaller than 2, placing them in the groove several hundred millimeters apart, temporarily blocking them from moving. You can release them only when the third sphere is in place, but there are so many things to consider! ••• CR

90. While assembling part of an electric generator, you realize that two pieces were not properly labeled. One piece is a nonconducting block, and the other is a conducting block, but without labels you don't know which is which. Because you had counted on the parts being properly labeled, you do not have a multimeter, batteries, or other standard electrical tools. All you have is your wool sweater, some nonconducting styrofoam "peanuts" used in packaging, and some string. You are about to go for help when you realize that your knowledge of static electricity should be enough. ••• CR

91. Working on a system to collect solar energy, you are trying to move some charged particles through the open interior of a uniformly charged ring. A colleague vaguely remembers Newton's and Priestley's argument that no electrostatic force is exerted on a charged particle inside a uniformly charged sphere. He suggests that the same must be true for a charged ring, and so you can send the charged particles through any part of the ring interior without the particles feeling an electric force and being deflected by it. You are skeptical, wondering if there might at least be a restriction on the path over which you send the particles such that they experience no electric force. ••• CR

Answers to Review Questions

1. The gravitational interaction between the balloon and Earth makes the balloon fall. After charging, the electric interaction between your hair and the balloon dominates. (Friction between your hair and the balloon is the source of the force that opposes the gravitational interaction between the balloon and Earth.)
2. The electric interaction is much stronger than the gravitational interaction. The electric interaction can be attractive or repulsive, while the gravitational interaction is only attractive.
3. A charged object can interact in different ways with a second charged object, either repelling or attracting that object. This means there are different possibilities for the type of charge on the second object.
4. Without further information, it's impossible to say who is right. Positive charge carriers moved from an object A to an object B or negative charge carriers moved from B to A have the same effect. However, because we know that plastic combs become negatively charged when rubbed through hair, and the hair acquires positive charge, we could speculate that the hair transfers electrons to the balloon.
5. Zero. Charge can only be moved from one place to another or created or destroyed in equal positive and negative portions. Because charge is a conserved quantity, the amount of charge in a closed system is constant.
6. The surplus charge causing the spark entered your body at your feet but interacted with the knob at your fingers. That the charge migrated tells you that your body is a fair electrical conductor.
7. Paper is an electrical insulator; to see this for yourself, insert a slip of paper between two batteries in a flashlight and turn on the switch. A paper clip is metal and thus an electrical conductor. Seawater is an electrical conductor because of the presence of dissolved ions. Tires are rubber and so electrical insulators, just as the rubber insulation on electrical power cords is. Air is usually an electrical insulator, but as with most other electrical insulators, a sufficient electric force exerted on a volume of air can cause a breakdown, or spark, and then charge carriers can flow through the air, making it an electrical conductor in the breakdown region.
8. Breaking wood leaves two pieces of similar material. There's no reason the symmetrical result (same material on both sides of the break) should leave a positive charge on one piece and a negative charge on the other. It is usually in the breaking of bonds in *dissimilar* materials that a surplus of charge is left behind on the two materials.
9. The charged rod attracts opposite charges and repels like charges on the neutral object, causing the object to become polarized. An oppositely charged region forms near the rod, while a like-charged region forms farther away. The proximity of the oppositely charged region causes the object to be attracted (weakly) to the rod.
10. There would be no difference. Opposite charges would still be opposite and attract, and like charges would still be like and repel.
11. Polarization is accomplished by bringing an already charged item near the object to be polarized. In each case the polarization effect creates regions of surplus charge in the object, with the region of charge opposite to those on the charged item forming closest to the charged item. In a conductor, some electrons are free to move throughout the material, and it is these mobile electrons that move from one part of the object to another as the object becomes polarized. In an insulator, electrons are not free to move through the material, but rather the electron cloud in each atom shifts slightly toward or away from the charged item (depending on the sign of its surplus charge). The effect of many superposed atomic cloud shifts creates thin regions of surplus charge on the surface of the insulating object.
12. (*a*) Positively charged or neutral; (*b*) negatively charged only.
13. The magnitude F^E_{AB} is proportional to the charge on B, experimentally. Likewise, the magnitude F^E_{BA} is proportional to the charge on A. Because Newton's third law tells you that these two forces must be equal in magnitude, they must both be proportional to both the charge on A and the charge on B. The only way to make this happen is for the product $q_A q_B$ to appear in the expression for the force. Note that the sum $q_A + q_B$ does not reproduce the proportionality behavior; doubling q_B does not double the sum.
14. Doubling both charges without changing the distance would increase the force exerted on each by a factor of 4. Doubling the distance would compensate for this factor of 4, because the force is inversely proportional to the square of the distance.
15. The magnitude of the force exerted on either partner in the interaction pair is identical, as is always the case with any interaction.
16. The last term does not involve charge carrier 1 and therefore has nothing to do with the force exerted on 1. This term should be omitted from the expression.
17. Because particles 1 and 2 carry charges of opposite types, the situation requires that particle 3 not be placed between 1 and 2 in order that the directions of the two forces oppose each other. To obtain equal magnitudes for the two forces, particle 3 must be placed closer to the particle with smaller charge (particle 1). Thus the answer is (*c*).

Answers to Guided Problems

Guided Problem 22.2 Let α be the angle that each thread makes with respect to vertical. Then

$$Q = d\sqrt{\frac{mg\tan\alpha}{k}} = (0.093\text{ m})\sqrt{\frac{(0.017\text{ kg})(9.8\text{ m/s}^2)(0.4203)}{9.0\times10^9\text{ N}\cdot\text{m}^2/\text{C}^2}}$$

$$= 2.6\times10^{-7}\text{C},$$

$$\text{where } \alpha = \sin^{-1}\left(\frac{d}{2\ell}\right) = \sin^{-1}\left(\frac{93\text{ mm}}{2\times120\text{ mm}}\right) = 22.80°,$$

and $\tan\alpha = 0.4203$.

Guided Problem 22.4

$$(a)\ v = e\sqrt{\frac{k}{mR}}$$

$$= (1.6\times10^{-19}\text{ C})\sqrt{\frac{9.0\times10^9\text{ N}\cdot\text{m}^2/\text{C}^2}{(9.1\times10^{-31}\text{ kg})(5.3\times10^{-11}\text{ m})}}$$

$$= 2.2\times10^6\text{ m/s};$$

$$(b)\ T = \frac{2\pi R}{v} = \frac{(2\pi)(5.3\times10^{-11}\text{ m})}{2.2\times10^6\text{ m/s}} = 1.5\times10^{-16}\text{ s}.$$

Guided Problem 22.6 The force on the top ion points upward, away from the central base ion, and has magnitude

$$F = ke^2\left[\frac{1}{h^2} + \frac{4}{a^2\sqrt{2}}\right] = 6.6\times10^{-8}\text{ N, where } h = \frac{a}{\sqrt{2}}.$$

PRACTICE

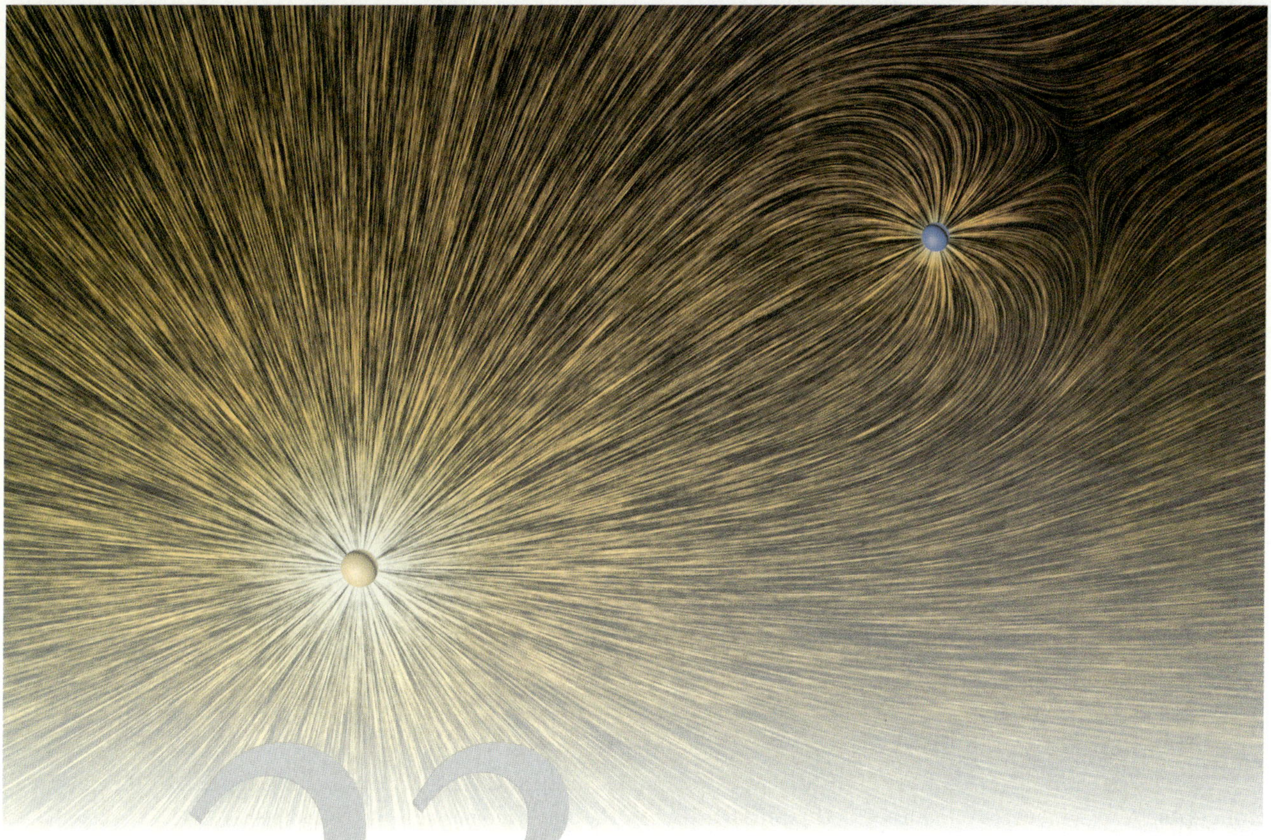

23

PRACTICE
The Electric Field

Chapter Summary

Electric fields (Sections 23.1–23.3, 23.5)

Concepts In the field model of long-range interactions, interacting object A fills the space around itself with a **field** (or **interaction field**). When an object B is placed in this field, the field acts on B. If A and B have mass, the field is a *gravitational field;* if they are charge carriers, it is an *electric field.*

A **test particle** is one whose mass and/or charge is so small that the particle does not perturb the objects generating the field being measured.

The direction of the **electric field** at a given location is the same as the direction of the electric force exerted on a positive test particle at that location.

Quantitative Tools If a test particle located at position P and carrying charge q_t experiences a force $\vec{F}^E_t$, then the **electric field** $\vec{E}$ (N/C) at P is

$$\vec{E} \equiv \frac{\vec{F}^E_t}{q_t}. \tag{23.1}$$

If the source particle is at position $\vec{r}_s$ and carries charge q_s, the electric field it creates at any position P is

$$\vec{E}_s(P) = k\frac{q_s}{r^2_{sP}}\hat{r}_{sP}, \tag{23.4}$$

where $\hat{r}_{sP}$ is a unit vector pointing from the source particle to P and $k = 9.0 \times 10^9\ \text{N}\cdot\text{m}^2/\text{C}^2$.

Principle of **superposition of electric fields:** The combined electric field $\vec{E}$ created by a system of particles that carry charges $q_1, q_2, \ldots$ is

$$\vec{E} = \vec{E}_1 + \vec{E}_2 + \cdots = \Sigma k\frac{q_i\hat{r}_{iP}}{r^2_{iP}}. \tag{23.5}$$

Electric dipoles (Sections 23.4, 23.6, 23.8)

Concepts A *uniform electric field* has a constant magnitude and direction at all locations; a *nonuniform electric field* can vary in magnitude and/or direction from one location to another. A uniform electric field gives a charged particle a constant acceleration.

An **electric dipole** consists of equal quantities q_p of positive and negative charge separated by a small distance.

When an electrically neutral object is placed in an electric field, the field causes the object's positive and negative charge centers to separate, producing an **induced dipole.**

Quantitative Tools The **dipole moment** $\vec{p}$ (C · m) of a dipole is

$$\vec{p} \equiv q_p\vec{r}_p, \tag{23.9}$$

where $\vec{r}_p$ is the vector from the center of negative charge to the center of positive charge.

The torque $\Sigma\vec{\tau}$ produced on a dipole by a uniform electric field is

$$\Sigma\vec{\tau} = \vec{p} \times \vec{E}. \tag{23.21}$$

The **induced dipole moment** $\vec{p}_{ind}$ of a neutral atom placed in an external electric field that is not too large is

$$\vec{p}_{ind} = \alpha\vec{E}, \tag{23.24}$$

where α is the **polarizability** of the atom.

For positions far from an electric dipole, the electric field due to the dipole is inversely proportional to the cube of the distance r from the dipole. In particular, at distant points along the bisector axis (x axis)

$$E_y \approx -k\frac{p}{|x^3|}, \tag{23.10}$$

and at distant points along the dipole separation axis ($+y$ axis)

$$E_y \approx 2k\frac{p}{y^3}. \tag{23.13}$$

Electric fields of continuous charge distributions (Section 23.7)

Concepts **Charge density** can be linear (λ, C/m), over a surface area (σ, C/m^2), or throughout a volume (ρ, C/m^3).

Quantitative Tools The electric field due to a set of infinitesimal source particles of charge dq_s is

$$\vec{E} = k\int \frac{dq_s}{r_{sP}^2}\hat{r}_{sP}. \quad (23.15)$$

See the Procedure box on page 414.

Linear, area, and *volume charge densities* are

$$\lambda \equiv \frac{q}{\ell} \quad (23.16)$$

$$\sigma \equiv \frac{q}{A} \quad (23.17)$$

$$\rho \equiv \frac{q}{V}. \quad (23.18)$$

A uniformly charged rod of length ℓ carrying charge q oriented along the y axis and centered at the origin produces an electric field

$$E_x = \frac{kq}{x\sqrt{\ell^2/4 + x^2}}$$

along the x axis.

A uniformly charged ring of charge q and radius R oriented with the plane of the ring perpendicular to the z axis and the ring center at the origin produces an electric field

$$E_z = k\frac{qz}{(z^2 + R^2)^{3/2}}$$

along the z axis.

A uniformly charged disk of surface charge density σ and radius R oriented with the disk face perpendicular to the z axis and the disk center at the origin produces an electric field

$$E_z = 2k\pi\sigma\left[1 - \frac{z}{(z^2 + R^2)^{1/2}}\right]$$

along the z axis.

Outside a solid sphere of radius R carrying a uniformly distributed charge q, the electric field produced by the sphere is

$$E_{\text{sphere}} = k\frac{q}{r^2},$$

where $r > R$ is the distance from the sphere's center. This field is the same as the field that would be produced if all the charge were concentrated at the sphere's center.

Review Questions

Answers to these questions can be found at the end of this chapter.

23.1 The field model

1. What is the physics definition of *field*?
2. What are the two major reasons for introducing the field concept?
3. When two charged Ping-Pong balls, A and B, are held a small distance apart, which ball is the source of the electric field that acts on ball B?
4. What is the difference between a scalar field and a vector field? Give an example of each type.
5. What is a vector field diagram, and how is it useful?

23.2 Electric field diagrams

6. How can a charged test particle be used to determine the electric field at a point P caused by a charged source object S located nearby?
7. A positively charged styrofoam pellet is placed in the electric field surrounding a charged sphere. If the charge on the pellet is changed from positive to negative, what happens to the magnitude and direction of the sphere's electric field at the pellet's location?
8. A negatively charged test particle is placed at position P in an electric field, and it experiences an electric force directed to the west. What is the direction of the electric field at point P?

23.3 Superposition of electric fields

9. Balloon 1 is charged and taped to a board, and a pushpin is inserted at a different location on the board. The electric field at the pushpin due to balloon 1 is measured to have magnitude E_1. Balloon 1 is removed and the process is repeated with balloon 2, taped at a third location. The electric field at the pin due to balloon 2 is measured to have magnitude E_2. If both balloons are present, is the magnitude of the electric field at the pin equal to $E_1 + E_2$?

23.4 Electric fields and forces

10. An electron initially moving horizontally near Earth's surface enters a uniform electric field and is deflected upward. What can you say about the direction of the electric field (assuming no other interaction)? What can you say about the direction of the electric field if the electron is deflected downward?
11. A uniform electric field is directed to the right. Sketch the trajectory of a proton and an electron launched straight up in this field.
12. Is it possible for a dipole that is initially moving in a straight line to be deflected by a uniform electric field?
13. An electron is traveling in circular motion at constant speed due to the effect of an electric field. Is it possible for the electric field to be uniform?

23.5 Electric field of a charged particle

14. If the charge on particle 2 in *Principles* Figure 23.23 were doubled, what aspects of the electric field at point P would change: the magnitude, the direction, or both?
15. A delicate instrument is two paces away from a highly charged metallic sphere. If you want to reduce the magnitude of the electric field at the instrument to 1% of its present value, how many paces away from its present position must you move the instrument?

23.6 Dipole field

16. Which is greater, the magnitude of the electric field a distance r from a small sphere carrying charge q or the magnitude of the electric field a distance r from a small electric dipole of dipole moment qd, where d is the dipole separation and $r \gg d$?
17. What is the definition of *dipole moment*?
18. An electric dipole is fixed at the origin of a coordinate system, and an electric field detector can be moved anywhere along the surface of an imaginary sphere of radius R that is centered on the origin. The radius of this sphere greatly exceeds the dipole separation, $R \gg d$. As the detector is moved over the spherical surface, what is the ratio of the largest and smallest magnitudes of the electric field it detects, $E_{\text{maximum}}/E_{\text{minimum}}$?

23.7 Electric fields of continuous charge distributions

19. A hemispheric shell made of a material that is an electrical insulator has a radius R and a charge q distributed uniformly over it. It is placed in the $z \geq 0$ region of an xyz coordinate system, centered about the z axis, with its base resting on the xy plane. Write the expression for the charge dq on an infinitesimally thin ring portion of the shell of width $Rd\theta$, where θ is the angle from the z axis to the ring.
20. What is the distinguishing radial dependence of the electric field (*a*) around a charged particle (charge distributed in no dimensions), (*b*) around a long uniformly charged wire (charge distributed in one dimension), and (*c*) around a large uniformly charged sheet (charge distributed in two dimensions)?

23.8 Dipoles in electric fields

21. What are the SI units of polarizability?
22. The magnitude of the electric field due to a permanent dipole decreases as the cube of distance r from the dipole: $E \propto 1/r^3$. The electric force exerted by the dipole on a charged particle placed in the electric field of the dipole is also proportional to $1/r^3$: $F^E_{\text{dp}} \propto 1/r^3$. How does the force exerted by the charged particle on the dipole depend on r?
23. What are the similarities and differences between permanent and induced dipoles?

PRACTICE

Developing a Feel

Make an order-of-magnitude estimate of each of the following quantities. Letters in parentheses refer to hints below. Use them as needed to guide your thinking.

1. The electric field magnitude 0.1 nm from a proton (P, B)
2. The electric field magnitude 1 m from a ball of 10^6 electrons (I)
3. The charge-to-mass ratio for a sodium (Na^+) ion (G, P)
4. The charge-to-mass ratio for either of two identical particles whose gravitational and electric interactions cancel each other (E, R)
5. The volume charge density of a hydrogen nucleus (F, K, P)
6. The surface charge density on a 200-mm length of a freshly pulled strip of transparent tape (D, H, M, Q, U)
7. The linear charge density on a rubbed plastic rod that is 300 mm long (C, H, L, Q, T)
8. The electric field strength 0.1 m from the long axis of the plastic rod of Question 7 (Answer to Question 7, A)
9. The magnitude and direction of the uniform electric field required to "float" a proton near Earth's surface (N, P, S)
10. The electric dipole moment of a water molecule (J, O)

Hints

A. Is this location close or far enough from the rod to use an approximation for the magnitude of $\vec{E}$?
B. What is 0.1 nm in meters?
C. What is the mass of the rod?
D. What is the mass of the tape strip?
E. If you equate the gravitational and electric force expressions, what factor cancels?
F. What is the radius of a hydrogen nucleus?
G. What is the mass of a sodium ion?
H. What fraction of this mass is due to protons?
I. What is the charge on the ball?
J. How should you model the charge distribution?
K. What is the formula for the volume of a sphere?
L. What is the number of electrons in the rod?
M. What is the number of electrons in the strip?
N. What is the mass of a proton?
O. What is the separation of the centers of charge?
P. What is the charge of a proton in coulombs?
Q. What fraction of the electrons is redistributed during charging?
R. What is the ratio of the gravitational constant to the proportionality constant in Coulomb's law?
S. If the electric field points upward, what is the direction of the electric force it exerts on the proton?
T. What is the length along which the surplus charge is distributed?
U. What is the surface area of the strip?

Key (all values approximate)

A. No, which means you must use the expression in the Chapter Summary: $E_x = kq/x(\ell^2/4 + x^2)^{1/2}$; **B.** 1×10^{-10} m; **C.** 0.1 kg; **D.** 1×10^{-4} kg; **E.** the factor for the distance between the particles; **F.** 1×10^{-15} m; **G.** 4×10^{-26} kg; **H.** half, assuming the atoms contain equal numbers of protons and neutrons; **I.** -2×10^{-13} C; **J.** there is an imbalance of about one elementary charge, so the dipole consists of one "surplus" proton centered between the H atoms and one surplus electron centered on the O atom; **K.** $V = 4\pi r^3/3$; **L.** 3×10^{25}; **M.** same as the number of protons, 3×10^{22}; **N.** 2×10^{-27} kg; **O.** 5×10^{-11} m, because of the bonding angle of 105° between the H atoms; **P.** $+2 \times 10^{-19}$ C; **Q.** about one in 10^{12} (see *Principles* Section 22.3); **R.** $G/k \approx 7 \times 10^{-21}$, with both constants in SI units; **S.** upward; **T.** 0.2 m, or two-thirds the length of the rod; **U.** 0.002 m^2

Worked and Guided Problems

Procedure: Calculating the electric field of continuous charge distributions by integration

To calculate the electric field of a continuous charge distribution, you need to evaluate the integral in Eq. 23.15. The following steps will help you evaluate the integral.

1. Begin by making a sketch of the charge distribution. Mentally divide the distribution into small segments. Indicate one such segment that carries a charge dq_s in your drawing.
2. Choose a coordinate system that allows you to express the position of the segment in terms of a minimum number of coordinates (x, y, z, r, or θ). These coordinates are the integration variables. For example, use a radial coordinate system for a charge distribution with radial symmetry. Unless the problem specifies otherwise, let the origin be at the center of the object.
3. Draw a vector showing the electric field caused by the segment at the point of interest. Examine how the components of this vector change as you vary the position of the segment along the charge distribution. Some components may cancel, which greatly simplifies the calculation. If you can determine the direction of the resulting electric field, you may need to calculate only one component. Otherwise express $\hat{r}_{sP}$ in terms of your integration variable(s) and evaluate the integrals for each component of the field separately.
4. Determine whether the charge distribution is one-dimensional (a straight or curved wire), two-dimensional (a flat or curved surface), or three-dimensional (any bulk object). Express dq_s in terms of the corresponding charge density of the object and the integration variable(s).
5. Express the factor $1/r_{sP}^2$, where r_{sP} is the distance between dq_s and the point of interest, in terms of the integration variable(s).

At this point you can substitute your expressions for dq_s and $1/r_{sP}^2$ into Eq. 23.15 and carry out the integral (or component integrals), using what you determined about the direction of the electric field (or substituting your expression for $\hat{r}_{sP}$).

These examples involve material from this chapter but are not associated with any particular section. Some examples are worked out in detail; others you should work out by following the guidelines provided.

Worked Problem 23.1 Charge square

Four charged particles are arranged in a square as shown in Figure WG23.1, with $q = 3.9 \times 10^{-4}$ C and $a = 6.9$ mm. Determine the magnitude and direction of the electric field at the center of the square.

Figure WG23.1

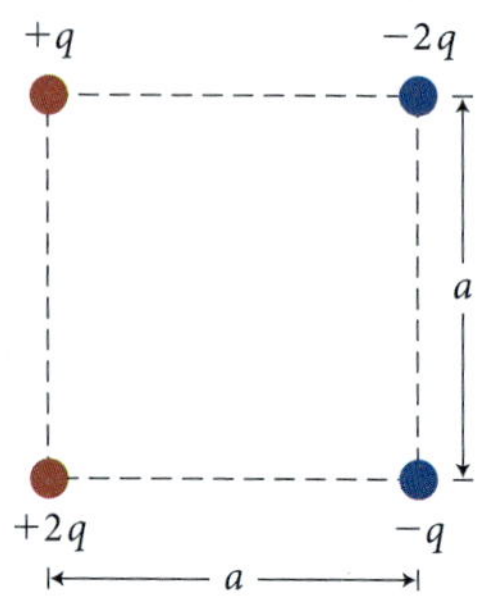

❶ GETTING STARTED We use the superposition principle, expressed in Eq. 23.5, on the individual electric fields created by the four particles to determine the electric field at the center.

❷ DEVISE PLAN We could calculate the electric field due to each particle and then add the components to get the field at the square's center. However, we can simplify the problem by exploiting the symmetry of the configuration. One way to use that symmetry is to separate the four particles into two pairs: $+q/-q$ having separation distance $a\sqrt{2}$ and contributing an electric field $\vec{E}_1$ to the center and $+2q/-2q$ having separation distance $a\sqrt{2}$ and contributing an electric field $\vec{E}_2$ to the center (Figure WG23.2).

Figure WG23.2

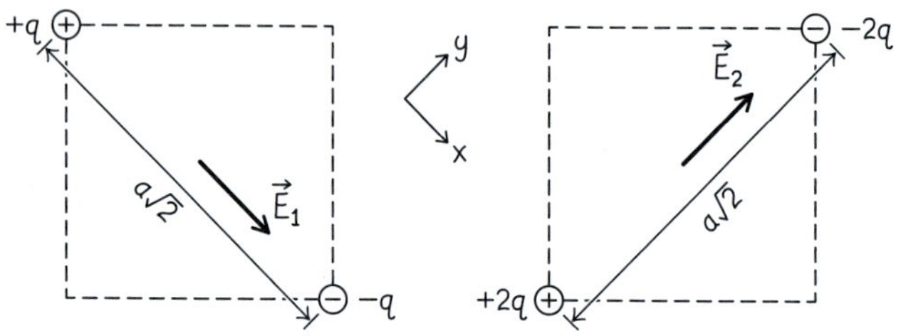

Each of the two fields is produced by a pair of charged particles carrying charges of equal magnitude but opposite signs, with the fields pointing away from the positively charged particle and toward the negatively charged particle. Note in Figure WG23.2 that we have aligned the axes of our coordinate system in a way that facilitates the calculation of components. Because we seek the electric field at the center of the square, we know that the magnitudes E_1 and E_2 are related by a factor of 2 (that is, $2E_1 = E_2$) due to the similarities of distance and charge. All we have to do is add the electric field vectors $\vec{E}_1$ and $\vec{E}_2$ to obtain the electric field at the center.

❸ EXECUTE PLAN For the $+q/-q$ pair, the electric field at the square's center is

$$\vec{E}_1 = k\frac{q}{r_{+q}^2}\hat{r}_{+q} + k\frac{(-q)}{r_{-q}^2}\hat{r}_{-q}$$

$$= k\frac{q}{(\frac{1}{2}a\sqrt{2})^2}\hat{\imath} + k\frac{(-q)}{(\frac{1}{2}a\sqrt{2})^2}(-\hat{\imath})$$

$$= 4k\frac{q}{a^2}\hat{\imath}.$$

For the $+2q/-2q$ pair, we note that $\vec{E}_2$ is produced along the y direction by particles that carry charges that are twice as large as in the $+q/-q$ pair. We can therefore infer that

$$\vec{E}_2 = 8k\frac{q}{a^2}\hat{\jmath},$$

which means that the electric field at the center of the square is

$$\vec{E} = \vec{E}_1 + \vec{E}_2 = 4k\frac{q}{a^2}\hat{\imath} + 8k\frac{q}{a^2}\hat{\jmath}.$$

The magnitude of this electric field is

$$E = \sqrt{E_x^2 + E_y^2} = \sqrt{\left(\frac{4kq}{a^2}\right)^2 + \left(\frac{8kq}{a^2}\right)^2} = 4\sqrt{5}k\frac{q}{a^2},$$

and its direction is

$$\theta = \tan^{-1}\frac{E_y}{E_x} = \tan^{-1}\frac{8kq/a^2}{4kq/a^2} = \tan^{-1} 2 = 63°.$$

Substituting values yields

$$\vec{E} = \frac{4\sqrt{5}(9.0 \times 10^9\ \mathrm{N \cdot m^2/C^2})(3.9 \times 10^{-4}\ \mathrm{C})}{(0.0069\ \mathrm{m})^2}$$

$$= 6.6 \times 10^{11}\ \mathrm{N/C},$$

at 63° above the positive x axis as oriented in Figure WG23.2. ✓

❹ EVALUATE RESULT The electric field we obtained is large, but the charge on these particles is large and the separation distance is small. The direction makes sense because it points approximately along the line that connects the two particles carrying a charge $\pm 2q$.

Guided Problem 23.2 Charge triangle

Three particles form an equilateral triangle with side length a. Two of the particles carry a positive charge $+q$, and the third particle carries a charge $-2q$. What are the magnitude and direction of the electric field at the center of the triangle?

❶ GETTING STARTED

1. Draw a diagram showing the particles, charges, and distances.
2. Locate the center of the triangle.
3. What causes the electric field at the center? Account for all sources that contribute to this field.
4. Is there any symmetry you can use to simplify your work?

❷ DEVISE PLAN

5. Must you work with vectors to solve this problem? You know that particles carrying the same type of charge repel each other and particles carrying opposite types of charge attract each other. Be sure to take this aspect of the interaction into account in your diagram.

❸ EXECUTE PLAN

6. What are the relevant distances to the center of the triangle?

❹ EVALUATE RESULT

7. Does your answer behave in a physically plausible way when the side lengths or charge magnitudes are varied?

Worked Problem 23.3 Torqued dipole

Figure WG23.3 shows an electric dipole located near a fixed charged particle A that carries charge $+q_A$. The dipole charge is q_D. (*a*) What torque does the electric force exerted by A create about the dipole's midpoint? (*b*) Sketch a graph showing how the torque caused by $\vec{F}^E_{AD}$ changes as the dipole separation d increases while the distance a between particle A and the dipole remains constant.

Figure WG23.3

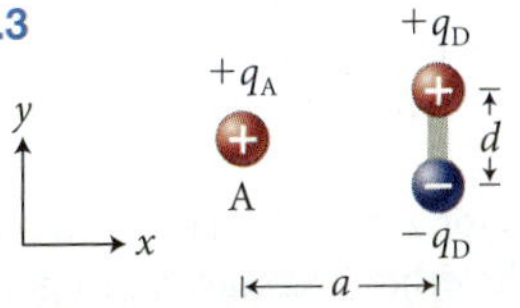

❶ GETTING STARTED The positive pole of the dipole is repelled by A, and the negative pole is attracted to A. This combination of attraction and repulsion causes a torque about the dipole midpoint that tends to rotate the dipole clockwise. The right-hand rule tells us that this torque is directed into the page. The two electric forces exerted on the dipole are not parallel to each other because the electric field created by A is directed radially outward.

❷ DEVISE PLAN One way to approach this problem is by brute force: Calculate the electric force exerted by A on one pole of the dipole, determine the torque caused by it about the dipole midpoint, do the same for the other pole, and then add the torques to get their vector sum. If we think of the dipole and particle A as a system, however, all the interactions are internal: The system is isolated. This means the vector sum of torques on the system about a chosen reference point is zero. The dipole midpoint is the reference point specified in the problem statement, so we choose it as the origin of our coordinate system. The torque on the dipole is the negative of the torque on particle A. Because the *Principles* volume derives a formula for the magnitude, at any position, of the electric field created by a dipole (Eq. 23.8, which using our symbols for variables is $E = -kq_Dd/[a^2 + (d/2)^2]^{3/2}$), we can solve this problem.

❸ **EXECUTE PLAN** To keep track of the dipole variables in our calculations, we label them with subscript D.

(*a*) From Eq. 23.1 we know that the electric force exerted by the dipole on particle A is

$$\vec{F}^E_{\rm DA} = q_{\rm A}\vec{E}_{\rm D}. \qquad (1)$$

From Eq. 23.8, the electric field surrounding the dipole at the position of particle A (on the x axis) is

$$\vec{E}_{\rm D} = -k\frac{q_{\rm D}d}{[a^2 + (d/2)^2]^{3/2}}\hat{\jmath}. \qquad (2)$$

The torque on A about the midpoint of the dipole is

$$\vec{\tau}_{\rm DA} = \vec{r}_{\rm DA} \times \vec{F}^E_{\rm DA} = (-a\hat{\imath}) \times q_{\rm A}\left(-k\frac{q_{\rm D}d}{[a^2 + (d/2)^2]^{3/2}}\hat{\jmath}\right).$$

By remembering that $\hat{\imath} \times \hat{\jmath} = \hat{k}$ (out of the page) and that the torque on the particle is equal and opposite to the torque on the dipole, we obtain the torque that the force $F^E_{\rm AD}$ causes on the dipole:

$$\vec{\tau}_{\rm AD} = -\vec{\tau}_{\rm DA} = -k\frac{q_{\rm A}q_{\rm D}ad}{[a^2 + (d/2)^2]^{3/2}}\hat{k}. \checkmark \qquad (3)$$

(*b*) Figure WG23.4 shows the magnitude of this torque as a function of d, with a held fixed. At $d = 0$, the torque is zero. For small values of d ($d < a$), the torque increases almost linearly as d increases because the denominator is nearly equal to a^3. As the dipole separation approaches $d = \sqrt{2}a$, the torque reaches a maximum value. For larger values of d, the denominator is dominated by the d term and is nearly equal to d^3. This means that the torque decreases almost quadratically as d increases in this region, as illustrated in Figure WG23.4.

Figure WG23.4

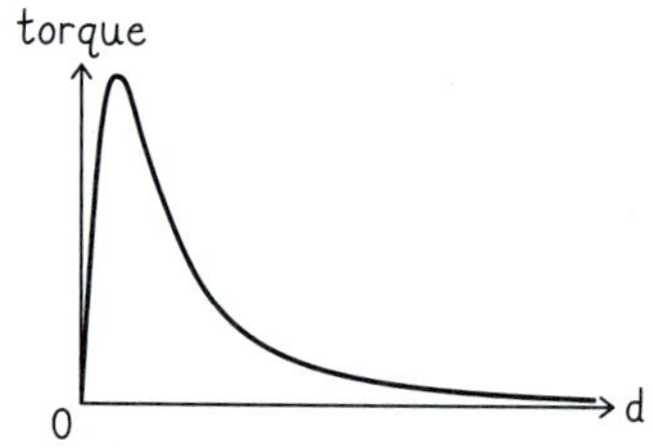

❹ **EVALUATE RESULT** Equation 3 says that if $q_{\rm A} > 0$, the torque on the dipole is in the negative z direction—that is, into the page. This information combined with the right-hand rule of Section 12.4 means that the dipole should rotate clockwise. This is what we expect because a positively charged particle A causes the top of the dipole to rotate away from A and pulls the bottom of the dipole toward A.

We could also check the result by using the brute force method mentioned above. The direction of the torque for $q_{\rm A} < 0$ is also as we expect, twisting the dipole counterclockwise. The electric force exerted on the particle is in the downward y direction, as we see by substituting Eq. 2 into Eq. 1. In what direction is the electric force exerted by the particle on the dipole? Does this result make sense? We have seen from Eq. 3 that as the dipole separation d gets large, the torque magnitude decreases. Why is this?

Figure WG23.4 shows that there is a maximum torque. Why is this? Think about what happens to the lever arm of the torque as the dipole separation decreases.

Guided Problem 23.4 Interacting dipoles

The centers of the two dipoles in Figure WG23.5 are separated from each other by a center-to-center distance a. Both dipoles have a dipole charge $q_{\rm p}$ and a dipole separation d. What are the magnitude and direction of the electric force exerted by one dipole on the other?

Figure WG23.5

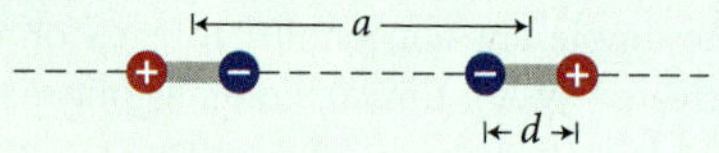

❶ **GETTING STARTED**

1. For a dipole aligned along a y axis, Eq. 23.11,

$$E_y = k\frac{q_{\rm p}}{[y - (d/2)]^2} - k\frac{q_{\rm p}}{[y + (d/2)]^2},$$

gives the magnitude of the electric field at any position on the y axis (the dipole's axis). How can you use this equation to determine the electric forces exerted by one dipole on the two poles of the other dipole? (Hint: A useful approach is to model one dipole as a set of source particles for an electric field and the other as a set of two oppositely charged test particles in that field. You need to identify the source particles and test particles so that you do not double count.)

❷ **DEVISE PLAN**

2. Can you take advantage of any symmetry in the problem?
3. How can you keep track of the various relevant distances in your diagram? Be careful not to use the same symbol to represent two different things.

❸ **EXECUTE PLAN**

❹ **EVALUATE RESULT**

4. Does the electric force in your result point in the direction you expect? Consider the relative sizes of the various terms in your result.
5. What happens to the force as the center-to-center distance a from one dipole to the other becomes much greater than the dipole separation d in each dipole?

PRACTICE

Worked Problem 23.5 Electric field created by a straight charged rod

A charged rod of length ℓ has a uniform linear charge density λ. What are the magnitude and direction of the electric field at a point P that is a distance a from one end of the rod and lies along the rod's long axis?

❶ **GETTING STARTED** First we make a diagram displaying the given information (Figure WG23.6). This problem is similar to examples in the *Principles* volume for a continuous charge distribution. However, in this problem we are not given the charge q carried by the rod; all we know is the charge per unit length. Nonetheless, we should be able to use similar techniques to obtain the electric field.

Figure WG23.6

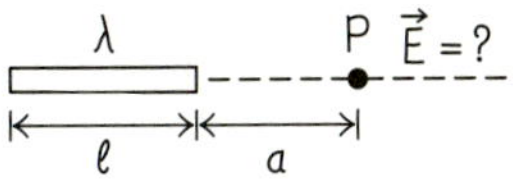

❷ **DEVISE PLAN** We can determine the electric field $\vec{E}$ created by a continuous charge distribution by dividing the rod into a large number of small segments and then summing their contributions $d\vec{E}$ to the electric field:

$$\vec{E} = \int d\vec{E} = \int k\frac{dq}{r^2}\hat{r}_{\rm P},$$

where dq is the charge on any segment and r is the distance from that segment of the rod to P. To keep track of the contributions from the various segments we will draw a diagram. From symmetry, we know the electric field points along the rod's long axis.

❸ **EXECUTE PLAN** We draw a diagram that shows one rod segment dx and all the variables needed for our calculation (Figure WG23.7).

Figure WG23.7

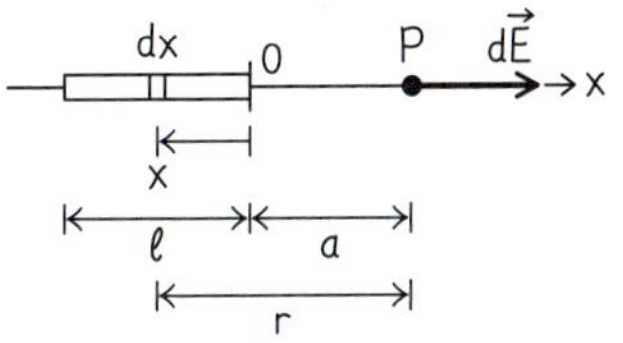

For convenience, we choose the x axis to be along the rod's axis and locate the origin of this axis at the right end of the rod. If we choose the positive x axis to the right, $\hat{r}_{\rm P} = \hat{\imath}$ and $d\vec{E} = \hat{\imath}\,dE$ is the electric field created by segment dx centered at position x. Remembering that the coordinate x represents a signed quantity (the position), we see from Figure WG23.7 that the distance r from any segment to P is $a - x$ in our coordinate system. The charge dq on the segment is $dq = \lambda dx$. The electric field at P is thus

$$\vec{E} = \hat{\imath}\int_{-\ell}^{0} k\frac{\lambda dx}{(a-x)^2} = k\frac{\lambda}{a-x}\bigg|_{-\ell}^{0}\hat{\imath}$$

$$= k\left[\frac{\lambda}{a} - \frac{\lambda}{a-(-\ell)}\right]\hat{\imath}.$$

$$= k\lambda\left[\frac{1}{a} - \frac{1}{a+\ell}\right]\hat{\imath}. ✔$$

❹ **EVALUATE RESULT** We first want to make sure our expression gives the correct direction for the electric field. If the charge on the rod is positive, the electric field at P should point to the right because that is the direction a small positively charged test particle would move. This is in the positive x direction for our coordinate system. For positive λ, the factor in front of $\hat{\imath}$ is indeed positive, meaning the component of the electric field in the x direction is positive, as expected.

If the rod length ℓ is much greater than the distance a from the rod end to P, we can assume ℓ is effectively infinite. As ℓ approaches infinity, the term $1/(a+\ell)$ inside the square brackets drops out and the electric field magnitude becomes $E = k\lambda/a$; that is, the field magnitude for positions very close to the rod is independent of ℓ.

As we move P closer and closer to the right end of the rod (a goes to zero), the electric field becomes infinite. At the right end of the rod, P is presumably right on top of a charged particle (zero separation), so the electric field should become very large because of the $1/r^2$ dependence of Coulomb's law. Note also that as ℓ approaches zero, the electric field becomes zero—which is what we expect because there is no charge on a rod of zero length.

Guided Problem 23.6 Electric field created by a curved charged rod

A thin semicircular rod of radius R carries a charge q uniformly distributed along its length. What are the magnitude and direction of the electric field at the center of the arc formed by the rod?

❶ **GETTING STARTED**

1. Draw a sketch with the rod as a half circle and the given quantities placed appropriately.
2. How do you deal with the effects of a continuous charge distribution when the direction from the point of interest to one segment of the charge distribution is different from the direction from the point of interest to another segment?

❷ **DEVISE PLAN**

3. How are you going to determine the contributions to the electric field from different segments of the rod?
4. What is the most natural variable to use in doing the integration required in this circular arc problem? How can an angular measure be related to the lengths of various rod segments?
5. What simplifications, if any, does the symmetry of the half circle allow you to make? Think in terms of the components of the vectors at the position of interest (center of the arc).

❸ **EXECUTE PLAN**

❹ **EVALUATE RESULT**

6. Is the direction of the electric field you obtained plausible?
7. Does your expression behave in a physically plausible way when you vary either R or q?

Worked Problem 23.7 Dipole corrections

In any direction far away from a dipole, the electric field surrounding the dipole decreases approximately as the inverse cube of distance. For a dipole with dipole charge q_p, dipole separation d, and dipole moment magnitude $p = q_p d$, what is the first level of correction to this inverse-cube approximation (*a*) at any position on the dipole axis that is an intermediate distance (neither very close nor very far) from either end of the dipole and (*b*) at any position on the perpendicular bisector of the dipole axis that is an intermediate distance from the dipole?

1 GETTING STARTED Figure WG23.8 shows the dipole along with the information given in the problem statement and labels for the electric fields at an arbitrary location along the dipole axis ($\vec{E}_{\parallel}$)

Figure WG23.8

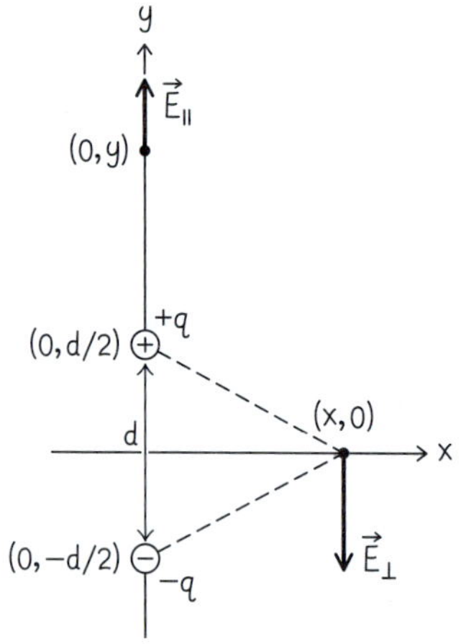

and at an arbitrary location on the perpendicular bisector ($\vec{E}_{\perp}$). *Principles* Section 23.6 derives the expression for the nonzero components of the electric fields along the dipole axis (Eq. 23.12) and perpendicular to it (Eq. 23.8):

$$E_{\parallel} = E_y = k\frac{q_p}{y^2}\left[\left(1 - \frac{d}{2y}\right)^{-2} - \left(1 + \frac{d}{2y}\right)^{-2}\right]$$

$$E_{\perp} = E_y = -k\frac{q_p d}{[x^2 + (d/2)^2]^{3/2}}$$

(Remember that E_x is zero in both cases.) We then saw how these equations yield the approximations $E_{\parallel} = E_y \approx 2kq_p d/y^3$ (Eq. 23.13) and $E_{\perp} = E_y \approx -kq_p d/x^3$ (Eq. 23.10) when the distance from the dipole is much greater than the dipole separation d ($y \gg d/2$ and $x \gg d/2$). We just have to make the approximations more accurate, keeping in mind that the corrections for the two cases may differ slightly from each other because the expression for $E_{\perp} = E_y$ in the x direction is different from the expression for $E_{\parallel} = E_y$ in the y direction.

2 DEVISE PLAN The approximations $E_{\parallel} = E_y \approx 2kq_p d/y^3$ and $E_{\perp} = E_y \approx -kq_p d/x^3$ were obtained using only the first-order term in a binomial expansion. To make the approximations more accurate, we need to take the next term in the expansion into account. The expansion is $(1 + z)^n = 1 + nz/1! + n(n-1)z^2/2! + n(n-1)(n-2)z^3/3! + n(n-1)(n-2)(n-3)z^4/4! + \cdots$. We hope to get by with just the terms through z^2 because the long-range expressions used only $1 + nz$, but we'll go to the z^3 term in case there is an exact cancellation.

3 EXECUTE PLAN (*a*) Consider first the electric field $\vec{E}_{\parallel}$ along the dipole axis, given by Eq. 23.12. Noting that $n = -2$ in this equation and using the expansion of $(1 + z)^n$ to the z^3 term with $z = d/2y$, we have

$$\left(1 \pm \frac{d}{2y}\right)^{-2} \approx 1 \pm (-2)\frac{d}{2y} + \frac{(-2)(-2-1)}{2}\left(\frac{d}{2y}\right)^2 \pm \frac{(-2)(-3)(-4)}{6}\left(\frac{d}{2y}\right)^3$$
$$= 1 \mp \frac{d}{y} + \tfrac{3}{4}\frac{d^2}{y^2} \mp \tfrac{1}{2}\frac{d^3}{y^3}.$$

Substituting this expression into Eq. 23.12, we see that the first-level correction for intermediate distances is

$$E_{\parallel} = E_y \approx k\frac{q_p}{y^2}\left[\left(1 + \frac{d}{y} + \tfrac{3}{4}\frac{d^2}{y^2} + \tfrac{1}{2}\frac{d^3}{y^3}\right) - \left(1 - \frac{d}{y} + \tfrac{3}{4}\frac{d^2}{y^2} - \tfrac{1}{2}\frac{d^3}{y^3}\right)\right] = k\frac{q_p}{y^2}\left(2\frac{d}{y} + \frac{d^3}{y^3}\right)$$
$$= 2k\frac{q_p d}{y^3}\left(1 + \frac{d^2}{2y^2}\right). \checkmark$$

This result is similar to Eq. 23.13, $E_{\parallel y} \approx 2kq_p d/y^3$, except that now we have the additional factor $[1 + d^2/2y^2]$. It is good that we kept terms through $z^3 = (d/2y)^3$ because the z^2 term cancels in the difference.

(*b*) We carry out a similar calculation for intermediate distances from the dipole along the perpendicular bisector. We start by writing Eq. 23.8 in the form

$$E_{\perp} = E_y = -\frac{kq_p d}{[x^2 + (d/2)^2]^{3/2}} = -\frac{kq_p d}{x^3}\left(1 + \tfrac{1}{4}\frac{d^2}{x^2}\right)^{-3/2}.$$

Using the same expansion procedure we used to obtain a first-level correction for $E_{\parallel}$, we see that the first-level correction for this direction is

$$E_{\perp} = E_y \approx -\frac{kq_p d}{x^3}\left[1 + (-\tfrac{3}{2})\tfrac{1}{4}\frac{d^2}{x^2}\right]$$
$$= -\frac{kq_p d}{x^3}\left(1 - \tfrac{3}{8}\frac{d^2}{x^2}\right). \checkmark$$

It is gratifying to note that in both cases the correction term ($1 + d^2/2y^2$ for $E_{\parallel}$, $1 - 3d^2/8x^2$ for $E_{\perp}$) is on the order of $(d/y)^2$ or $(d/x)^2$. We expect that these two cases should bracket the actual correction for arbitrary directions at intermediate distances, because the electric field contribution from each charged particle is spherically symmetrical, suggesting significant dependence on distance but not so much on direction.

4 EVALUATE RESULT If we let either x or y get very large relative to d (that is, at locations very far from the dipole), then $d/x \to 0$ and $d/y \to 0$. At these locations, our expression for $E_{\parallel}$ becomes Eq. 23.13 and our expression for $E_{\perp}$ becomes Eq. 23.10. The plus sign in front of the $(d^2/2y^2)$ term in the correction for $(E_{\parallel})_y$ is plausible. To see why, imagine holding a positively charged test particle at a location on the dipole axis far beyond the positive end—for instance, at location $(0, y)$ in Figure WG23.8—and then moving the test particle closer and closer to the dipole. As you do this, the magnitude of the repulsive force exerted by the dipole's positive end on the test particle increases more rapidly than does the magnitude of the attractive force exerted by the more distant negative end.

Guided Problem 23.8 Cathode ray tube

A cathode ray tube uses an electric field to steer electrons to various locations on a screen. In Figure WG23.9, an electron fired from the "electron gun" passes between two parallel plates, and the uniform vertical electric field between the plates deflects the electron's trajectory in the y direction. As the electric field magnitude is varied, the electron can be directed to hit the screen anywhere vertically from top to bottom. (A separate set of plates controls the horizontal position.) If the plates are 30 mm long and located 0.20 m behind a screen that is 0.30 m high, what electric field magnitude is required to deflect an electron to the bottom of the screen if the electron has an initial horizontal velocity of 3.0×10^5 m/s?

Figure WG23.9

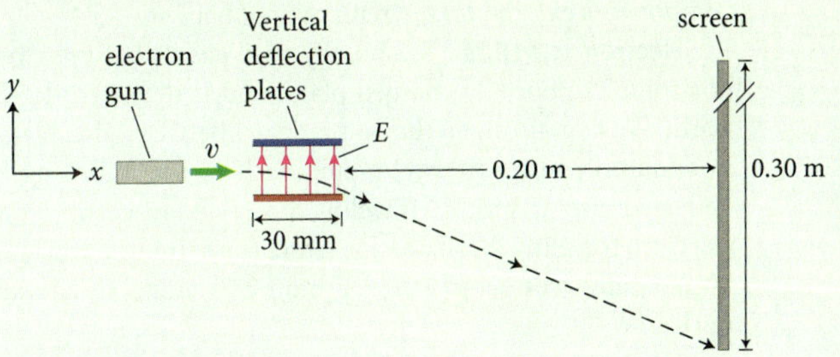

1 GETTING STARTED

1. What physical interactions control the electron's trajectory? What simplifications and assumptions can or must you make?
2. What happens to its motion as the electron travels from gun to screen, and why?

2 DEVISE PLAN

3. How can you determine the electron's trajectory? Remember that you have done trajectory calculations before with the gravitational force as the dominant one. Is there a similarity with the electric force in this case?
4. Does the electron experience a constant force? Does the answer to this question depend on whether the electron is between the plates or in the region from the plates to the screen? Whether or not the answer depends on the electron's position, remember that the trajectory must be continuous at the boundary between the regions.

3 EXECUTE PLAN

4 EVALUATE RESULT

Questions and Problems

For instructor-assigned homework, go to MasteringPhysics® MP

Dots indicate difficulty level of problems: • = *easy,* •• = *intermediate,* ••• = *hard;* CR = *context-rich problem.*

23.1 The field model

1. What is the magnitude of the gravitational field that Earth feels due to the Sun? •
2. Determine the magnitude of Earth's gravitational field for (a) a 70.0-kg person standing at Earth's surface, (b) a 700.0-kg satellite in orbit 150 km above Earth's surface, and (c) the Moon (use 3.844×10^8 m for the center-to-center distance between Earth and the Moon. •
3. Sketch the gravitational field at 15 positions uniformly distributed along the comet orbit in Figure P23.3. ••

Figure P23.3

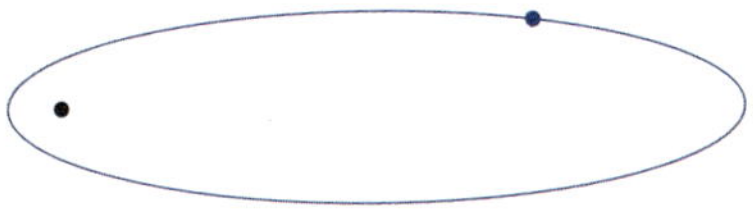

4. Suppose there is an electric field pointing horizontally toward the east at some location near Earth's surface. Does it make sense to add the gravitational and electric *fields* to determine the behavior of a proton at that location? ••

23.2 Electric field diagrams

5. The units of the gravitational field are those of acceleration. Is that true of the electric field as well? If not, why not? •
6. Two electrons initially repel each other with an electric force of magnitude 2.5×10^{-20} N. What is the magnitude of the electric field at one electron due to the other? •
7. The dwarf planet Pluto and its moon Charon have very similar masses. Suppose the masses are equal, and draw a gravitational field diagram for this system of two source objects. ••
8. Draw two vector field diagrams, one for a particle carrying charge $+q$ and located at the origin of a rectangular coordinate system and one for a particle carrying charge $-2q$ and located at the origin. Describe the principal differences between the two diagrams. ••

23.3 Superposition of electric fields

9. The two Ping-Pong balls in Figure P23.9 carry charges that have the same magnitude but opposite signs. Sketch the vectors that represent the electric fields the balls produce at locations A, B, C, D, and E, which all lie in a common plane that includes the line joining the centers of the balls. Use a ruler to estimate that relative distances between locations. •

Figure P23.9

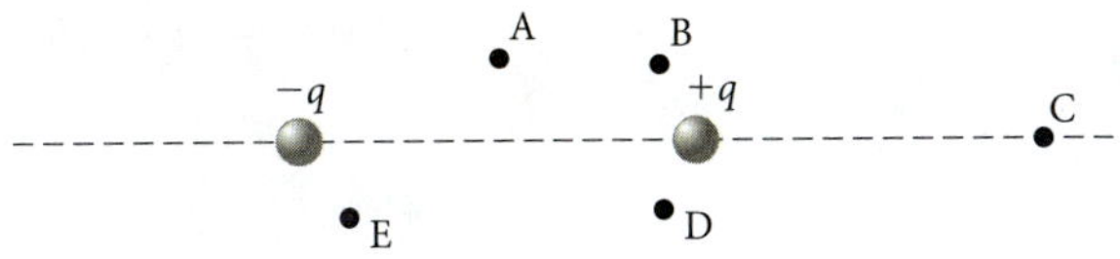

PRACTICE

10. Positive charge is distributed uniformly on a plastic rod bent to form a quarter-circular arc (Figure P23.10). What is the direction of the electric field at the center of the circle? •

Figure P23.10

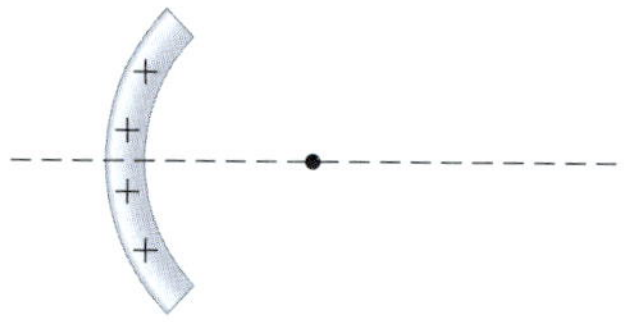

11. Repeat Problem 9 for the case where the positive charge in Figure P23.9 remains $+q$ but the negative charge is changed to $-2q$. ••

12. The two particles in Figure P23.12 carry identical charges. Sketch the vectors that represent the electric fields the particles produce at locations A, B, and C, which all lie in the plane that is midway between the two particles and perpendicular to the line connecting them. ••

Figure P23.12

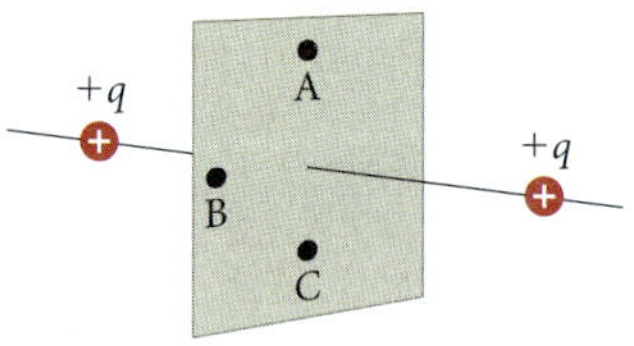

13. Charged beads are placed at the corners of a square in the various configurations shown in Figure P23.13. Each red bead carries a charge $+q$, and the blue bead carries a charge $-q$. Rank the configurations according to the magnitude of the electric field at the center of the square, smallest magnitude first. ••

Figure P23.13

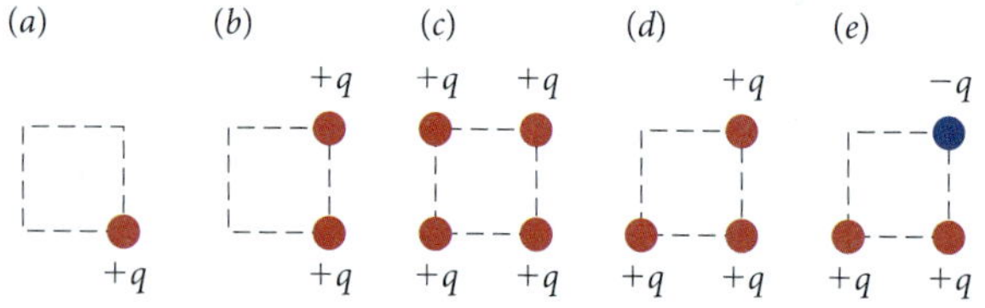

14. The charge on a nonconducting rod increases linearly from end A to end B. The rod is bent in a circle so that ends A and B almost meet very near the top of the circle (Figure P23.14). What is the direction of the electric field at the center of the circle? (Hint: Consider contributions from diametrically opposite segments!) •••

Figure P23.14

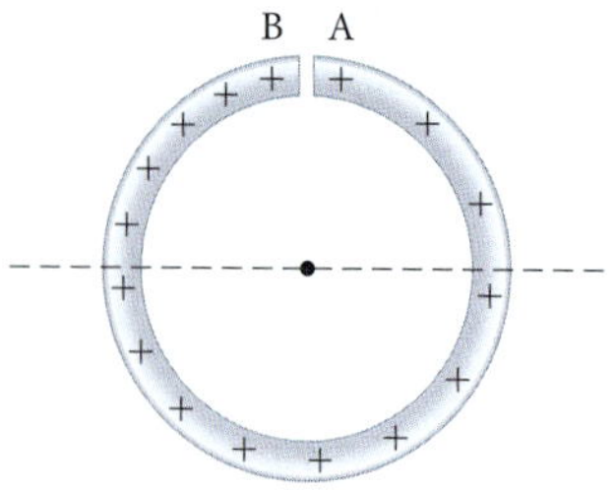

23.4 Electric fields and forces

15. To what extent is the gravitational field uniform inside the room in which you are sitting? •

16. A positively charged test particle is placed midway between two fixed, identical positively charged source particles. (*a*) Is the test particle in a stable or unstable equilibrium at that location? (*b*) If the test particle is replaced by a negatively charged test particle, is it in a stable or unstable equilibrium at that location? •

17. A box full of charged plastic balls sits on a table. The electric force exerted on a ball near one upper corner of the box has components 1.2×10^{-3} N directed north, 5.7×10^{-4} N directed east, and 2.2×10^{-4} N directed vertically upward. The charge on this ball is 120 nC. If this ball were replaced with one that has a charge of -50 nC, what would be the force components exerted on the replacement ball? ••

18. An electron traveling horizontally east passes between two horizontal, oppositely charged plates and is deflected downward. Passing through the same space between the plates, in which direction (if any) would each of the following be deflected: (*a*) a proton traveling horizontally east, (*b*) an electron traveling horizontally west, (*c*) a proton traveling horizontally west, and (*d*) a proton traveling horizontally north? ••

19. A 30.0-mg oil drop carrying a charge of $+3.5\ \mu$C passes undeflected through a region in which there is a uniform, constant electric field. What are the magnitude and direction of the electric field? ••

20. Each dipole in Figure P23.20 is free to rotate about an axis that is perpendicular to the plane of the page (represented by the dot in the center of each dipole). The dipoles are initially held fixed in a horizontal line as shown but are then released and begin rotating. What is their most likely final orientation if there is a mechanism for energy dissipation? ••

Figure P23.20

21. Suppose two plates lie in parallel horizontal planes, one plate in the xy plane at $z = 0$ and the other plate in the plane that is parallel to the xy plane at $z = 10$ mm. Between the plates is a constant electric field directed vertically upward (that is, in the positive z direction). A proton and an electron are launched in the positive x direction with the same initial velocity from position (0, 0, 5.0 mm). If the proton strikes a plate at (200 mm, 0, 10 mm), where does the electron strike? •••

23.5 Electric field of a charged particle

22. Two uniformly charged pellets A and B are held some distance from each other, and then the charge on A is doubled. Which of the following statements is most correct? (*a*) The magnitude of the electric force exerted on A is doubled because the electric field at the position of A is doubled. (*b*) The magnitude of the electric force exerted on A is doubled because the electric field at the position of B is doubled. (*c*) The magnitude of the electric force exerted on B is doubled because the electric field at the position of B is doubled. •

23. What is the magnitude of the electric field 200 mm away from a particle carrying 3.0 μC of charge? •

24. A small, charged, spherical object at the origin of a Cartesian coordinate system contains 3.30×10^4 more electrons than protons. What are the magnitude and direction of the electric field at the position (2.00 mm, 1.00 mm)? •

25. Two protons A and B are separated by a distance $d = 9.00\ \mu$m. What are the magnitude and direction of the electric field along the line connecting the protons (*a*) halfway between them and (*b*) a distance $d/4$ away from A and $3d/4$ away from B? Use the relationship between electric force and electric field. •

26. A positively charged particle initially at rest on the ground accelerates upward to 100 m/s in 2.00 s. If the particle has a charge-to-mass ratio of 0.100 C/kg and the electric field in this region is constant and uniform, what are the magnitude and direction of the electric field? ••

27. A proton is located in the xy plane at (4.00 mm, 3.00 mm) and experiences an electric force exerted by a particle at the origin carrying a positive charge of 6.95 μC. (*a*) Determine the magnitude and direction of the electric force exerted on the proton. (*b*) Using the relationship between electric field and electric force and the result from part *a*, determine the magnitude and direction of the electric field at (4.00 mm, 3.00 mm) due to the positive charge at the origin. (Assume the proton has been removed.) ••

28. A particle at the origin of a Cartesian coordinate system carries a charge of 3.89×10^{-9} C. What are the magnitude and direction of the electric field at (*a*) (4.00 mm, 0), (*b*) (0, 4.00 mm), and (*c*) (−2.829 mm, 2.829 mm)? ••

29. (*a*) Plot the value of the radial component of the electric field due to a positively charged pellet as a function of distance from the pellet center. (*b*) Repeat for a negatively charged pellet. Take each pellet to be a uniformly charged nonconducting sphere having a radius of 18.5 mm and carrying a charge of 1.11 nC. ••

30. An electron initially placed 0.10 m to the right of a small charged sphere moves to the right with an initial acceleration of 4.0×10^7 m/s^2. What is the magnitude of the charge on the sphere? (Ignore gravity.) ••

31. A small sphere carrying 6.0 nC of charge is placed 100 mm from a small sphere carrying 3.0 nC of charge. Assume the spheres are tiny relative to the 100-mm separation distance. At what position on the line joining the spheres is the electric field magnitude zero? ••

32. Two beads, one carrying charge $+q$ and the other carrying charge $+4q$, are separated by a distance d that is much greater than the radius of each bead. (*a*) Is there any location along the line between them where the electric field magnitude is zero? If so, what is that location in terms of d? (*b*) Is there any other position where the electric field magnitude is zero? ••

33. In an inkjet printer, tiny drops of ink of inertia m are given a charge q and then fired toward the paper at speed v. They first pass between two charged plates of length ℓ that create a uniform electric field of magnitude E between them (Figure P23.33). The field direction is perpendicular to the plates and to the initial path of the drops. The electric field deflects each drop from its initial horizontal path and is used to control what is printed on the paper. (*a*) Derive an expression for how far in the vertical direction a drop is deflected as it passes between the plates. (*b*) For a drop inertia of 1.5×10^{-10} kg, an electric field strength of 1.2×10^6 N/C, a plate length of 10 mm, and a drop speed of 20 m/s, calculate the drop charge necessary to result in a deflection of 1.3 mm. (*c*) Is it acceptable to ignore the effects of gravity in this case? ••

Figure P23.33

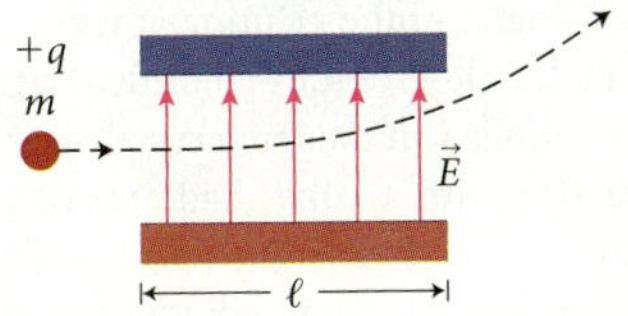

34. (*a*) What electric field magnitude is needed to balance the gravitational force exerted by Earth on an electron near Earth's surface? (*b*) Relative to the electron's position, where would you have to place a proton in order to create an equivalent electric force on the electron? ••

35. Consider a rectangle with diagonal length $2a$ in the yz plane with the origin at the center of the rectangle. Four beads, each carrying charge q, are placed on the rectangle perimeter, one bead at each corner. Show that the electric field along the x axis is given by ••

$$E_x = k\left(\frac{4qx}{(x^2+a^2)^{3/2}}\right)\hat{\imath}.$$

36. A particle carrying a charge of 6.0 μC is located at the origin of a rectangular coordinate system, and a particle carrying a charge of 4.0 μC is located at (0, 5.0 m). What are the magnitude and direction of the electric field at the positions (*a*) (5.0 m, 0), (*b*) (−5.0 m, 0), and (*c*) (0, −5.0 m)? ••

37. Five charged particles are equally spaced around a semicircle of radius 100 mm, with one particle at each end of the semicircle and the remaining three spaced equally between the two ends. The semicircle lies in the region $x < 0$ of an xy plane, such that the complete circle is centered on the origin. (*a*) If each particle carries a charge of 1.00 nC, what is the electric field at the origin? (*b*) Where could you put a single particle carrying a charge of −5.00 nC to make the electric field magnitude zero at the origin? ••

38. A positively charged particle 1 is at the origin of a Cartesian coordinate system, and there are no other charged objects nearby. You need the electric field magnitude at the position (3.00 nm, 4.00 nm) to be zero, so that no electric force is exerted on any charged object placed at that location. (*a*) Make a plot of all positions where a single additional charged particle 2 (of arbitrary charge) could be placed to make the electric field magnitude zero at (3.00 nm, 4.00 nm). Explain some of the key points of your graph. (*b*) Where would you need to place particle 2 if it carried the same charge as particle 1? ••

39. Three particles carrying equal positive charge are located at the corners of an equilateral triangle with side length a. What are the magnitude and direction of the electric field (*a*) at the center of the triangle, (*b*) at the midpoint of any side of the triangle, and (*c*) a distance a above the triangle apex? •••

40. Two nonconducting spheres 1 and 2 carry the same charge, and the magnitude of the electric force exerted by each sphere on the other is 0.10 N when they are 50 mm apart. (*a*) What is the magnitude of the charge on each sphere, assuming each has a diameter much smaller than 10 mm? (*b*) What is the magnitude of the electric field 50 mm directly above sphere 1 if sphere 2 is located to the left of sphere 1? (*c*) Would your answers change if each sphere had a radius of 10 mm? •••

41. A particle carrying a charge of $-5.0\ \mu\text{C}$ is located at the origin of a rectangular coordinate system, and a particle carrying a charge of $12.0\ \mu\text{C}$ is located at (1.0 m, 0.50 m). Determine the coordinates of the position at which $E = 0$. ●●●

42. In table salt—sodium chloride, NaCl—the Na^+ and Cl^- ions are arranged in a cubic crystal structure. You can observe in this structure a cube made up of eight ions: four Na^+ and four Cl^- in alternating corners. Each Na^+ has a radius of 99 pm, each Cl^- has a radius of 181 pm, and the ions are spaced as though they were solid balls of these sizes, touching their neighbors. (*a*) For a single cube of this arrangement, what are the magnitude and direction of the electric field at one of the Na^+ ions due to the other seven ions in the cube? (*b*) What are the magnitude and direction of the vector sum of the electric forces exerted on this Na^+ ion by the other seven ions? ●●●

23.6 Dipole field

43. A water molecule (Figure P23.43) has a dipole moment of $6.19 \times 10^{-30}\ \text{C}\cdot\text{m}$. If the O–H bonds were ionic bonds (in reality they are polar covalent bonds), the electrons from the two hydrogen atoms would be completely transferred to the oxygen atom. Using the measured dipole moment and the fact that the centers of positive and negative charge are 0.058 nm apart, can you rule out the hypothesis that the O–H bonds are ionic? ●

Figure P23.43

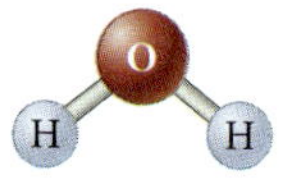

44. Two plastic bowling balls, 1 and 2, are rubbed with cloth until they each carry a uniformly distributed charge of magnitude 0.10 nC. Ball 1 is negatively charged, and ball 2 is positively charged. If the balls are held apart by a 600-mm stick stuck through the holes so that it runs from the center of one ball to the center of the other, what is the dipole moment of the arrangement? ●

45. As Figure P23.45 shows, the water molecule is bent, and the angle formed by the three atoms is 104.5°. Given that the permanent dipole moment of the molecule is $6.186 \times 10^{-30}\ \text{C}\cdot\text{m}$, determine the dipole moment of each OH bond. ●●

46. A proton located several proton diameters away from a small charged object carrying charge q is subject to an electric field of magnitude E. As the proton moves a distance d along the x axis away from the object, the electric field magnitude drops to $E/4$. If the charged object had instead been an electric dipole (with a charge of magnitude q on each end) oriented in the z direction, by what factor would the initial electric field magnitude E have dropped as the proton receded by distance d along the x axis? ●●

47. A dipole consisting of a proton and an electron held a distance d apart is aligned along a z axis. A second proton is then placed at the midpoint of the line joining the electron and proton of the dipole. What is the ratio of the electric field magnitude at $(0, 0, 10d)$ to the electric field magnitude at $(0, 0, 20d)$? ●●

48. Equation 23.12,

$$E_y = k\frac{q_p}{y^2}\left[\left(1 - \frac{d}{2y}\right)^{-2} - \left(1 + \frac{d}{2y}\right)^{-2}\right],$$

was derived for the case $y > d/2$. Explain why this equation holds for the case $y < -d/2$. ●●

49. An electric *quadrupole* can be constructed by placing four charged objects at the corners of a square (Figure P23.49). The objects are identical except for the charge they carry: The two objects in one diagonally opposed pair each carry charge $+q$, and the other two objects carry charge $-q$. (Note that there is no charge on the quadrupole overall and that the combination of four charges has no dipole moment.) How does the magnitude of the electric field depend on the distance r from the center of the quadrupole? Take the side length for the square to be d and assume $r \gg d$. ●●

Figure P23.49

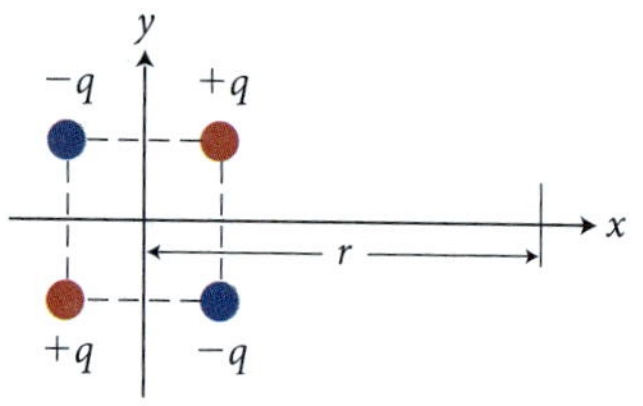

50. A dipole is centered at the origin of a coordinate system, and a small charged sphere is some distance away along the perpendicular bisector of the dipole. The particle carries a uniformly distributed charge of -3.0 nC, and experiences a 200 nN electric force in the positive y direction. (*a*) If the dipole charge is 10 nC and the dipole separation is 20 mm, how far away from the dipole is the sphere? (*b*) How is the dipole moment oriented? ●●

51. Two thin plastic rods, each of length ℓ, are joined end to end. One rod is positively charged with a uniform linear charge density λ, and the other carries a negative charge density $-\lambda$. What is the effective dipole moment of the rod? ●●

52. An electric dipole that has dipole separation d is aligned along the y axis of an xy coordinate system, pointed in the positive y direction. (*a*) Show that for x and y much greater than d, the x and y components of the electric field of the dipole are given by

$$E_x = \frac{3kpxy}{(x^2 + y^2)^{5/2}}; \quad E_y = \frac{kp(2y^2 - x^2)}{(x^2 + y^2)^{5/2}}.$$

(*b*) Show that this general result includes the special results derived in *Principles* Section 23.6. ●●●

23.7 Electric fields of continuous charge distributions

53. You've been given the task of charging a spherical weather balloon made of a conducting material, and you want to put as much charge on it as possible. An experienced colleague advises you that the air surrounding the balloon becomes conducting when the electric field at the balloon surface reaches 100,000 N/C, causing a spark that discharges the balloon. Because the balloon must stay charged, you cannot allow this air breakdown to occur. By measuring the balloon's shadow, you calculate the balloon diameter to be 3.5 m. This gives you enough information to estimate the maximum charge the balloon can have without causing air breakdown. ●

54. A positively charged particle is released from rest along the axis of symmetry of a fixed ring carrying a uniformly distributed negative charge. Describe the motion of the particle. ●

55. A uniformly charged rod lies along the z axis of an xyz coordinate system, from $z = -100$ mm to $z = +100$ mm. The linear charge density on the rod is 100 nC/m. What is the vector expression for the electric field at (40 mm, 30 mm, 0)? •

56. In the uniform charge distribution shown in Figure P23.56, each of the three arcs forms one-fourth of the circumference of a ring. The upper right and lower left arcs each carry a positive charge q, while the upper left arc carries a charge $-q$. Determine the electric field at P, the ring center, in terms of q and R. ••

Figure P23.56

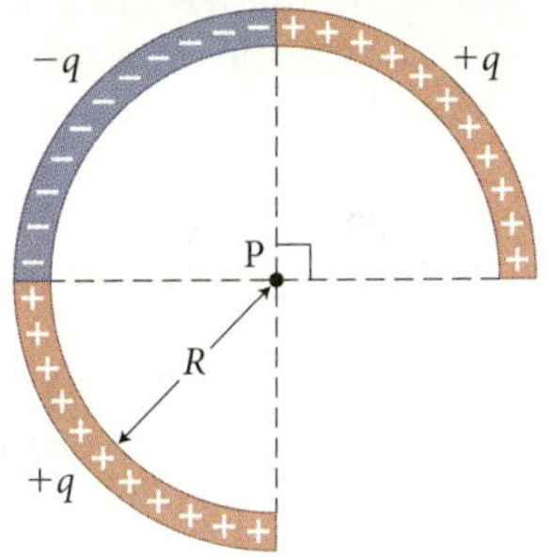

57. The thin glass rod of length ℓ in Figure P23.57 has a linear charge density that starts out as zero at the left end of the rod and increases linearly from left to right. The positive charge on the rod is q_{rod}. (*a*) What is the electric field along the rod's axis at position P, which lies a distance d from the right end of the rod? (*b*) What is the approximate expression for the magnitude of the electric field at distances $d \gg \ell$—that is, far enough away to make the rod look small? ••

Figure P23.57

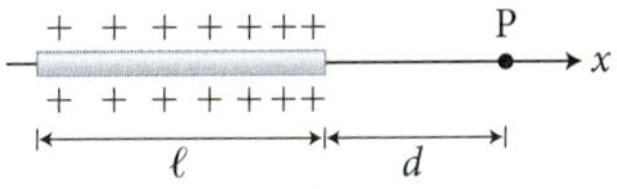

58. You have two disks, 1 and 2, both of radius $R = 25.0$ mm and both made of the same nonconducting material. Disk 1 carries a uniformly distributed charge $q_1 = 1.50\ \mu$C, and the uniformly distributed charge q_2 on disk 2 is unknown. You place disk 1 at $z_1 = 0$ and disk 2 at $z_2 = +32.0$ mm such that the symmetry axis of each disk coincides with the z axis. Using a small charged pith ball, you locate one position on the z axis where the electric force exerted on the pith ball is zero; this position is $z_{E=0} = +88.0$ mm. What is the charge on disk 2? ••

59. What percentage error in the electric field magnitude do you introduce by approximating the charged disk of *Principles* Figure 23.29 as an infinite charged sheet with the same surface charge density for (*a*) $z = 0.1R$, (*b*) $z = 0.5R$, and (*c*) $z = R$? ••

60. You wish to determine the electric field magnitude along the perpendicular bisector of a 250-mm line along which 30 nC of charge is distributed uniformly. You want to get by with a minimal amount of work, so you need to know when it is sufficient to approximate the line of charge as a charged particle. At what distance along the perpendicular bisector does your error in E reach 5% when you use this approximation? ••

61. For a uniformly charged disk of radius 90 mm, you wish to determine the electric field magnitude along the axis that runs through the disk center and perpendicular to the disk face. You want to get by with a minimal amount of work, so you need to know when you can get by with approximating the disk as an infinite sheet. At what distance along the perpendicular axis does your error in E reach 10% when you use this approximation? ••

62. Three narrow concentric rings of radii 50 mm, 70 mm, and 90 mm are centered about the origin, with the axis of symmetry of each ring oriented along the y axis. The charge on the inner ring is 1.0 μC, that on the middle ring is $-2.0\ \mu$C, and that on the outer ring is 1.0 μC. (*a*) What is the electric field magnitude at (0, 100 mm, 0)? (*b*) What quantity of charge must be placed at (0, -100 mm, 0) to make the electric field magnitude zero at the position calculated in part *a*? ••

63. Two large oppositely and uniformly charged parallel plates are separated by 10 mm. An electron is projected halfway between the plates and parallel to them with an initial speed of 4.0×10^6 m/s. The electron hits the top plate 20 mm from where the electron was projected. (*a*) Which plate is negatively charged, top or bottom? (*b*) What is the surface charge density on the plates if you know that the densities have the same magnitude? ••

64. A particle of inertia m that carries charge q is held above an infinite sheet on which the surface charge density is σ. The charge on the sheet is of the same type as the charge on the particle. The particle is then released from rest. (*a*) Describe its motion. (*b*) What is its acceleration? (*c*) What is the change in its kinetic energy after it has traveled a distance s? ••

65. A uniformly charged thin rod lies along the x axis from $x = 0$ to $x = +\infty$. (*a*) Derive an expression for the magnitude E_y of the electric field along the positive y axis, and (*b*) show that the electric field at positions on this axis makes an angle of 135° with the rod. •••

66. One half of a charged thin ring of radius R carries a charge q_1 uniformly distributed over it, and the other half of the ring carries a charge q_2 uniformly distributed over it. For any position along the axis of symmetry of the ring, derive an expression for (*a*) the component of the electric field parallel to the axis and (*b*) the component of the electric field perpendicular to the axis. •••

67. In Figure P23.67, determine the x and y components of the electric field at position P, which is a distance d above one end of a rod of length ℓ carrying uniformly distributed charge q •••.

Figure P23.67

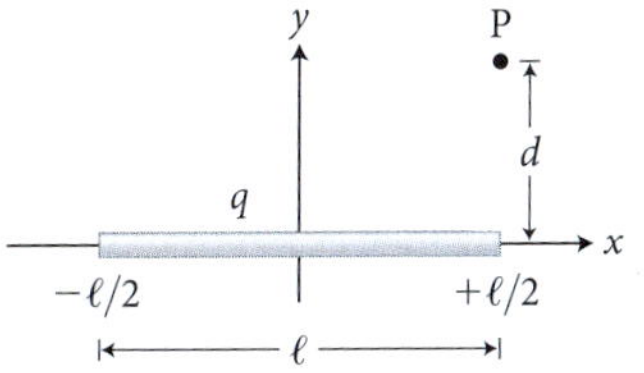

68. A thin rod of length 2ℓ has a linear charge density that is λ_0 at the left end but decreases linearly with distance going from left to right in such a way that the charge on the entire rod is zero. (*a*) What is the magnitude of the electric field along the rod's axis at a position P that is a distance $d > \ell$ to the right of the center of the rod? (*b*) Does your expression simplify to a familiar result for the limiting case $d \gg \ell$? (Hint: The dipole moment of the rod has magnitude $p = 2\lambda_0\ell^2/3$.) •••

69. You place 2.2 μC of charge along a long nonconducting rod. The rod extends from $x = 0$ farther than you can see along the positive x axis. The charge distribution has the form of a decreasing exponential: $q(x) = q_0 e^{-x/\ell}$, where $\ell = 28.6$ mm. Calculate the electric field magnitude 20 mm from the near end of the rod, along its long axis. •••

23.8 Dipoles in electric fields

70. The water molecule is a permanent dipole with a dipole moment of 6.186×10^{-30} C·m. If a single water molecule were oriented such that its dipole moment is along a z axis, what torque is caused on it by the electric force due to an 8500-N/C electric field if that field is in the xz plane and directed 42° above the x axis? •

71. A microwave oven, which fills the oven chamber with oscillating electric fields, works well at heating food that has a high water content. However, it does not work well with frozen food or with food that has a high oil content but low water content. Can you think of a reason for this? (Hint: Water molecules in ice are much more rigidly constrained than they are in liquid, and oil molecules are nonpolar.) •

72. The electric force due to a uniform external electric field causes a torque of magnitude 10.0×10^{-9} N·m on an electric dipole oriented at 30° from the direction of the external field. The dipole moment of the dipole is 8.0×10^{-12} C·m. (*a*) What is the magnitude of the external electric field? (*b*) If the two particles that make up the dipole are 2.5 mm apart, what is the magnitude of the charge on each particle? •

73. A dipole is to be released in a region where there is a uniform electric field and no dissipative forces. Describe the motion of the dipole if it is released from rest in an orientation (*a*) parallel to the electric field and (*b*) almost perpendicular to the electric field. •

74. A small object with dipole moment p is released near its equilibrium orientation in a uniform electric field of magnitude E. The rotational inertia of the dipole is I. (*a*) What is the effective torsional constant κ of this simple harmonic system? (*b*) Calculate the angular frequency ω of small oscillations about the equilibrium orientation. ••

75. A dipole that is free to move is placed near a fixed dipole, with the midpoint of the free dipole on the perpendicular bisector of the fixed dipole. The distance from the free dipole to the fixed one is much greater than the dipole separation d of the fixed dipole. Draw a diagram to illustrate the motion of the free dipole if it is placed with its dipole moment (*a*) in the same direction as the direction of $\vec{p}_{\text{fixed}}$, the dipole moment of the fixed dipole, (*b*) in the direction opposite that of $\vec{p}_{\text{fixed}}$, and (*c*) perpendicular to the direction of $\vec{p}_{\text{fixed}}$. ••

76. In a particular region of space, an electric field has a constant direction but its magnitude increases smoothly along that direction. A dipole is placed in this field, its dipole moment is oriented perpendicular to the field, and it is released from rest. If no dissipative forces are present, describe the dipole's motion, paying particular attention to how it differs from what the motion would be if the electric field were uniform. ••

77. A particle carrying 5.0×10^{-7} C of charge is located on the perpendicular bisector of a small dipole, 300 mm from the center of the line joining the two poles of the dipole. The magnitude of the electric force exerted on the particle is 10.0×10^{-6} N. Draw a diagram showing the dipole and indicating the direction of its dipole moment. On this diagram, show (*a*) the direction of the electric force exerted on the particle and (*b*) the direction of the electric force exerted on the dipole. (*c*) Determine the magnitude of the electric force exerted on the dipole. ••

78. There are two possible alignments of a dipole in an external electric field where the dipole is in equilibrium. (*a*) Draw a field diagram for a uniform electric field and show these two alignments. (*b*) Are both alignments stable? (Consider what would happen in each case if you gave the dipole a slight twist.) (*c*) Based on your answer to part *b* and your experience in mechanics, in which orientation does the dipole have less potential energy? ••

79. In very rare cases, the polarizability of a molecule may be negative. (*a*) Draw a picture showing the resultant charge distribution when such a molecule is placed in the electric field surrounding a positively charged particle. (*b*) Describe the motion of the molecule that would result. ••

80. Two identical particles, each carrying charge q, are a distance r apart. A dipole for which the dipole moment magnitude is p and the dipole separation is $d < r$ is placed on the (imaginary) line joining the two particles in such a way that the center of the dipole coincides with the center of the line joining the two particles. Determine the electric force exerted on the dipole. (Hint: You may wish to use a Taylor series expansion to determine the small difference in the electric forces exerted on the two poles of the dipole.) •••

81. An electrically neutral molecule is collinear with (and located between) two charged particles, one carrying a charge of $+3.56\ \mu$C and the other carrying a charge of $-1.05\ \mu$C. The center of the molecule is 2.57 μm from each particle. If the vector sum of the electric forces exerted on the molecule is 45.0 nN, what is the polarizability of the molecule? •••

Additional Problems

82. Express the SI unit of electric field in terms of joules and other SI base units. •

83. Four particles are located at the corners of a square that is 50 mm on a side. All four particles carry a charge of magnitude 3.0 nC, with positive charge at the lower left corner and negative charge at the other corners. Draw the electric field vectors at the center of the square caused by each of the four source charges, then determine the magnitude and direction of the electric field at the center of the square. •

84. Determine the electric field (magnitude and direction) at the position (8.00 nm, 6.00 nm) caused by a particle located at the origin and carrying a charge of (*a*) 8.00 μC, (*b*) $-23.0\ \mu$C, (*c*) 10.0 nC. •

85. Each of the two particles in Figure P23.85 carries a charge of magnitude q. Determine a position, if one exists, where the electric field magnitude is zero if the charge (*a*) is of the same type on the two particles and (*b*) is positive on one particle and negative on the other. •

Figure P23.85

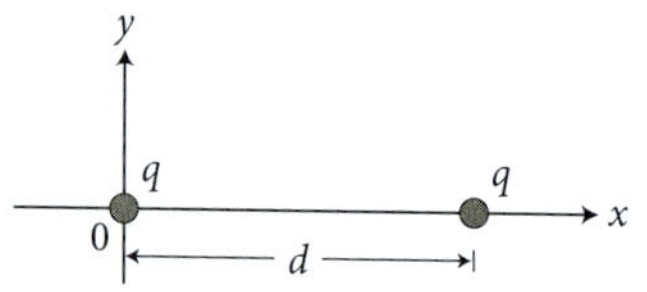

86. An electron is launched into a region of constant electric field, $\vec{E} = 2 \times 10^4$ N/C directed along the positive y axis of a rectangular coordinate system, with an initial velocity of 2.1×10^7 m/s in the positive x direction. How far has the electron traveled in the y direction during the time interval it takes to move 40 mm in the x direction? (Even though the speed at which the electron moves is an appreciable fraction of the speed of light, ignore relativistic effects.) ••

87. An electrically neutral, linear, polar molecule has positive charge equivalent to the charge on one proton centered

0.30 nm from its center of mass and an equal quantity of negative charge centered 0.10 nm from its center of mass (opposite the positive charge). In an electric field of magnitude 100.0 N/C, what are (*a*) the greatest possible and (*b*) the smallest possible torque experienced by this molecule? ••

88. You have a pair of objects that interact with each other electrically. The objects initially are separated by a distance r and exert a force of magnitude F^E on each other. If the separation is increased to $2r$, calculate the new force magnitude between the objects if they are (*a*) charged particles, (*b*) permanent dipoles with their separation along their dipole axis, (*c*) permanent dipoles with their separation perpendicular to their dipole axis, (*d*) a charged particle and a permanent dipole with the dipole pointing directly away from the charged particle, (*e*) a charged particle and an induced dipole. ••

89. A particle carrying a charge of +32.0 nC is located at (10.0 nm, 95.0 nm), and a particle carrying a charge of +98.0 nC is located at (45.0 nm, 56.0 nm). Calculate the electric force exerted on a charged particle placed at the origin if the charge on that particle is (*a*) 3.50 μC, (*b*) 7.22 μC, (*c*) 95.1 nC, (*d*) −77.5 nC, (*e*) 1.00 mC, and (*f*) 33.2 C. (Hint: Once part *a* is done, there is a fast way to do this.) ••

90. Figure P23.90 shows four charged particles, each having a charge equal to +3.00 μC, arranged in a square. What are the magnitude and direction of the electric field at P, located midway between the top two particles? ••

Figure P23.90

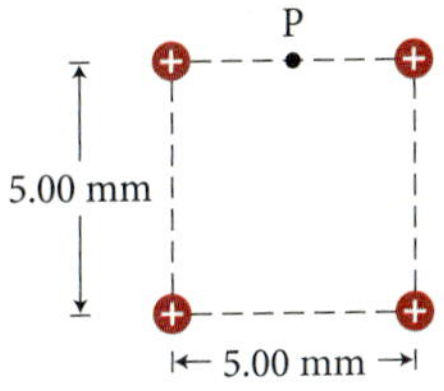

91. A uniformly charged rod extends from $y = -150$ mm to $y = +150$ mm along the y axis of an xy coordinate system. The charge on the rod is 30 nC. (*a*) With the goal of eventually calculating the electric field magnitude along the rod's perpendicular bisector, approximate the rod as three charged particles, and draw a picture showing the locations of the three particles you will use for the calculation and the magnitude of the charge on each one. (*b*) What is the electric field magnitude at $x = 200$ mm using this approximation? (*c*) What is the error in your result in part *b*? (*d*) If you were unable to integrate, what could you do to your approximation to make it better? ••

92. A small sphere 1 carrying charge q_1 and having inertia m_1 is constrained to moving inside a narrow vertical tube (Figure P23.92). Fixed at the bottom of the tube is a small sphere 2 carrying charge q_2. (*a*) Determine the equilibrium height h for sphere 1 (ignore friction). (*b*) Show that if sphere 1 is displaced from this equilibrium position by a small amount and then released, it moves in simple harmonic motion with angular frequency $\omega = (2g/h)^{1/2}$. •••

Figure P23.92

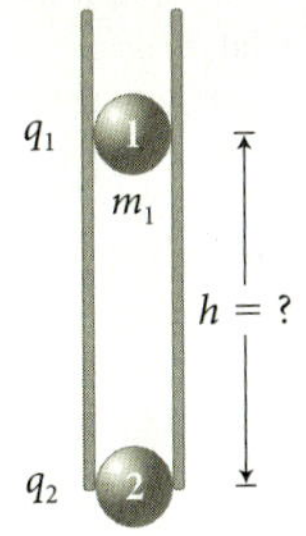

93. Your boss is designing a new data storage system that will have a lot of dipoles very close to one another. They will point in the z direction and be closely spaced in the x and y directions. The data reader will detect E_z as it passes some small distance above the sheet of dipoles. You know that Equation 23.13 is valid only for large distances from the dipole, but it is much easier to apply than the exact result. You prefer the easiest calculation possible, but your boss demands 1.00% accuracy at distances only a few dipole separations from one of the source dipoles. ••• CR

94. You are designing a new guidance mechanism for an inkjet printer. You believe that a circular arc of charge, mounted in the xy plane, is needed in order to deflect the ink droplets most efficiently from their original path along the z axis. You want to use a uniformly charged arc of arc length s that subtends an angle 2θ along a circle of radius R through whose center the ink droplets will pass. The amount of charge that can easily be transferred to the arc is q, which limits the magnitude of the electric field that can be attained at the center of the circle. ••• CR

95. A rod of length πR is composed of three nonconducting segments of equal length. The middle segment is electrically neutral, and each end segment carries a uniformly distributed negative charge $-q$. The rod is bent into a semicircle of radius R. Determine the magnitude of the electric field at the center of the semicircular arc. •••

PRACTICE

Answers to Review Questions

1. A field is a set of values, each value associated with a position in space surrounding one or more field sources.
2. It is impossible to deal with the interactions of moving charged particles without the field concept, and it is often easier to deal with fields than with distributions of charge.
3. Ball A is the source of the electric field that acts on B; the electric field created by B does not act on B.
4. A scalar field, such as the temperature at any position in the space of interest, specifies a scalar value (magnitude only) at each position. A vector field, such as the gravitational field, specifies a vector value (magnitude and direction) at each position.
5. A vector field diagram is a map that uses small vector arrows to represent, at selected positions in space, the field created by a field source. Such a diagram is useful in illustrating how the magnitude and direction of the field vary from one location to another in the field.
6. Place the charged test particle at point P and measure the electric force exerted on the particle by the source. Divide this electric force by the charge of the test particle to obtain the electric field of source S at point P.
7. Nothing. The pellet contributes nothing to the electric field created by the sphere. Because nothing has changed with the source of the field (the sphere), the field the pellet experiences doesn't change.
8. The electric field is defined to be in the direction that a positive test particle would experience an electric force, which is opposite the force on the negative test particle in this question. Hence the electric field is directed toward the east.
9. No, because the two electric field contributions must be added as vectors. The magnitude of the electric field at the pushpin can be anywhere from $|E_1 - E_2|$ to $|E_1 + E_2|$.
10. A negatively charged particle placed in a uniform electric field is accelerated in the direction opposite the direction of $\vec{E}$, and so the upward acceleration of the electron tells you that $\vec{E}$ must have a component that is directed vertically downward. (There might also be a component parallel to the initial motion of the electron. This would change the electron's speed but not its direction.) If the electron is accelerated downward, $\vec{E}$ must have a component that is directed vertically upward.
11. See Figure RQA23.11.

Figure RQA23.11

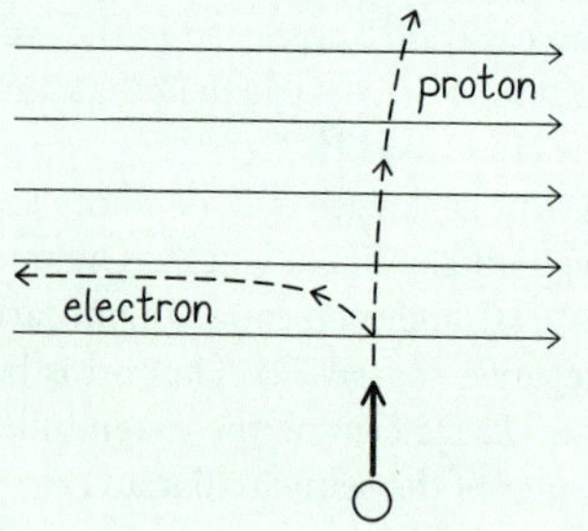

12. No, because the forces exerted on the two charged regions of the dipole are equal in magnitude but opposite in direction, making the vector sum of forces zero.
13. No. The acceleration is not constant (it is centripetal and always changing direction). Therefore the electric force exerted on the electron must be nonconstant, implying the electric field is not uniform.
14. Both. The contribution E_2 makes to the electric field at P would increase, affecting both the x and y components of the electric field (and not in the same proportion).
15. The field magnitude decreases in proportion to the square of the distance between the two objects. To reduce the field by a factor of 100, therefore, you must increase the separation distance by a factor of 10, which means moving it to a position 20 paces from the sphere. Moving the instrument another 18 paces out will do the trick.
16. The magnitude of the electric field due to the sphere is proportional to $1/r^2$, while that due to the dipole is proportional to $1/r^3$. The ratio $E_{\text{dipole}}/E_{\text{sphere}}$ is thus $(qd/r^3)/(q/r^2) = d/r < 1$. That is, the dipole field is weaker at this distance.
17. The dipole moment is a vector pointing from the negative charge in an electric dipole to the positive charge. The magnitude of the dipole moment is $p = qd$, where q is the magnitude of either charge on the dipole and d is the dipole separation.
18. The ratio is 2. The magnitude of the field differs along the axis of the dipole and along the perpendicular bisector of that axis, as given by Equations 23.10 and 23.13. These two, which differ by a factor of 2, are the extreme cases at a given distance R. In the space between these axes the field smoothly varies between these extremes.
19. The radius of the annular ring is $R \sin\theta$, and its width is $R\,d\theta$. Thus the area of the ring is $2\pi(R\sin\theta)R\,d\theta = 2\pi R^2 \sin\theta\,d\theta$. Since the hemispheric half-shell has an area of $2\pi R^2$, the ratio of the ring areas to the shell area is $\sin\theta\,d\theta$. This ratio of the areas also represents the ratio of the infinitesimal charge on the ring dq to the charge on the shell q: $dq/q = \sin\theta\,d\theta$. Thus the infinitesimal charge on the ring is $dq = q\sin\theta\,d\theta$.
20. (*a*) $1/r^2$, (*b*) $1/r$, (*c*) constant.
21. The units are $\text{C}^2 \cdot \text{m/N}$.
22. Because the two forces form an interaction pair, the force magnitude F^E_{pd} must equal the magnitude F^E_{dp}; thus $F^E_{\text{pd}} \propto 1/r^3$. The electric field around the charged particle decreases as the distance squared, not the distance cubed, but the electric force exerted on the dipole decreases more rapidly than the surrounding field does. This is because the electric force exerted on the dipole is the result of a near cancellation of the electric forces exerted on the two ends of the dipole. This cancellation gets more complete as the dipole separation becomes small relative to the distance between the dipole and the particle.
23. Permanent dipoles have separation between their centers of positive and negative charge even in the absence of external electric fields, whereas charge separation for an induced dipole is created only when the object is placed into an external electric field. The charge separation in an induced dipole is proportional to the external field strength E, at least for small values of E.

Answers to Guided Problems

Guided Problem 23.2 At the center, $\vec{E}$ points toward the negatively charged particle and has magnitude $E = 9kq/a^2$. Clever trick: Due to symmetry, adding charge $-q$ to each of the three vertices will not change $\vec{E}$ at the center.

Guided Problem 23.4 In the orientation shown in the figure, the force between the two dipoles is repulsive, with magnitude

$$F = \frac{kq_\text{p}}{(a+d)^2} + \frac{kq_\text{p}}{(a-d)^2} - \frac{2kq_\text{p}}{a^2},$$

which for $d \ll a$ can be approximated as $F \approx 6kq_\text{p}d^2/a^4$.

Guided Problem 23.6 If we take the semicircular rod to be the top half of a circle, then $\vec{E}$ at the circle center points downward (for $q > 0$) and has a magnitude

$$E = \frac{kq}{\pi R^2}\int_{\phi=0}^{\pi} \sin\phi\,d\phi = \frac{2kq}{\pi R^2}.$$

Guided Problem 23.8 To accelerate the electrons downward, the electric field between the plates points upward with magnitude

$$E = \frac{mv_\text{i}^2 h}{e\ell(\ell + 2d)}$$

$$= \frac{(9.1 \times 10^{-31}\,\text{kg})\left(3.0 \times 10^5\,\dfrac{\text{m}}{\text{s}}\right)^2(0.30\,\text{m})}{(1.6 \times 10^{-19}\,\text{C})(0.030\,\text{m})(0.030\,\text{m} + 2 \times 0.20\,\text{m})}$$

$$= 12\,\text{N/C}.$$

24 PRACTICE
Gauss's Law

Chapter Summary

Electric field lines and electric flux (Sections 24.1–24.3, 24.6)

Concepts **Electric field lines** let us visualize the electric field around any charge distribution. The lines are drawn so that at any point the electric field $\vec{E}$ is tangent to the lines.

The number of electric field lines that emanate from a positively charged object or terminate on a negatively charged object is proportional to the charge carried by the object.

The **field line density** at a given position in an electric field is the number of field lines per unit area that cross a surface perpendicular to the field lines at that position. At every position in a field line diagram, the magnitude of the electric field is proportional to the field line density at that position.

The electric flux through a closed surface depends only on the amount of charge enclosed by the surface. The flux through a closed surface due to charge carriers outside the surface is always zero.

Quantitative Tools The *area vector* $\vec{A}$ associated with a flat surface area has a magnitude A equal to the surface area and is directed normal to the plane of the area.

The **electric flux** Φ_E ($\text{N} \cdot \text{m}^2/\text{C}$) through a surface due to an electric field $\vec{E}$ is

$$\Phi_E = \begin{cases} \int \vec{E} \cdot d\vec{A} & (24.4) \\ \oint \vec{E} \cdot d\vec{A} \quad \text{(closed surface)}, & (24.5) \end{cases}$$

where $d\vec{A}$ is an infinitesimal surface area segment and $\vec{E}$ is the electric field at that location. If the surface is closed, the direction of $d\vec{A}$ is chosen to point outward.

Gauss's law (Sections 24.4, 24.7)

Concepts A **Gaussian surface** is any closed surface used to apply Gauss's law. When using Gauss's law to determine an electric field, we choose a Gaussian surface such that the electric field is the same (and possibly zero) everywhere along as many regions of the surface as possible.

The electric field outside a uniformly charged spherical shell is the same as the electric field due to a particle that carries an equal charge and is located at the shell center. The shell's contribution to the electric field is zero everywhere inside the shell.

Quantitative Tools **Gauss's law:** The electric flux through a Gaussian surface is

$$\Phi_E = \oint \vec{E} \cdot d\vec{A} = \frac{q_{\text{enc}}}{\epsilon_0}, \tag{24.8}$$

where q_{enc} (the **enclosed charge**) is the sum of all the charge inside the surface, and

$$\epsilon_0 \equiv \frac{1}{4\pi k} = 8.85 \times 10^{-12}\ \text{C}^2/(\text{N} \cdot \text{m}^2) \tag{24.7}$$

is the **permittivity constant** ($k = 9.0 \times 10^9\ \text{N} \cdot \text{m}^2/\text{C}^2$, Eq. 22.5).

PRACTICE

Calculating electric fields (Sections 24.5, 24.8)

Concepts A Gaussian surface used to determine an electric field should have the same symmetry (spherical, cylindrical, planar) as the symmetry of the charge distribution producing the field. See *Principles* Figure 24.27 and the Procedure box.

A system in which the distribution of charge does not change is in **electrostatic equilibrium.** The electric field inside a conducting object that is in electrostatic equilibrium is zero. Any surplus charge placed on the object arranges itself at the surface of the object, and the electric field at the surface is perpendicular to the surface. A metal reaches electrostatic equilibrium so quickly that this rearrangement is virtually instantaneous.

Quantitative Tools The magnitude of the electric field a distance r from the center of a sphere that has radius $R \geq r$ and contains charge of magnitude q distributed uniformly throughout the sphere volume is

$$E = \frac{1}{4\pi\epsilon_0}\frac{q}{R^3}r = k\frac{q}{R^3}r.$$

The magnitude of the electric field a distance r from an infinite rod having a uniform linear charge density λ is

$$E = \frac{\lambda}{2\pi\epsilon_0 r} = \frac{2k\lambda}{r}.$$

The magnitude of the electric field produced by a nonconducting sheet having a uniform surface charge density σ is

$$E = \frac{\sigma}{2\epsilon_0}.$$

The magnitude of the electric field produced by an infinite conducting plate having a uniform surface charge density σ is

$$E = \frac{\sigma}{\epsilon_0}. \quad (24.17)$$

Review Questions

Answers to these questions can be found at the end of this chapter.

24.1 Electric field lines

1. Describe how to draw an electric field line for a given charge distribution.
2. Explain how to determine the number of field lines to draw around a given charged object.

24.2 Field line density

3. Explain how electric field lines represent both the direction and the magnitude of the electric field at a given location in an electric field.
4. What is the definition of *field line density*?
5. Why do we measure field line density only through a surface that is perpendicular to the field lines?

24.3 Closed surfaces

6. The field line flux through a certain closed surface is zero. Does that mean there are no charged objects inside the closed surface?
7. The enclosed charge for a closed surface is zero. Does that mean there are no electric field lines crossing the surface?
8. Eight electrons are the only charged particles inside an isolated balloon, producing a field line flux through its surface. (*a*) If eight additional electrons are set outside the balloon to form the eight corners of a cube, how does the field line flux through the balloon change? (*b*) How does the flux change if the eight additional electrons are all placed at one location outside the balloon instead of being distributed at the corners of a cube?
9. Given a drawing of the electric field lines surrounding a closed surface, explain how to determine the field line flux through that surface.

24.4 Symmetry and Gaussian surfaces

10. Describe the electric fields inside and outside a uniformly charged spherical shell.
11. Describe the characteristics of planar symmetry.

24.5 Charged conducting objects

12. Under what conditions is the electric field magnitude equal to zero inside a conducting material?
13. Under what conditions is the electric field magnitude nonzero inside the cavity enclosed by a hollow conducting sphere?
14. A hollow conducting object in electrostatic equilibrium carries a surplus electric charge. Without additional information, what must be true about the distribution of this surplus charge?

24.6 Electric flux

15. What is the distinction between *field line flux* and *electric flux*? Why is electric flux the preferred variable for analyzing electric fields?
16. In the formula for electric flux, $\Phi_E = EA \cos\theta$, what does A represent? What does θ represent?
17. When working with irregular surfaces and/or nonuniform electric fields, we obtain the electric flux by integrating a scalar product of the electric field and a small segment of the area of the surface. Why is the scalar product needed?
18. In flux calculations for a closed surface, why is it important to define the area vector as pointing outward, away from the interior of the surface?

24.7 Deriving Gauss's law

19. A spherical surface encloses one electron and one proton. Is the enclosed charge positive, negative, or zero?
20. Would Gauss's law hold if the electric field due to a charged particle had a $1/r$ dependence rather than a $1/r^2$ dependence?

24.8 Applying Gauss's law

21. Inside a ball of volume V and radius R that carries a uniformly distributed charge q, you draw a spherical Gaussian surface that is concentric with the ball and has radius $r < R$. Write an expression for the charge q_{enc} enclosed by the Gaussian surface.
22. A thin spherical metal shell of radius R carries a uniformly distributed charge $+q$. It is surrounded by a concentric thin spherical metal shell of radius $2R$ that carries a uniformly distributed charge $-q$. For which of the following regions enclosed by a concentric spherical Gaussian surface of radius r is the electric field zero: $r < R$, $R < r < 2R$, $r > 2R$?
23. In sketching a Gaussian surface for an infinitely long charged rod when you need to determine the electric field at some distance r from the rod axis, it makes sense to draw a cylinder of radius r for the Gaussian surface, but what value should you use for the length of the cylindrical Gaussian surface? Must this length be infinity just as the rod length is?

Developing a Feel

Make an order-of-magnitude estimate of each of the following quantities. Letters in parentheses refer to hints below. Use them as needed to guide your thinking.

1. The gravitational flux that enters the roof of a typical one-story house due to Earth's gravitational field (E, I, P, L)
2. The electric flux through a horizontal cake pan held 10 m directly above a small object that carries a charge of 100 μC (B, H, M)
3. The surface charge density that results when you place 50 μC of charge on a metal baking sheet (D, J)
4. The surface charge density required to "float" an electron 10^{-2} m above a plastic cutting board (C, G, K, N, A)
5. The surface charge density on the ground that is required to create an upward electric field of magnitude 100 N/C a few meters above the ground (O, F)

Hints

A. What electric field strength is required to create the electric force needed to cancel the gravitational force exerted on the electron?
B. What is the bottom surface area of a cake pan?
C. What forces must cancel in order to float the electron?
D. What is the area of a baking sheet?
E. What is the floor area of a typical one-story house?
F. Does it matter exactly how far above the ground you are?
G. What are the dimensions of a cutting board?
H. What is the magnitude of the electric field at the location of the cake pan?
I. What should you do about the tilt angle θ of the roof surface?
J. How does the charge distribute itself?
K. What does the order-of-magnitude difference between the 10-mm separation distance and the surface area of the board tell you about the board?
L. What are the gravitational quantities that correspond to these electrical quantities?
M. Is the electric field uniform over the cake pan surface?
N. What is the inertia of an electron?
O. Which geometry is more appropriate here: spherical or planar?
P. If this estimate were of electric flux, which quantities would you need?

Key (all values approximate)

A. 6×10^{-11} N/C; **B.** 0.04 m^2; **C.** the electric force exerted by the charged board and the gravitational force exerted by Earth; **D.** 0.2 m^2; **E.** 150 m^2; **F.** this value is not needed as long as you approximate Earth's surface as an infinite sheet; **G.** 0.3 m $\times$ 0.4 m; **H.** 9000 N/C; **I.** nothing—the floor area, $A \cos\theta$, includes the roof slope; **J.** approximately uniformly on both sides of the sheet; **K.** the board might as well be infinitely large at this small separation distance; **L.** $\vec{E} \leftrightarrow \vec{g}$, $\vec{A} \leftrightarrow \vec{A}$; **M.** because the pan is about 0.3 m across, the variation in the angular direction of $\vec{E}$ over the surface is diameter/distance = 0.3 m/10 m = 0.03 rad $\approx 2°$, small enough to consider the field uniform; **N.** 9×10^{-31} kg; **O.** planar because Earth's curvature is negligible for such a small separation distance; **P.** $\vec{E}$, $\vec{A}$

Worked and Guided Problems

Procedure: Calculating the electric field using Gauss's Law

Gauss's law allows you to calculate the electric field for charge distributions that exhibit spherical, cylindrical, or planar symmetry without having to carry out any integrations.

1. Identify the symmetry of the charge distribution. This symmetry determines the general pattern of the electric field and the type of Gaussian surface you should use (see Figure 24.27).
2. Sketch the charge distribution and the electric field by drawing a number of field lines, remembering that the field lines start on positively charged objects and end on negatively charged ones. A two-dimensional drawing should suffice.
3. Draw a Gaussian surface such that the electric field is either parallel or perpendicular (and constant) to each face of the surface. If the charge distribution divides space into distinct regions, draw a Gaussian surface in each region where you wish to calculate the electric field.
4. For each Gaussian surface determine the charge q_{enc} enclosed by the surface.
5. For each Gaussian surface calculate the electric flux Φ_E through the surface. Express the electric flux in terms of the unknown electric field E.
6. Use Gauss's law (Eq. 24.8) to relate q_{enc} and Φ_E and solve for E.

You can use the same general approach to determine the charge carried by a charge distribution given the electric field of a charge distribution exhibiting one of the three symmetries in Figure 24.27. Follow the same procedure, but in steps 4–6, express q_{enc} in terms of the unknown charge q and solve for q.

These examples involve material from this chapter but are not associated with any particular section. Some examples are worked out in detail; others you should work out by following the guidelines provided.

Worked Problem 24.1 Pair of charged spheres

(*a*) Draw the electric field line pattern that arises from two very small spheres, each carrying a charge $+q$. (Assume that the radius of each sphere is much smaller than the distance between the spheres.) (*b*) What is the electric flux through the plane that bisects and is perpendicular to a line segment drawn between the centers of the two spheres? (c) How would the field line pattern change if the charge on each small sphere were $-q$?

❶ **GETTING STARTED** We have two spheres that carry equal charge, and we must show the field line pattern for the electric field they create in two cases: both spheres positively charged and both negatively charged. We must also determine the electric flux through a plane midway between the spheres. We start with the sketch of Figure WG24.1, showing our given information and the quantities we must determine.

Figure WG24.1

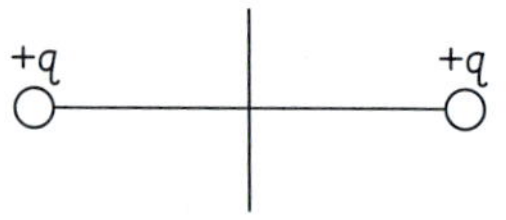

We know the relationship between the type of charge an object carries and the direction of the electric field around the object, and we know how to draw the field lines for a known electric field. We therefore need to figure out the electric field direction at several locations in the space around the spheres and then connect these points to draw the field lines. To determine the electric flux through the bisecting plane, we need to sum over the entire plane the quantity $\vec{E} \cdot d\vec{A}$, which is $E_x dA$ if we take the separation between the two spheres to be in the x direction. This seems as if it could be a lengthy calculation, but we hold out hope that once we start drawing field lines, we may find that symmetry simplifies the problem. Because we are told that the spheres are much smaller than their separation distance, we will treat each sphere as a particle in drawing field lines.

❷ **DEVISE PLAN** We obtain the direction of the electric field by determining the direction of the electric force exerted on a positively charged test particle located near the spheres. We could determine this force direction at many locations around the spheres and from these electric force vectors determine the direction of $\vec{E}$ and then draw the field lines. For a complex charge distribution, this is the only way. In this problem, however, we can use the symmetry of our two-sphere system to figure out the field line pattern.

Once we have the field line diagram, we can use Eq. 24.4 to express the electric flux through the specified plane. We can answer part *c* from our knowledge of the relationship between charge type and field line direction.

❸ **EXECUTE PLAN** (*a*) Because the charge on each sphere is positive, the electric field is directed radially outward from each sphere. We know that, no matter where we put it, the test particle is repelled by both spheres. We also know that wherever we place the test particle it is repelled more strongly by the sphere closer to it. In the plane midway between the spheres, the electric forces exerted on the test particle by the two spheres must be of equal magnitude because the spheres are equidistant from the plane. Thus for the test particle placed in the plane between the spheres, the force $\vec{F}^E_{sp}$, which is the vector sum of forces exerted on the test particle by the two spheres, has no x component. Drawing in a few electric force vectors gives the pattern shown in Figure WG24.2. Using the force vectors as a guide and the fact that field lines cannot cross each other, we trace out a dozen or so lines for the electric field due to the two spheres (Figure WG24.3). ✓

Figure WG24.2

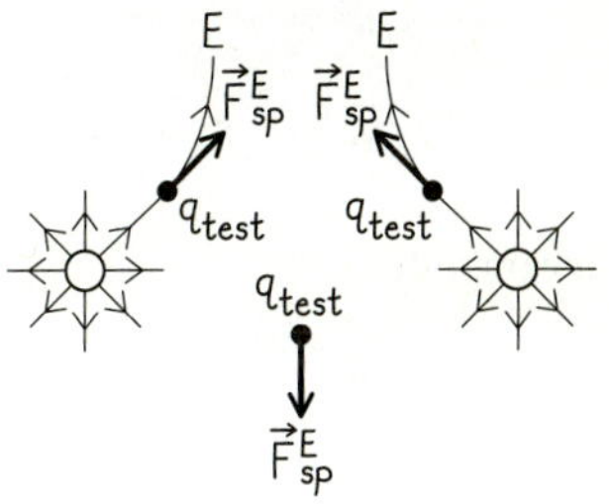

(*b*) Notice in Figure WG24.3 that no electric field lines cross the plane between the two spheres. This tells us that the normal component E_x of the electric field is zero, and thus the electric flux through this plane is zero. ✓

(*c*) If both spheres were negatively charged, the field line pattern would look the same except the directions of the field lines would be reversed. ✓

Figure WG24.3

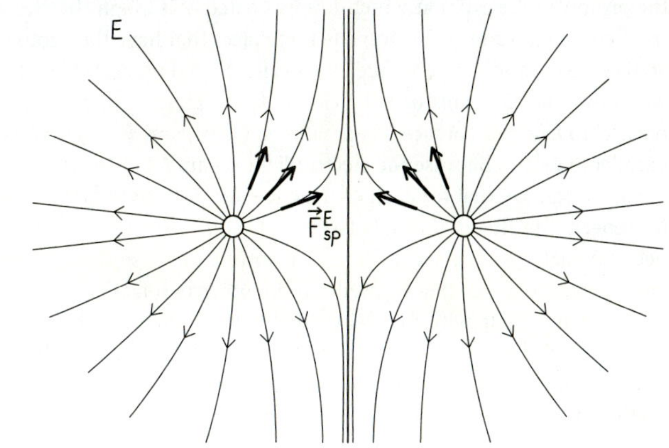

❹ **EVALUATE RESULT** We know from *Principles* Section 24.1 that electric field lines between two objects that are oppositely charged run from the positively charged object to the negatively charged one. Thus, we expect that the field lines between two objects that carry the same type of charge should look as if they are pushing the objects apart, just as Figure WG24.3 shows. It makes sense that the electric flux through the bisecting plane is zero because the electric field component perpendicular to the plane is zero by symmetry: The charge distribution is unchanged when reflected about the bisecting plane.

Guided Problem 24.2 Charged square sheet

A square sheet carries a charge $+q$ uniformly distributed over its surface. Make a sketch of the sheet, and draw the electric field lines outside the sheet in the plane that contains the sheet. Based on this sketch, what is the electric flux through a plane perpendicular to the sheet and passing through its center?

❶ **GETTING STARTED**

1. After drawing your sketch, describe the problem in your own words. What is the problem asking you to determine? Are you asked for a qualitative or a quantitative answer?
2. What do you know about the direction of the electric field near the sheet edges?
3. What should the electric field look like at distances far from the sheet?

❷ **DEVISE PLAN**

4. Are there any symmetries you can use to simplify the problem?
5. What equation helps you get the electric flux? Can you already guess what the flux is?

❸ **EXECUTE PLAN**

6. Draw several field lines connecting the two limiting cases: close to the sheet and far away from it.

❹ **EVALUATE RESULT**

7. What can you say about the electric flux through any plane that is perpendicular to the sheet through a symmetry axis of the sheet?

Worked Problem 24.3 Flux through a cube

As you ponder your drink, you notice an ice cube floating in your glass. Because you are studying electric flux, this floating cube leads you to formulate an interesting question: What electric flux is produced though each face of an imaginary cube of side length a, at one corner of which is a single proton?

❶ **GETTING STARTED** We are given the size of a cube and the fact that one corner is occupied by a proton. We are asked to determine the electric flux through the cube's faces. We draw a sketch containing this information (Figure WG24.4). We treat the proton as a particle with a uniform charge distribution, which means that it creates a spherically symmetrical electric field. This means that the field line density across any face of the cube is nonuniform, with most (but not all) field lines missing the cube entirely.

Figure WG24.4

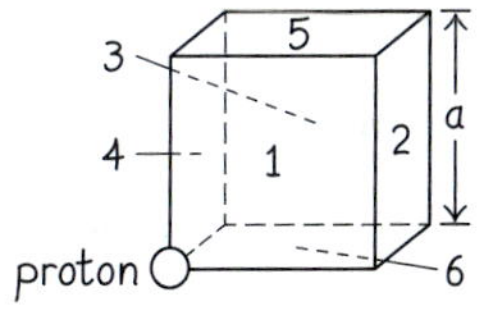

❷ **DEVISE PLAN** We know the flux is given by Eq. 24.5, and because the electric field is not constant over each face of the cube, the integration may be challenging. However, we can treat each cube face separately and hope to exploit symmetry to simplify the flux calculation. We also know that the electric field due to the single proton is given by Eq. 24.15, with $q = +e$:

$$\vec{E} = \frac{1}{4\pi\epsilon_0}\frac{e}{r^2}\hat{r},$$

where q is the charge on the proton and r is the radial distance from the proton to the point at which $\vec{E}$ is evaluated. Although the electric field magnitude varies over the three faces that have the proton at their common corner (faces 1, 4, and 6 in Figure WG24.4), we know the *directions* of the field at these faces: $\vec{E}$ at face 1 is parallel to face 1, $\vec{E}$ at face 4 is parallel to face 4, and $\vec{E}$ at face 6 is parallel to face 6. Because the electric field is parallel to these three faces, we can say that for each of them $\vec{E} \cdot d\vec{A} = E \cos 90° \, dA = 0$. Moreover, the fluxes through faces 2, 3, and 5 are all the same because each vector area segment $d\vec{A}$ on one of these three faces has a corresponding area segment on the other two faces, all making the same angle with the electric field. Thus, the only thing we need to calculate is the flux through one of the three faces that have nonzero flux. Figure WG24.5, showing face 2, helps us with setting up the integral. With the xyz axes shown in Figure WG24.5, the area

Figure WG24.5

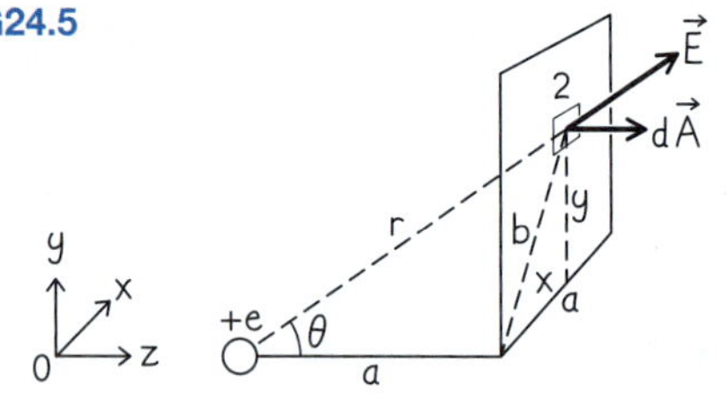

segment dA equals $dx\,dy$. For the right triangle that has the proton at one vertex, we have $\cos\theta = a/r$ and $r^2 = a^2 + b^2$, where b is the distance from the area segment $d\vec{A}$ to the corner of face 2 that is nearest the proton: At that corner, $x = y = 0$ and $z = a$. For the right triangle inside face 2, we have $b^2 = x^2 + y^2$. Thus $r = \sqrt{a^2 + (x^2 + y^2)}$. The flux through face 2 is

$$\Phi_E = \int \vec{E} \cdot d\vec{A} = \int E \cos\theta \, dA = \int \frac{1}{4\pi\epsilon_0} \frac{e}{r^2} \cos\theta \, dA$$

$$= \int_0^a \int_0^a \frac{1}{4\pi\epsilon_0} \frac{ea}{\sqrt{(a^2 + x^2 + y^2)^3}} dx\,dy.$$

❸ EXECUTE PLAN Referring to integral tables (or using a computer program to do symbolic integration), we determine that integration over x yields

$$\Phi_E = \frac{ea}{4\pi\epsilon_0} \int_0^a \left[\frac{x}{(a^2 + y^2)\sqrt{a^2 + x^2 + y^2}} \right]_0^a dy$$

$$= \frac{ea^2}{4\pi\epsilon_0} \int_0^a \frac{dy}{(a^2 + y^2)\sqrt{2a^2 + y^2}}.$$

If you cannot find this last integral in a reference source, the integration over y is not easy, but a substitution of variables can put the integral in a form found in most integral tables. The substitutions

$$u^2 = a^2 + y^2$$

$$dy = \frac{u}{y} du$$

transform the integral into

$$\Phi_E = \frac{ea^2}{4\pi\epsilon_0} \int_a^{\sqrt{2}a} \frac{(u/y)du}{u^2\sqrt{u^2 + a^2}}$$

$$= \frac{ea^2}{4\pi\epsilon_0} \int_a^{\sqrt{2}a} \frac{du}{u\sqrt{u^2 + a^2}\sqrt{u^2 - a^2}}$$

$$= \frac{ea^2}{4\pi\epsilon_0} \int_a^{\sqrt{2}a} \frac{du}{u\sqrt{u^4 - a^4}}$$

Checking a table of integrals, we obtain

$$= \frac{ea^2}{4\pi\epsilon_0} \left[\frac{-2}{4a^2} \arcsin \frac{a^2}{u^2} \right]_a^{\sqrt{2}a}$$

$$= -\frac{e}{8\pi\epsilon_0} \left[\arcsin\left(\tfrac{1}{2}\right) - \arcsin(1) \right] = -\frac{e}{8\pi\epsilon_0} \left[\frac{\pi}{6} - \frac{\pi}{2} \right].$$

The electric flux through faces 2, 3, and 5, the three faces that do not contain the proton at one corner, is thus

$$\Phi_E = \frac{e}{24\epsilon_0}. \checkmark$$

As noted in Devise Plan, the electric flux through the other three faces is zero.

❹ EVALUATE RESULT You might say "There must be an easier way!" Sometimes there is; sometimes not. (In this case there *is* a much easier way, shown in Worked Problem 24.5.) Nonetheless, you should not be afraid to tackle integration problems like this. The important thing is to set up the physics properly, as we did in Devise Plan. Then use the math tools you know or can find to obtain an answer.

Although it might seem surprising that the flux through faces 2, 3, and 5 is independent of the cube side length a, this is to be expected when you think of the "rays" of the electric field that radiate from the proton. Doubling the size of the cube would still catch the same number of field lines on these three faces and thus not affect the flux through them.

Guided Problem 24.4 Charged rod, cubed

An infinitely long, positively charged rod whose linear charge density is λ, runs through a cube of side length a. The rod passes through the cube's center and is perpendicular to the top and bottom faces. Use integration to determine the electric flux through each face.

❶ GETTING STARTED

1. What information are you given? What quantity are you asked to determine? Make a sketch showing all this information.
2. In what sense is this problem similar to Worked Problem 24.3? In what sense is it different?
3. What physical symmetry can you use to simplify the problem? What does the electric field due to an infinitely long charged wire look like?

❷ DEVISE PLAN

4. Is the electric flux through any face zero? Why?
5. Which equations allow you to express the unknown quantities in terms of known ones? What information can help you determine the electric field at a position on, the location of, and the surface normal direction of a face of the cube that has nonzero flux?

6. Begin with the definition of electric flux. Determine the direction of the electric field at any location on each face so that you can integrate over the surface. Rewrite dA in terms of the coordinates of that location (probably x, y, z).
7. The scalar product includes the factor $\cos\theta$. Can you relate this cosine function to the coordinate variables? What about the distance from the rod to area segment dA?
8. Once you have the flux through one face, can you use symmetry or analogy to infer the flux through the other faces?

❸ EXECUTE PLAN

9. Perform the integration over one face that has nonzero flux and extend the result to the other faces.

❹ EVALUATE RESULT

10. As we will work out in detail in Guided Problem 24.6, you can cleverly calculate the answer without using integration, as a check on the brute-force answer. Using symmetry to argue that two faces have zero flux and four faces have equal fluxes, see whether the sum of the fluxes through the nonzero faces equals q_{enc}/ϵ_0, as Gauss's law requires.

Worked Problem 24.5 Revisiting flux through a cube

Use Gauss's law to determine the electric flux through each face of the cube of Worked Problem 24.3.

❶ GETTING STARTED As in Worked Problem 24.3, our given information is that the cube side length is a and the cube has an isolated proton embedded at one corner (Figure WG24.4). Our task here is to use Gauss's law, Eq. 24.8, to solve the problem of how much electric flux passes through each face of the cube. We know how to calculate the electric field surrounding the proton, and we know the locations and orientations of the faces. We also know that a cube possesses symmetries that we can exploit to simplify the problem.

❷ DEVISE PLAN Because the proton is at the corner of the cube, the cube does not enclose it and so cannot be our Gaussian surface. However, we can enclose the proton by attaching seven additional cubes, each of side length a, to our original cube, creating a cube of side length $2a$ and having the proton at its geometric center (Figure WG24.6). This large cube is our Gaussian surface. We can apply Gauss's law to get the electric flux through any face of this surface and then use symmetry to get the flux through any face of our original cube of side length a.

Figure WG24.6

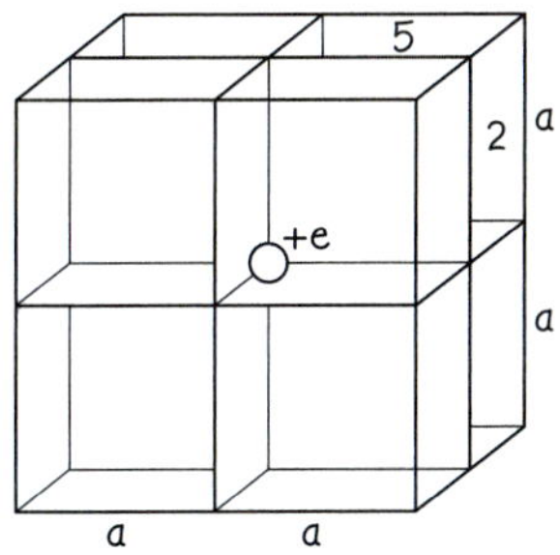

❸ EXECUTE PLAN From Gauss's law, we know that the flux through the large cube enclosing a single proton is e/ϵ_0. Because the proton is at the geometric center, symmetry tells us that the electric flux is the same through all six faces of the large cube. As Figure WG24.6 shows, each face of the large cube is composed of four squares, each of side length a: One face of the large cube contains four faces of our original cube. Thus, if we apply Gauss's law and symmetry, the flux through each of these smaller faces must be

$$\Phi_E = \frac{1}{(6)(4)}\frac{e}{\epsilon_0} = \frac{e}{24\epsilon_0}.$$

This is the same answer we obtained in Worked Problem 24.3 by tedious integration!

This result gives us the flux through sides 2, 3 and 5 of our original cube. The fact that the electric field is parallel to faces 1, 4, and 6 of the original cube tells us that the flux through sides 1, 4, and 6 is still zero. ✔

❹ EVALUATE RESULT Using Gauss's law is much easier than the method we used in Worked Problem 24.3 to do the same task. This law is extremely powerful in cases where symmetry can be exploited. It takes practice and experience to see how to construct Gaussian surfaces, but as this example shows, learning to do so is well worth the effort.

Guided Problem 24.6 Revisiting charged rod cubed

Use Gauss's law to determine the electric flux through each face of the cube of Guided Problem 24.4.

❶ GETTING STARTED

1. Because this problem asks you to determine the same quantity as in Guided Problem 24.4, should you draw the same sketch?
2. In what sense is this problem similar to Worked Problem 24.5? In what sense is it different?
3. What physical symmetry can you use to simplify the problem? What does the electric field due to an infinitely long charged wire look like?

❷ DEVISE PLAN

4. Is the electric flux through any face zero? Why?
5. Which equations allow you to express the unknown quantities in terms of known ones? What information can help you determine these unknown quantities?
6. What should you draw as your Gaussian surface? What is the amount of charge enclosed by this surface?

❸ EXECUTE PLAN

7. Apply Gauss's law, using the symmetry of the system.

❹ EVALUATE RESULT

8. Should your answer agree with your answer in Guided Problem 24.4? Does it?

Worked Problem 24.7 Nonuniformly charged cylinder

A very long, solid nonconducting cylinder of radius R has a volume charge density that is proportional to the radial distance r from the long central axis of the cylinder according to the expression $\rho(r) = \rho_0 r$, where ρ_0 is a constant with units C/m^4. (*a*) For any location near the midpoint of the cylinder's length, obtain an expression for the magnitude of the electric fields inside and outside the cylinder in terms of ρ_0, R, and r. (*b*) Sketch a graph showing the electric field magnitude as a function of the radial distance r from the cylinder's long central axis.

1 GETTING STARTED We are given an equation showing how volume charge density changes inside a solid cylinder and told that the cylinder is very long. Our tasks are (*a*) to determine expressions for the magnitude of the electric field inside and outside the cylinder, in both cases working near the middle of the cylinder's length, and (*b*) to graph how the electric field changes as we move radially away from the cylinder's long central axis.

The cylinder's symmetry makes this a prime candidate for the application of Gauss's law. Because our task is to determine the magnitude of the electric field midway along the length and we're told that the cylinder is very long, we assume that we can ignore any deviation from cylindrical symmetry of the electric field near the cylinder ends. Thus we can assume that the field in the region we concentrate on is directed radially outward from the long axis of the cylinder.

2 DEVISE PLAN We'll use Gauss's law to obtain expressions for the electric fields inside and outside the cylinder, making use of cylindrical symmetry. For our task in part *b*, we will take the expressions obtained in part *a*, insert numerical constants where needed, and graph E versus r, making sure that the expressions agree at $r = R$.

3 EXECUTE PLAN (*a*) Because the symmetry is cylindrical, we use a cylindrical Gaussian surface and show it surrounding a portion of the charge inside the cylinder (Figure WG24.7). As usual, we use r for the Gaussian surface radius and show the surface extending some distance h along the cylinder's length. Because it is radial, the electric field is perpendicular to this Gaussian surface everywhere except on the two end caps of the surface. On the end caps, $d\vec{A}$ is perpendicular to $\vec{E}$ (because the surface is parallel to $\vec{E}$, and $d\vec{A}$ is normal to the surface) and so $\vec{E} \cdot d\vec{A} = E \cos 90° \, dA = 0$. By symmetry, the magnitude of the electric field is the same everywhere on the curved part of the Gaussian surface. Thus, we need to integrate only over the area of the curved part:

$$\Phi_E = \oint \vec{E} \cdot d\vec{A} = \oint E \cos 0° \, dA = E \oint dA = E(2\pi r h).$$

Figure WG24.7

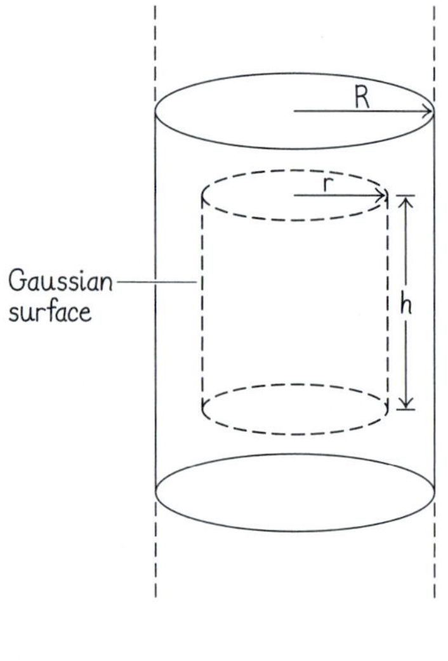

Note that the scalar product leads us to an integral over the scalar area segment dA rather than over the vectorial area segment $d\vec{A}$. Using the vectorial form would yield $\oint d\vec{A} = \vec{0}$! (You should be able to explain why.) Applying Gauss's law, we say

$$\Phi_E = E(2\pi r h) = \frac{q_{enc}}{\epsilon_0}$$

$$E = \frac{q_{enc}}{2\pi r h \epsilon_0}.$$

In determining the charge enclosed by our Gaussian surface, we must remember that the volume charge density $\rho = \rho(r) = \rho_0 r$ varies with the radial distance r from the cylinder's axis. We therefore divide the interior of the Gaussian surface into a series of thin-walled cylindrical shells each of radius r_{shell}, wall thickness dr_{shell}, and wall length h (Figure WG24.8). The infinitesimal amount of charge contained in the wall of each shell is $dq = \rho(r = r_{shell})dV$, where $dV = 2\pi r_{shell} h dr_{shell}$ is the volume of the wall. The charge contained within the Gaussian surface of radius r is thus

$$q_{enc} = \int dq = \int \rho(r_{shell}) dV = \int_0^{r_{shell}=r} \rho_0 r_{shell} [2\pi r_{shell} h dr_{shell}]$$

$$= \frac{2\rho_0 \pi h r^3}{3}.$$

Figure WG24.8

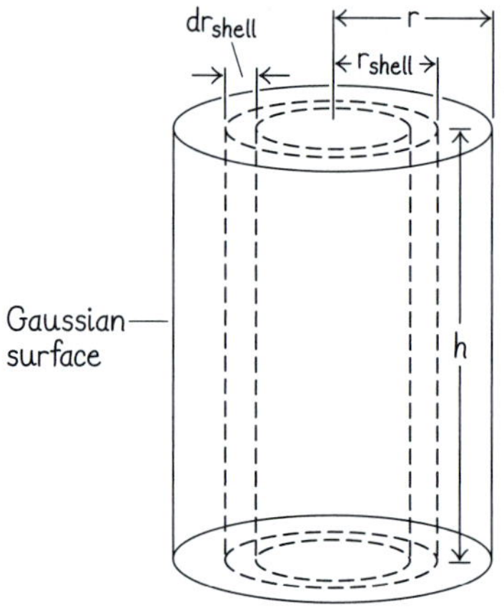

The magnitude of the electric field at radius r inside the solid cylinder ($r < R$) is thus

$$E_{inside} = \frac{2\rho_0 \pi h r^3/3}{2\pi r h \epsilon_0} = \frac{\rho_0}{3\epsilon_0} r^2. ✔$$

Outside the cylinder, the amount of charge enclosed by the Gaussian surface is independent of the radial distance because the charge distribution ends at the surface of the cylinder. Thus we evaluate the charge enclosed at distance $r = R$, which means $q_{enc} = 2\pi h \rho_0 R^3/3$. This gives an electric field magnitude at radial distance r outside the cylinder ($r > R$) of

$$E_{outside} = \frac{2\rho_0 \pi h R^3/3}{2\pi r h \epsilon_0} = \frac{\rho_0 R^3}{3\epsilon_0} \frac{1}{r}. ✔$$

PRACTICE

(*b*) Plotting the magnitude E as a function of the radial distance r from the cylinder's central axis yields the graph of Figure WG24.9. The shape of the curve tells us that the field magnitude is proportional to r^2 up to the cylinder's surface ($r = R$) and then is proportional to $1/r$ for $r > R$. ✔

Figure WG24.9

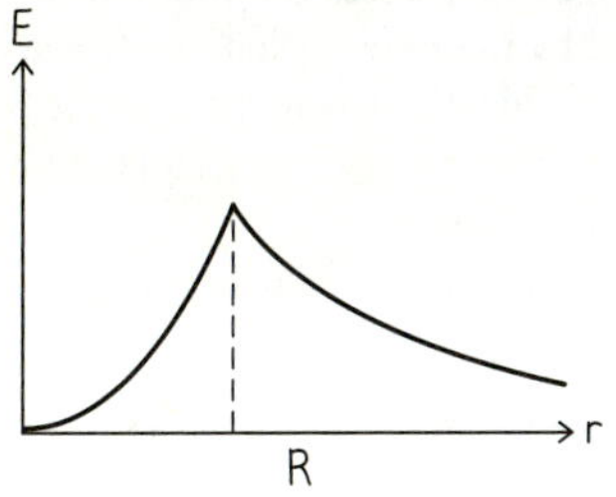

❹ **EVALUATE RESULT** It makes sense that the electric field magnitude is an increasing function of r inside the solid cylinder but is a decreasing function of r outside. As we go radially outward from the cylinder's center to its surface, more and more charge is enclosed by the Gaussian surface and so the electric field becomes stronger and stronger until we reach $r = R$. Once outside the solid cylinder, the field magnitude decreases as we get farther away, just as in *Principles* Exercise 24.7 for an infinitely long thin rod. We also check to make sure that our expressions for the electric fields inside the rod and outside the rod agree at the rod's boundary at $r = R$, and gratifyingly we determine that they give the same result for the limiting case of $r \rightarrow R$ from either side; in both cases, $E(r = R) = \rho_0 R^2/3\epsilon_0$.

Guided Problem 24.8 Nonuniformly charged sphere

A solid nonconducting sphere of radius R carries a charge q in its interior. The charge is distributed throughout the region $r < R$ nonuniformly, but with spherical symmetry. The volume charge density as a function of the radial distance r from the center of the solid sphere is proportional to $1/r$. Determine the electric fields for positions inside and outside the solid sphere, and then sketch a graph showing the field magnitude as a function of r.

❶ **GETTING STARTED**

1. List the information you are given, and then describe what you must determine. Make a sketch of the situation.
2. In what sense is this problem similar to Worked Problem 24.7? In what sense is it different?
3. Do you have enough information to work the problem? Are there any assumptions you must make?

❷ **DEVISE PLAN**

4. What physical symmetry can you use to simplify the problem? What does the electric field look like for a sphere of charge?
5. What is the volume charge density as a function of the radius, in terms of quantities given in the problem statement?
6. What is an appropriate Gaussian surface?
7. What amount of charge is enclosed in this Gaussian surface?

❸ **EXECUTE PLAN**

8. Apply Gauss's law, using the symmetry of the system. The volume charge density is not uniform in this case, so determining the enclosed charge involves an integral. Be attentive!

❹ **EVALUATE RESULT**

9. Does the way the electric field inside the sphere depends on r make sense? Explain why this behavior of E is reasonable.

Questions and Problems

For Instructor-assigned homework, go to MasteringPhysics®

Dots indicate difficulty level of problems: • = *easy,* •• = *intermediate,* ••• = *hard;* CR = *context-rich problem.*

24.1 Electric field lines

1. Suppose a charged particle is located at the origin. What is the direction of the electric field at the point (0.6, 1.2) if the particle is (*a*) positively charged and (*b*) negatively charged? •
2. Because of the presence of positively charged ions in Earth's atmosphere, on a calm day free electrons (that is, electrons not bound to atoms) just above Earth's surface generally experience a small upward electric force. Sketch the electric field lines near Earth's surface. •
3. Can you draw an electric field line through a location in space where the electric field magnitude is zero? •
4. You and a friend are asked to draw the two-dimensional electric field line pattern for two charged objects located near each other. The charge on the first object is $+2q$ (with q positive), and the charge on the second object is $-q$. You show 32 field lines emanating from the first charge and 16 field lines terminating on the second charge. Your friend shows 24 field lines emanating from the first object and 12 terminating on the second object. Which diagram is correct? •
5. A positively charged test particle is released from rest in a uniform electric field. The only force experienced by the particle is the electric force exerted by the sources of the uniform field. (*a*) Describe the trajectory the particle follows. (*b*) How does the trajectory change, if at all, if the particle is given an initial velocity in the direction of the electric field? (*c*) How does the trajectory change if the particle has an initial velocity that makes an angle $\theta \neq 0$ with the electric field? (*d*) Repeat parts *a–c* for a negatively charged test particle. ••
6. A certain field line diagram illustrates the electric field due to three particles that carry charges 5.0 μC, -3.0 μC, and -2.0 μC. If 20 field lines emanate from the positively charged particle, how many field lines terminate on each of the negatively charged particles? ••
7. Figure P24.7 shows the electric field produced by an electric dipole. How would a positively charged test particle begin to move when released from rest (*a*) at point A, (*b*) at point B, (*c*) at point C, and (*d*) at point D? Assume that no other objects exert forces on the test particle. (*e*) How does your answer to part *a* change if the test particle has an initial velocity that makes some angle $\theta \neq 0$ with the electric field at A? ••

Figure P24.7

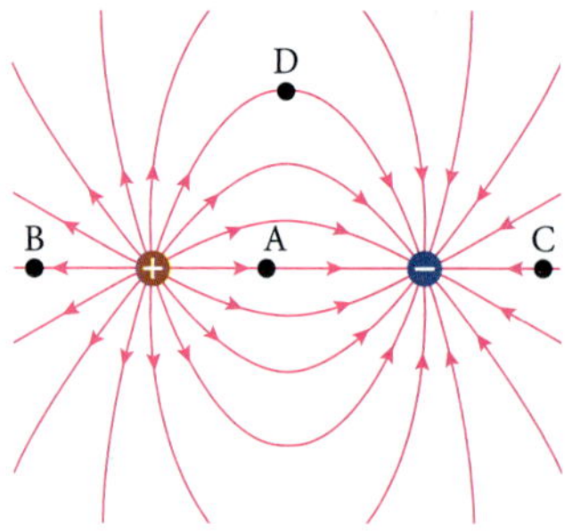

8. Two particles of charge $+q$ are located at opposite ends of one diagonal of a square, and two particles of charge $-q$ are located at opposite ends of the square's other diagonal. Sketch the pattern of electric field lines created, showing eight lines per particle in the plane that contains the square. ••
9. Assume that a test particle is released from rest in an electric field and experiences no forces other than the electric force exerted by the objects that create the electric field. Does an electric field line passing through the particle's initial position represent the particle's trajectory over time? If not, illustrate with an example. ••
10. Draw several field lines surrounding the three charged particles shown in Figure P24.10. ••

Figure P24.10

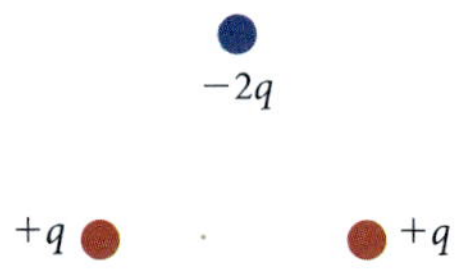

11. Two classmates sitting next to you have made an electric field diagram. You are looking at it (not during a test) to see if they did it correctly, but part of the diagram is covered by a quarter, as shown in Figure P24.11. If your classmates made the diagram correctly, what can you say about the region covered by the quarter? State all the information you can determine about any charged particles in that region. ••

Figure P24.11

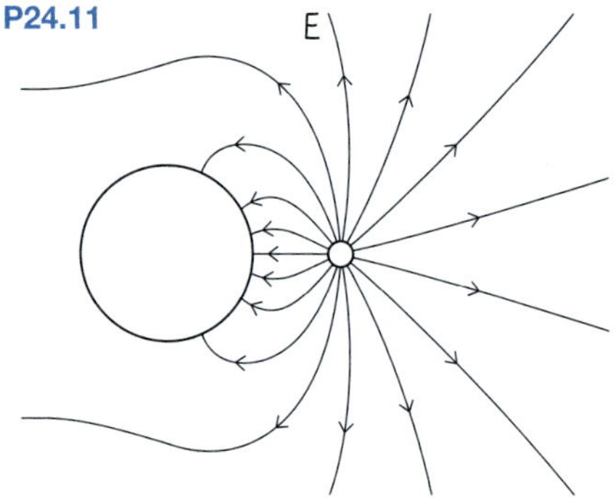

12. Outline an algorithm for a computer program that traces out the electric field lines surrounding a charged object. Assume that functions have already been provided to draw the charged object itself and to draw line segments between pairs of points that your program chooses. •••
13. There are many parallels between gravitational phenomena and electrical phenomena: One can think of a test object with mass in a gravitational field as analogous to a test object with positive charge in an electric field. (*a*) Draw the gravitational field line pattern for the Earth-Moon system, showing arrows on the lines to indicate direction. (*b*) Now consider a system made up of two charged objects. Which type of charge (positive or negative) must each object carry in order to have an electric field line pattern match the gravitational field line pattern that you drew in part *a*? (*c*) Do you see any differences between electrical and gravitational phenomena? •••

24.2 Field line density

14. A small charged ball is suspended at the center of a spherical balloon that is nestled snugly inside a cubical cardboard box. On one side, the balloon touches the wall of the box. (*a*) At this point of contact, is the electric field magnitude on the balloon

surface equal to the electric field magnitude on the box surface? Assume neither object is polarized. (*b*) At this point of contact, is the number of field lines per unit of balloon surface area equal to the number of field lines per unit of box surface area? •

15. Where in Figure P24.15 does the electric field have the greatest magnitude? •

Figure P24.15

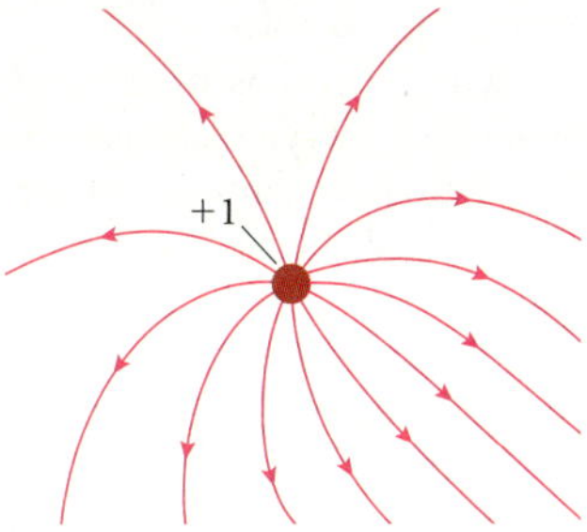

16. Suppose a certain planar surface has 2000 field lines passing through each square meter, normal to the surface. How many field lines pass through each square meter if the surface is tilted by 60° ? •

17. Consider the pattern of five field lines shown in Figure P24.17. Rank positions A, B, and C according to the magnitude of their electric fields, from greatest to smallest. •

Figure P24.17

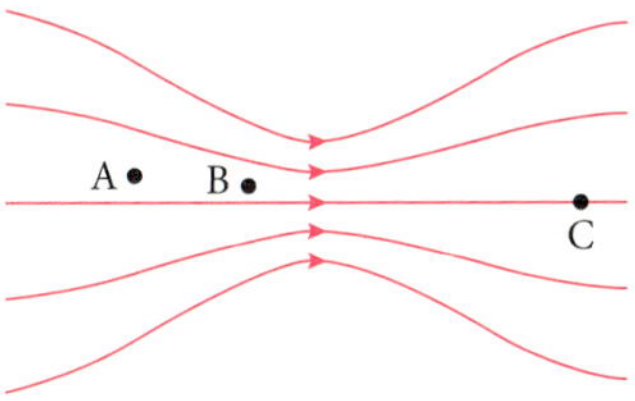

18. Make a geometric argument, based on how the field lines spread out into space, that the magnitude of the electric field surrounding a long, straight, charged wire is proportional to $1/r$, where r is the radial distance from the long axis of the wire. ••

19. Make a geometric argument, based on the pattern of electric field lines, that the magnitude of the electric field surrounding a large, flat, charged metal plate is constant and independent of the distance d from the plate as long as d is small relative to the area of the plate. ••

20. Figure P24.20 shows electric field lines due to a distribution of charge (not shown). The labeled regions of space are all equal in size. In which of the labeled regions, A, B, and C, is (*a*) the electric field greatest and (*b*) the electric field smallest? (*c*) How much greater is the largest labeled electric field than the smallest nonzero labeled electric field? ••

Figure P24.20

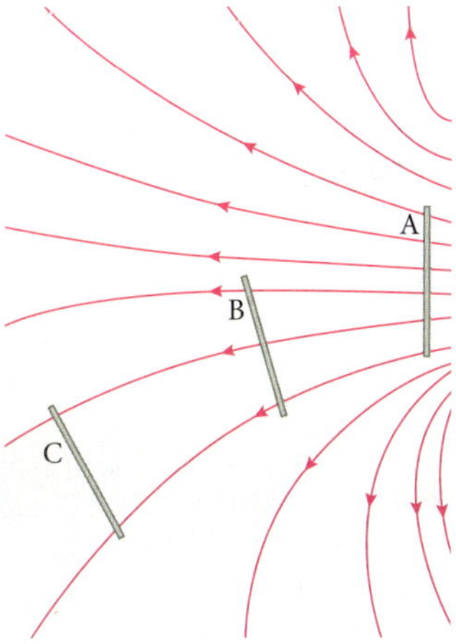

21. Identical charged pellets are released from rest from equidistant starting lines A, B, and C in Figure P24.21, in a region of nonuniform electric field. (*a*) Rank the pellets according to the time interval it takes the pellet on line A to cross line B, the pellet on B to cross C, and the pellet on C to cross D, smallest interval first. (*b*) How does your answer to part *a* change if each pellet is given an identical initial velocity directed upward along lines A, B, and C? ••

Figure P24.21

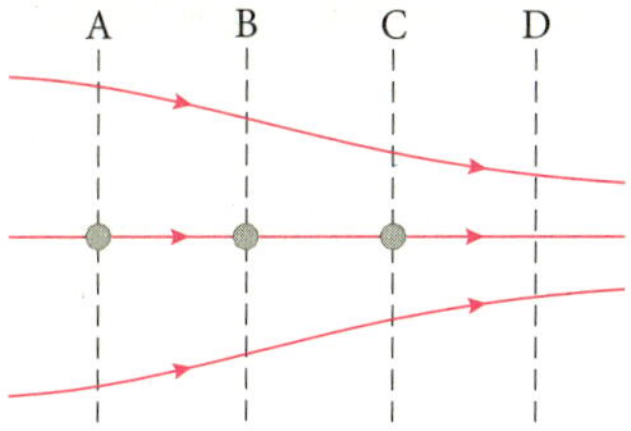

22. You decide to make an electric field line diagram in two dimensions, with 16 lines per coulomb of charge. (*a*) How many lines should you draw surrounding a particle that carries $+1.5$ C of charge? Should the lines enter or leave that particle? (*b*) Answer the same questions for a particle that carries -0.375 C of charge. (*c*) Could you represent a particle that carries $+0.8$ C in this diagram? ••

23. Two surfaces are near two different charged objects, and the surfaces are identical in size. Surface A has N field lines passing perpendicularly through it. Surface B has only $N/2$ field lines passing through it, and they pass through at an angle 72° from normal. Is the field line density greater near surface A or surface B, and by how much? •••

24.3 Closed surfaces

24. Imagine a system that consists of only a single positively charged object. Is it possible to have in this system a closed surface that has a negative field line flux through it? (Note: The charged object need not lie inside the surface.) •

25. Closed surface A is a sphere of radius R, closed surface B is a sphere of radius $2R$, and closed surface C is a cube with side length R. At the geometric center of each closed surface is a small ball that is completely enclosed by the surface and carries electrical charge $+q$. Assuming there are no other charged objects inside any of the closed surfaces, rank the surfaces according to the electric field line flux through them, largest first. •

26. Three charged pellets are arranged along a line. Three hypothetical closed surfaces are drawn around this set of three pellets. The three surfaces have identical cylindrical walls but different top caps (Figure P24.26). Rank the closed surfaces from smallest to greatest in terms of the electric field line flux through them. •

Figure P24.26

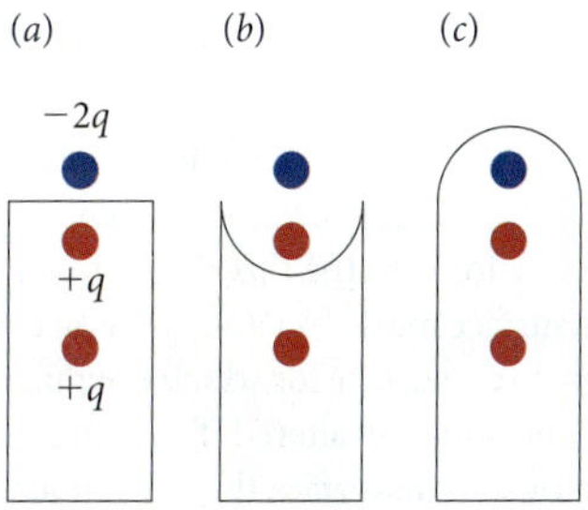

27. In Figure P24.27, assume that a Gaussian surface drawn to surround only sphere 1 would have an electric field line flux of +4. Sketch Gaussian surfaces that contain sphere 1 plus one or more additional spheres and have field line fluxes of (*a*) +24, (*b*) −4, and (*c*) +8. ••

Figure P24.27

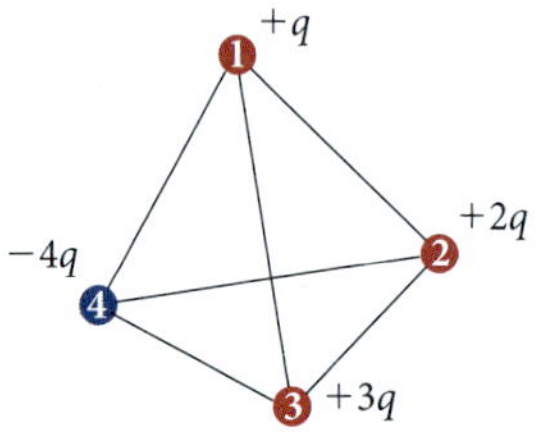

28. In the electric field line diagram for the charge arrangement shown in Figure P24.28, 12 field lines emanate from the object of charge +1 C. What is the field line flux through closed surfaces (*a*) A, (*b*) B, (*c*) C, (*d*) D, and (*e*) H? ••

Figure P24.28

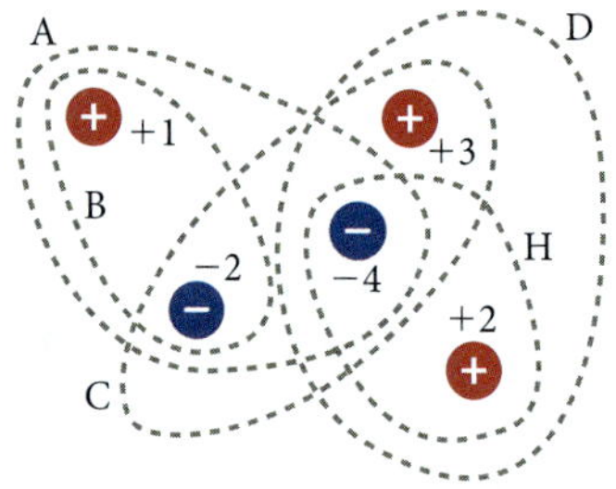

29. In a certain field line diagram, a single electron is drawn that has four field lines terminating on it. If a closed surface in another part of this diagram is shown to have 16 field lines coming out of it, what can be said about the number of charge carriers inside the surface and the type of charge they carry? ••

30. For the dipole in Figure P24.30, can you draw a two-dimensional closed surface through which the field line flux is (*a*) zero, (*b*) +16, (*c*) −16, and (*d*) +3? ••

Figure P24.30

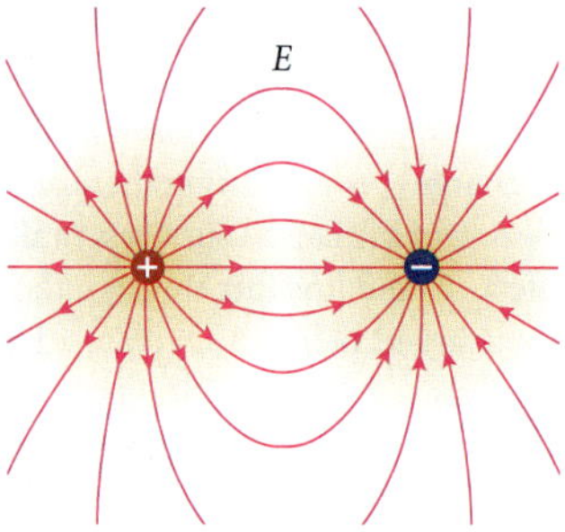

31. Make an argument based on Gauss's law that a charged object cannot be held in stable translational equilibrium by electric fields alone. For a start, assume there is no other charged object in the region of interest even though the external electric field can be due to charged objects outside this region. •••

32. The chapter explains that the charge inside a closed surface is proportional to the flux through that surface. To illustrate why the surface must be closed, draw an example of a charge distribution and a surface for which the flux through the surface would be considerably altered if the surface had any holes (unclosed regions of the surface through which flux is not counted). •••

24.4 Symmetry and Gaussian surfaces

33. (*a*) Can you draw a Gaussian surface that offers a simple way to compute the electric field surrounding a charged dipole? (*b*) If not, does this mean that the relationship between field line flux and enclosed charge and the relationship between field line density and magnitude of the electric field do not apply to charged dipoles? •

34. An isolated system consists of one object carrying charge $+q$ and one object carrying charge $-q$. Are all the electric field lines for the system contained inside some boundary? •

35. When a charged particle is placed at the center of a spherical Gaussian surface, the field line flux through the surface is $+\Phi$. Suppose that the spherical Gaussian surface is to be replaced by a cubical Gaussian surface composed of six square plates. Square plates are positioned above and below the charged particle to form two sides of the cubical Gaussian surface that is centered on the charged particle, as shown in Figure P24.35. What is the field line flux through each plate? •

Figure P24.35

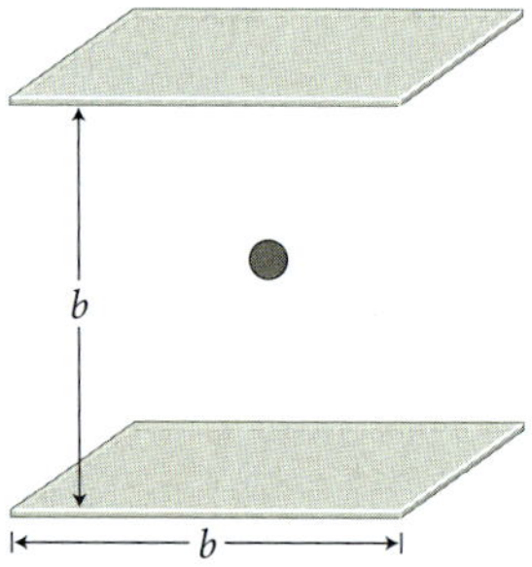

36. Figure P24.36 shows a cross section through an infinitely long, uniformly charged hollow cylinder. How does the magnitude of the electric field vary with the radial distance r from the cylinder's long central axis (*a*) inside the hole in the cylinder and (*b*) outside the cylinder? ••

Figure P24.36

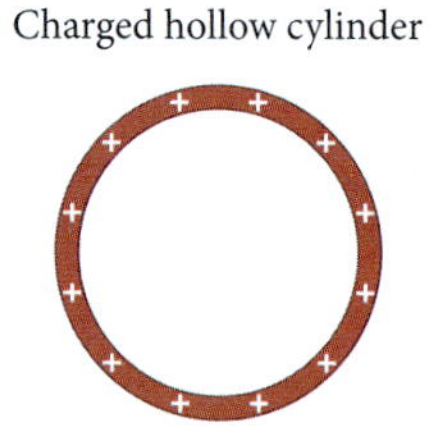

37. Figure P24.37 shows a cylindrical Gaussian surface straddling a charged sheet. Are there any other shapes that would be appropriate for the Gaussian surface in this situation? ••

Figure P24.37

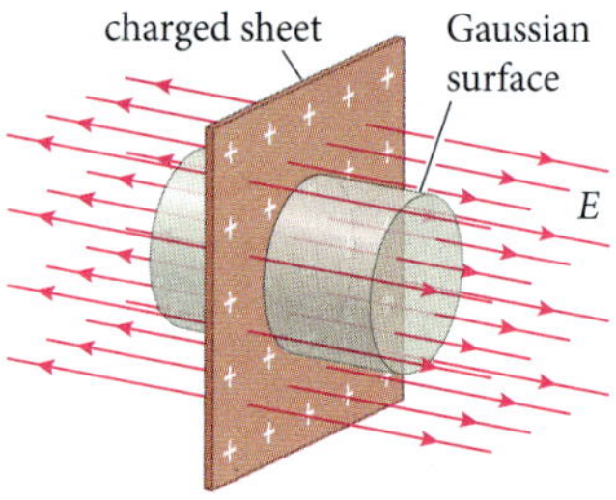

38. Suppose you want to determine the amount of charge on a spherical shell. You start out by surrounding the shell with a cylindrical Gaussian surface. Is it possible to use the flux everywhere on the surface of the cylinder to determine the charge on the spherical shell? Why isn't this recommended in the chapter? ••

39. The magnitude of the electric field a distance R away from a particle carrying charge q is E_0. Now consider this same quantity of charge q distributed uniformly throughout the volume of a nonconducting solid sphere of radius R. What is the electric field magnitude, in terms of E_0, (*a*) a distance $2R$ from the center of the sphere, (*b*) at the sphere surface, and (*c*) a distance $R/4$ from the sphere center? ••

40. You are given a uniformly charged spherical shell that has a radius R and carries a positive charge q. In order to measure the electric field magnitude inside, you drill a small hole that removes 0.01% of the shell's material and insert a probe into the shell. What are the direction and approximate magnitude of the electric field at the shell center? (Hint: The answer is small but not zero.) •••

41. You and your friend are working in a lab and wish to measure the surface charge density on a slab of metal. The slab is very long and very wide, but flat. You begin adding up the field line flux through a cylindrical Gaussian surface that passes through the slab as in Figure P24.37. Your friend begins adding up the field line flux through a cubical Gaussian surface that passes through the slab. Her cube is a little shorter than your cylinder, and it is wider than your cylinder. Will the two of you still obtain the same result for the surface charge density? If so, why? If not, what needs to be changed about your friend's cube? •••

42. You have a hollow spherical shell of radius R that carries a positive charge. The shell is very thin. You make many Gaussian surfaces concentric with the shell to determine the electric field line density at various distances from the center. Qualitatively plot the electric field line density as a function of the distance from the center of the shell. Show regions inside the shell as well as outside. •••

24.5 Charged conducting objects

43. The two-cavity metal object in Figure P24.43 is electrically neutral, but each cavity contains a charged particle as shown. What are (*a*) the charge on the surface of each cavity and (*b*) the charge on the outer surface of the object? •

Figure P24.43

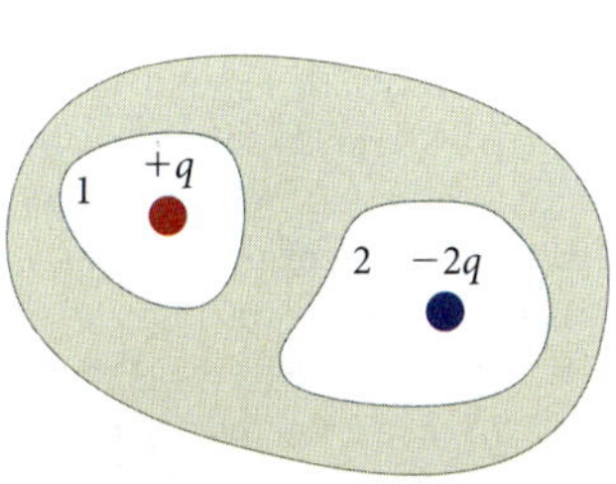

44. Some charged particles are suspended inside a hollow metal object by supports made of a material that is an electrical insulator. The metal object has charge $+q$ distributed over its outer surface and charge $-2q$ distributed over its inner surface. (*a*) How much charge is suspended in the cavity? (*b*) What is the charge on the object? (Hint for part *b*: What is the electric field a very large distance r from the center of the object?) ••

45. Delicate electronic devices are sometimes enclosed inside metal boxes to protect them from external electric fields. Explain what physical phenomena might cause this protection. ••

46. A *coronal discharge* occurs when the electric field magnitude just above the surface of a conductor exceeds approximately 3×10^6 N/C, a magnitude strong enough to ionize atoms in the air by ripping electrons from them. Coronal discharge is most likely to occur near a sharp tip of a conductor. (This is why solder joints in electronics must not have sharp protrusions and why it's easier to draw a spark from your fingertip than from your knee after scuffing your feet on a carpet.) (*a*) Make an argument based on the geometry of the field lines emerging from a conducting surface that charge is more likely to concentrate on a convex region of the surface than on a concave region. (*b*) Sketch a paring knife that has a surplus charge on it, and shade the regions where charge is most likely to concentrate on the surface. ••

47. Two concentric spherical metal shells are insulated from each other and from the surroundings. The inner shell carries a charge $+2q$, and the outer shell carries a charge $-q$. In electrostatic equilibrium, what is the charge on (*a*) the outer surface of the inner shell, (*b*) the inner surface of the outer shell, and (*c*) the outer surface of the outer shell? (*d*) The shells are then connected to each other by a metal wire. Do parts *a–c* for the situation obtained after electrostatic equilibrium is reached. ••

48. A small ball carrying a charge $-2q$ is placed at the center of a spherical metal shell that carries a charge $+q$. What are the sign and magnitude of the charge (*a*) on the inner surface of the shell and (*b*) on the outer surface of the shell? (*c*) Do your answers change if the ball is not at the center of the shell? If so, how? ••

49. Figure P24.49 shows a neutral conducting block with four hollow chambers inside. A charge of $-5q$ has collected on the outer surface of the block. Inside three of the chambers are particles that carry charges $+q$, $+q$, and $+2q$. Determine the charge inside the fourth chamber in terms of q. ••

Figure P24.49

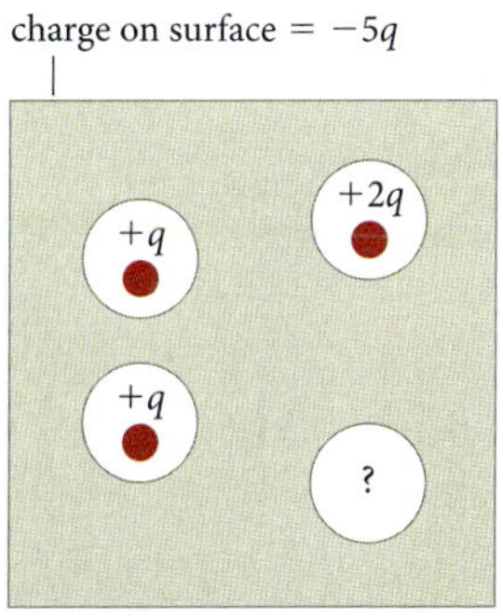

50. A pellet carrying charge $+q$ is centered inside a spherical cavity that has been cut off-center in a solid metal sphere that carries charge $-2q$ (Figure P24.50 on next page). (*a*) How much charge resides on the inner surface of the cavity? Is this charge

PRACTICE

distributed uniformly or nonuniformly? (*b*) How much charge resides on the outer surface of the metal sphere? Is this charge distributed uniformly or nonuniformly? •••

Figure P24.50

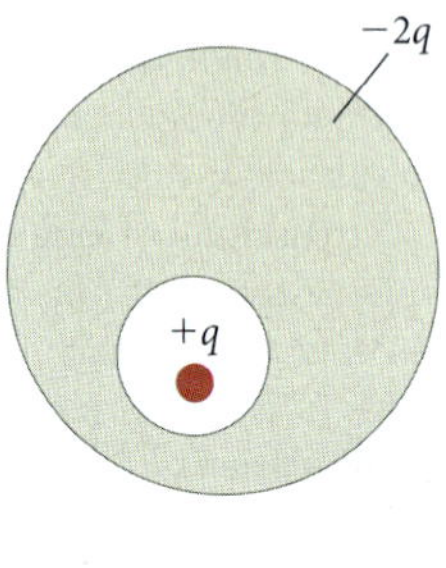

51. A particle carries a charge of $2q$ and is located at the origin. The particle is surrounded by a conducting shell of inner radius R and thickness t. The shell carries a charge of $-3q$. Determine (*a*) the charge on the inner surface of the shell and (*b*) the charge on the outer surface of the shell. (*c*) Make a qualitative plot of the electric field line density as a function of distance from the origin. Be sure to show the field line density in the hollow region, inside the material of the shell, and outside. •••

24.6 Electric flux

52. Imagine a cubical Gaussian surface snugly surrounding a volleyball that is charged uniformly over its surface. The electric flux through one side of the cube is 5.2×10^2 N · m^2/C. What is the charge on the volleyball? •

53. A flat sheet that has an area of 3.0 m^2 is placed in a uniform electric field of magnitude 10 N/C. While keeping the sheet flat, can you orient it so that the electric flux through it is 6 N · m^2/C? So that the flux is 60 N · m^2/C? •

54. Figure P24.54 shows a cylindrical Gaussian surface enclosing a segment of a long charged wire. Consider using a spherical Gaussian surface to enclose the same segment of the wire. (*a*) Which surface, cylindrical or spherical, has the greater electric flux through it? (*b*) Which surface is more appropriate for calculating the electric flux? Justify your answer. •

Figure P24.54

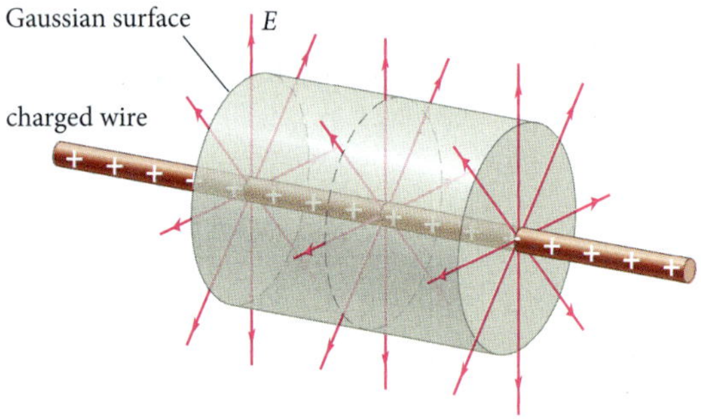

55. A particle carries a charge of 6.0 μC. Calculate the electric flux through a spherical Gaussian surface that is centered on the particle and has a radius of (*a*) 0.04 m and (*b*) 0.08 m. •

56. Use a symmetry argument to determine the electric flux through a Gaussian surface that encloses both charged particles that form an electric dipole. Does the value calculated for the flux depend on the shape of the surface? ••

57. Figure P24.57 shows a charged particle surrounded by three different closed surfaces, (*a*), (*b*), and (*c*). In each case, the charge on the particle and the geometry of the left side (left of the dashed line) of the surface are identical. The closed surfaces have different geometries to the right of the dashed line. In which case is the flux through the right side of the surface the greatest? In which case is it the smallest? ••

Figure P24.57

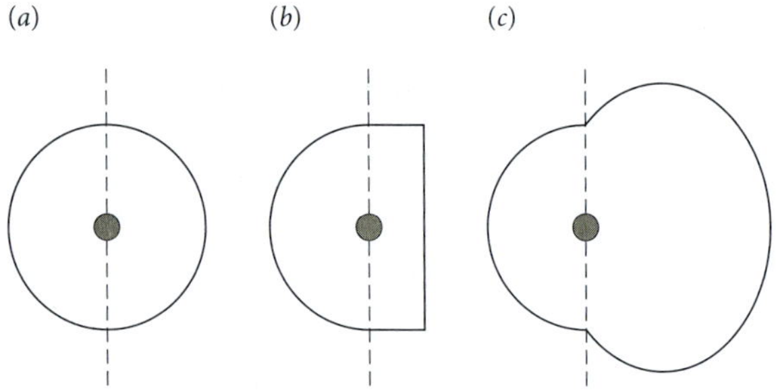

58. A butterfly net hangs from a circular loop of diameter 400 mm. You hold the loop horizontally in a region where the electric field is 150 N/C downward, as shown in Figure P24.58. (*a*) What is the electric flux through the net? (*b*) Does the flux through the net increase or decrease if you rotate the loop so that it lies in a vertical plane? ••

Figure P24.58

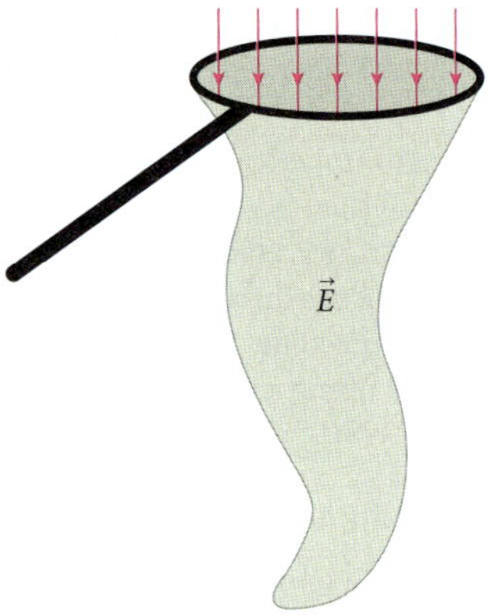

59. A particle that carries an unknown amount of charge is placed at the center of a hollow metal sphere of inner radius R_i and outer radius R_o. The magnitude of the electric field outside the sphere at any radial distance r from the center is $3kq/r^2$ (with $q > 0$), directed toward the center, and the charge on the inner surface of the sphere is $-2q$. What are (*a*) the charge on the particle and (*b*) the charge on the sphere? ••

60. A small conducting ball that carries a charge of 30.0 nC is located at the center of an electrically neutral hollow conducting sphere of inner radius 100 mm and outer radius 150 mm. What is the surface charge density (*a*) on the sphere's inner surface and (*b*) on its outer surface? (*c*) Determine the electric field as a function of r, the radial distance from the center of the sphere. ••

61. A solid conducting sphere 60 mm in radius carries a charge of 5.0 nC. A thick conducting spherical shell of inner radius 100 mm and outer radius 120 mm carries a charge of -4.0 nC and is concentric with the sphere. (*a*) Draw the electric field lines for the situation, marking the location of all charge on your diagram. (*b*) Calculate the surface charge density on the surface of the solid sphere and on the inner and outer surfaces of the thick shell. (*c*) Determine the electric field as a function of *r*, the radial distance from the center of the sphere. •••

24.7 Deriving Gauss's law

62. Three particles each carrying charge $+q$ are located at the corners of an equilateral triangle of side length a, and the triangle is centered on the origin of a Cartesian coordinate system. What is the electric flux through a spherical Gaussian surface centered at the origin if the radius of the Gaussian surface is (*a*) $a/4$ and (*b*) $2a$? •

63. A particular closed surface has four sides. The electric flux is $+5.0\ \mathrm{N \cdot m^2/C}$ through side 1, $+8.0\ \mathrm{N \cdot m^2/C}$ through side 2, and $-9.0\ \mathrm{N \cdot m^2/C}$ through side 3. (*a*) If there is no surplus charge enclosed by the surface, what is the flux through side 4? (*b*) If the flux through side 4 is $-8.0\ \mathrm{N \cdot m^2/C}$, how much charge is enclosed by the surface? •

64. A particular cylindrical Gaussian surface encloses no charge. If 20 electric field lines pass into the cylinder through one of the flat ends of the cylinder and 16 of these lines emerge from the other flat end, what can you conclude about the other 4 electric field lines? •

65. Consider a rod of length ℓ that carries a uniform charge distribution. Is Gauss's law appropriate for calculating the electric field at a radial distance r from the midpoint of the rod's length (*a*) when $r \ll \ell$, (*b*) when $r = \ell$, and (*c*) when $r \gg \ell$? For each case in which your answer is yes, describe the shape of the most useful Gaussian surface. ••

66. Any collection of N charged particles can be divided into N collections each containing one of the particles. Use the superposition property of electric fields to show that the electric flux through any Gaussian surface due to a collection of N charged particles is the sum of the fluxes through the same Gaussian surface produced by the N individual particles. ••

67. A horizontal rectangular sheet of length ℓ and width w is positioned with its center a vertical distance $w/2$ below an infinitely long positively charged rod that has a uniform linear charge density λ. (*a*) If the sides of length ℓ are parallel to the rod's axis, what is the magnitude of the electric flux through the sheet? (*b*) If the vertical distance between the sheet center and the rod is reduced to $w/4$, does the flux magnitude increase, decrease, or stay the same? ••

68. A cubical shell with edges of length a is positioned so that two adjacent sides of one face are coincident with the $+x$ and $+y$ axes of a rectangular coordinate system and the corner formed by these two sides is at the origin. (*a*) Sketch the electric field vectors in the region of the shell if an electric field of magnitude $E = bx^2$ directed along the $+x$ axis exists in this region. (*b*) How much charge is contained in the volume of the shell? ••

69. A cubical Gaussian surface 30 mm on each side is centered on a particle that carries a charge of $+3.0\ \mu\mathrm{C}$. (*a*) If you draw a field line diagram with four field lines per microcoulomb, how many lines pass through the Gaussian surface? In which direction are these lines? (*b*) Ignoring corners and edges, how many field lines pass through each face of the Gaussian surface? (*c*) What is the electric flux through the Gaussian surface? (*d*) What is the electric flux through one face? (*e*) Which of your answers change if the particle is moved 10 mm away from the center of the Gaussian surface? (You don't need to obtain new values for the answers that change, if any.) ••

70. There is a Gauss's law for gravity analogous to Gauss's law for electricity. (*a*) If the electric flux through a closed surface is proportional to the enclosed charge, what is the gravitational flux proportional to? (*b*) Write an equation for Gauss's law for gravity. ••

71. A dipole that carries charges $\pm q$ is aligned along the y axis of an xyz rectangular coordinate system, with the midpoint of the dipole at the origin. (*a*) Use Gauss's law to calculate the electric flux through the xz plane, which bisects the dipole and is perpendicular to the dipole moment. (Hint: Calculate the electric flux for each charge separately and apply the principle of superposition.) (*b*) Calculate the flux through the xz plane by integrating the electric field in Eq. 23.8 over the plane. (You'll need to generalize Eq. 23.8 to any point on the xz plane by making the substitution $x^2 \rightarrow r^2 = (x^2 + z^2)$.) (*c*) Which of the two techniques lets you obtain the flux through the xz plane more easily? •••

24.8 Applying Gauss's law

72. A positively charged hollow sphere of radius +100 mm has a uniform surface charge density of $10\ \mathrm{nC/m^2}$. Determine the electric field (*a*) 20 mm, (*b*) 90 mm, and (*c*) 110 mm from the center of the sphere. •

73. A positively charged solid sphere of radius 100 mm has a uniform volume charge density of $250\ \mathrm{nC/m^3}$. Determine the electric field (*a*) 20 mm, (*b*) 90 mm, and (*c*) 110 mm from the center of the sphere. •

74. A positively charged thin cylindrical shell of length 10 m and radius 50 mm has no end caps and a uniform surface charge density of $9 \times 10^{-9}\ \mathrm{C/m^2}$. (*a*) What is the charge on the shell? Determine the electric field magnitude far from either end of the shell at (*b*) $r = 49$ mm and (*c*) $r = 51$ mm, where r is the radial distance from the long central axis of the shell. •

75. An infinitely long positively charged cylindrical shell of radius a has a uniform linear charge density λ_a. An infinitely long cylindrical shell of radius $b > a$ is concentric with the first and has a uniform linear charge density λ_b. (*a*) Determine $\vec{E}$ in all regions. (*b*) If $\lambda_a = +5.0\ \mathrm{nC/m}$, which type of charge must the shell of radius b carry and what value must λ_b have in order for the electric field to be zero for radial distances $r > b$? (*c*) Sketch the electric field lines for this situation. ••

76. Two parallel vertical sheets of infinite extent carry surplus charge and are 50 mm apart. Determine the magnitude and direction of the electric field in all regions of space (*a*) when each sheet has a uniform surface charge density $\sigma = +3.0\ \mathrm{nC/m^2}$ and (*b*) when $\sigma = +3.0\ \mathrm{nC/m^2}$ for the left sheet and $\sigma = -3.0\ \mathrm{nC/m^2}$ for the right sheet. (*c*) Draw a diagram showing the sheets and the electric field lines for the situations described in parts *a* and *b*. ••

77. A long, thin, positively charged wire runs along the long central axis of a hollow conducting cylinder of length 10 m, inner radius 50 mm, and outer radius 70 mm. The wire has a uniform linear charge density of $+1.5\ \mu\mathrm{C/m}$. (*a*) Ignoring the regions near the two ends, calculate the surface charge density on the cylinder's inner and outer surfaces. Again ignoring the ends, determine the electric field magnitude at (*b*) $r = 49$ mm, (*c*) $r = 51$ mm, and (*d*) $r = 100$ mm, where r is the radial distance from the wire. ••

78. A positively charged nonconducting hollow sphere of outer radius R and inner radius $R/2$ has a uniform volume charge density ρ. Determine the magnitude and direction of the electric field as a function of r, the radial distance from the sphere center. ••

79. A positively charged nonconducting sphere of radius a has a uniform volume charge density ρ_0. It is snugly surrounded by a positively charged thick, nonconducting spherical shell of inner radius a and outer radius b. This thick shell has a volume charge density $\rho_0 r/a$ for $a < r \leq b$. Determine the electric field in all regions as a function of r, the radial distance from the center of the sphere. ••

80. An infinitely long nonconducting solid cylinder of radius R has a nonuniform but cylindrically symmetrical charge distribution. The volume charge density is given by $\rho(r) = c/r$, where c is a positive constant having units C/m^2 and r is the radial distance from the long central axis of the cylinder. (*a*) What is the charge in a section of the cylinder of length ℓ? Write an expression for the electric field magnitude for (*b*) $r < R$ and (*c*) $r > R$. ••

81. An infinitely long positively charged wire with a uniform linear charge density $+\lambda$ is parallel to the y axis of a Cartesian coordinate system and passes through the x axis at $x = -d$. At the origin, the electric field due to this charged wire has magnitude E_0 and is directed to the right along the positive x axis. A second infinite charged wire, parallel to the first and with a uniform linear charge density, passes through the x axis at $x = +3d$. The vector sum of the electric field at the origin due to the two lines of charge has magnitude $2E_0$. What is the linear charge density of the second charged wire? Obtain all the possible answers. ••

82. Figure P24.82 shows a cross section through a system that consists of an infinitely long charged rod centered in a thick cylindrical shell of inner radius R and outer radius $2R$. The shell is made of a conducting material; the rod is made of a nonconducting material and has a uniform linear charge density. The electric field associated with the system is indicated by the field lines in the diagram. For each finite length ℓ of the system, there is a charge of $-q$ on the shell inner surface. For that same finite length ℓ, determine the charge on (*a*) the rod and (*b*) the shell outer surface. (*c*) In length ℓ, what is the charge on the shell? (*d*) What is the ratio of the surface charge density on the shell's inner surface to the surface charge density on the outer surface? ••

Figure P24.82

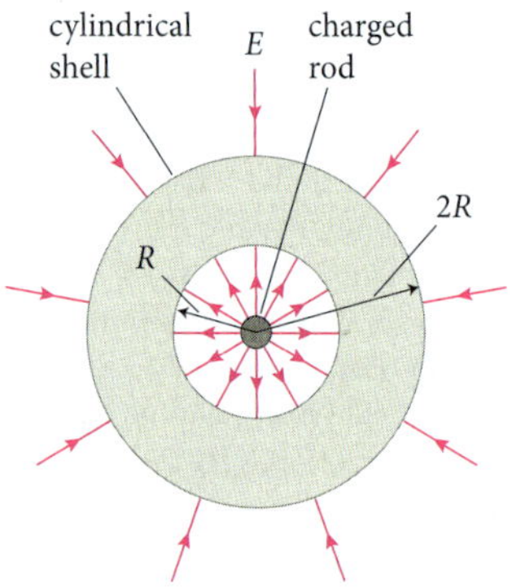

83. A positively charged solid nonconducting cylinder of length $\ell = 10$ m and radius $R = 50$ mm has uniform volume charge density $+9.0 \times 10^{-9}\ C/m^3$. (*a*) What is the charge inside the cylinder? Avoiding the regions near the ends, determine the electric field magnitude at (*b*) $r = 40$ mm and (*c*) $r = 60$ mm, where r is the radial distance from the long central axis of the cylinder. ••

84. Three nonconducting infinite sheets are parallel to the yz plane of an xyz coordinate system. Each sheet has a uniform surface charge density. Sheet 1, negatively charged with surface charge density $-\sigma$, passes through the x axis at $x = 1.0$ m. Sheet 2 has an unknown surface charge density and passes through the x axis at $x = 2.0$ m. Sheet 3, negatively charged with surface charge density -3σ, and passes through the x axis at $x = 4.0$ m. The electric field due to the sheets is zero at $x = 1.5$ m. (*a*) What is the surface charge density on sheet 2? If the electric field at $x = 0$ is $\vec{E}_0$, what is the electric field at (*b*) $x = -2.0$ m (*c*) $x = 3.0$ m, and (*d*) $x = 6.0$ m? ••

85. A particle that carries positive charge $+q$ is located at the center of one or more concentric, thick or thin spherical shells. The shells are either made of a conducting material but are electrically neutral or made of a nonconducting material and have uniform surface charge densities. Figure P24.85 is the graph of the electric flux passing through spherical Gaussian surfaces centered on the particle, as a function of radial distance r from the particle. (*a*) What is the minimum number of spherical shells required to produce the graph? (*b*) Describe each shell completely, specifying its charge, its inner and outer radii, and whether it is made of a conducting or nonconducting material. ••

Figure P24.85

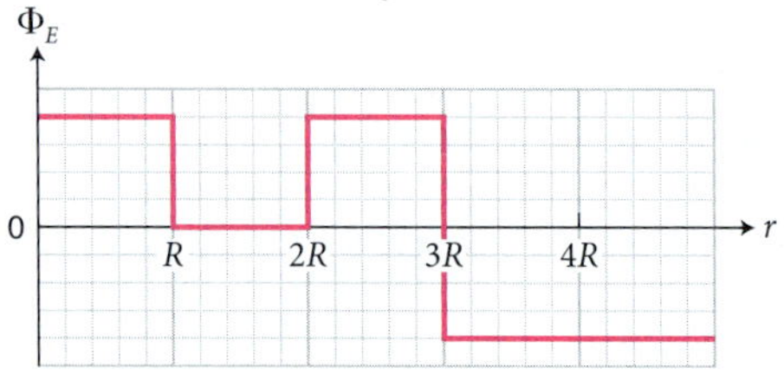

86. Can the graph in Figure P24.87 be produced by a system that consists of only charged particles? If not, explain why not. If so, describe the system that contains the minimum number of charged particles. ••

87. At what radius along the perpendicular bisector of a wire of length 0.25 m carrying 30 nC of charge does the assumption of cylindrical symmetry in applying Gauss's law give you an answer whose error exceeds 5%? ••

88. An infinitely long positively charged wire that carries a uniform linear charge density λ passes through the origin of an xy coordinate system and lies on the y axis. At the position $x = d$ on the x axis, the electric field created by this wire has magnitude E and is directed to the right along the positive x axis. A charged particle is then placed on the x axis at $x = 2d$. At $x = d$ on the x axis, the electric field created by this particle has magnitude $2E$ and is directed to the left along the x axis. (*a*) At what positions on the x axis is the vector sum of the electric fields zero? (*b*) What is the magnitude of the electric field produced by the wire at the locations you identified in part *a*? ••

89. The origin of an x axis is placed at the center of a nonconducting solid sphere of radius R that carries a charge $+q_{sphere}$ distributed uniformly throughout its volume. A particle that carries an unknown charge q_{part} is located on the x axis at $x = +2R$. The magnitude of the electric field due to the sphere-particle combination is zero at $x = +R/4$ on the x axis. (*a*) What is q_{part} in terms of q_{sphere}? (*b*) At what other locations on the x axis is the electric field zero? •••

PRACTICE

90. A particle that carries charge $+4q$ is located at the origin of an x axis, and a uniformly charged nonconducting solid sphere of radius R and carrying charge $+q$ is centered at $x = +6R$ on the x axis. (*a*) At what locations on the x axis is the electric field zero? (*b*) If the nonconducting sphere is replaced by a conducting sphere of the same radius and carrying the same charge, would the answers to part *a* change? ●●●

91. The nonuniform volume charge density inside a positively charged solid nonconducting sphere of radius R is $\rho(r) = \rho_0 r/R$, where r is the radial distance from the sphere center. (*a*) Calculate the electric field as a function of r for $r < R$ and $r > R$. Repeat for volume charge densities of (*b*) $\rho(r) = \rho_0(1 - \frac{1}{2}R/r)$ and (*c*) $\rho(r) = \rho_0(1 - R/r)$. ●●●

92. A positively charged nonconducting solid sphere of radius R has a nonuniform volume charge density given by ρ_0 for $r \leq R/2$ and given by $2\rho_0(1 - r/R)$ for $R/2 \leq r \leq R$, where r is the radial distance from the sphere center. (*a*) Determine the charge q on the sphere in terms of ρ_0 and R. (*b*) Determine $\vec{E}$ in terms of ρ_0, r, and R. (*c*) Show that the electric field is continuous at the boundaries. ●●●

Additional problems

93. Can an electric field line have a kink in it? ●

94. Three particles each carrying charge $+q$ are located at the corners of an equilateral triangle whose side length is a. The triangle is centered on the origin of a Cartesian coordinate system. (*a*) Draw the electric field line diagram for this configuration of charge. What is the electric flux through a Gaussian surface that contains (*b*) one of the particles and (*c*) two of the particles? ●

95. A particle of charge q and mass m is placed above an infinite charged sheet for which the surface charge density is σ. The sheet carries the same type of charge as the particle. What is the acceleration of the particle as a function of its distance d above the sheet? ●

96. Infinite positively charged sheet 1 has uniform surface charge density $\sigma_1 = +4.0\ \text{nC/m}^2$ and is located in the yz plane of a Cartesian coordinate system. Infinite negatively charged sheet 2 is parallel to sheet 1 and has uniform surface charge density $\sigma_2 = -8.0\ \text{nC/m}^2$. Sheet 2 is 4 m to the right of sheet 1 along the $+x$ axis. (*a*) Determine the magnitude and direction of the electric field in all regions of space. (*b*) Draw a diagram showing the locations of the two sheets, labeling the regions and drawing the field lines for each region. ●●

97. A conducting, thick spherical shell of inner radius 100 mm and outer radius 120 mm has a particle carrying a 3.0-nC charge placed at its center. (*a*) Draw the electric field line diagram for the situation, marking the location of all charge on your diagram. (*b*) Calculate the surface charge density at the inner and outer shell surfaces. (*c*) Determine the electric field as a function of r, the radial distance from the center of the shell. (*d*) Draw an electric field line diagram for the situation when the particle is displaced by 30 mm from the shell's center. ●●

98. A system is composed of two infinitely long concentric cylinders, an outer cylinder O and an inner cylinder I. Each is either conducting or nonconducting, and both have a uniform surface or volume charge density. Cylinder O is a shell, and cylinder I is either solid or a shell. The graph in Figure P24.98 shows the magnitude of the electric field as a function of the radial distance r from the long central axis of the concentric cylinders. At all values of r, the electric field either is zero or has a nonzero magnitude and is directed away from the long central axis. (*a*) Deduce whether the cylinders are conducting or nonconducting, and give the relevant radii R (inner and outer radii for O; either one radius or two for I depending on whether it is solid or a shell) in terms of the general radius R shown in the graph. (*b*) What is the ratio of the charge on cylinder I to the charge on cylinder O? ●●

Figure P24.98

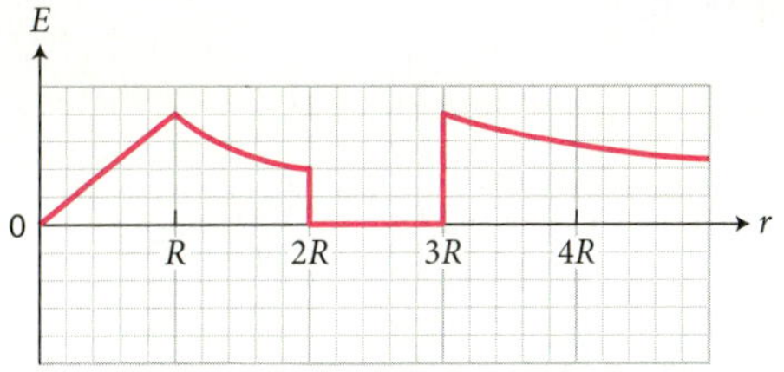

99. Near Earth's surface, the electric field has a magnitude of 150 N/C and points downward. Treating Earth's surface as a conducting sphere, calculate the surface charge density necessary to produce this electric field. ●●

100. An electron initially 3.00 m from a nonconducting infinite sheet of uniformly distributed charge is fired toward the sheet. The electron has an initial speed of 400 m/s and travels along a line perpendicular to the sheet. When the electron has traveled 2.00 m, its velocity is instantaneously zero, and it then reverses its direction. (*a*) What is the surface charge density on the sheet? (*b*) Given the same initial velocity, from what distance should the electron be fired if it is to just reach the sheet? ●●

101. Figure P24.101 shows four charge distributions in an xyz coordinate system. A is a charged particle at the origin, B is a charged conducting solid sphere of radius R centered at the origin, C is a uniformly charged nonconducting solid sphere of radius R centered at the origin, and D is a nonconducting infinite sheet of uniformly distributed charge in the yz plane, shown in cross section. In each case the electric field at $x = R$ is the same. Rank the magnitudes of the electric fields for the four cases, largest first, at (a) $x = 2R$ and (*b*) $x = R/2$. ●●

Figure P24.101

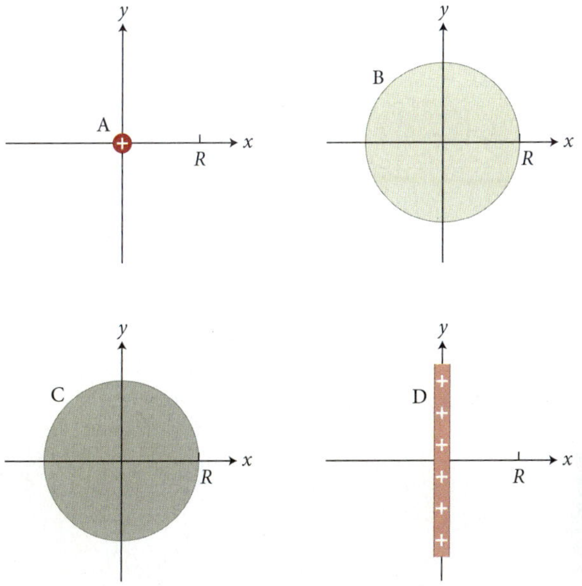

102. A positively charged nonconducting infinite sheet that has a uniform surface charge density σ lies in an xy plane. As shown in Figure P24.102, a circular region of radius R has been cut out of the sheet. (*a*) What is the electric field magnitude at the center of the circle? (*b*) Use superposition to calculate the electric field, both magnitude and direction, at a distance $z = 4R$ above the center of the circle. ••

Figure P24.102

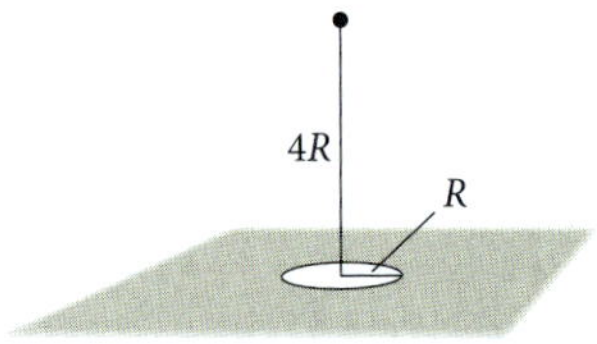

103. A nonconducting positively charged slab 1 of thickness $2a$ has a nonuniform but symmetrical volume charge density $\rho_0 x/a$. The sheet is centered, at $x = 0$, on the yz plane of a Cartesian coordinate system. (*a*) Determine the magnitude and direction of the electric field in all regions of space as a function of x, the distance from the yz plane. (*b*) A nonconducting charged slab 2, of thickness $2t$, is placed parallel to sheet 1 such that sheet 2 intersects the x axis at $x = d$. Sheet 2 is positively charged and has a uniform volume charge density ρ_0. Determine the electric field in all regions of space as a function of x. •••

104. A quantity of positive charge is distributed throughout the volume of a long nonconducting rod, which lies on the z axis and is centered at $z = 0$. The rod's radius R is much smaller than its length ℓ. For positions $r \ll \ell$ and $|z| \ll \ell$, calculate the electric fields inside and outside the rod as a function of the radial distance r from the rod's long central axis if the volume charge density is (*a*) ρ_0 and (*b*) $\rho_0(1 - 2r/R)$. •••

105. You are a crewmember on a space station orbiting Earth. To investigate some physics you remember from college, you drill a small hole all the way through a large solid nonconducting sphere of radius R that has a negative charge q_s evenly distributed throughout its volume, making sure the hole goes through the sphere's center. You then go outside the station with the sphere and release a small pellet carrying positive charge $+q_p$ at one entrance of the hole. You are gratified to observe that the pellet oscillates with the frequency you calculated beforehand based on Gauss's law and your knowledge of simple harmonic motion. ••• CR

106. You need to create a uniform electric field in a small region of space, and all you have to work with is one large styrofoam ball that carries a uniform volume charge distribution ρ. You cut the ball into two sections and scoop a hemispherical hole out of each section so that putting the sections back together results in a spherical cavity *off-center* inside the ball. You know that the cavity can be described as a region composed of equal amounts of uniformly distributed positive and negative charge carriers, giving it a charge of zero. You suspect the principle of superposition might be useful. ••• CR

107. Electrical power lines are often not insulated, and the magnitude of the electric field of the surrounding air is about 3×10^6 N/C. At greater electric field magnitudes, the air dissociates into charged particles, causing a breakdown and a big spark. You've been given a long sample of wire to test in the lab under electrostatic conditions, and you measure its diameter to be 16.6 mm. You have lots of equipment to produce a uniform linear charge density on the wire sample, and you figure you'd better build in a safety factor of 3 to account for humid days and so forth. ••• CR

108. An infinitely large positively charged nonconducting sheet 1 has uniform surface charge density $\sigma_1 = +130.0\ \text{nC/m}^2$ and is located in the xz plane of a Cartesian coordinate system. An infinitely large positively charged nonconducting sheet 2 has uniform surface charge density $\sigma_2 = +90.0\ \text{nC/m}^2$ and intersects the xz plane at the z axis, making an angle of 30° with sheet 1. (*a*) Draw a diagram showing the end view of the sheets in the xy plane. (*b*) Determine the expression for the electric field in the region between the sheets for positive values of x and y. Calculate the value of the electric field at (3 m, 1 m, 0). •••

PRACTICE

Answers to Review Questions

1. Imagine placing a positively charged test particle near any charged object in the distribution—call it object 1—and then imagine dragging the test particle a short distance in the direction of the electric force exerted by object 1 on the particle. Draw a directed line segment along the drag path, with the arrowhead of the segment pointing in the direction of the test particle's motion. This directed line segment is the first portion of the field line. Examine the surroundings of the test particle in its new position and then imagine dragging it a short distance in the direction of the vector sum of the electric forces it now experiences due to the charge distribution. Extend the line segment along this drag path, again showing an arrowhead pointing in the direction of the test particle's motion. Repeat until you reach a charged object in the distribution (or until you reach the edge of the area you are using for your field drawing).
2. The number is arbitrary, subject to the constraint that, in a given field line diagram, the number of lines that begin or terminate on any charged object contributing to the electric field is proportional to the magnitude of the charge on that object.
3. The direction of the electric field vector at any point is tangent to the field line at that point. The density of the electric field lines in any region represents the magnitude of the electric field in that region.
4. Field line density is the number of lines per unit area that cross a surface that is perpendicular to the electric field.
5. If the surface were parallel to the electric field, no field lines would cross the surface. At an intermediate angle θ from the perpendicular, a fraction $\cos\theta < 1$ as many field lines would cross the surface. To define field line density unambiguously, we choose the surface to be perpendicular to the field lines.
6. Not necessarily. That the flux through the surface is zero tells you only that the enclosed charge (the algebraic sum of the charges on all charged objects inside the surface) is zero. There may be several charged objects inside, whose charges sum to zero. A closed surface surrounding the one proton and one electron that make up a hydrogen atom is one example.
7. Not necessarily. If any electric field lines cross the surface, then there must be one outgoing field line for every incoming field line, so that the field line flux through the surface is zero. One example is a closed surface surrounding an electric dipole. Another example is a charged particle outside a closed surface whose enclosed charge is zero.
8. (*a*) Because the amount of charge enclosed by the balloon does not change, the field line flux through its surface does not change. (*b*) Again the field line flux does not change because the enclosed charge does not change. (However, in either case the field line *pattern* changes when the electrons are placed outside the balloon.)
9. Count the number of field lines that penetrate the surface going outward as $+1$ for each penetration; count the number of field lines that penetrate the surface going inward as -1 for each penetration. Do not count field lines that do not penetrate the surface. The algebraic sum of the inward and outward values is the field line flux.
10. The electric field in the space enclosed by a uniformly charged spherical shell is zero. The electric field at points outside a uniformly charged spherical shell is the same as the electric field due to a particle carrying an equal charge located at the center of the shell.
11. Planar symmetry is the symmetry of an infinite sheet. The appearance of the sheet remains unchanged if it is rotated by any amount about an axis perpendicular to the sheet, or translated by any amount along either of the two axes perpendicular to this perpendicular axis.
12. The electric field is zero under conditions of electrostatic equilibrium (any condition where the distribution of the charged particles in the conductor does not vary with time) because the vector sum of the electric forces exerted on a test particle within the conducting material is zero.
13. If there are no charged particles inside the cavity, then the electric field is zero inside the cavity, no matter what the charge distribution is outside the sphere. The electric field inside the cavity can be nonzero when there are charged particles inside the cavity. In either case, the electric field is zero within the conducting material of the sphere itself.
14. The surplus charge must be distributed on the surfaces of the conducting object. The surplus charge resides on the outer surface of the conducting material in the absence of other charged objects, and possibly also on the inner surface surrounding the cavity if there is a charged object in the cavity.
15. The two are proportional to each other. The field line flux has an arbitrary value, depending on how many lines are drawn to represent a certain amount of charge. The electric flux is uniquely defined by Eq. 24.4.
16. A represents the area of a flat surface through which we wish to measure the electric flux. θ represents the angle between the electric field and the surface normal. So $\cos\theta = \pm 1$ if the surface is perpendicular to the electric field (that is, if the surface normal vector is parallel or antiparallel to the electric field).
17. For each small segment of the area of the surface, we need to compute the contribution $\Phi_E = EA\cos\theta$. If we simply multiplied the magnitudes of $\vec{E}$ and $\vec{A}$ without using the scalar product, we would miss the factor $\cos\theta$. The scalar product correctly incorporates the magnitude of $\vec{E}$, the magnitude of $\vec{A}$, and the cosine of the angle between $\vec{E}$ and the surface normal.
18. If we had defined the area vector as pointing inward, we would have obtained the wrong sign for Φ_E. Just as the field line density for a closed surface enclosing a positively charged particle is defined to be positive, we want the electric flux to be positive through a closed surface enclosing a positively charged particle.
19. The enclosed charge is zero because we must compute the algebraic sum of the charges on the individual particles enclosed by the spherical surface.
20. No. Checkpoint 24.20 makes a similar point. Gauss's law is a direct consequence of the $1/r^2$ dependence of the electric field due to a charged particle. Any deviation from this behavior renders Gauss's law invalid.
21. Because the charge distribution is uniform, the ratio of the charge enclosed by the Gaussian surface to the charge enclosed by the ball is the same as the ratio of the volumes of the two spheres. Therefore $q_{enc}/q = V_{enc}/V = (4\pi r^3/3)/(4\pi R^3/3)$, or $q_{enc} = q(r/R)^3$.
22. The electric field is zero anywhere the algebraic sum of the charge inside the Gaussian surface is zero. This happens for $r < R$ and $r > 2R$.
23. It doesn't matter how long you make the cylindrical Gaussian surface because this length cancels as you do the calculation coming out of Eq. 24.8. (Such a cancellation is a feature of many types of physics problems. You have to define a variable to completely specify the calculation, but if that variable is not important for the physics—and the details of an imaginary surface certainly should not be important—that variable should cancel somewhere during your calculation. If it does not, you've probably made a mistake somewhere.)

PRACTICE

Answers to Guided Problems

Guided Problem 24.2 The electric flux is zero because the charge distribution is symmetrical under reflection through this plane.

Guided Problem 24.4 The electric flux through the top and bottom faces is zero. The electric flux through each of the other four faces is $\lambda a/4\epsilon_0$.

Guided Problem 24.6 The electric flux through the top and bottom faces is zero. The electric flux through each of the other four faces is $\lambda a/4\epsilon_0$.

Guided Problem 24.8 For $r \leq R$, $E = q/(4\pi R^2\epsilon_0)$. For $r \geq R$, $E = q/(4\pi r^2\epsilon_0)$.

Figure WGA24.8

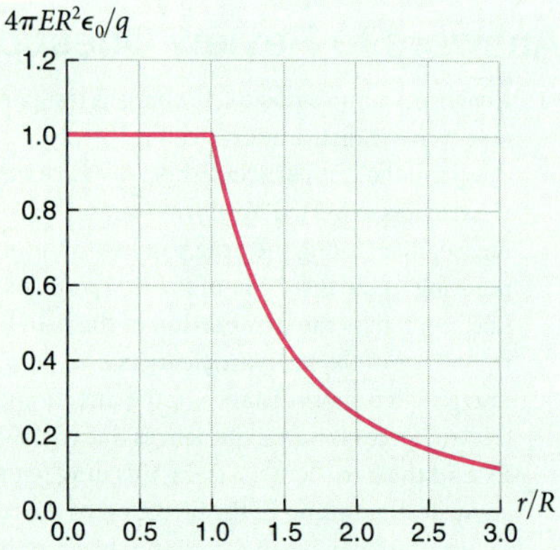

25

PRACTICE

Work and Energy in Electrostatics

Chapter Summary

Energy and work (Sections 25.1, 25.2, 25.4)

Concepts **Electric potential energy** is the potential energy associated with the relative positions of charged objects.

The **electrostatic work** done by an electric field on a charged particle as the particle moves from one position to another is independent of the path taken and depends on only the particle's initial and final positions.

The constant electric field created by stationary charged objects is sometimes called an *electrostatic field.*

Quantitative Tools If two particles carrying charges q_1 and q_2 are separated by a distance r_{12}, their **electric potential energy** U^E is

$$U^E = \frac{q_1 q_2}{4\pi\epsilon_0}\frac{1}{r_{12}}, \tag{25.8}$$

where U^E is taken as zero at infinite separation. The electric potential energy of a system of charged particles is the sum of the potential energies of all possible particle pairs. For three particles, the energy is

$$U^E = \frac{q_1 q_2}{4\pi\epsilon_0}\frac{1}{r_{12}} + \frac{q_1 q_3}{4\pi\epsilon_0}\frac{1}{r_{13}} + \frac{q_2 q_3}{4\pi\epsilon_0}\frac{1}{r_{23}}. \tag{25.14}$$

Electrostatic potential (Sections 25.2, 25.3, 25.5)

Concepts The **potential difference** between points A and B in an electrostatic field is equal to the negative of the electrostatic work per unit charge done by the field on a charged particle as it moves from A to B.

An **equipotential surface** is a surface over which the electrostatic potential is constant. The electric field lines associated with a stationary charge distribution are always perpendicular to the equipotential surfaces for the charge distribution. The electrostatic work done on a charged particle moving along an equipotential surface is zero.

An electrostatic field is directed from points of higher potential to points of lower potential. The electric force pushes positively charged particles toward regions of lower potential, whereas it pushes negatively charged particles toward regions of higher potential.

Quantitative Tools If we set the zero of potential at infinity, the potential $V(r)$ at a distance r from a particle carrying a charge q is

$$V(r) = \frac{1}{4\pi\epsilon_0}\frac{q}{r}. \tag{25.21}$$

Potential is measured in **volts:**

$$1\ \text{V} \equiv 1\ \text{J/C}. \tag{25.16}$$

If we set the zero of potential at infinity, the potential at a point P due to a group of n charged particles of charge q_n at distances r_{nP} from point P is

$$V_P = \frac{1}{4\pi\epsilon_0}\sum_n \frac{q_n}{r_{nP}}. \tag{25.30}$$

The work W_q done on a charged particle q by an electric field $\vec{E}$ as the particle moves from point A to point B is

$$W_q(\text{A} \to \text{B}) = q\int_A^B \vec{E}\cdot d\vec{\ell}. \tag{25.24}$$

The potential difference V_{AB} between points A and B due to an electrostatic field $\vec{E}$ is

$$V_{AB} \equiv \frac{-W_q(\text{A} \to \text{B})}{q} = -\int_A^B \vec{E}\cdot d\vec{\ell}. \tag{25.25}$$

For any electrostatic field,

$$\oint \vec{E}\cdot d\vec{\ell} = 0. \tag{25.32}$$

Continuous charge distributions (Section 25.6)

Quantitative Tools At any point P, the potential due to an extended charged object is

$$V_P = \frac{1}{4\pi\epsilon_0}\int \frac{dq_s}{r_{sP}}, \tag{25.34}$$

where r_{sP} is the distance from the infinitesimal charge element dq_s to P and the integral is taken over the object. (See the Procedure box "Calculating the electrostatic potential of continuous charge distributions.")

If a thin rod of length ℓ carries a uniformly distributed charge q, the potential due to the rod at any point P on a line that runs perpendicular to the rod and passes through either end is

$$V_P = \frac{1}{4\pi\epsilon_0}\frac{q}{\ell}\ln\left(\frac{\ell + \sqrt{\ell^2 + d^2}}{d}\right),$$

where d is the distance from P to the rod.

If a thin disk of radius R carries a uniform surface charge density σ, the potential due to the disk at any point P on a line that runs perpendicular to the plane of the disk and passes through the disk center is

$$V_P = \frac{\sigma}{2\epsilon_0}(\sqrt{z^2 + R^2} - |z|),$$

where z is the distance from P to the disk.

Calculating the electrostatic field from the potential (Section 25.7)

Quantitative Tools If we know the potential due to a charge distribution, we can use the equation

$$\vec{E} = -\frac{\partial V}{\partial x}\hat{\imath} - \frac{\partial V}{\partial y}\hat{\jmath} - \frac{\partial V}{\partial z}\hat{k} \tag{25.40}$$

to calculate the value of the electrostatic field due to the distribution at any point $P(x, y, z)$.

We can also calculate individual components of the electric field from the potential. For example, $E_x = -\partial V/\partial x$ and $E_r = -\partial V/\partial r$.

Review Questions

Answers to these questions can be found at the end of this chapter.

25.1 Electric potential energy

1. What is electric potential energy?
2. In what way is electric potential energy more complicated than gravitational potential energy?
3. How does the electric potential energy of a dipole placed near a stationary charged object depend on the orientation of the dipole relative to the charged object?

25.2 Electrostatic work

4. What is electrostatic work?
5. When a charged particle moves in an electrostatic field, on which aspects of its path does the electrostatic work done on the particle depend? Which aspects of the path have no bearing on the amount of electrostatic work done on the particle?
6. What is electrostatic potential difference?
7. What is the distinction between the potential difference in an electric field and the potential at any point in the field?

25.3 Equipotentials

8. What are equipotential lines? Equipotential surfaces? Equipotential volumes?
9. How are equipotential lines and surfaces spatially related to electric field lines?
10. In an electric field, how does the electrostatic potential vary along a given field line?
11. What characteristic of a charged particle determines whether it tends to move from a region of higher electrostatic potential to a region of lower electrostatic potential or from a region of lower potential to one of higher potential?

25.4 Calculating work and energy in electrostatics

12. What is the mathematical expression for the electrostatic work done on a charged particle in moving the particle from one location to another in the electrostatic field created by a second charged particle?
13. What is the relationship between the electrostatic work done on a charged particle in moving it around in an electric field and the path of the motion?
14. What is the mathematical relationship between the electrostatic work done on a charged particle in moving it from point A to point B and the electrostatic potential difference between points A and B?
15. How can the electric potential energy of a system made up of two charged particles be defined when only differences in potential energy are physically meaningful?
16. What is the electric potential energy for any system of charged particles?

25.5 Potential difference

17. What is the SI unit of potential difference?
18. For (*a*) a system of charged particles and (*b*) an electric circuit, what is the common reference position used to allow us to assign a unique value of electrostatic potential to each position in the system?
19. What is the expression for determining the electrostatic potential at any given position in a system of charged particles when the potential at infinity is assigned a value of zero?
20. Is it possible to extract energy from an electrostatic field by going around a closed path?

25.6 Electrostatic potentials of continuous charge distributions

21. How can the expression for the electrostatic potential of an object that carries a continuous distribution of charge be obtained from the expression for the electrostatic potential of a system of charged particles?
22. Is there any advantage to computing the electrostatic potential of a distribution of charge rather than the electric field due to the distribution?

25.7 Obtaining the electric field from the potential

23. Can the field line pattern for the electrostatic field created by a charged object be determined from a map of the equipotentials?
24. What is the relationship between the electrostatic field and the electrostatic potential?

Developing a Feel

Make an order-of-magnitude estimate of each of the following quantities. Letters in parentheses refer to hints below. Use them as needed to guide your thinking.

1. The electrostatic work done while assembling one proton and one electron to form a hydrogen atom (F, X, A)
2. The minimum work done by an external agent to bring two protons together to form a helium nucleus (F, M, A)
3. The potential difference needed to give 10^{-12} J of kinetic energy to a proton that is initially at rest (Q, A)
4. The electrostatic potential at a point that is 30 mm from one end of a charged glass rod and lies on the line that runs through that end perpendicular to the rod's long axis (C, R, W)
5. The surface charge density on a utility-hole cover charged with a car battery (D, V, I, N, S)
6. The potential difference between floor and ceiling needed to "float" a proton in your room (Z, K, AA, U, P)
7. The potential difference required to stop an electron whose initial speed is 1×10^6 m/s (H, Q, A)
8. The initial speed, expressed as a multiple of the speed of light c, of an alpha particle (which is a helium atom stripped of its two electrons) that approaches to within 9×10^{-15} m of the center of a gold nucleus (BB, B, G, L, Q)
9. The minimum work needed to assemble eight protons, one at each of the eight corners of a 5-mm cube (E, J, O, T, Y)

Hints

A. What is the magnitude of charge on any proton or electron?
B. What is the electrostatic potential at the particle's initial position? At its final position?
C. What is the length of the charge distribution on a typical glass rod used in the laboratory?
D. How can this be done physically, and what type of charged object results?
E. How much work is required to place the first proton at the lower left front corner?
F. What is the initial separation between the two particles?
G. What is the charge of a gold nucleus?
H. What is K_{initial}?
I. What equipotential surface is at a potential of 12 V?
J. How much work is required to place the second proton at the lower left rear corner?
K. Which of the two surfaces, floor or ceiling, must be positively charged?
L. What is the particle's final speed?
M. What is their final separation?
N. What is a typical radius of a utility-hole cover?
O. How much work is required to place the third proton at the lower right rear corner?
P. What is the distance from floor to ceiling?
Q. How are ΔV and ΔK related for the particle?
R. What is a reasonable guess for how much charge the rubbed rod can carry?
S. How does this situation relate to the charged disk in *Principles* Example 25.7?
T. Do you see a trend in the number of terms?
U. What value of E is required in order to have the electric force balance this gravitational force?
V. What is the potential difference between the terminals of a car battery?
W. Where is the potential equal to zero?
X. What is their final separation?
Y. How many terms must be combined to get the minimum work required to place all eight protons?
Z. What forces must balance to float the proton?
AA. What is the magnitude of the gravitational force exerted?
BB. What is the initial separation distance?

Key (all values approximate)

A. elementary charge, $e = 1.6 \times 10^{-19}$ C; **B.** zero at initial position, $V = (1/4\pi\epsilon_0)(q/r)$ at final position; **C.** 0.2 m; **D.** place cover on nonconducting stand, attach positive battery terminal to cover, and negative battery terminal to ground, producing a charged disk; **E.** none, because there is no potential difference to move through; **F.** essentially infinite; **G.** 79 protons, thus $+79e$; **H.** 5×10^{-19} J; **I.** the surface of the cover; **J.** $W = q\Delta V = (1/4\pi\epsilon_0)(q^2/r)$, where r is cube edge length and q is proton charge; **K.** the floor; **L.** zero; **M.** nuclear separation distance, 2×10^{-15} m; **N.** 0.3 m; **O.** $q\Delta V = (1/4\pi\epsilon_0)(q^2/r) + (1/4\pi\epsilon_0)(q^2/\sqrt{2}r)$; **P.** 3 m; **Q.** assuming only electrostatic work, $q\Delta V + \Delta K = 0$; **R.** 1×10^1 μC; **S.** both upper and lower surfaces of the cover are charged, so there are two thin disks to superpose; **T.** each proton added requires one term for each proton already in place; **U.** $E = mg/q \approx 1 \times 10^{-7}$ V/m; **V.** 12 V; **W.** infinitely far from the rod; **X.** the atom's radius, 5×10^{-11} m; **Y.** 28, counting each pair of protons once: 12 edge terms, 12 face diagonals, and 4 body diagonals; **Z.** gravitational force exerted by Earth on proton and electric forces exerted by charged floor and ceiling on it; **AA.** 2×10^{-26} N; **BB.** infinite

Worked and Guided Problems

Procedure: Calculating the potential difference between two points in an electric field

The potential difference between two points in an electric field is given by Eq. 25.25. The following steps will help you evaluate the integral:

1. Begin by making a sketch of the electric field, indicating the points corresponding to the two points between which you wish to determine the potential difference.
2. To facilitate evaluating the scalar product $\vec{E} \cdot d\vec{\ell}$, choose a path between the two points so that $\vec{E}$ is either parallel or perpendicular to the path. If necessary, break the path into segments. If $\vec{E}$ has a constant value along the path (or a segment of the path), you can pull it out of the integral; the remaining integral is then equal to the length of the corresponding path (or the segment of the path).
3. Remember that to determine V_{AB} ("the potential difference between points A and B"), your path begins at A and ends at B. The vector $d\vec{\ell}$ therefore is tangent to the path, in the direction that leads from A to B (see also Appendix B).

At this point you can substitute the expression for the electric field and carry out the integral. Once you are done, you may want to verify the algebraic sign of the result you obtained: *negative* when a positively charged particle moves along the path in the direction of the electric field, and *positive* when it moves in the opposite direction.

Procedure: Calculating the electrostatic potential of continuous charge distributions

To calculate the electrostatic potential of a continuous charge distribution (relative to zero potential at infinity), you need to evaluate the integral in Eq. 25.34. The following steps will help you work out the integral:

1. Begin by making a sketch of the charge distribution. Mentally divide the distribution into infinitesimally small segments carrying a charge dq_s. Indicate one such segment in your drawing.
2. Choose a coordinate system that allows you to express the position of dq_s in the charge distribution in terms of a minimum number of coordinates (x, y, z, r, or θ). These coordinates are the integration variables. For example, use a radial coordinate system for a charge distribution with radial symmetry. Never place the representative segment dq_s at the origin.
3. Indicate the point at which you wish to determine the potential. Express the factor $1/r_{sP}$, where r_{sP} is the distance between dq_s and the point of interest, in terms of the integration variable(s).
4. Determine whether the charge distribution is one dimensional (a straight or curved wire), two dimensional (a flat or curved surface), or three dimensional (any bulk object). Express dq_s in terms of the corresponding charge density of the object and the integration variable(s).

At this point you can substitute your expressions for dq_s and $1/r_{sP}$ into Eq. 25.34 and work out the integral.

These examples involve material from this chapter but are not associated with any particular section. Some examples are worked out in detail; others you should work out by following the guidelines provided.

PRACTICE

Worked Problem 25.1 Relocating a charged particle

Consider a group of charged toner particles and how one of them can be moved around in the group. Four charged particles form a square with side length $a = 6.9\ \mu$m. Particles 1, 3, and 4 carry charge $+q = 3.9 \times 10^{-15}$ C, and particle 2 carries charge $-2q$. Particles 2 and 4 are diagonally opposite each other. How much work must be done by an external agent on particle 4 to pull it out of its corner, slide it around outside the perimeter of the square past particles 3, 2, and 1, and then place it stationary at the center of the square?

Figure WG25.1

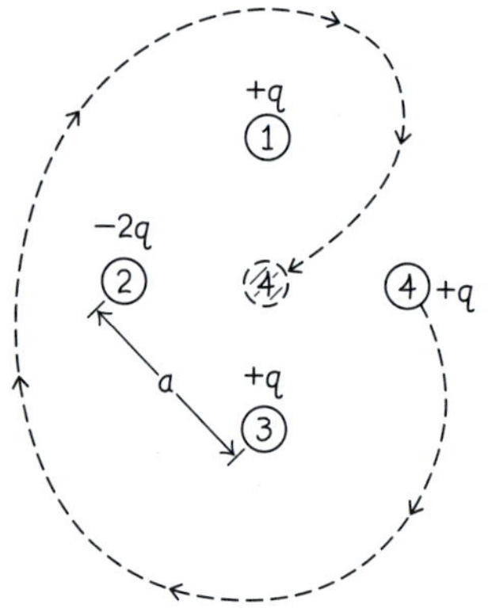

❶ GETTING STARTED We begin with a sketch of the arrangement and what we want to do with particle 4 (Figure WG25.1). We are not given much information about the external agent that causes particle 4 to move, but we do know that the change in the particle's kinetic energy is zero because it starts out with zero kinetic energy and has zero kinetic energy again after it is placed at the center of the square. Thus the work done by the external agent, the quantity we must calculate, is the negative of the electrostatic work done by the other three particles as particle 4 is moved.

❷ **DEVISE PLAN** Because the change in kinetic energy for particle 4 is zero, we can use

$$W_{\text{on }4} = W_{\text{by agent}} + W_{\text{by }1,2,3} = \Delta K = 0.$$

Because electrostatic interactions are nondissipative, we know that the work done by particles 1, 2, and 3 on particle 4 equals the negative of the change in electric potential energy of the system. Thus we can use

$$W_{\text{by agent}} = -W_{\text{by }1,2,3} = -(-q_4\Delta V) = q_4\Delta V. \quad (1)$$

For particle 4 at any given location, the electrostatic potential at that location due to particles 1, 2, and 3 is given by

$$V = \frac{1}{4\pi\epsilon_0}\sum_{j=1}^{3}\frac{q_j}{r_j}, \quad (2)$$

where r_j is the separation distance between particle 4 and particle j (where $j = 1, 2, 3$).

We need to determine the difference between the electrostatic potential at the initial and final positions of particle 4. We can calculate this difference in potential in two ways: use Eq. 2 with either the final or initial separation distances to calculate the potentials at those positions and then substitute the values obtained into Eq. 1, or substitute Eq. 2 into Eq. 1 and sum the potential differences due to each particle separately. We choose the latter method because it allows us to consolidate common factors easily.

❸ **EXECUTE PLAN** The work done by the external agent on particle 4 is

$$W_{\text{by agent}} = q_4[V_f - V_i] = q_4\frac{1}{4\pi\epsilon_0}\left[\sum_{j=1}^{3}\frac{q_j}{r_{j,f}} - \sum_{j=1}^{3}\frac{q_j}{r_{j,i}}\right]$$

$$= \frac{q_4}{4\pi\epsilon_0}\left\{\sum_{j=1}^{3} q_j\left[\frac{1}{r_{j,f}} - \frac{1}{r_{j,i}}\right]\right\} = \frac{q_4}{4\pi\epsilon_0}\left\{q_1\left[\frac{1}{\frac{1}{2}a\sqrt{2}} - \frac{1}{a}\right]\right.$$

$$\left. + q_2\left[\frac{1}{\frac{1}{2}a\sqrt{2}} - \frac{1}{a\sqrt{2}}\right] + q_3\left[\frac{1}{\frac{1}{2}a\sqrt{2}} - \frac{1}{a}\right]\right\}.$$

Removing the subscripts on q to simplify, with $q_4 = q_1 = q_2 = q$ and $q_2 = -2q$, we have

$$W_{\text{by agent}} = \frac{q}{4\pi\epsilon_0}\left[q\left(\frac{1}{\frac{1}{2}a\sqrt{2}} - \frac{1}{a}\right) + (-2q)\left(\frac{1}{\frac{1}{2}a\sqrt{2}} - \frac{1}{a\sqrt{2}}\right)\right.$$

$$\left. + q\left(\frac{1}{\frac{1}{2}a\sqrt{2}} - \frac{1}{a}\right)\right] = \frac{2q^2}{4\pi\epsilon_0 a}\left(\frac{1}{\sqrt{2}} - 1\right)$$

$$= \frac{2(3.9\times10^{-15}\text{ C})^2}{4\pi(8.85\times10^{-12}\text{ C}^2/\text{N}\cdot\text{m}^2)(6.9\times10^{-6}\text{ m})}\left[\frac{1}{\sqrt{2}} - 1\right]$$

$$= -1.2\times10^{-14}\text{ J.} ✔$$

❹ **EVALUATE RESULT** As a check on this result, let's try the alternative approach of calculating the potential V_f at particle 4's final position, due to particles 1, 2, and 3; then calculating V_i at particle 4's initial position, due to particles 1, 2, and 3; and directly using $W_{\text{by agent}} = q_4[V_f - V_i]$. Taking the potential at infinity to be zero, we obtain

$$V_f = \frac{1}{4\pi\epsilon_0}\left(\frac{q}{a/\sqrt{2}} + \frac{q}{a/\sqrt{2}} + \frac{(-2q)}{a/\sqrt{2}}\right) = 0,$$

and we get

$$V_i = \frac{1}{4\pi\epsilon_0}\left(\frac{q}{a} + \frac{q}{a} + \frac{(-2q)}{a\sqrt{2}}\right) = \frac{q}{4\pi\epsilon_0 a}(2 - \sqrt{2}).$$

So

$$q_4[V_f - V_i] = 0 - \frac{q^2}{4\pi\epsilon_0 a}(2 - \sqrt{2}) = -1.2\times10^{-14}\text{ J},$$

just as we found above. It makes sense that $V_f = 0$ because particle 4's final position is equidistant from three charged particles whose charges sum to zero. And it makes sense that $V_i > 0$ because particle 4's initial position is closer to the two positively charged particles than to the negatively charged particle. The electrostatic work done on particle 4 as it moves from $V_i > 0$ to $V_f = 0$ (negative potential difference) is positive. Because particle 4's kinetic energy does not change, this positive electrostatic work is balanced by negative work done by the external agent. So it makes sense that our answer is negative.

Guided Problem 25.2 Forming and straightening a charged triangle

You have three charged particles that are initially very far apart from one another, and you must bring them together to form an equilateral triangle of side length ℓ. Particles A and B each carry a charge $-q$, and particle C carries a charge $4q$. How much work must you do to form the triangle? How much work must you do to rearrange the particles so that they are in a straight line with particle C in the center and a distance ℓ between adjacent particles?

❶ **GETTING STARTED**

1. Sketch the triangle and the line, and describe the problem in your own words. What two values are you asked to determine?

❷ **DEVISE PLAN**

2. How can you relate the work you need to do in forming the triangle to the electric potential energy of the configuration?
3. What kind of drawing should you make to show the process of forming the triangle? What kind to show the straightening process?
4. How many terms are in the potential-energy sum for each configuration? What are those terms?

❸ **EXECUTE PLAN**

5. By comparing the initial and final potential differences, compute the work done in forming the triangle. Repeat for the work done in forming the straight line.
6. Is there a shortcut for evaluating the amount of work needed to form the straight line?

❹ **EVALUATE RESULT**

7. Which configuration do you expect to have a greater potential energy?

Worked Problem 25.3 Nonuniformly charged rubber ball

A solid rubber ball of radius R carries a charge q_{ball}, with the volume charge density increasing linearly from zero at the center to the ball's surface. What is the difference in potential between a position B on the ball's surface and any position D located a distance $d < R$ from the ball's center?

❶ **GETTING STARTED** As usual we begin with a sketch of the situation (Figure WG25.2). Note that the problem statement does not specify that positions B and D must be on the same radial line. We could just as easily have shown D on, say, the radius that runs from the center to the 12 o'clock position at the ball's surface. Because of symmetry, the electrostatic potential is the same at each point on a spherical shell concentric with the ball, however, and so we arbitrarily show B and D on the same radial line.

Figure WG25.2

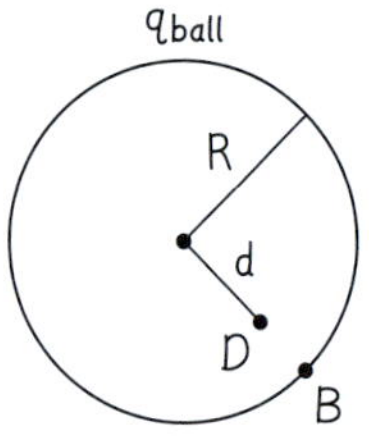

The difference in potential between B and D is a line integral of the electric field from the initial position at B, where radial distance $r = R$, to the final position at D, where $r = d$. Thus we must determine $\vec{E}$. We know from symmetry that the electric field is directed radially, and we also know that the field magnitude is affected by the charge distribution, so we must determine a way to calculate that magnitude as a function of the charge distribution.

❷ **DEVISE PLAN** The difference in potential between B and D is given by Eq. 25.25, $V_{BD} = -\int_B^D \vec{E} \cdot d\vec{\ell}$. We know from Chapter 24 that we can determine the electric field at any radial distance r from the center by using the symmetry of the problem and Gauss's law (Eq. 24.8), $\Phi_E = \oint \vec{E} \cdot d\vec{A} = q_{enc}/\epsilon_0$, where q_{enc} in our case is the quantity of charge enclosed within a sphere that is concentric with the ball and has a radius $r = d$. We can get q_{enc} by noting that the volume charge density increases linearly from zero with distance x from the center, $\rho(x) = \rho_0 x$, where ρ_0 is a constant of dimension C/m^4, and using

$$q_{enc}(r) = \int \rho dV,$$

where dV is the volume of a thin spherical shell concentric with the ball. The value of ρ_0 can be determined by noting that q_{ball} is the charge carried by the ball—that is, $q_{ball} = q_{enc}(R)$.

❸ **EXECUTE PLAN** The charge enclosed by a solid sphere of arbitrary radius r is the sum of the contributions from a series of spherical shells each of radius x and thickness dx:

$$q_{enc}(r) = \int \rho dV = \int_0^r (\rho_0 x)(4\pi x^2 dx) = \pi \rho_0 r^4.$$

From this, we can express ρ_0 in terms of q_{ball}:

$$q_{enc}(R) = \pi \rho_0 R^4 = q_{ball}$$

$$\rho_0 = \frac{q_{ball}}{\pi R^4}.$$

Now we use Gauss's law (Eq. 24.8). Because the ball's symmetry requires that the electric field be radially directed, we have at any radial distance r from the ball's center

$$\oint \vec{E}(r) \cdot d\vec{A} = E(r)A(r) = \frac{q_{enc}(r)}{\epsilon_0}$$

$$E(r)(4\pi r^2) = \frac{\pi \rho_0 r^4}{\epsilon_0} = \frac{q_{ball} r^4}{\epsilon_0 R^4}$$

$$E(r) = \frac{q_{ball}}{4\pi\epsilon_0 R^4} r^2.$$

The difference in potential between point B on the ball's surface ($r = R$) and point D a distance $r = d$ from the ball's center is then

$$V_d - V_R = -\int_R^d \vec{E}(r) \cdot d\vec{r} = -\int_R^d E(r)dr$$

$$= -\int_R^d \frac{q_{ball}}{4\pi\epsilon_0 R^4} r^2 dr = -\frac{q_{ball}}{4\pi\epsilon_0 R^4} \left[\tfrac{1}{3} r^3\right]_R^d$$

$$= \frac{q_{ball}}{12\pi\epsilon_0 R^4}(R^3 - d^3). ✔$$

❹ **EVALUATE RESULT** If q_{ball} is positive, the electric field is directed radially outward. This means that as we move from B to D, we are moving in the direction opposite the direction of the electric field, thereby increasing the electrostatic potential. Consequently, the potential difference should be positive, which is what our answer says. The opposite is true if q_{ball} is negative, which is also consistent with our equation. Our equation says that the potential difference is a linear function of q_{ball}, and we expect $V_d - V_R$ to be greater if the ball carries more charge. We note that if we locate D such that $d = R$, the potential difference is zero, as it must be.

Guided Problem 25.4 Charged plastic sphere

A quantity q_{sphere} of charge is uniformly distributed throughout a solid plastic sphere of radius R. What is the potential difference between the center and a point A located a distance r from the center when $r < R$ and when $r > R$?

1 GETTING STARTED

1. Sketch the sphere.
2. What information is given, and what variable or variables are you asked to determine?

2 DEVISE PLAN

3. How do you determine the potential difference between any two positions inside the sphere? What quantities do you need to know in order to determine this difference?
4. How do you determine the charge enclosed within a spherical shell of any radius?
5. How do you relate the potential at any position outside the plastic sphere to the potential at any position inside by matching expressions at a boundary of these two regions?

3 EXECUTE PLAN

4 EVALUATE RESULT

6. Does your expression give the correct result for the potential at a location very far from the sphere center?

Worked Problem 25.5 Line of charge

A plastic rod of length ℓ is rubbed with fur to uniformly distribute a quantity q_{rod} of surplus charge. It is then placed on a nonconducting stand, and the stand is positioned so that the rod lies along the x axis of an xy coordinate system and the rod's center is at the origin. Determine the electrostatic potential at any point P located at an arbitrary position (x_P, y_P) outside the rod.

1 GETTING STARTED This problem is similar to *Principles* Example 25.6, which determines the electrostatic potential for points along a line that runs through one end of a rod and is perpendicular to the rod's long axis. However, we're now asked to determine the potential at *any* location in the space surrounding the rod. We need to calculate the electrostatic potential that a charge distribution creates at a point P, and for this we need Eq. 25.34:

$$V = \int \frac{1}{4\pi\epsilon_0}\frac{dq}{r},$$

where r is the distance from P to an infinitesimal charge element dq in the charge distribution. We draw a diagram that shows the necessary information (Figure WG25.3).

Figure WG25.3

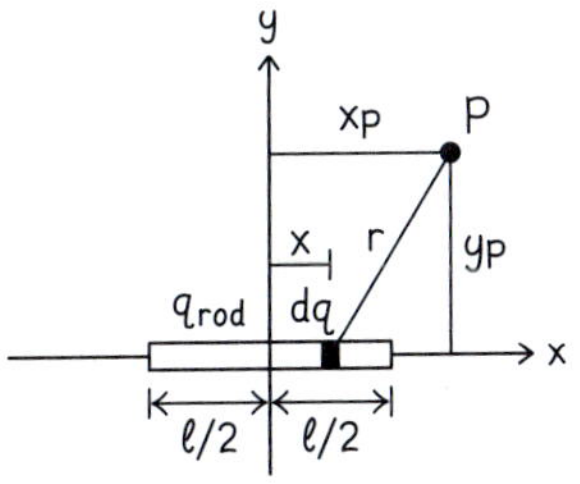

2 DEVISE PLAN We need to determine the contribution to the potential from each infinitesimal charge element dq of the rod because the distance from P to the rod is different for each element. Then we integrate all the contributions to get the potential due to all the charge distributed in the rod. We need to determine appropriate values for r and dq for each position x along the rod. The amount of charge in an infinitesimal rod length dx is $dq = \lambda dx$, where $\lambda = q_{rod}/\ell$ is the linear charge density. We then integrate from one end of the rod to the other to add up the contribution of each dq to the potential.

3 EXECUTE PLAN The charge on the element dq is

$$dq = \frac{q_{rod}}{\ell}dx$$

and the distance from the element to P is

$$r = \sqrt{(x_P - x)^2 + y_P^2}.$$

Substituting gives us our expression for the potential at P:

$$V = \frac{1}{4\pi\epsilon_0}\frac{q_{rod}}{\ell}\int_{-\ell/2}^{\ell/2}\frac{dx}{\sqrt{(x_P - x)^2 + y_P^2}}.$$

By making a simple substitution, we can put the integral in a form we can look up:

$$u = x_P - x$$

$$du = -dx$$

$$V = \frac{1}{4\pi\epsilon_0}\frac{q_{rod}}{\ell}\int_{x_P+\ell/2}^{x_P-\ell/2}\frac{-du}{\sqrt{u^2 + y_P^2}}.$$

Note how the limits of integration have changed to match the change of variable to u. This integral is identical to the integral in Example 25.6:

$$V = \frac{1}{4\pi\epsilon_0}\frac{q_{rod}}{\ell}\left[-\ln\left(u + \sqrt{u^2 + y_P^2}\right)\right]_{x_P+\ell/2}^{x_P-\ell/2}$$

$$= \frac{1}{4\pi\epsilon_0}\frac{q_{rod}}{\ell}\left[\ln\left(x_P + \ell/2 + \sqrt{(x_P + \ell/2)^2 + y_P^2}\right)\right.$$

$$\left.-\ln\left(x_P - \ell/2 + \sqrt{(x_P - \ell/2)^2 + y_P^2}\right)\right]$$

$$= \frac{1}{4\pi\epsilon_0}\frac{q_{rod}}{\ell}\ln\left(\frac{x_P + \ell/2 + \sqrt{(x_P + \ell/2)^2 + y_P^2}}{x_P - \ell/2 + \sqrt{(x_P - \ell/2)^2 + y_P^2}}\right). \checkmark \quad (1)$$

We now use this equation to plot the potential due to the rod everywhere in the xy plane. A contour plot of the potential for a rod 2.0 m long is shown in Figure WG25.4 on the next page.

PRACTICE

Figure WG25.4

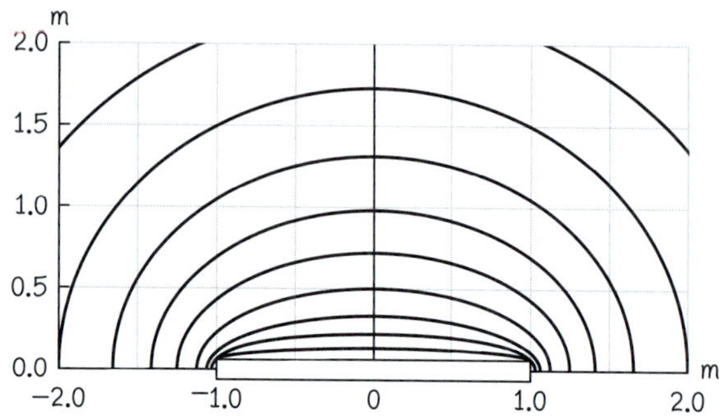

❹ EVALUATE RESULT If P is located on a line parallel to the y axis above or below the end of the rod, then $x_P = \ell/2$. You should check Eq. 1 for V in this special case of $x_P = \ell/2$ to confirm that we get the same expression as in Example 25.6:

$$V = \frac{q}{4\pi\epsilon_0\ell}\ln\left(\frac{\ell + \sqrt{\ell^2 + d^2}}{d}\right),$$

with the modification that our y_P corresponds to d in the *Principles* equation. Equation 1 is a complicated expression, but with it we can calculate the potential anywhere in the xy plane outside the rod. If P is very far from the rod, the rod viewed from P looks like a particle, and the potential at P calculated with Eq. 1 should be that due to a particle carrying charge q_{rod}: zero. If we let either x_P, y_P, or both become infinite in Eq. 1, the argument of the natural logarithm is unity, and $\ln(1) = 0$, yielding the expected potential of zero.

Guided Problem 25.6 Charged ring

A thin, flat ring made of a nonconducting material has inner radius R_{in} and outer radius R_{out}. Its surface charge density $\sigma(a)$ decreases with distance a from the center as $\sigma(a) = \sigma_0/a$, where σ_0 is a constant with units C/m. Determine the electrostatic potential at any location along the axis that passes through the ring's center and is perpendicular to the plane of the ring.

❶ GETTING STARTED

1. Draw a sketch of the system.
2. What makes locations on this axis special for determining electrostatic potential?

❷ DEVISE PLAN

3. What expression can you use to determine the contributions from all the charge elements dq on the ring?
4. What symmetry of the ring can you exploit to establish a group of charge elements that are all at the same distance from the desired location?
5. What mathematical quantities can you use to specify this group of charge elements?
6. What is the distance between this group of charge elements and the location you are interested in?
7. What variable(s) do you integrate to account for all the charge elements on the ring, and what are the appropriate limits of integration?

❸ EXECUTE PLAN

8. Where can you obtain an analytic expression for the value of the resulting integral?

❹ EVALUATE RESULT

9. Does the expression you obtained for electrostatic potential behave properly at large distances from the ring?

PRACTICE

Worked Problem 25.7 Electric field around a charged rod

The electric field surrounding a charged object that lacks sufficient symmetry to use Gauss's law can be determined either from Coulomb's law (as we saw in Chapter 23) or from the electrostatic potential as given by Eq. 25.40. Use the latter method to determine, for any location in space, the component of the electric field perpendicular to the rod in Worked Problem 25.5.

❶ GETTING STARTED We are given, from Worked Problem 25.5, the orientation of a charged rod of length ℓ and charge q_{rod} in an xy coordinate system and are asked to use Eq. 25.40 to obtain an expression, valid at any location in the space surrounding the rod, for the perpendicular component of the electric field due to the rod. From Figure WG25.3 we see that the y component of the electric field is the one perpendicular to the rod.

❷ DEVISE PLAN We need to calculate $E_y = -\partial V/\partial y$. We have to take the partial derivative of the potential with respect to y while holding all other variables constant; in other words, we treat the position x as a constant. At any arbitrary location (x, y) the electrostatic potential is given by

$$V(x, y) = \frac{1}{4\pi\epsilon_0}\frac{q_{rod}}{\ell}\ln\left(\frac{x + \ell/2 + \sqrt{(x + \ell/2)^2 + y^2}}{x - \ell/2 + \sqrt{(x - \ell/2)^2 + y^2}}\right).$$

Taking the derivative of the logarithm's argument appears daunting, but we can simplify things by using the identity $\ln(a/b) = \ln a - \ln b$.

❸ EXECUTE PLAN

$$E_y = -\frac{\partial V}{\partial y} = \frac{1}{4\pi\epsilon_0}\frac{q_{\text{rod}}}{\ell}\frac{\partial}{\partial y}\left\{\ln\left[x - \ell/2 + ((x - \ell/2)^2 + y^2)^{1/2}\right] - \ln\left[x + \ell/2 + ((x + \ell/2)^2 + y^2)^{1/2}\right]\right\}$$

$$= \frac{1}{4\pi\epsilon_0}\frac{q_{\text{rod}}}{\ell}\left\{\left[\frac{\frac{1}{2}((x - \ell/2)^2 + y^2)^{-1/2}2y}{x - \ell/2 + ((x - \ell/2)^2 + y^2)^{1/2}}\right] - \left[\frac{\frac{1}{2}((x + \ell/2)^2 + y^2)^{-1/2}2y}{x + \ell/2 + ((x + \ell/2)^2 + y^2)^{1/2}}\right]\right\}$$

$$= \frac{1}{4\pi\epsilon_0}\frac{q_{\text{rod}}}{\ell}y\left\{\left[\frac{((x - \ell/2)^2 + y^2)^{-1/2}}{x - \ell/2 + ((x - \ell/2)^2 + y^2)^{1/2}}\right] - \left[\frac{((x + \ell/2)^2 + y^2)^{-1/2}}{x + \ell/2 + ((x + \ell/2)^2 + y^2)^{1/2}}\right]\right\}. ✔$$

This algebra is complicated but very useful because it is much easier to get the electric field component via the known potential than from superposition of electric fields as was done in Chapter 23. The expression for the x component of $\vec{E}$ is even more complicated than this expression for E_y, but the procedure for obtaining it is the same. You should try it.

❹ EVALUATE RESULT We can check to see that our expression for E_y is not unreasonable by looking at a few limiting cases. If the location we're interested in is along the x axis, E_y should be zero by symmetry. We see that setting $y = 0$ gives $E_y(x, 0) = 0$ as expected. If the location is along the perpendicular bisector of the rod ($x = 0$), the expression we get for $E_y(0, y)$ should match the expression obtained in *Principles* Example 23.4 once we note that our rod is along the x axis whereas the rod in Example 23.4 is along the y axis:

$$E_y(0, y) = \frac{1}{4\pi\epsilon_0}\frac{q_{\text{rod}}}{\ell}y\left\{\left[\frac{((\ell/2)^2 + y^2)^{-1/2}}{((\ell/2)^2 + y^2)^{1/2} - \ell/2}\right] - \left[\frac{((\ell/2)^2 + y^2)^{-1/2}}{((\ell/2)^2 + y^2)^{1/2} + \ell/2}\right]\right\}$$

$$= \frac{1}{4\pi\epsilon_0}\frac{q_{\text{rod}}}{\ell}y\left\{\frac{\ell((\ell/2)^2 + y^2)^{-1/2}}{y^2}\right\}$$

$$= \frac{1}{4\pi\epsilon_0}\frac{q_{\text{rod}}}{y((\ell/2)^2 + y^2)^{1/2}} = k\frac{q_{\text{rod}}}{y(\frac{1}{4}\ell^2 + y^2)^{1/2}}.$$

This indeed matches the result of *Principles* Example 23.4. (Remember that from Eq. 24.7 defining the permittivity constant ϵ_0, we know $k = 1/4\pi\epsilon_0$.)

Guided Problem 25.8 Electric field due to a charged disk

A thin disk of radius R has a uniform surface charge density σ. Use Eq. 25.40 to obtain an expression for the electric field along the axis that runs through the disk center and is perpendicular to the plane of the disk. Orient the disk in the xy plane of an xyz coordinate system, with the disk center at the origin, so that the axis you work with is the z axis.

❶ GETTING STARTED

1. What are your knowns in this problem? What must you determine? Obtain the expression for the potential for this system from the Chapter Summary above.

❷ DEVISE PLAN

2. What is the expression for the potential $V(z)$ along the z axis ($x = y = 0$)?
3. What is the relationship between an electric field and the electrostatic potential at any location in the field?
4. Which component or components of the electric field are zero by symmetry?
5. Which quantities should you hold constant when you take the appropriate partial derivative?

❸ EXECUTE PLAN

❹ EVALUATE RESULT

6. Is the result obtained the same as that derived in *Principles* Example 23.6? That result expressed E_z in terms of ϵ_0 and R:

$$E_z = \frac{1}{2\epsilon_0}\sigma z\left(\frac{1}{\sqrt{z^2}} - \frac{1}{\sqrt{z^2 + R^2}}\right).$$

Questions and Problems

For instructor-assigned homework, go to MasteringPhysics® MP

Dots indicate difficulty level of problems: • = *easy,* •• = *intermediate,* ••• = *hard;* CR = *context-rich problem.*

25.1 Electric potential energy

1. What orientation of an electric dipole in a uniform electric field has the greatest electric potential energy? What orientation has the least? (Let the system comprise both the electric dipole and the sources of the uniform electric field.) •
2. Identical positively charged objects A, B, and C are launched with the same initial speed from the same position above a negatively charged sheet that produces a uniform electric field. The directions of the initial velocities are shown in Figure P25.2. Assuming the objects do not interact with one another, rank them in order of their speeds at the instant they reach the sheet, greatest speed first. •

Figure P25.2

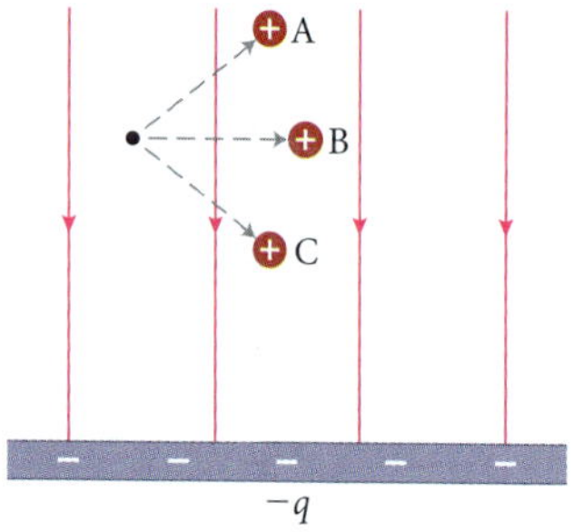

3. You release three balls simultaneously from the same height above the floor. The balls all carry the same quantity of surplus positive charge, but they have different masses: 1 kg, 2 kg, and 3 kg. In addition to the gravitational field due to Earth, there is a uniform electric field directed downward. Assume that the balls are far enough apart that they have negligible influence on one another and that air resistance can be ignored. (*a*) Which ball has the greatest speed when it reaches the floor? (*b*) If all three were negatively charged, which ball would reach the floor first? ••
4. A proton, a deuteron (a hydrogen nucleus containing one proton and one neutron), and an alpha particle (a helium nucleus consisting of two protons and two neutrons) initially at rest are all accelerated through the same distance in the uniform electric field created by a very large charged plate. Compare their final (*a*) kinetic energies, (*b*) momentum magnitudes, (*c*) speeds, and (*d*) time intervals needed to cover the distance. (*e*) How do the changes in electric potential energy compare? ••
5. A proton, a deuteron (a hydrogen nucleus containing one proton and one neutron), and an alpha particle (a helium nucleus consisting of two protons and two neutrons) initially at rest are all accelerated for the same time interval in the uniform electric field created by a very large charged plate. Compare their final (*a*) kinetic energies, (*b*) momentum magnitudes, (*c*) speeds, and (*d*) distances traveled. (*e*) How do the changes in electric potential energy compare? ••
6. Consider an isolated system of two identical electric dipoles as in Figure P25.6. For which orientation is the electric potential energy smaller? ••

Figure P25.6

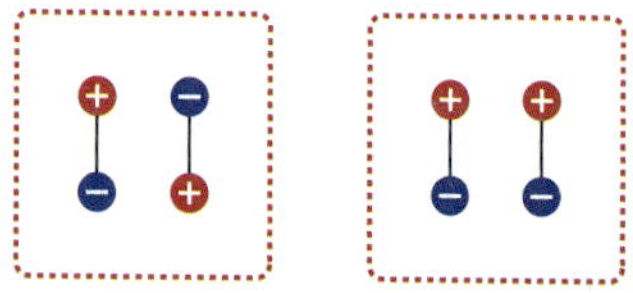

7. A dipole carrying charges $+q$ and $-q$ separated by a distance d is rotated 180° in a uniform electric field (Figure P25.7). What is the change in electric potential energy associated with this rotation? (Consider a system comprising both the dipole and the sources of the electric field.) ••

Figure P25.7

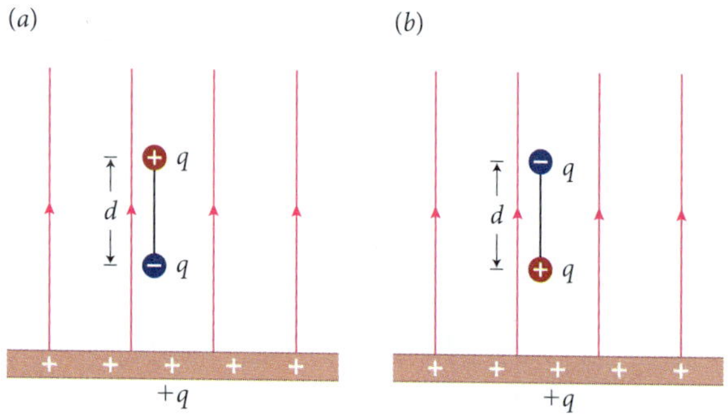

25.2 Electrostatic work

8. In an electrostatic field, path 1 between points A and B is twice as long as path 2. If the electrostatic work done on a negatively charged particle that moves from A to B along path 1 is W_1, how much work is done on this particle if it later goes from A to B along path 2? •
9. The electrostatic work done on a particle carrying charge q as the particle travels from point A to point B in an electric field is W. How much electrostatic work is done on a particle carrying charge $-2q$ that travels from B to A in the field? •
10. Electrostatic work W is done on a charged particle as it travels 10 mm along a straight path from point A to point B in an electric field. If you return the particle to point A and then exert a force on it to move it from A to B along a curved path that is 20 mm long, how much electrostatic work is done on the particle relative to the work W done along the straight path? •
11. Points A and B are on the same electric field line. If the potential difference between A and B is positive, is the field directed from A to B or from B to A? •
12. In three separate experiments, an object is moved from point A to point B in the uniform electric field of a large charged plate (Figure P25.12). The object is at rest in both the initial and final positions. Object 1 carries charge $+q$ and has mass m; object 2 carries charge $+q$ and has mass $2m$; object 3 carries charge $-q$ and has mass m. Rank the objects in order of

PRACTICE

the changes their displacements produce in the electric potential energy of the object-plus-plate system, greatest change first. ••

Figure P25.12

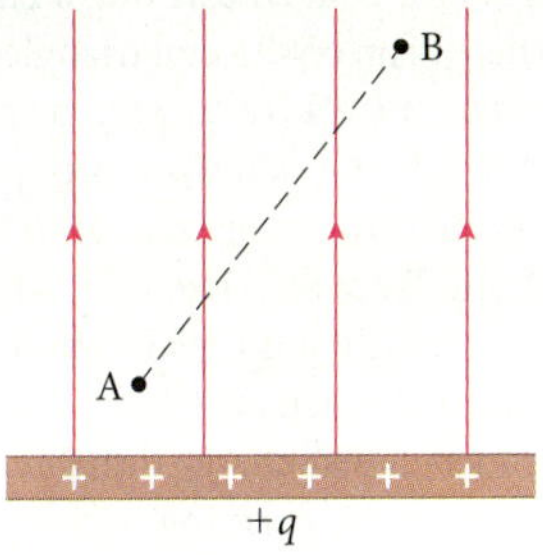

13. Electrostatic work W is done on a charged particle as the particle travels from point A to point B in an electric field. You then apply a force to move the particle back to A, increasing its kinetic energy by an amount equal to $2W$. How much work did you do? ••

14. Points A, B, and C form the vertices of a triangle in a nonuniform electrostatic field. The electrostatic work done on a particle of charge q as the particle travels from A to B is W_{AB}, and that done on the particle as it travels from A to C is $W_{AC} = -W_{AB}/2$. How much electrostatic work is done on the particle as it travels from B to C? ••

15. In the presence of an electrostatic field, you find that you must do positive work on an electron to move it from point A to point B without changing its kinetic energy. (*a*) Considering just the electron as our system, has the system's electric potential energy increased, decreased, or remained the same? (*b*) What if your system consists of both the electron and the charged particles that are the source of the electrostatic field? (*c*) Is the electrostatic potential difference between A and B positive, negative, or zero? ••

16. In the presence of an electrostatic field, you find that you must do positive work on a proton to move it from point A to point B without changing its kinetic energy. (*a*) Considering just the proton as your system, have you increased, decreased, or left unchanged its electric potential energy? (*b*) What if your system consists of both the proton and the charged particles that are the source of the electrostatic field? (*c*) Is the potential difference between A and B positive, negative, or zero? ••

17. An electron moves from point A to point B under the influence of an electrostatic field in which the potential difference between A and B is negative. (*a*) If your system includes both the electron and the particles generating the electrostatic field, does the system's electric potential energy increase, decrease, or remain the same? (*b*) Does the electron's kinetic energy increase, decrease, or remain the same? (*c*) How would the answers in parts *a* and *b* change if your system included only the electron? ••

18. A proton moves from point A to point B under the influence of an electrostatic field in which the potential difference between A and B is negative. (*a*) If your system includes both the proton and the particles generating the electrostatic field, does the system's electric potential energy increase, decrease, or remain the same? (*b*) Does the proton's kinetic energy increase, decrease, or remain the same? (*c*) How would the answers in parts *a* and *b* change if your system included only the proton? ••

19. Four objects are moved in various ways in the electrostatic field of Figure P25.19. Rank the following motions in order of the amount of electrostatic work done on the object, smallest amount first: (*a*) an object carrying charge $+q$ is moved from A to B, (*b*) an object carrying charge $+q$ is moved from A to C, (*c*) an object carrying charge $+q$ is moved from B to C, (*d*) an object carrying charge $-q$ is moved from A to B. ••

Figure P25.19

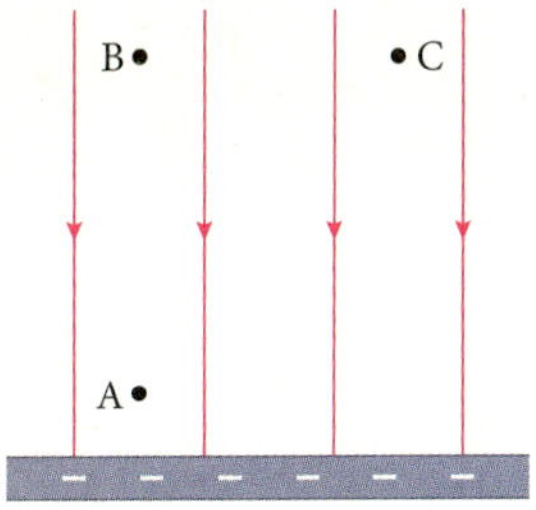

20. Points A, B, C, and D are at the corners of a square area in an electric field, with B adjacent to A and C diagonally across from A. The potential difference between A and C is the negative of that between A and B and twice that between B and D. In terms of the potential difference between A and B, what is the potential difference (*a*) between B and C, (*b*) between C and D, and (*c*) between A and D? •••

25.3 Equipotentials

21. Can an equipotential line ever cross itself? •

22. Can you draw an equipotential surface through a position where the electric field vanishes? •

23. Describe the equipotential surfaces associated with an infinitely long charged wire that has a uniform linear charge density. •

24. Sketch some equipotential lines for the electric field line pattern of a electric dipole. ••

25. Sketch some electric field lines and equipotential lines associated with two identical charged particles spaced horizontally. ••

26. Some equipotential lines surrounding a negatively charged object are shown in Figure P25.26, where the potential difference between any two adjacent lines is the same. (*a*) In which region is the electric field magnitude greatest? (*b*) What is the direction of the electric field in that region? (*c*) Which equipotential line has the greatest potential? ••

Figure P25.26

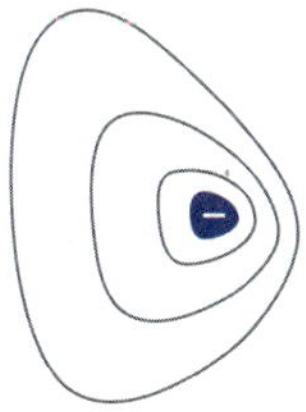

27. You determine that it takes no electrostatic work to move a charged object from point A to point B along a particular path. (*a*) Can you conclude that A and B are on the same equipotential surface? (*b*) Can you say that the path is part of an equipotential surface that includes A and B? Justify your answers. ••

PRACTICE

28. Figure P25.28 shows that the spacing between equipotential surfaces surrounding a charged particle increases with radial distance r away from the particle. (*a*) How would the potential have to depend on r in order to make the spacing between equipotential surfaces uniform? (*b*) How would the electric field depend on r in that case? ••

Figure P25.28

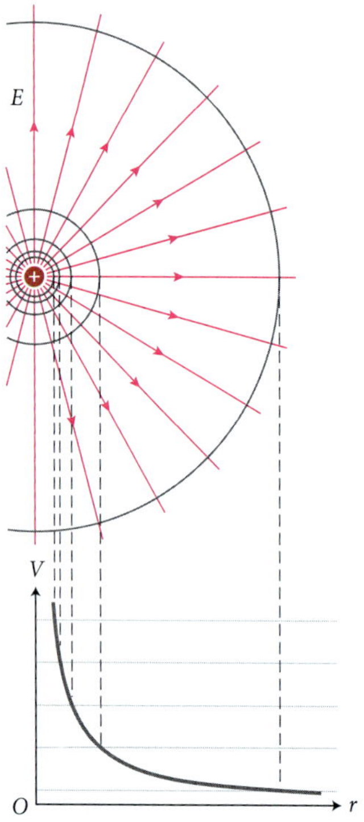

25.4 Calculating work and energy in electrostatics

29. Particle A carrying a charge of 3.0 nC is at the origin of a Cartesian coordinate system. (*a*) What is the electrostatic potential (relative to zero potential at infinity) at a position $r = 4.0$ m from the origin? (*b*) With particle A held in place at the origin, how much work must be done by an outside agent to bring particle B, also carrying a 3.0-nC charge, from infinity to $r = 4.0$ m? (*c*) Particle B is returned to infinity, and particle A is moved to $r = 4.0$ m and held there. How much work must be done by an outside agent to bring particle B from infinity to the origin? •

30. A particle carrying a charge of 6.0 nC is released from rest in a uniform electric field of magnitude 2.0×10^3 N/C. What are (*a*) the electrostatic work done on the particle after it has moved 4.0 m and (*b*) the particle's kinetic energy at that instant? •

31. Particles A, B, C, and D in Figure P25.31 each carry a charge of magnitude 3.0 nC. Calculate the electric potential energy for the charge distribution in this 3.0-m square (*a*) if all the charges are positive; (*b*) if B, C, and D are positive and A is negative; (*c*) if B and C are positive and A and D are negative; and (*d*) if A and C are positive and B and D are negative. ••

Figure P25.31

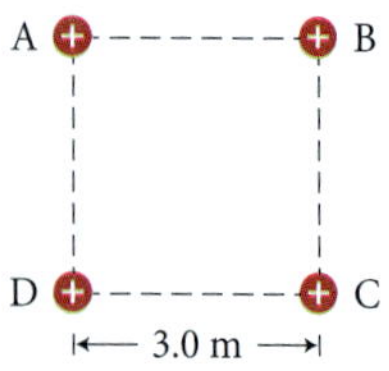

32. Particles A and B, each carrying a charge of 2.0 nC, are at the base corners of an equilateral triangle 2.0 m on a side. (*a*) What is the potential (relative to zero at infinity) at the apex of the triangle? (*b*) How much work is required to bring a positively charged particle carrying a charge of 5.0 nC from infinity to the apex if A and B are held fixed? (*c*) Answer parts *a* and *b* for the case where particle B is replaced by a particle carrying a charge of −3.0 nC. (*d*) Calculate the electric potential energy for each of the two triangular charge distributions. ••

33. Six particles, each carrying a charge of 3.0 nC, are equally spaced along the equator of a sphere that has a radius of 0.60 m and has its center at the origin of a rectangular coordinate system. What is the electrostatic potential (relative to zero at infinity) (*a*) at the sphere center and (*b*) at either pole of the sphere? ••

34. An electron and a proton are held on an x axis, with the electron at $x = +1.000$ m and the proton at $x = -1.000$ m. (*a*) How much work is required to bring an additional electron from infinity to the origin? (*b*) If, instead of the second electron coming in from infinity, it is initially at $x = +20.00$ m on the axis and is given an initial velocity of 500.0 m/s toward the origin, does it reach the origin? If so, what is its speed at the instant it reaches the origin? If not, how close to the origin does it come? ••

35. Four objects, each carrying a charge of magnitude q, are placed at the corners of a square measuring d on each side. Two of the objects are positively charged, and two are negatively charged, with like-charged objects placed at opposite corners of the square. (*a*) Is the electric potential energy associated with this charge distribution positive, negative, or zero? (*b*) Confirm your answer to part *a* by calculating the electric potential energy. ••

25.5 Potential difference

36. Show that the units of electric field, newtons per coulomb, are equivalent to the units volts per meter. •

37. Four possible paths for a positively charged object traveling from a 2-V equipotential to a 3-V equipotential are shown in Figure P25.37. Rank the paths in order of the electrostatic work done on the object along each path, greatest value first. •

Figure P25.37

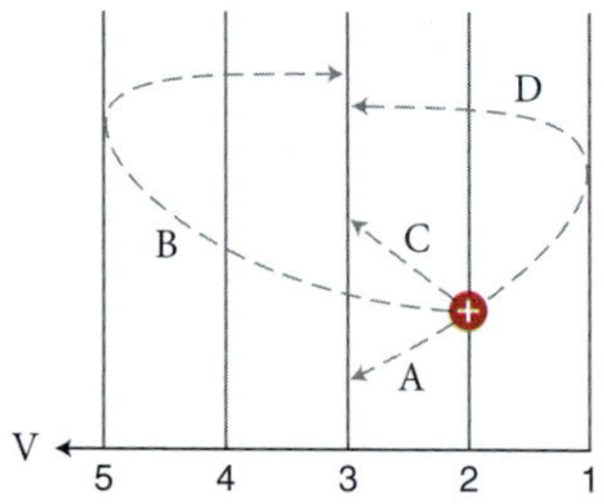

38. An infinite sheet carries a surface charge density of $3.5\ \text{nC/m}^2$. How far apart are the equipotential surfaces whose potentials differ by 100 V? •

39. Four particles, each carrying a charge of magnitude 3.0 nC, are at the corners of a square that has a side length of 3.0 m. For zero potential set at infinity, calculate the potential at the center of the square (*a*) if all particles are positively charged, (*b*) if three particles are positively charged and one is negatively charged, and (*c*) if two particles are positively charged and two are negatively charged. ••

40. A particle carrying charge $+9.00$ nC is at the origin of a rectangular coordinate system. Taking the electrostatic potential to be zero at infinity, locate the equipotential surfaces at 20.0-V intervals from 20.0 V to 100 V, and sketch them to scale. Are these surfaces equally spaced? ••

41. A particle carrying charge $+q$ is located on the x axis at $x = +d$. A particle carrying charge $-3q$ is located on the x axis at $x = -7d$. (*a*) With zero potential at infinity, at what locations on the x axis is the electrostatic potential zero? (*b*) At what locations on the y axis is the potential zero? (*c*) Answer the questions of parts *a* and *b* for the case where the object at $x = -7d$ carries charge $+3q$. ••

42. In a rectangular coordinate system, a positively charged infinite sheet on which the surface charge density is $+2.5\ \mu\text{C/m}^2$ lies in the yz plane that intersects the x axis at $x = 0.10$ m. What are (*a*) $\vec{E}$ for $x > 0.10$ m and (*b*) the potential difference $V(0.20\text{ m}) - V(0.50\text{ m})$? (*c*) A $+1.5$-nC charged particle is initially at $x = 0.50$ m. How much work must an external agent do to move this particle to $x = 0.20$ m? (*d*) Taking the potential to be zero at the sheet, draw three equipotential surfaces at 20-V intervals on each side of the plane, labeling each surface with its potential value. ••

43. In a rectangular coordinate system, an infinite sheet having a positive surface charge density lies in the yz plane that intersects the x axis at $x = 0.50$ m. Points A and B are on the x axis at $x = 2.0$ m and $x = 7.0$ m, respectively. (*a*) Is the potential difference $V_B - V_A$ positive or negative? If the magnitude of the potential difference is 15.0 V, what are (*b*) $\vec{E}$ in this region and (*c*) the numerical value of $+\sigma$? ••

44. Figure P25.44 shows three configurations of charged particles. All the particles are the same distance from the origin. Rank the configurations in terms of (*a*) the electrostatic potentials at the origin, greatest first, and (*b*) the electric potential energies of the three-particle system, greatest first. ••

Figure P25.44

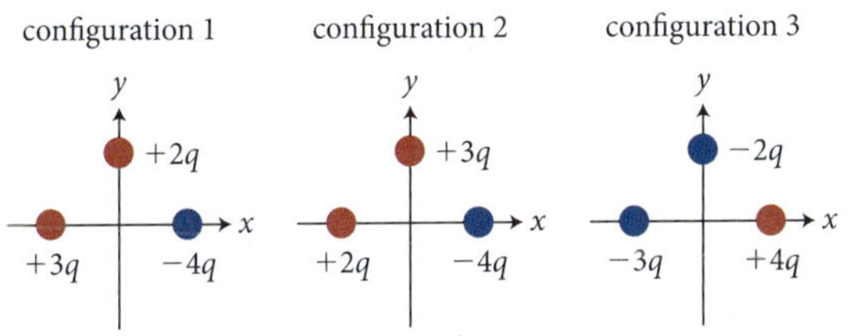

45. Two parallel conducting plates are 0.10 m apart and carry equal and opposite charges. They are large enough relative to the 0.10-m separation distance that we can assume the electric field between them is uniform. The potential difference between them is 500 V. An electron is released from rest at the negative plate. (*a*) Draw the electric field between the plates, indicating the sign of the charge on each plate and which plate is at the higher electrostatic potential. (*b*) What is the magnitude of the electric field between the plates? (*c*) What is the change in the potential energy of the system comprising the plates and the electron when the electron moves from the negative plate to the positive plate? (*d*) How much work is done by the electric field on the electron as it makes this trip? (*e*) What is the electron's kinetic energy when it reaches the positive plate? ••

46. Two parallel conducting plates carry equal and opposite charges. The plates are large relative to their separation distance, so we can assume the electric field between them is uniform. The potential difference between them is 0.25 V, and the magnitude of the electric field between them is 50 V/m. (*a*) What is the surface charge density on the plates? (*b*) What is the separation distance? (*c*) How much work is done by the electric field on an electron as it moves from the negative plate to the positive plate? ••

47. Particle 1 carrying charge $+q_1$ is placed on the x axis at $x = -d$. Particle 2 carrying some unknown charge q_2 is placed somewhere on the x axis. The potential energy associated with the charges is $+q_1^2/(2\pi\epsilon_0 d)$, and the electrostatic potential due to the charges is $+q_1/(\pi\epsilon_0 d)$ at the origin and zero at an infinite distance. (*a*) What is the sign of the charge on particle 2? (*b*) What is the magnitude of the charge on particle 2, and where on the x axis was particle 2 placed? Determine all possible answers. ••

48. Two charged particles are placed near the origin of an xyz coordinate system. Particle 1 carries charge $+q$ and is on the x axis at $x = +d$. Particle 2 carries an unknown charge and is at an unknown location. The magnitude of the electric field at the origin is $q/(2\pi\epsilon_0 d^2)$, and the electrostatic potential at the origin, relative to $V = 0$ at infinity, is $+3q/(4\pi\epsilon_0 d)$. (*a*) If particle 2 is on the x axis, what are its charge and location? (*b*) If particle 2 is on the y axis, what are its charge and location? Determine all possible solutions. •••

25.6 Electrostatic potentials of continuous charge distributions

49. A thin disk of radius $R = 62.5$ mm has uniform surface charge density $\sigma = 7.5\ \text{nC/m}^2$. Calculate the potential on the axis that runs through the disk center and is perpendicular to the disk face at distances (*a*) 5.0 mm, (*b*) 30 mm, and (*c*) 62.5 mm from the disk. •

50. Charge $q = +10$ nC is uniformly distributed on a spherical shell that has a radius of 120 mm. (*a*) What are the magnitude and direction of the electric field just outside and just inside the shell? (*b*) What is the electrostatic potential just outside and just inside the shell, relative to zero at infinity? (*c*) What are the electrostatic potential and electric field magnitude at the shell's center? •

51. A very long positively charged wire on which the linear charge density λ is 150 nC/m lies on the z axis of a rectangular coordinate system. Calculate the electrostatic potential (*a*) 2.0 m, (*b*) 4.0 m, and (*c*) 12 m from the wire, assuming that $V = 0$ at 2.5 m. ••

52. A particle carrying charge $+q$ is placed at the center of a thick-walled conducting shell that has inner radius R and outer radius $2R$ and carries charge $-4q$. A thin-walled conducting shell of radius $3R$ carries charge $+4q$ and is concentric with the thick-walled shell. Defining $V = 0$ at infinity, calculate all distances from the particle at which the electrostatic potential is zero. ••

53. Four uniformly charged nonconducting rods, each of length ℓ and carrying charge $+q$, are arranged in a square of side length ℓ. At the center of the square, what are (*a*) the magnitude of the electric field and (*b*) the electrostatic potential? ••

54. Figure P25.54 shows three charge distributions. In A, a particle carrying a charge $+q$ is located a distance R from the origin. In B, $+q$ charge is spread uniformly over a semicircle of radius R centered at the origin. In C, $+q$ charge is spread uniformly over a circle of radius R centered at the origin. Rank these distributions in terms of (*a*) the electric field magnitude at the origin, smallest first, and (*b*) the electrostatic potential at the origin, smallest first. (*c*) Using infinity as the location where the electrostatic potential is zero, write an expression for the electrostatic potential at the origin in distribution B. ••

Figure P25.54

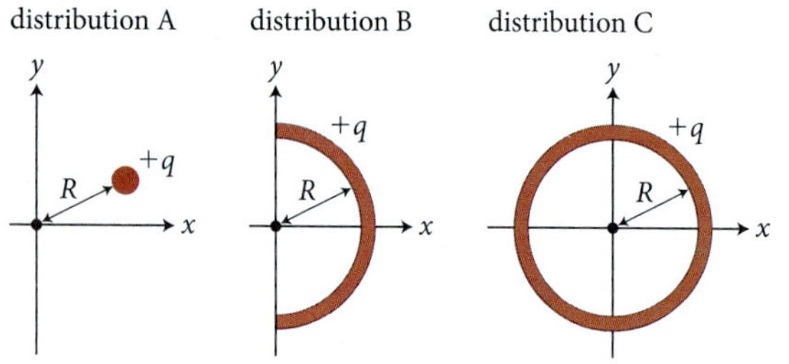

55. A particle carrying charge $q_p = +10$ nC is located at $y_p = 0.030$ m on the y axis of an xy coordinate system. A nonconducting rod of length $\ell = 0.10$ m carrying charge $q_r = -10$ nC lies on the x axis, extending from $x = 0$ to $x = 0.10$ m. Write an expression for the electrostatic potential for any position along the y axis. ••

56. A disk of radius R has positive charge uniformly distributed over an inner circular region of radius a and negative charge uniformly distributed over the outer annular (ring-shaped) region (Figure P25.56). The surface charge density on the inner region is $+\sigma$, and that on the annular region is $-\sigma$. The electrostatic potential at P, located on the central perpendicular axis a distance $z = R$ from the disk center, is zero. What is a in terms of R? •••

Figure P25.56

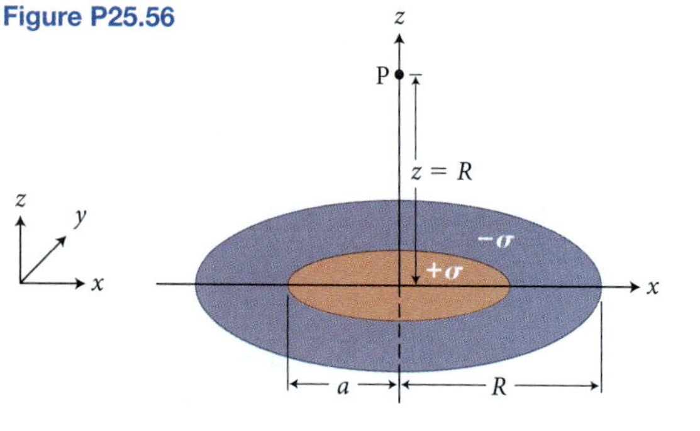

57. The surface charge density on a nonconducting disk of radius R varies with the radius as $\sigma(r) = cr$, where c is a positive constant ($c > 0$). Derive an expression for the electrostatic potential as a function of position x along an x axis that runs through the disk center and is perpendicular to the disk face, with the disk center at $x = 0$ on this axis. •••

58. A very long, solid, positively charged cylinder has a radius R and is made of a nonconducting material. The nonuniform volume charge density is given by $\rho = +ar$, where r is the radial distance away from the long central axis of the cylinder. Calculate the difference in electrostatic potential between a location on the axis and a location on the outer surface of the cylinder. •••

25.7 Obtaining the electric field from the potential

59. The electrostatic potential in some region of space is given by $V(x) = A + Bx$, where V is in volts, x is in meters, and A and B are positive constants. Determine the magnitude of the electric field in this region. In what direction is the field? •

60. The electrostatic potential in a particular xy coordinate system is given by $V(x, y) = 3xy - 5y^2$. Obtain the expression for the electric field. •

61. A particle carrying $+3.00$ nC of positive charge is at the origin of an xy coordinate system. Take $V(\infty)$ to be zero for these calculations. (*a*) Calculate the potential V on the x axis at $x = 3.0000$ m and at $x = 3.0100$ m. (*b*) Does the potential increase or decrease as x increases? Compute $\Delta V/\Delta x$ for distances along the x axis, where ΔV is the difference in potential between $x = 3.0000$ m and $x = 3.0100$ m, and $\Delta x = 0.0100$ m. (*c*) Calculate the electric field magnitude at $x = 3.0000$ m, and compare this magnitude with value calculated for $\Delta V/\Delta x$ in part *b*. (*d*) Calculate the electrostatic potential at the position $x = 3.0000$ m, $y = 0.0100$ m, and compare your result with the potential at $x = 3.0000$ m calculated in part *a*. Discuss the significance of this result. ••

62. Two particles, each carrying positive charge q, are on the y axis, one at $y = +a$ and the other at $y = -a$. (*a*) Calculate the potential for any point on the x axis. (*b*) Use your result in part *a* to determine the electric field at any point on the x axis. ••

63. Figure P25.63 shows a two-dimensional slice through a set of equipotential surfaces. (*a*) At which of the locations marked A, B, C, and D is the magnitude of the electric field greatest? (*b*) Is the magnitude of the electric field greater at B or at F? (*c*) Sketch some electric field lines to support your arguments. ••

Figure P25.63

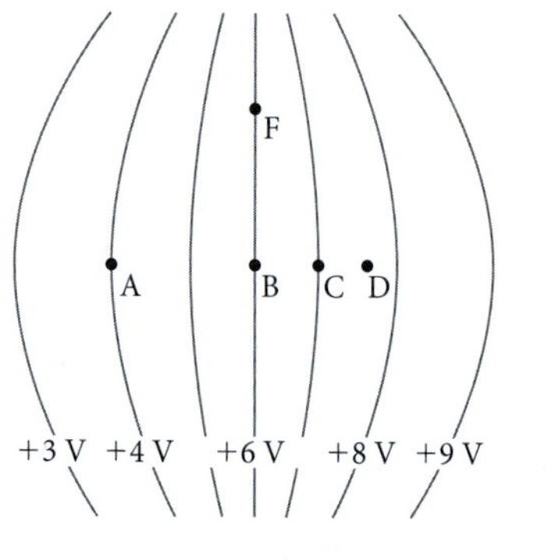

64. A particle carrying 3.00 nC of positive charge is at the origin of a rectangular coordinate system, and a particle carrying 3.00 nC of negative charge is on the x axis at $x = 6.00$ m. (*a*) Calculate the potential on the x axis at $x = 3.00$ m, relative to zero potential at infinity. (*b*) Calculate the electric field on the x axis at $x = 3.00$ m. (*c*) Calculate the potential on the x axis at $x = 3.01$ m. (*d*) Compute $\Delta V/\Delta x$ for ΔV between $x = 3.00$ m and $x = 3.01$ m, and $\Delta x = 0.01$ m, and compare your result with your result in part *b*. ••

65. A ring of radius a carrying a uniformly distributed charge q is located in the yz plane of a rectangular coordinate system, with the center of the ring at the origin. (*a*) Sketch a graph of the electrostatic potential $V(x)$ as a function of distance along the x axis. (*b*) At what position is $V(x)$ a maximum? (*c*) What is E_x at this position? •••

PRACTICE

66. Consider a spherically symmetrical distribution of charged particles. The magnitude of charge for the distribution is q, and the radius of the distribution is R. The electrostatic potential varies with radial distance r away from the center of the distribution. For $r > 2R$, $V(r) = -q/(4\pi\epsilon_0 r)$; for $R < r < 2R$, $V(r) = -q/(8\pi\epsilon_0 R)$; and for $r < R$, $V(r) = -3q/(4\pi\epsilon_0 r) + 5q/(8\pi\epsilon_0 R)$. *(a)* What is the electric field in these three regions? Use $V(\infty) = 0$ in your calculations. *(b)* Describe a set of objects that could produce an electrostatic potential that behaves in this way. •••

Additional problems

67. An electron travels from point A to point B in an electrostatic field and gains kinetic energy. *(a)* Is the electrostatic work done on the electron positive, negative, or zero? *(b)* Is the potential at A higher than, lower than, or the same as the potential at B? •

68. A proton travels from point A to point B in an electrostatic field and gains kinetic energy. *(a)* Is the electrostatic work done on the proton positive, negative, or zero? *(b)* Is the potential at A higher than, lower than, or the same as the potential at B? •

69. Calculate E_x for each potential: (a) $V(x) = a + bx$, $a = 4000$ V, $b = 6000$ V/m. (b) $V(x) = ax + b/x$, $a = 1500$ V/m, $b = 2000$ V · m. (c) $V(x) = ax - bx^2$, $a = 2000$ V/m, $b = 3000$ V/m^2. (d) $V(x) = -2000$ V (independent of x). •

70. Consider an isolated, uniformly charged spherical shell of radius R carrying positive charge q. Point A is on the shell, point B is a distance $2R$ from the center, point C is a distance $R/2$ from the center, and point D is at the center. Is the potential difference positive or negative *(a)* between A and B, *(b)* between A and C, *(c)* between A and D? ••

71. You are sketching equipotentials for a positively charged particle, having defined $V = 0$ at infinity. If you draw the 5.0-V equipotential as a circle with a radius of 50 mm, what is the radius of *(a)* the 10-V equipotential and *(b)* the 2.0-V equipotential? ••

72. A uniformly charged rod of length ℓ and charge $+q$ lies on the x axis of a Cartesian coordinate system, extending from the origin to $x = -\ell$. What is the electric potential due to this rod at a position on the positive x axis that is a distance d from the origin? ••

73. A solid sphere of radius R is concentric with a conducting spherical shell that carries charge $+q_{shell}$ and has an inner radius of $2R$ and outer radius of $3R$. If the electrostatic potential at the common center of the sphere and shell is the same as the potential at infinity, what is the charge q_{sphere} on the solid sphere *(a)* if the sphere is conducting and *(b)* if the sphere is nonconducting and has a uniform charge distribution throughout it? •••

74. You really like your new job at the atomic physics lab. Your boss casually mentions that the electron in a helium ion (He^+) emits energy in the form of radiation as it jumps from an orbit that has a radius of 0.42 nm to an orbit that has a radius of 0.24 nm. Sensing a chance to make a good impression, you wonder if any more information is needed in order to figure out the energy carried off by the emitted radiation. ••• CR

75. You have always wondered exactly how strong is the interaction called the *strong nuclear interaction*, and you suspect that an element like uranium could make a good test case. You begin to wonder if the electric potential energy discussed in this chapter might provide a path to an answer. As you search for a starting point, you return to *Principles* Example 25.4, which examines the energy associated with holding the hydrogen atom together. But there is only one proton in the hydrogen nucleus, whereas a uranium nucleus has 92 protons, separated from one another by about 2×10^{-15} m. Clearly something must be able to hold all those protons so close to one another. ••• CR

76. Two charged objects 1 and 2 are held a distance r apart. Object 1 has mass m and charge $+2q$, and object 2 has mass $2m$ and charge $+q$. The objects are released from rest. Assume that the only force exerted on either object is the electric force exerted by the other object. *(a)* When the objects are in motion, what is the ratio of their kinetic energies K_2/K_1? When the objects are a distance $4r$ apart, what is the speed of *(b)* object 1 and *(c)* object 2? When the objects are very far apart, what is the speed of *(d)* object 1 and *(e)* object 2? •••

Answers to Review Questions

1. Electric potential energy is the potential energy associated with the relative positions of objects that carry electrical charge.
2. The gravitational interaction can be only attractive, but the electric interaction can be either attractive or repulsive, depending on whether the charged objects carry charge of the same type (interaction is repulsive) or charge of opposite types (interaction is attractive). For oppositely charged objects, electric potential energy (like gravitational potential energy) decreases with decreasing separation, but for charged objects of the same sign, electric potential energy increases with decreasing separation.
3. The electric potential energy of the dipole is at its minimum when the dipole is oriented in the direction of the electric field created by the charged object and increases as the angle between the dipole orientation and the field direction increases.
4. Electrostatic work is the work done by an electrostatic field on a charged particle or charged object.
5. The amount of electrostatic work done on the particle depends on the two endpoints of the path. The work done is not affected by either path length or path shape.
6. The electrostatic potential difference between any two points A and B in an electrostatic field is the negative of the electrostatic work per unit charge done on a charged particle moved along any path from A to B.
7. Potential difference is a quantity related to *two locations* in an electric field and is numerically equivalent to the electrostatic work per unit charge done on a charged particle moved from one location to the other. Potential is a quantity that is related to any *one location* in an electric field; a value for potential can be assigned to any location in the field once we choose a reference location at which the potential in the field is zero.
8. Equipotential lines and surfaces are any lines and surfaces in an electric field along which the electrostatic potential is the same everywhere. An equipotential volume is the interior of a conducting object in electrostatic equilibrium, because the electric field magnitude in that interior is zero, making the whole interior an equipotential volume.
9. Equipotential lines and surfaces in an electric field are always perpendicular to the field lines.
10. The potential decreases as you move along the field line in the direction of the field.
11. The type of charge the particle carries. The electric force exerted on a positively charged particle is in the direction of the electric field, which means the force tends to move the particle in the direction from higher to lower electrostatic potential. The electric force exerted on a negatively charged particle is in the opposite direction and so tends to move the particle from a region of lower potential to a region of higher potential.
12. The expression, derived from a line integral of the electric force over the path of the particle's motion, is given by Eq 25.5.
13. There is no relationship. The amount of electrostatic work done is independent of the path; it depends on only the initial and final positions of the particle.
14. The electrostatic work per unit charge done on a charged particle as it moves from A to B is the negative of the potential difference between point A and point B.
15. We define the system's electric potential energy by choosing some reference configuration of the particles in which the electric potential energy is defined to be zero. Usually, the best choice for this zero-potential-energy configuration is infinite separation between the particles (which corresponds to zero electric force between them). The potential energy of the system when the separation distance is some finite value is then the difference between U^E at that separation distance and $U^E(=0)$ at infinity.
16. For a system of charged particles, the electric potential energy is the sum of the potential energies for each pair of particles, as given in Eq. 25.14 for a system of three particles.
17. The volt, which equals one joule per coulomb.
18. (*a*) The reference position at which electrostatic potential is defined to be zero is either infinity (which means infinite separation between particles) or (*b*) in dealing with electric circuits the ground.
19. Equation 25.30, $V_P = (1/4\pi\epsilon_0)\sum_n q_n/r_{nP}$, where r_{nP} is the distance between the particle whose charge is q_n and the position P at which the electrostatic potential is being measured.
20. No, because the work done by an electrostatic field is path-independent, which means the work done by the field is zero for a closed path because the beginning and end of the path are at the same location.
21. Treat each infinitesimal element of charge as a particle and integrate over the object, obtaining Eq. 25.34, $V = (1/4\pi\epsilon_0)\int(dq/r)$, where r is the distance between the infinitesimal element that carries charge dq and the position at which the potential is being measured.
22. Yes, because electrostatic potential is a scalar (which is easier to calculate than an electric field, which is a vector) and potential and field represent two different ways of expressing equivalent information.
23. Yes, because we know that the field lines are perpendicular to the equipotentials and that the direction of the field is the same as the direction of decreasing potential. The field magnitude correlates with the density of the equipotentials: The more closely spaced the equipotentials, the greater the field magnitude.
24. The component of the electrostatic field in any of the Cartesian directions x, y, z is equal to the negative of the derivative of the electrostatic potential with respect to distance in that direction (Eq. 25.40).

Answers to Guided Problems

Guided Problem 25.2 To form the triangle: $W_1 = U^E_i = -\dfrac{7q^2}{4\pi\epsilon_0\ell}$. To rearrange:

$$W_2 = U^E_f - U^E_i = -\frac{q^2}{8\pi\epsilon_0\ell}.$$

Guided Problem 25.4 The potential difference from the center of the sphere to radius r is $V_{0r} = -\dfrac{q_{\text{sphere}}r^2}{8\pi\epsilon_0 R^3}$ for $r < R$ and $V_{0r} = \dfrac{q_{\text{sphere}}}{8\pi\epsilon_0}\left(\dfrac{2}{r} - \dfrac{3}{R}\right)$ for $r > R$.

Guided Problem 25.6 With the ring centered at the origin of the z axis,

$$V(z) = \frac{\sigma_0}{2\epsilon_0}\ln\left(\frac{R_{\text{out}} + \sqrt{R^2_{\text{out}} + z^2}}{R_{\text{in}} + \sqrt{R^2_{\text{in}} + z^2}}\right).$$

Guided Problem 25.8 $E_z = \dfrac{1}{2\epsilon_0}\sigma z\left(\dfrac{1}{\sqrt{z^2}} - \dfrac{1}{\sqrt{z^2 + R^2}}\right)$

26 PRACTICE
Charge Separation and Storage

Chapter Summary

Capacitors (Sections 26.1, 26.2, 26.5)

Concepts A **charge-separating device** (such as a battery) has some mechanism that moves charge carriers *against* an electric field. The work done in this process increases the system's electric potential energy.

A **capacitor** consists of a pair of conducting objects separated by a nonconducting material or vacuum. The objects store electric potential energy once charge has been transferred from one to the other.

A *parallel-plate capacitor* consists of two parallel conducting plates of surface area A separated by a gap of width d. The electric field is uniform between the plates.

A *coaxial capacitor* consists of two coaxial conducting cylinders of radii R_1 and $R_2 > R_1$ and length $\ell \gg R_2$.

A spherical capacitor consists of two concentric conducting spherical shells of radii R_1 and $R_2 > R_1$.

Quantitative Tools The conducting objects in a capacitor carry charges of equal magnitude q but opposite sign. The charge separation produces a potential difference of magnitude V_{cap} between the objects. The **capacitance** C of this arrangement is

$$C \equiv \frac{q}{V_{\text{cap}}}. \qquad (26.1)$$

Capacitance is measured in **farads** F, where

$$1\text{ F} \equiv 1\text{ C/V}.$$

The capacitance of a *parallel-plate capacitor* is

$$C = \frac{\epsilon_0 A}{d}.$$

The capacitance of a *coaxial capacitor* is

$$C = \frac{2\pi\epsilon_0 \ell}{\ln(R_2/R_1)}.$$

The capacitance of a spherical capacitor is

$$C = 4\pi\epsilon_0 \frac{R_1 R_2}{R_2 - R_1}.$$

Electric field energy and emf (Sections 26.4, 26.6)

Concepts The **energy density** of an electric field is the energy per unit volume stored in the field.

The **emf** of any charge-separating device is the work per unit charge done by nonelectrostatic interactions in separating positive and negative charge carriers.

Quantitative Tools The electric potential energy U^E stored in a capacitor is

$$U^E = \tfrac{1}{2}\frac{q^2}{C} = \tfrac{1}{2}CV_{\text{cap}}^2 = \tfrac{1}{2}qV_{\text{cap}}. \qquad (26.4)$$

In air or vacuum, the **energy density** u_E of an electric field is

$$u_E = \tfrac{1}{2}\epsilon_0 E^2. \qquad (26.6)$$

The **emf** $\mathscr{E}$ of a charge-separating device is

$$\mathscr{E} \equiv \frac{W_{\text{nonelectrostatic}}}{q}. \qquad (26.7)$$

PRACTICE

Dielectrics (Sections 26.3, 26.7, 26.8)

Concepts A **dielectric** is a polarizable nonconducting material. A *polar* dielectric is made up of molecules that have a permanent dipole moment, whereas a *nonpolar* dielectric consists of molecules that do not have a dipole moment in the absence of an electric field.

Quantitative Tools The **dielectric constant** κ of a material between capacitor plates is

$$\kappa \equiv \frac{V_0}{V_d}, \qquad (26.9)$$

where V_0 is the potential difference across the capacitor without the dielectric and V_d is the potential with the dielectric in place.

A dielectric inserted between the plates of a capacitor becomes polarized by the electric field of the capacitor. This polarization gives the two faces of the dielectric thin layers of charge of equal magnitude but opposite sign. This charge is **bound** because the charge carriers are not free to move. The charge on the capacitor plates is **free** because the charge carriers are free to move.

If a capacitor has capacitance C_0 without a dielectric, its capacitance with a dielectric is

$$C_d = \kappa C_0. \quad (26.11)$$

If q_{free} is the **free charge** on a capacitor, then the **bound charge** q_{bound} is

$$q_{bound} = \frac{\kappa - 1}{\kappa} q_{free}. \quad (26.18)$$

Gauss's law in matter is

$$\oint \kappa \vec{E} \cdot d\vec{A} = \frac{q_{free,\,enc}}{\epsilon_0}, \quad (26.25)$$

where $q_{free,\,enc}$ is the free charge enclosed by the Gaussian surface.

Review Questions

Answers to these questions can be found at the end of this chapter.

26.1 Charge separation

1. What is the difference between the potential difference in a system and the system's electric potential energy?
2. When two charged objects that make up a system are separated by some distance, on what quantities does the system's electric potential energy depend?
3. In a system of charged objects separated from one another, where in space should one say that the system's electric potential energy is stored?
4. What does a Van de Graaff generator produce?

26.2 Capacitors

5. What is a capacitor?
6. Describe a parallel-plate capacitor. What geometric approximation is usually made in treating parallel-plate capacitors, and what simplification for its electrical properties results?
7. How is the amount of charge on each plate of a parallel-plate capacitor related to the potential difference between the plates?
8. For a given potential difference between the plates of a parallel-plate capacitor, how does the quantity of charge on each plate vary with plate area and separation distance?
9. In practice, what limits the quantity of charge that can be stored on the plates of a parallel-plate capacitor?

26.3 Dielectrics

10. Distinguish between the two general types of dielectrics, including a description of how each type behaves in an external electric field.
11. From a macroscopic point of view, what happens to a dielectric material when it is placed in an external uniform electric field?
12. What is the distinction between bound charge and free charge?
13. Why is the electric field magnitude in a parallel-plate capacitor with no dielectric between the plates greater than the electric field magnitude when a dielectric is inserted between the plates?
14. Does the electric field created in a polarized dielectric store less, the same, or more energy than an electric field of equal magnitude in a vacuum? Why?

26.4 Voltaic cells and batteries

15. What is a battery, and what does it do?
16. What is emf?

26.5 Capacitance

17. How is the capacitance of a capacitor defined?
18. On what properties of a capacitor does capacitance depend?
19. What is the unit of capacitance? Is its size appropriate to most practical applications in electronic devices?

26.6 Electric field energy and emf

20. How does the electric potential energy stored in a capacitor depend on the quantity of charge on each conductor?
21. How does the electric potential energy stored in a capacitor depend on the potential difference between the conductors?
22. What is energy density, and what is the algebraic relationship between the energy density of an electric field and the field magnitude?
23. How is the potential difference between the negative and positive terminals of the charge-separating device related to the emf in an ideal device and in a real-world device?

26.7 Dielectric constant

24. What is the definition of dielectric constant for a dielectric material?
25. Why is the dielectric constant of liquid water greater than that of other common materials used in capacitors, like paper or mica?
26. For a parallel-plate capacitor with a dielectric material filling the space between its plates, how is the bound charge on either dielectric surface related to the free charge on the surface of the adjacent conducting plate?
27. Why does the energy stored in an isolated charged capacitor decrease as a dielectric is inserted into the capacitor?

26.8 Gauss's law in dielectrics

28. When Gauss's law is used to calculate the electric field in a dielectric, the charge enclosed by any Gaussian surface we choose is $q_{free,\,enc} - q_{bound,\,enc}$. How can we use the law for a dielectric when we know nothing about $q_{bound,\,enc}$?
29. What is Gauss's law in a dielectric material, and what is its relationship to the form of Gauss's law we worked with in Chapter 24?

Developing a Feel

Make an order-of-magnitude estimate of each of the following quantities. Letters in parentheses refer to hints below. Use them as needed to guide your thinking.

1. The maximum potential difference between two metal baking sheets separated by 100 mm of air (A, D)
2. The maximum quantity of charge that can be placed on a metal-coated basketball in air (A, J, S, Q)
3. The potential difference that causes a lightning strike (A, O)
4. The dimensions of the plates in a square, 1-F parallel-plate capacitor with air between the plates (T, U, F, K, P)
5. The capacitance of a raindrop in dry air (B, G)
6. The plate area of a 50-fF capacitor on a computer memory chip (C, N)
7. The maximum energy density achievable in an electric field in air (A, V)
8. The maximum amount of electrical energy that can be stored in an electric field that fills your physics laboratory (A, H)
9. The capacitance of the coaxial cable that connects the cable box sitting atop your television to the cable outlet in the wall (E, I, M, R)
10. The capacitance of a metal-coated softball (G, L)

Hints

A. What is the electric field at the breakdown threshold of air?
B. What is the radius of a raindrop?
C. What is between the plates?
D. How does the magnitude of the electric field between two parallel plates E relate to the magnitude of the potential difference V between them?
E. What is the length of the cable?
F. For a given capacitance, what is the relationship between plate area and plate separation distance?
G. What is the radius of the "other" sphere serving as a conductor in this "capacitor"?
H. What is the laboratory volume?
I. What are the radii of the conductors?
J. Where is the magnitude of potential greatest?
K. What is a reasonable value for the smallest gap that can be maintained between two large metal plates?
L. What is the radius of a softball?
M. What shape can you assume for the cable?
N. What is the gap width?
O. What is the length of a lightning bolt?
P. What plate area is needed in order to have 1-F capacitance when the plate separation distance is 2 mm?
Q. What is the radius of a basketball?
R. What is a reasonable dielectric constant value for the cable?
S. If you model the ball as a conducting sphere, how do you determine its capacitance?
T. Is 1 F considered a common capacitance value or an extremely high value?
U. What does having such a large capacitance suggest about plate size?
V. What is the relationship between the energy density of an electric field and the field magnitude?

Key (all values approximate)

A. 3×10^6 V/m; **B.** 0.004 m; **C.** some dielectric material, probably silicon dioxide (κ approximately 5); **D.** $V = Ed$; **E.** 3 m; **F.** as separation distance increases, plate area must increase proportionally to maintain constant capacitance, which means you want a small gap; **G.** infinite; **H.** 4×10^2 m^3; **I.** $R_{inner} = 5 \times 10^{-4}$ m, $R_{outer} = 3 \times 10^{-3}$ m; **J.** near the ball surface; **K.** 2 mm; **L.** 50 mm; **M.** ignore any bends and loops, assuming all radii of curvature are much greater than R_{outer}, so that you can treat the cable as a cylinder; **N.** 1×10^{-8} m; **O.** 2×10^3 m; **P.** 2×10^8 m^2; **Q.** 0.1 m; **R.** with plastic insulation, κ is approximately 2; **S.** imagine the ball being concentric with a sphere of infinitely large radius so that you form a capacitor in which the ball surface is one conductor, the surface of the infinite sphere is the other conductor, and the gap is filled with air; **T.** extremely high; **U.** plates must be quite large; **V.** the energy density is proportional to the square of the field magnitude, with $\epsilon_0/2$ as the proportionality constant.

PRACTICE

Worked and Guided Problems

Procedure: Calculating the capacitance of a pair of conductors

To calculate the capacitance of a pair of conductors:

1. Let the conductors carry opposite charges of magnitude q.
2. Use Gauss's law, Coulomb's law, or direct integration to determine the electric field along a path leading from the negatively charged conductor to the positively charged conductor.
3. Calculate the electrostatic work W done on a test particle carrying a charge q_t along this path (Eq. 25.24) and determine the potential difference across the capacitor from Eq. 25.15,

$$V_{cap} = -W_{q_t}(- \rightarrow +)/q_t.$$

4. Use Eq. 26.1, $C \equiv q/V_{cap}$, to determine C.

These examples involve material from this chapter but are not associated with any particular section. Some examples are worked out in detail; others you should work out by following the guidelines provided.

Worked Problem 26.1 Roll-up capacitor

In a roll-up parallel-plate capacitor (Figure WG26.1), the plates are thin sheets of metal foil with a Mylar dielectric between them. Suppose that the foil and Mylar sheets are each 0.0500 mm thick and the capacitor is 20.00 mm tall and has a radius of 6.00 mm. Estimate the charge stored in the capacitor when there is a 25-V potential difference across the capacitor leads.

Figure WG26.1

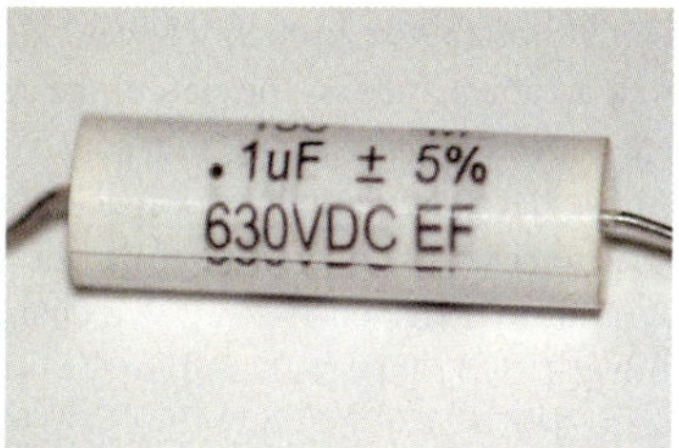

❶ GETTING STARTED We must first visualize how this capacitor is constructed. As usual, we begin with a sketch, in this case a sketch of the components—two foil sheets separated by a Mylar sheet—before the capacitor is rolled up (Figure WG26.2). We label the thickness of each sheet t. We assume that the Mylar completely fills the space between the foil sheets, so that the plate separation distance is equal to the Mylar thickness. Now we roll it up. However, there's a trick here: If we roll up the three-sheet sandwich of foil-Mylar-foil, the bottom foil touches the top foil, connecting the two plates and effectively nullifying the capacitor. To avoid this, the unrolled capacitor we start with has to be a four-sheet sandwich configured foil-Mylar-foil-Mylar (Figure WG26.3). The thickness of this sandwich is $4t$, where $t = 0.0500$ mm is the thickness of each sheet, and the radius of the rolled-up capacitor is $R = 6.00$ mm.

Figure WG26.2

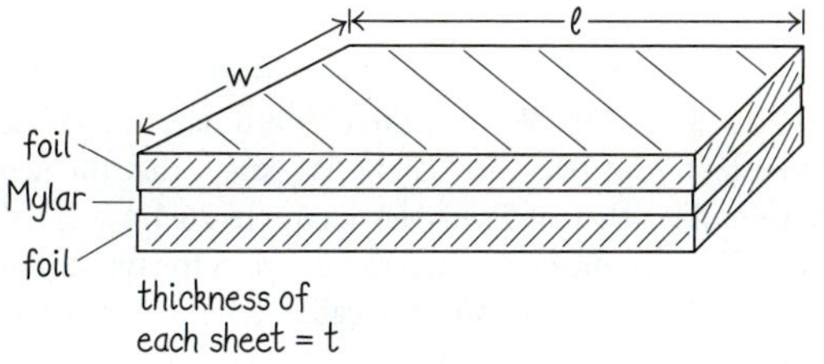

Figure WG26.3

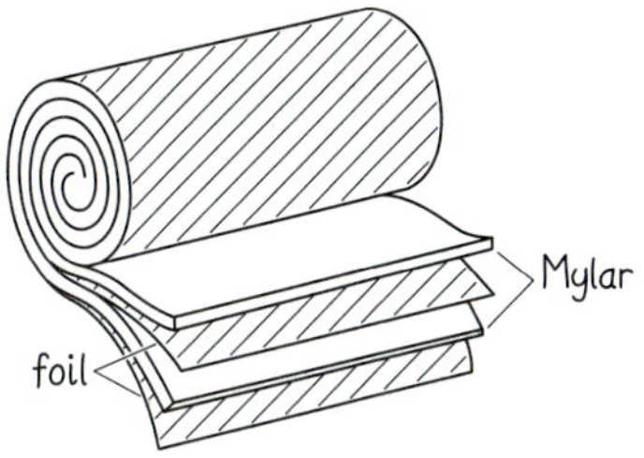

❷ DEVISE PLAN The radius R of the capacitor is related to the sheet thickness t and to the number of sheets in the length R. Because we are given values for the capacitor height and radius, as well as the thickness of each sheet, we should be able to unroll the sandwich and compute the capacitance of the equivalent parallel-plate capacitor. The problem asks how much charge can be stored in this capacitor when the potential difference across it is 25 V. Because capacitance is defined as the quantity of charge that can be stored for a given potential difference, calculating the capacitance should allow us to determine the quantity of stored charge.

If we unroll the capacitor, we have two foil sheets (the parallel plates) separated by a Mylar sheet of the same size. (The second Mylar sheet shown in Figure WG26.3 lies outside the capacitor and hence is irrelevant to the capacitance.) From Eq. 26.11 and the result of *Principles* Example 26.2, $C = \epsilon_0 A/d$, we know that the capacitance of parallel plates with a dielectric between them is

$$C = \frac{\kappa\epsilon_0 A}{d}.$$

In this expression, d is the separation distance between the plates, and in our problem that distance is the thickness $t = 0.0500$ mm of the Mylar sheet. After we look up the dielectric constant of Mylar ($\kappa = 3.3$), what we need to do is estimate the area $A = \ell w$ of each foil sheet. When the capacitor is unrolled, the height of the capacitor is one dimension of either foil sheet—let's say the width, so that $w = 20.00$ mm. We know how long the foil and Mylar sheets are (the ℓ in $A = \ell w$), and their combined thickness determines the radius $R = 6.00$ mm of the rolled-up capacitor. So we can infer the length of the foil sheets from what we know about their thickness, the Mylar thickness, and the radius of the rolled-up capacitor.

❸ **EXECUTE PLAN** One way to estimate the length of the unrolled foil sheets is to assume the capacitor is rolled as tightly as possible and then use the volume of the rolled-up capacitor. When you imagine starting with the four-sheet sandwich (foil-Mylar-foil-Mylar) and rolling it up, the width $w = 20.00$ mm in Figure WG26.2 becomes the height of the capacitor. The other dimension of the four sheets, ℓ, is related to the capacitor radius ($R = 6.00$ mm). When the capacitor is fully rolled up, the volume of the unrolled parallel-plate sandwich ($w \times \ell \times 4t$) must match the volume of the cylindrical capacitor ($\pi R^2 w$). Thus we have

$$V = \pi R^2 w = w\ell(4t)$$

$$\ell = \frac{\pi R^2}{4t}.$$

Another way to estimate the sheet length ℓ is to note that it requires many turns to roll up the capacitor. Each turn is a spiral ring of thickness $4t$, but because there are many turns, we can model the capacitor as if the spirals were circles. That means the capacitor is composed of a set of nested cylindrical shells, each of thickness $4t$ but with different radii, ranging from $r = 2t$ for the inner shell to $r = R - 2t$ for the outer shell. Then $R/4t$ gives the number of four-sheet shells across the capacitor radius. If we add up the circumferences of these shells, we have our ℓ. The average circumference of the shells in the roll is then $2\pi R/2$, so the length ℓ becomes

$$\ell = (\text{number of four-sheet shells}) \times (\text{average circumference})$$

$$= \left(\frac{R}{4t}\right)\left(\frac{2\pi R}{2}\right) = \frac{\pi R^2}{4t}.$$

It is reassuring that both methods give the same estimate for sheet length ℓ.

Now we obtain our expression for the capacitance of this Mylar-filled capacitor, noting that the separation distance d between "plates" is the thickness t of the Mylar between the two foil sheets:

$$C = \frac{\kappa\epsilon_0 A}{d} = \frac{\kappa\epsilon_0 \ell w}{t} = \frac{\kappa\epsilon_0\left(\frac{\pi R^2}{4t}\right)w}{t} = \frac{\kappa\epsilon_0 \pi R^2 w}{4t^2}. \quad (1)$$

Finally, the quantity of charge that can be stored with a 25-V potential difference across the capacitor is

$$q = CV = \frac{\kappa\epsilon_0 \pi R^2 w V}{4t^2}$$

$$= \frac{3.3(8.85 \times 10^{-12}\ \text{F/m})\pi(6.00 \times 10^{-3}\ \text{m})^2(20.0 \times 10^{-3}\ \text{m})(25\ \text{V})}{4(5.00 \times 10^{-5}\ \text{m})^2}$$

$$= 1.7 \times 10^{-7}\ \text{C}. ✓$$

❹ **EVALUATE RESULT** Our algebraic result shows that a larger capacitor (greater R or w) means that more charge can be stored for a given value of V, which makes sense. It also says that if the sheets are packed more tightly (smaller t), the quantity of charge that can be stored also increases because more foil is packed in the same volume. (However, you then need to worry about electrical breakdown of the Mylar film.) Equation 1 yields a capacitance of 6.6×10^{-9} F. Although you probably haven't developed a feel yet for capacitors, a capacitance in the nanofarad range is not unreasonable for a capacitor of this size and construction. Typical capacitors in most electric circuits have capacitances ranging from a few picofarads to several hundred microfarads. Because we know that $q = CV$ and we are given $V = 25$ V, a charge in the hundred-nanocoulomb (10^{-7} C) range makes sense for this capacitor.

Guided Problem 26.2 Home-made capacitor

Estimate the greatest capacitance you might achieve at home by rolling layers of aluminum foil and waxed paper around a number 2 pencil.

❶ **GETTING STARTED**

1. Are the results of Worked Problem 26.1 applicable?

❷ **DEVISE PLAN**

2. What is the length of an unused number 2 pencil?
3. What is the greatest length of foil or waxed paper you can (*a*) easily obtain and (*b*) handle without aid while creating the roll?
4. How are these lengths related to the capacitance?

❸ **EXECUTE PLAN**

5. What is a reasonable value for the dielectric constant of waxed paper?

❹ **EVALUATE RESULT**

6. Is your numerical value reasonable?
7. Try it and see if you are able to construct such a capacitor.

Worked Problem 26.3 Capacitance of television cable

Estimate the capacitance of a length L of the "RG-6" coaxial cable used for cable television. This type of cable consists of an inner wire of 0.50-mm radius and a concentric outer conductor of 6.8-mm diameter, with the space between the two conductors filled with polyethylene (dielectric constant $\kappa = 2.3$).

❶ **GETTING STARTED** We are asked to estimate the capacitance of a given length of television cable. We know that the geometry closely resembles that of *Principles* Example 26.3, except that we need to include the dielectric material between the two conductors. Because doubling the length of the cable doubles the surface area of each conductor while keeping the separation unchanged, we expect the capacitance to be proportional to L. We know that putting charge $+q$ on the inner wire and charge $-q$ on the outer conductor results in an electric field pointing radially outward from the inner wire, and hence a potential difference between the two conductors. Because the space between the two conductors is filled with a dielectric material, we need to account for the effect of the dielectric material on the electric field in the region between the two conductors.

❷ **DEVISE PLAN** We will follow the Procedure box on page 471 to calculate the capacitance. For the path over which electrostatic work is done, we choose the straight path that goes radially inward from the inner surface of the outer conductor (radius 3.4 mm) to the outer surface of the inner conductor (radius 0.50 mm). To compute the electric field, we will use Gauss's law in matter, Eq. 26.25.

❸ **EXECUTE PLAN** Let $R_1 = 0.50$ mm be the radius of the inner conductor, and let $R_2 = 3.4$ mm be the radius of the outer conductor. The electric field in the region $R_1 < r < R_2$ is given by Gauss's law in matter: $\oint \kappa \vec{E} \cdot d\vec{A} = q_{\text{free, enc}}/\epsilon_0$. We choose a cylindrical Gaussian surface of radius r and length L, concentric with the two conductors. The electric field points radially outward, so $\vec{E} \cdot d\vec{A} = 0$ on the two flat ends of the cylinder. On the curved surface of the cylinder (area $A = 2\pi r L$), the electric field is constant due to cylindrical symmetry, so the Gauss's-law integral simplifies to $\kappa E A = q/\epsilon_0$, where the charge $+q$ on the inner conductor is the free charge enclosed by the Gaussian surface. The electric field for $R_1 < r < R_2$ points radially outward and has magnitude

$$E = \frac{q}{\kappa A \epsilon_0} = \frac{q}{\kappa 2\pi r L \epsilon_0}.$$

The potential difference between the capacitor's two conductors is then (using Eq. 26.25)

$$V_{21} = -\int_{R_2}^{R_1} \vec{E} \cdot d\vec{\ell} = -\int_{R_2}^{R_1} E\, dr = -\frac{q}{2\pi\kappa\epsilon_0 L}\int_{R_2}^{R_1} \frac{dr}{r}$$

$$= -\frac{q}{2\pi\kappa\epsilon_0 L}\left[\ln(r)\right]_{R_2}^{R_1} = -\frac{q}{2\pi\kappa\epsilon_0 L}\ln\left(\frac{R_1}{R_2}\right)$$

$$= \frac{q}{2\pi\kappa\epsilon_0 L}\ln\left(\frac{R_2}{R_1}\right).$$

Then using $q = CV$, we obtain

$$C = \frac{q}{V_{21}} = \frac{2\pi\kappa\epsilon_0 L}{\ln(R_2/R_1)}.$$

Putting in numbers, we calculate the capacitance per unit length to be

$$\frac{C}{L} = \frac{2\pi\kappa\epsilon_0}{\ln(R_2/R_1)} = \frac{(6.283)(2.3)(8.85 \times 10^{-12}\,\text{F/m})}{\ln(3.4/0.50)}$$

$$= 6.7 \times 10^{-11}\,\text{F/m} = 67\,\text{pF/m}. ✔$$

❹ **EVALUATE RESULT** *Principles* Example 26.3 found the capacitance of a coaxial cable (with air or vacuum between the inner and outer conductors) to be $C = (2\pi\epsilon_0 L)/\ln(R_2/R_1)$. Our expression is greater by a factor $\kappa = 2.3$. This makes sense, as we have seen in other examples that filling the space between a capacitor's two conductors with a nonconductor having dielectric constant κ increases the capacitance by a factor κ. We can also check online that the numerical value 67 pF/m agrees with tabulated values for the capacitance per unit length of commercial RG-6 television cable.

Guided Problem 26.4 Laptop power

The rechargeable batteries needed in laptop computers are both heavy and expensive. Moreover, the lifetime of many rechargeable batteries is relatively short—perhaps at best a few thousand charge-discharge cycles. Because of this, capacitors have been considered as one possible option to store the required energy. Capacitors are quickly charged, and because no chemical reaction is involved, they have a much longer lifetime than do batteries. Let us say your ultra-low-power laptop requires a potential difference of 8 V to run, and you'd like it to run for a minimum of 4 h using an average power of 1 W. Assume it is possible to "tap" a constant 8 V from a capacitor that has a potential difference greater than or equal to 8 V, but whose potential difference cannot exceed 48 V. (*a*) In order to use this capacitor in your laptop, what would its capacitance have to be? (*b*) If this were a parallel-plate capacitor, how large would the plate area have to be if the plates were separated by a Mylar layer 0.05 mm thick? Does this type of capacitor seem a feasible alternative to today's rechargeable batteries?

❶ **GETTING STARTED**

1. How much energy must be available for use?
2. Can the capacitor be fully discharged at the end of 4 h, or must it still be partially charged?

❷ **DEVISE PLAN**

3. Express the required capacitance in terms of initial and final potential differences and the required energy that must be supplied by the capacitor.
4. How does capacitance depend on surface area, separation distance, and dielectric constant in a parallel-plate capacitor?

❸ **EXECUTE PLAN**

❹ **EVALUATE RESULT**

5. Work out numbers for the energy removed from the capacitor and for the energy needed to run the computer for 4 h. Do they agree?
6. Is the plate area feasible for a capacitor that must fit inside a laptop computer?
7. Modern dielectric materials and construction techniques (see, for example, Problem 79 in this chapter) allow capacitors on the order of 1 F to fit into a volume of 10^{-5} m^3. Would knowing this change your answer about feasibility?

Worked Problem 26.5 Earth-sized capacitor

What is the capacitance of Earth when you model it as a conducting sphere?

❶ GETTING STARTED It is hard to think of Earth as being part of an electronic device, in this case a gigantic capacitor, but let's accept that premise for the sake of argument. We know the definition of capacitance: the amount of charge that can be stored per unit of potential difference between the two conductors of a capacitor. If Earth is one conductor in our capacitor, what can act as the other conductor? That the potential of a spherical object is typically measured by defining infinitely far away as the position of zero potential gives us the clue we need: We should consider the other conductor to be an infinitely large spherical shell that is concentric with Earth.

❷ DEVISE PLAN We know from Eq. 26.1 that capacitance is given by $C = q/V_{\text{cap}}$, but in this problem q is the charge on Earth's surface, a quantity we do not know. To use Eq. 26.1, however, we also need to know the potential V_{cap} at Earth's surface. We found in *Principles* Section 25.5 that the potential at some radial distance r from a charged particle is given by Eq. 25.21, $V(r) = q/4\pi\epsilon_0 r$. When we use this expression for V in Eq. 26.1, the two q factors cancel, and so our not knowing a value for q is not an obstacle here.

❸ EXECUTE PLAN In this problem, r in Eq. 25.21 is Earth's radius R_E. Substituting the expression for V given by Eq. 25.21 into Eq. 26.1 therefore yields

$$C_E = \frac{q}{(q/4\pi\epsilon_0 R_E)} = 4\pi\epsilon_0 R_E$$

$$= 4\pi(8.85 \times 10^{-12}\ \text{C}^2/\text{N}\cdot\text{m}^2)(6.4 \times 10^6\ \text{m}) = 0.71\ \text{mF}. ✔$$

❹ EVALUATE RESULT We see from the algebraic expression that the capacitance of Earth would increase if it had a larger radius. This increase is to be expected because the charge carriers on the surface would then be farther apart, and thus more charge could be stored on the surface. It is also gratifying to note that this is exactly the result we obtained in *Principles* Example 26.4 for a spherical capacitor, $C = 4\pi\epsilon_0 R_1 R_2/(R_2 - R_1)$, when we make the outer sphere's radius infinite.

Guided Problem 26.6: Tin can capacitor

A certain capacitor consists of a solid cylindrical core surrounded by a metal shell. The shell is capped at both ends with metal covers, forming a connected metal surface with the shell but not the rod. The shell has radius R_{shell} and length L. The core is separated from the shell by a distance d and has length $L - 2d$. Assume that $d \ll R_{\text{shell}}$ and also that $d \ll L$. What is the capacitance of this capacitor?

❶ GETTING STARTED

1. Start by drawing a sketch of the capacitor, labeling all the given variables and indicating the quantity you must determine.
2. How is this capacitor similar to a coaxial capacitor? How does it differ from a coaxial capacitor?
3. Are the metal covers on the ends at the same potential as the metal shell?
4. What are the appropriate surface areas of the conductors?
5. Is the distance between core and shell (including covers) constant over all but a negligible portion of the capacitor?

❷ DEVISE PLAN

6. What is the expression for capacitance in a coaxial capacitor?
7. What distances correspond to the two radii in this expression?
8. How can you account for the effects of the end caps on the capacitance?

❸ EXECUTE PLAN

❹ EVALUATE RESULT

9. Pick some numerical values and compare this capacitance with that of a roll-up capacitor of similar dimensions from Worked Problem 26.1. What do you conclude?

Worked Problem 26.7 Variable capacitance

A variable capacitor can be constructed by inserting a slab of dielectric material partway between a pair of parallel plates. One such capacitor has plates of length ℓ and area A, where the plates are separated by a distance d. If the dielectric constant of the inserted material is κ, what is the capacitance as a function of how far into the space between the plates the dielectric is inserted?

❶ GETTING STARTED Figure WG26.4 shows our given information. Aligning the x axis along the plate length allows us to use x to represent the inserted length. Our drawing shows that this capacitor has two regions: region 1 with plate length $\ell - x$ and air between the plates and region 2 with plate length x and the dielectric between the plates. Because of the presence of the dielectric, we know that the electric field magnitude is not the same in the two regions. We probably need to use the general definition of capacitance, $C = q/V$, and figure out, for a given potential difference V, what surface charge is required on the plates above and below each of these two regions.

Figure WG26.4

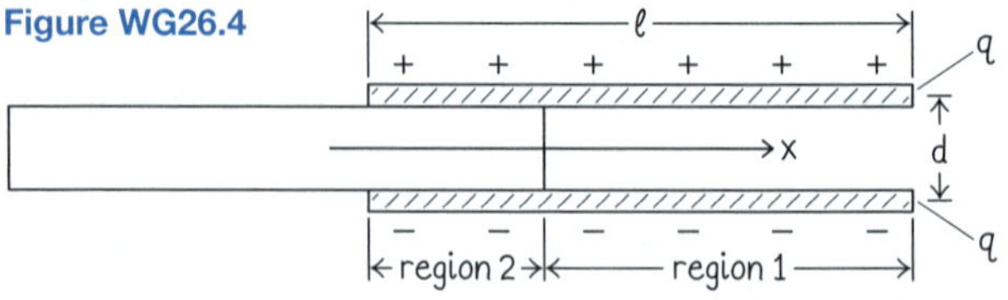

❷ DEVISE PLAN Because there are two regions in this capacitor, we have to be careful when we use our capacitance equation. We want to know how much free charge $q_{\text{cap,free}}$ the capacitor can store for a given potential difference across the plates. We know that the potential is the same everywhere on each plate, and so the potential difference V_{cap} is the same everywhere across the plates. Because this potential difference is related to the electric field in each region by $V_{cap} = Ed$ and because d is constant, we conclude that the electric field must be the same in both regions. Because a dielectric decreases the electric field by a factor κ for a fixed density of free charge on the plates, the free-charge density must be greater by a factor κ in region 2 (dielectric-filled region) than in region 1 (air-filled region). The free charge q_{1free} or q_{q2free} on the plates in each region is the free-charge density (charge per unit area) in that region multiplied by the corresponding surface area. The charge $q_{cap,free}$ stored by the capacitor is the sum of q_{1free} and q_{2free}. Then taking the ratio of $q_{cap,free}$ and V_{cap} will give us the capacitance for this variable capacitor.

❸ **EXECUTE PLAN** Because the plate area is A, the plate width is $w = A/\ell$. The plate area for region 1 is $A_1 = (\ell - x)w$, and the plate area for region 2 is $A_2 = xw$. There is no dielectric in region 1, and so in this region Eq. 26.12 tells us that the electric field is

$$E_1 = \frac{V_{cap}}{d} = E_{1free} = \frac{\sigma_{1free}}{\epsilon_0} = \frac{q_{1free}}{\epsilon_0 A_1},$$

which leads us to

$$q_{1free} = \frac{V_{cap}}{d}\epsilon_0 A_1. \quad (1)$$

From Eq. 26.14, the field in region 2 is

$$E_2 = \frac{V_{cap}}{d} = E_{2free} - E_{2bound} = \frac{\sigma_{2free} - \sigma_{2bound}}{\epsilon_0}$$
$$= \frac{q_{2free} - q_{2bound}}{\epsilon_0 A_2}.$$

But from Eq. 26.17 ($q_{free} - q_{bound} = q_{free}/\kappa$), we see that this last equation can be rewritten in the form

$$\frac{V_{cap}}{d} = \frac{q_{2free}}{\kappa\epsilon_0 A_2}.$$

The free charge on the plates is therefore

$$q_{cap,free} = q_{1free} + q_{2free} = \frac{V_{cap}}{d}\epsilon_0 A_1 + \frac{V_{cap}}{d}\kappa\epsilon_0 A_2$$
$$= \frac{V_{cap}}{d}\epsilon_0[(\ell - x)w + \kappa x w],$$

which means that the capacitance of our variable capacitor is given by

$$C(x) = \frac{q_{cap,free}}{V_{cap}} = \frac{\epsilon_0 w}{d}[(\ell - x) + \kappa x]$$
$$= \frac{\epsilon_0 w}{d}[\ell + (\kappa - 1)x] = \frac{\epsilon_0 A}{d}\left[1 + (\kappa - 1)\frac{x}{\ell}\right]. ✔$$

❹ **EVALUATE RESULT** We know that dielectrics are used in capacitors to increase capacitance. Therefore $C(x)$ should increase as we insert more of the dielectric into the space between the plates (increase x). This is just what our result says because $\kappa - 1 > 0$ (remember, κ is always greater than unity). We should also check the limits $x = 0$ and $x = \ell$. With $x = 0$ (no dielectric), our equation reduces to the result from *Principles* Example 26.2 for a dielectric-free parallel-plate capacitor: $C_0 = \epsilon_0 A/d$. When the capacitor is entirely filled with dielectric, $x = \ell$ and our equation becomes

$$C(\ell) = \frac{\epsilon_0 A}{d}\left[1 + (\kappa - 1)\frac{\ell}{\ell}\right] = \frac{\epsilon_0 A}{d}[1 + \kappa - 1]$$
$$= \kappa\frac{\epsilon_0 A}{d} = \kappa C_0,$$

which agrees with Eq. 26.11 giving the capacitance of a capacitor entirely filled with a dielectric.

Guided Problem 26.8 Vacuum Capacitors

Devices used in high-power radio-frequency applications require capacitors that can store large quantities of charge without electrical breakdown. Dielectric materials may be undesirable in these applications because of the materials' finite breakdown thresholds. Instead, high storage capacity is achieved with *vacuum capacitors*, which consist of conducting plates separated by a fairly large distance and sealed inside an evacuated canister so that there is vacuum between the plates rather than air. One problem with these capacitors is that the vacuum is not perfect (that is, some air molecules are present); another problem is that a sufficiently large electric field can ionize the metal plates, ripping off electrons from the plates and leading to electrical breakdown. Suppose the largest electric field that can be supported by a vacuum capacitor is 10 times greater than the breakdown threshold of air. What is the maximum potential difference that can be applied to a 1.0-nF parallel-plate vacuum capacitor with a plate separation of 1.0 mm? What is the maximum charge that can be stored without discharging?

❶ **GETTING STARTED**

1. How are potential difference and electric field related for a parallel-plate capacitor?
2. Where can you find the value for the maximum electric field in air and then for this capacitor?

❷ **DEVISE PLAN**

3. How are stored charge and potential difference related for a capacitor?
4. What dielectric constant should be used for a vacuum capacitor?

❸ **EXECUTE PLAN**

❹ **EVALUATE RESULT**

5. Is the maximum potential difference quite large compared with potentials encountered in commonplace low-power devices?
6. Is the maximum stored charge fairly large?

Questions and Problems

For instructor-assigned homework, go to MasteringPhysics® MP

Dots indicate difficulty level of problems: • = *easy,* •• = *intermediate,* ••• = *hard;* CR = *context-rich problem.*

26.1 Charge separation

1. When two objects are charged by a charge-separating process or device, how are their charges related? •
2. Positive work is done on a system containing positively and negatively charged particles. All work goes into changing the electric potential energy of the system. What can be said about the electric field between positively and negatively charged particles? What can be said about the electric field everywhere else? ••
3. You are designing a Van de Graaff generator, and you want it to hold as many electrons as possible. Should you make the radius of the sphere very large or very small? ••
4. Draw energy diagrams for the processes of separating charge carriers by (*a*) rubbing, (*b*) increasing the separation distance between a positively charged object and a negatively charged object, and (*c*) increasing the separation distance between two positively charged objects. ••
5. A plastic rod is rubbed with wool, producing a distribution of positive and negative surplus charge that is concentrated in two locations on the rod and two on the wool. This distribution can be approximated as two pairs of small balls of charge as shown in Figure P26.5. The distance d is 30.0 mm, and the magnitude of the charge on each ball is 2.00 μC. If 34.0 J of work went into thermal energy as the rod and wool heated up, how much work was done on the system? ••

Figure P26.5

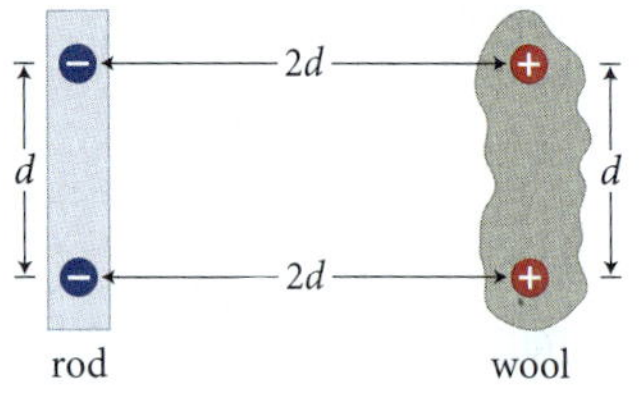

6. A piece of wool is used to charge two plastic spheres. When the spheres are held 200 mm apart, they repel each other with 7.00 N of force. If the wool ends up with a surplus positive charge of 23.5 μC, what is the charge on each of the two spheres? ••
7. Two 0.0450-kg spheres are identical (including the charge they carry) and are initially pinned in place 200 mm apart. You unpin them and push on each sphere with a force of 0.15 N. After their separation increases to 400 mm, each sphere has a speed of 500 mm/s. What is the charge on each sphere? Is there more than one possible answer? ••
8. A fellow scientist heard that a Van de Graaff generator built 70 years ago could collect 5.0 C of charge on its dome, which had a radius of 1.1 m, and has challenged you to do the same. The belt you plan to use is 100 mm wide and 10.0 m long (5.0 m to go up to the dome, and 5.0 m to come back down). Charging the belt gives it a surface charge density of 45 $\mu C/m^2$. How much force must your motor be able to exert on the belt in order to accomplish your goal? If you had more freedom in the design, what changes would you make to make the charging process easier on your motor, and why? Would your changes alter only the force required for your motor, or would they also affect the energy required for charging? State any assumptions you make, and state whether or not they are physically reasonable. •••

26.2 Capacitors

9. The plates of a capacitor are charged using a battery, and they produce an electric field across the separation distance d between them. The two plates are now to be pushed together to a separation of $d/2$. The pushing together can be done either with the battery connected or with it disconnected. Which way would result in the greater electric field magnitude, and by what factor? •
10. Two parallel-plate capacitors have the same plate area. Capacitor 1 has a plate separation twice that of capacitor 2, and the quantity of charge you place on capacitor 1 is twice the quantity you place on capacitor 2. How do the potential differences across each of the two capacitors compare to each other? •
11. Two parallel-plate capacitors have the same plate area. Capacitor 1 has a plate separation twice that of capacitor 2, and the potential difference you impose across the plates of capacitor 1 is twice the potential difference you impose across capacitor 2. How do the quantities of charge stored on the two capacitors compare to each other? •
12. Suppose a capacitor is fully charged by a battery and then disconnected from the battery. The positive plate has a charge $+q$ and the negative plate has a charge $-q$. The plate area is doubled, and the plate separation is reduced to half its initial separation. What is the new charge on the negative plate? ••
13. Explain why there must always be some nonzero electric field outside the plates of a parallel-plate capacitor (Figure P26.13*a*), which means that the idealization shown in Figure P26.13*b*, with all the field lines confined to the region between the plates, can never be exact. (Hint: Consider the potential difference between the plates for paths outside the edges.) ••

Figure P26.13

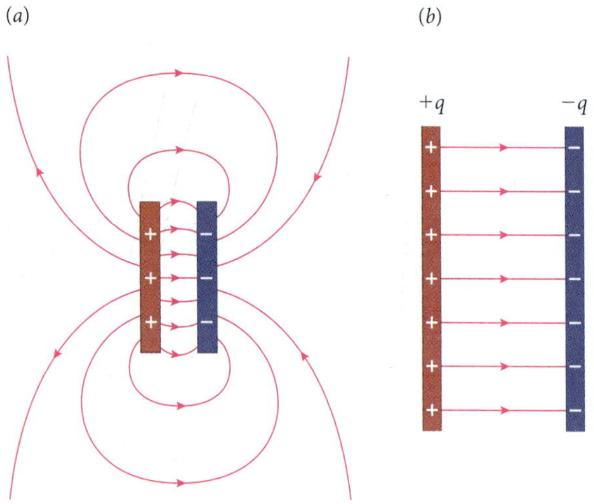

14. Figure P26.14 is a graph of the electric field between two capacitor plates as a function of distance from the left plate. The distance between the plates is d, the direction of the field is to the right, and a battery is connected to the plates. (*a*) Which plate carries a positive charge? (*b*) How many slabs of material have been inserted between the plates? (*c*) What can you say about the slab(s) inserted? (*d*) Make a graph of the electric field between the plates when the slabs between the plates are removed and the battery remains connected. ••

Figure P26.14

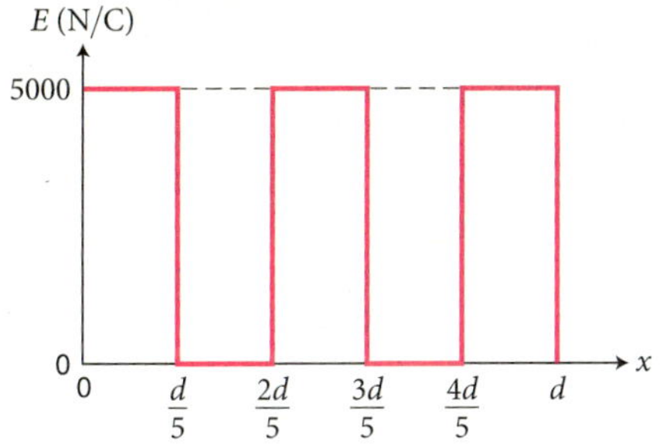

15. When two parallel plates separated by a distance d are connected to a battery that maintains a potential difference of magnitude V between the plates, a charge of magnitude q accumulates on each plate. If the plate separation is increased to $2d$ and the battery is replaced with one that has potential difference $2V$ between the terminals, what is the new charge on each plate? ••

16. Suppose two capacitor plates have an area of $0.0100\ \text{m}^2$ and are initially separated by 1.00 mm. Each plate holds $3.30\ \mu\text{C}$ of charge. How much energy is required to increase the plate separation to 2.00 mm? ••

17. A certain capacitor is fully charged by a battery, such that the positive plate holds a charge $+q$ and the negative plate holds a charge $-q$. The plates of the capacitor are then pulled apart to twice their initial separation. Determine the new charge on the positive plate if (*a*) the battery is kept attached to the capacitor as the separation is increased, and (*b*) the battery is disconnected before the plate separation is increased. ••

18. You need to insert a metal slab between the two plates of a parallel-plate capacitor. The plates are a distance d apart, and a battery maintains a constant potential difference V_{batt} between them. In order to avoid dielectric breakdown, the electric field in any region cannot exceed $4V_{\text{batt}}/d$. (*a*) What is the maximum thickness of the metal slab that can be used without causing dielectric breakdown? (*b*) If this maximum thickness is used, does the insertion of the metal slab affect the amount of charge stored on the capacitor? •••

26.3 Dielectrics

19. Either a dielectric or a conductor could be inserted between the plates of a capacitor. (*a*) State at least two similarities between the effects of inserting a dielectric and inserting a conductor. (*b*) State at least two differences between the effects of inserting a dielectric and inserting a conductor. •

20. A fully charged capacitor initially has an air gap and is disconnected from the battery. A dielectric material is inserted between the plates. What happens to (*a*) the free charge at the surface of the capacitor plates and (*b*) the total charge (free and bound) at the surface of the capacitor plates? •

21. Two parallel-plate capacitors have the same dimensions, but the space between the plates is filled with air in capacitor 1 and with plastic in capacitor 2. The magnitude of the charge on the plates is the same in both capacitors. Compare (*a*) the magnitudes of the electric fields E_1 and E_2 between the plates, (*b*) the potential differences V_1 and V_2 between the plates, and (*c*) the energies stored in the capacitors. ••

22. Two parallel-plate capacitors have the same dimensions, but the space between the plates is filled with air in capacitor 1 and with plastic in capacitor 2. The potential difference between the plates is the same in both capacitors. Compare (*a*) the magnitudes of the electric fields E_1 and E_2 between the plates, (*b*) the magnitudes of the charges on the plates q_1 and q_2, and (*c*) the energies stored in the capacitors. ••

23. A capacitor connected to a battery initially holds a charge of $+q$ on its positive plate and $-q$ on its negative plate. The electric field between the plates is initially $\vec{E}$. A dielectric material is then inserted that polarizes in such a way as to produce an electric field of $-0.30\vec{E}$ (where the $-$ sign indicates that this field opposes the initial field $\vec{E}$). Determine the new charge stored on the positive plate. ••

24. A parallel-plate capacitor with air between the plates and plate separation distance d is connected to a battery that maintains a potential difference V_{batt} between the plates. Sketch a graph of V as a function of x when x is defined as position between the plates, running from $x = 0$ at the surface of the positively charged plate to $x = d$ at the surface of the other plate. Plot the points $x = 0$, $x = d/4$, $x = d/2$, $x = 3d/4$, and $x = d$. A slab that is made of a dielectric material and has a thickness of $d/2$ is inserted between the plates such that the midpoint of the slab thickness is at the position $d/2$ in the space between the plates. Sketch a graph of $V(x)$ for the capacitor now. Comment on how your graph is affected by the magnitude of the bound charge induced on the surface of the dielectric slab. ••

25. A capacitor initially has a charge of magnitude q on each plate. When a dielectric is inserted between the plates, the bound surface charge on the two dielectric surfaces facing the plates has a magnitude $q/3$. What is the ratio of the electric field magnitude in the empty capacitor to the electric field magnitude in the capacitor with the dielectric (*a*) if the battery stays connected to the plates and (*b*) if the battery is removed before the dielectric is inserted? ••

26. A capacitor has a plate area of $0.0045\ \text{m}^2$ and a charge of magnitude q on each plate. The space between plates has been filled with a dielectric that has a bound surface charge of magnitude $3q/4$ on either side. When the dielectric material is removed, the electrical breakdown of air is observed between the plates. What is the smallest possible value of q? ••

27. The night before an exam, your study partner asks what you can do to a parallel-plate capacitor to avoid the problem of the electrical breakdown of air. You answer that a nonconducting dielectric material can be inserted. Your friend is confused as to why other things wouldn't work. Why wouldn't it help, for example, to add a conducting slab? Why isn't increasing plate separation also a valid answer? After all, moving charge carriers very far apart must decrease their effect on the air between them. Why do these alternatives not work? •••

26.4 Voltaic cells and batteries

28. The term *emf* is an acronym for *electromotive force*. Why is this a misnomer? •

29. As a battery is used to charge a capacitor, does the overall charge inside the battery get smaller, greater, or stay the same? •

30. What limits the lifetime of a battery? •

31. The reactions in a lead-acid battery are

Positive terminal: $PbO_2 + HSO_4^- + 3H^+ + 2e^- \rightarrow PbSO_4 + 2H_2O$

Negative terminal: $HSO_4^- + Pb \rightarrow PbSO_4 + H^+ + 2e^-$

If a certain battery supplies 1.0×10^8 electrons per second to the negative terminal and the battery contains 3.00 moles of electrolytic solution (which means the solution contains 3.00 moles of HSO_4^-), what fraction of the solution undergoes a chemical reaction each second? ••

32. One electrode in an alkaline battery is zinc, and the other is manganese dioxide. (*a*) Fill in the blank for the chemical reaction at the zinc electrode: $Zn + 2OH^- \rightarrow ZnO +$ ____ $+ 2e^-$. (*b*) Fill in the blank for the reaction at the manganese electrode: $2MnO_2 + H_2O +$ ____ $\rightarrow Mn_2O_3 + 2OH^-$. (*c*) Which electrode is positive and which is negative? ••

33. Suppose that the metal electrodes in a battery are shaped like large parallel plates and are 1.00 mm apart, so that they are essentially a parallel-plate capacitor. If the battery supplies a potential difference of 4.5 V between the electrodes, what is the surface charge density on the electrodes (before anything has been connected to the battery)? ••

26.5 Capacitance

34. A parallel-plate capacitor initially has capacitance C. The distance between the plates is then doubled, with a 9.0-V battery connected. The battery is then disconnected, and the plate area is doubled. Finally, a 20-V battery is connected across the plates. What is the new capacitance? •

35. A capacitor consisting of two concentric spheres and one consisting of two coaxial cylinders both have an inner radius of 10.0 mm and an outer radius of 30.0 mm. If the two capacitors have the same capacitance, what is the length of the cylinders? •

36. A parallel-plate capacitor initially has capacitance C. What is the capacitance after each of the following single changes is made: (*a*) plate separation distance doubled, (*b*) dielectric material inserted, (*c*) potential difference across plates doubled, (*d*) plate area halved, (*e*) applied emf increased until plate charge doubles. •

37. A coaxial capacitor consisting of an inner wire and an outer cylindrical shell has a length of 80.0 mm and an outer diameter of 10.0 mm. When connected to an 18.0-V battery, this capacitor can hold 1.1 nC of charge on the wire. What is the wire radius? ••

38. Consider a parallel-plate capacitor with charge $+q$ on the top plate and $-q$ on the other, and a plate area that is large relative to the separation distance. Contrast this with a spherical capacitor consisting of two concentric spherical shells, one smaller than the other, with a charge of $+q$ uniformly distributed on the outer shell and a charge of $-q$ uniformly distributed on the inner shell. (*a*) Do the positive and negative charges distribution contribute equally to the electric field inside each capacitor? If not, what fraction of the field comes from the negative distribution? (*b*) What is the electric field magnitude outside each capacitor? ••

39. One way to double the capacitance of a parallel-plate capacitor is to reduce the plate separation distance by a factor of 2. Doubling the capacitance of a spherical capacitor is a bit more complex, though. (*a*) If you had a spherical capacitor consisting of two concentric spherical shells of radii R_{inner} and $R_{outer} > R_{inner}$, you could double the capacitance by changing the radius of the outer shell from R_{outer} to some value d. What is d in terms of R_{inner} and R_{outer}? (*b*) You could also double the capacitance by changing the radius of the inner shell from R_{inner} to some value d. What is d in terms of R_{inner} and R_{outer}? (*c*) Repeat parts *a* and *b* for a capacitor consisting of two long concentric cylindrical shells of radii R_{inner} and $R_{outer} > R_{inner}$. ••

40. A spherical capacitor consists of two concentric conducting spherical shells of radii R and $2R$. (*a*) How long would a coaxial cylindrical capacitor made of two concentric cylindrical conductors of radii R and $2R$ have to be in order to have the same capacitance as the spherical capacitor? (*b*) What plate separation distance would be required for a parallel-plate capacitor made of two circular conductors each of radius R in order to have the same capacitance as the spherical capacitor? ••

41. Two small, irregularly shaped conducting objects, one carrying charge $+q$ and one carrying charge $-q$, are placed on an x axis at $x = -4.0$ m and $x = +4.0$ m, respectively. Between the objects, the electric field on the x axis is given by $E(x) = aq(x^2 + b)$, where a and b are constants. (*a*) What are the units of a and b? (*b*) What is the capacitance of this configuration? •••

42. The expression for the capacitance of a parallel-plate capacitor that has plates of area A separated by a distance d is given in *Principles* Example 26.2. (*a*) Show that the expression for a spherical capacitor, given in *Principles* Example 26.4, reduces to the expression for a parallel-plate capacitor in the limit that R_1 approaches R_2, with $d = R_2 - R_1$. (*b*) Show that the expression for a cylindrical capacitor, given in Example 26.3, reduces to the expression for a parallel-plate capacitor in the limit that R_1 approaches R_2, with $d = R_2 - R_1$. (Hint: You might find the Taylor series expansion of $\ln(1 + x)$ useful.) •••

26.6 Electric field energy and emf

43. A parallel-plate capacitor with air between its plates carries a charge of 6.60 μC when a 9.00-V battery is connected to it. How much energy is stored in the capacitor? •

44. Suppose a certain battery has an internal emf of 9.00 V but the potential difference across its terminals is only 85.0% of that value. If that battery is connected to a 56.0-μF capacitor, how much energy is stored when the capacitor is fully charged? •

45. A parallel-plate capacitor connected to a battery maintaining a potential difference V across the capacitor initially stores electric potential energy U_i^E. If the plate area is doubled and the battery is replaced with one that maintains a potential difference of $2V$ across the capacitor, how much electric potential energy is stored now? •

PRACTICE

46. Two parallel-plate capacitors 1 and 2 are identical except that capacitor 1 has charge $+q$ on one plate and $-q$ on the other, and capacitor 2 has charge $+2q$ on one plate and $-2q$ on the other. Compare the two capacitors based on their (*a*) capacitance, (*b*) potential difference between the plates, (*c*) electric field magnitude between the plates, and (*d*) energy stored. ••

47. Three parallel-plate capacitors are separately connected to identical batteries. Capacitor 1 has a plate area A and a plate separation d. Capacitor 2 has a plate area $2A$ and a plate separation d. Capacitor 3 has a plate area A and a plate separation $2d$. Rank the three capacitors, largest first, based on (*a*) capacitance, (*b*) charge stored, (*c*) electric field magnitude between the plates, (*d*) energy stored, and (*e*) energy density. ••

48. Three parallel-plate capacitors each store the same amount of charge. Capacitor 1 has a plate area A and a plate separation d. Capacitor 2 has a plate area $2A$ and a plate separation d. Capacitor 3 has a plate area A and a plate separation $2d$. Rank the three capacitors, largest first, based on their (*a*) capacitance, (*b*) potential difference between the plates, (*c*) electric field magnitude between the plates, (*d*) energy stored, and (*e*) energy density. ••

49. (*a*) A spherical capacitor consists of two concentric conducting spheres of radii R and $2R$. If the two spheres carry charges of $+q$ and $-q$, what is the average energy density inside the capacitor in terms of R and q? (*b*) A cylindrical capacitor of length ℓ consists of two coaxial conducting cylinders of radii R and $2R$. If the two cylinders carry charges of $+q$ and $-q$, what is the average energy density inside the capacitor? ••

50. A parallel-plate capacitor has plates of area A. The plates are initially separated by a distance d, but this distance can be varied. If the capacitor is connected to a battery, what should the plate separation be if you want to quadruple (*a*) the capacitance, (*b*) the charge stored, (*c*) the energy stored, and (*d*) the energy density? ••

51. A parallel-plate capacitor has plates of area A. The plates are initially separated by a distance d, but this distance can be varied. If the capacitor is charged by a battery and the battery is then removed so that the capacitor is isolated, what should the plate separation be if you want to quadruple (*a*) the capacitance, (*b*) the charge stored, (*c*) the energy stored, and (*d*) the energy density? ••

52. A parallel-plate capacitor has an initial charge q and a plate separation distance d. How much work must you do, in terms of q, d, and plate area A, to increase the separation distance to $3d$ if (*a*) the capacitor is isolated and (*b*) the capacitor is connected to a battery? (*c*) The work you do is positive in both cases. Explain why in one situation the electric potential energy increases and in the other it decreases. •••

26.7 Dielectric constant

53. (*a*) Does it make sense to talk about a dielectric constant for a conductor? If so, what value does the constant have? (*b*) What is the breakdown threshold for a conductor? •

54. The potential difference across the plates of a parallel-plate capacitor is gradually increased. (*a*) What happens when the breakdown threshold is exceeded? (*b*) If you want to increase the potential difference before breakdown occurs, what capacitor variables might you change? •

55. (*a*) Make a list of ways to increase the capacitance of a parallel-plate capacitor. (*b*) Does *Increase quantity of charge stored* or *Decrease potential difference* belong on the list? •

56. When you remove a dielectric slab from between the plates of a charged isolated capacitor, what happens to the energy stored in the capacitor? Why does this happen to the stored energy? ••

57. Two parallel-plate capacitors are identical except that capacitor 1 has vacuum between the plates and capacitor 2 has a dielectric slab of dielectric constant κ filling the space between the plates. The capacitors are connected to identical batteries. Compare the two based on (*a*) capacitance, (*b*) charge stored, (*c*) energy stored, (*d*) electric field magnitude, and (*e*) energy density. ••

58. Two parallel-plate capacitors are identical except that capacitor 1 has vacuum between the plates and capacitor 2 has a dielectric slab of dielectric constant κ filling the space between the plates. Each capacitor is isolated (that is, not connected to a battery), and they store equal quantities of charge. Compare the two based on (*a*) capacitance, (*b*) potential difference between the plates, (*c*) energy stored, (*d*) electric field magnitude between the plates, and (*e*) energy density. ••

59. When a dielectric slab completely fills the space between the plates of a parallel-plate capacitor, the magnitude of the bound charge is one-fourth the magnitude of the free charge. (*a*) What is the dielectric constant of the material of which the slab is made? (*b*) If the slab does not fill the space between the plates, but instead has a width equal to half the distance between the plates, does the magnitude of the bound charge change? If so, how? ••

60. If you want to maintain a potential difference of 6000 V between the plates of a parallel-plate capacitor, what is the minimum value of the plate separation if the space between the plates is completely filled by (*a*) a slab of mica and (*b*) a slab of barium titanate? (*c*) What is the ratio of the maximum charges that could be put on a plate of the capacitor in part *b* to the capacitor in part *a*. ••

61. A parallel-plate capacitor with a plate area of 50 mm^2 and air between the plates can hold 5.5 pC of charge per volt of potential difference across its plates. When a barium titanate dielectric slab completely fills the space between the plates and the capacitor is connected to a 9.0-V battery, what is the electric field magnitude inside the capacitor? ••

62. You are working on charge-storage devices for a research center. Your goal is to store as much charge on a given device as possible. The facilities allow you to generate almost any potential difference V you need, but you are restricted to using a single parallel-plate capacitor. The area and separation distance of the plates are fixed, and the dielectric materials available to you are paper ($\kappa = 3.0$, $E_{max} = 4.0 \times 10^7$ V/m), Mylar ($\kappa = 3.3$, $E_{max} = 4.3 \times 10^8$ V/m), quartz ($\kappa = 4.3$, $E_{max} = 8 \times 10^6$ V/m), and mica ($\kappa = 5$, $E_{max} = 2 \times 10^8$ V/m). What properties of these materials must you consider in choosing the best dielectric for your needs? Rank the materials in order of their ability to meet your needs, first choice first. ••

63. A spherical capacitor has an inner radius of 8.00 mm and an outer radius of 8.50 mm. With air between the spheres, the capacitor is connected to a battery and allowed to charge fully. With the battery still connected, oil is poured in, filling the volume between the spheres. As the oil is added, the battery does an additional 8.90 nJ of work on the capacitor. What is the potential difference supplied by the battery? •••

64. A dielectric slab completely fills the space between the plates of a parallel-plate capacitor. The magnitude of the bound

charge on each side of the slab is 75% of the magnitude of the free charge on each plate. The capacitance is $480\epsilon_0\ell$, where ℓ is a constant with dimensions of length, and the maximum charge that can be stored on the capacitor is $240\ell^2\epsilon_0 E_{max}$, where E_{max} is the breakdown threshold. What are (*a*) the dielectric constant for the slab, (*b*) the plate separation distance in terms of ℓ, and (*c*) the plate area in terms of ℓ? •••

26.8 Gauss's law in dielectrics

65. Two very long wires each carry a linear charge density λ. They initially repel each other with a force F. If the wires are immersed in distilled water, with what force do they repel each other? •
66. A solid conducting sphere of radius R and carrying charge $+q$ is embedded in an electrically neutral nonconducting spherical shell of inner radius R and outer radius $2R$. The material of which the shell is made has a dielectric constant of 3.0. (*a*) Relative to a potential of zero at infinity, what is the potential at the center of the conducting sphere? (*b*) If the dielectric constant of the shell is increased, what happens to the potential at the center of the sphere? ••
67. A solid conducting sphere of radius R is embedded in an electrically neutral nonconducting spherical shell that has inner radius R, has outer radius $2R$, and is made of a material having dielectric constant κ. Inside the shell the electric field magnitude is $E = 3Q/(4\pi\epsilon_0 r^2)$ and, relative to a potential of zero at infinity, the potential at the surface of the sphere is $+15Q/(16\pi\epsilon_0 R)$, where Q is a constant with dimensions of electrical charge. What are (*a*) the charge on the sphere and (*b*) the dielectric constant of the shell? ••
68. A conducting sphere has a radius of 2.25 m and carries a positive surplus charge of 35.0 mC. A protective layer of barium titanate is applied to the surface of the sphere to make it safe for laboratory workers nearby. Safety considerations dictate that the potential difference between the surface of the conductor and the outside of the nonconductive layer must be 20,000 V (though this is by no means safe under all conditions). How thick must the protective layer be? •••

Additional problems

69. (*a*) Explain how treating the electric field lines between two oppositely charged objects as elastic bands can help you to understand what happens to the electric potential energy of the system when you increase the separation distance between the objects. (*b*) Can you think of any limitations to this elastic-band analogy for analyzing field lines? •
70. Why would two objects made of nonconducting material make a poorer capacitor than two objects of the same shape made of material that is an electrical conductor? •
71. Two parallel-plate capacitors have the same plate separation. The plate area of capacitor 1 is twice that of capacitor 2. (*a*) How do the potential differences across the two capacitors compare if the quantity of charge you place on capacitor 1 is twice the quantity you place on capacitor 2? (*b*) How do the charge magnitudes on either plate of the two capacitors compare if the potential difference between the plates of capacitor 1 is twice that between the plates of capacitor 2? •
72. During a lightning strike, on the order of 10 C of charge is typically transferred to the ground over a potential difference of 3×10^8 V. (*a*) What is the capacitance of the cloud-ground system? (*b*) How much energy is stored in the system just before the strike? (*c*) As a check on the order of magnitude of your answer for part *b*, convert the energy released in the lightning strike into liters of gasoline (gasoline has a stored chemical energy of 36 MJ/liter). ••
73. Given that charge separation increases the electric potential energy of a system, what can you conclude about the criteria for keeping a system of positively and negatively charged particles in static equilibrium, in the presence of electrostatic interactions only? ••
74. A parallel-plate capacitor in which the plates are extendable is connected to a battery and charged until there is a charge $+q$ on one plate and a charge $-q$ on the other plate. (*a*) With the battery still connected, the area of each plate is doubled by sliding the extension out. How much charge is on each plate now? (*b*) In which case, before the plate area is expanded or after, is more force required to keep the plates apart? Use the elastic-band model described in Problem 69 to explain your answer. ••
75. A parallel-plate capacitor carries a charge $+q$ on one plate and a charge $-q$ on the other plate. The plates have an area A. How much force, in terms of q and A, does one plate exert on the other? ••
76. A 30.5-μF parallel-plate capacitor initially has air between its plates and is connected to a 24.0-V battery. The capacitor is then submerged in distilled water. What is the charge on the plates (*a*) if the capacitor is submerged with the battery connected and (*b*) if the battery is removed before submersion? ••
77. Your firm uses a large parallel-plate capacitor to store energy, and you measure the electric field strength between the plates to determine the amount of energy stored. During a test run with a new renewable energy source, you realize that the electric field magnitudes being produced are too small to be accurately detected by your equipment. The capacitor plates are fixed in place, and you cannot yet control the energy source to give you a greater potential difference. All you have to work with are four large flat slabs of metal, one $d/2$ thick, one $d/3$ thick, one $d/4$ thick, and one $d/5$ thick, where d is the fixed plate separation distance. You realize that it is necessary to increase E by at least an order of magnitude, but it takes you a while to figure out what to do. ••• CR
78. You are working for a car-battery manufacturer, and your boss complains that to be more competitive, the company needs to produce batteries that will last longer while minimizing the amount of metal or metal oxide used. She is not concerned about the amount of electrolyte used, but the battery must be powerful enough to supply a great deal of energy quickly when needed. You begin to think about what the shape of the electrodes might have to do with battery life and power, starting with what seem to be the extremes: electrodes shaped like sheets similar to parallel plates and rod-shaped electrodes that extend down into the electrolyte solution. ••• CR
79. In the endless endeavor to make electronic devices as small as possible, you have been hired to make a capacitor that has the greatest capacitance possible in a cubic volume of (10 mm) × (10 mm) × (10 mm). You are allowed to use any capacitor geometry you wish, as well as any combination of geometries. For simplicity, assume a dielectric constant of 1000 (as better materials are found, you can multiply the capacitance appropriately). You begin thinking about the minimum thickness of the conductors and dielectrics, and the scale of about 0.5 μm seems reasonable. There is the question of how to fill the volume while maintaining exactly two conducting surfaces. ••• CR

PRACTICE

Answers to Review Questions

1. Potential difference is a measure of the work per unit charge done by the electric field in moving a charged test particle (not part of the system) from one location in the system to another. The system's electric potential energy is determined by the configuration of the charged particles that make up the system.
2. The potential energy depends on the amount of charge on the objects and on their separation distance.
3. Electric potential energy is stored in the system's electric field, in any region of space where that field exists.
4. A Van de Graaff generator produces a very large separation of charge between Earth's surface ("ground") and a metal sphere attached to a nonconducting support, and hence a very large potential difference.
5. A capacitor is a pair of conducting objects separated by a nonconducting material or vacuum. Any such pair of objects stores electric potential energy when charge has been transferred from one object to the other.
6. A parallel-plate capacitor is an arrangement of two parallel conducting plates that have the same area A and are separated by a distance d. When d is small relative to the lateral dimensions of the plates, the electric field is approximately localized and uniform between the charged plates and zero outside them.
7. The magnitude of the charge on each plate is proportional to the potential difference between the plates. For a parallel-plate capacitor, this is because the potential difference equals the product of the electric field strength and the plate separation distance, and the field strength is proportional to the surface charge density on either plate.
8. The quantity of charge on a plate varies directly with plate surface area and inversely with separation distance.
9. Electrical breakdown occurs when the charge on the plates is great enough to produce an electric field sufficient to ionize the air (or other material) between the plates.
10. A dielectric is a nonconducting material. *Polar* dielectrics are made up of molecules that have a permanent dipole moment, whereas *nonpolar* dielectrics consist of molecules that do not have a dipole moment in the absence of an electric field. When either type is placed in an external electric field, the centers of positive and negative charge in the molecules are displaced, producing an induced dipole moment. Molecules in polar dielectrics can also align themselves with the external electric field.
11. In a uniform external field, no surplus charge is induced on any volume that lies entirely inside the material, but uncompensated induced charge densities appear on the surfaces.
12. Bound charge is the surplus of charge in polarized matter due to charge carriers that are bound to atoms and cannot move freely within the bulk of the material. Free charge is the surplus of charge due to charge carriers that can move freely within the bulk of a material.
13. The direction of the electric field $\vec{E}_{cap}$ due to the plates is from the positive plate to the negative plate, but the direction of the electric field $\vec{E}_{dielec}$ due to the polarized dielectric between the plates is in the opposite direction: from the positive induced surface charge near the negative plate to the negative induced surface charge near the positive plate. The vector sum of $\vec{E}_{cap}$ and $\vec{E}_{dielec}$ gives a field magnitude for the dielectric-filled capacitor that is smaller than the magnitude of the capacitor without the dielectric.
14. The field in the dielectric stores more energy than the vacuum field. Work must be done by an external electric field on the dielectric in order to separate the positive and negative charge carriers, and this work done increases the electric potential energy stored in the dielectric's electric field, so that the amount of energy stored is greater than in a field of equal magnitude that exists in a vacuum.
15. A battery is an assembly of one or more voltaic cells that separates charge carriers by converting energy released in chemical reactions into electric potential energy.
16. Emf is the work done per unit charge by nonelectrostatic interactions in a charge-separating device (such as a battery) in order to separate positive and negative charge carriers in the device.
17. The capacitance is the ratio of the magnitude of the charge on either conductor that forms the capacitor and the magnitude of the potential difference between the conductors.
18. In the absence of a dielectric, capacitance depends on only the size and geometric properties of a capacitor—that is, on the shape of the conductors making up the capacitor and on the separation of the conductors. The capacitance also depends on the properties of the dielectric material inserted between the conductors.
19. The unit of capacitance is the farad, which is 1 C/V. Because 1 C is an enormous quantity of charge relative to the quantity of charge on conductors in electronic devices, capacitances in the range of microfarads to picofarads are more commonly used.
20. The electric potential energy is proportional to the square of the charge on each conductor: $U^E = q^2/2C$ (Eq. 26.4).
21. The electric potential energy is proportional to the square of the potential difference: $U^E = CV_{cap}^2/2$ (Eq. 26.4).
22. Energy density is the electric potential energy stored in an electric field per unit volume of the field: $u_E = U^E/\text{field volume}$. The energy density for a given field is proportional to the field magnitude squared, as given (for air or vacuum) by Eq. 26.6: $u_E = \frac{1}{2}\epsilon_0 E^2$.
23. In an ideal charge-separating device, none of the energy associated with the work done by nonelectrostatic interactions is dissipated, and the potential difference between the terminals is equal to the emf. In a nonideal device, some energy is dissipated inside the device and thus not available to be turned into electrostatic work; now the potential difference between the device's terminals is smaller than the emf. (See the discussion in the *Principles* paragraphs that surround Equation 26.8.)
24. The dielectric constant for the material is the potential difference between a capacitor's conductors without any of the dielectric material between the conductors divided by the potential difference between the conductors with the dielectric material completely filling the space between them.
25. The constant for water is greater because water molecules are polar and can align themselves with the electric field, whereas the molecules in paper and mica are nonpolar. The induced polarization in liquid water is therefore much greater than that in paper or mica.
26. The sign of the bound charge on the dielectric surface is opposite the sign of the free charge on the plate, and the quantity of bound charge is smaller than the quantity of free charge. The relationship is given by Eq. 26.18: $q_{bound} = (\kappa - 1)(q_{free})/\kappa$.
27. The stored energy must decrease because as the dielectric comes near the capacitor, the capacitor does positive work on it, pulling it into the space between the conductors.
28. We use Gauss's law for determining the electric field inside a dielectric by substituting $q_{free}[(\kappa - 1)/\kappa]$ (Eq. 26.18) for q_{bound}. This substitution gives us an expression that does not contain q_{bound}. The result is that Gauss's law may be applied using only the free charge enclosed by the Gaussian surface and the electric field inside the dielectric material, Eq. 26.25.

29. Gauss's law in a dielectric material is $\oint \kappa \vec{E} \cdot d\vec{A} = q_{\text{free, enc}}/\epsilon_0$ (Eq. 26.25), where κ is the dielectric constant for the dielectric material and $q_{\text{free, enc}}$ is that portion of the free charge that is enclosed by the chosen Gaussian surface. When no dielectric is present, $\kappa = 1$ and this expression reduces to the Chapter 24 form of Gauss's law, $\oint \vec{E} \cdot d\vec{A} = q_{\text{enc}}/\epsilon_0$ (Eq. 24.8).

Answers to Guided Problems

Guided Problem 26.2 $C = \dfrac{\epsilon_0 \kappa \ell w}{d} = 0.3\ \mu\text{F}$.

Guided Problem 26.4 (*a*) $C = \dfrac{2P\Delta t}{V_i^2 - V_f^2} = 13\ \text{F}$;

(*b*) $A = \dfrac{Cd}{\epsilon_0 \kappa} = 2.2 \times 10^7\ \text{m}^2 = (4.7\ \text{km})^2$.

Guided Problem 26.6 $C = \dfrac{\epsilon_0 A}{d} = \dfrac{2\pi\epsilon_0 R_{\text{shell}}}{d}(L + R_{\text{shell}})$.

Guided Problem 26.8 $V_{\text{max}} = E_{\text{max}} d = 30\ \text{kV}$; $Q_{\text{max}} = CV_{\text{max}} = 30\ \mu\text{C}$.

PRACTICE

27

PRACTICE

Magnetic Interactions

Chapter Summary

Magnetic field (Sections 27.1, 27.2)

Concepts Every **magnet** has two *magnetic poles.* The pole attracted to Earth's North Pole is called a *north pole;* the magnet's opposite pole is called a *south pole.*

Like magnetic poles repel each other, and opposite magnetic poles attract each other. Earth's North Pole is a magnetic south pole because it attracts the north pole of a compass needle.

Magnetic materials are attracted to both types of magnetic poles. The presence of a magnet induces **magnetic polarization** in magnetic materials.

A magnet is surrounded by a **magnetic field.** This field exerts a force on the poles of other magnets and is represented by **magnetic field lines.** At any position, the direction of the magnetic field is tangent to the magnetic field line passing through that position. Magnetic field lines form loops that exit a magnet at its north pole and reenter the magnet at its south pole. Near (but outside of) a magnet, magnetic field lines point away from north poles and toward south poles. At any location, the magnitude of the magnetic field is proportional to the field line density at that location.

Currents and magnetic fields (Sections 27.3, 27.5)

Concepts A flow of charged particles, called a **current,** causes a magnetic field.

The *direction of current* through a conductor is the direction in which positive charge carriers would flow, which is from high potential to low potential.

Right-hand current rule: If you point the thumb of your right hand in the direction of the current, the fingers curl in the direction of the magnetic field produced by that current.

Right-hand rule for vector product $I\vec{\ell} \times \vec{B}$

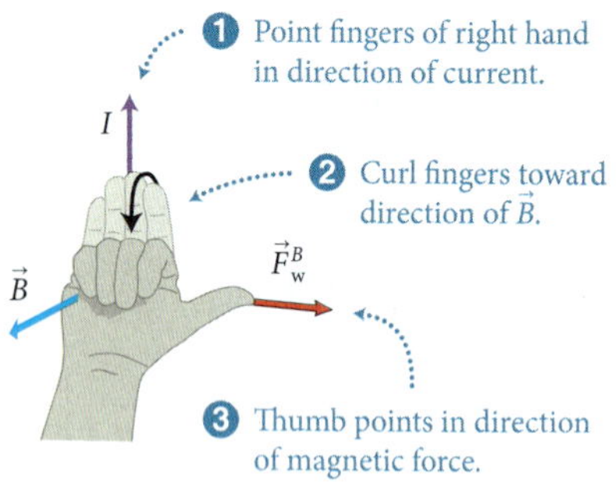

Quantitative Tools If a particle carrying charge dq passes a given section of a conductor in a time interval dt, the current I through that section is

$$I \equiv \frac{dq}{dt}. \tag{27.2}$$

We measure current in **amperes** (A), where

$$1\ \mathrm{C} \equiv 1\ \mathrm{A \cdot s}. \tag{27.3}$$

If a straight wire of length ℓ carrying a current I perpendicular to a uniform magnetic field $\vec{B}$ experiences a force $\vec{F}^B_{\mathrm{w,\,max}}$, the magnitude of the magnetic field is

$$B \equiv \frac{F^B_{\mathrm{w,max}}}{|I|\ell}. \tag{27.5}$$

The SI unit of the magnetic field is the **tesla** (T), where

$$1\ \mathrm{T} \equiv 1\ \mathrm{N/(A \cdot m)} = 1\ \mathrm{kg/(s^2 \cdot A)}. \tag{27.6}$$

The **magnetic force** $\vec{F}^B_{\mathrm{w}}$ exerted on a straight wire in a uniform magnetic field is

$$\vec{F}^B_{\mathrm{w}} = I\vec{\ell} \times \vec{B}, \tag{27.8}$$

where the direction of $\vec{\ell}$ is the direction of the current through the wire. The direction of $\vec{F}^B_{\mathrm{w}}$ is obtained by curling the fingers of the right hand from the direction of the current to $\vec{B}$.

Table 27.1 Right-hand rules in magnetism

	Thumb points in direction of	Fingers curl
Current rule	Current	Along magnetic field
Force rule	Magnetic force	From current to magnetic field

It is sometimes helpful to write out Eq. 27.8 component by component:

$$F^B_{\text{w}x} = I\ell_y B_z - I\ell_z B_y$$
$$F^B_{\text{w}y} = I\ell_z B_x - I\ell_x B_z$$
$$F^B_{\text{w}z} = I\ell_x B_y - I\ell_y B_x.$$

Magnetic flux (Section 27.6)

Concepts The **magnetic flux** through a surface is a measure of the number of magnetic field lines crossing the surface. The magnetic flux through any closed surface is zero because magnetic field lines always form closed loops.

Quantitative Tools The **magnetic flux** Φ_B through a surface is

$$\Phi_B \equiv \int \vec{B} \cdot d\vec{A}, \tag{27.10}$$

where the integral is taken over the surface.

Magnetic flux is measured in **webers** (Wb), where

$$1\ \text{Wb} \equiv 1\ \text{T} \cdot \text{m}^2 = 1\ \text{m}^2 \cdot \text{kg}/(\text{s}^2 \cdot \text{A}).$$

For any closed surface, **Gauss's law for magnetism** is

$$\Phi_B = \oint \vec{B} \cdot d\vec{A} = 0. \tag{27.11}$$

Forces exerted on moving particles (Section 27.7)

Quantitative Tools If a charged particle of charge q moves with velocity $\vec{v}$ in the presence of an electric field and a magnetic field, the **electromagnetic force** $\vec{F}^{EB}_{\text{p}}$ exerted on the particle by the fields is

$$\vec{F}^{EB}_{\text{p}} = q(\vec{E} + \vec{v} \times \vec{B}). \tag{27.20}$$

It is sometimes helpful to write out Eq. 27.20 component by component:

$$F^{EB}_{\text{p}x} = q(E_x + v_y B_z - v_z B_y) \quad F^{EB}_{\text{p}y} = q(E_y + v_z B_x - v_x B_z) \quad F^{EB}_{\text{p}z} = q(E_z + v_x B_y - v_y B_x).$$

A charged particle of charge q and mass m moving at speed v perpendicular to a uniform magnetic field $\vec{B}$ follows a circular path of radius R given by

$$R = \frac{mv}{|q|B}. \tag{27.23}$$

The time interval T for one revolution is

$$T = \frac{2\pi m}{|q|B}, \tag{27.24}$$

and the angular frequency ω is

$$\omega = \frac{|q|B}{m}. \tag{27.25}$$

Magnetism and electricity unified (Sections 27.4, 27.8)

Concepts The interaction observed between charge carriers depends on their motion relative to the observer: The interaction can be purely electric, purely magnetic, or a combination of the two. Magnetic and electric interactions are two aspects of one *electromagnetic* interaction, with magnetism being a relativistic correction to the electric interaction.

Review Questions

Answers to these questions can be found at the end of this chapter.

27.1 Magnetism

1. What is a magnet? What is a magnetic material?
2. What are magnetic poles? How are the two types of magnetic poles defined?
3. How do magnetic poles interact with each other?
4. What is an elementary magnet? How does a model based on elementary magnets explain magnetization?

27.2 Magnetic fields

5. How is the concept of a magnetic field used to describe the action of a magnet?
6. What information about a magnetic field is conveyed by its magnetic field line pattern?
7. How does the magnetic field line flux through a closed surface depend on the number and strength of the elementary magnets enclosed by the surface?

27.3 Charge flow and magnetism

8. This section describes another source of magnetic fields besides a magnet. What is this source, and how is it defined?
9. Describe the magnetic field produced near a straight current-carrying wire.
10. In what direction would electrons need to flow in order to produce the same magnetic field as an equal flow of positive ions moving from left to right?
11. When electrons flow upward through a wire, how do we describe the direction of the corresponding current?
12. If you are looking at the face of a clock and see a current toward you from the center of the clock, do the magnetic field lines encircle the current in a clockwise or counterclockwise sense?
13. When a current-carrying wire is aligned perpendicular to a bar magnet, what is the relationship between the direction of the magnetic force exerted by the magnet on the wire and the direction of the magnetic field due to the magnet (call this the *external* magnetic field to distinguish it from the magnetic field due to the current in the wire)? What is the relationship between the direction of the magnetic force exerted by the magnet on the wire and the current direction?

27.4 Magnetism and relativity

14. Why should we expect any observed magnetic interaction to depend on the reference frame of the observer?
15. If the magnetic force exerted by a current-carrying wire is merely a relativistic correction to the internal electric forces in the wire, why is the magnetic force exerted by the wire so readily observable?
16. To an observer at rest relative to a current-carrying wire, how does the linear charge density of the fixed ions in the wire compare with the linear charge density of the moving electrons? How do these charge densities compare according to an observer moving along with the electrons?

27.5 Current and magnetism

17. For a current-carrying wire placed in an external magnetic field, for what orientation is the magnitude of the magnetic force exerted by the external field on the wire a maximum? For what orientation is it a minimum?
18. On what factors does the magnitude of the magnetic force exerted by an external magnetic field on a current-carrying wire depend?
19. A current through a wire is in the positive x direction in the presence of an external magnetic field that points in the positive y direction. In what direction does the magnetic force on the wire point?

27.6 Magnetic flux

20. For a flat surface located in a uniform magnetic field, how is the magnetic flux through the surface defined?
21. What is Gauss's law for magnetism, and what does it imply about magnetic sources?
22. How does the magnetic flux through one surface bounded by a loop compare with the magnetic flux through a different surface bounded by the same loop?

27.7 Moving particles in electric and magnetic fields

23. The magnetic force exerted by an external magnetic field on a current-carrying wire is a combination of what?
24. If a charged particle is moving in a magnetic field, what is the direction of the magnetic force exerted by the field on the particle?

27.8 Magnetism and electricity unified

25. Why does an observer moving along with electrons in a current-carrying wire measure the linear charge density of the fixed positive ions in the wire as being greater than the linear charge density of the electrons?
26. In the Earth reference frame, a positively charged particle moves parallel to a current-carrying wire. What is the difference between how an observer moving along with electrons in the wire interprets the force exerted by the wire on the particle and how an observer in the Earth reference frame interprets that force?

PRACTICE

Developing a Feel

Make an order-of-magnitude estimate of each of the following quantities. Letters in parentheses refer to hints below. Use them as needed to guide your thinking.

1. The current needed in a long straight wire to produce, 1 m away from the wire, a magnetic field magnitude equal to the magnitude of the magnetic field due to Earth (C, Q)
2. The magnitude of the flux of Earth's magnetic field through the top of your desk (C, K, F)
3. The magnitude and direction of the magnetic force exerted by Earth on an electron moving west along Earth's equator at 10^5 m/s (C, L, G)
4. The magnitude of the magnetic field contributed by a single elementary magnet in a small iron bar magnet (A, I, M, U)
5. The magnitude of a uniform magnetic field required to keep a proton moving in the field at 10^6 m/s in a circular orbit having the same radius as a basketball (L, P, T)
6. The magnitude of a uniform magnetic field needed to keep an electron moving in the field in a circular orbit if the electron is to complete 1 revolution each microsecond (D, H, L)
7. The minimum current needed to "float" a piece of 18-gauge copper wire in a horizontal magnetic field of magnitude 0.5 T (V, R, N, J, B)
8. The maximum acceleration of a copper rod that is 100 mm long has a radius of 5 mm and carries a current of 100 A in a uniform magnetic field of magnitude 1 T (O, J, S, E)

Hints

A. What is the magnitude of the magnetic field due to a small bar magnet?
B. What is the mass of a length ℓ of this wire?
C. What is the magnitude of the magnetic field near Earth's surface?
D. What is the mass of an electron?
E. What maximum magnetic force is available?
F. What is the area of an average desktop?
G. In what direction does Earth's magnetic field point along the equator?
H. How is the period related to the magnetic field strength?
I. What is the volume of a small bar magnet?
J. What is the mass density of copper?
K. What is the angle between the direction of Earth's magnetic field and the horizontal?
L. What is the magnitude of the charge carried by this particle?
M. What is the mass density of iron?
N. What is the volume of a length ℓ of this wire?
O. What is the volume of the rod?
P. What is the radius of a basketball?
Q. How are magnetic field magnitude B and current I related for a long straight wire?
R. What is the diameter of 18-gauge wire?
S. What is the mass of the rod?
T. What is the mass of a proton?
U. What is the mass of an iron atom?
V. What forces must balance to float the wire?

Key (all values approximate)

A. 0.01 T, from *Principles* Table 27.1; **B.** $(7 \times 10^{-3}\ \text{kg/m})\ell$; **C.** 5×10^{-5} T; **D.** 9×10^{-31} kg; **E.** $I\ell B \sim 10$ N; **F.** 2 m^2; **G.** horizontal and north; **H.** $T = 2\pi m/qB$; **I.** 1×10^{-5} m^3; **J.** 9×10^3 kg/m^3; **K.** this varies in the continental United States from 50° to 75°, so say 60°; **L.** elementary charge, $e = 1.6 \times 10^{-19}$ C; **M.** 8×10^3 kg/m^3; **N.** $\pi r^2 \ell \approx (8 \times 10^{-7}\ \text{m}^2)\ell$; **O.** 8×10^{-6} m^3; **P.** 0.1 m; **Q.** $B = 2kI/c_0^2$; **R.** 1×10^{-3} m; **S.** 0.07 kg; **T.** 1.7×10^{-27} kg; **U.** 9×10^{-26} kg; **V.** gravitational and magnetic.

Worked and Guided Problems

These examples involve material from this chapter but are not associated with any particular section. Some examples are worked out in detail; others you should work out by following the guidelines provided.

Worked Problem 27.1. Rail gun

A *rail gun* is a device used to accelerate projectiles without the use of explosives. Figure WG27.1 shows an overhead view of one such gun. A crossbar slides on two identical rails that are 100 mm apart. Charge carriers flow along one rail, into the crossbar, and then along the other rail. A uniform external magnetic field pointing up out of the page accelerates the crossbar. (*a*) In which direction is the crossbar accelerated? (*b*) What is the coefficient of kinetic friction μ_k between rails and crossbar if the current is 10 A, the magnetic field magnitude is 0.12 T, and the crossbar has a mass of 2.0 kg and moves at constant speed once it has been accelerated?

Figure WG27.1

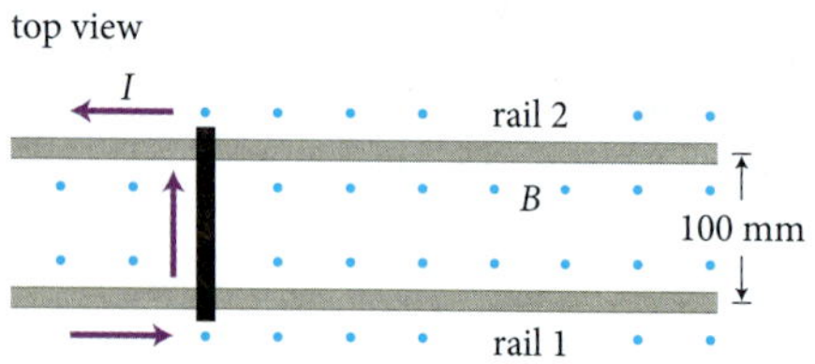

❶ **GETTING STARTED** A current-carrying wire—or, in this case, a current-carrying crossbar—is subject to a force exerted by the external magnetic field. The force due to this field accelerates the crossbar, and our first task is to determine whether this acceleration is to the left or to the right in Figure WG27.1. (We know the acceleration cannot be up out of the page or down into the page because the magnetic force must be perpendicular to the magnetic field, which points out of the page.) Because the crossbar slides on the rails, we know it must experience a frictional force that opposes the magnetic force. We're given the magnitude and direction of the uniform magnetic field, the separation distance for the rails, values for the current and the crossbar mass, and the fact that the final crossbar speed is constant. We use this information for our second task: calculating the coefficient of kinetic friction.

❷ **DEVISE PLAN** For part *a*, the direction of the magnetic force $\vec{F}^B_c$ exerted by the external field on the crossbar determines in which direction the crossbar is accelerated. We can determine the direction of this force from the right-hand force rule, $\vec{F}^B = I\vec{\ell} \times \vec{B}$. For part *b*, as for all problems involving forces, we begin with a free-body diagram, this one for the crossbar viewed from the side, end-on (Figure WG27.2).

Figure WG27.2

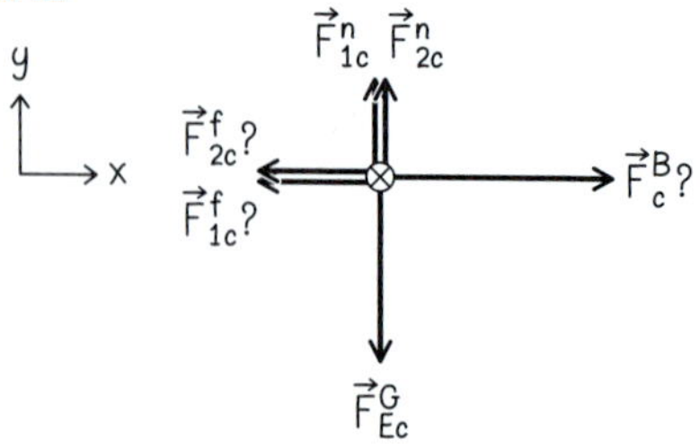

We don't yet know the direction of the magnetic force $\vec{F}^B_c$ exerted on the crossbar, and so we arbitrarily draw that force arrow to the right and add a question mark to remind us that its direction may have to be changed. Because the direction of the frictional forces opposes the magnetic force, we show $\vec{F}^f_{1c}$ and $\vec{F}^f_{2c}$ to the left, but also add question marks. We also show the downward gravitational force and two upward normal forces, one exerted by each rail.

We can use Eq. 27.8, $\vec{F}^B_c = I\vec{\ell} \times \vec{B}$, in its scalar form, $F^B_c = |I|\ell B \sin\theta$ (Eq. 27.7), to get the magnetic force in terms of our given numerical values. Each frictional force exerted by a rail on the crossbar is related to the upward normal force exerted by each rail on the crossbar by Eq. 10.55: $F^f_{2c} = \mu_k F^n_{2c}$ and $F^f_{1c} = \mu_k F^n_{1c}$, where μ_k is the coefficient of kinetic friction.

❸ **EXECUTE PLAN** (*a*) Applying the right-hand force rule, we position our right hand above the crossbar in Figure WG27.1, with fingers pointing up in the direction of the current and the palm toward us so that the fingers can curl toward our face, in the direction of the external magnetic field. The thumb points to the right, telling us this is the direction of $\vec{F}^B_c$. We guessed correctly! ✔

The magnetic force accelerates the crossbar to the right. The two frictional forces $\vec{F}^f_{2c}$ and $\vec{F}^f_{1c}$ therefore must be leftward. Because these frictional forces and the magnetic force oppose each other, they can cancel and allow the crossbar to move at constant velocity.

(*b*) Let us work with the *x* and *y* components of the forces, using the coordinate axes shown in Figure WG27.2. In the *x* direction, $a_x = 0$, so the vector sum of the forces exerted on the crossbar becomes

$$\Sigma F_x = ma_x$$

$$F^B_c - (F^f_{2c} + F^f_{1c}) = 0. \quad (1)$$

Because the rails are identical and the crossbar is placed symmetrically, $F^f_{2c} = F^f_{1c}$ and $F^n_{2c} = F^n_{1c}$, which means we can simplify our notation to F^f_{rc} for the frictional force exerted by *each* rail on the crossbar and F^n_{rc} for the normal force exerted by *each* rail on the crossbar. When we make these changes in notation and substitute $I\ell B\sin\theta$ for F^B_c, Eq. 1 becomes

$$I\ell B\sin\theta - 2F^f_{rc} = I\ell B\sin\theta - 2\mu_k F^n_{rc} = 0.$$

Because the magnetic field and the current through the crossbar run at right angles to each other, $\theta = 90°$, $\sin 90° = 1$, and we have

$$I\ell B - 2\mu_k F^n_{rc} = 0. \quad (2)$$

In the *y* direction, we have for the identical rails $F^n_{2c} = F^n_{1c} = F^n_{rc}$. Newton's second law in this direction gives us

$$\Sigma F_y = ma_y = 0$$

$$2F^n_{rc} - F^G_{Ec} = 0$$

$$F^n_{rc} = mg/2. \quad (3)$$

Combining Eqs. 2 and 3 and rearranging, we obtain

$$\mu_k = \frac{I\ell B}{mg} = \frac{(10\text{ A})(0.100\text{ m})(0.12\text{ T})}{(2.0\text{ kg})(9.8\text{ m/s}^2)} = 6.1 \times 10^{-3}. ✔$$

❹ **EVALUATE RESULT** That the crossbar is accelerated to the right makes sense because the magnetic force on the crossbar points to the right, as we found by applying the right-hand force rule to Figure WG27.1. Our μ_k value seems like a very small coefficient of friction, but that's exactly what you want in a rail gun because its purpose is to move objects. The idea is that at currents much greater than the 10 A we have here (1000 A, say), you can accelerate the crossbar to very high speeds.

Guided Problem 27.2 Magnetic scale

Figure WG27.3 shows a sensitive device for measuring an object's mass. The object hangs by a string from a horizontal rod through which an electric current is directed from left to right. The rod is free to slide up and down a pair of vertical columns with negligible friction, but the rod's orientation remains fixed. The entire unit is placed in an external magnetic field, and the current in the circuit is adjusted until the rod and object are motionless. Once this equilibrium has been attained, the object's mass is calculated from the magnitude of the magnetic force required to balance the gravitational force on the object.

In which direction must the external magnetic field point—into or out of the page in Figure WG27.3—in order for the scale to work? What current is required to balance the rod if the combined mass of the object and the rod is 0.157 kg and the magnetic field has magnitude 0.150 T?

Figure WG27.3

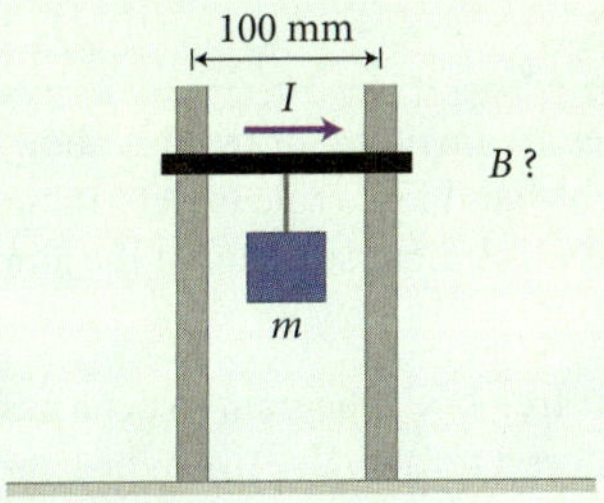

❶ **GETTING STARTED**

1. Describe the problem in your own words. What information are you given, and what quantities must you determine using the given information?
2. Draw a free-body diagram—but of the rod, the object, or something else?
3. Which concepts and principles concerning magnetism apply here?

❷ **DEVISE PLAN**

4. What is your plan for determining the magnetic field direction?
5. For a given current value, which equations allow you to express the unknown current in terms of known quantities?
6. What is the angle between the electric current in the rod and the magnetic field?

❸ **EXECUTE PLAN**

7. Determine the field direction.
8. Work through the algebra and solve for the desired unknown quantity; then substitute known values to get a numerical answer.

❹ **EVALUATE RESULT**

9. Does your direction for the magnetic field make sense?
10. Is your value for the current large or small? Compare it to maximum household current by noting the capacity of the circuit breakers or fuses in your home.

Worked Problem 27.3 Torque on a Wire

A straight current-carrying wire is oriented at an angle of 37.00° to a uniform external magnetic field of magnitude 0.0110 T (Figure WG27.4). The current in the wire is 10.0 A, and the portion within the field has length $\ell = 790$ mm. (*a*) What is the direction of the magnetic force exerted by the external field on the wire? (*b*) If the bottom end of the wire is fixed but the rest of the wire is free to move, what is the torque about the fixed end of the wire? In which direction does the torque cause the wire to rotate?

Figure WG27.4

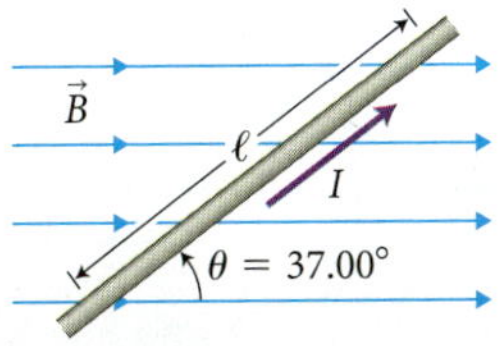

❶ **GETTING STARTED** We must determine three things about a current-carrying wire placed in an external magnetic field: the direction of the force exerted by the magnetic field on the wire, the torque this force causes about one end of the wire, and the direction in which the wire tends to rotate because of this torque. For part *a*, we can determine the magnetic force direction from the right-hand force rule. For part *b*, we can use the principles we learned in Chapter 12 to determine the magnitude and direction of the torque due to the magnetic force on the wire.

❷ **DEVISE PLAN** The force $\vec{F}^B_w$ exerted by the external field on the wire is given by Eqs. 27.8 and 27.7:

$$\vec{F}^B_w = I\vec{\ell} \times \vec{B} \quad \text{or} \quad F^B_w = I\ell B \sin\theta. \tag{1}$$

Each small wire segment of length $d\ell$ experiences the same magnitude and direction of force $d\vec{F} = Id\vec{\ell} \times \vec{B}$, so the force computed in Eq. 1 is uniformly exerted along the length of the wire. Thus, when calculating the torque, we can place the point of application of the force at the wire's midpoint—just as we take the point of application of the force of gravity to be at an object's center of mass. The torque is given by Eq. 12.1, $\tau = rF\sin\theta$, where θ is the angle between the vector $\vec{r}$ (that locates the point of application of the force relative to the rotation axis) and the line of action of the force.

❸ **EXECUTE PLAN** (*a*) Applying the right-hand force rule, we align our right hand along the current direction in Figure WG27.4 in such a way that we can curl the fingers toward the field lines representing $\vec{B}$. When we do this, our thumb points into the page, which is the direction of $\vec{F}^B_{\text{w}}$. ✔

(*b*) In working with the torque in this problem, we have to be careful about notation because θ in Eq. 1 is not the same as θ in Eq. 12.1 for the torque. To keep things straight, we keep θ as the angle between the magnetic field direction and the current direction, and we change Eq. 12.1 to $\tau = rF\sin\phi$, so that ϕ is the angle between $\vec{F}^B_{\text{w}}$ (into the page) and the vector $\vec{r}$ pointing from the rotation axis (the wire's fixed end) to the point of application of $\vec{F}^B_{\text{w}}$ (Figure WG27.5). Using these angle symbols, Eq. 12.1 gives us

$$\begin{aligned}\tau &= rF\sin\phi = r(I\ell B\sin\theta)\sin\phi \\ &= \frac{\ell}{2}(I\ell B\sin\theta)(\sin 90°) = \tfrac{1}{2}I\ell^2 B\sin\theta \\ &= \tfrac{1}{2}(10.0\ \text{A})(0.790\ \text{m})^2(0.0110\ \text{T})(\sin 37.00°) \\ &= 0.0207\ \text{N}\cdot\text{m}. ✔\end{aligned}$$

Figure WG27.5

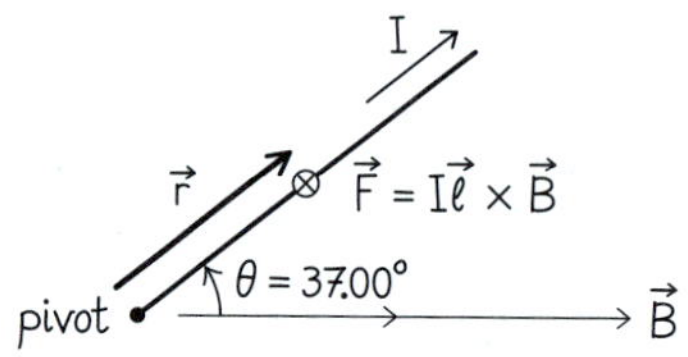

Because $\vec{F}^B_{\text{w}}$ is into the page and the wire initially lies in the plane of the page, the free end of wire tends to rotate into the page. ✔

❹ **EVALUATE RESULT** Our expression above for the torque is proportional to B. This makes sense, given that a greater magnetic field results in a proportionally greater force, and thus a proportionally greater torque. The torque is zero when θ is 0 or 180°, which makes sense because there is no magnetic force on a wire that runs parallel to the magnetic field: The magnetic force (and thus the torque) is greatest when the wire is perpendicular to the field. It also makes sense that the torque is proportional to ℓ^2: one factor of ℓ for the magnetic force ($\vec{F}^B = I\vec{\ell} \times \vec{B}$) and a factor of $\ell/2$ for the lever arm in the definition of torque. We also note that newton-meters are the correct units for torque.

Guided Problem 27.4 Torque on a Current Loop

A square loop of wire carrying a 1.7-A current is oriented so that the plane of the loop is parallel to a uniform external magnetic field as shown in Figure WG27.6. Each straight segment of the loop is 10 mm long, and the magnetic field magnitude is 0.23 T. Name all of the forces exerted on the loop. Compute the vector sum of these forces. Does the loop experience a torque? If it does, determine the direction of rotation and the torque magnitude. If the loop does not experience a torque, explain why not.

❶ **GETTING STARTED**

1. State the problem in your own words. How do the magnetic field and current affect the loop?

Figure WG27.6

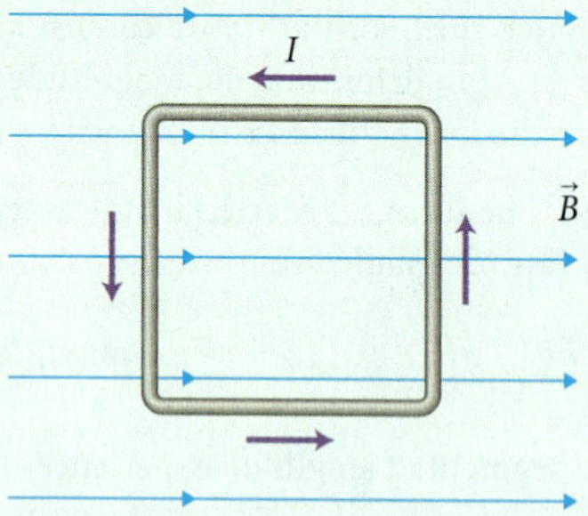

2. Because forces are involved, draw a free-body diagram. Apply the right-hand force rule to determine the direction of the force on each straight segment of the loop.

❷ **DEVISE PLAN**

3. Examine your free-body diagram to determine whether the loop experiences a torque. Use the right-hand rule for torque direction either to determine the torque direction or to conclude that there is no torque.
4. Decide which algebraic expression you can use to calculate the vector sum of the forces and, if appropriate, the torque magnitude.

❸ **EXECUTE PLAN**

5. Substitute numbers to get numerical answers.

❹ **EVALUATE RESULT**

6. Are your force and torque magnitudes reasonable? How do your calculated values compare with the values that you expected?
7. Is the torque direction what you expect?

Worked Problem 27.5. Bad picture?

Televisions manufactured during the 20th century work by shooting electrons at a screen to create the image that you see. The key component of these televisions is a *cathode ray tube* (CRT) that sprays a stream of electrons onto the screen (Figure WG27.7). The electrons are emitted from an *electron gun* located at the back of the CRT and then steered to various parts of the screen by means

PRACTICE

of variable magnetic fields. But any other magnetic field could also deflect these electrons. (*a*) Estimate the maximum deflection, due to Earth's magnetic field, of an electron aimed at the center of the screen 300 mm away from the electron gun emitting electrons that travel at 3.0×10^7 m/s. Assume that Earth's magnetic field is directed northward, is oriented at an angle of 45° below the horizontal, and has a magnitude of 3.0×10^{-5} T. (*b*) How much, and in which direction, is the image on the screen shifted by Earth's magnetic field when the screen faces east? (*c*) What if the screen faces north?

Figure WG27.7

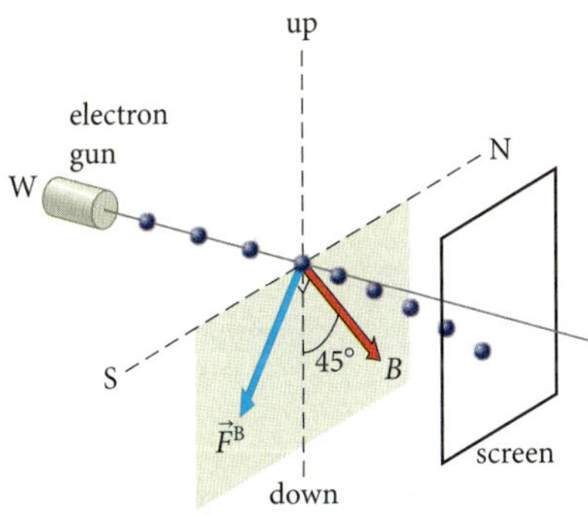

❶ **GETTING STARTED** We are told that the electron beam in a television CRT might be deflected by Earth's magnetic field, and we are asked to determine the greatest possible deflection as each electron travels 300 mm through the field. We must then determine the magnitude and direction of this deflection for two possible orientations of the CRT.

❷ **DEVISE PLAN** The force exerted by a magnetic field on a charged particle—an electron in this case—moving through the field is given by Eq. 27.19, $\vec{F}^B = q\vec{v} \times \vec{B}$. This force is always perpendicular to the direction in which the particle moves, so as each electron is deflected, the direction of the magnetic force exerted on it changes. To simplify the problem, we will assume that the electron isn't deflected very much. We can then make the approximation that the force direction is constant and points perpendicular to the electron's initial direction. Then we can use Newton's second law and kinematics with constant acceleration to determine the electron's deflection, as we would do for projectile motion under constant gravitational acceleration. (We will check at the end whether the small-deflection approximation is justified.) First, however, we need to determine the orientation of the television that gives maximum deflection.

We assume that we can ignore the effect of gravity. Because the spatial directions in this problem are somewhat complicated, we will first write out $\vec{F}^B = q\vec{v} \times \vec{B}$ in vector components, then use the right-hand force rule as a check of our results.

❸ **EXECUTE PLAN** (*a*) We will define Cartesian coordinates such that $\hat{\imath}$ points east, $\hat{\jmath}$ points north, and $\hat{k}$ points up. We can check with the right-hand rule for vector products that $\hat{\imath} \times \hat{\jmath} = \hat{k}$, as the math requires. Then we can write Earth's magnetic field as $\vec{B} = (\hat{\jmath}\cos 45° - \hat{k}\sin 45°)B_0$, which points north and 45° below the horizontal plane, with magnitude $B_0 = 3.0 \times 10^{-5}$ T. The electron beam travels in the same direction as the television screen faces. Defining θ_C to be the compass direction (0° for north, 90° for east) in which the electrons travel, we can write the electron velocity as $\vec{v} = (\hat{\jmath}\cos\theta_C + \hat{\imath}\sin\theta_C)v_0$, with magnitude $v_0 = 3.0 \times 10^7$ m/s. Now we write out the components of $\vec{F}^B = q\vec{v} \times \vec{B}$:

$$F_x^B = q(v_yB_z - v_zB_y) = (-ev_0B_0)(-\cos\theta_C \sin 45°)$$

$$F_y^B = q(v_zB_x - v_xB_z) = (-ev_0B_0)(\sin\theta_C \sin 45°)$$

$$F_z^B = q(v_xB_y - v_yB_x) = (-ev_0B_0)(\sin\theta_C \cos 45°)$$

$$F^B = \left(\frac{ev_0B_0}{\sqrt{2}}\right)\sqrt{1 + \sin^2\theta_C},$$

where, in writing the magnitude F^B, we used $\cos 45° = \sin 45° = 1/\sqrt{2}$. We can see from the expression for F^B that the electrons experience a nonzero magnetic force, whichever compass direction the CRT screen faces, but that the magnitude varies with the compass direction.

To calculate how far each electron is deflected, we first compute the time interval $\Delta t = \ell/v_0$ required for the electron to travel, at speed v_0, the length $\ell = 300$ mm from the electron gun to the screen. Then we compute the deflection d due to the magnetic force $\vec{F}^B$, where we are approximating $\vec{F}^B$ to be constant and perpendicular to the length of the CRT. From Newton's second law, the electron's acceleration is $\vec{a} = \vec{F}^B/m_e$, where $m_e = 9.11 \times 10^{-31}$ kg is the electron's mass. For constant $\vec{F}^B$, the acceleration is constant and is perpendicular to the initial velocity, so we can write the deflection d due to $\vec{F}^B$ as

$$d = \tfrac{1}{2}a\Delta t^2 = \tfrac{1}{2}\left(\frac{F^B}{m_e}\right)\Delta t^2 = \tfrac{1}{2}\left(\frac{F^B}{m_e}\right)\left(\frac{\ell}{v_0}\right)^2 = \frac{F^B\ell^2}{2m_ev_0^2}$$

$$d = \frac{ev_0B_0\ell^2}{2\sqrt{2}m_ev_0^2}\sqrt{1 + \sin^2\theta_C} = \frac{eB_0\ell^2}{2\sqrt{2}m_ev_0}\sqrt{1 + \sin^2\theta_C}.$$

The maximum deflection occurs for $\sin\theta_C = \pm 1$, which occurs when $\theta_C = 90°$ (screen faces east) or $\theta_C = 270°$ (screen faces west). Substituting $\sin\theta_C = \pm 1$ and then canceling the $\sqrt{2}$ in numerator and denominator, we obtain the maximum deflection:

$$d_{max} = \frac{eB_0\ell^2}{2m_ev_0} = \frac{(1.6 \times 10^{-19}\text{ C})(3.0 \times 10^{-5}\text{ T})(0.300\text{ m})^2}{(2)(9.11 \times 10^{-31}\text{ kg})(3.0 \times 10^7\text{ m/s})}$$

$$= 7.9\text{ mm.} ✔$$

(*b*) If the screen faces east, then $\theta_C = 90°$, so $\sin\theta_C = 1$, $\cos\theta_C = 0$, and the magnitude of the deflection is 7.9 mm. The deflection is in the direction of $\vec{F}^B$, which has components $F_x^B = 0$, $F_y^B < 0$, and $F_z^B = F_y^B$. So the deflection points diagonally downward, 45° below south. From the perspective of the viewer, who is facing west, the image is shifted diagonally down and to the left, with a magnitude of 7.9 mm. ✔

(*c*) If the screen faces north, then $\theta_C = 0$, so $\sin\theta_C = 0$, $\cos\theta_C = 1$, and the magnitude of the deflection is 5.6 mm. Now $\vec{F}^B$ has components $F_x^B > 0$, $F_y^B = 0$, and $F_z^B = 0$. So the deflection points due east. From the perspective of the viewer, who is facing south, the image is shifted 5.6 mm to the left. ✔

❹ **EVALUATE RESULT** That seems like a pretty big deflection, one big enough to notice by turning the television to different positions. In fact, turning the screen right or left, you can actually see the picture shift by a few mm. We can check our approximation that the direction of $\vec{F}^B$ is constant by evaluating the maximum angle $\alpha = \tan^{-1}(at/v_0) = 3.0°$ (for $\sin\theta_C = \pm 1$) between the electron's initial and final velocities: 3° is a pretty small angle, justifying the approximation. You should calculate the effect of gravity on the electron to check our assumption that it was all right to ignore the gravitational force.

We can use the right-hand force rule to check the directions of the deflections in parts *b* and *c*. For the east-facing screen, the electric current is traveling west and the viewer is facing west. From the viewer's perspective, Earth's magnetic field points diagonally down and to the right, so the right-hand force rule gives a magnetic force that is diagonally down and to the left, in agreement with our calculation. For the north-facing screen, the current travels south. Earth's magnetic field points downward and toward the south-facing viewer, so the right-hand force rule gives a magnetic force that is directly to the left, again in agreement with our result.

Guided Problem 27.6 Fusion energy

Nuclear fusion, the process that powers the Sun, can be made to occur in a laboratory by superheating a gas of electrons and protons (called a plasma) to temperatures exceeding 10^6 K. When their energy is high enough, the protons combine to create helium nuclei, and energy is liberated as the protons fuse. These hot, charged particles are trapped by a "containment vessel" formed by a strong magnetic field. Alcator C-mod at the Massachusetts Institute of Technology can achieve magnetic fields greater than 8 T. Assume that the C-mod's containment vessel has a circular cross section and that the magnetic field is uniform and has a constant magnitude of 8.0 T. What is the minimum radius of the vessel so that both electrons and protons are trapped? What is the period of the orbit in which the particles travel? Assume that the average speed of the particles is about 2.0×10^7 m/s.

1 GETTING STARTED

1. Describe the problem in your own words. What two variables must you determine?
2. What type of motion is implied by "containment"?
3. Which particle, proton or electron, is harder to contain?

2 DEVISE PLAN

4. What simplification results from seeking the minimum vessel radius?
5. How is the radius related to the given information?
6. What expressions must you use to determine the orbit period?

3 EXECUTE PLAN

7. Work through the algebra and solve for the desired unknown quantities, and then substitute values you know to get numerical answers.

4 EVALUATE RESULT

8. Is your value for the vessel radius unreasonable? That is, would such a device fit in a reasonably sized laboratory room?
9. Check that a particle moving in a circular orbit at your calculated radius and period would have the speed given in the problem statement.
10. How should the ratio of the two calculated radii relate to the ratio of the proton and electron masses? Does your answer check out?

Worked Problem 27.7. Going with the flow

A proton moves parallel to a current-carrying wire, at a distance 10 mm from the long axis of the wire, with the proton's velocity equal to the average velocity of the electrons in the wire. The interaction between the wire and the proton is observed from two reference frames: Observer E is at rest in the Earth reference frame, while observer M is moving relative to the Earth reference frame. To observer E, the wire is at rest, carries a 5.0-A current, has an ion charge density $\lambda_{E,ions} = +1.60 \times 10^3$ C/m, and has an electron charge density $-\lambda_{E,ions}$, making the wire electrically neutral. (*a*) What must M's velocity be, relative to the Earth reference frame, such that M observes only an electric force (and no magnetic force) between the wire and the proton? (*b*) What magnitude does observer M measure for this electric force? (*c*) What acceleration does this force give the proton?

PRACTICE

1 GETTING STARTED We are told that a proton moving along with the electrons in a current-carrying wire is examined by two observers: E in the Earth reference frame and M in a reference frame moving relative to E. We are also told that M sees the proton-wire interaction as purely electric and from this information must determine her speed relative to E. We must also calculate what M measures for the magnitude of the electric force exerted by the wire on the proton and the resulting acceleration of the proton.

2 DEVISE PLAN For part *a*, the only way that M can see the wire-proton interaction as purely electric is if the proton is at rest relative to M. Therefore her speed must be the same as that of the proton (and thus of the electrons), which is related to the current and the linear charge density through Eq. 27.36, $I = \lambda_{proper}v$, where $\lambda_{proper} = \lambda_{E,ions}$ is what E measures for the linear charge density of the ions in the wire.

We can then use the calculated value of v to obtain the magnitude of the electric force needed in part *b*. This electric force is given by Eq. 27.32, $\vec{F}^E_{Mwp} = q\vec{E}_M$, with the electric field magnitude measured by M given by Eq. 27.31:

$$E_M = \frac{2k\lambda_{proper}}{r}\gamma\frac{v^2}{c_0^2},$$

where $\gamma = 1/\sqrt{1-(v/c_0)^2}$

For part *c*, once we have F^E_{Mwp}, we can obtain the proton's acceleration by dividing the magnitude of this force by the proton mass.

3 EXECUTE PLAN (*a*) The speed of the electrons measured by E is, from Eq. 27.36,

$$v = \frac{I}{\lambda_{proper}} = \frac{5.0\text{ A}}{1.60 \times 10^3\text{ C/m}} = 0.0031\text{ m/s.} ✔$$

This then must be the speed at which M moves relative to the Earth reference frame.

(*b*) Using the expression for E_M given by Eq. 27.31, we get for the electrostatic force measured by M

$$F^E_{Mwp} = qE_M = q\frac{2k\lambda_{proper}}{r}\gamma\frac{v^2}{c^2}.$$

Here q is the charge on the proton, which is the elementary charge e, and the electron linear charge density is λ_{proper} as we saw in part a, so we have

$$F^E_{\text{Mwp}} = (1.6 \times 10^{-19}\,\text{C})\frac{2(9.0 \times 10^9\,\text{N}\cdot\text{m}^2/\text{C}^2)(1.60 \times 10^3\,\text{C/m})}{0.010\,\text{m}}$$

$$\times (1.09 \times 10^{-22}) = 5.0 \times 10^{-26}\,\text{N}. ✔$$

(c) A force of this magnitude gives the proton an acceleration that has a magnitude of

$$a = \frac{F^E_{\text{Mwp}}}{m_{\text{p}}} = \frac{5.0 \times 10^{-26}\,\text{N}}{1.67 \times 10^{-27}\,\text{kg}} = 30\,\text{m/s}^2. ✔$$

❹ **EVALUATE RESULT** Notice that the speed of the electrons, 0.003 m/s, is very small. The density of electrons in the wire is so great that even a very small average speed can create a current of several amperes. The force we calculated is extremely small, as we expect because of the tiny magnitude of the elementary charge e, but the acceleration of the proton is not so small because of its very small mass: The proton's acceleration is greater than that of a freely falling particle in Earth's gravitational field.

Guided Problem 27.8. Half speed

Suppose that in the situation described in Worked Problem 27.7 the proton is moving at only half the speed of the electrons. If you are an observer at rest relative to the wire, what magnitude do you measure for the electric force exerted by the wire on the proton? Would you observe a magnetic force exerted on the proton? If so, what is the magnitude of this force?

❶ **GETTING STARTED**

1. What portions of Worked Problem 27.7 can you use in this problem?
2. Which equations can help you determine the two types of interaction?

❷ **DEVISE PLAN**

3. Which equations can help you calculate the electric and magnetic fields in this relativistic situation?
4. What important simplification should you make?

❸ **EXECUTE PLAN**

5. Work out the needed quantities algebraically and then substitute numbers to get a numerical answer.

❹ **EVALUATE RESULT**

6. How does the magnitude of the electric force exerted on the proton compare to that found in Worked Problem 27.7? Is this sensible?

Questions and Problems

For instructor-assigned homework, go to MasteringPhysics®

Dots indicate difficulty level of problems: • = *easy,* •• = *intermediate,* ••• = *hard;* CR = *context-rich problem.*

27.1 Magnetism

1. Which way does the north pole of a compass needle point in the Southern Hemisphere? •
2. Which type of magnetic pole is located near Earth's geographic South Pole? •
3. How are the elementary magnets aligned in the magnet in Figure P27.3? •

Figure P27.3

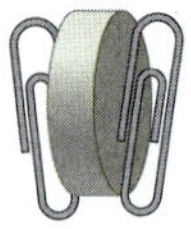

4. Can a magnet have more than two magnetic poles, one north and one south? ••
5. You are given three bars of metal. Two of them are magnets, and the third is made of a magnetic material but is not magnetized. Describe how, using only the three bars, you could determine which of them is not a magnet. ••
6. You are given two metal rods. One is a magnet, and the other is made of magnetic material but does not have the elementary magnets aligned. Using no other objects, how can you determine which is the magnet? ••
7. Sketch and describe the magnetic poles of a spherical piece of uniformly magnetized material. •••

27.2 Magnetic fields

8. Which field line patterns in Figure P27.8 can represent a magnetic field? •

Figure P27.8

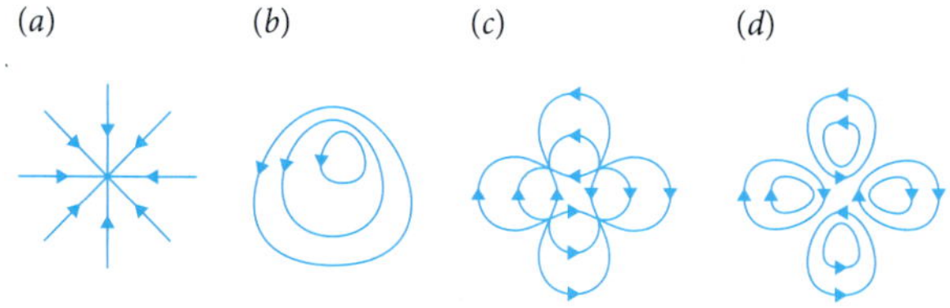

9. A bar magnet is enclosed by a spherical surface. (*a*) What is the flux through the entire surface? (*b*) If the magnetic flux through the hemisphere closest to the magnet's north pole is positive, what is the flux through the hemisphere closest to the magnet's south pole positive, negative, or zero? (*c*) The magnet is now moved so that its north half is outside the surface. What is the flux through the entire surface now (*d*) The portion of the magnet outside the surface is sawed off. What is the flux through the surface now? •
10. Is the field line pattern created by a magnetic dipole the same as the field line pattern created by an electric dipole? Draw both field line patterns. ••
11. Describe what happens to a bar magnet placed in the nonuniform external magnetic field shown in Figure P27.11. ••

Figure P27.11

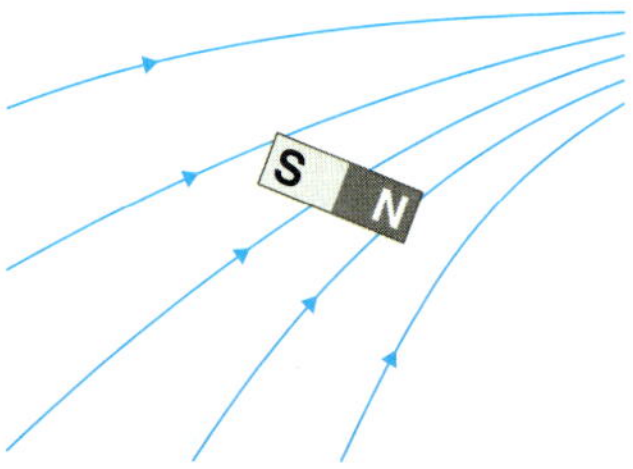

12. Describe what happens to a bar magnet placed in the nonuniform external magnetic field shown in Figure P27.12. ••

Figure P27.12

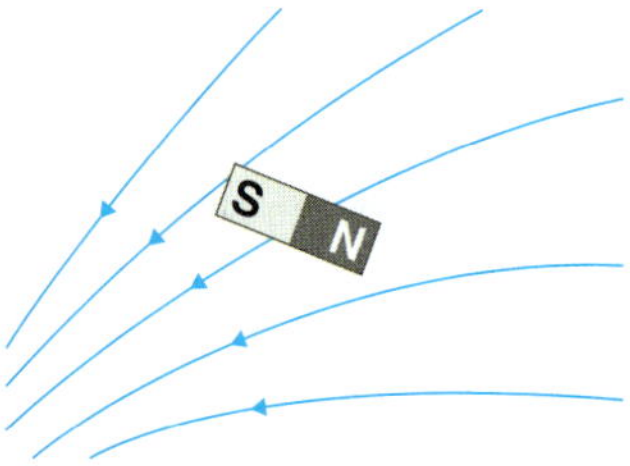

13. Is there a field line pattern that could everywhere represent either the magnetic field due to a magnet or the electric field due to a system of fixed charged particles? ••
14. Estimate the magnitude of the magnetic field at location 2 in Figure P27.14 if the magnetic field magnitude at location 1 is 0.27 T. Note that real magnetic field lines spread out in three dimensions. The spreading is shown in only two dimensions here, but you must imagine that the spreading also occurs into and out of the page. ••

Figure P27.14

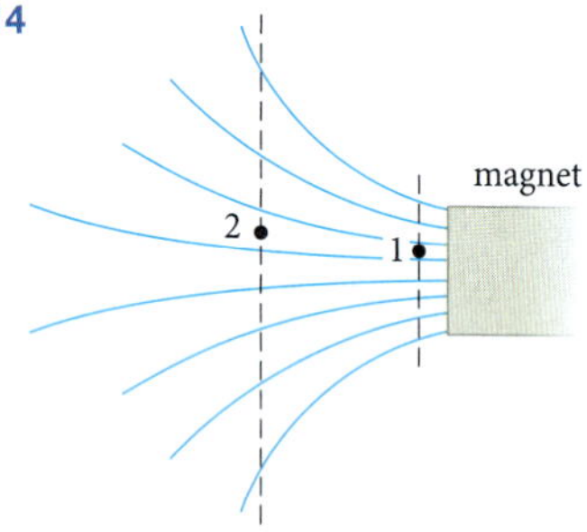

15. Rank the magnet pairs in Figure P27.15 in order of the amount of torque on magnet 2, smallest torque first. Assume all the magnets are equal in strength and the spacing between magnets is comparable in all pairs. •••

PRACTICE

Figure P27.15

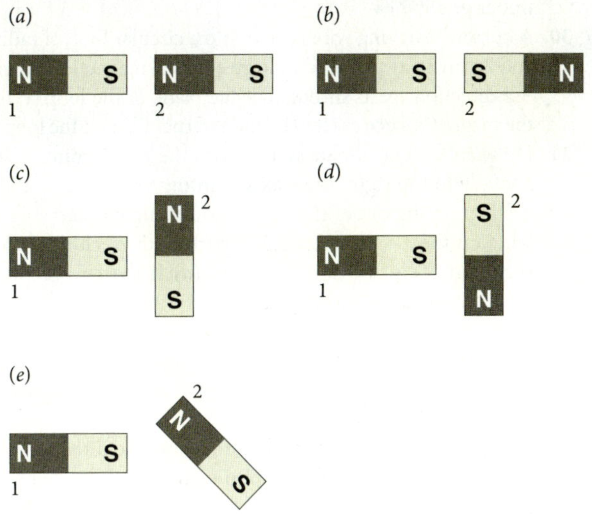

27.3 Charge flow and magnetism

16. The long, straight current-carrying wire of Figure P27.16 lies in the plane of the page, and the magnetic field it produces at position P points out of the page. (*a*) In what direction does the magnetic field point at position S? (*b*) What is the current direction in the wire? •

Figure P27.16

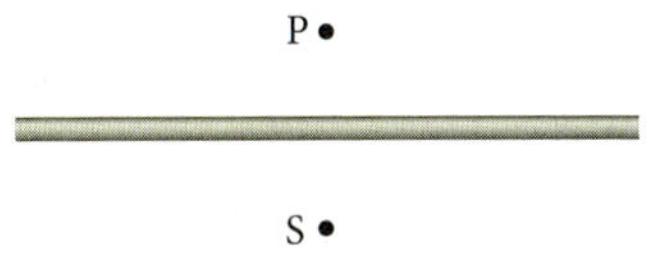

17. Figure P27.17 shows a long, straight current-carrying wire running perpendicular to the plane of the page. The current produces a magnetic field that points to the right at position P. (*a*) In what direction does the magnetic field point at position S? (*b*) What is the current direction in the wire? •

Figure P27.17

18. Figure P27.18 shows three particles passing near the north end of a bar magnet. Particle 1 is an electron, and particles 2 and 3 are protons. All three particles move at the same speed. (*a*) Determine the direction of the magnetic force exerted on each particle as it passes over the magnet. (*b*) What is the direction of the force (if any) exerted by each particle on the magnet? •

Figure P27.18

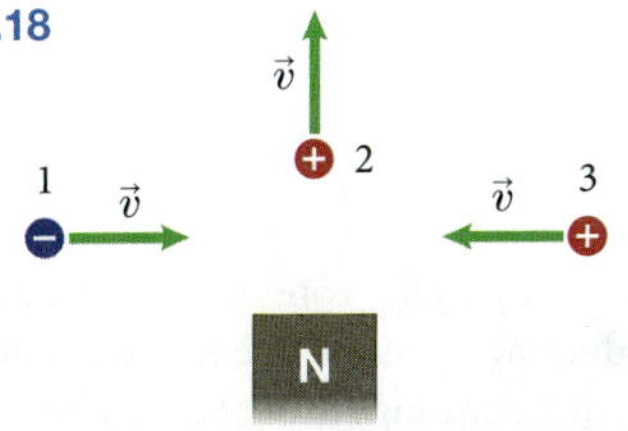

19. Figure P27.19 shows a conducting rod suspended from a spring in a region where a uniform magnetic field points horizontally out of the page. The rod can be supplied with current by two thin wires connecting its ends to the terminals of a battery (not shown). (*a*) Does the tension in the spring depend on whether or not the wires are connected to the battery? (*b*) Does the tension depend on which wire is connected to which battery terminal? If so, which wire should be connected to the positive terminal in order to increase the tension in the spring? ••

Figure P27.19

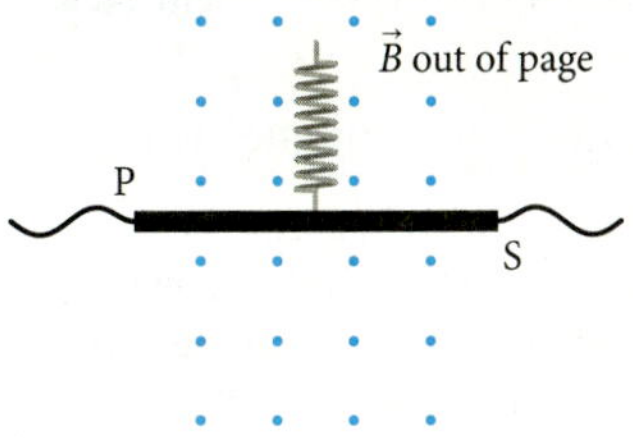

20. A wire is coiled in the shape of a helical spring with closely spaced turns. (*a*) When current is passed through it, does the coil tend to lengthen, shorten, or stay the same length? (*b*) Does your answer depend on the current direction? ••

21. The square loop of wire in Figure P27.21 carries a current, and an external magnetic field is directed out of the page everywhere. If the magnetic force exerted on side 1 is to the right, determine (*a*) the direction of the current in the loop and (*b*) the directions of the magnetic forces exerted on sides 2, 3, and 4. ••

Figure P27.21

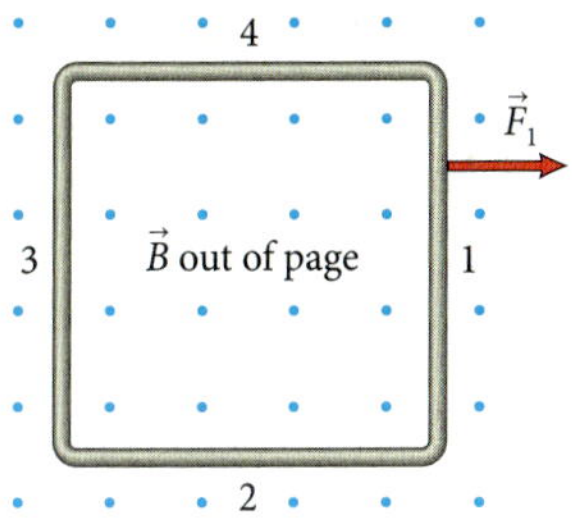

22. The two metal rods in Figure P27.22 are perpendicular to each other. Describe the magnetic force each rod exerts on the other, and then describe the torque caused by each force. •••

Figure P27.22

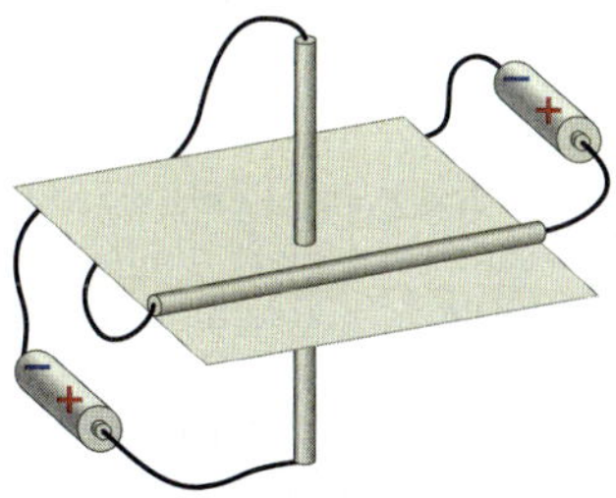

27.4 Magnetism and relativity

23. If two charged particles M and S are at rest relative to each other, there is no magnetic force between them. Suppose instead that particle M is moving relative to particle S while S is at rest in the Earth reference frame. Is a magnetic force exerted on S? •

24. A positively charged particle is at rest on the positive z axis in reference frame S. Reference frame S′ is moving along the positive x axis of S, reference frame S″ is moving along the negative x axis, and reference frame S‴ is moving along the y axis, all with speed v relative to S. The axes of all the reference frames are oriented the same way, and their origins coincide at instant $t = 0$, when observers in each reference frame make measurements. In which reference frames do observers measure an electric field? •

25. Write expressions for the magnitudes and directions of the electric fields measured in Problem 24. ••

26. Compare the magnitudes and directions of the magnetic fields measured in Problem 24. ••

27.5 Current and magnetism

27. A wire 0.70 m long carries a current of 1.4 A. The wire is at an angle of 53° to a uniform external magnetic field. If the force exerted by the field on the wire is 0.20 N, what is the magnitude of the magnetic field? •

28. In Figure P27.28, an external magnetic field is directed upward throughout a region that contains four current-carrying wires having the lengths and currents shown. Rank the wires according to the magnitude of the magnetic force exerted on them by the external field, smallest force first. Ignore any interactions between the wires. •

Figure P27.28

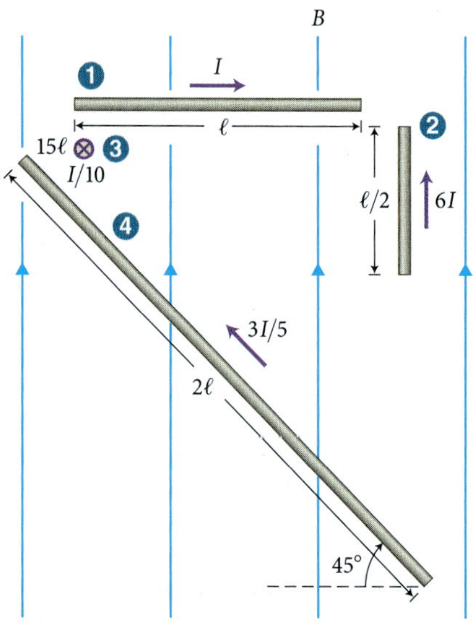

29. Two vertical parallel rails made of material that is an electrical conductor are 80.0 mm apart (Figure P27.29). A wire 80.0 mm long is free to slide along the rails, and the rails allow a current to be maintained through the wire as it slides. An external magnetic field of magnitude 0.250 T is directed into the page in Figure P27.29. If the mass of the wire is 4.00 g, what is the current in the wire if the wire doesn't fall under gravity? ••

Figure P27.29

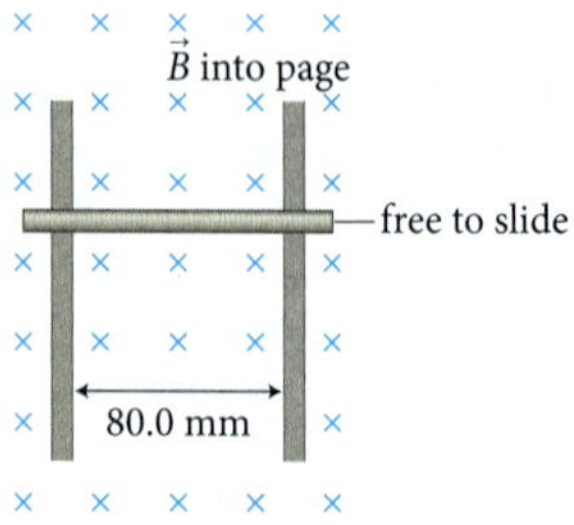

30. A current-carrying wire is bent into a circular loop of radius R and lies in an xy plane. A uniform external magnetic field in the $+z$ direction exists throughout the plane of the loop. What is the magnetic force exerted by the external field on the loop? ••

31. Draw an xyz coordinate system with the x axis pointing horizontally to the right, the y axis pointing up the page, and the z axis pointing out of the page. Show a current-carrying wire lying on the x axis, and a 2.5-A current through the wire directed in the positive x direction. (*a*) If the charge carriers are only electrons, how many of them pass through a cross-sectional area of the wire each second? (*b*) In which direction are the electrons moving? (*c*) If this wire is in a 0.20-T external magnetic field directed into the page, what is the force magnitude per unit length exerted by the external field on the wire? (*d*) On your diagram, show the direction of the magnetic field and the direction of the force exerted by the external field on the wire. ••

32. A wire 70.0 mm long is bent in a right angle such that the wire starts at the origin and goes in a straight line to $x = 30.0$ mm, $y = 0$, and then in another straight line from $x = 30.0$ mm, $y = 0$ to $x = 30.0$ mm, $y = 40.0$ mm. The wire is in an external uniform 0.500-T magnetic field in the $+z$ direction, and the current through the wire is 4.10 A, directed from the origin into the wire. (*a*) Determine the magnitude and direction of the magnetic force exerted by the external field on the wire. (*b*) This wire is removed and replaced by one that is 50.0 mm long and runs directly from the origin to the location $x = 30.0$ mm, $y = 40.0$ mm. If the current through this wire is also 4.10 A, what are the magnitude and direction of the magnetic force exerted by the external field on the wire? ••

33. Figure P27.33 on the next page shows the arrangement we looked at in *Principles* Example 27.2: a metal bar 0.20 m long suspended from two springs, each having a spring constant $k = 0.10$ N/m. Initially there is no current through the bar, and it is suspended at rest below the ceiling. With a current of 0.45 A, the bar rises a distance $d = 1.5$ mm. Suppose that the current is turned off, the bar drops down to its original position, and we attach a 5.0-mg piece of plastic to the center of the bar. Now how much current must there be through the bar to make it rise a distance $d = 1.5$ mm? ••

Figure P27.33

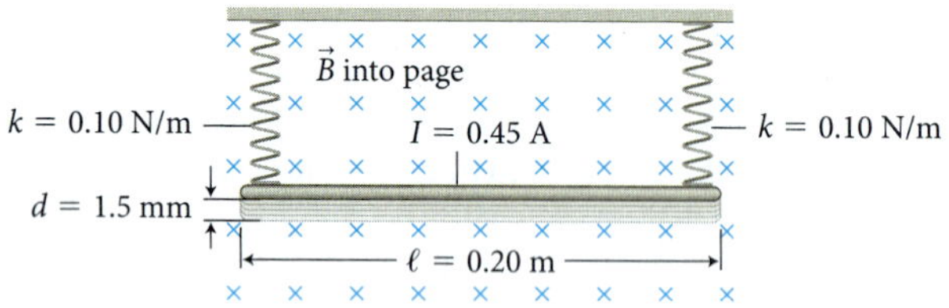

34. Two horizontal parallel conducting rods are connected such that a conducting crossbar free to slide along them has a constant current I running through it (Figure P27.34). The rods are separated by a distance ℓ and are in an external uniform magnetic field of magnitude B directed out of the page. The crossbar has a length ℓ and mass m. (*a*) In which direction

does the crossbar move? (*b*) If there is a coefficient of static friction μ_s between rods and crossbar, what is the minimum current I_0 necessary for the crossbar to move? ••

Figure P27.34

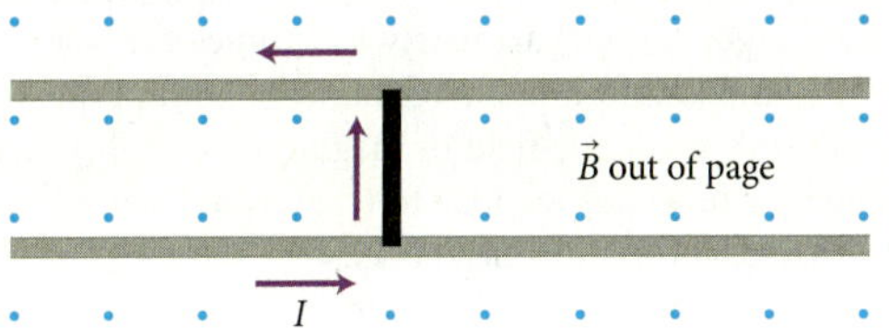

35. The top left portion of Figure P27.35 shows a current-carrying wire shaped into a rectangular loop that is very flexible. The loop is mounted on a base (not shown) that allows it to spin in any direction, and in this way any forces that cause the loop to move, spin, or distort can be detected. If the current direction through the loop is counterclockwise as indicated, what magnetic field direction(s) could cause the shape and orientation changes shown in parts (*a*)–(*e*) of Figure P27.35? If no magnetic field is necessary to make a shown change, write "none." If there is no way a magnetic field could cause a shown change, write "not possible." ••

Figure P27.35

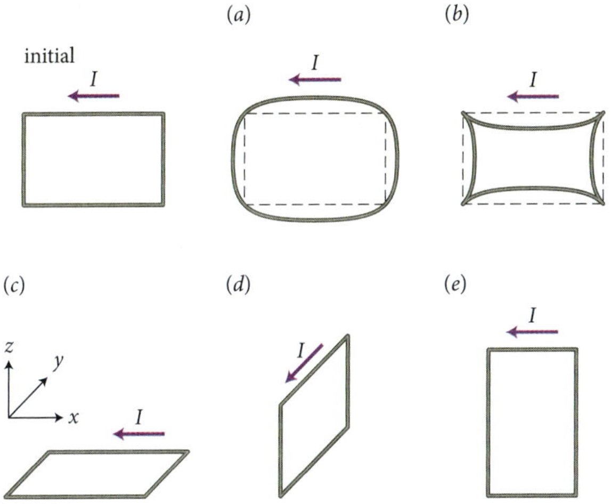

36. An arbitrary-shaped tangle of wire is connected such that it carries a current I_0 from position $\vec{r}_1$ to position $\vec{r}_2$ in a region where there is an external uniform magnetic field $\vec{B}_0$. Show that the magnetic force exerted by the external field on the wire is given by $\vec{F}^B_w = I_0(\vec{r}_2 - \vec{r}_1) \times \vec{B}_0$. •••

37. A 1.00-m metal bar that has a mass of 0.900 kg is initially pinned in place on an incline 65.0° above the horizontal (Figure P27.37). There is a 0.850-T magnetic field directed upward in the region around the bar, and metal contacts along the incline allow a current through the bar. If the coefficient of static friction between bar and contacts is 0.200, (*a*) what are the minimum magnitude and the direction of the current that must pass through the bar to keep it from moving once it is released? (*b*) Is there a maximum current that can be used in that same direction that will also hold the bar in place? •••

Figure P27.37

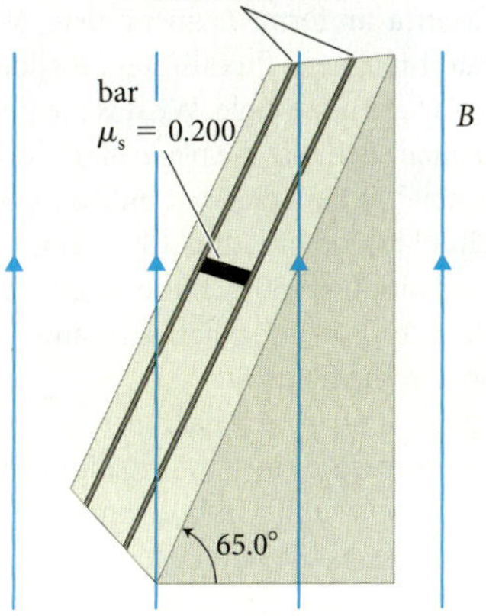

27.6 Magnetic flux

38. Figure P27.38 shows a bar magnet placed at four positions on and near a spherical shell. Rank the positions according to the amount of magnetic flux through the shell, smallest flux first. •

Figure P27.38

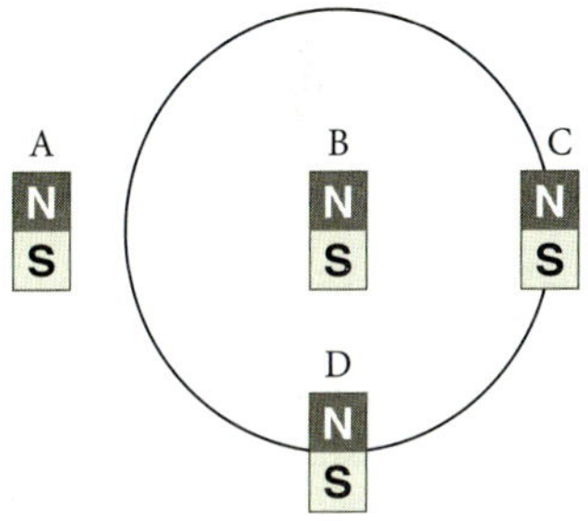

39. Figure P27.39 on the next page shows five objects, all placed in the same uniform, upward-directed external magnetic field. Rank the objects according to the amount of magnetic flux through them, smallest flux first. •

Figure P27.39

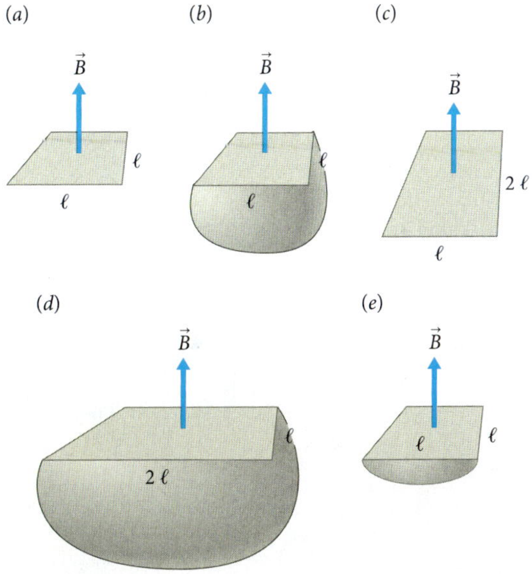

PRACTICE

40. A square loop of side length 100 mm is placed on a wooden table in a uniform magnetic field of magnitude 0.25 T. The greatest magnetic flux through the loop is measured when the loop is flat on the table. What is the flux through the loop when it is tilted such that the plane of the loop makes a 60° angle with the table? Draw a diagram indicating all necessary vectors. ••

41. A circular loop of radius 100 mm is placed in a magnetic field of magnitude 0.030 T. If the magnetic flux through the loop is $3.00 \times 10^{-4}\ \mathrm{T \cdot m^2}$, what is the angle between the plane of the loop and the field? ••

42. A square loop of wire has a perimeter of 4.00 m and is oriented such that two of its parallel sides form a 25.0° angle with the horizontal. A uniform horizontal magnetic field of magnitude 0.100 T passes though the loop. (*a*) Calculate the magnetic flux through the loop. (*b*) Another loop lies in the same plane but has an irregular shape, resembling a starfish. Its area equals that of the square loop. Calculate the flux through this loop. ••

43. The loop of Figure P27.43 is partially in a region where there is a 2.0-T magnetic field pointing out of the page and partially in a region where there is a 1.0-T magnetic field pointing into the page. Calculate the magnetic flux through the loop. ••

Figure P27.43

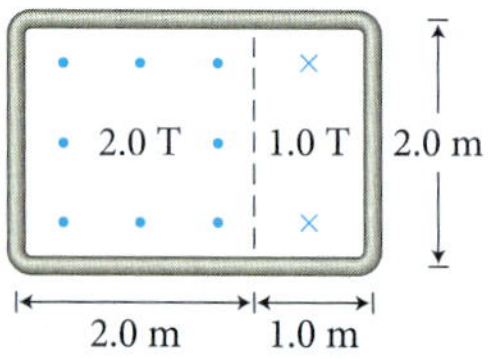

44. A hemispherical bowl of radius R is placed in a uniform magnetic field that has magnitude B_0 and is in the positive z direction. The open top of the bowl is in the xy plane. Obtain an expression for the magnetic flux through the hemispherical surface of the bowl. ••

27.7 Moving particles in electric and magnetic fields

45. A proton moves at 6.67×10^5 m/s undeflected in the $+x$ direction through a velocity selector, a device containing crossed electric and magnetic fields. You measure the electric field to be 2.0×10^5 N/C in the positive z direction. (*a*) What are the magnitude and direction of the magnetic field $\vec{B}$? (*b*) If the proton's speed doubles, in which direction is it deflected? •

46. Figure P27.46 shows the semicircular path through which charged particles travel in the magnetic field of a mass spectrometer. If the particles are oxygen ions carrying a charge of $-2e$ and the magnetic field magnitude is 0.20 T, how long does it take each ion to travel the semicircular path through the magnetic field? The mass of an O^{2-} ion is 2.6×10^{-26} kg. •

Figure P27.46

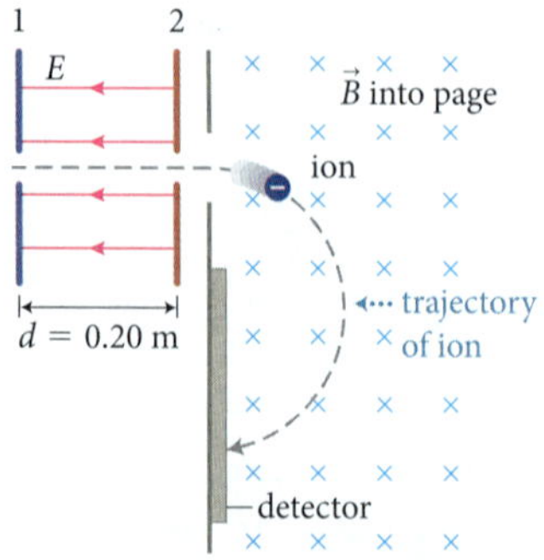

47. An alpha particle ($m = 6.64 \times 10^{-27}$ kg), which has twice the charge and approximately four times the mass of a proton, is moving in a circle of radius 0.75 m perpendicular to a uniform magnetic field of magnitude 0.75 T. Calculate the alpha particle's (*a*) angular frequency and period of motion, (*b*) speed, and (*c*) kinetic energy. ••

48. A proton moves in a circular orbit 150 mm in radius that is perpendicular to a uniform 0.25-T magnetic field. Determine the proton's (*a*) angular frequency and period of motion, (*b*) speed, and (*c*) kinetic energy. ••

49. An electron that has a kinetic energy of 7.5×10^{-17} J moves in a circular orbit perpendicular to a uniform magnetic field of magnitude 0.35 T. For this electron, determine (*a*) the radius of its orbit, (*b*) its angular frequency and period of motion, and (*c*) its speed. ••

50. A deuteron is a charged particle that has the same charge as a proton but approximately twice the mass. An alpha particle has twice the charge and approximately four times the mass of a proton. For this problem, assume the mass ratios are exactly 2 and 4. If a proton, a deuteron, and an alpha particle move in a uniform magnetic field in circles having the same radii, compare their (*a*) speeds, (*b*) kinetic energies, and (*c*) angular momentum magnitudes. ••

51. The isotopes magnesium-24 (mass 3.983×10^{-26} kg) and magnesium-26 (mass 4.315×10^{-26} kg) are to be separated using a mass spectrometer in which the magnetic field magnitude is 0.577 T. The ions used are the ones that have lost one electron each, $^{24}\mathrm{Mg}^+$ and $^{26}\mathrm{Mg}^+$. What is the minimum value of the potential difference through which these ions must be accelerated if the separation distance between them on the detector screen must be 2.60 mm? (Assume the mass ratio is 26/24.) ••

52. A particle that has mass m and charge q enters a uniform magnetic field that has magnitude B and is directed along the x axis. The initial velocity of the particle is in the xy plane. (*a*) Describe the particle's path as it travels through the magnetic field. (*b*) If the particle enters the magnetic field at $t = 0$, what is its angular displacement at $t = 2\pi m/qB$? ••

53. A horizontal metal strip 1.0 mm thick and 20 mm wide carries a 20-A current along its length, and both the length and the width are perpendicular to a uniform magnetic field of magnitude 2.0 T that is directed vertically up. The potential difference across the strip width is 4.27 μV. (*a*) If the side of the strip width that is to your left as you look in the direction of the current is at the higher potential, what is the sign of the mobile charge carriers? What are (*b*) the speed and (*c*) the number density of the charge carriers? ••

54. The cross section of a copper strip is 1.0 mm thick and 20 mm wide. There is a 10-A current through this cross section, with the charge carriers traveling down the length of the strip. The strip is placed in a uniform magnetic field that has a magnitude of 2.0 T and is directed perpendicular to both the length and the width of the strip. If the number density of free electrons in copper is $8.47 \times 10^{19}\ \mathrm{mm^{-3}}$, calculate (*a*) the speed of the electrons in the strip and (*b*) the potential difference across the strip width. ••

55. A proton is accelerated through a potential difference of 120 V, as shown in Figure P27.55, and fired into a chamber. There is no electric field in the chamber, but there is a 0.15-T magnetic field in the positive z direction. The proton enters the chamber at a 25° angle above the horizontal, and this entry location is the origin of the xyz coordinate system. Determine the coordinates of the location at which the proton will later strike this same wall from the inside. ••

Figure P27.55

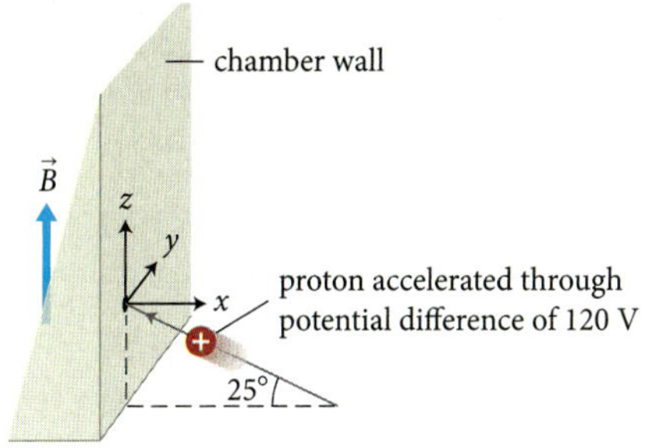

56. A beam of protons enters the network of five chambers shown in Figure P27.56 with an initial speed of 300 m/s and moves through the network along the path indicated by the dashed black line. In each chamber, the electric field is as specified, and the radius of curvature R is 0.40 m wherever it is shown. For each chamber, calculate the component of the magnetic field perpendicular to the path of the protons. •••

Figure P27.56

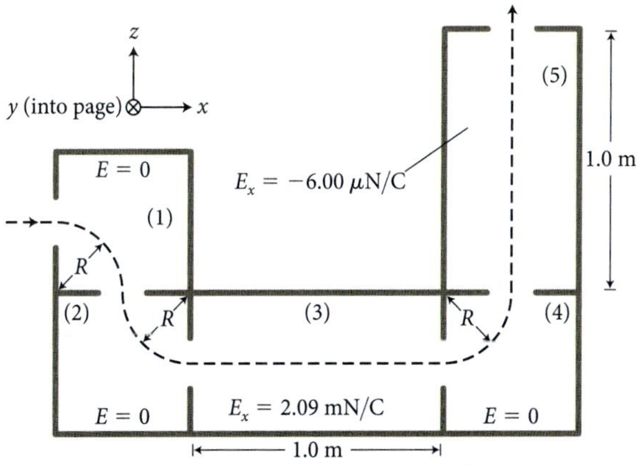

57. Electrons are made to flow through the copper strip of Figure P27.57. The strip's cross section is 1.00 mm high and 30.5 mm wide, and the strip is placed in a 2.00-T magnetic field that is directed out of the page. If the number of electrons per unit volume in the copper is $8.46 \times 10^{28}\ \mathrm{m^{-3}}$ and the current in the strip is 12 A, calculate the potential difference across the width of the strip when conditions have been allowed to equilibrate. •••

Figure P27.57

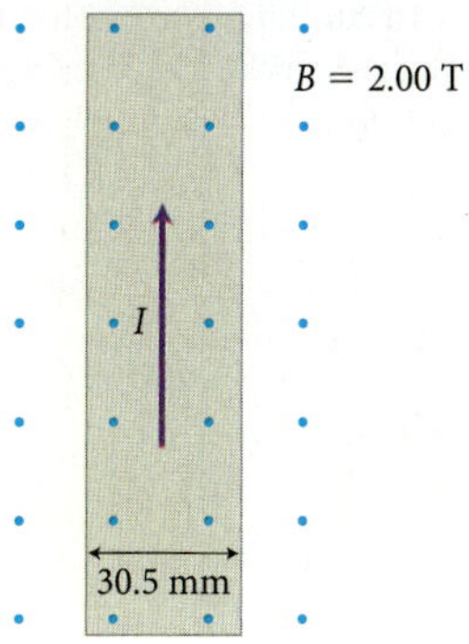

27.8 Magnetism and electricity unified

58. On average, the number density of free electrons in copper is $8.46 \times 10^{19}\ \mathrm{mm^{-3}}$. (*a*) Calculate what the linear charge density λ for a copper wire 1.00 mm in radius would be if this quantity of electrons were missing. (*b*) Assume this copper wire is electrically neutral in the Earth reference frame, in which it is at rest and carrying a current. Calculate the linear charge density λ' of the copper wire in a reference frame moving along with the electrons if the electrons are moving at 4.70×10^{-4} m/s. ••

59. A square loop of wire 1.00 m on a side is at rest and has a linear charge density of zero in the Earth reference frame. The loop lies in the xy plane of an xyz coordinate system, and there is a clockwise electric current through the loop as seen by a person looking down the positive z axis to the xy plane. The electrons move at speed v, and an observer M, moving at this same speed v, approaches the loop along the y axis (moving in the positive y direction). In which side(s) of the loop ($+x, +y, -x, -y$) does M see the linear charge density as being due (*a*) to surplus positive charge carriers and (*b*) to surplus negative charge carriers? ••

60. Suppose electrons move through a copper wire at speed v. Call the linear charge densities in the Earth reference frame λ_{Ep} for the fixed positive ions in the wire and λ_{En} for the (negative) electrons. Observer E in the Earth reference frame (which is also the reference frame of the positive ions) measures the wire to be electrically neutral. Observer M is moving along with the electrons (in the same direction as the electrons and at speed v). Calculate the linear charge density of the wire as measured by M in terms of λ_{En} if the speed is (*a*) 3.0×10^{5} m/s and (*b*) 3.0 mm/s (an achievable speed for electrons in copper wire). ••

61. A long wire that is at rest in the Earth reference frame initially carries no current. Observer E in this reference frame measures linear charge densities of $\lambda_{\mathrm{En}} = 45.00\ \mu$C/m for the (negative) electrons in the wire and $\lambda_{\mathrm{Ep}} = 60.00\ \mu$C/m for the positive ions. A current is created as electrons are made to move through the wire at speed v, and observer M moves along with the electrons at their speed v. What value must v have in order for M to measure an electric field of magnitude $E = 3.00 \times 10^{7}$ N/C at a distance 0.0100 m above the wire? •••

Additional problems

62. In Figure P27.62, an external magnetic field is directed out of the page, and six wires are placed, one at a time, in this field. Each wire carries a current in the direction indicated; if there is no indicated direction, the current is zero. Determine the direction of the magnetic force exerted by the magnetic field on each wire. •

Figure P27.62

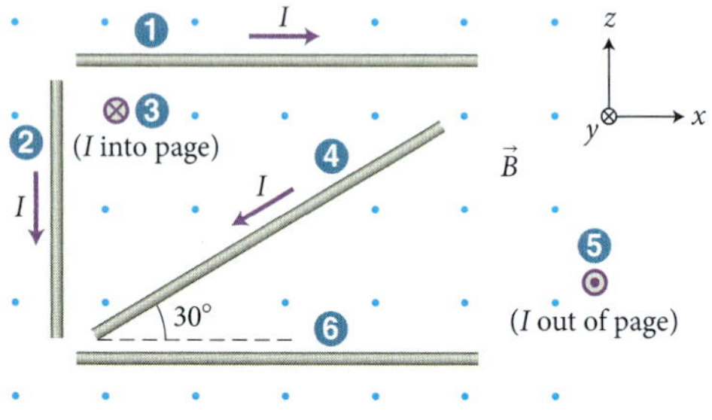

63. Three charged particles initially have identical masses, charges, and speeds and are traveling perpendicular to the same magnetic field. Because they are all in the same magnetic field and have identical masses and charges, all particles have the same initial cyclotron frequency and revolve with the same period T. The speed of particle 1 is doubled; particle 2 enters a region in which the magnetic field has been reduced by a factor of 2; and particle 3 collides with and sticks to a neutral particle of the same mass, causing a change in speed. Determine the new period of each particle in terms of the initial period T. •

64. At the equator, the direction of Earth's magnetic field is horizontal and to the north, and the magnitude is 3.5×10^{-5} T. (*a*) What is the magnetic flux through a circular loop of radius 0.10 m, lying flat on the ground at the equator? The loop is now balanced on its edge and the axis that runs perpendicular to the plane of the loop is pointed in different directions. What is the magnetic flux through the loop when this axis is pointed (*b*) northwest, (*c*) due north, and (*d*) west? •

65. When a wire 1.0 m long carries a 20-A current in the $+x$ direction in a uniform external magnetic field, the magnetic force exerted by the field on the wire is given by $F_x^B = 0, F_y^B = 3.0$ N, $F_z^B = 2.0$ N. When the wire is rotated until the charge carriers travel in the $+y$ direction, the magnetic force exerted by the field on the wire is given by $F_x^B = -3.0$ N, $F_y^B = 0, F_z^B = -2.0$ N. What are the magnitude and direction of the magnetic field? ••

66. Blood contains both positive and negative ions. In a certain patient being tested, the speed of these ions in a large artery is measured at 0.60 m/s. The patient is placed in a uniform magnetic field of magnitude 0.20 T. If a potential difference of 1.0×10^{-3} V is measured across the diameter of the artery, what is that diameter? ••

67. Electrons enter a region of perpendicular electric and magnetic fields (similar to *Principles* Example 27.5). The region occupied by the fields is 40.0 mm long in the x direction, where x is taken to be the original direction of motion. After passing through this region, the electrons then travel an additional 300 mm in the x direction before hitting a phosphorescent screen that lights up where the electrons strike it. The electrons pass undeflected through the region of perpendicular fields when $E = 2.0 \times 10^3$ N/C and $B = 1.2 \times 10^{-5}$ T. (*a*) Determine the speed of the undeflected electrons. (*b*) If the magnetic field is turned off but the electric field is left on, by what distance have the electrons been deflected when they reach the phosphorescent screen? ••

68. A particle of mass m and charge q moves in a circle of radius r in a uniform magnetic field of magnitude B. Show that (*a*) the particle's momentum is given by Bqr and (*b*) its kinetic energy is given by $B^2q^2r^2/2m$. ••

69. You are designing magnetic motors. A colleague insists that like magnetic poles attract—north poles attract north poles and south poles attract south poles. You feel the need to remove this idea from his head. You possess three unlabeled bar magnets. Surely that will be enough . . . ••• CR

70. Figure P27.70 shows a 1.0-m, 0.350-kg horizontal metal rod attached to two ropes, each of which makes an angle of 30° with the horizontal. Each rope then drapes over a pulley and is attached to a vertical rod of mass m. Assume the pulleys have negligible mass. There is a 0.25-T magnetic field in the region of the rod, parallel to the xy plane, oriented 45° from the long axis of the horizontal rod. When the horizontal rod is made to carry a current I, suddenly the rod moves upward until the ropes holding it make an angle of 5.0° with the horizontal. What was the value of I? •••

Figure P27.70

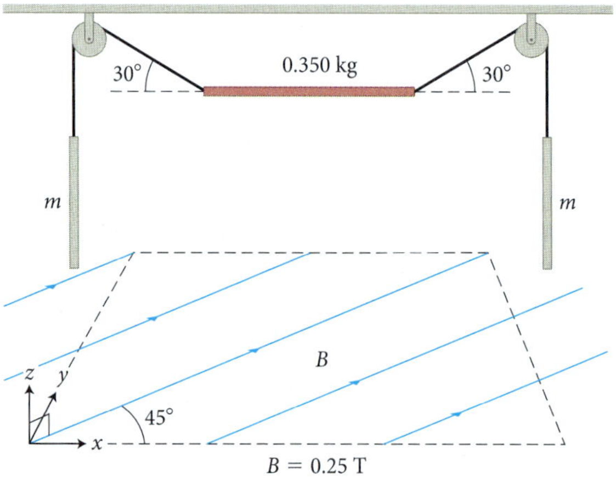

71. A wire bent into a semicircle of radius R lies in a plane that is perpendicular to a uniform external magnetic field $\vec{B}$. If the wire carries a current I, what are the magnitude and direction of the magnetic force exerted by the external field on the wire? •••

72. You are working with the square wire loop shown in Figure P27.72. The loop lies in a magnetic field, is connected to a battery, and is attached to an axis that runs through its center and is parallel to the plane of the loop. Initially the loop is held in place, but once it is released, it immediately rotates 180° about this axis. You know that magnetic fields can induce a torque on a current-carrying wire, but you are surprised by the rotation of exactly 180°. In an attempt to explain why this happened, you determine the direction of the current in the loop and the direction of the magnetic field in the region of the loop. You begin to wonder if multiple answers might be possible and if there is any way to keep the loop rotating in the same direction. ••• CR

Figure P27.72

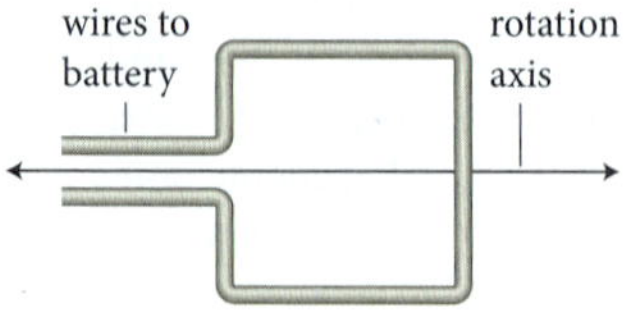

Answers to Review Questions

1. A magnet is an object that attracts objects made of iron, nickel, cobalt, or certain alloys, including most types of steel. A magnetic material is one that is attracted to a magnet.
2. Magnetic poles are the places on a magnet where a magnetic material is attracted most strongly. In a magnet that is free to align in any direction, the pole that settles toward geographic north is defined to be the magnet's north pole, and the opposite pole is the south pole.
3. Two like magnetic poles repel each other; two magnetic poles of opposite types attract each other.
4. An elementary magnet is the tiny magnetic dipole corresponding to a single atom of magnetic material such as iron, nickel, or cobalt, or to an elementary particle such as an electron or proton. In the elementary-magnet model for magnetism, a large number of the elementary magnets in a magnetic material have their north poles aligned in one direction and their south poles aligned in the opposite direction. This alignment of elementary N and S poles creates the overall N and S poles of the magnet.
5. A magnet is surrounded by a magnetic field, which exerts a force on the poles of another magnet.
6. Magnetic field lines tell us the direction and relative magnitude of the magnetic field. The field lines point in the direction of the magnetic field, and the density of field lines is proportional to the magnetic field's magnitude. For the field created by a magnet, magnetic field lines on the outside of the magnet point from the magnet's north pole to its south pole; within the magnet, magnetic field lines point from the magnet's south pole to its north pole.
7. It doesn't; the magnetic field line flux through a closed surface is always zero, because magnetic field lines always form closed loops.
8. The magnetic field source described is moving charge carriers, which constitute a *current*, defined as the flow of charge carriers.
9. The magnetic field lines are circles, centered on the wire and in planes perpendicular to it.
10. The electrons would need to flow from right to left, because a flow of positive charge in one direction produces the same magnetic field as an equal flow of negative charge in the opposite direction.
11. Because electrons are negatively charged particles, the current direction is downward.
12. Counterclockwise, as shown using the right-hand current rule. If you point the thumb of your right hand in the direction of the current (that is, toward yourself), the fingers curl counterclockwise, indicating the direction of the magnetic field produced by that current.
13. The direction of the force exerted by the magnet on the wire is perpendicular to the direction of the external magnetic field and also perpendicular to the current direction, as determined by the right-hand force rule. When the outstretched fingers of your right hand align with the current such that they can curl toward the direction of the external magnetic field, the thumb points in the direction of the force exerted by the external field on the wire.
14. We expect this because electric currents, which both cause and interact with magnetic fields, depend on velocity, and velocity is always relative to an observer's reference frame.
15. The huge internal electric forces between the charged constituents in the wire balance to zero because there are equal amounts of positive and negative charge carriers. Because the electric forces are so huge, however, even a small relativistic correction to them is measurable, so the magnetic force is observable.
16. The observer at rest relative to the wire sees equal charge densities for the ions and the electrons, and so the wire appears electrically neutral to this observer. The observer moving with the electrons sees a greater linear charge density for the ions than for the electrons, and thus to this observer the wire is not electrically neutral.
17. The magnetic force is a maximum when the wire is perpendicular to the external field and a minimum (zero) when the wire and external field are either parallel or antiparallel.
18. It depends on the magnitude of the external magnetic field, the absolute value of the current, the length of wire in the field, and the sine of the angle between the directions of the current and the field: $F^B_w = |I|\ell B \sin\theta$ (Eq. 27.7).
19. From the right-hand force rule and Eq. 27.8, the force exerted by the field on the wire points in the positive z direction: $\hat{\imath} \times \hat{\jmath} = \hat{k}$.
20. The magnetic flux through the surface is the scalar product of the magnetic field vector and the area vector for the surface.
21. The magnetic flux through any closed surface is zero. This implies that there are no isolated magnetic monopoles (analogous to isolated charged particles).
22. The flux is the same through *all* surfaces bounded by a given loop, except for a plus or minus sign determined by the chosen direction of the normal area vector.
23. The magnetic force exerted on the wire is the vector sum of the magnetic forces exerted by the field on the moving charged particles that make up the current in the wire. The force exerted on each particle is $\vec{F}^B_p = q\vec{v} \times \vec{B}$ (Eq. 27.19).
24. The force is directed perpendicular to the magnetic field direction and perpendicular to the particle's velocity, in accordance with the right-hand force rule.
25. The ions are moving relative to the observer, so she sees the distance between ions decrease because of the length contraction due to special relativity. Decreased distance between ions means increased linear charge density for them.
26. The observer in the Earth reference frame interprets the force as a purely magnetic interaction between the particle and the current, as the wire carries no surplus charge when observed from the Earth reference frame. The observer moving along with the electrons interprets the force as a combination of electric and magnetic interactions: The electric interaction arises because the wire appears positively charged to the observer who moves along with the electrons; the magnetic interaction is now due to the motion of the positive ions as seen from the reference frame of the electrons. For the special case in which the velocity of the positively charged particle equals the velocity of the electrons, the interaction observed from the moving reference frame is purely electric.

Answers to Guided Problems

Guided Problem 27.2 $\vec{B}$ points into the page; $I = \dfrac{mg}{\ell B} = 103$ A.

Guided Problem 27.4 There is no force on the top or bottom side of the square. The force on the right side is into the plane of the figure, and the force on the left side is out of the plane of the figure, as shown in Figure WGA27.2. The vector sum of these two forces is zero. The torque tends to rotate the loop about the dashed line in the figure. The right side moves into the plane of the figure, while the left side moves out. The magnitude of the torque is $\tau = 2(\ell/2)(I\ell B) = 3.9 \times 10^{-5}\,\text{N} \cdot \text{m}$.

Figure WGA27.2

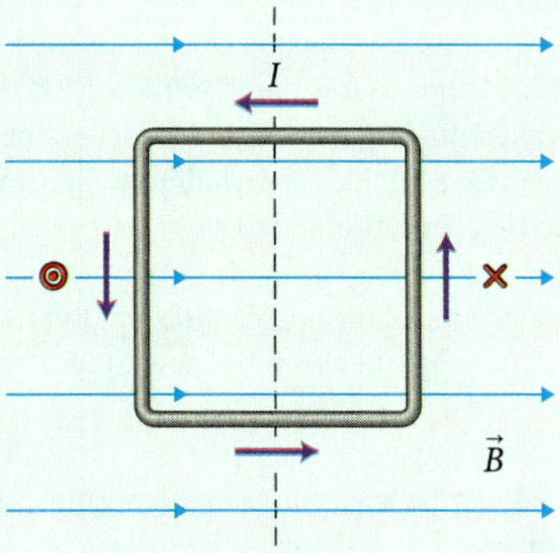

Guided Problem 27.6

For protons, $R = \dfrac{m_\text{p} v}{eB} = 0.026$ m, $T = \dfrac{2\pi m_\text{p}}{eB} = 8.2$ ns. For electrons, $R = \dfrac{m_\text{e} v}{eB} = 14\ \mu\text{m}$ and $T = \dfrac{2\pi m_\text{e}}{eB} = 4.5$ ps. So the minimum vessel radius is 26 mm.

Guided Problem 27.8 In the Earth reference frame (at rest with respect to the wire), I measure no electric force exerted by the wire on the proton: $F^E_{\text{Ewp}} = 0$. But I do measure a magnetic force: $F^B_{\text{Ewp}} = |q| v_\text{p} \dfrac{2kI}{rc_0^2} = 2.5 \times 10^{-26}\,\text{N}$.

PRACTICE

28 PRACTICE Magnetic Fields of Charged Particles in Motion

Chapter Summary

Current loops (Sections 28.1–28.3)

Concepts A magnetic field is produced by magnets, by current-carrying wires, and by moving charged particles.

The magnetic field pattern produced by a wire carrying a current and bent into a circular **current loop** is similar to the field pattern of a magnetic dipole.

A spinning charged particle has a magnetic field identical to that of an infinitesimally small magnetic dipole.

The **magnetic dipole moment** $\vec{\mu}$ is a vector that specifies the orientation and magnitude of a magnetic dipole. The direction of $\vec{\mu}$ is the same as the direction of the magnetic field at the dipole center. For a bar magnet, the direction of $\vec{\mu}$ is from south pole to north pole. For a current loop, the direction of $\vec{\mu}$ is the direction in which your thumb points when you curl the fingers of your right hand in the direction of the current.

A current loop placed in a magnetic field tends to rotate such that the direction of $\vec{\mu}$ aligns with the direction of the magnetic field.

Ampère's law (Sections 28.4, 28.5)

Concepts **Ampère's law** states that the line integral of the magnetic field along a closed path, called an **Ampèrian path,** is proportional to the current encircled by the path. See the Procedure box before the Worked and Guided Problems for how to apply Ampère's law.

Quantitative Tools If a constant current I_{enc} is encircled by an **Ampèrian path,** then by **Ampère's law,** the line integral of the magnetic field around the path is

$$\oint \vec{B} \cdot d\vec{\ell} = \mu_0 I_{enc}, \tag{28.1}$$

where $d\vec{\ell}$ is an infinitesimal segment of length of the Ampèrian path and μ_0, called the **permeability constant,** has the value

$$\mu_0 = 4\pi \times 10^{-7}\ \mathrm{T \cdot m/A}.$$

If a long, straight wire carries a current I, the magnitude of the magnetic field it produces at a distance d from the wire is

$$B = \frac{\mu_0 I}{2\pi d}.$$

The magnitude of the magnetic field produced by a large sheet carrying a uniformly distributed current is

$$B = \tfrac{1}{2}\mu_0 K,$$

where K is the current magnitude per unit width of the sheet.

PRACTICE

Solenoids and toroids (Section 28.6)

Concepts A **solenoid** is a long, tightly wound helical coil of wire. The diameter of the coil is much smaller than its length. Outside an infinitely long solenoid, the magnetic field approaches zero; inside the solenoid, the magnetic field is directed parallel to the solenoid length.

A **toroid** is a solenoid bent into a circle. The entire magnetic field is contained within the windings of the toroid, and the magnetic field lines form circles around the center of the toroid.

Quantitative Tools If an infinitely long **solenoid** that has n windings per unit length carries a current I, the magnetic field the solenoid produces in its interior has magnitude

$$B = \mu_0 nI. \tag{28.6}$$

If a **toroid** that has N windings carries a current I, the magnetic field the toroid produces inside the windings at a distance r from the toroid center has magnitude

$$B = \mu_0 \frac{NI}{2\pi r}. \tag{28.9}$$

Biot-Savart law (Section 28.7)

Quantitative Tools **Biot-Savart law:** If a small segment of wire $d\vec{\ell}$ carries a constant current I, the magnetic field produced by the segment at a point P a distance r_{sP} from the segment is

$$d\vec{B}_s = \frac{\mu_0}{4\pi}\frac{I\,d\vec{\ell} \times \hat{r}_{sP}}{r_{sP}^2}, \tag{28.12}$$

where $d\vec{\ell}$ points in the current direction and $\hat{r}_{sP}$ points from the segment to P. The magnetic field is

$$\vec{B} = \int_{\text{current path}} d\vec{B}_s. \tag{28.10}$$

A circular arc of radius R spanning an angle ϕ and carrying a current I produces a magnetic field at the center of the circle of magnitude

$$B = \frac{\mu_0 I\phi}{4\pi R}.$$

Magnetic field of a moving charged particle (Section 28.8)

Quantitative Tools A particle that has charge q and velocity $\vec{v}$ produces at a point P a magnetic field

$$\vec{B} = \frac{\mu_0}{4\pi}\frac{q\vec{v} \times \hat{r}_{pP}}{r_{pP}^2} \tag{28.21}$$

where $\hat{r}_{pP}$ points from the particle to P and r_{pP} is the distance from the particle to P.

If charged particles 1 and 2 carrying charges q_1 and q_2 are a distance r_{12} apart and have velocities $\vec{v}_1$ and $\vec{v}_2$, the electromagnetic force exerted by particle 1 on particle 2 is

$$\vec{F}^{EB}_{12} = \frac{1}{4\pi\epsilon_0}\frac{q_1 q_2}{r_{12}^2}\left[\hat{r}_{12} + \frac{\vec{v}_2 \times (\vec{v}_1 \times \hat{r}_{12})}{c_0^2}\right], \tag{28.26}$$

where $\hat{r}_{12}$ points from particle 1 to particle 2 and

$$c_0 = \frac{1}{\sqrt{\mu_0 \epsilon_0}}$$

is the speed of light. Equations 28.21 and 28.26 are valid only if $v \ll c_0$.

Review Questions

Answers to these questions can be found at the end of this chapter.

28.1 Source of the magnetic field

1. What is the fundamental source of magnetic fields?
2. Are all magnetic forces central?
3. Is it possible to have a magnetic field without any magnetic poles?

28.2 Current loops and spin magnetism

4. What do the patterns of magnetic field lines from a current loop and from a bar magnet have in common?
5. What does the magnetic field surrounding a spinning charged particle look like?

28.3 Magnetic dipole moment and torque

6. What is the direction of the magnetic dipole moment vector used to specify the orientation of a magnetic dipole?
7. Describe the three right-hand rules used in studying magnetism.
8. Describe the magnetic interaction experienced by a current loop placed in a uniform external magnetic field.
9. What does the commutator do in an electric motor?

28.4 Ampèrian paths

10. Magnetic flux through any closed surface is zero, but electric flux need not be. How can this difference be accounted for in terms of the properties of electrostatic field lines and magnetic field lines?
11. How does the value of the line integral of the electrostatic field along a closed path encircling a charge distribution compare with the value of the line integral of the magnetic field along a closed path encircling a current-carrying wire?
12. State Ampère's law.
13. How can you determine whether a current encircled by an Ampèrian path makes a positive or negative contribution to the line integral of the magnetic field around the path?

28.5 Ampère's law

14. The proportionality constant in Ampère's law shows the relationship between what two variables associated with a current-carrying wire?
15. What kind of symmetry is displayed by a long straight wire carrying a steady current? How does this symmetry determine what you choose for the Ampèrian path when using Ampère's law to calculate the magnitude of this magnetic field?
16. How does the magnitude of the magnetic field around a long, straight current-carrying wire of radius R depend on radial distance $r > R$ from the long axis of the wire? Assuming that the current is steady and uniformly distributed within the wire, how does the field magnitude depend on the radial distance $r < R$ from the wire axis? From the point of view of Ampère's law, why is this?
17. Describe the magnetic field produced by a large flat sheet of uniformly distributed current for which the current per unit width is K. What are the magnitude and direction of the field above and below the sheet?

28.6 Solenoids and toroids

18. What is a solenoid? Describe the magnitude and direction of the magnetic field produced by a long solenoid carrying a steady current.
19. What is a toroid? Describe the magnitude and direction of the magnetic field produced by a toroid carrying a steady current.
20. Does the magnetic field inside a very long solenoid differ from that inside a toroid if the two devices carry the same current in the same number of turns? If so, how?

28.7 Magnetic fields due to currents

21. Compare and contrast the expression for the infinitesimal magnetic field at some location P near a small segment of current-carrying wire given by the Biot-Savart law (Eq. 28.12) and the expression for the electrostatic field at some location P near a source charged particle, which we obtained from Coulomb's law in Section 23.7, $d\vec{E}_s(\mathrm{P}) = k(dq_s\hat{r}_{s\mathrm{P}}/r_{s\mathrm{P}}^2)$ (Eq. 23.14).
22. What steps can we follow to calculate the magnetic force between two parallel straight wires of length ℓ, carrying constant currents I_1 and I_2 and separated by a distance d?
23. Comment on the range of applicability of the Biot-Savart law relative to the range of applicability of Ampère's law.

28.8 Magnetic field of a moving charged particle

24. What is the origin of each of the two vector products in Eq. 28.26, the expression for the electromagnetic force between two moving charged particles 1 and 2?
25. What is the numerical value of the product of the proportionality constants μ_0 and ϵ_0? How does it relate to the speed of light c_0?
26. Does the force between two moving charged particles obey Newton's third law?

Developing a Feel

Make an order-of-magnitude estimate of each of the following quantities. Letters in parentheses refer to hints below. Use them as needed to guide your thinking.

1. The maximum magnetic field magnitude you are exposed to due to current in the electrical wiring in your house (E, K, P)
2. The straight-wire current needed to reverse the deflection of a compass needle sitting on your laboratory table (H, A, O, W)
3. The maximum magnetic field strength 10 m from a typical lightning bolt (G, R)
4. The maximum magnitude of the magnetic field you can produce in a solenoid sitting on your laboratory table when the core contains only air (D, N, Q, U)
5. The maximum magnetic force per meter between the antiparallel currents in your household wiring (P, E)
6. The electric current around the equator needed to produce Earth's magnetic field at the North Pole (B, I, M, S)
7. The magnitude of the magnetic field at the center of a Bohr-model hydrogen atom caused by the electron orbiting the nucleus (C, J, T)
8. The magnitude of the magnetic field at the North Pole that might be attributed to Earth's rotation, assuming a uniformly charged surface (F, L, I, V)

Hints

A. What is the horizontal component of Earth's magnetic field in your neighborhood?
B. What is the magnetic field magnitude at the North Pole?
C. What is the orbit radius?
D. What are the crucial variables to maximize?
E. What is the current configuration?
F. What is the magnitude of the electric field near Earth's surface?
G. How should you model the current?
H. How should the wire be oriented?
I. What is the radius of Earth?
J. What is the electron's speed?
K. How close do you come to the wiring?
L. What surface charge density could create this electric field magnitude?
M. What is the straight-line distance from a point on the equator to the North Pole?
N. What maximum current is reasonable?
O. What magnetic field strength is needed?
P. What is the maximum likely current in each conductor?
Q. What is a typical wire diameter used to carry currents of this magnitude in household or building wiring?
R. What is the peak current?
S. How can you compute the vector sum of the magnetic field magnitudes due to a large number of tiny segments of the current loop?
T. What magnitude of charge does the electron carry, and what is its inertia?
U. What is the maximum number of turns n per meter of solenoid?
V. How should you model the current?
W. How close to the wire can you place the compass?

Key (all values approximate)

A. 2×10^{-5} T; **B.** 7×10^{-5} T; **C.** 5×10^{-11} m; **D.** because $B = \mu_0 nI$, both I and n (number of windings per unit length) should be maximized; **E.** paired conductors separated by 10^{-2} m (two copper wires inside a nonconducting sheath) and carrying equal-magnitude currents in opposite directions; **F.** 100 V/m; **G.** approximately a vertical line; **H.** the compass detects horizontal magnetic fields, so orient the wire vertically; **I.** 6×10^6 m; **J.** electrical attraction provides centripetal force, so 2×10^6 m/s; **K.** 0.1 m if you stand near a wall; **L.** from Coulomb's law, 10^{-9} C/m^2; **M.** 9×10^3 km; **N.** laboratory tables are powered with 20 A, 120 V circuits, so the available current will be on the order of 20 A; **O.** enough to more than cancel Earth's magnetic field, say 4×10^{-5} T; **P.** 20 A for large appliances; **Q.** About 2 mm wire diameter; **R.** 10^5 A; **S.** by using the Biot-Savart law; **T.** $e = 1.6 \times 10^{-19}$ C, $m_e = 9.11 \times 10^{-31}$ kg; **U.** with 2-mm wire diameter, 500 turns per meter (or some small multiple of 500 turns per meter, if the wire is wound in more than one layer) are possible; **V.** as a stack of horizontal current loops of different radii (careful: current depends on radius); **W.** 0.02 m.

Worked and Guided Problems

Procedure: Calculating the magnetic field using Ampère's law

For magnetic fields with straight or circular field lines, Ampère's law allows you to calculate the magnitude of the magnetic field without having to carry out any integrations.

1. Sketch the current distribution and the magnetic field by drawing one or more field lines using the right-hand current rule. A two-dimensional drawing should suffice.
2. If the field lines form circles, the Ampèrian path should be a circle. If the field lines are straight, the path should be rectangular.
3. Position the Ampèrian path in your drawing such that the magnetic field is either perpendicular or tangent to the path and constant in magnitude. Choose the direction of the Ampèrian path so that, where it runs parallel to the magnetic field lines, it points in the same direction as the field. If the current distribution divides space into distinct regions, draw an Ampèrian path in each region where you wish to calculate the magnetic field.
4. Use the right-hand current rule to determine the direction of the magnetic field of each current encircled by the path. If this magnetic field and the Ampèrian path have the same direction, the contribution of the current to I_{enc} is positive. If they have opposite directions, the contribution is negative.
5. For each Ampèrian path, calculate the line integral of the magnetic field along the path. Express your result in terms of the unknown magnitude of the magnetic field B along the Ampèrian path.
6. Use Ampère's law (Eq. 28.1) to relate I_{enc} and the line integral of the magnetic field and solve for B. (If your calculation yields a negative value for B, then the magnetic field points in the opposite direction you assumed in step 1.)

You can use the same general approach to determine the current given the magnetic field of a current distribution. Follow the same procedure, but in steps 4–6, express I_{enc} in terms of the unknown current I and solve for I.

These examples involve material from this chapter but are not associated with any particular section. Some examples are worked out in detail; others you should work out by following the guidelines provided.

Worked Problem 28.1 Electrical wiring

A hobbyist has decided to install several new electrical accessories in her houseboat. To power these devices, she lays two wires along the ceiling of her boat as indicated in Figure WG28.1. (The plane of the drawing corresponds to the boat ceiling.) The wires are designed to carry the currents indicated in the figure, but she worries that the magnetic field near the wires might be strong enough to disrupt the operation of the compass that is already mounted to the ceiling. To reassure her that there will be no such problems, determine the magnitude and direction of the magnetic field at the position $x = 0$, $y = 4.0$ m, where the compass is located.

Figure WG28.1

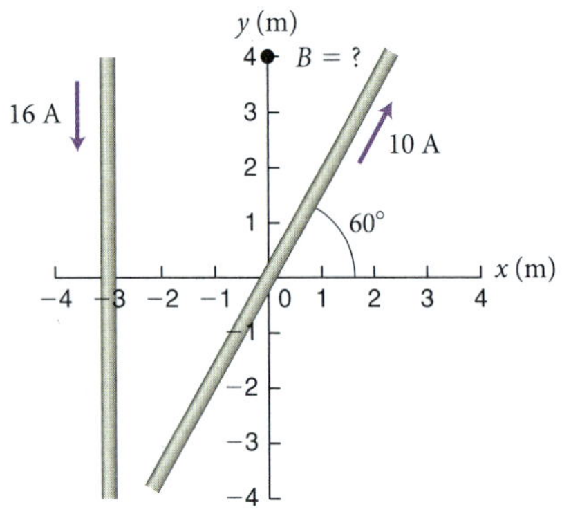

❶ **GETTING STARTED** Currents generate magnetic fields. Here two current-carrying wires contribute to a magnetic field at the position indicated. We are asked to determine the magnitude and direction of this magnetic field.

❷ **DEVISE PLAN** We know from *Principles* Example 28.3 that the magnitude of the magnetic field generated at a radial distance r from a long, straight current-carrying wire is $B = \mu_0 I/2\pi r$. Because the magnetic field is a vector, we need to determine the vector sum of the individual fields created by the two wires. We also know that near a current-carrying wire, magnetic field lines form concentric circles around the wire. We can use this information and the right-hand current rule to determine the field direction.

❸ **EXECUTE PLAN** Let's call the 10-A current I_1 and the corresponding magnetic field $\vec{B}_1$, and let's call the 16-A current I_2 and its magnetic field $\vec{B}_2$. Using the right-hand current rule, we point our right thumb in the direction of I_1 and notice that $\vec{B}_1$ points out of the plane of the page (i.e., points in the $+\hat{k}$ direction) at the position $x = 0, y = 4.0$ m, which we'll call position P. Similarly, by pointing our right thumb along I_2, we see that $\vec{B}_2$ also points out of the plane of the page at position P. The distance r_1 from the first wire to P, measured along a path perpendicular to the wire, is $r_1 = y\cos(60°) = 2.0$ m. The distance from the second wire to P is $r_2 = 3.0$ m. So the two wires' contributions to the magnetic field at point P are $\vec{B}_1 = +(\mu_0 I_1/2\pi r_1)\hat{k}$ and $\vec{B}_2 = +(\mu_0 I_2/2\pi r_2)\hat{k}$. The combined field $\vec{B}$ at point P is then

$$\vec{B} = \frac{\mu_0}{2\pi}\left(\frac{I_1}{r_1} + \frac{I_2}{r_2}\right)\hat{k} = \frac{4\pi \times 10^{-7}\ \mathrm{T \cdot m/A}}{2\pi}\left(\frac{10\ \mathrm{A}}{2.0\ \mathrm{m}} + \frac{16\ \mathrm{A}}{3.0\ \mathrm{m}}\right)\hat{k}$$

$$= +(2.1 \times 10^{-6}\ \mathrm{T})\hat{k}. \checkmark$$

❹ EVALUATE RESULT A magnitude of 2.1×10^{-6} T for the magnetic field associated with these two currents is reassuring because it is about 20 times smaller in magnitude than Earth's magnetic field, and thus unlikely to affect the compass reading. It is also reassuring that the magnetic field points up toward the sky, while the compass is designed to measure the horizontal component of Earth's magnetic field. Finally, a value smaller than Earth's magnetic field makes sense for a current of several amperes at a distance of several meters, because I know from experience that a compass is affected by everyday electrical wiring only when it is held very close to a wire.

Guided Problem 28.2 Bell wire

A student runs a long wire along one wall of her room, curves the wire at the corner, and continues to run it to a bell on the adjacent wall. The wire at the corner forms a circular arc of radius 10 mm (Figure WG28.2). What are the magnitude and direction of the magnetic field at position P if the current in the wire is 540 mA?

Figure WG28.2

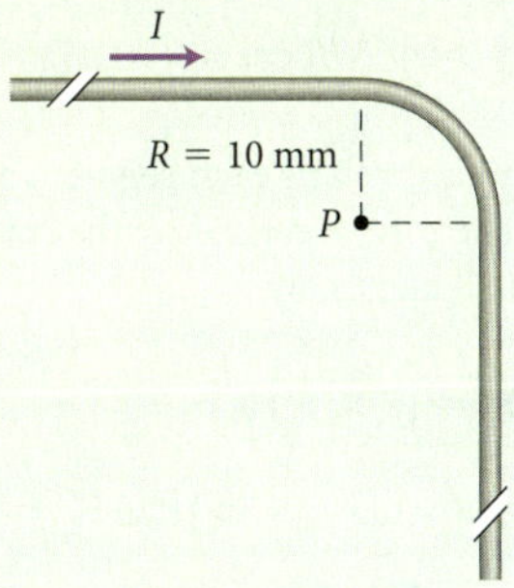

❶ GETTING STARTED

1. Describe the problem in your own words.
2. What concept(s) apply to this situation?
3. What assumptions must you make?

❷ DEVISE PLAN

4. Can you break the problem into parts?
5. Which equations will help you get the magnetic field for the various parts?
6. Can the equations specific to a slightly different situation be modified for this situation?
7. Magnetic field is a vector. How can you determine the vector direction?

❸ EXECUTE PLAN

8. Solve for the desired unknown quantity. Substitute values you know to get a numerical answer. Be sure to determine the vector direction and include it in your answer.

❹ EVALUATE RESULT

9. Does your answer behave as you expect it to as you change the radius of curvature?

Worked Problem 28.3 Galvanometer

A galvanometer is an old-fashioned device used to measure current. The simple model shown in Figure WG28.3 consists of a coil of wire, a vertical spring, a permanent magnet, and an indicator needle. A rigid rod (not shown) that runs perpendicular to the page is attached to the coil, and the coil is free to rotate about this rod axis. (The rod is also wired to allow the current to enter and leave the coil.) One end of the spring is attached to the coil, and the other end of the spring is attached to a fixed support. With no current through the device, the coil is horizontal, the spring is relaxed, and the needle points straight up. When there is a current in the coil, a torque is induced on the coil, causing it to rotate about the rigid rod, and the spring becomes either stretched or compressed. This rotation of the coil causes the needle to swing right or left, indicating the magnitude and sign of the current on a numerical scale (not shown in Figure WG28.3). As long as the angle ϕ through which the needle deflects from the vertical is not too large, the spring is stretched or compressed only vertically. (*a*) Viewed from above, what is the current direction with the coil rotated to the position shown? (*b*) Derive an algebraic expression for ϕ as a function of the current in the coil. (*c*) Calculate the current required to deflect the needle to an angle of 5.7°.

Figure WG28.3

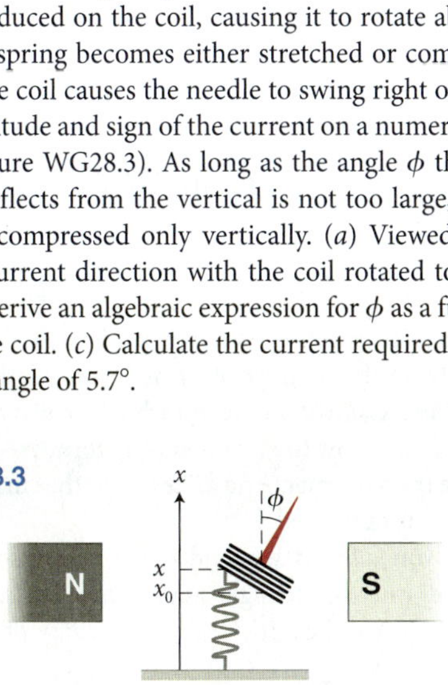

The coil has a square cross section, with sides of length ℓ. The coil has $N = 100$ turns, the magnet produces a uniform magnetic field of magnitude 0.010 T, and the spring constant is 2.0 N/m.

❶ GETTING STARTED We are given data for a galvanometer and asked to determine (*a*) the direction of the current in the coil, (*b*) an expression for the needle-deflection angle as a function of the current, and (*c*) the value of the current when that angle is 5.7°. We know that the magnet produces a magnetic field that is directed from the north pole to the south pole—that is, left to right in Figure WG28.3. We also know that a current loop experiences a torque when placed in an external magnetic field, and we know how to compute the magnitude of such a torque.

❷ DEVISE PLAN To deduce the current direction, we can use the right-hand force rule to determine the direction of the magnetic force on each side of the coil.

To derive an expression for ϕ as a function of I, we recall that Newton's second law applied to rotational motion tells us that the rotational acceleration of an object is proportional to the sum of the torques it experiences. We have two torques in this system: one due to the spring force and one due to the magnetic force between the external magnetic field and the current in the coil. These two torques balance to give the needle zero rotational acceleration once it reaches the position on the numerical scale corresponding to the amount of current in the coil. We can compute these torques because we know that the torque an object experiences when a force is exerted on it is $\vec{\tau} = \vec{r} \times \vec{F}$ (Eq. 12.38). The spring is stretched in the view shown in Figure WG28.3, and so the spring force is exerted downward on the left side of the coil. We know from Hooke's law

PRACTICE

(Eq. 8.20) that its magnitude is $F^c = |-k(x - x_0)|$, where k is the spring constant.

Each of the four sides of the coil experiences a magnetic force. Regardless of what the current direction is, the side of the coil facing us in Figure WG28.3 and its parallel side (behind the page) must feel forces that are perpendicular to the page and pointing in opposite directions. These forces not only cancel but also create zero torque on the coil because they are directed along the axis of rotation. Thus the only magnetic torques on the coil are those caused by the forces exerted on the two sides of the coil that face the two poles of the magnet. Because Figure WG28.3 shows the needle rotated to the right through angle ϕ, we know that the force direction is upward on the coil side facing the north pole and downward on the coil side facing the south pole. The magnitude of the force exerted on any straight wire segment in the coil can be found from Eq. 28.13,

$$F^B = |I\vec{\ell} \times \vec{B}| = \ell IB;$$

where ℓ is the length of each coil side. Note that the angle in this vector product is always 90° as the coil rotates, but the angle in the vector product for the torque, $\vec{\tau} = \vec{r} \times \vec{F}$, depends on ϕ. We just need to put these pieces together to get ϕ as a function of I and then a value for I when $\phi = 5.7°$.

❸ **EXECUTE PLAN** (*a*) The force exerted by the stretched spring is downward, and so to keep the left side of the coil tilted upward as shown, the magnetic force exerted on this side must be upward. By the same reasoning, the right side of the coil must experience a downward magnetic force. Thus we know two of the three variables covered by the right-hand force rule—magnetic force direction and magnetic field direction—and so let's use this rule to determine the current direction. The current is either clockwise or counterclockwise as viewed from above. In the left side of the coil, a clockwise current means that, in order to make the fingers of our right hand able to sweep from I direction to $\vec{B}$ direction, we must position the hand with the fingers touching the coil's left side and pointing into the page with the palm facing to the right. Our thumb, which indicates the direction of the magnetic force on this side of the coil, points downward, but we know that this force is directed upward. Thus the current is not clockwise; it must be counterclockwise. ✔

To confirm that the current is counterclockwise as viewed from above, we apply the right-hand force rule to the right side of the coil. A counterclockwise current in this side means that when we point our fingers at this side in such a way that we can sweep them from I direction to $\vec{B}$ direction, the thumb points down for the direction of $\vec{F}^B$. Knowing that this is indeed the direction of $\vec{F}^B$ here, we have confirmed that the current in the coil is counterclockwise. ✔

(*b*) Because the needle does not accelerate once there is a steady current through the coil, the magnitude τ^B of the combined torques due to the two magnetic forces must be equal to the magnitude τ^c of the torque due to the spring force. Because these two torques must be of equal magnitude in order to balance each other, we have $\tau^B = \tau^c$:

$$\tau^B_\vartheta + \tau^c_\vartheta = \tau^B + (-\tau^c) = 0$$

$$\tau^B = \tau^c.$$

The coil is composed of a stack of N turns, and each turn consists of four segments. We know that only the segments facing the north and south magnetic poles contribute to the torque, so we must consider the magnetic force on these two segments of each turn. The torque due to the magnetic force exerted on each segment is the vector product of the force due to the magnetic field and the radius vector $\vec{r}$ pointing from the axis of rotation (the central axis of the coil) to the segment. The magnitude of this vector product is $rF^B \sin\theta = rF^B \cos\phi$, where $\theta = \frac{\pi}{2} - \phi$ is the angle between $\vec{r}$ and $\vec{F}$. Because there are N turns in the coil, there are N wire segments on each side of the coil. Because there are two sides experiencing the magnetic force that creates the torque, the torque on the coil due to the magnetic field is

$$\begin{aligned}\tau^B &= 2|\vec{r} \times \vec{F}^B| \\ &= 2\left[\tfrac{1}{2}\ell(\ell NIB)\sin\left(\tfrac{\pi}{2} - \phi\right)\right] \\ &= \ell^2 NIB\cos\phi,\end{aligned}$$

where I is the current through each segment and thus the current through the coil. The torque caused by the spring force can be approximated, for small angles, by

$$\begin{aligned}\tau^c &= |\vec{r} \times \vec{F}^c| \\ &= \tfrac{1}{2}\ell\,|k(x - x_0)|\sin\left(\tfrac{\pi}{2} - \phi\right) \\ &= \tfrac{1}{2}\ell\,|k(\tfrac{1}{2}\ell\sin\phi)|\cos\phi \\ &\approx \tfrac{1}{4}k\ell^2\sin\phi\cos\phi.\end{aligned}$$

The substitution we just used, $\Delta x = \frac{1}{2}\ell\sin\phi$, is an approximation because we have assumed that the spring stretches only vertically, whereas in reality it is also pulled slightly to the right. Nevertheless, our approximation should be fine for small angles of rotation. Setting the two torques' magnitudes equal to each other, we get for the current

$$I = \frac{k}{4NB}\sin\phi.$$

For small angles, $\sin\phi \approx \phi$ (in radians), which means that the angle of deflection is approximately linear with the current:

$$I = \frac{k}{4NB}\phi, \quad \text{or} \quad \phi = \frac{4NBI}{k}. ✔$$

(*c*) For $\phi = 5.7°$, we get

$$I = \frac{2.0\ \text{N/m}}{4(100)(0.010\ \text{T})}(5.7°)\left(\frac{1\ \text{rad}}{57.3°}\right) = 50\ \text{mA}. ✔$$

❹ **EVALUATE RESULT** In the equation we derived for I, notice how the needle-deflection angle does not depend on the size of the coil; it depends only on the number of turns N and on the strength of the magnetic field. Can you figure out why the coil size doesn't play a role? Hint: Look at how the two opposing torques—one from the spring and one from the magnetic force due to the current—depend on the dimensions of the coil.

Make sure you fully understand each vector product used in the solution and where each angle comes from. The torques caused by magnetic forces can be fairly complex because of all the angles involved.

The magnitude of the current is neither excessively large nor small. Galvanometers often have a switch to allow you to measure different ranges of current while keeping the needle-deflection angle small. Moreover, a real galvanometer has a construction somewhat different from the version shown in Figure WG28.3. A spiral spring is typically used, and the magnets are designed so that the magnetic field direction is mostly radial. What would this accomplish?

This problem is a good example of how to solve a seemingly complex problem by putting several smaller pieces together. You may need to reach back to Chapter 8 to review how springs work and to Chapter 12 to review torque.

Guided Problem 28.4 Force on a rectangular current loop

A circuit board has a rectangular loop of wire next to a long straight wire located a distance $x = 0.300$ mm away from the loop (Figure WG28.4), with a 39-mA current through each element. What is the magnetic force exerted by the wire on the loop? The rectangle dimensions are $\ell = 5.7$ mm and $w = 0.90$ mm.

Figure WG28.4

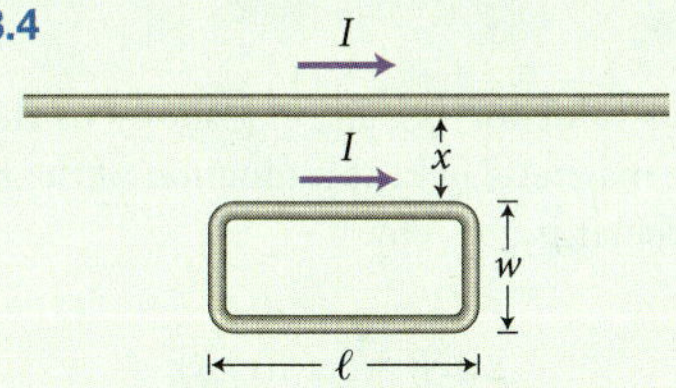

1 GETTING STARTED

1. Can you break the problem into parts?
2. What simplification can you make immediately just by looking at the problem?
3. What assumptions do you need to make?

2 DEVISE PLAN

4. Along each side of the rectangle, in what direction does the magnetic field generated by the wire point? In what direction does the magnetic force exerted on that side point?
5. Are there any two sides of the rectangle whose magnetic forces cancel one another?
6. What is an expression for the magnetic force between two parallel current-carrying wires?

3 EXECUTE PLAN

7. Apply the right-hand current rule to determine the direction of the magnetic field, and the right-hand force rule to obtain the directions of the forces.
8. Obtain an algebraic expression for the vector sum of the forces exerted on the loop. Then substitute numbers to get a numerical answer.

4 EVALUATE RESULT

9. Is your value for the magnitude of the magnetic force exerted on the loop unreasonable? Do you expect this force magnitude to be large or small?
10. How does the force depend on the dimensions of the loop? If ℓ and w become so large that only one side of the rectangle is near the wire, does the force per unit length reduce to a familiar expression? Does your algebraic expression also make sense if w becomes so small that the two long sides of the rectangle lie on top of one another, with equal but oppositely directed currents?

Worked Problem 28.5 Wire with nonuniform current

A long, straight wire that has a cross-sectional radius R carries a current I, but this current is not uniformly distributed over the circular cross section of the wire. Instead, the number density of charge carriers n depends linearly on the radial distance r from the wire's central axis: $n(r) = n_R r/R$, where n_R is the number density of charge carriers at the wire surface; these charge carriers all move at the same velocity v. (*a*) Derive an expression for the magnetic field magnitude B as a function of r for $r < R$ and for $r > R$. (*b*) Plot B as a function of r.

1 GETTING STARTED We are asked to derive expressions for the magnetic field magnitude inside and outside a current-carrying wire when the current is distributed nonuniformly across the wire cross section (rather than just outside an infinitesimally thin wire, as we did in the *Principles* discussion). We know that the magnetic field due to current in a wire has field lines that form closed loops around the wire. Ampère's law will be useful, but the nonuniform current requires a careful computation of the enclosed current for each value of r, the radial distance away from the wire center. This means we must break the wire cross section into a large number of small elements, with each element small enough to have a uniform current through it, and then integrate to obtain the current enclosed at any value of r. We can then draw a graph showing B as a function of r.

2 DEVISE PLAN Because of the cylindrical symmetry, we use Ampère's law:

$$\oint \vec{B} \cdot d\vec{\ell} = \mu_0 I_{enc}$$

for a tiny segment $d\vec{\ell}$ along some chosen Ampèrian path. The current enclosed inside any Ampèrian path we choose must be computed with an integral, but how can we set that up? From Chapter 27, we know that the current in a wire is related to the number density of charge carriers by Eq. 27.16, $I = nAqv$. Because we are dealing with an electric current, the charge q is the magnitude of the elementary charge e carried by an electron, and we are told that v does not depend on the distance r from the wire center. However, n is a function of r, so we cannot simply multiply the number density by the volume of the wire. We must imagine breaking the wire into small volume elements, but what kind? Because nothing varies with length along the wire, we can allow our elements to have any length. That is good because length along the wire is absorbed into the speed v of the charge carriers.

The cross-sectional area factor in our volume is another matter: Because n depends on r, we must break the cross-sectional area A of the wire into tiny portions, with n approximately constant over each portion. This suggests that we use very thin rings so that all portions of the cross section of a ring have the same value of r. The cross-sectional area dA of such a ring (Figure WG28.5) of radius r and thickness dr is its circumference times its thickness: $dA = 2\pi r\,dr$. This can be seen by imagining the ring being sliced through the thickness dr and unrolled to produce a rectangle of length $2\pi r$ and height dr.

Putting all this together in applying Eq. 27.16, with the substitutions $n = n(r)$, $A = 2\pi r\,dr$, and $q = e$, we get for the current dI through any infinitesimally thin cylindrical shell of radius r:

$$dI = n(r)ev2\pi r\,dr.$$

At any radial distance r from the wire center, the current enclosed by a circular Ampèrian path can be found by integrating this expression from the wire center out to r. We should have no trouble applying Ampère's law in this case of a nonuniform current distribution, as long as we can do the integrals.

Figure WG28.5

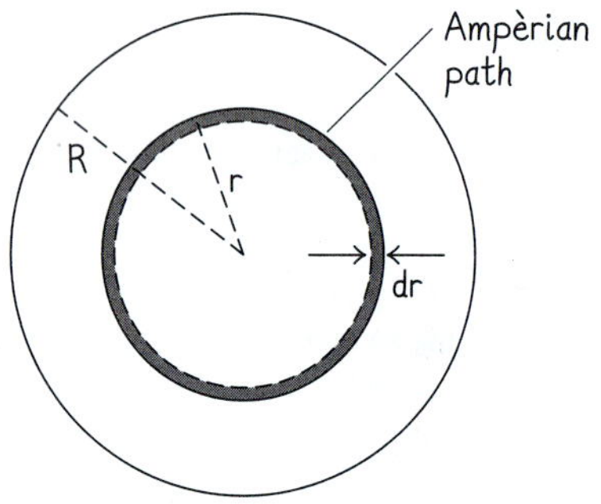

3 EXECUTE PLAN (*a*) We draw a circular Ampèrian path at a radius r inside the wire (Figure WG28.5). $\vec{B}$ and $d\vec{\ell}$ are parallel all along the Ampèrian path, so $\vec{B}\cdot d\vec{\ell} = B\,d\ell\cos 0 = B\,d\ell$. Because the current depends only on the distance r from the wire center, the symmetry is not disturbed for any given path radius. Thus the magnitude of the magnetic field at all points along this circular Ampèrian path has the same value, and we can bring it outside the integral:

$$B\oint d\ell = \mu_0 I_{enc}$$

$$2\pi r B = \mu_0 I_{enc}. \qquad (1)$$

We must now compute the current enclosed by integrating over a large number of infinitesimally thin cylindrical shells, each of radius r and thickness dr and carrying current dI:

$$I_{enc}(r) = \int dI = \int_0^r 2\pi evn(r)r\,dr$$

$$= 2\pi ev\int_0^r n_R\frac{r}{R}r\,dr = \frac{2\pi evn_R}{R}\int_0^r r^2 dr$$

$$= \frac{2\pi evn_R}{R}\frac{r^3}{3}, \qquad (2)$$

where R is the wire radius.

We could next substitute this expression for I_{enc} into Ampère's law, but there is a great simplification to be made. We do not know values for n_R and v, but we do know that the current in the wire is I. Perhaps we can eliminate some unknowns by computing the integral all the way to the wire surface (where $r = R$), which must give us an expression that represents the wire current I:

$$I = \frac{2\pi evn_R}{R}\int_0^R r^2 dr = \frac{2\pi evn_R}{R}\frac{R^3}{3}.$$

This allows us to simplify Eq. 2 for the current enclosed at any Ampèrian path radius r to

$$I_{enc}(r) = I\frac{r^3}{R^3}.$$

Substituting this value for I_{enc} in Eq. 1 shows us that inside a wire of radius R, the magnetic field as a function of the radial distance r from the wire center is given by

$$2\pi r B = \mu_0 I (r/R)^3$$

$$B = \frac{\mu_0 I}{2\pi}\frac{r^2}{R^3}.$$

Outside the wire, $r > R$, the enclosed current is just I at any path radius r, and so the expression for the magnetic field magnitude at any radial distance r from the wire center is the same as that for a thin wire:

$$B = \frac{\mu_0 I}{2\pi r}. ✔$$

(*b*) Figure WG28.6 is a graph of the magnetic field magnitude B as a function of the radial distance r from the wire center. ✔

Figure WG28.6

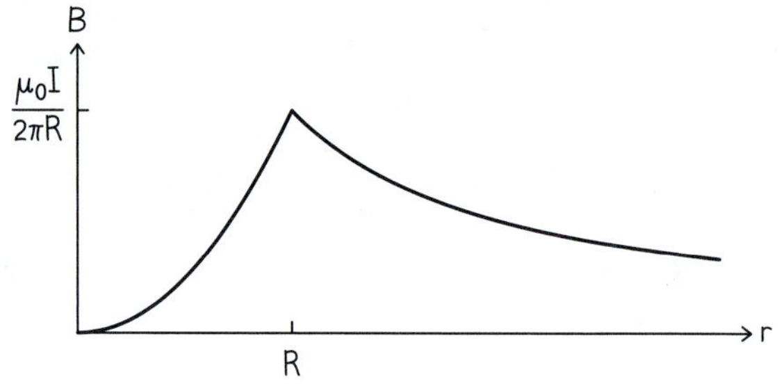

4 EVALUATE RESULT The problem statement tells us that n increases linearly with the radial distance r from the wire center. This nonuniform current distribution means that as we move radially away from the wire center, more and more current is enclosed by our Ampèrian path. Thus, the magnetic field magnitude increases quadratically until we reach the wire surface. Outside the wire, the current enclosed is always I, as it is for a wire carrying a uniformly distributed current, and so the magnetic field magnitude drops off as $1/r$. In this region our result agrees with what we found for an infinitesimally thin wire (see *Principles* Example 28.3)

PRACTICE

Guided Problem 28.6 Magnetic field in a coaxial cable

A coaxial cable consists of two concentric elements, an inner conducting wire and an outer conducting shell, typically separated by some dielectric material. One reason for using this type of cable is that when there is a current in it, the magnetic field due to the current is "trapped" inside the cable. Show that this is true by deriving one expression for the magnetic field magnitude in the region between the inner wire and the outer shell, and another expression for the magnetic field outside of the outer shell. Assume a uniform current and model that current as having one direction in the inner wire and the opposite direction in the outer shell. You can treat the outer shell as if its thickness were infinitesimal.

1 GETTING STARTED

1. How is this problem similar to Worked Problem 28.5?
2. What approach seems best to attack this problem?

2 DEVISE PLAN

3. Assign symbols for each radius you need. How many different radii must you use to establish the results you need?
4. What portions of Worked Problem 28.5 are relevant?

3 EXECUTE PLAN

5. Apply Ampère's law as many times as needed.
6. Sketch a graph of the magnetic field magnitude as a function of distance from the center of the inner wire to check the behavior inside and outside the cable.

4 EVALUATE RESULT

7. What is the radial dependence of the magnetic field in each region? Are your results unreasonable?
8. Do your results match what the problem statement says about the magnetic field being trapped inside the cable? If not, you probably made an error somewhere. Go back and check your work.

Worked Problem 28.7 Equivalence

A charged particle moves parallel to a long, straight current-carrying wire. The particle is a perpendicular distance a away from the wire, and the direction of the particle's velocity is the same as the direction of the current in the wire. Show that F^B_{wp}, the magnitude of the magnetic force exerted by the wire on the particle, is equal to F^B_{pw}, the magnitude of the magnetic force exerted by the particle on the wire, and that these two forces are in opposite directions.

1 GETTING STARTED We are told that a charged particle moves alongside a current-carrying wire, that the perpendicular distance between the particle and the wire is a, and that the particle's direction of motion is the same as the current direction. Our task is to show that the magnetic force exerted by the wire on the particle, which moves in the magnetic field created by the current in the wire, is equal in magnitude to the force exerted by the particle on the wire and that these two forces point in opposite directions. That the two forces should be equal and opposite—that is, $\vec{F}^B_{wp} = -\vec{F}^B_{pw}$—is not true in general for magnetic interactions, as discussed in *Principles* Section 28.8, but we are told that it should be true in this special case.

Let's spell out the concepts that will help us to solve this problem. We know that a long, straight current-carrying wire generates a magnetic field whose field lines encircle the wire, and we know that a charged particle moving through this magnetic field will experience a magnetic force that is perpendicular both to the field and to the particle's velocity. Similarly, we know that a moving charged particle generates a magnetic field and that a current-carrying wire will experience a force due to this magnetic field.

2 DEVISE PLAN As we've drawn in Figure WG28.7, we let the current I in the wire run in the $+x$ direction, along the x axis. We let the position P of the charged particle be on the y axis at $x = 0$, $y = a$, $z = 0$. We call the particle's charge q, and we let the particle's velocity $\vec{v}$ point in the x direction: $\vec{v} = v\hat{\imath}$.

To evaluate the magnetic field $\vec{B}_w$ due to the wire at position P, we can use Ampère's law, Eq. 28.1, as applied in *Principles* Example 28.3, where we found the magnitude of the magnetic field at a distance d from a long, straight wire to be

$$B = \frac{\mu_0 I}{2\pi d}. \quad (1)$$

Figure WG28.7

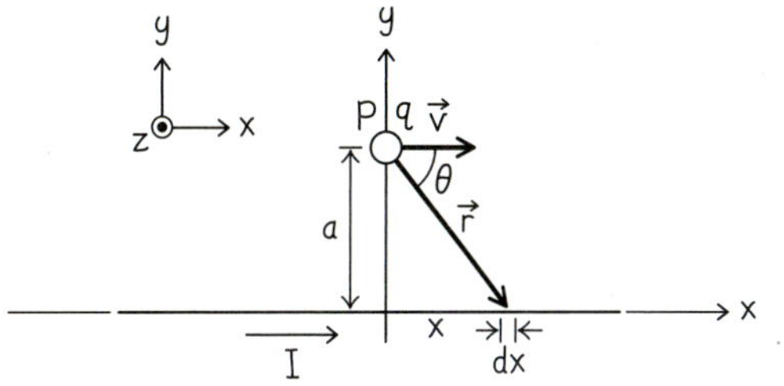

To compute the force $\vec{F}^B_{wp}$ exerted on a charged particle moving in the field of the wire, we can use Eq. 27.19:

$$\vec{F}^B_p = q\vec{v} \times \vec{B}. \quad (2)$$

To evaluate at any position $(x, 0, 0)$ along the wire the magnetic field $\vec{B}_p$ due to the moving particle, we can use the expression for the magnetic field of a moving charged particle, Eq. 28.21, with the vector $\vec{r}$ indicated in Figure WG28.7 pointing from the moving charged particle (the source of the magnetic field) to the segment dx along the wire at $(x, 0, 0)$. Finally, to compute the force $\vec{F}^B_{pw}$ exerted on the wire, we can break the wire up into infinitesimal segments $d\vec{\ell} = dx\hat{\imath}$ along the x axis and calculate each segment's infinitesimal contribution $d\vec{F}^B_w$ to the force using Eq. 27.8:

$$d\vec{F}^B = I\, d\vec{\ell} \times \vec{B}. \quad (3)$$

We can then integrate Eq. 3 over the entire length of the wire to obtain $\vec{F}^B_{pw}$.

Finally, we can use the right-hand current rule and the right-hand force rule to check that the directions make sense for the magnetic fields and forces that we calculate.

3 EXECUTE PLAN Substituting the distance a into Eq. 1 yields the magnitude $B_w = \mu_0 I/2\pi a$ at the point P where the charged particle is located. Using the right-hand current rule, we point our right thumb along the positive x axis and our fingers point out of the page at P. Because $\hat{\imath} \times \hat{\jmath} = \hat{k}$ is a vector identity, the z axis in Figure WG28.7 must point out of the page. Thus the magnetic field at point P due to the wire is

$$\vec{B}_{\text{w}} = \frac{\mu_0 I}{2\pi a}\hat{k}. \tag{4}$$

We obtain the magnetic force $\vec{F}^B_{\text{wp}}$ exerted on the charged particle by substituting $\vec{B}_{\text{w}}$ from Eq. 4 into Eq. 2:

$$\vec{F}^B_{\text{wp}} = q\vec{v} \times \left(\frac{\mu_0 I}{2\pi a}\hat{k}\right) = (qv\hat{\imath}) \times \left(\frac{\mu_0 I}{2\pi a}\hat{k}\right) = \frac{\mu_0 Iqv}{2\pi a}(-\hat{\jmath}),$$

where we used the vector identity $\hat{\imath} \times \hat{k} = -\hat{\jmath}$ to see that the force points downward, in the $-y$ direction, for $q > 0$. We can check this direction using the right-hand force rule: If $q > 0$, then the vector $q\vec{v}$ points to the right, while $\vec{B}_{\text{w}}$ points out of the page. Pointing the fingers of our outstretched right hand to the right and then curling them out of the page leaves our thumb pointing downward, confirming that the force on the particle points down toward the wire (along $-\hat{\jmath}$) if $q > 0$.

We evaluate the magnetic field $\vec{B}_{\text{p}}$ at position $(x, 0, 0)$ along the wire due to the moving charged particle by substituting the vector $\vec{r} = x\hat{\imath} - a\hat{\jmath}$ into Eq. 28.21:

$$\vec{B}_{\text{p}} = \frac{\mu_0}{4\pi}\frac{q\vec{v} \times \hat{r}}{r^2} = \frac{\mu_0}{4\pi}\frac{(qv\hat{\imath}) \times \left(\dfrac{x\hat{\imath} - a\hat{\jmath}}{\sqrt{x^2 + a^2}}\right)}{(\sqrt{x^2 + a^2})^2}.$$

Remember that $\vec{r}$ points from the moving charged particle, at location $(0, a, 0)$, to the point $(x, 0, 0)$ at which $\vec{B}_{\text{p}}$ is evaluated. The length of this vector is $r = \sqrt{x^2 + a^2}$, and the unit vector pointing along $\vec{r}$ is

$$\hat{r} = \frac{\vec{r}}{r} = \frac{x\hat{\imath} - a\hat{\jmath}}{\sqrt{x^2 + a^2}}.$$

Collecting the square roots into the denominator and simplifying, we get

$$\vec{B}_{\text{p}} = \frac{\mu_0 qv}{4\pi}\frac{\hat{\imath} \times (x\hat{\imath} - a\hat{\jmath})}{(x^2 + a^2)^{3/2}} = \frac{\mu_0 qva}{4\pi(x^2 + a^2)^{3/2}}(-\hat{k}),$$

where in the last step we used $\hat{\imath} \times (x\hat{\imath} - a\hat{\jmath}) = (\hat{\imath} \times x\hat{\imath}) - (\hat{\imath} \times a\hat{\jmath}) = -a\hat{k}$, because $\hat{\imath} \times \hat{\imath} = \vec{0}$ and $\hat{\imath} \times \hat{\jmath} = \hat{k}$. This magnetic field points in the $-z$ direction, which is into the plane of the page. We can check this direction by noting that a positively charged particle (assuming $q > 0$) moving to the right constitutes an electric current directed to the right. So we can point our right thumb along the charged particle's velocity vector, with our fingers wrapping around the particle, and notice that along the x axis (where the current-carrying wire is) our fingers are directed into the page, confirming the direction $-\hat{k}$.

Now we can substitute $\vec{B}_{\text{p}}$ into Eq. 3 to calculate the magnetic force $d\vec{F}^B_{\text{pw}}$ exerted on segment dx of the current-carrying wire. We also note that the current is in the $+x$ direction and substitute $Id\vec{\ell} = Idx\hat{\imath}$ to get

$$d\vec{F}^B_{\text{pw}} = Id\vec{\ell} \times \vec{B}_{\text{p}} = [\,Idx\hat{\imath}\,] \times \left[\frac{\mu_0 qva}{4\pi(x^2 + a^2)^{3/2}}(-\hat{k})\right]$$

$$= \frac{\mu_0 Iqva\,dx}{4\pi(x^2 + a^2)^{3/2}}\hat{\jmath},$$

where we used the vector identity $\hat{\imath} \times \hat{k} = -\hat{\jmath}$ to determine that the force points upward $(+\hat{\jmath})$ toward the charged particle, if $q > 0$. We can use the right-hand force rule to check that the force (for $q > 0$) points upward by pointing the outstretched fingers of our right hand to the right, along the current, and curling our fingers into the page, along $\vec{B}_{\text{p}}$; when we do this, our thumb points upward. Next we integrate $d\vec{F}^B_{\text{pw}}$ along the length of the wire to calculate the force $\vec{F}^B_{\text{pw}}$ exerted on the wire:

$$\vec{F}^B_{\text{pw}} = \frac{\mu_0 Iqv}{4\pi}\hat{\jmath}\left(\int_{x=-\infty}^{\infty}\frac{a\,dx}{(x^2 + a^2)^{3/2}}\right) = \frac{\mu_0 Iqv}{4\pi}\hat{\jmath}\left(\frac{2}{a}\right) = \frac{\mu_0 Iqv}{2\pi a}\hat{\jmath}.$$

We found that the integral in parentheses equals $2/a$ by looking it up on-line, but it turns out that by integrating over the angle θ shown in Figure WG28.7 instead of the coordinate x, we obtain an integral that is much easier to solve. Because we can see from the figure that $a/x = \tan\theta$, we can write $x = a/\tan\theta$ and differentiate to get $dx = -(a\,d\theta/\sin^2\theta)$. Then, because $a/\sqrt{x^2 + a^2} = a/r = \sin\theta$, we can write

$$\frac{a\,dx}{r^3} = -\frac{\sin\theta\,d\theta}{a}.$$

Now we can change the integration variable from x to θ and get

$$\int_{x=-\infty}^{\infty}\frac{a\,dx}{(x^2 + a^2)^{3/2}} = \int_{\theta=\pi}^{0}\left(-\frac{\sin\theta\,d\theta}{a}\right) = \frac{1}{a}\int_{\theta=0}^{\pi}\sin\theta\,d\theta = \frac{2}{a}.$$

Looking at the expressions we obtained above for $\vec{F}^B_{\text{wp}}$ and $\vec{F}^B_{\text{pw}}$, we can see that $\vec{F}^B_{\text{pw}} = -\vec{F}^B_{\text{wp}}$, as we were told in the problem statement to expect. ✔

❹ **EVALUATE RESULT** The force magnitude depends linearly on the current and on the speed and charge of the moving particle, as we expect. That Newton's third law applies here is reassuring, though we know that this is not necessarily to be expected in magnetic interactions. It makes sense that the particle and the wire are attracted toward one another for $q > 0$ and are repelled from one another for $q < 0$, because we can view the motion of the charged particle as an electric current, and we know that the magnetic force between two parallel currents is attractive, while the magnetic force between two antiparallel currents is repulsive.

Guided Problem 28.8 Tubular current

A very long, hollow cylindrical conductor of inner radius R_{in} and outer radius R_{out} carries current I distributed uniformly throughout its cross-sectional area (Figure WG28.8). Derive an expression for the magnitude of the magnetic field due to this current as a function of the radial distance r from the central axis in all regions: (*a*) $0 \leq r \leq R_{in}$, (*b*) $R_{in} \leq r \leq R_{out}$, (*c*) $r > R_{out}$.

Figure WG28.8

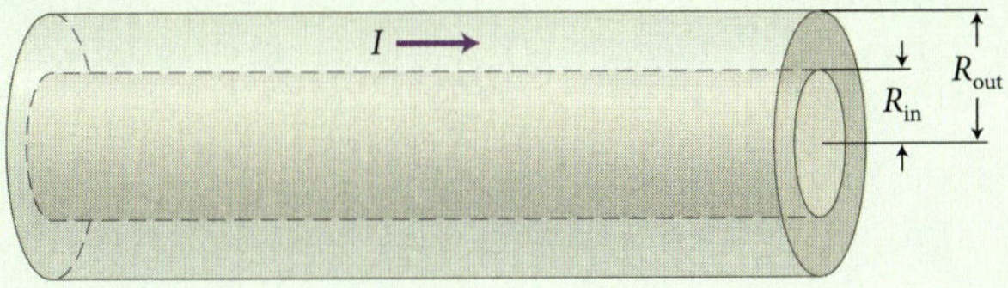

1 GETTING STARTED

1. What is the symmetry of the current distribution?
2. What general law provides the easiest method to compute the magnetic field in each region?

2 DEVISE PLAN

3. How many different applications of your chosen general law will be required to determine the magnetic field in each region?
4. In which region(s) will it be necessary to perform a calculation to determine the current encircled?

3 EXECUTE PLAN

5. In region *b*, what fraction of the current is encircled by a circle of radius *r*?

4 EVALUATE RESULT

6. How does your answer behave as *r* varies over the full range in each region? Does the result from one region match the result from the adjacent region at the boundary?

Questions and Problems

For instructor-assigned homework, go to MasteringPhysics® MP

Dots indicate difficulty level of problems: • = easy, •• = intermediate, ••• = hard; CR = context-rich problem.

28.1 Source of the magnetic field

1. A negatively charged particle sits midway between the two magnets in Figure P28.1, at rest relative to the magnets. If the magnet on the left is twice as strong as the magnet on the right, what is the direction of the magnetic force exerted on the particle? •

Figure P28.1

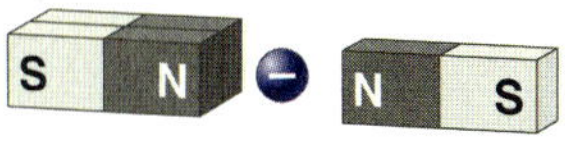

2. Two parallel wires each carry a current I in the positive x direction. What is the direction of the magnetic field at any point that lies midway between the wires and in the plane defined by them? •
3. Consider a square loop of wire that carries a clockwise current when viewed from above. What is the direction of the magnetic field at the center of the square loop due to (*a*) the left side, (*b*) the top side, (*c*) the right side, and (*d*) the bottom side? •
4. A negatively charged particle is at rest in a region where a uniform magnetic field points in the positive x direction and a uniform electric field points in the positive y direction. What is the direction of the vector sum of the forces exerted on the particle? ••
5. Suppose two electrons move on parallel, closely spaced paths in the $+z$ direction, each with velocity $\vec{v}$ in the Earth reference frame. Discuss all forces exerted on the electrons. ••
6. Two protons are fired toward each other on closely spaced paths, one moving in the $+z$ direction and one in the $-z$ direction. As they pass close to each other, is the magnetic force between them attractive, repulsive, or neither? ••
7. The two insulated, current-carrying wires in Figure P28.7 cross at right angles, and each carries a current I. The locations labeled 1–4 are all in the plane defined by the wires, with each location a perpendicular distance d from both wires. At how many of these four locations is the magnetic field (*a*) directed out of the page, (*b*) directed into the page, and (*c*) equal to zero? ••

Figure P28.7

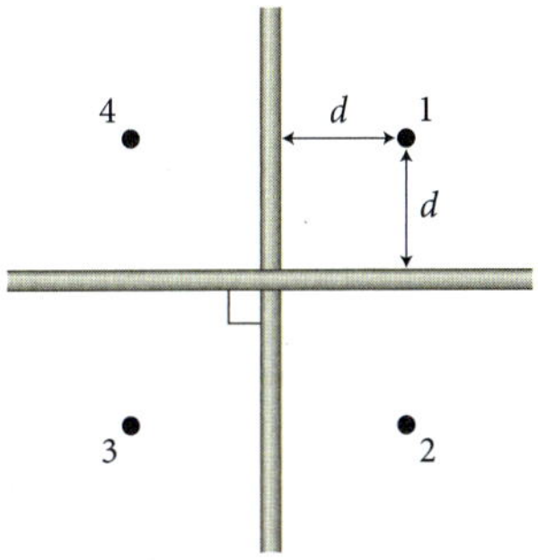

8. Two of the three wires in Figure P28.8 carry current I, and the third wire carries current $6I$. The location labeled P is a distance d from each of the wires carrying current I. What is the direction of the magnetic field at P? ••

Figure P28.8

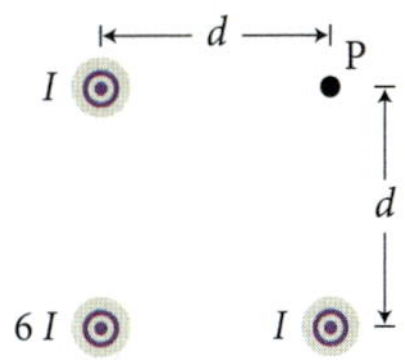

PRACTICE

9. Two positively charged particles 1 and 2 are moving in the same plane, with the velocity of particle 1 perpendicular to the velocity of particle 2. At the instant shown in Figure P28.9, particle 2 is on the line that defines the velocity of particle 1. For this instant, describe and sketch the direction of the magnetic force that each particle exerts on the other. ●●●

Figure P28.9

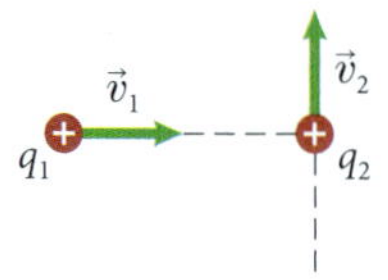

10. In Figure P28.10, (*a*) specify the direction of the magnetic field at the location labeled P due to each of the four sides 1–4 of the current loop. (*b*) Which side produces the strongest magnetic field at P? (*c*) What additional information is needed to determine the direction of the magnetic field at P due to the loop? ●●●

Figure P28.10

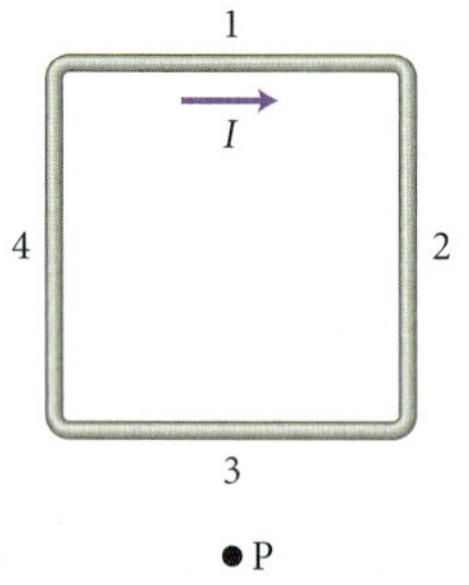

28.2 Current loops and spin magnetism

11. Where do you expect the magnitude of the magnetic field due to a circular current loop to be greatest? ●

12. Could Figure P28.12 represent the magnetic field due to a bar magnet that has a rectangular cross section rather than a circular cross section? ●

Figure P28.12

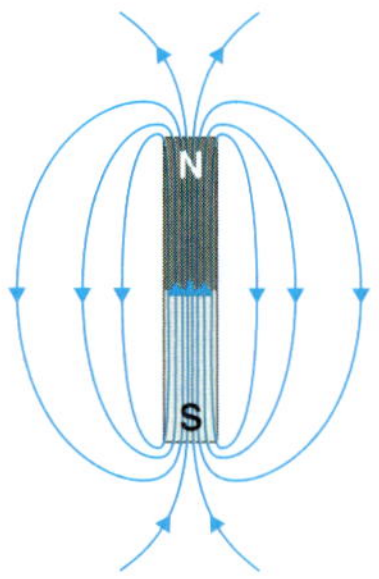

13. A loop of wire carries a current I as shown in Figure P28.13. Determine the direction of the magnetic field at the points labeled. ●

Figure P28.13

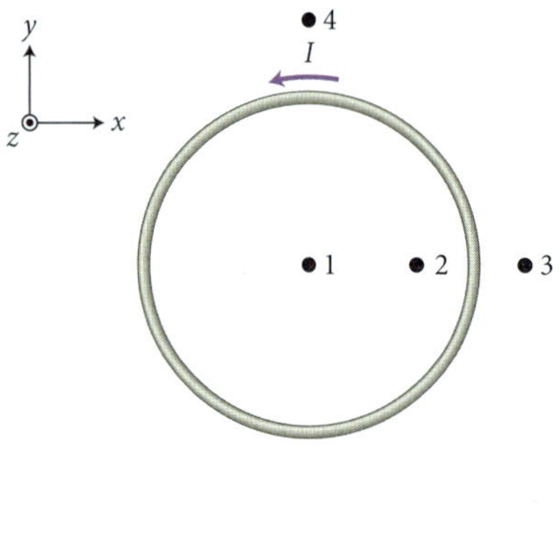

14. Figure P28.14 shows a positively charged spherical object that is spinning. For each of the labeled points, state the direction of the magnetic field. Assume all points lie in the xy plane. ●●

Figure P28.14

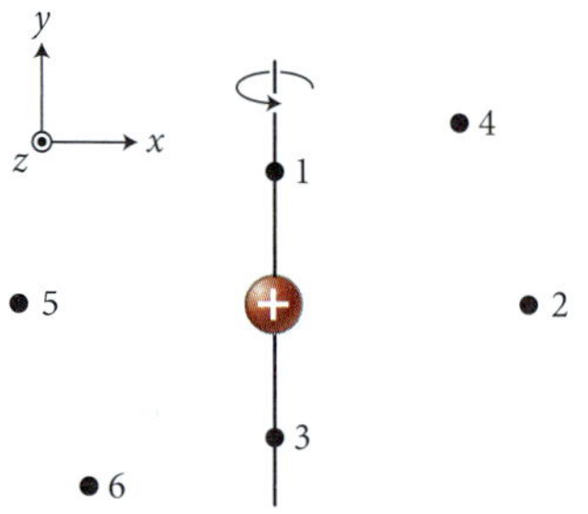

15. Sometimes when a current loop is constructed, a rectangular geometry is more convenient than a circular geometry. How would the magnetic field from a small square current loop compare with that from a small circular current loop? ●●

16. Consider two charged particles 1 and 2, each of them able to translate (move from place to place) and to spin. In which of the following circumstances is there a magnetic interaction between the particles: (*a*) neither particle translating, neither particle spinning; (*b*) neither translating, only particle 1 spinning; (*c*) neither translating, both spinning; (*d*) 1 at rest and not spinning, 2 translating and not spinning; (*e*) 1 at rest and not spinning, 2 translating and spinning; (*f*) 1 spinning and not translating, 2 translating and not spinning; (*g*) 1 spinning and not translating, 2 translating and spinning; (*h*) both translating, neither spinning; (*i*) both translating, only 2 spinning; (*j*) both translating, both spinning. ●●

17. A circular current-carrying wire loop produces a magnetic field. A spinning disk of uniformly distributed charge produces a similar magnetic field. How would you expect the field due to a spinning disk to compare to the field due to a current-carrying wire loop? ●●

18. For the bar magnet in Figure P28.18, which of the four locations labeled 1, 2, 3, 4 has the greatest density of magnetic field lines? ●●

Figure P28.18

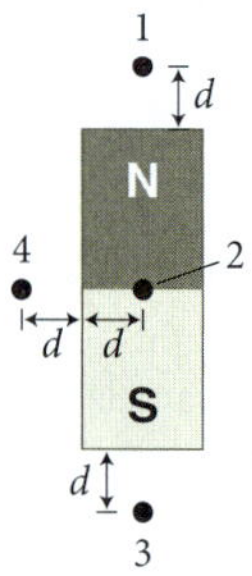

19. A negatively charged particle located at the origin of an xyz coordinate system is spinning clockwise about the x axis (that is, clockwise when you look at the particle while standing somewhere on the positive x axis). What is the direction of its magnetic field at all positions along (*a*) the x axis, (*b*) the y axis, and (*c*) the z axis? ●●

PRACTICE

20. Figure P28.20 shows a wire segment bent into a half-circle, with the center of curvature labeled P. If the wire of which this segment is a part is extremely long and carries a current I, what is the direction of the magnetic field at P? ••

Figure P28.20

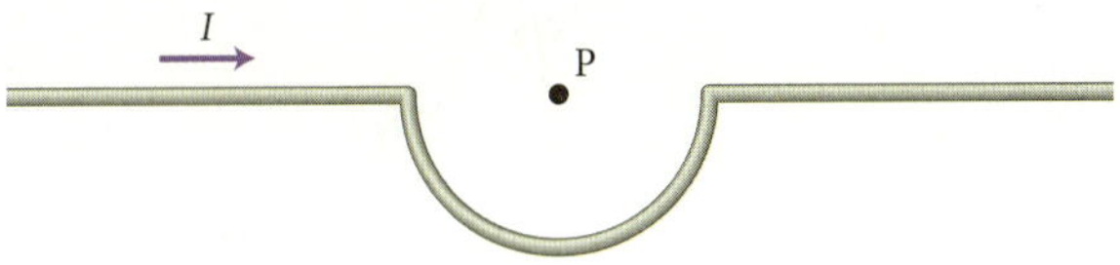

21. In the Bohr model of the hydrogen atom, an electron orbits a nucleus consisting of one proton. Given that the electron and proton are both spinning, describe the types of magnetic interactions you expect to be associated with the hydrogen atom. •••

28.3 Magnetic dipole moment and torque

22. In the space surrounding Earth, the main component of the planet's magnetic field is the field due to a magnetic dipole. In what direction is Earth's magnetic dipole moment? •

23. Earth's magnetic field is thought to be generated by currents in the planet's core. In what direction (clockwise or counterclockwise, when viewed along the rotation axis from north to south) does this current circulate? •

24. The disk shown in Figure P28.24 is charged with electrons and spins counterclockwise when viewed from above. From this perspective, what is the direction of the magnetic dipole moment of the disk? •

Figure P28.24

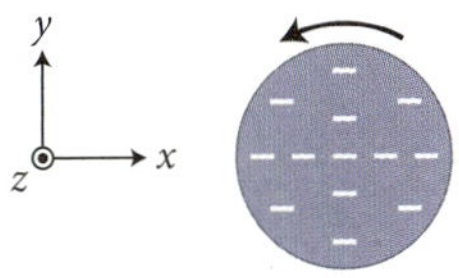

25. In the open wire loop of Figure P28.25, end 1 is held at a higher potential than end 2. (*a*) In which direction do electrons move through the loop? (*b*) What is the direction of the current? (*c*) What is the direction of the loop's magnetic dipole moment? ••

Figure P28.25

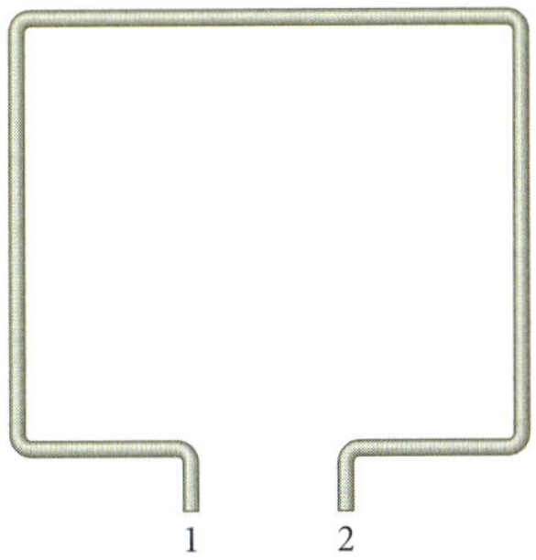

26. Figure P28.26 shows part of the rotation of an electric motor, during which the magnetic dipole moment of the loop points to the left or has some component to the left. If the entire rotation were shown, during what fraction of the rotation would the magnetic dipole moment have some component pointing to the right? ••

Figure P28.26

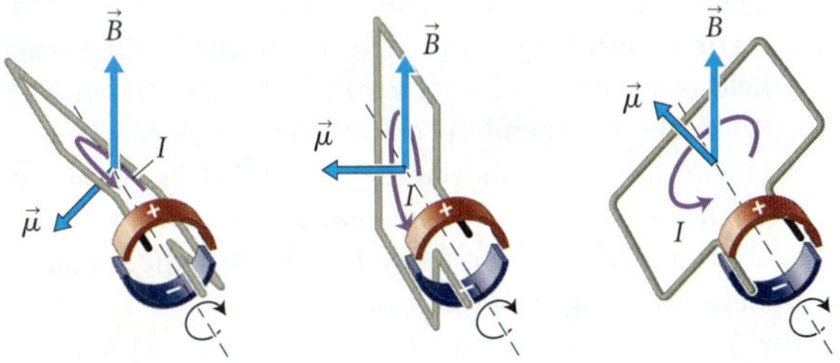

27. A current loop lying in the xy plane of an xyz coordinate system experiences a torque that is clockwise about the y axis when viewed looking down from the positive y axis toward the origin. This torque is due to a uniform external magnetic field that points in the positive x direction. What is the direction of the current in the loop? ••

28. A current loop lies in the xy plane of an xyz coordinate system, with the current circulating counterclockwise when viewed looking down the positive z axis toward the origin. The loop experiences a torque about the x axis that is counterclockwise when viewed looking down the positive x axis toward the origin. Describe the direction of the uniform external magnetic field responsible for this torque. ••

29. Determine the direction of the magnetic dipole moment in each current loop or charge distribution in Figure P28.29. In (*c*), the higher potential end of the loop is marked +. ••

Figure P28.29

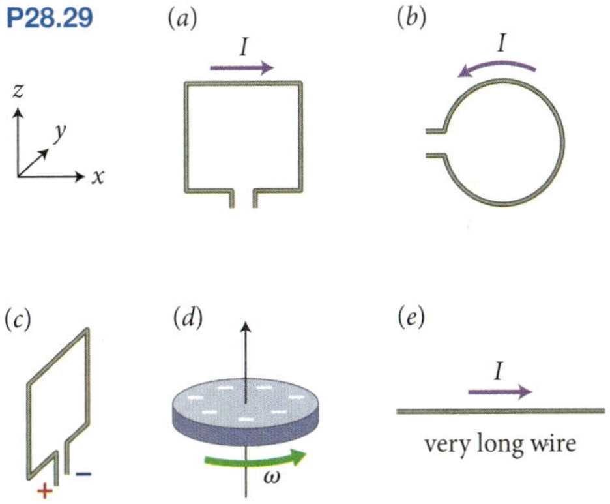

30. (*a*) As the electric motor shown schematically in Figure P28.30 operates, which of the arrows shown could represent the magnetic dipole moment at various instants? (*b*) If there are any arrows that are not possible magnetic dipole moment vectors, state why they are not allowed. ••

Figure P28.30

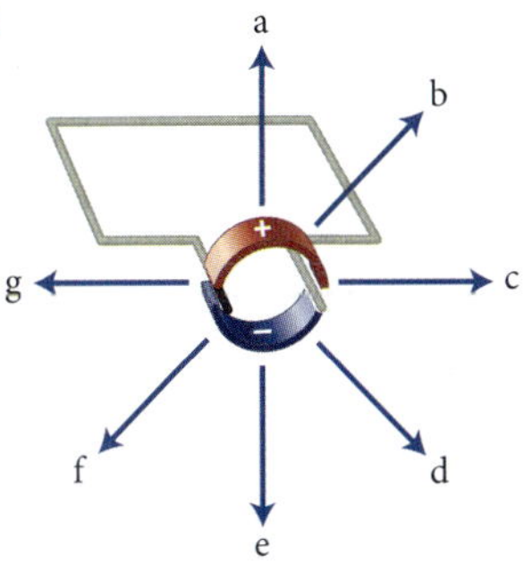

31. Figure P28.31 shows a rectangular loop of current in an external magnetic field. Initially the plane of the loop makes a 65° angle with the magnetic field. (*a*) Determine the direction of the magnetic force exerted on each side of the loop. Treat side 4 as though it were one unbroken wire. (*b*) Determine the direction of the torque on the loop about the axis shown as a dashed line. (*c*) What is the orientation of the loop once the system reaches equilibrium? ••

Figure P28.31

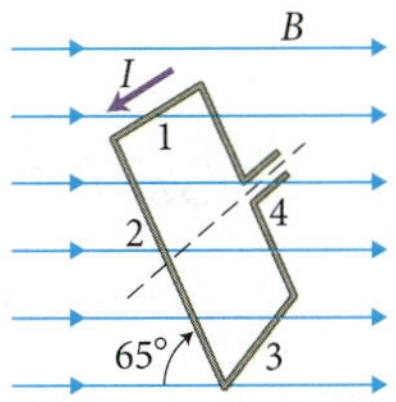

32. *Principles* Figure 28.10 shows a current loop in an external magnetic field and the forces exerted on the different lengths of the wire. Assume that the loop is attached to a pivot that allows it to spin (as between *Principles* Figures 28.10 and 28.11). (*a*) Determine the directions of all the forces on the loop if the current were reversed. (*b*) Is this new situation any different from that shown in *Principles* Figure 28.11? •••

33. A negatively charged particle is held in position and then released in a region where a uniform magnetic field points in the positive x direction and a uniform electric field points in the positive y direction. The particle is spinning about an axis parallel to the z axis, and the spin is clockwise when viewed looking down from the positive z axis toward the origin. (*a*) Is the electromagnetic force exerted on the particle different from what it would be if the particle were not spinning? (*b*) Would there be any other changes if the particle were not spinning? If so, describe them. •••

28.4 Ampèrian paths

34. The current loop in Figure P28.34 lies in the xy plane. For each of the Ampèrian paths (*a*)–(*e*), is the line integral of the magnetic field positive, negative, or zero? •

Figure P28.34

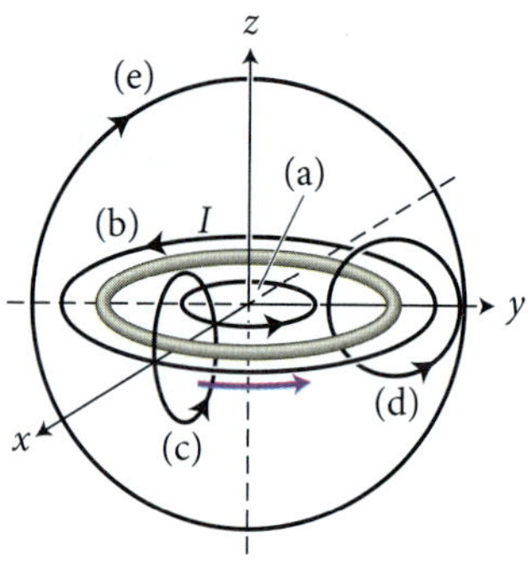

35. Wires 1 to 5 in Figure P28.35 carry current either into or out of the page. What is the magnitude of the current enclosed by the Ampèrian path indicated? Is the line integral of the magnetic field around this path, in the direction indicated, positive, negative, or zero? •

Figure P28.35

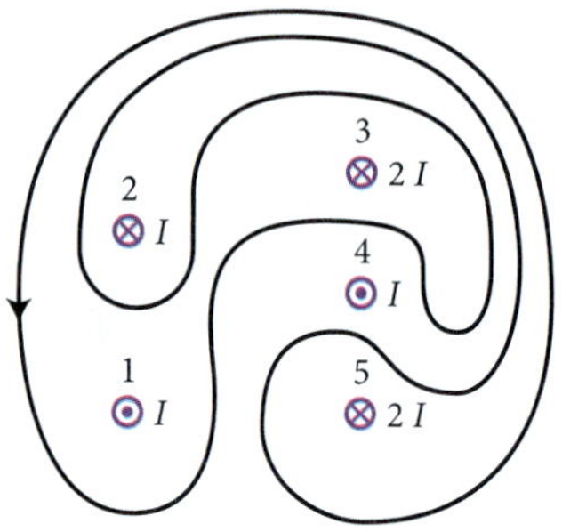

36. Is the line integral of the magnetic field along the closed path in Figure P28.36 positive, negative, or zero? The direction of integration is shown with arrows on the path. •

Figure P28.36

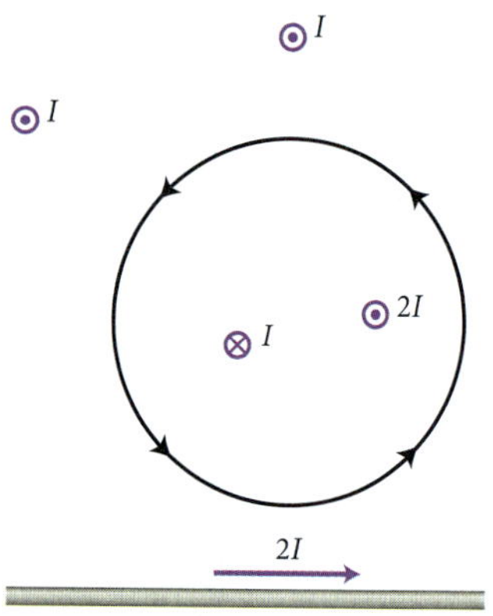

37. Figure P28.37 shows a series of current-carrying wires, and in each case an Ampèrian path is shown. Rank the six cases according to the magnitude of the line integral of the magnetic field calculated along the Ampèrian path shown in each case, smallest value of $|\oint \vec{B} \cdot d\vec{\ell}|$ first. ••

Figure P28.37

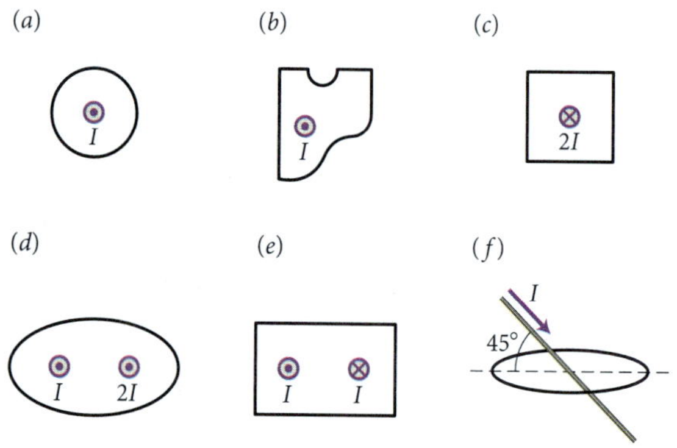

38. The line integral of the magnetic field around a certain closed path is initially L. The current that penetrates this path is then doubled. What can you say about the current through the path if the new integral of the magnetic field around the closed path is (*a*) L and (*b*) $2L$? ••

39. Each of the wires 1 to 3 in Figure P28.39 carries a current perpendicular to the page. The line integrals of the magnetic field around the three Ampèrian paths shown all have the same positive value. How do the magnitudes and directions of the three currents compare? ••

Figure P28.39

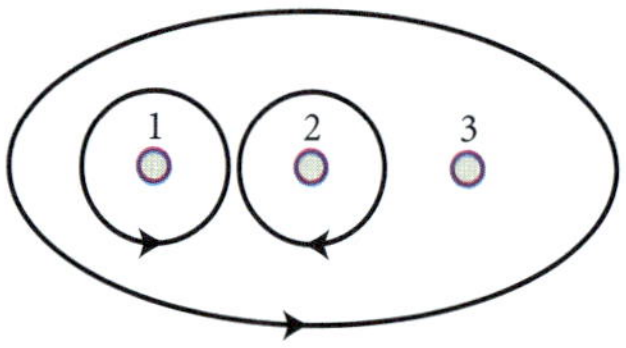

40. A positively charged particle located at the origin of an xyz coordinate system spins about the z axis, and the spin is counterclockwise when viewed looking down from the positive z axis toward the origin. Is the line integral of the magnetic field positive, negative, or zero for an Ampèrian path going (*a*) clockwise around the origin in the xy plane when viewed looking down from the positive z axis, (*b*) clockwise around the origin in the yz plane when viewed looking from the positive x axis, and (*c*) clockwise around the origin in the xz plane when viewed looking from the positive y axis? ••

41. Eleven wires and one Ampèrian path are shown in Figure P28.41, with current values and directions as indicated. Is the line integral of the magnetic field along the Ampèrian path shown greater than, smaller than, or equal to zero? ••

Figure P28.41

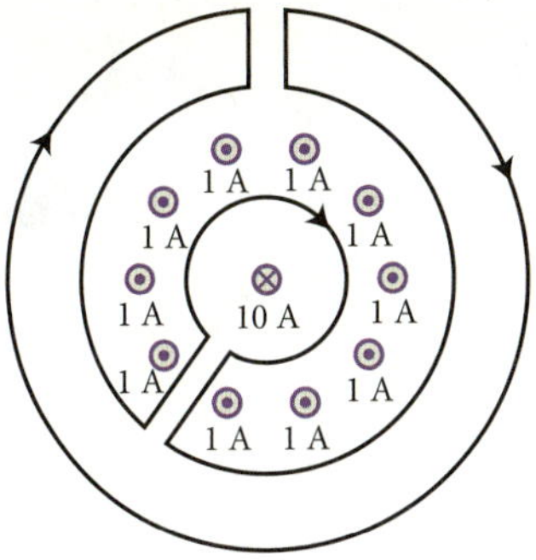

42. Figure P28.42 shows magnetic field lines in a certain region. Are there any locations where there must be a current directed into or out of the plane of the diagram? (Consider locations near the numbers on the vertical axis.) At which of the locations 1–9 does a current exist? What is the current direction in each case? ••

Figure P28.42

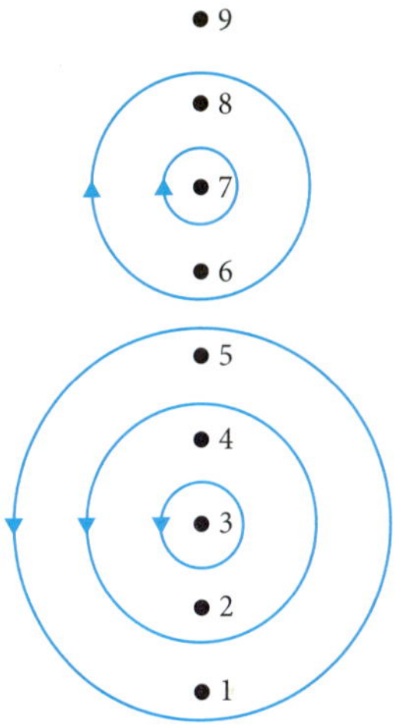

43. Figure P28.43 shows two paths (A and B) around a wire that carries current I. (*a*) Along which path is the line integral of the magnetic field greater? (*b*) Along which path is the average magnetic field greater? (*c*) Explain how your answers to parts *a* and *b* are consistent. •••

Figure P28.43

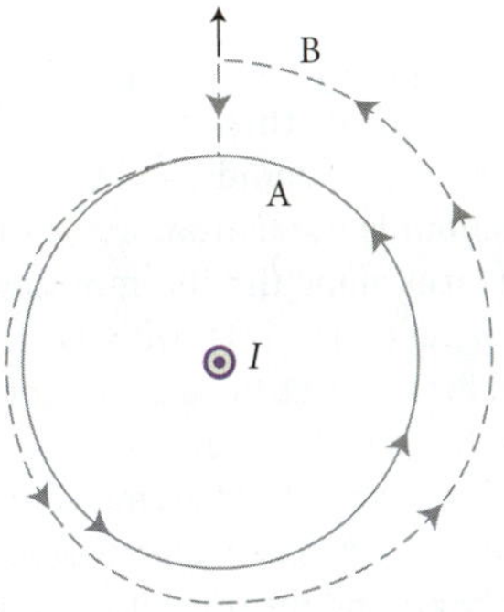

44. Figure P28.44 shows a very long wire that carries a current I in the z direction and is centered in the xy plane at the position (0, 0). The line integral of the magnetic field along Ampèrian path 1 is $-5.50\ \text{T} \cdot \text{m}$. Determine the line integral of the magnetic field along path 2. •••

Figure P28.44

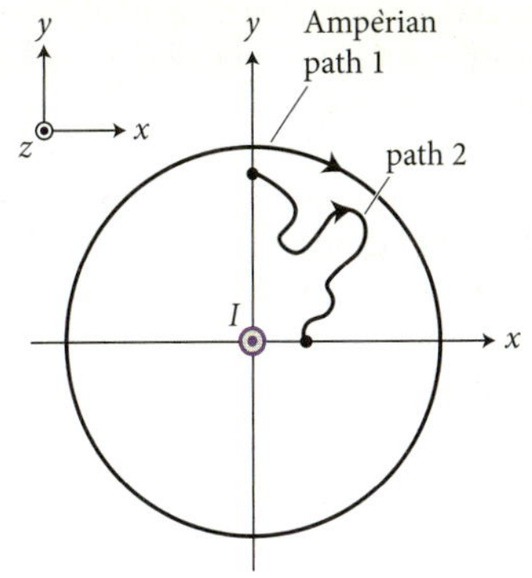

28.5 Ampère's law

45. At a location 25 mm away from a long, straight current-carrying wire, the magnitude of the magnetic field due to the wire is 2.0×10^{-5} T. Calculate the magnitude of the current in the wire. •

46. A long, straight wire carrying 1.5 A of current to the left is placed above a large, flat sheet through which the current per unit width is 3.0 A/m to the left. What are the magnitude and direction of the magnetic force exerted on each 1.0-m length of the wire? •

47. The magnetic field magnitude is 4.0 mT at a position 6.2 mm radially away from a long current-carrying wire. Calculate (*a*) the current in the wire and (*b*) the magnetic field magnitude at a position 77 mm radially away from the wire. •

48. Two straight wires separated by a very small distance run parallel to each other, one carrying a current of 3.0 A to the right and the other carrying a current of 4.0 A to the left. Give the approximate value for the magnitude of the magnetic field a large distance r from both wires. ••

49. A moving particle carrying charge e traveling to the right at 2.5×10^7 m/s initially feels no magnetic force. When a long current-carrying wire is placed parallel to the line of motion of the particle at a location 3.0 μm away from the particle, an initial force of magnitude 7.0×10^{-13} N is exerted on the particle. What is the magnitude of the current in the wire? ••

50. An electric current is uniformly distributed throughout a long, straight wire that has a diameter of 50 mm. If the current through the wire is 6.0 A, calculate the magnitude of the magnetic field (*a*) 20 mm radially away from the wire center and (*b*) 50 mm radially away from the wire center. (*c*) What must the current be to create a magnetic field of magnitude 1.0 T 50 mm radially away from the wire center? ••

51. Two large, flat current-carrying sheets are placed parallel to each other, one sheet above the other. The upper sheet carries a current 2.0 A per unit of width to the left, and the lower sheet carries a current 5.0 A per unit of width to the right. Calculate the magnitude of the magnetic field (*a*) between the sheets, (*b*) above the upper sheet, and (*c*) below the lower sheet. (*d*) Draw a diagram showing the direction of the magnetic field in each of these regions. ••

52. A electron travels to the right at 3.0×10^6 m/s between two large, flat sheets that are parallel to each other and to the electron's line of motion. If currents per unit width of 8.0 A/m to the right through the top sheet and 8.0 A/m to the left through the bottom sheet are then generated, what is the magnitude of the magnetic force exerted on the electron? Draw a diagram showing the direction of the magnetic field between the sheets and the direction of the magnetic force exerted on the electron. ••

53. A certain wire has a circular cross section of radius R and carries a current I. Suppose that the charge carriers all move along the cylindrical surface of the wire, not through its cross-sectional area. (*a*) Derive an expression for the magnetic field magnitude $B(r)$ as a function of distance r from the center of the wire; check that your expression makes sense for $r < R$ and for $r > R$. (*b*) Make a graph showing the magnitude of the magnetic field in and around the wire as a function of the radial distance r from the center. Mark the wire radius R on your graph. ••

54. Point P is a distance $d_1 = 4.0$ mm above a large sheet of metal that carries a current of 40 A in the positive x direction and a distance $d_2 = 3.0$ mm below a very long wire that carries a current of 0.35 A in the positive x direction. If the magnetic field magnitude at P is zero, calculate the width of the metal sheet. ••

55. Two large, parallel, current-carrying plates are oriented horizontally and the vertical distance between them is 5.0 mm. The current per unit width in each plate is 100 A/m, and both currents are in the positive x direction. Determine the magnitude and direction of the magnetic force per unit area exerted by the lower plate on the upper plate. ••

56. A coaxial cable carries a current I_{wire} in its inner conducting wire and a current I_{shell}in its outer conducting shell. The radius of the wire is R_{wire}, the distance from the cable center to the inside of the shell is R_{shell}, and the distance from the center to the outer edge of the shell is $2R_{shell}$. Determine all locations (if any exist) at which the magnetic field magnitude is zero if (*a*) $I_{wire} = I_{shell}$, (*b*) $I_{wire} = -I_{shell}$, and (*c*) $I_{wire} = -I_{shell}/2$. •••

57. A particle of mass 9.1×10^{-31} kg and carrying an unknown quantity of charge is shot at a velocity of 2.0×10^4 m/s to the right and enters the magnetic field generated by a large, flat current-carrying sheet. The current in the sheet is parallel to the particle's initial line of motion. The particle exits the magnetic field 90 mm directly above the location where it enters. If the sheet carries a current of 4.0 A per unit width, what is the magnitude of the charge of the particle? •••

28.6 Solenoids and toroids

58. A long solenoid with 300 windings per meter of length carries a current of 1.0 A. Calculate the magnitude of the magnetic field inside the solenoid. •

59. You need to use a long solenoid to produce a magnetic field of magnitude 0.070 T. If the maximum current you are able to run through the windings is 20 A, what is the minimum number of windings per meter the solenoid must have? •

60. A small solenoid is inserted into a larger solenoid (Figure P28.60). The current in the small solenoid is from A to B. (*a*) Determine the initial direction of the magnetic dipole moment of the small solenoid. (*b*) Assuming the large solenoid is fixed in place and the small solenoid is free to rotate, determine the equilibrium direction of the magnetic dipole moment of the small solenoid. •

Figure P28.60

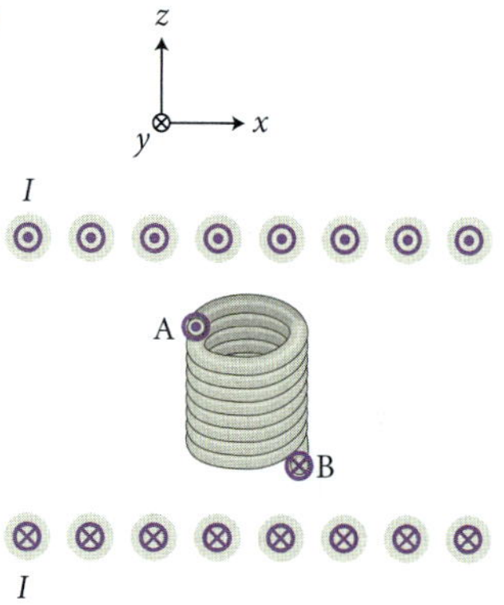

61. A long, straight wire carrying a current of 2.5 A to the left is placed directly below and parallel to the central axis of a solenoid that has 1000 windings per meter of length and a current of 45 mA. Calculate the magnitude and direction of the magnetic field at the center of the solenoid if the wire is 50 mm away from the solenoid center. Does it matter whether the wire is inside or outside the solenoid coils? ••

62. Calculate the magnitude of the magnetic force exerted on a wire that is 20 mm long and carries a current of 4.0 A when it is suspended inside a solenoid at an angle of 45° to the magnetic field. The solenoid has 700 turns per meter of length and carries a current of 3.0 A. ••

63. A toroid has 250 square windings carrying a current of 3.0 mA. Each side of each square winding is 50 mm long, and the distance from the toroid center to the inner surface of the windings is 120 mm. What is the magnitude of the magnetic field (*a*) at the center of any square winding, (*b*) midway between the toroid center and the inner surface of the windings, and (*c*) 30 mm beyond the outer surface of the windings? ••

64. At what radial distance r from the center of a toroid of 200 windings does the magnitude of the magnetic field equal that found inside a solenoid that has 500 turns per meter of length? Assume that the current is the same through both devices. ••

65. A toroid carries a current I and has n circular windings per unit length measured along the inside edge of the windings. The radius of each circular winding is $R_{winding}$, and the inner radius of the toroid is R_{toroid}. Derive an expression for the magnetic field magnitude at any location inside the circular windings. ••

66. An electron is fired into one end of the solenoid in Figure P28.66. Viewed along the positive x axis from a negative x coordinate, the electron enters from below at a 65° angle to the horizontal, just inside the bottom edge of the solenoid. From this viewpoint the solenoid carries a 10-A clockwise current. The solenoid is made from a 33.0-m length of wire, and it has 400 turns along the 200-mm length shown in the figure. (*a*) Ignoring end effects, what is the smallest time interval required for the electron to pass through the solenoid without striking the coils? (*b*) If the electron follows the quickest path through the solenoid as determined from the time interval you calculated in part *a*, how many revolutions does the electron's path make around the solenoid axis? •••

Figure P28.66

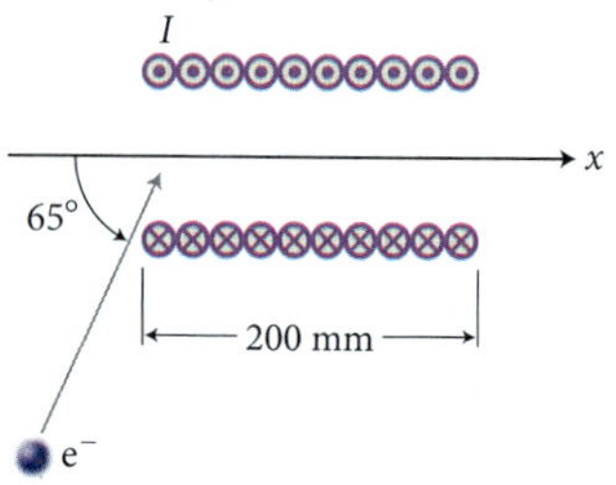

67. You are calibrating magnetic coils for a particle detector. One step involves checking the magnetic field at different positions inside a toroid, and you are asked to measure the field at the positions labeled 1, 2, 3, 4 in Figure P28.67. Your partner, knowing that the magnetic field inside a *solenoid* is uniform, asks why anyone would measure more than one position inside the toroid, which is a solenoid bent into a ring. How can you explain the need to compare the field magnitudes at positions 1 and 2? Why compare the magnitudes at positions 3 and 4? Can you explain to your partner why the magnetic field is not uniform in a toroid even though a toroid is nothing more than a solenoid bent into a donut shape? •••

Figure P28.67

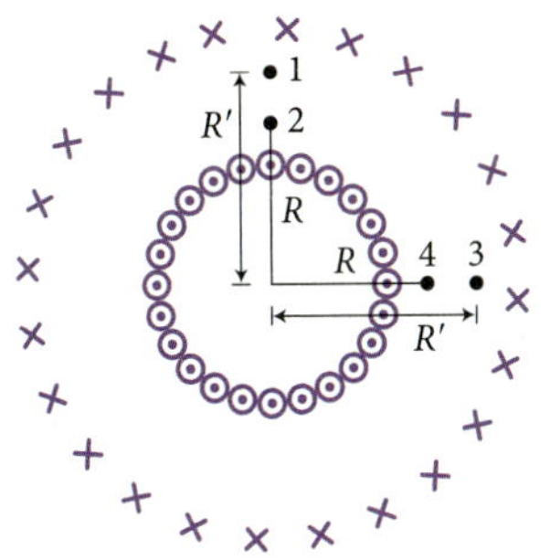

28.7 Magnetic fields due to currents

68. Calculate the magnitude of the magnetic field at the center of a circular arc of radius 25 mm spanning an angle of $\pi/2$ and carrying a current of 3.0 A. •

69. Wire 1, 5.0 m long and carrying a current of 3.0 A, experiences a magnetic force of magnitude 4.0×10^{-7} N when placed 90 mm away from wire 2 running parallel to wire 1. What must the magnitude of the current in wire 2 be? •

70. Use the Biot-Savart law to determine the magnetic field 70 mm above the center of a loop of wire that has a radius of 0.22 m and carries 3.0 A of current. ••

71. Wire 1, 3.0 m long and of linear mass density 0.010 kg/m, is initially held in place and carries 10 A of current to the right. Very long wire 2 is placed parallel to and 5.0 mm directly above wire 1. When wire 1 is released, it stays in place. What are the magnitude and direction of the current in wire 2? ••

72. Suppose that we can use wire of 1.0-mm diameter to make either a single loop of wire or a solenoid, and we wish to compare, for a given current, the magnetic fields at the center of each. (*a*) Use the Biot-Savart law to derive an expression for the magnetic field magnitude at the center of a circular current loop. (*b*) Compare the magnitude of the magnetic field at the center of a circular current loop of radius 10 mm with the magnitude of the magnetic field at the center of a solenoid of the same radius and with 1.0 turn per millimeter. Assume the current is the same through the current loop and the solenoid. ••

73. In Figure P28.73, point P is the common center of two circular arcs of wire, the larger of radius 70 mm and the smaller of radius 20 mm. What are the magnitude and direction of the magnetic field at P if the current through the wire is 3.0 mA? ••

Figure P28.73

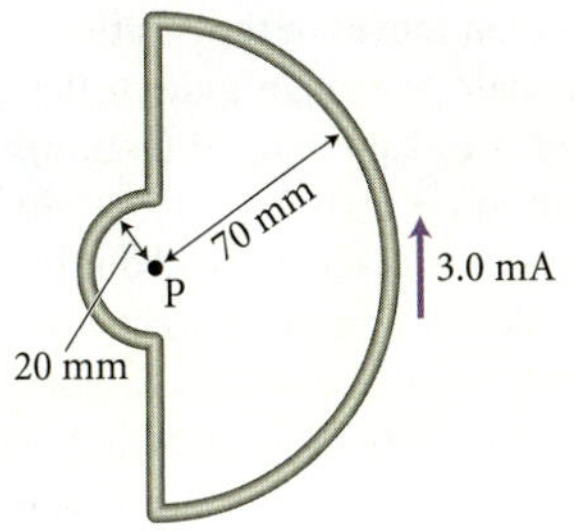

74. A current-carrying wire has been bent into the form shown in Figure P28.74, with a half-circle of radius R_1 lying in the *xy* plane connected via two straight segments to a half-circle of radius R_2 lying in the *yz* plane. The current direction is as indicated. If $R_2 = 1.5\,R_1$, what is the direction of the magnetic field at P, which lies at the common center of the half-circles? ••

Figure P28.74

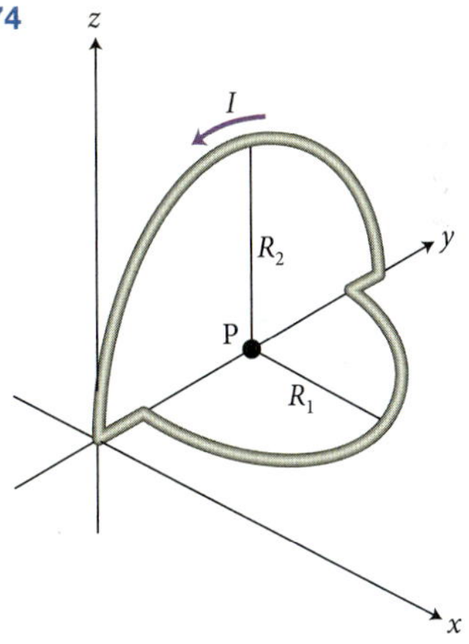

75. A wire carrying a 3.0-A current lies along the *x* axis of an *xy* coordinate system, extending from $x = 0$ to $x = 10$ m. What is the magnitude of the magnetic field at point P located at $x = 0$, $y = 2.0$ m? •••

76. The horizontal portion of the wire in Figure P28.76 has a length $\ell = 0.100$ m, and position P is a perpendicular distance $d = 30.0$ mm above the center of the horizontal portion. The wire carries a 45.0-A current, and the two slanted portions of the wire are extremely long. Calculate the magnitude of the magnetic field at P. •••

Figure P28.76

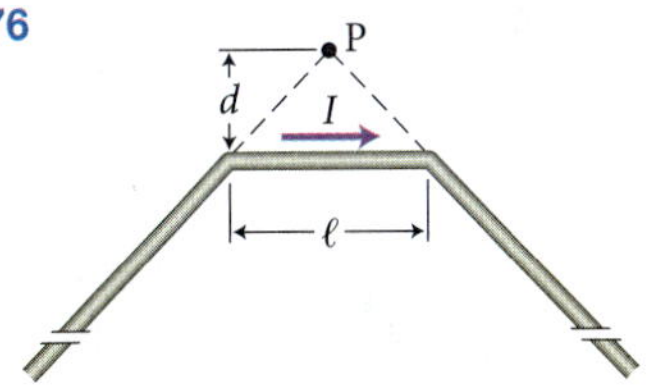

28.8 Magnetic field of a moving charged particle

77. An electron moves in a straight line at a speed of 6.0×10^7 m/s. Calculate the magnitude and direction of the magnetic field at a position 5.0 mm behind the electron and 15 mm below its line of motion. •

78. A proton moves in the positive x direction at 4.00×10^4 m/s. Calculate the magnitude of the magnetic field at the point $(x, y) = (+2.00 \text{ mm}, +1.00 \text{ mm})$ as the proton passes through the origin. •

79. Express the magnetic field due to a uniformly moving charged particle in terms of the electric field of the particle. ••

80. Two electrons 1 and 2 move along antiparallel paths separated by a distance of 10 nm, traveling at speeds $v_1 = 4.0 \times 10^7$ m/s and $v_2 = 7.0 \times 10^6$ m/s. What is the magnitude of the magnetic force exerted by electron 2 on electron 1? ••

81. Proton 1, traveling in the negative x direction at speed v_1, is directly below proton 2, which is traveling at speed v_2 at an angle of 45° above the positive x axis. If the protons are separated by a distance r, calculate the magnitude of the magnetic force each proton exerts on the other. ••

82. A charged particle is traveling through a uniform magnetic field, with its velocity perpendicular to the field direction. In Section 27.7 you learned that such a particle experiences a magnetic force that causes it to move in a circular path. Also, because it is moving, the charged particle creates its own magnetic field $\vec{B}_p$. (*a*) Derive an expression for the magnetic field magnitude B_p at the center of the circular path in terms of the magnitude B_{ext} of the external uniform magnetic field, the particle's orbit radius R, the charge q on the particle, and the particle's mass m. (*b*) Using $c_0 = 1/\sqrt{\mu_0 \epsilon_0}$, show that your expression can be cast in the form below. ••

$$\frac{q^2}{4\pi\epsilon_0 R} \frac{1}{mc_0^2} B_{ext}$$

83. Electron 1, initially traveling to the right at 1.5×10^6 m/s, is accelerated upward at 900 m/s² by the electromagnetic force exerted by electron 2, which is directly beneath electron 1 and traveling to the left at 4.0×10^6 m/s. What must the distance between the electrons be? ••

84. An electron and a proton are fired in opposite directions, and at the instant they are nearest each other, their separation distance is 3.0 μm (Figure P28.84). At that instant, the two particles are both moving at 3.0×10^4 m/s but in opposite directions. (*a*) Determine the magnitude and direction of the magnetic force exerted by the proton on the electron at this instant. (*b*) Show that the ratio of the magnetic to electric forces at this instant equals v^2/c_0^2, where $v = 3.0 \times 10^4$ m/s and c_0 is the speed of light. ••

Figure P28.84

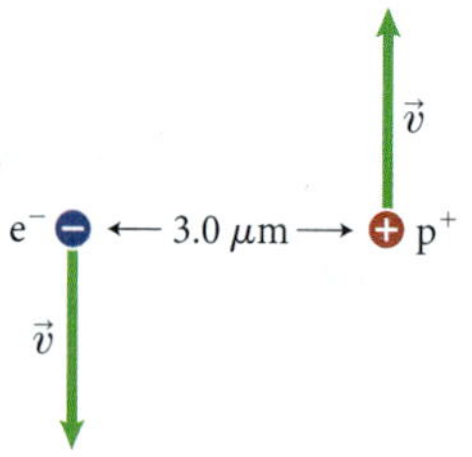

85. Two electrons move near each other and at the instant shown in Figure P28.85 are 2.0 mm apart. The speed of electron 1 is $v_1 = 300$ m/s, that of electron 2 is $v_2 = 500$ m/s, and the directions of motion are as shown in Figure P28.85. Determine the magnitude and direction of (*a*) the magnetic force exerted by electron 1 on electron 2 and (*b*) the magnetic force exerted by electron 2 on electron 1. ••

Figure P28.85

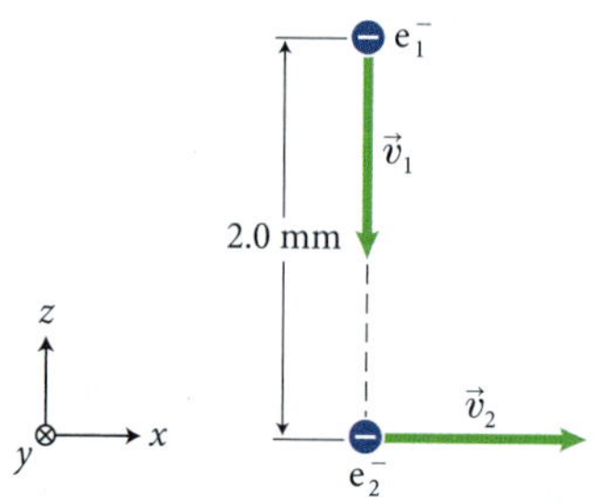

86. At $t = 0$, electron 1 is shot out of an accelerator at a speed of 2.0×10^3 m/s. At $t = 1.0$ μs, electron 2 is shot out of the accelerator and travels on a path that is parallel to and 10 mm below the path of electron 1. The speed of electron 2 is 5.0×10^3 m/s. (*a*) At $t = 3.0$ μs, what is the magnitude of the magnetic field at a point that is 3.0 mm ahead of electron 1 and 5.0 mm below it? Assume that the magnetic forces the electrons exert on each other for the 2.0 μs before you make your calculations do not alter the electrons' paths significantly. (*b*) Show whether or not it is valid to assume that the magnetic forces the electrons exert on each other during the interval from $t = 1.0$ μs to $t = 3.0$ μs do not alter the electrons' paths significantly. •••

Additional Problems

87. A current loop lies in the xy plane, with the current circulating counterclockwise when viewed from the positive z axis. Is there a torque on the loop, and if so, in what direction, if a uniform magnetic field is applied along the positive (*a*) x axis, (*b*) y axis, and (*c*) z axis? •

88. A solenoid that is 200 mm long has 200 turns. What current I in the solenoid is required to produce a magnetic field of magnitude 1.0 T inside the solenoid? •

89. Wire 1 is 2.3 m long and carries a current of 2.2 A to the right. Wire 2 is also 2.3 m long, and it carries a current of 3.0 A to the left. The wires are parallel to each other and separated by a distance of 0.25 m. Determine the direction and magnitude of the magnetic force exerted by wire 2 on wire 1. ••

90. Figure P28.90 shows two square loops of wire. The loop on the right is fixed in place, and the one on the left is free to pivot in any direction. Both loops carry a current that is counterclockwise when viewed from above. (*a*) What is the direction of the magnetic field created by the right loop at the left loop? (*b*) What is the initial direction of the magnetic dipole moment of the left loop? (*c*) How does the left loop rotate? (*d*) After the left loop is allowed to rotate and the system reaches equilibrium, are the magnetic dipole moments of the two loops parallel, antiparallel, or neither? ••

Figure P28.90

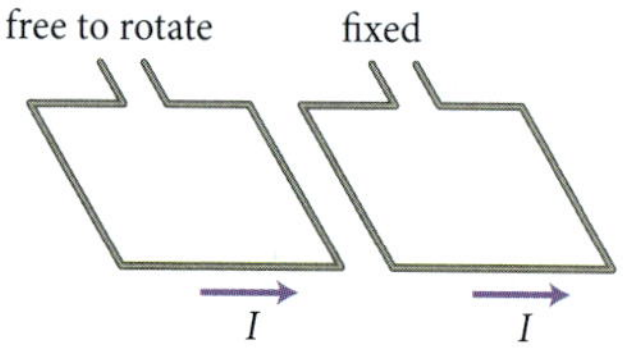

91. Wire 1, with mass 0.010 kg and length 1.0 m, has a square cross section and is initially at rest on a table. It is connected by flexible leads to a battery and carries a steady current of 1.5 A. When wire 2 is placed parallel to wire 1 a distance 2.0 mm away, wire 1 begins to slide across the table away from wire 2. If the coefficient of static friction between wire 1 and the table is 0.050, what must be the minimum current through wire 2? ••

92. Two of your friends separately calculated a magnetic field line integral around a long, straight current-carrying wire in a homework problem, but they arrived at different answers. Now they want your help, so they send you a copy of their work. Andy chose a square path for his line integral, a path centered on the wire in a plane perpendicular to the wire. Beth chose a path in the shape of an equilateral triangle encircling the wire in the same plane, with one side exactly equal in length to and aligned with one side of Andy's square path. The wire penetrates the center of the square but not the center of the triangle. Andy came up with a value of 64 T · m for the line integral, and Beth calculated 89 T · m. Andy's integral along the common side was 10 T · m, and Beth's integral along this side was 45 T · m. Unfortunately they forgot to send you any details about the current in the wire. You begin to text them for more information, but you suddenly realize that you need nothing more to evaluate quite a bit about their work. ••• CR

93. Your design team is working on an air-core toroid that is to have the greatest feasible magnetic field per ampere of current but in which the greatest magnetic field magnitude must be exactly four times the smallest magnetic field magnitude. Because of space and cost restrictions, the maximum length of wire you can use is 100 m and the core radius must be at least 30 mm. You begin to speculate about how many turns the toroid needs to have, its inner and outer radii, and how much magnetic field you might achieve. ••• CR

Answers to Review Questions

1. Particles in motion—either moving in a straight line or spinning about an axis—cause magnetic fields.
2. Magnetic forces are generally not central; that is, they do not point along the line joining two source elements.
3. Yes. For example, the magnetic field due to a charged particle moving in a straight line has no poles.
4. The two field line patterns are similar to each other, and both resemble the pattern of the magnetic field due to an infinitesimally small magnetic dipole.
5. The magnetic field due to a spinning charged particle is identical to the magnetic field due to an infinitesimally small magnetic dipole.
6. The direction of the magnetic dipole moment vector is the same as the direction of the magnetic field line passing through the center of the dipole. This is from S to N in a bar magnet or according to the right-hand dipole rule for a current loop.
7. The right-hand current rule gives magnetic field direction when current direction is known, and vice versa. The right-hand force rule gives magnetic force direction when current direction and magnetic field direction are known, and vice versa. The right-hand dipole rule gives magnetic dipole moment direction when current direction is known, and vice versa. These rules are illustrated in *Principles* Figure 28.9.
8. The vector sum of forces exerted on the current loop is zero, but there is a nonzero vector sum of torques that tends to align the loop's magnetic dipole moment vector with the external magnetic field.
9. The commutator reverses the direction of the current through the motor's current loop every time the loop rotates one-half turn (just as the loop's magnetic dipole moment aligns with the external field), so that the magnetic torque keeps the loop always rotating in the same direction.
10. Electrostatic field lines originate and terminate on charged particles; magnetic field lines form closed loops. Therefore, the electric flux through a closed surface is proportional to the amount of charge inside, but the corresponding magnetic flux through the surface is always zero.
11. The line integral of the electrostatic field is always zero, regardless of the quantity of charge; that of the magnetic field depends on the amount of current encircled.
12. The line integral of the magnetic field along a closed path is proportional to the current encircled by the path.
13. If the direction in which the Ampèrian path encircles the current is the same as the direction of the magnetic field created by the current, the current makes a positive contribution to the line integral; otherwise, the current makes a negative contribution.
14. The constant shows the relationship between the line integral of the magnetic field around an Ampèrian path and the amount of current encircled by the path.
15. The wire has cylindrical symmetry. Because of its cylindrical symmetry, the magnetic field lines are concentric circles with constant magnitude at each radius. In using Ampère's law to determine this magnitude, you should choose an Ampèrian path that coincides with one of the field lines.
16. The magnitude of the magnetic field at any point outside the wire is inversely proportional to the radial distance from the wire axis. This is true because all the current in the wire is encircled by the Ampèrian path, and the length of the path is proportional to the radial distance from the axis. At points inside the wire, the magnitude is directly proportional to the radial distance from the axis because in this case only a fraction of the current is encircled by the magnetic field line used as the Ampèrian path. How large that fraction is depends on the ratio of the area encircled by the Ampèrian path to the cross-sectional area of the wire (see *Principles* Checkpoint 28.12).
17. The magnetic field is uniform on either side of the sheet; in other words, it has the same magnitude at all distances above and below the sheet, with the field magnitude given by the result of *Principles* Example 28.4: $B = \frac{1}{2}\mu_0 K$, where K is the current per unit width carried by the sheet. The field direction lies in the plane of the sheet and is perpendicular to the current, as given by the right-hand current rule. The field direction is diametrically opposite on the two sides.
18. A solenoid is a tightly wound, long coil of wire used to produce a magnetic field. The field pattern is like that of a bar magnet oriented along the axis of the solenoid, and the field is much greater inside the solenoid than outside. The field is approximately uniform inside, proportional to the current and the number of turns per unit length (Eq. 28.6), and approximately zero outside.
19. A toroid is a tightly wound, donut-shaped coil of wire, as would result from bending a solenoid into a circle so that it ends meet. Its magnetic field is confined to the donut-shaped interior cavity, with magnitude inversely proportional to the distance from the center of the circle (the distance from the central axis of the donut hole), and direction in accordance with the right-hand current rule.
20. The magnetic field inside the solenoid is approximately uniform, but the field inside the toroid is not—it depends inversely on the distance from the axis about which the toroid would roll if it were a car tire.
21. Both fields are directly proportional to the strength of the source ($I d\vec{\ell}$ for the magnetic field, dq_s for the electrostatic field) and inversely proportional to the square of the radial separation distance, but the electrostatic field is directed along the unit vector to the field point, while the magnetic field depends on the vector product of the current segment and this unit vector.
22. First use Ampère's law (Eq. 28.1) along a circular path of radius d centered on wire 1, to determine the magnetic field at the location of wire 2 due to the current in wire 1. Then use the magnetic force law (Eq. 27.8) to calculate the force exerted on wire 2 due to the magnetic field of wire 1. The result is $F^B_{12} = \mu_0 \ell I_1 I_2/(2\pi d)$ (Eq. 28.16).
23. Ampère's law is useful only in situations where the field direction is known from symmetry and only the magnitude must be determined. The Biot-Savart law is not limited to symmetrical situations and can be used to compute the magnetic field due to a steady current circulating in any closed circuit, provided, of course, that the integral of Eq. 28.10 is amenable to analytic or numerical evaluation.
24. The vector product $\vec{v}_1 \times \hat{r}_{12}$ comes from the magnetic field produced by particle 1 at the location of particle 2, as given by the Biot-Savart law. The vector product $\vec{v}_2 \times (\vec{v}_1 \times \hat{r}_{12})$ comes from the magnetic interaction between the particles: Particle 2 is subject to the magnetic field created by particle 1.
25. $\epsilon_0\mu_0 = (8.85 \times 10^{-12}\ \mathrm{C^2/N \cdot m^2})(4\pi \times 10^{-7}\ \mathrm{T \cdot m/A}) = 1.11 \times 10^{-17}\ \mathrm{s^2/m^2} = 1.11 \times 10^{-17}(\mathrm{m/s})^{-2} = 1/(8.99 \times 10^{16}\ \mathrm{m^2/s^2}) = 1/(3.00 \times 10^8\ \mathrm{m/s})^2$. This is the reciprocal of the square of the speed of light.
26. No. Newton's third law requires that the forces exerted by two objects on each other be equal in magnitude and opposite in direction. The magnetic forces exerted by two moving charged particles on each other are typically neither equal in magnitude nor oriented in opposite directions, although some special cases (e.g. two charged particles moving in parallel, side by side) can satisfy $\vec{F}^B_{12} = -\vec{F}^B_{21}$. The reason is that Newton's law, $\vec{F}_{12} = -\vec{F}_{21}$, requires that the system's momentum be constant, and when fields are involved it is not enough to consider only the particles in doing a third-law analysis. Instead, the system for this analysis must include both the particles and their electric and magnetic fields.

PRACTICE

Answers to Guided Problems

Guided Problem 28.2

$\frac{\mu_0 I}{2\pi R} + \frac{(\mu_0 I)(\pi/2)}{4\pi R} = 1.9 \times 10^{-5}$ T, pointing into the plane of the page.

Guided Problem 28.4

$F = \frac{\mu_0 I^2 \ell}{2\pi}\left(\frac{1}{x} - \frac{1}{x + w}\right) = 4.3 \times 10^{-9}$ N, attracting the loop toward the wire.

Guided Problem 28.6

For $R_{wire} < r < R_{shell}$, $B(r) = \frac{\mu_0 I}{2\pi r}$. For $r > R_{shell}$, $B(r) = 0$ because $I_{enc} = 0$.

Guided Problem 28.8

(*a*) $B = 0$. (*b*) $B = \frac{\mu_0 I}{2\pi r}\frac{(r^2 - R_{in}^2)}{(R_{out}^2 - R_{in}^2)}$. (*c*) $B = \frac{\mu_0 I}{2\pi r}$.

29

PRACTICE

Changing Magnetic Fields

PRACTICE

Chapter Summary

Induced emf and current (Sections 29.1, 29.2, 29.4, 29.5)

Concepts A changing magnetic flux through the area enclosed by a conducting loop causes an **induced current** through the loop. This process is called **electromagnetic induction.**

According to **Lenz's law**, the direction of an induced current is always such that the magnetic flux produced by the induced current opposes the change in the magnetic flux that induces the current.

Quantitative Tools If a straight rod of length ℓ moves with speed v perpendicular to a magnetic field of magnitude B, the magnitude of the **induced emf** across the ends of the rod is

$$|\mathscr{E}_{\text{ind}}| = B\ell v. \tag{29.3}$$

According to **Faraday's law**, the induced emf in a closed path due to a changing magnetic flux through the area enclosed by the path is

$$\mathscr{E}_{\text{ind}} = -\frac{d\Phi_B}{dt}, \tag{29.8}$$

where $d\Phi_B/dt$ is the rate at which the magnetic flux changes. The **induced current** in a conducting loop of resistance R is

$$I_{\text{ind}} = \frac{\mathscr{E}_{\text{ind}}}{R}. \tag{29.4}$$

Reminder: The **magnetic flux** Φ_B through a surface is

$$\Phi_B \equiv \int \vec{B} \cdot d\vec{A}, \tag{27.10, 29.5}$$

where the integral is taken over the surface. Magnetic flux is measured in **webers** (Wb), where $1\ \text{Wb} \equiv 1\ \text{T} \cdot \text{m}^2$.

The electric field accompanying a changing magnetic field (Sections 29.3, 29.6)

Concepts A changing magnetic field is accompanied by an electric field. Unlike an electrostatic field, this electric field does not necessarily do zero work on a charged particle that travels around a closed path.

Quantitative Tools The integral around any closed path of the electric field that accompanies a changing magnetic field is given by

$$\oint \vec{E} \cdot d\vec{\ell} = -\frac{d\Phi_B}{dt}, \tag{29.17}$$

where the line integral is around a closed path, and the magnetic flux is through a surface bounded by that same closed path.

Inductance (Section 29.7)

Quantitative Tools If an emf $\mathscr{E}_{\text{ind}}$ is induced in a loop when the current through it changes at the rate dI/dt, the **inductance** L of the loop is given by

$$\mathscr{E}_{\text{ind}} = -L\frac{dI}{dt}. \tag{29.19}$$

See the Procedure box for guidance on how to calculate L. The SI unit of inductance is the **henry** (H):

$$1\ \text{H} \equiv 1\ \text{V} \cdot \text{s/A} = 1\ \text{kg} \cdot \text{m}^2/\text{C}^2. \tag{29.20}$$

The inductance of a solenoid of length ℓ and cross-sectional area A with N turns is

$$L = \frac{\mu_0 N^2 A}{\ell}.$$

Magnetic energy (Section 29.8)

Quantitative Tools The **magnetic potential energy** U^B stored in the magnetic field of an inductor that has inductance L and carries a current I is

$$U^B = \tfrac{1}{2}LI^2. \quad (29.25)$$

The **energy density** u_B of the potential energy stored in a magnetic field of magnitude B, defined as the magnetic potential energy per unit volume, is

$$u_B \equiv \frac{1}{2}\frac{B^2}{\mu_0}. \quad (29.29)$$

Review Questions

Answers to these questions can be found at the end of this chapter.

29.1 Moving conductors in magnetic fields

1. What happens when a vertical conducting rod moves east through an external magnetic field that points north?
2. What happens when a conducting loop, moving east, gradually leaves a region of zero magnetic field and enters a region of uniform, north-pointing magnetic field? Assume that the area vector of the loop points north.
3. What is an induced electric current?
4. Do the effects induced in a conducting object that is moving in an external magnetic field depend on the direction of the object's motion relative to the field direction?

29.2 Faraday's law

5. How does changing the reference frame from which you make your measurements affect your explanation of induced current in a conducting loop that is moving from a region of zero magnetic field into a region of uniform external magnetic field?
6. What is Faraday's law?
7. What is electromagnetic induction?

29.3 Electric fields accompany changing magnetic fields

8. Must a magnetic force be exerted on the charge carriers in a conducting loop in order for a current to be induced in the loop?
9. Does the nature of the force that causes electromagnetic induction depend on the choice of reference frame? If so, how? If not, why?
10. What is the difference, if any, between the field lines of the electric field that accompanies a changing magnetic field and the field lines of the electric field of a stationary charged particle?

29.4 Lenz's law

11. What does Lenz's law say about the direction of a current induced in a conducting loop?
12. What general physical principle underlies Lenz's law (that is, why would it make no sense to reverse the direction of Lenz's law)?
13. What are eddy currents?

29.5 Induced emf

14. What is induced emf?
15. When a conducting loop moves through a nonuniform external magnetic field, a current is induced as charge carriers inside the loop start moving. This is true even when the loop is oriented such that the direction of the magnetic force is perpendicular to the direction of the induced current, so the magnetic force does no work on the charge carriers. Where does the energy that causes the charge carriers to move come from?
16. What are (*a*) the quantitative statement of Faraday's law and (*b*) the significance of the negative sign in the equation?
17. Describe two differences between induced emf and potential difference.
18. How does the emf induced in a flat conducting loop that is rotating at a constant rotational speed ω in a uniform magnetic field change as the loop rotates?

29.6 Electric field accompanying a changing magnetic field

19. How is the electric field that accompanies a changing magnetic field related to the induced emf in the region of changing magnetic flux?
20. How does the direction of the electric field vary inside and outside a solenoid whose magnetic field is changing with time?
21. How does the magnitude of the electric field that accompanies the changing magnetic field described in Review Question 18 vary inside and outside the solenoid?

29.7 Inductance

22. Does changing the current in a conducting loop induce an emf in the loop?
23. What is the SI unit of inductance?
24. What is an inductor, and what purpose does it serve in electric circuits?
25. What characteristic of a conducting loop or device does inductance describe? On what properties of the conducting loop or device does inductance depend?

29.8 Magnetic energy

26. Work must be done against the induced emf in an inductor in order to change the current in it. What change in energy occurs to account for the work done?
27. How does the magnetic potential energy stored in an inductor depend on the current through the inductor? Does this energy also depend on other properties of the inductor?
28. How does the magnetic potential energy stored in the magnetic field of an inductor depend on the field magnitude? Is this relationship applicable to magnetic fields other than those of inductors?

Developing a Feel

Make an order-of-magnitude estimate of each of the following quantities. Letters in parentheses refer to hints below. Use them as needed to guide your thinking.

1. The emf you can generate along a rotating metal clothes hanger without using magnets (P, K, G, B)
2. The maximum potential difference developed when you swing a metal curtain rod around your body (H, S, K, G)
3. The maximum current induced when you drop a small but powerful bar magnet through a metal key ring of resistance $R = 0.1\ \text{V/A}$ (R, I, M)
4. The magnetic potential energy stored in a volume of 1 m^3 near Earth's surface (G)
5. The maximum emf induced around the loop formed by your metal key ring when you walk under a 100-A residential power line (W, A, Q, L, F)
6. The maximum magnetic potential energy stored in a doghouse placed under a 100-A neighborhood power line (W, A, Q, C)
7. The magnitude of the electric field due to changing magnetic fields around the outside of your car when you park it under a high-tension power line leading away from a nuclear-powered electricity-generating plant (W, D, J, Q, U, F, X)
8. The magnetic field magnitude needed to have the same energy density as gasoline (N)
9. The length of wire needed to make a 1-H inductor in the form of a solenoid wrapped on a pencil (E, O, V)
10. The maximum potential difference between the two ends of a 2-m metal rod dropped from the top of a 10-story building so that it maintains a horizontal orientation as it falls (K, G, T)

Hints

A. How far above you is the power line?
B. How rapidly can you rotate the loop?
C. What is the volume of a doghouse?
D. What is the magnitude of the current carried by a power line?
E. How is inductance related to the radius and length of the pencil?
F. How does the current vary with time?
G. What is the magnetic field magnitude?
H. What is a typical length of a curtain rod?
I. Over what area is the magnetic flux changing?
J. How far above the car is the power line?
K. What is the source of the magnetic field?
L. What is the area of the conducting loop?
M. What is the smallest likely time interval for the change in flux?
N. What is the energy content of a liter of gasoline?
O. What are the length and radius of a standard pencil?
P. What is the area enclosed by the loop formed by the hanger?
Q. How can you estimate the maximum magnetic field strength?
R. What is the magnetic field strength near a pole of the magnet?
S. What is the average translational speed of points on the rod?
T. What is the maximum speed of the rod?
U. What is the "radius" of the car?
V. What is the circumference of each winding?
W. How should you model the power line?
X. How are the induced emf and electric field related for a circular path of radius R that encircles a changing magnetic flux?

Key (all values approximate)

A. 6 m; **B.** spinning at the end of a string—say, three times/s; **C.** 1 m^3; **D.** for a 1-GW nuclear plant, about 1×10^3 A; **E.** $L = \mu_0 N^2(\pi R^2)/\ell$; **F.** it goes from positive maximum to negative maximum and back in $\frac{1}{60}$ s; **G.** 5×10^{-5} T; **H.** 1 m; **I.** the magnet cross section—say, $10^{-4}\ \text{m}^2$; **J.** 20 m; **K.** Earth; **L.** $10^{-3}\ \text{m}^2$; **M.** the time interval during which the magnet passes through the ring, 10^{-2} s; **N.** about 3×10^7 J; **O.** $\ell = 0.2$ m, $R = 3 \times 10^{-3}$ m; **P.** $3 \times 10^{-2}\ \text{m}^2$; **Q.** from the form of Ampere's law given in *Principles* Example 28.3: $B = \mu_0 I/2\pi d = (2 \times 10^{-7}\ \text{T} \cdot \text{m/A})I/d$; **R.** 1 T; **S.** 5 m/s, assuming a rotation rate slower than 2 rev/s; **T.** 2×10^1 m/s; **U.** 1 m; **V.** $2\pi R$; **W.** as a long, straight current-carrying wire; **X.** $\mathscr{E} = 2\pi RE$

Worked and Guided Problems

Procedure: Calculating inductances

The inductance of a current-carrying device or current loop is a measure of the emf induced in the device or loop when current is changed. To determine the inductance of a particular device or current loop, follow these four steps.

1. Derive an expression for the magnitude of the magnetic field in the current-carrying device or current loop as a function of the current. Your expression should depend only on the current I and possibly—but not necessarily—the position within the device or current loop.
2. Calculate the magnetic flux Φ_B through the device or current loop. If the expression you derived in step 1 depends on position, you will have to integrate that expression over the volume of the device or circuit. Use symmetry to simplify the integral and divide the device into segments on which B is constant.
3. Substitute the resulting expression you obtained for Φ_B into Eq. 29.21. As you take the derivative with respect to time, keep in mind that only the current varies with respect to time, so you should end up with an expression that contains the derivative dI/dt on both sides of the equal sign.
4. Solve your expression for L after eliminating dI/dt.

These examples involve material from this chapter but are not associated with any particular section. Some examples are worked out in detail; others you should work out by following the guidelines provided.

Worked Problem 29.1 Rectangular loop near a wire

The long, straight wire in Figure WG29.1 carries a current i that varies as a function of time according to $i(t) = a + bt$, where $a = 0.50$ A and $b = 4.0$ A/s during the time interval $0 < t \leq 2.0$ s. For all instants $t > 2.0$ s, the current is constant. The wire is placed a distance $h = 0.040$ m above and in the plane of a stationary rectangular loop of wire. The loop dimensions are width $w = 0.10$ m and length $\ell = 0.60$ m, and its resistance is $R = 2.8$ V/A. For the time interval $0 < t \leq 2.0$ s and for all instants $t > 2.0$ s, determine the induced emf in the loop and the magnitude and direction of the induced current in the loop.

Figure WG29.1

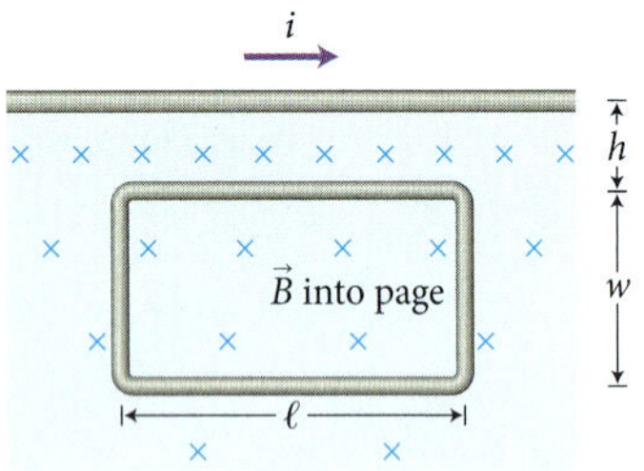

❶ **GETTING STARTED** We are given a description of a current-carrying, straight wire positioned above a rectangular loop made of conducting material, with the wire sitting in the plane defined by the loop. Our tasks are to obtain values for the emf and the current induced in the loop and to determine the direction of that induced current. We know that the emf and current are induced by a changing magnetic flux, and we know that the magnetic flux through the loop is changing because that flux is due to the magnetic field created by the current in the wire. Because that current changes during the time interval $0 < t \leq 2.0$ s, the magnetic field around the wire is also changing.

❷ **DEVISE PLAN** We can calculate the magnetic field created by the current in the straight wire using Ampere's law. Recall from *Principles* Example 28.3 that the magnitude of this magnetic field is inversely proportional to the perpendicular distance r from the wire: $B = \mu_0 I/(2\pi r)$. Because the field lines of this magnetic field form circles around the wire, there is a magnetic flux through the rectangular loop, given by Eq. 29.5:

$$\Phi_B = \int \vec{B} \cdot d\vec{A}.$$

Because the magnetic field magnitude at any location enclosed by the loop is a function of how far from the wire that location is, we need to integrate the magnetic field over the loop area in order to calculate the magnetic flux.

Once we have the changing magnetic flux, we can use Faraday's law to calculate the induced emf, which depends on a time-varying magnetic flux. Hence we need to analyze the derivative of the magnetic flux with respect to time for the interval $0 < t \leq 2.0$ s in order to calculate the emf induced in the loop:

$$\mathscr{E}_{\text{ind}} = -\frac{d\Phi_B}{dt} = -\frac{d}{dt}\int \vec{B} \cdot d\vec{A}.$$

Our final step is to use Eq. 29.4, $I_{\text{ind}} = \mathscr{E}_{\text{ind}}/R$, to calculate the magnitude of the induced current and to use Lenz's law to establish its direction.

❸ **EXECUTE PLAN** The current in the wire and hence the magnetic flux are changing only during the interval $0 < t \leq 2.0$ s. For all instants $t > 2.0$ s, the current in the wire, the magnetic field this current creates, and the magnetic flux through the loop are all constant, and therefore both the induced emf and the induced current are zero for $t > 2.0$ s. ✔

For the time interval $0 < t \leq 2.0$ s, the magnitude of the magnetic field due to a current-carrying wire is given by

$$B = \frac{\mu_0 i}{2\pi r} = \frac{\mu_0(a + bt)}{2\pi r},$$

where r is a perpendicular distance away from the wire. We begin by drawing, across the loop area, a thin strip of width dr, length ℓ, and area $dA = \ell\, dr$ (Figure WG29.2). We can consider the magnetic field to be essentially constant over the area of this infinitesimal strip. The differential magnetic flux $d\Phi_B$ through the differential area element dA is then

$$d\Phi_B = B\,dA = B\ell\,dr = \frac{\mu_0(a + bt)}{2\pi r}\ell\,dr.$$

Figure WG29.2

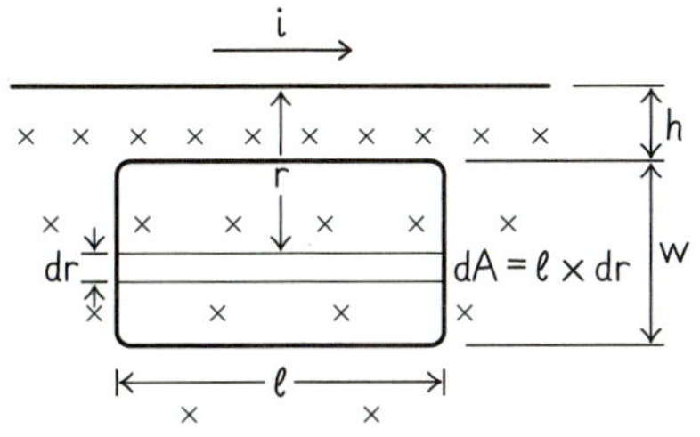

The magnetic flux through the loop is found by integrating this expression from $r = h$ to $r = h + w$:

$$\Phi_B = \int \vec{B}\cdot d\vec{A} = \frac{\mu_0(a + bt)}{2\pi}\int_{r=h}^{r=h+w}\frac{\ell\,dr}{r}$$

$$= \frac{\mu_0(a + bt)\ell}{2\pi}\ln\left(\frac{h + w}{h}\right).$$

Applying Faraday's law gives us

$$\mathscr{E}_{\text{ind}} = -\frac{d\Phi_B}{dt} = -\frac{d}{dt}\left[\frac{\mu_0(a + bt)\ell}{2\pi}\ln(1 + w/h)\right]$$

$$= -\frac{\mu_0 b\ell}{2\pi}\ln(1 + w/h).$$

The magnitude of the induced emf is thus

$$|\mathscr{E}_{\text{ind}}| = (2 \times 10^{-7}\ \text{T}\cdot\text{m/A})(4.0\ \text{A/s})(0.60\ \text{m}) \times \ln[1 + (0.10\ \text{m}/0.040\ \text{m})]$$

$$= 6.0 \times 10^{-7}\ \text{T}\cdot\text{m}^2/\text{s}.$$

(Note that the induced emf is independent of t for the interval $0 < t \leq 2.0$ s.)

Because the volt is the unit of emf, we need to check the unit in this equation before we can say we are done. Using the substitution $1\ \text{T} = 1\ \text{N}/(\text{A}\cdot\text{m})$ gives us

$$\frac{\text{T}\cdot\text{m}^2}{\text{s}} = \frac{\text{N}\cdot\text{m}^2}{\text{A}\cdot\text{m}\cdot\text{s}} = \frac{\text{N}\cdot\text{m}}{\text{A}\cdot\text{s}} = \frac{\text{N}\cdot\text{m}}{\text{C}} = \frac{\text{J}}{\text{C}} = \text{V}.$$

Thus the magnitude of the induced emf is

$$|\mathscr{E}_{\text{ind}}| = 6.0 \times 10^{-7}\ \text{V}. ✔$$

The current $i(t)$ in the wire produces a magnetic flux that within the area of the loop is directed into the page in Figure WG29.2. The magnetic field increases as time passes, and hence the magnetic flux through the loop also increases. By Lenz's law, the direction of the current induced in the loop must be counterclockwise in order to produce an induced magnetic field out of the plane of the page to counteract the increase in flux due to the time-varying magnetic field. ✔

The magnitude of the induced current is

$$I_{\text{ind}} = \frac{|\mathscr{E}_{\text{ind}}|}{R} = \frac{6.0 \times 10^{-7}\ \text{V}}{2.8\ \text{V/A}} = 2.1 \times 10^{-7}\ \text{A}. ✔$$

❹ **EVALUATE RESULT** Moving a magnet through the many windings of a solenoid induces a current on the order of microamperes, so we should not be surprised that the current through one turn of wire is about 0.2 μA even though the current in the wire is fairly great and the loop is close to the wire. Inductive effects are small.

Looking at the loop center gives us a way of checking our $\mathscr{E}_{\text{ind}}$ value. The distance from the wire to the center of the loop is $r = h + (w/2) = 0.090$ m, and we can use Ampere's law to obtain the magnetic field magnitude at this location at $t = 0$:

$$B(t = 0) = \frac{\mu_0 i}{2\pi r} = \frac{\mu_0(a + bt)}{2\pi r}$$

$$= (2 \times 10^{-7}\ \text{T}\cdot\text{m/A})\left(\frac{0.50\ \text{A}}{0.090\ \text{m}}\right)$$

$$= 1.1 \times 10^{-6}\ \text{T}.$$

At $t = 2.0$ s, the magnetic field at the loop center is 17 times greater than this value: $B(t = 2.0\ \text{s}) = 1.9 \times 10^{-5}$ T. [The factor 17 is the ratio of the currents at these two values of t: $(8.5\ \text{A})/(0.50\ \text{A}) = 17$.] The average change in the magnetic field at the center is then

$$\frac{\Delta B}{\Delta t} = \frac{(17 - 1)(1.1 \times 10^{-6}\ \text{T})}{2.0\ \text{s}}$$

$$= 8.9 \times 10^{-6}\ \text{T/s}.$$

We can estimate the average time derivative of the magnetic flux by multiplying this value by the area of the loop:

$$\frac{\Delta\Phi_B}{\Delta t} \approx \left(\frac{\Delta B}{\Delta t}\right)(\ell w) = (8.9 \times 10^{-6}\ \text{T/s})(0.60\ \text{m})(0.10\ \text{m})$$

$$= 5.3 \times 10^{-7}\ \text{V}.$$

This is close to our calculated value, $\mathscr{E}_{\text{ind}} = 6.0 \times 10^{-7}$ V, which gives us some assurance that our work is correct.

Guided Problem 29.2 Moving loop

A rectangular loop of length ℓ and width w moves at constant velocity $\vec{v}$ away from a long, straight wire carrying a current I (Figure WG29.3). The wire lies in the plane defined by the loop, and the loop's resistance is R. What are the direction and magnitude of the current induced in the loop at the instant the side nearest the wire is a perpendicular distance r away from the wire?

Figure WG29.3

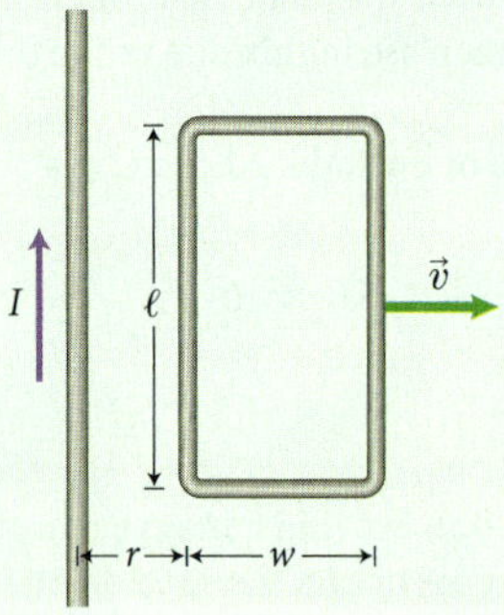

1 GETTING STARTED

1. Look for similarities and differences between this problem and Worked Problem 29.1. Will a modification of the approach we used in that problem work here?
2. Which portions of the results of Worked Problem 29.1 can be used directly?

2 DEVISE PLAN

3. Determine an expression for the magnetic field at a perpendicular distance r from the wire.
4. Do you need to integrate the magnetic field over the loop in order to calculate the magnetic flux? If so, can you use the same differential area element we used in Worked Problem 29.1?
5. You will likely need to differentiate the magnetic flux through the loop with respect to t to determine the rate of change of the magnetic flux. Remember that because the loop is moving, r is a function of time.
6. Will calculating the time derivative of the magnetic flux allow you to express the induced emf in terms of the loop velocity? If so, will that result lead you to the induced current?

3 EXECUTE PLAN

7. What are the appropriate limits of integration for the flux integral?
8. Here are two possibly useful derivatives:

$$\frac{d}{dt}\ln(r + w) = \frac{1}{r + w}\frac{dr}{dt} \quad \text{and} \quad \frac{d}{dt}\ln(r) = \frac{1}{r}\frac{dr}{dt}.$$

9. Use Lenz's law to determine the direction of I_{ind}. Remember to consider not only the direction of the magnetic field through the loop but also whether the magnetic flux is *increasing* or *decreasing* over time.

4 EVALUATE RESULT

10. Check that the current direction you found opposes the change in the magnetic flux. You can check by determining which way the magnetic force exerted by the wire on the loop points according to your direction for the induced current. The magnetic force exerted on the loop must oppose the loop's motion.
11. How does your result for emf compare with the value obtained in Worked Problem 29.1? Is this reasonable?

PRACTICE

Worked Problem 29.3 Electric field accompanying a changing magnetic field

Figure WG29.4 shows three conducting loops, A, C, and D, positioned in a uniform magnetic field whose magnitude increases with time. The concentric circles are all equidistant from one another, at radii R, $2R$, $3R$, and $4R$, and the radial lines divide each circle into 12 equal segments. The region of nonzero magnetic field ends at $r = \frac{5}{2}R$. Obtain expressions for the magnitude of the induced emf in each of the three conducting loops A, C, and D. Then use Lenz's law to determine the direction of the induced current in each of the three loops.

Figure WG29.4

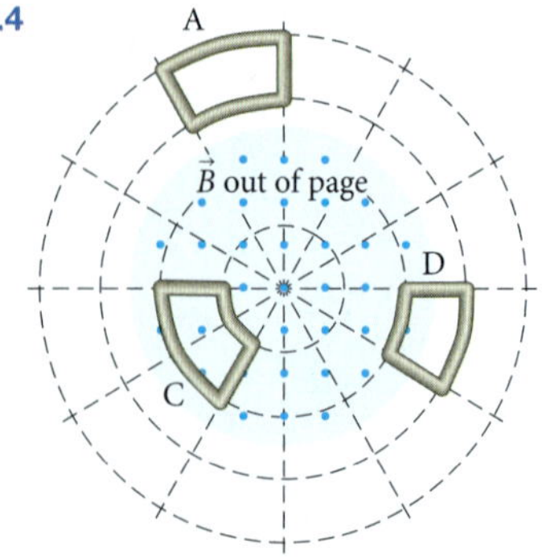

1 GETTING STARTED The figure shows three conducting loops, each perpendicular to a changing magnetic field. We need to determine the induced emf, induced current, and direction of the induced current in each loop. It looks as if there is a changing magnetic flux through two of the three loops, so we expect to obtain a nonzero induced emf and therefore an induced current in loops C and D. We also expect that we will be able to simplify the problem by exploiting the cylindrical symmetry of the shaded region of the figure and by using the fact that the magnetic field is uniform within this shaded region. Finally, we remember seeing a similar example of cylindrical symmetry worked out in *Principles* Example 29.7.

2 DEVISE PLAN Because of the cylindrical symmetry of the changing magnetic field, we know that the electric field lines that accompany this changing magnetic field must be concentric circles, such as the circles drawn in the figure.

The magnitude $E(r)$ of the electric field that accompanies the changing magnetic field can be obtained using Eq. 29.17, $\oint \vec{E} \cdot d\vec{\ell} = -d\Phi_B/dt$. We compute the line integral around each of the four circles at radii $r = R$, $2R$, $3R$, $4R$. Because each of the circles lies along an electric field line, and the electric field magnitude is constant along any field line, we can write $|\oint \vec{E} \cdot d\vec{\ell}| = 2\pi r\, E(r)$ for the circular path at radius r, leaving us with

$$2\pi r\, E(r) = \left| -\frac{d\Phi_B}{dt} \right|. \quad (1)$$

We take the absolute value because $E(r)$ is a magnitude and therefore must be non-negative.

Because the magnetic field is uniform within the shaded region of the diagram, we can write the magnetic flux through each circle simply as the product $\Phi_B = BA$, where B is the magnetic field magnitude and A is the *shaded* area enclosed by the circle. If we call the radius of the shaded area $R_{\text{shaded}} = \frac{5}{2}R$, then for $r \leq R_{\text{shaded}}$, we have $\Phi_B = \pi r^2 B$, and for $r \geq R_{\text{shaded}}$, we have $\Phi_B = \pi R^2_{\text{shaded}} B$.

Once we have the electric field magnitude $E(r)$, we can combine Eqs. 29.8 and 29.17 to determine the emf induced around each of the three conducting loops: $\mathscr{E}_{\text{ind}} = \oint \vec{E} \cdot d\vec{\ell}$. We must break the line integral around each conducting loop into four parts: the two radial sides and the two arc sides. Because the electric field lines are concentric circles, the line integral of the electric field for each loop is zero along the radial sides and nonzero along the arcs.

Finally, we can apply Lenz's law to determine the direction of the induced current in each loop.

❸ **EXECUTE PLAN** Combining Eq. 1 with our expressions for the magnetic flux Φ_B through each of the concentric circles, we see that for $r \leq R_{\text{shaded}}$, we have $2\pi r E = \pi r^2 |dB/dt|$, so $E(r) = (r/2)|dB/dt|$. For $r \geq R_{\text{shaded}}$, we have $2\pi r E = \pi R^2_{\text{shaded}} |dB/dt|$, and thus $E(r) = (R^2_{\text{shaded}}/2r)|dB/dt|$. Because the magnetic field points out of the page and increases in magnitude with time, by Lenz's law the electric field must point clockwise around each circle.

Loop A is entirely outside the magnetic field, which means there is no magnetic flux through this loop and therefore no induced emf and no induced current. (Note that there is a nonzero electric field along the two arcs of loop A. However, the integral of the electric field along the inner arc must be the negative of the integral along the outer arc, so the line integral around the closed path is zero. We can see that the two canceling contributions to the emf are equal in magnitude because (for $r > R_{\text{shaded}}$) the arc length $\propto r$, and the electric field $\propto 1/r$.) ✔

Loop C lies entirely inside the magnetic field. The radius of the inner arc is R, and the radius of the outer arc is $2R$. Moving clockwise around loop C as we evaluate the line integral $\mathscr{E}_{\text{ind}} = \oint \vec{E} \cdot d\vec{\ell}$, we determine a positive contribution for the outer arc ($\vec{E}$ points in the same direction as $d\vec{\ell}$), zero for the radial segment ($\vec{E} \perp d\vec{\ell}$), a negative contribution for the inner arc ($\vec{E}$ points opposite $d\vec{\ell}$), and zero again for the second radial segment, thus completing the loop. Because each arc subtends $\frac{1}{6}$ of a circle, the arc lengths are $2\pi r/6$ for $r = 2R$ and $r = R$. Adding the four contributions gives

$$\mathscr{E}_C = \frac{2\pi(2R)E(2R)}{6} + 0 - \frac{2\pi R E(R)}{6} + 0.$$

Then substituting $E(r) = (r/2)(dB/dt)$ at both $r = 2R$ and $r = R$ gives us

$$\mathscr{E}_C = \frac{2\pi}{6}\left(\frac{4R^2}{2} - \frac{R^2}{2}\right)\frac{dB}{dt} = \frac{\pi R^2}{2}\frac{dB}{dt}$$

for the magnitude of the emf induced in loop C. Because the magnetic flux through the loop points out of the page and is increasing in magnitude, the direction of the induced current must be clockwise around loop C. ✔

We determine the induced emf for loop D in a similar manner. In this case, the outer arc, at $r = 3R$, is outside the magnetic field, while the inner arc, at $r = 2R$, is inside the magnetic field. Also, each arc subtends only $\frac{1}{12}$ of a circle, so the arc lengths are $2\pi r/12$ for $r = 3R$ and $r = 2R$. Integrating $\mathscr{E}_{\text{ind}} = \oint \vec{E} \cdot d\vec{\ell}$ clockwise over the four sides of loop D (outer arc, radial segment, inner arc, and radial segment) gives us

$$\mathscr{E}_D = \frac{2\pi(3R)E(3R)}{12} + 0 - \frac{2\pi(2R)E(2R)}{12} + 0.$$

For the inner arc, because $2R < R_{\text{shaded}}$, we again use $E(r) = (r/2)(dB/dt)$ and obtain $E(2R) = R(dB/dt)$. For the outer arc, because $3R > R_{\text{shaded}}$, we instead use $E(r) = (R^2_{\text{shaded}}/2r)(dB/dt)$, so then

$$E(3R) = \frac{(5R/2)^2}{6R}\frac{dB}{dt} = \frac{25R}{24}\frac{dB}{dt}.$$

Substituting these values for the electric field, we obtain the magnitude of the induced emf in loop D:

$$\mathscr{E}_D = \frac{2\pi}{12}\left[(3R)\frac{25R}{24} - (2R)R\right]\frac{dB}{dt} = \frac{3\pi R^2}{16}\frac{dB}{dt}.$$

Because the magnetic flux through the loop again points out of the page and is increasing in magnitude, the induced current must be clockwise around loop D. ✔

❹ **EVALUATE RESULT** Because loop A is completely outside the magnetic field, it is reasonable that this loop has no induced emf. Loops C and D experience the changing magnetic flux to different degrees, so we expect their induced emfs to differ. Loop D, with the smaller area affected by the magnetic flux, has the smaller induced emf, as we expect.

Guided Problem 29.4 A falling loop

Under the influence of gravity, a rectangular wire loop of mass m, width w, length ℓ, and resistance R falls out of a uniform magnetic field $\vec{B}$ (Figure WG29.5 on the next page). The loop is released from rest at the instant its lower edge is just barely inside the magnetic field. At the instant shown in the figure, the loop is exiting the magnetic field at speed $v(t) > 0$ (that is, the loop is moving downward). Obtain an expression for the speed of the loop as a function of time, for the time interval from the instant the loop is released to the instant just before its top edge exits the magnetic field. What happens after the top edge of the loop has left the field?

Figure WG29.5

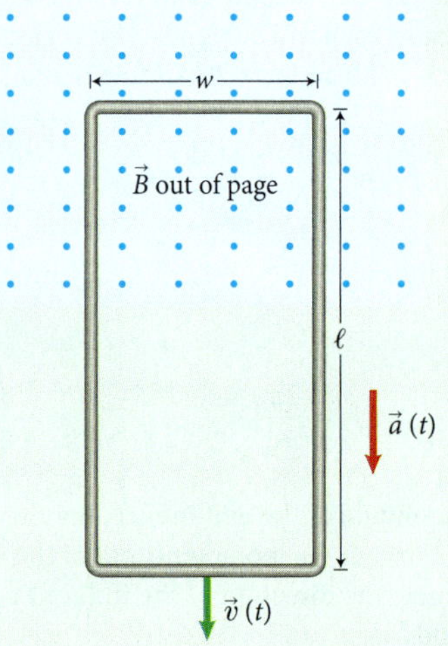

1 GETTING STARTED

1. As the loop falls, the magnetic flux through the loop changes, and that change in flux induces a current in the loop. The induced current slows the loop down (Lenz's law). A good first step is to seek a relationship between the magnetic flux through the loop at some instant t and the downward velocity of the loop. Be careful, though; at any instant, the magnetic field is zero over the lower region of the loop area and uniform and nonzero over the upper region.
2. Induced emf and induced current may be more useful here than simple magnetic flux.
3. You may need additional information to solve for the speed, so consider force analysis or energy analysis. Remember that you seek a relationship between speed and time.
4. It may be necessary to solve a differential equation to determine $v(t)$, so do not rule out acceleration as a useful quantity.

2 DEVISE PLAN

5. Obtain an expression for $d\Phi_B/dt$ that involves $v(t)$.
6. Current may relate to both magnetic flux and magnetic force. What is the magnitude of the induced current in the loop at the instant shown in Figure WG29.5? (Use $I_{ind} = \mathscr{E}_{ind}/R$.)
7. Would a free-body diagram for all the vertical forces exerted on the loop be helpful? Recall that a magnetic force is exerted on the loop. Express the magnitude and direction of this force in terms of the quantities given. (Hint: Use Eq. 28.13, $\vec{F} = I_{ind}\vec{\ell} \times \vec{B}$.) Use the vertical component of this force to obtain an expression for the vertical motion of the loop.
8. You know that $a = dv/dt$, so is it possible to write a differential equation for the speed as a function of time?

3 EXECUTE PLAN

9. If you get a differential equation of the form $dv/dt = \alpha - \beta v$, where $v(0) = 0$, you might want to try a solution of the form $v = (\alpha/\beta)(1 - e^{-\beta t})$.

4 EVALUATE RESULT

10. Taking a derivative of your expression for $v(t)$ should yield acceleration, giving you a test of the reasonableness of your result.

Worked Problem 29.5 Inductance of a toroid

Determine an expression for the inductance L of a toroid (see Section 28.6) for which the windings have a circular cross section of radius R_w and the toroid radius is $R_t \gg R_w$.

1 GETTING STARTED We begin by making a sketch of the toroid (Figure WG29.6). We know from *Principles* Section 28.6 that the magnetic field is entirely contained within the cavity formed by the windings of the toroid and that the magnetic field lines are circular loops centered on the toroid's central axis (an axis perpendicular to the plane of the figure).

Figure WG29.6

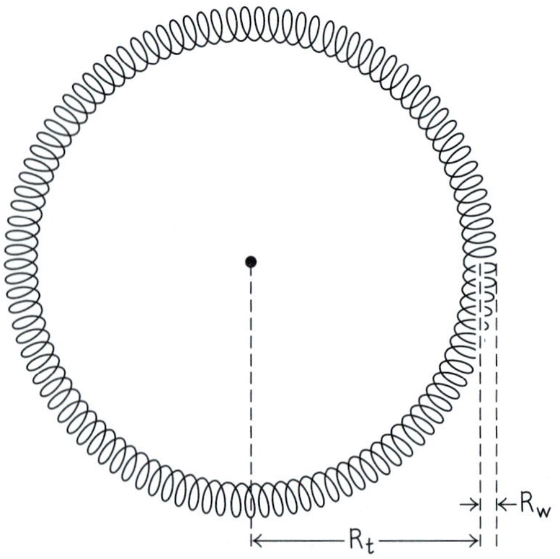

2 DEVISE PLAN To calculate the inductance of the toroid, we can follow the steps in the Procedure box at the beginning of this *Practice* chapter. We first need to determine the magnetic field magnitude in terms of the current I through the toroid. We derived this expression in Section 28.6 and found that at a radial distance r from the center of a toroid that has N windings, $B = \mu_0 NI/(2\pi r)$ (Eq. 28.9). The condition $R_t \gg R_w$ means that r in Eq. 28.9 can be approximated as $r \approx R_t$, so we have $B = \mu_0 NI/(2\pi R_t)$. Having this expression for B, we can calculate the magnetic flux as a function of the current. We can then substitute this result into Eq. 29.21, $d\Phi_B/dt = L(dI/dt)$, and solve for L.

3 EXECUTE PLAN The magnetic flux through one winding is the area of one winding, πR_w^2, multiplied by the magnetic field magnitude B inside the winding. For the entire toroid, therefore, the magnetic flux is

$$\Phi_B = N(\pi R_w^2)B = \frac{\mu_0 N^2 I R_w^2}{2R_t}.$$

Substituting this expression for Φ_B into Eq. 29.21 yields

$$\frac{d}{dt}\frac{\mu_0 N^2 I R_w^2}{2R_t} = L\frac{dI}{dt}.$$

The only time-dependent factor on the left is the current, so

$$L = \frac{\mu_0 N^2 R_w^2}{2R_t}. \checkmark$$

PRACTICE

❹ **EVALUATE RESULT** Our result shows that the inductance of a toroid increases as the square of the number of windings N. This makes sense because both the magnetic field in the toroid cavity and the magnetic flux through the toroid windings increase with N. That inductance also depends on the square of the winding radius R_w makes sense because increasing R_w increases the area enclosed by each winding and therefore increases the magnetic flux by the factor R_w^2.

Finally, the inductance is inversely proportional to the radius R_t of the toroid, which makes sense because the magnetic field and therefore the magnetic flux decrease as $1/R_t$. (Note: This expression for inductance is valid only for toroids in which $R_t \gg R_w$.)

Guided Problem 29.6 Coaxial cable inductance and magnetic energy

Figure WG29.7 shows a coaxial cable that consists of two concentric long, hollow cylinders of negligible resistance. The inner cylinder has radius R_{inner}, the outer cylinder has radius R_{outer}, and the length of both cylinders is $\ell \gg R_{outer}$. There is a current I in the cable, and the current direction is from the battery into the inner cylinder and then through the outer cylinder to the battery. What is the magnetic potential energy stored in the magnetic field? What is the inductance of the cable?

Figure WG29.7

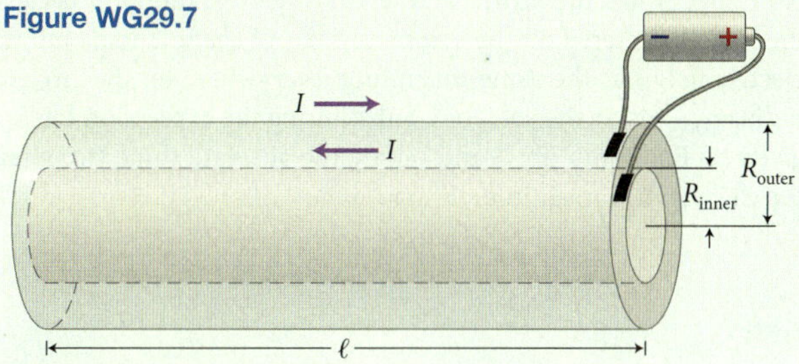

❶ **GETTING STARTED**

1. We must know the magnetic field magnitude as a function of the radius in order to determine the amount of magnetic potential energy stored. Is Ampere's law (Eq. 28.1) useful for this?
2. What is the relationship between the energy stored in the magnetic field of an inductor and the inductance?

❷ **DEVISE PLAN**

3. To obtain expressions for the magnetic field magnitude everywhere, apply Ampere's law, $\oint \vec{B} \cdot d\vec{\ell} = \mu_0 I_{enc}$ (Eq. 28.1), outside the cable, where the radial distance $r > R_{outer}$; then inside the inner cylinder, where $r < R_{inner}$; and finally between the cylinders, where $R_{inner} < r < R_{outer}$.
4. For the region where the magnetic field magnitude is nonzero, use Eq. 29.29 to determine the magnetic energy density.
5. The quantity of magnetic potential energy stored can be found by integrating the magnetic energy density over the volume of space where $B \neq 0$. Is the magnetic field uniform or nonuniform in this region? You may need to choose a volume element for your integral. Based on the symmetry in the problem, the volume element for a cylindrical shell of radius r, thickness dr, and length ℓ is $dV = 2\pi r \ell \, dr$.
6. What are the appropriate limits of integration?
7. Once you have U^B, you can use it and Eq. 29.25 to determine the inductance in the cable.

❸ **EXECUTE PLAN**

❹ **EVALUATE RESULT**

8. Consider what happens to the stored energy as the dimensions of the coaxial cable are changed.

Worked Problem 29.7 Electric fields and Faraday's law

A solenoid is made by wrapping a wire 100 times around a hollow, nonmagnetic cylinder (Figure WG29.8). The solenoid's length is $\ell = 2.5 \times 10^{-1}$ m, and its radius is $a = 3.0 \times 10^{-2}$ m. A small wire loop of radius $r_{loop} = 1.0 \times 10^{-2}$ m is placed at the midpoint of the solenoid's length and concentric with the solenoid. The loop has resistance $R = 5.0$ V/A. During the time interval $t = 0$ to $t = 2.0$ s, the current through the solenoid increases as $I(t) = bt$, where $b = 2.0 \times 10^{-1}$ A/s. After $t = 2.0$ s, the current remains constant. For $0 < t < 2.0$ s and for $t > 2.0$ s, what are (*a*) the emf induced in the loop, (*b*) the magnitude and direction of the electric field that accompanies the changing magnetic flux in the loop, and (*c*) the magnitude and direction of the current induced in the loop?

Figure WG29.8

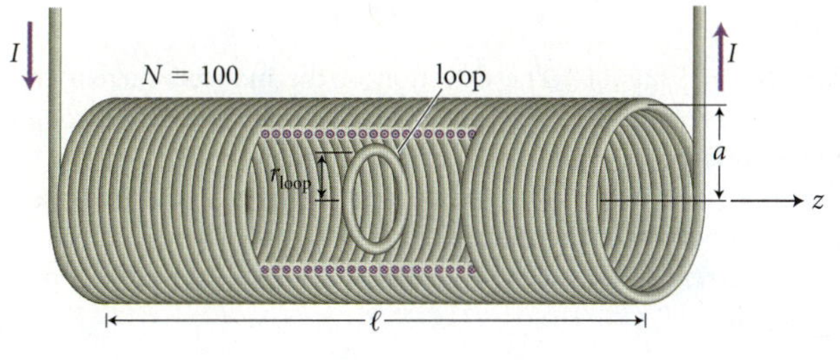

❶ **GETTING STARTED** For $t > 2.0$ s, the current is not changing, so the induced emf, electric field, and induced current are all zero. Thus we have already completed one part of our task. ✔

All we need to consider now is what happens during the interval $0 < t < 2.0$ s, when the current *is* changing. During this interval, there is a changing magnetic flux through the solenoid cavity and hence through the area enclosed by the loop. Therefore, by the Eq. 29.17 form of Faraday's law, there must be an electric field accompanying the changing magnetic flux through the loop area. This electric field is responsible for the emf that drives the induced current around the loop. We can determine the direction of the induced current by using Lenz's law or by determining the direction of the electric field. Note that the direction of the current through the solenoid is shown in Figure WG29.8.

❷ **DEVISE PLAN** In order to determine the induced emf in the loop, we must first calculate the magnetic field inside the solenoid. For this we can use Eq. 28.6, $B = \mu_0 nI$, where n is the number of windings per unit length of the solenoid:

$$B = \mu_0 nI = \mu_0 \frac{N}{\ell} I.$$

We can integrate this expression for B to determine the magnetic flux inside the loop from Eq. 29.5:

$$\Phi_B = \int \vec{B} \cdot d\vec{A},$$

where $d\vec{A}$ is the area vector perpendicular to the solenoid axis. Then the Eq. 29.8 form of Faraday's law gives us the emf induced in the loop:

$$\mathscr{E}_{\text{ind}} = -\frac{d\Phi_B}{dt} = -\frac{d}{dt}\left(\int \vec{B} \cdot d\vec{A}\right).$$

We should then be able to obtain the electric field magnitude by using the definition of emf as the line integral of the electric field around the loop. Combining Eqs. 29.8 and 29.17, we have

$$\mathscr{E}_{\text{ind}} = \oint_{\text{loop}} \vec{E} \cdot d\vec{l} = -\frac{d}{dt}\int \vec{B} \cdot d\vec{A}, \qquad (1)$$

where the line integral is taken along the circle of radius r, centered on the solenoid axis, around which we wish to determine the electric field magnitude $E(r)$ due to the changing magnetic field. To determine the direction of the electric field, we infer by analogy with *Principles* Checkpoint 29.12 that the electric field lines will form circles centered around the solenoid axis, in the direction required by Lenz's law.

Finally, we can use Eq. 29.4 to obtain the induced current in the loop from the emf and the resistance of the loop:

$$I_{\text{ind}} = \frac{|\mathscr{E}_{\text{ind}}|}{R}.$$

❸ **EXECUTE PLAN** (*a*) The magnetic field inside the solenoid is

$$\vec{B} = \mu_0 nI\,\hat{k} = \frac{\mu_0 NI}{\ell}\hat{k} = \frac{\mu_0 Nbt}{\ell}\hat{k}.$$

(From the orientation of the solenoid loops and the direction of the current in Figure WG27.8, we see that the magnetic field produced by the solenoid is in the positive z direction, so the direction of $\vec{B}$ is given by $\hat{k}$.) We choose the orientation of the area element $d\vec{A}$ in the magnetic flux integral to point in the positive $\hat{k}$ direction, parallel to the magnetic field: $d\vec{A} = dA\,\hat{k}$. The magnetic flux integral through the loop is then

$$\Phi_B = \int \vec{B} \cdot d\vec{A} = \int B\,\hat{k} \cdot dA\,z = \int B\,dA.$$

Because the magnetic field is constant inside the solenoid and the area of the loop is $A = \pi r_{\text{loop}}^2$, the magnetic flux inside the loop is given by

$$\Phi_B = \int B\,dA = \frac{\mu_0 Nbt}{\ell}\int dA = \frac{\mu_0 Nbt}{\ell}\pi r_{\text{loop}}^2.$$

The induced emf is then

$$\mathscr{E}_{\text{ind}} = -\frac{d\Phi_B}{dt} = -\frac{d}{dt}\left(\frac{\mu_0 Nbt}{\ell}\right)\pi r_{\text{loop}}^2 = -\frac{\mu_0 Nb\pi r_{\text{loop}}^2}{\ell} \qquad (2)$$

$$= -\frac{(4\pi \times 10^{-7}\,\text{T}\cdot\text{m/A})(100)(2.0 \times 10^{-1}\,\text{A/s})\pi(1.0 \times 10^{-2}\,\text{m})^2}{(2.5 \times 10^{-1}\,\text{m})}$$

$$= -3.2 \times 10^{-8}\,\text{T}\cdot\text{m}^2/\text{s} = -3.2 \times 10^{-8}\,\text{V}. ✔$$

(*b*) We obtain the electric field that accompanies the changing magnetic flux by extracting $\vec{E}$ from the line integral of Eq. 1. For this case, that equation becomes

$$\mathscr{E}_{\text{ind}} = \oint_{\text{loop}} \vec{E} \cdot d\vec{l} = E(2\pi r_{\text{loop}}). \qquad (3)$$

Note that E has the same value everywhere on the loop because the loop is centered on the symmetry axis of the solenoid, and the electric field has the same magnitude everywhere on the circle of radius r_{loop} inside the solenoid. Substituting the expression for $\mathscr{E}_{\text{ind}}$ given by Eq. 2 into Eq. 3 and taking the absolute value (to obtain the electric field magnitude E) give us

$$E(2\pi r_{\text{loop}}) = \frac{\mu_0 Nb\pi r_{\text{loop}}^2}{\ell}$$

$$E = \frac{1}{2\pi r_{\text{loop}}}\frac{\mu_0 Nb\pi r_{\text{loop}}^2}{\ell} = \frac{\mu_0 Nb r_{\text{loop}}}{2\ell}$$

$$= \frac{(4\pi \times 10^{-7}\,\text{T}\cdot\text{m/A})(100)(2.0 \times 10^{-1}\,\text{A/s})(1.0 \times 10^{-2}\,\text{m})}{2(2.5 \times 10^{-1}\,\text{m})}$$

$$= 5.0 \times 10^{-7}\,\text{T}\cdot\text{m/s}. ✔$$

Because $\vec{B}$ points along the z axis and increases with time, the resulting electric field lines must loop around clockwise, as viewed from the positive z axis: This is the direction in which our fingers curl if we point our right thumb in the $-z$ direction, to oppose $d\vec{B}/dt$ (using the right-hand dipole rule). ✔

(*c*) The direction of the induced current is the same direction as the electric field. So the direction of the induced current in the loop is opposite the direction of the current in the solenoid. ✔

The magnitude of the induced current in the loop is

$$I_{\text{ind}} = \frac{|\mathscr{E}_{\text{ind}}|}{R} = \frac{\mu_0 Nb\pi r_{\text{loop}}^2}{R\ell} = \frac{3.2 \times 10^{-8}\,\text{V}}{5.0\,\text{V/A}}$$

$$= 6.4 \times 10^{-9}\,\text{A}. ✔$$

❹ **EVALUATE RESULT** The direction of the induced current can also be determined from Lenz's law. The magnetic flux through the loop is positive (the magnetic field points in the positive z direction) and increases as the current in the solenoid increases. So, the direction of the induced current is opposite the direction of the current in the solenoid in order to oppose the change that created it.

PRACTICE

Guided Problem 29.8 Betatron

An electron of mass m and charge $q = -e$ located in a nonuniform magnetic field between the north and south poles of a magnet travels in a circular orbit of radius R (Figure WG29.9, illustrating a type of particle accelerator known as a betatron). The magnetic field magnitude is $B(r)$, where r is radial distance from an axis that is perpendicular to the plane defined by the circular orbit and passes through the center of the circle. Although B varies with r, the field is symmetrical about this axis. The magnetic field direction is perpendicular to the plane of the orbit. The average value of the field magnitude over the area bounded by the orbit is

$$B_{av} = \frac{1}{\pi R^2} \int_{\text{area}} B(r)\, dA.$$

Suppose that $B(r)$ varies with time. What relationship between dB_{av}/dt, the rate of change of the average magnetic field enclosed by the electron's orbit, and $dB(R)/dt$, the rate of change of the magnetic field at the orbit radius $r = R$, is necessary for the electron to stay in its circular orbit?

Figure WG29.9

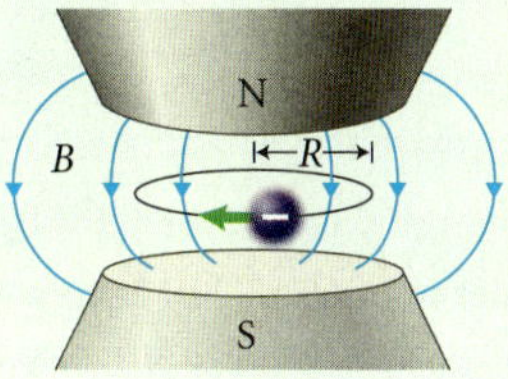

❶ GETTING STARTED

1. Assume that the electron moves in a circular orbit at constant radius R, but that the electron's speed may vary with time. (Changing the electron's speed is the purpose of a particle accelerator.) To keep the electron moving in a circle, what must be the direction of the magnetic force exerted by the magnetic field on the moving electron?
2. If the magnitude $B(R)$ of the magnetic field at the orbit radius R varies with time, what must happen to the electron's speed in order to maintain the circular motion in the orbit?
3. What relates speed to force for circular motion? Is the magnetic force exerted on the electron related to the magnetic field magnitude?

❷ DEVISE PLAN

4. Write an expression for the magnetic force exerted on the electron in terms of the electron's speed v, orbit radius R, and magnetic field magnitude $B(r)$ when $r = R$.
5. What radial force (perpendicular to the particle's velocity) is needed to keep a particle traveling in circular motion at a given speed?
6. Use the relationship between force and acceleration to obtain an expression for the speed of the electron.
7. Differentiate the electron's speed with respect to time to obtain an expression for the time rate of change of the electron's speed in terms of $dB(r)/dt$, R, $-e$, and m.
8. When the magnetic field magnitude starts to increase at a rate $dB(r)/dt$, the changing magnetic flux is accompanied by an electric field. Can you express the changing magnetic flux in terms of dB_{av}/dt and R?
9. Write an expression that gives the electric field a distance R from the center of the orbit in terms of dB_{av}/dt and R. Does the electric field point in the direction of the electron's velocity or in the opposite direction?
10. Relate dv/dt to the electric field magnitude a distance R from the orbit center.
11. Determine an expression for dv/dt in terms of dB_{av}/dt, R, $-e$, and m.

❸ EXECUTE PLAN

12. Compare your two expressions for dv/dt to obtain a condition that relates B_{av} and $B(r)$ and is mandatory in order for the electron to stay in its circular orbit at radius R.

❹ EVALUATE RESULT

13. Consider limiting cases.

PRACTICE

Questions and Problems

For instructor-assigned homework, go to MasteringPhysics®

Dots indicate difficulty level of problems: • = *easy*, •• = *intermediate*, ••• = *hard*; CR = *context-rich problem.*

29.1 Moving conductors in magnetic fields

1. What happens if the conducting rod in Figure P29.1 moves (*a*) in either direction along the z axis and (*b*) in either direction along the y axis? •

Figure P29.1

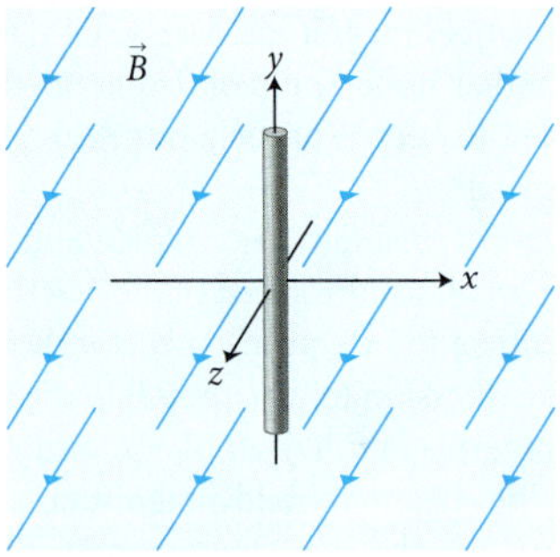

2. The Air Force Thunderbirds aerial demonstration team is performing at an air show located on Earth's magnetic equator. In what directions can the airplanes fly so that there is no charge separation on their metal surfaces? •

3. How should any one of the airplanes described in Problem 2 fly in order to produce the maximum charge separation between its wing tips? (Consider both the direction of motion and the orientation of the wings.) ••

4. Figure P29.4 shows a square conducting loop centered on the x axis, with its sides parallel to the y and z axes. The loop moves with constant velocity in the negative x direction toward a small bar magnet that is centered on the origin and has its polar axis aligned along the x axis. At the instant shown, what is the direction of the magnetic force exerted on an electron sitting at the midpoint of each side? Does the motion of the loop cause any separation of the charge carriers in the loop? Does the motion induce a current in the loop? If so, what is the direction of that current? ••

Figure P29.4

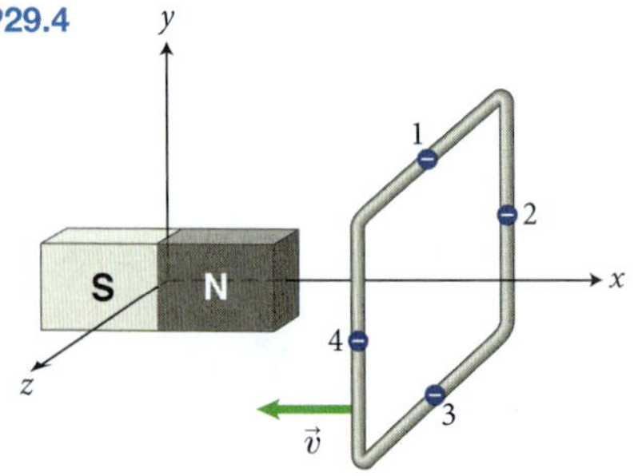

5. What happens if the conducting rod in Figure P29.1 rotates (*a*) clockwise about the z axis as viewed looking down the positive z axis toward the origin, (*b*) clockwise about the x axis as viewed looking down the positive x axis toward the origin, and (*c*) clockwise about the y axis as viewed looking down the positive y axis toward the origin? ••

29.2 Faraday's law

6. The large loop of wire in Figure P29.6*a* carries into and out of a lamp an electric current whose direction alternates back and forth with time. A circular ring of wire of radius R is at one of the three positions labeled A, C, and D. (*a*) At which position is the induced current in the ring greatest? At which position is it smallest? (*b*) Instead of being spread out in large loops, the actual wiring in houses and other buildings has the wires entering and leaving the lamp close and parallel to each other, as shown in Figure P29.6*b*. How is the induced current in the ring affected by this geometry? •

Figure P29.6

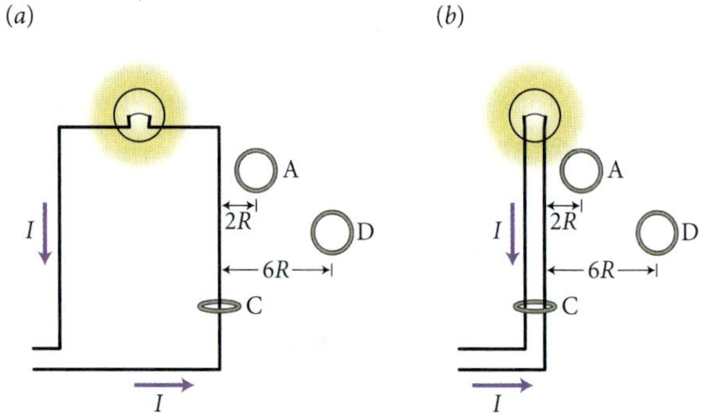

7. The bar magnet in Figure P29.7 is rotated about an axis that runs perpendicular to the page and passes through the center of the magnet. The magnet rotates with rotational speed ω. A loop of wire is placed alongside the magnet as shown. The loop is positioned so that the axis that runs perpendicular to the face of the loop and that passes through the center of the loop lies in the plane in which the magnet rotates. (*a*) Is a current induced in the loop? (*b*) If so, is the induced current constant, or does it vary with time? •

Figure P29.7

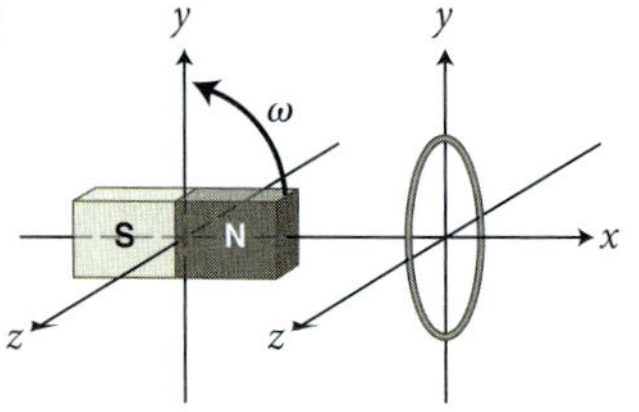

8. Suppose you used a circular loop of the same area rather than the rectangular loop in *Principles* Example 29.1. What similarities and differences would you observe in each portion of Figure P29.8 parts *a–e*? ••

Figure P29.8

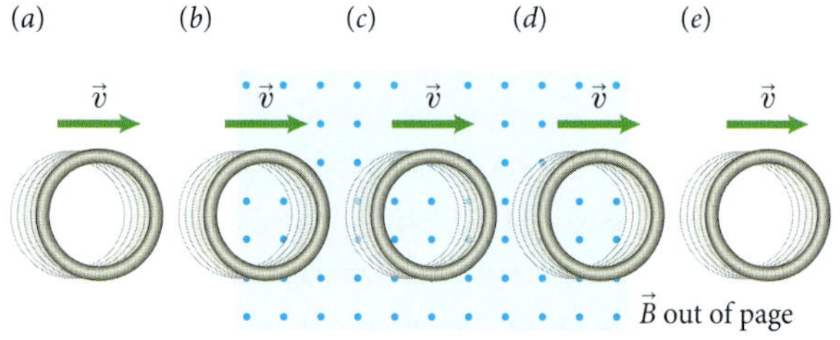

9. A large region of space contains a uniform magnetic field that is increasing with time. You have a piece of wire of length ℓ and want to form a coil from it. What shape should you use for your windings and how many windings should you have to generate the maximum induced current in the coil when it is placed in the changing magnetic field? ••

10. A 1.00-m length of wire is shaped into a rectangle, and another 1.00-m length of identical wire is shaped into a circle. Both wires then move at the same speed into and then out of a region of uniform magnetic field. Is the induced current in the rectangle greater than, smaller than, or the same as the induced current in the circle? •••

29.3 Electric fields accompany changing magnetic fields

11. You observe a small charge separation between the ends of a conducting rod that is lying on the table in front of you. This is puzzling because the rod is not connected to a battery or other power source; it is at rest on the nonconducting table, pointed toward a nearby window. You call your friend, who calmly asks where you are. You reply that you are riding the high-speed train between Paris and Avignon. Your friend offers explanations for the charge separation in two different inertial reference frames. What are those explanations? •

12. A flat conducting plate lies in the xy plane of an xyz coordinate system in which the xy plane is horizontal. A bar magnet is lowered vertically toward the plate. If the magnet is oriented so that its north pole faces the origin as the magnet moves toward the plate, what do the electric field lines in the plate look like? What do the field lines look like if the south pole faces the origin as the magnet moves? •

13. A metal pipe is held vertically, and a bar magnet is dropped into it. What do the electric field lines in the pipe look like as the magnet falls through it? ••

14. You have a bar magnet and a circular conducting loop, and you wish to induce a current in the loop that changes direction regularly: clockwise, counterclockwise, clockwise, and so on. Explain how to do this while the loop remains at rest on a wooden table. ••

29.4 Lenz's law

15. You have a bar magnet and a loop of wire. The loop lies in the plane of this page, and we define a positive current as one for which the current direction is clockwise around the loop as viewed from above. How can you move the magnet so as to induce a positive current in the loop? (There are several answers to this question; provide as many as you can.) •

16. If you drop a magnet through a length ℓ of copper pipe, the time interval needed for the magnet to travel through the pipe (even if the magnet never touches the sides of the pipe) is much greater than the time interval the magnet takes to drop the same distance ℓ in air. Why? •

17. The long straight wire in Figure P29.17 carries a current I that varies in time as $I = I_0 \sin(\omega t)$, and a loop of wire is held stationary near the straight wire. When is the induced current in the loop clockwise? When is it zero? When is it counterclockwise? ••

Figure P29.17

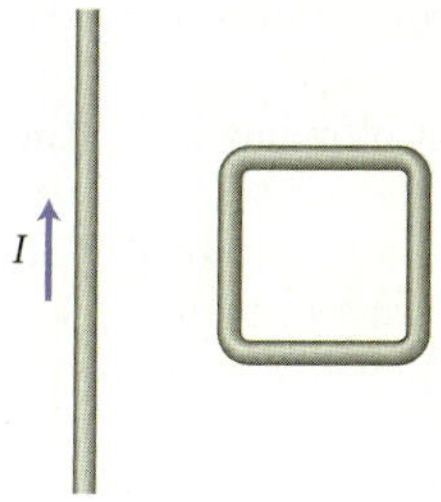

18. A pendulum consists of a rod with an aluminum disk attached, suspended from a pivot. First the pendulum is held at a 30° angle to the vertical and released so that it begins to swing. The disk passes between the poles of a powerful magnet on each swing (Figure P29.18a). Next a series of vertical slits are cut completely through the disk (Figure P29.18b). The pendulum is again held at a 30° angle and released, and the disk again passes between the magnet's poles on each swing. Describe the motion of the pendulum in each case and explain your answer. Ignore any frictional force exerted at the pivot. ••

Figure P29.18

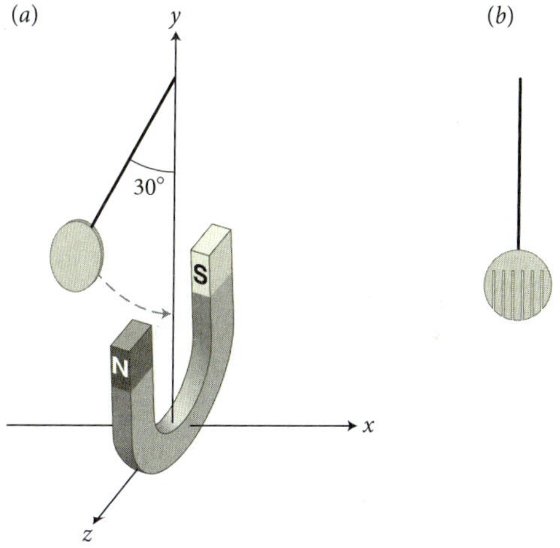

29.5 Induced emf

19. The magnetic flux through a conducting loop increases at a rate of $3.0\ \mathrm{T \cdot m^2/s}$. What is the magnitude of the induced emf in the loop? •

20. Initially there is no magnetic flux through a conducting loop. A magnetic field near the loop is then suddenly turned on, and 5.0 s later the magnetic flux through the loop is $1.0\ \mathrm{T \cdot m^2}$. What is the average magnitude of the induced emf in the loop during the 5.0-s time interval? •

21. A rectangular loop of length $\ell = 80$ mm, width $w = 60$ mm, and internal resistance $R = 20$ V/A is located in a homogeneous magnetic field of magnitude $B = 0.50$ T. The area vector of the loop makes a 45° angle with the magnetic field direction. In 0.40 s, the magnetic field completely reverses direction. What is the average current in the loop during this time interval? •

22. You are building an instrument to measure the orientation of Earth's magnetic field. Your device consists of a single conducting coil that encloses an area $A = 400\ \mathrm{mm^2}$ and rotates

at a speed of 10,000 rotations/min. What peak induced emf should you expect if the magnitude of Earth's magnetic field is 50 μT? •

23. A circular coil of radius $R = 50$ mm rotates about an axis that is perpendicular to a uniform magnetic field of magnitude $B = 0.50$ T (Figure P29.23). If the coil completes 60 rotations each second, how many windings must the coil have in order to power an appliance that requires an emf that varies as $\mathscr{E}_{ind}(t) = V_{max} \sin(\omega t)$, where $V_{max} = 155$ V? ••

Figure P29.23

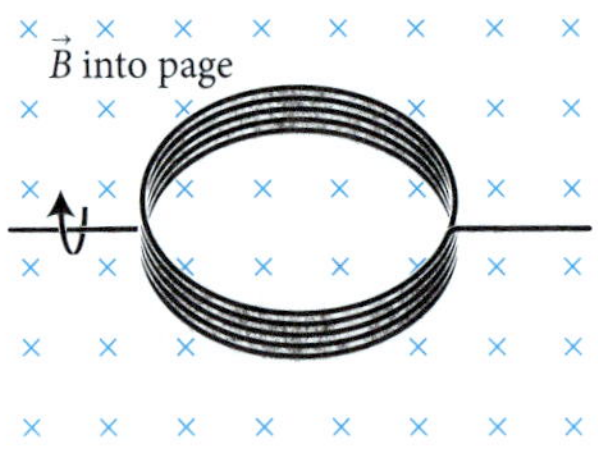

24. The square conducting loop in Figure P29.24 lies in the xy plane of an xyz coordinate system. The loop is in a uniform magnetic field that points in the positive z direction and is decreasing at a rate of 0.070 T/s. What are (*a*) the magnitude of the induced emf in the loop and (*b*) the direction of the induced current in the loop? ••

Figure P29.24

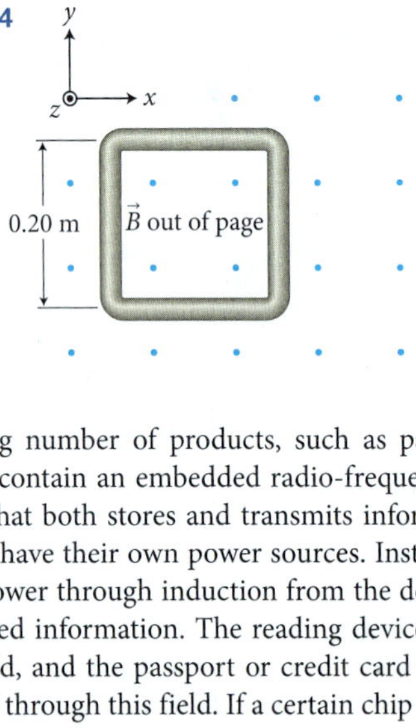

25. An increasing number of products, such as passports and credit cards, contain an embedded radio-frequency identification chip that both stores and transmits information. The chips do not have their own power sources. Instead, they receive their power through induction from the device used to read the stored information. The reading device generates a magnetic field, and the passport or credit card containing a coil is passed through this field. If a certain chip needs a peak induced emf of 4.0 V to operate and the magnetic field varies with time as $B(t) = B_{peak} \sin(\omega t)$, where $B_{peak} = 5.0$ mT is the maximum magnetic field and $\omega = 8.52 \times 10^7\ s^{-1}$, what value must the product AN have in order for the chip to operate, where A is the coil's surface area and N is number of turns in the coil? ••

26. A 100-mm-long metal rod is placed in a uniform magnetic field with the rod length perpendicular to the field direction (Figure P29.26). The rod moves at 0.20 m/s, and its velocity vector makes an angle of 60° with the rod length. If the magnitude of the magnetic field is 0.40 T, what is the potential difference between the two ends of the rod? ••

Figure P29.26

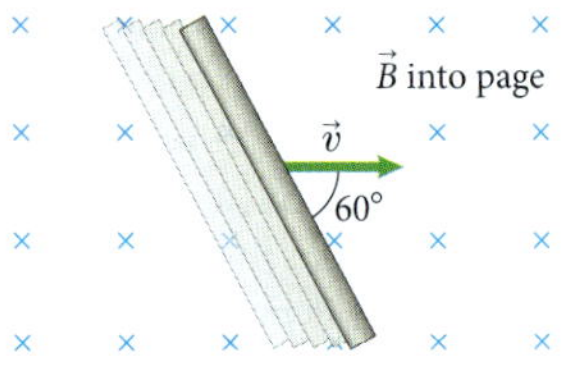

27. The very long cylindrical solenoid of Figure P29.27 has a radius of 0.50 m and 1000 windings per meter along its length. A circular conducting loop of radius 1.0 m encircles the solenoid, with the long central axis of the solenoid passing through the center of the loop, and with the area vector of the loop parallel to the solenoid axis. The solenoid initially carries a steady current I, but the current is then reduced to zero during a 0.100-s time interval. If the average emf induced in the loop during that interval is 0.10 V, what was the initial current magnitude? ••

Figure P29.27

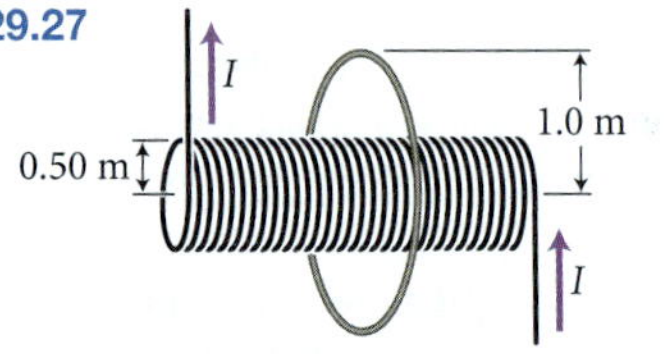

28. The space to the right of the y axis in Figure P29.28 contains a uniform magnetic field of unknown magnitude that points in the positive z direction. As a conducting square loop placed in the xy plane (oriented with its horizontal and vertical sides parallel to the x and y axes) moves to the right across the y axis at a constant speed of 2.0 m/s, a 0.24-V emf is induced in the loop. (*a*) If the side length of the loop is 0.30 m, what is the magnitude of the magnetic field? (*b*) What is the direction of the induced current in the loop? ••

Figure P29.28

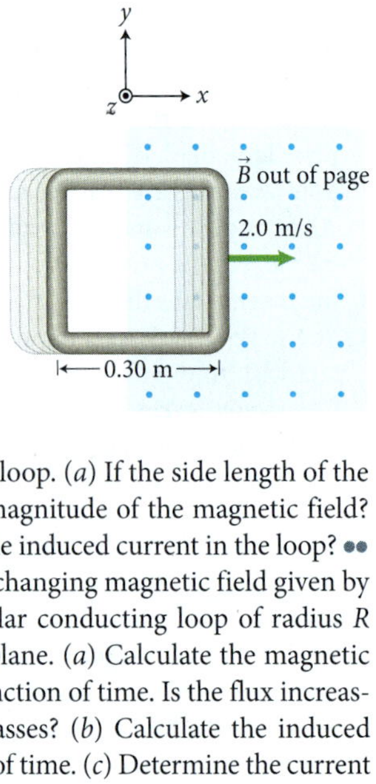

29. A region of space contains a changing magnetic field given by $\vec{B}(t) = B_0 e^{-t/\tau} \hat{k}$, and a circular conducting loop of radius R lies in this region in the xy plane. (*a*) Calculate the magnetic flux through the loop as a function of time. Is the flux increasing or decreasing as time passes? (*b*) Calculate the induced emf in the loop as a function of time. (*c*) Determine the current direction in the loop. ••

30. The coil in a generator has 100 windings and a cross-sectional area of 0.0100 m². (*a*) If the coil turns at a constant rotational speed and the magnetic field in the generator is that of Earth ($B = 0.500 \times 10^{-4}$ T), how many 360° rotations must the coil complete each second to generate a maximum induced emf of 1.00 V? (*b*) Based on this calculation, does it seem practical to use Earth's magnetic field in electric generators? ••

31. You have two cylindrical solenoids, one inside the other, with the two cylinders concentric. The outer solenoid has length $\ell_{outer} = 400$ mm, radius $R_{outer} = 50$ mm, and $N_{outer} = 1000$ windings. The inner solenoid has length $\ell_{inner} = 40$ mm,

PRACTICE

radius $R_{\text{inner}} = 20$ mm, and $N_{\text{inner}} = 150$ windings. The inner solenoid is centered within the outer solenoid. When the outer solenoid carries a current given by $I(t) = I_0 \sin(\omega t)$, with $I_0 = 600$ mA and $\omega = 100\ \text{s}^{-1}$, what is the peak emf in the inner solenoid? ••

32. A rectangular wire loop enclosing an area $A = 0.40\ \text{m}^2$ is inside a long cylindrical solenoid with two windings per mm. The area vector of the loop is aligned with the axis of the solenoid, and the current in the solenoid varies according to the graph shown in Figure P29.32. What is the induced emf in the loop at $t = 10$ s? ••

Figure P29.32

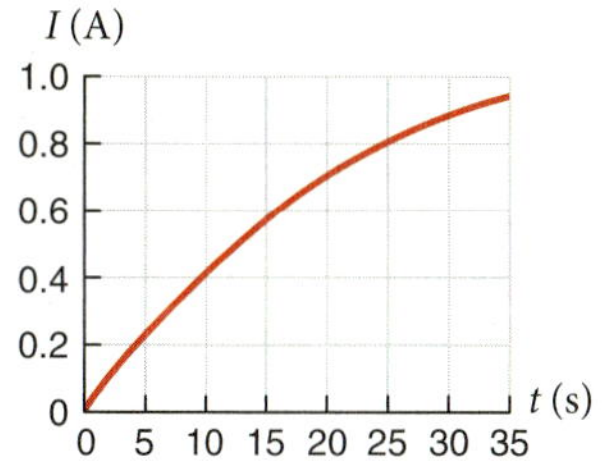

33. A circular metal disk with a shaft through its center rotates about a central axis as shown in Figure P29.33. The unit is placed in a uniform magnetic field of magnitude 1.5 T, directed parallel to the shaft. Two small sliding contacts are placed against the unit, one touching the edge of the disk and the other touching the end of the shaft. (*a*) If the disk radius is 100 mm and the disk completes 300 rotations per minute, what is the value of the emf induced between the two contacts? (*b*) Which contact is at the greater potential? ••

Figure P29.33

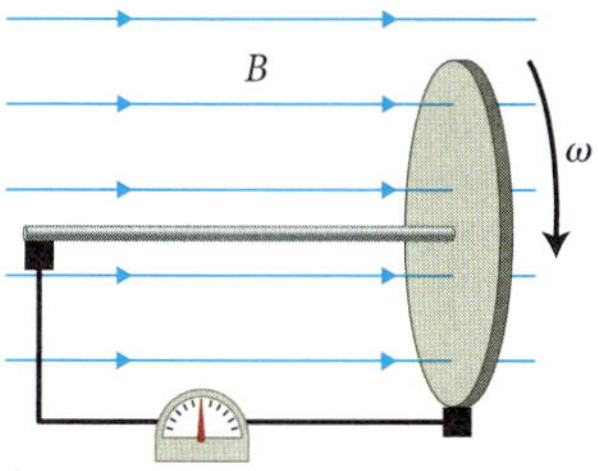

34. The dimensions of the rectangular loop of wire in Figure P29.34 are $\ell = 50$ mm and $w = 40$ mm. The loop moves at speed $v = 30$ mm/s through the magnetic field shown. The field magnitude increases linearly from $B_i(x_i) = 10$ mT at $x_i = 300$ mm to $B_f(x_f) = 60$ mT at $x_f = 900$ mm. The area vector of the loop is parallel to the magnetic field direction. What is the induced emf in the loop? •••

Figure P29.34

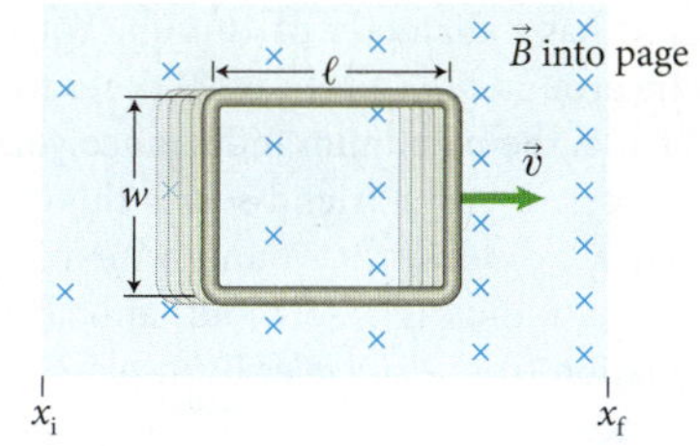

35. The dimensions of the rectangular loop of wire in Figure P29.35 are $\ell = 400$ mm and $w = 120$ mm. The mass of the loop is 10 g, its resistance is 5.0 V/A, and before entering the magnetic field shown the loop is moving at a constant speed v_i. The magnetic field magnitude is 5.0 T, and the loop's area vector is parallel to the field direction. How many seconds after the leading edge of the loop enters the magnetic field is the loop's speed half its initial value? Ignore any friction effects. •••

Figure P29.35

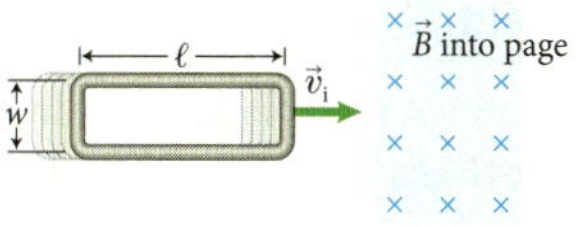

36. (*a*) A rectangular loop of wire is $\ell = 800$ mm long and $w = 500$ mm wide. You bend the ℓ sides into a semicircle while keeping the w sides straight, as shown in Figure P29.36, and then move the curved loop at speed $v = 0.800$ m/s into a uniform magnetic field of magnitude $B = 0.600$ T. One of the sides labeled w is the leading edge of the moving loop, and the magnetic field direction is perpendicular to those sides. What is the value of the emf induced in the loop? (*b*) What is the induced emf if the loop is rotated 90° so that the side leading into the magnetic field is one of the curved sides? •••

Figure P29.36

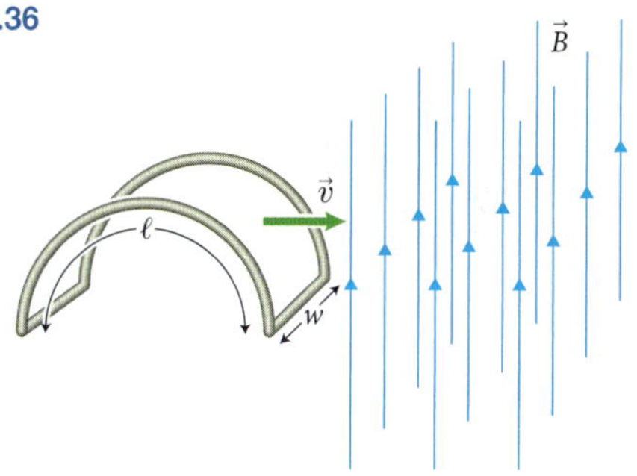

37. A bar is sliding along a set of connected conducting rails as shown in Figure P29.37. The bar is given an initial velocity $\vec{v}_i$ to the right and then allowed to move freely. The bar has mass m, and the distance between the rails (which is also the bar length) is ℓ. The resistance of the conducting loop comprising the bar and conducting rails is R. Show that the speed of the bar decreases exponentially with time, and determine the time constant. •••

Figure P29.37

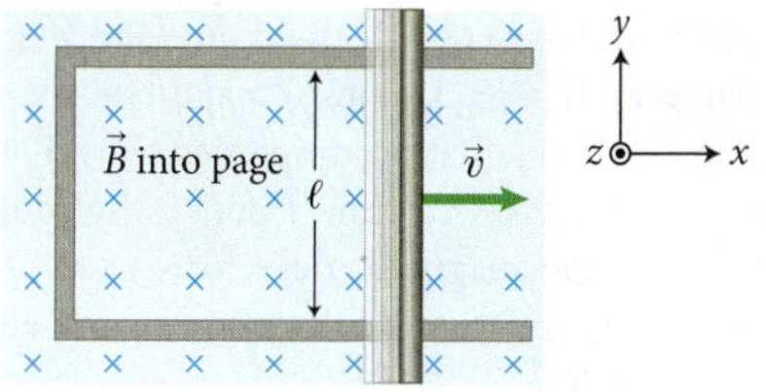

38. The area vector of a rectangular loop that is initially $\ell_i = 300$ mm long and $w_i = 200$ mm wide is aligned with the direction of a uniform magnetic field that has initial magnitude $B_i = 500$ mT. You want to increase the field magnitude smoothly to $B_f = 700$ mT in 10 s, but you want to have zero induced current in the loop. You plan to accomplish this by changing the loop's length ℓ as you increase the magnetic field. In order to have $I_{ind} = 0$, what must the loop length be after 3.00 s and after 10.0 s? •••

29.6 Electric field accompanying a changing magnetic field

39. A uniform magnetic field exists in a circular area. A particle carrying charge $q = 5.0$ mC is placed in the field a distance $r_p = 20$ mm from the center of the circular area. If the particle experiences a force that has magnitude $F = 4.00\ \mu$N and is perpendicular to the direction of the magnetic field, at what rate is the magnetic field changing? •

The next four problems are based on the situation illustrated in Figure P29.40. A uniform magnetic field pointing in the positive z direction fills a cylindrical volume of space of radius R whose central axis is the z axis. Outside this region, there is no magnetic field.

Figure P29.40

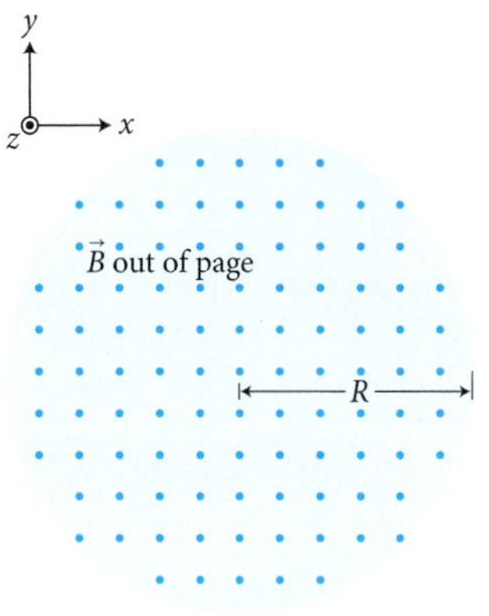

40. In Figure P29.40, $R = 0.12$ m and a changing magnetic field creates an electric field that has magnitude $E = 10$ V/m at a radial distance $r = 0.060$ m from the center of the magnetic field. What is the instantaneous magnitude of the time rate of change of the magnetic field? •
41. If in Figure P29.40 $R = 0.25$ m and the magnetic field magnitude is decreasing at a rate of 0.30 T/s, what is the magnitude of the electric field created by this changing magnetic field (*a*) at radial distance $r = 0.20$ m from the magnetic field center and (*b*) at $r = 0.50$ m from the center? (*c*) Do the electric field lines encircle the z axis clockwise or counterclockwise, when viewed looking down the positive z axis toward the origin? ••
42. If the magnitude of the magnetic field in Figure P29.40 changes with time as $B = B_{max}\sin(\omega t)$, calculate the magnitude of the electric field that accompanies this changing magnetic field as a function of time t and radial distance r from the center of the magnetic field for (*a*) $r < R$ and (*b*) $r > R$. (*c*) At $t = 0$, what is the direction of the electric field? ••
43. The magnitude of the magnetic field in Figure P29.40 changes with time, and the magnitude of the accompanying electric field inside the magnetic field is given by $E(r, t) = 3Crt^2$, where C is a positive constant and r is the radial distance from the center of the magnetic field. For the case where $B = 0$ at $t = 0$, derive an expression for the magnitude of the magnetic field as a function of time for $t > 0$. ••
44. A uniform magnetic field fills a cylindrical volume of radius R, and the field magnitude changes with time at an unknown rate. At a certain instant, the electric field magnitude at a radial distance $r_1 < R$ from the magnetic field center is E_1. At this instant, at what radial distance r from the magnetic field center is the electric field magnitude E equal to $E_1/3$ (*a*) if $r < R$ and (*b*) if $r > R$? ••
45. It takes an electric field magnitude of about 10^6 V/m to ionize atoms in the air and produce a spark. Is it possible to increase the magnetic field inside a long solenoid quickly enough to generate a spark inside? Take the solenoid radius to be 30 mm. •••

29.7 Inductance

46. A 2.0-H inductor carries a current that is increasing at a rate of 0.40 A/s. What is the magnitude of the emf induced in the inductor? Does this induced emf aid or oppose the flow of the charge carriers? •
47. When the current through an inductor is decreasing at a rate of 2.0 A/s, the magnitude of the induced emf is 6.0 V. What is the inductance of the inductor? •
48. The radius of a toroid is $R_t = 0.10$ m, and the windings have a circular cross section. The radius of each winding is $R_w = 10$ mm, and the number of windings is $N = 400$. Calculate the inductance of the toroid. •
49. The current through an inductor of inductance L is given by $I(t) = I_{max}\sin(\omega t)$. (*a*) Derive an expression for the induced emf in the inductor as a function of time. (*b*) At $t = 0$, is the current through the inductor increasing or decreasing? (*c*) At $t = 0$, is the induced emf opposing or aiding the flow of the charge carriers? (Remember that the direction of a positive induced emf is the same as the current direction and the direction of a negative induced emf is opposite the current direction.) (*d*) How are the answers to parts *b* and *c* consistent with the behavior of inductors discussed in the text? ••
50. The induced emf in an inductor of inductance L varies with time according to $\mathscr{E}_{ind}(t) = -2Ct$, where C is a positive constant. (*a*) If there is no current through the inductor at $t = 0$, calculate the current as a function of time for $t > 0$. (*b*) Is the current increasing or decreasing when $t > 0$? (*c*) Discuss how your answer to part *b* is consistent with the sign of $\mathscr{E}_{ind}$ and what you know about the behavior of inductors. ••
51. You and a friend have a 0.65-m length of copper wire that has a diameter of 4.115 mm and a wooden rod that is 85 mm long and has a diameter of 10 mm. You're aiming to wind the wire around the rod about 40 times to form an inductor. (*a*) What is the maximum inductance you can achieve with this device? (*b*) Your friend solves this problem by reasoning that a cylindrically wound wire whose length greatly exceeds its radius is a solenoid, and therefore he can use the equation from *Principles* Example 29.8 to determine the inductance:

$$L = \frac{\mu_0 N^2 A}{\ell} = \frac{(4\pi \times 10^{-7}\ \mathrm{T \cdot m/A})(40^2)\pi(0.0020575\ \mathrm{m})^2}{0.65\ \mathrm{m}}$$

$$= 4.1 \times 10^{-8}\ \mathrm{H}.$$

Evaluate your friend's work. ••

52. The toroid in Figure P29.52 has 200 rectangular windings, and the toroid radii are $R_{in} = 160$ mm and $R_{out} = 240$ mm. The height of each winding is $h = 20$ mm, such that the rectangular cross section of each winding is $(R_{out} - R_{in}) \times h = (80\ \mathrm{mm}) \times (20\ \mathrm{mm})$. What is the inductance of the toroid? •••

Figure P29.52

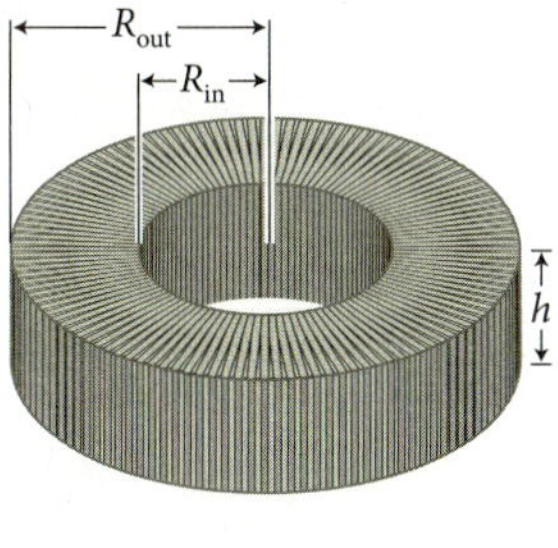

29.8 Magnetic energy

53. Calculate the amount of magnetic potential energy stored in a 0.60-H inductor when the current in the inductor is 6.0 A. •
54. If 10 J of magnetic potential energy is stored in a 5.0-H inductor, what is the current in the inductor? •
55. A cylindrical volume of space contains a uniform magnetic field of magnitude 0.12 T but unknown direction. If the dimensions of the cylindrical volume are length $\ell = 0.060$ m and radius $R = 0.040$ m, how much magnetic potential energy is stored in the field? ••
56. When you unplug a coffee maker that plugs into the utility outlet of your car, you notice a spark. Worried that the coffee maker might be broken, you take it apart and find that the heating element is a tungsten wire that, according to the label, is wound 600 times around what appears to be a nonmagnetic core. The core has radius $R = 2.0$ mm and length $\ell = 200$ mm. On the outside of the coffee maker, it says 12 V, 3.2 A. Where does the spark come from? ••
57. The magnitude of the magnetic field in a magnetic resonance imaging (MRI) machine can be as great as $B = 3.0$ T. Under normal circumstances, this field cannot be shut off by just flipping a switch. Instead the magnitude needs to be carefully decreased to zero. In an emergency, however, the magnet can be "quenched" so that B reduces to zero in 20 s. Such a quench can cost thousands of dollars and likely damages the magnets. Assume that the magnetic field exists inside a cylinder of radius $R = 300$ mm and length $\ell = 200$ mm. How much magnetic potential energy is dissipated when the magnetic field is quenched in this way, and what is the average rate at which energy is dissipated? ••
58. What is the magnetic potential energy stored in a cylindrical volume of height $h_{cylin} = 50$ mm and radius $R_{cylin} = 24$ mm that symmetrically surrounds an infinitely long wire that has radius $R_{wire} = 2.1$ mm and carries current $I = 2.3$ A? •••
59. A cylindrical solenoid of length ℓ and radius R has n windings per unit length and carries a current I. (*a*) Use the inductance expression $L = (\mu_0 N^2 A)/\ell$ from *Principles* Example 29.8 and Eq. 29.25, $U^B = LI^2/2$, to derive an expression for the magnetic potential energy in the solenoid as a function of the current and the solenoid's dimensions. (*b*) Derive this same expression by beginning with Eq. 29.30, $U^B = \int u_B\, dV$. •••

Additional problems

60. Calculate the inductance of a 2000-windings cylindrical solenoid that is 0.20 m long if the radius of each winding is 0.03 m. •
61. The current in a cylindrical solenoid is increased smoothly from $I_i = 0.40$ A at $t_i = 3.0$ s to $I_f = 1.2$ A at $t_f = 5.0$ s. What is the induced emf during this time interval if the solenoid length is $\ell = 150$ mm, the radius of each winding is $R = 20$ mm, and there are 400 windings? •
62. A uniform magnetic field exists in a cubic volume of space with a 50-mm side length. If the magnetic energy stored in this volume is 12 J, what is the magnetic field magnitude? •
63. In a large laboratory electromagnet, the poles have a circular cross section with a diameter of 100 mm and are 25 mm apart. If there is a uniform 1.3-T magnetic field between the poles, how much magnetic potential energy is stored in the magnetic field? •
64. The rate at which the magnetic flux inside a wire loop decays is given by $\Phi_B(t) = \Phi_{B,i} e^{-\beta t}$, where $\beta = 0.50$/s and $\Phi_{B,i} = 4.0$ Wb. What is the magnitude of the induced current at $t = 10$ s if the resistance of the wire is $R = 2.0$ V/A? ••
65. You build a solenoid containing 400 windings over a 0.20-m length, with a loop radius of 0.025 m for each winding. If the current in the unit is 3.0 A, what are (*a*) the magnitude of the magnetic field produced and (*b*) the inductance of the solenoid? (*c*) Use your value of B from part *a* to calculate the amount of magnetic potential energy stored in the solenoid. (*d*) Use your value of L from part *b* to calculate the amount of magnetic potential energy stored. ••
66. A conducting bar that is $\ell = 40$ mm long can slide with negligible friction on two parallel conducting rails positioned at an incline of $\theta = 15°$ (Figure P29.66). Initially, the bar is at rest in a magnetic field of magnitude $B = 0.60$ T. What is the emf between the rails 0.20 s after the bar starts sliding while it is still inside the magnetic field? ••

Figure P29.66

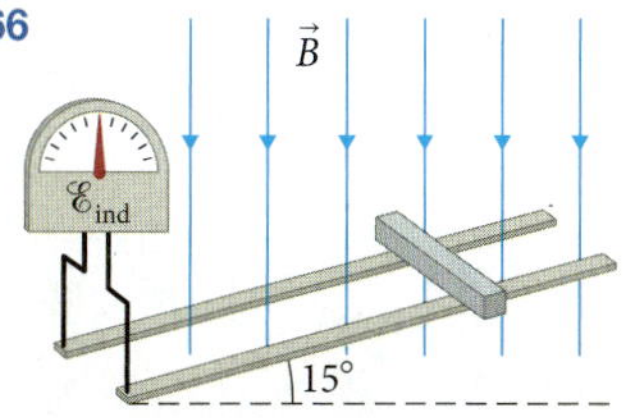

67. You have a circular wire loop of radius $a = 0.50$ m. It carries a current that increases linearly from 0 to 4.5 A in 0.30 s. At the center of this loop is a wire loop of radius $b = 0.0020$ m and resistance $R = 0.80$ V/A. The loops are coplanar. What is the current induced in the smaller loop? ••

68. You shape a flexible wire into a loop of initial radius r_i = 30 mm. You then place the loop in a uniform magnetic field and pull the two ends of the wire in opposite directions at v = 6.0 mm/s so that the loop starts closing up (Figure P29.68). If the field magnitude is B = 0.70 T, what is the emf between the ends of the wire 2.0 s after you begin pulling? ••

Figure P29.68

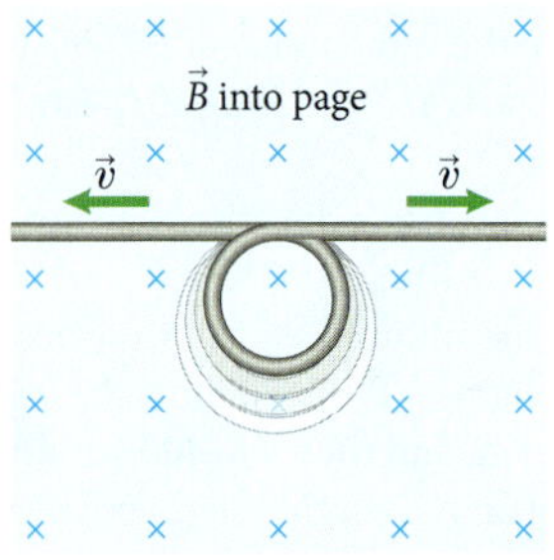

69. A rod of length ℓ rotates about one end at a constant rotational speed ω. The rod is in a uniform magnetic field $\vec{B}$, and the axis of rotation is parallel to $\vec{B}$ (Figure P29.69). (*a*) In terms of ℓ, B, and ω, what potential difference develops between the two ends of the rod? (*b*) Which end of the rod has a greater potential? (*c*) If ℓ = 0.15 m, B = 1.0 T, and ω = 377 s^{-1}, what is the potential-difference value? ••

Figure P29.69

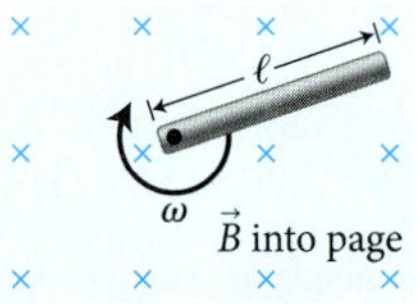

70. A uniform magnetic field of magnitude B fills all space and points in the positive z direction (Figure P29.70). A circular conducting loop in the xy plane is growing larger, with its radius as a function of time given by $r(t) = vt$, where v is a positive constant. (*a*) Derive an expression for the magnitude of the emf induced in the loop as a function of time. (*b*) What is the direction of the induced current? ••

Figure P29.70

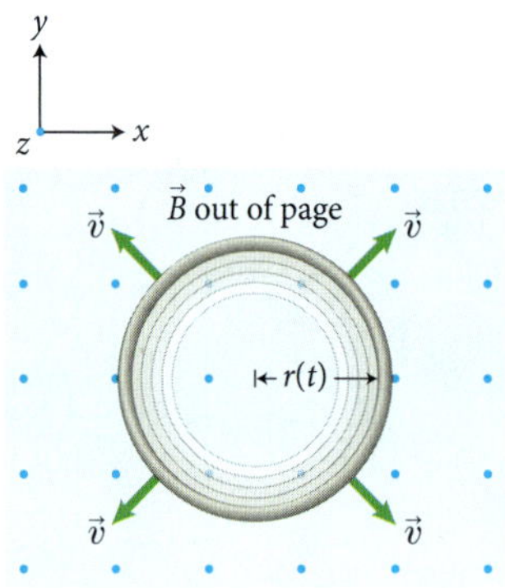

71. A conducting bar of width w = 0.12 m and mass m = 8.0 g can slide freely on two parallel conducting rails positioned at an incline of θ = 15° (Figure P29.71). The rails are connected at their base by a piece of conducting material. The distance between the rails is w, and the resistance in the rails is R = 0.20 V/A. A uniform magnetic field $\vec{B}$ is exactly vertical as indicated in the drawing, with B = 0.50 T. At what constant (terminal) speed does the bar slide down the incline? Ignore friction. ••

Figure P29.71

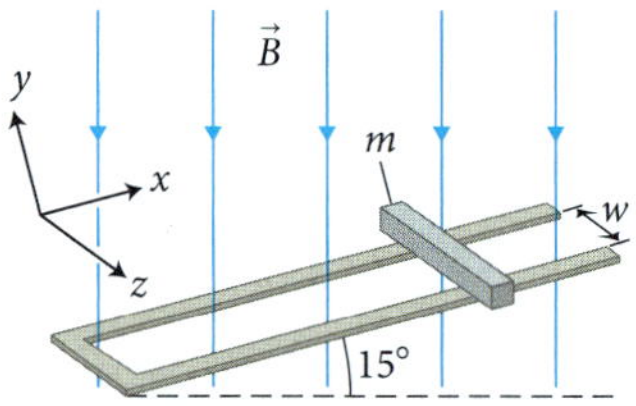

72. For the system described in Problem 71, you measure a constant speed of 1.0 m/s. Because this is not the value you calculated when you ignored friction in the system, you conclude that the friction in the rails is too great to be ignored. What value for the coefficient of kinetic friction μ_k yields the 1.0-m/s speed you measured? •••

73. A square loop of wire of side length a and resistance R lies a distance x to the right of a long, straight wire that carries a current I. The straight wire lies in the plane defined by the loop, parallel to one side of the square, and the current direction in the wire is upward. The loop is held stationary, and the current in the wire varies sinusoidally as $I = I_{max} \sin(\omega t)$. Derive an expression for the emf induced in the loop as a function of I_{max}, ω, a, x, and t. •••

74. You are working for a company that is interested in mapping geological formations in Earth's crust by examining variations in the magnitude of the magnetic field at Earth's surface. Your assignment is to design a device that can detect small variations in this magnetic field at ground level. Deciding on a system that uses a rotating coil, you realize that the design (number of windings, winding cross-sectional area, rotational speed, and so forth) must give a 1-mV signal in Earth's magnetic field in order to be useful. ••• CR

75. On the fifth floor of the physics building, you are in a laboratory class studying induction. You are using a computer to measure emf values from a solenoid when suddenly a thunderstorm breaks out. You see a large blip on the computer screen and 2.0 s later hear a loud thunderclap. Looking out the window, you see that straight ahead a tree was struck by lightning. You quickly save the data on your computer (plotted in Figure P29.75) and note that the solenoid happens to be oriented at an angle of θ = 40° with respect to your line of sight to the tree. The solenoid windings have cross-sectional area A = 0.10 m^2, and there are N = 100 windings. You wonder about the current involved in the lightning flash that struck the tree. ••• CR

Figure P29.75

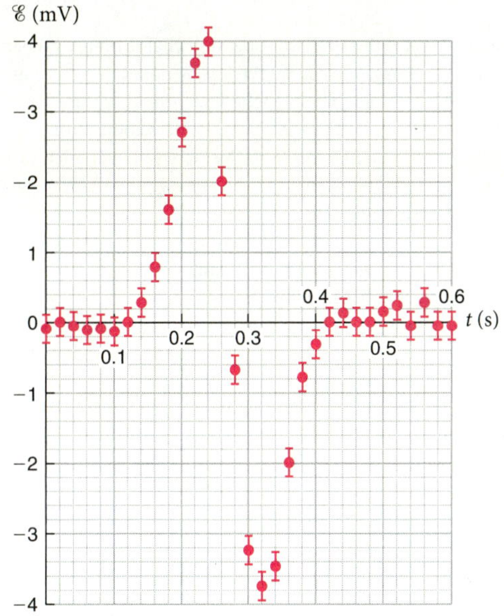

76. An electromagnet in a physics laboratory is damaging electronic apparatus in its vicinity. You suspect that the damage is due to unusually large induced currents created each time the electromagnet power supply is turned on, so you decide to monitor the magnet's magnetic field. Figure P29.76 shows the field magnitude as a function of time during the first 18 s after you connect the magnet to a power supply. Instead of smoothly increasing to its designed value of 0.90 T, the field magnitude starts to decrease after about 3.0 s, very likely due to fluctuations in its power supply. What is not clear is whether these fluctuations can account for the damage, because the electronic apparatus is designed with the expectation that the change in magnetic field strength will be linear with time. ••• CR

Figure P29.76

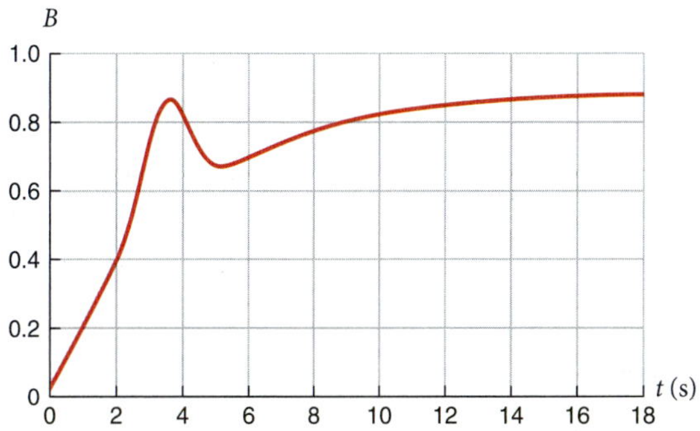

77. Analog cassette players read sound recorded on magnetic tape. The sound is recorded by magnetizing the tape longitudinally (magnetization parallel to the tape's length) with varying magnetic field magnitudes in either direction. The tape is usually divided into longitudinal tracks so that different signals can be recorded in parallel. In the player, as the tape is pulled across the reading head, a varying emf is induced in a coil wound around the C-shaped metal core of the head (Figure P29.77). This emf is then amplified and sent to the speakers. Trying to learn more about the physics of this technology, you read that the recorded signal magnitude is usually given in terms of *fluxivity,* which is the peak magnetic flux per track width. In particular, you find a paper that gives a fluxivity of 320 nWb/m for a 1000-Hz sine wave recorded on a track 6.3 mm wide [O. Schmidbauer, *J. Audio Eng. Soc.,* 46(10), 859 (1998)]. Naturally, not all of the flux generated threads through the coil, but your search shows that reading heads can have a "flux efficiency" of 98% [J. G. McKnight, B. E. Cortez, and J. A. McKnight, *J. Audio Eng. Soc.,* 46(10), 845 (1998)] and that 250 coil windings are typical. You begin to wonder about the emf induced in the coil and how the frequency of the recorded sound relates to the speed v with which the tape runs. ••• CR

Figure P29.77

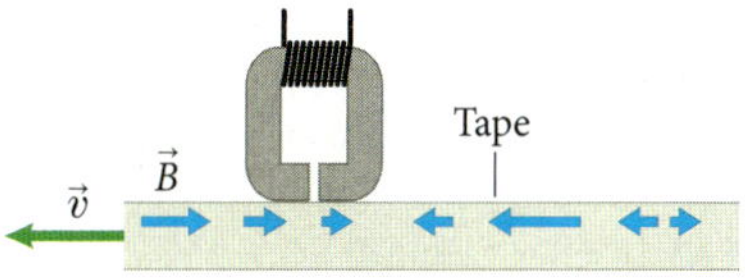

Answers to Review Questions

1. The magnetic force exerted by the external magnetic field on the charge carriers that move with the rod drives the positive carriers upward and the negative carriers downward. The result is a separation of charge and a small potential difference between the bottom and top of the rod.
2. For the portion of the loop that is in the nonzero-field region, the magnetic force exerted by the magnetic field on the charge carriers drives the positive carriers upward and the negative carriers downward. As long as part of the loop is in the nonzero-field region and part of the loop is in the zero-field region, the result is to create an electric current in the loop. When the entire loop is within the region of nonzero, uniform magnetic field, the current is no longer induced.
3. An induced electric current is the flow of charge carriers caused by electromagnetic induction, as opposed to a current that is caused by a source of potential difference such as a battery. Although the causes are different, there is no *physical* difference between induced currents and other currents.
4. Yes. The induced effects are reversed when the direction of the object's velocity is reversed, and the effects are zero when the object's velocity is parallel to the magnetic field.
5. Changing the reference frame does not affect the explanation. Whether you say the loop moves through the external magnetic field created by a stationary source or the external source moves and the loop is stationary, the result is the same: An electric current is induced in the loop as it moves between regions of differing magnetic fields.
6. Whenever the magnetic flux through a conducting loop changes, an electric current is induced in the loop.
7. Electromagnetic induction is the process by which a changing magnetic flux causes charge carriers in a conducting object to move. When the magnetic flux through a conducting loop changes, a current is induced in the loop.
8. No. In the reference frame in which the loop is at rest, there is no magnetic force to create the current in the loop. Rather, the changing magnetic field is accompanied by an electric field, and this electric field is the source of an electric force exerted on the charge carriers, creating a current in the loop.
9. Yes. In a reference frame in which a conducting loop is at rest and a magnetic field source is moving, the electric field caused by the time-varying magnetic flux is the source of the electromagnetic induction. In a reference frame in which the conducting loop moves through a nonuniform external magnetic field, the magnetic force exerted on the charge carriers in the loop is the source of the electromagnetic induction.
10. The field lines of an electric field that accompanies a changing magnetic field form closed loops, whereas the field lines of the field of stationary charged particles, which originate on positively charged particles and terminate on negatively charged ones, do not.
11. The current is induced by a changing magnetic flux through the loop, and Lenz's law says that the direction of the induced current is the direction that makes the magnetic field created by the induced current oppose the changing magnetic flux through the loop.
12. The law of conservation of energy underlies Lenz's law. If the direction of an induced current were to enhance the change in the magnetic flux rather than oppose that change, the result would be an increase in the system's energy without any work being done on the system.
13. Eddy currents are electric currents induced in a conducting object by a changing external magnetic field near the object. These currents are generally not confined to a single path, as in a wire, but circulate as tiny whirlpools.
14. Induced emf is the emf (work per unit charge done in separating positive and negative charge carriers by nonelectrostatic means) associated with changing magnetic flux through a closed path.
15. The energy acquired by the charge carriers comes from the agent that causes the loop to move. If the loop is being pulled through the magnetic field, for example, that mechanical work done on the loop is transferred to the charge carriers.
16. (*a*) Faraday's law states that the emf induced around a closed path is equal to the negative of the time rate of change of magnetic flux through an area bounded by the path: $\mathscr{E}_{ind} = -d\Phi_B/dt$. (*b*) The negative sign reflects Lenz's law by making the expression say that the direction of $\mathscr{E}_{ind}$ is such that the induced current opposes the magnetic-flux change generating that current.
17. (1) Both induced emf and potential difference are related to the work done per unit charge on charged particles. In the case of potential difference, the work is done by electrostatic forces, but the work is done by nonelectrostatic forces in the case of emf.
(2) Potential difference is path-independent, which means that the work done by electrostatic forces on charged particles depends only on the particles' starting and ending locations, not on the path they take to get to those locations. The work done by the emf induced by a changing magnetic field does depend on the path taken by the charged particles; that is, the work done by nonelectrostatic forces depends on the shape of the loop in which the emf is induced.
18. The induced emf oscillates sinusoidally according to the expression $\mathscr{E}_{ind} = \omega BA \cos \omega t$ (where A is the area enclosed by the loop).
19. The induced emf is the line integral of the electric field that accompanies the changing magnetic field, around the path bounding the area through which the magnetic flux is changing.
20. The direction of the electric field is tangent to the electric field lines, which form loops centered on the solenoid axis. The electric field lines lie in planes perpendicular to the solenoid axis and point in the direction dictated by Lenz's law. This is true both inside and outside the solenoid.
21. The magnitude of the electric field is proportional to the time derivative of the magnetic field strength, $E \propto (dB/dt)$. From *Principles* Example 29.7 you know that inside the magnetic field region E varies directly with distance from the solenoid axis, and from Checkpoint 29.13 you know that outside the magnetic field region E varies inversely with the distance from the solenoid axis.
22. Yes. The changing current changes the magnetic flux through the loop, and Faraday's law tells you that the changing magnetic flux induces an emf to oppose the flux change.
23. The SI unit is the henry, which equals one volt-second per ampere.
24. An inductor is an electrical component that has a specified inductance, such that a given dI/dt results in a known, specified emf. Because the induced emf opposes changes in current, one use of an inductor is to even out any current fluctuations in a current-carrying loop.
25. The inductance of a conducting loop or device describes how much the magnetic flux through it changes when the current changes. The inductance depends only on the geometric properties of the loop or device—that is, on its size and shape. For example, the inductance of a solenoid depends on its length, cross-sectional area, and the number of windings: $L \propto N^2A/\ell$.
26. The work done to change the current in an inductor goes into, or comes out of, the magnetic potential energy stored in the magnetic field of the inductor. That is, a reduction in the current is accounted for by a decrease in the stored magnetic potential energy. Some external source is needed to account for the work done to increase the current, work that increases the stored magnetic potential energy.

27. The magnetic potential energy depends on the square of the current in the inductor and on the inductance: $U^B = LI^2/2$. Because inductance depends on the physical dimensions of the inductor, you can also say that the magnetic potential energy stored in an inductor depends on the square of the current and on the size and shape of the inductor; for a solenoidal inductor, for example, $U^B \propto N^2AI^2/\ell$.
28. The magnetic potential energy in an inductor is equal to the volume integral of the energy density in the magnetic field: $U^B = \int u_B dV$. The energy density is proportional to the square of the field strength, $u_B = B^2/(2\mu_0)$, which is a general relationship for any magnetic field. (If the field strength is approximately uniform over the volume of the inductor, the energy is just the product of the energy density and the volume.)

Answers to Guided Problems

Guided Problem 29.2 $I_{\text{ind}} = \dfrac{\mathscr{E}_{\text{ind}}}{R} = \dfrac{\mu_0 I \ell v}{2\pi R}\left(\dfrac{1}{r} - \dfrac{1}{r+w}\right)$. In the configuration of Figure WG29.3, the direction of the induced current is clockwise around the loop.

Guided Problem 29.4 While the top of the loop is still in the magnetic field, $v = (g\tau)(1 - e^{-t/\tau})$, with $\tau = (mR/w^2B^2)$. After the top edge of the loop has left the magnetic field, v increases with time at constant acceleration g.

Guided Problem 29.6 $U^B = \dfrac{\mu_0 \ell I^2}{4\pi}\ln\left(\dfrac{R_{\text{outer}}}{R_{\text{inner}}}\right)$, $L = \dfrac{\mu_0 \ell}{2\pi}\ln\left(\dfrac{R_{\text{outer}}}{R_{\text{inner}}}\right)$

Guided Problem 29.8 $\dfrac{dB(R)}{dt} = \dfrac{1}{2}\left(\dfrac{dB_{\text{av}}}{dt}\right)$

30

PRACTICE
Changing Electric Fields

Chapter Summary

Changing electric fields (Sections 30.1, 30.4)

Concepts A changing electric field is accompanied by a magnetic field, and a changing magnetic field is accompanied by an electric field.

Table 30.1 Properties of electric and magnetic fields

	Electric field	Magnetic field
associated with	charged particle	moving charged particle
	changing magnetic field	changing electric field
exerts force on	any charged particle	moving charged particle

Quantitative Tools The **displacement current** due to a changing electric flux through a surface is

$$I_{\text{disp}} \equiv \epsilon_0 \frac{d\Phi_E}{dt}. \quad (30.7)$$

The *Maxwell-Ampère law* is

$$\oint \vec{B} \cdot d\vec{\ell} = \mu_0(I_{\text{int}} + I_{\text{disp}}), \quad (30.8)$$

where I_{int} is the current intercepted by a surface spanning an Ampèrian path.

Maxwell's equations (Section 30.5)

Concepts **Maxwell's equations** provide a complete mathematical description of electric and magnetic phenomena and the relationship between the two.

Quantitative Tools **Maxwell's equations** are

$$\Phi_E \equiv \oint \vec{E} \cdot d\vec{A} = \frac{q_{\text{enc}}}{\epsilon_0} \quad (30.10)$$

$$\Phi_B \equiv \oint \vec{B} \cdot d\vec{A} = 0 \quad (30.11)$$

$$\oint \vec{E} \cdot d\vec{\ell} = -\frac{d\Phi_B}{dt} \quad (30.12)$$

$$\oint \vec{B} \cdot d\vec{\ell} = \mu_0 I_{\text{int}} + \mu_0\epsilon_0 \frac{d\Phi_E}{dt}. \quad (30.13)$$

Electromagnetic waves (Sections 30.2, 30.3, 30.6, 30.7)

Concepts An **electromagnetic wave** is a propagating disturbance in a combined electric and magnetic field. The electric and magnetic fields in these waves are perpendicular to each other, and the direction of wave propagation is the direction of $\vec{E} \times \vec{B}$.

A **planar electromagnetic wave** is one in which the wavefronts are planes perpendicular to the direction of propagation. At each point on a planar wavefront, the instantaneous magnitude of the electric field has the same value, as does the instantaneous magnitude of the magnetic field.

Oscillating dipoles and antennas to which an alternating potential is applied emit electromagnetic waves.

The **polarization** of an electromagnetic wave is the orientation of the electric field as seen by an observer looking in the direction of propagation.

Quantitative Tools The speed of an electromagnetic wave in vacuum is

$$c_0 = \frac{1}{\sqrt{\epsilon_0\mu_0}}. \quad (30.26)$$

The speed of an electromagnetic wave in a dielectric of dielectric constant κ is

$$c = \frac{c_0}{\sqrt{\kappa}}.$$

The **Poynting vector** $\vec{S}$ gives the energy transported by an electromagnetic wave per unit time across a unit area perpendicular to the direction of propagation of the wave:

$$\vec{S} \equiv \frac{1}{\mu_0}\vec{E} \times \vec{B}. \quad (30.37)$$

The power transported by an electromagnetic wave crossing a surface is

$$P = \int_{\text{surface}} \vec{S} \cdot d\vec{A}. \quad (30.38)$$

Review Questions

Answers to these questions can be found at the end of this chapter.

30.1 Magnetic fields accompany changing electric fields

1. What besides electric current produces a magnetic field?
2. How is the direction of the magnetic field that accompanies a changing electric field related to the direction of the changing electric field?
3. Describe the similarities and differences in the sources that produce electric and magnetic fields.
4. What is the main difference between the effects of electric fields on charged particles and the effects of magnetic fields on charged particles?
5. Describe the main similarity and the main difference in the spatial appearance of electric and magnetic field lines.

30.2 Fields of moving charged particles

6. Is the electric field surrounding a charged particle moving with constant velocity spherically symmetrical or asymmetrical? If asymmetrical, describe what the field looks like.
7. What determines how asymmetrical the electric field surrounding a charged particle moving at constant velocity is?
8. When do kinks appear in the field line pattern of the electric field that surrounds a charged particle? What two regions of a given field line does a kink join?
9. What are the two components of an electromagnetic wave?

30.3 Oscillating dipoles and antennas

10. Describe at the instant $t = T$ the electric field lines in three regions of interest near an electric dipole whose polarity changes once (from positive above negative to negative above positive) during the time interval $t = 0$ to $t = T/2$ and then remains fixed from $t = T/2$ to $t = T$.
11. In a transverse electromagnetic wave, how are the electric and magnetic fields oriented relative to each other and relative to the direction in which the wave propagates?
12. What does it mean to say that the electric and magnetic fields in an electromagnetic wave are *in phase*?
13. How is the polarization of an electromagnetic wave defined?
14. What is an antenna?
15. How is an oscillating current created in an emitting antenna?

30.4 Displacement current

16. What electrical device can be used to demonstrate that the form of Ampère's law given in Chapter 28, $\oint \vec{B} \cdot d\vec{\ell} = \mu_0 I_{enc}$, is incomplete? Describe an Ampèrian path around the device and a surface spanned by the path that you can use to illustrate this incompleteness.
17. What is the generalized form of Ampère's law, which applies when electric fields are changing?
18. In the generalized form of Ampère's law, what does each term to the right of the equal sign represent?
19. Is displacement current really a current? If not, why is it called a current?
20. How must the displacement-current term in the generalized form of Ampère's law be modified when the capacitor being analyzed contains a dielectric between its plates?

30.5 Maxwell's equations

21. Write the four equations from the *Principles* text that are collectively called Maxwell's equations, and name each one.
22. Given that all four of the laws for electric and magnetic fields were discovered before Maxwell modified one of them, why is it still fitting to refer to all of them as Maxwell's equations?
23. Describe the experimental evidence for each of Maxwell's equations.

30.6 Electromagnetic waves

24. For an electromagnetic wave pulse emanating from an accelerated charge carrier, what does the transverse (kinked) portion of the pulse look like far from the location where the acceleration occurred?
25. What is the relationship between the magnitudes of the electric and magnetic fields for an electromagnetic wave pulse traveling in vacuum?
26. What is the relationship between the magnitudes of the electric and magnetic fields for an electromagnetic wave pulse traveling through a dielectric material?
27. In terms of the electric constant ϵ_0 and the magnetic constant μ_0, what is the speed of an electromagnetic wave pulse traveling in vacuum and traveling through a dielectric?
28. For a planar electromagnetic wave, what is the directional relationship among the magnetic field, the electric field, and the wave's propagation velocity?
29. Do electromagnetic waves of different frequencies travel at different speeds in vacuum?
30. How is the speed at which an electromagnetic wave travels in vacuum related to the wave's frequency and wavelength?
31. What are the names of the major divisions of the electromagnetic spectrum?

30.7 Electromagnetic energy

32. How do the energy densities in the electric and magnetic fields of a planar electromagnetic wave in vacuum compare with each other?
33. (*a*) What is the expression for the energy density u of an electromagnetic wave in vacuum in terms of its electric and magnetic components? (*b*) How can you express the energy density if you know the electric component of the wave but do not know the magnetic component? (*c*) How can you express the energy density if you know the magnetic component but not the electric component?
34. What is the Poynting vector of an electromagnetic wave in vacuum, and what properties of the wave does this vector represent?
35. What is the intensity of an electromagnetic wave?
36. What is the relationship between the intensity of an electromagnetic wave and its energy density?

Developing a Feel

Make an order-of-magnitude estimate of each of the following quantities. Letters in parentheses refer to hints below. Use them as needed to guide your thinking.

1. The shortest-wavelength electromagnetic wave you can generate by waving a charged rod (T, F, B)
2. The wavelength of a radio station that is called FM 104 (A, K, F, B)
3. The frequency of a radio wave if one wavelength occupies the length of a tennis court (F, B, U)
4. The maximum magnitude of the electric field 1 m from an electron that has 10^{-12} J of energy and is moving at a constant speed $v \approx c_0$ (W, G, DD, S, FF)
5. The time interval needed for a radio wave pulse emitted from ground level to travel to and then back from a communications satellite moving in a geostationary orbit at 3×10^3 m/s (A satellite in geostationary orbit moves at a translational speed equal to the product of Earth's rotational speed and the orbit's radius, so it always stays above a single location on Earth's surface.) (B, P, CC, N, H)
6. The average displacement current caused when a 1-μF capacitor is charged to 10 V in 0.1 s (J, O)
7. The root mean square (rms) value of the electric field magnitude 1 km from an AM radio station emitting antenna (E, I, X, Q, V, M)
8. The maximum magnetic field magnitude 100 mm from a 125-mW cell phone (E, Z, X, Q, BB)
9. The change in electric flux in the region between your finger and a metal doorknob when a spark jumps from your finger to the knob (Y, EE, C, R)
10. The power radiated by all the AM radio stations in the United States (M, D, L, AA)

Hints

A. What does the radio station number refer to?
B. What is the wave speed?
C. What is the electric field magnitude at which air breaks down (that is, when sparks form)?
D. How many AM stations are there in an average-size city?
E. What is the relationship between the rms values of the electric and magnetic field magnitudes?
F. What is the relationship between wavelength and frequency?
G. What is the electric field magnitude 1 m from an electron at rest?
H. What is the height above Earth's surface to geostationary orbit?
I. What is the relationship between E_{rms} and the average intensity of the wave?
J. What is the quantity of charge on each plate when the capacitor is fully charged?
K. What is the frequency unit for FM radio?
L. How many average-size cities are in the United States?
M. What power is radiated by a typical commercial radio station?
N. What is Earth's radius?
O. What is the conventional current required to charge the capacitor?
P. What is the orbital period of a geostationary orbit?
Q. What is the relationship between the average intensity of the wave and the average power of the wave source at a radial distance $r = R$ from the source?
R. What is the cross-sectional area where the electric field magnitude is greatest?
S. For a moving electron, how does the magnitude of the component of the electric field perpendicular to the line of motion 1 m from the electron compare with the magnitude of the electric field 1 m from an electron at rest?
T. At what maximum frequency can you wave the rod?
U. What is the length of a tennis court?
V. What is the relationship between P_{av} and E_{rms}?
W. What is the charge on the electron?
X. What is the area of a sphere of radius R?
Y. How should you model this situation to relate it to material covered in the *Principles* text?
Z. What is the relationship between B_{rms} and the average intensity of the wave?
AA. What is a reasonable value for the number of AM stations in the United States that are outside cities?
BB. What is the relationship between P_{av} and B_{rms}?
CC. How does the period of an object in circular motion at constant speed relate to the circle's radius?
DD. Where is the electric field due to the electron's motion greatest?
EE. Is the electric field between the plates of a charged capacitor uniform or nonuniform?
FF. What is the γ factor for a 10^{-12}-J electron?

Key (all values approximate)

A. the frequency of the electromagnetic waves emitted by the station's emitting antenna; **B.** 3×10^8 m/s; **C.** 3×10^6 V/m; **D.** 30 stations; **E.** $B_{rms} = E_{rms}/c_0$; **F.** $f = c_0/\lambda$; **G.** $ke/r^2 = 1 \times 10^{-9}$ V/m ($k = 9 \times 10^9$ N·m²/C², Coulomb's law); **H.** $R - R_E \sim 4 \times 10^7$ m; **I.** $S_{av} = E_{rms}^2/c_0\mu_0$; **J.** $q_{max} = CV = 10^{-5}$ C; **K.** megahertz; **L.** at least one per state, and more in populous states—say 100 cities; **M.** 10^4 W; **N.** 6×10^6 m; **O.** $I = \Delta q/\Delta t = 10^{-4}$ A; **P.** $T = 1$ day $= 9 \times 10^4$ s; **Q.** $P_{av} = S_{av}A = S_{av}4\pi R^2$; **R.** the cross-sectional area of the smaller object, your finger—10^{-4} m²; **S.** the two magnitudes differ by the same factor that scales length contraction: $\gamma = 1/\sqrt{1 - v^2/c_0^2}$; **T.** 5 Hz; **U.** 3×10^1 m; **V.** $P_{av} = E_{rms}^2 4\pi R^2/c_0\mu_0$; **W.** -1.6×10^{-19} C; **X.** $A = 4\pi R^2$; **Y.** as a parallel-plate capacitor with your finger as one plate and the knob as the other plate; **Z.** $S_{av} = c_0 B_{rms}^2/\mu_0$; **AA.** 20 in each state = 1000 stations; **BB.** $P_{av} = c_0 B_{rms}^2 4\pi R^2/\mu_0$; **CC.** $T = 2\pi R/v$ (Eq. 11.20); **DD.** perpendicular to the line of motion; **EE.** uniform; **FF.** 1×10^1

Worked and Guided Problems

These examples involve material from this chapter but are not associated with any particular section. Some examples are worked out in detail; others you should work out by following the guidelines provided.

Worked Problem 30.1 Magnetic from electric

The electric field of a planar sinusoidal electromagnetic wave is given by $\vec{E}(z, t) = E\sin(kz - \omega t)\hat{\imath}$, where $k = 9.0\ \text{m}^{-1}$ and $E = 6.0 \times 10^2\ \text{V/m}$. (*a*) What are the wavelength and angular frequency of the wave? (*b*) What are the magnitude and direction of the magnetic field associated with this electric field?

❶ **GETTING STARTED** We are given the equation that describes the electric field of an electromagnetic wave and the values for the field magnitude E and the wave number k. From the z and the minus sign in the argument of the sine function, we know that the wave is traveling in the positive z direction (Eq. 16.12). Because the wave is planar, we see from *Principles* Figure 30.38 that, on each planar surface $z = a$, the electric field has a uniform value and lies along the x direction.

❷ **DEVISE PLAN** For part *a* we can determine the wavelength from Eq. 16.7, $k = 2\pi/\lambda$, and the angular frequency from Eqs. 16.11 and 16.9, $\omega = 2\pi/T$ and $\lambda = cT$, where in this case $c = c_0 = 3.0 \times 10^8\ \text{m/s}$. For part *b* we use our knowledge that in a planar sinusoidal electromagnetic wave, the electric and magnetic fields are perpendicular to each other and the direction in which the wave they constitute travels is given by $\vec{E} \times \vec{B}$. We also know that the relationship between the field magnitudes is $B = E/c_0$ (Eq. 30.24) and that the fields are in phase.

❸ **EXECUTE PLAN** (*a*) From Eq. 16.7 $k = 2\pi/\lambda$, the wavelength is $\lambda = 2\pi/k = 2\pi/(9.0\ \text{m}^{-1}) = 7.1 \times 10^{-2}\ \text{m}$. ✔

The angular frequency of the wave is therefore

$$\omega = \frac{2\pi c_0}{\lambda} = \frac{2\pi(3.0 \times 10^8\ \text{m/s})}{(2\pi/9.0)\ \text{m}} = 2.7 \times 10^9\ \text{s}^{-1}. ✔$$

(*b*) Consider a pair of values (z, t) such that $0 < kz - \omega t < \pi/2$. At the location and instant specified by (z, t), the sine function is positive and so the electric field points in the positive x direction. The wave travels in the positive z direction. Therefore, at (z, t), $\vec{E} \times \vec{B}$ must point in the positive z direction. We know that $\hat{\imath} \times \hat{\jmath} = \hat{k}$, so we know that the magnetic field must point in the positive y direction and be of the form

$$\vec{B}(z, t) = B\sin(kz - \omega t)\hat{\jmath}.$$

The magnitude of the magnetic field is

$$B = \frac{E}{c_0} = \frac{6.0 \times 10^2\ \text{V/m}}{3.0 \times 10^8\ \text{m/s}} = 2.0 \times 10^{-6}\ \text{V}\cdot\text{s/m}^2.$$

We know that $1\ \text{V} = 1\ \text{N}\cdot\text{m/C}$, so $1\ \text{V}\cdot\text{s/m}^2 = 1\ \text{N}\cdot\text{s/C}\cdot\text{m}$. We also know that the unit of magnetic field is the tesla, where $1\ \text{T} = 1\ \text{N}\cdot\text{s/m}\cdot\text{C}$. So the magnitude of the magnetic field is $B = 2.0 \times 10^{-6}\ \text{T}$, and if we include its direction the result is

$$\vec{B}(z, t) = (2.0 \times 10^{-6}\ \text{T})\sin[(9.0\ \text{m}^{-1})z - (2.7 \times 10^9\ \text{s}^{-1})t]\hat{\jmath}. ✔$$

❹ **EVALUATE RESULT** The values we calculated in part *a* lie in the range between commercial radio waves and microwaves and satisfy $c_0 = \lambda f$. In part *b* our calculated magnetic field magnitude is about 1/25 the magnitude of Earth's magnetic field near the equator. The electric field magnitude of this wave is about six times the magnitude of typical atmospheric electric fields, 100 V/m. Thus the results we obtained are not unreasonable.

Guided Problem 30.2 Electric from magnetic

The magnetic field vector of a planar electromagnetic wave is given by

$$\vec{B}(y, t) = B\cos(ky + \omega t)\hat{k},$$

where $B = 2.0 \times 10^{-5}\ \text{T}$, $\omega = 3.0 \times 10^9\ \text{s}^{-1}$, and $\hat{k}$ is the unit vector in the z direction. What are (*a*) the value of the wave number k and (*b*) the expression for the magnitude and direction of the electric field associated with this magnetic field?

❶ **GETTING STARTED**

1. Is the approach used in Worked Problem 30.1 useful here?
2. In which direction is the wave traveling?
3. Along which axis does the direction of the magnetic field oscillate?

❷ **DEVISE PLAN**

4. How is the wave number k related to the angular frequency ω?
5. Along which axis does the electric field oscillate?
6. How are the magnitudes of the electric and magnetic fields related?
7. You should now be able to write an expression for the electric field.

❸ **EXECUTE PLAN**

8. Calculate the value of k.
9. Write an expression for the wave's electric-field component.
10. What is the magnitude of the electric field?
11. Do you have the correct units for the electric field?

❹ **EVALUATE RESULT**

12. How do your values for E and B compare with the magnitude of Earth's magnetic field near the equator and the magnitude of a typical atmospheric electric field, which is about 100 V/m?

Worked Problem 30.3 Antenna reach

A certain type of FM radio receiver requires a minimum radio signal with a root-mean-square electric field magnitude of 1.2×10^{-2} N/C to operate. How far from a radio station broadcasting its electromagnetic signal at an average power of 100 kW can this receiver be used?

❶ **GETTING STARTED** We are given the power at which a radio station broadcasts its signal, 100 kW, and we must calculate the distance from the emitting antenna to the position at which the electric-field portion of the electromagnetic waves has a root-mean-square magnitude of 1.2×10^{-2} N/C. We begin by assuming that the waves are broadcast uniformly in all directions, which allows us to model the power at any instant as being distributed on a spherical surface. Thus the distance we seek is the radius r of the sphere at the position where $E_{rms} = 1.2 \times 10^{-2}$ N/C.

❷ **DEVISE PLAN** We can use Eq. 30.38 to obtain the relationship between the area of any spherical surface through which the waves pass and the average power and average intensity of the waves. Thus from $A_{sphere} = 4\pi r^2$ we can obtain a value for r, the distance we seek. In order to use Eq. 30.38, however, we must know the average intensity of the waves, so our first step should be to calculate that value from Eq. 30.40, $S_{av} = E_{rms}B_{rms}/\mu_0$.

❸ **EXECUTE PLAN** Substituting E_{rms}/c_0 for B_{rms} in Eq. 30.40, we get for the average intensity

$$S_{av} = \frac{E_{rms}^2}{\mu_0 c_0} = \frac{(1.2 \times 10^{-2}\text{ N/C})^2}{(4\pi \times 10^{-7}\text{ N}\cdot\text{s}^2/\text{C}^2)(3.0 \times 10^8\text{ m/s})}$$

$$= 3.8 \times 10^{-7}\text{ N/m}\cdot\text{s}.$$

Recall that $1\text{ W} = 1\text{ N}\cdot\text{m/s}$, so $S_{av} = 3.8 \times 10^{-7}\text{ W/m}^2$. The time-average version of Eq. 30.38 is

$$P_{av} = \int \vec{S}_{av} \cdot d\vec{A} = S_{av} 4\pi r^2.$$

Therefore the distance r at which $E_{rms} = 1.2 \times 10^{-2}$ N/C is

$$r = \sqrt{\frac{P_{av}}{4\pi S_{av}}} = \sqrt{\frac{1.0 \times 10^5\text{ W}}{(4\pi)(3.8 \times 10^{-7}\text{ W/m}^2)}} = 1.4 \times 10^5\text{ m.} ✔$$

❹ **EVALUATE RESULT** Our result—about 100 miles—is close to the distance at which FM stations fade out when we are driving across the country and therefore in agreement with our experience.

Guided Problem 30.4 Beam from outer space

A spacecraft 120 AU above Earth (1 AU = 1 astronomical unit = 1.5×10^8 km) has a 20-W directional dish antenna emitting at 8.0 GHz (Figure WG30.1). This emitting antenna is aimed at a 34-m-diameter receiving antenna located on Earth. Suppose you want the signal to have a root-mean-square electric field magnitude of 1.0×10^{-3} V/m at the receiving dish on Earth's surface. What must the beam width angle θ be?

Figure WG30.1

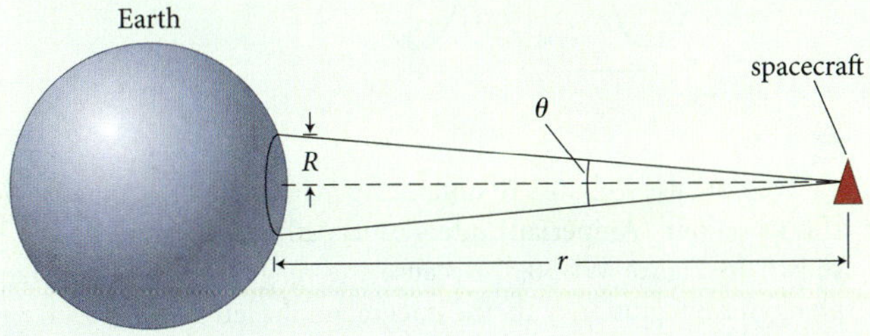

❶ **GETTING STARTED**

1. How does a directional antenna differ from an antenna that emits waves equally in all directions?
2. What assumptions should you make about how the power is emitted directionally?
3. Assume the signal projects to a circular area on Earth's surface. Draw a diagram showing how the beam width is related to the radius R of that circular area and to r, the distance from the spacecraft to Earth.

❷ **DEVISE PLAN**

4. How can you calculate the average intensity of the signal's electromagnetic waves?
5. What relationship can you use to determine the maximum area on Earth that the signal is directed toward in order to be detected? What relationship can you use to determine the maximum area on Earth's surface that the beam can cover and still be detectable?
6. How can you determine the maximum beam width once you know the maximum area that the signal should cover on Earth?

❸ **EXECUTE PLAN**

7. Calculate the maximum intensity associated with the signal root-mean-square electric field magnitude.
8. Calculate the maximum area on Earth's surface that the beam can cover and still be detectable.
9. Calculate the radius R of the circular area on Earth's surface covered by the signal.
10. Use your values for R and r and your diagram from step 3 to obtain the beam width angle.

❹ **EVALUATE RESULT**

11. With the beam angle you calculated, do you think the 34-m-diameter receiving antenna can detect the signal?

Worked Problem 30.5 Discharge radiation

A capacitor consists of two circular parallel plates of radius $R = 150$ mm separated by distance $d = 20$ mm. The initial magnitude of the charge on the capacitor is $q_0 = 9.0 \times 10^{-8}$ C, and after discharge is initiated, it discharges via a steady current $I = 3.0$ mA. What is the power that crosses the closed cylindrical surface surrounding the space between the plates 2.0×10^{-5} s after discharge begins?

1 GETTING STARTED We begin with a sketch showing the discharging capacitor and a few of the associated electric and magnetic field lines (Figure WG30.2). The closed cylindrical surface surrounding the space between the capacitor plates consists of two end faces, one coinciding with each plate, and a curved surface that joins the end faces and encloses the space between the plates. Because the distance between the plates is small relative to the radius of the plates, we assume that at any instant t, the charge $q(t)$ on the plates is uniformly distributed and the electric field $\vec{E}(t)$ is uniform between the plates (that is, we ignore edge effects). We show this uniform field in our sketch. While the capacitor is discharging, the magnitude of $\vec{E}$ is decreasing, and therefore there is a displacement current I that points in the direction of $\Delta\vec{E}$, which is opposite the direction of $\vec{E}$.

Figure WG30.2

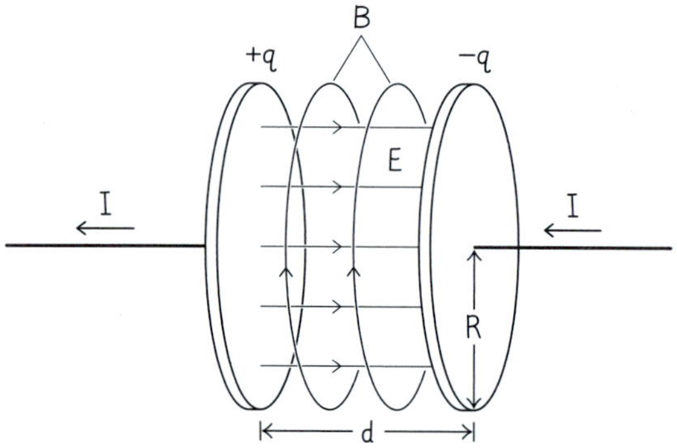

While the electric field is changing, there is an associated magnetic field $\vec{B}(t)$ between the plates, and we know that the magnetic field lines form circular loops. We determine the direction of these loops by applying the right-hand current rule to the displacement current and add the loops to our Figure WG30.2.

At each location in the space between the plates, the electric and magnetic fields are perpendicular to each other. Because the electric field is decreasing, the energy stored in this field is also decreasing. Using our drawing and this information, we must determine, at $t = 2.0 \times 10^{-5}$ s, the power P that crosses the closed cylindrical surface defined by the capacitor volume.

2 DEVISE PLAN In order to calculate P, we must determine the flux of the Poynting vector (Eq. 30.38). We know from Eq. 30.37 that this vector is proportional to $\vec{E} \times \vec{B}$, and so we must determine the magnitudes of the electric and magnetic fields between the plates. We can use Gauss's law (Eq. 30.10) to obtain E, which depends on the charge on the plates. Because the current is steady, we can determine the charge on the plates as a function of time. After we use Eq. 30.8 to determine B, we can calculate the flux of the Poynting vector on the closed cylindrical surface and obtain the power that crosses the surface.

3 EXECUTE PLAN Figure WG30.3 shows a circle of radius R that is centered on and perpendicular to the line passing through the centers of the two circular plates. Consider a point Z lying on this circle. Our first task is to use Gauss's law to calculate the magnitude of $\vec{E}(t)$ at Z. We choose as our Gaussian surface the closed cylinder shown in Figure WG30.4*a*. Note that the cylinder lies partly inside the space between the capacitor plates and partly outside that space and that Z lies on the end face that is in the space between the plates, as shown in Figure WG30.4*b*. In this space, there is nonzero

Figure WG30.3

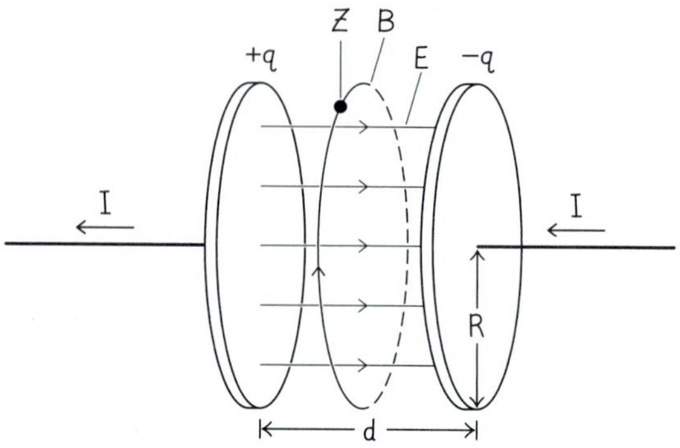

flux only through this end face. Thus with $A_{endface}$ as the face area, Gauss's law, $\Phi_E = \oint \vec{E} \cdot d\vec{A} = q_{enc}/\epsilon_0$ (Eq. 24.8), becomes

$$EA_{endface} = \frac{\sigma A_{endface}}{\epsilon_0} = \frac{q(t)A_{endface}}{\pi R^2 \epsilon_0}$$

$$E(t) = \frac{q(t)}{\pi R^2 \epsilon_0}. \qquad (1)$$

Figure WG30.4

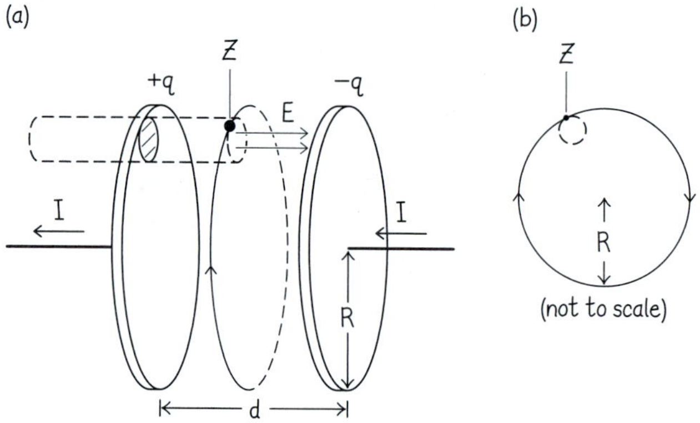

We now use Eq. 30.8 to obtain the magnitude of $\vec{B}(t)$ at Z. We choose as our (Ampèrian) integration path the circle of radius R shown in Figure WG30.3. Because the magnitude B is constant along this integration path, the integral on the left side of Eq. 30.8 is $B(2\pi R)$. On the right side of the equation, $I_{int} = 0$ because the integration path defines an open surface, a disk of radius R, and there is no current through the disk. Because the electric field is uniform, its flux is $\Phi_E = E(\pi R^2)$, so the magnitude of the displacement current is, from Eq. 30.7,

$$I_{disp} = \epsilon_0 \frac{dE}{dt} \pi R^2.$$

Substituting Eq. 1 for E gives us

$$I_{disp} = \epsilon_0 \frac{d}{dt}\left[\frac{q(t)}{\pi R^2 \epsilon_0}\right]\pi R^2 = \frac{dq(t)}{dt}.$$

Because the current is steady and the charge is decreasing, the steady current $I = -dq(t)/dt$. Thus the magnitude of the displacement current is equal to the magnitude of the steady current. Therefore Eq. 30.8 becomes $B(2\pi R) = \mu_0 I$, and we have

$$B = \frac{\mu_0 I}{2\pi R}. \qquad (2)$$

We now apply Eq. 30.37 to calculate the magnitude and direction of the Poynting vector $\vec{S}(t)$ at point Z. Because point Z could be chosen on any circle inside the capacitor, the expression for the Poynting vector should be general. Applying the right-hand rule for the vector product $\vec{E} \times \vec{B}$ in Figure WG30.5*a*, we see that the direction of the vector product points away from the curved part of the closed cylinder—that is, radially outward at Z in Figure WG30.5*b*. This is therefore the direction of $\vec{S}$. From Eqs. 1 and 2, the magnitude is

$$S(t) = \frac{1}{\mu_0}EB = \frac{q(t)}{\pi R^2 \epsilon_0}\frac{I}{2\pi R}.$$

Figure WG30.5

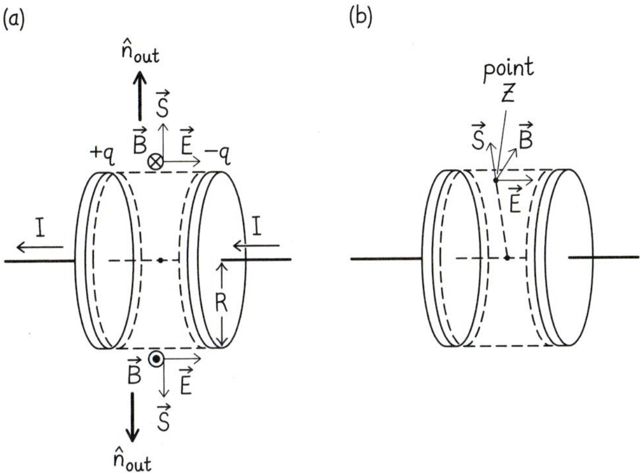

Note that the Poynting vector is directed radially outward at each point inside the capacitor, so energy will not cross the flat ends of the cylindrical space. The power that crosses the curved part of our closed cylindrical surface can be computed using Eq. 30.38. For a closed surface, we always choose $\hat{n}_{out}$ as the outward-pointing normal to the surface. Because $\vec{S}(t)$ points outward on all portions of our curved surface, the only thing we need to do is multiply S by the area of that curved surface, $A = 2\pi Rd$. The power that crosses the surface is then

$$P(t) = S(t)A = \frac{q(t)}{\pi R^2 \epsilon_0}\frac{I}{2\pi R}2\pi Rd = \frac{q(t)I}{\pi R^2 \epsilon_0}d.$$

Because the current is steady, the charge on the plates as a function of time is given by $q(t) = q_0 - It$. Therefore the power that crosses the curved part of our closed cylindrical surface as a function of time is given by

$$P(t) = \frac{(q_0 - It)I}{\pi R^2 \epsilon_0}d,$$

and at $t = 2.0 \times 10^{-5}$ s the power is

$$P = \frac{[(9.0 \times 10^{-8}\text{ C}) - (3.0 \times 10^{-3}\text{ A})(2.0 \times 10^{-5}\text{ s})]}{\pi(0.150\text{ m})^2(8.85 \times 10^{-12}\text{ C}^2/\text{N}\cdot\text{m}^2)}$$

$$\times (3.0 \times 10^{-3}\text{ A})(2.0 \times 10^{-2}\text{ m}) = 2.9\text{ W.} ✔$$

❹ **EVALUATE RESULT** In *Principles* Example 30.10, a parallel-plate capacitor with circular plates of radius $R = 0.10$ m, plate separation distance $d = 0.10$ mm, and a steady charging current of 1.0 A had $(3.6 \times 10^8\text{ W/s})\Delta t$ of power crossing into the cylindrical space between the plates. For that capacitor, therefore, the power at $\Delta t = 2.0 \times 10^{-5}$ s would be 7.2×10^3 W. From Example 30.10, we know that the power is proportional to I^2 and to d and inversely proportional to R^2. Using that relationship for our capacitor, where $I_{discharging} = 3.0$ mA, $R = 150$ mm, and $d = 20$ mm, we expect a power of

$$\frac{P_{discharging}(\Delta t = 2.0 \times 10^{-5}\text{ s})}{P_{charging}(\Delta t = 2.0 \times 10^{-5}\text{ s})} =$$

$$\frac{(q_0 - I_{discharging}\Delta t)I_{discharging}}{(I_{charging}\Delta t)I_{charging}}\frac{d_{discharging}}{d_{charging}}\frac{(R_{charging})^2}{(R_{discharging})^2}$$

$$P_{discharging}(\Delta t = 2.0 \times 10^{-5}\text{ s}) =$$

$$(7.2 \times 10^3\text{ W})\frac{(3.0 \times 10^{-8}\text{ C})}{(2.0 \times 10^{-5}\text{ C})}\frac{(3.0 \times 10^{-3}\text{ A})}{(1.0\text{ A})}$$

$$\times \frac{(20\text{ mm})}{(0.10\text{ mm})}\frac{(0.10\text{ m})^2}{(0.150\text{ m})^2} = 2.9\text{ W},$$

in excellent agreement with our result.

Guided Problem 30.6 Charge it!

A capacitor consists of two circular parallel plates, each with a radius $R = 200$ mm, separated by a distance $d = 15$ mm (Figure WG30.6). A steady current charges the capacitor for a time interval $\Delta t = 7.7 \times 10^{-6}$ s. During this time interval, the maximum magnitude of the magnetic field between the plates is $B_{max} = 1.2 \times 10^{-8}$ T. What is the maximum power that crosses the closed cylindrical surface surrounding the space between the plates?

Figure WG30.6

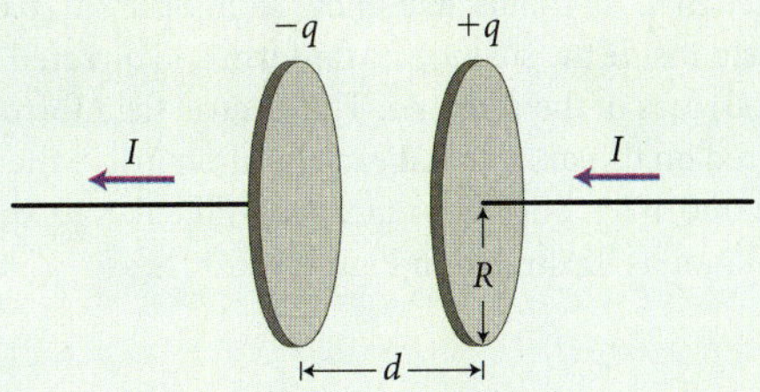

PRACTICE

❶ GETTING STARTED

1. What quantities do you need to know in order to determine the maximum power that crosses the closed cylindrical surface that defines the space between the plates?
2. Which of these quantities are given in the problem statement?

❷ DEVISE PLAN

3. Which Maxwell equation gives you a relationship between the current and B_{max}?
4. Along what closed path does the magnetic field have its maximum magnitude?
5. Which Maxwell equation allows you to determine the maximum value of the electric field magnitude, E_{max}?
6. What is the relationship between the current and q_{max}, the maximum value of the charge on the capacitor plates?
7. How do you calculate the maximum power that crosses into the space between the plates?

❸ EXECUTE PLAN

8. Write an expression for the current.
9. Write an expression for q_{max}.
10. Write an expression for E_{max}.
11. Determine the direction of the Poynting vector, and write an expression for the maximum value of the magnitude of the Poynting vector.
12. Determine the maximum value of the power that crosses the cylindrical surface.

❹ EVALUATE RESULT

13. Does your value for the steady current seem reasonable?
14. Does your value for P_{max} seem reasonable?

Worked Problem 30.7 Solenoid antenna

The solenoid of Figure WG30.7 has radius $a = 0.10$ m and height $h = 0.60$ m. The current is decreasing as $I(t) = I_0 - bt$, where $I_0 = 0.40$ A and $b = 0.200$ A/s, and the current direction is as shown in the figure. If the solenoid has $N = 500$ windings, at what rate is electromagnetic energy leaving the cylindrical space inside the solenoid at $t = 1.0$ s?

Figure WG30.7

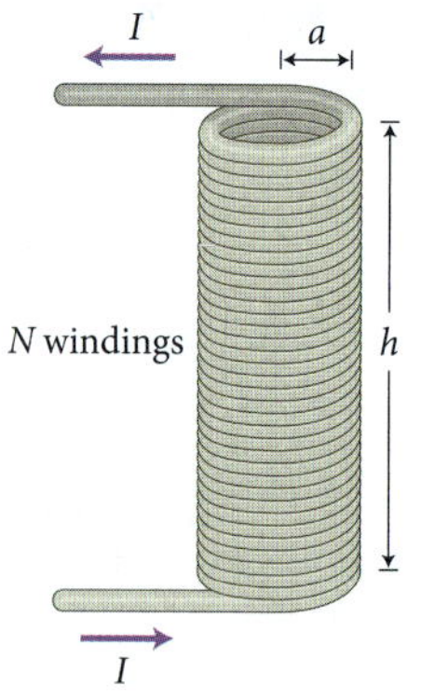

Figure WG30.8

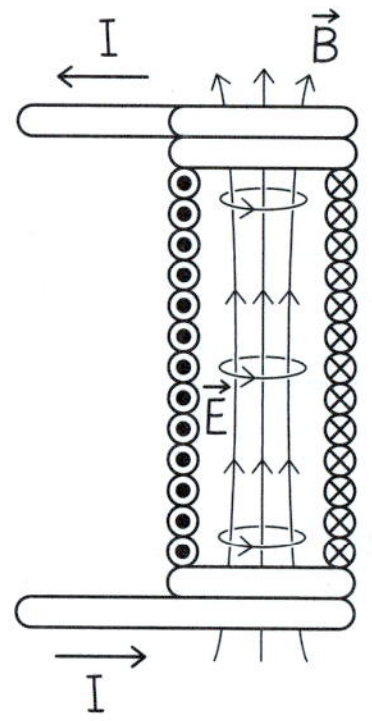

❶ GETTING STARTED The solenoid has N/h windings per unit of height, and the current in the solenoid is decreasing. While the current is decreasing, the magnetic field inside the solenoid is decreasing. This changing magnetic field is accompanied by an electric field. Because the magnetic field is decreasing, we expect electromagnetic energy to leave the inside of the solenoid, and our task is to determine the rate at which this energy leaves.

We can ignore edge effects because the height of the solenoid is much greater than its radius. We know from Section 28.6 that the magnetic field inside the solenoid is uniform and directed along the long (vertical) axis of the solenoid. The electric field forms circular loops centered on this axis, and at each location inside the solenoid, the electric and magnetic fields are perpendicular to each other. This information is illustrated in Figure WG30.8.

❷ DEVISE PLAN The rate at which electromagnetic energy leaves the cylindrical space inside the solenoid—the power—is given by the flux of the Poynting vector through the curved surface of the solenoid. Energy leaves the space inside the solenoid, and from this we know the direction of the Poynting vector—parallel to the end faces of the cylinder and directed outward, away from the long central axis.

We can use Eq. 30.36 to calculate the magnitude of the Poynting vector. In order to use this equation, we must know the magnitudes E and B. We can use the Eq. 30.12 form of Faraday's law to calculate E. Because the current decreases linearly with time, the rate of change of the magnetic flux in the solenoid, $d\Phi_B/dt$, is constant and therefore the electric field magnitude is constant. Thus there is no displacement current associated with the electric field. This means Eq. 30.6, the generalized form of Ampère's law, $\oint \vec{B} \cdot d\vec{\ell} = \mu_0 I_{int} + \mu_0 \epsilon_0 (d\Phi_E/dt)$, reduces to Eq. 28.1, so we can use the latter to calculate the magnetic field magnitude.

To determine the power, we must integrate the Poynting vector over the cylindrical surface just surrounding the space inside the solenoid. Because the electric and magnetic fields are perpendicular to each other, tangent to and uniform over this surface, the power is the product of the Poynting vector magnitude and the area of the cylindrical surface.

PRACTICE

❸ **EXECUTE PLAN** We begin with Ampère's law with no displacement current, $\oint \vec{B} \cdot d\vec{\ell} = \mu_0 I_{enc}$ (Eq. 28.1), where $d\vec{\ell}$ is a small segment of the Ampèrian path of length ℓ shown in Figure WG30.9. The direction of integration is clockwise. The magnetic field is zero outside the solenoid and points upward inside, so the left side of Eq. 28.1 is $\oint \vec{B} \cdot d\vec{\ell} = B\ell$. In the region of the solenoid we've chosen for our Ampèrian path, the current is into the plane of the page, so $I_{enc} = (N/h)\ell I$. Therefore the magnitude of the magnetic field is

$$B\ell = \frac{\mu_0 N I(t)\ell}{h} \Rightarrow B(t) = \frac{\mu_0 N(I_0 - bt)}{h}. \quad (1)$$

Figure WG30.9

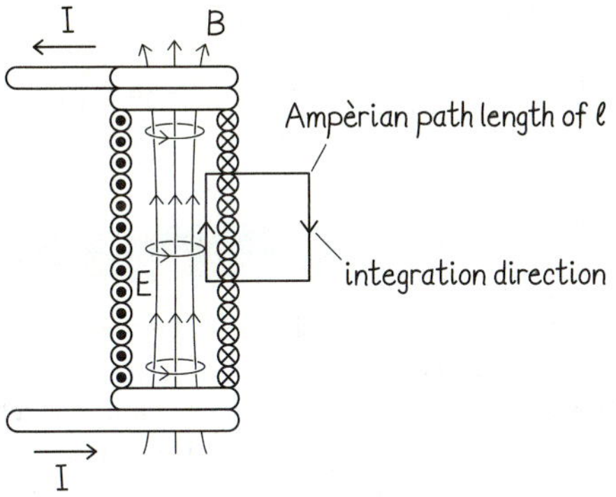

Next, to obtain an expression for E, we apply the Eq. 30.12 form of Faraday's law, $\oint \vec{E} \cdot d\vec{\ell} = -d\Phi_B/dt$. This time $d\vec{\ell}$ represents a small segment of the circumference ℓ of the closed path of radius r shown in Figure WG30.10. Again we integrate clockwise (as viewed from below). The changing magnetic flux is

$$\frac{d\Phi_B}{dt} = \frac{dB}{dt}\pi r^2,$$

and we can use Eq. 1 to rewrite this equation in the form

$$-\frac{d\Phi_B}{dt} = -\frac{\mu_0 N \pi r^2}{h}\frac{d(I_0 - bt)}{dt} = \frac{\mu_0 N \pi r^2 b}{h}.$$

Because the electric field forms circular loops, the line integral of the electric field around this closed path is $\oint \vec{E} \cdot d\vec{\ell} = E 2\pi r$. Therefore Faraday's law implies that the magnitude of the electric field is

$$E 2\pi r = \frac{\mu_0 N \pi r^2 b}{h} \Rightarrow E = \frac{\mu_0 N r b}{2h}. \quad (2)$$

Figure WG30.10

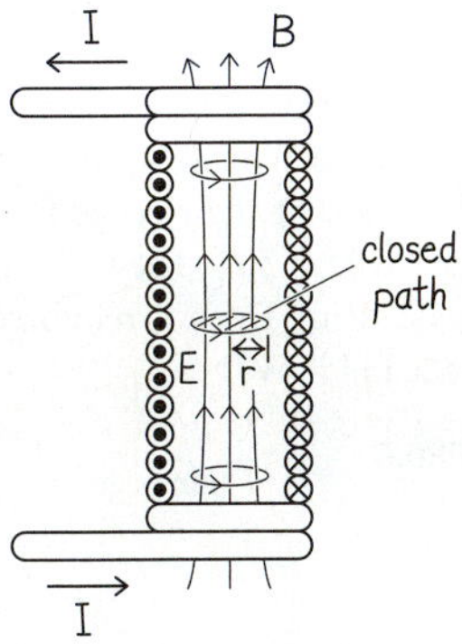

Because the sign of the electric field is positive in Eq. 2, the direction of the electric field is the same as the integration direction.

Now we have all we need to determine the rate at which electromagnetic energy leaves the region inside the solenoid. We do this by calculating the flux of the Poynting vector through the cylindrical surface of the solenoid, where $r = a$. First we check the direction of the Poynting vector by determining the direction of $\vec{E} \times \vec{B}$, which points radially away from the center of the solenoid. We now use Eqs. 1 and 2 in Eq. 30.36 to calculate the magnitude of the Poynting vector:

$$S(r = a) = \frac{1}{\mu_0}EB = \frac{\mu_0 N^2 a b(I_0 - bt)}{2h^2}.$$

To determine the power at $t = 1.0$ s, we multiply S by the area of the curved surface of the cylinder, $2\pi a h$:

$$P = 2\pi a h S(r = a) = \frac{\mu_0 N^2 b(I_0 - bt)}{h}\pi a^2$$

$$= \frac{(4\pi \times 10^{-7}\ \mathrm{N \cdot s^2/C^2})(500)^2(0.200\ \mathrm{A/s})}{(0.60\ \mathrm{m})}$$

$$\times \left[0.40\ \mathrm{A} - (0.200\ \mathrm{A/s})(1.0\ \mathrm{s})\right]\pi(0.10\ \mathrm{m})^2$$

$$= 6.6 \times 10^{-4}\ \mathrm{W}. ✔$$

❹ **EVALUATE RESULT** This is a very small rate of energy leaving the solenoid. We have no clear standard of comparison for this value for the power. However, we expect that the electromagnetic energy leaving the cylindrical space inside the solenoid is equal to the time rate of change of the magnetic field energy stored in the space. The energy density of the magnetic field is given by Eq. 30.28, $u_B = B^2/2\mu_0$. Because the magnetic field is uniform, the energy U^B stored in it is the product of the energy density and the volume $\pi a^2 h$ of the cylindrical space:

$$U^B = \frac{B^2}{2\mu_0}\pi a^2 h = \frac{\mu_0 N^2 (I_0 - bt)^2}{2h^2}\pi a^2 h.$$

The time rate of change of the stored magnetic energy is thus

$$\frac{dU^B}{dt} = \frac{d}{dt}\left[\frac{\mu_0 N^2 (I_0 - bt)^2}{2h}\pi a^2\right] = -\frac{\mu_0 N^2 b(I_0 - bt)}{h}\pi a^2.$$

This expression has the same magnitude as the one we obtained for P, the rate at which electromagnetic energy leaves the solenoid, giving us confidence that our calculation is correct. The minus sign makes sense because energy is leaving the solenoid interior and hence the stored energy decreases.

Guided Problem 30.8 Coiled again!

The solenoid in Figure WG30.7 has N windings, radius a, and height $h \gg a$. The current through the windings is given by $I(t) = bt$, where b is a positive constant and has units of amperes per second. At what rate does electromagnetic energy cross the cylindrical surface defined by the windings? In which direction is this energy transfer?

1 GETTING STARTED

1. How does the situation in this solenoid differ from the situation in Worked Problem 30.7?
2. Do you have enough information to determine the magnitude and direction of the electric and magnetic fields inside the solenoid? Are any assumptions needed?
3. Make a sketch of the solenoid, showing the current direction and the directions you've determined or assumed for $\vec{E}$ and $\vec{B}$.

2 DEVISE PLAN

4. What is a convenient generic location to choose in order to write an expression for the magnitudes of $\vec{B}(t)$ and $\vec{E}(t)$?
5. What equation can you use to calculate the direction and magnitude of $\vec{B}(t)$?
6. What equation can you use to determine $\vec{E}(t)$?
7. How can you determine the direction and magnitude of $\vec{S}(t)$?
8. What equation can you use to determine the power?

3 EXECUTE PLAN

4 EVALUATE RESULT

9. Write an expression for the energy stored in the magnetic field at instant t.
10. What is the time derivative of the stored magnetic energy?

Questions and Problems

For instructor-assigned homework, go to MasteringPhysics®

Dots indicate difficulty level of problems: • = *easy,* •• = *intermediate,* ••• = *hard;* CR = *context-rich problem.*

Unless directed otherwise, use $c_0 = 3.0 \times 10^8$ m/s for the speed of electromagnetic waves traveling in vacuum.

30.1 Magnetic fields accompany changing electric fields

1. The magnitude of the electric field of Figure P30.1 is changing with time. As a result of this change, there is an upward-pointing magnetic field at position P. Is the electric field magnitude increasing or decreasing? •

Figure P30.1

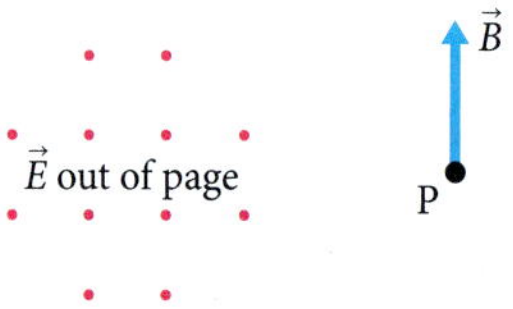

2. Figure P30.2 shows two electric fields, one in a region of circular cross-section and one in a long flat region. In both cases, the electric field decreases over time. What is the direction of the accompanying magnetic field in each case? •

Figure P30.2

3. A parallel-plate capacitor is charged until it carries charge $+q$ on one plate and charge $-q$ on the other plate. The capacitor is then disconnected from the power supply and isolated. What is the direction of the magnetic field that surrounds the charged capacitor? •

4. The uniform electric field shown in Figure P30.4 points out of the page and is contained in a cylindrical volume of space. If the electric field is rapidly turned off, a magnetic field is produced. (*a*) What is the direction of this magnetic field? (*b*) Does this magnetic field exist only in the volume where the electric field exists, only outside that volume, or both inside and outside that volume? ••

Figure P30.4

5. The capacitor of Figure P30.5 is being charged by a steady current I. What are the directions of (*a*) the electric field between the plates, (*b*) the change in the electric field, and (*c*) the magnetic field between the plates? ••

Figure P30.5

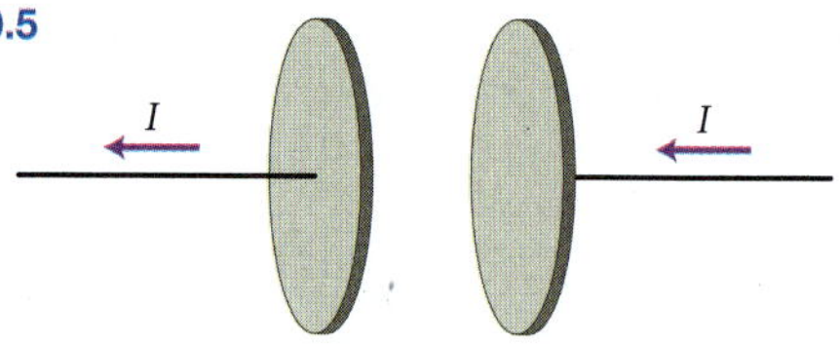

6. Figure P30.6 shows an increasing magnetic field and the electric field that accompanies it according to Faraday's law. If the magnetic field is increasing at an increasing rate, (*a*) is the electric field magnitude constant, increasing, or decreasing? (*b*) Does the behavior of the electric field produce an additional magnetic field? If so, what is the direction of the additional magnetic field? Does it reinforce or counteract the original magnetic field? ••

Figure P30.6

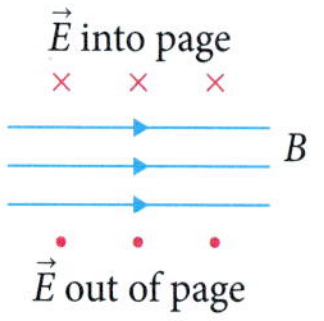

PRACTICE

30.2 Fields of moving charged particles

7. Are the radiating electric field lines around a charged particle straight lines when the particle (*a*) is stationary, (*b*) moves at constant velocity, (*c*) accelerates? •

8. Which field line patterns in Figure P30.8 could represent (*a*) electric field lines and (*b*) magnetic field lines? •

Figure P30.8

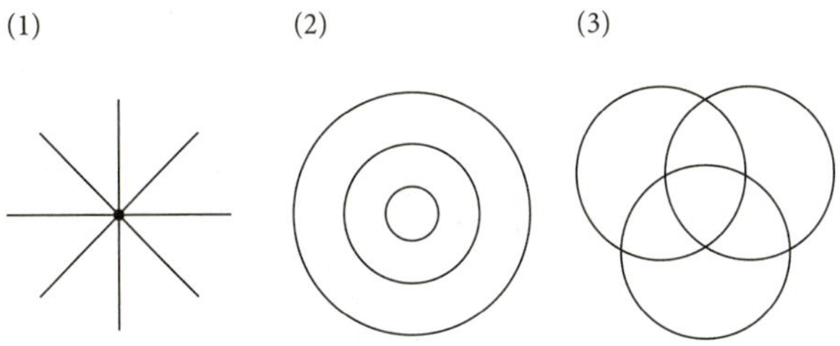

9. Would a charged particle moving at a high speed in a circle create kinks in its electric field? •

10. A positively charged particle moving to the right is stopped rapidly. Sketch the resultant radiated pulse. ••

11. Is any type of electric field produced when (*a*) a wire having zero surplus charge carries a constant current, (*b*) a wire having zero surplus charge carries a time-varying current, (*c*) a bar magnet moves translationally at constant velocity, (*d*) a bar magnet rotates about an axis that passes symmetrically through its poles? ••

12. Is any magnetic field produced when (*a*) a uniformly charged sphere rotates at constant rotational speed about an axis that passes through its fixed center, (*b*) a charged particle moves translationally at constant velocity, (*c*) a charged particle that is moving translationally accelerates? ••

13. Sketch the electric and magnetic field line patterns produced by the four situations shown in Figure P30.13: (*a*) a stationary charged rod carrying a linear charge density of $+\lambda$, (*b*) a charged rod carrying a linear charge density of $+\lambda$ that moves at constant velocity along the length of the rod, (*c*) a stationary charged rod carrying a linear charge density of $+\lambda$ that is infinitesimally close to a parallel stationary charged rod carrying a linear charge density of $-\lambda$, (*d*) a charged rod carrying a linear charge density of $+\lambda$ that moves at constant velocity along the length of rod and is infinitesimally close to a parallel charged rod carrying a linear charge density of $-\lambda$ and moving in the opposite direction. ••

Figure P30.13

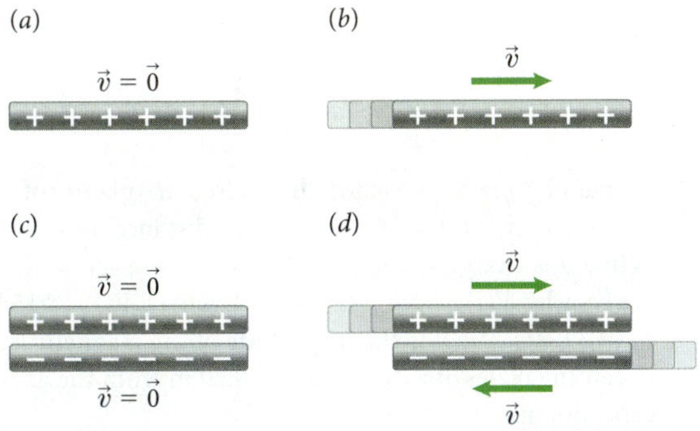

30.3 Oscillating dipoles and antennas

14. What antenna length should be used to create a dipole antenna that emits 100-MHz electromagnetic waves, a frequency typical of FM radio broadcasts? •

15. An electromagnetic wave is traveling eastward. If at a given instant the magnetic field for one section of the wave points south, in which direction does the electric field for that section point at that instant? •

16. An electric dipole with its center located at the origin of a Cartesian coordinate system oscillates along the x axis, creating an electromagnetic wave. At a position on the z axis far from the origin, (*a*) what is the polarization of the wave and (*b*) which axis are the magnetic field lines parallel to? ••

17. Figure P30.17 shows a magnetic field line pattern radiating from an oscillating electric dipole. (*a*) What is the direction of the change, over the next infinitesimal time interval, in the magnetic field at P? (*b*) Use your answer to part *a* to determine the direction of the electric field loop around P. (*c*) Is the dipole oscillating right-left, up-down, or in-out of the page? ••

Figure P30.17

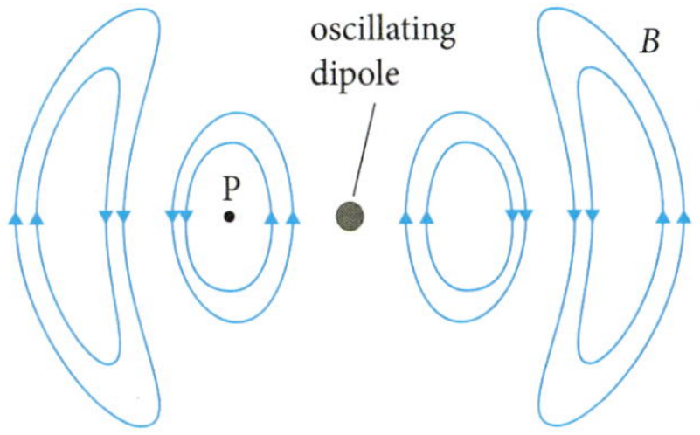

18. A router used for wireless Internet access follows the 802.11g standard, which operates at 2.4 GHz. (*a*) What is the wavelength of the electromagnetic waves emitted by the router? (*b*) How tall would a dipole antenna need to be? Is this length comparable to the length of any router antennas you've seen? ••

19. Why are radio transmission towers oriented vertically rather than laid horizontally on the ground? ••

20. To detect an incoming planar electromagnetic wave, we observe a single charged particle that begins at rest and is free to move only in the xy plane. If we observe the particle oscillating along the y axis, with no motion along the x axis, what can we say about the direction of the electric and magnetic fields and the direction of wave propagation? ••

21. In Figure P30.21, a charged particle has been suddenly accelerated downward, producing the electric field line pattern shown. When the kinks in the field lines reach the metal rod at the left, they produce a downward current in the rod. Is the particle that has been accelerated positively or negatively charged? ••

Figure P30.21

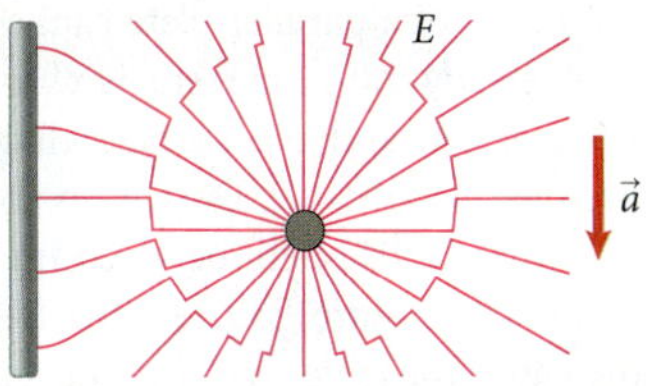

22. As we saw in *Principles* Checkpoint 30.9, a receiving dipole antenna has to be aligned with the oscillating electric field in order to produce a measurable potential difference in the antenna. What if we wanted to detect the potential difference caused by the changing magnetic field? (*a*) What antenna shape would we need? (*b*) How would this antenna need to be oriented relative to the wave in order to maximize its ability to detect the wave? (*c*) Use Faraday's law to explain whether this antenna is a better detector for low-frequency waves or for high-frequency waves. •••

30.4 Displacement current

23. A parallel-plate capacitor with circular plates has a steady charging current of 5.0 A. The wires into and out of the plates attach to the plate centers. If the radius of each plate is 40 mm and there is no dielectric between the plates, what is the magnetic field magnitude at a position that lies between the plates and is 30 mm from the (imaginary) line joining their centers? •
24. A specified volume of space contains an electric field for which the magnitude is given by $E = E_0 \cos(\omega t)$. Suppose that $E_0 = 10 \text{ V/m}$ and $\omega = 1.0 \times 10^7 \text{ s}^{-1}$. (*a*) What is the maximum displacement current through a 0.50-m^2 cross-sectional area of this volume? (*b*) How would this area have to be oriented relative to the electric field to get this maximum displacement current? •
25. Instead of a capacitor in a circuit, we can get the same effect by slicing a thick wire in two, making our cut perpendicular to the wire's long axis. If the wire diameter is 10.0 mm and we place the two parallel circular surfaces of the cut wire 0.010 mm apart, what is the magnetic field magnitude at a position that lies between the two surfaces and is 2.0 mm from the long central axis of the wire at the instant the current in the wire is 2.0 A? Assume the charge carriers that create the current are uniformly distributed over the cross-sectional area of the wire. ••
26. A parallel-plate capacitor has a steady charging current of 5.0 A. What are (*a*) the time rate of change of the electric flux between the plates and (*b*) the displacement current between the plates? (*c*) How do your answers to parts *a* and *b* change if there is a dielectric for which $\kappa = 1.5$ between the plates? Assume the area of the plates is much greater than the separation distance between them. ••
27. A parallel-plate capacitor is charging with constant current I. At some instant, $B = 1.6 \times 10^{-8}$ T at a position that is 7.0 mm from the center of the wire leading to the capacitor. (*a*) Calculate the current magnitude at that instant. (*b*) Draw the current in the left plate to show why you get the same value of B no matter where you place the surface bounded by your Ampèrian path. Draw the lengths of your current arrows to scale to show how the current magnitude does or does not change at various positions in the plate. ••
28. For a capacitor of capacitance C, show that the displacement current between the capacitor's plates is given by $C(dV/dt)$, where V is the potential difference across the capacitor. ••
29. The circular plates of a parallel-plate capacitor have a radius of 30 mm. A steady 2.0-A current is charging the initially uncharged capacitor, and the surface charge on the plates is distributed uniformly. (*a*) Derive an expression for the magnitude of the electric field between the plates as a function of time. (*b*) In Figure P30.29*a*, the flat circular surface between the capacitor plates has a radius of 10 mm. What is the displacement current through this flat circular surface? (*c*) Consider the open surface shown in Figure P30.29*b*, a cylindrical shell open at the right end that passes through the left capacitor plate. If the radius of the flat circular end is 10 mm, what is the displacement current through the open shell? (*d*) Why is your answer to part *c* different from your answer to part *b*? Why are both these answers different from $I = 2.0$ A, the current through the capacitor? ••

Figure P30.29

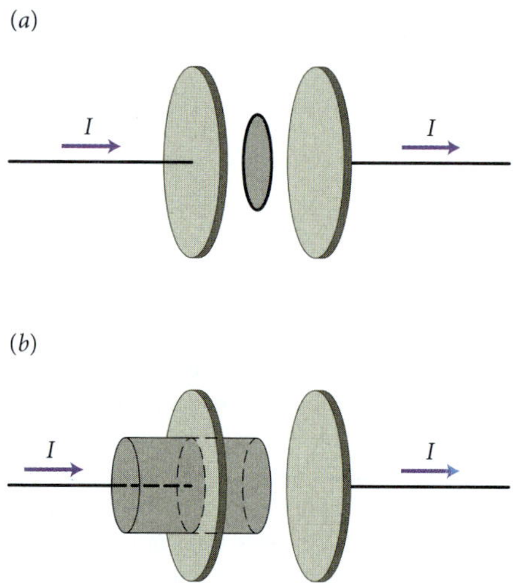

30. A short wire runs along an x axis from $x = a$ to $x = -a$ (Figure P30.30). At $t = 0$, there is a small sphere carrying charge $+q_0$ at $x = a$ and a small sphere carrying charge $-q_0$ at $x = -a$. As the spheres discharge and a current is established in the wire, show that, for $t > 0$, the generalized form of Ampère's law (Eq. 30.13) and the Biot-Savart law (Eq. 28.12) give the same result for the magnitude of the magnetic field a distance b up the y axis. (Hint: Obtain the electric flux through a circular disk in the yz plane, centered at the origin. Because the electric field is not constant over the surface of the disk, you must divide the disk into a nested set of rings of various radii and integrate. A representative ring should have radius r and radial extent dr.) •••

Figure P30.30

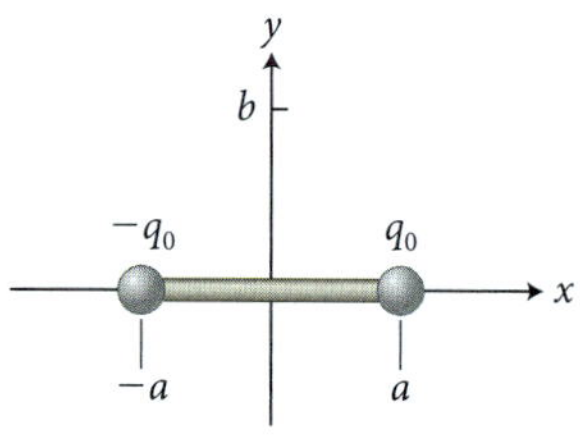

31. A parallel-plate capacitor has circular plates of radius $R = 0.300$ m and plate separation distance $d = 0.10$ mm. While it is charging, the potential difference across the plates is given by $V(t) = V_{max}(1 - e^{-t/\tau_0})$, where $V_{max} = 15$ V and $\tau_0 = 3.0$ ms. What is the magnitude of the magnetic field between the plates at a distance $r = 0.20$ m from the axis of the capacitor at $t = 1.30$ ms? •••

PRACTICE

30.5 Maxwell's equations

32. When you use Maxwell's equations to determine electric and magnetic fields, a lot depends on making the "right" choice for the integration path. What happens if you choose the "wrong" path? Do the equations still hold? Consider a parallel-plate capacitor with circular plates, but use a rectangular integration path that has two sides parallel to the plates and two sides perpendicular to them, as in Figure P30.32. What do you get? •

Figure P30.32

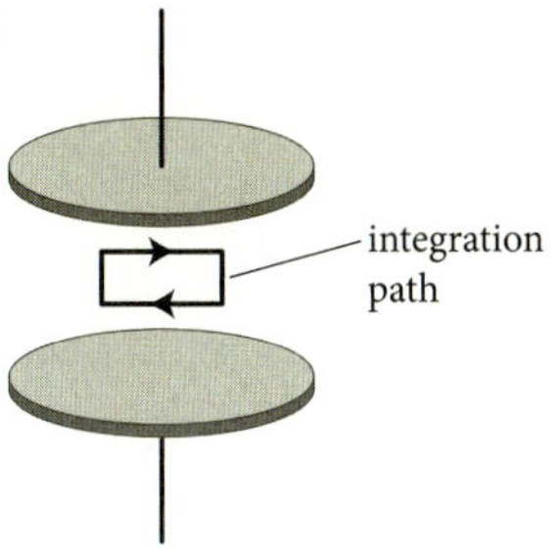

33. Using Eq. 30.11, show that the normal component of the magnetic field is continuous across any surface. ••
34. In free space, Maxwell's equations simplify greatly. The two equations involving surface integrals of the fields (Eqs. 30.10 and 30.11) are zero, and the two equations involving line integrals of the fields (Eqs. 30.12 and 30.13) have values proportional to the rate of flux change of the other field. Because the fluxes are surface integrals of the fields, why don't all four equations reduce to zero? ••
35. For a perfect conductor, $E = 0$ everywhere inside, and all the charge resides on the surface even when charge carriers are flowing. (*a*) Use Maxwell's equations to show that the magnetic field inside a conductor is constant. (*b*) Use Maxwell's equations to show that the magnetic flux through a perfect conducting loop is constant. (*c*) A superconductor is more than just a perfect conductor. It also has the property that $B = 0$ inside the superconductor. Use Maxwell's equations to show why the current in a superconductor is confined to the surface. •••
36. A physics teacher tries to build a device that illustrates Maxwell's generalization of Ampère's law. She drills a hole in the center of each plate of a parallel-plate capacitor and then runs a wire through the holes (Figure P30.36). There is no connection between the wire and the plates, and the potential difference across the plates can be controlled. Can the teacher adjust this potential difference so that there is no magnetic field at a distance r from the wire? In particular, what must be the rate of change of the potential difference if she wants no magnetic field at a distance $r = 20$ mm from the wire when it carries a steady current of 0.0200 A and the distance between the plates is $d = 3.0$ mm? •••

Figure P30.36

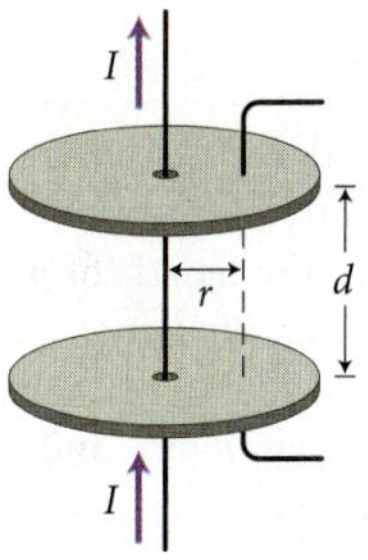

30.6 Electromagnetic waves

37. The frequency of AM radio channels is typically on the order of 10^5 Hz or 10^6 Hz. What is the wavelength of these waves? FM waves have wavelengths between 1.0 m and 10 m. What is the frequency of these waves? •
38. The speed of light drops to 2.26×10^8 m/s in water. What is the dielectric constant of water? •
39. The optical fibers used for telecommunications links have dielectric constant $\kappa = 1.6$. How long does a signal originating in California take to reach New York in a fiber-optic cable? •
40. A phone call you make from the United States to Germany is routed via a satellite that is in a geostationary orbit at an altitude of 36,000 km. How long is the time interval between the instant you say "Hello" to the instant your greeting arrives in Germany? Ignore the distance between the United States and Germany. •
41. The antenna of a WiFi access point has a length of about 80 mm. What does this say about the likely frequency of the wireless network? •
42. (*a*) At a distance from an emitting antenna where the electric field has a maximum magnitude of 15 V/m when the air is dry, what is the maximum magnetic field magnitude? (*b*) How does the value of E_{max} change when the air is very damp, increasing the dielectric constant of the air? (*c*) How does the value of B_{max} change in the damp air? Assume that the antenna's potential difference is unaffected by the damp air. ••
43. Using electromagnetic waves, you generally cannot resolve any structures that are smaller than the wavelength you are using. CD, DVD, and Blu-ray players use small "pits" that encode the 0s and 1s of the digital information stored on them—the smaller the pits, the more information you can store. A DVD can store 4.7 GB, and a Blu-ray can store 25 GB. If a DVD player typically uses lasers that emit red light in the wavelength range from 640 nm to 660 nm, what do you expect the wavelength and color of a Blu-ray laser to be? ••
44. Blue light has a wavelength of 430 nm in vacuum. What is its wavelength after it enters a medium for which the dielectric constant $\kappa = 1.45$? ••
45. *3K cosmic background radiation* is energy left over from events that occurred when the universe was in a very early stage of development. Given that the amount of energy associated with any radiation is linearly proportional to the radiation frequency and that the energy associated with a 10^6-Hz radio wave is 6.6×10^{-28} J, what is the frequency of the cosmic background radiation? Assume that the energy of this radiation can be approximated as $k_B T$, where $T = 3.0$ K (thus the name given to this radiation). ••
46. If the electric field in an electromagnetic wave 100 mm from a radio-emitting antenna has a maximum magnitude of 6.0×10^5 V/m, what is the maximum magnetic field magnitude 500 m from the antenna? ••

30.7 Electromagnetic energy

47. An electromagnetic wave has an average Poynting vector magnitude of 8.00×10^{-7} W/m^2. What is the maximum value of the magnitude of the electric field? •
48. An electromagnetic wave has root-mean-square magnetic field magnitude $B_{rms} = 1.5 \times 10^{-6}$ T. What are the root-mean-square electric field magnitude and the average intensity of the wave? •

49. The power of a laser is much smaller than the power of an incandescent light bulb, but the laser light does not spread out very much. Explain why this tendency not to spread has such an effect over long distances. •
50. A 1.0-mW laser has a beam radius of 0.6 mm. What is the intensity of this beam? •
51. The intensity of the HERCULES laser, one of the world's most powerful, is 2.0×10^{20} W/mm². Granted, the beam pulse lasts for only 30 fs, but if we assume the beam is an electromagnetic pulse, what is its average energy density, and what energy can one pulse deliver to a 1.0-μm² target? ••
52. Radio signals typically have a very small intensity. Imagine that a vehicle receives a signal of 10 μW/m². (*a*) What are the maximum magnitudes of the electric and magnetic fields? (*b*) If the tower emitting the radio waves is located 8.0 km away from the vehicle, how powerful is the emitting antenna? ••
53. For a constant current of 0.20 A, what time interval is required to deliver 1.0 MW of power to the space between the plates of a capacitor if the plates are circular and parallel, their diameter is 150 mm, and their separation distance is 0.200 mm? ••
54. Assume a 60-W incandescent light bulb radiates uniformly in all directions. At a distance of 2.0 m from the bulb, determine (*a*) the intensity of the electromagnetic waves, (*b*) the maximum electric field magnitude, and (*c*) the maximum magnetic field magnitude. ••
55. The emitting antenna of a 100-kW radio station radiates equally in all directions. What are the magnitudes E_{max} and B_{max} (*a*) 100 m from the antenna and (*b*) 50 km from the antenna? (*c*) For these two distances from the antenna, calculate the maximum potential difference caused between the ends of a receiving antenna that is 1.0 m long, assuming the antenna is aligned perfectly with the electric field of the radio wave. ••
56. A laser beam has a radius of 1.5 mm. How powerful does the laser have to be for the maximum magnitude of the magnetic field in the beam to be 5.0 μT? ••
57. Sunlight on Earth has an intensity of about $S = 1.0$ kW/m². How much power can be harvested from a solar energy panel that is 2.0 m long and 1.6 m wide if the sunlight comes in at an angle of $\theta = 20°$ with respect to the surface normal vector of the panel and the panel is 20% efficient? ••
58. You want to use your microwave oven to heat 0.20 L of water from room temperature to boiling. The water is in a cup that has a radius of 30 mm, and you want the water to reach its boiling point in 3.00 min. What are the required (*a*) average power, (*b*) average intensity, and (*c*) root-mean-square electric field of the microwaves? Assume all the microwaves come in from the top and are completely absorbed by the water. ••
59. The human eye can detect light intensities as small as $S_{min} = 10^{-12}$ W/m². If an incandescent 100-W light bulb is about 10% efficient, how far away could you see it under the simplest assumptions? Does your result make sense? ••
60. Similar to perceived loudness in hearing, the brightness the human eye and brain perceive for light is logarithmic rather than linear. For example, you do not perceive light that has an intensity of S as being twice as bright as light of intensity $S/2$. What happens to the perceived brightness of a light bulb if you double the distance from it? ••
61. The Poynting vector for an electromagnetic wave is given by $(100 \text{ W/m}^2) \sin^2[(1000 \text{ m}^{-1})z - (3.0 \times 10^{11} \text{ s}^{-1})t]\hat{k}$. What are (*a*) the wave's propagation direction and (*b*) the time-averaged energy per unit time radiated through a 1.0-m² surface aligned with its normal parallel to the direction of propagation? (*c*) At an instant when the electric field is in the $+x$ direction, in what direction is the magnetic field? What are (*d*) the wavelength and frequency of this electromagnetic wave (you may need to review material in Chapter 16) and (*e*) the electric and magnetic field vectors, as a function of position and time? •••
62. A cylindrical solenoid of radius R and height h consists of N windings. There is a current through the windings, and this current increases with time as $I = \alpha t$, where α is a constant. (*a*) Describe the directions of the electric field, the magnetic field, and the Poynting vector. (*b*) Determine the magnitude of the Poynting vector at a radial distance $r = R$ from the center of the long center axis of the solenoid. (*c*) Use the result of part *b* to derive an expression for the power input to the solenoid as a function of time. (*d*) Using the formula for the inductance of an ideal solenoid, calculate the power from the rate of change of the stored magnetic energy. Does this answer agree with your answer in part *c*? •••
63. A polarizing filter is a plastic sheet that allows only certain components of the electric field in an electromagnetic wave to pass through, and a wave that has passed through such a filter is said to be *polarized*. After a wave has passed through the filter shown in Figure P30.63*a*, for instance, the wave's electric field contains only the vertical components of all the electric field vectors present before the wave passed through. Because the horizontal components have been blocked, the wave has lost half of its initial intensity. If this polarized wave then passes through the filter of Figure P30.63*b*, where the filter-polarizing direction is at an angle θ to the direction of the vertically polarized wave, the wave loses more of its intensity. If the polarized wave has an intensity $S_{before} = 200$ W/m² before passing through the filter of Figure P30.63*b* and $\theta = 20.0°$, what is the intensity after the wave passes through? •••

Figure P30.63

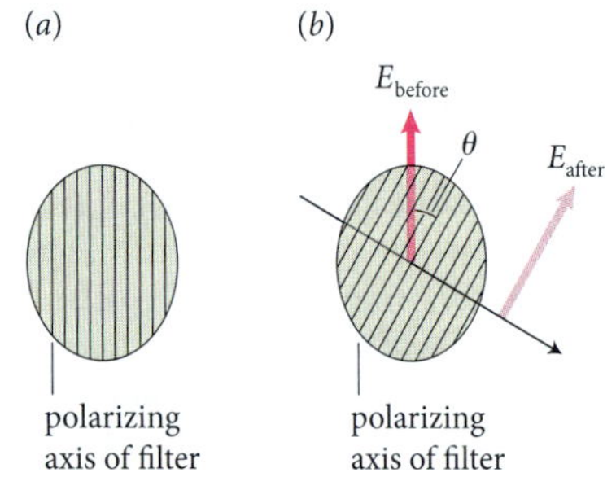

Additional problems

64. Liquid argon has a dielectric constant of 1.5. What is the speed of an electromagnetic wave pulse through this medium? •
65. What needs to be the length of a half-wave antenna for a radio station that emits its signal at 90.5 MHz? •
66. Full-body scanners at airports are sometimes referred to as *millimeter-wave scanners* and sometimes as *terahertz scanners*. Does this make sense? •

PRACTICE

67. A home microwave oven typically uses 2.45-GHz microwaves, and a microwave oven in a restaurant kitchen is more likely to run at 915 MHz. Calculate the wavelength for each frequency and the length of the emitting antenna needed in each case. •

68. A sinusoidal electromagnetic wave has a maximum electric field magnitude of $E_{max} = 500$ N/C. What is the root-mean-square value of the electric field? •

69. By focusing an ultraviolet laser pulse, you can produce an apparently hovering plasma point in midair. If it takes an electric field magnitude of 1.0×10^6 N/C to ionize air, what must the intensity of the pulse be? ••

70. For a particular electromagnetic wave, B_{rms} is 0.30×10^{-6} T. For this wave, calculate (*a*) E_{rms} , (*b*) the average energy density, and (*c*) the intensity. ••

71. A 500-W industrial carbon dioxide cutting laser is capable of cutting 3.0-mm thick steel at a rate of 20 mm/s. Carbon dioxide lasers operate at a wavelength of 10.6 μm. If the spot size of the cutting laser is 0.17 mm in diameter and the intensity is uniform in this spot, what are the magnitudes of the Poynting vector, the rms magnetic field, and the rms electric field for this laser? ••

72. A radio station sends out its signal via a 20-kW emitting antenna. Assuming the signal is emitted equally in all directions and no signal strength is lost, how much power per unit area remains in the signal at a location 10 km from the emitting antenna? ••

73. It takes sunlight about 8 min to travel from the Sun to Earth, where it has an average intensity of 1400 W/m^2. If it takes 44 min for light to travel from the Sun to Jupiter, what is the sunlight intensity there? ••

74. The intensity of sunlight striking Earth's upper atmosphere is approximately 1.35×10^3 W/m^2. (*a*) Calculate E_{max} and B_{max} at this location. (*b*) Given that Earth is 1.5×10^{11} m from the Sun, what is the power output of the Sun? (*c*) If all the sunlight that strikes the upper atmosphere reached Earth's surface, how many watts of power would reach Earth's surface? (Hint: The Earth–Sun distance is so great that you can assume all the sunlight is perpendicular to the cross section of Earth.) ••

75. At a distance of 50 mm (about the distance from your ear to the center of your brain), the 824.6-MHz microwave radiation from a cell phone has an intensity of 35 W/m^2. The maximum permissible radiation leaking from a microwave oven at the same distance is 10 W/m^2. It occurs to you that you could estimate the average magnetic fields generated by the two devices. You also know that people concerned about the possible effects of cell phone radiation on the brain often use a Bluetooth headset, which has an intensity of 0.080 W/m^2 at a distance of 50 mm. But in this case the cell phone itself is probably near your waist—on a belt or in a pocket or purse. There must be an improvement in intensities and field magnitudes at the center of the brain or people would not do this. While contemplating these things, you realize that there may also be a concern that the wavelength of cell phone radiation is comparable to the size of the skull. ••• CR

76. Some people are concerned about "electromagnetic smog" and install meshes on their windows to absorb electromagnetic waves. A particular product advertises "50-dB attenuation in the range from 10 MHz to 3 GHz," with attenuation defined as

$$\text{attenuation (dB)} = 10 \log\left(\frac{\text{input intensity}}{\text{output intensity}}\right).$$

The meshes (sometimes called *Faraday cages* or *Faraday meshes*) generally work if the diameter of the holes is smaller than the wavelength of the radiation. You naturally wonder what this means in terms of reductions in the wave intensity and field strengths. However, it is also curious that the manufacturer advertises a frequency range, so you begin to think about the maximum mesh diameter allowed and whether a minimum is required. ••• CR

Answers to Review Questions

1. A changing electric field produces a magnetic field.
2. The magnetic field forms loops around the changing electric field. The direction of the magnetic field at any location can be found using the right-hand current rule by substituting the direction of $\Delta\vec{E}$ as the direction of "current."
3. Electric fields produced by charged particles are produced both by moving charged particles and by charged particles at rest; magnetic fields produced by charged particles are produced only when the particles are moving. Fields of either kind are produced by changing fields of the other kind.
4. Electric fields exert forces on charged particles, whether the particles are moving or at rest. Magnetic fields exert forces only on moving charged particles.
5. The main similarity occurs for fields whose source is a changing counterpart field: Magnetic field lines form closed loops around a changing electric field, and electric field lines form closed loops around a changing magnetic field. The main difference occurs for fields whose source is a charged particle: Magnetic field lines form closed loops around moving charged particles, but electric field lines do not; instead, electric field lines spread outward from positively charged particles and converge on negatively charged particles, whether moving or at rest.
6. The electric field is not spherically symmetrical. It is weakest along the line of the velocity and strongest in directions perpendicular to the velocity.
7. The extent of the asymmetry is determined by the particle's speed: The faster the particle moves, the more the field surrounding it deviates from spherical symmetry.
8. Kinks appear when the charged particle is accelerated. The kink in any given electric field line joins the part of the line created by the particle before acceleration began with the part of the field line created after the particle's velocity has changed.
9. An electromagnetic wave is made up of an electric field and a magnetic field.
10. The field lines near the dipole are directed from the positive pole to the negative pole and are connected to both poles. This is true in a region of space centered on the dipole and extending in all directions by the distance that changes in the electric field could have traveled since the last change in the dipole sources: $d = cT/2$, where $T/2$ is the interval from $t = T/2$ to $t = T$. The lines far from the dipole are unconnected to the dipole sources, but they reproduce the field that existed when the dipole had its original orientation. "Far from the dipole" means far enough that electric field changes could not have traveled to this region during the time interval since the first change in the dipole sources began—that is, in the interval T between $t = T$ and $t = 0$. Between these two regions the field is not that of a dipole. Rather, the field in this region must form closed loops because there are no charged sources in the region for field lines to begin or terminate on. These loops connect the "broken ends" of the dipolar fields in the near region and in the far region. This region contains a set of loops that are "disconnected" from the dipole sources. See *Principles* Figure 30.13.
11. The magnetic field is perpendicular to the electric field, and both are perpendicular to the direction in which the wave propagates.
12. *In phase* means that the two fields oscillate with the same frequency and simultaneously reach their maxima (or minima).
13. The polarization is defined to be the direction of the electric field of the wave, as seen by an observer looking along the direction of propagation.
14. An antenna is a conducting device that either emits or receives electromagnetic waves.
15. The oscillating current is created by applying across the antenna an alternating potential difference that drives charge carriers in the antenna back and forth. This oscillating motion of the carriers constitutes a current in the antenna.
16. A charging capacitor demonstrates that the Chapter 28 form of Ampère's law is incomplete. The Ampèrian path should encircle the wire leading to one of the plates, and the surface chosen to test the law should pass between the capacitor plates. The current through this surface is zero, so I_{int} for this surface is zero. There is a magnetic field between the plates, however, and so the Chapter 28 form of the law must be incomplete.
17. The generalized form of Ampère's law is $\oint \vec{B} \cdot d\vec{\ell} = \mu_0 I_{\text{int}} + \mu_0\epsilon_0(d\Phi_E/dt)$.
18. The term $\mu_0 I_{\text{int}}$ represents the contribution to $\oint \vec{B} \cdot d\vec{\ell}$ of any current intercepted by a surface spanning any chosen Ampèrian path. The term $\mu_0\epsilon_0(d\Phi_E/dt)$ represents the contribution to $\oint \vec{B} \cdot d\vec{\ell}$ of any changing electric flux through the surface.
19. Displacement current is not a current in the sense of being moving charge carriers. The name is given to the factor $\epsilon_0(d\Phi_E/dt)$ in the generalized form of Ampère's law because this term is associated with a magnetic field in a region in which no charge carriers are moving. The name reminds us that we can use the right-hand *current* rule to determine the direction of the magnetic field associated with the changing electric field $\Delta\vec{E}$.
20. When a dielectric is present, the factor κ that represents the dielectric constant must be included in the displacement-current term: $\mu_0\epsilon_0\kappa(d\Phi_E/dt)$.
21. Equation 30.10, $\Phi_E = \oint \vec{E} \cdot d\vec{A} = (q_{\text{enc}}/\epsilon_0)$, is Gauss's law; Eq. 30.11, $\Phi_B = \oint \vec{B} \cdot d\vec{A} = 0$, is Gauss's law for magnetism; Eq. 30.12, $\oint \vec{E} \cdot d\vec{\ell} = -(d\Phi_B/dt)$, is a quantitative form of Faraday's law; and Eq. 30.13, $\oint \vec{B} \cdot d\vec{\ell} = \mu_0 I_{\text{int}} + \mu_0\epsilon_0(d\Phi_E/dt)$, is Maxwell's generalization of Ampère's law.
22. It is fitting because Maxwell was the first to recognize that—along with conservation of charge—these four expressions completely describe all electromagnetic phenomena.
23. Equation 30.10 (Gauss's law): From the experimentally determined inverse-square relationship between the electric forces two charged particles exert on each other and the distance between the particles, and from the result that in a steady state there is no surplus charge inside a hollow charged conductor. Equation 30.11 (Gauss's law for magnetism): from the observation that magnetic monopoles do not exist, an absence that guarantees zero magnetic flux through any closed surface. Equation 30.12 (Faraday's law): from experiments on electromagnetic induction. Equation 30.13 (generalized form of Ampère's law): from measurements of the force between current-carrying wires and from observations concerning electromagnetic waves.
24. Far from where the charge carrier was accelerated, the transverse part of the pulse looks like a three-dimensional slab that extends infinitely in two dimensions and has some small finite thickness in the third dimension. The slab moves away from the charge carrier along the direction corresponding to the dimension of finite thickness.
25. The ratio E/B equals the propagation speed c_0 of the pulse.
26. The ratio E/B equals the propagation speed c of the pulse, which equals the speed of light in vacuum divided by the square root of the dielectric constant.
27. In vacuum, the speed is equal to the reciprocal of the square root of these two constants: $c_0 = 1/\sqrt{\epsilon_0\mu_0}$. In the dielectric, the speed is c_0 divided by the square root of the dielectric constant: $c = c_0/\sqrt{\kappa} = 1/\sqrt{\epsilon_0\mu_0\kappa}$.

PRACTICE

28. The magnetic field, the electric field, and the velocity are perpendicular to one another. The direction of propagation is the same as the direction of $\vec{E} \times \vec{B}$.
29. No. In vacuum, electromagnetic waves of all frequencies travel at the same constant speed c_0.
30. The speed at which the wave travels is equal to the product of the wave's frequency and the wavelength, $f\lambda$.
31. From lowest to highest frequency, the names are radio waves, infrared, visible light, ultraviolet, x rays, and gamma rays.
32. The electric and magnetic energy densities are numerically equal to each other.
33. (*a*) $u = EB\sqrt{\epsilon_0/\mu_0}$; (*b*) $u = \epsilon_0 E^2$; (*c*) $u = B^2/\mu_0$
34. The Poynting vector is the vector product of the wave's electric field and magnetic field vectors divided by the magnetic constant. It represents the flow of energy per unit time per unit area in the wave.
35. The intensity is the magnitude of the wave's Poynting vector. For a planar electromagnetic wave, this magnitude is equal to the instantaneous electromagnetic power that crosses a unit area oriented perpendicular to the direction of $\vec{E} \times \vec{B}$.
36. The intensity of the wave equals the product of the wave's energy density and its speed: $S = uc_0$ (Eq. 30.35).

Answers to Guided Problems

Guided Problem 30.2 (*a*) $k = \dfrac{\omega}{c_0} = \dfrac{3.0 \times 10^9\ \text{s}^{-1}}{3.0 \times 10^8\ \text{m/s}} = 1.0 \times 10^1\ \text{m}^{-1}$;

(*b*) $\vec{E}(y, t) = (6.0 \times 10^3\ \text{V/m}) \cos[(1.0 \times 10^1\ \text{m}^{-1})y + (3 \times 10^9\ \text{s}^{-1})t]\hat{\imath}$

Guided Problem 30.4 $\theta = 5.4 \times 10^{-9}$ rad

Figure WGA_30.4

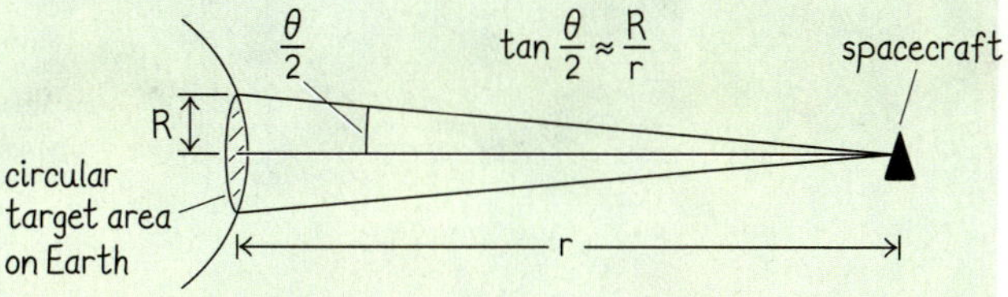

Guided Problem 30.6 $P_{max} = 15$ W

Guided Problem 30.8 $\dfrac{dU^B}{dt} = \dfrac{\mu_0 N^2}{h} b^2 t \pi a^2$; power crosses into the solenoid

31 PRACTICE Electric Circuits

Chapter Summary

The basic circuit (Section 31.1)

Concepts An **electric circuit** is an interconnection of electrical components (*circuit elements*). A **loop** is any closed conducting path through a circuit. A **power source** is any device that provides electric potential energy to an electric circuit. The potential difference across the terminals of the power source drives charge carriers through the circuit and thereby creates a current in the circuit. The **load** in an electric circuit is all the circuit elements connected to the power source. In the load, electric potential energy is converted to other forms of energy.

Quantitative Tools Standard representations of some common circuit elements used in circuit diagrams:

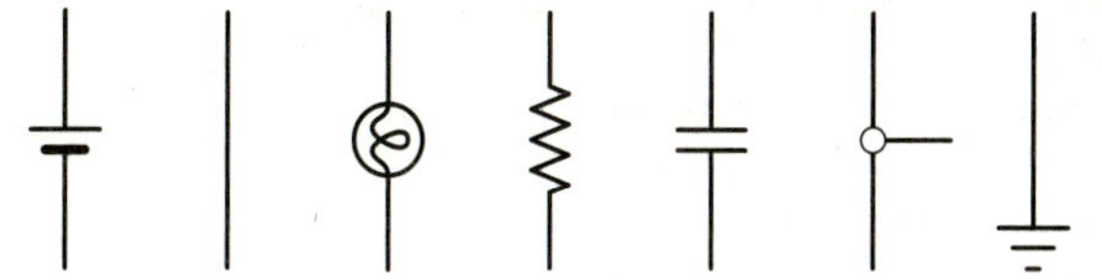

Current and resistance (Sections 31.2, 31.4, 31.5, 31.8)

Concepts A circuit is in **steady state** when the current has a constant value at all points in the circuit. The **current continuity principle** states that in steady state, the current is the same at all locations along a single-loop circuit.

The **resistance** of a circuit element is a measure of the potential difference across that element for a given current in it. The SI unit of resistance is the **ohm** Ω, where $1\,\Omega \equiv 1\text{ V/A}$. The **conductivity** σ of a material is a measure of its ability to conduct charge carriers through the material and is measured in SI units of $\text{A}/(\text{V}\cdot\text{m})$.

When there is a current in a conductor, there must be an electric field in the conductor to cause the current. In a conductor of uniform cross section at steady state, this electric field has the same magnitude everywhere and is parallel to the walls of the conductor.

The **drift velocity** $\vec{v}_\text{d}$ of the charge carriers in a metal in which a current is present is the average velocity with which the carriers are moving.

The **current density** $\vec{J}$ in an electrical conductor is a vector whose direction is the same as the drift velocity direction when the charge carriers are positive and opposite the drift velocity direction when the charge carriers are negative.

Quantitative Tools The magnitude J of the **current density** is

$$J \equiv \frac{|I|}{A} = n|q|v_\text{d}, \tag{31.5}$$

where n is the number of charge carriers per unit volume of the conductor and v_d is the magnitude of the drift velocity of the charge carriers. If the electric field in a metal is $\vec{E}$, the **drift velocity** of the charge carriers (free electrons) is

$$\vec{v}_\text{d} = -\frac{e\vec{E}}{m_\text{e}}\tau, \tag{31.3}$$

where m_e is the mass of an electron and τ is the average time interval between collisions of the electrons with the metal ions.

The **conductivity** of a metal is

$$\sigma \equiv \frac{J}{E} = \frac{ne^2\tau}{m_\text{e}}. \tag{31.8, 31.9}$$

The **resistance** of any circuit element is

$$R \equiv \frac{V}{I}, \tag{31.10}$$

where V is the applied potential difference across the element and I is the resulting current in the element. If the curve of I versus V for a conductor is a straight line, the conductor obeys **Ohm's law** $I = V/R$ (Eq. 31.11) and we call it *ohmic*.

The resistance of a conductor of length ℓ and cross-sectional area A is

$$R = \frac{\ell}{\sigma A}. \tag{31.14}$$

The rate at which energy is dissipated in a resistor is

$$P = I^2R. \tag{31.43}$$

The rate at which a power source delivers energy is

$$P = I\mathscr{E}, \tag{31.45}$$

where $\mathscr{E}$ is the emf of the source.

PRACTICE

Circuit loops (Sections 31.3, 31.6, 31.7)

Concepts A **junction** is a location in a circuit where more than two wires are connected. A **branch** in a circuit is a conducting path between two junctions that is not intercepted by another junction. According to the **branch rule,** the current in a branch of a multiloop circuit is the same throughout the branch.

Two or more circuit elements are connected in *series* if there is only a single current path through them and the charge carriers flow through one element after the other. The potential difference across circuit elements connected in series is equal to the sum of the individual potential differences across each circuit element.

Two or more circuit elements are connected in *parallel* if their ends are connected to the same two junctions. The potential differences across circuit elements connected in parallel are always equal.

Quantitative Tools By the **loop rule,** the sum of the emfs and the potential differences around any loop under steady-state conditions is zero:

$$\Sigma\mathscr{E} + \Sigma V = 0. \qquad (31.21)$$

For a steady-state multiloop circuit, the **junction rule** states that the sum of the charge carriers going into a junction equals the sum of the carriers coming out of that junction:

$$I_{\text{in}} = I_{\text{out}}. \qquad (31.27)$$

See the Procedure boxes "Applying the loop rule in single-loop circuits" and "Analyzing multiloop circuits."

The **equivalent resistance** of resistors *in series* is given by

$$R_{\text{eq}} = R_1 + R_2 + R_3 + \cdots. \qquad (31.26)$$

The **equivalent resistance** of resistors *in parallel* is given by

$$\frac{1}{R_{\text{eq}}} = \frac{1}{R_1} + \frac{1}{R_2} + \frac{1}{R_3} + \cdots. \qquad (31.33)$$

Review Questions

Answers to these questions can be found at the end of this chapter.

31.1 The basic circuit

1. What is the main difference between how a direct-current electric circuit is powered and how an alternating-current electric circuit is powered?
2. What is a *loop* in an electric circuit?
3. What is the *load* in an electric circuit?
4. Are the wires in an electric circuit part of the load?
5. Describe the energy conversion that takes place in a direct-current electric circuit.

31.2 Current and resistance

6. In electric circuits, to what situation does the term *steady state* refer?
7. What is the current continuity principle?
8. What does the current continuity principle say about the accumulation or depletion of charge carriers at any location in a single-loop electric circuit?
9. When a charge carrier moves from one location in a circuit to another location, how much electric potential energy is converted to some other form of energy?
10. How are circuit elements connected in a series connection?
11. What electrical property of a circuit element determines how great a potential difference must be applied across it in order to maintain a given current in it?

31.3 Junctions and multiple loops

12. In steady state, what does the current continuity principle require for (*a*) the current in any branch of a multiloop circuit and (*b*) the current into and out of a junction?
13. What electrical quantity is the same for two light bulbs that are connected in series? For two light bulbs connected in parallel?
14. What is a short in an electric circuit, and what does it do?
15. Does the orientation of elements in a circuit diagram make any difference in whether or not the diagram correctly represents the circuit? Does the length or bending of the connecting wires make any difference?

31.4 Electric fields in conductors

16. What is the electric field like inside a conductor of uniform cross section carrying a steady current?
17. On what three factors does the resistance of an electrical conductor of uniform cross section depend?

31.5 Resistance and Ohm's law

18. Describe what a metallic electrical conductor looks like at the atomic level.
19. How does the Drude model describe the average motion of free electrons in an electrical conductor in the presence of an electric field?
20. What is the conductivity of a material, and what property of the material does conductivity measure?
21. Which properties determine the conductivity of a material?
22. How is the resistance of a circuit element defined?
23. What is an ohmic material?
24. What information about resistance can be found by plotting current as a function of applied potential difference? What does such a curve look like for a circuit element made of an ohmic material?

31.6 Single-loop circuits

25. What two conditions apply to a single-loop circuit in steady state?
26. What is the equivalent resistance of a number of resistors in series?
27. What is the internal resistance of a battery, and how is it accounted for when we analyze a circuit that contains the battery?

31.7 Multiloop circuits

28. What is the equivalent resistance of a number of resistors connected in parallel?
29. Summarize the suggested strategy for analyzing multiloop circuits.

31.8 Power in electric circuits

30. What is the general expression for the rate at which electrical energy is converted to other forms of energy in a circuit element?
31. What is the expression for the rate at which energy is dissipated in a resistor in terms of the current through it? Which type of energy conversion does this dissipation represent?

Developing a Feel

Make an order-of-magnitude estimate of each of the following quantities. Letters in parentheses refer to hints below. Use them as needed to guide your thinking.

1. The resistance of a glowing 100-W light bulb (W, E, R)
2. The resistance of a 5-W nightlight plugged into a bathroom outlet (W, E, R)
3. The height from which you must fall to gain the kinetic energy equivalent to the energy two 100-W light bulbs use in 1 h (H, A, O)
4. The length of tungsten filament in a 100-W light bulb (J, C, M)
5. The diameter of the copper wires in a 15-m heavy-duty extension cord (D, L, P, S)
6. The electric field inside the filament of a glowing 100-W light bulb (E, T)
7. The energy available for conversion in a C battery (Q, U)
8. The cost of 1 MJ (10^6 J) of C-battery energy (I, F)
9. The average rate at which electrical energy is used by the average U.S. home (N, G, V)
10. The annual cost of electricity to run the average U.S. home at \$0.15/kW-h (\$0.04/MJ) (K, B)

Hints

A. How do you determine your kinetic energy at the end of the fall?
B. How much energy does the home use in a year?
C. What is the diameter of the filament?
D. What potential difference is allowed for the cord?
E. What is the potential difference?
F. What is the cost of one C battery?
G. What is the rate of energy consumption when most items are in use?
H. How much energy do the bulbs use in 1 h?
I. How many C batteries are needed in order to have 1 MJ of energy?
J. What is the resistance of the filament?
K. How much power does the home use?
L. How much current can a heavy-duty cord carry?
M. What is the conductivity of tungsten at operating temperature?
N. How many lights and appliances are used in an average home?
O. What is your inertia?
P. What is the conductivity of copper?
Q. How long can a flashlight remain on before it dims dramatically?
R. If you opt to use $R = P/I^2$, how can you calculate current when you know the power and potential difference?
S. Describe the circuit you must analyze.
T. What is the length of the filament?
U. What is the power of a flashlight bulb?
V. During what fraction of the average day is home energy consumption near maximum?
W. What expression gives the resistance in a circuit element when you know the element's power rating?

Key (all values approximate)

A. all your gravitational potential energy *mgh* before the fall is converted to kinetic energy; **B.** 3×10^{10} J/y; **C.** 5×10^{-2} mm; **D.** wires should be almost ideal, so a few percent of household potential difference, or 5 V; **E.** 1×10^2 V, typical in household wiring; **F.** \$1 each in bulk; **G.** heating/cooling dominates, so say 5 kW; **H.** 7×10^5 J; **I.** 10 batteries, see Developing a Feel question 7; **J.** 10^2 Ω, see Developing a Feel question 1; **K.** 1 kW, see Developing a Feel question 9; **L.** 2×10^1 A; **M.** 1×10^6 A/(V·m); **N.** a dozen lights, a refrigerator, stove, TV, computer, and heating/cooling system; **O.** 6×10^1 kg; **P.** 6×10^7 A/(V·m); **Q.** 5 h; **R.** $P = IV$; **S.** two 15-m wires side by side inside a sheath made of nonconducting material, an unknown circuit element (load) plugged into the female end of the cord joins the two wires into a single-loop circuit, and the house wiring at 120 V provides the power source for the circuit; **T.** 10^{-1} m, see Developing a Feel question 4; **U.** 5 W; **V.** 1/3; **W.** either $R = P/I^2$ or $R = V^2/P$

PRACTICE

Worked and Guided Problems

Procedure: Applying the loop rule in single-loop circuits

When applying the loop rule to a single-loop circuit consisting of resistors, batteries, and capacitors, we need to make several choices in order to calculate the current or the potential difference across each circuit element.

1. Choose a reference direction for the current in the loop. (This direction is arbitrary and may or may not be the direction of current, but don't worry, things sort themselves out in step 4.) Indicate your chosen reference direction by an arrowhead, and label the arrowhead with the symbol for the current (I).
2. Choose a direction of travel around the loop. This choice is arbitrary and separate from the choice of the reference direction for the current in step 1. (You may want to indicate the travel direction with a circular clockwise or counterclockwise arrow in the loop.)
3. Start traversing the loop in the direction chosen in step 2 from some arbitrary point on the loop. As you encounter circuit elements, each circuit element contributes a term to Eq. 31.21. Use Table 31.2 to determine the sign and value of each term. Add all terms to obtain the sum in Eq. 31.21. Make sure you traverse the loop completely.
4. Solve your expression for the desired quantity. If your solution indicates that $I < 0$, then the direction of current is opposite the reference direction you chose in step 1.

Table 31.2 Signs and values of potential differences across batteries and resistors (Figure 31.35)

Circuit element	Plus sign when traversing	Value
ideal battery	from − to +	$\mathscr{E}$
capacitor	from − to +	$q(t)/C$
resistor	opposite reference direction of current	IR

Procedure: Analyzing multiloop circuits

Here is a series of steps for calculating currents or potential differences in multiloop circuits.

1. Identify and label the junctions in the circuit.
2. Label the current in each branch of the circuit, arbitrarily assigning a direction to each current.
3. Apply the junction rule to all but one of the junctions. (The choice of which junctions to analyze is arbitrary; choose junctions that involve the quantities you are interested in calculating.)
4. Identify the loops in the circuit and apply the loop rule (see the Procedure box on page 831) enough times to obtain a suitable number of simultaneous equations relating the unknowns in the problem. The choice of loops is arbitrary, but every branch must be in at least one of the loops. Traverse each loop in whichever direction you prefer, but be sure you traverse each loop completely and stick with the direction of travel and with the chosen directions of the currents.

There are several simplifications you can make during your analysis.

1. Multiloop circuits can sometimes be simplified by replacing parallel or series combinations of resistors by their equivalent resistances. If you can reduce the circuit to a single loop, you can solve for the current in the source. You may then need to "unsimplify" and undo the resistor simplification to calculate the current or potential difference across a particular resistor.
2. In general when solving problems, you should solve equations analytically before substituting known numerical values. When solving the simultaneous equations you obtain for multiloop circuits, however, you can often simplify the algebra if you substitute the known numerical values earlier on.

These examples involve material from this chapter but are not associated with any particular section. Some examples are worked out in detail; others you should work out by following the guidelines provided.

Worked Problem 31.1 Battery power

A battery of emf $\mathscr{E}$ has internal resistance R_{batt}. When it is new, the battery can maintain this emf while transporting an amount of charge q between its terminals, but then further charge transport is accompanied by a rapid reduction in the value of this emf. Suppose the battery is connected to a resistive load of resistance R. (*a*) What value of R maximizes the rate at which energy is converted in the load? (*b*) Derive an expression for the maximum rate at which energy is converted in the load. (*c*) Derive an expression for the amount of electric potential energy converted to thermal energy in the load before the battery dies.

❶ **GETTING STARTED** We are given the emf and internal resistance for a battery in a circuit that contains a load of resistance R. The battery is capable of transporting an amount of charge q before dying. Our tasks are (*a*) to determine what value of R maximizes the rate at which energy is delivered by the battery and to express (*b*) that maximum power and (*c*) the amount of energy converted in the load in terms of the given variables. Let's first draw the circuit and show the reference direction we choose for the current and the direction in which we shall travel around the circuit as we analyze the potential differences across the various circuit elements (Figure WG31.1).

Figure WG31.1

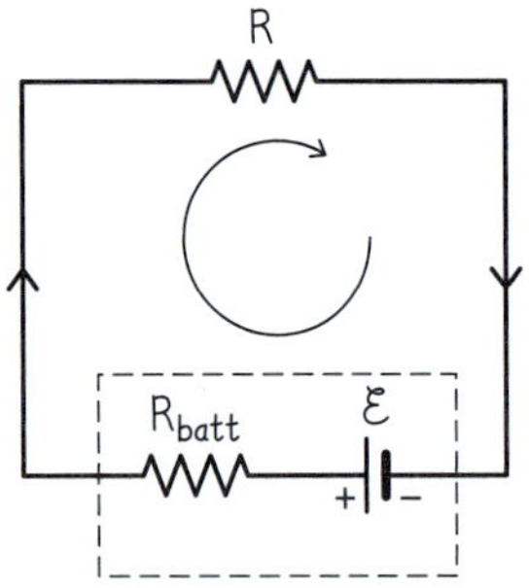

❷ **DEVISE PLAN** We first apply the loop rule (Eq. 31.21) to determine the current in the circuit. We then use Eq. 31.43 to obtain an expression for the power P, which is the rate at which energy is converted in the load. In order to calculate the value of R that maximizes P, we need to differentiate P with respect to R and then determine the value of R for which $dP/dR = 0$. Once we have this value of R, we can use Eq. 31.43 again to solve part *b*. For part *c*, we can use Eq. 31.41 to determine how much energy is converted in the load before the battery dies.

❸ **EXECUTE PLAN** (*a*) With our choices for the current reference direction and the direction in which we travel around the circuit, the loop rule takes the form

$$\mathscr{E} - IR_{batt} - IR = 0,$$

so the current is

$$I = \frac{\mathscr{E}}{R_{batt} + R}. \quad (1)$$

The rate at which energy is converted in the load is, from Eq. 31.43,

$$P = I^2R = \left(\frac{\mathscr{E}}{R_{batt} + R}\right)^2 R.$$

Next we take the derivative of this power with respect to R and set it equal to zero:

$$\frac{dP}{dR} = \mathscr{E}^2\left[\left(\frac{1}{R_{batt} + R}\right)^2 - 2R\left(\frac{1}{R_{batt} + R}\right)^3\right] = 0.$$

This equation solved for R gives us

$$\left(\frac{1}{R_{batt} + R}\right)^2 = 2R\left(\frac{1}{R_{batt} + R}\right)^3$$

$$R_{batt} + R = 2R$$

$$R = R_{batt}. ✔$$

The rate at which energy is converted in the load is greatest when the load resistance is the same as the battery's internal resistance.

(*b*) Substituting R_{batt} for R in Eq. 1 gives us an expression for the current that maximizes the power:

$$I_{max} = \frac{\mathscr{E}}{R_{batt} + R} = \frac{\mathscr{E}}{2R_{batt}}.$$

Thus the maximum power is

$$P_{max} = I_{max}^2 R = \left(\frac{\mathscr{E}}{2R_{batt}}\right)^2 R_{batt} = \frac{1}{4}\frac{\mathscr{E}^2}{R_{batt}}. ✔$$

(*c*) We can now use Eq. 31.41 to obtain an expression for the energy converted in the load:

$$\Delta E = -qV_{ab} = IRq = \frac{\mathscr{E}}{2R_{batt}}R_{batt}q = \frac{\mathscr{E}q}{2}. ✔$$

❹ **EVALUATE RESULT** The chemical energy converted in the battery before it dies is $\Delta E = \mathscr{E}q$, so our result tells us that half of this chemical energy is converted in the load. The other half of the chemical energy must be converted in the internal resistance of the battery! All of this chemical energy is dissipated into thermal energy due to the internal resistance of the battery or the external resistance of the load. This is reasonable for a resistive load, such as a hair dryer or toaster, but it might surprise you that by maximizing the rate of energy conversion in the load we have "wasted" 50% of the chemical energy of the battery. Returning to Eq. 1, we see that if the load resistance is considerably greater than the internal resistance of the battery, the current will be much smaller. Suppose $R = 100R_{batt}$. Then the rate of energy conversion in the load is much smaller, but Eq. 31.41 allows 99% of the converted chemical energy to appear in the load, with only 1% "wasted" in the battery. By taking a much longer time to convert energy, we use the energy stored in the battery much more efficiently.

Guided Problem 31.2 Battery-powered lift

A standard D cell battery can supply 25 mA at 1.5 V for about 300 h, and its internal resistance is about 1.0 Ω. A multispeed winch powered by such a battery is 50% efficient and is being used to lift a 60-kg object that is initially on the ground. When the winch is set to a very slow speed, the load resistance is much greater than the internal resistance of the battery. The greatest speed of the winch is limited by the maximum power supplied by the battery. (*a*) In each case, how high can the winch lift the object before the battery uses all of its energy? (*b*) What are the maximum speed at which the winch lifts the object and the minimum time interval required for the lift? Assume the battery capacity (product of current and time) is independent of the discharge rate, which is not accurate for real batteries.

❶ GETTING STARTED

1. Draw a circuit diagram. Which circuit element symbol should represent the winch?
2. When the winch is run at a very slow speed, how does the amount of energy dissipated due to the battery's internal resistance compare with the amount of energy converted to mechanical potential energy of the rising object?

❷ DEVISE PLAN

3. What relationship tells you the quantity of charge the battery delivers before it dies?
4. What relationship tells you how much energy the battery delivers before it dies?
5. How can you use energy relationships to determine the height to which the object rises before the battery dies?
6. What expression allows you to compute the rate of energy transfer to the load?
7. How do you maximize the rate at which energy is delivered to the load?
8. How do you determine the greatest speed at which the winch can lift the object?

❸ EXECUTE PLAN

9. Calculate the quantity of charge delivered and the energy delivered before the battery dies.
10. Calculate how high off the ground the object is lifted at very slow speed.
11. What is the greatest speed the object attains?
12. At this greatest lift rate, what is the maximum height that the winch can lift the object before the battery dies?
13. What minimum time interval is required for the object to reach this height?

❹ EVALUATE RESULT

14. Are your results for the time interval required to raise the load to its maximum height at the greatest speed reasonable? Examine some limiting cases.

Worked Problem 31.3 Designing an ohmmeter

An ammeter that has a resistance of 20 Ω reads 50 μA when the needle on the meter scale is fully deflected. By combining the ammeter with a 1.5-V battery and resistors 1 and 2 that have resistances R_1 and R_2, you can convert it to an ohmmeter. When the leads of this ohmmeter are connected to each other (which is equivalent to connecting the leads across a circuit element of zero resistance), the needle on the meter scale is fully deflected. This full deflection represents both a current of 50 μA and a resistance of 0. In order to use the meter to measure the resistance of any circuit element, you must convert the meter-scale readings from amperes to ohms. Once you have done this calibration and connected the meter leads across a circuit element of unknown resistance R_u, the reading on your hand-calibrated scale indicates the resistance of the element. (*a*) If you want half-scale deflection to indicate 15 Ω, how should you connect the circuit elements to one another, and what values should you choose for R_1 and R_2? (*b*) When you align your ohm scale with the ampere scale on the meter, with the full-deflection reading $R = 0$ aligned with 50 μA on the ampere scale, which value on the ampere scale aligns with the 5.0-Ω position on your scale? With the 50-Ω position on your scale?

❶ GETTING STARTED We have an ammeter that has a resistance of 20 Ω, a 1.5-V battery, and resistors 1 and 2 that have resistances R_1 and R_2, and we must connect these four elements in an electric circuit in such a way that the combination acts as an ohmmeter and measures the resistance R_u of a fifth element we place in the circuit. We begin by drawing our ohmmeter as a box containing our four given elements not yet connected to one another (Figure WG31.2). We must connect the ends of our fifth element of resistance R_u to two wires that emerge from this ohmmeter "box."

Figure WG31.2

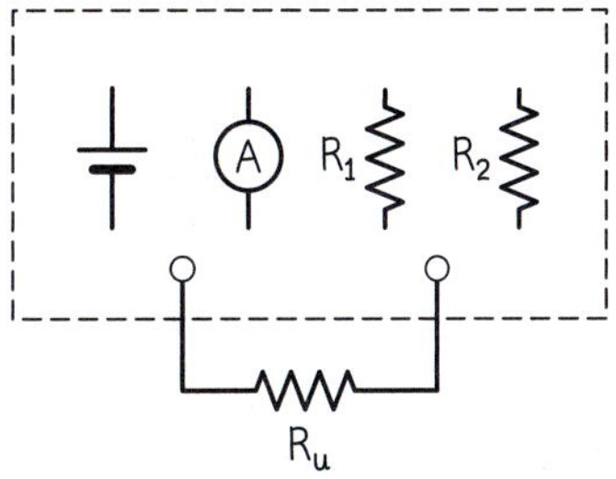

❷ DEVISE PLAN (*a*) To see why we need two resistors and how they must be connected, suppose at first that both R_1 and R_2 are very small and can be replaced by wires. Then we must connect only a battery, an ammeter, and the external resistance R_u. But if $R_u = 0$, then we obtain just a battery in series with an ammeter, and the current is $I_{\text{no resistors}} = \mathscr{E}_{\text{batt}}/R_A = 1.5\text{ V}/20\ \Omega = 75\text{ mA}$. This sounds small, but it is 1500 times the full-scale deflection current! We need a resistor to limit the current to the 50-μA scale of the meter. We can place this resistor in series with the ammeter and the battery so that the equivalent resistance of the meter + resistor combination is very great. However, we will also need to adjust the circuit so that a half-scale meter deflection corresponds to external resistance $R_u = 15\ \Omega$, without noticeably changing the portion of the circuit that secures the earlier value. Thus at least one more resistor connected in a parallel branch will be needed, and its value will need to be small (so as not to affect the earlier value very much). The numerical values can be computed using

PRACTICE

our knowledge of series and parallel resistances and the behavior of the current and potential difference for series and parallel connections.

(*b*) Having calibrated the ohmmeter, we should be able to apply the junction and loop rules to compute the scale reading for any other external resistance. If we solve for the current in the ammeter, we can determine the fraction of full-scale deflection. We can then make an appropriate mark for the corresponding scale reading in ohms.

❸ **EXECUTE PLAN** (*a*) We calibrate the meter scale by using the restrictions that our new "ohmmeter" requires full-scale deflection when $R_u = 0$ and half-scale deflection when $R_u = 15\ \Omega$. To satisfy the first requirement, we connect the battery, ammeter, and resistor 1 in series inside our ohmmeter "box" and place zero resistance (a wire) for R_u (Figure WG31.3). The value of R_1 must allow full-scale deflection, so

$$I_{\text{full-scale}} = \frac{\mathscr{E}_{\text{batt}}}{R_1 + R_A}$$

$$R_1 = \frac{\mathscr{E}_{\text{batt}} - R_A I_{\text{full-scale}}}{I_{\text{full-scale}}} = \frac{1.5\ \text{V} - (20\ \Omega)(50 \times 10^{-6}\ \text{A})}{50 \times 10^{-6}\ \text{A}}$$

$$= 3.0 \times 10^4\ \Omega.$$

Figure WG31.3

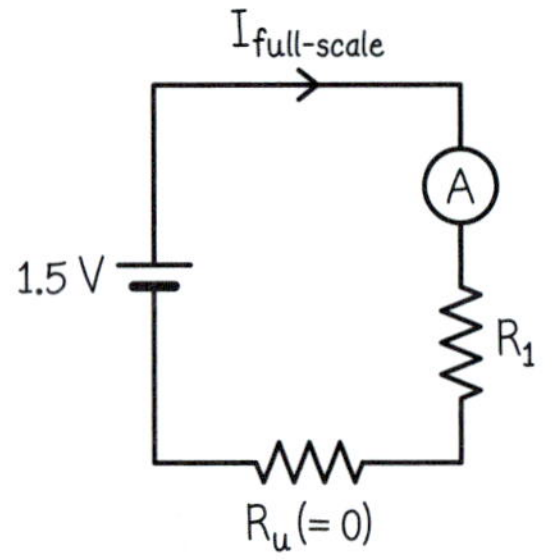

Now we add resistor 2 in a parallel branch and replace the external resistance with $R_u = 15\ \Omega$ (Figure WG31.4). We now have a two-loop circuit, and we add labels for currents and direction of travel around loops. This allows us to write the single junction equation and two loop equations:

$$I_u = I_1 + I_2 \quad (1)$$

$$+\mathscr{E}_{\text{batt}} - I_2R_2 - I_uR_u = 0 \quad (2)$$

$$+I_2R_2 - I_1R_A - I_1R_1 = 0. \quad (3)$$

Figure WG31.4

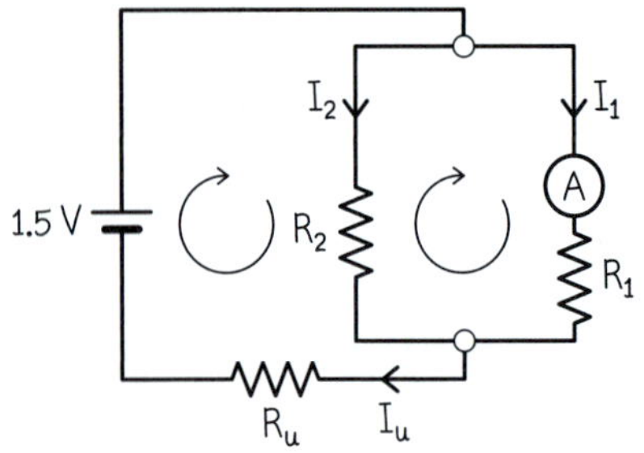

We know that the current in the ammeter for this special case is $I_1 = 0.25\ \mu\text{A}$. Thus Eq. 3 allows us to compute the potential difference across resistor 2:

$$I_2R_2 = I_1(R_A + R_1) = (25 \times 10^{-6}\ \text{A})(20\ \Omega + 3.0 \times 10^4\ \Omega)$$
$$= 0.75\ \text{V}.$$

Next we obtain the potential difference across R_u from Eq. 2:

$$+\mathscr{E}_{\text{batt}} - I_2R_2 - I_uR_u = 0$$
$$1.5\ \text{V} - 0.75\ \text{V} - I_uR_u = 0$$
$$I_uR_u = 0.75\ \text{V}.$$

The current in the external resistor must therefore be

$$I_u = \frac{V_u}{R_u} = \frac{0.75\ \text{V}}{15\ \Omega} = 50\ \text{mA}.$$

The current in the battery must equal the current in the external resistor because these elements are connected in series. Because the current in the ammeter is known, the current in the battery can be computed from Eq. 1:

$$I_2 = I_u - I_1 = 50\ \text{mA} - 25\ \mu\text{A} = 50\ \text{mA}.$$

Notice that the current in the ammeter is entirely negligible on the scale of the current in the battery, resistor 2, and the external resistor. In fact, these three currents are identical to two significant digits. This allows us to determine the resistance R_2:

$$R_2 = \frac{V_2}{I_2} = \frac{0.75\ \text{V}}{50 \times 10^{-3}\ \text{A}} = 15\ \Omega.$$

The design of our ohmmeter is complete. ✔

(*b*) The two specific cases to be solved use the same circuit shown in Figure WG31.4. Thus we can employ Eqs. 1–3, changing only the value of R_u. In each case all resistances are known, which leaves three unknown currents to be determined from our three equations. Because we wish to solve for I_1, it is convenient to use Eq. 1 to eliminate I_u from Eq. 2, leaving us with two equations in two unknowns:

$$I_2R_2 - I_1(R_A + R_1) = 0 \quad (3)$$

$$+\mathscr{E}_{\text{batt}} - I_1R_u - I_2(R_2 + R_u) = 0. \quad (4)$$

Next we use Eq. 3 to eliminate I_2 from Eq. 4 and solve for I_1:

$$+\mathscr{E}_{\text{batt}} - I_1R_u - \frac{I_1(R_A + R_1)(R_2 + R_u)}{R_2} = 0$$

$$I_1 = \frac{\mathscr{E}_{\text{batt}}R_2}{R_2R_u + (R_A + R_1)(R_2 + R_u)}. \quad (5)$$

Suppose $R_u = 5.0\ \Omega$. Then

$$I_1 = \frac{(1.5\ \text{V})(15\ \Omega)}{(15\ \Omega)(5.0\ \Omega) + (20\ \Omega + 3.0 \times 10^4\ \Omega)(15\ \Omega + 5.0\ \Omega)}$$
$$= 37\ \mu\text{A}.$$

The ammeter needle would move to 37 μA, or 75% of full-scale deflection, which is where we make the 5.0-Ω mark. ✔

PRACTICE

Similarly, if $R_u = 50\ \Omega$, the ammeter current is

$$I_1 = \frac{(1.5\ \text{V})(15\ \Omega)}{(15\ \Omega)(50\ \Omega) + (20\ \Omega + 3.0 \times 10^4\ \Omega)(15\ \Omega + 50\ \Omega)}$$

$$= 12\ \mu\text{A}.$$

The needle is at 12 μA, or 23% of full-scale deflection, for the 50-Ω mark. ✔

❹ **EVALUATE RESULT** Our circuit is a reasonable design because we can easily find resistors that have the values we need: 15 Ω and $3.0 \times 10^4\ \Omega$. An alternative design employing the first resistor in parallel with the ammeter and the second in series with that combination and the battery would produce a first resistor with an uncomfortably small resistance that would be difficult to find and small enough to call into question our assumption that the resistance of the connecting wires can be ignored. Try it!

Our assumption of zero internal resistance in the battery is the only way to proceed. The value should be small in any case, but we are not given enough information about the battery (alkaline? rechargeable? lead-acid?) to allow us to look up a reasonable value.

The expression we obtained for the ammeter current, Eq. 5, shows that the current decreases as the external resistance R_u increases. This makes sense because the resistance scale runs backward compared to the current scale. The zero of current in Eq. 5 also corresponds to an infinitely large value of R_u, which is consistent with the nonlinear resistance scale that our numerical results require.

We should examine the effect of resistor 2 on our original calculation of full-scale deflection for zero external resistance. Solving Eq. 5 for the current in the ammeter for zero external resistance gives

$$I_1 = \frac{(1.5\ \text{V})(15\ \Omega)}{(15\ \Omega)(0) + (20\ \Omega + 3.0 \times 10^4\ \Omega)(15\ \Omega + 0)}$$

$$= 50\ \mu\text{A}.$$

Thus the added small parallel resistance indeed had no effect on the full-scale deflection, at least to two significant digits.

Guided Problem 31.4 Four resistors

Resistors 1, 2, 3, and 4 are connected to a battery as shown in Figure WG31.5. Express the current through each resistor in terms of R_1 and the battery emf $\mathscr{E}$.

Figure WG31.5

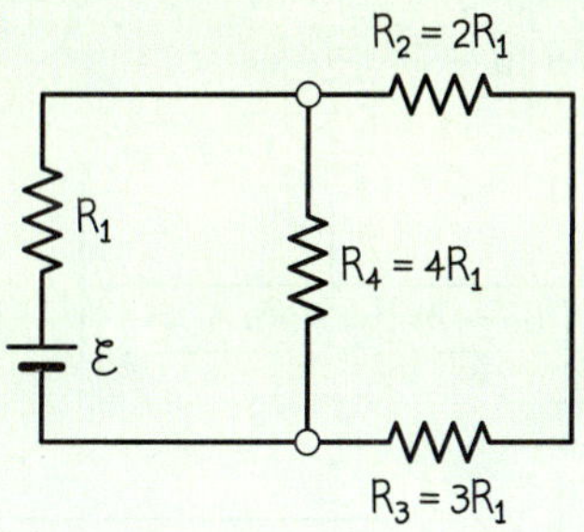

❶ **GETTING STARTED**

1. Apply the steps in the Procedure box "Analyzing multiloop circuits." Choose a reference direction for each current and label the currents I_1, I_2, and I_4 through the three branches. Draw curved arrows to indicate the (arbitrary) direction in which you will travel around each loop.
2. Why isn't it necessary to show current I_3 in your diagram?

❷ **DEVISE PLAN**

3. How many independent equations do you need to solve the problem?
4. Is there a useful simplification for this circuit?

❸ **EXECUTE PLAN**

5. Compute equivalent resistances as needed.
6. What is the current through resistor 1?
7. What is the current through resistor 4?
8. What is the current through resistors 2 and 3?

❹ **EVALUATE RESULT**

9. Check that the junction rule is satisfied.

Worked Problem 31.5 Resistance of a truncated cone

Consider a resistor constructed of a material of conductivity σ that has the shape of a truncated cone of length ℓ, base radius b, and top face radius a (Figure WG31.6). The base and top face are parallel to each other. Derive an expression in terms of these variables for the resistance between the base and the top face.

Figure WG31.6

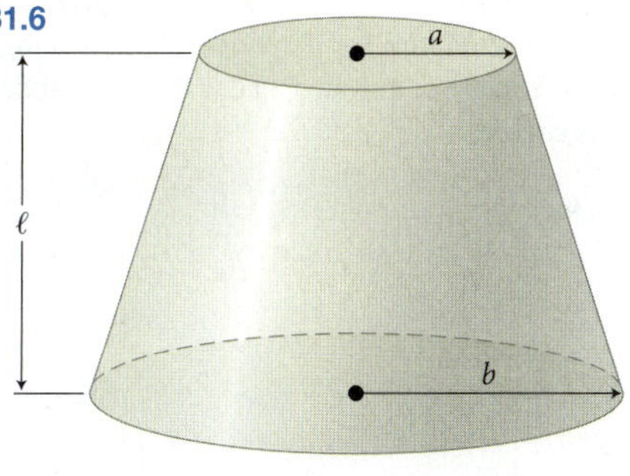

❶ **GETTING STARTED** We know how to compute the resistance of a conductor of uniform cross section, but the cross-sectional area of this cone varies along its length. That suggests we need to integrate. We can model the cone as a stack of thin disks, oriented parallel to the base of the cone, each disk of variable radius r and thickness dx. Because the thickness is infinitesimal, each disk is essentially of uniform cross-sectional area $A = \pi r^2$. The disks are connected in series because charge carriers must flow through each disk in the order they occur in the stack.

PRACTICE

❷ **DEVISE PLAN** Figure WG31.7 shows the truncated cone in cross section, with a representative thin disk of radius r and thickness dx. We can use Eq. 31.14 to determine the resistance dR of each disk as a function of x, the distance from the base. From the geometry of the cone, we can determine how the disk radius r varies with x and therefore how the disk area A varies with x. Because the disks are connected in series, the sum of their resistances is the resistance of the cone. To determine this sum, we can integrate the resistance $dR(x)$ from $x = 0$ to $x = \ell$.

Figure WG31.7

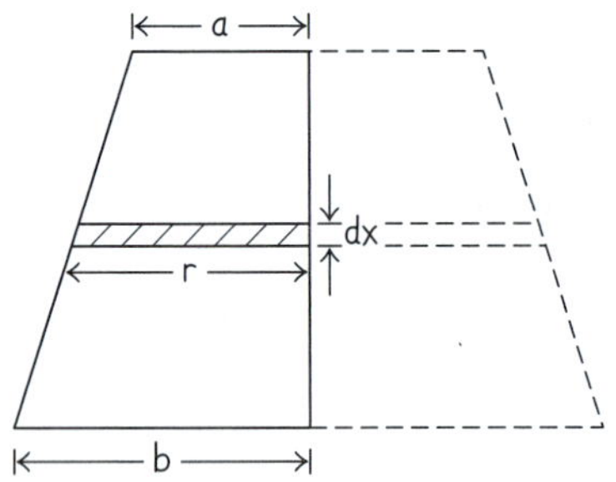

❸ **EXECUTE PLAN** We determine how the radius r of any disk and its distance x from the base are related by working with the similar triangles shown in Figure WG31.8*b*. Figure WG31.8*a* shows their origin: In the view of the cone shown in Figure WG31.7, we draw a vertical line from the left edge of the top face to the base. From the similar triangles, r and x are related by

$$\frac{b - r}{x} = \frac{b - a}{\ell}.$$

Figure WG31.8

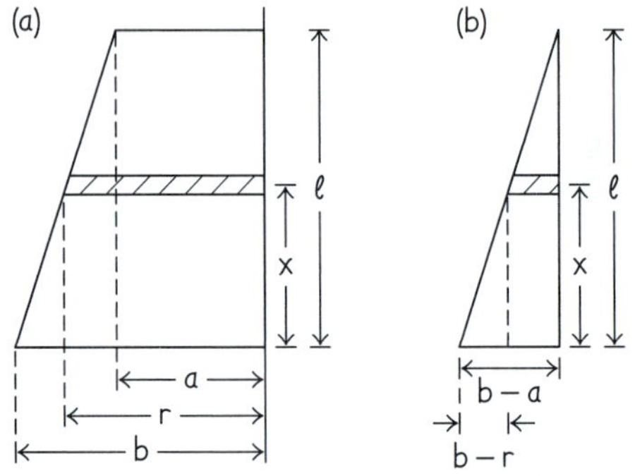

Rearranging this equation gives us an expression for $r(x)$:

$$r(x) = b + \frac{(a - b)}{\ell}x.$$

The area of the disk as a function of x is then

$$A(x) = \pi\left[b + \frac{(a - b)}{\ell}x\right]^2.$$

We now use Eq. 31.14 to obtain the resistance $dR(x)$ for any disk of thickness dx located a distance x from the base:

$$dR(x) = \frac{dx}{\sigma\pi\left[b + \frac{(a - b)}{\ell}x\right]^2}.$$

The resistance of the cone is therefore

$$R = \int_{x=0}^{x=\ell} \frac{dx}{\sigma\pi\left[b + \frac{(a - b)}{\ell}x\right]^2}.$$

Using the identity (see Appendix B)

$$\int \frac{dx}{(\alpha + \beta x)^2} = -\frac{1}{\beta(\alpha + \beta x)},$$

we have

$$R = \int_{x=0}^{x=\ell} \frac{dx}{\sigma\pi\left[b + \frac{(a - b)}{\ell}x\right]^2}$$

$$= -\frac{1}{\sigma\pi}\frac{1}{\left[\frac{(a - b)}{\ell}\right]\left[b + \frac{(a - b)}{\ell}x\right]}\Bigg|_{x=0}^{x=\ell}$$

$$= -\frac{1}{\sigma\pi}\left\{\frac{1}{\left[\frac{(a - b)}{\ell}\right](b + (a - b))} - \frac{1}{\left[\frac{(a - b)}{\ell}\right](b)}\right\}$$

$$= -\frac{1}{\sigma\pi}\left\{\frac{(b - a)}{\left[\frac{(a - b)}{\ell}\right](ab)}\right\} = \frac{\ell}{\sigma\pi ab}. \checkmark$$

❹ **EVALUATE RESULT** Our expression involves the dimensions of the cone in a sensible fashion; that is, the resistance increases as the cone length increases and the resistance decreases as either the base or top face increases in size. If $b = a$, the cross-sectional area of the cone is a uniform $A = \pi a^2$ and our resistance expression becomes $R = \ell/\sigma\pi a^2 = \ell/\sigma A$. That this expression is identical to Eq. 31.14, the resistance for a cylindrical or rectangular resistor, gives us confidence that our answer for the resistance of the truncated cone is correct.

PRACTICE

Guided Problem 31.6 Conductivity of seawater

An oceanographer uses electrical conductivity to study how the ion concentration in seawater depends on depth. She does this by lowering into the ocean a device consisting of a metallic solid cylinder of radius $r_{\text{inner}} = 10.0$ mm concentric with a metallic cylindrical shell of radius $r_{\text{outer}} = 40.0$ mm (Figure WG31.9). The length of both the solid cylinder and the shell is $\ell = 400$ mm. The device is attached to the end of a cable, and the cable is lowered to a depth $D = 4000$ m, where the water temperature is 0.00 °C and the salinity is 3.50×10^4 mg per liter of solution. With the device at that depth, the oceanographer applies a potential difference $V_{\text{outer}} - V_{\text{inner}} = 0.500$ V between the solid cylinder and the cylindrical shell, producing an outward radial current $I = 2.93$ A. What is the conductivity of the seawater at that depth?

Figure WG31.9

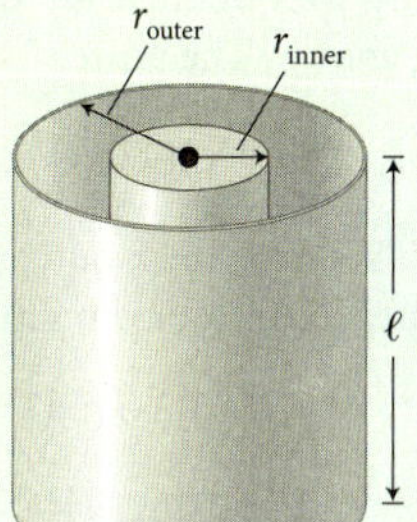

❶ GETTING STARTED

1. How can you model the seawater that fills the space between the solid cylinder and the cylindrical shell as a resistor?
2. Is your model a combination of thin shells connected in series or parallel?

❷ DEVISE PLAN

3. How can you calculate the resistance dR of the individual shells of seawater?
4. How can you determine the contribution of all the seawater shells to get the resistance of the seawater?
5. What expression relates resistance to potential difference and current?
6. How can you calculate the seawater conductivity?

❸ EXECUTE PLAN

7. Express the resistance dR of one seawater shell in terms of the shell radius r, thickness dr, and length ℓ. (Be careful: Which dimension corresponds to the length of this shell resistor?)
8. Integrate to sum the resistances of all the seawater shells.
9. Use Eq. 31.11 to relate this expression for R to the potential difference and current.
10. Use this relationship to calculate the conductivity of the seawater.

❹ EVALUATE RESULT

11. Look up the value of the conductivity of seawater. Does your answer make sense based on that value?

Worked Problem 31.7 Multiple batteries

Calculate the rate at which each of the three batteries in Figure WG31.10 either delivers or absorbs (specify which in each case) energy. Assume all the batteries have zero internal resistance, and use numerical values $R_1 = R_3 = 1.0\ \Omega$, $R_2 = 2.0\ \Omega$, $\mathscr{E}_1 = 2.0$ V, and $\mathscr{E}_2 = \mathscr{E}_3 = 4.0$ V.

Figure WG31.10

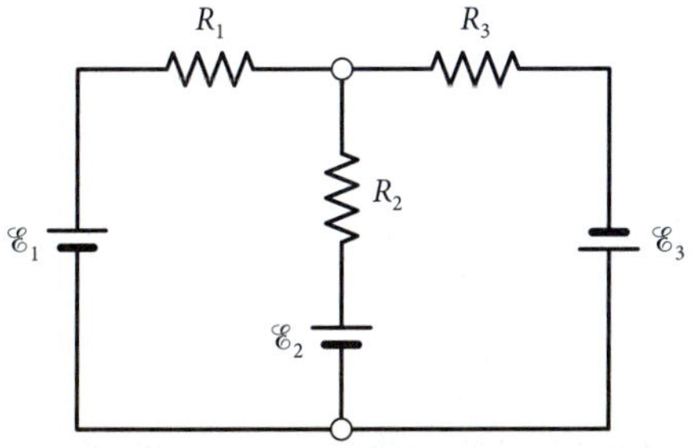

❶ GETTING STARTED We begin by observing that this is a multiloop circuit containing two junctions. We redraw the circuit diagram and label various locations along the wires to have a convenient way of identifying each loop we'll work with; our junctions are at b and d in the arbitrary lettering we use. Next we label the directions we choose for currents I_1, I_2, and I_3 through the three branches and add a clockwise arrow in the center of the left and right loops to show the direction in which we'll travel around each loop (Figure WG31.11).

Figure WG31.11

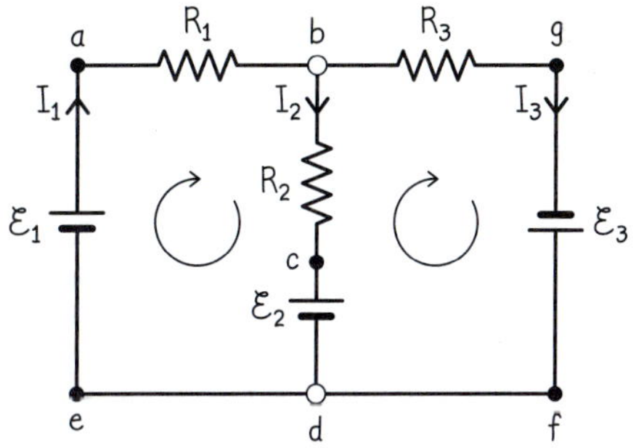

❷ DEVISE PLAN To solve this problem, we must determine the value of the current in each branch and then use our current values to calculate the power for each battery. To determine the current values, we apply the junction rule (Eq. 31.27) to one of the junctions and then the loop rule (Eq. 31.21) to as many loops as necessary. Because we have three unknown currents, we need three independent equations. With only two junctions, we know that the junction rule can give us only one independent equation, and so we must use the loop rule on two loops to get our three equations. Once we have values for I_1, I_2, and I_3, we can use Eq. 31.45 to calculate the power for each battery.

❸ EXECUTE PLAN The junction rule applied to junction b, with $I_{\text{in}} = I_1$ and $I_{\text{out}} = I_2 + I_3$, yields

$$I_1 = I_2 + I_3. \quad (1)$$

For loop abcdea, moving clockwise from a, we have

$$-I_1R_1 - I_2R_2 - \mathscr{E}_2 + \mathscr{E}_1 = 0. \quad (2)$$

For loop bgfdcb, moving clockwise from b, we have

$$-I_3R_3 + \mathscr{E}_3 + \mathscr{E}_2 + I_2R_2 = 0. \quad (3)$$

Now we must use these three equations to obtain expressions for I_1, I_2, and I_3. Let's begin with Eq. 2 solved for I_1:

$$I_1 = \frac{-I_2R_2 - \mathscr{E}_2 + \mathscr{E}_1}{R_1}, \quad (4)$$

and next Eq. 3 solved for I_3:

$$I_3 = \frac{\mathscr{E}_3 + \mathscr{E}_2 + I_2R_2}{R_3}. \quad (5)$$

We can now substitute these expressions for I_1 and I_2 into Eq. 1:

$$\frac{-I_2R_2 - \mathscr{E}_2 + \mathscr{E}_1}{R_1} = I_2 + \frac{\mathscr{E}_3 + \mathscr{E}_2 + I_2R_2}{R_3}.$$

Solving for I_2 and substituting given values yield

$$I_2 = \frac{-\mathscr{E}_2(R_3 + R_1) + \mathscr{E}_1R_3 - \mathscr{E}_3R_1}{R_1R_3 + R_1R_2 + R_2R_3}$$

$$= \frac{-(4.0\text{ V})(1.0\ \Omega + 1.0\ \Omega) + (2.0\text{ V})(1.0\ \Omega) - (4.0\text{ V})(1.0\ \Omega)}{(1.0\ \Omega)(1.0\ \Omega) + (1.0\ \Omega)(2.0\ \Omega) + (2.0\ \Omega)(1.0\ \Omega)}$$

$$= -2.0\text{ A}.$$

The minus sign means that the direction of I_2 is the opposite of the direction we chose in Figure WG31.11. Hence battery 2 is delivering energy.

We can now calculate I_1 by substituting values in Eq. 4:

$$I_1 = \frac{-(-2.0\text{ A})(2.0\ \Omega) - (4.0\text{ V}) + (2.0\text{ V})}{1.0\ \Omega} = +2.0\text{ A}.$$

The positive result for this current indicates that battery 1 is delivering energy.

Equation 5 gives us

$$I_3 = \frac{(4.0\text{ V}) + (4.0\text{ V}) + (-2.0\text{ A})(2.0\ \Omega)}{1.0\ \Omega} = +4.0\text{ A},$$

and this positive value for I_3 tells us that battery 3 is delivering energy.

The rate at which energy is delivered to the circuit by battery 1 is, from Eq. 31.45,

$$P_1 = \mathscr{E}_1I_1 = (2.0\text{ V})(2.0\text{ A}) = 4.0\text{ W}, ✔$$

and that rate for battery 2 is

$$P_2 = \mathscr{E}_2|I_2| = (4.0\text{ V})(2.0\text{ A}) = 8.0\text{ W} ✔$$

Note we use the absolute value for I_2 because we have concluded that the negative value we obtained for this current meant that battery 2 is delivering energy. The power for battery 3 is

$$P_3 = \mathscr{E}_3I_3 = (4.0\text{ V})(4.0\text{ A}) = 16\text{ W}. ✔$$

❹ **EVALUATE RESULT** We can check our results in two ways. First we check that our values for the current satisfy the junction rule:

$$I_{in} = I_1 = 2.0\text{ A}$$

$$I_{out} = I_2 + I_3 = -2.0\text{ A} + 4.0\text{ A} = 2.0\text{ A}.$$

Next we check that the rate at which energy is delivered by the batteries is equal to the rate at which energy is dissipated in the resistors. That rate for the batteries is 4.0 W + 8.0 W + 16 W = 28 W, and for the resistors it is

$$P_1 = (I_1^2)(R_1) = (2.0\text{ A})^2(1.0\ \Omega) = 4.0\text{ W}$$

$$P_2 = (I_2^2)(R_2) = (2.0\text{ A})^2(2.0\ \Omega) = 8.0\text{ W}$$

$$P_3 = (I_3^2)(R_3) = (4.0\text{ A})^2(1.0\ \Omega) = 16\text{ W}$$

$$4.0\text{ W} + 8.0\text{ W} + 16\text{ W} = 28\text{ W}.$$

PRACTICE

Guided Problem 31.8 Resistor network power

Consider the circuit shown in Figure WG31.12 that consists of resistors 1, 2, 3, and 4 with values $R_1 = 2.0\ \Omega$, $R_2 = 4.0\ \Omega$, $R_3 = 4.0\ \Omega$, and $R_4 = 2.0\ \Omega$, and two batteries with emfs $\mathscr{E}_1 = 50$ V and $\mathscr{E}_2 = 20$ V. Calculate the rate at which energy is delivered to each resistor.

Figure WG31.12

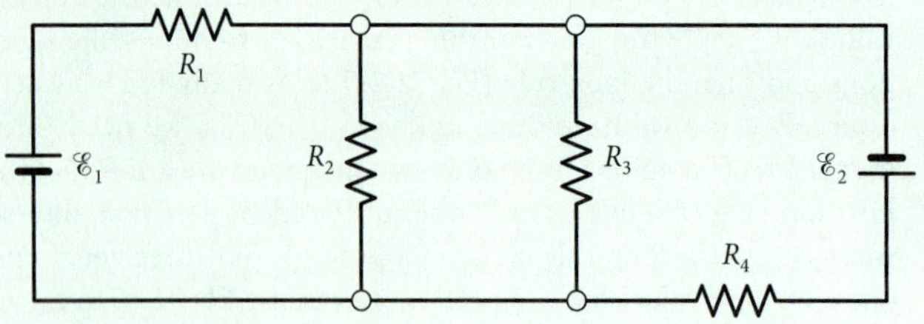

❶ **GETTING STARTED**

1. How can you simplify the circuit?
2. Redraw the circuit diagram, applying the steps in the "Analyzing multiloop circuits" Procedure box.

❷ **DEVISE PLAN**

3. How many unknown currents must you determine?
4. Use the junction and loop rules to obtain the equations you need.
5. How do you calculate the power for each resistor?

❸ **EXECUTE PLAN**

6. Apply the junction rule.
7. Apply the loop rule.
8. Solve your set of equations for the current in each branch.
9. What is the current through resistors 2 and 3 in the original circuit of Figure WG31.12?
10. Calculate the rate at which energy is delivered to each resistor.

❹ **EVALUATE RESULT**

11. Check that your current values satisfy the junction rule.
12. Check that the rate at which energy is delivered by the batteries is equal to the rate at which it is dissipated in the resistors.

Questions and Problems

Dots indicate difficulty level of problems: • = *easy,* •• = *intermediate,* ••• = *hard;* CR = *context-rich problem.*

Unless instructed otherwise, assume all batteries and all wires in circuits are ideal and thus have zero (internal) resistance.

31.1 The basic circuit

1. A battery that initially contains 3.0×10^{24} electrons is used to power a light bulb for some time interval, pumping 1.1×10^{24} electrons through the bulb during that interval. How many electrons remain in the battery? •
2. How can the energy conversions in an electric circuit be represented in terms of two generalized circuit elements? •
3. A battery and four identical light bulbs are arranged in the circuit of Figure P31.3. Rank the current magnitudes at the nine lettered locations from greatest to smallest. •

Figure P31.3

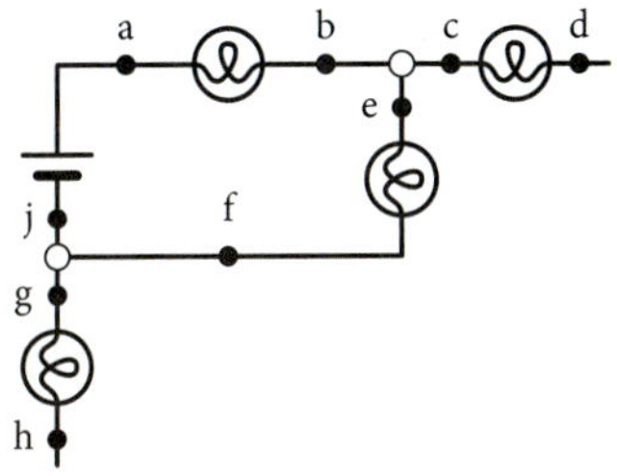

4. Which of the seven identical light bulbs in the circuit of Figure P31.4 light up? •

Figure P31.4

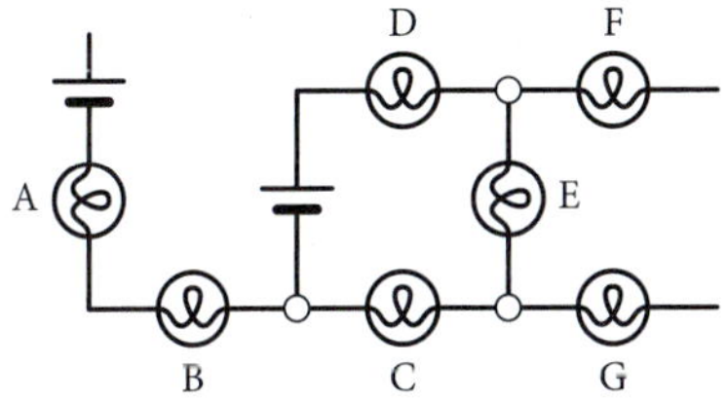

5. You have a light bulb, a battery, and one wire (which you cannot cut into two pieces). Draw the four ways of connecting these elements so that the bulb lights up. ••
6. Name any devices other than the three mentioned in Section 31.1—battery, solar cell, and electric generator—that can act as a power source in an electric circuit. ••
7. Draw a circuit diagram for a typical home hair dryer. To which form (or forms) of energy is electric potential energy converted when you use the dryer? ••
8. Figure P31.8 shows five identical light bulbs A–E connected to a battery. Initially, some of the bulbs light up because the two terminals of each bulb are connected to opposite terminals of the battery. If any wire in the circuit is cut, some bulbs may go out. Which bulbs, if any, go out when a single cut is made at (*a*) location a, (*b*) location b, (*c*) location c, and (*d*) location d? •••

Figure P31.8

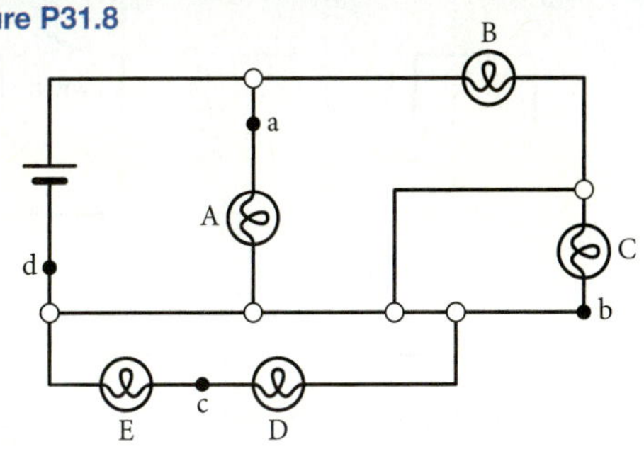

9. You and a colleague want to light a light bulb using a parallel-plate capacitor as a power source. Your colleague objects to this design, stating that the bulb cannot light up if the circuit is not continuous and the circuit is not continuous because the air gap between the capacitor plates constitutes a break in the circuit. He argues that charge carriers do not jump across the gap, so how can there be any current? What is your counterargument? •••

31.2 Current and resistance

10. Which of the light bulbs (if any) in Figure P31.10 are connected in series to each other? •

Figure P31.10

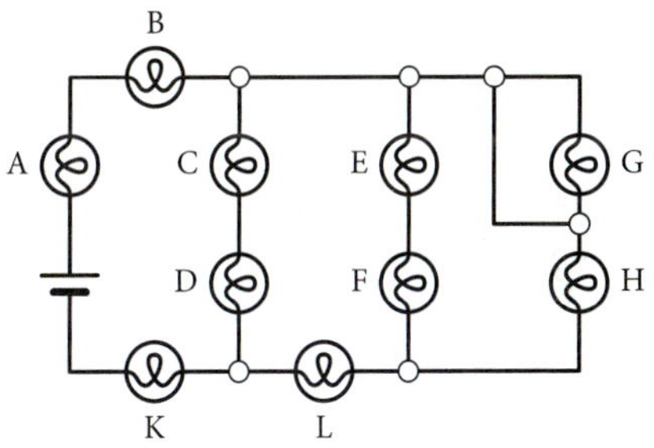

11. (*a*) In the circuit of Figure P31.11, do all four bulbs light up? (*b*) Rank the bulbs according to how brightly they light up, brightest first. •

Figure P31.11

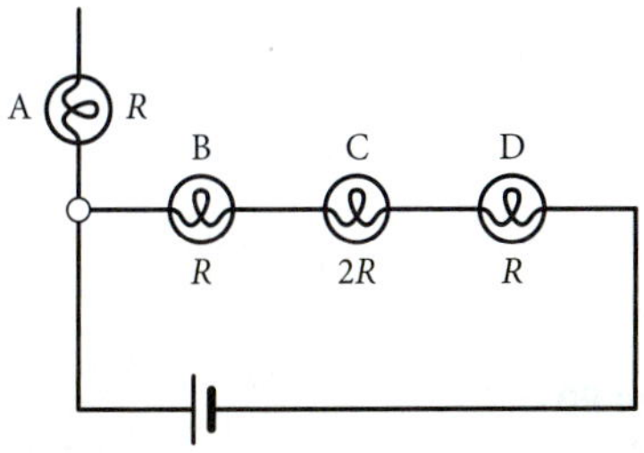

12. All the power sources (batteries or capacitors) in Figure P31.12 on the next page start with a potential difference of 9.0 V between their terminals, and all of them run down (decrease in potential difference) over time. Rank the brightness of these identical light bulbs from least bright to most bright. The *t* values in parts *d* through *g* refer to the time interval that has passed since the power source was connected to the load. ••

Figure P31.12

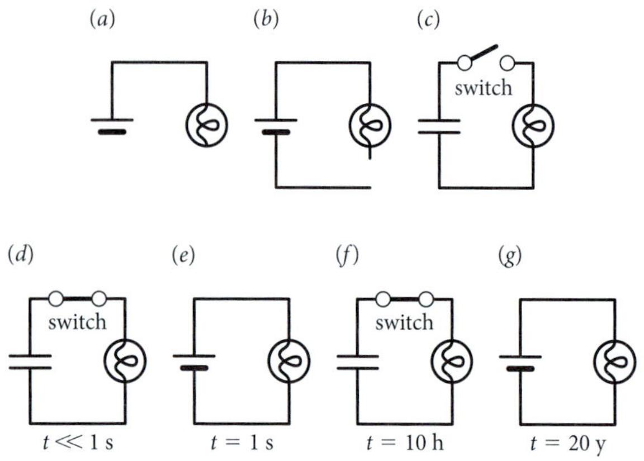

13. In Figure P31.13, bulb A is brighter than bulb B, B is brighter than C, and C is brighter than D. Is it possible for the potential difference across bulb C to be (*a*) 3 V and (*b*) 2 V? ••

Figure P31.13

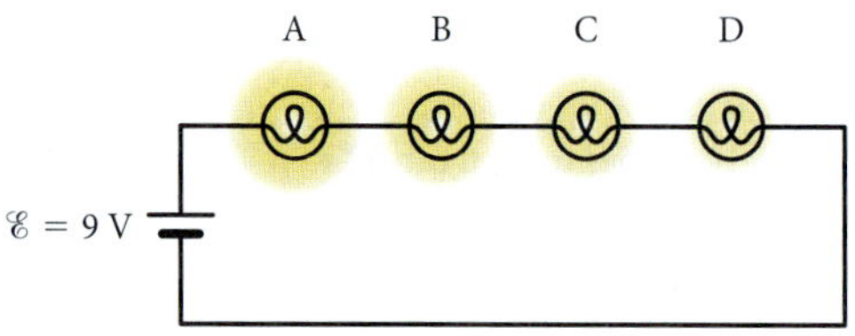

14. When light bulbs A and B are connected in series to a battery, A glows brightly and B glows dimly. You remove bulb B so that the circuit is just the battery and bulb A and connect bulb B to an identical battery. With the two bulbs connected to identical batteries but in separate circuits, do they glow equally brightly now? ••

15. Bulb B produces twice as much light and thermal energy as bulb A, and bulb C produces three times as much light and thermal energy as bulb A. The bulbs are connected in series to a 9.0-V battery, and the steady current through bulb A is 1.0 A. In 1.0 s, how much energy is dissipated as light and thermal energy by each bulb? •••

31.3 Junctions and multiple loops

16. Wires A, B, and C meet at a junction. The current in wire A is 3.2 mA into the junction, and the current in wire B is 4.3 mA out of the junction. What is the current in wire C, and in what direction, into or out of the junction, is this current? •

17. Which (if any) of the light bulbs in Figure P31.17 are connected to other bulbs in parallel? •

Figure P31.17

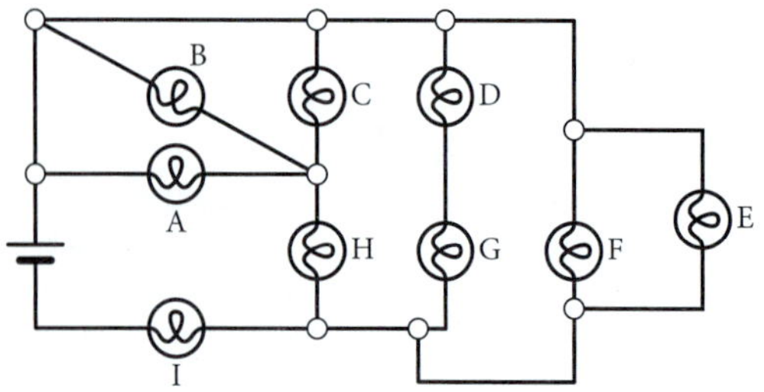

18. Which of the light bulbs in Figure P31.18 are connected to each other in series? Which are connected to each other in parallel? •

Figure P31.18

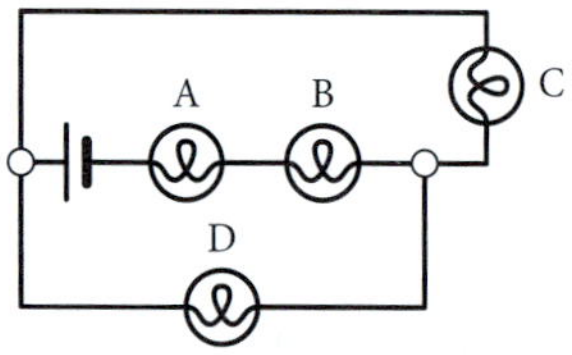

19. Draw a circuit diagram for the circuit of Figure P31.19 ••.

Figure P31.19

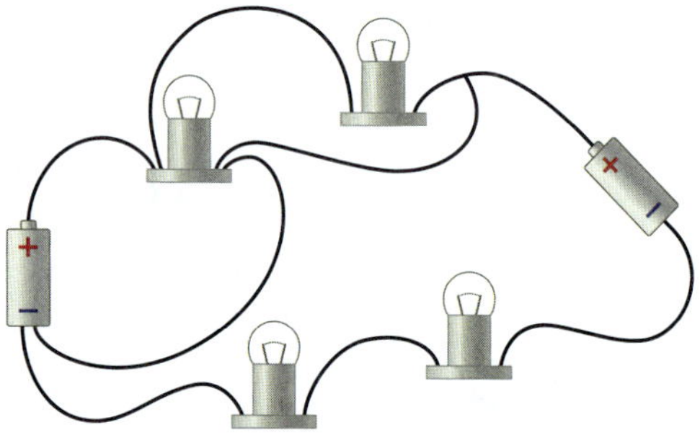

20. In the circuit of Figure P31.20, bulb A is bright and bulb B is dim. Which bulb (*a*) has the greater potential difference across it, (*b*) carries the greater current, and (*c*) has the greater resistance? ••

Figure P31.20

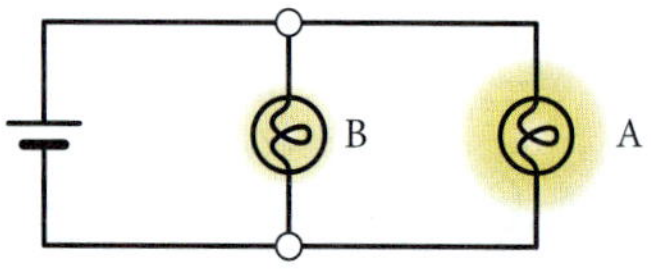

21. (*a*) Draw a circuit diagram for the circuit shown in Figure P31.21, which consists of a battery and four identical light bulbs. (*b*) Do all the bulbs light up? (*c*) Which bulb is brightest? Dimmest? (*d*) Which bulbs are connected to each other in parallel? Which are connected in series? ••

Figure P31.21

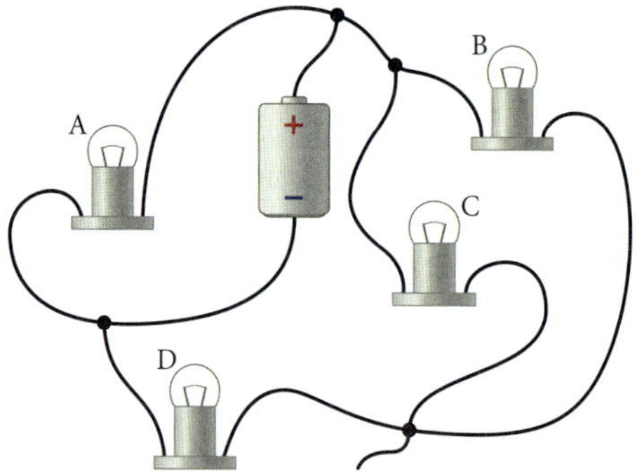

PRACTICE

22. Decades ago, holiday lights were wired in series, so that if one bulb in a string burned out, all the lights in the string went dark because the burned-out bulb interrupted the circuit. Today's lights are wired at least partially in parallel, so that if one light goes out, many others in the string remain lit. In which circuits in Figure P31.22 does one bulb burning out leave all other bulbs lit? In which does one bulb burning out cause one or more of the other bulbs to go out? ••

Figure P31.22

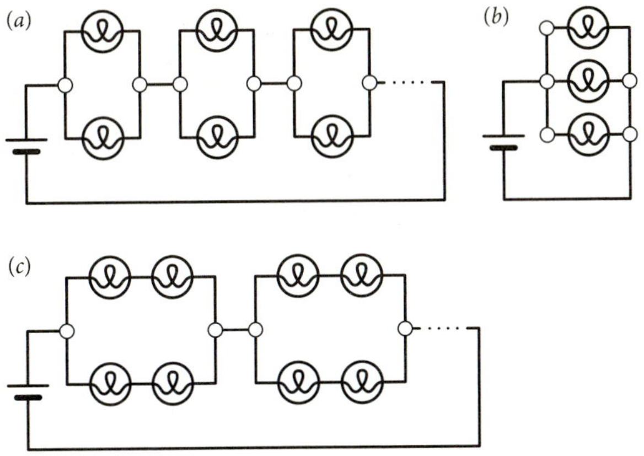

23. Are the lights in a house wired in series, in parallel, or a combination of the two? •••

31.4 Electric fields in conductors

24. In Figure P31.24, the wire connecting the positive battery terminal to the top end of the resistor is 100 mm long, and the wire connecting the negative battery terminal to the bottom end of the resistor is also 100 mm long. If the resistor is 10 mm long, what are the electric field magnitudes at locations a, b, and c? •

Figure P31.24

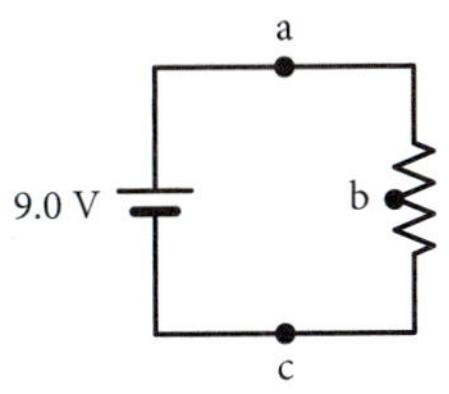

25. Once the switch in the circuit in Figure P31.25 is closed, the circuit can be used to charge the capacitor. Sketch the electric field inside wire A (*a*) when the switch is open, (*b*) at the instant just after the switch is closed, and (*c*) at some instant long after the switch is closed. •

Figure P31.25

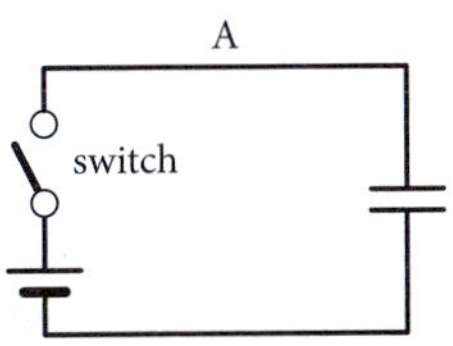

26. A cylindrical wire initially has resistance R and length ℓ. The wire is clamped in place at its midpoint, and the portion to the left of the clamp remains unchanged. The portion to the right of the clamp is stretched out to a length ℓ. Express the new resistance R' of the wire in terms of R. Assume the stretching is done uniformly and the wire remains cylindrical. ••

27. You want to use a length of insulated rigid metal rod to discharge the plates of a parallel-plate capacitor without allowing the electric field in the rod to exceed 1000 N/C. The area A of each plate is 1.00 m^2, the plate separation distance is $d = 100$ mm, and there is no dielectric material between the plates. Initially, each plate holds a charge of magnitude 4.51×10^{-8} C. If one end of the rod is attached to the center of one edge of plate 1, describe all the positions on plate 2 to which the other end of the rod could be attached. Illustrate your answer with a sketch. •••

31.5 Resistance and Ohm's law

28. A copper wire that is 600 mm long and has a radius of 1.0 mm is connected to the terminals of a 9.0-V battery. What is the current through the wire [$\sigma_{copper} = 5.9 \times 10^7$ A/(V · m)]? •

29. The nickel-chromium alloy nichrome is often used for heating elements. A typical household toaster heating element has a resistance of 12 Ω. If you make this element using nichrome wire 0.40 mm in diameter, how long must the wire be? How long must it be if you use copper wire of the same diameter [$\sigma_{nichrome} = 6.7 \times 10^5$ A/(V · m), $\sigma_{copper} = 5.9 \times 10^7$ A/(V · m)]?•

30. A 6-gauge copper wire (4.115-mm diameter) carries a current of 1.20 A. What is the wire's current density?

31. How strong must an electric field in a metal be in order for electrons in the field to have a drift speed of 10 mm/s if the time interval between electron-ion collisions is 1.0×10^{-14} s? •

32. Figure P31.32 is a graph of the current through a light-emitting diode as a function of the potential difference across the diode. What is the resistance of the diode at a potential difference of 3.0 V? ••

Figure P31.32

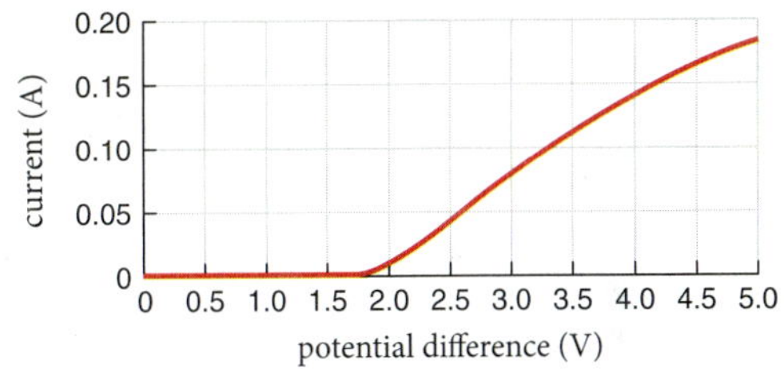

33. *Gauge* is a term used to describe the size of a wire: The greater the gauge, the smaller the wire diameter. At room temperature, 4-gauge wire has a diameter of 5.19 mm, and 22-gauge wire has a diameter of 0.64 mm. For copper, how long would a wire of each gauge need to be to have a resistance of 1.0 Ω [$\sigma_{copper} = 5.9 \times 10^7$ A/(V · m)]? ••

34. Two wires are made of the same material. If both are at the same temperature, but one has twice the diameter and three times the length of the other, which has the greater resistance, and by what factor? ••

35. When a potential difference of 1.00 V is maintained across a cube made of a metal for which the charge carrier number density is $n = 6.60 \times 10^{28}$ charge carriers/m^3, the cube carries current $I = 6.10 \times 10^5$ A. What is the average time interval τ between collisions in this metal if each side of the cube is 10.0 mm long? ••

36. What is the magnitude of the applied electric field inside an aluminum wire of radius 1.0 mm that carries a 4.0-A current [$\sigma_{aluminum} = 3.6 \times 10^7$ A/(V · m)]? ••

37. For each of these changes in a metal, predict whether the average time interval between collisions of an electron with a lattice ion increases or decreases: (*a*) spatial density of the lattice ions is increased, (*b*) size of the lattice ions is decreased, (*c*) charge of the lattice ions is increased. ••

38. In a copper wire that has a diameter of 1.63 mm, the drift velocity is 7.08×10^{-4} m/s. If we assume one free electron per copper atom, what are (*a*) the current in the wire and (*b*) the current density? (*c*) This wire connects a light bulb, power source, and switch in a circuit, and the distance between the switch and bulb is 3.00 m. How long does it take for an electron initially at the switch to reach the bulb? ••

39. In a particle accelerator, the particles in a beam of protons are traveling toward a target at a speed equal to $0.100c_0$. If the beam has a radius of 0.100 μm and carries a current of 2.00 nA, how many protons strike the target in 1.00 s? Assume the target is large enough to intercept the entire beam. •

40. When you step on the brake pedal in your car, charge carriers flow from the battery to the rear brake lights. Suppose the wire connecting the switch at the pedal to the brake lights is made of copper and has a diameter of 1.1 mm. If the current through the wire is 2.0 A, how long on average does it take an electron to travel from the switch at the pedal to one of the brake lights? The number density of free electrons in copper is $n = 8.4 \times 10^{28}$ electrons/m^3. ••

41. Even though silver is a better electrical conductor than copper, most electrical cables are made from copper. The main reason is cost: The per-kilogram price of silver is about 100 times the per-kilogram price of copper. If you want a length ℓ of wire to have a resistance R, by what factor does the cost of silver exceed that of copper? (The mass density of silver is ρ_S = 10,490 kg/m^3, and that of copper is ρ_C = 8960 kg/m^3.) ••

42. You have a piece of copper wire and a piece of carbon rod, each 1.5 m long and each having a cross-sectional area of 8.0×10^{-6} m^2. When you connect the copper wire to the terminals of a 9.0-V battery, the current in the wire is I. If you want to connect the carbon rod to another battery and have the same current I in the wire, what must the potential difference of the battery be [$\sigma_{copper} = 5.9 \times 10^7$ A/(V · m), $\sigma_{carbon} = 7.3 \times 10^4$ A/(V · m)]? ••

43. An electric field of magnitude 4.50×10^2 V/m is created in a wire that is 300 mm long and has a radius of 1.00 mm. The number density of the charge carriers in the wire is 1.20×10^{27} charge carriers/m^3. How much energy is gained by the lattice of metal ions in the time interval it takes for the average electron to travel the length of the wire? •••

31.6 Single-loop circuits

44. What are the magnitude and direction of the current in each circuit in Figure P31.44? •

Figure P31.44

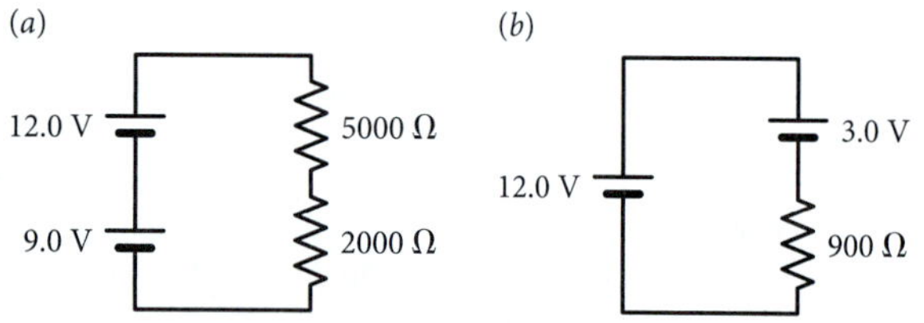

45. What are the magnitude and direction of the current in the circuit in Figure P31.45? •

Figure P31.45

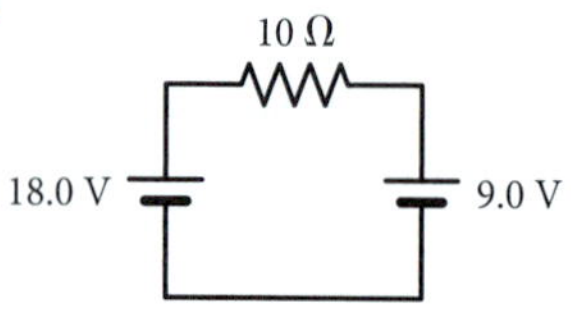

46. Three resistors are connected in series to a battery. If the resistances are $R_1 = 15\ \Omega$, $R_2 = 20\ \Omega$, and $R_3 = 25\ \Omega$ and the current through the 15-Ω resistor is 2.3 A, what is the potential difference across the battery terminals (*a*) if the battery is ideal and (*b*) if the battery has an internal resistance of 5.0 Ω? •

47. What are the magnitude and direction of the current in each circuit in Figure P31.47? ••

Figure P31.47

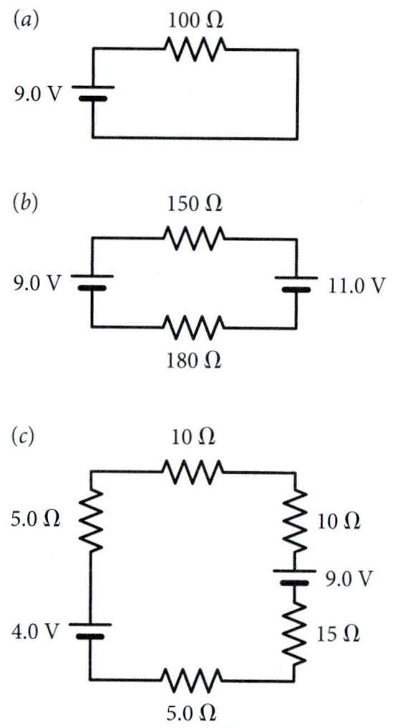

48. When using the loop rule, what problems do you encounter with the circuit in Figure P31.48*a*? What do you expect for the current in the more realistic circuit in Figure P31.48*b*, which includes a small nonzero resistance in the wire and internal resistance in the battery? ••

Figure P31.48

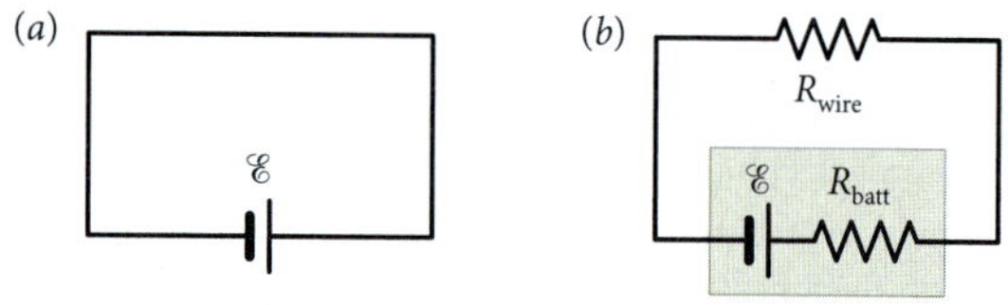

49. When a nonideal battery is connected to a 2.0-Ω resistor in a circuit, the current in the circuit is 2.0 A. When the same battery is connected to a 1.0-Ω resistor in a circuit, the current in the circuit is 3.0 A. What are (*a*) the internal resistance of the battery and (*b*) its emf? ••

50. Two resistors connected in series have an equivalent resistance of 8.0 Ω. The same resistors connected in parallel have an equivalent resistance of 1.5 Ω. What is the resistance of each resistor? ••

51. The potential difference between positions a and b in Figure P31.51 is 5.5 V, and $R_1 = 5.0\ \Omega$, $\mathscr{E}_1 = 8.0$ V, and $\mathscr{E}_2 = 4.0$ V. What is the value of the resistance R_2? ••

Figure P31.51

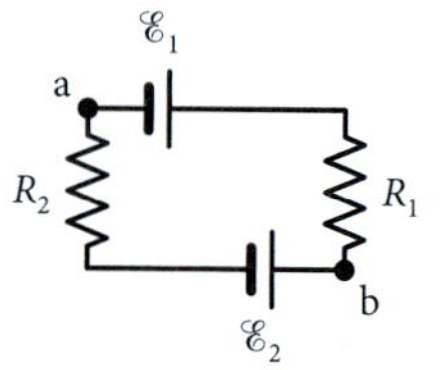

52. A typical car battery can be modeled as an ideal source $\mathscr{E}$ connected in series with an internal resistance R_{batt}. Using a good battery of this design to "jump start" a dead one can be dangerous if done incorrectly. (*a*) If you want to connect a good battery to a dead one in such a way that you have the smallest possible current through the dead one, should you connect them in series (+ to − and − to +) or in parallel (+ to + and − to −)? Assume you have a good battery for which $\mathscr{E}_{\text{good}} = 12.0$ V and $R_{\text{batt, good}} = 0.0200\ \Omega$ and a dead one for which $\mathscr{E}_{\text{dead}} = 11.0$ V and $R_{\text{batt, dead}} = 0.200\ \Omega$. Calculate the current through the batteries connected (*b*) in series and (*c*) in parallel. ••

53. For the circuit shown in Figure P31.53, calculate (*a*) the magnitude and direction of the current and (*b*) the potential differences V_{ab}, V_{bc}, V_{cd}, and V_{da}. Use these values: $R_1 = 5.0\ \Omega$, $R_2 = 3.0\ \Omega$, $R_3 = 6.0\ \Omega$, $\mathscr{E}_1 = 10$ V, and $\mathscr{E}_2 = 2.0$ V. ••

Figure P31.53

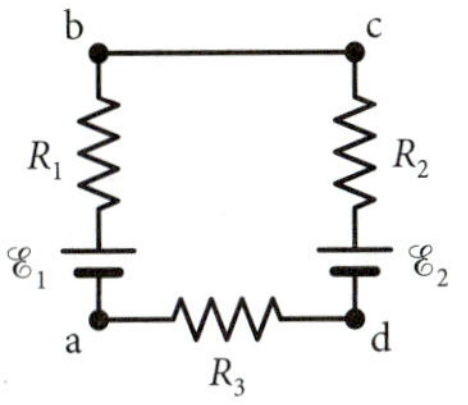

54. The internal resistance of a battery is relatively small when the battery is new but increases as the battery ages. When a new 12.0-V battery is attached to a 100-Ω load, the potential difference across the load is 11.9 V. After the circuit has operated for a while, the potential difference across the load is 11.5 V. By how much has the internal resistance of the battery changed? ••

55. (*a*) What is the equivalent resistance of the circuit in Figure P31.55? Use the values $R_1 = 200\ \Omega$, $R_2 = 900\ \Omega$, and $R_3 = 100\ \Omega$. (*b*) What is the current in the circuit? Assume $\mathscr{E} = 12$ V. (*c*) The electric potential at location d is defined to be 0, because the negative terminal of the battery is attached to ground. What is the electric potential at locations a, b, and c? ••

Figure P31.55

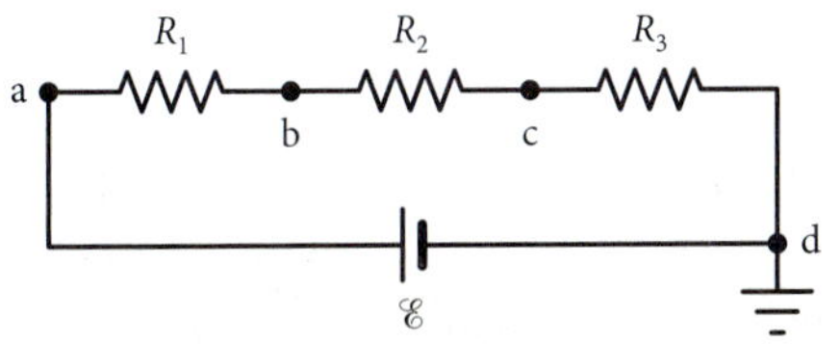

56. Resistors 1 and 2—$R_1 = 40\ \Omega$, $R_2 = 70\ \Omega$—are connected in series to a 4.5-V battery. (*a*) What is the potential difference across resistor 1? (*b*) If you decrease the value of R_1, what happens to the current in the circuit and to the potential difference across resistor 1? ••

57. A light bulb has resistance $R_{\text{bulb}} = 5.0\ \Omega$ and should be operated at a potential difference of $V_{\text{bulb}} = 3.0$ V. If you must use this bulb in a circuit powered by a battery of emf $\mathscr{E} = 9.0$ V, how much resistance must you add in series to the circuit in order to have a 3.0-V potential difference across the bulb? ••

58. You must complete the circuit of Figure P31.58 in such a way that it draws a current of 0.300 A from the battery. The battery maintains a potential difference of 10.0 V with no load, but has an internal resistance of $R_{\text{batt}} = 18.0\ \Omega$. The only material you have is 20.0 mm^3 of nichrome, and you must use all of it. If your plan is to form the nichrome into a cylindrical resistor, what must the cylinder length and cross-sectional area be? [The conductivity of nichrome is 6.7×10^5 A/(V · m).] •••

Figure P31.58

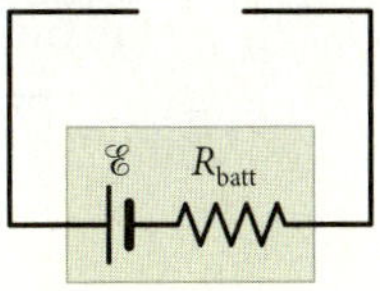

31.7 Multiloop circuits

59. What is the equivalent resistance of the circuit in Figure P31.59? Use the values $R_1 = 2.0\ \Omega$, $R_2 = 1.5\ \Omega$, $R_3 = 2.0\ \Omega$, $R_4 = 1.5\ \Omega$, $R_5 = 2.0\ \Omega$, and $R_6 = 1.5\ \Omega$. •

Figure P31.59

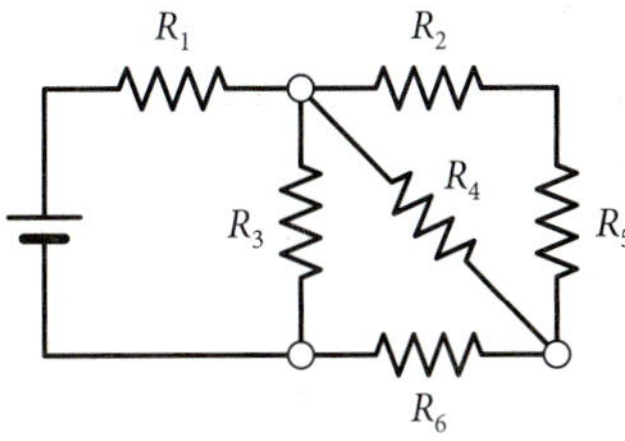

60. Figure P31.60 shows three circuits containing four identical resistors, each having resistance *R*. Which circuit has the smallest equivalent resistance? Which has the greatest equivalent resistance? •

Figure P31.60

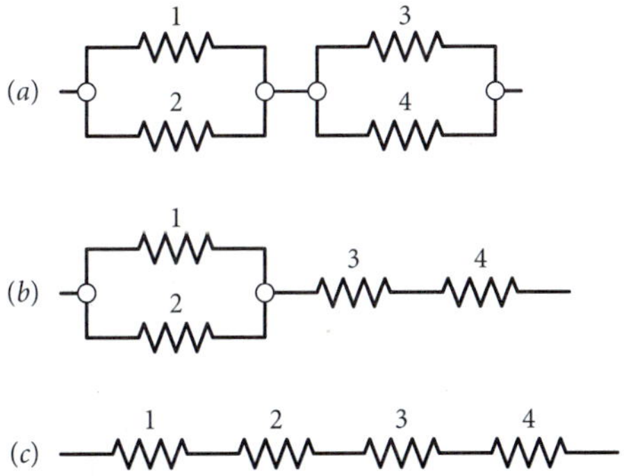

61. A nonideal ammeter that has an internal resistance of 0.503 Ω is connected in series with a 3.00-V battery and a 40.0-Ω resistor. By what percentage does the presence of the ammeter change the current measurement? •

62. In Figure P31.62 on the next page, the brightness of each bulb depends on the magnitude of the current through it. Rank these identical bulbs according to brightness, brightest first, (*a*) before the wire ab connecting the two junctions is cut and (*b*) after the wire is cut. (*c*) Does cutting the wire increase or decrease the brightness of A? Of B? Of C? ••

Figure P31.62

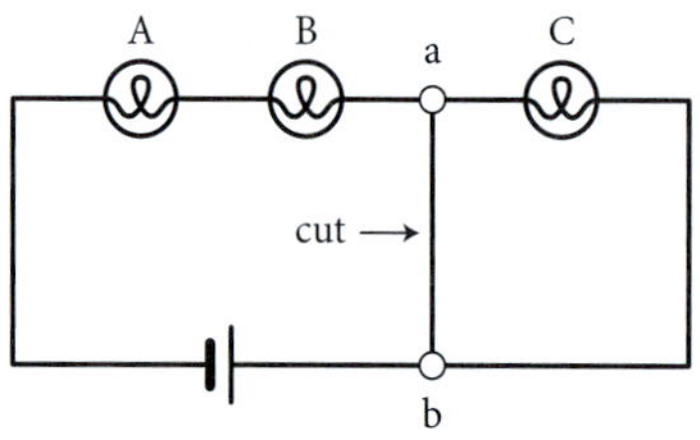

63. Using only 10.0-Ω resistors (but as many as you like), build a circuit that has a resistance of 27.5 Ω. ••

64. A copper wire has a diameter of 0.20 mm and is $\ell_{wire} = 10$ m long. (*a*) What is the resistance of the wire? (*b*) The wire is cut into *N* identical pieces, and the pieces are connected in parallel to form a single resistor. What is the minimum value of *N* that gives this resistor a resistance smaller than $R_{resistor} = 1.0\ \Omega$? [The conductivity of copper is 5.9×10^7 A/(V · m).] ••

65. For the circuit in Figure P31.65, assume the electric potential is zero at the negative terminal of the battery. Calculate (*a*) the equivalent resistance of the circuit, (*b*) the electric potential at position a, and (*c*) the magnitude and direction of the current through each resistor. ••

Figure P31.65

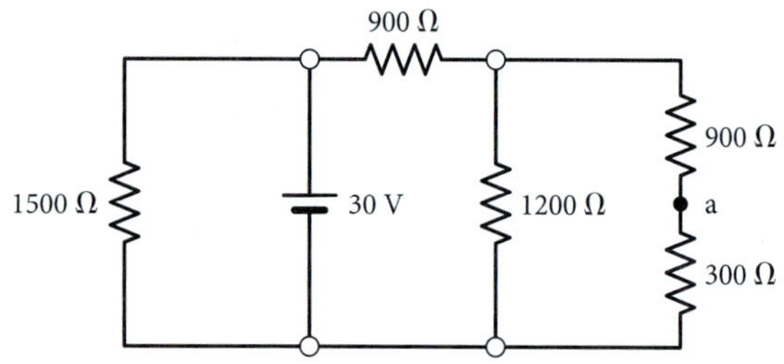

66. In Figure P31.66, determine the magnitude of current I_1. ••

Figure P31.66

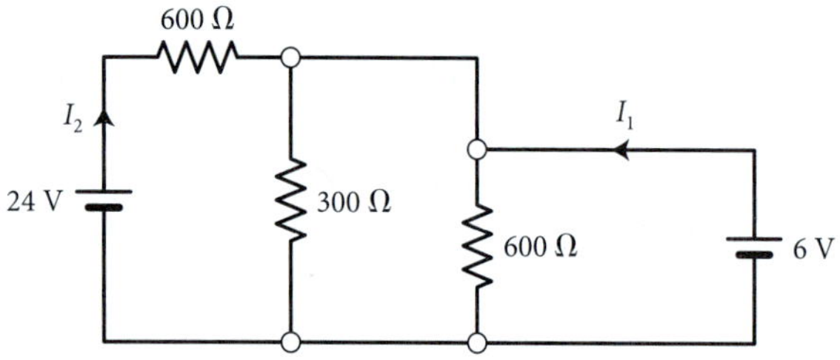

67. In Figure P31.67, calculate the magnitudes of currents I_1, I_2, and I_3. ••

Figure P31.67

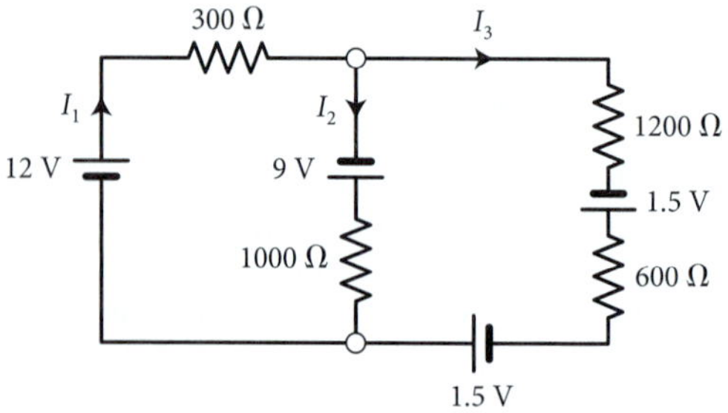

68. In Figure P31.68, the circuit has been completed for several minutes. Calculate (*a*) the current through each resistor and (*b*) the magnitude of charge on each capacitor plate. ••

Figure P31.68

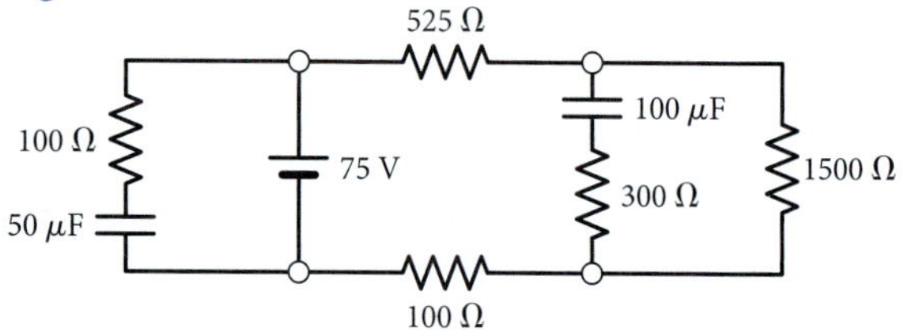

69. In Figure P31.69, calculate (*a*) the equivalent resistance of the circuit and (*b*) the magnitude of the current through each resistor. Use these values: $R_1 = 1.0\ \Omega$, $R_2 = 2.0\ \Omega$, $R_3 = 2.0\ \Omega$, $R_4 = 3.0\ \Omega$, $R_5 = 1.0\ \Omega$, $R_6 = 1.0\ \Omega$, and $\mathscr{E} = 14$ V. ••

Figure P31.69

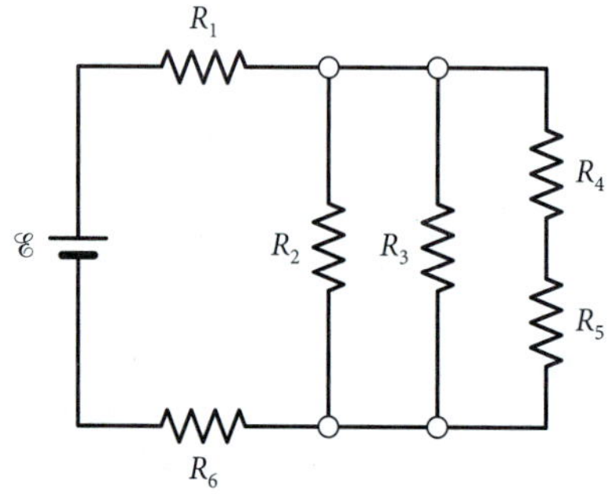

70. In Figure P31.70, determine the magnitudes of the currents I_1, I_2, and I_3 and whether the direction shown for each current is correct or should be reversed. Assume that $R_1 = 8.0\ \Omega$, $R_2 = 8.0\ \Omega$, $\mathscr{E}_1 = 6.0$ V, $\mathscr{E}_2 = 6.0$ V, and $\mathscr{E}_3 = 9.0$ V. ••

Figure P31.70

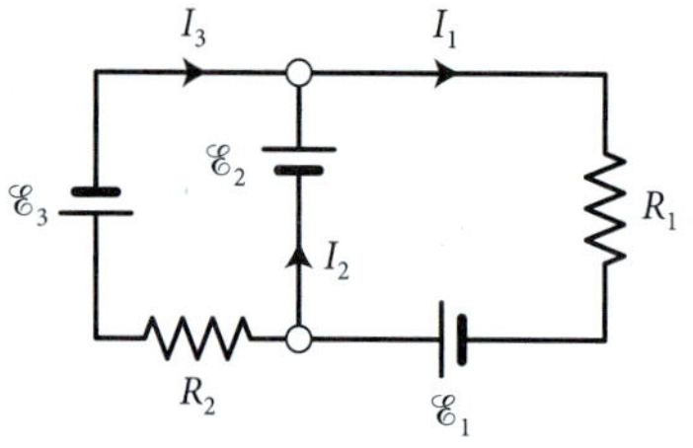

71. The eight resistors in Figure P31.71 are identical to one another, all having resistance $R = 200\ \Omega$. What is the magnitude of the current drawn from the battery? ••

Figure P31.71

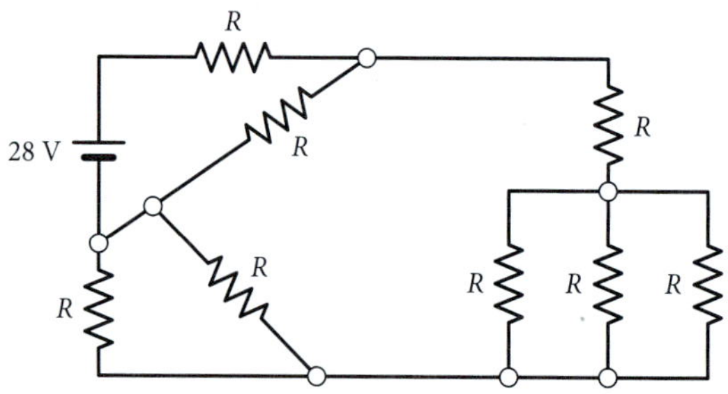

72. In Figure P31.72, $\mathscr{E}_1 = 5.0$ V, $\mathscr{E}_2 = 5.0$ V, $\mathscr{E}_3 = 1.5$ V, $R_1 = 50\ \Omega$, $R_2 = 50\ \Omega$, and $R_3 = 50\ \Omega$. What are (*a*) the current in each branch of the circuit and (*b*) the potential differences V_{ab}, V_{bc}, V_{cd}, V_{de}, V_{ef}, and V_{fa}? ••

Figure P31.72

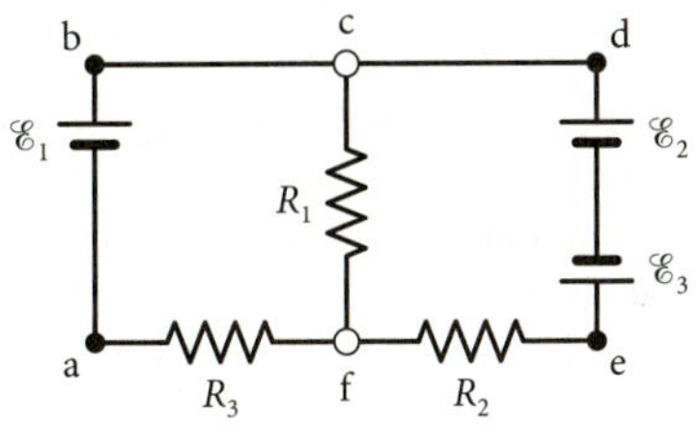

73. A string of winter holiday lights consists of *N* bulbs, each having resistance R_b (Figure P31.73). Wired in parallel with each bulb is a resistor of resistance R_p. What is the resistance of the string? If one of the bulbs burns out, what happens to the other *N*-1 bulbs? ••

Figure P31.73

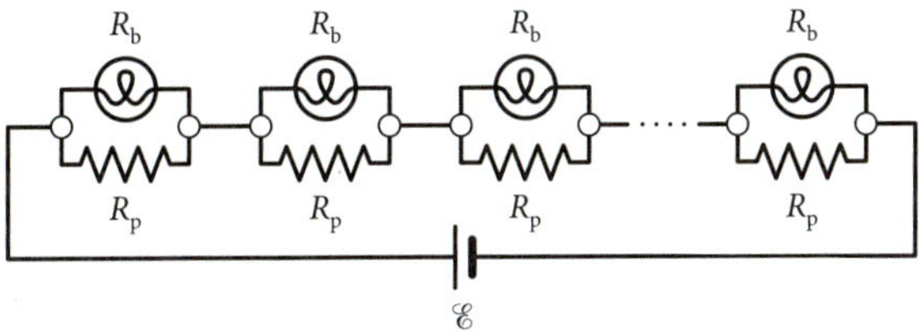

74. An ammeter that has internal resistance $R_{am} = 0.504\ \Omega$ is designed to measure a maximum current of $I_{max} = 100$ mA. You want to use this ammeter to measure the current in a circuit that consists of a 3.00-V battery and a resistor that has a resistance of 4.00 Ω. (*a*) What problem do you encounter? (*b*) How can you overcome this problem by inserting a second resistor into the circuit and rescaling the meter readout (that is, by multiplying the readout value by some constant)? ••

75. If each resistor in Figure P31.75 has resistance $R = 5.0\ \Omega$, what is the equivalent resistance of the combination? ••

Figure P31.75

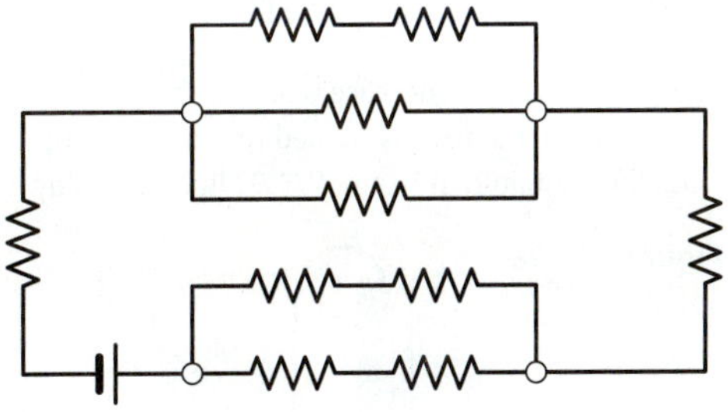

76. In Figure P31.76, $R_1 = 2.0\ \Omega$, $R_2 = 1.5\ \Omega$, $R_3 = 2.0\ \Omega$, $R_4 = 1.0\ \Omega$, $R_5 = 2.0\ \Omega$, $R_6 = 1.0\ \Omega$, $C_1 = 20\ \mu$F, $C_2 = 40\ \mu$F, and $\mathscr{E} = 12.0$ V. Assume that the circuit has been connected for several minutes. (*a*) Calculate the current through the battery and through each resistor. (*b*) Compute the magnitude of charge on each plate of both capacitors. •••

Figure P31.76

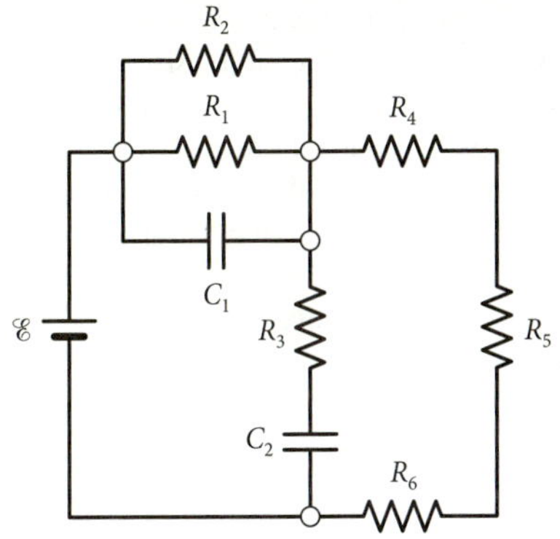

77. In Figure P31.77, each of the three batteries supplies an emf of 6.0 V and each of the four resistors has a resistance of 3.0 Ω. Calculate the magnitudes of the five currents I_1–I_5. •••

Figure P31.77

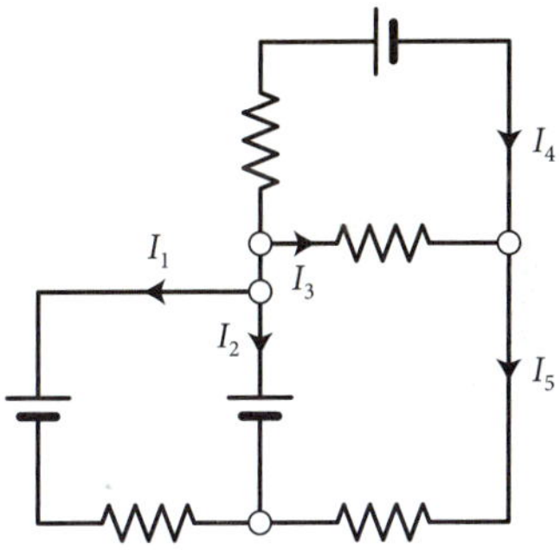

78. If the ammeter in the Wheatstone bridge of Figure P31.78 measures zero current when the resistance R_{var} of the variable resistor is set to 185 Ω, what is the current I_L through the left side of the bridge? •••

Figure P31.78

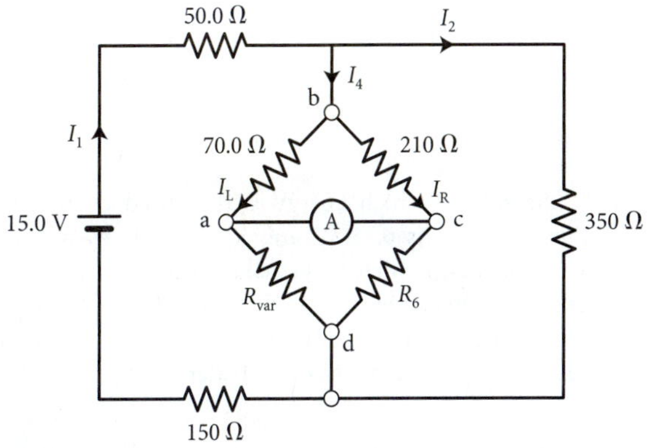

PRACTICE

31.8 Power in electric circuits

79. If a light bulb has a resistance of 5.5 Ω and is dissipating energy at a rate of 9.0 W, what are (*a*) the current through the bulb and (*b*) the potential difference across its terminals? •

80. If the current through a 10-Ω resistor is 2.0 A, how much energy is dissipated by the resistor in 1.0 h? •

81. Two light bulbs 1 and 2 are connected in parallel to an 8.00-V battery. (*a*) If the bulb resistances are $R_1 = 4.0\ \Omega$ and $R_2 = 6.0\ \Omega$, what is the rate at which each bulb consumes energy? (*b*) At what rate does the circuit consume energy? (*c*) Calculate the same three power values for the bulbs connected in series rather than in parallel. •

82. A car battery is labeled "12 V 40 Ah." You forget to switch off the light in your glove compartment, which draws 0.80 A. How long until the battery is drained? •

83. (*a*) Determine the current through and the potential difference across each resistor in Figure P31.83. Assume that $R_1 = R_2 = R_3 = R_4 = 50.0\ \Omega$, $\mathscr{E}_1 = 10.0$ V, and $\mathscr{E}_2 = 5.00$ V. (*b*) At what rate is energy dissipated in each resistor? (*c*) What is the power of each battery, and is energy used by or supplied by each battery? ••

Figure P31.83

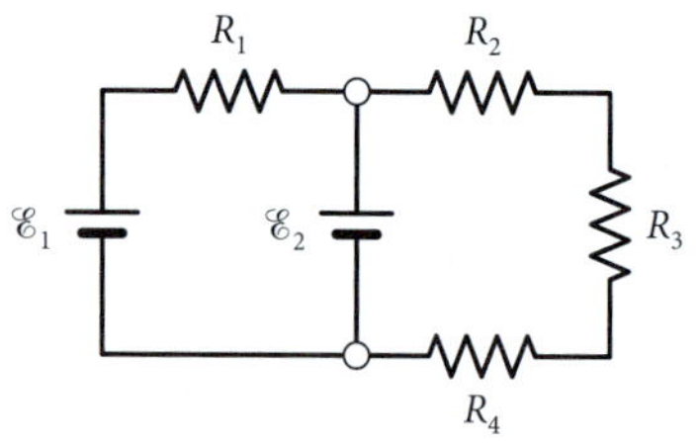

84. A 60-W light bulb has resistance $R = 10.00\ \Omega$ when connected to a battery with emf $\mathscr{E} = 120.0$ V. What is the internal resistance R_{batt} of the battery? ••

85. Determine the current through each resistor and the magnitude of the charge on either capacitor plate after the circuit in Figure P31.85 has been connected for a few minutes. ••

Figure P31.85

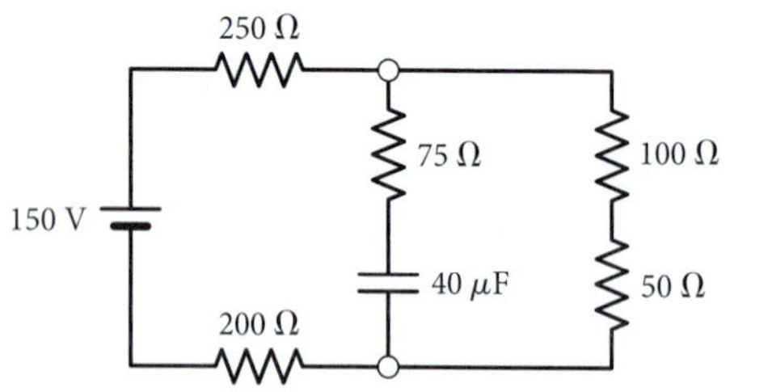

86. If the rate at which energy is dissipated by resistor 1 in Figure P31.86 is 0.75 W, and $R_1 = 12\ \Omega$, $\mathscr{E}_1 = 4.5$ V, and $\mathscr{E}_2 = 8.0$ V, (*a*) what is the value of R_2? (*b*) At what rate is energy dissipated in resistor 2? (*c*) Which battery supplies energy to the circuit, and at what rate does it do so? (*d*) At what rate is energy used by the other battery? ••

Figure P31.86

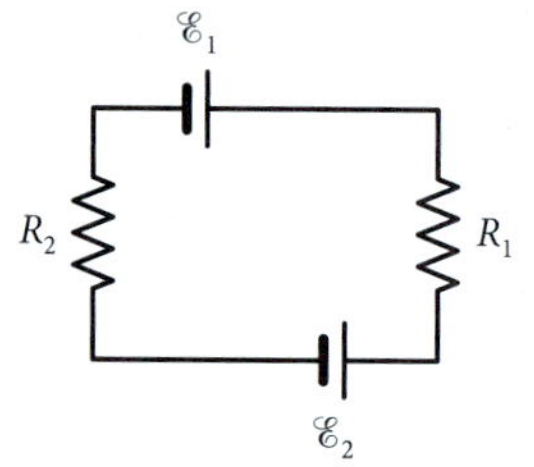

87. A copper wire of length $\ell = 1.0$ km and radius $r = 1.2$ mm carries current $I = 20$ A. At what rate is energy lost from the wire? Why do long electrical transmission lines usually work with "high voltage"? ••

88. In Figure P31.88, in which resistor is energy dissipated (*a*) at the greatest rate and (*b*) at the smallest rate? •••

Figure P31.88

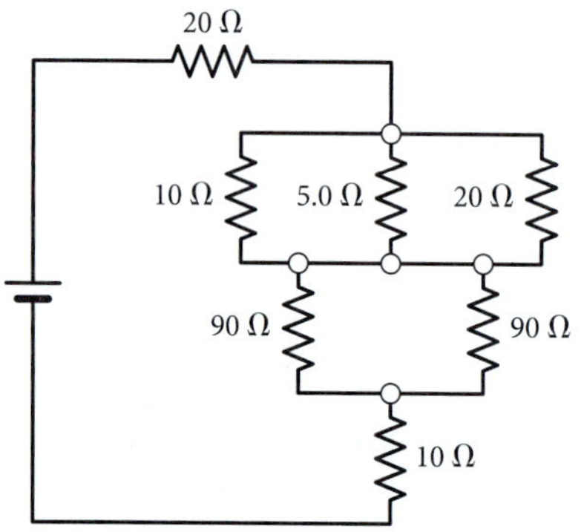

89. At what rate is energy either delivered by or delivered to each battery in Figure P31.67? At what rate is energy dissipated in each resistor? Does the power summed over all the elements make sense? •••

90. A physics student who needs a magnetic field for a project makes a solenoid coil from "magnet wire," which is copper wire coated with a very thin enamel insulation. (The insulation is so thin that you can ignore its thickness.) He chose 28-gauge wire, which is 0.321 mm in diameter, and winds a solenoid that is 50 mm in diameter and 0.20 m long. He then runs a 3.0-A current through the solenoid but is disappointed at how small the magnetic field magnitude is and horrified at how hot the magnet gets after a few minutes. Calculate the magnetic field magnitude and the rate at which energy is lost as thermal energy as the coil heats up. What would you suggest the student do to get a greater magnetic field and less thermal energy loss? •••

Additional problems

91. The filament in an incandescent light bulb is a resistor that has a resistance of 9.5 Ω at room temperature. By what factor does the resistance increase when a 100-W bulb connected to a 120-V power source is turned on and heats up? •

92. Does the light bulb in Figure P31.92 light up? Why or why not? •

Figure P31.92

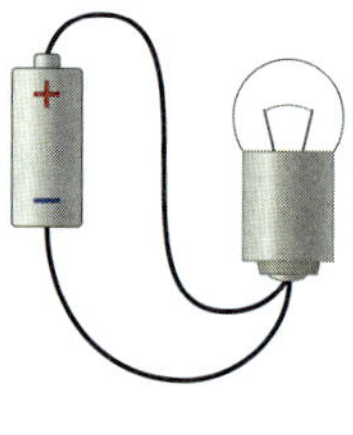

PRACTICE

93. In what type of electrical conductor could the charge on the charge carriers in a current have a magnitude other than e? •

94. The potential difference across a resistor in a circuit is 12 V when a current of 1.0 A passes through the resistor. What is the potential difference across the resistor when the current through it is 3.5 A? •

95. The battery in Figure P31.95 has internal resistance $R_{batt} = 13.0\ \Omega$ and maintains an emf $\mathscr{E} = 20.0$ V. What is the resistance R of the resistor connected in series with the battery if the current through the circuit is 0.100 A? •

Figure P31.95

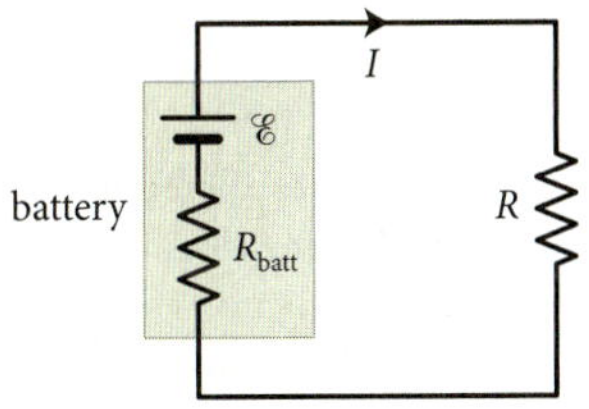

96. Calculate the values of I_1 and I_2 in the circuit shown in Figure P31.96 if all the resistors have resistance 240 Ω and $I_3 = 2.0$ A. ••

Figure P31.96

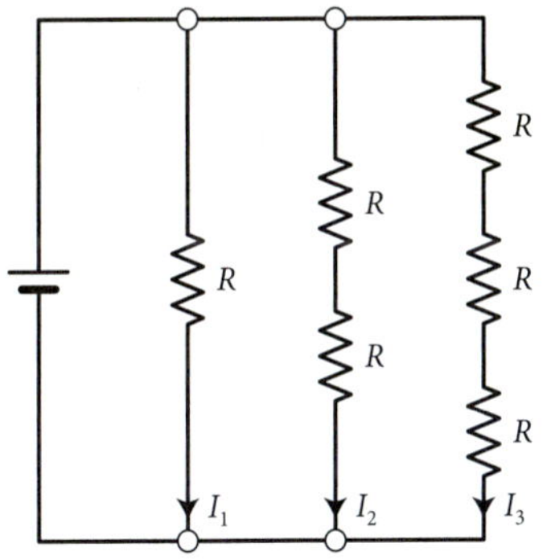

97. If each battery in Figure P31.97 has an emf of 9.0 V, what is the potential difference across the light bulb in each circuit? ••

Figure P31.97

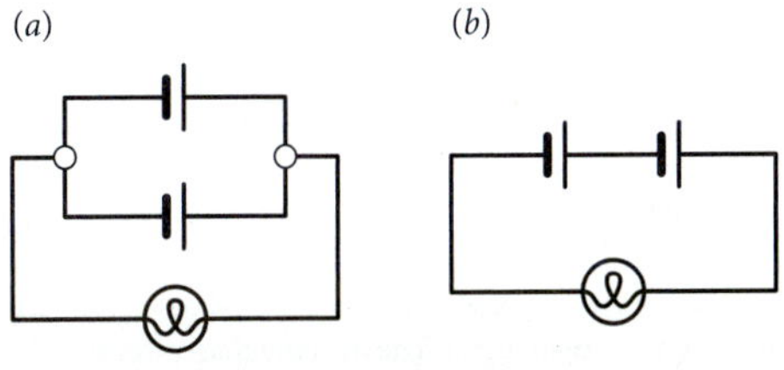

98. The two resistors in Figure P31.98 are made of the same material and are of equal length. The only difference between them is that the radius of the top one is greater than the radius of the bottom one. (*a*) Through which resistor is the current greater? (*b*) Across which resistor is the potential difference greater? (*c*) How does the resistance of the circuit compare with the individual resistances of the two resistors? ••

Figure P31.98

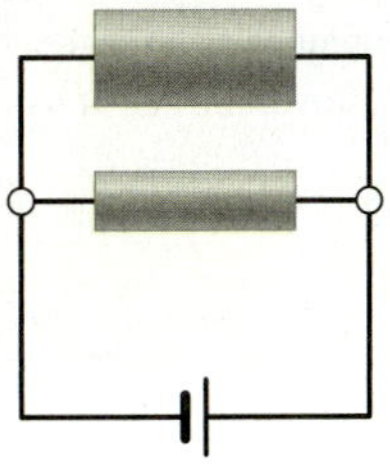

99. If you want to add a third resistor to the circuit in Figure P31.98 to reduce the circuit resistance as much as possible, should you connect it in series or in parallel? Should you add a resistor with a large cross-sectional area, like the top one in Figure P31.98, or one with a small cross-sectional area, like the bottom one? ••

100. In Figure P31.100, $\mathscr{E}_1 = 3.0$ V and $\mathscr{E}_2 = 5.0$ V. (*a*) What value of $\mathscr{E}_3$ causes the potential difference across resistor 1 to be zero? (*b*) In that situation, what is the current through resistor 2? ••

Figure P31.100

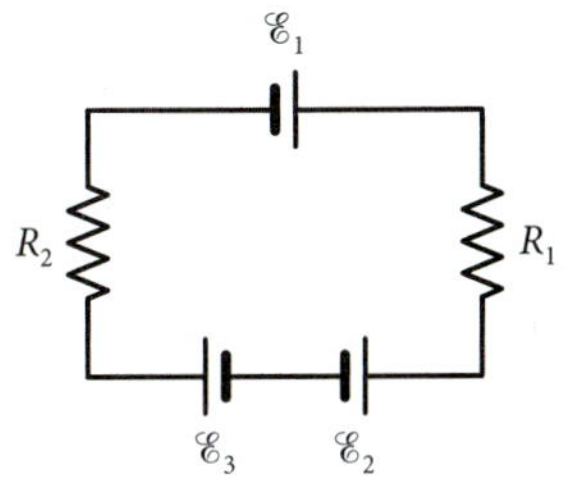

101. Your boss has given you the incomplete circuit shown in Figure P31.101 and charged you with determining the greatest and smallest currents that can be drawn from the battery using this circuit. The catch is that you must close the gap with a resistor from your laboratory. You rummage around and find a huge cabinet full of resistors ranging from very small to very large resistance. •••

Figure P31.101

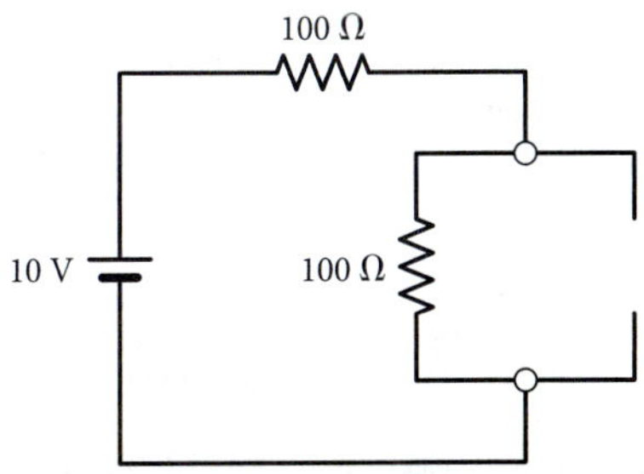

102. You illuminate a photovoltaic cell with a halogen light bulb. The cell is connected to an ammeter, a voltmeter, and a variable resistor (Figure P31.102*a* on the next page), and the current through and potential difference across the resistor are measured for different settings of the resistor. Figure P31.102*b* shows the data from these measurements, where each data point represents the potential difference and current at a particular value of R_{var}. What values of R_{var} do the data points at low and high potential differences correspond to? When is the power of the photovoltaic cell at its maximum value? •••

Figure P31.102

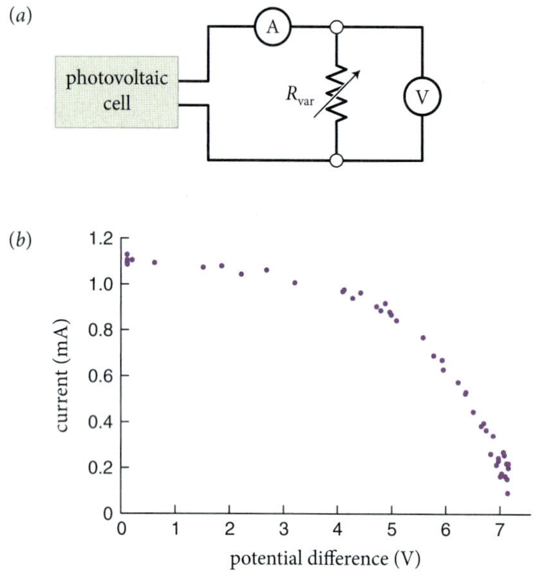

103. The circuit shown in Figure P31.103 has been connected for a few minutes. Determine the current through each resistor and the battery, and determine the magnitude of charge on either plate of each capacitor. Use resistor values $R_1 = R_2 = 5.00\ \Omega$, $R_3 = 4.00\ \Omega$, $R_4 = 6.00\ \Omega$, $R_5 = 10.0\ \Omega$, $R_6 = 0.500\ \Omega$, $R_7 = 1.00\ \Omega$, and $R_8 = 0.500\ \Omega$. •••

Figure P31.103

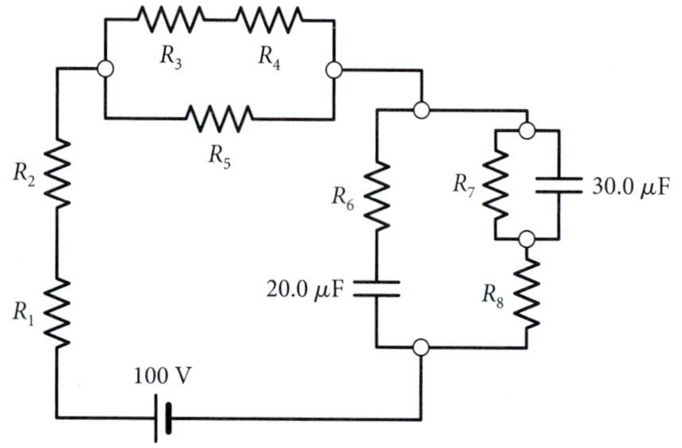

104. Three students rent a third-floor apartment. After signing the lease, they realize there's no electricity on the third floor! They run a 30.5-m, 18-gauge extension cord up from the second floor and plug everything into some power strips plugged into this cord. An electrician visiting the apartment says, "You can't do that; you'll burn the house down! Get a heavy-duty cord made with 12-gauge wire." You don't see how that could make a significant difference, so you begin to look up wire sizes in a reference table. ••• CR

105. You need a liquid electrical conductor for a project you are working on, and as one possibility you try seawater. You know the number density of the charge carriers and the average time interval between collisions. Your preliminary calculations using *Principles* Eq. 31.9 and the mass and charge of an electron give you a theoretical conductivity, σ_{theory}. When testing the seawater, though, you obtain a conductivity less than two thousand times smaller than σ_{theory} ($\sigma_{test} < \sigma_{theory}/2000$). You struggle to understand this discrepancy. ••• CR

Answers to Review Questions

1. In a direct-current circuit, the potential difference supplied by the power source stays constant, and in an alternating-current circuit, the potential difference of the power source changes (*alternates*) over time.
2. A loop is any closed conducting path through the circuit.
3. The load is all the circuit elements connected to the power source.
4. In a nonideal circuit, yes, because some of the potential difference of the power source is converted to other forms of energy in the wires. In this chapter, however, we consider such conversions to be negligible relative to the conversion taking place in the circuit elements, and so we do not consider the wires part of the load.
5. Electric potential energy initially in charge carriers in the power source is converted to some other form of energy in the circuit load.
6. Steady state for an electric circuit means that the current in every part of the circuit is constant over time.
7. For a single-loop electric circuit in a steady state, the current is the same at all locations in the circuit.
8. The principle states that when the circuit is in steady state, charge carriers do not accumulate at any location in the circuit. For example, every charge carrier moving from the power source into the rest of the circuit is accompanied by a charge carrier moving from the rest of the circuit into the power source.
9. The amount of electric potential energy converted is equal to the potential difference between the two locations multiplied by the charge on the carrier.
10. The elements are connected such that there is only a single current path through them, so that charge carriers must flow first through one element, then the next element, and so on.
11. The resistance of the element is the determining property.
12. (*a*) The current is the same everywhere in any given branch of a multiloop circuit (the branch rule). (*b*) The number of charge carriers going into a junction equals the number exiting the junction (junction rule).
13. The electrical quantity that is the same for the bulbs connected in series is the current through them. The quantity that is the same for the bulbs connected in parallel is the potential difference across each one.
14. A short in an electric circuit is a branch of negligible resistance connected in parallel to some other element in the circuit. Essentially all the charge carriers moving through the circuit flow through the short, and essentially none flow through the element connected in parallel.
15. No. Any orientation is allowed in a diagram as long as the connections between elements are accurately portrayed. Because the wires are treated as ideal, neither the length you draw them nor whether you show them bent or straight affects the accuracy of the diagram.

PRACTICE

16. The electric field has the same magnitude everywhere inside the conductor, and the direction of the field is parallel to the walls of the conductor (in the direction of the current).
17. The resistance of an electrical conductor of uniform cross section depends on the material the conductor is made of and the length and cross-sectional area of the conductor. The resistance is directly proportional to the length and inversely proportional to the area.
18. A metal consists of a lattice of positive ions held in fixed positions and vibrating about those positions. The ions are metal atoms that have lost one or more of their outermost electrons, and these electrons are free to move about the lattice at very high speeds, colliding occasionally with the ions.
19. At any instant, the velocity of each electron is equal to its velocity before the last collision plus the impulse per unit of mass due to the electric force exerted on the electron. The average velocity of all the electrons is then the average velocity just after their last collision plus the average impulse per unit of mass. Because an electron can move in any direction after a collision, the average velocity of the electrons just after their last collision is zero. Therefore the average velocity of the electrons at any instant is due only to the average impulse per unit of mass due to the electric force exerted on the electrons between collisions. The average impulse per unit of mass is the product of the force and the average time interval between collisions divided by the mass of the electron. This average velocity due to the impulse is the *drift velocity* of the electrons, and its direction is opposite that of the electric field.
20. The conductivity is the proportionality factor between the current density and the electric field in any conductor made of the material. It measures how well or how poorly the material conducts an electric current.
21. The conductivity depends on the number density of the charge carriers, their charge and mass, the average time interval between collisions, and temperature.
22. The resistance is the ratio of the potential difference across the element to the current through it.
23. An ohmic material is one that obeys Ohm's law, $I = V/R$ (Eq. 31.11).
24. The slope of the curve is the reciprocal of the resistance of the element. For a circuit element made of an ohmic material, the curve is a straight line, which means that the resistance is independent of the potential difference across the element.
25. Current continuity requires that the current is the same at all locations in the circuit. Energy conservation requires that the algebraic sum of the emfs and the potential differences around the loop is zero (loop rule).
26. The equivalent resistance of resistors in series is the sum of the individual resistances.
27. A battery's internal resistance accounts for the (usually small) amount of energy dissipated inside the battery and thus not available as electric potential energy outside the battery. When we analyze the circuit, a small resistor of resistance R_{batt} is added in series with the battery of emf $\mathscr{E}$.
28. The equivalent resistance of resistors connected in parallel is the reciprocal of the sum of the reciprocals of the individual resistances.
29. Identify all junctions and label the currents in each branch. Write the junction rule for all but one junction, and write the loop rule for as many loops as necessary to obtain, along with the junction rule, as many independent equations as there are unknowns to solve for. Then perform the required algebra to solve for the unknowns.
30. The rate at which energy is converted is power, and the general expression for power in a circuit element is the product of the current through the element and the magnitude of the potential difference across it.
31. The rate of energy conversion in a resistor is equal to the current squared times the resistance and represents the conversion of electric potential energy to thermal energy (Eq. 31.43).

Answers to Guided Problems

Guided Problem 31.2 (*a*) $h_{slow} = \dfrac{\Delta E_{batt}}{2\,mg} = \dfrac{(4.1 \times 10^4\ \text{J})}{2(60\ \text{kg})(9.8\ \text{m/s}^2)} = 34\ \text{m},$

$$h_{max} = \tfrac{1}{4}\left(\frac{\Delta E_{batt}}{mg}\right) = \tfrac{1}{4}\frac{(4.1 \times 10^4\ \text{J})}{(60\ \text{kg})(9.8\ \text{m/s}^2)} = 17\ \text{m};$$

$$(b)\ v_{max} = \frac{(\text{efficiency})(P_{max})}{mg} = 4.8 \times 10^{-4}\ \text{m/s},$$

$$\Delta t_{min} = \frac{2R_{batt}\Delta E_{batt}}{\mathscr{E}^2} = \frac{(2)(1.0\ \Omega)(4.1 \times 10^4\ \text{J})}{(1.5\ \text{V})^2}$$

$$= 3.6 \times 10^4\ \text{s} = 10\ \text{h}$$

Guided Problem 31.4 $I_1 = \dfrac{\mathscr{E}}{R_1 + R_{eq2,3,4}} = \dfrac{9}{29}\dfrac{\mathscr{E}}{R_1},$

$$I_4 = \frac{\mathscr{E} - I_1R_1}{R_4} = \frac{5}{29}\frac{\mathscr{E}}{R_1},$$

$$I_2 = \frac{\mathscr{E} - I_1R_1}{R_{eq2,3}} = \frac{4}{29}\frac{\mathscr{E}}{R_1}$$

Guided Problem 31.6 $\sigma = \dfrac{I}{\Delta V 2\pi \ell}\left(\ln\dfrac{r_{outer}}{r_{inner}}\right) = 3.23\ \text{A}/(\text{V}\cdot\text{m})$

Guided Problem 31.8 $P_{R1} = I_1^2R_1 = 8.0 \times 10^2\ \text{W}, P_{R2} = 25\ \text{W},$

$$P_{R3} = 25\ \text{W}, P_{R4} = 4.5 \times 10^2\ \text{W}$$

PRACTICE

32 PRACTICE Electronics

Chapter Summary

AC circuits (Sections 32.1, 32.2, 32.5)

Concepts **Alternating current (AC)** is current that periodically changes direction.

In an AC circuit that contains a capacitor, the current through the capacitor leads the potential difference by 90° (one-fourth of an oscillation).

In an AC circuit that contains an inductor, the current through the inductor lags the potential difference by 90°.

In any circuit that contains a capacitor and/or an inductor, **reactance** is the proportionality constant between the potential-difference amplitude and the current amplitude.

The **phase constant** ϕ for an AC circuit, which is the phase difference between the source emf and the current, is negative when the current leads the source emf and positive when the current lags the source emf.

Quantitative Tools The instantaneous emf supplied by an AC source is

$$\mathscr{E} = \mathscr{E}_{\max} \sin \omega t. \tag{32.1}$$

The instantaneous current in an AC circuit is

$$i = I \sin (\omega t - \phi), \tag{32.16}$$

where I is the amplitude (maximum value) of the current and ϕ is the **phase constant**. In an AC circuit that contains a capacitor, the *capacitive reactance* is

$$X_C \equiv \frac{1}{\omega C}, \tag{32.14}$$

and the amplitude of the potential difference across the capacitor is

$$V_C = IX_C. \tag{32.15}$$

In an AC circuit that contains an inductor, the *inductive reactance* is

$$X_L \equiv \omega L, \tag{32.26}$$

and the amplitude of the potential difference across the inductor is

$$V_L = IX_L. \tag{32.27}$$

RC and *RLC* series circuits (Section 32.6)

Concepts The **impedance** of a load connected to an AC source is a proportionality constant between the amplitudes of the potential difference and the current through the load.

Quantitative Tools
In an ***RC* series circuit,** the sum of all the instantaneous potential differences equals the emf of the source:

$$\mathscr{E} = v_R + v_C. \tag{32.28}$$

The current amplitude is

$$I = \frac{\mathscr{E}_{\max}}{Z}, \tag{32.33}$$

where Z is the **impedance** of the load. For an RC series circuit, the impedance is

$$Z_{RC} \equiv \sqrt{R^2 + 1/\omega^2 C^2}. \tag{32.34}$$

The amplitudes of the potential differences are

$$V_R = IR = \frac{\mathscr{E}_{\max} R}{\sqrt{R^2 + 1/\omega^2 C^2}} \tag{32.35}$$

$$V_C = IX_C = \frac{\mathscr{E}_{\max}/\omega C}{\sqrt{R^2 + 1/\omega^2 C^2}}, \tag{32.36}$$

and the **phase constant** for the circuit is

$$\phi = \tan^{-1}\left(-\frac{1}{\omega RC}\right). \tag{32.38}$$

In an ***RLC* series circuit,** the sum of all the instantaneous potential differences equals the emf of the source:

$$\mathscr{E} = v_R + v_L + v_C. \tag{32.39}$$

The **impedance** of the *RLC* series circuit is

$$Z_{RLC} \equiv \sqrt{R^2 + \left(\omega L - \frac{1}{\omega C}\right)^2}, \tag{32.43}$$

and so the current amplitude is

$$I = \frac{\mathscr{E}_{\max}}{Z_{RLC}} = \frac{\mathscr{E}_{\max}}{\sqrt{R^2 + (\omega L - 1/\omega C)^2}}. \tag{32.42}$$

The **phase constant** for the circuit is given by

$$\tan\phi = \frac{\omega L - 1/\omega C}{R}. \tag{32.44}$$

Resonance and power in AC circuits (Sections 32.7, 32.8)

Concepts At the **resonant angular frequency**, the current in a series *RLC* circuit is a maximum.

The **power factor** is a measure of the efficiency with which the source in an AC circuit delivers energy to the load.

Quantitative Tools The **resonant angular frequency** is

$$\omega_0 = \frac{1}{\sqrt{LC}}. \tag{32.47}$$

For a sinusoidally varying current, the **root-mean-square** current is

$$I_{\text{rms}} = \frac{I}{\sqrt{2}}, \tag{32.53}$$

and the root-mean-square potential difference is

$$V_{\text{rms}} = \frac{V}{\sqrt{2}} \qquad \mathscr{E}_{\text{rms}} = \frac{\mathscr{E}_{\max}}{\sqrt{2}}. \tag{32.55}$$

The average power is

$$P_{\text{av}} = \mathscr{E}_{\text{rms}} I_{\text{rms}} \cos\phi, \tag{32.61}$$

where the cosine term is the **power factor** for the circuit:

$$\cos\phi = \frac{R}{Z}. \tag{32.62}$$

Semiconductor devices (Sections 32.3, 32.4)

Concepts A **semiconductor** is a material that contains a limited number of charge carriers that can move freely and that has an electrical conductivity intermediate between that of electrical conductors and that of electrical insulators.

An *intrinsic* semiconductor is made of atoms of only one element. An *extrinsic* (*doped*) semiconductor contains, interspersed among the atoms of its main element, trace amounts of atoms of other elements. These *dopant* atoms alter the number of electrons that can move freely and so change the electronic properties of the semiconductor.

A **hole** is an incomplete bond in a semiconductor that behaves like a freely moving positive charge carrier.

In a *p-type* semiconductor, holes are the free charge carriers. In an *n-type* semiconductor, electrons are the free charge carriers.

A **diode** is made by bringing a piece of *p*-type semiconductor into contact with a piece of *n*-type semiconductor. It behaves like a one-way valve for current.

The **depletion zone** in a diode is a thin insulating region at the junction between the *p*-type and *n*-type semiconductors where the positive and negative charge carriers have recombined and become immobile.

A **transistor** consists of a thin layer of one type of extrinsic semiconductor sandwiched between two layers of the opposite type of extrinsic semiconductor (such as *npn*). It behaves either like an on/off switch for current or like a current amplifier.

Review Questions

Answers to these questions can be found at the end of this chapter.

32.1 Alternating currents

1. What is an alternating current?
2. Describe how the current changes in a circuit that consists of a charged capacitor connected to an inductor.
3. What property specific to AC circuits must be considered when you apply the junction rule, the loop rule, or Ohm's law to such circuits?

32.2 AC circuits

4. What two quantities must you know in order to specify the time dependence of a sinusoidally varying function?
5. What is a phasor? Which phasor properties are used in analyzing oscillating quantities?
6. What do the descriptions *lead* and *lag* mean when applied to two oscillating quantities A and B that vary with the same angular frequency?
7. In a series AC circuit that contains a capacitor, an inductor, and a resistor, how is the current through each circuit element related to the potential difference across the element?

32.3 Semiconductors

8. What is a semiconductor?
9. What is the difference between an intrinsic semiconductor and an extrinsic semiconductor?
10. Describe how holes in an extrinsic semiconductor behave like positively charged particles.
11. How are doped silicon semiconductors classified, and what do the classifications mean?

32.4 Diodes, transistors, and logic gates

12. What are the two main components of a diode?
13. What is the depletion zone in a diode?
14. Describe how a depletion zone forms in a diode.
15. What happens when the *n* side of a diode is connected to a battery's positive terminal and the *p* side is connected to the negative terminal? What happens when the connections are *n* side to negative terminal and *p* side to positive terminal?
16. What is a bias potential difference, and what is its purpose in an *npn* transistor?
17. What two main functions can transistors perform in electric circuits?
18. Explain how a current is created in a field-effect transistor.
19. What is a logic gate?

32.5 Reactance

20. For a capacitor connected to an AC generator, compare the current through the capacitor and the potential difference across the capacitor in terms of their angular frequencies, amplitudes, and phase constants.
21. What is capacitive reactance in an AC circuit, and on what properties of the circuit does it depend?
22. For an inductor connected to an AC generator, compare the current through the inductor and the potential difference across the inductor in terms of their angular frequencies, amplitudes, and phase constants.
23. What is inductive reactance in an AC circuit? On what properties of the circuit does it depend?

32.6 *RC* and *RLC* series circuits

24. How can the sum of two or more quantities that vary sinusoidally at the same angular frequency be determined from the phasors representing the quantities?
25. How is the impedance of a load in an AC circuit defined?
26. Explain why the combination of a resistor and a capacitor connected in series to an AC source acts as a frequency filter.

32.7 Resonance

27. What does resonant angular frequency ω_0 refer to in a series *RLC* circuit, and which properties of the circuit determine its resonant angular frequency?
28. How does the amplitude of the current in a series *RLC* circuit vary with the angular frequency of the source?
29. Which properties of a series *RLC* circuit determine the maximum amplitude of the current?

32.8 Power in AC circuits

30. What is the advantage of using the root-mean-square value of the sinusoidally oscillating current or emf when analyzing power in an AC circuit?
31. What is the average power at a resistor in an AC circuit? What happens to the energy associated with this power?
32. What is the average power at a capacitor or an inductor in an AC circuit? Describe the instantaneous power at either element.
33. What is the power factor for a load connected to an AC source?

Developing a Feel

Make an order-of-magnitude estimate of each of the following quantities. Letters in parentheses refer to hints below. Use them as needed to guide your thinking.

1. The maximum displacement of an electron in the electrical wire leading to a lamp in your home (E, Q, K)
2. The reactance of a 1-μF capacitor in a 60-Hz circuit (H, A)
3. The reactance of a 1-μF capacitor in a circuit that oscillates at a typical FM radio frequency (H, O)
4. The reactance of a 5-mH inductor in a circuit that oscillates at a typical FM radio frequency (C, O)
5. The capacitance needed for a high-pass filter for the 8-Ω tweeter (high-frequency speaker) in a home stereo system (F, M)
6. The inductance needed for a low-pass filter for the 8-Ω subwoofer (very-low-frequency speaker) in a home stereo system (J, D)
7. The inductance needed for resonance in an *RLC* series circuit that consists of the inductor plus a 10-μF capacitor, 1-kΩ resistor, and a 60-Hz source (L)
8. The rate at which energy is consumed in a household AC circuit for a 100-W light bulb wired in series with a 5-μF capacitor (R, S, T, I, K, A, B, P)
9. The rate at which energy is consumed by a 100-W light bulb wired in series with a 10-mH inductor in an AC household circuit (R, S, T, I, K, A, B, N)
10. The inductance of the 200-W motor running a food processor in your kitchen at maximum power if the unit has a 5-μF capacitor (K, G)

Hints

A. How does angular frequency depend on frequency?
B. What is the formula for the power factor?
C. How does inductive reactance depend on angular frequency?
D. How does the cutoff angular frequency depend on inductance?
E. What is the typical drift speed of electrons in household wiring?
F. What is a typical cutoff angular frequency for a tweeter fitted with a high-pass filter?
G. What is the requirement for maximizing the power factor?
H. How does capacitive reactance depend on angular frequency?
I. What is *R* for the circuit?
J. What is a typical cutoff angular frequency for a subwoofer fitted with a low-pass filter?
K. What is the frequency of household AC power?
L. What is the condition for resonance?
M. How does the cutoff angular frequency depend on capacitance?
N. What is the impedance?
O. What is a typical broadcast frequency for an FM station?
P. What is the impedance?
Q. What is the maximum time interval that an electron travels in one direction?
R. How is the rate at which the bulb consumes energy determined?
S. What is $\mathscr{E}_{max}$ for household wiring?
T. What is *I* for the circuit?

Key (all values approximate)

A. $\omega = 2\pi f$; **B.** $\cos\phi = R/Z$; **C.** $X_L = \omega L$; **D.** $\omega_c = R/L$; **E.** 10^{-4} m/s (from *Principles* Example 31.7); **F.** $10^4\ s^{-1}$; **G.** the system angular frequency must be the resonant angular frequency, which happens when $\omega L = 1/\omega C$; **H.** $X_C = 1/\omega C$; **I.** that of the bulb, $R = \mathscr{E}^2_{max}/(100\ W) = 10^2\ \Omega$; **J.** $10^3\ s^{-1}$; **K.** 60 Hz; **L.** $\omega_0 = 1/\sqrt{LC}$; **M.** $\omega_c = 1/RC$; **N.** $1 \times 10^2\ \Omega$; **O.** 10^8 Hz; **P.** $5 \times 10^2\ \Omega$; **Q.** half the AC period; **R.** $P_{av} = \frac{1}{2}\mathscr{E}_{max} I \cos\phi$; **S.** 170 V; **T.** $I = \mathscr{E}_{max}/Z$

PRACTICE

Worked and Guided Problems

Procedure: Analyzing AC series circuits

When analyzing AC series circuits we generally know the properties of the various circuit elements (such as R, L, C, and $\mathscr{E}$), but not the potential differences across them. To determine these, follow the procedure below.

1. To develop a feel for the problem and to help you evaluate the answer, construct a phasor diagram for the circuit.
2. Determine the impedance of the load using Eq. 32.43. If there is no inductor, then ignore the term containing L; if there is no capacitor, ignore the term containing C, and so on.
3. To determine the amplitude of the current in the circuit, you can now use Eq. 32.42; to determine the phase of the current relative to the emf, use Eq. 32.44.
4. Determine the amplitude of the potential difference across any reactive element using $V = XI$, where X is the reactance of that element. For a resistor use $V = RI$.

These examples involve material from this chapter but are not associated with any particular section. Some examples are worked out in detail; others you should work out by following the guidelines provided.

Worked Problem 32.1 *LC* circuit

In the LC circuit of Figure WG32.1, $C = 80\ \mu\text{F}$. Initially, with switch S open, the capacitor is charged by an amount q_0. The switch is then closed, and 20 ms later the electric potential energy stored in the capacitor is one-fourth its initial value. What is the inductance L?

Figure WG32.1

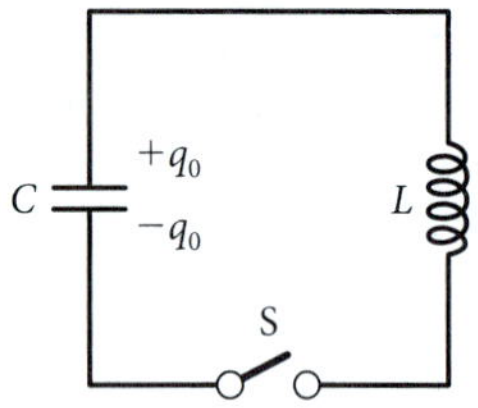

❶ **GETTING STARTED** The potential energy in an LC circuit is stored in both the inductor and the capacitor. We are told that initially the capacitor has charge q_0, and we know there is no current through the inductor because the switch is open. We are also told that 20 ms after the switch is closed, the energy stored in the capacitor is one-fourth its initial value. Our goal is to determine the inductance of the inductor.

❷ **DEVISE PLAN** Because the energy in an LC circuit is constant, the circuit behaves like a simple harmonic oscillator, with energy that oscillates back and forth between the capacitor and the inductor. The energy stored in the capacitor is proportional to the charge squared (see Eq. 26.4), and we know that the potential difference across the capacitor oscillates sinusoidally according to $v_C = V_0 \cos \omega_0 t$ (*Principles* Figure 32.4). For capacitors, we also know that $q/v_C = C$ (Eq. 26.1), so $q = Cv_C = CV_C \cos \omega_0 t$. Because the initial ($t = 0$) value of q is known to be $q(0) = q_0 = CV_C \cos(0) = CV_C$, the charge on the capacitor at any instant can be written as $q = q_0 \cos \omega_0 t$. We know that at the instant $t_1 = 20$ ms, the capacitor has only one-fourth of its initial energy. Therefore we can determine the value of ω_0 in terms of t_1. Knowing that $\omega_0 = 1/\sqrt{LC}$, we can use C and t_1 to determine the value of L.

❸ **EXECUTE PLAN** The electric potential energy stored in the capacitor at any instant t is given by Eq. 26.4

$$U_C^E(t) = \frac{q^2}{2C} = \frac{(q_0 \cos \omega_0 t)^2}{2C} = \frac{q_0^2}{2C} \cos^2 \omega_0 t.$$

Thus we can use the fact that at $t_1 = 20$ ms the energy in the capacitor is one-fourth the energy at $t = 0$ to say

$$\frac{U_C^E(t_1)}{U_C^E(0)} = \frac{\cos^2 \omega_0 t_1}{\cos^2(0)} = \frac{\cos^2 \omega_0 t_1}{1} = \tfrac{1}{4} \Rightarrow \cos \omega_0 t_1 = \tfrac{1}{2}.$$

Solving this cosine expression for $\omega_0 t_1$ yields

$$\omega_0 t_1 = \cos^{-1}(\tfrac{1}{2}) = \frac{\pi}{3}\,\text{rad} = 60°.$$

Therefore, with $\omega_0 = 1/\sqrt{LC}$, we obtain

$$t_1 = \frac{\pi}{3\omega_0} = \frac{\pi}{3}\sqrt{LC},$$

and the inductance is

$$L = \frac{1}{C}\left(\frac{3t_1}{\pi}\right)^2 = \frac{1}{(80 \times 10^{-6}\ \text{F})}\left[\frac{3(20 \times 10^{-3}\ \text{s})}{\pi}\right]^2$$

$$= 4.6\ \text{s}^2/\text{F} = 4.6\ \text{H}. ✔$$

❹ **EVALUATE RESULT** Our value for the inductance, $L = 4.6$ H, is not unreasonably large compared to the inductor in *Principles* Example 32.6. We can check our result by calculating the energy stored in the magnetic field of the inductor. The current in the circuit is given by

$$i = dq/dt = -\omega_0 q_0 \sin \omega_0 t.$$

PRACTICE

The energy stored in the inductor is given by

$$U^B_L(t_1) = \tfrac{1}{2}Li^2 = \tfrac{1}{2}L\omega_0^2 q_0^2 \sin^2 \omega_0 t_1$$
$$= \tfrac{1}{2}L\frac{1}{LC}q_0^2 \sin^2 \omega_0 t_1 = \frac{q_0^2}{2C}\sin^2 \omega_0 t_1.$$

When $\omega_0 t_1 = \pi/3$ rad, $\sin^2\omega_0 t_1 = \frac{3}{4}$. Therefore $U^B_L(t_1) = \frac{3}{4}q_0^2/2C$ and the energy stored in the circuit at t_1 is

$$U^B_L(t_1) + U^E_C(t_1) = \tfrac{3}{4}\frac{q_0^2}{2C} + \tfrac{1}{4}\frac{q_0^2}{2C} = \frac{q_0^2}{2C} = U^E_C(0).$$

Because there is no current through the circuit just before the switch is closed, $U^B_L(0) = 0$ and

$$U^B_L(t_1) + U^E_C(t_1) = U^E_C(0) + U^B_L(0).$$

Therefore the energy is constant, as we expect because there is no resistor in the circuit.

Guided Problem 32.2 *RLC* circuit

Consider the circuit of Figure WG32.2, consisting of an inductor of inductance $L = (8.0/\pi^2) \times 10^{-3}$ H, a resistor of resistance R, a capacitor of capacitance $C = 0.50$ nF, a battery for which $\mathscr{E} = 4.0$ V, and two switches S_1 and S_2. Initially S_1 is closed and S_2 is open. After a long time interval $\Delta t \gg RC$, S_1 is opened and S_2 is closed. What is the current in the circuit at the instant t_{equal} when the magnetic potential energy stored in the inductor is equal to the electric potential energy stored in the capacitor?

Figure WG32.2

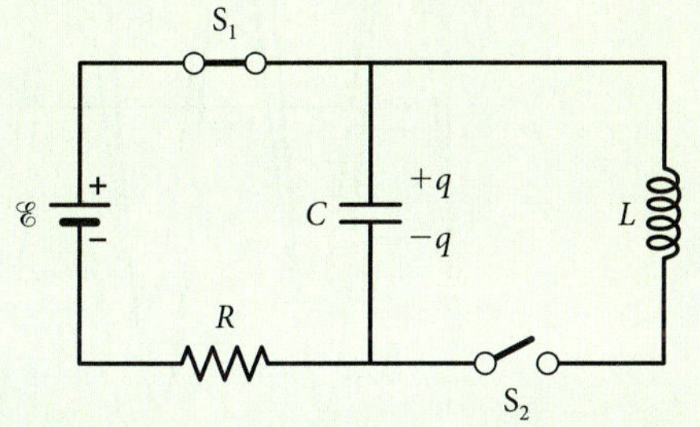

1 GETTING STARTED

1. What happens at the capacitor while switch 1 is closed and switch 2 is open?
2. How do the capacitor potential difference and the current behave after switch 1 is opened and switch 2 is closed?

2 DEVISE PLAN

3. How does the electric potential energy stored in the capacitor depend on the potential difference and capacitance?
4. How does the magnetic potential energy stored in the inductor depend on the current and inductance?
5. How can you use energy considerations to determine the current through the inductor at the instant t_{equal}?

3 EXECUTE PLAN

6. What are the potential difference across the capacitor and the potential energy in the circuit at the instant switch 1 is opened and switch 2 is closed?
7. What is the stored energy in the inductor at the instant t_{equal}?
8. At that instant, what is the current amplitude in the circuit?

4 EVALUATE RESULT

9. Is this value for the current in the range that can be easily measured with equipment from your undergraduate physics laboratory?
10. How does this value for the current magnitude I at the instant the inductor energy equals the capacitor energy compare with the maximum possible value for the current I_{max}?
11. What is I_{max}?
12. How does this value for the maximum current compare with the value you calculated?

Worked Problem 32.3 Driven *RL* circuit

Consider the *RL* circuit of Figure WG32.3, where the AC source produces a time-varying emf given by $\mathscr{E} = \mathscr{E}_{\text{max}} \sin \omega t$. The amplitude of the emf is $\mathscr{E}_{\text{max}} = 120\sqrt{2}$ V, and the angular frequency is $\omega = 120\pi$ s^{-1}. If $R = 3.0\ \Omega$ and $L = 4.0 \times 10^{-3}$ H, what is the average power delivered by the AC source?

Figure WG32.3

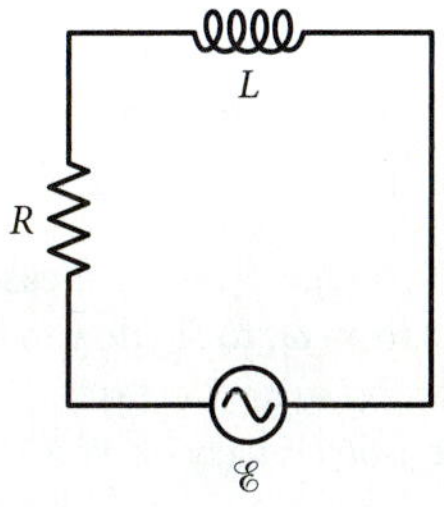

1 GETTING STARTED We begin by drawing a phasor diagram for the circuit showing V_R, V_L, and I (Figure WG32.4). We know that V_R and I are in phase in an AC circuit, and so we show these two phasors superimposed on each other. We also know that in an AC circuit the potential difference across the inductor leads the current by 90°, and so we draw phasor V_L at a right angle to our other two phasors. Our goal is to calculate the average power delivered by the source, which is the average rate at which the source delivers energy.

Figure WG32.4

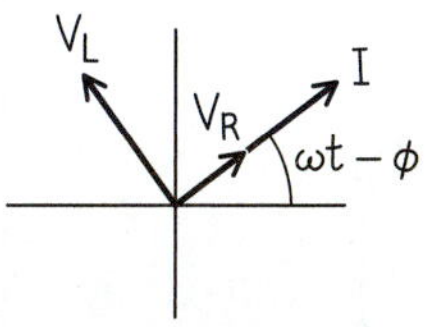

2 DEVISE PLAN We can use Eq. 32.60, $P_{\text{av}} = \frac{1}{2}\mathscr{E}_{\text{max}} I \cos \phi$, to calculate the average power delivered by the AC source, which means we must know $\mathscr{E}_{\text{max}}$, I, and $\cos \phi$. We are given the value for $\mathscr{E}_{\text{max}}$ but must determine I and $\cos \phi$. We can use Eq. 32.42 without the capacitance term (because our circuit contains no capacitors) for I, and for the power factor $\cos \phi$ we have Eq. 32.62. In order to use this relationship, however, we must know the circuit impedance Z, and we are given all the values needed to determine Z from Eq. 32.43.

❸ **EXECUTE PLAN** From Eq. 32.42, the current amplitude expressed in terms of values we know is

$$I = \frac{\mathcal{E}_{max}}{\sqrt{R^2 + (\omega L)^2}}.$$

The impedance of the circuit is, from Eq. 32.43,

$$Z = \sqrt{R^2 + (\omega L)^2},$$

and substituting this expression for Z in Eq. 32.62 gives us the power factor $\cos\phi$:

$$\cos\phi = \frac{R}{Z} = \frac{R}{\sqrt{R^2 + (\omega L)^2}}.$$

Therefore the average power delivered by the AC source is, from Eq. 32.60,

$$P_{av} = \tfrac{1}{2}\mathcal{E}_{max} I \cos\phi = \frac{1}{2}\frac{\mathcal{E}^2_{max}R}{[R^2 + (\omega L)^2]}$$

$$= \frac{1}{2}\frac{(120\sqrt{2}\text{ V})^2(3.0\ \Omega)}{[(3.0\ \Omega)^2 + (120\pi\text{ s}^{-1})^2(4.0 \times 10^{-3}\text{ H})^2]}$$

$$= 3.8 \times 10^3\text{ W}.\ ✔$$

❹ **EVALUATE RESULT** With this large value for the average power, we expect the current amplitude to be large, so we can check that value:

$$I = \frac{\mathcal{E}_{max}}{\sqrt{R^2 + (\omega L)^2}}$$

$$= \frac{120\sqrt{2}\text{ V}}{\sqrt{(3.0\ \Omega)^2 + (120\pi\text{ s}^{-1})^2(4.0 \times 10^{-3}\text{ H})^2}}$$

$$= 5.1 \times 10^1\text{ A}.$$

This relatively large value for I gives us confidence that our power calculation is the right order of magnitude.

Another check for evaluating our result is to look at the phase difference, which we expect to satisfy the condition $0 < \phi < \pi/2$. From Eq. 32.44,

$$\phi = \tan^{-1}\frac{\omega L}{R}$$

$$= \tan^{-1}\frac{(120\pi\text{ s}^{-1})(4.0 \times 10^{-3}\text{ H})}{3.0\ \Omega} = 0.47\text{ rad},$$

again giving us confidence in our result.

As a third check, we can plot on the same graph the AC source potential difference as a function of time and the current as a function of time (Figure WG32.5). The potential difference leads the current, as we expect.

Figure WG32.5

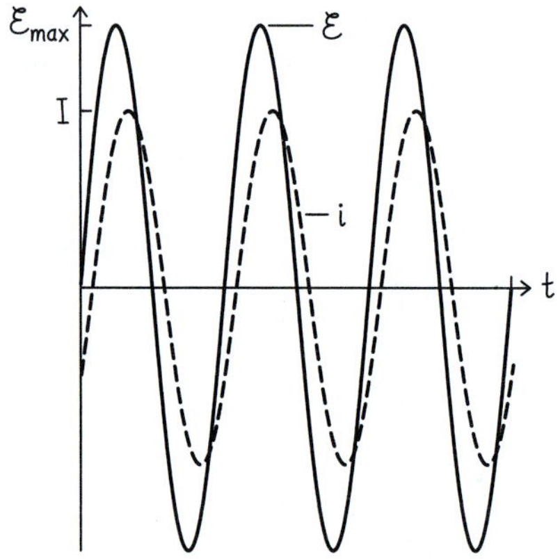

Guided Problem 32.4 Driven *RC* circuit

In the *RC* circuit of Figure WG32.6, the emf of the AC source is given by $\mathcal{E} = \mathcal{E}_{max}\sin\omega_1 t$. The emf amplitude is $\mathcal{E}_{max} = 10$ V, and the angular frequency is $\omega_1 = 100\text{ s}^{-1}$. When the angular frequency is changed to a new value ω_2, the time average of the power delivered by the source decreases by a factor of 2. If $R = 3.0\ \Omega$ and $C = 5.0 \times 10^{-2}$ F, what is the value of ω_2?

Figure WG32.6

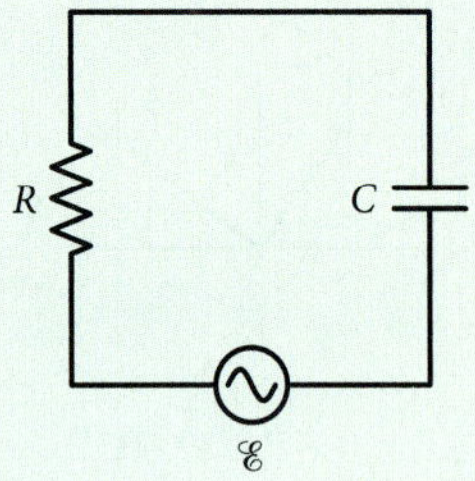

❶ **GETTING STARTED**

1. Draw a phasor diagram for the circuit, showing V_R, V_C, and I.

❷ **DEVISE PLAN**

2. What is the current amplitude as a function of ω?
3. What is the phase difference as a function of ω?
4. What is the time average of the power delivered by the AC source as a function of ω?
5. Write an expression showing the ratio of the average power when $\omega = \omega_1$ and the average power when $\omega = \omega_2$.
6. Solve this expression for ω_2.

❸ **EXECUTE PLAN**

7. Determine ω_2 from the given values.

❹ **EVALUATE RESULT**

8. Knowing that the average power decreases when the angular frequency changes from ω_1 to ω_2, do you expect the amplitude of the current to increase or decrease?
9. Does the average power vary as you expect as a function of ω?
10. Does your answer for ω_2 agree with what you expect?

Worked Problem 32.5 Unknown circuit element I

Figure WG32.7 shows a circuit containing an AC source for which the emf varies with time as $\mathscr{E} = \mathscr{E}_{max} \sin \omega t$ and a resistor of resistance R. The square with the question mark represents either an inductor or a capacitor (but not both). The amplitude of the emf is $\mathscr{E}_{max} = 100\sqrt{2}$ V, and the angular frequency is $\omega = 10\ s^{-1}$. The time-dependent current is given by $i = (10\ A)\sin(\omega t + \pi/4)$. Is the unknown element a capacitor or an inductor? What is the value of R? What is the value of the capacitance or of the inductance of the unknown element?

Figure WG32.7

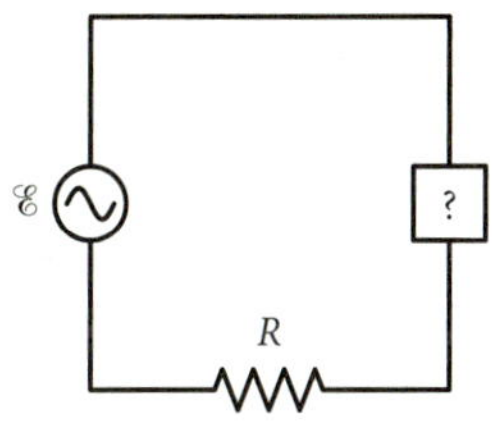

❶ **GETTING STARTED** We know from the current expression $i = (10\ A)\sin(\omega t + \pi/4)$ that the phase difference between the AC source emf and the current is $\phi = -\pi/4$. The minus sign tells us that the current leads the AC source emf. Therefore the unknown element must be a capacitor, and we have the answer to the first question this problem asks. ✔

With this information, we can draw a phasor diagram for the circuit showing V_R, V_C, and I (Figure WG32.8).

Figure WG32.8

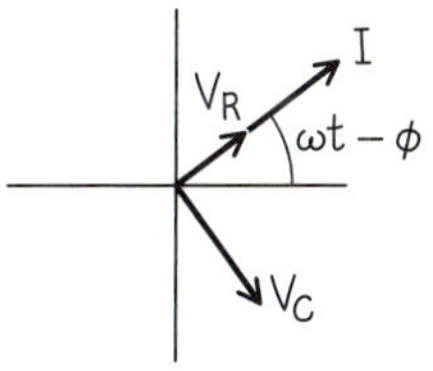

❷ **DEVISE PLAN** We have two unknowns, R and C, so our plan should be to obtain two independent equations containing these unknowns. We know that the unknown element is a capacitor, and we know the phase constant ϕ. Thus we can use Eq. 32.44 without the inductance term as one equation containing C and R. The current equation given in the problem statement shows the amplitude of current $I = 10$ A, and we are told the value of $\mathscr{E}_{max}$. Therefore we can use Eq. 32.42 without the inductance term as our second equation containing C and R.

❸ **EXECUTE PLAN** We know that $\phi = -\pi/4$ and $\tan(-\pi/4) = -1$. Thus Eq. 32.44 yields

$$-1 = \frac{-1/\omega C}{R}$$

$$\frac{1}{\omega C} = R. \qquad (1)$$

With this result, we can eliminate $1/\omega C$ from Eq. 32.42, solve that equation for R, and use our numerical values:

$$I = \frac{\mathscr{E}_{max}}{\sqrt{R^2 + (1/\omega C)^2}} = \frac{\mathscr{E}_{max}}{\sqrt{R^2 + R^2}} = \frac{\mathscr{E}_{max}}{\sqrt{2}R}$$

$$R = \frac{\mathscr{E}_{max}}{\sqrt{2}I} = \frac{100\sqrt{2}\ V}{\sqrt{2}(10\ A)} = 10\ V/A = 10\ \Omega. ✔$$

Now that we know R, we solve Eq. 1 for the capacitance:

$$C = \frac{1}{\omega R} = \frac{1}{(10\ s^{-1})(10\ \Omega)} = 1.0 \times 10^{-2}\ F. ✔$$

❹ **EVALUATE RESULT** Our value for the capacitance is somewhat large, and our value for the resistance is small but reasonable. Because $\phi = -\pi/4$, the reactance of the capacitor is equal to the resistance, the impedance of the circuit is $Z = \sqrt{R^2 + X_C^2} = \sqrt{2}R$, and therefore the amplitude of current

$$I = \frac{\mathscr{E}_{max}}{\sqrt{2}R} = \frac{100\sqrt{2}\ V}{\sqrt{2}(10\ \Omega)} = 10\ A.$$

This agrees with our result above, which gives us confidence in our calculation.

We can also check our result by comparing the average power delivered by the AC source—the average rate at which the source delivers energy to the resistor—and the power at the resistor—the average rate at which that energy is dissipated by the resistor. We know that $\cos\phi = \cos(-\pi/4) = 1/\sqrt{2}$. Hence the average power delivered by the source is, from Eq. 32.60,

$$P_{av} = \tfrac{1}{2}\mathscr{E}_{max}\frac{\mathscr{E}_{max}}{\sqrt{2}R}\frac{1}{\sqrt{2}} = \frac{1}{4}\frac{\mathscr{E}^2_{max}}{R}.$$

The average rate at which energy is dissipated in the resistor is, from Eq. 32.52,

$$P_{av} = \tfrac{1}{2}I^2R = \tfrac{1}{2}\left(\frac{\mathscr{E}_{max}}{\sqrt{2}R}\right)^2 R = \frac{1}{4}\frac{\mathscr{E}^2_{max}}{R}.$$

We see that these two are equal, which is what we expect because the phasors V_C and I are 90° out of phase, and so no energy is dissipated in the capacitor.

Guided Problem 32.6 Unknown circuit element II

Figure WG32.9 on the next page shows a circuit containing an AC source for which the emf varies with time as $\mathscr{E} = \mathscr{E}_{max}\sin\omega t$. The emf amplitude is $\mathscr{E}_{max} = 6.0$ V, and the resistor is rated at $R = 3.0\ \Omega$. The square with the question mark represents an inductor, a capacitor, *or both*. When the angular frequency is $\omega_1 = 1.0\ s^{-1}$, the current is in phase with the source emf. When the angular frequency is $\omega_2 = 2.0\ s^{-1}$, the current is out of phase with the emf by $|\pi/4|$ rad. What is the average rate at which energy is dissipated in this circuit when the angular frequency is ω_1? Repeat for angular frequency ω_2.

Figure WG32.9

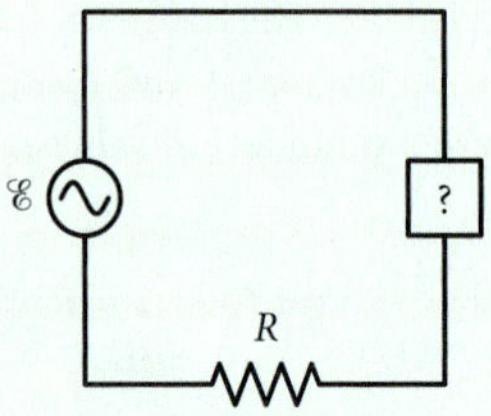

❶ **GETTING STARTED**

1. Does the square represent an inductor, a capacitor, or both?
2. When the angular frequency is $\omega_2 = 2.0\ \mathrm{s}^{-1}$, what reactance(s) must be accounted for?
3. Draw a phasor diagram for the circuit.

❷ **DEVISE PLAN**

4. What is the appropriate expression relating angular frequency to the inductance and/or capacitance?
5. How can you determine whether the source emf leads or lags the current at angular frequency ω_2?
6. How can you determine the values of L and/or C?
7. How can you determine the current amplitude when the angular frequency is ω_1? ω_2?
8. How can you determine the average rate at which energy is dissipated in the resistor?
9. Is there any energy dissipated in the inductor and/or capacitor?

❸ **EXECUTE PLAN**

10. Write the expressions relating L and/or C at both given frequencies.
11. Calculate values for L and/or C.
12. Calculate the current amplitude at ω_1 and ω_2.
13. Determine the average rate at which energy is dissipated at ω_1 and ω_2.

❹ **EVALUATE RESULT**

14. What is the average power delivered by the AC source at angular frequency ω_1? Did you expect that result?

Worked Problem 32.7 FM radio tuner

Suppose you want a series *RLC* circuit to tune to a radio station that broadcasts at a frequency of 89.7 MHz, but you do not want to pick up the signal from a station that broadcasts at 89.5 MHz. To achieve this, for a given input signal from your antenna, you want your resonance curve to be narrow enough to make the current in the circuit at 89.5 MHz be 100 times smaller than the current in the circuit at 89.7 MHz. You cannot avoid having a resistance of $R = 0.100\ \Omega$, and practical considerations also dictate that you use the smallest possible value for L. What values of L and C must you use?

❶ **GETTING STARTED** We begin by drawing a phasor diagram showing V_R, V_C, V_L, and I (Figure WG32.10). We first draw phasors V_R and I in phase, and then draw V_L leading I by 90° and V_C lagging I by 90°. We model the time-dependent input signal by the sinusoidal function $\mathscr{E} = \mathscr{E}_{\max} \sin \omega t$ and the time-dependent current in the circuit by $i = I \sin(\omega t - \phi)$. We want resonance to occur at $\omega_{89.7} = (2\pi)(89.7 \times 10^6\ \mathrm{Hz})$. We also require that the current amplitude $I(\omega_{89.5})$ at $\omega_{89.5} = (2\pi)(89.5 \times 10^6\ \mathrm{Hz})$ be one-hundredth the maximum current at resonance $I(\omega_{89.7})$: $I(\omega_{89.5}) = 0.0100 I(\omega_{89.7})$. We are given that $R = 0.100\ \Omega$.

Figure WG32.10

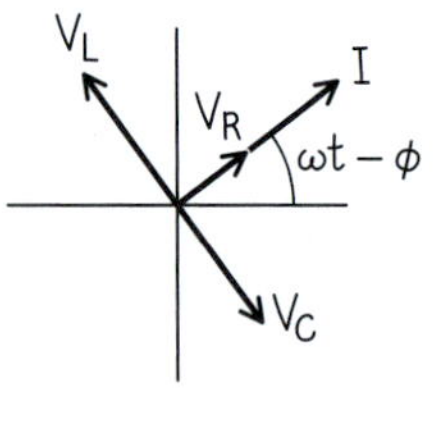

❷ **DEVISE PLAN** The current amplitude I is a function of ω (Eq. 32.42). We also use the resonance condition Eq. 32.47 to simplify the expression for $I(\omega_{89.7})$. We have two expressions, one for $I(\omega_{89.7})$ and one for $I(\omega_{89.5})$, and the condition that $I(\omega_{89.5}) = 0.0100 I(\omega_{89.7})$. We can thus obtain a relationship between L and C. We again use the resonance condition Eq. 32.47, which gives a second condition for L and C. We now solve our system of equations for the values of L and C.

❸ **EXECUTE PLAN** Equation 32.42 gives the current amplitude as a function of ω:

$$I = \frac{\mathscr{E}_{\max}}{\sqrt{R^2 + (\omega L - 1/\omega C)^2}}. \tag{1}$$

We know from Eq. 32.46 that at resonance, $\omega L = 1/\omega C$, which means that at our resonant angular frequency $\omega_{89.7}$, Eq. 1 reduces to

$$I(\omega_{89.7}) = \frac{\mathscr{E}_{\max}}{R}. \tag{2}$$

Once we set $\omega = \omega_{89.5}$ in Eq. 1:

$$I(\omega_{89.5}) = \frac{\mathscr{E}_{\max}}{\sqrt{R^2 + (\omega_{89.5} L - 1/\omega_{89.5} C)^2}}, \tag{3}$$

we are ready to determine values for L and C. To keep the notation simple, let's for now use h to represent the factor by which the two current amplitudes must differ: $h = 0.0100$. Thus

$$I(\omega_{89.5}) = hI(\omega_{89.7}),$$

and from Eqs. 2 and 3 we have

$$\frac{\mathscr{E}_{\max}}{\sqrt{R^2 + (\omega_{89.5} L - 1/\omega_{89.5} C)^2}} = h\frac{\mathscr{E}_{\max}}{R}.$$

Squaring both sides and eliminating $\mathscr{E}_{\max}$ yield

$$\frac{1}{R^2 + (\omega_{89.5} L - 1/\omega_{89.5} C)^2} = h^2 \frac{1}{R^2}. \tag{4}$$

A little algebraic manipulation yields the condition that

$$\frac{R^2}{R^2 + (\omega_{89.5} L - 1/\omega_{89.5} C)^2} = h^2$$

$$\Rightarrow (\omega_{89.5} L - 1/\omega_{89.5} C)^2 = \left(\frac{1}{h^2} - 1\right) R^2.$$

Taking square roots, we have

$$\omega_{89.5}L - \frac{1}{\omega_{89.5}C} = -\sqrt{\frac{1}{h^2} - 1}\,R.$$

We show a minus sign on the term on the right because the circuit is below resonance, which means that $(\omega_{89.5}L - 1/\omega_{89.5}C) < 0$. Using Eq. 32.47 in the form $C = 1/L\omega_{89.7}^2$, where $\omega_{89.7}$ is the resonant angular frequency, we obtain

$$\omega_{89.5}L\left[1 - \left(\frac{\omega_{89.7}}{\omega_{89.5}}\right)^2\right] = -\sqrt{\frac{1}{h^2} - 1}\,R,$$

which yields

$$L = \frac{\sqrt{\left(\frac{1}{h^2} - 1\right)}R}{\omega_{89.5}\left[(\omega_{89.7}/\omega_{89.5})^2 - 1\right]}$$

$$= \frac{\sqrt{(1.00 \times 10^4 - 1)}(0.100\ \Omega)}{(5.62 \times 10^8\ \text{s}^{-1})\left[(89.7/89.5)^2 - 1\right]} = 3.97 \times 10^{-6}\ \text{H}. ✔$$

The capacitance is therefore

$$C = \frac{1}{L\omega_{89.7}^2} = \frac{1}{(3.97 \times 10^{-6}\ \text{H})(5.63 \times 10^8\ \text{s}^{-1})^2}$$

$$= 7.92 \times 10^{-13}\ \text{F}. ✔$$

❹ **EVALUATE RESULT** Suppose the antenna produces a maximum signal $\mathscr{E}_{max} = 100\ \mu\text{V}$. Then at resonance, where $\phi = 0$, the time average of the signal's power is, from Eq. 32.60,

$$P_{av}(\omega_{89.7}) = \tfrac{1}{2}\mathscr{E}_{max}I(\omega_{89.7}) = \frac{1}{2}\frac{\mathscr{E}_{max}^2}{R}$$

$$= \frac{(1.00 \times 10^{-4}\ \text{V})^2}{2(0.100\ \Omega)} = 5.00 \times 10^{-8}\ \text{W}, \qquad (5)$$

where we have substituted from Eq. 2 for $I(\omega_{89.7})$. The signal's average power at $\omega = \omega_{89.5}$ is

$$P_{av}(\omega_{89.5}) = \tfrac{1}{2}\mathscr{E}_{max}I(\omega_{89.5})\cos\phi.$$

The power factor at 89.5 MHz is given by Eq. 32.62:

$$\cos\phi = \frac{R}{Z} = \frac{R}{\sqrt{R^2 + (\omega_{89.5}L - 1/\omega_{89.5}C)^2}}.$$

Therefore the average power at 89.5 MHz, when we substitute this expression for $\cos\phi$ and the expression for $I(\omega_{89.5})$ using Eq. 1, is

$$P_{av}(\omega_{89.5}) = \frac{1}{2}\frac{\mathscr{E}_{max}^2 R}{R^2 + (\omega_{89.5}L - 1/\omega_{89.5}C)^2}.$$

We can use Eqs. 4 and 5 to write this as

$$P_{av}(\omega_{89.5}) = \frac{1}{2}\frac{\mathscr{E}_{max}^2}{R}h^2 = P_{av}(\omega_{89.7})h^2$$

$$= (5.00 \times 10^{-8}\ \text{W})(1.00 \times 10^{-4}) = 5.00 \times 10^{-12}\ \text{W}.$$

So the current at 89.5 MHz is 100 times smaller than the peak current $I(\omega_0)$ at resonance, and the time average of the power of the input signal at 89.5 MHz is down by a factor of 10^4, which is a very small power value compared to the signal we want.

Guided Problem 32.8 *RLC* circuit

A series *RLC* circuit with $R = 10.0\ \Omega$, $L = 400\ \text{mH}$, and $C = 2.0\ \mu\text{F}$ is connected to an AC source of emf $\mathscr{E} = \mathscr{E}_{max}\sin\omega t$, which has amplitude $\mathscr{E}_{max} = 100\ \text{V}$. The angular frequency is $\omega = 4000\ \text{s}^{-1}$, and the time-dependent current is given by $i = I\sin(\omega t - \phi)$.

(*a*) Calculate the amplitude I of the current and the phase constant ϕ that represents the phase difference between the current and the source emf.

(*b*) What is the ratio of the potential-difference amplitude V_L across the inductor to the potential-difference amplitude V_C across the capacitor?

❶ **GETTING STARTED**

1. Draw a phasor diagram for the circuit.

❷ **DEVISE PLAN**

2. What quantities must you know in order to calculate the current amplitude?
3. What quantities must you know in order to calculate the phase constant?
4. How can you determine the values of the amplitudes V_C and V_L?
5. How can you determine the value of X_C you need for Eq. 32.15 and the value of X_L you need for Eq. 32.27?

❸ **EXECUTE PLAN**

6. You have all the data you need to obtain a value for I from Eq. 32.42. However, you have surely noticed by now that many circuit problems require you to calculate ωL and $1/\omega C$, so it is usually most efficient to begin by calculating these two values and then the impedance.
7. Calculate the current amplitude.
8. Calculate the phase constant.
9. Calculate the ratio V_L/V_C.

❹ **EVALUATE RESULT**

10. Compute the resonant angular frequency ω_0.
11. When $\omega = 4000\ \text{s}^{-1}$, is the circuit being driven at an angular frequency greater than or less than the resonant angular frequency?
12. What does this tell you about the expected current? About the expected ratio V_L to V_C?

Questions and Problems

For instructor-assigned homework, go to MasteringPhysics® MP

Dots indicate difficulty level of problems: • = *easy*, •• = *intermediate*, ••• = *hard*; CR = *context-rich problem.*

32.1 Alternating currents

1. A fully charged parallel-plate capacitor is connected to an inductor as shown in Figure P32.1. What is the time average of the magnitude of the magnetic field produced in the inductor? •

Figure P32.1

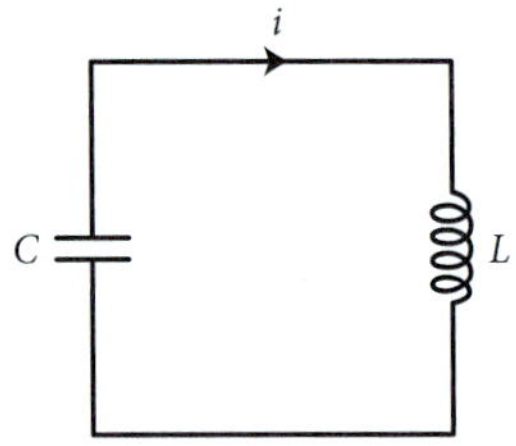

2. (*a*) If each vertical gray line in *Principles* Figure 32.4*b* represents 0.020 s, what is the frequency of the oscillation? (*b*) What is the average potential difference across the capacitor in one cycle? •
3. For the circuit shown in *Principles* Figure 32.4*a*, let the period T of the oscillation be 1.0 s. Identify the instant(s) at which the energy stored in the inductor reaches a maximum. •
4. (*a*) For the circuit shown in Figure P32.4*a*, draw (qualitative) curves showing the current as a function of time and the potential difference across the parallel-plate capacitor as a function of time. Assume that the capacitor is fully charged at $t = 0$ and that the potential is positive when the upper plate is positively charged, and use the current reference direction shown. (*b*) Repeat for the circuit in Figure P32.4*b*. ••

Figure P32.4 (*a*) (*b*)

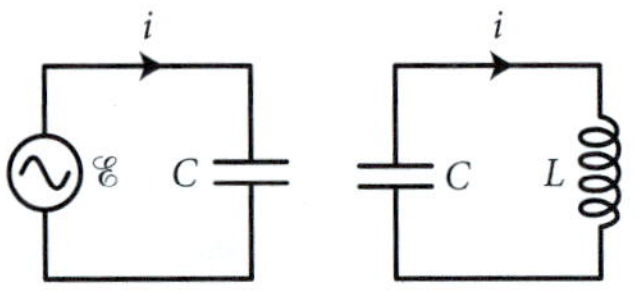

5. Two circuits X and Y each contain a parallel-plate capacitor and may contain other elements as well. The capacitors are identical, and the potential difference across each is shown in Figure P32.5. Which circuit—X, Y, or both—could contain a resistor, and under what circumstances could it/they contain a resistor? ••

Figure P32.5

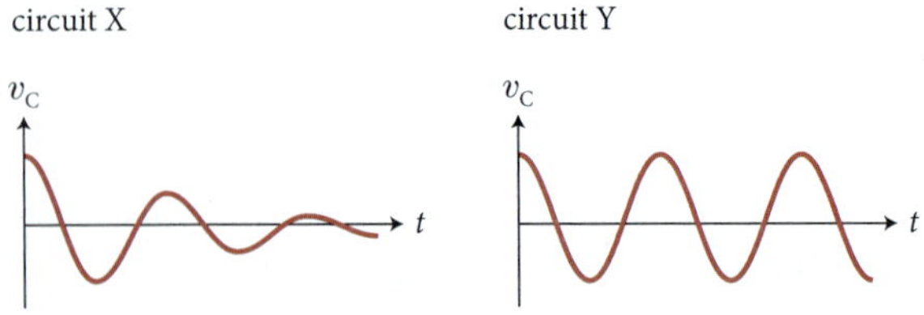

6. In an LC circuit like the one shown in Figure P32.1, which of these quantities simultaneously reach their maximum values: $|v_C|$, $|q_C|$, $|i|$, $|B|$, $|U^E|$, $|U^B|$? ••
7. A parallel-plate capacitor is fully charged and connected to an inductor. The capacitor initially stores charge q and electric potential energy U^E. Once the circuit is closed, charge carriers flow from the capacitor, producing a current in the circuit. When the charge on the capacitor has been reduced to $q/2$, what is the magnetic potential energy U^B stored in the inductor? Report your answer in terms of U^E. ••
8. If the circuit in Figure P32.8 operates at 60 Hz with $\mathscr{E}_{max} = 170$ V and $R = 9.0\ \Omega$, how much energy is dissipated in the resistor in 0.75 s? ••

Figure P32.8

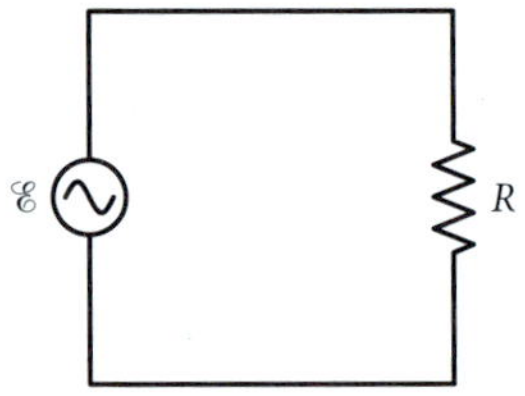

9. A circuit consists of a parallel-plate capacitor, an inductor, and a switch, which is initially open. The capacitor plates have an area of 1.00×10^{-4} m^2 and are held 0.100 mm apart by a thin layer of barium titanate. The capacitor is charged to a potential difference of 10 V, and then the switch is closed. How much charge remains on the capacitor at the instant the energy stored in the inductor has increased to 85% of its maximum? •••
10. In an LC circuit, there is always some energy dissipation as electrical energy is converted to thermal energy. (*a*) What property of the circuit is responsible for electrical energy being converted to thermal energy? (*b*) Describe the shape of a graph showing the charge on one capacitor plate as a function of time. (*c*) What sort of function would describe the rate at which energy is converted? [Hint: See the discussion of damped mechanical oscillators in Chapter 15.] •••

32.2 AC circuits

11. Draw a phasor diagram at instant t_0 for the circuit element whose instantaneous current and instantaneous potential difference are shown in Figure P32.11. •

Figure P32.11

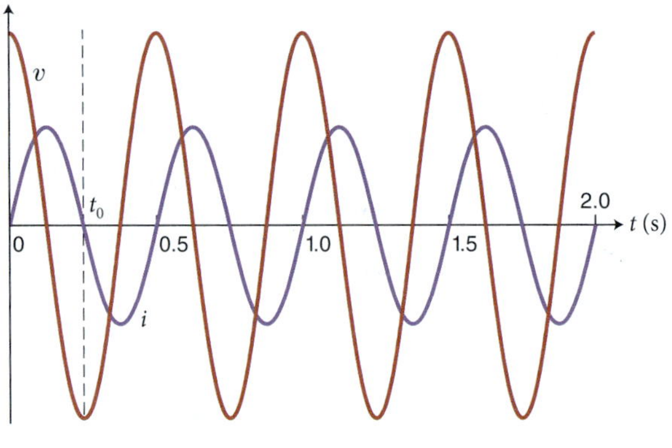

12. Draw a phasor diagram for the current and potential difference represented in Figure P32.12 at the instant $t = T$. Be sure to note which way it is rotating. •

Figure P32.12

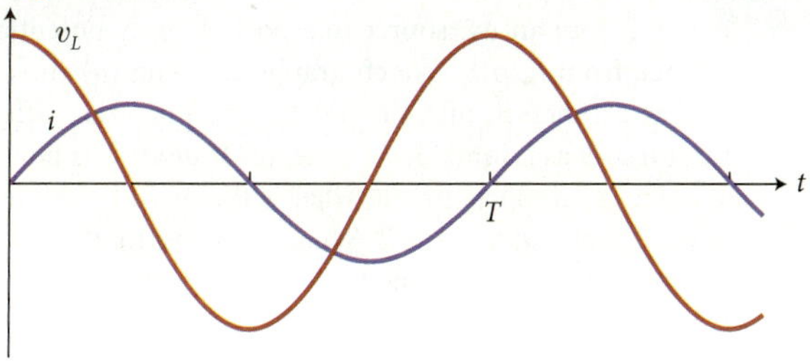

13. In a circuit consisting of an inductor connected to a nonsinusoidal AC source, the current varies as a function of time as shown in Figure P32.13. Sketch the potential difference across the inductor as a function of time. ••

Figure P32.13

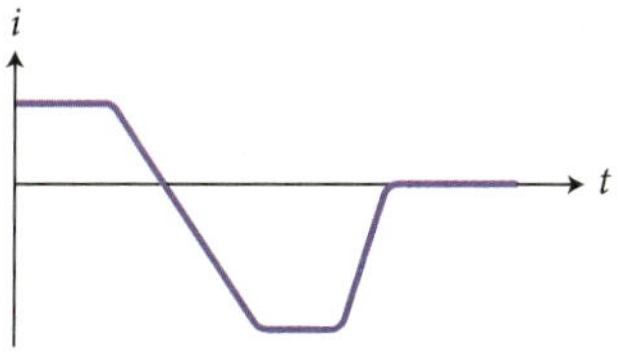

14. The phasor diagram in Figure P32.14 shows the potential difference across a circuit element and the current through the element at $t = 0$. (*a*) Is the element a resistor, capacitor, or inductor? (*b*) On a single graph, sketch a curve showing v as a function of time and a curve showing i as a function of time. ••

Figure P32.14

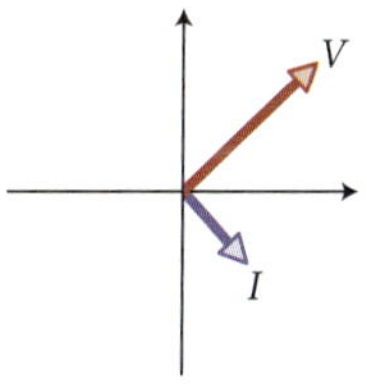

15. Figure P32.15 shows, for an AC circuit, the current phasor and a potential difference phasor at $t = 0$ and at $t = 1.0$ s. In each case, assume phasor magnitudes $I = 1.0$ A and $V = 9.0$ V. Give as many details about this circuit as you can. ••

Figure P32.15

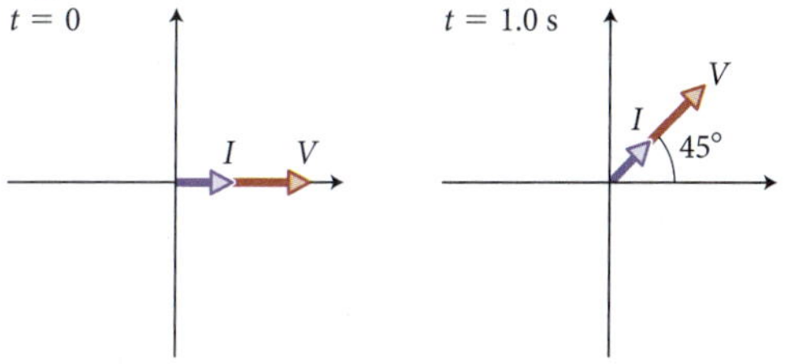

16. Figure P32.16 shows, for a circuit consisting of one element and an AC source, the current through the element as a function of time and the potential difference across the element. Is the element an inductor, a capacitor, or a resistor? ••

Figure P32.16

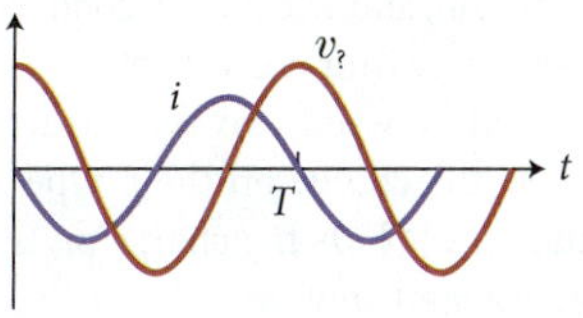

17. In a circuit consisting of a nonsinusoidal AC source plus one additional element, the instantaneous current varies as shown in Figure P32.17. Sketch the potential difference across the additional element as a function of time if that element is (*a*) a capacitor and (*b*) an inductor. •••

Figure P32.17

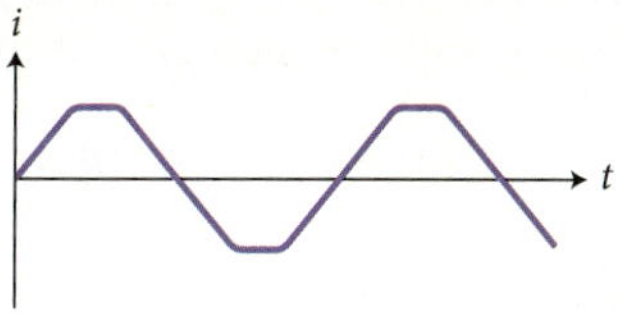

18. A friend has built an AC circuit for you to analyze. You know the circuit contains a resistor, but it also contains another element. Because you know the circuit components available to your friend, you know that the unknown element must be a 0.32-F capacitor, a 0.32-mF capacitor, a 6.28-mH inductor, or a 62.8-mH inductor. Figure P32.18 shows curves for the current through the unknown element and the potential difference across it. The maximum current is 1.00 mA, and the maximum potential difference is 1.00 V. Which of the four available elements did your friend use, and how do you know? •••

Figure P32.18

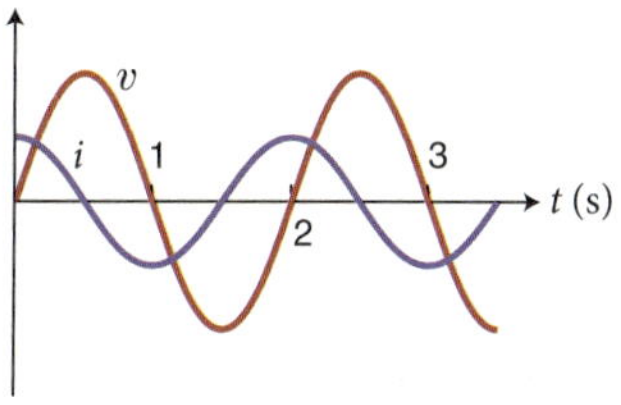

32.3 Semiconductors

19. A sample contains 3.0×10^{22} Si atoms and nothing else. (*a*) How many valence electrons does the sample contain? (*b*) How many of the valence electrons in the sample can conduct electricity? •
20. Silicon is doped with the following elements. In each case, is the resultant extrinsic semiconductor n-type or p-type: indium, gallium, phosphorus, boron, arsenic, aluminum, antimony? •
21. Conduction in a semiconductor can be greatly enhanced by the addition of very small quantities of dopant atoms, even in the parts-per-million range. Explain how the addition of such a tiny percentage of dopant atoms can increase the conduction by a significant factor. •
22. Unlike electrons, the holes in a semiconductor do not leave the semiconductor in which they are formed. Yet, holes can be thought of as positive charge carriers. When a hole has traveled to the edge of the semiconductor and reaches an electrical lead, where does it go? ••
23. You have an intrinsic semiconductor, a p-type semiconductor, and an n-type semiconductor. The doped samples each contain the same number density of dopant atoms. Which of the three semiconductors do you expect to have (*a*) the greatest ability to carry current when the three are connected to identical batteries, (*b*) the greatest number of electrons, and (*c*) the greatest number of holes entering the battery as they leave the semiconductor? ••
24. You have ordered a 10.00 mm × 10.00 mm × 2.000 mm sheet of pure silicon from a laboratory supply company, but the sheet the company sends has a mass of 463.05 mg. You know that the company also produces silicon doped with

boron, and you wonder if there may have been some contamination. The mass densities are $\rho_{Si} = 2329.6\ kg/m^3$ and $\rho_B = 2340\ kg/m^3$, and the atomic weights are B = 10.81 atomic units, Si = 28.085 atomic units. Determine as much information as possible about the contamination of your sheet. If you need pure silicon for its conduction properties, is this sheet likely to meet your needs? •••

32.4 Diodes, transistors, and logic gates

25. Which circuit in Figure P32.25 produces the greatest current in the emitter? •

Figure P32.25

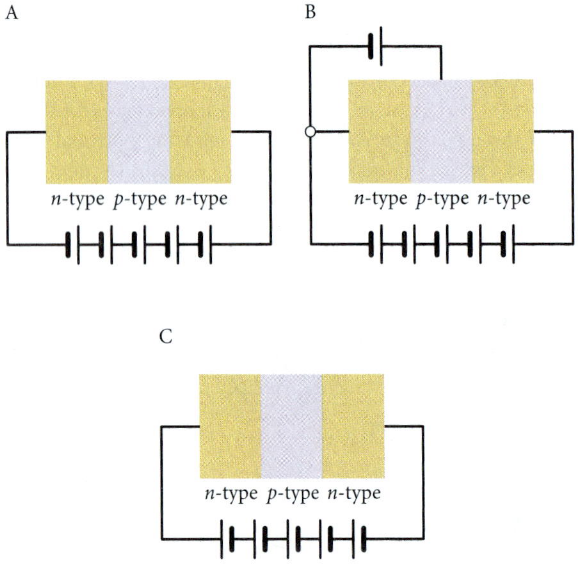

26. The two transistors in Figure P32.26 are connected to each other by wires and also connected to input wires at terminals A and B. The output of this combination depends on the inputs at A and B. In terms of this circuit's reaction to input at A and B, which type of logical operation is performed? •

Figure P32.26

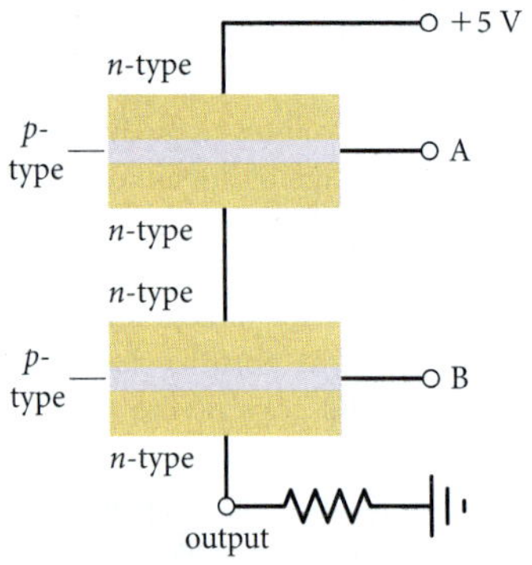

27. Is the light bulb in Figure P32.27 lit? •

Figure P32.27

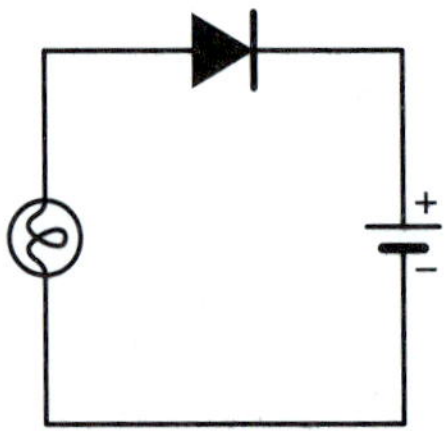

28. The rectifier shown in Figure P32.28 converts the alternating emf from an AC source to a positive-only potential difference from *a* to *b*. Sketch graphs showing (*a*) the source emf as a function of time and (*b*) the potential difference from *a* to *b* as a function of time. (*c*) If diode 1 is blown out and acts as an open circuit, what is the output potential difference from *a* to *b*? (*d*) What happens to the potential difference from *a* to *b* if diode 1 operates normally but diode 2 is blown out? ••

Figure P32.28

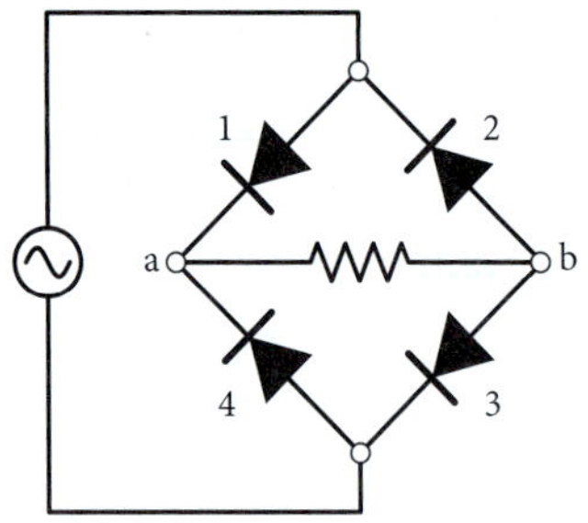

29. The circuit diagram for a rectifier is typically drawn with a resistor in the center. Would the rectifier function if this resistor were replaced by a capacitor? ••

30. The logic gate in Figure P32.30 contains four field-effect transistors. Each of the gates A–D of the transistors may be positively biased (Y in the table) or not (N in the table). Depending on the various bias combinations, charge carriers may or may not flow through the circuit. Fill in the output column of the table. ••

Figure P32.30

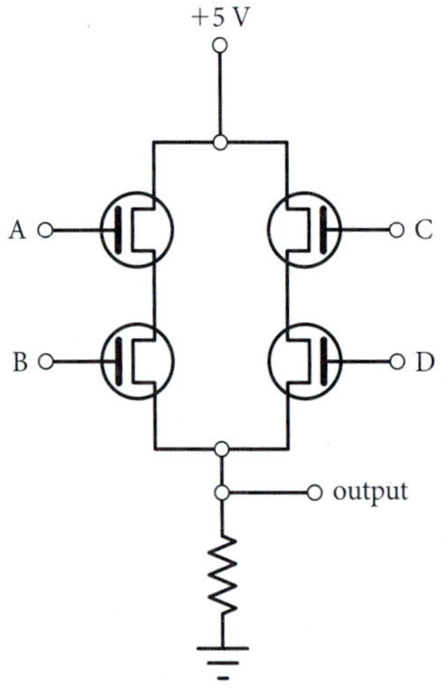

A	B	C	D	output
Y	Y	Y	Y	
Y	N	Y	Y	
Y	Y	Y	N	
N	N	Y	Y	
N	Y	Y	N	
N	N	N	Y	

31. You have two regions, A and B, of differently doped silicon, with the regions joined together to make a continuous silicon wafer. When the positive terminal of a battery is connected to region A and the negative terminal is connected to region B, no charge carriers flow. When the terminal connections are switched, charge carriers flow. (*a*) When there is a current, in which direction—A to B or B to A—do the positive charge carriers move? (*b*) In which direction do the electrons move? (*c*) Which region is *p*-type and which is *n*-type? (*d*) Which region may contain boron, and which may contain phosphorus? ••

32. Suppose a transistor consists of a very narrow *p*-type material sandwiched between two very wide regions of *n*-type material. (*a*) Is the charge on the *p*-type region positive or negative, and why? (*b*) Is the charge on the *n*-type region positive or negative, and why? ••

33. In Figure P32.33, what combinations of positive bias (input signals) A, B, C, D allow the light bulb to light up? ••

Figure P32.33

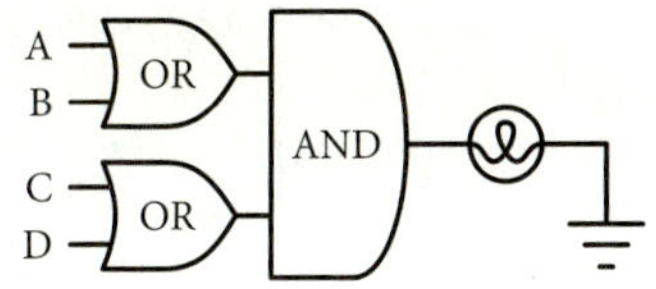

34. If in Figure P32.33 the two gates on the left were both AND and the gate on the right was OR, what combinations of positive bias (input signals) A, B, C, D would allow the light bulb to light up? ••

35. You are using the logic gate of Figure P32.35 to test some transistors and emf sources. The output produced by the logic gate depends on the potential relative to ground at inputs A and B. The only emf sources available to you are AC sources, but using one of them to bias either input A or input B results in an oscillating input potential. Consider how using an AC source affects the potential relative to ground at either A or B. Describe how using an AC source differs from using a DC source, both in general and in the specific function of this circuit. Could any modifications or additions be made to the circuit so that the way it functions with an AC source more closely resembles the way it would function with a DC source? Draw a circuit diagram of any useful modifications. •••

Figure P32.35

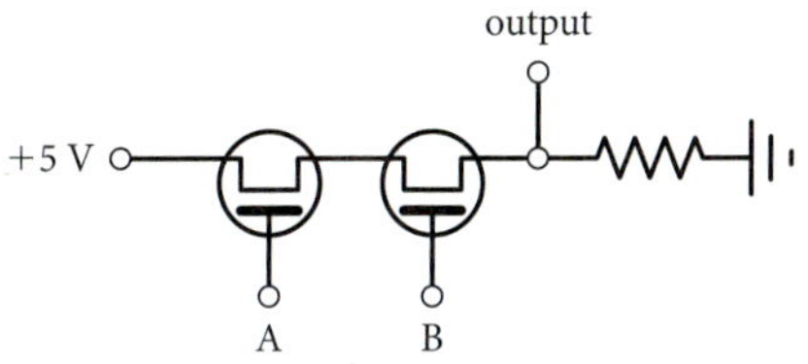

32.5 Reactance

36. What is the reactance of a 50.0-mH inductor when connected to an AC current source that has a frequency of 120 Hz? ••

37. The reactance of a 30.0-μF capacitor is $X_C = 1.0 \times 10^4\ \Omega$. What is the angular frequency of the current through the capacitor? •

38. For the circuit shown in Figure P32.38, what must the frequency f of the AC source be in order for the amplitude V_C of the potential difference across the capacitor to equal the amplitude V_R of the potential difference across the resistor? •

Figure P32.38

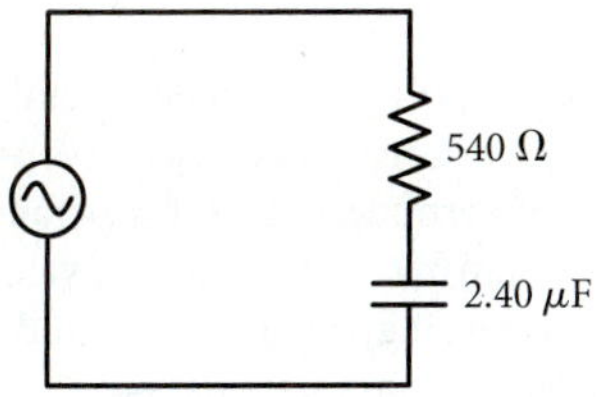

39. A capacitor for which $C = 10$ mF is connected to an AC source. The source emf is given by $\mathscr{E} = \mathscr{E}_{max} \sin \omega t$, with $\mathscr{E}_{max} = 5.0$ V and $\omega = 20\ s^{-1}$. (*a*) What is the amplitude of the current through the capacitor? (*b*) How does the current amplitude change as you increase the source angular frequency? ••

40. An inductor for which $L = 10$ mH is connected to an AC source. The source emf is given by $\mathscr{E} = \mathscr{E}_{max} \sin \omega t$, with $\mathscr{E}_{max} = 5.0$ V and $\omega = 200\ s^{-1}$. (*a*) What is the amplitude of the current through the inductor? (*b*) How does the current amplitude change as you lower the source angular frequency? As you lower the inductance? ••

41. Figure P32.41 shows resistors $R_1 = 30.0\ \Omega$ and $R_2 = 10.0\ \Omega$ connected in parallel to an AC source. (*a*) If the maximum current in the circuit is 2.03 A, what is the amplitude $\mathscr{E}_{max}$ of the AC source? (*b*) If the source emf peaks at $t = 0$, and the frequency is 60.0 Hz, what is the potential difference across each resistor at $t = 20.2$ ms? ••

Figure P32.41

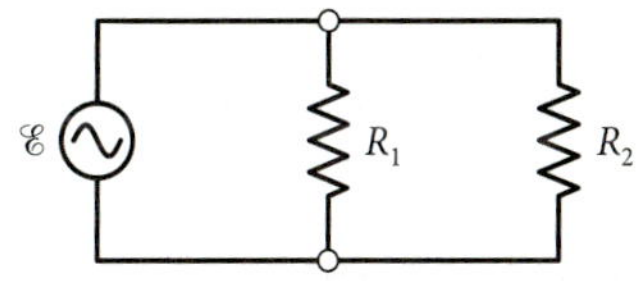

42. You must use a resistor, a capacitor, or an inductor to fill a gap in a circuit. You want to have as much current as possible through this circuit element to ensure that it can be easily detected. Which element should you use if the current through it is (*a*) very high frequency (VHF), (*b*) very low frequency (VLF), (*c*) DC, (*d*) time-varying so that it is sometimes VHF and other times VLF? ••

43. A device is connected to a 60.0-Hz AC source for which the emf is given by $\mathscr{E} = \mathscr{E}_{max} \sin(\omega t)$. If after 5.00 ms the current is 30.9% of its maximum value, is the current leading or lagging the source emf? ••

44. A resistor for which $R = 60.0\ \Omega$ is connected to an AC source. The source emf is given by $\mathscr{E} = \mathscr{E}_{max} \sin(\omega t + \phi_i)$, where $\mathscr{E}_{max} = 5.00$ V, $\omega = 2\pi(30\ \text{Hz})$, and $\phi_i = \pi/4$. At what instants is there no current in the circuit? If you replace the resistor with a capacitor for which $C = 200$ mF, at what instants is there no current in the circuit? ••

45. In the parallel circuit of Figure P32.45, the current amplitude is the same through the inductor branch, the capacitor branch, and the resistor branch. If $L = 20.0$ mH and $C = 10.0$ mF, what are the source angular frequency and the resistance R? •••

Figure P32.45

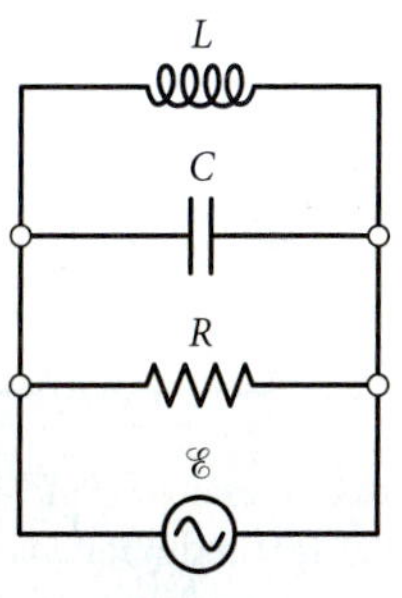

32.6 *RC* and *RLC* series circuits

46. A circuit contains a 1.00×10^3-Ω resistor and a 5.00×10^2-mH inductor in series. What is the impedance of the circuit when a 1.00-kHz AC source is used? ••

47. In an *RLC* series circuit driven by an AC source, the amplitude of the potential difference across the inductor is 29.0 V and that across the capacitor is 13.0 V. If the amplitude of the current through the 900-Ω resistor is 5.00 mA, what is the amplitude of the source emf? •

48. An *RC* series circuit consists of an AC source, a 6.00-mF capacitor, and a 20.0-Ω resistor. If the source emf is given by $\mathscr{E} = \mathscr{E}_{max}\sin(\omega t)$, where $\mathscr{E}_{max} = 5.00$ V and $\omega = 10.0\ s^{-1}$, what is the current amplitude? •

49. A circuit consists of an AC source wired in series to a 1000-Ω resistor and a 1.00-μF capacitor. For a source emf amplitude $\mathscr{E}_{max} = 35.0$ V, calculate the phase constant ϕ and the amplitudes V_C and V_R if the source frequency is (*a*) 60 Hz and (*b*) 2100 Hz. ••

50. A circuit consists of an AC source, for which $\mathscr{E}_{max} = 18$ V, in series with a 1200-Ω resistor and a capacitor. If the amplitude of the potential difference across the resistor is $V_R = 9.0$ V when the source operates at 1500 Hz, what is the capacitance of the capacitor? ••

51. A 120-V AC source has a frequency of 60.0 Hz and produces the same maximum current in two series circuits. Each circuit contains a 100-Ω resistor. Circuit 1 contains a 4.50-mF capacitor, and circuit 2 contains an inductor. What is the inductance in circuit 2? ••

52. You need a filter circuit to eliminate a 60-Hz signal and lower frequencies. The load you are trying to drive has a resistance of 50 Ω. You decide to design a low-pass filter that has a cutoff frequency of 200 Hz. If you use the circuit shown in Figure P32.52, what capacitance *C* should you use? What fraction of any 60-Hz signal potential difference passes through this circuit? ••

Figure P32.52

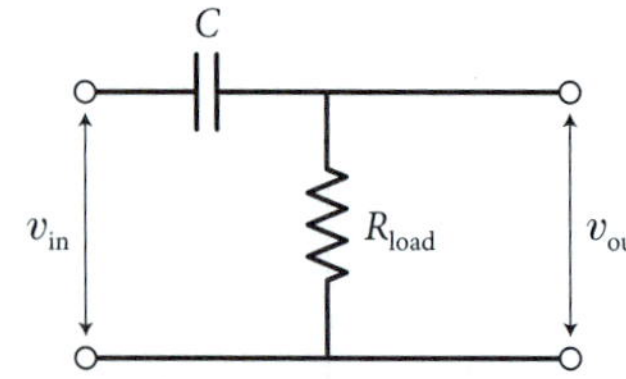

53. (*a*) Construct a phasor diagram for the circuit shown in Figure P32.53. (*b*) What is the phase constant if $C_1 = 1.00\ \mu F$, $C_2 = 3.00\ \mu F$, $R_1 = 200\ \Omega$, $R_2 = 400\ \Omega$, and $\omega = 4000\ s^{-1}$? ••

Figure P32.53

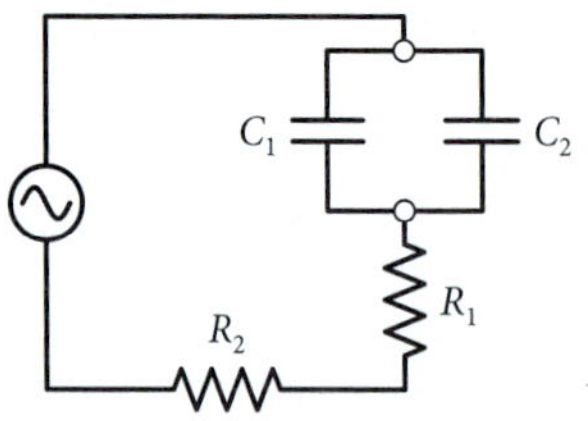

54. A loudspeaker has a resistance of 8.00 Ω. If you connect it in series with a 10.0-mH inductor, what percentage of the original maximum current are you going to get for a sound that has a pure frequency of 1000 Hz? ••

55. In the circuit shown in Figure P32.55, the current amplitude through the *RL* branch is the same as that through the *RC* branch. If $R = 10.0\ \Omega$ and $C = 50.0\ \mu F$, and the source operates at $\omega = 80.0\ s^{-1}$, what is the inductance *L*? ••

Figure P32.55

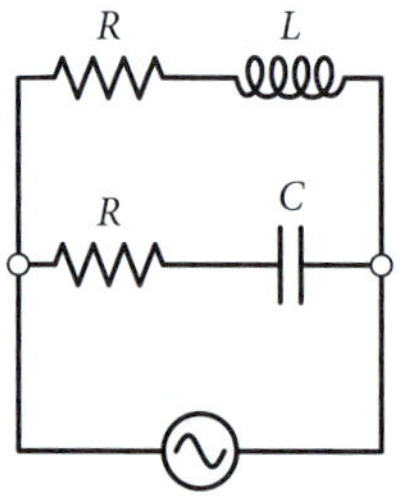

56. In an *RC* series circuit consisting of a 20.0-Ω resistor, a 300-μF capacitor, and an AC source, the source frequency is $150\ s^{-1}$. If the current has its maximum value at $t = 0$, at what later instant is the source emf at its maximum value? ••

57. A 200-Hz power source in a series *RLC* circuit applies an AC potential difference that has an amplitude of 60 V. The current amplitude is 1.0 A, and the phasor diagram for the circuit is shown in Figure P32.57. What is the resistance of the circuit? ••

Figure P32.57

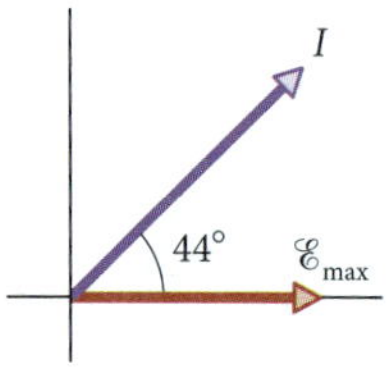

58. (*a*) What can you say, at all instants, about v_R, v_C, and v_L in the parallel circuit of Figure P32.58? (*b*) Construct a phasor diagram for V_R, V_C, V_L, and $\mathscr{E}$ and a phasor diagram for i_R, i_C, and i_L. (*c*) What is the current in the source? (*d*) Show that the current is a minimum at the frequency $\omega = \sqrt{1/LC}$. •••

Figure P32.58

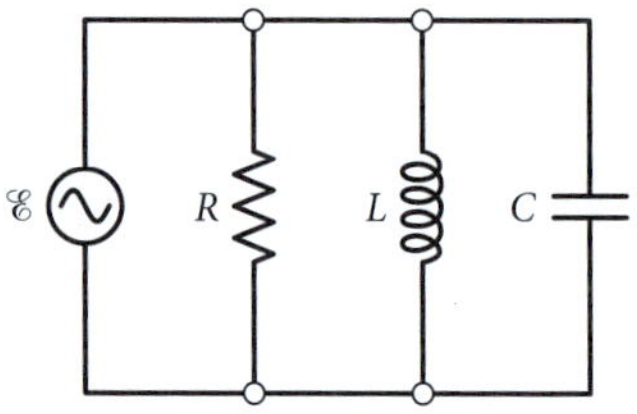

59. Two AC potential differences $v_1 = V_1\sin(\omega t + \phi_1)$ and $v_2 = V_2\sin(\omega t + \phi_2)$ are added according to

$$v_{sum} = V\sin(\omega t + \phi) = v_1 + v_2 = V_1\sin(\omega t + \phi_1) + V_2\sin(\omega t + \phi_2),$$

with $\omega = 10.0\ s^{-1}$, $V_1 = 5.00$ V, and $V_2 = 8.00$ V. At $t = 0$, $v_1(t = 0) = 4.50$ V and $v_2(t = 0) = 3.70$ V. (*a*) Use phasors to determine values for *V* and ϕ in the expression $v_{sum} = V\sin(\omega t + \phi)$ and a value for $v(t = 0.0500\ s)$. (*b*) Repeat using trigonometry, and then compare your results from the two methods. •••

60. In the circuit shown in Figure P32.60, $\mathscr{E} = \mathscr{E}_{max}\sin\omega t$ and $\omega = 100\ s^{-1}$. If $R = 20.0\ \Omega$, $R_C = 18.0\ \Omega$, and $R_L = 15.0\ \Omega$, what must the values of *L* and *C* be in order for the current amplitude *I* to be the same in branches 1, 2, and 3? •••

Figure P32.60

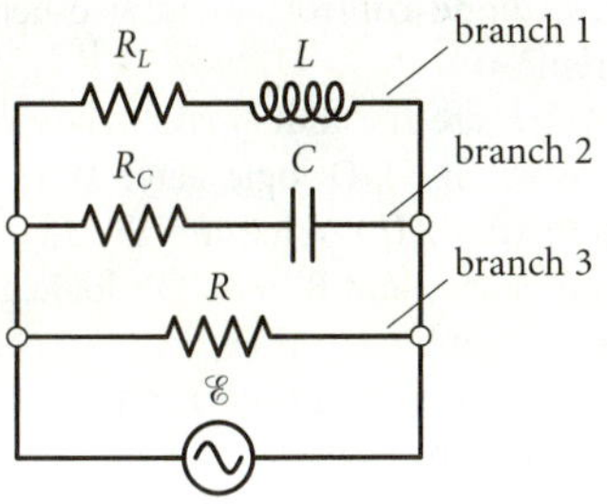

32.7 Resonance

61. An *RLC* circuit consists of a 20-μF capacitor, a 300-Ω resistor, and a 50-mH inductor connected in series with an AC source. What is the resonant angular frequency for this circuit? •

62. A 6.00-mH solenoid is connected in series with a 1.0-μF capacitor and an AC source. The solenoid has internal resistance 3.0 Ω, which can be treated as a series resistor in the circuit. (*a*) What is the resonant angular frequency? (*b*) If the source emf amplitude is $\mathscr{E}_{max} = 15$ V, what is the current amplitude at the resonant angular frequency? •

63. A circuit contains an electromagnet that can be modeled as an inductor of inductance 0.80 H in series with a resistance of 0.50 Ω. If you want to add a capacitor in series with the electromagnet to make the circuit resonate at 380 s^{-1}, what value of *C* must you use? •

64. A series *RLC* circuit is driven by an AC source at resonance. The resistor has a resistance of $R = 10\ \Omega$, and the AC source has an emf amplitude of $\mathscr{E}_{max} = 12$ V. What is the current amplitude? •

65. An *RLC* series circuit initially has resonant angular frequency ω_{0i}. Circuit elements are then changed such that, for any fixed operating angular frequency, both the capacitive reactance and the inductive reactance are twice their initial values. What is the resonant angular frequency ω_{0f} after the changes are made? ••

66. An *RLC* series circuit has $X_C = X_L = R$. When the circuit is operating at resonance, the current amplitude is 1.0 A. When the angular frequency of the current is doubled, what is the new current amplitude? ••

67. An inductor resonates at $4.08 \times 10^4\ s^{-1}$ when placed in series with a 2.00-μF capacitor. When driven at that resonant angular frequency, an AC source for which $\mathscr{E}_{max} = 5.00$ V produces a 0.400-A current in the circuit. What is the inductance? What is the resistance in the circuit? ••

68. In Figure P32.68, $C_1 = 1.00\ \mu$F, $C_2 = 2.00\ \mu$F, and $L = 47.0$ mH. Which circuit has the lower resonant angular frequency, and what is that resonant angular frequency? ••

Figure P32.68

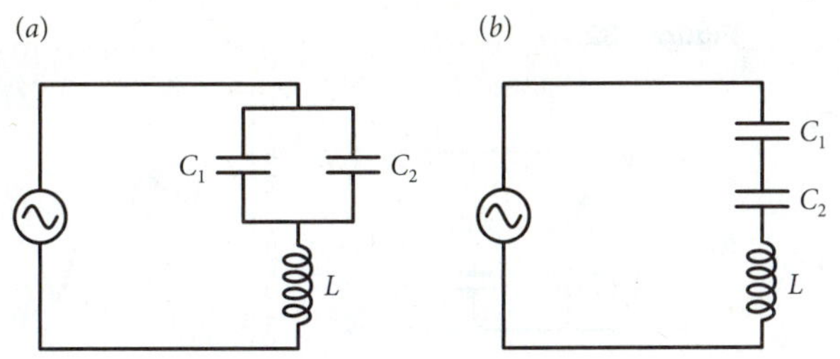

69. An *RLC* series circuit contains an AC source of emf for which $\mathscr{E}_{max} = 30.0$ V, a 5.00-Ω resistor, a 4.00-mH inductor, and an 8.00-μF capacitor. What are (*a*) the resonant angular frequency and (*b*) the current amplitude if it is driven at the resonant angular frequency? (*c*) If a 1.00-kHz, 30.0-V source is used, what is the current amplitude? ••

70. An *RLC* series circuit has a 350-mH inductor and a 25.0-Ω resistor connected to a 50.0-Hz AC power source, and a variable capacitor. (*a*) To what capacitance value must it be set in order to have the circuit be at resonance? (*b*) If the source produces $\mathscr{E}_{rms} = 120$ V, what is the maximum potential difference across the inductor and the capacitor at resonance? ••

71. You want to build an AM radio that uses an *RLC* circuit for tuning. The circuit consists of a 30.0-Ω resistor, a 15.0-μH inductor, and an adjustable capacitor. At what capacitance should the capacitor be set in order to receive the signal from a station that broadcasts at 870 kHz? How would you make the tuning more selective? ••

72. The resonant angular frequency is ω_0 in two identical *RLC* circuits 1 and 2. After determining that the power delivered by the source at resonance is too high, you reduce the angular frequency of the source of circuit 1 to $\omega_1 = \omega_0/2$. To what value $\omega_2 \neq \omega_1$ must you change the angular frequency of the source of circuit 2 in order to have the power delivered by the source of circuit 1 equal that of circuit 2? •••

32.8 Power in AC circuits

73. An *RLC* circuit consists of a 200-Ω resistor, a 300-μF capacitor, and a 3.00-H inductor. The circuit is connected to a power outlet that has a peak emf of 170 V and oscillates at 400 Hz. What is the average rate at which energy is dissipated in this circuit? •

74. A toaster oven has a resistive heating element. The average rate at which it dissipates energy as thermal energy is 1.00 kW. In the United States, emf amplitude in household circuits is $\mathscr{E}_{max} = 170$ V and the AC oscillation rate is 60 Hz. What is the root-mean-square current through the heating element? •

75. An AC power line has a current amplitude of 4.00 A and a resistance of 0.500 Ω. At what average rate is energy lost from the line? •

76. For household electrical outlets in the United States, the root-mean-square value of the source emf is 120 V. (*a*) For a hair dryer rated at 1875 W, what are the root-mean-square current and the current amplitude? Ignore any capacitive and inductive reactance in the hair dryer circuit. (*b*) If an equally powerful hair dryer is to be sold in Germany, where household outlets have $\mathscr{E}_{rms} = 220$ V, what are I_{rms} and *I*? ••

77. In the first 100.0 ms after the switch on an *RLC* circuit is closed, the resistor dissipates 5.005 J of energy. In the first 200.0 ms, the resistor dissipates 10.03 J of energy. If the circuit contains a 70.0-mH inductor, what is the smallest possible inductive reactance of the circuit? ••

78. For the circuit of Problem 69, what is the average rate at which energy is delivered by the source when the circuit is operated at the resonant frequency? When it is operated at 1.00 kHz? What is the power factor in each case? ••

79. An *RLC* series circuit containing a 6.00-mH inductor, a 100-Ω resistor, a 4.00-μF capacitor, and an AC source for which $\mathscr{E}_{max} = 30.0$ V is operated at an angular frequency of 5000 s^{-1}. Determine the phase constant, the power factor, the impedance, the rms emf for the source, the rms current, and the average rate at which energy is delivered by the source. ••

80. A 120-V AC circuit has a 20.0-Ω resistor connected in series to a capacitor for which the capacitive reactance is $X_C = 35.0\ \Omega$. (*a*) What is the phase constant? (*b*) What is the average rate at which energy is dissipated in the circuit? (*c*) If the resistance in the circuit is 25.0 Ω, what would the capacitive reactance have to be in order for the power factor to be 0.25? ••

81. An *RLC* series circuit containing a 5.0-Ω resistor, a 15-mH inductor, and a 10-mF capacitor is driven at a frequency of 8.0 Hz by an AC source for which $\mathscr{E}_{max} = 8.0$ V. At what average rate is energy dissipated? What is the average dissipation rate at resonance? ••

82. You need to design a power cable to connect an energy-storage facility located at the ocean shore to a wind turbine farm 2 km offshore (Figure P32.82). The farm can deliver energy at an average rate of 45 MW, and you need to run a single cable to deliver energy at this rate (the turbines and the storage facility share a common ground). The cable has a resistance *R*, leading to a loss of energy during transmission. Assume that all other loads on the circuit (electrical appliances in all the buildings serviced by this facility) have no capacitive or inductive reactance. Using different transformers at either end, you can change the value of $\mathscr{E}_{max}$ and *I* while maintaining the same rate at which electrical energy is delivered to the cable. Should you choose a high or a low value for $\mathscr{E}_{max}$? •••

Figure P32.82

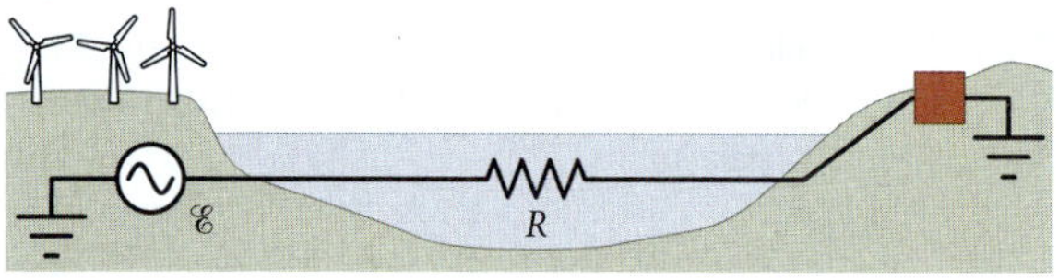

83. An *RLC* series circuit consists of a 450-Ω resistor, a 3.00-mF capacitor, and a 1.00-H inductor. The circuit is driven by a power source that oscillates at 20.0 Hz and has an $\mathscr{E}_{rms}$ value of 60.0 V. The power source is switched on at $t = 0$, and at that instant the emf is at its maximum value. Calculate the power supplied at (*a*) $t = 0.0200$ s, (*b*) $t = 0.0375$ s, and (*c*) $t = 0.500$ s. •••

Additional problems

84. Sketch the phasor diagram for v_C, v_L, and the instantaneous current for the circuit shown in Figure P32.84 at an arbitrary instant $t \neq 0$. If the potential difference across the capacitor is a maximum at $t = 0$, what are the initial phases of v_C, v_L, and *i*? •

Figure P32.84

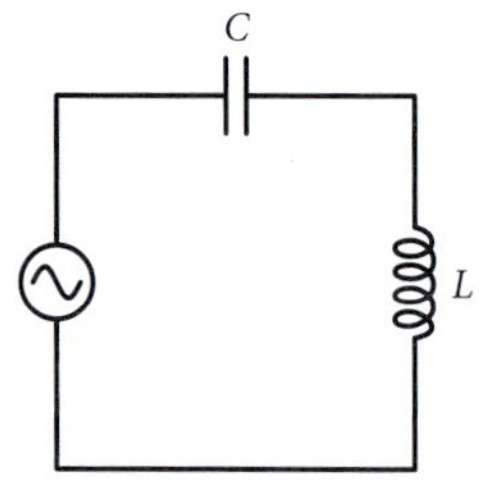

85. A capacitor is connected to an AC source. Sketch a graph showing how the current amplitude changes as you increase the AC angular frequency. •

86. Can a diode control anything other than the direction of current? ••

87. (*a*) What are the four possible combinations for input at A and B in an AND logic gate? What is the output for each combination? (*b*) What are the four possible combinations for input at A and B in an OR logic gate? What is the output for each combination? ••

88. A solenoid can be treated as a series *RL* circuit. If such a solenoid driven by a 60-Hz, 15-V AC source has an inductance of 6.0 mH and a resistance of 3.0 Ω, what are the phase constant and the current amplitude? ••

89. A circuit consisting of an AC source, a 100-Ω resistor, and a 1.00-μF capacitor has an impedance of 1330 Ω. (*a*) What is the source frequency? (*b*) What is the phase difference between the current and the source emf? ••

90. An *RLC* series circuit containing a 20.0-Ω resistor, a 30.0-mH inductor, and a 300-μF capacitor is driven by an AC source at a very high frequency. If the source amplitude is $\mathscr{E}_{max} = 12.0$ V, what can you say about the current in the circuit? ••

91. In the circuit shown in Figure P32.91, the AC source oscillates at 60 Hz and its emf is given by $\mathscr{E} = \mathscr{E}_{max} \sin(2\pi ft)$, where $\mathscr{E}_{max} = 15$ V and $R = 150\ \Omega$. The voltage source is operating at 60 Hz. Sketch, as functions of time, the current, the potential difference, and the power to the resistor. ••

Figure P32.91

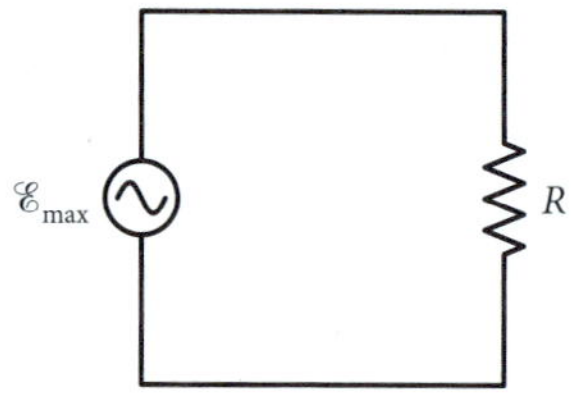

92. What happens with the light bulb shown in Figure P32.92 as you increase the frequency of the AC source? ••

Figure P32.92

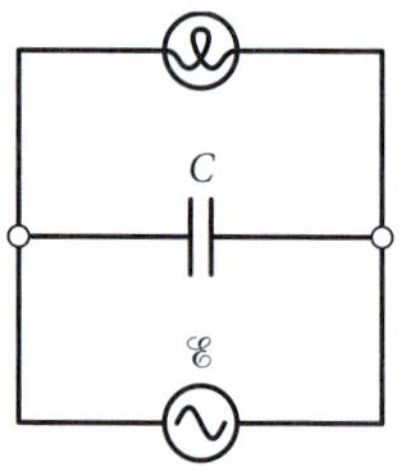

93. A diode *clipper* is a circuit used to eliminate extremes in input potential. If the graph in Figure P32.93 represents input potential as a function of time for the circuit shown, sketch a graph showing the output potential as a function of time. ••

Figure P32.93

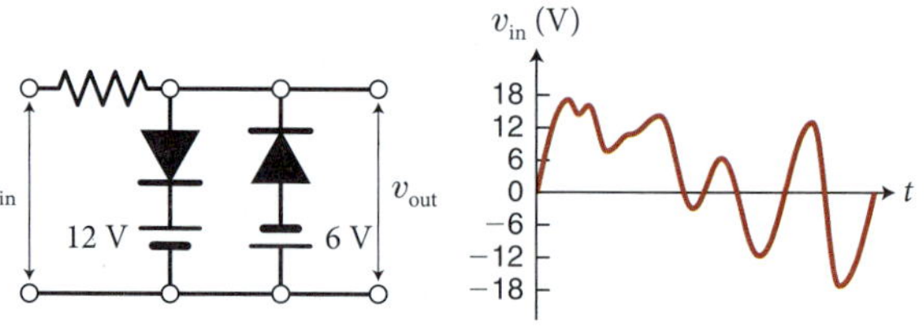

94. Figure P32.94 shows, for an AC circuit, the instantaneous current through a circuit element and the potential difference across the element. What can you determine about the element? ●●●

Figure P32.94

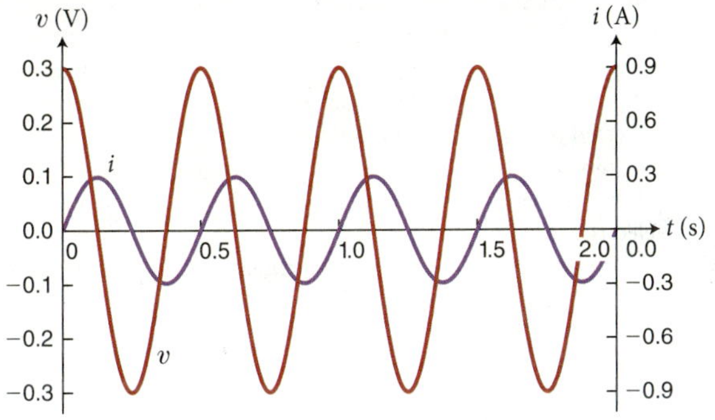

95. Your boss has purchased a new AC power source to run a high-voltage, low-current display, but it is not working. While he is fuming, you look at the owner's manual and discover that this power source produces only half the peak potential difference needed to operate the display. Because you are pretty sure you have a transformer on your workbench that will solve the problem, you tell your boss that you can fix it. When you return to your workbench, you are horrified to discover that the other members of your team have scavenged not only the transformer but most of your other supplies as well! Ignoring hookup wire and solder, you have only two identical capacitors and two identical diodes at your disposal. You collapse onto your lab stool and start thinking about how to word your apology to the boss, when suddenly you realize you can solve the problem after all! ●●● CR

96. The circuit in Figure P32.96 represents your planned design for a wall power supply that will run a radio that usually runs on a 9-V battery. The power supply uses a transformer (not shown) to convert the 110-V AC household emf of the wall outlet to a 9-V AC emf. If you do not add any additional components to this circuit, the potential difference over time is as shown in graph *a*, a typical sinusoidally varying $v(t)$ curve. Batteries supply direct current, however, and a radio designed to run on batteries cannot run on alternating current. If you address this problem by adding a rectifier to your circuit, the potential difference over time is as shown in graph *b*. The radio still will not run properly, though, because the 120-Hz cycle would either render the radio dysfunctional or result in an annoying 120-Hz buzz. By adding a large capacitor in parallel with the rectifier, you can smooth out the potential difference as the capacitor charges and discharges over the course of a cycle. Still, there is going to be a residual 120-Hz "wiggle" on top of the DC signal, as shown in graph *c*. You can filter out this wiggle by using an inductor as a low-pass filter. If the radio has an internal resistance of $R = 20.0\ \Omega$, what inductance value do you need in order to reduce the wiggle by a factor of 2? ●●●

Figure P32.96

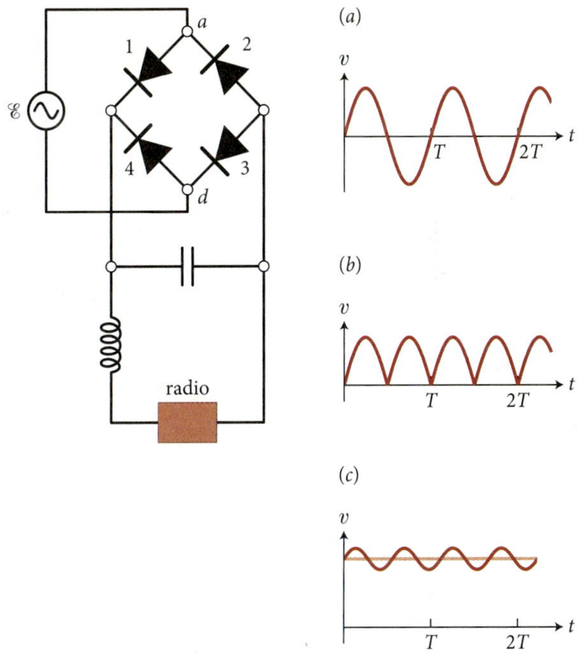

97. The research laboratory you work in is less than a block away from the transmitting antenna of a radio station that broadcasts at 1100 kHz. You notice that every piece of equipment in the lab has 1100-kHz noise in addition to the signals you want, which are in the range from 2 kHz to 5 kHz. You wonder if there is some sort of simple circuit you could add to the lab equipment that would allow your desired frequencies to pass through without much loss, while reducing the 1100-kHz signal by at least a factor of ten. ●●● CR

Answers to Review Questions

1. An alternating current is a time-dependent electric current that periodically changes direction.
2. The current varies sinusoidally. Before the capacitor begins to discharge, the current is zero. As the capacitor discharges, the current increases to its maximum magnitude in one direction, then returns to zero, then increases to its maximum magnitude in the opposite direction, and then returns to zero again to end one cycle. In any nonideal circuit, the amplitude of the current oscillations decays because there is resistance in the circuit.
3. The property is that the potential differences and currents in AC circuits are time-dependent rather than constant.
4. The phase of a sinusoidal function describes how the function depends on time. The two quantities necessary to specify the phase at any instant t are ω, the angular frequency, and ϕ_i, the value of the phase at the instant $t = 0$. Then the phase at any instant t is given by $\omega t + \phi_i$.
5. A phasor is a rotating arrow whose component on a vertical axis can be used to represent oscillating quantities. The vertical component of the phasor represents the value of the oscillating quantity, the phasor length represents the quantity's amplitude, and the angle of the phasor measured counterclockwise from the horizontal axis of the reference circle at any instant represents the quantity's phase $\omega t + \phi_i$ at that instant.
6. Quantity A is said to *lead* quantity B when the maximum value of A during one oscillation cycle occurs before the maximum value of B occurs. Quantity A is said to *lag* quantity B when the maximum value of A during one cycle occurs after the maximum value of B occurs.
7. The current leads the potential difference across the capacitor by 90°, lags the potential difference across the inductor by 90°, and is in phase with the potential difference across the resistor.
8. A semiconductor is a material that has a limited supply of free charge carriers, so that its electrical conductivity is intermediate between that of conductors and that of insulators.
9. An intrinsic semiconductor is chemically pure and its conductivity too small for many practical applications (except as an electrical insulator). An extrinsic semiconductor (also called a doped semiconductor) has a precisely controlled level of impurity atoms (called dopants) introduced so that the conductivity can be adjusted to suit specific applications.
10. In a p-type semiconductor, dopant atoms have fewer valence electrons than the host lattice atoms, creating a deficit of one electron—a hole—in the surrounding covalent bonds. An electron from another covalent bond can move into the hole, as if the hole "attracted" the electron. The hole has now moved to the site previously occupied by the electron, and the process can be repeated. Because the hole moves in a direction opposite the moving electrons, the hole behaves like a positively charged particle moving between lattice sites.
11. Doped silicon semiconductors are classified as p-type (p for *positive*) or n-type (n for *negative*). A p-type semiconductor contains dopant atoms that have fewer valence electrons than the host lattice atoms and thus create holes in the semiconductor lattice; the holes behave like free positive-charge carriers. An n-type semiconductor contains dopant atoms that have more valence electrons than the host lattice atoms, providing free negative-charge carriers.
12. A diode is made up of a p-type silicon semiconductor and an n-type silicon semiconductor in contact with each other.
13. The depletion zone is a thin region containing no free charge carriers that develops at the junction between the n-type and p-type sides of the diode.
14. The depletion zone forms as electrons from the n-type side cross into the p side and fill up holes there, while holes from the p-type side cross into the n side and combine with electrons there. These electron-hole recombinations result in the accumulation of negative charge on the p-type side of the depletion zone and accumulation of positive charge on the n-type side of the zone, with the resulting electric field directed from the n side to the p side.
15. Connecting the n side to the positive terminal and the p side to the negative terminal creates an electric field across the depletion zone directed from n to p; this external field broadens the depletion zone and maintains the condition of no charge carriers able to flow in the diode. Connecting the n side to the negative terminal and the p side to the positive terminal creates an electric field across the zone directed from p to n; when sufficiently strong, this external field shrinks and then eliminates the depletion zone with the result that charge carriers can flow through the diode. Thus, a diode allows electric current in one direction only.
16. It is a potential difference between emitter and base that shrinks the base-collector depletion zone enough to allow electrons to move from emitter to collector, thus creating a current through the transistor.
17. Transistors can function as switches or as current amplifiers.
18. First, two n-type wells are created in a layer of p-type material, then an insulating layer and a metal gate are added above the p-type region. Depletion zones form between the n- and p-type regions, preventing the flow of charge carriers between regions. When the gate receives a small positive charge, holes are driven from the p-type material beneath the gate, and the depletion zones at the boundaries of the two regions of n-type material become joined. A greater positive charge on the gate causes the depletion zone beneath it to be pushed away, creating an n-type channel connecting the two n-type wells and allowing conduction through the n-type materials.
19. A logic gate is a device that accepts two input signals, performs a logical operation on them, and emits the result as an output signal. In integrated circuits such as computer chips, logic gates are often implemented with field-effect transistors.
20. The current and the potential difference oscillate at the same angular frequency. The current amplitude I is directly proportional to the potential-difference amplitude V_C according to $I = \omega C V_C$. The current leads the potential difference by 90°, and so the phase constant of the current is $\phi = -\pi/2$ relative to $\phi = 0$ for the generator.
21. For a circuit containing a capacitor, the amplitude of the potential difference across the capacitor is proportional to the amplitude of the current through the capacitor, and the proportionality constant is the capacitive reactance of the circuit. Capacitive reactance depends on the angular frequency of the oscillation and on the capacitance: $X_C = 1/\omega C$.
22. The current and the potential difference oscillate at the same angular frequency. The current amplitude I is directly proportional to the potential-difference amplitude V_L according to $I = V_L/\omega L$. The current lags the potential difference by 90°, and so the phase constant of the current is $\phi = +\pi/2$ relative to $\phi = 0$ for the generator.
23. For a circuit containing an inductor, the amplitude of the potential difference across the inductor is proportional to the amplitude of the current through the inductor, and the proportionality constant is the inductive reactance of the circuit. Inductive reactance depends on the angular frequency of the oscillation and on the inductance: $X_L = \omega L$.
24. The sum at any given instant is determined by adding up the vertical components of the phasors of all the quantities. The result of this addition is the vertical component of the phasor of the sum, which equals the vector sum of the phasors.
25. The impedance is the ratio of the amplitude of the source emf to the amplitude of the current through the load: $Z = \mathscr{E}_{max}/I$.
26. Equation 32.34 shows that the impedance of a load consisting of a resistor and a capacitor connected in series is very great at low angular frequencies and nearly equal to the resistance at high angular frequencies. Therefore the amplitude of the potential difference across the resistor (the output) is very small if the angular frequency of the source (the input) is low but is nearly equal to the amplitude $\mathscr{E}_{max}$ of the source emf if the source angular frequency is high. This difference

PRACTICE

in impedance allows high-frequency signals to pass through the circuit but weakens low-frequency signals so that they cannot pass through the circuit—the low-frequency signals are filtered out.

27. The resonant angular frequency is the source angular frequency that results in the greatest current amplitude. This occurs when ωL is equal to $1/\omega C$, which means $\omega_0 = 1/\sqrt{LC}$. Inductance and capacitance are the circuit properties that determine the value of ω_0.
28. The current amplitude has its maximum value when the source angular frequency ω equals the circuit's resonant angular frequency ω_0 and decreases both as ω gets smaller than ω_0 and as ω gets greater than ω_0.
29. The maximum current amplitude depends on the resistance in the circuit and on the amplitude of the source emf.
30. The time average of any sinusoidally oscillating quantity is zero, and $I_{av} = 0$ and $\mathscr{E}_{av} = 0$ give no insight into how these quantities change over time. The root-mean-square value of a sinusoidally oscillating quantity is nonzero, however, and so is a more meaningful measure of the quantity.
31. The average power at a resistor is $P_{av} = I^2_{rms}R = \frac{1}{2}I^2R$. The energy is dissipated as thermal energy.
32. The average power at a capacitor or an inductor is zero because the potential difference across either of these circuit elements is 90° out of phase with the current through the element (i leads v_C by 90°, i lags v_L by 90°). In those parts of the oscillation cycle where i and either v_C or v_L have the same sign, the instantaneous power to the element is positive (energy is added to the element by the source); in those parts of the cycle where i and v have opposite signs, the instantaneous power is negative (energy is removed from the element by the source).
33. The power factor is the cosine of the phase difference between the source emf and the current. Because the average power to a load is $P_{av} = \frac{1}{2}\mathscr{E}_{max}I\cos\phi$, the power factor is a measure of the efficiency with which the source delivers energy to the load.

Answers to Guided Problems

Guided Problem 32.2 $I = \sqrt{\dfrac{C}{2L}}\mathscr{E} = 2.2 \times 10^{-3}$ A

Guided Problem 32.4 $\omega_2 = \sqrt{\dfrac{1}{C^2R^2 + 2/\omega_1^2}} = 6.6\ \text{s}^{-1}$

Guided Problem 32.6 The box contains a capacitor and an inductor in series, and $P_{av} = \frac{1}{2}I^2R = 6.0$ W at ω_1 and $P_{av} = 3.0$ W at ω_2.

Guided Problem 32.8 (*a*) $I = \dfrac{\mathscr{E}_{max}}{\sqrt{R^2 + (\omega L - 1/\omega C)^2}} = 6.8 \times 10^{-2}$ A

and $\phi = \tan^{-1}\dfrac{\omega L - 1/\omega C}{R} = 1.6$ rad. (*b*) $\dfrac{V_L}{V_C} = \dfrac{X_L}{X_C} = 13$

PRACTICE

33 PRACTICE Ray Optics

PRACTICE

Chapter Summary

Rays (Sections 33.1, 33.2, 33.3, 33.5)

Concepts A **ray** is a line that represents the direction in which light travels.

For **reflected light,** the **angle of incidence** θ_i is the angle between the incident ray and the normal to the reflecting surface, and the **angle of reflection** θ_r is the angle between the reflected ray and the normal to the surface. The **law of reflection** says that when a ray strikes a smooth surface, $\theta_r = \theta_i$ and the two angles are in the same plane.

Refraction is the bending of light when it travels from one medium to another. The **angle of refraction** is the angle between the refracted ray and the normal to the surface at the interface between the materials.

Light passing from a high-density medium into a lower-density medium is bent away from the normal to the surface at the interface between the media. The **critical angle** θ_c is the angle of incidence for which the angle of refraction is 90°, which means the refracted rays emerge along the interface. If the angle of incidence is greater than θ_c, the light is all reflected back into the denser medium (**total internal reflection**).

An **image** is formed when light rays emanating from an object either intersect or appear to intersect at some location in space. The image is *real* when the rays actually do intersect at the location of the image and *virtual* when the rays do not pass through the location of the image.

Dispersion is the spatial separation of waves of different wavelengths in a light ray. When caused by refraction, the separation occurs because the speed at which each wave in the ray moves through a medium depends on the frequency of the wave.

Fermat's principle states that the path taken by a light ray between any two locations is the path for which the time interval needed for the ray to travel between those locations is a minimum.

Quantitative Tools The **index of refraction** n of a medium is

$$n \equiv \frac{c_0}{c}, \tag{33.1}$$

where c_0 is the speed of light in vacuum and c is the speed of light in the medium.

If light has wavelength λ in vacuum, its wavelength λ_1 in a medium having index of refraction n_1 is

$$\lambda_1 = \frac{\lambda}{n_1}. \tag{33.3}$$

Snel's law: When light passes from a medium having index of refraction n_1 into a medium having index of refraction n_2, the angles and indices satisfy the relationship

$$n_1 \sin\theta_1 = n_2 \sin\theta_2, \tag{33.7}$$

where θ_1 is the angle of incidence and θ_2 is the angle of refraction.

For light traveling from a high-density medium having index of refraction n_2 to a lower-density medium having index of refraction $n_1 < n_2$, the **critical angle** is

$$\theta_c = \sin^{-1}\left(\frac{n_1}{n_2}\right). \tag{33.9}$$

Forming images using thin lenses (Sections 33.4, 33.5, 33.6, 33.8)

Concepts A **lens** is an optical element that redirects light rays by refraction such that they form images. The *axis* of a lens is a line that passes through the lens center and is perpendicular to the lens surface. Rays that run close to the lens axis are called *paraxial* rays. They can be either parallel to the lens axis or at a small angle to it.

Quantitative Tools The **lens equation** is

$$\frac{1}{f} = \frac{1}{o} + \frac{1}{i}, \tag{33.16}$$

where f is the **focal length** of the thin lens, o is the *object distance,* and i is the *image distance.* The sign possibilities for f, o, and i are given in Table 33.2 on the next page.

Rays that are parallel to and close to the axis of a thin *converging* (*convex*) lens converge to a point called the **focal point** (or **focus**) of the lens. For a thin *diverging* (*concave*) lens, rays entering the lens from the left parallel to and close to the axis diverge as though they came from a single point to the left of the lens, called the **focal point.**

The **focal length** of a lens is the distance from the focal point to the center of the lens.

To determine the location and orientation of an image formed by a lens, make a ray diagram using the **principal rays.** See the accompanying Procedure boxes.

The **magnification** of a lens is

$$M \equiv \frac{h'}{h} = -\frac{i}{o}, \qquad (33.17)$$

where h' is the image height and h is the object height. The image is upright if M is positive and inverted if M is negative.

Lensmaker's formula: The focal length of a lens made of material of index of refraction n, having radii of curvature R_1 and R_2, and surrounded by air is given by

$$\frac{1}{f} = (n-1)\left(\frac{1}{R_1} + \frac{1}{R_2}\right). \qquad (33.36)$$

The radii are positive for convex surfaces, negative for concave surfaces, and infinity for planar surfaces.

Table 33.2 Sign conventions for f, i, and o (positive = real; negative = virtual)

Sign	Lens	Mirror
$f > 0$	converging lens	converging mirror
$f < 0$	diverging lens	diverging mirror
$o > 0$	object in front[b] of lens	object in front of mirror
$o < 0$[a]	object behind lens	object behind mirror
$i > 0$	image behind lens	image in front of mirror
$i < 0$	image in front of lens	image behind mirror
$h_i > 0$	image upright	image upright
$h_i < 0$	image inverted	image inverted
$\|M\| > 1$	image larger than object	image larger than object
$\|M\| < 1$	image smaller than object	image smaller than object

[a] Encountered only with lens or mirror combinations.
[b] For both lenses and mirrors, *in front* means *on the side where the rays originate; behind* refers to the opposite side.

PRACTICE

Optical instruments (Section 33.6)

Concepts The lens of the eye forms an image on the retina. The *near point* is the closest object distance at which the eye can focus comfortably, about 0.25 m from the eye for an adult.

A compound microscope uses two converging lenses to form its image. The image formed by the first lens (the *objective* lens) serves as the object for the second lens (the *eyepiece* lens).

A refracting telescope uses two converging lenses to form its image. They are positioned so that the objective lens forms a real image of a distant object and the eyepiece lens forms, at infinity, a virtual image of this real image.

Quantitative Tools The **angular magnification** M_θ of a lens is

$$M_\theta = \left|\frac{\theta_i}{\theta_o}\right|, \qquad (33.18)$$

where θ_i is the angle subtended by the image and θ_o is the angle subtended by the object. For small angles, the angular magnification of a converging lens placed between an object and the eye is

$$M_\theta \approx \frac{0.25\text{ m}}{f}. \qquad (33.21)$$

The *strength* d of a lens measured in diopters is

$$d \equiv \frac{1\text{ m}}{f}. \qquad (33.22)$$

The magnification M of a compound microscope is

$$M = M_1 M_{\theta 2} = \frac{-0.25\text{ m}}{f_2\left(\dfrac{o_1}{f_1} - 1\right)},$$

where M_1 is the magnification of the objective lens, $M_{\theta 2}$ is the angular magnification of the eyepiece lens, o_1 is the distance from the object to the objective lens, f_1 is the focal length of the objective lens, and f_2 is the focal length of the eyepiece lens.

The angular magnification M_θ of a refracting telescope is

$$M_\theta = \left|\frac{\theta_i}{\theta_o}\right| \approx \left|\frac{f_1}{f_2}\right|,$$

where f_1 is the focal length of the objective lens and f_2 is the focal length of the eyepiece lens.

Mirrors (Sections 33.2, 33.7)

Concepts A flat mirror forms a virtual image of an object. The image is just as far behind the mirror as the object is in front of the mirror.

A *concave* spherical mirror focuses incident rays that are parallel to and close to the axis of the mirror to a point in front of the mirror (the **focal point**), corresponding to a real focus. A *convex* spherical mirror disperses the parallel incident rays such that they appear to come from a point behind the mirror (the **focal point**), corresponding to a virtual focus.

To determine the location and orientation of an image formed by a mirror, make a ray diagram showing the three **principal rays.** See the accompanying Procedure boxes.

Quantitative Tools The focal length of a spherical mirror is one-half its *radius of curvature*:

$$f = \frac{R}{2}. \tag{33.23}$$

For a spherical mirror, the relationship of focal length f, object distance o, and image distance i is given by the lens equation:

$$\frac{1}{f} = \frac{1}{o} + \frac{1}{i}. \tag{33.24}$$

The sign possibilities for f, o, and i are given in Table 33.2.

PRACTICE

Review Questions

Answers to these questions can be found at the end of this chapter.

33.1 Rays

1. What has to happen in order for you to see an object?
2. What is a light ray? What is the relationship between a light ray and a light beam?
3. What is a shadow?

33.2 Absorption, transmission, and reflection

4. Describe the three possibilities for what happens to light that falls on an object.
5. What happens to most of the light that strikes an opaque object? To most of the light that strikes a translucent object?
6. State the law of reflection.
7. What is the difference between specular reflection and diffuse reflection?
8. If every ray that strikes a rough surface obeys the law of reflection, why is no image formed?
9. What is an image?
10. What is the difference between a real image and a virtual image?
11. Explain what it means to form an image of an object—for example, in a mirror. Why does an observer see the image of an object placed in front of a mirror as being located behind the mirror?
12. What do the colors of visible light correspond to?
13. How are the wavefronts and rays that represent the propagation of light drawn relative to the direction of propagation and relative to each other?

33.3 Refraction and dispersion

14. What is refraction, and why does it occur?
15. Does the wavelength change when light passes from a medium that has a high mass density into one that has a lower mass density, and if so, how?
16. For a refracting light ray, what are the names of the two angles associated with the bending, and how are their relative sizes related to the relative densities of the media?
17. What is the definition of *critical angle* for light rays undergoing refraction as they move from one medium into another?
18. Describe how total internal reflection occurs.
19. What is Fermat's principle?
20. What is dispersion, and why does it occur?

33.4 Forming images

21. A light ray traveling along a path in medium A is refracted when it enters medium B. If the ray's direction of travel is then reversed, how does its path change as the ray moves through medium B and back into medium A?
22. What are paraxial light rays?
23. For light moving from left to right through a lens, describe the paths of the three principal rays used to locate the image formed by the lens.
24. Describe the difference between the shapes of converging and diverging lens surfaces and the difference in what happens to light rays passing through them.

33.5 Snel's law

25. What is the definition of the index of refraction of a material through which light can pass?
26. How does the wavelength of light traveling in a transparent material depend on the material's index of refraction?
27. What is Snel's law?
28. How does the critical angle for total internal reflection at the boundary between two media with different mass densities depend on the indices of refraction of the media?

33.6 Thin lenses and optical instruments

29. What is the lens equation? What are the sign conventions for the distances f, o, and i in it?
30. What is the expression for determining the magnification of an image? What does the sign of the magnification tell you?
31. What is the near point of the human eye?
32. How is the angular magnification of an image formed by a lens defined?
33. What is a diopter?

33.7 Spherical mirrors

34. How does the focal length of a spherical mirror depend on the radius of curvature of the mirror?
35. Can the lens equation, $1/f = 1/o + 1/i$, be used for analyzing the image formed by a spherical mirror? If so, what are the sign conventions for the three variables?
36. What determines whether the image formed by a converging mirror is real or virtual?

33.8 Lensmaker's formula

37. What restrictions apply to the lensmaker's formula?
38. What is the sign convention for the radii of curvature in the lensmaker's formula?

Developing a Feel

Make an order-of-magnitude estimate of each of the following quantities. Letters in parentheses refer to hints below. Use them as needed to guide your thinking.

1. The thickness of glass needed to delay light by 1 μs compared to an equal thickness of vacuum (H, A, L)
2. The thickness of air (at STP) needed to delay light by 1 μs compared to an equal thickness of vacuum (H, D, L)
3. The vertical displacement of a horizontal light ray passing through a car windshield (I, A, M, Y)
4. The angular range in water through which you can see objects in the air when looking up from underwater (J, V)
5. The angular displacement of the Sun by the atmosphere when sunlight is tangent to Earth's surface (D, Q, K, I, X)
6. The time interval during which you can see the Sun after it has dropped below the horizon (F, R)
7. The change in the eye's average focal length needed to make either distant or nearby objects visible (G, S, Z, N)
8. The radius of curvature of a funhouse mirror that makes you look very fat (U, B, O, W)
9. The radius of curvature of one side of a +5-diopter glass lens if the other side is flat (A, P, E, AA)
10. The altitude at which a large airplane casts no shadow on the ground (C, T)

Hints

A. What is the index of refraction of glass?
B. What is the object distance?
C. How large is an airplane?
D. By how much does the index of refraction of air at standard temperature and pressure exceed the index of refraction of vacuum?
E. What is the lensmaker's formula?
F. By what angle is the Sun displaced by the atmosphere when sunlight is tangent to Earth's surface?
G. What is the lens equation?
H. For any material, how are distance traveled, speed, and travel time interval related?
I. At an interface between medium 1 and medium 2, how are the incident and refracted angles related?
J. What is the critical angle?
K. If you model the atmosphere as a spherical shell of uniform mass density (hence, uniform index of refraction), what is its effective height?
L. For any material, how are the speed of light and the index of refraction related?
M. What is the windshield thickness?
N. What is the distance from the eye's lens to the image?
O. What is the relationship between magnification and o, i, and f?
P. What is the relationship between diopters and focal length?
Q. Does the index of refraction of air vary in the atmosphere?
R. How fast does Earth rotate on its axis?
S. What is the minimum distance from an object that can be clearly seen to the eye's lens?
T. What is the angular size of the Sun?
U. By how much must your image be magnified horizontally to make you look very fat?
V. What is the index of refraction of water?
W. What is the relationship between focal length and radius of curvature?
X. How can you determine the angle of refraction?
Y. What is the angle of incidence for light entering the windshield?
Z. What is the maximum distance from an object to the eye's lens?
AA. What is the radius of curvature for a flat surface?

Key (all values approximate)

A. $n = \frac{3}{2}$; **B.** 1 m; **C.** about 50 m (either length or wingspan); **D.** 3×10^{-4}; **E.** $1/f = (n - 1)(1/R_1 + 1/R_2)$; **F.** 10^{-2} rad (see Developing a Feel 5); **G.** $1/f = 1/o + 1/i$; **H.** $d_{mat} = c_{mat}\Delta t_{mat}$; **I.** $n_1 \sin\theta_1 = n_2 \sin\theta_2$; **J.** $\theta_c = \sin^{-1}(n_1/n_2)$; **K.** to produce atmospheric pressure, a spherical shell of uniform mass density ($1\ \mathrm{kg/m^3}$) must have height $h = P_0/\rho g = 1 \times 10^4$ m; **L.** $c_{mat} = (3 \times 10^8\ \mathrm{m/s})/n_{mat}$; **M.** 5 mm; **N.** diameter of the eyeball, 25 mm; **O.** $M = -i/o$ and $1/f = 1/o + 1/i$; **P.** $d = (1\ \mathrm{m})/f$; **Q.** yes, the index decreases as the mass density of the atmosphere decreases nonlinearly from sea level to vacuum; **R.** $\omega = 2\pi/\mathrm{day} = 7 \times 10^{-5}\ \mathrm{s^{-1}}$; **S.** about 0.25 m; **T.** about the same angular size as a finger held at arm's length: $\theta = 0.01\ \mathrm{m}/1\ \mathrm{m} = 0.01$ rad; **U.** by a factor of 3; **V.** $n = \frac{4}{3}$; **W.** $f = R/2$; **X.** sketch Earth with a refracted ray tangent to the surface, and the angle of refraction appears in a right triangle in which two of the sides are Earth's radius ($R_E = 6 \times 10^6$ m) and the radius to the top of the atmosphere ($R_E + h$); **Y.** 50°; **Z.** infinity; **AA.** $R = \infty$

Worked and Guided Problems

Procedure: Simplified ray diagrams for lenses

To determine the location and orientation of an image formed by a lens, follow this procedure.

1. Draw a horizontal line representing the lens axis (the line perpendicular to the lens through its center). In the center of the diagram, draw a vertical line representing the lens. Put a + above the line to represent a converging lens or a – to represent a diverging lens.
2. Put two dots on the axis on either side of the lens to represent the foci of the lens. The dots should be equidistant from the lens.
3. Represent the object by drawing an upward pointing arrow from the axis at the appropriate relative distance to the lens. For example, if the distance from the object to the lens is twice the focal length of the lens, put the arrow twice as far from the lens as the dot you drew in step 2. The top of the arrow should be at about half the height of the lens.
4. From the top of the arrow representing the object draw two or three of the three *principal rays* listed in the following Procedure Box Principal rays for lenses.
5. The top of the image is at the point where the rays *that exit the lens* intersect (if they diverge, trace them backward to determine the point of intersection). If the intersection is on the opposite side of the lens from the object, the image is real; if it is on the same side, the image is virtual. Draw an arrow pointing from the axis to the intersection to represent the image (use a dashed arrow for a virtual image).

In general it is sufficient to draw two principal rays, but depending on the situation, some rays may be easier to draw than others. You can also use a third ray to verify that it, too, goes through the intersection. (If it doesn't, you have made a mistake.)

Procedure: Principal rays for lenses

The propagations of principal rays for converging and diverging lenses are very similar. The description below holds for rays that travel from left to right.

Converging lens

1. A ray that travels parallel to the lens axis before entering the lens goes through the right focus after exiting the lens.
2. A ray that passes through the center of the lens continues undeflected.
3. A ray that passes through the left focus travels parallel to the lens axis after exiting the lens. If the object is between the focus and the lens, this ray doesn't pass through the focus but lies on the line from the focus to the point where the ray originates.

Diverging lens

1. A ray that travels parallel to the lens axis before entering the lens continues along the line from the left focus to the point where the ray enters the lens.
2. A ray that passes through the center of the lens continues undeflected.
3. A ray that travels toward the right focus travels parallel to the lens axis after exiting the lens.

Procedure: Ray diagrams for spherical mirrors

Ray diagrams for spherical mirrors are very similar to those for lenses. The procedure below is for rays traveling from the left to the right.

1. Draw a horizontal line representing the mirror axis. In the center of the diagram, draw a circular arc representing the mirror. A converging mirror curves toward the left; a diverging mirror curves toward the right.
2. Put a dot on the axis at the center of the circular arc and label it C. Add another dot on the axis, halfway between C and the mirror. This point is the focus. Label it f.
3. Represent the object by drawing an upward pointing arrow from the axis at the appropriate relative distance to the left of the mirror. For example, if the distance from the object to a converging mirror is one-third the radius of curvature of the mirror, put the arrow a bit to the right of the focus The top of the arrow should be at about half the height of the mirror.
4. From the top of the arrow representing the object draw two or three of the following three so-called *principal rays* listed in the Procedure Box Principal rays for spherical mirrors on page 619.
5. The top of the image is at the point where the rays that are reflected by the mirror intersect. If the intersection is on the left side of the lens, the image is real; if it is on the right, the image is virtual. Draw an arrow pointing from the axis to the intersection to represent the image (use a dashed arrow for a virtual image).

Procedure: Principal rays for spherical mirrors

The description below holds for rays that travel from left to right.

Converging mirror

1. A ray that travels parallel to the mirror axis before reaching the mirror goes through the focus after being reflected.
2. A ray that passes through the center of the sphere on which the mirror surface lies is reflected back onto itself. If the object is between the center and the mirror, this ray doesn't pass through the center but lies on the line from the center to the point at which the ray originates.
3. A ray that passes through the focus is reflected parallel to the axis. If the object is between the focus and the mirror, this ray doesn't pass through the focus but lies on the line from the focus to the point at which the ray originates.

Diverging mirror

1. A ray that travels parallel to the mirror axis before reaching the mirror is reflected along the line that goes through the focus and the point where the ray strikes the surface.
2. A ray that passes through the center of the sphere on which the mirror surface lies is reflected back onto itself.
3. A ray whose extension passes through the focus is reflected parallel to the axis.

For both converging and diverging mirrors a ray that hits the mirror on the axis is reflected back symmetrically about the axis.

These examples involve material from this chapter but are not associated with any particular section. Some examples are worked out in detail; others you should work out by following the guidelines provided.

Worked Problem 33.1 Aquarium beams

You shine a laser pointer into a filled aquarium tank from above. The laser beam strikes the water surface at 40.0° from the normal and then travels to one of the glass sidewalls of the tank. Does the beam pass through that wall into the air, and if so, at what angle of refraction?

❶ GETTING STARTED This problem involves a sequence of encounters of a laser beam with interfaces between materials that have different indices of refraction. Our goal is to determine whether the beam passes through a sidewall of the tank and enters the air and, if so, at what angle of refraction. The question we must answer is: At each interface—(1) air–water, (2) water–glass, (3) glass–air—is the beam totally reflected, or does it enter the second material and become refracted? Consequently, we need to work out the change of direction of the beam at each interface.

To visualize the situation, we arbitrarily choose the right sidewall of the tank and make a sketch showing that wall, the water surface, and the laser beam (Figure WG33.1). If the beam is to pass all the way through and end up back in the air, it travels first through the air to the water surface, then through the water to the left surface of the right sidewall, and then through the glass to the right surface of this wall. To keep the diagram simple, we omit any reflected rays. We number the three interfaces and show the beam bending toward the normal to interfaces 1 and 2 as it crosses those interfaces (moving in each case from the lower-density material to the higher-density material) and bending away from the normal as it crosses interface 3 because now it moves from higher density to lower density. We label the six angles the beam makes to the interface normals θ_{a1}, θ_{w1}, θ_{w2}, θ_{g2}, θ_{g3}, and θ_{a3}.

Figure WG33.1

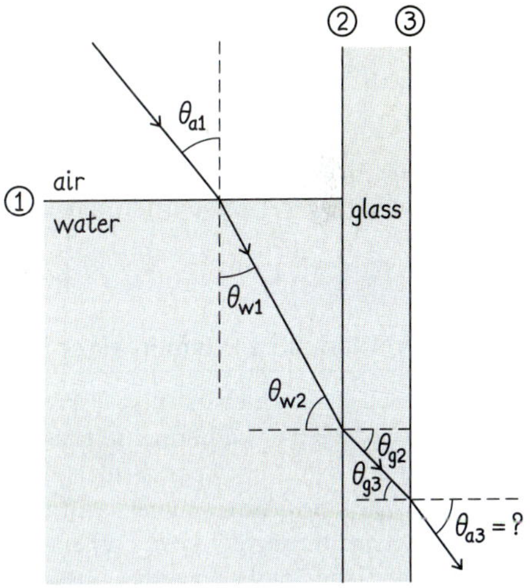

❷ DEVISE PLAN We know from *Principles* Table 33.1 that the index of refraction of air is smaller than that of water, which is smaller than that of glass. Thus total internal reflection—if it happens—can happen only at the glass–air interface because this is the only place the beam might move from a material of greater n value to a material of smaller n value. If total internal reflection occurs, Snel's law applied to the glass–air interface cannot be satisfied, and so the value of the critical angle is exceeded. We then obtain the indices of refraction we need in *Principles* Table 33.1. Two types of glass are listed, and we arbitrarily assume the aquarium is made of flint glass.

Table 33.1 Indices of refraction for common transparent materials

Material	n (for λ = 589 nm)
Air (at standard temperature and pressure)	1.00029
Liquid water	1.33
Sugar solution (30%)	1.38
Sugar solution (80%)	1.49
Microscope cover slip glass	1.52
Sodium chloride (table salt)	1.54
Flint glass	1.65
Diamond	2.42

We repeatedly apply Snel's law, along with some trigonometry, to determine the angles and thereby determine whether the Snel's law condition at interface 3 can be met. If no value of θ_{a3} exists, total internal reflection occurs and the beam does not pass from glass to air; if a value exists, θ_{a3} is the exit angle.

3 EXECUTE PLAN We apply Snel's law at each interface in numerical order, beginning with interface 1: the air–water interface.

$$n_{\text{air}} \sin\theta_{a1} = n_{\text{water}} \sin\theta_{w1}.$$

We are given $\theta_{a1} = 40.0°$, and from *Principles* Table 33.1 we see that $n_{\text{air}} = 1.00029$ and $n_{\text{water}} = 1.33$. Thus

$$\theta_{w1} = \sin^{-1}\left(\frac{n_a \sin\theta_{a1}}{n_w}\right) = \sin^{-1}\left(\frac{1.00029 \sin 40.0°}{1.33}\right) = 28.9°.$$

Next we note that the normals to interfaces 1 and 2 form a right triangle that has the in-water portion of the beam as its hypotenuse. Therefore $\theta_{w1} + \theta_{w2} = 90°$ and

$$\theta_{w2} = 90.0° - 28.9° = 61.1°.$$

Now we apply Eq. 33.7 to interface 2:

$$n_w \sin\theta_{w2} = n_g \sin\theta_{g2}$$

$$\theta_{g2} = \sin^{-1}\left(\frac{n_w \sin\theta_{w2}}{n_g}\right) = \sin^{-1}\left(\frac{1.33 \sin 61.1°}{1.65}\right) = 44.9°.$$

Interfaces 2 and 3 are parallel, which means $\theta_{g2} = \theta_{g3}$, allowing us to calculate θ_{a3}:

$$n_g \sin\theta_{g3} = n_a \sin\theta_{a3}$$

$$\theta_{a3} = \sin^{-1}\left(\frac{n_g \sin\theta_{g3}}{n_a}\right) = \sin^{-1}\left(\frac{1.65 \sin 44.9°}{1.00029}\right) = \sin^{-1}(1.16).$$

Because the argument of the inverse sine function exceeds 1, no angle exists that can satisfy this condition. This tells us that θ_{g3} exceeds the critical angle for the glass–air interface. The beam must undergo total internal reflection at interface 3 and thus does not exit the tank. ✔

4 EVALUATE RESULT We know that total internal reflection can happen only to light traveling from a medium with a higher index of refraction into a medium with a lower index of refraction, and this is the case here, as the beam moves from glass ($n_g = 1.65$) to air ($n_a = 1.00029$). For total internal reflection to occur, $\theta_{g3} = \theta_{g2} = 44.9°$ must exceed the critical angle θ_c for the glass–air interface. To see whether or not $\theta_{g3} > \theta_c$, we can use Eq. 33.9 with glass for medium 2 and air for medium 1:

$$\sin\theta_c = \frac{n_a}{n_g} = \frac{1.00029}{1.65} = 0.606; \quad \theta_c = \sin^{-1}\left(\frac{n_a}{n_g}\right) = 37.3°.$$

Thus $\theta_{g3} > \theta_c$, consistent with total internal reflection at interface 3 (the glass–air interface).

Guided Problem 33.2 Prism in air or liquid

A beam of light enters a flint-glass prism as shown in Figure WG33.2, entering normal to face AB. When the prism is surrounded by air, the beam is totally internally reflected at face AC. When the prism is immersed in a clear liquid, the beam exits the prism through face AC. What minimum value of the index of refraction of the liquid permits the beam to exit?

Figure WG33.2

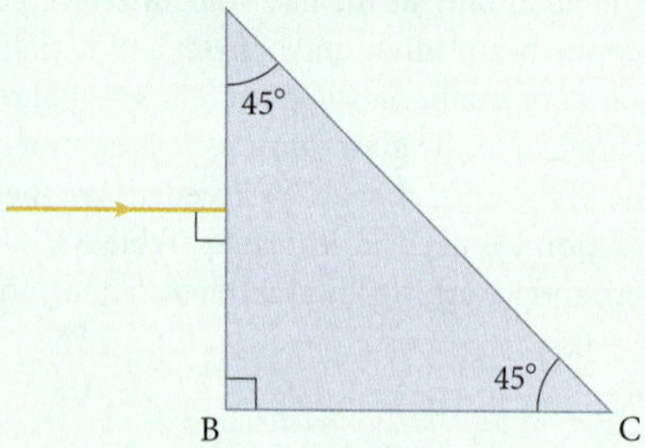

1 GETTING STARTED

1. In Figure WG33.2, draw the path the beam follows when the prism is surrounded by air, and label the angles.
2. What principle determines the beam's path?
3. Does the beam change direction on entering the prism?

2 DEVISE PLAN

4. How does the path of the beam *in the prism* depend on whether the prism is surrounded by air or by liquid?
5. Draw a diagram showing the beam's path when the prism is surrounded by liquid.
6. What determines the angle at which the beam strikes face AC?
7. How can you use the angle from question 6 and total internal reflection to determine the minimum index of refraction of the liquid?
8. What value do you need to look up to calculate the liquid's index of refraction?

3 EXECUTE PLAN

4 EVALUATE RESULT

9. Is your result plausible, and why?

Worked Problem 33.3 Magnified insect

Using a magnifying lens outdoors to examine an insect, you notice that when you hold a piece of paper underneath the lens and let sunlight fall on the lens, the smallest bright spot forms when the paper is 150 mm from the lens. Where should you hold the lens to form an image of the insect that is upright and three times larger than the insect?

❶ **GETTING STARTED** This is a problem about image formation with a magnifying lens. We need to determine the lens–object distance that produces an upright image three times larger than the object. We know that magnifying lenses are converging lenses. Because the smallest bright spot of sunlight is formed when the lens is 150 mm from the paper, we know that the sunlight is focused there, and thus the focal length f of the lens is $+0.150$ m (positive because the lens is converging). We start by drawing a simplified ray diagram (Figure WG33.3). Because our image must be upright, we position our object closer to the lens than the focal point.

Figure WG33.3

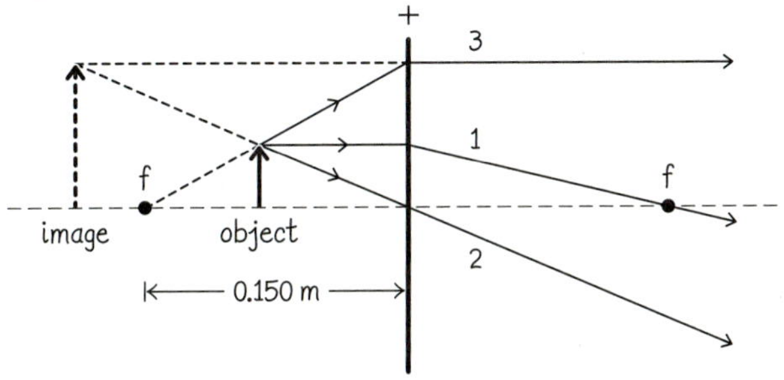

❷ **DEVISE PLAN** We can use Eq. 33.17 to determine the image distance i in terms of the object distance o. Then we can use the lens equation (Eq. 33.16) together with our known value of f to determine o. Figure WG33.3 shows that the image is on the same side of the lens as the object and therefore the image distance i is negative. The image is upright, and therefore the image height and magnification are positive.

❸ **EXECUTE PLAN** Equation 33.17 gives us $i = -Mo$. This result substituted in Eq. 33.16 yields

$$\frac{1}{f} = \frac{1}{i} + \frac{1}{o} = -\frac{1}{Mo} + \frac{1}{o} = \left(\frac{M-1}{M}\right)\frac{1}{o}.$$

Solving this expression for o yields

$$o = \left(\frac{M-1}{M}\right)f = \left(\frac{3-1}{3}\right)(0.150\text{ m}) = 0.100\text{ m}. \checkmark$$

❹ **EVALUATE RESULT** From our simplified ray diagram, we expect to obtain $o < f$, and we do. An object distance of 0.100 m is fairly short, but it is reasonable because we know from experience that we hold a magnifying glass close to the object we are viewing.

Guided Problem 33.4 Image on paper

Your friend holds a lens and a sheet of paper near a flower so that an image of the flower appears on the paper. The flower is 0.10 m away from the lens, and the image is four times the size of the flower. Which lens did your friend borrow from the physics lab to produce this image?

❶ **GETTING STARTED**

1. What quantity (value and sign) can you use to identify a lens? What algebraic symbol is used to denote this quantity?
2. Which type of lens—converging or diverging—can produce an image on a sheet of paper, or can both types of lens do so?
3. Draw a simplified ray diagram showing an enlarged image that can appear on a sheet of paper, using the type of lens you identified in question 2, and label the relevant distances. If you identified more than one type of lens, draw a simplified ray diagram for each type and identify which can produce an enlarged image.

❷ **DEVISE PLAN**

4. What equations relate image size and object size to image distance and object distance?
5. What equation relates image distance, object distance, and focal length?

❸ **EXECUTE PLAN**

❹ **EVALUATE RESULT**

6. Is your answer plausible?

Worked Problem 33.5 Corrective lenses

Your friend's eyeglass lenses, made of a material for which the index of refraction is 1.498, have one convex surface and one concave surface. The concave surface is on the side nearer to the eye and has a radius of curvature of magnitude 71.3 mm, and the convex surface has a radius of curvature of 125 mm. If your friend looks at her computer screen at a distance of 500 mm, how far from her eyes is the image of the screen formed? Is she near-sighted (has difficulty seeing distant objects) or far-sighted (has difficulty seeing nearby objects)?

❶ **GETTING STARTED** We need to determine the image distance for eyeglass lenses used to view a computer screen (the object) at an object distance of 500 mm. We are given the index of refraction for the lens material ($n = 1.498$), the radii of curvature for the two surfaces of each lens—$R_{\text{convex}} = 125$ mm and $R_{\text{concave}} = -71.3$ mm—and the object distance $o = 500$ mm.

To determine whether your friend is near-sighted or far-sighted, we must identify the overall effect of each lens as being converging or diverging. We also need this information to draw a ray diagram. That the convex surface has a greater magnitude of radius of curvature than the concave surface means that the convex surface is flatter than the concave surface. Thus the concave surface refracts light rays more, and the lens overall is a diverging lens. We indicate this by showing a minus sign above the lens in our simplified ray diagram (Figure WG33.4). As this illustration shows, it doesn't matter, with a diverging lens, whether the object is farther or closer than the focal point. Either way, the image is virtual and appears between the lens and the object.

Figure WG33.4

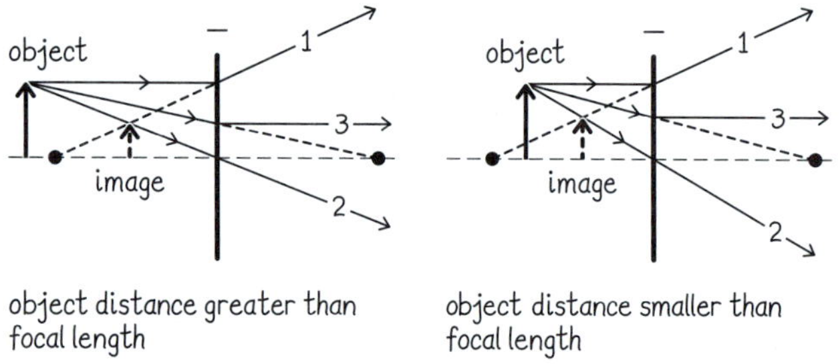

❷ **DEVISE PLAN** We can use the lens equation (Eq. 33.16) to obtain i in terms of f and o. First, though, we must calculate f, which we can do by using the lensmaker's formula (Eq. 33.36).

❸ **EXECUTE PLAN** In Eq. 33.36, a convex radius of curvature is positive and a concave radius of curvature is negative. Substituting the values provided in this equation gives us

$$\frac{1}{f} = (1.498 - 1)\left(\frac{1}{125 \times 10^{-3}\,\text{m}} + \frac{1}{-71.3 \times 10^{-3}\,\text{m}}\right) = -3.00/\text{m}.$$

Now we solve Eq. 33.16 for i and calculate its value using this value for $1/f$ and our known value for o:

$$\frac{1}{f} = \frac{1}{i} + \frac{1}{o}$$

$$i = \frac{1}{\frac{1}{f} - \frac{1}{o}} = \frac{1}{-3.00/\text{m} - \frac{1}{0.500\,\text{m}}} = -0.200\,\text{m}.$$

A negative image distance means the image is on the same side of the lens as the object, so the image appears to be between the computer screen and your friend's eyes, 0.200 m from her eyes. ✔

From the fact that the image distance is shorter than the object distance, we infer that your friend is near-sighted, meaning she sees near objects well. She thus needs her contact lenses to bring the image of a faraway object closer to her eyes, so that the image appears where her eyes can focus on it. ✔

❹ **EVALUATE RESULT** The relative radii of curvature told us that the lens is overall diverging, which means the image distance must be negative, as our result is. According to the ray diagram, the image distance should be shorter than the object distance, giving us added support for the reasonableness of our result.

Guided Problem 33.6 Correcting near-sightedness

A near-sighted person's eyes cannot create focused images of distant objects on the retina because the retina is too far from the eye's lens. Near-sighted individuals see nearby objects clearly because images of closer objects form farther from the eye's lens and can reach the retina. Therefore corrective lenses for near-sightedness are designed to form images of distant objects at the person's "far point" (the farthest distance at which a person can see clearly). If a person has an eyeglass prescription of -3.00 diopters but is not wearing his glasses, what is the far point?

❶ **GETTING STARTED**

1. Is a -3.00-diopter lens converging or diverging? How do you know?
2. Where does this lens form an image of a distant object?
3. Draw a ray diagram showing the image of a distant object formed by this lens.
4. What quantity must you determine? How does it relate to your ray diagram?

❷ **DEVISE PLAN**

5. What distance in your ray diagram can you determine from the lens strength?
6. What equation can you use to relate the distances in your ray diagram?

❸ **EXECUTE PLAN**

❹ **EVALUATE RESULT**

7. Is your answer plausible?

Worked Problem 33.7 Mirror image

You are looking at your face in a spherical mirror and see an upright image that is enlarged 1.50 times.

(*a*) Is the mirror diverging or converging? (*b*) Is the distance from you to the mirror surface longer or shorter than the mirror's focal length? (*c*) If the absolute value of the radius of curvature of the mirror is 0.96 m, where is the image?

❶ **GETTING STARTED** We are told that a spherical mirror produces an upright image that is 1.50 times larger than the object and asked whether the mirror is converging or diverging and where the object is located relative to the mirror's focal point. We are also given the absolute value of the mirror's radius of curvature and asked to determine the image distance.

❷ **DEVISE PLAN** We know that all diverging spherical mirrors form images that are smaller than the objects, so the mirror in this problem must be a converging mirror. For part *b*, we know that a spherical converging mirror forms an upright image only when the object distance is shorter than the mirror's focal length. To determine the image distance, we have Eq. 33.24 relating focal length f, object distance o, and image distance i. To obtain i from this relationship, however, we must know f and o. The magnification, which we know, relates o to i through Eq. 33.17, and so we have a way of expressing o in terms of i:

$$M = 1.50 = \frac{-i}{o}.$$

For f, we know that in spherical mirrors, $|f| = R/2$.

❸ **EXECUTE PLAN**

(*a*) This is a converging mirror, indicated by the enlarged image. ✔

(*b*) The fact that the image is upright tells us that the distance from the object (your face) to the mirror must be shorter than the focal length. ✔

(*c*) The focal length of a converging mirror is positive. Thus, for this mirror, $f = 0.96\text{ m}/2 = +0.48\text{ m}$. Equation 33.17 lets us express o in terms of i:

$$M = -\frac{i}{o}$$

$$o = -\frac{i}{1.50}.$$

We now have what we need to determine i:

$$\frac{1}{f} = \frac{1}{i} + \frac{1}{o} = \frac{1}{i} + \left(\frac{-1.50}{i}\right) = \frac{-0.50}{i}$$

$$i = -0.50f = -0.50(+0.48\text{ m}) = -0.24\text{ m}.$$

The image of your face is 0.24 m behind the mirror surface. ✔

❹ **EVALUATE RESULT** We can use a ray diagram to check that our result is reasonable (Figure WG33.5). The figure shows that we have a virtual image, and so we expect to obtain a negative value for i. The image seems to be about 1.5 times larger than the object. Although we haven't calculated o, we can confirm that $o < f$ is correct by this reasoning: $|i| = 0.24$ m is less than $f = 0.48$ m. When an image is larger than its object, the object–mirror distance is shorter than the image–mirror distance. Thus, because $|i| < f$ and $o < |i|$, we know that $o < f$.

Figure WG33.5

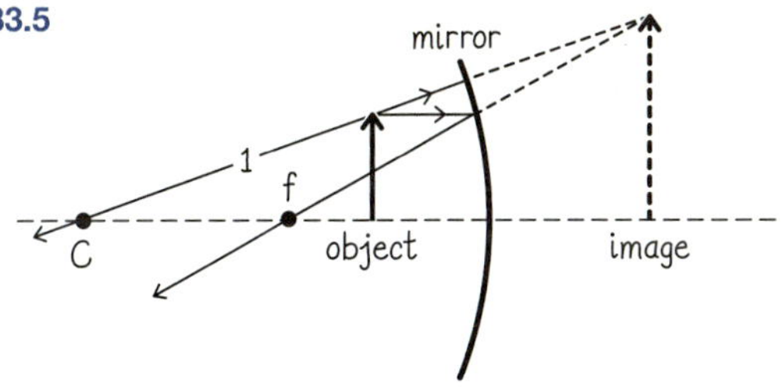

Guided Problem 33.8 Reflecting flames

You want to use a spherical mirror to cast an image of a candle flame on a sheet of paper.

(*a*) Should you use a diverging mirror or a converging mirror?
(*b*) If the absolute value of the radius of curvature of the mirror you use is 300 mm and you position the candle 360 mm in front of the mirror, do you see the image of the flame on the paper? If so, at what distance from the mirror must you hold the paper, and how big is the image?

❶ **GETTING STARTED**

1. Which type of image can be viewed on a sheet of paper: real or virtual?
2. Which type of image is created by a converging mirror? By a diverging mirror?
3. Combine your answers to questions 1 and 2 to answer part *a*.

❷ **DEVISE PLAN**

4. Draw a ray diagram showing the candle, the mirror, and two principal rays that allow you to locate the image. Check that you obtain the correct type of image.
5. How does the shape of the mirror determine the sign of the focal length?
6. How can you use the mirror radius of curvature and the object–mirror distance to determine where to hold the paper?

❸ **EXECUTE PLAN**

❹ **EVALUATE RESULT**

7. Is the paper–mirror distance you calculated consistent with your answer to question 1? Is this distance reasonable?
8. Is your result for image size plausible?

Worked Problem 33.9 Reflecting telescope

A *Cassegrain telescope* (Figure WG33.6) uses a large converging spherical mirror, the *primary*, to collect light from distant stars and a small diverging spherical mirror, the *secondary*, to send the light through a gap in the primary to a detector located outside the telescope. If the primary has a focal length of 1.00 m, the secondary is mounted 0.85 m from the surface of the primary, and the final real image forms 0.12 m behind the surface of the primary, what is the focal length of the secondary?

Figure WG33.6

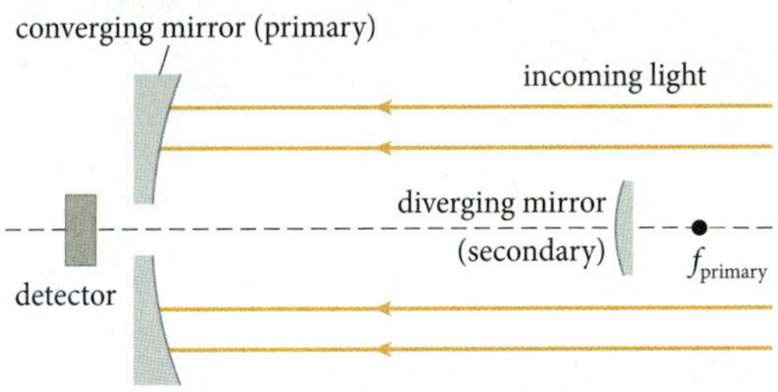

❶ **GETTING STARTED** This is a problem about image formation by two mirrors, so we apply the principle that the image formed by the first mirror (the primary) serves as the object for the second mirror (the secondary). Because a telescope is used to observe distant objects, light from the objects enters the telescope as parallel rays. We start by drawing a ray diagram for the primary, showing these parallel rays reflected from this mirror (Figure WG33.7*a* on the next page). Parallel rays converge in the primary's focal plane, which means that the distance $i_{primary}$ from the primary to the image it forms is equal to the focal length $f_{primary}$.

Next we draw a diagram showing both mirrors (Figure WG33.7*b*). It is difficult to draw principal rays showing how light reflects from the secondary. However, the problem tells us the location of the final image—0.12 m behind the primary—and so in this diagram we show the rays reflected from the secondary as meeting at this location. We also label the other distances specified in the problem. Our task is to calculate the focal length of the secondary $f_{secondary}$, that places the final image at the proper location.

Figure WG33.7

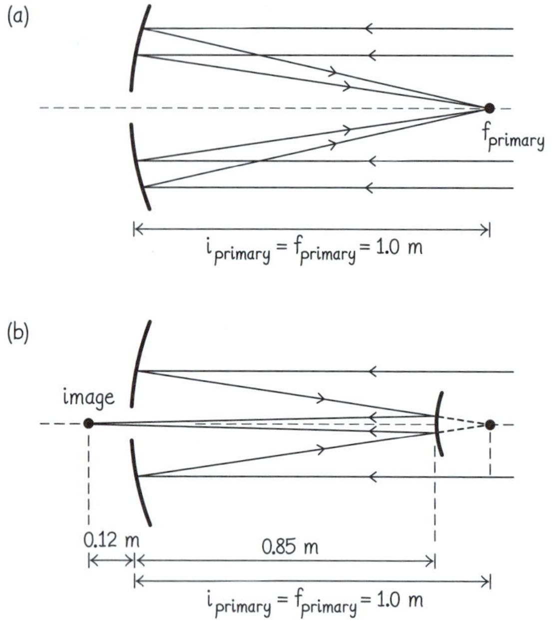

❷ **DEVISE PLAN** The image formed by the primary is *behind* the secondary. Light does not actually reach that location, however, because the secondary is in the way. Therefore the object distance for the secondary, $o_{secondary}$, is negative. The image distance, $i_{secondary}$, is positive because the image is real. We can use the distance between the two mirrors and the distance from the final image to the primary, along with $f_{primary} = 1.00$ m, to obtain values for $o_{secondary}$ and $i_{secondary}$, and then use these distances in Eq. 33.24 to determine $f_{secondary}$.

❸ **EXECUTE PLAN** The distance from the primary to $f_{primary}$ is 1.00 m, and the distance between the mirrors is 0.85 m. Because the object for the secondary is the image formed by the primary, we have $|o_{secondary}| = 1.00\text{ m} - 0.85\text{ m} = 0.15\text{ m}, o_{secondary} = -0.15\text{ m}$. Also, $i_{secondary} = 0.85\text{ m} + 0.12\text{ m} = 0.97\text{ m}$. These two values in Eq. 33.24 yield

$$f_{secondary} = \left(\frac{1}{o_{secondary}} + \frac{1}{i_{secondary}}\right)^{-1}$$

$$= \left(\frac{1}{-0.15\text{ m}} + \frac{1}{0.97\text{ m}}\right)^{-1} = -0.18\text{ m.} ✓$$

❹ **EVALUATE RESULT** We expect $f_{secondary}$ to be negative because the secondary is a diverging mirror. Because $|i_{secondary}| \gg |o_{secondary}|$, and thus $|1/i_{secondary}| \ll |1/o_{secondary}|$, we expect $f_{secondary}$ to be comparable to $o_{secondary}$. Our result agrees with both expectations and so seems reasonable.

Guided Problem 33.10 Double lens

You have a camera in which the lens is a combination of a diverging lens of focal length -120 mm and a converging lens of focal length 42 mm. The two are mounted 60 mm apart, and the converging lens is the one closer to the camera body. To focus the image produced on the sensor in the camera body, you move the pair of lenses closer to or farther from the sensor, keeping the distance between the lenses fixed at 60 mm. Suppose you are photographing a plant that is 400 mm tall and is located 500 mm in front of the diverging lens. When you have this object in focus, how far is the converging lens from the sensor?

❶ **GETTING STARTED**

1. What principle determines how the image forms after the light from the object passes through both lenses?
2. Draw a diagram showing the object, the two lenses, and the camera sensor. Label the important distances. If a distance is not known, label it with an appropriate symbol.
3. What quantity must you determine? How is this quantity related to the image distance for the converging lens?

❷ **DEVISE PLAN**

4. What ray diagrams should you draw?
5. What equation can you use to calculate the distance from the converging lens to the sensor?

❸ **EXECUTE PLAN**

6. Draw a diagram showing the rays for the image formed by the diverging lens.
7. Draw a ray diagram showing both lenses and the rays for the image formed by the converging lens. Remember that for a combination of two lenses, the principal rays for the second lens are not necessarily the continuation of the rays from the first lens.
8. Calculate the image distance for the converging lens.

❹ **EVALUATE RESULT**

9. Is your answer for the distance between the converging lens and the sensor plausible?

PRACTICE

Questions and Problems

For instructor-assigned homework, go to MasteringPhysics®

33.1 Rays

1. Figure P33.1 shows eight point sources of light, a–h, and two detectors, A and B. The point sources are evenly spaced, with 0.10 m between adjacent sources, and detector A shields part of detector B from the point sources. If no light is reflected from any nearby objects, how many of the point sources illuminate any part of (*a*) detector A and (*b*) detector B? •

Figure P33.1

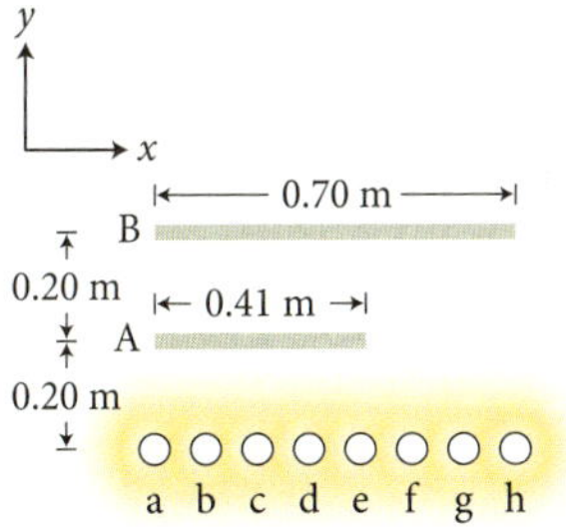

2. A point source is fixed 1.0 m away from a large screen. Call the line normal to the screen surface and passing through the center of the point source the z axis. When a sheet of cardboard in which a square hole 0.040 m on a side has been cut is placed between the point source and the screen, 0.50 m from the point source with the hole centered on the z axis, a bright square shows up on the screen. If, instead, a second sheet of cardboard with a similar square hole is placed between the point source and screen, 0.25 m from the point source with the hole centered on the z axis, the bright square it casts on the screen is identical to the bright square from the first sheet. What are the dimensions of the hole in this sheet? •
3. A thin, flat object in which a square hole 30.0 mm on a side has been cut is illuminated with a point source. Light that passes through the hole strikes a screen 300 mm behind the object. Call the direction normal to the screen the z direction. The point source is shifted away from the center of the hole by 150 mm in the positive x direction. The point source is centered on the hole in the y direction and is 300 mm in front of the object in the z direction. What are (*a*) the dimensions of the bright region on the screen and (*b*) the x and y coordinates of the perimeter of the bright region? ••
4. Sunlight that reaches Earth is blocked by Earth from traveling any farther, so that the region on the side of Earth facing away from the Sun is in shadow. The portion of this region in complete shadow is the *umbra*, and the portion in partial shadow is the *penumbra*. The Sun's radius is 7.0×10^5 km, Earth's radius is 6.4×10^3 km, and the Sun–Earth distance is 1.5×10^8 km. (*a*) What is the shape of the umbra? Of the penumbra? (*b*) Consider an observer in space on the side of Earth facing away from the Sun—that is, in the shadow region. Does this observer see the Sun when he is in the umbra? When he is in the penumbra? ••
5. Two models of light emitted from a light bulb are illustrated in Figure P33.5. (*a*) Describe the difference in the behavior of light in each model. (*b*) Describe an experiment that can determine which model of light is more accurate. ••

Figure P33.5

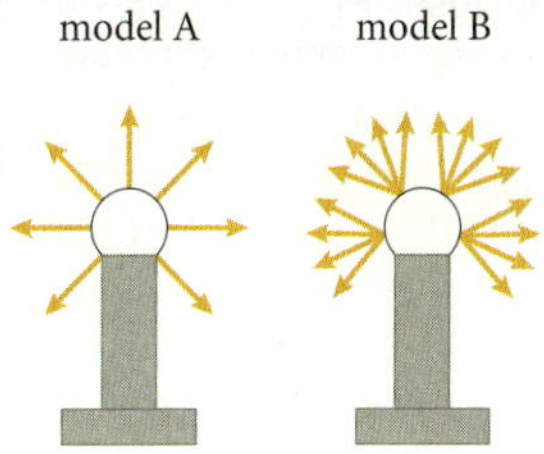

6. An aquarium light bulb has a long, straight glowing filament surrounded by a tubular, clear glass bulb. This lighted bulb, with its filament oriented vertically, is placed 1.0 m from a screen in an otherwise dark room. A thin sheet of cardboard is placed halfway between the filament and the screen so that no light can reach the screen. If a small hole, shaped like an equilateral triangle, is cut through the center of the cardboard sheet, describe the pattern of light that appears on the screen. •••
7. A burning candle is placed in front of a screen, and a sheet of cardboard with a small round hole in it is inserted between the candle and the screen as shown in Figure P33.7. Describe the pattern of light that appears on the screen. •••

Figure P33.7

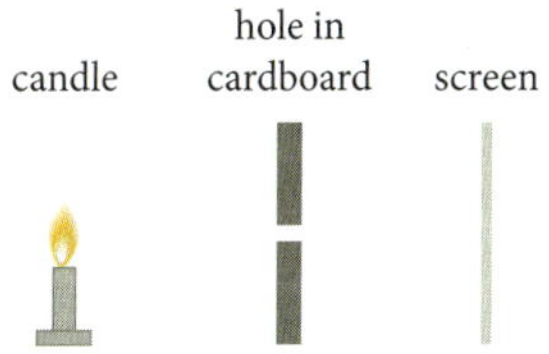

33.2 Absorption, transmission, and reflection

8. Figure P33.8 shows light rays reflected from a smooth surface. Draw three wavefronts along the rays that have not yet struck the surface and three wavefronts along the reflected rays. •

Figure P33.8

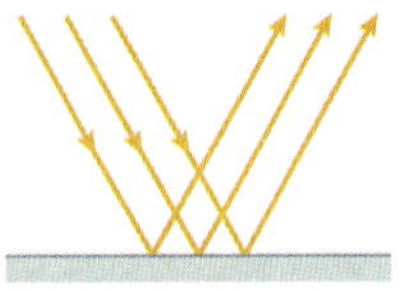

9. Where in the room shown in Figure P33.9 should a mirror be mounted so that a person sitting in the chair has a full view of the gate in the fence outside? •

Figure P33.9

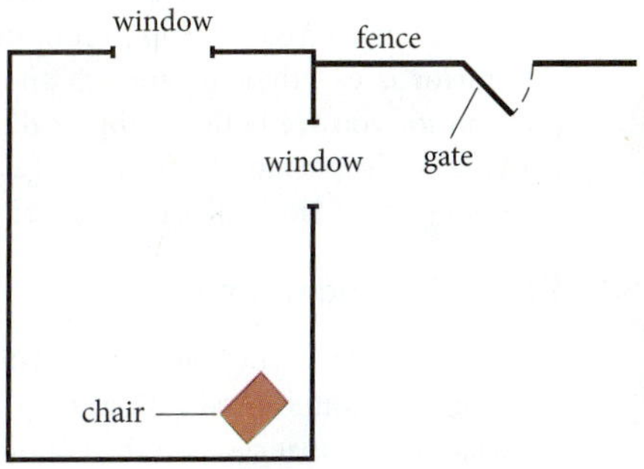

PRACTICE

10. A classmate exclaims about the professor's bright blue shirt, "Wow, that shirt has a lot of blue in it!" Evaluate your classmate's statement. •
11. A flat mirror oriented perpendicular to the y axis of a Cartesian coordinate system extends along the x axis from $x = 0$ to $x = 4.0$ m. An object is located in the xy plane at the point (1.0 m, 2.0 m). With your eye in the xy plane in the range $y < 0$ and x equal to any value, you cannot see the image of this object in the mirror. For what range of x and y in the xy plane can you see the image in the mirror? ••
12. The bottom edge of a wall-mounted mirror aligns with your waist, and the top edge aligns with a point somewhere above your head. Draw a diagram that illustrates, when you stand in front of this mirror, the portion of your whole body that you can see in the image. ••
13. The minimum height for a wall mirror in which you can view your entire body is half your height, with the distance from the floor to the bottom of the mirror equal to half the distance between your eyes and feet. This relationship between object height and mirror height/position does not hold for distant objects, however. How large (height, width, or both) a reflecting surface is needed in order for you to see the entire image of a large distant object—a tree, say? (Hint: What quantity is different when you view your own image as opposed to when you view the image of a distant object?) ••
14. Standing 1.0 m away from a large mirror, you see an image of a flashlight in the mirror. If the image appears to be 2.0 m behind the mirror, 1.0 m vertically above your eyes, and 3.0 m to your right (your actual right, not your reflection's right), what is the flashlight's location relative to you? ••
15. A classmate believes that the image you see in a mirror is on the mirror surface rather than behind the mirror. What is something you can do to convince your classmate he is incorrect? ••
16. A woman holds a mirror stationary and perfectly vertical as a boy runs toward it at a speed of 1.0 m/s. (*a*) In her reference frame, what does the woman observe for the speed at which the boy and his reflection move toward the mirror? (*b*) In the reference frame of the boy, what does he observe for the speed at which the woman and his reflection move toward him? ••
17. Consider this statement: Think of the reflection of the Moon on a cloudless night: Look in the ocean, you see a large moon. Look in a pond; the same moon is there. In a puddle, in a teacup—everywhere, diminished somewhat in size, but all the features are there. (*a*) What physical attribute (referred to only indirectly in the statement) is it that differs in size for the ocean, pond, puddle, and cup? (*b*) What other quantities determine this attribute? Draw a diagram showing how the image of the Moon forms and relating all the quantities you've identified to one another. •••
18. You want to see how your new belt buckle matches your new hat. Your eyes are 110 mm below the top of the hat and 800 mm above the buckle. You walk up to your mirror and notice that the mirror is exactly large enough and exactly in the right position for you see both the top of the hat and the buckle. (*a*) What is the position of the top edge of the mirror relative to your eyes? (*b*) How tall is the mirror? •••

33.3 Refraction and dispersion

19. The light bulb in a bathroom ceiling is directly over a toy boat floating in a bathtub filled with water to a depth x. How does the shadow the boat casts on the bottom of the tub compare with the shadow it casts when the water is drained out and the boat is held the same distance x above the tub bottom? Treat the bulb as a point source. •
20. While scuba diving, you have injured yourself and must signal the boat on the surface for help. You have five laser pointers, each emitting light of a different color: red, orange, yellow, green, and blue. When you shine the yellow light up toward the boat, the beam makes such a small angle with the surface that all the light is reflected back into the water. (*a*) If you are not able to move closer to the boat, which color or colors of light might you try? (*b*) Are these other lights likely to be successful in penetrating the surface at that point? •
21. The observer in Figure P33.21 is looking at a coin near the edge of a pool filled with water. To this observer, does the water appear to be shallower or deeper than it really is? •

Figure P33.21

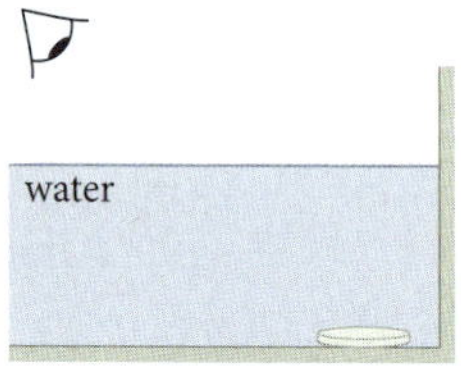

22. In Figure P33.22, a straight plank of lumber enters a pool of water at an angle. What does the plank look like to the observer? ••

Figure P33.22

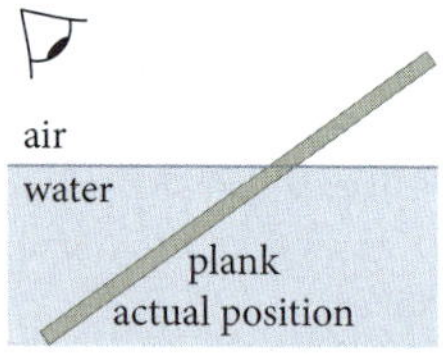

23. Figure P33.23 shows incident and all reflected or refracted light rays in three cases, A, B, and C. For each case, state (*a*) in which material, 1 or 2, the light travels faster and (*b*) in which material, 1 or 2, the ray originates. ••

Figure P33.23

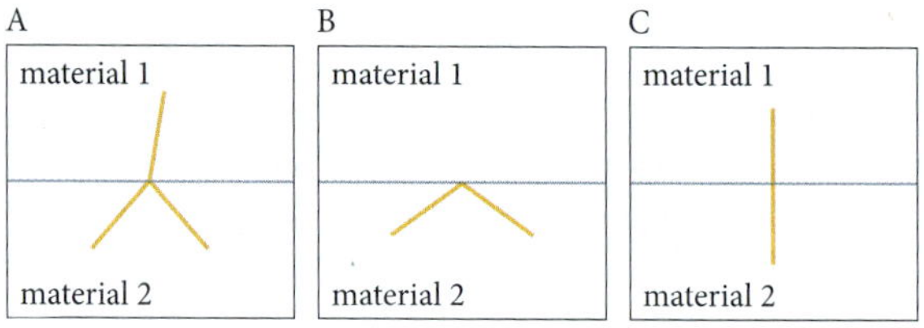

24. Parallel red and green laser rays are incident on a glass slab as shown in Figure P33.24. Sketch the rays as they pass through the slab and after they have entered the air to the right of the slab. Are the rays parallel after they exit the slab? Is the distance between the rays after they exit the slab equal to the distance between them before they entered? ••

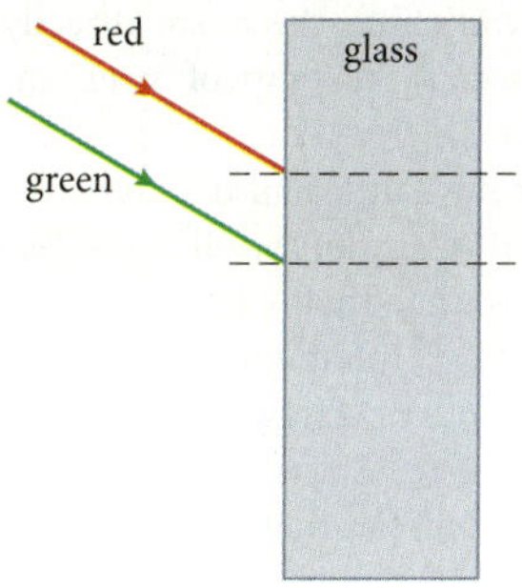

Figure P33.24

25. A thick layer of transparent oil floats on top of water. Sketch what happens to a ray of light coming in at a 30° angle away from the normal to the surface. ••
26. Suppose a small flashlight bulb is on the bottom of the bathtub of Problem 19, directly under the toy boat. When this bulb is lit and the ceiling light is turned off, how does the size of the shadow cast by the boat on the ceiling change when the water in the tub is replaced by a liquid in which the speed of light is (*a*) faster than the speed of light in water and (*b*) slower than the speed of light in water? ••
27. Suppose the prism in Figure WG33.2 is immersed in a liquid in which the speed of light is lower than the speed of light in glass. Describe what happens to the light shown entering at normal incidence in the figure. ••
28. Driving down a long straight highway, you see a reflection of the sky in the road ahead. It disappears before you get to it but reappears down the road continually. Because there is nothing different about the road from one location to another, explain what is happening in terms of refraction. ••
29. White light passing through a prism is dispersed into its constituent colors. Describe how this rainbow of colors can be changed back to white light. •••
30. A glass cylinder is placed inside a large beaker, and corn oil is poured into the combination until the beaker is full. If the glass cylinder is now invisible inside the oil, what must you conclude about how light interacts with the oil and the glass? •••

33.4 Forming images

31. (*a*) Draw a simplified ray diagram showing the three principal rays for an object located outside the focal length of a converging lens. (*b*) Is the image real or virtual? (*c*) Is it upright or inverted? (*d*) What happens to the image as the object is moved farther from the lens? •
32. (*a*) Draw a simplified ray diagram showing the three principal rays for an object located outside the focal length of a diverging lens. (*b*) Is the image real or virtual? (*c*) Is it upright or inverted? (*d*) What happens to the image as the object is moved farther from the lens? •
33. The lens in a magnifying glass is a converging lens, but parallel light rays that pass through a converging lens must converge to a point. This being true, how can a magnifying glass form an image that is larger than the object? Why isn't the image reduced to a point? •
34. A lens has a radius of curvature of magnitude R on its left surface and a radius of curvature of magnitude $2R$ on its right surface. Parallel rays entering the lens from the left are focused to a point 100 mm to the right of the right surface. At what distance from the lens is the point at which parallel rays entering from the right are focused? •
35. Looking at an object through a thin lens, you see a virtual image. Which side of the lens is the image on, or does it appear to be inside the lens? What property of this image tells you whether the lens is converging or diverging? ••
36. (*a*) Draw a simplified ray diagram showing the three principal rays for an object located inside the focal length of a diverging lens. (*b*) Is the image real or virtual? (*c*) Is it upright or inverted? (*d*) What happens to the image as the object is moved toward the focal point? ••
37. (*a*) Draw a simplified ray diagram showing the three principal rays for an object located inside the focal length of a converging lens, closer to the lens than to the focal point. (*b*) Is the image real or virtual? (*c*) Is it upright or inverted? (*d*) What happens to the image as the object is moved closer to the focal point? ••
38. An object 20 mm tall is placed 70 mm to the left of a converging lens that has a focal length of 100 mm. (*a*) Draw a scale diagram showing the three principal rays, and use them to locate the image. Is the image (*b*) real or virtual, (*c*) inverted or upright, (*d*) larger or smaller than the object? ••
39. An object is placed 80 mm to the left of a diverging lens for which the focus is 100 mm from the lens. (*a*) Draw a scale diagram showing the three principal rays, and use them to locate the image. Is the image (*b*) real or virtual, (*c*) inverted or upright, (*d*) larger or smaller than the object? ••
40. Complete the table below for a converging lens. ••

		Image		
Object Location	Image Location	Real or virtual?	Upright or inverted?	Larger or smaller than the object?
Between lens and focus	Between positive infinity and lens (same side)	Virtual	Upright	Larger
At focus				
Between focus and twice the focal length				
At twice the focal length				
Beyond twice the focal length				
At infinity				

41. Figure P33.41 shows light passing first through a diverging lens and then through a converging lens placed 100 mm to the right of the diverging lens. The rays emerge from the converging lens parallel to one another. Calculate the distance from each lens to its focus. ••

Figure P33.41

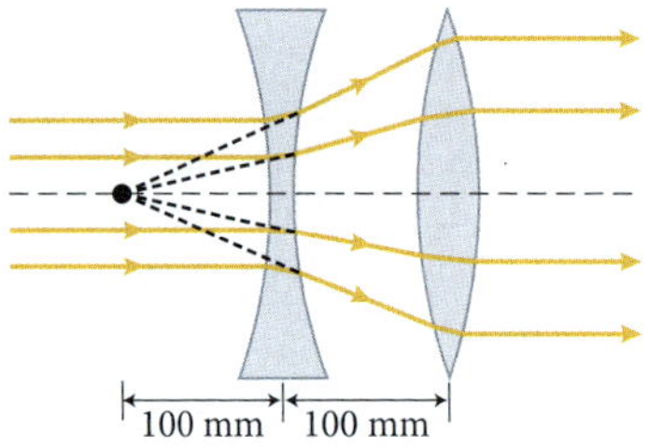

42. Two identical converging lenses of focal length 100 mm are placed 400 mm apart, and an object 40 mm tall is placed 230 mm to the left of the left lens. (*a*) Draw a scale diagram showing the three principal rays for the left lens, and use them to locate the image formed by this lens. (*b*) Draw the principal rays for the right lens, and use them to locate the image formed by this lens. Is the image formed by the right lens (*c*) real or virtual, (*d*) inverted or upright, (*e*) larger or smaller than the object? •••

33.5 Snel's law

43. Light is traveling at a speed of 1.24×10^8 m/s through a certain material. Determine what material it is likely traveling through. •

44. What is the index of refraction of a material in which the speed of light is 7.50% slower than the speed of light in vacuum? •

45. Green light has a wavelength of 530 nm in air. What are the frequency and wavelength of this light in flint glass (index of refraction $n = 1.65$)? •

46. A light ray traveling through medium 1, index of refraction $n_1 = 1.45$, reaches the interface between medium 1 and medium 2, index of refraction $n_2 = 1.24$. (*a*) At what minimum angle with respect to the normal must the ray be incident on the interface in order to be totally internally reflected? (*b*) How would the situation change if the ray were traveling in medium 2 when it reached the interface? •

47. A light ray travels up from the bottom of a tank containing mineral water (index of refraction $n = 1.37$). Assuming that the water surface is smooth, at what angle from the normal to that surface would the light ray have to strike the surface in order to reflect back into the tank and not escape? •

48. You shine a laser pointer at an angle of 30° from the normal onto the surface of a thick block of glass for which the index of refraction is $n = 1.5$. (*a*) What is the angle of refraction of the laser beam? (*b*) Draw a diagram showing the normal, the surface of the block, and the incident and refracted wavefronts and rays. (*c*) How would the angles in parts *a* and *b* change if the incident angle were 45°? ••

49. In vacuum, the wavelength of the light in your laser pointer is 538 nm. Standing at the shore of a calm pond, you shine the laser beam onto the water surface at an angle of 60° from the normal to the surface. If the index of refraction for the water is $n = 1.333$, how do each of the following properties of the light change as the light enters the water: (*a*) wavelength, (*b*) frequency, (*c*) speed, and (*d*) direction of propagation? (*e*) If you shine the beam directly onto the surface (along the normal), do any of your answers change, and if so, how? ••

50. A light ray is incident on a layer of oil floating on water. The index of refraction of oil is greater than that of water, which is greater than that of air. Call the angle of incidence in air θ_a, the angle of refraction in oil θ_o, and the angle of refraction in water θ_w. (*a*) Draw a diagram showing all three layers and all angles. (*b*) Show that $n_a \sin\theta_a = n_w \sin\theta_w$. (*c*) The result in part *b* implies that in calculating the final direction (θ_w) of a light ray passing from medium 1 into medium 2 and then into medium 3, all having different n values, we can ignore the presence of medium 2. Can you also ignore medium 2 if what you are calculating is the *location* where the ray strikes the bottom of the container of water? ••

51. The index of refraction in flint glass is 1.66 for blue light and 1.61 for red light, with the values for other colors between these limits. A ray of white light traveling from left to right through a slab of flint glass undergoes dispersion as it exits the slab and enters the air. If the exiting ray strikes the right surface of the slab at an angle of 30.0° from the normal to the surface, what is the angle of refraction (*a*) for the blue light and (*b*) for the red light? (*c*) A flat opaque screen is placed in the path of the refracted rays such that the red ray strikes perpendicular to the screen. If the distance along the refracted red ray from slab to screen is 0.50 m, what is the distance between the point of red light and the point of blue light in the rainbow produced on the screen? (Use the small-angle approximation.) ••

52. What is the critical angle for total internal reflection for an optical fiber cable surrounded by air if the index of refraction is (*a*) 1.4 and (*b*) 1.8? (*c*) Which fiber could have a sharper bend (smaller radius of curvature) and still be capable of total internal reflection? ••

53. Show that the ray exiting the block in Figure P33.53 is parallel to the ray entering the block. ••

Figure P33.53

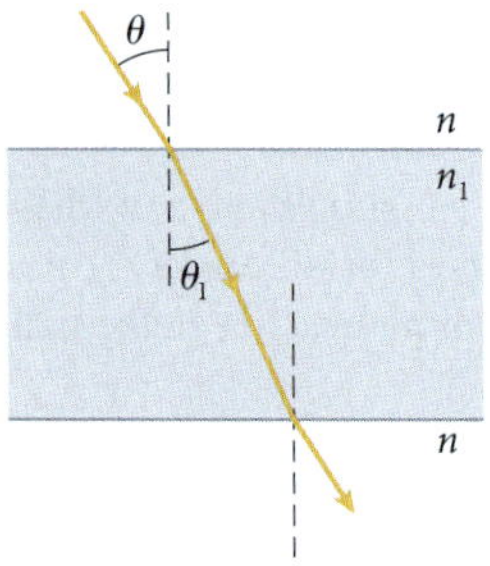

54. Red light for which the wavelength in air is 700 nm strikes a diamond ($n_{diamond} = 2.42$) at an angle of 40.0° from the normal to the air–diamond interface. Calculate (*a*) the wavelength and frequency of the light inside the diamond and (*b*) the angle of refraction. ••

55. A light ray travels through medium 1, index of refraction $n_1 = 1.1$, into medium 2, index of refraction $n_2 = 1.5$ (Figure P33.55). At what angle with respect to the normal to the interface between the media does the light need to strike the interface so that the reflected and the refracted rays are at right angles to each other? ••

Figure P33.55

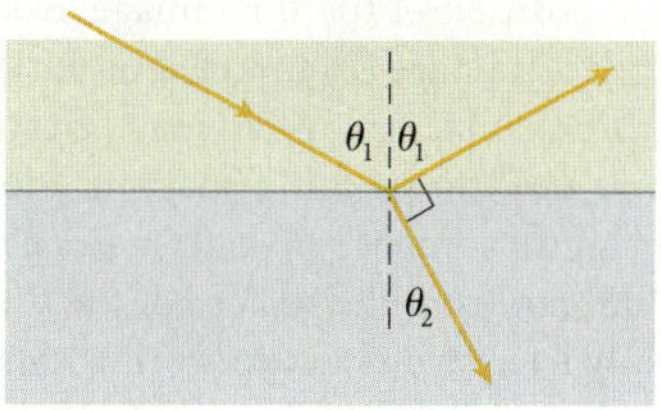

56. A researcher stands at the end of a lakeside pier, 4.0 m above the water surface and 6.0 m away from a buoy floating on the lake (Figure P33.56). A rope hangs from the bottom of the buoy down into the water, with a light attached to its end. When the researcher looks at the light from a position at which his line of sight intersects the water surface exactly halfway between the pier and the buoy, the light appears to be 4.0 m below the water surface. How far under the surface is the light? ••

Figure P33.56

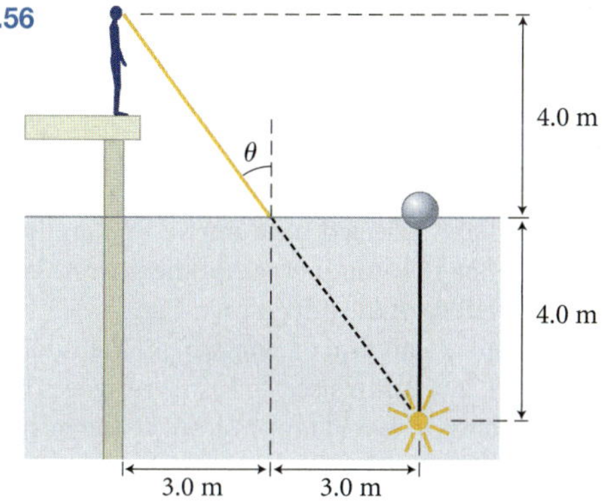

57. Figure P33.57 depicts a light ray entering an optical fiber from air and being transmitted through the fiber by total internal reflection. (*a*) If the index of refraction of the fiber is n, what is the maximum value of θ, the angle the entering ray makes with the normal to the flat end of the fiber, for which total internal reflection occurs? (*b*) When n is greater than a certain value n_0, the light ray can enter the fiber at any angle θ between 0 and 90° and total internal reflection still occurs inside the fiber. What is n_0? •••

Figure P33.57

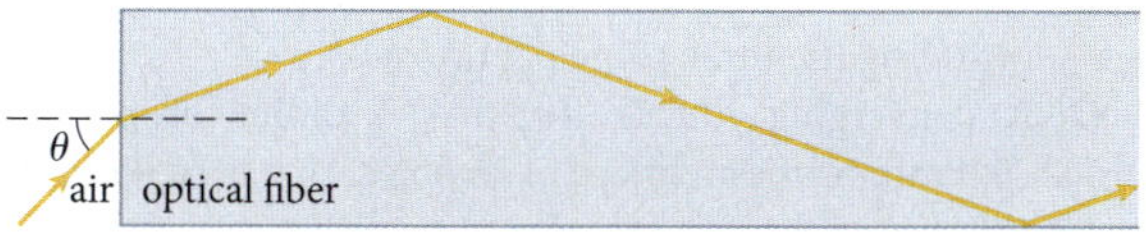

58. A ray traveling through a large vat filled with medium 1, index of refraction $n_1 = 1.3$, is incident on a flat layer (thickness $d = 12$ mm) of medium 2, index of refraction $n_2 = 1.6$. If the light enters medium 2 at an angle $\theta_1 = 40°$ with respect to the normal to the interface between the media, how far is it shifted from its original path once it exits medium 2? •••

59. A child's toy sits on the bottom of a swimming pool in which the water depth is $d = 1.8$ m (Figure P33.59). To a child standing at the pool edge and a distance $h = 3.5$ m above the pool bottom, the toy appears to be a horizontal distance $y = 4.2$ m away from the sidewall. At what horizontal distance from the sidewall is the toy located? •••

Figure P33.59

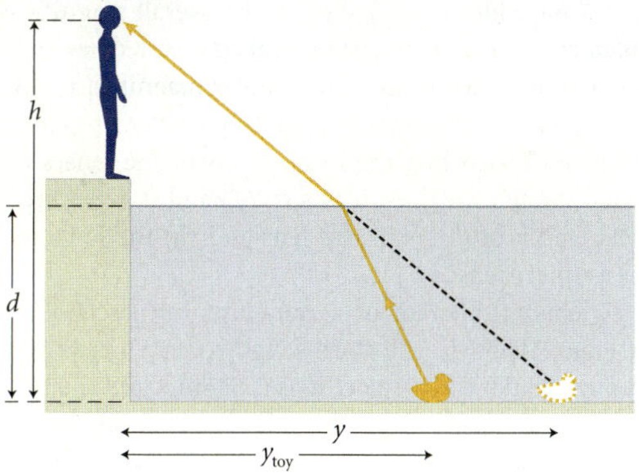

33.6 Thin lenses and optical instruments

60. What is the lens strength of a diverging lens that has a focal length of magnitude 400 mm? •
61. Mathematically, why can't a single diverging lens produce a real image? •
62. What is the focal length of eyeglasses that have a lens strength of +1.5 diopters? •
63. Using a converging lens that has focal length $f = 100$ mm, how far behind the lens do you expect to see a sharp image of an object located 2.00 m in front of the lens? •
64. A cheap cell phone camera uses a single lens to form an image on a sensor that is 10 mm high and 5.8 mm behind the lens. How far do you need to be away from the Eiffel Tower (height 324 m) to get its whole length in a photograph? Ignore the tilting that occurs as you take the photo from the ground. •
65. The objective lens in a telescope that produces a 40-fold angular magnification has a focal length of 2.0 m. What is the focal length of the eyepiece lens? •
66. An object is placed 800 mm away from a thin converging lens that has a focal length of 500 mm. What are (*a*) the image distance and (*b*) the magnification? (*c*) Draw a simplified ray diagram for this case. ••
67. An object is placed 150 mm away from a converging thin lens that has a focal length of 400 mm. What are (*a*) the image distance and (*b*) the magnification? (*c*) Draw a simplified ray diagram for this case. ••
68. An object is placed 600 mm away from a diverging thin lens for which the focal length is –300 mm. What are (*a*) the image distance and (*b*) the magnification of the image? ••
69. An object is placed 200 mm from a diverging thin lens that has a focal length of −500 mm. What are (*a*) the image distance and (*b*) the magnification? (*c*) Draw a simplified ray diagram for this case. ••
70. A bug is 30 mm away from a lens. As you look through the lens, the bug appears to be just at your near point (0.250 m in front of your eyes). If the actual distance between your eyes and the bug is 130 mm, what is the lens focal length? ••
71. A woman is not able to focus on objects that are closer to her eyes than 400 mm unless she wears eyeglasses. Her glasses enable her to clearly see objects at the near point of an average human (and no closer). What is the strength of the lenses in her glasses? ••
72. Two converging lenses are placed facing each other and 600 mm apart, with lens 1 to the left of lens 2. An object is placed 400 mm to the left of lens 1, which has a focal length

of 150 mm. (*a*) If the focal length of lens 2 is 200 mm, where is the image located? (*b*) What is the overall magnification of the image? (*c*) Is the image upright or inverted? ••

73. An astronomical telescope of angular magnification M_θ consists of an objective lens and an eyepiece lens separated by a distance d, such that the focal points of the lenses coincide inside the telescope. In terms of M_θ and d, what are (*a*) the focal length of the objective lens and (*b*) the focal length of the eyepiece lens? ••

74. A schematic diagram of a refractive microscope is shown in Figure P33.74. The focal length of the objective lens is 25 mm, that of the eyepiece lens is 63 mm, and the two lenses are 200 mm apart. If the object is 30 mm away from the objective lens, what are (*a*) the distance between the eyepiece lens and the image produced by that lens and (*b*) the overall magnification of this image? ••

Figure P33.74

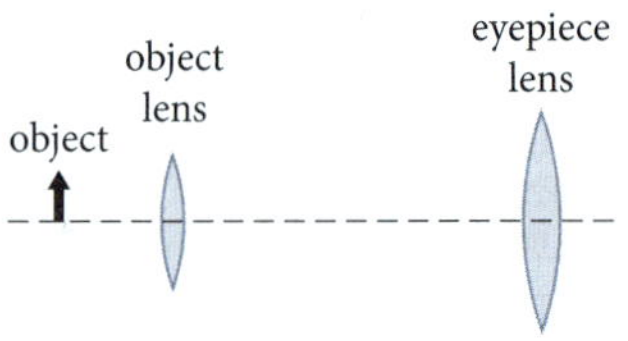

75. Two converging lenses, 1 and 2, are positioned facing each other, with lens 1 on the left. The focal length of lens 1 is 100 mm, that of lens 2 is 180 mm, and the two lenses are 150 mm apart. If an object is 50 mm to the left of lens 1, (*a*) at what distance from lens 2 should a screen be placed if the object's image is to be focused on the screen? (*b*) What is the overall magnification of the image? (*c*) Is the image upright or inverted? ••

76. Two lenses with focal lengths $f_1 = 100$ mm and $f_2 = 200$ mm are placed facing each other a distance $d = 550$ mm apart, with lens 1 to the left of lens 2. What is the location of the image formed of an object placed 150 mm to the left of lens 1? ••

77. The focal points of the two converging lenses shown in Figure P33.77 are denoted by solid dots for the left lens and open dots for the right lens. Describe the final image. ••

Figure P33.77

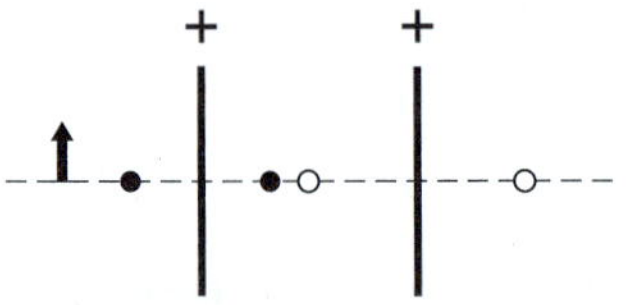

78. In Figure P33.78, a converging lens 1, of focal length 100 mm, and a diverging lens 2, of focal length –80.0 mm, are 160 mm apart. If the object is 180 mm away from lens 1, what are (*a*) the distance between lens 2 and the image produced by that lens and (*b*) the overall magnification of this image? •••

Figure P33.78

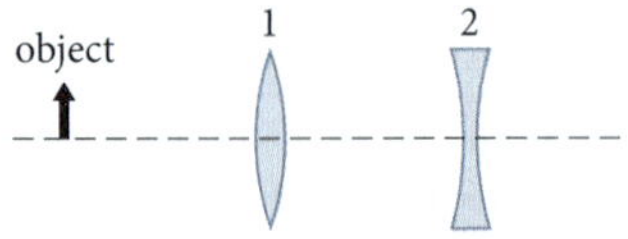

79. Problem 42 describes a setup of two identical converging lenses spaced 400 mm apart. Each lens has a focal length of 100 mm, and a 40-mm-tall object stands 230 mm to the left of the left lens. (*a*) Use an analytical approach to determine the position of the final image. Based on your calculation, is the final image (*b*) inverted or upright and (*c*) real or virtual? (*d*) Calculate the overall magnification. •••

80. You need to design a magnification system that provides a magnification of 3.00 and creates a real, upright image located 300 mm from the surface of the final lens in the system. The only lenses you have to work with are two converging lenses, each having a focal length of 100 mm. How should you place them with respect to the object, as well as with respect to each other, so as to achieve your goals? •••

81. You are trying to look at a geosynchronous communications satellite that is 5.500 m long. A typical human eye can resolve objects that are 0.1000 mm wide when the objects are at the person's near point, and the same angular size applies to objects farther away than the near point. Suppose the telescope you are using is 1.000 m long from one lens to the other. Describe what must be true of the lenses in order for you to be able to look at the satellite. Assume the satellite is exactly resolvable when viewed through your telescope. Is your result reasonable? What modifications could you make to the telescope in order to make it easier to see the satellite? •••

33.7 Spherical mirrors

82. Sunlight reflected off a mirror you are holding is focused at a point 160 mm in front of the mirror. What is the radius of curvature of the mirror? •

83. A spherical mirror for which the radius of curvature is $R = 250$ mm is used to form an image of an object placed a distance $d = 200$ mm in front of the mirror. Where does the image appear? •

84. A bathroom shaving mirror has radius of curvature $R = 400$ mm. Describe the image of your face formed when you stand (*a*) a distance $d_{close} = 100$ mm from the mirror and (*b*) a distance $d_{far} = 1.20$ m from the mirror. •

85. Passenger-side car mirrors often carry the warning "Objects in mirror are closer than they appear." If the mirror on your car has radius of curvature $R = -800$ mm and the car behind you and one lane to the right is a distance $o = 20.0$ m away, how far away does it appear? •

86. An object is placed 60 mm in front of a converging spherical mirror for which the radius of curvature is 200 mm. What are (*a*) the image distance and (*b*) the magnification of the image? (*c*) Is the image real or virtual? (*d*) Is it upright or inverted? (*e*) Draw a ray diagram illustrating this situation and including the three principal rays. ••

87. A converging mirror that has a radius of curvature of 70.0 mm forms an image of an object that is 20.0 mm tall and 150 mm in front of the mirror. (*a*) What is the image height? (*b*) Is the image real or virtual? (*c*) Is it upright or inverted? (*d*) Draw a ray diagram illustrating this situation and including the principal rays. ••

88. You stand 0.50 m in front of a diverging mirror for which the radius of curvature is −3.5 m. (*a*) Is your image real or virtual? (*b*) Is it upright or inverted? (*c*) How far away from the mirror surface is it located? (*d*) What is its magnification? ••

89. When you look at yourself in a converging mirror, you appear to be one-fourth your actual size. If you are standing 1.0 m in front of the mirror, what is the mirror's radius of curvature? ••

90. You wish to use a converging mirror to form an image that is N times larger than the object. In terms of N and R, the radius

of curvature of the mirror, at what distance o from the mirror should you place the object? ••

91. A spherical mirror produces a real image of your face that is twice as large as your face. If your face is 750 mm from the mirror, what is the radius of curvature of the mirror? ••

92. A converging mirror has a focal length of 300 mm. Calculate the image distance and magnification for an object located (*a*) halfway between the focal point and the mirror, (*b*) at the focal point, (*c*) halfway between the focal point and the center of curvature, (*d*) at the center of curvature, (*e*) a distance f beyond the center of curvature, and (*f*) at infinity. ••

93. Repeat Problem 92 for a diverging mirror. Comment on any similarities or differences with the two types of mirrors. ••

94. A security mirror in a shop is designed to give a wide-angle view, but as a result the images it forms are much smaller than their objects. If you want an image that appears 10.0 m behind the mirror to have a magnification of 10.0%, what radius of curvature must the mirror have? ••

95. The optical system of Figure P33.95 consists of a converging lens and a converging mirror. The focal points of the lens are marked by open dots and the center of curvature of the mirror by a solid dot. Draw a simplified ray diagram, and describe the final image. •••

Figure P33.95

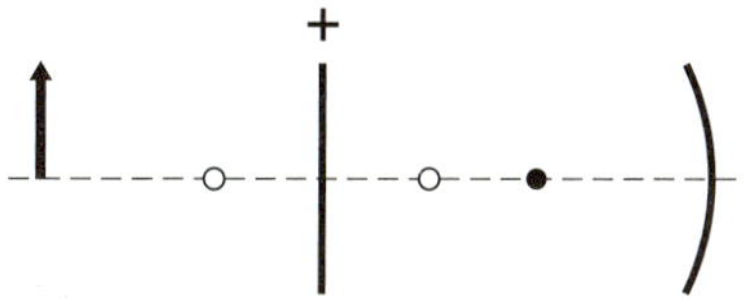

96. The kind of image a spherical mirror produces for a real object depends on where the object is located relative to the focal point of the mirror. There are three types of spherical mirrors—converging, diverging, and flat—if you consider a flat mirror as being one portion of a curved surface for which the radius of curvature is infinitely large. For a real object placed in front of each type of mirror, characterize the image as real or virtual; upright or inverted; in front of or behind the mirror; and enlarged, shrunken, or the same size as the object. •••

97. You position an object in front of a spherical mirror for which the magnitude of the radius of curvature is R_1. The image formed is real, inverted, and twice as large as the object. You then replace this spherical mirror with one that has a radius of curvature of magnitude R_2 (keeping the object distance unchanged). The image formed by this mirror is virtual, upright, and twice as large as the object. Calculate a value for the ratio R_2/R_1. •••

33.8 Lensmaker's formula

98. All the lenses in Figure P33.98 are surrounded by air. Which of the lenses are converging, and which are diverging? •

Figure P33.98

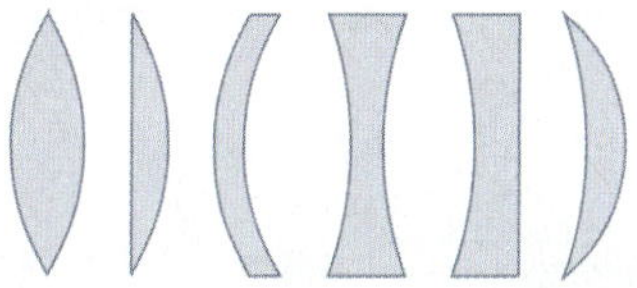

99. You have a thin lens that is convex on both surfaces. The material of which the lens is made has index of refraction $n = 1.40$, and the radii of curvature are $|R_1| = 300$ mm and $|R_2| = 500$ mm. What is the lens focal length in air? •

100. To correct the vision of a near-sighted patient, an optician needs to make a pair of eyeglasses using −3.0-diopter lenses. The lenses are plano-concave, and the front surface (that is, the surface farthest from the eye) is the flat surface. If the glass used for the lenses has an index of refraction of 1.5, what radius of curvature must the remaining surface have? •

101. A plano-convex lens has a focal length of 170 mm, and the material of which the lens is made has an index of refraction of 1.6. What is the radius of curvature of the convex surface? •

102. The radius of curvature of one surface of a glass lens ($n = 1.45$) is 1.50 m. If sunlight is focused at a point 0.300 m away from the lens, what is the radius of curvature of the other surface? ••

103. The two surfaces of a double convex, thin lens made of plastic each have an absolute value of radius of curvature of 1.8 mm. If the focal length of the lens is 4.5 mm, what is the index of refraction of the plastic? ••

104. A lens has an index of refraction of 1.50. Its left side curves outward with an absolute value of radius of curvature of 0.15 m, and its right side curves inward with an absolute value of radius of curvature of 0.25 m. What is its focal length if you look through it (*a*) from the left side and (*b*) from the right side? ••

105. A thin lens is made of material that has an index of refraction of 1.50. When an object 10 mm tall is placed 500 mm away from the lens, an upright image 21.5 mm tall is formed. One surface of the lens is concave, with an absolute value of radius of curvature of 350 mm. What is the radius of curvature of the other surface? ••

106. A lens made of glass for which the index of refraction is 1.55 has a focal length of 0.500 m in air. What is its focal length when this lens is submerged in water? ••

107. The convex surface of a plano-convex lens has an absolute value of radius of curvature of 40 mm. The index of refraction for the glass of which the lens is made is 1.5. (*a*) What is the focal length of the lens? (*b*) You take some measurements and determine that the 40-mm radius of curvature is correct but the focal length is 100 mm instead of the value calculated in part *a*. What must the index of refraction for the glass be? ••

108. A thin lens of focal length f_A is made of a material for which the index of refraction is $n_A = 1.1$. If you make a lens B that is identical to lens A in every way except that the index of refraction of the material used to make B is $n_B = 2n_A$, how does the focal length f_B for this lens compare with f_A? ••

109. The thin lens in air of Figure P33.109 is drawn showing $|R_1| < |R_2|$. (*a*) Is this lens converging or diverging? (*b*) If the lens were drawn showing $|R_1| = |R_2|$, would it be converging or diverging? (*c*) If it were drawn showing $|R_1| > |R_2|$, would it be converging or diverging? ••

Figure P33.109

110. The two surfaces of a lens made of an unknown material have the same magnitude of radius of curvature $|R|$. When an object is placed a distance R away from the lens, the image formed is real and twice as large as the object. What is the index of refraction of the material of which the lens is made? •••

Additional problems

111. When you shine a laser-beam pointer at a wall, why do you see a dot on the wall but not the beam running from pointer to wall? •

112. A man spearfishing from a dock sees a fish in the water. In order to hit the fish, should he aim the speargun above, below, or directly at the image he sees? •

113. Traveling through an optical cable for which the index of refraction is 1.6, how long does it take a light signal to travel from New York to Los Angeles, a distance of 4.0×10^3 km? •

114. In about the years 214–212 BC, the Greek philosopher and scientist Archimedes is said to have repelled a Roman attack with a "death-ray" converging mirror, using sunlight to set the approaching fleet on fire. Assume an early morning attack from the east, with the Sun directly behind the ships. If the approaching fleet is 100 m away from the mirror, what would the mirror's radius of curvature have to be in order to achieve the maximum effect? •

115. What is an application of a converging lens for these situations: (*a*) object is at twice the focal length, (*b*) object is at the focal length, and (*c*) object is at infinity? ••

116. An object that is 40 mm tall is placed 60 mm in front of a converging thin lens. If the image is inverted and 80 mm tall, what are (*a*) the distance from the image to the lens and (*b*) the focal length of the lens? ••

117. A converging lens for which $f = 50$ mm forms an image that is three times larger than the object. How far from the lens is the object? ••

118. In vacuum, the wavelength of a certain light wave is 550 nm. (*a*) What is the wavelength in a medium where the wave speed is 2.4×10^8 m/s? What is the frequency of this light (*b*) in vacuum and (*c*) in the medium? ••

119. The focal length of a lens can be different for different colors of light. (*a*) What optical principle causes this problem? (*b*) Can the problem be corrected? (*c*) Does the same problem affect mirrors? ••

120. When an object is placed 1.2 m in front of a diverging mirror, an image of the object is formed 0.75 m away from the mirror. (*a*) Is the image real or virtual? (*b*) Is it upright or inverted? (*c*) What is the mirror's radius of curvature? ••

121. The focal points of the two converging lenses shown in Figure P33.121 are denoted by solid dots for the left lens and open dots for the right lens. Draw a simplified ray diagram to locate the final image. ••

Figure P33.121

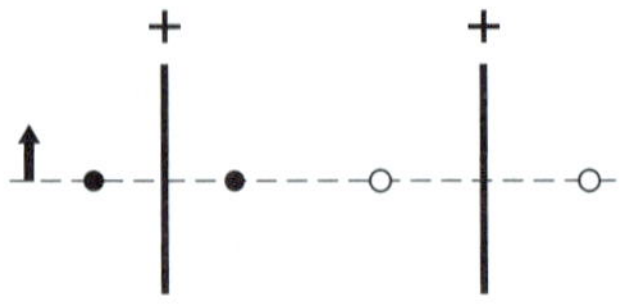

122. Using a camera fitted with a lens for which $f = 50$ mm, you take a photograph of a person who is 1.7 m tall and is standing 29 m away from you. What is the height of the person's image on the film? ••

123. A piece of electronic circuitry embedded in a layer of diamond ($n_{diamond} = 2.42$) emits light. The diamond is covered by a coating of flint glass ($n_{flint} = 1.65$). The interface between the two materials is flat, as is the interface between the flint glass and the surrounding air. The two interfaces are parallel. Relative to the direction normal to both interfaces, what are (*a*) the greatest angle at which light emitted in the diamond layer can enter the flint glass and (*b*) the greatest angle at which light emitted in the diamond layer travels through the flint glass and enters the surrounding air? •••

124. You and a friend are scuba diving on a calm day when you decide it would be neat to estimate the critical angle for light going from water into air. Your friend is underwater and has a laser pointer and a waterproof earpiece so that he can hear your instructions. He also has a floating marker attached to him that remains on the surface directly above him. Sitting in a small motorboat on the surface, you have a variety of tools for measuring distances (tape measures, fishing line that could be let out and later accurately measured, and so on). You think for a moment and decide on a course of action. ••• CR

125. You are in charge of the projector in a movie theater. The film passes through a holder, and light from a bright bulb passes first through the film and then through a lens. You have several additional lenses that can be swapped out, and the position of the lens holder is easily adjustable, but moving the film holder seems more troublesome. A single film frame is 20.00 mm tall. You notice that when the lens is placed 100.0 mm from the film, a sharp image 1450 mm tall is formed on the movie screen on the other side of the lens. This image is far too small, filling less than one-third of the screen. If the patrons do not see a much larger, well-focused image, you may be returned to your previous job making popcorn. ••• CR

126. For a lens in air, you have learned the conditions on its radii of curvature to make the lens converging or diverging. You have done some diving, and you realize that a lens has a different focal length underwater than it does in air. That starts you thinking about what would happen if a lens is placed in a medium with an index of refraction greater than that of the material of which the lens is made, but you are not even sure that it is possible to form images under such conditions. Lost in your thoughts, you drift off into dreamland. ••• CR

PRACTICE

Answers to Review Questions

1. The object has to either emit light or redirect light from a source, and this light must enter your eye and be formed into an image of the object.
2. A light ray is a line drawn in a diagram to represent the direction in which light from a source travels. A ray corresponds to a very thin beam of light emitted by the source.
3. A shadow is the dark region behind an object that is facing a light source, formed because the object blocks some of the light emitted by the source, preventing it from reaching the shadow region.
4. The light can be absorbed, which means it enters the object and does not come out; transmitted, which means it passes through the object; or reflected, which means it bounces off the object surface and is redirected away from the surface.
5. Most of the light striking an opaque object is absorbed by the object, which means that light goes into the object and does not come out. Most of the light striking a translucent object is transmitted diffusely through the object, meaning the rays are redirected randomly as they pass through the object.
6. For a ray striking a smooth surface, the angle of reflection is equal to the angle of incidence, and the two angles are in the same plane.
7. Specular reflection is reflection from a smooth surface (which is a surface for which the direction of the surface normal doesn't change on the scale of the wavelength of the light). Diffuse reflection is reflection from an irregular surface in which the irregularities are comparable in size to the wavelength of the light. Because the normal to an irregular surface varies randomly, the light is reflected in all directions.
8. No image is formed because different portions of the rough surface have randomly different normal directions, so that incoming rays are randomly scattered even though, for each ray, the angle of incidence and reflection are equal.
9. An image is an optical reproduction of an object formed by light rays that travel from the object.
10. Any rays that travel from a selected point on the object and reach the image must intersect or appear to intersect at a common point on the image. A real image is formed by light rays that intersect at a point on the image. A virtual image is formed by rays that do not intersect at a point on the image, but only appear to do so when traced backward.
11. The object either emits or reflects light rays in all directions, and some of those that reach the mirror surface are reflected to the observer's eye. When the observer traces these rays backward from his eye, they appear to pass through the mirror and intersect (hence apparently originate) at a location behind the mirror, causing the image to be located there.
12. The colors correspond to the different frequencies of the waves in the visible region of the electromagnetic spectrum.
13. Wavefronts are drawn perpendicular to the direction of propagation, and rays are drawn in the direction of propagation. Thus, rays and wavefronts representing the same light are drawn perpendicular to each other.
14. Refraction is the bending of light rays as they move from a medium A into a medium B when the media have different mass densities. The rays bend because as each wavefront crosses from A into B, the speed of that portion of the wavefront that has entered B is different from the speed of the portion still in A.
15. Yes. Because $\lambda = c/f$ and frequency does not change at a boundary, wavelength λ must change as wave speed c changes. Passing into a medium of lower mass density causes c to increase, and so λ also increases.
16. The angle the unrefracted ray forms with the normal to the interface between the media is the angle of incidence; the angle the refracted ray makes with the normal to the interface is the angle of refraction. When the ray moves from a high-density medium into a low-density medium, the angle of incidence is smaller than the angle of refraction because the refracted ray bends away from the normal to the interface. When the ray moves from a low-density medium into a high-density medium, the angle of incidence is greater than the angle of refraction because the refracted ray bends toward the normal.
17. The critical angle is the angle of incidence that causes the angle of refraction to be 90°, so that the refracted rays travel along the interface between the two media.
18. When light travels from a high-density medium into a low-density medium, the angle of refraction is greater than the angle of incidence. When the angle of incidence is greater than the critical angle, the light cannot be refracted because the angle of refraction cannot exceed 90° (if it did exceed 90°, the ray would no longer be in the low-density medium). With no refraction, the interface reflects all the light back into the high-density medium.
19. The path a light ray takes in moving from one location to another is that path for which the time interval needed for the trip is a minimum.
20. In a light beam consisting of rays of different frequencies, dispersion is the spreading out of the beam as the light is refracted. The speed of light in most materials depends slightly on the frequency of the light, so the amount by which each ray in the beam is refracted depends on the ray's frequency.
21. The ray's path is not changed when the travel direction is reversed, so the ray travels along its original path back through B to the interface and then into A.
22. Paraxial light rays are rays that enter a lens near its central axis and are either parallel to that axis or oriented at a small angle to it.
23. (1) A ray that is parallel to the lens axis before entering the lens on the left is refracted to pass through the focal point on the right side of the lens, (2) a ray that passes through the lens center continues on its original path, and (3) a ray that passes through the focal point on the left side of the lens is refracted to a path parallel to the lens axis on the right. Where these three rays intersect (or appear to intersect) is the location of the image.
24. A converging lens surface curves the way the outside of a sphere curves and causes parallel light rays passing through the lens to converge at a point after they leave the lens. A diverging lens surface curves the way the inside of a sphere curves and causes parallel rays passing through the lens to diverge from one another after they leave the lens, as if they had originated from a common point on the opposite side of the lens.
25. The index of refraction is the ratio of the speed of light in vacuum to the speed of light in the material: $n_{\text{material}} = c_0/c_{\text{material}}$ (Eq. 33.1).
26. The wavelength in the material is equal to the wavelength in vacuum divided by the material's index of refraction: $\lambda_{\text{material}} = \lambda_{\text{vac}}/n_{\text{material}}$ (Eq. 33.3).
27. Snel's law describes the relationship between the angles of incidence and refraction when light traveling in a medium 1 enters a medium 2 and is refracted: The product of the sine of the angle of refraction and the index of refraction of the refractive medium 2 equals the product of the sine of the angle of incidence and the index of refraction of the incident medium 1: $n_1 \sin\theta_1 = n_2 \sin\theta_2$ (Eq. 33.7).
28. The sine of the critical angle is equal to the index of refraction of the lower-density medium divided by the index of refraction of the higher-density medium: $\sin\theta_c = n_{\text{lower density}}/n_{\text{higher density}}$ (from Eq. 33.9).
29. The lens equation relates, for any image formed by the lens, the lens focal length f to the object distance o and image distance i: $1/f = 1/o + 1/i$ (Eq. 33.16). Focal length is positive for converging lenses and negative for diverging lenses. Image distance is positive if the object and image are on opposite sides of the lens and negative if they are on the same side of the lens. Object distance is positive if the object is in front of the lens and negative if it is behind the lens, where *front* means the side on which the rays forming the image originate.

30. Magnification is the ratio of image height to object height: $M = -i/o$ (Eq. 33.17). A positive value of M indicates an upright image; a negative value of M indicates an inverted image.
31. The near point is the closest distance at which the eye can see an object in sharp focus.
32. Angular magnification is the absolute value of the ratio of the angle subtended by the image to the angle subtended by the object: $M_\theta = |\theta_i/\theta_o|$ (Eq. 33.18).
33. The diopter is the unit in which the strength of eyeglass lenses is measured. The lens strength d is given by Eq. 33.22: $d = (1 \text{ m})/f$, where f is the lens focal length.
34. The focal length is half the radius of curvature: $f = R/2$ (Eq. 33.23).
35. Yes. Focal length is positive for converging mirrors and negative for diverging mirrors. Image distance is positive if the object and image are on the same side of the mirror and negative if they are on opposite sides of the mirror. Object distance is positive if the object is in front of the mirror and negative if it is behind the mirror.
36. Whether the image is real or virtual depends on where the object is located. When the object is between the focus and the mirror surface, the image forms behind the mirror and so is virtual because the rays cannot enter the space behind the mirror. When the object–mirror distance is greater than the focus–mirror distance, the image forms in front of the mirror and so is real because the rays pass through the image location.
37. The formula applies only to thin lenses and only when the rays used to calculate the radii of curvature are paraxial so that the small-angle approximation can be used.
38. The radii are positive for convex surfaces, negative for concave surfaces, and infinite for flat surfaces.

Answers to Guided Problems

Guided Problem 33.2 $n_{liq} = 1.17$

Guided Problem 33.4 A lens of focal length $f = 80$ mm

Guided Problem 33.6 0.333 m

Guided Problem 33.8 (*a*) Converging. (*b*) Yes. With the candle upright and its base on the mirror axis, place the paper 257 mm in front of the mirror and below the axis to capture the image, which is 71.4% the size of the candle.

Guided Problem 33.10 57 mm

34 PRACTICE Wave and Particle Optics

Chapter Summary

Diffraction (Sections 34.1–34.3, 34.6)

Concepts Light is diffracted as it passes through an opening only when the width of the opening is either comparable to or smaller than the wavelength of the light.

Interference fringes are a pattern of alternating bright and dark bands (called *fringes*) cast on a screen by coherent light passing through two or more slits. **Fringe order** is the numerical ordering of bright and dark fringes. The central bright fringe is the *zeroth-order bright fringe,* the bright fringes to the left and right of it are the first-order bright fringes, the next bright fringes to the left and right are the second-order bright fringes, and so on. The two dark fringes bordering the central bright fringe are the first-order dark fringes, and so on.

When the light passes through two slits, the interference pattern formed on a screen behind the slits consists of alternating bright and dark fringes. When light passes through three or more slits, each dark fringe contains one or more regions that are not as bright as the bright fringes but not completely dark. In these patterns, the brightest fringes are *principal maxima,* and the fainter bright regions are *secondary maxima.*

A **diffraction grating** is a barrier containing a large number of equally spaced slits or grooves. A transmissive diffraction grating contains slits that transmit light, and a reflective diffraction grating contains grooves that reflect light.

The **Bragg condition** states that a crystal reflects x rays of wavelength λ only at angles of incidence relative to the crystal plane given by $2d\cos\theta = m\lambda$, where m is an integer and d is the distance between adjacent crystal planes.

Quantitative Tools When light of wavelength λ passes through two slits a distance d apart, the bright fringes occur at angles given by

$$\sin\theta_m = \pm\frac{m\lambda}{d},\ m = 0, 1, 2, 3, \ldots, \tag{34.5}$$

and the dark fringes occur when

$$\sin\theta_n = \pm\frac{(n-\frac{1}{2})}{d}\lambda,\ n = 1, 2, 3, \ldots. \tag{34.7}$$

The integers m and n give the **fringe order.**

For light passing through N slits, the *principal maxima* occur when

$$d\sin\theta_m = \pm m\lambda,\ m = 0, 1, 2, 3, \ldots, \tag{34.16}$$

and the dark fringes occur when

$$d\sin\theta_{\text{min}} = \pm\frac{k}{N}\lambda, \tag{34.17}$$

where k is an integer that is not an integer multiple of N.

Thin-film interference (Section 34.7)

Concepts Thin-film interference occurs in transparent materials whose thickness is comparable to one of the wavelengths of visible light. Light reflecting from the front surface of the material interferes with light reflecting from the back surface.

Quantitative Tools Light reflects from a thin film of thickness t and index of refraction n_b. At normal incidence of the light, the phase difference ϕ between the light rays reflected from the front and back surfaces of the film is

$$\phi = \frac{4\pi n_b t}{\lambda} + \phi_{r2} - \phi_{r1}, \tag{34.23}$$

where the phase shifts ϕ_{r1} and ϕ_{r2} are due to reflection at the front and back surfaces. Each phase shift must be either 0 or π, depending on the indices of refraction of the media in front of and behind the film.

PRACTICE

Diffraction by single slits and circular apertures (Sections 34.8, 34.9)

Concepts Light passing through a circular aperture is diffracted, and the interference fringes are circular. The central bright fringe is called the *Airy disk.*

Quantitative Tools When light is diffracted by a thin slit of thickness a, the dark fringes occur when

$$\sin\theta_n = \pm n\frac{\lambda}{a}, n = 1, 2, 3, \ldots. \quad (34.26)$$

When light is diffracted by a small circular aperture of diameter d, the first dark fringe occurs when

$$\sin\theta_1 = 1.22\frac{\lambda}{d}. \quad (34.29)$$

Rayleigh's criterion: The minimum angular separation θ_r for which two light sources can be *resolved* by a lens of diameter d is

$$\theta_r \approx 1.22\frac{\lambda}{d}. \quad (34.30)$$

Matter waves and photons (Sections 34.4, 34.5, 34.10)

Concepts **Wave-particle duality** says that particles and light have both wave and particle properties.

The **de Broglie wavelength** expresses the wavelength of a particle.

A **photon** is the "particle" of light. It is an indivisible, discrete unit of light.

Photoelectric effect: When photons of light of sufficiently high frequency shine on a metal, electrons are ejected from the metal. The *stopping potential difference* is the potential needed to stop the ejected electrons. The **work function** E_0 of a metal is the minimum energy needed to free an electron from the metal surface.

Quantitative Tools **Planck's constant** is

$$h = 6.626 \times 10^{-34}\ \text{J}\cdot\text{s}.$$

The **de Broglie wavelength** of a particle having momentum p is

$$\lambda = h/p.$$

In the **photoelectric effect,**

$$E_{\text{photon}} = hf = K_{\max} + E_0, \quad (34.35)$$

where f is the frequency of the light hitting the metal, $K_{\max}$ is the maximum kinetic energy of the ejected electron, and E_0 is the work function of the metal.

The energy of a photon is

$$E_{\text{photon}} = hf_{\text{photon}}, \quad (34.39)$$

and its momentum is

$$p_{\text{photon}} = \frac{hf_{\text{photon}}}{c_0}. \quad (34.40)$$

Review Questions

Answers to these questions can be found at the end of this chapter.

34.1 Diffraction of light

1. What is diffraction?
2. For a beam of planar waves passing through a narrow gap in a barrier located in the path of the beam, what relationship between wavelength and wavefront width determines whether the beam undergoes diffraction?

34.2 Diffraction gratings

3. What are interference fringes?
4. What does the order of an interference fringe designate?
5. When a light beam passes through two slits in a barrier, what condition determines where on a screen placed behind the barrier the bright interference fringes fall? What condition determines where on the screen the dark fringes fall?
6. Is the condition for constructive interference in light passing through a barrier containing many equally spaced slits the same as or different from the condition for constructive interference in light passing through a two-slit barrier? Is the condition for destructive interference the same or different in the two cases?
7. What is the distinction between principal and secondary maxima in an interference pattern created by light passing through a many-slit barrier?
8. What is a diffraction grating? What are the two types?

34.3 X-ray diffraction

9. What property of a crystal lattice allows the lattice to act as a diffraction grating for x rays?
10. What information does the Bragg condition convey?

34.4 Matter waves

11. What happens to a beam of electrons passing through a crystal? What does this suggest about how electrons behave?
12. What quantity measures the wave nature of a particle?
13. Why isn't it possible to observe wave behavior in macroscopic objects?

34.5 Photons

14. What is a photon, and what determines its energy?
15. The pattern on adjacent detecting screens when very-low-intensity light travels directly from a source to the screens is different from the pattern when the light passes through adjacent slits before reaching a detecting screen. Describe how this difference supports the model of light as a stream of particles.

34.6 Multiple-slit interference

16. Given that the waves leaving two slits correspond to waves from in-phase point sources, why are the waves out of phase when they arrive at a given location on a detecting screen?
17. When planar light waves pass through two side-by-side slits and then travel to a detecting screen, how does the maximum intensity in the interference pattern on the screen compare with the sum of the intensities of the waves incident on the slits?
18. What is the limiting condition for resolving two wavelengths, λ_1 and $\lambda_2 < \lambda_1$, in the dispersed spectrum formed by a diffraction grating?

34.7 Thin-film interference

19. How does thin-film interference occur?
20. When visible light passes through a transparent material, what limit on the thickness of the material determines whether or not interference occurs?
21. In thin-film interference, what two factors determine the phase difference between a light beam reflected from the front film surface and a beam reflected from the back surface?
22. Consider a ray of light traveling from medium 1 with index of refraction n_1 to medium 2 with index of refraction n_2. Describe the phase shift undergone upon reflection of the beam at the interface between media 1 and 2.

34.8 Diffraction at a single-slit barrier

23. By dividing a planar wavefront passing through a slit into suitable pairs of point sources, what feature of the interference pattern can be determined?
24. What is the expression for determining the directions to minima in the interference pattern created by light passing through a single slit?
25. What does the interference pattern created by light waves passing through a single slit look like if the slit width is smaller than the wavelength of the waves?

34.9 Circular apertures and limits of resolution

26. What does the interference pattern created by light passing through a circular aperture look like?
27. What is an Airy disk?
28. What is Rayleigh's criterion?
29. What is a diffraction limit, and how is it defined by the Airy disk of an interference pattern?

34.10 Photon energy and momentum

30. What is the photoelectric effect?
31. In an electric circuit in which the current is due to the photoelectric effect, what is the stopping potential difference, and on what property of the incident light does it depend?
32. What is the relationship between the stopping potential difference in a photoelectric circuit and the kinetic energy of the electrons ejected from the target?
33. How does the fact that the stopping potential difference for a photoelectric circuit depends on the frequency of the incident light rather than on the light intensity support a particle interpretation of light over a wave interpretation?
34. In a photoelectric circuit, what is the relationship between the current and the intensity of the incident light?
35. What is the work function of a metal?

Developing a Feel

Make an order-of-magnitude estimate of each of the following quantities. Letters in parentheses refer to hints below. Use them as needed to guide your thinking.

1. The distance between the first and second maxima 20 km away from two AM radio towers separated by 3 km, if they were to emit at the same frequency (E, L, P)
2. The angular location of the first "dark" fringe (*dark* in this case indicating no sound rather than no light) in the diffraction pattern when the sound wave created by striking the middle C key on a piano passes through a garage door (D, I, V)
3. The angular location of the first dark fringe in the diffraction pattern when a microwave signal passes through a metal doorway set in a metal wall (W, J)
4. The diameter of the image formed on the back of your eye by a point source of bright light (A, Q, U)
5. The number of photons per second emitted by a 5-mW green laser pointer (X, T)
6. The force exerted on a sheet of aluminum by the beam from a 5-mW green laser pointer (K, B)
7. The number of photons per second entering your eye from a 5-W LED lamp located 2 m away (S, F, O)
8. The wavelength of a neutron traveling at 300 m/s (M, C)
9. The minimum thickness of an oil slick lying on a puddle of water that appears red (R, H)
10. The electron speed needed in order for an electron beam to image a single virus (N, G)

Hints

A. What is the average wavelength of visible light?
B. How much momentum is carried by the laser beam in 1 s?
C. What is the neutron's momentum?
D. What is the frequency of the middle C sound wave?
E. What is the average frequency of AM radio waves?
F. What is the surface area of your pupil?
G. What wavelength must the electrons have in order to image this virus?
H. What is the index of refraction of oil?
I. What is the wavelength of this sound wave?
J. What is a typical width for a doorway?
K. How much energy is carried by the laser beam in 1 s?
L. What is the average wavelength of AM radio waves?
M. What is the neutron's mass?
N. What is a typical diameter for a virus?
O. What is the surface area of a sphere that has a radius of 2 m?
P. What is the angular separation of the two maxima?
Q. What is the focal length of the eye?
R. What is the wavelength of red light?
S. How many photons per second are emitted by the lamp?
T. What is the energy of a green photon?
U. What is the diameter of the pupil of the eye in bright light?
V. What is a typical width for a garage door?
W. What is the average wavelength of microwaves?
X. What is the wavelength of green light?

Key (all values approximate)

A. 5×10^{-7} m; **B.** 2×10^{-11} kg · m/s; **C.** 6×10^{-25} kg · m/s; **D.** 262 Hz; **E.** 1 MHz; **F.** 10^{-5} m^2; **G.** 10 nm; **H.** $n = 1.5$; **I.** 1 m; **J.** 1 m; **K.** 5 mJ; **L.** 300 m; **M.** 2×10^{-27} kg; **N.** 100 nm; **O.** 50 m^2; **P.** 0.1 rad; **Q.** 3×10^{-2} m; **R.** 7×10^{-7} m; **S.** 10^{19}; **T.** 4×10^{-19} J; **U.** 3×10^{-3} m; **V.** 3 m; **W.** 0.1 m; **X.** 5×10^{-7} m

Worked and Guided Problems

These examples involve material from this chapter, but they are not associated with any particular section. Some examples are worked out in detail; others you should work out by following the guidelines provided.

Worked Problem 34.1 Distinguishing headlights

You are driving east on a straight highway at night, with the pupils of your eyes dilated to a diameter of 6.0 mm. Far down the road, you spot a lone car traveling west toward you, and the headlights on this car are 1.5 m apart. Assuming diffraction is the only factor limiting your vision, how far away is the approaching car when you start seeing its headlights as two separate objects?

❶ GETTING STARTED This is a problem about distinguishing two adjacent point sources of light in the image formed by the lens in each of your eyes. We can consider just one eye, however, because the situation is the same for both eyes. To visualize the situation, we sketch it, defining L to be the distance from your eye to the headlights of the approaching car and θ the angle subtended at your eye by those headlights (Figure WG34.1).

Figure WG34.1

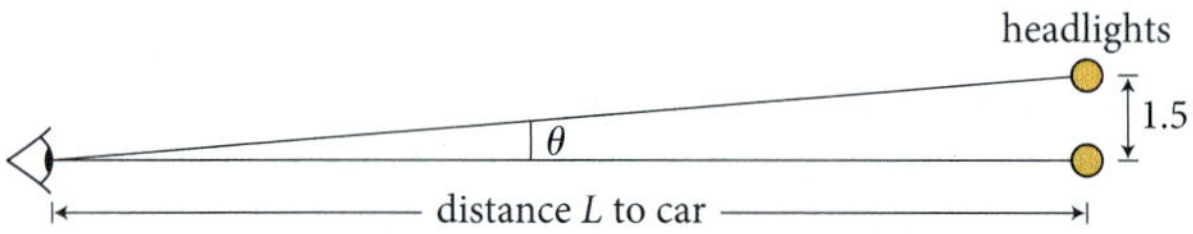

❷ DEVISE PLAN Figure WG34.1 shows that $\tan\theta = (1.5\text{ m})/L$, which means we can obtain L once we know θ. Because L is the distance at which the two headlights cease to be separate images, θ has to be the angle that satisfies Rayleigh's criterion. Equation 34.30 shows that this criterion depends on the diameter of the lens through which the light passes and on the wavelength of that light. In the eye, the pupil lies in front of the lens, which means the pupil diameter determines how much light passes through the lens. Thus we use the pupil diameter as the lens diameter. For wavelength, we choose a value near the center of the visible spectrum—$\lambda = 550$ nm—because the headlights emit visible light.

❸ EXECUTE PLAN Using y to represent the distance between the headlights, we have from Figure WG34.1 and the small-angle approximation

$$\theta \approx \tan\theta = \frac{y}{L}$$

Equation 34.30 says that the angle by which two objects must be separated if they are to satisfy Rayleigh's criterion is

$$\theta_r \approx \frac{y}{L} = \frac{1.22\lambda}{d}$$

and so—if diffraction is the only factor determining what you see—the distance at which you start to see the two headlights emerging from a single bright glow is

$$L = \frac{yd}{1.22\lambda} = \frac{(1.5\text{ m})(6.0\times10^{-3}\text{ m})}{1.22(550\times10^{-9}\text{ m})} = 1.3\times10^{4}\text{ m.} \checkmark$$

❹ EVALUATE RESULT You know that this distance, 8 miles, is much greater than the distance at which normally you can see an approaching car. (Of course, it's rare that you have a straight highway that is empty of cars over such a long distance!) In this case, the unreasonably large result suggests that diffraction is only one of the many phenomena limiting your vision. However, we can still tell that most likely the calculation is correct because the distance is on a reasonable scale—neither vastly too short (100 m or less) nor vastly too long (100 km or more).

We also notice that although we had to assume a wavelength for the light emitted by the headlights, L is inversely proportional to that wavelength. Because the range of the visible spectrum runs from 700 nm to 400 nm, the value of L we would get by choosing a different wavelength would change by at most 40%, not changing the order of magnitude of the result.

Guided Problem 34.2 Geosynchronous satellites

Television satellite dishes are approximately spherical mirrors that collect 12-GHz electromagnetic signals emitted by satellites in orbit around Earth. Each mirror serves as a circular aperture just as a lens does. How many satellites can be placed in geosynchronous orbit above the equator, at a height of 36,000 km above Earth's surface, if all of them are to send signals that can be distinguished by a satellite dish having a diameter of 0.45 m?

❶ GETTING STARTED
1. Draw a diagram showing two sources and the dish receiving their signals, labeling the relevant distances.
2. What condition determines whether the signals from two adjacent satellites are distinguishable? What distances does this condition depend on?

❷ DEVISE PLAN
3. What quantity must you determine to solve this problem? How does this quantity relate to the distance between adjacent distinguishable satellites?
4. What information do you need to look up to work this problem?
5. How can you determine the wavelength of the electromagnetic waves broadcast by the satellites?

❸ EXECUTE PLAN

❹ EVALUATE RESULT
6. Is the number of satellites you obtain plausibly large enough to satisfy telecommunications needs? Small enough to be consistent with any experience you have observing satellites in the night sky?

Worked Problem 34.3 Measuring the index of refraction of air

An *interferometer* (Figure WG34.2) exploits two-source interference to measure either very short distances or differences in indices of refraction. In the device, a laser beam is directed to a *beam splitter,* which reflects half of the light in the beam to adjustable mirror M_1, which can be moved closer to or farther from the beam splitter, and transmits the other half to stationary mirror M_2.

PRACTICE

The two beams follow the paths shown in Figure WG34.2, each traveling to its mirror M_1 or M_2, back to the beam splitter, and then to a detector that measures the intensity of the combined beams. For this problem, the laser has a wavelength in vacuum of 488 nm.

A sealed cylindrical chamber that is 50.0 mm long and has glass windows at both ends is initially filled with air. The chamber is placed so that the beam traveling to M_2 passes through it, and the position of adjustable mirror M_1 is set so that the intensity at the detector is a maximum. Then the air is gradually pumped out of the chamber. While the air is being pumped out, the intensity at the detector goes to a minimum and then returns to a maximum 60.0 times. Calculate the index of refraction of air.

Figure WG34.2

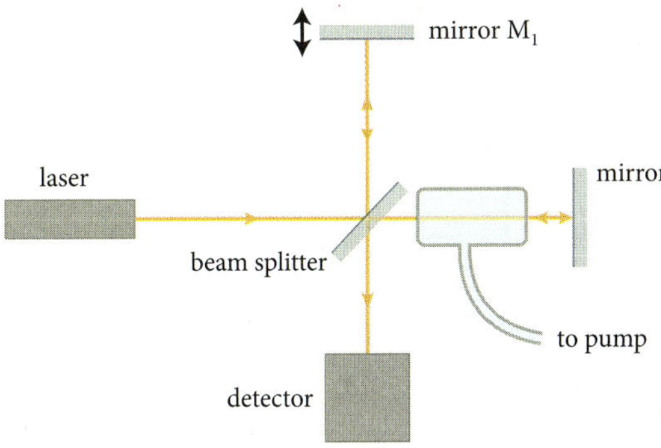

❶ GETTING STARTED This problem involves interference between light beams from two sources, M_1 and M_2. The amount of interference varies as the index of refraction of the contents of the chamber decreases as the air is pumped out. Changing the index of refraction changes the wavelength of the beam inside the chamber and thus changes the number of wavelengths along the path the beam travels from the splitter to M_2 and then back to the splitter.

Initially, when the chamber is filled with air, the combined intensity of the two beams at the detector is a maximum. This means that initially the beam passing through the chamber is in phase with the beam from M_1 when the two arrive at the detector. Then each intensity cycle down to a minimum and back to a maximum corresponds to decreasing the number of wavelengths in the chamber by 1 as the index of refraction decreases and consequently the wavelength gets longer. In the time interval during which the chamber goes from filled to evacuated, the minimum/maximum cycle occurs 60.0 times. We thus need to identify the index of refraction of air that causes the number of wavelengths to decrease by 60.0 as the index of refraction decreases to $n_{vacuum} = 1$.

❷ DEVISE PLAN The beam traveling to M_2 passes through the chamber twice, so the distance it travels through the chamber is $2L$, where L is the chamber length. We can express the number of wavelengths N_{air} in the air-filled chamber in terms of L, the beam wavelength in vacuum λ, and the index of refraction n_{air}. Likewise, we can express the number of wavelengths N_{vacuum} in the evacuated chamber in terms of L and λ. Then we can equate the difference $N_{air} - N_{vacuum}$ to 60.0 and solve for n_{air}.

❸ EXECUTE PLAN When the chamber is filled with air, the number of wavelengths in the chamber is

$$N_{air} = \frac{2L}{\lambda_{air}} = \frac{2L}{(\lambda/n_{air})} = \frac{2Ln_{air}}{\lambda},$$

and the number of wavelengths in the evacuated chamber is

$$N_{vacuum} = \frac{2L}{\lambda}.$$

Therefore

$$N_{air} - N_{vacuum} = \frac{2Ln_{air}}{\lambda} - \frac{2L}{\lambda} = \frac{2L}{\lambda}(n_{air} - 1)$$

$$n_{air} = \frac{\lambda(N_{air} - N_{vacuum})}{2L} + 1$$

$$= \frac{(488 \times 10^{-9}\ \text{m})(60.0)}{2(5.00 \times 10^{-2}\ \text{m})} + 1$$

$$= 2.93 \times 10^{-4} + 1 = 1.000293. ✔$$

Because the 1 in this calculation is an exact number and thus has an infinite number of significant digits, the number of significant digits in our value for n_{air} is determined by keeping all of the significant digits in the 2.93×10^{-4} value.

❹ EVALUATE RESULT This value is plausible because it is very close to but greater than 1, as it must be, and significantly smaller than the index of refraction for water (1.33) or other transparent materials. It also matches the value given in *Principles* Table 33.1.

Guided Problem 34.4 Colorful soap film

As a film of soap and water evaporates and thins, the dominant reflected color changes and eventually the film disappears. (*a*) What is the last color you see as the film thins? (*b*) How thick is the film just as the last vestige of color vanishes?

❶ GETTING STARTED

1. What principle determines the color reflected from the film? Based on this principle, what properties of the film affect the color?
2. As the film gets thinner, does the dominant reflected wavelength increase or decrease?
3. What reasonable assumption can you make about the angle at which you view the film?
4. Draw a sketch showing the film and the paths taken by reflected light.

❷ DEVISE PLAN

5. How can you use what you know about interference to determine the relationship between the film thickness and the dominant color reflected at that thickness?
6. At which film surface or surfaces is there a phase shift when the light is reflected?

❸ EXECUTE PLAN

7. What value is reasonable for the index of refraction of the film?

❹ EVALUATE RESULT

8. How does your result compare with the thickness of a piece of paper? Is the ratio of the two thicknesses reasonable?
9. To evaluate the reasonableness of your result another way, estimate the volume of soap solution a child might use to blow a single bubble and the size of the resulting bubble.

Worked Problem 34.5 Overlapping rainbows

White light (400–700 nm) is incident on a diffraction grating that has 300 lines/mm. As noted in *Principles* Section 34.2, the interference pattern in this case is not simply alternating bright and dark fringes but rather a sequence of red-to-violet rainbows located symmetrically to the left and right of a central white fringe. Which wavelengths in either third-order rainbow overlap the adjacent fourth-order rainbow?

❶ **GETTING STARTED** This is a problem about white light incident on a diffraction grating. To visualize the situation, we start with the interference pattern that results when monochromatic light strikes a grating (Figure WG34.3). Each wavelength produces an interference pattern consisting of narrow bright fringes separated by relatively wide dark fringes. The light in this problem is not monochromatic, however. It contains all visible wavelengths, so the interference pattern is a bright white spot at the center (where all colors undergo constructive interference) surrounded by a series of rainbows, each oriented with its violet end toward the center white spot. The orientation is this way because fringe position depends directly on wavelength. The shorter the wavelength, the closer to the midline of the interference pattern the fringe is. Because the wavelength of violet light is shorter than the wavelength of red light, in any rainbow in the interference pattern, the violet end of the rainbow is the end closer to the center. The rainbows overlap, and Figure WG34.4 shows this overlap for the first-order and second-order rainbows on either side of the central white spot.

Figure WG34.3

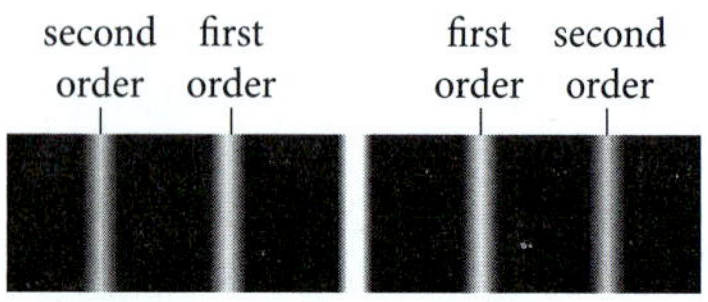

Figure WG34.4

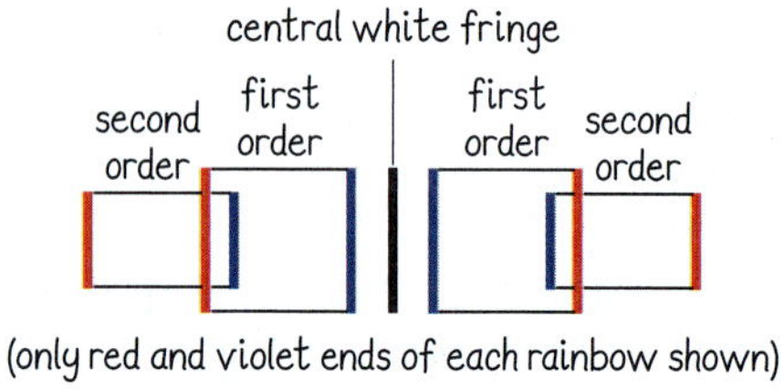

To solve this problem, we need to find the range of angular positions of the third- and fourth-order rainbows, and identify which wavelengths fall in the same angular range.

❷ **DEVISE PLAN** Figure WG34.4 shows that the longest wavelengths (those toward the red end) in the first-order rainbow overlap the shortest wavelengths (those toward the violet end) in the second-order rainbow. The same is true for all other orders, and Figure WG34.5 shows the overlap for the third- and fourth-order rainbows to the right of the central white spot. To determine the wavelength ranges that overlap, we calculate the angular position at which the fourth-order rainbow in Figure WG34.5 begins, which is the angular position of the violet end ($\lambda_{\text{short}} = 400$ nm). Next we calculate the wavelength in the third-order rainbow that falls at that same angular position, calling this wavelength $\lambda_{3,\text{overlap}}$. The third-order rainbow ends at its red end ($\lambda_{\text{long}} = 700$ nm), so the overlap extends from $\lambda_{3,\text{overlap}}$ to λ_{long}. For all these calculations, we use the Eq. 34.16 relationship between wavelength and angular position.

Figure WG34.5

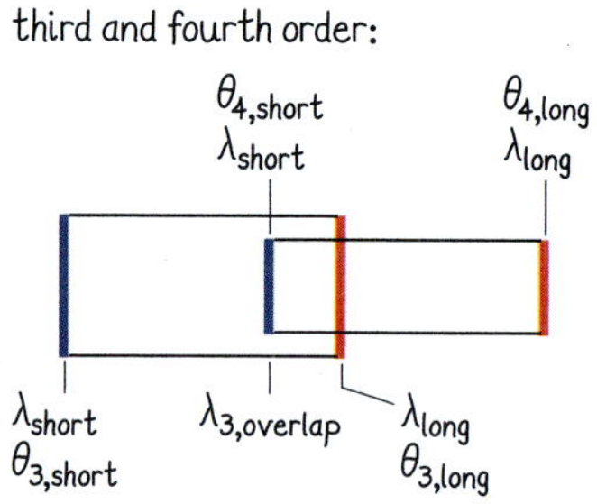

❸ **EXECUTE PLAN** The angular position of the violet end of the fourth-order rainbow is given by

$$d \sin \theta_{4,\text{short}} = 4\lambda_{\text{short}}, \tag{1}$$

where d is the grating spacing. Applying Eq. 34.16 to the wavelength $\lambda_{3,\text{overlap}}$ in the third-order rainbow where overlap begins gives us

$$d \sin \theta_{3,\text{overlap}} = 3\lambda_{3,\text{overlap}}. \tag{2}$$

Because the beginning of the overlap region and the violet end of the fourth-order rainbow occur at the same angular position, we can rewrite Eq. 2 as

$$d \sin \theta_{4,\text{short}} = 3\lambda_{3,\text{overlap}}. \tag{3}$$

Comparing Eqs. 1 and 3 tells us that $4\lambda_{\text{short}} = 3\lambda_{3,\text{overlap}}$, so

$$\lambda_{3,\text{overlap}} = \tfrac{4}{3}\lambda_{\text{short}} = \tfrac{4}{3}(400 \times 10^{-9}\ \text{m}) = 533 \times 10^{-9}\ \text{m}.$$

So, in the third-order rainbow, the wavelengths from 533 nm to 700 nm overlap with the fourth-order rainbow. ✔

❹ **EVALUATE RESULT** The wavelength in the third-order rainbow where overlap begins, 533 nm, is in the visible region of the electromagnetic spectrum, so our result is reasonable.

Guided Problem 34.6 Two colors

Light from a red laser ($\lambda_r = 633$ nm) passes through a narrow slit located 2.00 m from a screen and creates an interference pattern on the screen. When this laser is removed and light from a blue laser ($\lambda_b = 488$ nm) passes through the slit, the $n = 1$ minima of the interference pattern move by 3.00 mm. (*a*) In which direction do the minima move: toward the center of the interference pattern or away from the center? (*b*) What is the slit width?

❶ **GETTING STARTED**

1. How do the angular positions of the $n = 1$ minima depend on wavelength?
2. Draw a sketch showing the pattern formed by the red light and the pattern formed by the blue light.

❷ DEVISE PLAN

3. For a single-slit interference pattern, what equation relates the angular position of the minima to the wavelength of the light and the slit width?
4. What quantity do you need to determine in order to solve this problem?
5. Does the distance by which the $n = 1$ minima move depend on only one wavelength or on both wavelengths? How can you relate this distance to the wavelength(s) and the slit width?

❸ EXECUTE PLAN

❹ EVALUATE RESULT

6. How does the slit width compare with the wavelengths of the red and blue light? To the thickness of a piece of paper?

Worked Problem 34.7 Electron and neutron diffraction

Electrons moving at 2.0×10^6 m/s pass through a double-slit apparatus, producing an interference pattern in which adjacent bright fringes are separated by 1.5 mm. (*a*) What is the bright-fringe spacing when the electrons are replaced by neutrons moving at the same speed? (*b*) Can visible light be used with this apparatus to produce the same interference pattern as the electrons or neutrons?

❶ GETTING STARTED This is a problem about the interference pattern created on a screen by particles passing through a double-slit. In this case, electrons and neutrons rather than electromagnetic waves (photons) are interfering.

❷ DEVISE PLAN For any kind of waves, the bright-fringe separation distance y is determined by the center-to-center distance d between the slits, the normal distance L from the slits to the screen, and the wavelength λ of the interfering waves: $y = L\lambda/d$ (Eq. 34.15). The same apparatus is used for the electrons and neutrons, and so d and L remain unchanged.

To solve part *a*, we use Eq. 34.15 to express the bright-fringe spacing y_n obtained with neutrons in terms of the bright-fringe spacing y_e obtained with electrons and the electron and neutron wavelengths λ_e and λ_n. We can then use the de Broglie relationship, $\lambda = h/mv$ (Section 34.4), to substitute for λ_e and λ_n and obtain a value for y_n. For part *b*, we can compare the electron and neutron wavelengths with wavelengths in the visible region of the electromagnetic spectrum.

❸ EXECUTE PLAN (*a*) Equation 34.15 gives the relationship for y_n, y_e, and the electron and neutron wavelengths:

$$y_n = \frac{L\lambda_n}{d} \qquad \frac{y_n}{\lambda_n} = \frac{L}{d}$$

$$y_e = \frac{L\lambda_e}{d} \qquad \frac{y_e}{\lambda_e} = \frac{L}{d}$$

$$\frac{y_n}{\lambda_n} = \frac{y_e}{\lambda_e}.$$

We solve this expression for y_n, substitute the de Broglie relationship for the wavelengths, and substitute values:

$$y_n = y_e\frac{\lambda_n}{\lambda_e} = y_e\frac{h/m_n v_n}{h/m_e v_e} = y_e\frac{m_e}{m_n}$$

$$= (1.5 \times 10^{-3}\ \text{m})\left(\frac{9.11 \times 10^{-31}\ \text{kg}}{1.67 \times 10^{-27}\ \text{kg}}\right)$$

$$= 8.2 \times 10^{-7}\ \text{m} = 0.82\ \mu\text{m}. ✔$$

(*b*) The electron and neutron wavelengths are

$$\lambda_e = \frac{h}{mv} = \frac{6.626 \times 10^{-34}\ \text{J}\cdot\text{s}}{(9.11 \times 10^{-31}\ \text{kg})(2.0 \times 10^6\ \text{m/s})}$$

$$= 3.6 \times 10^{-10}\ \text{m} = 0.36\ \text{nm}$$

$$\lambda_n = \frac{h}{mv} = \frac{6.626 \times 10^{-34}\ \text{J}\cdot\text{s}}{(1.67 \times 10^{-27}\ \text{kg})(2.0 \times 10^6\ \text{m/s})}$$

$$= 2.0 \times 10^{-13}\ \text{m} = 2.0 \times 10^{-4}\ \text{nm}.$$

The electron wavelength is in the x-ray region of the electromagnetic spectrum, and the neutron wavelength is in the gamma-ray region. The visible spectrum extends roughly from 400 nm to 700 nm, meaning it is not possible for visible light to duplicate the interference pattern created by passing electrons or neutrons through a double slit. ✔

❹ EVALUATE RESULT Neutrons passing through a double slit at a given speed produce a much smaller bright-fringe spacing (by more than three orders of magnitude) than electrons passing through at the same speed. This makes sense because, with both having the same speed, the greater mass of the neutrons gives these particles greater momentum and hence shorter wavelength. Shorter wavelength results in closer bright-fringe spacing.

Because the speed in this problem is very large, the very small values we obtained for λ_e and λ_n are reasonable.

Guided Problem 34.8 Photoelectric effect with two light sources

For an experiment involving the photoelectric effect, you have two lasers for illuminating the target, and you can vary the potential difference between the target and the collector. With zero potential difference, the greatest value you measure for the kinetic energy of the electrons ejected from the target is 2.8 eV with laser 1 and 1.1 eV with laser 2. The wavelength of the light emitted by laser 2 is 50% greater than the wavelength of the light emitted by laser 1. What is the work function of the material of which the target is made?

❸ GETTING STARTED

1. Which conservation principle applies to this situation?
2. How is the work function related to the measured kinetic energies?

❸ DEVISE PLAN

3. With zero potential difference between target and collector, how is the maximum kinetic energy of the electrons measured at the collector related to the energy of the laser photons?
4. How can you relate the photon wavelength to photon energy?
5. What quantity do you need to determine in order to solve the problem?

❸ EXECUTE PLAN

❸ EVALUATE RESULT

6. Is the magnitude of your answer reasonable given the parameter values specified in the problem?

Questions and Problems

For instructor-assigned homework, go to MasteringPhysics® MP

Dots indicate difficulty level of problems: • = *easy,* •• = *intermediate,* ••• = *hard;* CR = *context-rich problem.*

34.1 Diffraction of light

1. Name some materials that allow you to observe light diffraction. •

2. Which wavelength of electromagnetic radiation do you expect to be diffracted by a window screen? What is the frequency of this radiation? •

3. Planar waves from a monochromatic light source are normally incident on a circular obstacle, which casts a shadow on a screen positioned behind the obstacle. What do the wave properties of light predict about how dark the center of the shadow is? ••

4. Light of wavelength λ is incident on an aperture of width a, producing diffraction. Describe the change(s) in the diffracted waves (*a*) when the aperture width is doubled and (*b*) when the wavelength is doubled. ••

5. A friend is standing behind a large tree and yelling. You can hear him, but not see him. Why? ••

34.2 Diffraction gratings

6. Coherent green light of wavelength 530 nm passes through two narrow slits for which the center-to-center separation distance is 100 μm. What is the difference in phase between the waves from the two slits for those that arrive at a distant screen at an angular position θ of (*a*) 15.4° and (*b*) 20.7°? •

7. A diffraction grating has adjacent slits separated by 4.00 μm. When yellow light (λ = 589 nm) is incident on the grating, what is the angular position of the second-order bright fringes? •

8. You shine a red laser beam on a diffraction grating and then shine a green laser beam on the grating. Is the spacing of the bright fringes for the red beam greater than, smaller than, or equal to the spacing of the bright fringes for the green beam? •

9. A reflection diffraction grating of width w has N grooves and is illuminated by normally incident monochromatic light. What condition determines how many orders of constructive interference can be seen in the interference pattern? ••

10. Violet light (λ = 400 nm) passing through a diffraction grating for which the slit spacing is 6.0 μm forms a pattern on a screen 1.0 m away from the grating. Is the fringe located at a linear distance y = 394 mm to the left of the central bright fringe a bright fringe, a dark fringe, or something in between? What is the order of this fringe? ••

11. Light passing through a two-slit grating makes a pattern on a screen located 500 mm away. In this pattern, the fifth-order dark fringe is 45.0 mm from the central bright fringe. How far from the central bright fringe is the third-order bright fringe? ••

12. A diffraction grating casts a pattern on a screen located a distance L from the grating. The central bright fringe falls directly in the center of the screen. For the highest-order bright fringe that hits the screen, $m = x$, and this fringe hits exactly on the screen edge. This means that $2x + 1$ bright fringes are visible on the screen. What happens to the number of bright fringes on the screen (*a*) if the wavelength of the light passing through the grating is doubled and (*b*) if the spacing d between adjacent slits is doubled? •••

13. (*a*) For the two-slit barrier shown in Figure P34.13, calculate the angle θ_1 for the first-order bright fringe if the slit separation distance is d_{orig} = 1.0 μm and the wavelength of the light passing through the slits is 546 nm. (*b*) Now consider a barrier in which one of the slits oscillates vertically and as a result the slit separation distance varies with time according to $d(t) = d_{orig} + A \sin \omega t$. Calculate θ_1 for the first-order bright fringe as a function of time for A = 0.25 μm and ω = 100 s^{-1}. (*c*) At what instant after $t = 0$ does θ_1 have its maximum value for the first time? What is this maximum value? (*d*) At what instant after $t = 0$ does θ_1 have its minimum value for the first time? What is this minimum value? (*e*) Which of the parameters A, ω, λ, d_{orig} affect the values of these angles?

Figure P34.13

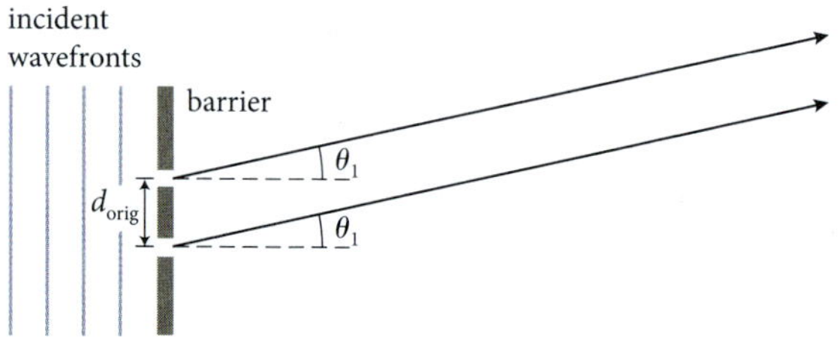

34.3 X-ray diffraction

14. Why are x rays rather than visible light used to determine structure in crystals? •

15. Do the bright spots in an x-ray diffraction pattern get closer together or farther apart when the energy of the x rays is doubled? •

16. A monochromatic x-ray beam that has a wavelength of 1.000×10^{-10} m strikes a sodium chloride crystal that has a lattice spacing of 2.815×10^{-10} m. What are (*a*) the $m = 1$ Bragg angle and (*b*) the highest-order Bragg angle? •

17. In an x-ray diffraction experiment on a crystal that has a cubic lattice, the greatest Bragg angle at which you see a peak in the intensity of diffracted x rays is 35.00°. If the x-ray wavelength is 1.000 nm, what is the atomic spacing in the crystal? Assume that only first-order fringes are visible in the diffraction pattern. ••

18. You are doing x-ray diffraction on a crystal that has a cubic structure, using 0.500-nm x rays. If the lattice spacing is $d = 6.70 \times 10^{-10}$ m, what are the two greatest Bragg angles at which you observe peaks in the intensity of the diffracted rays? ••

34.4 Matter waves

19. What is the order of magnitude of the de Broglie wavelength of a person walking down the street? •

20. How fast must a proton move in order to have the same de Broglie wavelength as the electron in Example 34.4, 1.5×10^{-10} m? •

21. A narrow solid obstacle is placed in the path of the electron in Figure P34.21. Does the electron have a chance of reaching the detector? •

PRACTICE

Figure P34.21

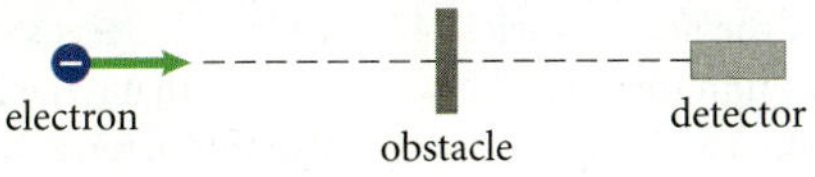

22. What is the de Broglie wavelength of a 0.17-kg hockey puck moving at 45 m/s? •

23. An alpha particle, which consists of two neutrons and two protons, has a mass of 6.645×10^{-27} kg and a charge of $2e$. What is the de Broglie wavelength of an alpha particle of kinetic energy 7.48×10^{-13} J? ••

24. Rank the following radiation and particles in order of increasing spacing between bright fringes in their diffraction patterns: yellow light, blue light, electrons moving at 1.04×10^3 m/s, protons moving at 1.04×10^3 m/s, and neutrons moving at 1.04×10^3 m/s. ••

25. You are accelerating electrons toward a diffraction grating to produce a diffraction pattern. If you want the pattern to contain 101 bright fringes and the spacing between slits in the grating is 7.00 μm, what speed must the electrons have? •••

34.5 Photons

26. Which photons contain more energy: those of blue light or those of red light? •

27. In a region of Earth's surface where the average amount of solar energy striking a square meter of ground each second is 200 J, how many photons strike each square meter each second? Use 580 nm for the average wavelength of this solar radiation. •

28. What is the smallest amount of (*a*) momentum and (*b*) energy that can be delivered using red light for which $\lambda = 700$ nm? •

29. At what rate do photons emitted by a green-light laser ($\lambda = 532$ nm) hit a wall 2.00 m from the laser if the power rating is 5.00 mW? What assumption must you make to solve this problem? ••

30. The sun has a power output of 3.83×10^{26} W. (*a*) How many photons does the Sun emit each second? What assumption(s) must you make to answer this question? (*b*) Installed on your roof is a solar panel that has a surface area of 1.00 m^2. How many photons from the Sun reach the panel? What assumption(s) must you make to answer this question? ••

31. (*a*) What is the energy of a 633-nm photon? (*b*) Two helium-neon lasers both emit 633-nm photons. Laser A has a power rating of 1.0 mW, but laser B has a power rating of only 0.25 mW. Why do the power ratings differ when the lasers emit the same wavelength of light? ••

34.6 Multiple-slit interference

32. Near the center of a diffraction pattern, adjacent maxima are separated by a distance of 20 mm. The diffraction grating is 0.200 m from the screen and has a slit spacing of 4.5 μm. What is the wavelength of light being used? •

33. A red laser beam ($\lambda = 650$ nm) is sent through a double slit to a screen that is 400 mm wide and 1.00 m away from the slits. (*a*) If the separation distance between the slits is 4000 nm, how many bright fringes appear on the screen? (*b*) Verify your answer to part *a* by calculating the distance between adjacent bright fringes. •

34. Laser light passes through a double-slit barrier with slit separation $d = 0.150$ mm onto a screen a distance $L = 5.00$ m away. The distance between the central and first-order bright fringes is $y = 23.0$ mm. What is the wavelength of the light? •

35. Using a diffraction grating with 200 slits/mm to create a diffraction pattern on a screen 2.00 m away from the grating, you see bright fringes 170 mm apart. What is the wavelength of the light? •

36. Green light ($\lambda = 510$ nm) shines through two slits separated by 2.30×10^{-6} m. The resulting diffraction pattern is cast on a screen 450 mm away. How far from the central bright fringe is the time-averaged intensity reduced to 12% of its maximum? ••

37. The radiation emitted by mercury vapor lamps includes green 546.1-nm light and blue 435.8-nm light. If this radiation passes through a transmission grating that has 600 slits/mm to form a diffraction pattern on a screen 0.500 m from the grating, what are the positions of the first-order and second-order bright fringes for each wavelength? Report your answers in terms of the linear distance y from the central bright fringe. ••

38. Cell phone radiation has a wavelength of about 300 mm. You are in the lobby of an office building in which the façade is a series of large, multistory panes of glass separated by vertical aluminum beams installed every 500 mm across the width of the building. Aluminum shields electromagnetic radiation. You are 10 m from the glass trying to make a phone call, but you don't get any reception. Could this have to do with interference? ••

39. You pass 589.0-nm radiation and 589.6-nm radiation through a diffraction grating that has 500.0 slits/mm. (*a*) In the diffraction pattern, what is the angular separation between the $m = 3$ peak for the 589.0-nm radiation and the $m = 3$ peak for the 589.6-nm radiation? (*b*) Are there fourth-order fringes in the diffraction pattern? ••

40. A beam of 550-nm light illuminates six parallel slits spaced 0.125 mm apart, and the resulting pattern is viewed on a screen. (*a*) What are the angular positions of the first-order and second-order principal maxima? (*b*) What are the angular positions of all the dark fringes between the central maximum and the first-order principal maximum? Between the central maximum and the first-order principal maximum, (*c*) how many dark fringes (minima) are there and (*d*) how many secondary maxima? ••

41. You shine a red ($\lambda = 650$ nm) laser beam and a green ($\lambda = 532$ nm) laser beam at a diffraction grating that has 400 slits/mm to create an interference pattern on a wall 3.00 m from the grating. If the two lasers are directly on top of each other, how far apart are the two $m = 1$ bright fringes from each other? Report your answer as a linear distance. ••

42. Is it possible to shine two laser beams of visible light into the same diffraction grating so that the dark fringes created by one beam overlay the bright fringes created by the other beam for all values of m? ••

43. Light of wavelength 570 nm passes through a pair of parallel slits that are 0.115 mm apart. It then falls on a screen that is 45.0 mm from the slits and centered directly opposite them. What must the minimum screen width be in order to have all the bright fringes fall on it? ••

44. A beam of light containing all the visible wavelengths from 400 nm to 700 nm passes through a pair of parallel slits that are 2.50 μm apart. These slits spread the beam into a series of full-color spectra. How many complete full-color spectra are formed? ••

45. You are designing a diffraction grating that, for 566.0-nm light, will produce second-order bright fringes that are an angular distance of 22.00° from the central bright fringe. How many equally spaced slits should this grating contain across its width if it is 24.00 mm wide? ••

46. You want to use a diffraction grating to resolve a beam of visible light into its component wavelengths, from 390 nm to 750 nm. Do the spectra from different orders overlap; that is, does a color from one order overlap with a different color from another order? If so, for which orders? ••

47. The spectrum of the radiation emitted by hydrogen atoms has a peak at $\lambda_r = 656.3$ nm (red) and a peak at $\lambda_b = 486.1$ nm (blue-green). (*a*) If this radiation is passed through a double-slit apparatus in which the slit separation is $d = 0.100$ mm and is then incident on a screen placed a distance $L = 2.10$ m from the slits, how far apart are the $m = 1$ maxima for the two wavelengths? Can these two maxima be resolved? (*b*) If, instead, a grating with 600 slits/mm is used, how far are the maxima be apart? •••

48. How many slits are needed in a diffraction grating that must resolve the $m = 1$ maxima of two spectral lines at $\lambda_s = 610$ nm and $\lambda_l = 615$ nm? •••

34.7 Thin-film interference

49. A 0.500-μm-thick flake of glass ($n_{glass} = 1.52$) from a broken cover slip is floating on water ($n_{water} = 1.33$). If white light initially traveling in the air ($n_{air} = 1.00$) is incident normal to the surface of the glass, what wavelengths in the visible spectrum undergo constructive interference as the white light is reflected from the top and bottom surfaces of the glass? •

50. You are designing a thin transparent reflective coating for the front surface of a sheet of glass. The index of refraction of the glass is 1.52, and when it is in use the coated glass has air on both sides. Because the coating is expensive, you want to use a layer that has the minimum thickness possible, which you determine to be 104 nm. What should the index of refraction of the coating be if it must cancel 550-nm light that hits the coated surface at normal incidence? ••

51. A sheet of glass ($n_{glass} = 1.5$) is coated with a 90.6-nm-thick layer of magnesium fluoride ($n_{coating} = 1.38$) to prevent reflection in the visible spectrum. What is the longest wavelength of light strongly reflected from this coated surface? Assume the incoming light is normal to the surface. ••

52. The thin film that forms a soap bubble has an index of refraction of 1.42. When white light strikes the outer surface of the film at normal incidence, 625-nm reflected light is especially bright. Derive an expression for the possible thicknesses of the film. ••

53. You are working with the mineral fluorite (CaF_2, $n_{fluorite} = 1.43$) and have a sample that is coated with a layer of liquid 158 nm thick. For various wavelengths of visible light incident normal to the surface of the liquid, you observe very strong reflection for green light ($\lambda = 510$ nm), essentially zero reflection for red light ($\lambda = 750$ nm), and intermediate levels of reflection for all wavelengths between the red and green extremes. What is the index of refraction of the liquid? •••

54. A thin film that is 175 nm thick and has an index of refraction smaller than 1.56 covers the front surface of a vertical sheet of glass that has an index of refraction of 1.56. The back surface of the glass interfaces with air, as does the front surface of the film. When a beam of light of variable wavelength is normally incident on the front surface of the film, we observe that, as the wavelength of the light is varied, 473-nm light reflects strongly from the front film surface. We also determine that if the film is any thinner than 175 nm, no constructive interference occurs. When the beam direction is changed so that the angle of incidence at which the light strikes the air–film interface is 51.0°, what is the angle of refraction for the beam in the film? •••

34.8 Diffraction at a single-slit barrier

55. When 633-nm light shines on a fracture-line crack in a thin piece of metal, a diffraction pattern is observed on a screen located $L = 0.90$ m from the metal. If the width of the central bright fringe is $w = 12$ mm, what is the width of the crack in the metal? •

56. How wide does a single slit have to be so that 650-nm light passing through the slit has its first dark fringe 30.0° from the center of the interference pattern? •

57. You send 400-nm violet light through a slit that is 0.500 mm wide. How far from the slit must you place a screen so that the distance between the $n = 1$ fringes is 10.0 mm? •

58. Red laser light ($\lambda = 656.5$ nm) passes through a slit of width $a = 0.100$ mm. On a screen a distance $L = 2.000$ m from the slit, what is the linear distance between the central bright fringe and either first-order dark fringe? •

59. Monochromatic 545-nm light is incident on a 15-μm-wide slit. If the diffraction pattern is cast on a screen 710 mm from the slit, what is the linear distance from the center of the pattern to the $n = 4$ dark fringe? •

60. A student makes the following claim: For radiation of any wavelength passing through a single slit, the separation distance between any two adjacent dark fringes is twice the source–screen distance when the slit width equals the wavelength. Evaluate this claim. ••

61. At sunset, red light travels horizontally through the doorway in the western wall of your beach cabin, and you observe the light on the eastern wall. What is the size of the interference pattern created by the doorway "slit"? ••

62. An experimental setup consists of a 550-nm laser, a screen at a distance of 0.50 m, and an adjustable-width single slit. At what slit width is the width of the central maximum of the interference pattern the same as that of the bright spot it would make in the absence of diffraction? In other words, for what slit width are the effects of wave optics and geometric optics comparable? ••

63. When 440-nm light is incident on a slit that is 75 μm wide, the diffraction pattern is cast on a screen 0.450 m from the slit. How wide is the central bright fringe? ••

64. A slit 0.002470 mm wide is used to study a light ray made up of two wavelengths, 482.0 nm and 517.3 nm, and the diffraction pattern is viewed on a screen 0.220 m from the slit. In the pattern, what is the distance between the $n = 2$ dark fringe for the 482.0-nm light and the $n = 2$ dark fringe for the 517.3-nm light? (Take both dark fringes to be on the same side of the central maximum.) ••

65. A 485-nm light beam passes through a slit and forms a diffraction pattern on a screen 0.320 m from the slit. The $n = 1$ and $n = 1$ dark fringes are 22.4 mm apart on the screen. (*a*) How wide is the slit? (*b*) What is the greatest angle from the original beam direction at which a dark fringe occurs? ••

66. Two extremely narrow, parallel slits are cut in a sheet of cardboard, with the width a of each slit very much smaller than the distance d between them. When the slits are illuminated by a coherent beam of 620-nm light, the angular position of the two third-order bright fringes is $\pm 4.27°$. The cardboard between the slits is then cut out so that the sheet contains only a single opening. When this opening is illuminated by the 620-nm light, what are the angular positions of the $n = 1, 2, 3$ dark fringes? ••

67. In the interference pattern created by 800-nm radiation passing through a single slit 45 μm wide, what is the angular separation between the $n = 3$ and $n = 5$ dark fringes on the same side of the central maximum? ••

68. In the interference pattern created by light diffracted from a single slit, which are wider: the first-order bright fringes or the third-order bright fringes? (Hint: Plot or plug in typical numerical values for the slit width and wavelengths to make an educated guess.) •••

69. A laser beam passes through a slit that is 1500 nm wide. In the interference pattern created on a distant screen, the angular position of the two first-order dark fringes is 25.0°. The beam then is shone on a soap film ($n_{film} = 1.40$) floating on water ($n_{water} = 1.33$). What is the minimum film thickness that causes light reflected at normal incidence from the air–film interface to cancel light reflected at normal incidence from the film–water interface? •••

34.9 Circular apertures and limits of resolution

70. A pinhole of diameter 0.20 mm is illuminated with 550-nm light. What is the width of the Airy disk on a screen 1.5 m away? •

71. The human eye is most sensitive to green light at 550 nm, which is why this wavelength is most frequently used when calculating the resolution limits of telescopes. A telescope for amateur astronomers has a focal length of 1200 mm and an aperture diameter of 200 mm. What is the radius of the Airy disk? •

72. You wish to use a lens to focus a beam of light that has a diameter of 40.0 mm. Which lens focuses the beam to the smallest point: lens A, 10.0-mm diameter, 25.0-mm focal length; lens B, 150-mm diameter, 50.0-mm focal length; or lens C, 30.0-mm diameter, 30.0-mm focal length? •

73. The Spitzer Space Telescope, launched in 2003, has a mirror that is 0.85 m in diameter and detects infrared light with wavelengths from 3.00 μm to 180 μm. If the instrument is used to study a pair of stars, what are the resolvable angular separations of the stars for the minimum and maximum wavelengths? •

74. For an eye in which the pupil has a radius of 3.0 mm, what is the smallest angular separation that can be resolved (*a*) when two violet ($\lambda = 400$ nm) objects are placed side by side and (*b*) when two red ($\lambda = 650$ nm) objects are placed side by side? When the objects are 100 m away from this eye, what minimum linear separation distance is needed for resolution (*c*) of the two violet objects and (*d*) of the two red objects? ••

75. A 530-nm laser beam passes through a circular aperture that has diameter 0.400 mm. What is the diameter of the first dark fringe on a screen 800 mm away from the aperture? ••

76. The pupil of the human eye can vary in diameter from 2.00 mm in bright light to 8.00 mm in dim light. The eye has a focal length of about 25 mm, and the visible spectrum extends from 390 nm (violet) to 750 nm (red). What range of Airy disk radii is possible for the eye? (Note that the light-sensitive cells on the retina have radii ranging from 0.75 μm to 3.0 μm.) ••

77. In vacuum, the Airy disk generated by a pinhole in a metal sheet has radius $y_{r,vac}$. How does the disk radius change when the sheet is submerged in water ($n = 1.33$)? ••

78. When 500-nm light is incident on a circular aperture that has diameter $d = 30.0$ μm, a diffraction pattern forms on a screen 350 mm from the aperture. Calculate the area of the central bright fringe. ••

79. Two objects emitting 550-nm light are placed side by side 30.0 mm apart. For an eye in which the pupil has a diameter of 6.00 mm, what is the minimum eye–objects distance L at which the objects are not resolvable? ••

80. You are using your telescope to view stars by observing the visible light they emit. If the diameter of the lens is 60.0 mm, what must the minimum angular separation of two stars be in order for you to resolve them? ••

81. A satellite studying Earth's surface uses a telescope mirror 2.75 m in diameter to focus light of wavelength 525 nm. If the satellite orbits at an altitude of 25,000 km and points the mirror straight downward, what is the diameter of the smallest surface feature it can resolve? ••

82. A beam of 650-nm light passes through a small round hole and falls on a screen 350 mm past the hole. If the diameter of the Airy disk on the screen is 139 mm, what is the diameter of the hole? ••

83. The red brake lights of a car are 2.00 m apart. Standing 300 m away from the rear of the car, you use a $f = 50$ mm lens with an aperture of diameter $d = 4.00$ mm to photograph the illuminated brake lights. Are the lights likely to be resolved in the photograph, or will they blur together? •••

84. You are building a pinhole camera, which uses a small hole instead of a lens to produce an image (Figure P34.84. (*a*) If the distance between the hole and the film is 100 mm and the hole diameter is 0.300 mm, what is the smallest resolved image point you can have on the film for light ranging from 390 nm to 750 nm? Consider both geometric optics (simply considering the shadow) and wave optics. (*b*) How can you determine the optimum pinhole size for a given wavelength of light? •••

Figure P34.84

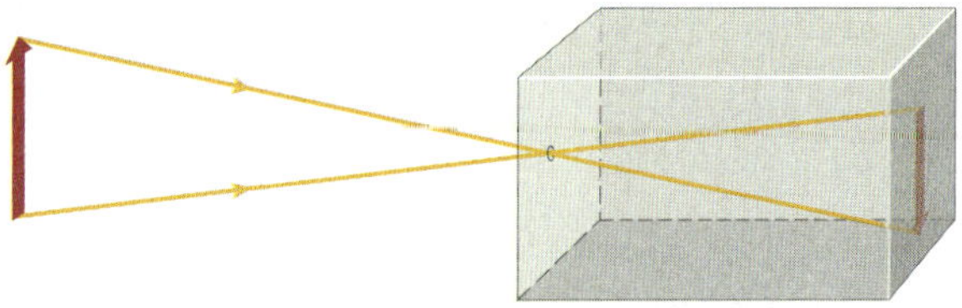

34.10 Photon energy and momentum

85. What happens to (*a*) the kinetic energy of a marble when its speed is reduced to half its initial speed and (*b*) the energy of a photon when its speed is reduced to half its initial speed (as, for instance, when the photon travels from a medium with an index of refraction of 1 into a medium with an index of refraction of 2)? •

86. What is the energy of (*a*) a 400-nm photon and (*b*) a 700-nm photon? •

87. What is the wavelength of a gamma-ray photon that has energy of 8.0×10^{-14} J? •

88. What is the momentum of a photon that has energy of 8.0×10^{-14} J? •

PRACTICE

89. Aluminum has a work function of $E_0 = 6.54 \times 10^{-19}$ J. What is the maximum wavelength of light that can free electrons from the surface? •

90. If the work function of a material is such that red light of wavelength 700 nm just barely initiates the photoelectric effect, what must the maximum kinetic energy of ejected electrons be when violet light of wavelength 400 nm illuminates the material? ••

91. When 410-nm light is incident on a sheet of metal, the maximum kinetic energy of electrons ejected from the metal surface is measured to be $K_{max} = 3.5 \times 10^{-20}$ J. What is the work function of the metal? ••

92. When three metals, 1, 2, and 3, are illuminated with light of frequency f in a photoelectric-effect experiment, the relationship of the stopping potential differences is found to be $V_{stop,1} > V_{stop,2} > V_{stop,3}$. Which material has (*a*) the lowest frequency below which no electrons are ejected and (*b*) the highest frequency below which the effect does not happen? ••

93. In a photoelectric-effect experiment, the stopping potential difference is found to be 3.4 V when 140-nm light is used. What is the work function of the metal? ••

94. A metal alloy has a work function of $E_0 = 4.6 \times 10^{-19}$ J. It is irradiated with light of different wavelengths, and the maximum kinetic energy of ejected electrons is measured. What are the maximum kinetic energy and the maximum electron speed (*a*) when 390-nm light is used and (*b*) when 750-nm light is used? ••

95. You determine that light of minimum-frequency 7.20×10^{14} Hz is needed to eject electrons from the surface of a certain metal. What frequency should the light have in order for the ejected electrons to have a maximum speed of 8.50×10^5 m/s? ••

96. A helium-neon laser that has a power rating of 0.250 mW operates at a wavelength of 633 nm and a beam diameter of 2.00 mm. Calculate (*a*) the energy per photon, (*b*) the number of photons emitted per second, (*c*) the momentum per photon, and (*d*) the pressure exerted on an absorber on which the beam is incident. ••

97. (*a*) If the kinetic energy of an electron and the energy of a photon are both 2.00×10^{-18} J, calculate the ratio of the de Broglie wavelength of the electron to the wavelength of the photon. Which particle has the shorter wavelength? (*b*) If the wavelength of a photon and the de Broglie wavelength of an electron are both 250 nm, calculate the ratio of the energy of the photon to the kinetic energy of the electron. Which particle has greater energy? ••

98. A 3.50-W beam of 216-nm laser light shines on the surface of a metal for which the work function is 2.00×10^{-19} J. What is the maximum number of electrons per second the beam can cause to be ejected from the metal? ••

99. A laser beam with an intensity of 60 W/m² shines on a black object of mass 2.3 mg. The beam hits an area of 4.5 mm² head-on (that is, the beam is perpendicular to the surface). Assuming a totally inelastic collision (meaning the incident photons are absorbed by the black object) and ignoring friction, what is the resulting acceleration of the object? •••

100. In the vacuum tube of Figure P34.98, the lower metal plate, the target, is irradiated with 400-nm light of intensity 5.50 W/m². The frequency of the light is great enough to cause electrons to be ejected from the target and travel to the upper metal plate, the collector. What is the maximum possible current in the circuit if the area of the target is 600 mm²? •••

Figure P34.98

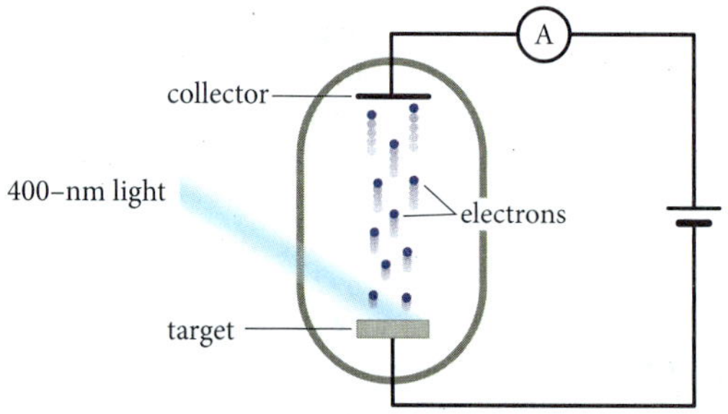

101. When 550-nm light passes through a thin slit and then travels to a screen, the first-order dark fringe in the interference pattern is at 32.5° from the center of the screen. When a beam of electrons, each having kinetic energy equal to the energy of the photons in the 550-nm beam, passes through the slit and travels to the screen, what is the smallest angle from the screen center at which no electrons are found? •••

102. A uniform film of a material that has index of refraction 1.30 covers the front surface of a pane made of glass with index of refraction 1.55. When a beam of monochromatic light initially traveling in air strikes the film at normal incidence, the minimum film thickness for which the light reflected from the air–film interface and the light reflected from the film–glass interface cancel is 123 nm. What is the energy of each photon in the light beam? •••

Additional problems

103. Monochromatic light of which wavelength diffracts the most through a 3.0-μm aperture: 400 nm, 500 nm, or 600 nm? •

104. A double-slit barrier with slit separation distance d is a distance L from a screen, with $L \gg d$. When green laser light ($\lambda_g = 532$ nm) passes through the barrier, the bright fringes on the screen are a distance y_g apart. When red laser light ($\lambda_r = 650$ nm) passes through the barrier, the bright fringes on the screen are a distance y_r apart. What is y_r expressed in terms of y_g? •

105. On a screen 2.5 m from a slit 0.0500 mm wide, you measure a separation distance of 31 mm between adjacent $n = 1$ and $n = 2$ dark fringes of a laser interference pattern. What is the wavelength of the laser radiation? The screen is far enough away and the fringes close enough together to justify the small-angle approximation. •

106. NASA plans to use x-ray diffraction to identify minerals on the surface of Mars. If the wavelength of the x rays is 0.155 nm, what is the lattice spacing in a crystalline sample if the crystal strongly reflects x rays at an incident angle of 51.7° in the first order? •

107. Babinet's principle states that, except for differences in intensity, the interference pattern created by light passing around an opaque object is the same as the pattern created by the same light passing through a hole of the same size and shape as the object. You shine a 690-nm laser beam on a human hair and observe an interference pattern on a screen 1.2 m from the hair. If each first-order dark fringe is 16 mm from the center of the pattern, what is the diameter of the hair? ••

108. Many hundreds of planets beyond our solar system have been discovered in recent years, but they have all been too far away to be resolved by present-day optical telescopes. Using light of wavelength 525 nm, what must the minimum mirror diameter of a space telescope be in order to resolve an Earth-sized planet at a distance of 10 light years? Are our present space telescopes nearing this size? The diameter of Earth is 1.27×10^7 m. ••

109. You shine light of frequency f_i on a diffraction grating and create a diffraction pattern on a screen made up of tiny photon detectors. (*a*) How does the pattern change if you increase the frequency of the light? (*b*) How does the pattern change if you replace the initial light source with one that emits brighter light of the same frequency f_i? (*c*) Is the number of photons detected at the screen smaller than, equal to, or greater than the number detected with the initial source? ••

110. A layer of oil ($n_{oil} = 1.48$) 0.0100 mm thick is resting on a puddle of water ($n_{water} = 1.33$). If white light is incident on the oil, what is the smallest angle from normal at which green light ($\lambda = 510$ nm) is strongly reflected? ••

111. When a monochromatic beam of light passes through a thin slit, the $n = 9$ dark fringe is 10° beyond the adjacent $n = 8$ dark fringe. What is the ratio of the wavelength of the light to the width of the slit? ••

112. In a double-slit interference pattern, it is the amplitudes of the light waves from each slit that add, not the light intensities. Usually, in the analysis of interference patterns, the radiation intensity (or amplitude) is assumed to be exactly the same for both slits. Because of inaccurate optical alignment, however, the illumination is often not the same for the two slits. If the intensity of light going through one slit is $0.010\ \text{mW/mm}^2$ while the intensity going through the second slit is $0.030\ \text{mW/mm}^2$, what is the intensity at an interference maximum and at an interference minimum? ••

113. Electrons are accelerated from rest through a 2.0-kV potential difference. What are (*a*) their speed after this acceleration and (*b*) their wavelength? (*c*) If the accelerated electrons are incident on a graphite crystal that has a lattice spacing of 0.123 nm, do you expect to observe diffraction? ••

114. You are designing a diffraction grating that will disperse white light into its spectrum (400-nm violet to 700-nm red). In the first-order spectrum, you want the angular separation between the shortest and longest wavelengths to be 12.0°. (*a*) How many slits per millimeter should the grating have? (*b*) How many complete full-color spectra will the grating produce, not counting the central bright fringe? ••

115. Monochromatic light passes through a small round hole 1.36 μm in radius. The light then strikes a detector 120 mm away from the hole and is absorbed by the detector surface. If the radius of the Airy disk on the detector is 33.3 mm, how much energy and momentum does each photon transfer to the detector? •••

116. A young adult with good vision is reading a document placed at her near point. She is using ordinary reading light of wavelength 500 nm, and the diameter of her pupil is 3.0 mm. Under these conditions, what is the height of the smallest letter she can resolve on the document? •••

117. In experiment 1, a laser beam of 750-nm light is passed through a double-slit barrier and creates a diffraction pattern on a screen. In experiment 2, one slit is covered with a semicylindrical piece of material that has an index of refraction of $n = 1.001$, as shown in Figure P34.117, and the 750-nm beam again passes through and creates a diffraction pattern on the screen. If the distance between the slits is $d = 1.2$ mm, what is the smallest radius of the semicylindrical piece that results in the screen locations that were bright fringes in experiment 1 being dark fringes in experiment 2, and the screen locations that were dark fringes in experiment 1 being bright fringes in experiment 2? •••

Figure P34.117

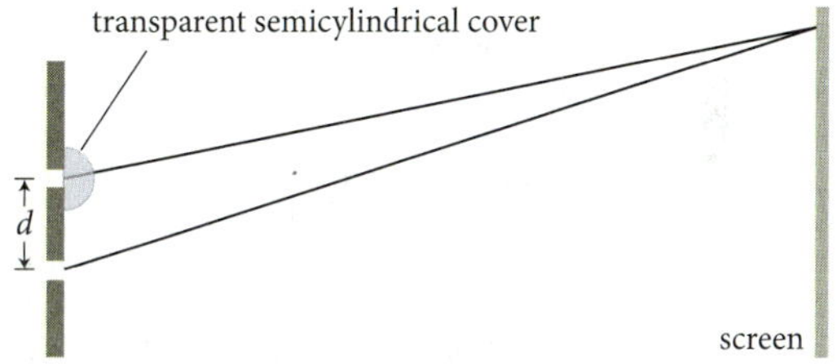

118. You have an unlabeled container in the laboratory that contains the solid lithium fluoride (LiF) and an identical unlabeled container that contains the solid sodium chloride (NaCl). You know that both materials crystallize in a cubic structure, with alternating Na and Cl ions in the NaCl lattice and alternating Li and F ions in the LiF lattice. The only testing instrument available is a diffraction apparatus that uses monochromatic 0.154-nm x rays. After reading in the literature that the lattice spacing is 0.202 nm for LiF and 0.283 nm for NaCl, you test one of the samples in the apparatus and observe the first intensity peak at a Bragg angle of 22.4°. ••• CR

119. As a mission engineer for NASA, you are working on a mission to map the surface of Mars. Your boss asks you to design the optical system for a satellite that can resolve surface features as small as 2.00 m across in the visible part of the electromagnetic spectrum. He tells you the instrument has to fit in a cubic bay of 1.0-m width. You know that to get sharp pictures, the satellite must take at least 17 hours to orbit the planet. Luckily you remember your physics classes on gravity, so you sit down to evaluate whether the job is feasible. ••• CR

Answers to Review Questions

1. Diffraction is the spreading out of a wave in the direction of wave propagation after the wave passes either through a small aperture or past the edge of a smooth barrier, such as a razor blade.
2. If the wavelength is comparable to the wavefront width, the beam diffracts after passing through the gap. If the wavefront width is much greater than the wavelength, there is no diffraction.
3. Interference fringes are the bright and dark bands formed on a screen when light passes through adjacent narrow slits in a barrier. As they travel to the screen, the beams emerging from the slits interfere with each other both constructively, producing bright fringes, and destructively, producing dark fringes.
4. The order refers to the numbering of fringes on either side of the central bright fringe, for which the order is zero. The symbol m is used for bright-fringe orders, and n is used for dark-fringe orders.
5. Bright fringes appear at any location on the screen where the difference in the slit-to-screen distance for the two slits is equal to a whole-number multiple of the wavelength. Dark fringes appear at any screen location where the difference in the slit-to-screen distance is equal to an odd multiple of $\lambda/2$.
6. The condition for constructive interference is the same in the two cases: If the path difference between adjacent slits is an integer number of wavelengths, constructive interference given by $d \sin \theta_m = \pm m\lambda$ results for N slits as for two slits. For destructive interference, the condition is not the same in the two cases. Rather than the alternating bright-dark sequence created by a two-slit barrier, the pattern created by a many-slit barrier has both strongly bright fringes called *principal maxima* and fainter bright fringes called *secondary maxima*. For a barrier containing N slits, there are $N - 1$ dark fringes between each pair of adjacent principal maxima and $N - 2$ secondary maxima between each pair of principal maxima. If N is large, the principal maxima are bright and narrow, and the minima and secondary maxima are essentially dark.
7. The principal maxima are the brightest fringes in the pattern, corresponding to constructive interference by *all* the beams created by the slits. The secondary maxima are weak bright fringes that break up the dark fringe between any two adjacent principal maxima. The secondary maxima are regions where the interference of all the beams is neither completely constructive nor completely destructive.
8. A diffraction grating is a barrier that consists of a large number of equally spaced slits or grooves. A barrier containing slits is called a transmission diffraction grating because the diffraction occurs after light passes—is transmitted—through the slits. A barrier containing grooves is called a reflective diffraction grating because the diffraction occurs after light reflects from the grooved surface of the barrier.
9. The atom-to-atom spacing in the lattice is generally of the same order of magnitude as x-ray wavelengths, so that adjacent planes of atoms act as a grating from which the x rays are diffracted.
10. For x rays diffracted by a crystal lattice, the Bragg condition defines the incidence angles θ that result in constructive interference of the rays reflected by the crystal. These angles are given by $2d \cos \theta_m = \pm m\lambda$, where d is the distance between planes in the lattice, m is any integer, and λ is the wavelength of the incident x rays.
11. The electrons are diffracted. Because diffraction is a wave phenomenon, this suggests that electrons exhibit wavelike behavior.
12. The wave nature of a particle is determined by its de Broglie wavelength $\lambda = h/p$, where $h = 6.626 \times 10^{-34}$ J · s is Planck's constant and p is the particle's momentum.
13. Observing macroscopic objects behaving like waves is not possible because the de Broglie wavelength of any macroscopic object is many orders of magnitude smaller than any length that can be measured.
14. A photon is a particle of light. The energy of a photon is proportional to the frequency of the light, with the proportionality constant being Planck's constant: $E = hf$.
15. Very-low-intensity light behaves like a beam of particles. When it is made to strike two small detecting screens placed close together, each particle of light in the beam strikes one screen or the other, and no matter for how long the experiment is run, the screens always record individual particle impacts. An interference pattern, which is characteristic of waves but not of particles, never builds up on the screens.
16. The waves are out of phase when they reach the screen because of the different distance each wave travels from its slit to the screen.
17. The maximum intensity in the interference pattern is four times the intensity of the waves incident on the slits because the intensity is proportional to the square of the electric field and the electric field is the sum of the fields of the waves from the two slits.
18. The wavelengths can be distinguished if, in the spectrum, the angular position of the mth-order principal maximum of λ_1 is greater than or equal to the angular position of the minimum adjacent to the mth-order principal maximum of λ_2.
19. Thin-film interference occurs when light reflected from the front surface of a thin film interferes with light reflected from the back surface of the film.
20. Interference occurs only if the thickness of the material is comparable to the wavelength of the light.
21. The phase difference is determined by the difference in path length of the two beams (the path of a beam reflected from the back surface is longer than the path of a beam reflected from the front surface) and by whether or not reflection from either surface inverts the wave.
22. There is a phase shift of π if the wave is inverted by the reflection, which happens when $n_2 > n_1$, and no phase shift if the wave is not inverted by the reflection, which happens when $n_1 > n_2$.
23. The directions to the dark fringes of the interference pattern can be determined.
24. The expression is $\sin \theta_n = n\lambda/a$, where θ is the angle between the direction to the minima and the original propagation direction of the light, n is any integer except zero, λ is the wavelength of the light, and a is the slit width.
25. The waves spread out in all directions once they pass through the slit, so there is no discernible interference pattern.
26. The interference pattern is a circular central maximum surrounded by alternating concentric dark fringes and secondary bright fringes.
27. An Airy disk is the circular central maximum in the interference pattern created by light passing through a circular aperture.
28. Rayleigh's criterion is a description of how close together two objects being viewed through a circular lens can be and still be distinguished from each other. The objects can be distinguished only if the distance between the centers of the two interference patterns is equal to or greater than the position of the first minimum of either pattern; this minimum separation occurs when the angular separation between the objects is at least $\theta = 1.22\lambda/d$, where d is the lens diameter.
29. A diffraction limit is a limit on how small the image of any object viewed through a lens can be; even if the object is a point, which has zero width, the image has some finite width because the light from the point diffracts as it passes through the lens. This smallest size is equal to the radius of the Airy disk.
30. The photoelectric effect is the emission of electrons from matter as a consequence of their absorption of energy from incident light with a photon energy greater than a certain minimum energy called the work function.

31. The stopping potential difference is the greatest positive value of the potential difference V_{CT} between the target and collector at which electrons ejected from the target can travel to the collector. It depends on the frequency of the incident light.
32. The stopping potential difference is proportional to the maximum kinetic energy the electrons can have: $K_{max} = eV_{stop}$ (Eq. 34.34).
33. In order to leave the target, an electron must acquire from the incident light a certain minimum amount of energy, proportional to the stopping potential difference, $K = eV_{stop}$. Because V_{stop} depends on the light's frequency rather than on its intensity, the energy delivered by the light must depend on frequency and not on intensity. In the wave model of light, the light energy is a function of intensity, and so this model does not work as an explanation of the photoelectric effect. In the particle model of light, the light consists of photons, with the energy in each photon proportional to the light frequency, agreeing with what is seen in the photoelectric effect.
34. The current is proportional to the intensity if the frequency of the light is great enough that a photon has enough energy to eject an electron from the metal surface. If the frequency of the light is too small, then there is no current, no matter how intense the incident light.
35. The work function is the minimum amount of energy necessary to free an electron from the surface of the metal.

Answers to Guided Problems

Guided Problem 34.2 110 satellites

Guided Problem 34.4 (*a*) The last color seen is violet, the color of visible light that has the shortest wavelength. (*b*) Assuming 400 nm is the shortest visible wavelength and the index of refraction of the soap film is that of water, the film thickness is 75 nm just before it becomes invisible.

Guided Problem 34.6 (*a*) The minima move toward the center of the pattern. (*b*) The slit is 0.097 mm wide.

Guided Problem 34.8 2.3 eV

Appendix A

Notation

Notation used in this text, listed alphabetically, Greek letters first.
For information concerning superscripts and subscripts, see the explanation at the end of this table.

Symbol	Name of Quantity	Definition	Where Defined	SI units
α (alpha)	polarizability	scalar measure of amount of charge separation occurring in material due to external electric field	Eq. 23.24	$C^2 \cdot m/N$
α	Bragg angle	in x-ray diffraction, angle between incident x rays and sample surface	Section 34.3	degree, radian, or revolution
α_ϑ	(ϑ component of) rotational acceleration	rate at which rotational velocity ω_ϑ increases	Eq. 11.12	s^{-2}
β (beta)	sound intensity level	logarithmic scale for sound intensity, proportional to $\log(I/I_{th})$	Eq. 17.5	dB (not an SI unit)
γ (gamma)	Lorentz factor	factor indicating how much relativistic values deviate from nonrelativistic ones	Eq. 14.6	unitless
γ	surface tension	force per unit length exerted parallel to surface of liquid; energy per unit area required to increase surface area of liquid	Eq. 18.48	N/m
γ	heat capacity ratio	ratio of heat capacity at constant pressure to heat capacity at constant volume	Eq. 20.26	unitless
Δ	delta	change in	Eq. 2.4	
$\Delta\vec{r}$	displacement	vector from object's initial to final position	Eq. 2.8	m
$\Delta\vec{r}_F$, Δx_F	force displacement	displacement of point of application of a force	Eq. 9.7	m
Δt	interval of time	difference between final and initial instants	Table 2.2	s
Δt_{proper}	proper time interval	time interval between two events occurring at same position	Section 14.1	s
Δt_v	interval of time	time interval measured by observer moving at speed v with respect to events	Eq. 14.13	s
Δx	x component of displacement	difference between final and initial positions along x axis	Eq. 2.4	m
δ (delta)	delta	infinitesimally small amount of	Eq. 3.24	
ϵ_0 (epsilon)	electric constant	constant relating units of electrical charge to mechanical units	Eq. 24.7	$C^2/(N \cdot m^2)$
η (eta)	viscosity	measure of fluid's resistance to shear deformation	Eq. 18.38	$Pa \cdot s$
η	efficiency	ratio of work done by heat engine to thermal input of energy	Eq. 21.21	unitless
θ (theta)	angular coordinate	polar coordinate measuring angle between position vector and x axis	Eq. 10.2	degree, radian, or revolution
θ_c	contact angle	angle between solid surface and tangent to liquid surface at meeting point measured within liquid	Section 18.4	degree, radian, or revolution
θ_c	critical angle	angle of incidence greater than which total internal reflection occurs	Eq. 33.9	degree, radian, or revolution
θ_i	angle of incidence	angle between incident ray of light and normal to surface	Section 33.1	degree, radian, or revolution

Symbol	Name of Quantity	Definition	Where Defined	SI units
θ_i	angle subtended by image	angle subtended by image	Section 33.6	degree, radian, or revolution
θ_o	angle subtended by object	angle subtended by object	Section 33.6	degree, radian, or revolution
θ_r	angle of reflection	angle between reflected ray of light and normal to surface	Section 33.1	degree, radian, or revolution
θ_r	minimum resolving angle	smallest angular separation between objects that can be resolved by optical instrument with given aperture	Eq. 34.30	degree, radian, or revolution
ϑ (script theta)	rotational coordinate	for object traveling along circular path, arc length traveled divided by circle radius	Eq. 11.1	unitless
κ (kappa)	torsional constant	ratio of torque required to twist object to rotational displacement	Eq. 15.25	$N \cdot m$
κ	dielectric constant	factor by which potential difference across isolated capacitor is reduced by insertion of dielectric	Eq. 26.9	unitless
λ (lambda)	inertia per unit length	for uniform one-dimensional object, amount of inertia in a given length	Eq. 11.44	kg/m
λ	wavelength	minimum distance over which periodic wave repeats itself	Eq. 16.9	m
λ	linear charge density	amount of charge per unit length	Eq. 23.16	C/m
μ (mu)	reduced mass	product of two interacting objects' inertias divided by their sum	Eq. 6.39	kg
μ	linear mass density	mass per unit length	Eq. 16.25	kg/m
$\vec{\mu}$	magnetic dipole moment	vector pointing along direction of magnetic field of current loop, with magnitude equal to current times area of loop	Section 28.3	$A \cdot m^2$
μ_0	magnetic constant	constant relating units of electric current to mechanical units	Eq. 28.1	$T \cdot m/A$
μ_k	coefficient of kinetic friction	proportionality constant relating magnitudes of force of kinetic friction and normal force between two surfaces	Eq. 10.55	unitless
μ_s	coefficient of static friction	proportionality constant relating magnitudes of force of static friction and normal force between two surfaces	Eq. 10.46	unitless
ρ (rho)	mass density	amount of mass per unit volume	Eq. 1.4	kg/m^3
ρ	inertia per unit volume	for uniform three-dimensional object, amount of inertia in a given volume divided by that volume	Eq. 11.46	kg/m^3
ρ	(volume) charge density	amount of charge per unit volume	Eq. 23.18	C/m^3
σ (sigma)	inertia per unit area	for uniform two-dimensional object, inertia divided by area	Eq. 11.45	kg/m^2
σ	surface charge density	amount of charge per unit area	Eq. 23.17	C/m^2
σ	conductivity	ratio of current density to applied electric field	Eq. 31.8	$A/(V \cdot m)$
τ (tau)	torque	magnitude of axial vector describing ability of forces to change objects' rotational motion	Eq. 12.1	$N \cdot m$
τ	time constant	for damped oscillation, time for energy of oscillator to decrease by factor e^{-1}	Eq. 15.39	s
τ_ϑ	(ϑ component of) torque	ϑ component of axial vector describing ability of forces to change objects' rotational motion	Eq. 12.3	$N \cdot m$
Φ_E (phi, upper case)	electric flux	scalar product of electric field and area through which it passes	Eq. 24.1	$N \cdot m^2/C$

Symbol	Name of Quantity	Definition	Where Defined	SI units
Φ_B	magnetic flux	scalar product of magnetic field and area through which it passes	Eq. 27.10	Wb
ϕ (phi)	phase constant	phase difference between source emf and current in circuit	Eq. 32.16	unitless
$\phi(t)$	phase	time-dependent argument of sine function describing simple harmonic motion	Eq. 15.5	unitless
Ω (omega, upper case)	number of basic states	number of basic states corresponding to macrostate	Section 19.4, Eq. 19.1	unitless
ω (omega)	rotational speed	magnitude of rotational velocity	Eq. 11.7	s^{-1}
ω	angular frequency	for oscillation with period T, $2\pi/T$	Eq. 15.4	s^{-1}
ω_0	resonant angular frequency	angular frequency at which current in circuit is maximal	Eq. 32.47	s^{-1}
ω_ϑ	(ϑ component of) rotational velocity	rate at which rotational coordinate ϑ changes	Eq. 11.6	s^{-1}
A	area	length $\times$ width	Eq. 11.45	m^2
A	amplitude	magnitude of maximum displacement of oscillating object from equilibrium position	Eq. 15.6	m (for linear mechanical oscillation; unitless for rotational oscillation; various units for nonmechanical oscillation)
$\vec{A}$	area vector	vector with magnitude equal to area and direction normal to plane of area	Section 24.6	m^2
$\vec{a}$	acceleration	time rate of change in velocity	Section 3.1	m/s^2
$\vec{a}_{Ao}$	relative acceleration	value observer in reference frame A records for acceleration of object o in reference frame A	Eq. 6.11	m/s^2
a_c	magnitude of centripetal acceleration	acceleration required to make object follow circular trajectory	Eq. 11.15	m/s^2
a_r	radial component of acceleration	component of acceleration in radial direction	Eq. 11.16	m/s^2
a_t	tangential component of acceleration	component of acceleration tangent to trajectory; for circular motion at constant speed $a_t = 0$	Eq. 11.17	m/s^2
a_x	x component of acceleration	component of acceleration directed along x axis	Eq. 3.21	m/s^2
$\vec{B}$	magnetic field	vector field providing measure of magnetic interactions	Eq. 27.5	T
$\vec{B}_{ind}$	induced magnetic field	magnetic field produced by induced current	Section 29.4	T
b	damping coefficient	ratio of drag force on moving object to its speed	Eq. 15.34	kg/s
C	heat capacity per particle	ratio of energy transferred thermally per particle to change in temperature	Section 20.3	J/K
C	capacitance	ratio of magnitude of charge on one of a pair of oppositely charged conductors to magnitude of potential difference between them	Eq. 26.1	F
C_P	heat capacity per particle at constant pressure	ratio of energy transferred thermally per particle to change in temperature, while holding pressure constant	Eq. 20.20	J/K
C_V	heat capacity per particle at constant volume	ratio of energy transferred thermally per particle to change in temperature, while holding volume constant	Eq. 20.13	J/K
$\mathrm{COP}_{cooling}$	coefficient of performance of cooling	ratio of thermal input of energy to work done on a heat pump	Eq. 21.27	unitless

Symbol	Name of Quantity	Definition	Where Defined	SI units
$\text{COP}_{\text{heating}}$	coefficient of performance of heating	ratio of thermal output of energy to work done on a heat pump	Eq. 21.25	unitless
c	shape factor	ratio of object's rotational inertia to mR^2; function of distribution of inertia within object	Table 11.3, Eq. 12.25	unitless
c	wave speed	speed at which mechanical wave travels through medium	Eq. 16.3	m/s
c	specific heat capacity	ratio of energy transferred thermally per unit mass to change in temperature	Section 20.3	J/(K · kg)
c_0	speed of light in vacuum	speed of light in vacuum	Section 14.2	m/s
c_V	specific heat capacity at constant volume	ratio of energy transferred thermally per unit mass to change in temperature, while holding volume constant	Eq. 20.48	J/(K · kg)
$\vec{D}$	displacement (of particle in wave)	displacement of particle from its equilibrium position	Eq. 16.1	m
d	diameter	diameter	Section 1.9	m
d	distance	distance between two locations	Eq. 2.5	m
d	degrees of freedom	number of ways particle can store thermal energy	Eq. 20.4	unitless
d	lens strength	1 m divided by focal length	Eq. 33.22	diopters
E	energy of system	sum of kinetic and internal energies of system	Table 1.1, Eq. 5.21	J
$\vec{E}$	electric field	vector field representing electric force per unit charge	Eq. 23.1	N/C
E_0	work function	minimum energy required to free electron from surface of metal	Eq. 34.35	J
E_{chem}	chemical energy	internal energy associated with object's chemical state	Eq. 5.27	J
E_{int}	internal energy of system	energy associated with an object's state	Eqs. 5.20, 14.54	J
E_{mech}	mechanical energy	sum of system's kinetic and potential energies	Eq. 7.9	J
E_{s}	source energy	incoherent energy used to produce other forms of energy	Eq. 7.7	J
E_{th}	thermal energy	internal energy associated with object's temperature	Eq. 5.27	J
$\mathscr{E}$	emf	in charge-separating device, nonelectrostatic work per unit charge done in separating positive and negative charge carriers	Eq. 26.7	V
$\mathscr{E}_{\text{ind}}$	induced emf	emf resulting from changing magnetic flux	Eqs. 29.3, 29.8	V
$\mathscr{E}_{\text{max}}$	amplitude of emf	amplitude of time-dependent emf produced by AC source	Section 32.1, Eq. 32.1	V
$\mathscr{E}_{\text{rms}}$	rms emf	root-mean-square emf	Eq. 32.55	V
e	coefficient of restitution	measure of amount of initial relative speed recovered after collision	Eq. 5.18	unitless
e	eccentricity	measure of deviation of conic section from circular	Section 13.7	unitless
e	elementary charge	magnitude of charge on electron	Eq. 22.3	C
$\vec{F}$	force	time rate of change of object's momentum	Eq. 8.2	N
$\vec{F}^B$	magnetic force	force exerted on electric current or moving charged particle by magnetic field	Eqs. 27.8, 27.19	N
$\vec{F}^{\text{b}}$	buoyant force	upward force exerted by fluid on submerged object	Eq. 18.12	N
$\vec{F}^{\text{c}}$	contact force	force between objects in physical contact	Section 8.5	N

Symbol	Name of Quantity	Definition	Where Defined	SI units
$\vec{F}^{d}$	drag force	force exerted by medium on object moving through medium	Eq. 15.34	N
$\vec{F}^{E}$	electric force	force exerted between electrically charged objects or on electrically charged objects by electric field	Eq. 22.1	N
$\vec{F}^{EB}$	electromagnetic force	force exerted on electrically charged objects by electric and magnetic fields	Eq. 27.20	N
$\vec{F}^{f}$	frictional force	force exerted on object due to friction between it and a second object or surface	Eq. 9.26	N
$\vec{F}^{G}$	gravitational force	force exerted by Earth or any object having mass on any other object having mass	Eqs. 8.16, 13.1	N
$\vec{F}^{k}$	force of kinetic friction	frictional force between two objects in relative motion	Section 10.4, Eq. 10.55	N
$\vec{F}^{n}$	normal force	force directed perpendicular to a surface	Section 10.4, Eq. 10.46	N
$\vec{F}^{s}$	force of static friction	frictional force between two objects not in relative motion	Section 10.4, Eq. 10.46	N
f	frequency	number of cycles per second of periodic motion	Eq. 15.2	Hz
f	focal length	distance from center of lens to focus	Section 33.4, Eq. 33.16	m
f_{beat}	beat frequency	frequency at which beats occur when waves of different frequency interfere	Eq. 17.8	Hz
G	gravitational constant	proportionality constant relating gravitational force between two objects to their masses and separation	Eq. 13.1	$\text{N} \cdot \text{m}^2/\text{kg}^2$
g	magnitude of acceleration due to gravity	magnitude of acceleration of object in free fall near Earth's surface	Eq. 3.14	m/s^2
h	height	vertical distance	Eq. 10.26	m
h	Planck's constant	constant describing scale of quantum mechanics; relates photon energy to frequency and de Broglie wavelength to momentum of particle	Eq. 34.35	$\text{J} \cdot \text{s}$
I	rotational inertia	measure of object's resistance to change in its rotational velocity	Eq. 11.30	$\text{kg} \cdot \text{m}^2$
I	intensity	energy delivered by wave per unit time per unit area normal to direction of propagation	Eq. 17.1	W/m^2
I	(electric) current	rate at which charged particles cross a section of a conductor in a given direction	Eq. 27.2	A
I	amplitude of oscillating current	maximum value of oscillating current in circuit	Section 32.1, Eq. 32.5	A
I_{cm}	rotational inertia about center of mass	object's rotational inertia about an axis through its center of mass	Eq. 11.48	$\text{kg} \cdot \text{m}^2$
I_{disp}	displacement current	current-like quantity in Ampère's law caused by changing electric flux	Eq. 30.7	A
I_{enc}	enclosed current	current enclosed by Ampèrian path	Eq. 28.1	A
I_{ind}	induced current	current in loop caused by changing magnetic flux through loop	Eq. 29.4	A
I_{int}	intercepted current	current intercepted by surface spanning Ampèrian path	Eq. 30.6	A
I_{rms}	rms current	root-mean-square current	Eq. 32.53	A
I_{th}	intensity at threshold of hearing	minimum intensity audible to human ear	Eq. 17.4	W/m^2
i	time-dependent current	time-dependent current through circuit; $I(t)$	Section 32.1, Eq. 32.5	A
i	image distance	distance from lens to image	Section 33.6, Eq. 33.16	m

Symbol	Name of Quantity	Definition	Where Defined	SI units
$\hat{i}$	unit vector ("i hat")	vector for defining direction of x axis	Eq. 2.1	unitless
$\vec{J}$	impulse	amount of momentum transferred from environment to system	Eq. 4.18	$kg \cdot m/s$
$\vec{j}$	current density	current per unit area	Eq. 31.6	A/m^2
J_ϑ	rotational impulse	amount of angular momentum transferred from environment to system	Eq. 12.15	$kg \cdot m^2/s$
$\hat{j}$	unit vector	vector for defining direction of y axis	Eq. 10.4	unitless
K	kinetic energy	energy object has because of its translational motion	Eqs. 5.12, 14.51	J
K	surface current density	current per unit of sheet width	Section 28.5	A/m
K_{cm}	translational kinetic energy	kinetic energy associated with motion of center of mass of system	Eq. 6.32	J
K_{conv}	convertible kinetic energy	kinetic energy that can be converted to internal energy without changing system's momentum	Eq. 6.33	J
K_{rot}	rotational kinetic energy	energy object has due to its rotational motion	Eq. 11.31	J
k	spring constant	ratio of force exerted on spring to displacement of free end of spring	Eq. 8.18	N/m
k	wave number	number of wavelengths in 2π units of distance; for wave with wavelength λ, $2\pi/\lambda$	Eqs. 16.7, 16.11	m^{-1}
k	Coulomb's law constant	constant relating electrostatic force to charges and their separation distance	Eq. 22.5	$N \cdot m^2/C^2$
k_B	Boltzmann constant	constant relating thermal energy to absolute temperature	Eq. 19.39	J/K
L	inductance	negative of ratio of induced emf around loop to rate of change of current in loop	Eq. 29.19	H
L_ϑ	(ϑ component of) angular momentum	capacity of object to make other objects rotate	Eq. 11.34	$kg \cdot m^2/s$
L_m	specific transformation energy for melting	energy transferred thermally per unit mass required to melt substance	Eq. 20.55	J/kg
L_v	specific transformation energy for vaporization	energy transferred thermally per unit mass required to vaporize substance	Eq. 20.55	J/kg
ℓ	length	distance or extent in space	Table 1.1	m
ℓ_{proper}	proper length	length measured by observer at rest relative to object	Section 14.3	m
ℓ_v	length	measured length of object moving at speed v relative to observer	Eq. 14.28	m
M	magnification	ratio of signed image height to object height	Eq. 33.17	unitless
M_θ	angular magnification	ratio of angle subtended by image to angle subtended by object	Eq. 33.18	unitless
m	mass	amount of substance	Table 1.1, Eq. 13.1	kg
m	inertia	measure of object's resistance to change in its velocity	Eq. 4.2	kg
m	fringe order	number indexing bright interference fringes, counting from central, zeroth-order bright fringe	Section 34.2, Eq. 34.5	unitless
m_v	inertia	inertia of object moving at speed v relative to observer	Eq. 14.41	kg
N	number of objects	number of objects in sample	Eq. 1.3	unitless
N_A	Avogadro's number	number of particles in 1 mol of a substance	Eq. 1.2	unitless
n	number density	number of objects per unit volume	Eq. 1.3	m^{-3}

Symbol	Name of Quantity	Definition	Where Defined	SI units
n	windings per unit length	in a solenoid, number of windings per unit length	Eq. 28.4	unitless
n	index of refraction	ratio of speed of light in vacuum to speed of light in a medium	Eq. 33.1	unitless
n	fringe order	number indexing dark interference fringes, counting from central, zeroth-order bright fringe	Section 34.2, Eq. 34.7	unitless
O	origin	origin of coordinate system	Section 10.2	
o	object distance	distance from lens to object	Section 33.6, Eq. 33.16	m
P	power	time rate at which energy is transferred or converted	Eq. 9.30	W
P	pressure	force per unit area exerted by fluid	Eq. 18.1	Pa
P_{atm}	atmospheric pressure	average pressure in Earth's atmosphere at sea level	Eq. 18.3	Pa
P_{gauge}	gauge pressure	pressure measured as difference between absolute pressure and atmospheric pressure	Eq. 18.16	Pa
p	time-dependent power	time-dependent rate at which source delivers energy to load; $P(t)$	Eq. 32.49	W
$\vec{p}$	momentum	vector that is product of an object's inertia and velocity	Eq. 4.6	$\text{kg}\cdot\text{m/s}$
$\vec{p}$	(electric) dipole moment	vector representing magnitude and direction of electric dipole, equal amounts of positive and negative charge separated by small distance	Eq. 23.9	$\text{C}\cdot\text{m}$
$\vec{p}_{\text{ind}}$	induced dipole moment	dipole moment induced in material by external electric field	Eq. 23.24	$\text{C}\cdot\text{m}$
p_x	x component of momentum	x component of momentum	Eq. 4.7	$\text{kg}\cdot\text{m/s}$
Q	quality factor	for damped oscillation, number of cycles for energy of oscillator to decrease by factor $e^{-2\pi}$	Eq. 15.41	unitless
Q	volume flow rate	rate at which volume of fluid crosses section of tube	Eq. 18.25	m^3/s
Q	energy transferred thermally	energy transferred into system by thermal interactions	Eq. 20.1	J
Q_{in}	thermal input of energy	positive amount of energy transferred into system by thermal interactions	Sections 21.1, 21.5	J
Q_{out}	thermal output of energy	positive amount of energy transferred out of system by thermal interactions	Sections 21.1, 21.5	J
q	electrical charge	attribute responsible for electromagnetic interactions	Eq. 22.1	C
q_{enc}	enclosed charge	sum of all charge within a closed surface	Eq. 24.8	C
q_{p}	dipole charge	charge of positively charged pole of dipole	Section 23.6	C
R	radius	radius of an object	Eq. 11.47	m
R	resistance	ratio of applied potential difference to resulting current	Eqs. 29.4, 31.10	Ω
R_{eq}	equivalent resistance	resistance that could be used to replace combination of circuit elements	Eqs. 31.26, 31.33	Ω
r	radial coordinate	polar coordinate measuring distance from origin of coordinate system	Eq. 10.1	m
$\vec{r}$	position	vector for determining position	Eqs. 2.9, 10.4	m
$\hat{r}_{12}$	unit vector ("r hat")	unit vector pointing from tip of $\vec{r}_1$ to tip of $\vec{r}_2$	Eq. 22.6	unitless
$\vec{r}_{\text{AB}}$	relative position	position of observer B in reference frame of observer A	Eq. 6.3	m
$\vec{r}_{\text{Ae}}$	relative position	value observer in reference frame A records for position at which event e occurs	Eq. 6.3	m

Symbol	Name of Quantity	Definition	Where Defined	SI units
$\vec{r}_{cm}$	position of a system's center of mass	a fixed position in a system that is independent of choice of reference frame	Eq. 6.24	m
$\vec{r}_p$	dipole separation	position of positively charged particle relative to negatively charged particle in dipole	Section 23.6	m
$r_\perp$	lever arm distance *or* lever arm	perpendicular distance between rotation axis and line of action of a vector	Eq. 11.36	m
$\Delta\vec{r}$	displacement	vector from object's initial to final position	Eq. 2.8	m
$\Delta\vec{r}_F$	force displacement	displacement of point of application of a force	Eq. 9.7	m
S	entropy	logarithm of number of basic states	Eq. 19.4	unitless
S	intensity	intensity of electromagnetic wave	Eq. 30.36	W/m^2
$\vec{S}$	Poynting vector	vector representing flow of energy in combined electric and magnetic fields	Eq. 30.37	W/m^2
s	arc length	distance along circular path	Eq. 11.1	m
s^2	space-time interval	invariant measure of separation of events in space-time	Eq. 14.18	m^2
T	period	time interval needed for object in circular motion to complete one revolution	Eq. 11.20	s
T	absolute temperature	quantity related to rate of change of entropy with respect to thermal energy	Eq. 19.38	K
$\mathcal{T}$	tension	stress in object subject to opposing forces stretching the object	Section 8.6	N
t	instant in time	physical quantity that allows us to determine the sequence of related events	Table 1.1	s
t_{Ae}	instant in time	value observer A measures for instant at which event e occurs	Eq. 6.1	s
Δt	interval of time	difference between final and initial instants	Table 2.2	s
Δt_{proper}	proper time interval	time interval between two events occurring at same position	Section 14.1	s
Δt_v	interval of time	time interval between two events measured by observer moving at speed v relative to an observer for whom the events occur at the same position	Eq. 14.13	s
U	potential energy	energy stored in reversible changes to system's configuration state	Eq. 7.7	J
U^B	magnetic potential energy	potential energy stored in magnetic field	Eqs. 29.25, 29.30	J
U^E	electric potential energy	potential energy due to relative position of charged objects	Eq. 25.8	J
U^G	gravitational potential energy	potential energy due to relative position of gravitationally interacting objects	Eqs. 7.13, 13.14	J
u_B	energy density of magnetic field	energy per unit volume stored in magnetic field	Eq. 29.29	J/m^3
u_E	energy density of electric field	energy per unit volume stored in electric field	Eq. 26.6	J/m^3
V	volume	amount of space occupied by an object	Table 1.1	m^3
V_{AB}	potential difference	negative of electrostatic work per unit charge done on charged particle as it is moved from point A to point B	Eq. 25.15	V
V_{batt}	battery potential difference	magnitude of potential difference between terminals of battery	Eq. 25.19	V
V_C	amplitude of oscillating potential	maximum magnitude of potential across circuit element C	Section 32.1, Eq. 32.8	V
V_{disp}	displaced volume	volume of fluid displaced by submerged object	Eq. 18.12	m^3

Symbol	Name of Quantity	Definition	Where Defined	SI units
V_P	(electrostatic) potential	potential difference between conveniently chosen reference point of potential zero and point P	Eq. 25.30	V
V_{rms}	rms potential	root-mean-square potential difference	Eq. 32.55	V
V_{stop}	stopping potential	minimum potential difference required to stop flow of electrons from photoelectric effect	Eq. 34.34	V
$\mathcal{V}$	"volume" in velocity space	measure of range of velocities in three dimensions	Eq. 19.20	$(m/s)^3$
v	speed	magnitude of velocity	Table 1.1	m/s
$\vec{v}$	velocity	time rate of change in position	Eq. 2.23	m/s
$\vec{v}_{12}$	relative velocity	velocity of object 2 relative to object 1	Eq. 5.1	m/s
$\vec{v}_{AB}$	relative velocity	velocity of observer B in reference frame of observer A	Eq. 6.3	m/s
v_C	time-dependent potential	time-dependent potential across circuit element C; $V_C(t)$	Section 32.1, Eq. 32.8	V
$\vec{v}_{cm}$	velocity, center of mass	velocity of the center of mass of a system, equal to the velocity of the zero-momentum reference frame of the system	Eq. 6.26	m/s
$\vec{v}_d$	drift velocity	average velocity of electrons in conductor in presence of electric field	Eq. 31.3	m/s
v_{esc}	escape speed	minimum launch speed required for object to reach infinity	Eq. 13.23	m/s
v_r	radial component of velocity	for object moving along circular path, always zero	Eq. 11.18	m/s
v_{rms}	root-mean-square speed	square root of average of square of speed	Eq. 19.21	m/s
v_t	tangential component of velocity	for object in circular motion, rate at which arc length is swept out	Eq. 11.9	m/s
v_x	x component of velocity	component of velocity directed along x axis	Eq. 2.21	m/s
W	work	change in system's energy due to external forces exerted on system	Eqs. 9.1, 10.35	J
$W_{P \to Q}$	work	work done along path from P to Q	Eq. 13.12	J
W_{in}	mechanical input of energy	positive amount of mechanical work done on system	Section 21.1	J
W_{out}	mechanical output of energy	positive amount of mechanical work done by system	Section 21.1	J
W_q	electrostatic work	work done by electrostatic field on charged particle moving through field	Section 25.2, Eq. 25.17	J
X_C	capacitive reactance	ratio of potential difference amplitude to current amplitude for capacitor	Eq. 32.14	Ω
X_L	inductive reactance	ratio of potential difference amplitude to current amplitude for inductor	Eq. 32.26	Ω
x	position	position along x axis	Eq. 2.4	m
$x(t)$	position as function of time	position x at instant t	Section 2.3	m
Δx	x component of displacement	difference between final and initial positions along x axis	Eq. 2.4	m
Δx_F	force displacement	displacement of point of application of a force	Eq. 9.7	m
Z	impedance	(frequency-dependent) ratio of potential difference to current through circuit	Eq. 32.33	Ω
z	zero-momentum reference frame	reference frame in which system of interest has zero momentum	Eq. 6.23	

Math notation

Math notation	Name	Where introduced
$\equiv$	defined as	Eq. 1.3
$\approx$	approximately equal to	Section 1.9
Σ (sigma, upper case)	sum of	Eq. 3.25
$\int$	integral of	Eq. 3.27
$\parallel$	parallel	Section 10.2
$\perp$	perpendicular	Section 10.2
$\propto$	proportional to	Section 13.1
$\cdot$	scalar product of two vectors	Eq. 10.33
$\times$	vector product of two vectors	Eq. 12.35
$\frac{\partial f}{\partial x}$	partial derivative of f with respect to x	Eq. 16.47
$\vec{b}$	vector b	Eq. 2.2
$\lvert\vec{b}\rvert$ or b	magnitude of $\vec{b}$	Eq. 2.3
b_x	x component of $\vec{b}$	Eq. 2.2
$\vec{b}_x$	x component vector of $\vec{b}$	Eq. 10.5
$\hat{\imath}$	unit vector ("i hat")	Eq. 2.1
$\hat{r}_{12}$	unit vector ("r hat")	Eq. 22.6

Note concerning superscripts and subscripts

Superscripts are appended to forces and potential energies to indicate the type of force or energy. They may be found in the main list under F, for forces, and U, for potential energies. Uppercase superscripts are used for fundamental interactions.

Subscripts are used on many symbols to identify objects, reference frames, types (for example, of energy), and processes. Object identifiers may be numbers, letters, or groups of letters. Reference frames are indicated by capital letters. Object identifiers and reference frames can occur in pairs, indicating relative quantities. In this case, the main symbol describes a property of whatever is identified by the second subscript relative to that of the first. In the case of forces, the first subscript identifies the object that causes the force and the second identifies the object on which the force is exerted. Types and processes are identified in various ways; many are given in the main list. Here are some examples:

m_1	inertia of object 1
$m_{\rm ball}$	inertia of ball
$\vec{v}_{\rm cm}$	velocity of center of mass of system
$\vec{r}_{12}$	position of object 2 relative to object 1; $\vec{r}_{12} = \vec{r}_2 - \vec{r}_1$
$\vec{p}_1$	momentum of object 1
$\vec{p}_{\rm Z2}$	momentum of object 2 as measured in zero-momentum reference frame
$\vec{v}_{\rm AB}$	velocity of observer B as measured in reference frame of observer A
$\vec{v}_{\rm Ao}$	velocity of object o as measured in reference frame A
$\vec{r}_{\rm Ee}$	position of event e as measured in Earth reference frame
$\vec{F}^c_{\rm pw}$	contact force exerted by person on wall
$\vec{F}^G_{\rm Eb}$	gravitational force exerted by Earth on ball
$E_{\rm th}$	thermal energy
$K_{\rm conv}$	convertible kinetic energy
$P_{\rm av}$	average power
$a_{\rm c}$	centripetal acceleration
$W_{\rm P\to Q}$	work done along path from P to Q

Initial and final conditions are identified by subscripts i and f, following other identifiers. For example:

$\vec{p}_{\rm 1i}$	initial momentum of object 1
$\vec{p}_{\rm Zball,f}$	final momentum of ball as measured in zero-momentum reference frame

Italic subscripts are used to identify components of vectors. These include x, y, z, r (radial), t (tangential), and ϑ (angular, with respect to given axis). They are also used to enumerate collections, for example, as indices of summation, and to indicate that a subscript refers to another variable. Here are some examples:

r_x	x component of position
a_t	tangential component of acceleration
L_ϑ	ϑ component of angular momentum
$p_{{\rm Zball}\,y,{\rm f}}$	final y component of momentum of ball as measured in zero-momentum reference frame
$\delta m_n r_n^2$	contribution to rotational inertia of extended object of small segment n, with inertia δm_n at position r_n
c_P	specific heat capacity at constant pressure
W_q	electrostatic work

Appendix B

Mathematics Review

1 Algebra

Factors

$$ax + bx + cx = (a + b + c)x$$
$$(a + b)^2 = a^2 + 2ab + b^2$$
$$(a - b)^2 = a^2 - 2ab + b^2$$
$$(a + b)(a - b) = a^2 - b^2$$

Fractions

$$\left(\frac{a}{b}\right)\left(\frac{c}{d}\right) = \frac{ac}{bd}$$
$$\left(\frac{a/b}{c/d}\right) = \frac{a}{b} \div \frac{c}{d} = \frac{a}{b}\cdot\frac{d}{c} = \frac{ad}{bc}$$
$$\left(\frac{1}{1/a}\right) = a$$

Exponents

$$a^n = \underbrace{a \times a \times a \times \cdots \times a}_{n \text{ factors}}$$

Any real number can be used as an exponent:

$$a^{-x} = \frac{1}{a^x}$$
$$a^0 = 1$$
$$a^1 = a$$
$$a^{1/2} = \sqrt{a}$$
$$a^{1/n} = \sqrt[n]{a}$$
$$a^x a^y = a^{x+y}$$
$$\frac{a^x}{a^y} = a^{x-y}$$
$$(a^x)^y = a^{x \cdot y}$$
$$a^x b^x = (ab)^x$$
$$\frac{a^x}{b^x} = \left(\frac{a}{b}\right)^x$$

Logarithms

Logarithm is the inverse function of the exponential function:

$$y = a^x \Leftrightarrow \log_a y = \log_a a^x = x \quad \text{and} \quad x = \log_a (a^x) = a^{\log_a x}$$

The two most common values for the base a are 10 (the common logarithm base) and e (the natural logarithm base).

$$y = e^x \Leftrightarrow \log_e y = \ln y = \ln e^x = x \quad \text{and} \quad x = \ln e^x = e^{\ln x}$$

Logarithm rules (valid for any base):

$$\ln(ab) = \ln(a) + \ln(b)$$
$$\ln\left(\frac{a}{b}\right) = \ln(a) - \ln(b)$$
$$\ln(a^n) = n\ln(a)$$
$$\ln 1 = 0$$

The expression $\ln(a + b)$ cannot be simplified.

Linear equations

A linear equation has the form $y = ax + b$, where a and b are constants. A graph of y versus x is a straight line. The value of a equals the slope of the line, and the value of b equals the value of y when x equals zero.

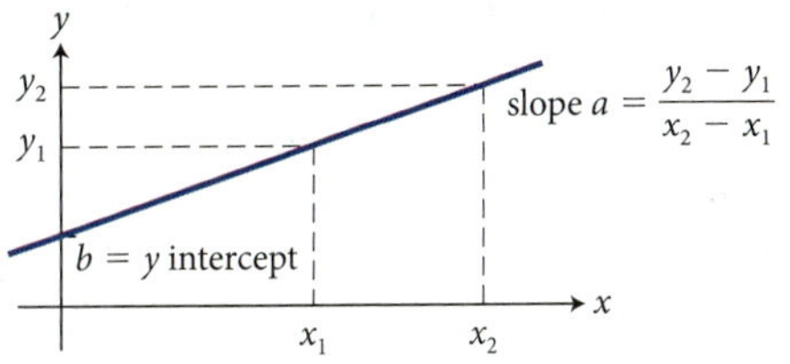

If $a = 0$, the line is horizontal. If $a > 0$, the line rises as x increases. If $a < 0$, the line falls as x increases. For any two values of x, say x_1 and x_2, the slope a can be calculated as

$$a = \frac{y_2 - y_1}{x_2 - x_1}$$

where y_1 and y_2 correspond to x_1 and x_2 (that is to say, $y_1 = ax_1 + b$ and $y_2 = ax_2 + b$).

Proportionality

If y is proportional to x (written $y \propto x$), then $y = ax$, where a is a constant. Proportionality is a subset of linearity. Because $y/x = a =$ constant for any corresponding x and y,

$$\frac{y_1}{x_1} = \frac{y_2}{x_2} \Leftrightarrow \frac{y_1}{y_2} = \frac{x_1}{x_2}.$$

Quadratic equation

The equation $ax^2 + bx + c = 0$ (the quadratic equation) has two solutions (called *roots*) for x:

$$x = \frac{-b \pm \sqrt{b^2 - 4ac}}{2a}$$

If $b^2 \geq 4ac$, the solutions are real numbers.

2 Geometry

Area and circumference for two-dimensional shapes

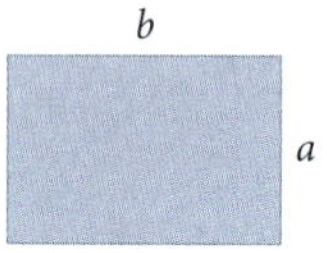

rectangle:
area $= ab$
circumference $= 2(a + b)$

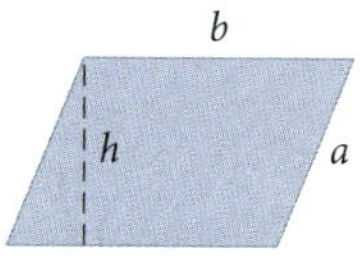

parallelogram:
area $= bh$
circumference $= 2(a + b)$

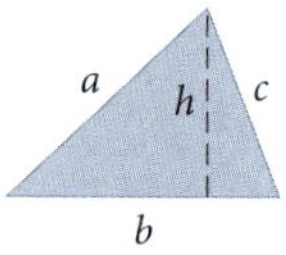

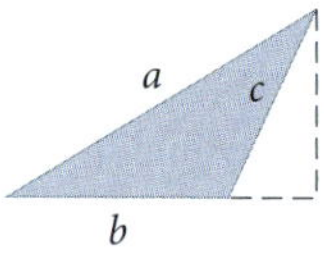

triangle:
area $= \frac{1}{2}bh$
circumference $= a + b + c$

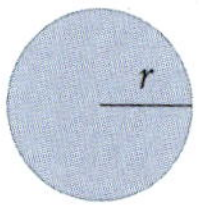

circle:
area $= \pi r^2$
circumference $= 2\pi r$

Volume and area for three-dimensional shapes

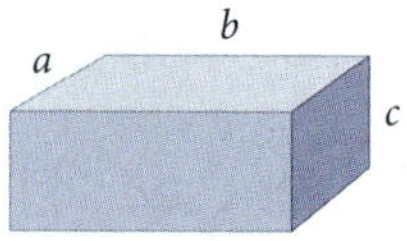

rectangular box:
volume $= abc$
area $= 2(a^2 + b^2 + c^2)$

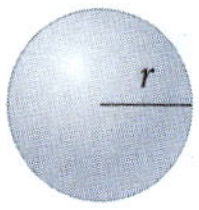

sphere:
volume $= \frac{4}{3}\pi r^3$
area $= 4\pi r^2$

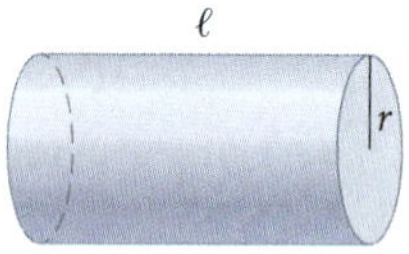

right circular cylinder:
volume $= \pi r^2 \ell$
area $= 2\pi r\ell + 2\pi r^2$

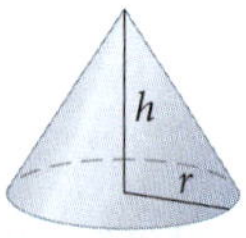

right circular cone:
volume $= \frac{1}{3}\pi r^2 h$
area $= \pi r^2 + \pi r\sqrt{r^2 + h^2}$

3 Trigonometry

Angle and arc length

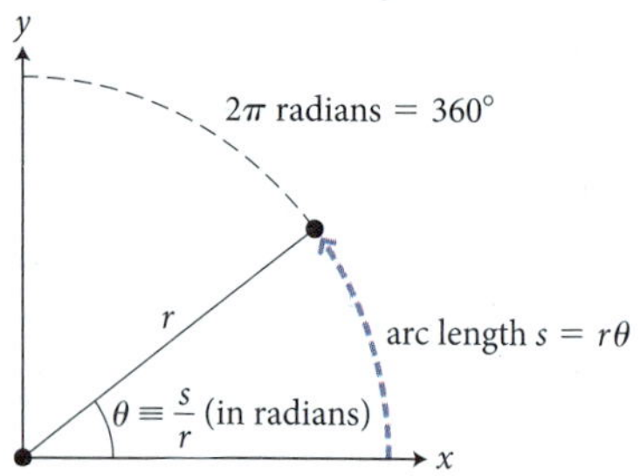

Right triangles

A right triangle is a triangle in which one of the angles is a right angle:

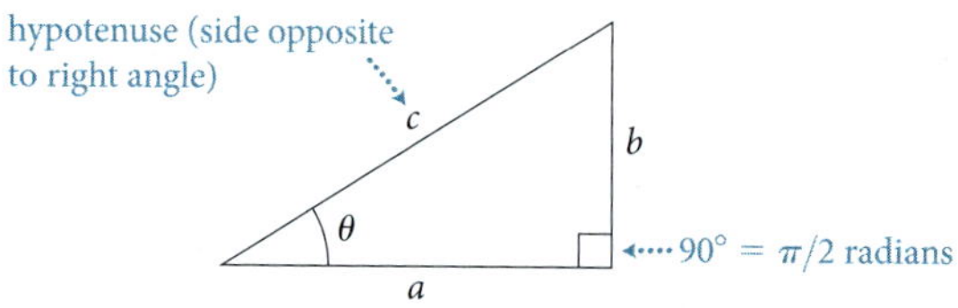

Pythagorean theorem: $a^2 + b^2 = c^2 \Leftrightarrow c = \sqrt{a^2 + b^2}$

Trigonometric functions:

$$\sin\theta = \frac{b}{c} = \frac{\text{opposite side}}{\text{hypotenuse}}, \quad \theta = \sin^{-1}\left(\frac{b}{c}\right) = \arcsin\left(\frac{b}{c}\right)$$

$$\cos\theta = \frac{a}{c} = \frac{\text{adjacent side}}{\text{hypotenuse}}, \quad \theta = \cos^{-1}\left(\frac{a}{c}\right) = \arccos\left(\frac{a}{c}\right)$$

$$\tan\theta = \frac{b}{a} = \frac{\text{opposite side}}{\text{adjacent side}}, \quad \theta = \tan^{-1}\left(\frac{b}{a}\right) = \arctan\left(\frac{b}{a}\right)$$

General triangles

For any triangle, the following relationships hold:

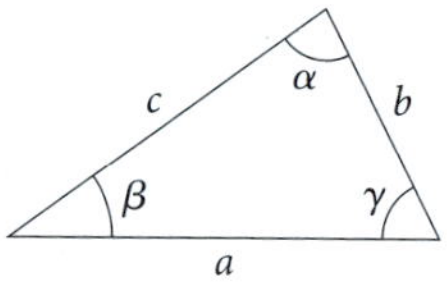

$$\alpha + \beta + \gamma = 180° = \pi \text{ rad}$$

Sine law: $\dfrac{\sin\alpha}{a} = \dfrac{\sin\beta}{b} = \dfrac{\sin\gamma}{c}$

Cosine law: $c^2 = a^2 + b^2 - 2ab\cos\gamma$

Identities

$$\tan\theta = \frac{\sin\theta}{\cos\theta}$$

$$\cot\theta = \frac{1}{\tan\theta} = \frac{\cos\theta}{\sin\theta}$$

$$\csc\theta = \frac{1}{\sin\theta}$$

$$\sec\theta = \frac{1}{\cos\theta}$$

Periodicity

$$\cos(\alpha + 2\pi) = \cos\alpha$$

$$\tan(\alpha + \pi) = \tan\alpha$$

Angle addition

$$\sin(\alpha \pm \beta) = \sin\alpha\cos\beta \pm \cos\alpha\sin\beta$$

$$\cos(\alpha \pm \beta) = \cos\alpha\cos\beta \mp \sin\alpha\sin\beta$$

Double angles

$\sin(2\alpha) = 2\sin\alpha\cos\alpha$

$\cos(2\alpha) = \cos^2\alpha - \sin^2\alpha = 1 - 2\sin^2\alpha = 2\cos^2\alpha - 1$

Other relations

$\sin^2\alpha + \cos^2\alpha = 1$

$\sin(-\alpha) = -\sin\alpha$

$\cos(-\alpha) = \cos\alpha$

$\sin(\alpha \pm \pi) = -\sin\alpha$

$\cos(\alpha \pm \pi) = -\cos\alpha$

$\sin(\alpha \pm \pi/2) = \pm\cos\alpha$

$\cos(\alpha \pm \pi/2) = \mp\sin\alpha$

The following graphs show $\sin\theta$, $\cos\theta$, and $\tan\theta$ as functions of θ:

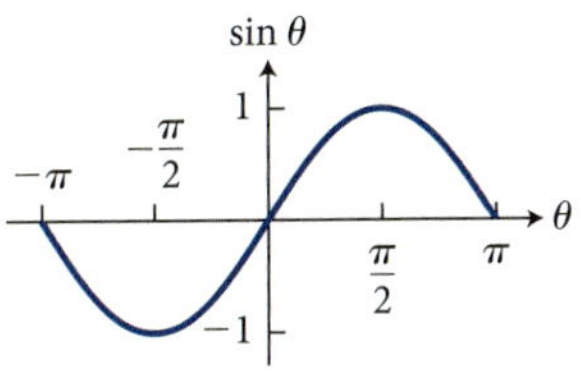

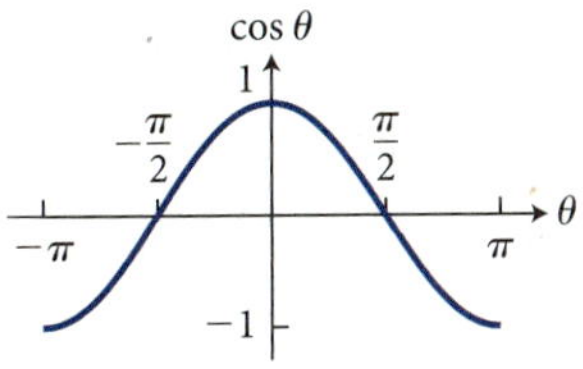

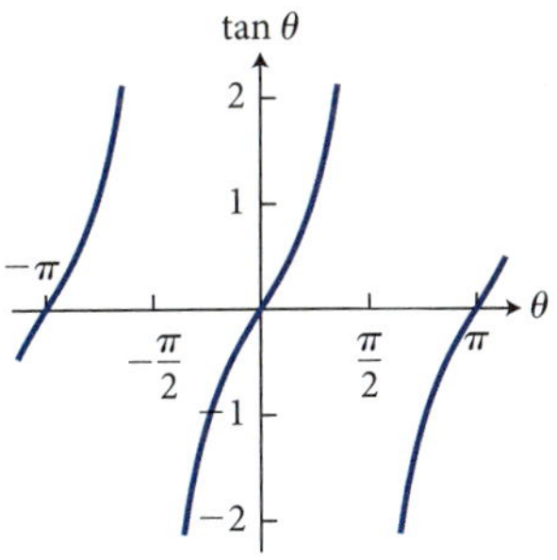

4 Vector algebra

A vector $\vec{A}$ in three-dimensional space can be written in terms of magnitudes A_x, A_y, and A_z of unit vectors $\hat{\imath}$, $\hat{\jmath}$, and $\hat{k}$, which have length 1 and lie along the x, y, and z axes:

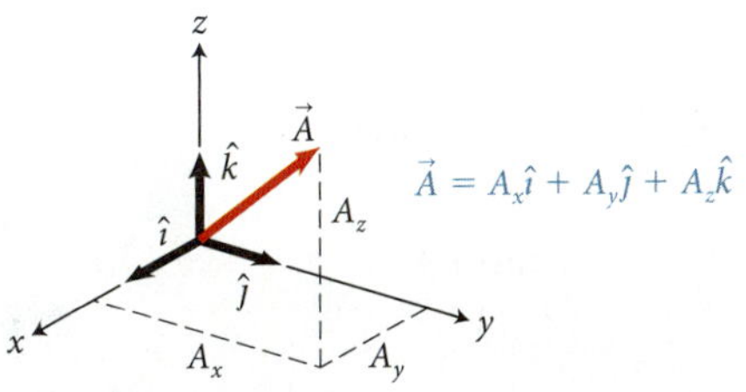

Dot products between vectors produce scalars:

$$\vec{A}\cdot\vec{B} = A_xB_x + A_yB_y + A_zB_z = |A||B|\cos\theta$$

(θ is the angle between vectors $\vec{A}$ and $\vec{B}$)

Cross products between vectors produce vectors:

$$\vec{A}\times\vec{B} = (A_yB_z - A_zB_y)\hat{\imath} + (A_zB_x - A_xB_z)\hat{\jmath} + (A_xB_y - A_yB_x)\hat{k}$$

$$|\vec{A}\times\vec{B}| = |\vec{A}||\vec{B}|\sin\theta \text{ (θ is the angle between vectors $\vec{A}$ and $\vec{B}$)}$$

The direction of $\vec{A}\times\vec{B}$ is given by the right-hand rule (see Figure 12.44).

5 Calculus

In this section, x is a variable, and a and n are constants.

Derivatives

Geometrically, the derivative of a function $f(x)$ at $x = x_1$ is the slope of $f(x)$ at x_1:

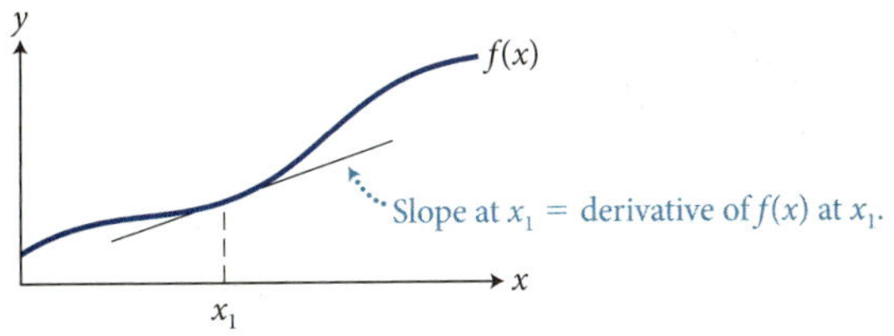

Derivatives of common functions

$$\frac{d}{dx}a = 0$$

$$\frac{d}{dx}x^n = nx^{n-1} \text{ (n need not be an integer)}$$

$$\frac{d}{dx}\sin x = \cos x$$

$$\frac{d}{dx}\cos x = -\sin x$$

$$\frac{d}{dx}\tan x = \frac{1}{\cos^2 x}$$

$$\frac{d}{dx}e^{ax} = ae^{ax}$$

$$\frac{d}{dx}\ln(ax) = \frac{1}{x}$$

$$\frac{d}{dx}a^x = a^x\ln a$$

Derivatives of sums, products, and functions of functions

Constant times a function: $\frac{d}{dx}[a\cdot f(x)] = a\cdot\frac{d}{dx}f(x)$

Sum of functions: $\frac{d}{dx}[f(x) + g(x)] = \frac{d}{dx}f(x) + \frac{d}{dx}g(x)$

Product of functions:

$$\frac{d}{dx}[f(x)\cdot g(x)] = g(x)\frac{d}{dx}f(x) + f(x)\frac{d}{dx}g(x)$$

Quotient of functions: $\frac{d}{dx}\left[\frac{f(x)}{g(x)}\right] = \frac{g(x)\frac{d}{dx}f(x) - f(x)\frac{d}{dx}g(x)}{[g(x)]^2}$

Functions of functions (the chain rule): If f is a function of u, and u is a function of x, then

$$\frac{d[f(u)]}{du}\cdot\frac{d[u(x)]}{dx} = \frac{d[f(x)]}{dx}$$

Second and higher derivatives The second derivative of a function f with respect to x is the derivative of the derivative:

$$\frac{d^2 f(x)}{dx^2} = \frac{d}{dx}\left(\frac{d}{dx}f(x)\right)$$

Higher derivatives are defined similarly:

$$\frac{d^n f(x)}{dx^n} = \underbrace{\cdots\frac{d}{dx}\left(\frac{d}{dx}\left(\frac{d}{dx}f(x)\right)\right)}_{n \text{ uses of } \frac{d}{dx}}$$ (where n is a positive integer).

Partial derivatives For functions of more than one variable, the partial derivative, written $\frac{\partial}{\partial x}$, is the derivative with respect to one variable; all other variables are treated as constants.

Integrals

Indefinite integrals Integration is the reverse of differentiation. An indefinite integral $\int f(x)dx$ is a function whose derivative is $f(x)$.

That is to say, $\frac{d}{dx}\left[\int f(x)dx\right] = f(x)$.

If $A(x)$ is an indefinite integral of $f(x)$, then so is $A(x) + C$, where C is any constant. Thus, it is customary when evaluating indefinite integrals to add a "constant of integration" C.

Definite integrals The definite integral of $f(x)$, written as $\int_{x1}^{x2} f(x)dx$, represents the sum of the area of contiguous rectangles that each intersect $f(x)$ at some point along one base and that each have another base coincident with the x axis over some part of the range between x_1 and x_2; the indefinite integral evaluates the sum in the limit of arbitrarily small rectangle bases. In other words, the indefinite integral gives the net area that lies under $f(x)$ but above the x axis between the boundaries x_1 and x_2.

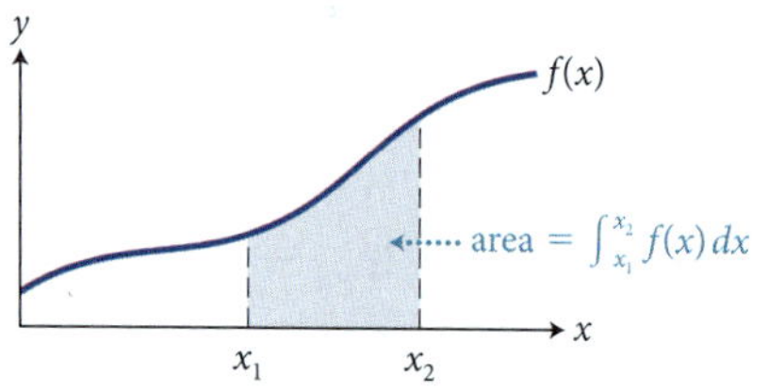

If $A(x)$ is any indefinite integral of $f(x)$, then the definite integral is given by $\int_{x1}^{x2} f(x)dx = A(x_2) - A(x_1) \equiv A(x)|_{x_1}^{x_2}$. The constant of integration C does not affect the value of definite integrals and thus can be ignored (i.e., set to zero) during evaluation.

Integration by parts $\int_a^b u dv$ is the area under the curve of $u(v)$. If $\int_a^b u dv$ is difficult to evaluate directly, it is sometimes easier to express the area under the curve as the area within part of a rectangle minus the area under the curve of $v(u)$. In other words:

$$\int_a^b u dv = uv|_a^b - \int_a^b v du.$$

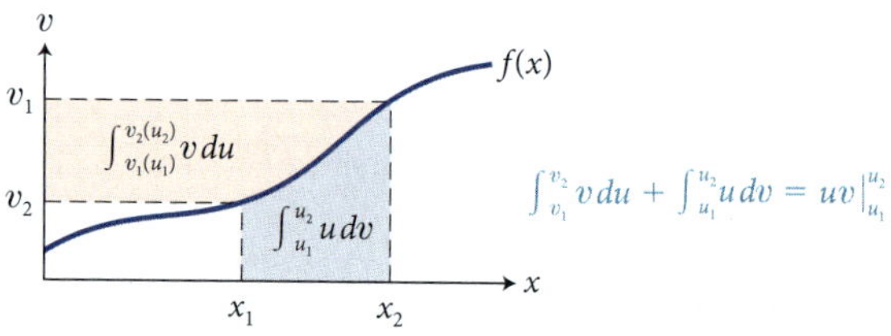

By choosing u and dv appropriately (both can be functions of x), this approach, called "integration by parts", can transform difficult integrals into easier ones.

Table of integrals In the following expressions, a and b are constants. An arbitrary constant of integration C can be added to the right-hand side.

$$\int x^n dx = \frac{1}{n+1}x^{n+1} \text{ (for } n \neq -1)$$

$$\int x^{-1}dx = \ln|x|$$

$$\int \frac{1}{a^2+x^2}dx = \frac{1}{a}\tan^{-1}\frac{x}{a}$$

$$\int \frac{1}{(a^2+x^2)^2}dx = \frac{1}{2a^3}\tan^{-1}\frac{x}{a} + \frac{x}{2a^2(x^2+a^2)}$$

$$\int \frac{1}{\sqrt{\pm a^2 + x^2}}dx = \ln|x + \sqrt{\pm a^2 + x^2}|$$

$$\int \frac{1}{\sqrt{a^2 - x^2}}dx = \sin^{-1}\frac{x}{|a|} = \tan^{-1}\frac{x}{\sqrt{a^2-x^2}}$$

$$\int \frac{x}{\sqrt{\pm a^2 - x^2}}dx = -\sqrt{\pm a^2 - x^2}$$

$$\int \frac{x}{\sqrt{\pm a^2 + x^2}}dx = \sqrt{\pm a^2 + x^2}$$

$$\int \frac{1}{(\pm a^2 + x^2)^{3/2}}dx = \frac{\pm x}{a^2\sqrt{\pm a^2 + x^2}}$$

$$\int \frac{x}{(a^2 + x^2)^{3/2}}dx = -\frac{1}{\sqrt{a^2+x^2}}$$

$$\int \frac{1}{a+bx}dx = \frac{1}{b}\ln(a+bx)$$

$$\int \frac{1}{(a+bx)^2}dx = -\frac{1}{b(a+bx)}$$

$$\int \sin(ax)dx = -\frac{1}{a}\cos(ax)$$

$$\int \cos(ax)dx = \frac{1}{a}\sin(ax)$$

$$\int \tan(ax)dx = -\frac{1}{a}\ln(\cos ax)$$

$$\int \sin^2(ax)dx = \frac{x}{2} - \frac{\sin 2ax}{4a}$$

$$\int \cos^2(ax)dx = \frac{x}{2} + \frac{\sin 2ax}{4a}$$

$$\int x\sin(ax)dx = \frac{1}{a^2}\sin ax - \frac{1}{a}x\cos ax$$

$$\int x\cos(ax)dx = \frac{1}{a^2}\cos ax + \frac{1}{a}x\sin ax$$

$$\int e^{ax}dx = \frac{1}{a}e^{ax}$$

$$\int xe^{ax}dx = \frac{e^{ax}}{a^2}(ax - 1)$$

$$\int x^2e^{ax}dx = \frac{x^2e^{ax}}{a} - \frac{2}{a}\left[\frac{e^{ax}}{a^2}(ax - 1)\right]$$

$$\int \ln ax\, dx = x\ln(ax) - x$$

$$\int_0^\infty x^ne^{-ax}dx = \frac{n!}{a^{n+1}}$$

$$\int_0^\infty e^{-ax^2}dx = \frac{1}{2}\sqrt{\frac{\pi}{a}}$$

Line integrals. A *line integral* is an integral of a function that needs to be evaluated over a path (that is, a curve connecting two points in space). Consider, for example, the two-dimensional path C from point A to point B in the figure below. (The procedure described below is equally applicable in three dimensions.)

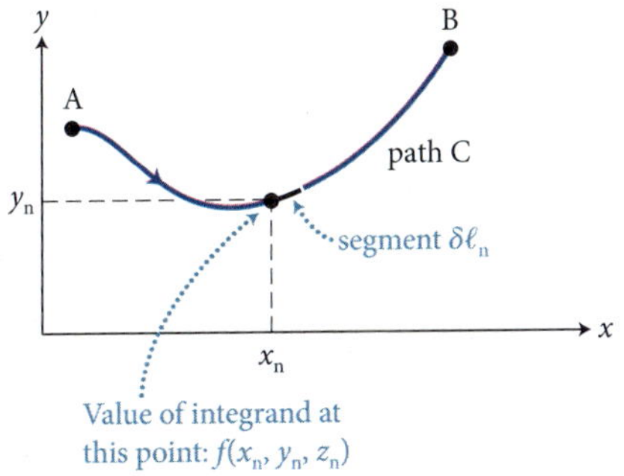

The path from A to B is *directed:* At any point the direction along the path away from A and toward B is forward (positive). Suppose we have a function $f(x, y, z)$ defined everywhere along the path. The function can be either a scalar or a vector; we will first discuss line integrals of scalar functions. We divide the path between A and B into small segments of length $\delta\ell_n$, each segment small enough that we can consider it essentially straight and small enough that the value of the function $f(x, y, z)$ can be considered constant over that segment. We then calculate the product $f(x_n, y_n, z_n)\delta\ell_n$ for each segment. The line integral of the function $f(x, y, z)$ along path C is then given by the sum of all those products along the path in the limit of infinitesimally small segments:

$$\int_C f(x, y, z)d\ell = \lim_{\delta\ell\to\infty} \sum_n f(x_n, y_n, z_n)\delta\ell_n.$$

To evaluate the integral on the right, we need to know the path C. Usually the path is specified in terms of the length parameter ℓ: $x = x(\ell)$, $y = y(\ell)$, $z = z(\ell)$. The line integral can then be written as an ordinary definite integral:

$$\int_C f(x, y, z)d\ell = \int_A^B f[x(\ell), y(\ell), z(\ell)]d\ell.$$

Next we consider the line integral of a vector function. We consider the same path C from A to B, but now we consider a vector function $\vec{F}(x, y, z)$. Instead of taking infinitesimally small scalar segments $d\ell_n$ along the path, we take small vector segments $d\vec{\ell}_n$ along the path, of length $d\ell_n$ and whose direction is tangent to the path in the direction of the path from A to B:

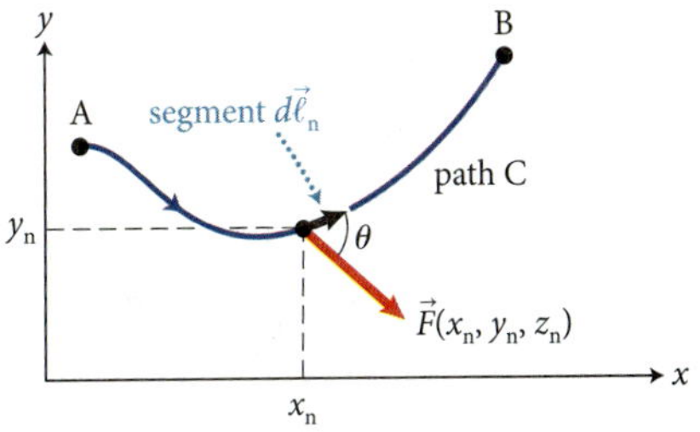

At each point we calculate the scalar product $\vec{F}(x_n, y_n, z_n) \cdot d\vec{\ell}_n$ and then sum these products over path C to obtain the line integral.

$$\int_C \vec{F}(x, y, z) \cdot d\vec{\ell}.$$

By writing out the scalar product, $\vec{F}(x, y, z) \cdot d\vec{\ell} = F(x, y, z)\cos\theta\, d\ell$, we can reduce the line integral of a vector function to that of a scalar function:

$$\int_C \vec{F}(x, y, z) \cdot d\vec{\ell} = \int_C F(x, y, z)\cos\theta\, d\ell.$$

In other words, we need to compute the line integral of the component of the vector $\vec{F}(x, y, z)$ along the tangent to the path.

If the path is closed—that is, the path returns to the starting point—we indicate that by putting a circle through the integration sign:

$$\oint_C \vec{F}(x, y, z) \cdot d\vec{\ell}.$$

Surface integrals. A *surface integral* is an integral of a function that needs to be evaluated over a surface. As with line integrals, the integrand of a surface integral can be a scalar or a vector function. We will only discuss the more general case of a vector function here.

The surface over which the integration is to be taken can be either *closed* or *open*. A closed surface, such as the surface of a sphere, divides space into two parts—an inside and an outside—and to get from one part to the other one has to go through the surface. An open surface does not have this property: For the surface S shown in the figure below, for example, one can go from one side of the surface to the other without passing through it.

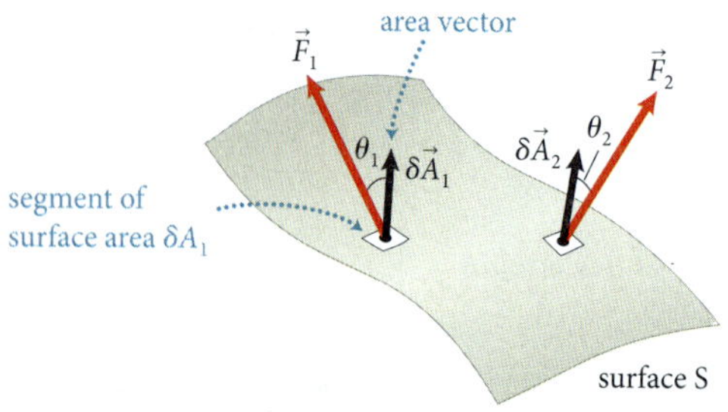

Consider a vector function $\vec{F}(x, y, z)$. To calculate the surface integral of this function over surface S, we begin by dividing the surface into small segments of surface area δA_n, each segment being small enough that we can consider it to be essentially flat and small enough so that the function $\vec{F}(x, y, z)$ can be considered constant over the segment. We then define an *area vector* $\delta\vec{A}_n$ whose magnitude is equal to the surface area δA_n of the segment and whose direction is normal to that segment. For each segment we then calculate the scalar product of the area vector and the value $\vec{F}_n$ of the vector function at that location: $\vec{F}_n(x_n, y_n, z_n) \cdot \delta\vec{A}_n$. The surface integral of the vector function over the surface S is then given by the sum of all those products for all the segments that make up the surface:

$$\int_S \vec{F}(x, y, z) \cdot d\vec{A} = \lim_{\delta A_n \to \infty} \sum_n \vec{F}_n(x_n, y_n, z_n) \cdot \delta\vec{A}_n.$$

If the surface is closed, we indicate that by putting a circle through the integration sign:

$$\oint_S \vec{F}(x, y, z) \cdot d\vec{A}$$

6 Complex numbers

A complex number $z = x + iy$ is defined in terms of its real part x and its imaginary part y. Both x and y are real numbers. i is Euler's constant, defined by the property $i^2 = -1$.

Each complex number z has a "complex conjugate" z^* which has the same real part but an imaginary part with opposite sign: $z = x + iy \Leftrightarrow z^* = x - iy$.

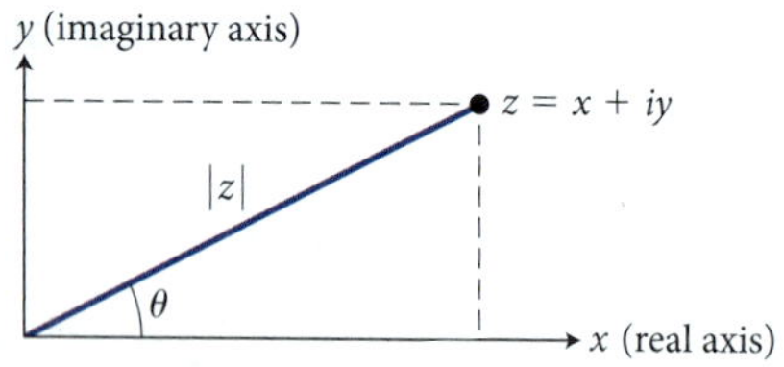

The real and imaginary parts can be expressed in terms of the complex number and its conjugate:

$$x = \tfrac{1}{2}(z + z^*)$$

$$y = \tfrac{1}{2i}(z - z^*)$$

A complex number is like a two-dimensional vector in a plane with a real axis and an imaginary axis. Thus, z can be described by a magnitude or length $|z|$ and an angle θ formed with the real axis (called the "phase angle"):

$z = |z|(\cos\theta + i\sin\theta)$, where $|z| = \sqrt{zz^*}$ and

$$\theta = \tan^{-1}\frac{y}{x} = \tan^{-1}\frac{(z - z^*)}{i(z + z^*)}.$$

Euler's formula says that $e^{i\theta} = \cos\theta + i\sin\theta$, allowing complex numbers to be written in the form $z = |z|e^{i\theta}$. This is a convenient form for expressing complex numbers. For example, it is easy to raise a complex number z to a power n: $z^n = |z|^n e^{in\theta}$.

7 Useful approximations

Binomial expansion

$$(1 + x)^n = 1 + nx + \frac{n(n-1)}{2}x^2 + \cdots$$

If $x \ll 1$, then $(1 + x)^n \approx 1 + nx$

Trigonometric expansions

$$\sin\alpha = \alpha - \frac{\alpha^3}{3!} + \frac{\alpha^5}{5!} - \frac{\alpha^7}{7!} + \cdots \quad (\alpha \text{ in rad})$$

$$\cos\alpha = 1 - \frac{\alpha^2}{2!} + \frac{\alpha^4}{4!} - \frac{\alpha^6}{6!} + \cdots \quad (\alpha \text{ in rad})$$

$$\tan\alpha = \alpha + \frac{1}{3}\alpha^3 + \frac{2}{15}\alpha^5 + \frac{17}{315}\alpha^7 + \cdots \quad (\alpha \text{ in rad})$$

If $\alpha \ll 1$ rad, then $\sin\alpha \approx \alpha$, $\cos\alpha \approx 1$, and $\tan\alpha \approx \alpha$.

Other useful expansions

$$\frac{1}{1 - x} = 1 + x + x^2 + x^3 + \cdots \quad \text{for } -1 < x < 1$$

$$e^x = 1 + x + \frac{1}{2}x^2 + \frac{1}{6}x^3 + \frac{1}{24}x^4 + \cdots$$

$$\ln(1 + x) = x - \frac{1}{2}x^2 + \frac{1}{3}x^3 - \frac{1}{4}x^4 + \cdots \quad \text{for } -1 < x < 1$$

$$\ln\left(\frac{1 + x}{1 + x}\right) = 2x + \frac{2}{3}x^3 + \frac{2}{5}x^5 - \frac{2}{7}x^7 + \cdots \quad \text{for } -1 < x < 1$$

Appendix C

SI Units, Useful Data, and Unit Conversion Factors

The seven base SI units		
Unit	Abbreviation	Physical quantity
meter	m	length
kilogram	kg	mass
second	s	time
ampere	A	electric current
kelvin	K	thermodynamic temperature
mole	mol	amount of substance
candela	cd	luminous intensity

Some derived SI units			
Unit	Abbreviation	Physical quantity	In terms of base units
newton	N	force	$kg \cdot m/s^2$
joule	J	energy	$kg \cdot m^2/s^2$
watt	W	power	$kg \cdot m^2/s^3$
pascal	Pa	pressure	$kg/m \cdot s^2$
hertz	Hz	frequency	s^{-1}
coulomb	C	electric charge	$A \cdot s$
volt	V	electric potential	$kg \cdot m^2/(A \cdot s^3)$
ohm	Ω	electric resistance	$kg \cdot m^2/(A^2 \cdot s^3)$
farad	F	capacitance	$A^2 \cdot s^4/(kg \cdot m^2)$
tesla	T	magnetic field	$kg/(A \cdot s^2)$
weber	Wb	magnetic flux	$kg \cdot m^2/(A \cdot s^2)$
henry	H	inductance	$kg \cdot m^2/(A^2 \cdot s^2)$

SI Prefixes					
10^n	Prefix	Abbreviation	10^n	Prefix	Abbreviation
10^0	—	—			
10^3	kilo-	k	10^{-3}	milli-	m
10^6	mega-	M	10^{-6}	micro-	μ
10^9	giga-	G	10^{-9}	nano-	n
10^{12}	tera-	T	10^{-12}	pico-	p
10^{15}	peta-	P	10^{-15}	femto-	f
10^{18}	exa-	E	10^{-18}	atto-	a
10^{21}	zetta-	Z	10^{-21}	zepto-	z
10^{24}	yotta-	Y	10^{-24}	yocto-	y

Values of fundamental constants

Quantity	Symbol	Value
Speed of light in vacuum	c_0	3.00×10^{8} m/s
Gravitational constant	G	6.6738×10^{-11} N · m²/kg²
Avogadro's number	N_A	6.0221413×10^{23}
Boltzmann's constant	k_B	1.381×10^{-23} J/K
Charge on electron	e	1.60×10^{-19} C
Electric constant	ϵ_0	$8.85418782 \times 10^{-12}\ C^2/(N \cdot m^2)$
Magnetic constant	μ_0	$4\pi \times 10^{-7}$ T · m/A
Planck's constant	h	6.626×10^{-34} J · s
Electron mass	m_e	9.11×10^{-31} kg
Proton mass	m_p	1.6726×10^{-27} kg
Neutron mass	m_n	1.6749×10^{-27} kg
Atomic mass unit	amu	1.6605×10^{-27} kg

Other useful numbers

Number or quantity	Value
π	3.1415927
e	2.7182818
1 radian	57.2957795°
Absolute zero ($T = 0$)	−273.15 °C
Average acceleration g due to gravity near Earth's surface	$9.8\ m/s^2$
Speed of sound in air at 20 °C	343 m/s
Density of dry air at atmospheric pressure and 20 °C	$1.29\ kg/m^3$
Earth's mass	5.97×10^{24} kg
Earth's radius (mean)	6.38×10^{6} m
Earth–Moon distance (mean)	3.84×10^{8} m

Unit conversion factors

Length

1 in. = 2.54 cm (defined)

1 cm = 0.3937 in.

1 ft = 30.48 cm

1 m = 39.37 in. = 3.281 ft

1 mi = 5280 ft = 1.609 km

1 km = 0.6214 mi

1 nautical mile (U.S.) = 1.151 mi = 6076 ft = 1.852 km

1 fermi = 1 femtometer (fm) = 10^{-15} m

1 angstrom (Å) = 10^{-10} m = 0.1 nm

1 light − year (ly) = 9.461×10^{15} m

1 parsec = 3.26 ly = 3.09×10^{16} m

Volume

1 liter (L) = 1000 mL = 1000 cm^3 = $1.0 \times 10^{-3}\ \text{m}^3$
= 1.057 qt (U.S.) = 61.02 in.^3

1 gal (U.S.) = 4 qt (U.S.) = 231 in.^3 = 3.785 L = 0.8327 gal (British)

1 quart (U.S.) = 2 pints (U.S.) = 946 mL

1 pint (British) = 1.20 pints (U.S.) = 568 mL

1 m^3 = 35.31 ft^3

Speed

1 mi/h = 1.4667 ft/s = 1.6093 km/h = 0.4470 m/s

1 km/h = 0.2778 m/s = 0.6214 mi/h

1 ft/s = 0.3048 m/s = 0.6818 mi/h = 1.0973 km/h

1 m/s = 3.281 ft/s = 3.600 km/h = 2.237 mi/h

1 knot = 1.151 mi/h = 0.5144 m/s

Angle

1 radian (rad) = 57.30° = 57°18'

1° = 0.01745 rad

1 rev/min (rpm) = 0.1047 rad/s

Time

1 day = 8.640×10^4 s

1 year = 365.242 days = 3.156×10^7 s

Mass

1 atomic mass unit (u) = 1.6605×10^{-27} kg

1 kg = 0.06852 slug

1 metric ton = 1000 kg

1 long ton = 2240 lbs = 1016 kg

1 short ton = 2000 lbs = 909.1 kg

1 kg has a weight of 2.20 lb where $g = 9.80\ \text{m/s}^2$

Force

1 lb = 4.44822 N

1 N = 10^5 dyne = 0.2248 lb

Energy and work

1 J = 10^7 ergs = 0.7376 ft · lb

1 ft · lb = 1.356 J = 1.29×10^{-3} Btu = 3.24×10^{-4} kcal

1 kcal = 4.19×10^3 J = 3.97 Btu

1 eV = 1.6022×10^{-19} J

1 kWh = 3.600×10^6 J = 860 kcal

1 Btu = 1.056×10^3 J

Power

1 W = 1 J/s = 0.7376 ft · lb/s = 3.41 Btu/h

1 hp = 550 ft · lb/s = 746 W

1 kWh/day = 41.667 W

Pressure

1 atm = 1.01325 bar = $1.01325 \times 10^5\ \text{N/m}^2$ = 14.7 lb/in.^2 = 760 torr

1 lb/in.^2 = $6.895 \times 10^3\ \text{N/m}^2$

1 Pa = 1 N/m^2 = $1.450 \times 10^{-4}\ \text{lb/in.}^2$

Periodic Table of the Elements

Period \ Group	1	2	3	4	5	6	7	8	9	10	11	12	13	14	15	16	17	18
1	1 **H** 1.008																	2 **He** 4.003
2	3 **Li** 6.941	4 **Be** 9.012											5 **B** 10.811	6 **C** 12.011	7 **N** 14.007	8 **O** 15.999	9 **F** 18.998	10 **Ne** 20.180
3	11 **Na** 22.990	12 **Mg** 24.305											13 **Al** 26.982	14 **Si** 28.086	15 **P** 30.974	16 **S** 32.065	17 **Cl** 35.453	18 **Ar** 39.948
4	19 **K** 39.098	20 **Ca** 40.078	21 **Sc** 44.956	22 **Ti** 47.867	23 **V** 50.942	24 **Cr** 51.996	25 **Mn** 54.938	26 **Fe** 55.845	27 **Co** 58.933	28 **Ni** 58.693	29 **Cu** 63.546	30 **Zn** 65.409	31 **Ga** 69.723	32 **Ge** 72.64	33 **As** 74.922	34 **Se** 78.96	35 **Br** 79.904	36 **Kr** 83.798
5	37 **Rb** 85.468	38 **Sr** 87.62	39 **Y** 88.906	40 **Zr** 91.224	41 **Nb** 92.906	42 **Mo** 95.94	43 **Tc** (98)	44 **Ru** 101.07	45 **Rh** 102.906	46 **Pd** 106.42	47 **Ag** 107.868	48 **Cd** 112.411	49 **In** 114.818	50 **Sn** 118.710	51 **Sb** 121.760	52 **Te** 127.60	53 **I** 126.904	54 **Xe** 131.293
6	55 **Cs** 132.905	56 **Ba** 137.327	71 **Lu** 174.967	72 **Hf** 178.49	73 **Ta** 180.948	74 **W** 183.84	75 **Re** 186.207	76 **Os** 190.23	77 **Ir** 192.217	78 **Pt** 195.078	79 **Au** 196.967	80 **Hg** 200.59	81 **Tl** 204.383	82 **Pb** 207.2	83 **Bi** 208.980	84 **Po** (209)	85 **At** (210)	86 **Rn** (222)
7	87 **Fr** (223)	88 **Ra** (226)	103 **Lr** (262)	104 **Rf** (261)	105 **Db** (262)	106 **Sg** (266)	107 **Bh** (264)	108 **Hs** (269)	109 **Mt** (268)	110 **Ds** (271)	111 **Rg** (272)	112 **Uub** (285)	113 **Uut** (284)	114 **Uuq** (289)	115 **Uup** (288)	116 **Uuh** (292)	117 **Uus** (294)	118 **Uuo**

Key: Number of protons → 29; Symbol for element → **Cu**; 63.546 ← Average atomic mass in g/mol. For elements having no stable isotope, value in parentheses is approximate atomic mass of longest-lived isotope.

Lanthanoids	57 **La** 138.905	58 **Ce** 140.116	59 **Pr** 140.908	60 **Nd** 144.24	61 **Pm** (145)	62 **Sm** 150.36	63 **Eu** 151.964	64 **Gd** 157.25	65 **Tb** 158.925	66 **Dy** 162.500	67 **Ho** 164.930	68 **Er** 167.259	69 **Tm** 168.934	70 **Yb** 173.04
Actinoids	89 **Ac** (227)	90 **Th** (232)	91 **Pa** (231)	92 **U** (238)	93 **Np** (237)	94 **Pu** (244)	95 **Am** (243)	96 **Cm** (247)	97 **Bk** (247)	98 **Cf** (251)	99 **Es** (252)	100 **Fm** (257)	101 **Md** (258)	102 **No** (259)

Answers to Selected Odd-Numbered Questions and Problems

Chapter 1

1. Undetectable

3. That the sequence is linear, meaning the difference between any two adjacent digits is 1.

5. 12 ways

7. One

9. T, A: reflection symmetry across vertical line passing through letter center. E, B: reflection symmetry across horizontal line passing through letter center. L, S: no reflection symmetry.

11. 9 axes of reflection symmetry, 13 axes of rotational symmetry

13. Two axes of reflection symmetry

15. (*a*) 1.5×10^{14} mm (*b*) 12,000 Earths

17. 10^4 gastrotrich lifetimes/tortoise lifetime

19. 10^9 to 10^{10} books

21. (*a*) Either one order of magnitude or none. Performing $V = \ell^3$ first yields $V_1 = \ell_1^3$, $V_2 = (2\ell_1)^3 = 8\ell_1^3$, which rounds to $10\ell_1^3$ so that $V_2 = 10V_1$, one order of magnitude. (*b*) Yes, because of the rules of rounding numerical values. For example, if $V_1 = 3.5\ \text{m}^3$, that value would round to an order of magnitude of $10\ \text{m}^3$. Then $V_2 = 8V_1 = 28\ \text{m}^3$, which also rounds to an order of magnitude of $10\ \text{m}^3$.

23. 10^5 leaves

25. Not reasonable. Because light travels much faster than sound, any thunder peal is delayed compared to the light signal caused by the lightning bolt event. From the principle of causality, the lightning you see after you hear the peal cannot have caused the peal.

27. That the barrier lowers time after time 30 s before a train passes is consistent with a causal relationship between the two events. The single negative result, however, tells you that the lowering of the barrier cannot be the *direct* cause of the passing of the train. More likely, the lowering is triggered when the train passes a sensor quite a distance up the tracks from the barrier and the sensor sends an electrical signal to the lowering mechanism. A malfunction in either the sensor, the electrical connections, or the lowering mechanism would account for the one negative result you observed.

29. $E = mc^2$; E is type of energy described, m is object mass, c is speed of light.

31. If the 30° angles must be interior to adjacent sides, the resulting zigzag pattern gives a distance of 1.0ℓ (to 2 significant digits). If the 30° angles must be exterior to adjacent sides, the result ranges from 3.4ℓ to 3.7ℓ. If a mixture of interior and exterior angles are allowed, the distance ranges from zero (parallelogram) to 2.4ℓ (one interior angle at end of chain).

33. 1.32×10^3 s

35. (*a*) The position decreases linearly as a function of time, from an initial position $x = 4.0$ m to a final position $x = 0$, reaching this final position at $t = 8.0$ s. (*b*) $x(t) = mt + b$ with $m = -0.5$ m/s, and $b = 4.0$ m

37. 352 in

39. (*a*) and (*b*). In both cases, the density of each piece is the same as the density of the original block.

41. No, because there is a significant difference (14 percent) in their mass densities.

43. Meters

45. (*a*) 10^{21} kg (*b*) 10^{25} kg (*c*) 10^{39} kg

47. (*a*) 3.00×10^8 m/s (*b*) $8.99 \times 10^{16}\ \text{m}^2/\text{s}^2$ (*c*) No. Because you should wait until the final answer to round off, the value in part *b* is $(2.99792 \times 10^8\ \text{m/s})^2 = 8.98752 \times 10^{16}\ \text{m}^2/\text{s}^2$ rounded to three significant digits. The square of the value in part *a* is $(3.00 \times 10^8\ \text{m/s})^2 = 9.00 \times 10^{16}\ \text{m}^2/\text{s}^2$.

49. Four significant digits

51. 35,987.1 km

53. 0.17 L. However, in the absence of information about volume measuring devices, mixing a standard one liter is probably best.

55. 7.4×10^{-3} g/s

57. 1.6 m

59. Place two coins on the balance, and hold the third in your hand. If the two coins balance, the one in your hand is the counterfeit. If the two coins do not balance, one must be the counterfeit. Swap the lighter of the two for the coin in your hand. If the two coins on the balance now balance, the counterfeit coin is the one you just removed, and it is lighter than real coins. If the two coins are still unbalanced, the counterfeit is the one that stayed on the balance during the whole experiment, and it is heavier than real coins.

61. 10^{56} mol

63. 2×10^3 boards

65. 10^4 m

67. 10^8

69. 0.349 mm

71. No. Atoms are typically 10^5 times larger than nuclei. If you make the nucleus diameter 500 mm, the atom diameter must be 50 km.

73. No. The swing will never get closer to the ground than about 0.80 m and will never rise above the ground more than about 2 m.

75. (*a*) $10^{17}\ \text{kg/m}^3$ (*b*) 13 orders of magnitude larger than Earth mass density, 14 orders of magnitude larger than water mass density (*c*) 10^{14} kg

Chapter 2

1. Time interval between adjacent frames and object size

3.

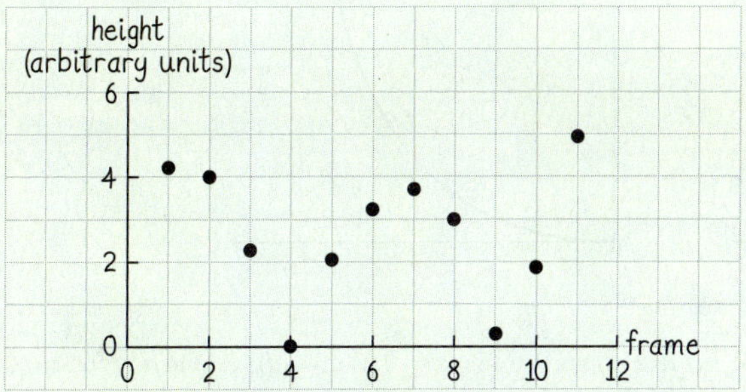

5. (*a*), (*c*), (*d*), (*e*), and (*f*)

7. Distance traveled 6.4 km, displacement zero

9. (*a*) Infinitely many (*b*) Infinitely many (*c*) Infinitely many (*d*) Two (one for each choice of positive direction)

11. If numerical values of time and distance are converted, but the scale of each axis still uses the same numerical labels (that is, "0.40 m" becomes "0.40 in"), then the curve would be much narrower and much taller. This is just a matter of perspective, though. If the scale of each axis is also converted, so that "0.40 m" becomes "16 in," then the shape of the graph is not changed by the conversion of units.

13. +1 block

15. The swimmer swims in the positive *x* direction at a constant speed (left sloping leg of curve, increasing *x* values). She stops briefly (horizontal leg, most probably at end of her lane) and then returns to the starting point (right sloping leg, decreasing *x* values) at a speed slightly lower than her initial speed (this leg not as steep as left leg).

17. Interpolation always gives a continuous path, but there is no reason to expect that the path is accurate everywhere. Suppose you are photographing a clock's pendulum at 1.0-s intervals, collecting data to use in a graph showing the pendulum's position as a function of time. Suppose further that the pendulum takes 1.0 s to swing from left to right and back left again. At this swing speed, the pendulum has just enough time between photographs to swing and return to its initial position, so that the photographs make it appear that the pendulum does not move at all. An interpolation of data points collected from the photographs would show a continuous horizontal line on a position-versus-time graph, which is certainly not correct.

19.

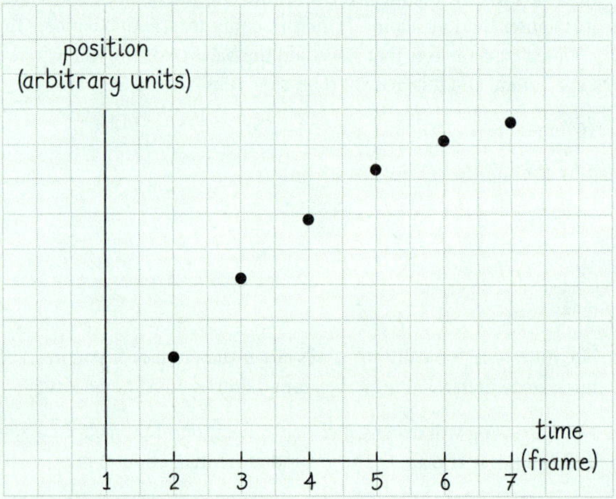

21. (*a*)

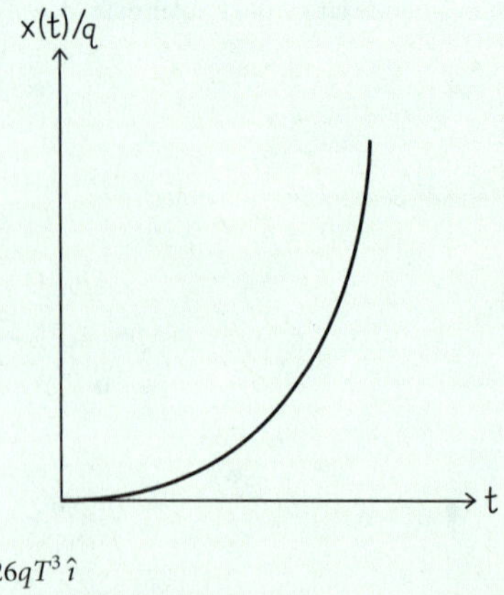

(*b*) $26qT^3\,\hat{\imath}$

25. (*a*) 10.2 m/s (*b*) 10.4 m/s (*c*) 9.24 m/s (*d*) 7.233 m/s (*e*) 6.3 m/s (*f*) 5.545 m/s

27. (*a*) Because the images were created at equal time intervals, the spacing between adjacent images is a function of the ball's speed. That the spacing between adjacent images has one value in the first five frames and a different value in the final five frames tells you that the ball moved at one speed at the beginning of the motion and at a different speed at the end of the motion. (*b*) During the first five frames.

29. (*a*) Just before instant t_2 and just after instant t_6. (*b*) From just before instant t_4 until instant t_6, which is where the bottom-curve slope is essentially the same as the top-curve slope.

31. B is closer to C than it is to A.

33. (*a*) 12 m/s (*b*) He likely treated the problem as though the cyclist rode at the two speeds for equal time intervals rather than for equal distances, and so just averaged the speeds: $(10\text{ m/s} + 16\text{ m/s})/2 = 13\text{ m/s}$.

35. 110 km/h

37. (1) No, because you could walk in either direction and so there are two possibilities for your final location. (2) Yes

39. (*a*) 3 m (*b*) 3 m/s (*c*) 3 m/s

41. (*a*) $A_x\hat{\imath}$ (*b*) $A_x\hat{\imath}$ (*c*) $A_x\hat{\imath}$

43. (*a*) 4.0 m (*b*) $(+4.0\text{ m})\,\hat{\imath}$

45. (*a*) +0.52 m (*b*) +0.80 m (*c*) 0 (*d*) $(+0.28\text{ m})\hat{\imath}$ (*e*) $(-0.80\text{ m})\hat{\imath}$ (*f*) $(-0.52\text{ m})\hat{\imath}$ (*g*) 0.66 m (*h*) 0.82 m (*i*) 1.5 m

47. $\vec{B} = -\vec{A}/2$

49. (*a*) $\vec{C} - \vec{A}$ (*b*) $\vec{A} - \vec{C}$

(*b*)

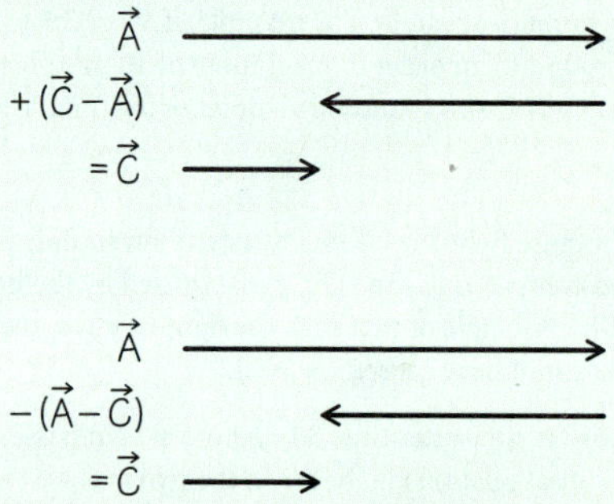

51. (*a*) $(-0.42\text{ m/s})\,\hat{\imath}$ (*b*) 1.3 m/s (*c*) Because average velocity considers only actual distance between initial and final positions, but average speed considers distance traveled between these two positions; average speed is path-dependent, average velocity is not.

53. 87 km/h

55. (*a*)

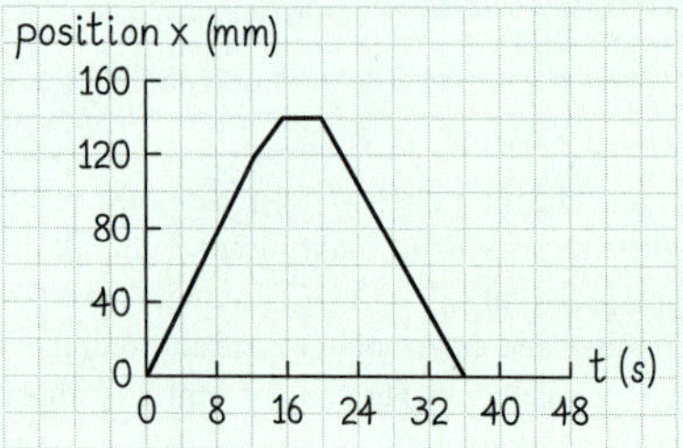

(*b*)

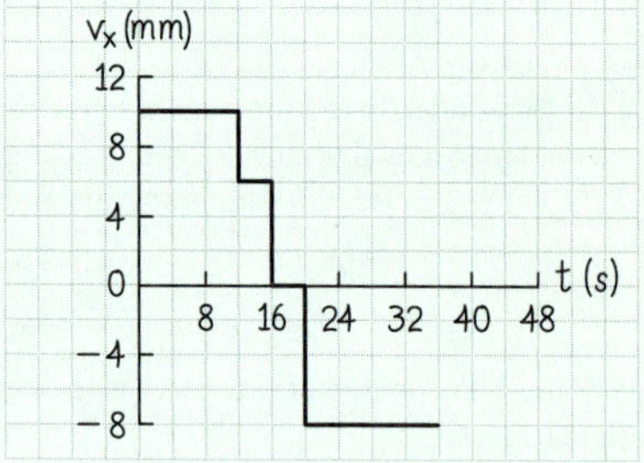

57. Object A

59.

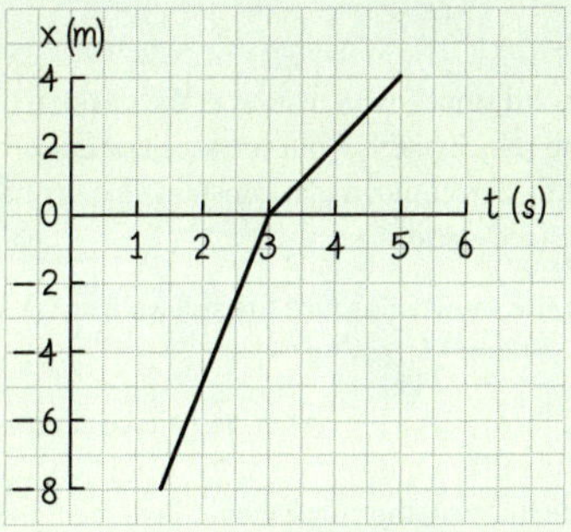

61. (*a*) 1.4 m/s (*b*) 10 m/s

63. 6.0×10^2 m

65. At 1.0 s: 45 m/s; at 4.0 s: 91 m/s

67. The fact that A passed B at 2:00 p.m. tells you that initially A was moving faster than 30 m/s. If A continued moving faster than 30 m/s eastward during the entire 1.0-h time interval, there is no way B could have caught up with A at 3:00 p.m. Therefore A must have slowed from a velocity above 30 m/s eastward to a velocity below 30 m/s eastward. Because a car cannot make discontinuous jumps in speed/velocity, B must have had a velocity of 30 m/s eastward at some instant. (Note that the speed could have always been greater than 30 m/s, but the velocity could not always have been greater than 30 m/s eastward.)

69. (*a*) Average speed of shadow leading edge (*b*) Yes, at the instant when the car is directly across from the light

71. (*a*) 21 m/s (*b*) 48 mi/h

73. (*a*) $x = -6.0$ m (*b*) $\vec{x} = (-6.0 \text{ m})\,\hat{\imath}$ (*c*) $x = 6.0$ m

75. By a time interval of $0.25(\Delta t)$, where Δt is A's time interval for the race

77. (*a*) 60 s (*b*) 3.6×10^2 m

79. (*a*) Greater than (*b*) Greater than

81. (*a*) 1:2 (*b*) 1:2

83. (*a*) +0.39 m/s (*b*) +0.3603 m/s (*c*) $\dfrac{x(t = 1.005) - x(t = 0.995)}{0.01 \text{ s}} =$ (+0.360003 m/s), whereas $v_x = \dfrac{dx}{dt} = 3ct^2$ such that $v_x(t = 1.0 \text{ s}) = 0.36$ m/s

85. (*a*) $d/2\Delta t$ (*b*) $2\Delta t$ (*c*) The distance traveled by the runner is an infinite series that requires infinitely many terms to approach *d*, but the time intervals that correspond to these distance intervals also get smaller and smaller in the series. At higher and higher terms in the series, the runner travels almost no distance in each term but does so in a time interval that is almost zero. Because the two effects cancel each other, the runner travels the distance from starting line to finish line in a finite time interval.

87. Tortoise wins by 0.2 mi, even with Hare running at his top speed, 6.0 mi/h. In order to cross the finish line first, Hare must run at 10 mi/h once he gets up from his nap, far above his top speed.

89. (*a*) $x(t) = -p - qt - rt^2$ (*b*) $x(t) = (p - 2) + qt + rt^2$

(*c*)

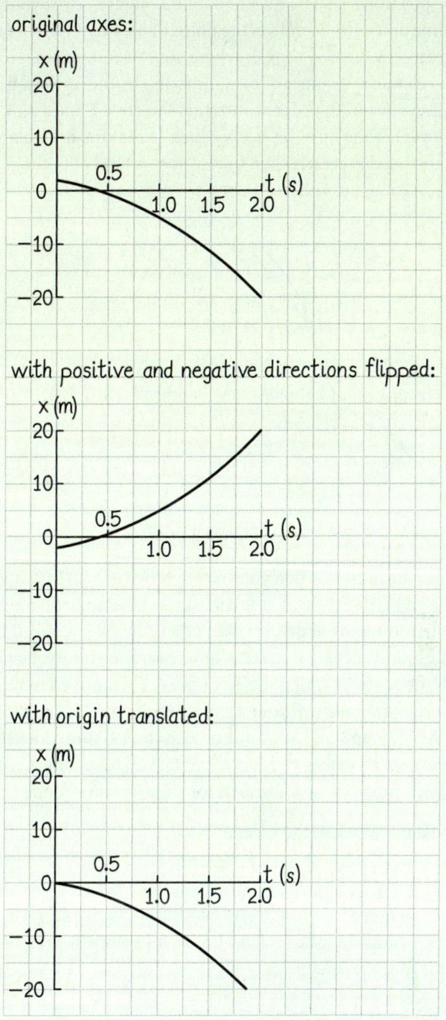

(*d*) −74 m, +74 m, −76 m

(*e*) −35 m/s, +35 m/s, −35 m/s

(*f*) There is no physical difference because the only things changed are position chosen as origin and direction chosen as positive.

91. You pass 12 empty trucks along the way, with a thirteenth pulling out of the mill just as you enter. The next day, you pass 12 full trucks , with a thirteenth pulling out of the mine just as you enter.

Chapter 3

1. (*a*) From first dot to fifth dot, evidenced by fact that space between adjacent dots increases for these five dots. (*b*) From fifth dot to ninth dot, evidenced by fact that space between adjacent dots decreases for these five dots. (*c*) The answers would be the same because the dots would be designated "first" through "ninth" starting at the right end of the sequence instead of the left end.

3. Not accelerating, indicated by the horse appearing in same position in each frame. With cameras equally spaced and triggered at equal time intervals, the unchanging position in all frames means the horse's speed did not change as the photographs were taken.

5. No. In the position-versus-time graph in the Figure below your car is the solid line and your friend's is the dotted line. Point A, where the lines intersect for the first time, is where your friend passes. To catch up, you accelerate at a constant rate, indicated by the upward bend of the solid line after A. In order to intersect the dotted line again, the slope of the solid line must be steeper than that of the dotted line. This means your speed is greater than that of your friend at B, the position at which you catch up with him.

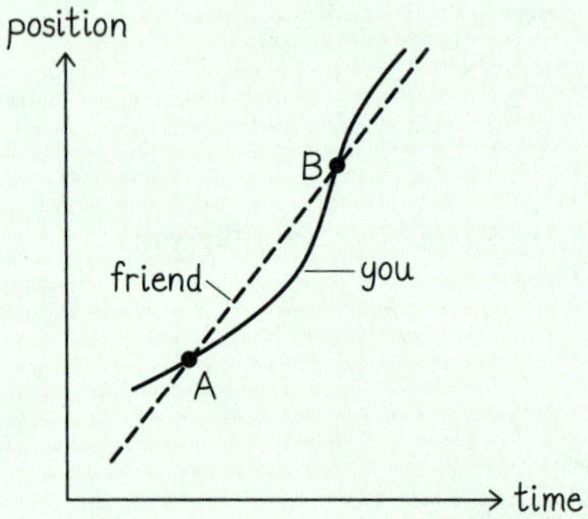

7. Initially you are at rest. When you start to move upward, your velocity has increased in the upward direction. If you take up to be the positive direction of motion, your acceleration is positive as you speed up from rest. This upward acceleration lasts for a short time interval, and soon, you reach the speed at which the elevator is programmed to move. Once that speed is reached, your acceleration is zero as you move at a constant velocity upward. As you approach the 19th floor, the elevator slows down, which makes your acceleration negative. This negative acceleration continues until the elevator stops at your floor.

9. The car that initially had the greater speed.

11. (*a*) 4.9 m/s (*b*) 15 m/s (*c*) 9.8 m/s

13. The curve in Figure 3.6*a* would still bend downward but not as much. Figure 3.6*b* would still be a straight line, but its slope would be about half what it is in that graph.

(*a*)

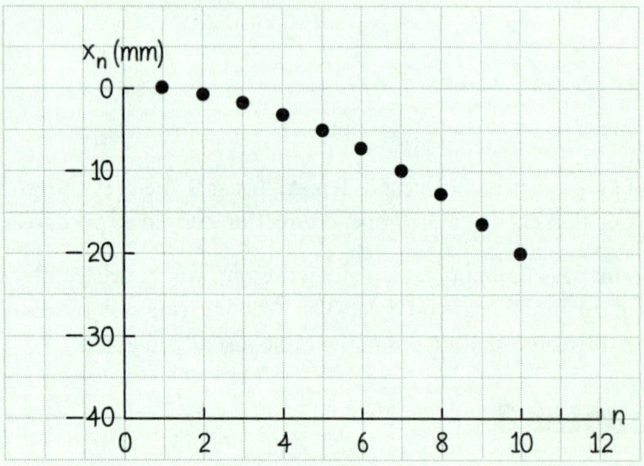

(*b*)

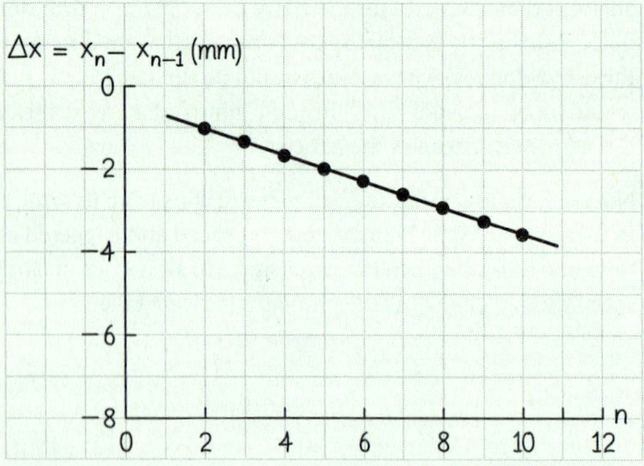

15. (*a*) Velocity 49 m/s upward, speed 49 m/s (*b*) Velocity 0, speed 0 (*c*) Velocity 49 m/s downward, speed 49 m/s (*d*) Velocity 98 m/s downward, speed 98 m/s

17. (*a*) Yes. A ball thrown upward stops for an instant at the peak of its path. At this instant, the velocity is zero but the acceleration is $g = -9.8\ \text{m/s}^2$. (*b*) Yes. Any object moving at constant velocity has nonzero velocity and zero acceleration.

19. The two techniques cause the snowballs to hit the sidewalk at the same speed.

21. The curve would start out identical to the no-air-resistance case, with a slope of $-9.8\ \text{m/s}^2$, but the magnitude of this slope would decrease with time. After some time interval, the curve would become horizontal, indicating a constant speed.

23.

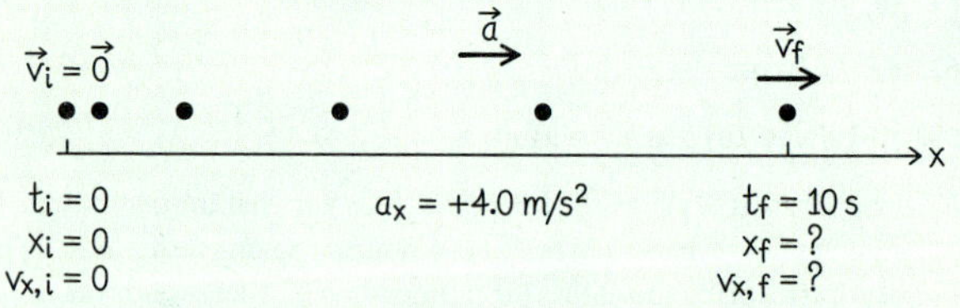

25. (*b*)

27.

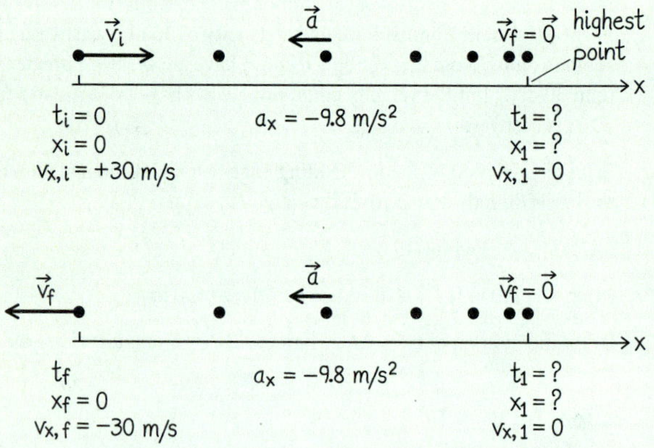

29. (*a*) $0.33\ \text{m/s}^2$ in direction of motion (*b*) 6.0×10^2 m

31. (*a*) 75 mm (*b*) $6.0 \times 10^{13}\ \text{m/s}^2$ in direction of motion

33. (*a*) You integrate. Determining the area under the curve is equivalent to adding up differential amounts of $v\delta t = \delta x$, and the sum of all such tiny steps is the displacement. (*b*) 1.0×10^2 m (*c*) No. In the figure below, the initial and final velocities are both zero, a case in which the equation from Worked Problem 3.3 yields zero for $v_{x,\text{av}}$. Yet the graph shows that the object has a positive velocity in the x direction for a significant time interval. Therefore the object must have a displacement in the x direction and its average velocity cannot be zero.

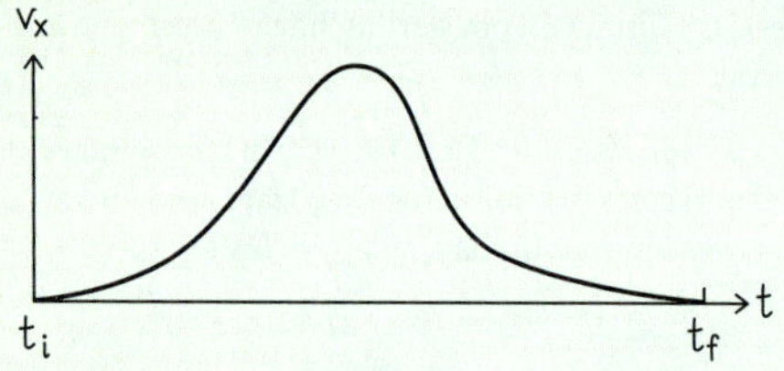

35. (*a*) 0.20 m downward (*b*) 0.22 m downward

37. (*a*) $4.2 \times 10^{15}\ \text{m/s}^2$ in direction of motion (*b*) 2.4 ns

39. (*a*) True. The fact that the curve is a straight line means the rate at which the velocity changes is constant. (*b*) Not necessarily true. The object could have started far enough from the origin that it never passes through position $x = 0$ on a position-versus-time plot. (*c*) True. The velocity is zero at the instant the curve crosses the time axis. (*d*) Not true. The fact that the curve crosses from positive v values to negative v values means the direction of the motion changed.

41. (*a*) 3.3×10^2 m (*b*) 38 s (*c*) 8.6 m/s

43. 13 m

45. 1.0 m

47. Factor of $\sqrt{2}$

49. The ball reaches its maximum height at $t = 3.0$ s, making the trajectory symmetric around that point. Between $t = 2.0$ s and $t = 3.0$ s, the ball moves upward and has a downward acceleration g; it moves some distance in this time interval. Between $t = 3.0$ s and $t = 4.0$ s, the ball, after having zero velocity for an instant, moves downward and has a downward acceleration g. Because the time intervals are equal, the distance the ball moves downward in 1.0 s equals the distance it moves upward in 1.0 s.

51. (*a*) 22 m/s (*b*) 2.3 s

53. (*a*) 0.65 s (*b*) 0.90 s

55. Let $\Delta y_{\Delta t} = \frac{1}{2}g(\Delta t)^2$ be the distance traveled after a time interval Δt and $\Delta y_{\Delta t+1} = \frac{1}{2}g(\Delta t + 1)^2$ be the distance traveled after time interval $\Delta t + 1$. The difference between these two distances is the distance traveled in the 1-s interval between these two intervals. Call this distance $h_{\Delta t} = g(\Delta t + \frac{1}{2})$, and because we are restricting ourselves to time intervals of 1 s, we could also write $h_N = g(N + \frac{1}{2})$ where N is an integer number of seconds. The ratio of the distance traveled in the first second to the distance traveled in the Nth second is

$$\frac{h_0}{h_N} = \frac{\frac{1}{2}}{N + \frac{1}{2}} = \frac{1}{2N + 1}.$$

Inserting the first few values for N yields 1/3, 1/5, 1/7, 1/9, . . .

57. 14 m

59. (*a*) 29 m/s upward (*b*) 36 m (*c*) 42 m

61. 13.6°

63. (*a*) Child on more-inclined slide (40°) (*b*) Child on more inclined slide (40°)

65. (*a*) 2.0 m/s^2 (*b*) 2.0 m/s^2 (*c*) 12 s (*d*) 20 m/s (*e*) 24 m/s

67. (*a*) 1.5 s (*b*) 3.1 m/s

69. (*a*) $\sqrt{2g\sin(\theta)\ell}$ (*b*) $\sqrt{g\sin(\theta)\ell}$

71. 35 °

73. 3.1 m

75. $a_x(t) = 6bt$

77. (*a*) Yes; acceleration constant (*b*) 6.12 m/s in $+x$ direction (*c*) 6.08 m/s in $+x$ direction, 6.16 m/s in $+x$ direction (*d*) 0.400 m/s^2 in $+x$ direction (*e*) 0.400 m/s^2 in $+x$ direction at both instants

79. (*a*) 10.0 m/s^2 in $+x$ direction (*b*) 50.0 m/s in $+x$ direction (*c*) 5.00 m/s^2 in $+x$ direction (*d*) 167 m

81. (*a*) 5.1 m (*b*) 1.8 s

83. (*a*) $a_x(t) = -v_{max}\,\omega\sin(\omega t)$ (*b*) $x(t) = (v_{max}/\omega)\sin(\omega t)$

85. 63 m

87. (*a*) 6.4×10^5 m/s^2 in direction opposite direction of motion (*b*) 0.25 ms (*c*) 0.18 m

89. (*a*) 2.24 m/s^2 (*b*) 21 m/s (*c*) 1.0×10^2 m

91. (*a*) 44.3 m/s (*b*) 4.52 s

93. (*a*) (20 m)$\hat{\imath}$, (29 m)$\hat{\imath}$, (29 m)$\hat{\imath}$, (20 m)$\hat{\imath}$ (*b*) (15 m/s)$\hat{\imath}$, (4.9 m/s)$\hat{\imath}$, (−4.9 m/s)$\hat{\imath}$, (−15 m/s)$\hat{\imath}$ (*c*) 0 (*d*) 12 m/s

95. 9.6×10^2 m/s^2 upward

97. $4g$, or 4×10^1 m/s^2 upward

99. (*a*) 6.0 m/s^2 upward (*b*) 3.3 s

101. (*a*) 11 m/s (*b*) upward (*c*) 5.2 m

103. 1.2 s

105. "Cloud-scraper" goes highest (1.5×10^2 m).

107. $a_1 = \frac{2d}{(\Delta t)^2} = 20.2\ \text{m/s}^2$, $a_2 = \frac{v_f^2}{2d} = 11.5\ \text{m/s}^2$, $a_3 = \frac{v_f - v_i}{t} =$ 15.3 m/s^2 (*b*) Student 3 calculated the average acceleration, and his value is approximately halfway between the values calculated by students 1 and 2. (*c*) Acceleration was not constant, but students 1 and 2 assumed it was.

109. Don't take the bet. You can throw a stone to a maximum height of 6.7 m.

Chapter 4

1. Puck 2 had twice the initial speed of puck 1.

3. No for object 1, yes for object 2. Friction between two objects opposes relative motion between them, but object 1 speeds up as it travels across the surface, meaning friction cannot account for the change in v_x. Object 2 slows down as it travels across the surface, meaning friction is one valid explanation for the change in v_x. (Though not the only explanation: A hockey stick slowing a puck sliding on ice, for instance, yields the same $v(t)$ curve as that shown for object 2.)

5. Object 2 has three times the inertia of object 1.

7.

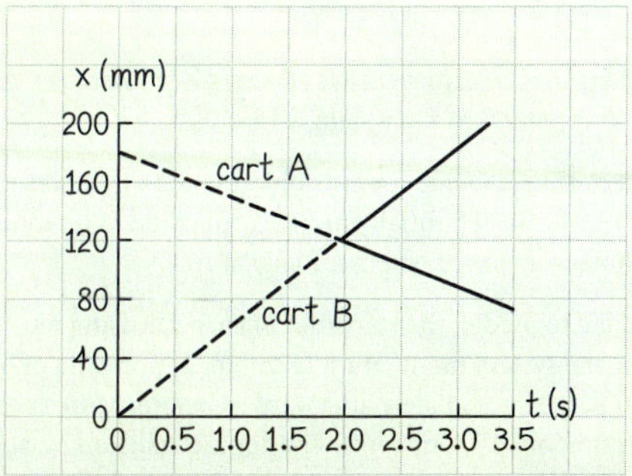

9. (*a*) Car A: upper solid line; car B: lower solid line (*b*) Car A

11. Inertia of A 2.5 times greater than inertia of B

13. Does not change

15. The inertia of just the bottle is the same in each case, but if the contents are included then the full bottle has the greater inertia because the water filling it has a greater inertia than the air filling the "empty" bottle.

17. Graph (*a*): smooth icy track; one wooden cart, one plastic cart; plastic cart initially at rest, wooden cart initially moving at 1.5 m/s. Graph (*b*): dusty unpolished track; carts made of same material but we cannot determine whether wood or plastic because we have no information about friction between each cart and surface; carts initially moving in same direction, one at 2.0 m/s and one at 5.0 m/s. Graph (*c*): rough damaged track; carts made of same material but we cannot determine whether wood or plastic because we have no information about friction between each cart and surface; one cart initially at rest, one initially moving.

19. (*a*) Extensive (*c*) No; number of passengers changes as people get on or off at each stop. In principle, people could also die or be born on the bus. (*d*) Yes, ignoring any deaths or births

21. 32 ways, assuming 5 objects named (person, truck, ball, friend, ground) cannot be subdivided.

23. 0.33 kg

25. 1.0 m/s to left

27. (*a*) $v_{1x,f} = -0.13$ m/s, $v_{2x,f} = +1.2$ m/s. (*b*) $\Delta v_{1x} = -1.6$ m/s, $\Delta v_{2x} = +1.2$ m/s. (*c*) 50 kg (*d*) $a_{1x} = -3.2\ \text{m/s}^2$, $a_{2x} = +2.4\ \text{m/s}^2$

29. Baseball

31. The two cars have the same change in momentum.

33. Yes. Momentum is a vector. Therefore the system has zero momentum if two conditions are met: The carts move in opposite directions and the absolute value of the product of inertia and velocity is the same for the two carts.

35. (*a*) $p_{1,i} = 0.196$ kg · m/s, $p_{1,f} = 0.131$ kg · m/s (*b*) $\vec{p}_{2i} = \vec{0}$, $\vec{p}_{2,f} = +0.327$ kg · m/s (*c*) $1.22 \times 10^3\ \text{kg/m}^3$

37. 46 m

39. 1.8 kg · m/s

41. 2.0 m/s

43. (*a*) No (*b*) No (*c*) Yes

45. 2.4 m/s

47. (*a*) 6 kg · m/s to the right (*b*) Zero (*c*) No. The wall does not move because it is attached to the ground or some underlying structure.

49. (*a*) +1.0 kg · m/s (*b*) +1.0 kg · m/s (*c*) Yes

51. (*a*) $\Delta\vec{p}_A = -8.0$ kg · m/s $\hat{\imath}$, $\Delta\vec{p}_B = +8.0$ kg · m/s $\hat{\imath}$ (*b*) Zero (*c*) Yes, because change in momentum for system is zero

53. (*a*) No, provided nothing outside the two-object system interacts with the system. (*b*) Yes, the object initially moving can come to rest and impart all its momentum to the object initially at rest.

55. (*a*) It is not possible to predict the velocities of each car using momentum. (*b*) Yes, the system momentum (combined momenta of both cars) must be the same immediately afterward as before. More specifically, the momentum of both cars together after the collision must be 2000 kg · m/s in the direction of the 1200-kg car's initial motion.

57. Remove your clothing and throw it toward the shore, so that it has a nonzero momentum. You gain equal momentum directed toward the opposite shore and drift toward that shore.

59. 80 kg

61. (*a*) 0.40 m/s (*b*) 7.0×10^2 kg · m/s in direction of initial motion (*c*) higher

63. (*a*) Before collision, cue ball has momentum directed toward 8 ball and 8 ball has zero momentum. After collision, cue ball has zero momentum and 8 ball has momentum equal in magnitude and direction to momentum of cue ball before collision. (*b*) Call direction of motion the $+x$ direction. For the isolated system of two balls, $m_8(v_{8x,f} - v_{8x,i}) = -m_c(v_{cx,f} - v_{cx,i})$. With $v_{8x,i} = 0$, $v_{cx,f} = 0$, and $m_8 = m_c$, this yields $v_{8x,f} = v_{cx,i}$. Because $m_8 = m_c$, this corresponds to $p_{8x,f} = p_{cx,i}$, or zero change in system momentum, consistent with zero impulse and with the answer in (*a*). Considering each ball separately, the non-zero change in momentum is also equal to the non-zero impulse, because the impulse affecting each ball is equal in magnitude and in the opposite direction, just as the momentum changes of each ball are equal and opposite. Each of the four quantities has magnitude mv.

65. 2.0×10^4 kg

67. (*a*) $v_{1x,i} = +2.0$ m/s, $v_{1x,f} = 0$ (*b*) $v_{2x,i} = -0.33$ m/s, $v_{2x,f} = +0.33$ m/s (*c*) $\Delta p_{1,x} = -2.0$ kg · m/s, $\Delta p_{2,x} = +2.0$ kg · m/s (*d*) Yes

(*e*)

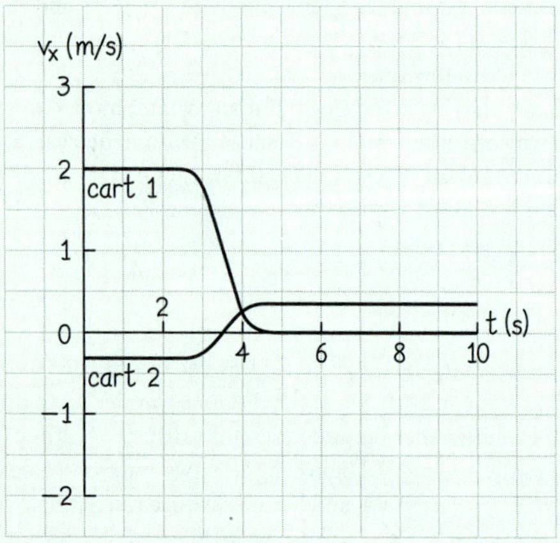

69. $m_{black} = 2m_{red}$

71. 2.0×10^2 kg

73. $p_{golf\ ball}/p_{baseball} = 1/2$

75. 5.6 kg

77.

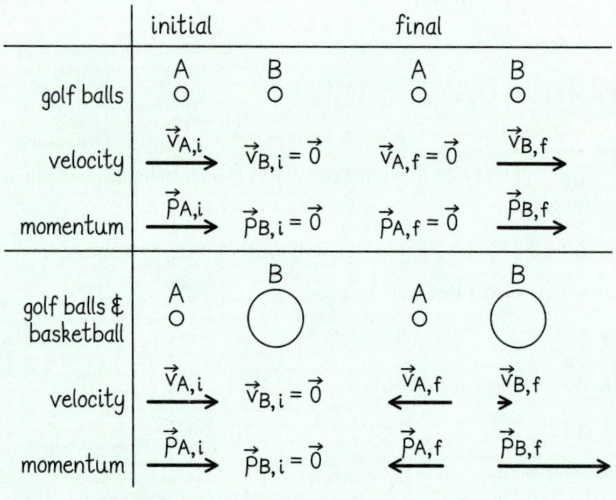

79. $v_{block,f} = \dfrac{m_{bullet}}{m_{block}}(v_{bullet,i} - v_{bullet,f})$

81. When a rocket is launched or a cannonball fired, the projectile has significant forward momentum. Because the momentum of the system is initially zero, after firing there must be momentum in the direction opposite the projectile direction. In a bazooka, material (largely burnt fuel) is expelled out the back, and so the required backward momentum need not come entirely from recoil. In a cannon, there is no outlet for air or debris at the back; consequently, the cannon must recoil with the same magnitude of momentum imparted to the cannonball.

83. In space, the rocket expels a huge number of gas particles at very high speeds. When these gas particles are ejected from the rear of the rocket, the rocket must acquire a forward velocity in order for system momentum to remain constant.

85. The two cars experience the same change in momentum $\Delta\vec{p} = m\Delta\vec{v}$ during the collision. If you are in the car of greater inertia, this momentum change is accomplished with a smaller velocity change. Because change in velocity over time is acceleration, being in the car of greater inertia means your body experiences the smaller acceleration in the collision, which is preferable in avoiding injury.

87. Don't drop the stereo because at the instant it reaches your friend its momentum is 53 kg · m/s downward. This could be harmful to both your friend and the stereo.

89. You get rid of the sandbags to decrease inertia and therefore momentum. If you simply drop them from the basket, your momentum when you reach the ground is 2.66×10^3 kg · m/s downward, below the critical value 2850 kg · m/s at which the basket is damaged. However, if you *throw* the sandbags downward, you increase their downward momentum and therefore decrease your downward momentum, making your momentum when you land far below the critical value.

91. (*a*) $3v_{ex}/4$ (*b*) $2v_{ex}/3$ (*c*) Two-stage, because each time a stage is detached, the inertia that must be accelerated in the next stage is decreased.

Chapter 5

1. (*a*) 3.0 m/s in negative x direction (*b*) 4.0 m/s in positive x direction

3. (*a*) Inelastic (*b*) Totally inelastic

5. Doubles momentum, quadruples kinetic energy

7. 2.5×10^6 kg

9. $m_A/m_B = 1/4$

11. For same momentum, $K_Y > K_X$. For same kinetic energy, $p_X > p_Y$.

13. The book slows down due to friction, and the book and table heat up slightly as the book's kinetic energy is converted to thermal energy.

15. Cannon: temperature, velocity (due to recoil), momentum. Ball: temperature, velocity, momentum, internal energy (due to slight deformation). Gunpowder: transformational energy (as solid converted to gas when ignited).

17. (*a*) I choose the system consisting of the two blocks only. It is not isolated; the blocks make contact with the spring outside the system, and this changes the momentum of the system.

(*b*)

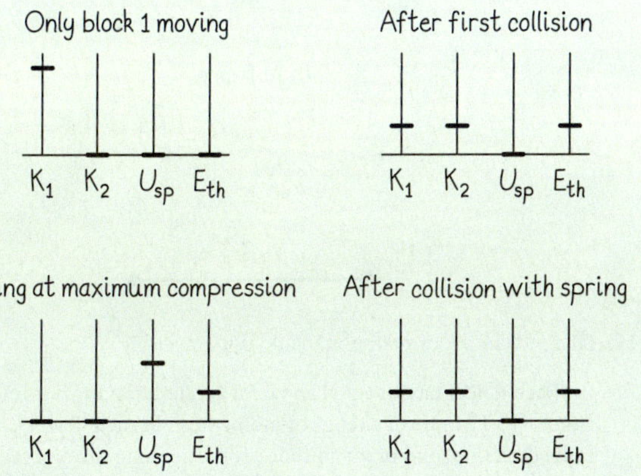

(*c*) The system starts out with kinetic energy. During the collision of the two blocks, this kinetic energy is changed into thermal energy. As the warmer blocks strike the spring, they momentarily come to a stop as their kinetic energy is changed to internal energy in the spring. Once the spring returns to its equilibrium length, the blocks regain kinetic energy. (*d*) $\frac{1}{2}v$

19. Kinetic energy of bike or car converted to thermal energy of brake pads and tires

21. The cars convert the same amount of kinetic energy to internal energy.

23. $|\Delta\vec{p}| = 2m|\vec{v}|$; $\Delta K = 0$; the answers are consistent because the change in momentum accounts for the change in velocity direction and the change in kinetic energy accounts for the change in velocity magnitude.

25. 6.3×10^{-3} J

27. (*a*) 5.0 m/s (*b*) −5.4 m/s (*c*) Yes (*d*) Zero

31. (*a*) No (*b*) Yes

33. $v_{1f} = -\dfrac{(m_1 - 2m_2)}{m_1 + m_2}v_{1i}$, $v_{2f} = \dfrac{1}{2}\left(\dfrac{5m_1 - m_2}{m_1 + m_2}\right)v_{1i}$

35. Inelastic, $m_B = 0.16$ kg

39. $\dfrac{\text{Conversion at 34 m/s}}{\text{Conversion at 25 m/s}} = 1.8$

43. Collision in which initial momenta have same magnitude

45. $\sqrt{\frac{3}{4}}v_{end}$

47. (*a*) 5.0 m/s (*b*) No (*c*) 0.50 J

51. Answers between 1×10^8 and 3×10^8 megatons are reasonable.

53. The coefficients are each other's multiplicative inverse; reversing the time order reverses *initial* and *final* in definition of coefficient, thus inverting it.

55. (*a*) 0.20 m/s, to left (*b*) $e = \infty$ (*c*) 0.20 m/s, to right (*d*) $e = \infty$ (*e*) $\Delta K = +200$ J; from chemical energy stored in her body (*f*) 0.047 Cal

57. (*a*) 7000 m/s in direction of initial velocity (*b*) 1.013×10^{10} J

59. $v_{shuttle} = 890$ m/s in direction of initial motion; $v_{rocket} = 790$ m/s in direction of initial motion

61. −0.60 m/s

63. $v_i + \sqrt{\dfrac{3m_B E_{spring}}{2m_A(m_B + m_A)}}$

65. (*a*)

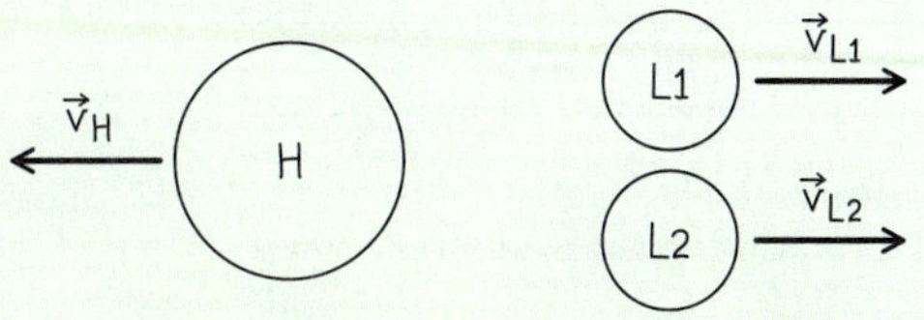

(*b*)

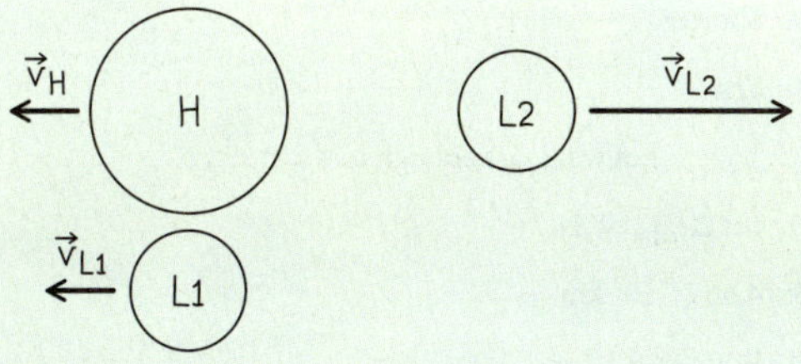

69. 1 m/s

71. (*a*) 2.0 m/s to right in Figure P5.70 (*b*) 0.098 J (*c*) $\vec{v}_{1f} = 0.66$ m/s to right, $\vec{v}_{2f} = 0.66$ m/s to right (*d*) 0.33 J (*e*) $e = 0$, as expected for a totally inelastic collision

77. Magnitude of momentum delivered by water each second is $\dfrac{\Delta p}{t} = \dfrac{Q^2\rho}{\pi r^2}$. You can determine whether the collision is elastic or inelastic by comparing the rate at which the ball's momentum changes with time to this momentum magnitude. You expect the collision to be inelastic because water droplets stick to the ball.

Chapter 6

1. Stepping on, move quickly enough to have your speed match the sidewalk speed; stepping off, stop walking as you reach the sidewalk end to minimize your speed relative to the ground.

3. 5.0 m/s in direction of motion of both cars

5. (*a*) Toward truck (*b*) Away from truck

7. The truck and the car traveling in the same direction: the truck driver sees the car initially moving backwards at 30 m/s, then accelerating in the direction of the truck travel, finally moving at zero velocity relative to the truck. The car and truck traveling in opposite directions: the truck driver sees the car initially approaching him at 30 m/s, then accelerating in the direction of the truck travel, finally approaching the truck at a speed of 60 m/s. The direction of acceleration is the same in both cases.

9. Before the truck slows, the truck and the cans have the same initial velocity. Because the cans are not attached to the truck, their velocity cannot change when the truck slows; they continue moving in the initial direction of motion until they hit up against the back of the cab.

11. (*a*) $\vec{p}_{A,i} = 2.5 \times 10^6$ kg · m/s west, $\vec{p}_{B,i} = 2.4 \times 10^6$ kg · m/s west, $\vec{p}_{A,f} = 3.0 \times 10^6$ kg · m/s west, $\vec{p}_{B,f} = 2.0 \times 10^6$ kg · m/s west (*b*) $\vec{p}_{A,i} = 1.7 \times 10^6$ kg · m/s east, $\vec{p}_{B,i} = 3.3 \times 10^5$ kg · m/s east, $\vec{p}_{A,f} = 1.2 \times 10^6$ kg · m/s east, $\vec{p}_{B,f} = 8.0 \times 10^5$ kg · m/s east

13. 4.00 m/s, or 12.0 m/s, depending on direction of officer's motion

15. 0.75 m/s

17. (*a*) +2.3 kg · m/s $\hat{\imath}$ (*b*) +3.8 m/s $\hat{\imath}$

19. Yes, in reference frame moving at speed v toward cart A

23.

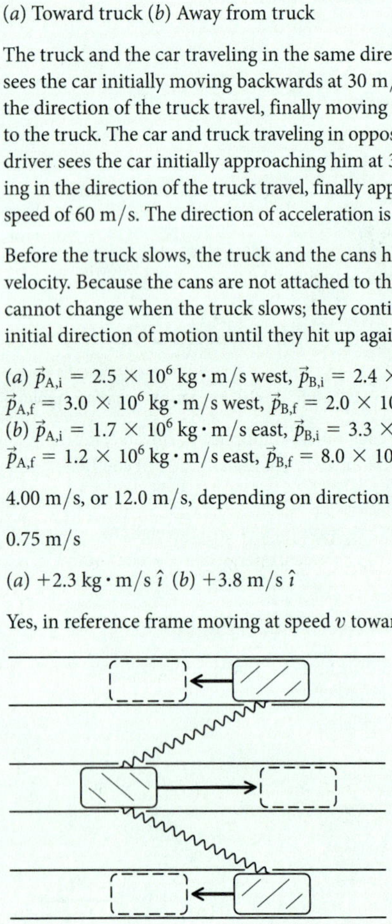

25. (*a*) 8.0 m/s (*b*) 5.0×10^4 kg · m/s in direction in which unit moves (*c*) 8.0 m/s in direction in which unit moves

27. Lightweight object; no

29. Shorter

31. Yes

33. You do not walk fast enough to do this.

35. (*a*) $\Delta t_{\text{calm}} = 2d/v$

37. 4.66×10^3 km

39. Boy's raft; 2.5 m.

41. (*a*) 0.38 m to right of origin (*b*) 0.63 m to left of origin (*c*) 1.38 m to right of origin. The center of mass location must be calculated for only one origin choice; that location can then be expressed relative to the other two origin choices with almost no calculation.

43. If the system's center of mass is not moving at constant velocity, the reference frame from which motion is measured is not inertial.

45.

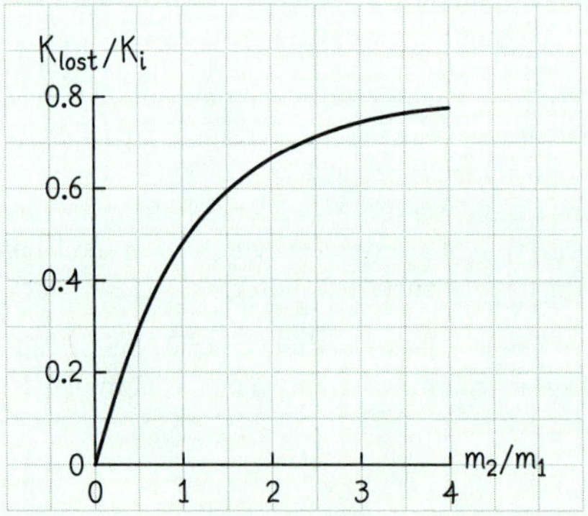

As m_2/m_1 approaches infinity, $K_{\text{lost}}/K_{\text{i}}$ approaches 1, meaning all kinetic energy is converted to other forms.

47. μ cannot be larger than m_1: $\mu_{\max} = m_1$. Smallest possible value is $\mu_{\min} = m_1/2$.

49. Reference frame in which ball is at rest before collision

51. (*a*) 11 m/s to the right (*b*) 0.030 kg (*c*) 60% (*d*) 1.8 J

53. (*a*) 9.3 m/s (*b*) 19 m/s toward each other (*c*) 0.27 kg (*d*) 99.7% (*e*) $\vec{v}_{1f} = 10$ m/s away from you; $\vec{v}_{2f} = 7.4$ m/s toward you

55. Collision between two objects of equal inertia m

57. (*a*) 0.25 m/s in direction in which ball is thrown (*b*) 4.6 m/s in direction in which ball is thrown (*c*) 16 J (*d*) 16 J

61. (*a*) 4.4 m/s (*b*) Before collision: (1.0 m/s)m_{mother} toward swimming penguin; after collision: (2.3 m/s)m_{mother} toward swimming penguin

63. (*a*) $\vec{v}_{\text{FG}} = \dfrac{\vec{v}_{\text{orange}}}{2}\left(\dfrac{2m_{\text{orange}} + m_{\text{apple}}}{m_{\text{orange}} + m_{\text{apple}}}\right)$

65. (*a*) $\vec{v}_{\text{rubber,f}} = 18$ m/s west, $\vec{v}_{\text{soft,f}} = 8.9$ m/s east. (*b*) 12-J increase. (*c*) Observer measures same 12-J conversion from kinetic energy to internal energy. (*d*) Observer measures same 12-J conversion.

67. (*a*) (*b*)

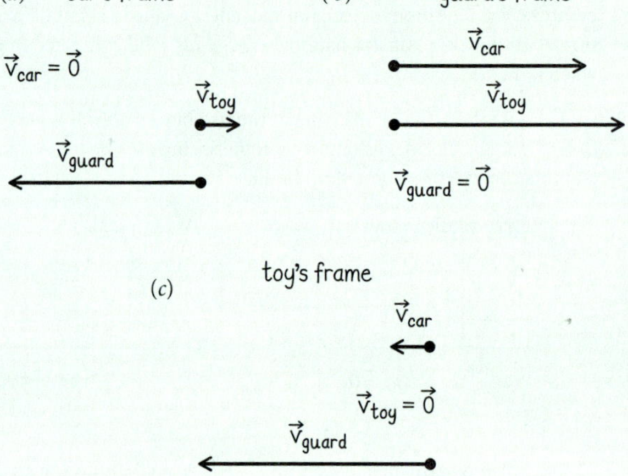

69. 0.86 m/s in the direction man and dog travel

71. (*a*) Each object has an equal apparent acceleration in your reference frame. (*b*) The rate of change of momentum of each object is in the same direction, and of magnitude proportional to the object's inertia.

73. Ball: 23 m/s in direction opposite its direction before collision; pot: 1.8 m/s in direction of ball's velocity before collision.

75. (*a*) 1.52×10^9 kg · m/s in direction in which A1 moves before collision (*b*) 317 m/s in direction in which A1 moves before collision (*e*) No dipping down, then rising again in either kinetic energy curve because all kinetic energy is converted to internal energy; none is converted back to kinetic energy after collision; kinetic energy drops to zero and remains there.

77. $\vec{v}_{0.30\text{ kg,f}} = 0.17$ m/s in direction of initial velocity, $\vec{v}_{0.50\text{ kg,f}} = 2.1$ m/s in direction of initial velocity

79. Call disk radius *R*. Draw horizontal *x* axis in plane of page, with axis origin at disk center and axis passing through hole center; center of mass is at $x_{cm} = -R/6$.

81. (*a*) 1.0 m/s (*b*) 6.9 m (*c*) 3.7 m from front end of car (*d*) 3.9 m from front end of car (*e*) Because speed changes as grain is added, grain is not evenly distributed over length of car.

Chapter 7

1. More than one (one between each piece of bread and salami)

3.

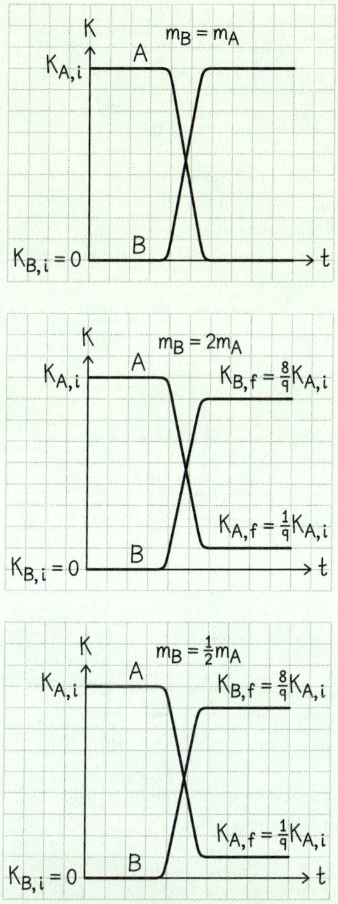

5. 1.80 m/s² to the left

7. (*a*) (*b*) (*c*)

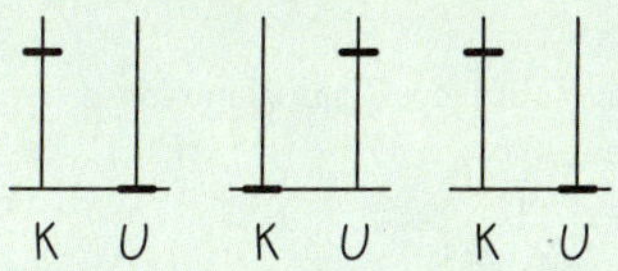

9. Case (*b*)

11. $K_m/K_{3m} = 3$

13. Trip down

15. (*a*) Into deforming metal (by breaking and re-forming chemical bonds) and heating it up (*b*) No, in fact you have to put in more energy to do a similar rearrangement of molecules to fix the slinky.

17. (*a*)

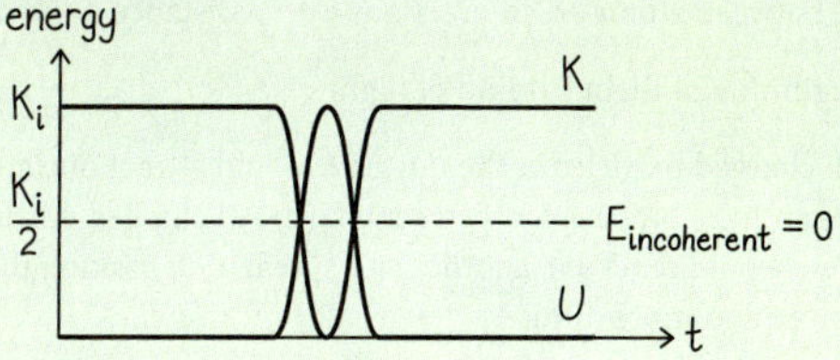

(*b*)

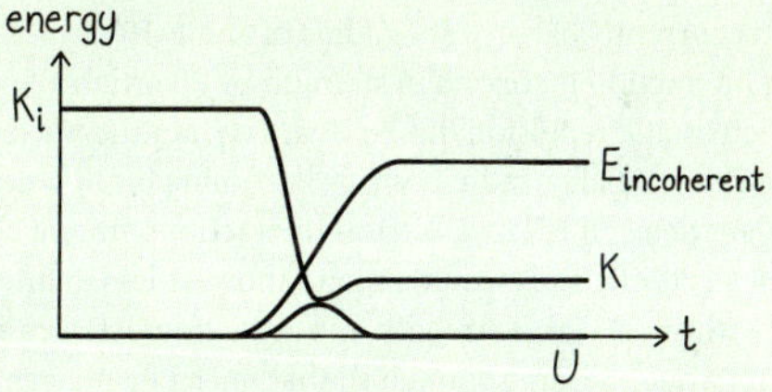

19. (*a*) System: ball, spring, air, Earth; air resistance not ignored

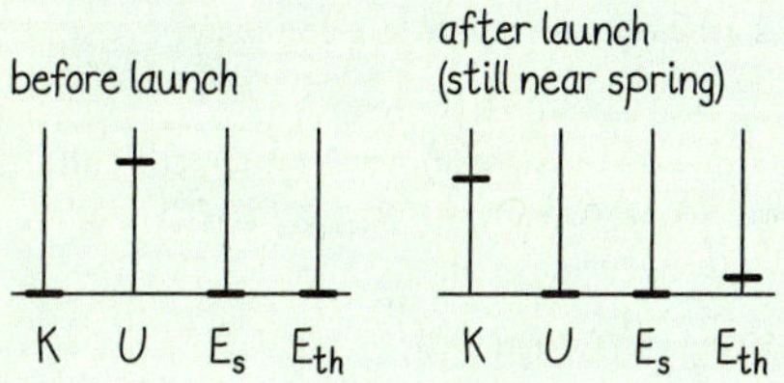

(*b*) System: ball, air, Earth; air resistance not ignored

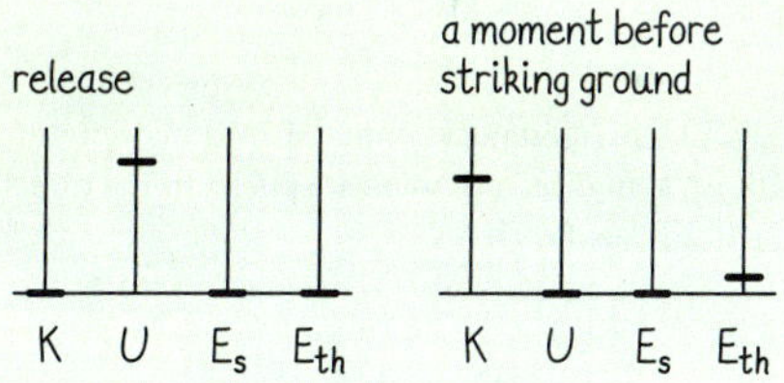

(*c*) System: bicycle, cyclist, air, road

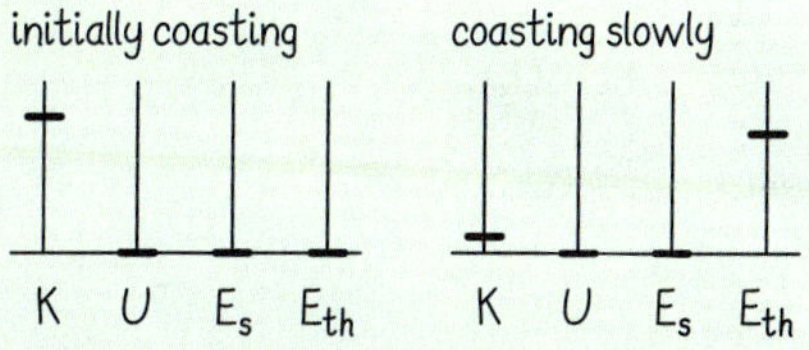

(*d*) System: car, air, road, fuel

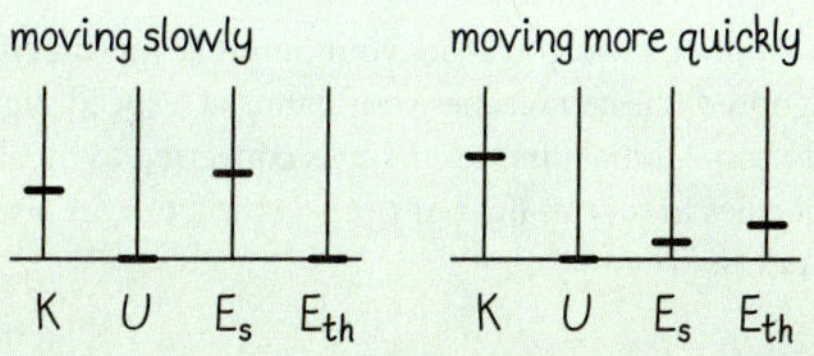

21. (*a*)

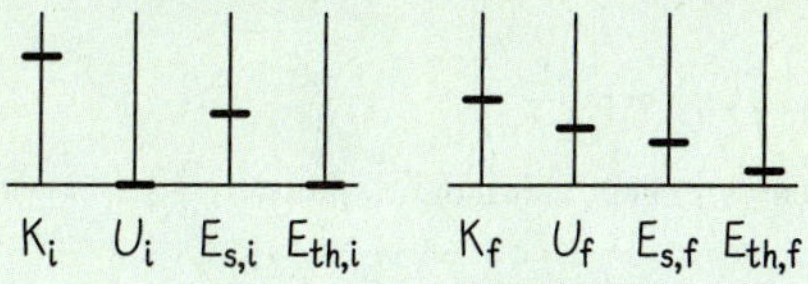

23. Yes. The copper atoms are likely joined to one another by chemical bonds, whereas contact between macroscopic objects typically involves repulsion at a distance. So the copper atoms may be pictured as being more "in contact" than your shoe is with the ground, but only because the atoms in copper are closer together. However, even the chemical bonds between atoms are interactions over a distance.

25. (*a*) Beginning of flight (*b*) End of flight

27. (*a*) All charged particles in the universe would attract one another and collapse into a compact charged center. (*b*) All charged particles in the universe would repel one another and spread out, making the universe ever more and more diffuse.

29. The strong interaction is responsible for holding atomic nuclei together against the electrical repulsion between protons. These interactions currently balance at a radius of about $10^{-14} - 10^{-15}$ m. If the strong interaction increased in strength by 20 orders of magnitude, but the electrostatic repulsion did not increase, atomic nuclei would be crushed to much smaller radii, perhaps becoming black holes! Atomic size scales are determined by electrical interactions among electrons and nuclei, so atomic sizes would remain more or less unaffected. However, with such a large strength, the attraction between neutrons and protons would be large enough so that nuclei in adjacent atoms could be drawn together. All matter might therefore be crushed. This new strong interaction would still not be large enough to affect interplanetary distances, where gravity would still dominate.

31. (*a*) 0.39 kg (*b*) $\vec{a}_{0.66\text{ kg}} = 3.2 \times 10^2\ \text{m/s}^2$ to the left, $\vec{a}_{0.39\text{ kg}} = 5.4 \times 10^2\ \text{m/s}^2$ to the right (*c*) Acceleration ratio and inverse of inertia ratio equal (Chapter 4): $|\vec{a}_{0.66\text{ kg}}/\vec{a}_{0.39\text{ kg}}| = 0.59$, $|m_{0.39\text{ kg}}/m_{0.66\text{ kg}}| = 0.59$

33. (*a*) −0.0020 (*b*) 250 m/s (*c*) 0.50 m/s

35. (*a*) 0.14 kg (*b*) $\vec{a}_{\text{glob,av}} = 25\ \text{m/s}^2$ to the left, $\vec{a}_{\text{cart,av}} = 6.7\ \text{m/s}^2$ to the right

37. 0.297 s

39. (*a*) $\vec{a}_{\text{goalie,av}} = 1.7 \times 10^{-2}\ \text{m/s}^2$ in puck's initial direction of motion, $\vec{a}_{\text{puck,av}} = 5.3 \times 10^3\ \text{m/s}^2$ in direction opposite puck's initial direction of motion (*b*) 90 kg. (*c*) 1.3×10^2 J

41. Position x_1:

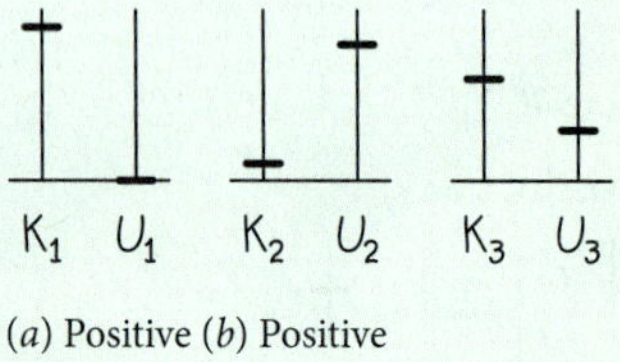

43. (*a*) Positive (*b*) Positive

45. 0.20 J

47. (*a*) 2.9 m/s (*b*) 3.2 m/s

49. (*a*) 0.59 J (*b*) $\vec{v}_{0.36\text{ kg,f}} = 1.1$ m/s to the left, $\vec{v}_{0.12\text{ kg,f}}$ 3.0 m/s to the right

51. If air resistance is ignored, the cap reaches your hands at speed v; if air resistance is not ignored, the cap reaches your hands at a speed slightly less than v because some initial kinetic energy is converted to incoherent energy of molecules in the air. Both answers come from the law of conservation of energy.

53. 4.59 km

55. 2.2 m/s

57. (*a*) 24 m/s (*b*) 49 J (*c*) 49 J

59. (*a*) 0.95 (*b*) 10 m/s, either upward or downward

61. $v_f = \frac{1}{4}\sqrt{15g\ell}$

63. Configuration (*b*)

65. 9.4%

67. (*c*) and (*d*)

69. (*a*) 57 J (*b*) 55 J

71. (*a*) Before the fall, the system's energy is all potential. During the fall, the system's potential energy is converted to kinetic energy. Just before impact, the system's energy is all kinetic. After impact, the system's kinetic energy has converted to thermal energy as Humpty Dumpty breaks.

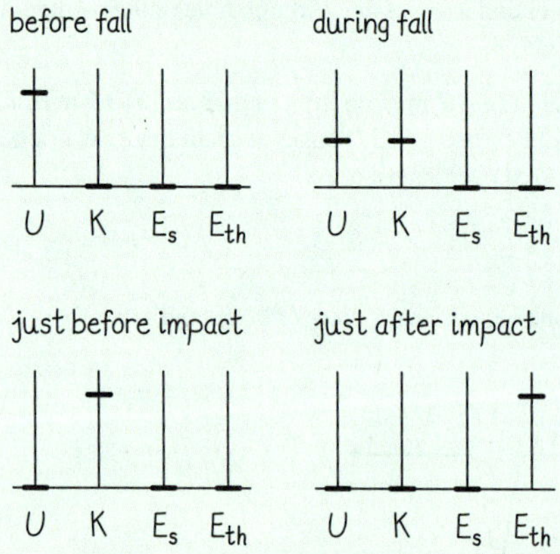

(*b*) Because conversion of coherent energy (kinetic, potential) into incoherent energy (thermal) is irreversible. If the men try to put Humpty Dumpty together, they constitute source energy. Although this can raise his pieces up to gain (coherent) potential energy, it cannot reverse the irreversible conversion of coherent kinetic energy to incoherent thermal energy. No matter how much source energy the men put in, Humpty Dumpty cannot be put back together.

(*c*)

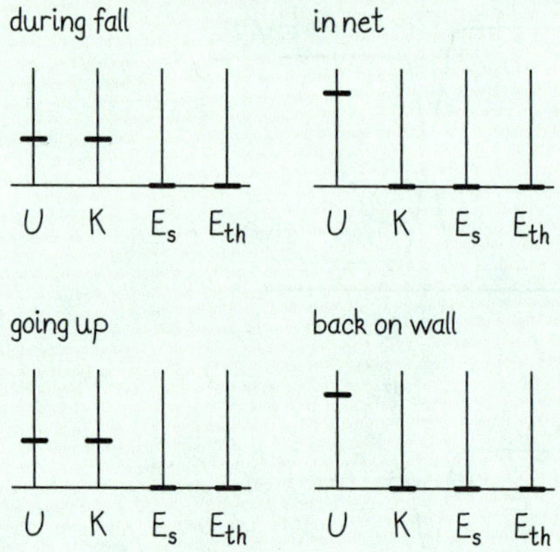

73. No, because some system coherent energy (kinetic) is converted to incoherent energy (mainly sound, small amount thermal energy).

75. 0.092 candy bars

77. Not impossible. The steam engine converts thermal energy (incoherent) to kinetic energy (coherent): Thermal energy causes liquid water to vaporize and expand, and the expanded volume moves pistons.

79. 0.0756 J

81. $a = 0.38\ \text{m/s}^2$ in the direction of the bicycle's initial motion

83. $\vec{v}_{1-\text{kg,f}} = \left(-\frac{2v}{3} - \sqrt{\frac{7}{9}v^2 + \frac{E}{2m}}\right)\hat{\imath}$,

$\vec{v}_{2-\text{kg,f}} = \left(+\frac{v}{3} - \sqrt{\frac{7}{9}v^2 + \frac{E}{2m}}\right)\hat{\imath}$, where $m = 1.00$ kg, $\hat{\imath}$ points to the right

Chapter 8

1. Neither; vector sum of forces exerted on truck = vector sum of forces exerted on cycle = 0

3. 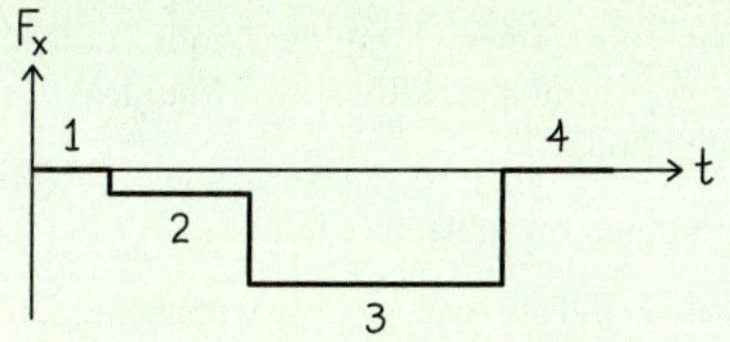

5. Object inertia is constant, which means change in momentum came from change in velocity, but knowing change in velocity does not tell you values of initial and final velocities; both are needed in order to determine change in kinetic energy.

7. (*a*) Magnitudes equal (*b*) Magnitudes equal (*c*) Magnitudes equal

9. (*a*)–(*f*) can all exert force.

11. (*a*) No. The force exerted by the pitcher on the ball results from contact between the pitcher's hand and the ball; once the ball leaves his hand, the pitcher no longer exerts force on it. (*b*) Drag force is exerted by the air on the ball, gravitational force is exerted by Earth on the ball.

13. No; at the top of the bounce, the cord has stopped exerting upward force but Earth's downward gravitational force is still exerted. The baby was moving upward, and gravitational force is changing the velocity's direction to downward. (The instant of zero velocity is the instant at which the velocity's direction changes from upward to downward.)

15. Because the vector sum of the forces exerted on the refrigerator is not zero. A force opposes your pushing force, probably frictional force exerted by the floor or, if the refrigerator back is against the wall, contact force exerted by the wall.

17. Downward contact force exerted by you on scale and upward contact force exerted by scale on you

19. $\vec{F}_{\text{by floor on you}}$; magnitude decreases

21. 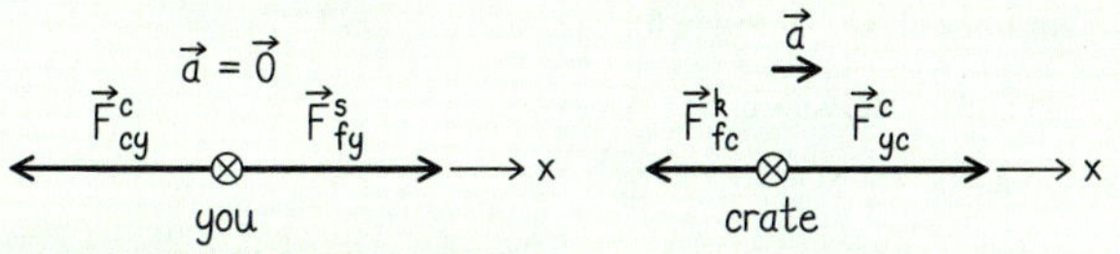

The crate moves because the magnitude of frictional force exerted by the floor on the crate is smaller than the magnitude of the contact force exerted by you on the crate. You do not move because the magnitude of the frictional force exerted by the floor on you is equal to the magnitude of the contact force exerted by the crate on you. (If you try to exert a force exceeding the available friction between your feet and the floor, your feet will slip.)

23. (*a*) 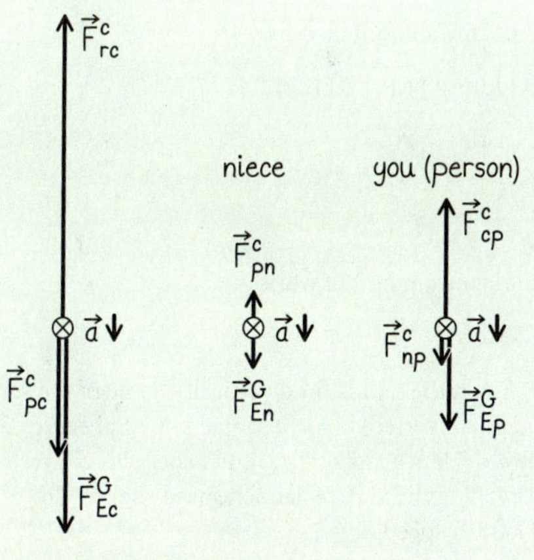

(*b*) $\vec{F}^{G}_{En} = 2.0 \times 10^2$ N downward, $\vec{F}^{c}_{pn} = 1.8 \times 10^2$ N upward, $\vec{F}^{G}_{Ep} = 4.9 \times 10^2$ N downward, $\vec{F}^{c}_{np} = 1.8 \times 10^2$ N downward, $\vec{F}^{c}_{cp} = 6.2 \times 10^2$ N upward, $\vec{F}^{G}_{Ec} = 9.8 \times 10^2$ N downward, $\vec{F}^{c}_{pc} = 6.2 \times 10^2$ N downward, $\vec{F}^{c}_{rc} = 1.5 \times 10^3$ N upward. Interaction pairs: $\vec{F}^{c}_{pn} - \vec{F}^{c}_{np}, \vec{F}^{c}_{cp} - \vec{F}^{c}_{pc}$ Gravitational force magnitudes given by mg. Interaction pairs are equal in magnitude, opposite in direction. Vector sum of forces exerted on each object must equal object's inertia times system acceleration (1.0 m/s^2 downward).

25. No; the tension in the upper portion is greater than the tension in the lower portion because the upward tensile force exerted by the upper portion on the lower portion must counteract the downward gravitational force exerted on the lower portion.

27. Forces equal in magnitude

29. 5.30×10^{17} m/s^2 in electron's initial direction of motion

31. Yes. Knowing the history of all the forces exerted on an object allows you to obtain the object's acceleration history and therefore the history of its velocity changes. Coupling this history with the known present position and velocity, you can work backwards to obtain the position and velocity at all previous instants.

33. (*a*) $\sum F_x(t) = \alpha - \beta t$, where $\alpha = 1.5 \times 10^3$ N and $\beta = 6.0 \times 10^3$ N/s (*b*) $\sum F_x > 0$ at $t < 0.25$ s, $\sum F_x < 0$ at $t > 0.25$ s, $\sum F_x = 0$ at $t = 0.25$ s

35. 59 m

37. (*a*) 9.8 N (*b*) 9.8 N

39. (*a*) 1500 N (*b*) 750 N

41. (*a*) 5.18×10^3 N (*b*) 3.2×10^2 N

43. (*a*) Tension equal to magnitude of gravitational force exerted by Earth on hanging block (*b*) Tension less than magnitude of gravitational force exerted on hanging block

45. (*a*) 4.9 m/s^2 to the right (*b*) 8.2 m/s^2 to the right

47. $a = b < d < c$

49. $m_W : m_M : m_P = \frac{1}{2} : 3 : \frac{3}{2}$

51. (*a*) 1.8×10^3 N/m (*b*) 0.41 m

53. $k_{\text{combination}} = k_1k_2(k_1 + k_2)$, therefore smaller than k_1

55. 60 mm

57. $\vec{a} = \dfrac{dk - gm}{3m}$ downward

59. (*a*) 5.4×10^2 N/m (*b*) 2.7 kg (*c*) 2.1 m/s^2 downward

63. (*a*) In segment attached to ceiling (*b*) In segment attached to tassel

65. (*a*) 4.2×10^4 N · s forward (*b*) 6.9×10^2 N forward

67. (*a*) 2.33 m/s (*b*) 381 N

69. (*a*) 0.22 N · s upward (*b*) 9.0 ms (*c*) 24 N (*d*) 6.1 N

71. (*a*) 0.45 N · s (*b*) 1.5×10^2 N (*c*) 2.3×10^2 N (*d*) 1.7 m/s in the direction of the serve

73. (*a*) 0.70 m/s^2 in direction of push (*b*) 1.4 m/s^2 in direction of push (*c*) 0.20 m/s^2 in direction of push

75. (*a*) $F/3m$ (*b*) $F/3$ to the right (*c*) $F/3$ to the left (*d*) (*a*) remains $F/3m$, (*b*) changes to $2F/3$ to the right, (*c*) changes to $2F/3$ to the left.

77. (*a*) Zero center-of-mass acceleration (*b*) $\sum \vec{F}_{\text{car}} = 1.2 \times 10^3$ N in direction car faces, $\sum \vec{F}_{\text{truck}} = 1.2 \times 10^3$ N in direction truck faces (*c*) 0.80 m/s^2 in direction truck faces

79. (*a*) 5.0 m/s^2 in direction of 50 N force (*b*) 18 m/s in direction away from 4.0-kg block

81. As you accelerate the child upward, the magnitude of the upward force you exert on her is greater than the magnitude F^G_{Ec} of the gravitational force exerted by Earth on her. This means that the magnitude of the downward force she exerts on you is also greater than F^G_{Ec}r. Hence, as you accelerate her upward, the scale reading increases for an instant or two. Once she is on your shoulders, however, the scale reading is the same as when the two of you stood side by side.

83. (*a*) $\vec{F}/3000$ kg toward the winch (*b*) 4.0×10^3 N toward the winch (*c*) 2.4×10^3 N toward the winch (which is now in front of trailer)

85. (*a*) 2.7×10^3 N forward (*b*) 3.0×10^3 N toward the tractor

87. (*a*) 0.25 m/s² to the right (*b*) $\vec{a}_{10\text{ kg red}} = 1.0$ m/s² in direction of your push, $\vec{a}_{20\text{ kg}} = \vec{a}_{10\text{ kg blue}} = \vec{0}$ (*c*) $\Sigma\vec{F}_{10\text{ kg red}} = 4.0$ N in direction of your push, $\Sigma\vec{F}_{20\text{ kg}} = 4.0$ N in direction of your push, $\Sigma\vec{F}_{10\text{ kg blue}} = 2.0$ N in direction of your push

89. For a car to stop from a given speed requires a fixed momentum change and therefore a fixed impulse. If we approximate the force magnitude as being constant in time, we can write $F = \Delta p/\Delta t$. If we allow a collision to occur over a greater distance (and therefore a longer time interval) the force magnitude at any given instant is smaller than the force magnitude when the car must stop in a shorter distance. The crumple zone allows more of the car to be destroyed, but it slows the passengers down over a greater distance, thereby exerting smaller-magnitude forces on them.

91. (*a*) 3.3 kg (*b*) The greatest tensile force is exerted when the elevator accelerates upward, which means when the elevator is either moving upward and increasing its speed or moving downward and decreasing its speed.

93. (*a*) 0.33 m/s² in direction of your push (*b*) $\vec{a}_{10\text{ kg}} = 1.0$ m/s² in direction of your push, $\vec{a}_{20\text{ kg}} = \vec{0}$ (*c*) 0.33 m/s² in direction of your push

95. The heavy pulley is attached to the beam, the light pulley is attached to the load. Run the rope twice around each pulley. Pull on the rope with force $\frac{9}{32}(m_\ell + m_p)g$.

97. There are at least two possibilities: (1) Use your arm strength to accelerate yourself up the free end of the rope at greater than 1.1 m/s². The tension in the rope will lift your friend off the ground. (2) Tie yourself to the same side of the rope as your friend, and pull on the other (free) end of the rope, lifting both of you with your amazing arm strength and the mechanical advantage of two rope segments to exert tension forces on your combined inertia.

99. The acceleration increases even though the force exerted on the rocket remains constant. In this case $\vec{a} = \vec{F}_{\text{thrust}}/m_{\text{rocket}}$, but the inertia is the inertia of everything attached to the rocket, including payload and fuel. Because the fuel is being expelled, the inertia is decreasing. This makes the effect of the constant force (the acceleration) increase.

Chapter 9

1. No

3. When you drop the brick from the greater height, the force of gravity is exerted on the brick over a greater distance, thus doing more work on the brick. When more work is done on the brick, it has more kinetic energy when it hits your foot and thus hurts more.

5. Initially, your hand exerts an upward force on the ball. The force displacement is nonzero because the point of application of the force is at the ball and therefore moves. Hence this force does work on the ball. Once you release the ball, the only force exerted on it is the gravitational force. The point of application is again at the ball, which is moving; thus the force displacement is nonzero, and the gravitational force does work on the ball as it rises. At the top of its path the ball reverses its motion and the gravitational force again does work on it because again the force displacement is nonzero. Finally, the laundry exerts an upward force on the ball as the ball moves downward; this force does work on the ball because again the force displacement is nonzero.

7. No. You push down on the floor, but the floor doesn't move, and so the force displacement is zero; you do no work on the floor. (You rise because your torso and hips push down on your legs, and your leg muscles push up on your torso and hips, lifting them. Your legs do positive work on your upper body.)

9. Both observers are right in their own reference frames.

11. No, work done on a system could also change its potential energy.

13. (*c*) The block alone should not be used as the system because friction occurs at the block-incline interface and it is not possible to know how much thermal energy produced by friction goes into the block (i.e., into the system) and how much goes into the incline (i.e., out of the system).

15. You push a block up an incline, with the block and incline part of a system that also includes Earth (but not you). The block increases in speed as you push (positive ΔK and positive ΔU), and some energy is lost to friction (positive ΔE_{th}). All these changes constitute work you do on the system (positive W).

17. The downward trip takes longer because the ball's initial kinetic energy is converted to other forms, making the downward speed lower than the upward speed. System 1—ball: Gravity does negative work as the ball rises but does an equal amount of positive work as the ball falls. The air does negative work on the ball both as it rises and as it falls, decreasing the system's energy. System 2—ball, Earth: As the ball rises, kinetic energy is converted to gravitational potential energy, and as the ball falls that potential energy is converted to kinetic energy. The air does negative work on the ball, making the system's final energy lower than its initial energy. System 3—ball, Earth, air: The same kinetic-potential-kinetic interconversion as in system 2, plus collisions between the ball and molecules in the air cause the molecules and ball to heat up, converting some mechanical energy to thermal energy.

19. No, the work magnitudes are the same, but the work done is positive for one ball and negative for the other.

21. The time interval doubles.

23. (*a*) 8.6×10^2 N (*b*) 2.4 m/s

27. (*a*) Yes (*b*) Gravitational force, tensile force exerted by rope, resistive force exerted by water , normal force exerted by bay floor

29. 13 J

31. (*a*) 3.1×10^2 N (*b*) 6.2×10^2 N (*c*) $(+9.2 \times 10^2\text{ N})\hat{\imath}$ where $\hat{\imath}$ points up (*d*) 1.5×10^2 J (*e*) 31 J (*f*) 1.5×10^2 J (*g*) 0 (*h*) -1.2×10^2 J

33. (*a*) 2.5×10^4 N (*b*) -1.3×10^4 J (*c*) -1.3×10^4 J

35. (*a*) 0.30 J (*b*) 75 mm (*c*) 0.15 J

37. They require the same amount of work.

39. (*a*) 2.0 J (*b*) 2.0 J (*c*) 1.0 J (*d*) 1.0 J (*e*) 1.0 J

41. 3 snowballs

43. $\dfrac{1}{2d}\left(\dfrac{mv^2}{5} - kd^2\right)$

45. They require the same amount of work.

47. 54 J

49. (*a*) 5.5 m/s (*b*) Yes, if the dart is fired vertically, some of the spring potential energy is converted to gravitational potential energy as the dart moves upward. Hence, not all the initial energy is converted to kinetic energy, making the vertical launch speed slightly slower than the horizontal launch speed.

51.

	Compression distance				
	0	0.050 m	0.10 m	0.15 m	0.20 m
K (J)	0.59	2.9	4.0	3.8	2.3
U^G (J)	0	−2.9	−5.9	−8.8	−12
U (J)	0	0.63	2.5	5.6	10

53. 6.1 J

55. (*a*)

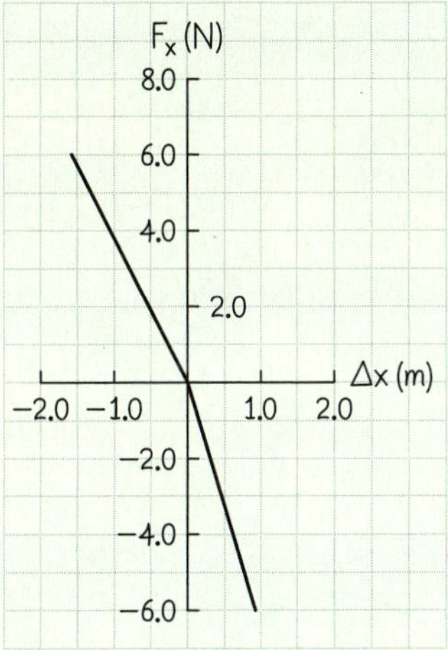

(*b*) Moves 0.77 m if pushed left, 0.63 m if pushed right (*c*) 1.2 J

57. 1.3×10^2 W

59. Because the zigzag path is spread out over a greater distance, the climber expends the same quantity of energy over a greater time interval, for a lower average power rating.

61. No. The work increases with time.

63. (*a*) 0.63 J (*b*) 1.3 W

65. (*a*) 9.0 W from the 3.0-N force, 6.0 W from the 2.0-N force (*b*) 3.0 W (*c*) Yes. The box is accelerating because the vector sum of the forces exerted on it is nonzero. Because power is equal to the product of force and speed, if the box moves at a higher speed, then the power from the same forces will increase in magnitude.

67. mgh

69. (*a*) If the initial velocity of the cart is in positive x direction, $\vec{F}_{avg} = -1.0 \times 10^3\ \text{N}\ \hat{\imath}$ (*b*) Zero, because the point of application does not move (*c*) $\Delta K_{cm} = -1.0 \times 10^2$ J

71. (*a*) 1.9×10^3 N (*b*) 1.2×10^{-3} candy bars

73. The block is moving at constant speed.

75. (*a*) With no dissipation, it doesn't matter which way you roll the ball. (*b*) With energy dissipation, you want to roll the ball down hill A, so that it travels a shorter distance. The shorter the path, the less energy dissipated, so the ball has a better chance of having sufficient mechanical energy to get over hill B.

77. Your center of mass must be 0.23 m above the floor. This is not practical.

79. 20 ± 10 N

Chapter 10

1. Parabolic, starting tangent to the vertical axis and curving toward the horizontal axis

3. 0.214 m

5. Ignoring air resistance, the acceleration is downward. Not ignoring air resistance, the acceleration is mostly down and a little bit in the direction opposite the velocity.

7. (*a*) No (*b*) Yes

9. (*a*) Acceleration to right as car speed increases (*b*) Very small downward acceleration but almost constant speed (*c*) Downward acceleration with small component to the left as car slows slightly (*d*) Very small acceleration downward and left, perpendicular to velocity (*e*) Acceleration upward and left, opposite velocity as car slows (*f*) Acceleration upward and left, opposite velocity as car stops

11. No

13. Five forces are exerted:

	Parallel to roof ridge	Normal to roof surface	Tangential to roof surface
Gravitational force by Earth, $\vec{F}^G_{Ep}$		X	X
Normal force by roof, $\vec{F}^n_{roof,p}$		X	
Tensile force by left rope, $\vec{F}^c_{left,p}$	X		X
Tensile force by right rope, $\vec{F}^c_{right,p}$	X	X	X
Force of static friction by roof, $\vec{F}^s_{rp}$	X		X

15. Static

17. (*a*) Force of static friction (*b*) The magnitude is equal to the magnitude of the gravitational force Earth exerts on the eraser. (*c*) No, unless you push with insufficient force to hold the eraser up at all. (*d*) It decreases to zero.

19. (*a*) pallet crate

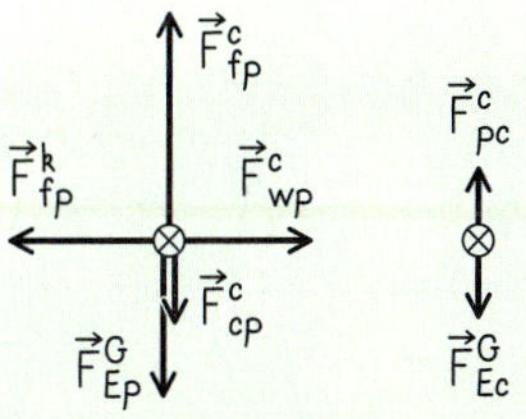

(*b*) pallet crate

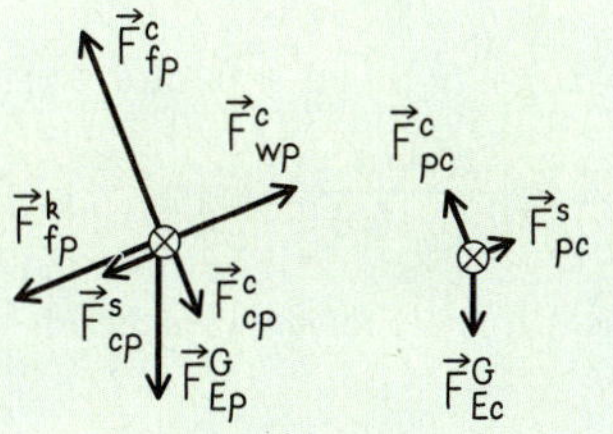

21. The normal force does positive work on the saw as the board and saw are lifted, no work as they are transported horizontally, and negative work as they are lowered onto the sawhorses; the algebraic sum of these work values is zero. The force of static friction does no work on the saw as the board and saw are lifted, positive work as their speed increases from zero to carrying speed, negative work as their speed decreases from carrying speed to zero at the sawhorses, and no work as they are lowered onto the horses; the algebraic sum of these work values is zero.

23. (*a*) 28° (*b*) 0.54

25. (*a*) They have the same speed at the bottom, but the child on the steeper slide arrives first. (*b*) The child on the steeper slide moves faster.

27. (*a*) $1.0\hat{\imath} + 4.0\hat{\jmath}$ (*b*) 4.1 units

29. (*a*) (30, −53°) (*b*) (18, −24)

31. 1.7 h

33. $(A, \omega t)$

35. (*a*) 0.93 km (*b*) 1.0 m/s at 31° north of east (*c*) 1.4 m/s

37. (*a*) One (*b*) Two (clockwise and counterclockwise equilateral triangles) (*c*) Three (*d*) N-1 distinct patterns for N arrows

39. Path (*a*) is the best representation. Path (*b*) is a poor representation because it ends up pointing directly downward, indicating no horizontal component to the velocity; as long as it moves, the cantaloupe always has a horizontal velocity component. Path (*c*) has two big issues: no vertical acceleration at first, then abrupt acceleration at the upper right corner.

41. 0.116 m

43. (*a*) 0.40 s (*b*) 1.2 m/s

45. (*a*) Never (*b*) Never (*c*) $t = 0.70$ s

47. A position that is more than half the range

49.

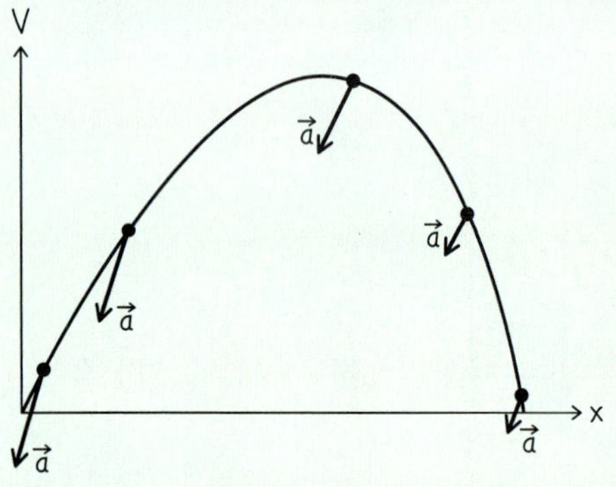

51. 6.0 m/s

53. (*a*) 1.5 s (*b*) 1.4 m (*c*) $v_{x,f} = 13$ m/s, $v_{y,f} = -7.6$ m/s (*d*) Yes

55. 15 m/s

57. (*a*) $\vec{a} = (-g\sin\phi)\hat{\jmath}$ (*b*) $\vec{v}(t) = (v_i\cos\theta)\hat{\imath} + (v_i\sin\theta - gt\sin\phi)\hat{\jmath}$ (*c*) $\Delta y = \dfrac{v_i^2\sin^2\theta}{2g\sin\phi}$ (*d*) $\Delta x = \dfrac{2v_i^2\sin\theta\cos\theta}{g\sin\phi}$

59. Assuming elastic collisions, (*a*) $v/16$ (*b*) $mv/16$ in the original direction of motion

61. (*a*) $v_1 = 0.28$ m/s, $v_2 = 0.44$ m/s (*b*) No

63. (*a*) $\vec{v} = 4.0$ m/s at $\theta = 44°$ (*b*) 69 mm

65. $-7.2\ \text{m}^2$

67. (*a*) 23° (*b*) 35 units^2

69. (*a*) 2.0 J (*b*) 79°

71. (*a*) 2.5 m/s (*b*) 49 mm

73. (*a*) 13 m/s (*b*) 34

77. (*a*) 1.0 m/s (*b*) 4.9 kJ (*c*) 2.0 m/s (*d*) 4.9 kJ

79. Pulling

81. $\mu_s = 0.40$, $\mu_k = 0.20$

83. (*a*) 4.3×10^2 N (*b*) 43 kJ

85. (*a*) 11 N (*b*) 13 N

87. (*a*) 3.4 s (*b*) 11 s (*c*) 1.5×10^2 m

89. 1.0 m

91. (*a*) 0.12 m (*b*) 0.15 m

93. (*a*) 14 m/s (*b*) 13 m/s (*c*) 13 m

95. 22 kW

97. 53 m/s

99.

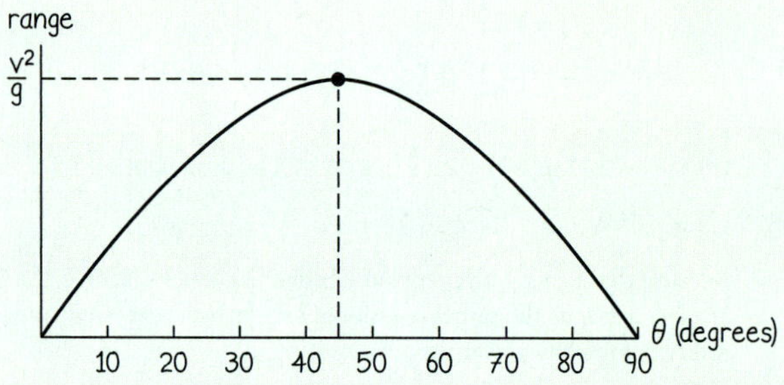

101. (*a*) 8.0×10^2 m (*b*) $(-20\ \text{m/s})\hat{\jmath}$ (*c*) -4.0×10^2 m

103. (*a*) $(1.49\ \text{N})\,\hat{\imath} + (5.33 \times 10^{-3}\ \text{N})\,\hat{\jmath}$ (*b*) 55.5 J

105. 75°

107. In order for a 100-kg pair to reach the top at a maximum speed of 5.0 m/s, the counterweight must have an inertia of 6.6×10^1 kg. For a 200-kg pair, the counterweight inertia must be 1.3×10^2 kg. The plan won't work. Either the 200-kg pair will not be accelerated or the 100-kg pair will be accelerated to a speed higher than 5.0 m/s.

109. (*a*) $y(x) = (\tan\theta)x - \dfrac{g}{2v^2\cos^2\theta}x^2$ (*b*) 23 m/s (*c*) 70 N

111. 51 mm

Chapter 11

1. Innermost track

3. The distance around the curved track is shorter in the inner lane, meaning the distance the passing car has to travel in order to pass is shorter in the inner lane than it would be in an outer lane.

5.

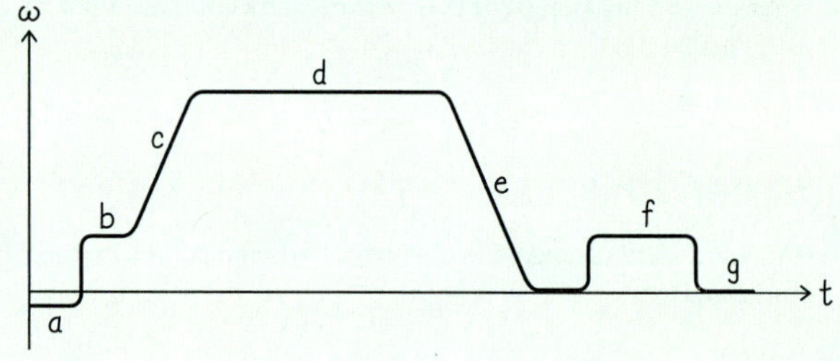

7. $p = 2, q = -1$

9. 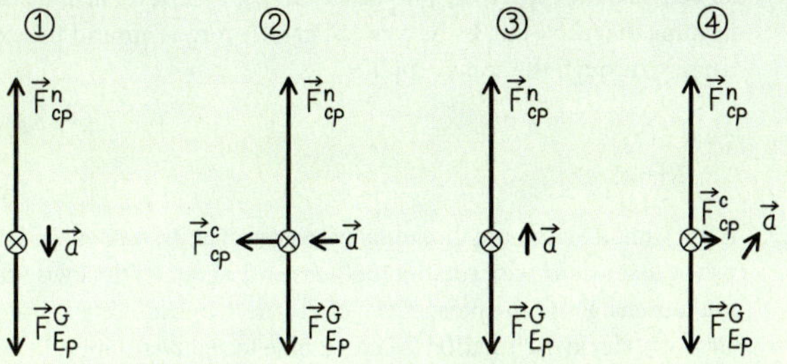

11. As the spinner rotates, the water and lettuce, because of their inertia, tend to move in a straight line tangent to the spinner circumference. Because it cannot fit through the holes in the spinner wall, the lettuce can't move in a straight line. The contact force exerted on it by the wall keeps it inside. Water drops can pass through the holes and do so, separating from the lettuce and leaving it dry. Initially, the drops might be held to the lettuce by cohesive forces, but as the spinner speeds up, these forces are insufficient to keep the drops moving in a circle, and they spin out of the spinner.

13. Ignoring friction between the car and track, the car climbs up the right wall as it enters the left turn. Because the student's body and the metal chunk climb this wall by the same amount as the car, the chunk stays between his knees, just as it was before the ride began.

15. (*a*)

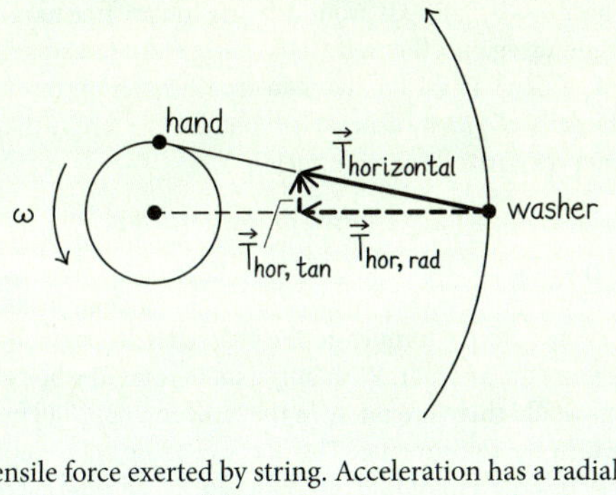

(*b*) Tensile force exerted by string. Acceleration has a radial and a tangential component. (*c*) Ignoring air resistance: hand stays at circle center; tensile force is directed toward circle center and acceleration has no tangential component.

17. Because the body's rotational inertia is greater in the layout position than in the tucked position. The radius of the circular path the head and feet travel during the flip is larger in the layout position than in the tucked position. Because the body remains airborne for roughly the same time interval in either position, the gymnast must have much greater kinetic energy in the layout position to complete the backflip.

19. (*a*) No, the inertia of the bowling ball is so much greater than that of the baseball that even placing the rotation axis on the outer surface of the baseball would not make it as difficult to spin as the bowling ball. (*b*) Yes. You could choose to revolve the baseball around an axis that passes no closer than, say, 5 m to the baseball, while choosing an axis passing just centimeters from the edge of the bowling ball. The rotational inertias are $I_{\text{bowl}} = m_{\text{bowl}} r_{\text{bowl}}^2$ and $I_{\text{base}} = m_{\text{base}} r_{\text{base}}^2$, where r is distance from either ball to the axis of revolution. Choose an arbitrary location for this axis and place the two balls at distances r_{bowl} and $r_{\text{base}} \gg r_{\text{bowl}}$ from the axis. Once the inequality $r_{\text{base}} \gg r_{\text{bowl}}$ is sufficiently large to make the difference between m_{bowl} and m_{base} insignificant, $I_{\text{base}} > I_{\text{bowl}}$.

21. (*a*) Rotational inertia decreases. (*b*) Carousel rotational speed increases.

23. $0.10\ \text{s}^{-1}$, $1.5 \times 10^{-4}\ \text{s}^{-1}$

25. $8.7 \times 10^{-3}\ \text{s}^{-2}$

27. Figure P11.27(*b*)

29. (*a*) $3mg \sin\theta$ (*b*) $3mg$

31. (*a*) $5.95 \times 10^{-3}\ \text{m/s}^2$ (*b*) 3.55×10^{22} N toward the center of mass of the Earth-sun system, which is essentially the center of the sun.

33. $19.6\ \text{m/s}^2$

35. (*a*) $58\ \text{s}^{-1}$ (*b*) 2.9×10^2 (*c*) 19 m/s (*d*) 96 m

37. (*a*) $\sqrt{2g(h-d)}$ (*b*) $mg\left(1 + \dfrac{2(h-d)}{R}\right)$ (*c*) $\sqrt{2g(h-d-R)}$ (*d*) $mg\left(\dfrac{2(h-d-R)}{R}\right)$ (*e*) $g\left(\dfrac{2(h-d-R)}{R}\right)$

39. (*a*) $18\ \text{m/s}^2$ (*b*) 0 (*c*) The vertical component of the normal force exerted by the cone on the ball (*d*) 0.92 m

41. 31 J

43. (*a*) $12\ \text{kg}\cdot\text{m}^2/\text{s}$ (*b*) $4.0\ \text{kg}\cdot\text{m}^2/\text{s}$

45. In order to continue moving in a circle at constant speed along with the pail, the water must have centripetal acceleration. This acceleration must be due to some force directed toward the center of the circle. When you whirl the pail rapidly, the forces exerted on the water are the force of gravity and a large contact force exerted by the bottom of the pail. When you whirl the pail at just the right speed, the gravitational force alone is sufficient to keep the water from spilling out. If you whirl too slowly, the acceleration due to gravity is larger than the necessary centripetal acceleration and the water spills out.

47. (*a*) $\dfrac{4v_i}{5\ell}$ (*b*) $\left(-\dfrac{3v}{5}\right)\hat{\imath}$ where $\hat{\imath}$ points in the direction of $\vec{v}_i$

49. $3.0\ \text{s}^{-1}$

51. $\omega_{\vartheta,i}/2$

53. $2mr^2 \sin^2\theta$

55. $\frac{5}{3}mR^2$

57. $0.16\ \text{s}^{-1}$

59. (*a*) $\frac{1}{2}mR^2$ (*b*) $\frac{1}{12}ma^2$

61. The day would lengthen.

63. 20 to 35 $\text{kg}\cdot\text{m}^2$, depending on your inertia

65. $2.0 \times 10^2\ \text{s}^{-1}$

67. $\frac{13}{8}mR_{\text{outer}}^2$

69. $0.28\ \text{kg}\cdot\text{m}^2$

71. 8.2×10^{-2} J

73. (*a*) $\dfrac{2m\ell^2}{3}$ (*b*) $\dfrac{m\ell^2}{6}$

75. $0.25\ \text{kg}\cdot\text{m}^2$

77. (*a*) 0.535° (*b*) 0.517°

79. The liquid inside the egg continues to rotate once you stop the egg. When stopped and released, viscous forces between the liquid and shell soon cause the shell to move along with the liquid, causing the entire egg to spin. In a hard-boiled egg, there is no liquid to continue rotating once you stop the egg. When you stop the outside of the hard-boiled egg, you stop everything.

81. (*a*) No work is done. (*b*) At the lowest point

83. (*a*) Force independent of r (*b*) Force proportional to $1/r^2$ (*c*) Force proportional to r

85. $\dfrac{6m_b v_b}{(3m_d + 4m_b)\ell_d}$

87. The acceleration due to gravity at her head is about 6.5 m/s^2. To avoid lightheadedness, you figure that the acceleration due to gravity at her head must be within 5% of the value at her feet. To accomplish this, the radius of the cylinder must be no less than 40 m.

89. You should maintain a constant tension of at least 74 N in the string while you unwind the entire string.

91. $\omega(x) = \dfrac{\sqrt{\left(\frac{3}{4}v\right)^2 - \frac{3}{2}g\left(\sqrt{d^2 - 4dx - 4x^2} - d\right)}}{d}$

Chapter 12

1. You can exert a greater torque by exerting a greater force tangential to the lid. The coefficient of static friction between the rubber and the lid is likely to be greater than the coefficient of static friction between your bare hand and the lid.

3. Torque is a better tightening specification because giving the specification in terms of the force exerted on the wrench you use does not provide a unique specification for how tight you fasten the bolts. You could use a wrench of any length, and the force necessary to get the correct tightness would be different for each different wrench length.

5. *c* and *e*

7. Option *a*. The baton's center of mass is closer to the larger sphere, making the lever arm distance between your hand and the center of mass longer in option a than in option *b*. The longer lever arm distance gives you finer control.

9. $\tau_B < \tau_A < \tau_C < \tau_D$

11. $C_A/C_B = 1/4$

13. The stick does not rotate, which means the torques caused by the contact forces exerted on it by your two fingers cancel each other. The farther a finger is from the stick's center of mass, the greater its lever arm distance and the smaller the contact force it exerts on the stick. So as you begin sliding your fingers, any slight difference in lever arm distance causes the finger farther from the center of mass—the left finger, say—to exert a smaller contact force and so slide more easily than the right finger. Once your left finger moves far enough toward the center of the stick to make the right lever arm distance greater than the left lever arm distance, the right finger exerts the smaller contact force and so speeds up, but only until its lever arm distance is less than that of the left finger. This tradeoff continues until the fingers meet, always at the 0.5-m mark.

15. *c*

17. (*a*)

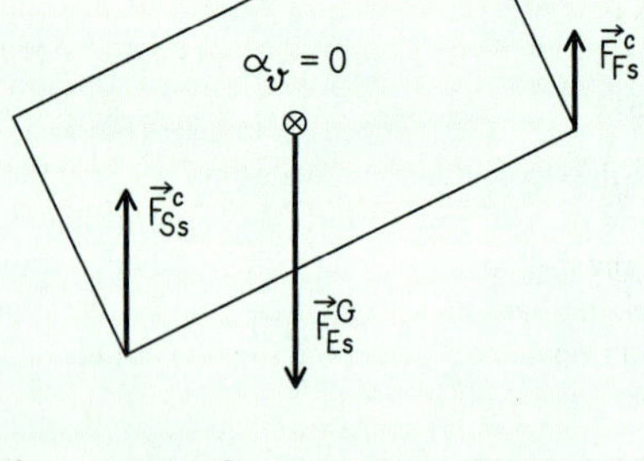

(*b*) The son carries the greater share of the load. (*c*) They would carry equal loads in the case of a sheet of plywood.

19. As the painter climbs, he moves farther from the point where the ladder contacts the carpeting. This gives him a greater lever arm distance, meaning that as he climbs he causes a greater torque around the axis running through the contact point.

21. $\tan^{-1}\left(\dfrac{1}{2\mu_s}\right)$

23. In the United States, the threading of nearly all bolts, screws, and nuts is such that a clockwise rotation tightens and a counterclockwise rotation loosens. From the perspective of the mechanic looking at his or her work, clockwise rotation is comparable to rightward motion and counterclockwise rotation is comparable to leftward motion. (Picture your hand placed on the 12 on a clock face: moving to the 1 is to the right, moving to the 11 is to the left.) Note that this clockwise-counterclockwise convention is consistent with the right-hand rule. With a nut on a bolt, for instance, the direction of the torque is the direction that the nut should move (down the body of the bolt to tighten, for example).

25. Positive *x* direction

27. 90° around the *y* axis followed by −90° around *x* axis

29. (*a*) 0.75 m from either end of the rod (*b*) 0.30 m from the heavier bucket

31. $8.2 \times 10^{-1}\ s^{-1}$

33. You fall backwards. The axis around which you are free to rotate (your toes) is right up against the wall. Your center of mass is not right up against the wall; it is near the (back-to-front) center of your body. Hence the force of gravity exerted on you causes a torque that tends to rotate you backwards about your toes.

35. $10^{-10}\ T_E$, where T_E is Earth's period of rotation, 24 h.

37. (*a*) 45 N (*b*) 30 N

39. If there are no external torques on the helicopter, its angular momentum must remain constant. With only a main rotor, the body of the helicopter would therefore rotate in the direction opposite the direction in which the rotor rotates. The purpose of the tail rotor is to exert a force on the air surrounding the craft, causing an external torque that keeps the body from rotating.

41. (*a*) 17 s^{-1} (*b*) 1.2×10^2 J (*c*) The additional energy comes from work done by the skater's muscles as she pulls her arms and weighted hands in toward her body. This force is not perpendicular to the motion because the hands and weights spiral in toward the center of her body.

43. (*a*) Stays the same (*b*) increases (*c*) increases

45. (*a*) The center of mass is a distance $\ell/3$ from the ball. (*b*) $v_f = v_i/3$ in the direction of the ball's initial motion. (*c*) $\omega_f = v/\ell$

47. (*a*) $7/17\ \omega$ clockwise (*b*) −0.42

49. The object continues to roll without slipping. Nothing changes when the coefficient of friction increases. Only the maximum possible force of static friction increases, not the actual force of static friction exerted.

51. (*a*) 3.5 m/s^2 (*b*) 4.2 N

53. $\sqrt{3}/6$

55. The two cans reach the bottom at the same instant.

57. $t_h/t_s = \sqrt{25/21}$

59. (*a*) $\frac{2}{7}g$ (*b*) $\frac{2}{5}g$

61. 1.7×10^{-1} J

63. 1.4 m

65. 0.15 MJ

67. $5.9\ s^{-2}$

69. $43\ s^{-1}$

71. (*a*) 5.0 J (*b*) 5.0 J (*c*) $7.6 \times 10^2\ s^{-1}$

73. (*a*) 3.4 m/s (*b*) $T = \dfrac{mv_i^2 r_i^2}{r^3} = 2.8$ N (*c*) 2.3×10^{-1} J

75. 54°

77. (*a*) Because $L = mrv_i$, treat the cube as a particle located at the cube's center, and insert $r = d/2$. This yields $L = mdv_i/2$. (*b*) At the instant of collision, the point of application of the contact force exerted by the lip on the cube is at the axis of rotation. The lever arm distance for this force is zero and thus this force cannot cause a torque about the axis. Hence there is no external torque on the cube and its angular momentum must be constant. (*c*) $3g/4d$ (*d*) $\sqrt{\dfrac{16gd}{3\sqrt{2}}}$

79. To change your angular momentum, there must be a torque on you. Otherwise your body continues moving in a straight line and you fall off the bike.

81. (*a*) 30 N · m (*b*) 26 N · m (*c*) 21 N · m (*d*) 15 N · m (*e*) 0 (*f*) 19 N · m

83. Writing $\vec{A} = A_x\hat{\imath} + A_y\hat{\jmath}$ and $\vec{B} = B_x\hat{\imath} + B_y\hat{\jmath}$, you can compute the vector product one component at a time, noting that for any two components along the same axis the vector product is always zero. Thus you have $\vec{A} \times \vec{B} = A_xB_y\hat{k} + A_yB_x(-\hat{k}) = (A_xB_y - A_yB_x)\hat{k}$.

85. (*a*) 20 N · m in the direction opposite the direction of motion (*b*) 68 N · m in the direction of motion

87. (*a*) 3.0 s (*b*) 4.9 rev

89. 0.37 N · m

91. $\hat{\jmath}$

93. (*a*) The engine is connected to the rear wheels, and so the force that accelerates the car forward is exerted at the bottom of the rear wheels. Because the line of action of this force goes below the center of mass of the car, the force causes a torque on the car that tends to lift the front wheels off the road. (*b*) With front-wheel drive, the force that accelerates the car forward is exerted at the bottom of the front wheels. The line of action of this force also goes below the center of mass of the car causing a torque on the car, but now the rear wheels are pushed into the road.

95. (*a*) 7.8×10^2 N (*b*) 6.0×10^2 N (*c*) 8.6×10^2 N and 6.6×10^2 N

97. $1 \times 10^4\ s^{-1}$

99. The torque is the gravitational force exerted on the cyclist times the lever arm distance, which is the length of the metal rod attaching each pedal to the bicycle. For a typical human ($m = 75$ kg) and bicycle (lever arm distance 0.3 m), this yields a torque of 10^2 N · m.

101. (*a*) $5.3\ m/s^2$ (*b*) 0.27

103. 4.0 m

105. (*a*) 3.1×10^2 N (*b*) 5.5×10^2 N

107. (*a*) $2.5\ m/s^2$ (*b*) $9.1\ s^{-1}$ (*c*) $9.1\ s^{-1}$ (*d*) 22 N (*e*) 60 W

109. The yo-yo accelerates downward, and the magnitude of the acceleration is $\dfrac{g}{1 + a/2b}$.

Chapter 13

1. The acceleration due to gravity increases linearly with radius.

3. 18 km

5. 6 : 1

7. $\dfrac{m_1}{m_2} = 1$

9. Torque can be interpreted as the second time derivative of the same area whose first derivative represents angular momentum.

11. (*a*) Yes, when you jump the scale shows a higher number at first. (*b*) No, the magnitude of the gravitational force exerted by Earth on you has not changed.

13. (*a*) $9.8\ m/s^2$ downward (*b*) $1.6\ m/s^2$ downward (*c*) Conclusion would not change.

15. The airplane moves downward at 2*g*. During the time interval in which this motion takes place, the person is in free fall, accelerating downward at *g*. This means that, relative to the plane, he is accelerating *upward* at *g*! This relative motion of plane and person is exactly like the person falling onto his head from an upside-down position on solid ground.

17. At least two possibilities to obtain a second scale reading: (1) Hold the tube horizontally and mark the unstretched (0 g) position, or (2) Add a second identical bob to find the 2 g position.

19. (*a*) The milk climbs the sides of the bowl, and the milk surface becomes concave. (*b*) Either a massive hemisphere placed near the milk or the combination of a toroid around the bowl and a massive object beneath the bowl.

21. 6.7×10^{-15} N

23. $\dfrac{4}{9}$

25. $3 \times 10^{11}g$

27. 3.2 km, 32 km, 3.5×10^2 km

29. 1×10^1 h

30. (*a*) Force exerted by Sun (*b*) $F^G_{SE}/F^G_{ME} = 1.8 \times 10^2$

31. 1.05×10^{18} kg

33. $Gm_{test}^2\sqrt{\left(\dfrac{1}{d^2} - \dfrac{2d}{(d^2 + \ell^2)^{3/2}}\right)^2 + \left(\dfrac{2\ell}{(d^2 + \ell^2)^{3/2}}\right)^2}$

35. $\dfrac{Gm_E r}{R_E^3}$

37. No. A 70-kg person can jump high enough to bring his center of mass to a height of 1.0 m to 1.5 m. That means the legs can exert forces capable of increasing the gravitational potential energy by about 10^3 J On the surface of Toro, this person's gravitational potential energy is -1.9×10^3 J, meaning he is bound to Toro by more energy than he can deliver in a jump.

39. Closer to object 1; specifically, a distance $(\sqrt{2} - 1)d$ from object 1 and a distance $(2 - \sqrt{2})d$ from object 2

41. (*a*) $\dfrac{Cm_E m_m}{2h^2}$ (*b*) $\sqrt{\dfrac{Cm_E}{h^2}}$

43. 9.4×10^2 km

45. $2.3 \times 10^{30}\ N \cdot m^2$

47. (*a*) $\vec{0}$ (*b*) -1.00×10^{-12} J/g (*c*) -5.0×10^{-13} J

49. Over a larger range

51. Elastic

53. 19 km/s

55. Being in very low orbit means that the radial distance from the satellite to the center of the moon is approximately the moon radius R_{moon}. The projectile reaches a distance $2R_{\text{moon}}$ from the moon's center, which is a height R_{moon} above the moon surface.

57. $v_{\text{comet}}/v_{\text{Mercury}} = \sqrt{2}$

59. $\sqrt{2C/a}$

61. 7.5 km/s

63. (*a*) $2.2 \times 10^{-7}\ \text{s}^{-1}$ (*b*) 89 km/s

67. To the right in the figure

69. $\dfrac{Gm_{\text{ring}}m_{\text{obj}}s}{(R_{\text{ring}}^2 + s^2)^{3/2}}$

70. (*a*) $0.54\dfrac{Gm_{\text{inner}}m_{\text{obj}}}{R^2}$ (*b*) $0.83\dfrac{Gm_{\text{inner}}m_{\text{obj}}}{R^2}$ (*c*) 0

71. (*a*) $-\dfrac{2Gm_{\text{part}}m_{\text{disk}}}{R^2}\left(1 - \dfrac{y}{\sqrt{R^2 + y^2}}\right)\hat{\jmath}$

73. From a theoretical standpoint, it does not matter. However, there may be logistical considerations, such as how much atmosphere you must traverse before reaching deep space, where air resistance is negligible. With these secondary considerations, it is best to launch vertically.

75. The acceleration vector is directed towards one focus of the ellipse. The tangential component could be greater than the perpendicular component of acceleration when the satellite is crossing a semiminor axis, provided $e^2 > \frac{1}{2}$. If the eccentricity is much greater, this condition could be satisfied elsewhere in the orbit. However, it can never be satisfied when the satellite is crossing a semimajor axis.

77. For $R_{\text{planetoid}} \approx 5$ m, mass density must be $6 \times 10^9\ \text{kg/m}^3$.

79. 4.24×10^7 m above the surface of Jupiter

81. Satellite is 2.7×10^2 km above Earth's surface.

83. (*a*) $\rho_{\max} = \dfrac{3H^2}{8\pi G} = 9.6 \times 10^{-27}\ \text{kg/m}^3$ (*b*) The estimate is about the same as what we found for part (*a*). As it is, the universe seems balanced between being open and being closed. If there were no dark matter or dark energy in the universe, it would be much less dense than estimated, and we would expect it to be open.

Chapter 14

1. (*b*), (*e*), (*f*)

3. A, 33 μs after noon; B, 67 μs after noon; C, 75 μs after noon; D, 94 μs after noon.

5. (*a*) Later (*b*) Same time (*c*) Earlier

7. c_0

9. 1.4×10^2 m

11. Straight calculation shows the speed of each end larger than the speed of light. This cannot happen because the concept of a rigid object is an approximation that breaks down under such extreme conditions: The rod would bend into a spiral shape so that no portion of it moves faster than the speed of light.

13. Longer than.

15. 1.4×10^3 m

17. 2.88×10^3 s

19. 0.5 km²

21. Zero

23. Energy, mass, and inertia

25. 3.59×10^6 m

27. (*a*) Lightlike (*b*) Lightlike (*c*) Timelike (*d*) Timelike

29. $v_{\text{A}} = 0.48c_0$, $v_{\text{B}} = 0.96c_0$

31. $0.99c_0$

33. $(1 - 2.47 \times 10^{-7})c_0$

35. (*a*) 8.00 km (*b*) 6.14×10^{-5} s

37. 2.13

39. (*a*) 7.62×10^3 km (*b*) 1.27×10^4 km

41. (*a*) 3.625×10^{14} m (*b*) 8.108×10^{15} m

43. (*a*) 59.5° (*b*) Length 5.00 m, wingspan 8.00 m, opening angle 77.3°.

47. (*a*) $x = 0$ (*b*) $t = 0$ (*c*) $x = 1.77 \times 10^8$ m (*d*) $t = 0.591$ s

49. (*a*) 5.93×10^3 s (*b*) 1.43×10^{12} m (*c*) 4.70×10^3 s

51. (*a*) 11.3° (*b*) 24.6°

53. (*a*) 1.00 (no increase) (*b*) 1.64

57. $9.46 \times 10^{-20}\ \text{kg}\cdot\text{m/s}$

59. Defining the direction of motion of the 150-kg probe to be the $+x$ direction, $\vec{v}_{150\ \text{kg}} = (+0.764c_0)\,\hat{\imath}$, $\vec{v}_{250\ \text{kg}} = (-0.578c_0)\,\hat{\imath}$

61. (*a*) $\gamma_{\text{C}} > \gamma_{\text{B}} > \gamma_{\text{A}}$ (*b*) $K_{\text{C}} > K_{\text{B}} > K_{\text{A}}$ (*c*) $|\vec{v}_{\text{C}}| > |\vec{v}_{\text{B}}| > |\vec{v}_{\text{A}}|$ (*d*) $p_{\text{C}} > p_{\text{B}} > p_{\text{A}}$

63. 1.73×10^{12} J; $E_{1\ \text{kg U}}/E_{1\ \text{kg coal}} = 5.8 \times 10^4$

65. $$E_1 = \frac{m_1c_0^2}{\sqrt{1 - \dfrac{(m_1 - m_2 - m_{\text{orig}})(m_1 + m_2 - m_{\text{orig}})(m_1 - m_2 + m_{\text{orig}})(m_1 + m_2 + m_{\text{orig}})}{(m_1^2 - m_2^2 + m_{\text{orig}}^2)^2}}}$$

$$p_1 = \frac{m_1c_0\sqrt{(m_1 - m_2 - m_{\text{orig}})(m_1 + m_2 - m_{\text{orig}})(m_1 - m_2 + m_{\text{orig}})(m_1 + m_2 + m_{\text{orig}})}}{\sqrt{(m_1^2 - m_2^2 + m_{\text{orig}}^2)^2 - (m_1 - m_2 - m_{\text{orig}})(m_1 + m_2 - m_{\text{orig}}) \times (m_1 - m_2 + m_{\text{orig}})(m_1 + m_2 + m_{\text{orig}})}}$$

67. (*a*) $v = (1 - 8.98 \times 10^{-9})c_0$ (*b*) $1.40 \times 10^4\ \text{GeV}/c_0^2$ or 2.49×10^{-23} kg

69. (*a*) 3.01×10^{-10} J (*b*) 9.0×10^8 m

71. 30.1 m, 24.2° away from vertical.

73. Yes, an observer in any reference frame moving along the perpendicular bisector of a line drawn between the two events sees the events as simultaneous.

75. (*a*) $0.986c_0$ (*b*) 91.1 s

77. If Orion's initial position is corrected for light travel time, the station will have just under 45 minutes to evacuate, so no re-write is required, just some hurry. If Orion's position is not corrected for travel time, so that the ship is seen at one location but has continued to travel toward the station while the light signal is in transit, there is no hope and a rewrite is definitely in order.

79. You can complete the race in the shortest time interval (measured in the Earth reference frame) by flying at speed $c_0/\sqrt{2}$.

Chapter 15

1. Least blurry at highest and lowest wing positions because at these positions vertical motion of wings is instantaneously zero.

3.

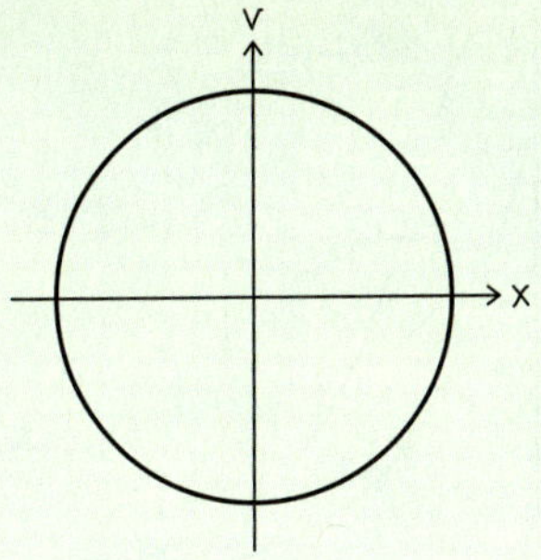

5. $0.5 < x < 3.5$

7. 5 s

9. Motion is periodic motion because it repeats itself over time but is not simple harmonic motion because its position and velocity cannot be described by a simple sine or cosine function. As yo-yo rises and falls, not all of its potential energy is converted to translational kinetic energy; some of it becomes rotational kinetic energy.

11. 127 Hz

13. Three harmonics

15. $\frac{4}{\pi}\sum_{n=1}^{\infty}\frac{1}{2n-1}\sin\left[(2n-1)\frac{2\pi t}{T}\right]$, where T is the period of one square "oscillation"

21. $x(t) = A\sin\left(\frac{2\pi t}{T} + \phi_i\right)$

$$v_x(t) = \frac{2\pi A}{T}\cos\left(\frac{2\pi t}{T} + \phi_i\right)$$

$$a_x(t) = -\left(\frac{2\pi}{T}\right)^2 A\sin\left(\frac{2\pi t}{T} + \phi_i\right)$$

23. (*a*) Yes (*b*) $-\pi/2$

29. 0.30 J

33. 0.69

35. 1/3

37. (*a*) Increase (*b*) It decreases.

39. (*a*) Yes (*b*) No (*c*) Yes (*d*) Yes (*e*) No (*f*) No (*g*) If the cup is glued to the table, the answers do not change. If the cup is free to move, then the coffee would not fly out of the cup even if the cup flew into the air in free fall (at least until it hit the table again).

41. (*a*) 0.059 m (*b*) $2.7\ \text{s}^{-1}$ (*c*) 4.6 mJ (*d*) 2.6 N/m (*e*) 5.6 rad (*f*) $x(t) = A\sin(\omega t + \phi_i)$ where $A = 0.059$ m, $\omega = 2.7\ \text{s}^{-1}$, $\phi_i = 5.6$ rad

43. 0.062 m

45. (*a*) 300 N/m (*b*) $x(t) = A\sin(\omega t + \phi_i)$, where $A = 0.020$ m, $\omega = 71\ \text{s}^{-1}$, $\phi_i = 1.6$

47. 0.060 m

49. 0.25 m

51. Pendulum on left

53. $v = \sqrt{2g\ell(\cos\vartheta_{max} - \cos\vartheta)}$

55. (*a*) $9.11 \times 10^{-4}\ \text{kg}\cdot\text{m}^2$ (*b*) 0.766 s

57. (*a*) 0.15 rad (*b*) 0.10 m/s

59. 0.90 s

61. $\Delta T = -\frac{1}{12}\frac{m_{rod}}{m_{bob}} + \frac{11}{288}\left(\frac{m_{rod}}{m_{bob}}\right)^2$ plus higher order terms

63. ω_d increases.

65. (*b*) 4.24 Hz (*c*) 0.0800 s (*d*) 2.13 rad

67. (*a*) 25 s (*b*) Instant $t = 18$ s

69. (*a*) $5.00\ \text{s}^{-1}$ (*b*) 2.00 kg/s (*c*) $y(t) = Ae^{-tb/2m}\sin(\omega_d t + \phi_i)$ where $A = 0.100$ m, $b = 2.00$ kg/s, $m = 0.500$ kg, $\omega_d = 4.58\ \text{s}^{-1}$

71. (*a*) 0.58% (*b*) 0.69

73. (*a*) $2\sqrt{mk}$ (*b*) Damping occurs so quickly that the spring returns to equilibrium position before being fully compressed. In the car, this means the system returns quickly to normal level rather than oscillating for a long time interval; the negative aspect is that springs do not absorb road-bump shocks as well as a spring system having $b \leq b_{crit}$.

75. $x(t) = Ae^{-t/2\tau}\sin(\omega t + \phi)$ where $A = 67$ mm, $\tau = 7.2$ s, $\omega = 2\pi\ \text{s}^{-1}$, and $\phi = 3\pi/2$

77. (*a*) Energy increases by factor of 4. (*b*) Maximum speed increases by factor of 2. (*c*) Period does not change.

79. $f_{half}/f_{whole} = \sqrt{2}$

83. $0.14\ \text{kg}\cdot\text{m}^2$

85. (*a*) $0.522\ \text{kg}\cdot\text{m}^2$ (*b*) $0.129\ \text{kg}\cdot\text{m}^2$ (*c*) 1.74 s

87. $mv^2/6$

89. You cut the wire to a length equal to the distance the ball stretches vertical spring.

91. Your mass is 71.4 kg.

Chapter 16

1. Yes, water can carry both transverse and longitudinal waves.

3. (*a*)

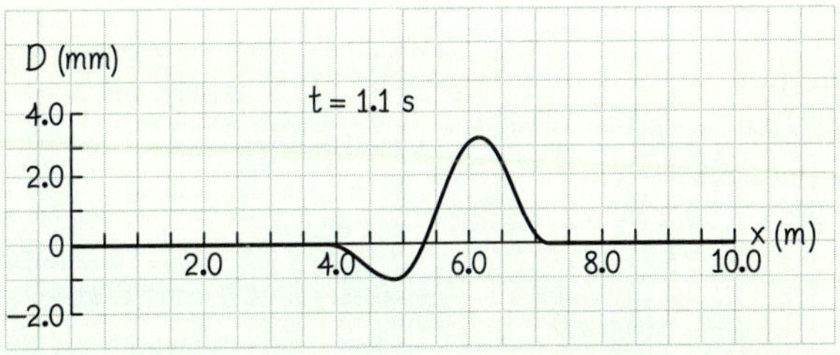

(*b*)

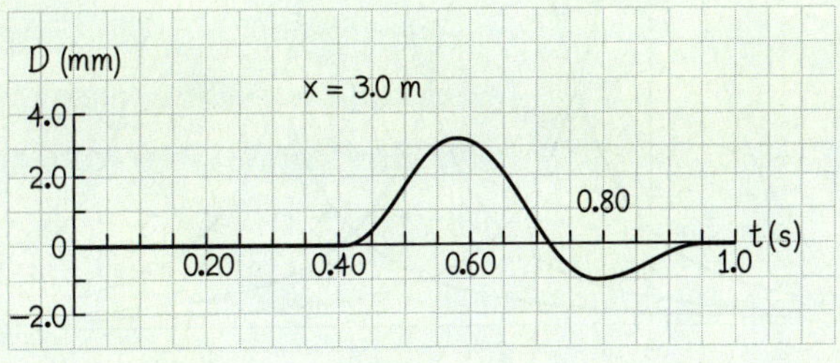

5.

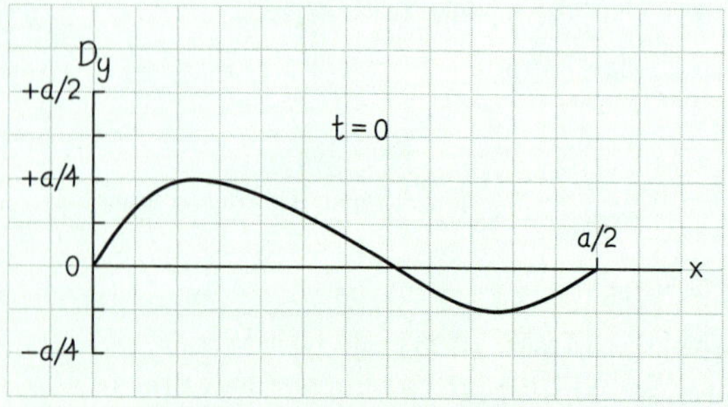

7. The definition is the same as for harmonic periodic wave: number of cycles per second executed by each medium particle.

9. The first crate must have struck when the cable was under minimal tension, resulting in low wave speed; the second crate must have struck when the cable was under significant tension, resulting in high wave speed. The tension change was probably the result of the ship's drifting away from the dock in the time interval between the two incidents.

13. (*a*) 0.10 m (*b*) 0.20 m (*c*) 0.30 m

15. Zero

17. Reflected wave not inverted

19. (*a*) Thinner string

(*b*)

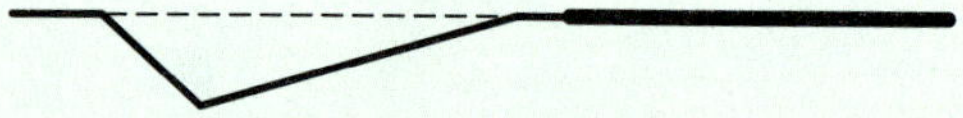

21.

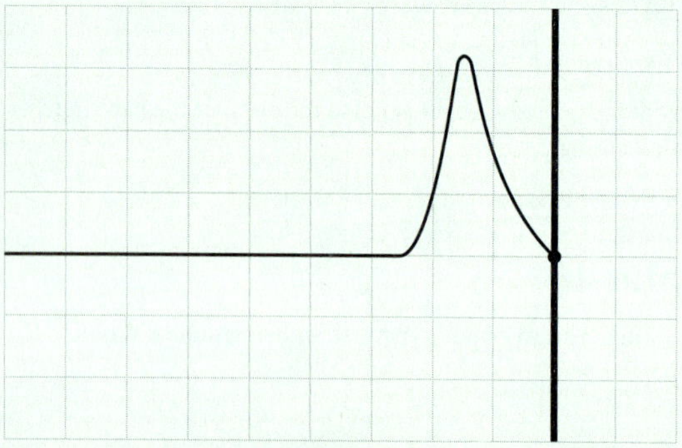

23. 30 m

25. (*a*)

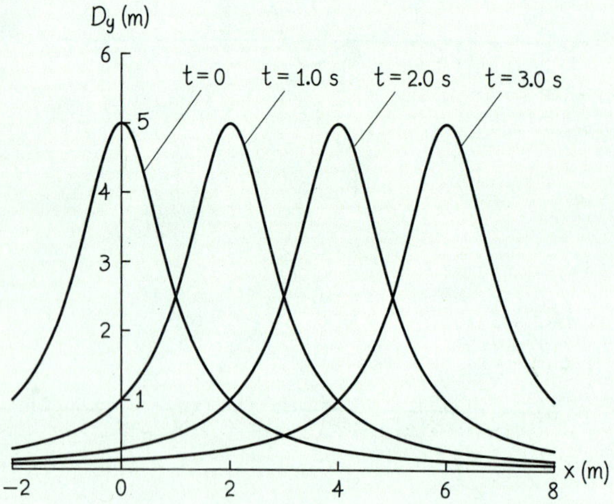

(*b*) 2.0 m/s

27. (*a*) $f(x, t) = \dfrac{a}{b^2 + (x - ct)^2}$, where $c = 1.75$ m/s

(*b*)

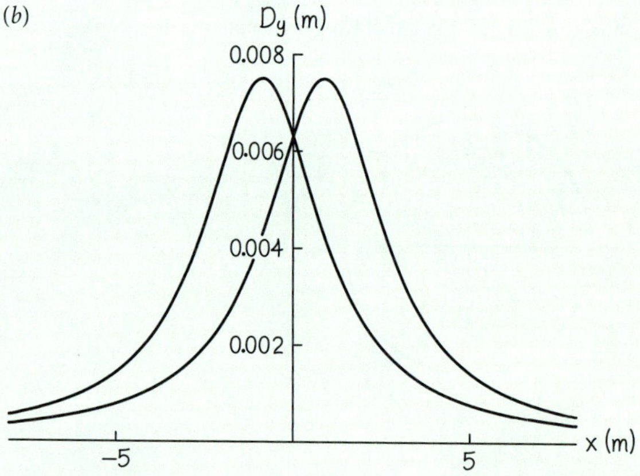

(*c*)

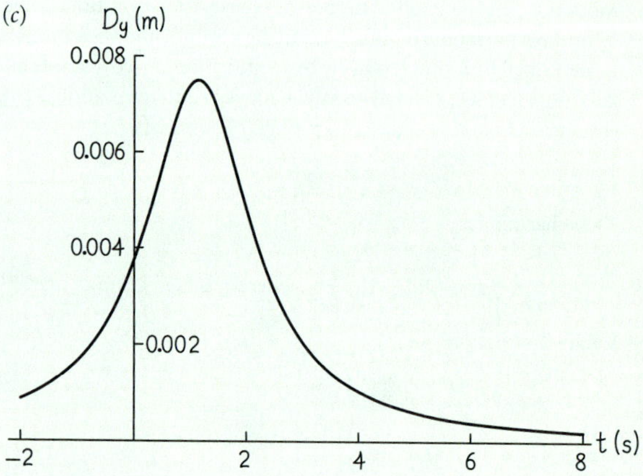

29. (*a*) 2.79 m (*b*) 6.09 Hz (*c*) 38.3 s^{-1}

31. 382 m/s in negative *x* direction

33. (*a*) 0.50 m (*b*) 5.7×10^2 s^{-1} (*c*) 90 Hz (*d*) 0.011 s

35. 0, 0.16 m, 0.32 m from tank edge

37. $f/5$

39. (*a*) 110 Hz (*b*) At frequencies *n*(110 Hz), where *n* is any integer

41. $A = 3.00 \times 10^{-2}$ m for both components; components travel in opposite directions at 1.20 m/s.

43. (*a*) 0.60 m (*b*) 10 mm in the *y* direction

(*c*) $f(x,t) = (0.010\text{ m}) \sin\left(\dfrac{2\pi}{0.60\text{ m}}x + \dfrac{\pi}{2}\right) \cos\left(\dfrac{2\pi}{0.60\text{ s}}t\right)$

45. 0.0578 m

47. 4.4 kg

49. (1) Shorten string by pinching off part of it; (2) replace string with one having lower linear mass density; (3) increase string tension.

51. 22 m/s

53. Fundamental frequency decreases by factor of 4

55. 4.62×10^6 N

57. 1.22 kW

59. (*a*) No change in power required. (*b*) Power required increased by factor of 16. (*c*) Power required decreased by factor of 0.25.

61. 2.3×10^5 J

63. 14.3 m/s

65. (*a*) $f(x,t) = a \sin(bx - qt)$, where $a = 0.0725$ m, $b = 2.09\ \text{m}^{-1}$, $q = 377\ \text{s}^{-1}$ (*b*) 89.6 W

67. The fact that the speed at which the surfer moves forward toward the wave base equals the speed at which the wave moves forward.

71. (*a*) No, because the pulse needs a nonzero time interval to travel the length of the rope. (*b*) No, again because the pulse needs a nonzero time interval to travel the length of the bar, though the pulse speed is much greater in the bar than in the rope.

73. $\Delta t_B = 0.87 \Delta t_A$

75. (*a*) 0.51 m/s (*b*) 12 s

77. (*a*) 0.500 m (*b*) 260 Hz (*c*) $f(x,t) = A \sin\left[\frac{2\pi}{\lambda} x\right] \cos[\omega t]$, where $A = 0.0200$ m, $\lambda = 0.500$ m, $\omega = 1.63 \times 10^3\ \text{s}^{-1}$

79. 1.9 m/s

81. For the pulse to travel end to end through a rope of length ℓ, $\Delta t = 2\sqrt{\ell/g}$.

Chapter 17

1. The approaching train emits waves that travel through the air and the track; those traveling through the air spread out spherically, those traveling in the track remain (largely) confined to the track, making the vibrations they cause detectable at greater distance. Also, the speed of vibrations through steel is greater than the speed of sound through air.

3. Yes, as long as the sound waves are free to spread out spherically from the source (professor's mouth). However, large lecture halls are often designed to have sound waves reflect off the walls and ceiling; in such cases, the amplitude may not drop off as $1/r$.

7. Because the bat feels air compressions created by your shout.

9. (*a*)

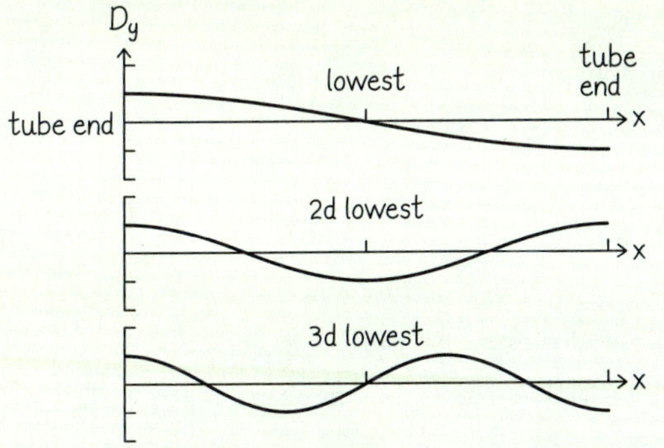

(*b*)

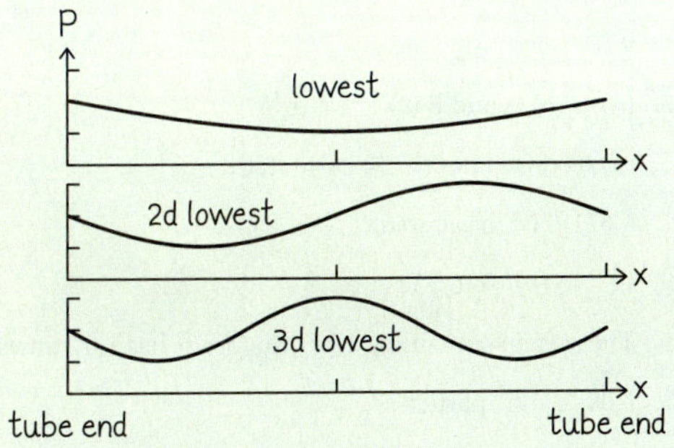

11. Nodal lines become antinodal lines, and vice-versa.

13. Because waves reflecting off the wall behind the speakers can travel to parts of the room that might otherwise be at the nodes.

15. The ripples are two-dimensional surface waves. The vibration causes the cup interior to act like a chain of sources. Because waves propagate away from sources, the wavefronts are parallel to the cup interior and therefore circular.

17. (*a*) $\theta = \sin^{-1}\left[\frac{(m + \frac{1}{2})c}{df}\right]$, $m = 0, 1, 2, \ldots$

(*b*) $\theta = \sin^{-1}\left[\left(m + \frac{1}{2} - \frac{\phi}{2\pi}\right)\frac{c}{df}\right]$, $m = 0, 1, 2, \ldots$

19. The sound waves she emitted diffracted around the corner and reached your ears.

21. (*c*) Nodal line locations in (*a*) are antinodal line locations in (*b*); antinodal line locations in (*a*) are nodal line locations in (*b*).

23. $5.0 \times 10^{-6}\ \text{W/m}^2$

25. 35 dB

27. 4.8 dB

29. 0.60 mW

31. (*a*) $3.2 \times 10^{-3}\ \text{W/m}^2$ (*b*) 7.9 W

33. 67 dB

35. (*a*) 70 dB (*b*) 6.0×10^2 W (*c*) 1.1×10^3 whales

37. The possible intensities at point R are $\frac{P}{4\pi}\left(\frac{1}{9\lambda} - \frac{1}{d}\right)^2$ where $d = 7.5\lambda, 8.5\lambda, 9.5\lambda$, or 10.5λ. The possible intensities at point Q are $\frac{P}{4\pi}\left(\frac{1}{6\lambda} + \frac{1}{d}\right)^2$ where $d = 4\lambda, 5\lambda, 6\lambda, 7\lambda$, or 8λ.

39. You hear both frequencies because the ear cannot resolve beats above $\Delta f = 20$ Hz.

41. 194 Hz, 198 Hz

43. $C < B < D < A$

45. 2 Hz, 4 Hz, 6 Hz

47. 6.6 Hz

49. Shift magnitude decreases.

51. 405 Hz

53. (*a*) 3 m/s (*b*) 34 m/s (*c*) 172 m/s

55. (*a*) 299 Hz (*b*) 298 Hz

57. (*a*) 450 Hz (*b*) 350 Hz

59. (*a*) 50 pulses (*b*) 6.2 s

61. 16 m/s away from whistle

63. 800 Hz

65. 4.7×10^2 m/s

67. 18.0 km/h

69. 50.3°

71. The reasoning is invalid because it is based on the boom being created at only one instant, the instant the plane attains Mach 1 speed. The boom is continuous at all speeds above Mach 1.

73. (*a*) 28° (*b*) 0.82 m

75. 19 m

77. No

79. (*a*) $f_1 = 399.8$ Hz, $f_2 = 409.8$ Hz (*b*) 10.0 Hz

81. Hyperbola

83. $f_b = 12.4$ Hz

85. Your current setup would only allow you to pick up radio stations 3.4 km down the road. You might try using a larger dish.

Chapter 18

1. 3.33 N

3. (*a*) $P_{C(top)} < P_{A,av} < P_{B,av} < P_{C(bottom)}$ (*b*) $F_{C(top)} < F_A < F_B < F_{C(bottom)}$

5. (*a*) $\vec{F}^c_{\ell w}$ at A directed to the right (*b*) No direction; pressure is scalar (*c*) $\vec{F}^c_{w\ell}$ at B directed upward (*d*) $\vec{F}^c_{\ell p}$ directed downward when piston pushed (*e*) $\vec{F}^c_{\ell p}$ directed upward when piston pulled (*f*) Answers (*d*), (*e*)

7. $\dfrac{1}{20}$

9. $45Gm^2_{planet}/64\pi R^4$

11. 25 N

13. (*a*) 125 kg/m^3 (*b*) Yes. (*c*) 1.75×10^7 kg

15. Water levels are identical.

17. Four friends

19. $\rho_1/\rho_2 = 2$

21. 2.99×10^{-3} m^3

23. (*a*) 0.133 kg/m^3 (*b*) He/H_2 = 0.479/0.521 = 0.919

25. 5.21 m/s

27. $v_B > v_A$, $P_B < P_A$, diameter at $B <$ diameter at A

29. The speed of the air outside the window is greater than the speed of the air inside, making the outside pressure lower than the inside pressure, so that the smoke is pulled out of the car.

31. (*a*) 3.56 m/s (*b*) 16.4 s

33. 2.53 N

35. (*a*) $\mathcal{T}_B < \mathcal{T}_C < \mathcal{T}_A$ (*b*) $P_A = P_B = P_C$

37. 2.92 mm

39. Wetting: $R_{tube} = R_{men} \cos\theta_c$; nonwetting: $R_{tube} = -R_{men}\cos\theta_c$

43. To top of tube

45. 6.3×10^4 N

47. (*a*) 1.5×10^4 N (*b*) 2.2×10^4 N (*c*) Because capsule mass increases as water enters through the leak

51. (*a*) 25 km (*b*) No, because at that height air resistance would not be negligible and because for water passing through such a small opening, viscosity would affect flow rate.

53. $F = P_{atm}wh/2 + gwh^2\rho/6$

55. $P = P_{atm} + mg/\pi R^2$

57. $\dfrac{P_A/P_B}{P_{A'}/P_{B'}} = 1.0$

59. 9.9×10^2 N

61. (*a*) 4.7×10^5 Pa (*b*) 80 m

63. 759 kg/m^3

69. 21.6 m/s

71. $v_2 = \sqrt{\dfrac{2gh}{1 - \left(\frac{d_2}{d_1}\right)^4}}$

73. 93%

75. (*a*) 4.84 m/s (*b*) 0.0974 m^3/s (*c*) 1.38 m/s

77. 2.3×10^{-5} kg

79. 2.05×10^{-7} m^3/s

81. 4.66 μJ

83. 5.43 m/s

85. $R_2/R_1 = \sqrt[4]{2}$

87. (*a*) 7.52 days (*b*) 51.5 years

89. $Q_2 = Q_1/256$

91. 6.09 m

93. (*a*) 1.68×10^3 N (*b*) 1.09×10^3 N

97. 4.88×10^{24} kg

99. $\mathcal{T}_A = 269$ N, $\mathcal{T}_B = 419$ N

101. (*a*) 0.0608 Hz (*b*) 0.0542 Hz

Chapter 19

1. (*a*) 1/13 (*b*) 4/13

3. 6.31×10^{-7} s

5. (*a*) 24 configurations (*b*) 624 configurations

7. 1/4

9. (*a*) HHHHH and HTHTH equally likely (*b*) Heads-up three times

11. 11 s

13. 3/10

15. $v_{av,N_2}/v_{av,O_2} = 1.069$

17. 1/14

19. 158 m/s

21. (*a*) 3.32×10^{-22} J (*b*) 102 m/s

23. (*a*) 1 basic state (*b*) 7 basic states

25. (*a*) 20 basic states (*b*) 64 basic states

27. 5 particles

29. 88 times

31. 9.79 times more likely

33. (*a*) C (*b*) A and E (*c*) 16 (*d*) 1/4

35. (*a*) 6 basic states (*b*) 30 basic states

37. 1.67×10^6 basic states

39. (*a*) No (*b*) No (*c*) Yes

41. The system containing 15.0-mm beads has 1.09 times more entropy.

43. 3.00×10^{18} particles

45. $S_B > S_C > S_D > S_E > S_A$

47. (*a*) 1.13×10^{15} (*b*) 34.7

49. 8 particles

51. 90 K

53. (*a*) 11.2 m/s (*b*) 12.5 m/s

55. 9

57. $\frac{7}{2}N\frac{1}{E_{th}} + \frac{2}{15}NE_{th}^{-13/15}$

59. 453 m/s

61. 1.1×10^4 m/s

63. (*a*) 5.05×10^{-20} J (*b*) $K_{particle}/K_{bacterium} = 1.0 \times 10^9$, $K_{particle}/K_{slug} = 1.0 \times 10^{-12}$

65. $m_B = 36m_A$

67. 181 kg · m/s

69. (*a*) Pressure due to helium 95.44%, pressure due to krypton 4.560%

71. (*a*) 4.13 m/s (*b*) 2.56×10^{-3} m/s

73. +0.432

75. $+8.73 \times 10^{24}$

77. $+3.50 \times 10^{23}$

79. +1.30

81. Increased by factor of 3.16

83. 8.59 K

85. (*a*) 2.50×10^{24}, mixed state (*b*) Zero

87. 1.07×10^9 basic states

89. $+2.08 \times 10^3$

91. (*a*) 3.69×10^{-25} kg (*b*) 6.38×10^{-21} J

93. 0.64%. Uranium-235

95. (*a*) 95.8 K (*b*) 1.19×10^{-21} J

97. (*a*) 18.6 (*b*) 4.31

99. 94.7 km

101. (*a*) 0.447 (*b*) 0.200

103. This is an unsafe container; its estimated life is less than 5 hours.

Chapter 20

1. Positive

3. (*a*) Neither (*b*) Quasistatic (*c*) Both

5. Ignoring collisions between molecules, the upper limit is about 10^3 cycles/s, because the piston must move more slowly in the *x* direction than the gas molecules. You can increase this frequency by increasing the gas temperature, by reducing the stroke length, or by using less massive gas particles.

7. (*a*) 100 K (*b*) 100 °C (*c*) 180 °F

11. (*a*) 22.1 °C (*b*) Yes

13. 2.14×10^3 °C

15. 1.5×10^7 J

17. 4.4×10^{14} J

19. (*a*) 1.46×10^{10} J (*b*) 1.5×10^2 km

21. 0.19 °C

23. 5.3×10^{-22} J (*b*) 6.11×10^{-21} J

25. 403 J/K³ · kg

27. B

29. 0

31. $T_A = 314$ K, $T_B = 176$ K, $T_C = 102$ K

33. $W_{on\ gas} = -P_iV_i$

35. -5.0×10^2 J

37. 0.0459 m

39. 14.1 kJ

41. 0

43. (*a*) 0.062 K, assuming $\rho_{air} = 1.2$ kg/m³ (*b*) 5.2×10^5 J

45. 1.09×10^{23} atoms

47. 2.68×10^3 J

49. Reason 1: Because $C_P = C_V + k_B$, $C_P/C_V > 1$ always, regardless of number of degrees of freedom. Reason 2: 6/9 corresponds to $d = 6/11$, which is not valid because d must be integer.

51. -2.70×10^3 J (*b*) $+2.70 \times 10^3$ J

53. $\frac{P_1V_1T_2}{T_1V_3}$

55. (*a*) 928 J (*b*) 928 J

57. $W = -Nk_BT\ln\left(\frac{V_f - nb}{V_i - nb}\right) - an^2\left(\frac{1}{V_f} - \frac{1}{V_i}\right)$.

$W(a = b = 0) = -Nk_BT\ln\left(\frac{V_f}{V_i}\right)$

59. 5.07×10^4 Pa

61. $4N(\ln 3)$

63. $C_P = 2.5k_B$

65. 1.9×10^2 K

67. (*a*) $d = 3$ (*b*) Particles are monatomic.

69. $W = (21/20)P_iV_i$

71. (*a*) 5.08×10^4 J (*b*) 1.36 km

73. 2.4×10^{23}

75. (*a*) °F (*b*) Either °F or °C

77. -5.28×10^3 Pa

79. In the process undergone by sample A, because $Q_A = 6Nk_BT_{tp}$ and $Q_B = 0$, $Q_A > Q_B$ by $6Nk_BT_{tp}$.

81. Half a dozen tubes, but better plan on 10 because of assumptions made.

Chapter 21

1. (*a*)

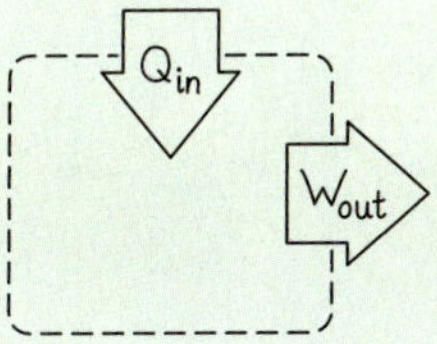

(*b*) System energy does not change; system entropy increases. (*c*) No

3. $\Delta S_3 < \Delta S_1 < \Delta S_2$

5. 425 J

7. (*a*) 9.6 J (*b*) 5.5×10^6 J (*c*) 2.8×10^4 kg

9. Material 2

11. 1.34×10^3 K

15. 4.09×10^3 J

17. (*a*) Reservoir 1 (*b*) Yes; device A

19. Cycle in (*a*)

21. 1.8 J

23. $\Delta S_{dev} = 0$, $\Delta S_{env} = 1.25 \times 10^{26}$

25. 1.0×10^{22}

27. 0.268

29. 18.8 MJ

31. $Q_{in} = 195$ J, $\eta = 0.44$

33. 0.396

35. System is reversible.

37. (*a*) 16 (*b*) 6.1

39. (*a*) 6.9 (*b*) 12 (*c*) 1.6×10^7 J

41. 3.1 kJ

43. 163 °C

45. $P_1 = 58.2$ kPa, $P_2 = 19.4$ kPa, $P_3 = 2.33$ kPa, $P_4 = 6.99$ kPa, $V_3 = 1.07$ m^3, $V_4 = 0.356$ m^3

47. 187 K

49. (*a*) 215 W (*b*) 6.28

51. 4.15×10^3 J

53. $\left(\dfrac{\Delta S}{\Delta t}\right)_{ocean} = -3.4 \times 10^{23}\ s^{-1}, \left(\dfrac{\Delta S}{\Delta t}\right)_{cabin} = +3.4 \times 10^{23}\ s^{-1}$

55. (*a*) 228 s (*b*) 6.38 (*c*) 1.93×10^5 J (*d*) -4.43×10^{25} (*e*) $+3.1 \times 10^{24}$ (not zero, because not all parts of the process are reversible).

57. 0.15

59. 0.0149

61. 431 K

63. 1.09×10^3 W

65. 7

67. 1.14×10^{24}

69. 4

71. (*a*) 478 K (*b*) 0.562 MJ

73. 2.2%

75. (*a*) 10.8 W (*b*) 1.17 W

77. (*a*) 0.71 (*b*) 12 km

79. (*a*) $COP_{cooling} = \dfrac{1}{\eta} - 1$ (*b*) $COP_{heating} = \dfrac{1}{\eta}$ (*c*) $COP_{cooling} > 0$, $COP_{heating} > 1$

81. (*a*) 20.5 kJ (*b*) 13.7 kJ

83. Five degrees of freedom

85.

	Car 1, Brayton cycle	Car 2, Carnot cycle
Efficiency	0.415	0.500
Work per cycle per unit mass (J/kg)	4.2	5.1
Power per unit mass (W/kg)	34	5.1
Speed after 11.5 s (m/s)	28	11
Drag force per unit mass due to air resistance at top speed[1] (N/kg)	1.2	0.33
Top speed[1] (m/s)	29	16

[1]Assuming drag force proportional to v^2.

Chapter 22

1. 9.8×10^{-4} N upward

3. 7.55 N downward

5. Any object carrying the third type of charge either would be attracted to both the T strip and the B strip or would be repelled by both of them.

7. (*a*) Stick C to a flat surface, then press A down on top of C such that the two pieces overlap along only half their lengths. Next press B down on top of the half of C that is not covered by A, so that B and C also overlap along only half their lengths. Holding A and B by the ends not stuck to C, remove A and B from C. The ends that were stuck to C have the same charge and repel each other. (*b*) No. Charge is a conserved quantity. This means that as A and B acquire a surplus charge of one type from C, C is left with a surplus of the opposite type of charge and so is attracted to A and B.

9. (*a*) 10^{-4} m^2, comparable to area of a fingernail (*b*) 2.6×10^{-5} m^2, making estimate off by one order of magnitude

11. The wriststrap allows any small amount of surplus charge that might build up on the technician to immediately discharge to the ground. This prevents a buildup of static charge and so eliminates any possibility of a spark.

13. Lightning occurs when there is an enormous surplus of one type of charge built up in clouds. The clouds then exert an attractive force on oppositely charged particles at Earth's surface. Once a large amount of charge collects on the ground where a person is standing, the charge moves into the person's body and travels to the head and along each strand of hair. Because each strand carries the same type of charge, the strands repel each other and stand out away from the person's head.

15. (*a*)

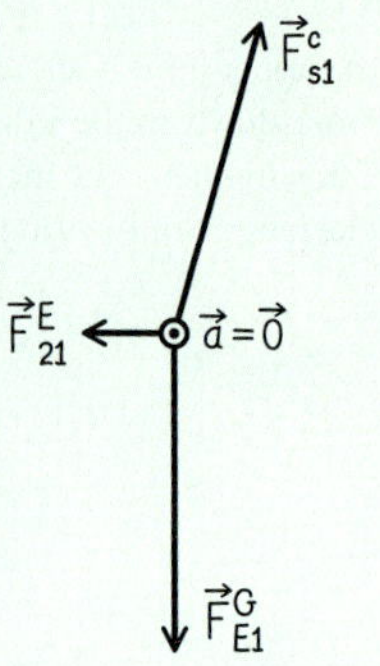

(*b*) 1.41×10^{-3} N directed away from clip exerting the force (*c*) No; that the strings form an angle tells you that the clips repel each other, meaning they carry the same type of charge, and so no discharge is possible.

17. (*a*) Place B and C on same side of A. (*b*) Place B and C on opposite sides of A.

19. Attractive

21.

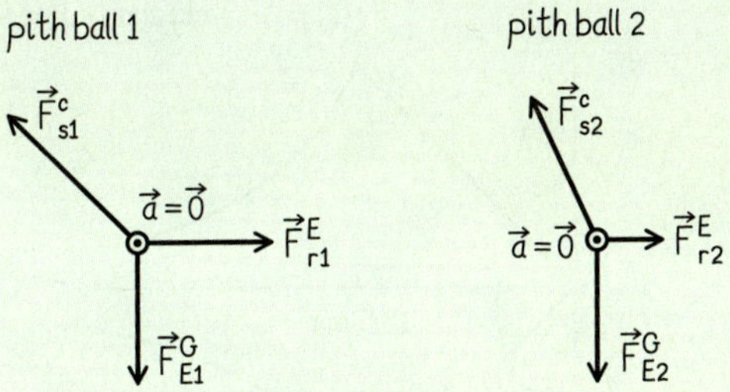

23. (*a*) The sphere rolls toward the rod. (*b*) If the quantity of the positive charge on the sphere is very small, polarization of the charge carriers in the sphere is the dominant effect and the sphere rolls toward the rod. If the quantity of the positive charge on the sphere is large, the sphere rolls away from rod.

25. (*a*) $F^E_A < F^E_C < F^E_B$ (*b*) $F^E_A < F^E_C < F^E_B$ (*c*) $F^E_B < F^E_C < F^E_A$

27. The polarized charge distribution in a larger chunk induces polarization in a smaller chunk. The two polarized chunks are therefore attracted to each other, collide, and cohere.

29. 1.02×10^{-10} N, repulsive

31. (*a*) $F^E_x = -3.6 \times 10^{-4}$ N, $F^E_y = 0$ (*b*) $F^E_x = 0$, $F^E_y = 1.0 \times 10^{-3}$ N

33. $-3.78\ \mu$C

35. $\dfrac{F^E}{F^G} = 1.35 \times 10^{20}$

37. (*a*) 4 units (*b*) 8 units

39. 8.51×10^{-6} C

41. (*a*) $F^E_{12}/8$ (*b*) Yes

43. (*a*) 1.6×10^{-5} N

(*b, c*)

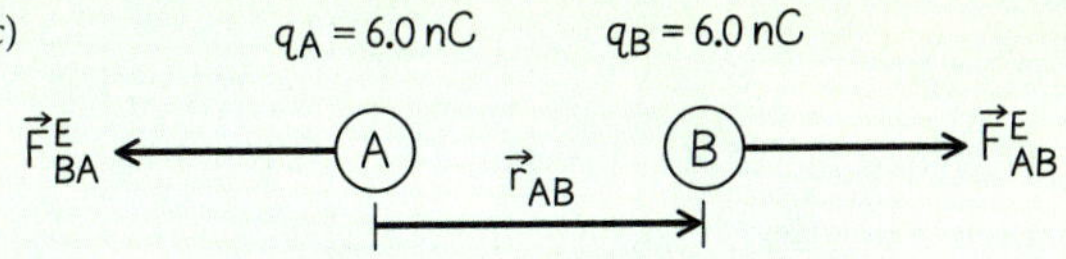

45. 2.0 μC and 4.0 μC

47. 2 electrons.

49. (*a*) The balls are initially attracted to each other due to polarization of the uncharged ball. Once they touch, they share charge and repel each other. When they come to rest, the two strings make the same angle with the vertical.

(*b*) $q = \sqrt{\dfrac{d^3 mg}{2k\sqrt{\ell^2 - d^2/4}}}$

51. Increased

53. 0.015 N directed along negative x axis

59. $\dfrac{\sqrt{2}}{2} + \dfrac{1}{4} \approx 0.952$

61. 1/8

63.

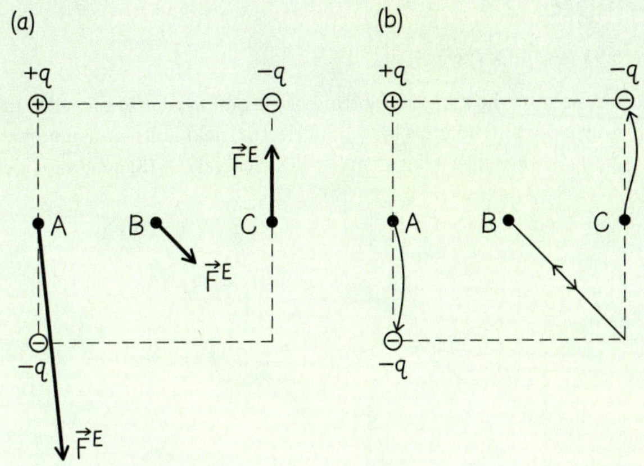

65. 3.0 μC

69. At $y = 10$ mm or $y = 40$ mm

71. Electrons in a piece of metal do not settle because gravitational forces exerted on them are negligible relative to electric forces exerted on them. Thus the difference between gravitational potential energy of an electron at the top of the piece and gravitational potential energy of an electron at the bottom of the piece is infinitesimally small.

73. 2.0×10^{-3} N upward

75. (*a*) 2.4×10^{-2} N directed along the positive y axis (*b*) 2.4×10^{-2} N directed along the negative y axis

77. -36 nC $-$ 36 nC

81. 47.1 N/m

83. At $5\pi/4$

85. (*a*) 8×10^{23} electrons. (*b*) 1×10^5 C (*c*) 2×10^{14} N (*d*) No

87. (*a*)

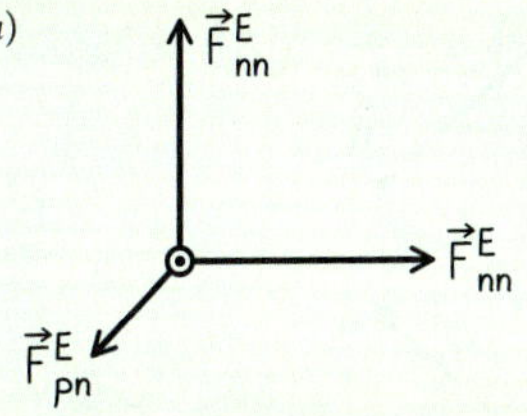

(b) 3.0×10^{-5} N along the line pointing from corner D to corner B and forming a 45° angle with side DC

91. The electric field is zero only at the center of the ring. Consider a location in the plane of the ring that is off-center. Call the distance from the location to the closest segment of the ring r_1 and call the distance to the farthest location on the ring r_2. Rather than picturing conical surfaces passing through the off-center location (as in Newton's and Priestley's arguments) you use a roughly triangular pie-slice off to either side of the location. If the charge is distributed evenly along the ring, the relationship between the charge q_1 on the smaller pie crust and the charge q_2 on the larger pie crust is $\frac{q_1}{r_1} = \frac{q_2}{r_2}$. The sum of the electric fields at the location due to the large and small pie crusts is $\vec{E} = \vec{E}_1 + \vec{E}_2 = k\left(\frac{q_1}{r_1^2} - \frac{q_2}{r_2^2}\right)$ in the direction of the larger pie crust. Using the charge ratio above, this simplifies to $\vec{E} = \frac{kq_2}{r_2}\left(\frac{1}{r_1} - \frac{1}{r_2}\right)$ in the direction of the larger pie crust. This is only zero if the two distances to the edges are equal (meaning the location is in the center of the ring).

Chapter 23

1. 5.93×10^{-3} N/kg

5. No, because the kilogram portion of the unit *newton* is cancelled in gravitational-field units but not in electric-field units. Gravitational: $\mathrm{N/kg} = (\mathrm{kg \cdot m/s^2})/\mathrm{kg} = \mathrm{m/s^2}$; electric: $\mathrm{N/C} = (\mathrm{kg \cdot m/s^2})/\mathrm{C}$

7. 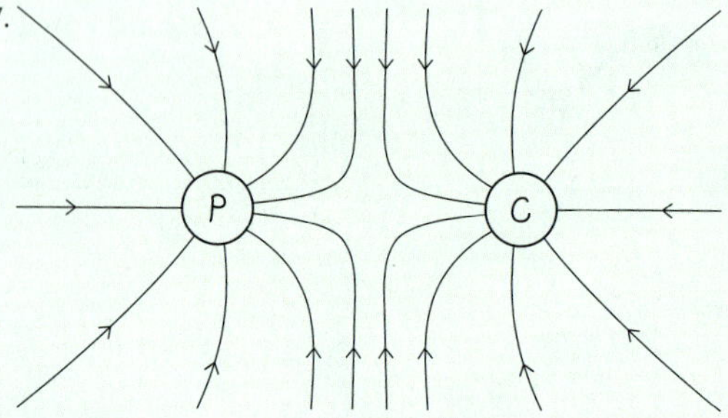

9. 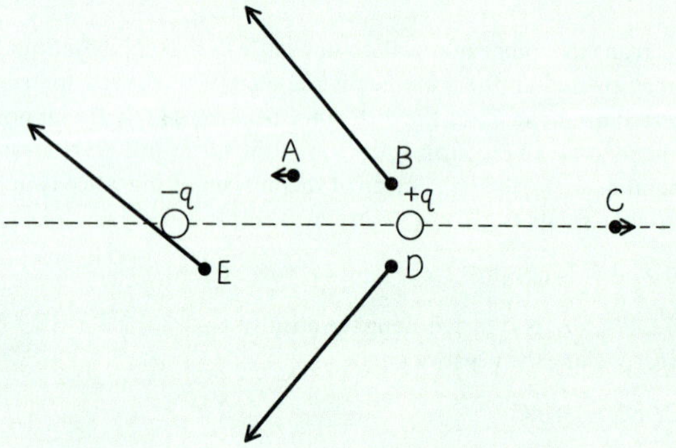

11. 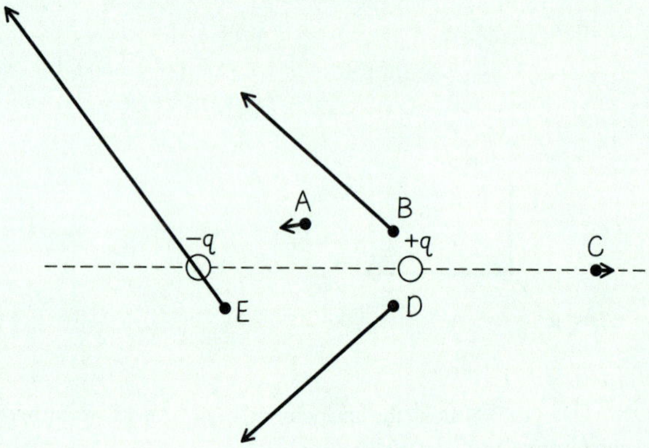

13. $|E|_c < |E|_a = |E|_d < |E|_b < |E|_e$

15. Very uniform because to a good approximation all points in the room are the same distance from Earth's center. Because the gravitational fields due to all other objects around you are extremely small, these fields cause negligible nonuniformity.

17. $\vec{F}^E = 5.0 \times 10^{-4}$ N south, 2.4×10^{-4} N west, 9.2×10^{-5} N downward

19. 84 N/C vertically upward

21. At (4.7 mm, 0, 0)

23. 6.8×10^5 N/C

25. (*a*) 0 (*b*) 2.5×10^2 N/C directed from A to B

27. (*a*) 4.0×10^{-10} N directed from the origin to the proton
(*b*) 2.5×10^9 N/C 2 directed from the origin to (4.00 mm, 3.00 mm)

29. (*a*)
(*b*) 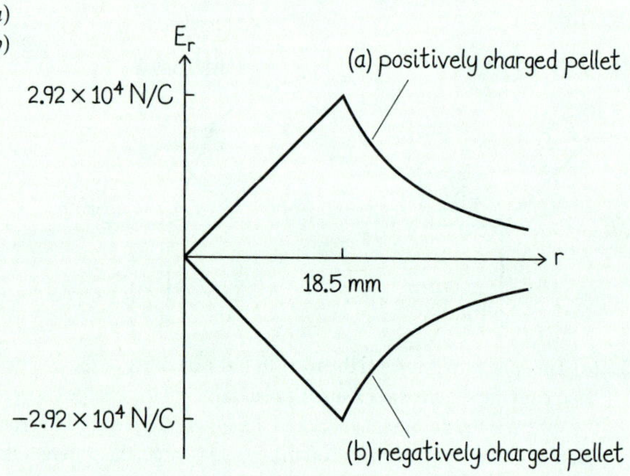

35. The beads are at $(0, y_0, z_0)$, $(0, -y_0, z_0)$, $(0, -y_0, z_0)$, $(0, -y_0, -z_0)$ and $a^2 = y_0^2 + z_0^2$. The electric field on the x axis is $\vec{E} = \sum_q \frac{kq}{x^2 + a^2}\hat{r}_{qx}$. The unit vectors are $\frac{1}{\sqrt{x^2 + a^2}}[(x, -y_0, -z_0), (x, y_0, -z_0), (x, y_0, z_0), (x, -y_0, z_0)]$, so $\vec{E} = \sum_q \frac{kq}{x^2 + a^2}\hat{r}_{qx} = \frac{4kqx}{(x^2 + a^2)^{3/2}}\hat{i}$.

37. (*a*) 2.17×10^3 N/C directed along positive x axis (*b*) At (−144 mm, 0)

39. (*a*) 0 (*b*) $\frac{4kq}{3a^2}$ directed away from the triangle's center
(*c*) $\frac{kq}{a^2}\left(1 + \frac{1}{\sqrt{2 + \sqrt{3}}}\right)$ directed upward

43. Treating the bonds as ionic yields $|\vec{p}_{H_2O}|$ 1.1×10^{-29} C·m, 1.8 times the measured value; these bonds cannot be ionic.

51. $\lambda \ell^2$

53. 3.4×10^{-5} C

61. 8.2 mm

63. (*a*) Bottom plate (*b*) $2.0 \times 10^{-8}\ \mathrm{C/m^2}$

65. (*a*) $E_y = \frac{k\lambda}{y}$ (*b*) $\tan^{-1}\frac{E_y}{E_x} = \tan^{-1}(-1) = 135°$

67. $E_x = \frac{kQ}{\ell}\left(\frac{1}{d} - \frac{1}{\sqrt{\ell^2 + d^2}}\right)$, $E_y = \frac{kQ}{d}\left(\frac{1}{\sqrt{\ell^2 + d^2}}\right)$

71. Any substance heats up when the kinetic energy of its molecules increases. In liquid water, the polar water molecules tend to align with the positive region of each molecule next to the negative region of neighboring molecules, and the molecules have a natural frequency associated with their oscillation around that equilibrium position. The transmitter in a microwave oven produces an oscillating electric field that matches that natural frequency. This increases the kinetic energy of the water molecules in a food placed in the oven, and the food is heated. Being nonpolar, oil molecules have a natural oscillation frequency different from that of liquid water, so the frequency of the microwaves is not a good match to the natural frequency of the oil molecules. The oil molecules in a food sample therefore do not increase their oscillation period, which means their kinetic energy does not increase and the food does not heat up. Because the water molecules in ice are constrained, their natural frequency differs from that of liquid water. Thus the frequency of the microwaves (that of liquid water) does not match that of water molecules in a sample of frozen food. Therefore the kinetic energy of the molecules does not increase, and the food does not heat up.

75. (*a*)

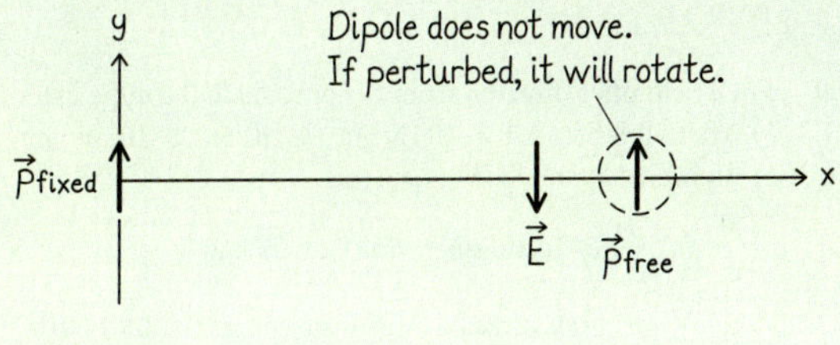

(*b*)

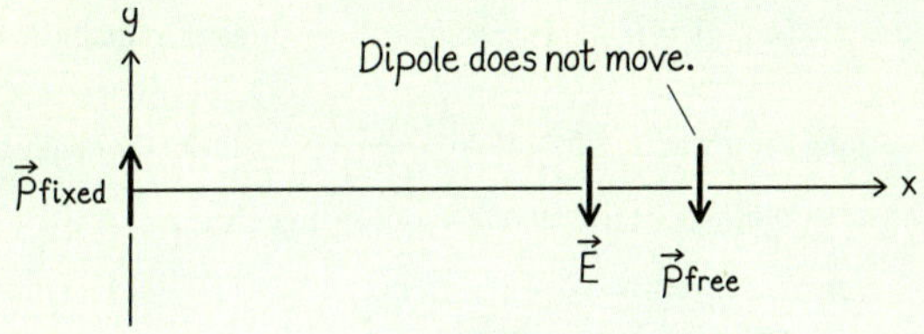

(*c*)

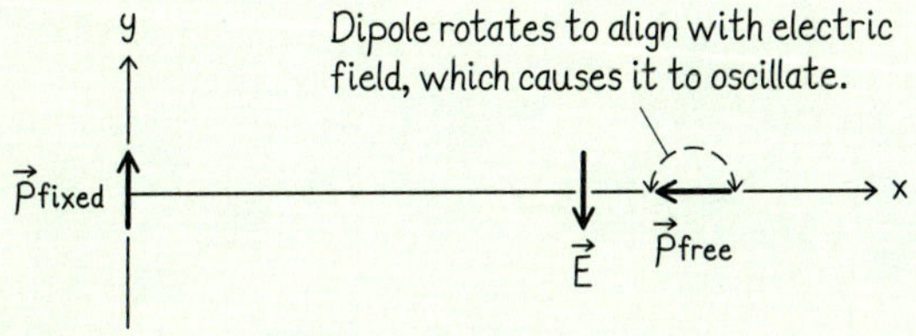

77. (*a*) and (*b*)

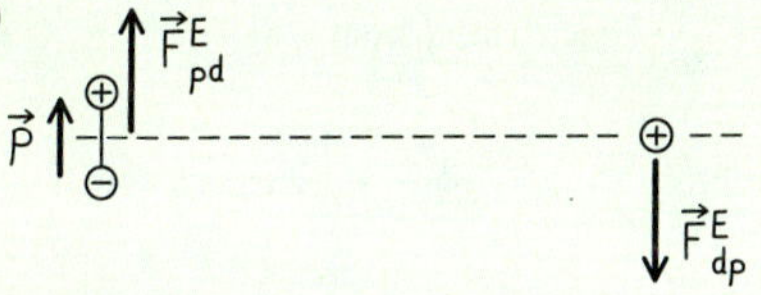

(*c*) 10.0×10^{-6} N

79. (*a*)

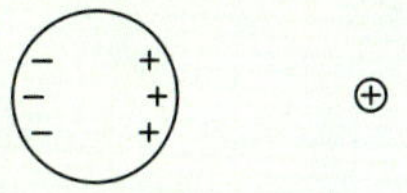

(*b*) The molecule would accelerate away from the positively charged particle.

81. $2.69 \times 10^{-45}\ C^2 \cdot m/N$

83.

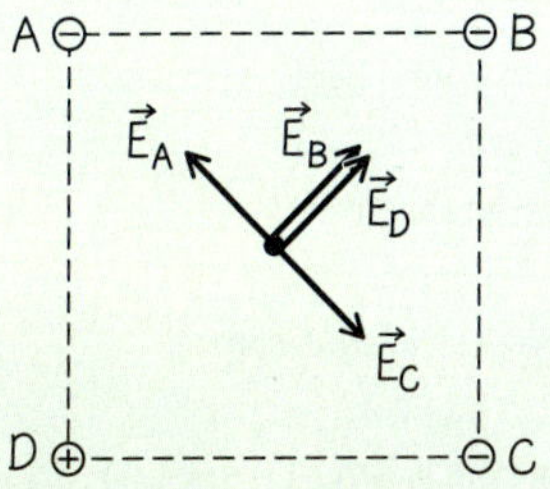

4×10^4 N/C pointing toward the negatively charged particle, that is, diagonally opposite the positively charged particle

85. (*a*) $(\frac{d}{2}, 0)$ (*b*) No such position exists.

87. (*a*) 6.4×10^{-27} N · m (*b*) 0

91. (*a*)

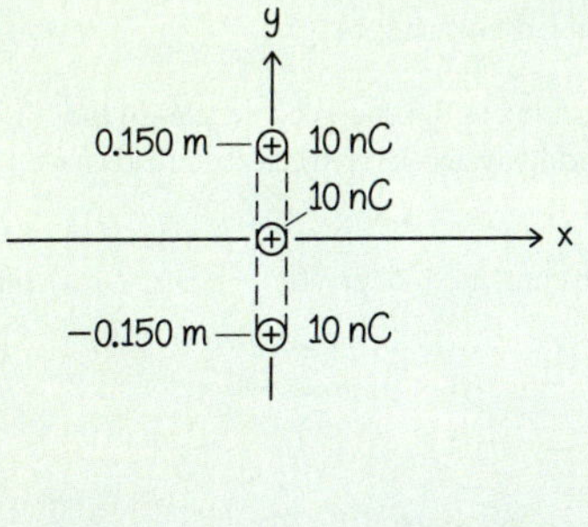

(*b*) 4.5×10^3 N/C. (*c*) 16% (d) Approximate the rod as five charged particles evenly spaced along the rod, each carrying one-fifth of a 30-nC charge.

95. $\dfrac{3kq}{\pi R^2}$

Chapter 24

1. (*a*) From origin to (0.6, 1.2) (*b*) From (0.6, 1.2) to origin

3. No

5. (*a*) The particle accelerates in the direction of $\vec{E}$. (*b*) The initial speed is different, but the trajectory does not change. (*c*) The component of the initial velocity parallel to $\vec{E}(v_i \cos\theta)$ increases the particle's speed; the component of the initial velocity perpendicular to $\vec{E}(v_i \sin\theta)$ changes trajectory from linear to parabolic. (*d*) In (*a*), the particle accelerates in the direction opposite the direction of $\vec{E}$. In (*b*), the particle initially moves in the direction of $\vec{E}$, then reverses course and travels in the direction opposite the direction of $\vec{E}$. In (*c*), the trajectory changes from linear to parabolic.

7. (*a*) Accelerates horizontally to the right (*b*) Accelerates horizontally to the left (*c*) Accelerates horizontally to the left (*d*) Accelerates to the right along the path that curves toward the negative end of the dipole (*e*) Accelerates to the right along the path that curves toward the negative end of the dipole

11. The quarter covers one or more charged particles carrying a combined negative charge equal in magnitude to 7/17 of the charge on the positively charged particle shown to the right of the quarter.

13. (*a*) With gravitational field lines defined as pointing in the direction of the gravitational force exerted on any object having mass, the Earth-moon gravitational field is as shown in the figure. (*b*) Both objects must carry negative charge. (*c*) All gravitational forces are attractive, but electric forces can be attractive or repulsive. Gravitational field lines always terminate on all objects in a field; electric field lines emanate from positively charged objects and terminate on negatively charged objects.

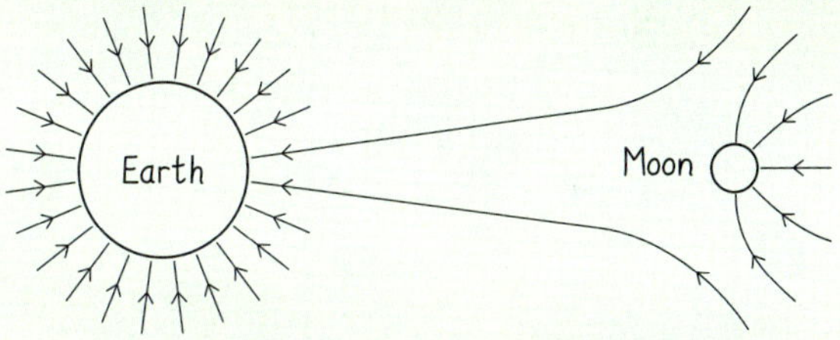

15. At lower right, where electric field line density is greatest

17. $E_B > E_A > E_C$

19. Treat the plate as infinite and lying horizontally in the *xy* plane. Because the arrangement is reflection symmetric about the *xz* and *yz* planes, the electric field can have only the E_z component. For the finite-sized plate, this symmetry is broken as you move away from the plate, but for the infinite plate, the symmetry argument holds for any distance from the plate. This means the field line density is constant around plate (the lines never bend toward or away from any region of space) and the electric field is uniform.

21. (*a*) $\Delta t_{C\to D} < \Delta t_{B\to C} < \Delta t_{A\to B}$ (*b*) No change as long as the pellets do not leave the electric field.

23. The field line density is greater near B by factor of 1.6.

25. $A = B = C$

29. The charge inside the closed surface must equal the charge on 4 protons, $+4e$. All that can be said about the number of particles over which this charge distributed is that the number must be even and there must be 4 or more particles.

33. (*a*) No (*b*) The relationship still applies to charged dipoles.

35. $+\Phi/6$

37. Many other shapes are equally useful, such as a cubic or rectangular box centered on a plate.

39. (*a*) $E_0/4$ (*b*) E_0 (*c*) $E_0/4$

41. Yes, because both the charge enclosed by the surfaces and the flux through the two surfaces are proportional to the area of the slab that is enclosed.

43. (*a*) $-q$ on cavity 1 inner surface; $+2q$ on cavity 2 inner surface (*b*) $-q$ on outer surface

45. Because metal is an electrical conductor, it remains in electrostatic equilibrium even when placed in an external electric field. The electric field inside a metal box is therefore zero and any device inside the box is not exposed to the electric field.

47. (*a*) $+2q$ (*b*) $-2q$ (*c*) $+q$ (*d*) Zero charge on outer surface of inner shell, zero charge on inner surface of outer shell, charge $+q$ on outer surface of outer shell

49. $-9q$

51. (*a*) $-2q$ (*b*) $-q$
(*c*)

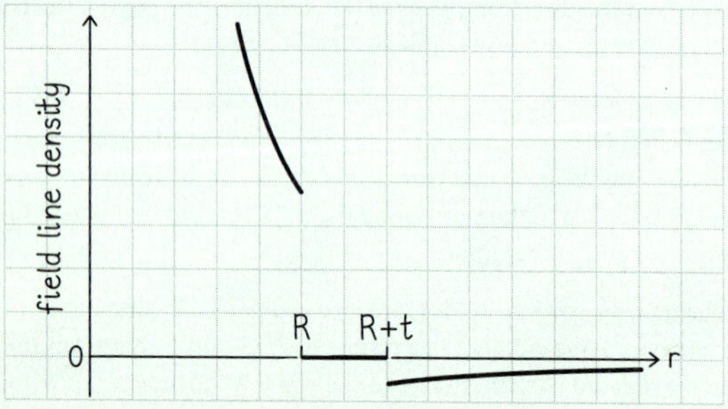

53. (*a*) Yes, by orienting the sheet such that the angle between the electric field direction and the direction normal to sheet is 78°. (*b*) No

55. (*a*) $6.8 \times 10^5\ \mathrm{N \cdot m^2/C}$ (*b*) $6.8 \times 10^5\ \mathrm{N \cdot m^2/C}$

57. $\Phi_{E,\text{ right side }(a)} = \Phi_{E,\text{ right side }(b)} = \Phi_{E,\text{ right side }(c)}$

59. (*a*) $+2q$ (*b*) $-5q$

61.

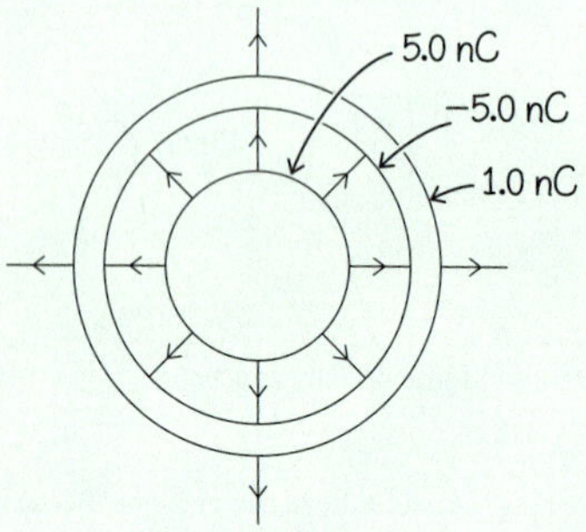

(*b*) $\sigma_{\text{solid}} = 1.1 \times 10^2\ \mathrm{nC/m^2}$ of positive charge, $\sigma_{\text{inner}} = 40\ \mathrm{nC/m^2}$ of negative charge, $\sigma_{\text{outer}} = 5.5\ \mathrm{nC/m^2}$ of positive charge (*c*) The electric field is directed away from the center and has magnitude:

$$E = \begin{cases} 0, & r \leq 60\text{ mm} \\ \dfrac{kq_1}{r^2}, & 60\text{ mm} < r < 100\text{ mm} \\ 0, & 100\text{ mm} \leq r \leq 120\text{ mm} \\ \dfrac{kq_2}{r^2}, & r > 120\text{ mm} \end{cases}$$

where $q_1 = 5.0$ nC and $q_2 = 1.0$ nC

63. (*a*) $-4.0\ \mathrm{N \cdot m^2/C}$ (*b*) -3.5×10^{-11} C

65. (*a*) Yes; use a cylindrical Gaussian surface. (*b*) No (*c*) Yes; use a spherical Gaussian surface.

67. (*a*) $\dfrac{\lambda \ell}{4\epsilon_0}$ (*b*) Increase

69. (*a*) 12 field lines directed from the particle to the cube exterior (*b*) 2 field lines (*c*) $3.4 \times 10^5\ \mathrm{N \cdot m^2/C}$ (*d*) $5.6 \times 10^4\ \mathrm{N \cdot m^2/C}$ (*e*) Answers (*b*) and (*d*) change.

71. (*a*) $\dfrac{q}{\epsilon_0}$ (*b*) $\dfrac{q}{\epsilon_0}$ (*c*) Technique using Gauss's law.

73. (*a*) 1.9×10^2 N/C directed away from sphere (*b*) 8.5×10^2 N/C directed away from sphere (*c*) 7.8×10^2 N/C directed away from sphere

75. (*a*) $E(r < a) = 0$, $\vec{E}(a < r < b) = \dfrac{2k\lambda_a}{r}$ directed radially away from long central axis, $\vec{E}(r > b) = \dfrac{2k(\lambda_a + \lambda_b)}{r}$ directed radially away from long central axis (*b*) 5.0 nC/m of negative charge

(*c*)

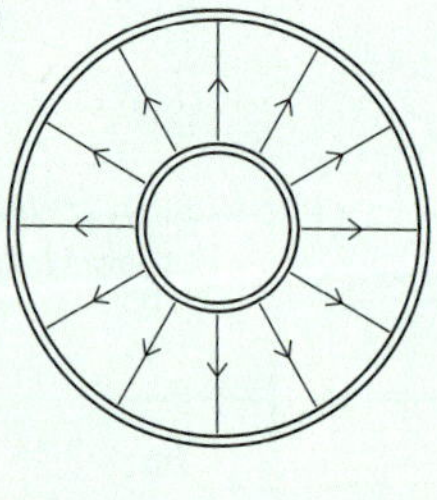

77. (*a*) $\sigma_{\text{inner}} = 4.8\ \mu\mathrm{C/m^2}$ of negative charge, $\sigma_{\text{outer}} = 3.4\ \mu\mathrm{C/m^2}$ of positive charge (*b*) 5.5×10^5 N/C (*c*) 0 (*d*) 2.7×10^5 N/C

79. $\vec{E}(r \leq a) = \dfrac{\rho_0 r}{3\epsilon_0}$ directed away from sphere;

$\vec{E}(a \leq r \leq b) = \dfrac{\rho_0 a^3}{\epsilon_0 r^2}\left[\frac{1}{12} + \frac{1}{4}\left(\dfrac{r}{a}\right)^3\right]$ directed away from sphere;

$\vec{E}(r \geq b) = \dfrac{\rho_0 a^3}{\epsilon_0 r^2}\left[\frac{1}{3} + \frac{1}{4}\left(\dfrac{b^4}{a^4} - 1\right)\right]$ directed away from sphere

81. Either -3λ or $+9\lambda$

83. (*a*) 7.1×10^{-10} C (*b*) 20 N/C (*c*) 21 N/C

85. (*a*) 2 shells (*b*) Inner shell: electrically neutral, thick, made of conducting material, inner radius R, outer radius $2R$; outer shell: carries charge $-2q$, thin, made of nonconducting material, radius $3R$

87. 0.040 m

89. (*a*) $q_{\text{part}} = \dfrac{49}{64} q_{\text{sphere}}$ (*b*) $x = \dfrac{R}{4}$, $x = \dfrac{16}{15}R$

91. (*a*) $\vec{E}(r < R) = \dfrac{\rho_0 r^2}{4\epsilon_0 R}$ directed away from sphere,

$\vec{E}(r > R) = \dfrac{\rho_0 R^3}{4\epsilon_0 r^2}$ directed away from sphere

(*b*) $\vec{E}(r < R) = \dfrac{\rho_0}{4\epsilon_0}\left(\frac{4}{3}r - R\right)$ directed away from sphere,

$\vec{E}(r > R) = \dfrac{\rho_0 R^3}{12\epsilon_0 r^2}$ directed away from sphere

(*c*) $\vec{E}(r < R) = \dfrac{\rho_0}{4\epsilon_0}\left(\frac{4}{3}r - 2R\right)$ directed away from sphere,

$\vec{E}(r > R) = \dfrac{\rho_0 R^3}{6\epsilon_0 r^2}$ directed toward sphere

93. No, in electrostatics (as long as the charged particles in the electric field are not suddenly accelerated) electric fields have no kinks.

95. The acceleration is constant and independent of *d*: $a = \sigma q/2m\epsilon_0$ away from sheet.

97. (*a*)

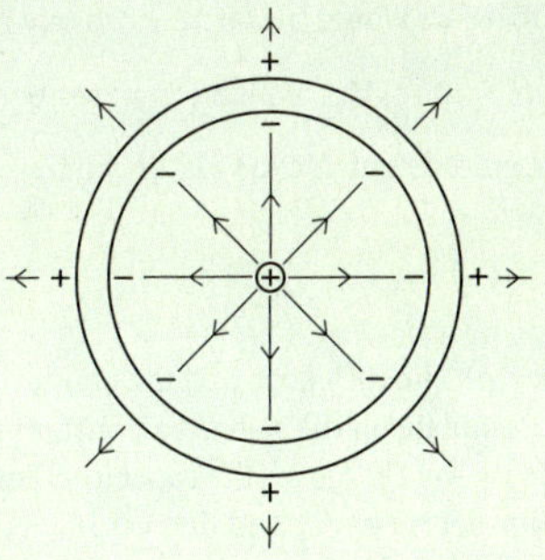

(*b*) $\sigma_{\text{inner shell surface}} = 24\ \text{nC/m}^2$ of negative charge, $\sigma_{\text{outer shell surface}} = 17\ \text{nC/m}^2$ of positive charge.

(*c*) $\vec{E}(r < R_{\text{inner}}) = \dfrac{kq}{r^2}$ directed from center to shell

$E(R_{\text{inner}} < r < R_{\text{outer}}) = 0$

$\vec{E}(r > R_{\text{outer}}) = \dfrac{kq}{r^2}$ directed away from shell outer surface

(*d*)

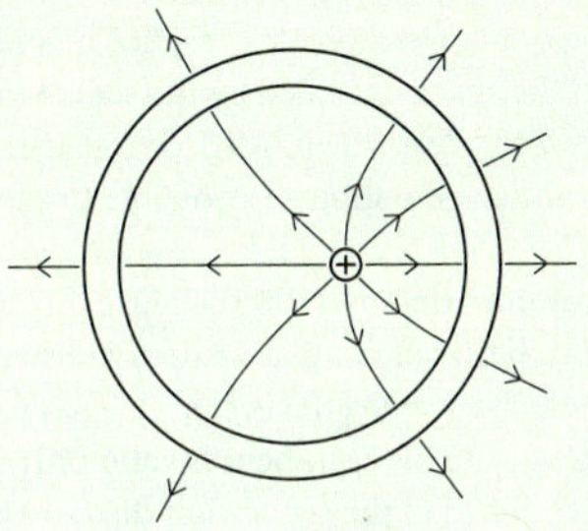

99. $1.3\ \text{nC/m}^2$ of negative charge

101. (*a*) $E_D > E_A = E_B = E_C$ (*b*) $E_A > E_D > E_C > E_B$

103. (*a*) $\vec{E}(-a < x < a) = \dfrac{\rho_0}{2\epsilon_0 a}(a^2 - x^2)$ in $-x$ direction; $E = 0$ everywhere outside slab.

(*b*) To left of 1, $\vec{E} = \rho_0 t/\epsilon_0$ in $-x$ direction; inside 1, $\vec{E}(x) = \left(\dfrac{\rho_0}{2\epsilon_0 a}(a^2 - x^2) + \dfrac{\rho_0 t}{\epsilon_0}\right)$ in $-x$ direction, between 1 and 2, $\vec{E} = \dfrac{\rho_0 t}{\epsilon_0}$ in $-x$ direction; inside left half of 2, $\vec{E}(x) = \dfrac{\rho_0}{\epsilon_0}(d - x)$ in $-x$ direction; inside right half of 2, $\vec{E}(x) = \dfrac{\rho_0}{\epsilon_0}(x - d)$ in $+x$ direction; to right of 2, $\vec{E} = \dfrac{\rho_0 t}{\epsilon_0}$ in $+x$ direction

105. $f = \dfrac{1}{2\pi}\sqrt{\dfrac{k|q_s|q_p}{mR^3}}$

107. Your wire should be positively charged at linear charge density $5 \times 10^2\ \text{nC/m}$.

Chapter 25

1. The greatest electric potential energy is when the direction of the dipole moment is antiparallel to the direction of the electric field; the least is when the direction of the dipole moment is parallel to the direction of the electric field.

3. (*a*) 1-kg ball (*b*) 3-kg ball

5. (*a*) $K_p = 2K_d = K_\alpha$ (*b*) $p_p = p_d = p_\alpha/2$ (*c*) $v_p = 2v_d = 2v_\alpha$ (*d*) $\Delta x_p = 2\Delta x_d = 2\Delta x_\alpha$ (*e*) $\Delta U^E_p = 2\Delta U^E_d = \Delta U^E_\alpha$

7. $\Delta U^E = 2qEd$

9. $2W$

11. From B to A

13. $3W$

15. (*a*) Remained the same (*b*) Increased (*c*) $V_B - V_A < 0$

17. (*a*) Increase (*b*) Decrease (*c*) Answer (*a*) would be "remain the same"; answer (*b*) would not change.

19. $W_{(a)} = W_{(b)} < W_{(c)} < W_{(d)}$

21. Yes, such as at the location where $E = 0$.

23. The equipotential surfaces are infinitely long cylindrical shells.

25.

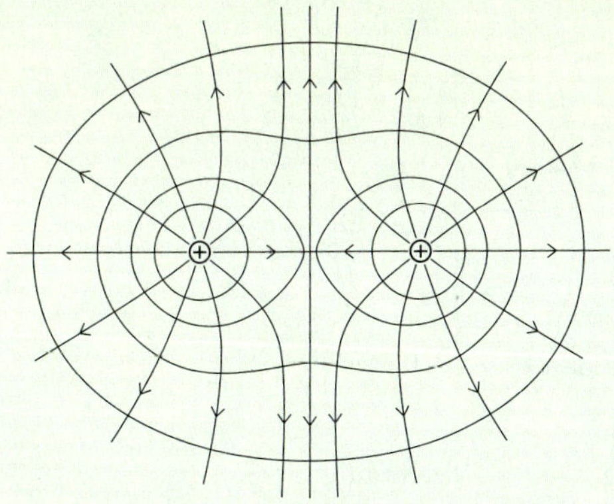

(*a*) Region to right of charged particle (*b*) To the left (*c*) Outermost line

27. (*a*) No (*b*) No

29. (*a*) 6.7 V (*b*) 2.0×10^{-8} J (*c*) 2.0×10^{-8} J

31. (*a*) 1.5×10^{-7} J (*b*) 0 (*c*) -3.8×10^{-8} J (*d*) -7.0×10^{-8} J

33. (*a*) 2.7×10^2 V (*b*) 1.9×10^2 V

35. (*a*) Negative (*b*) $\dfrac{q^2}{4\pi_0 d}(\sqrt{2} - 4)$

37. $W_A = W_B = W_C = W_D$.

39. (*a*) 51 V (*b*) 25 V (*c*) Zero

41. (*a*) $x = -d$ and $x = +5d$ (*b*) $y = \pm\sqrt{5}d$ (*c*) Nowhere (other than infinity)

43. (*a*) Negative (*b*) 3.0 V/m directed along the $+x$ axis (*c*) $5.3 \times 10^{-11}\ \text{C/m}^2$

45. (*a*)

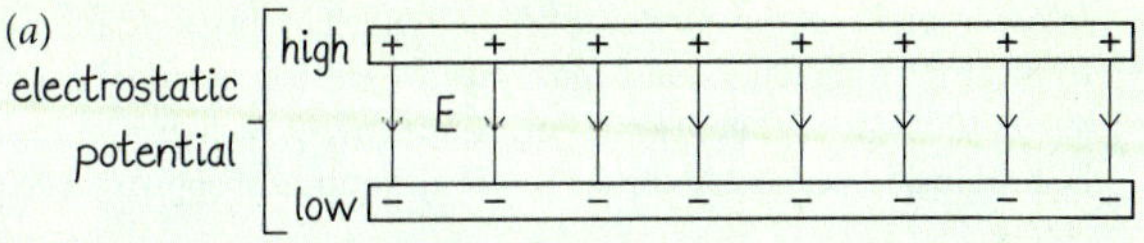

(*b*) 5.0×10^3 V/m (*c*) -8.0×10^{-17} J when the system is the electron and plates (*d*) $+8.0 \times 10^{-17}$ J when the system is the electron only and the electric field is external to the system (*e*) 8.0×10^{-17} J

47. (*a*) Positive (*b*) Particle 2 could carry charge $q_2 = 6q_1$ and be at $x_2 = 2d$, and it could carry charge $q_2 = 6q_1/5$ and be at $x_2 = -2d/5$.

49. (*a*) 24 V (*b*) 17 V (*c*) 11 V

51. (*a*) 6.0×10^2 V (*b*) -1.3×10^3 V (*c*) -4.2×10^3 V

53. (*a*) Zero (*b*) $V = \dfrac{q}{\pi\epsilon_0 \ell}\ln\left(\dfrac{\sqrt{2} + 1}{\sqrt{2} - 1}\right)$

55. $V = \dfrac{-q}{4\pi\epsilon_0 \ell}\ln\left[\dfrac{\ell + \sqrt{\ell^2 + y^2}}{y}\right] + \dfrac{q}{4\pi\epsilon_0(y - y_p)}$

57. $V = \dfrac{c}{8\epsilon_0}\left[2R\sqrt{R^2 + x^2} + x^2\ln\left(\dfrac{x^2}{(R + \sqrt{R^2 + x^2})^2}\right)\right]$

59. $E = B$; $-x$ direction.

61. (*a*) $\begin{matrix} V(x = 3.0000) = 8.99\ \text{V} \\ V(x = 3.0100) = 8.96\ \text{V} \end{matrix}$ (*b*) decreases, $\dfrac{\Delta V}{\Delta x} = -2.98\ \text{V/m}$
(*c*) $E(x = 3.0000) = 2.99\ \text{V/m}$. This has the opposite sign, as expected, and is close to the approximate value obtained in part *b*. (*d*) $E(x = 3.0000, y = 0.0100) = 3.00\ \text{V/m}$. Within the precision of the data, this is the same as the result found in part *c*, which is not surprising because the distance from the particle to the points in parts *c* and *d* are the same to within the precision of the data.

63. (*a*) B (*b*) F
(*c*)

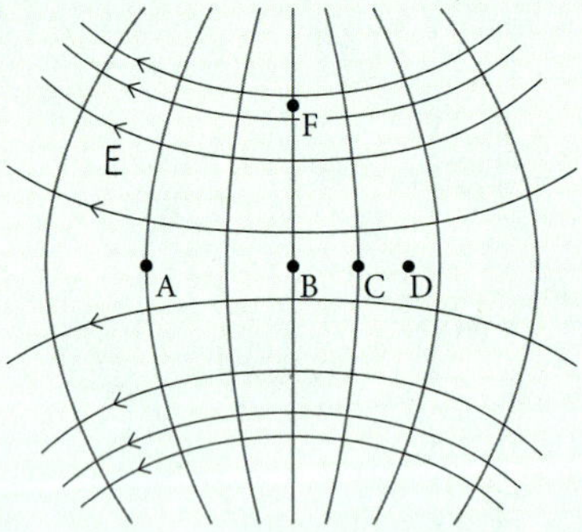

65. (*a*)

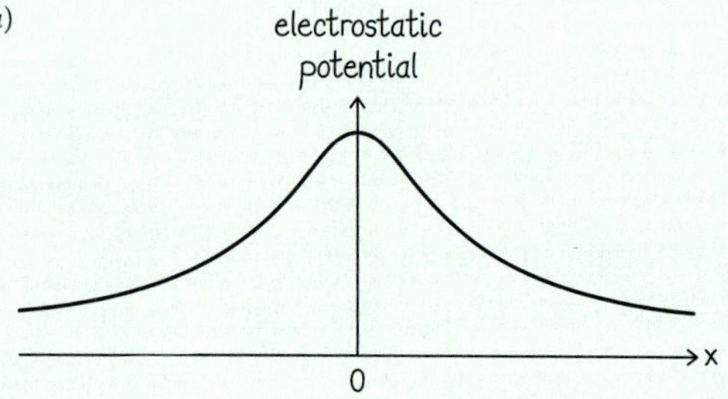

(*b*) At $x = 0$ (*c*) 0

67. (*a*) Positive (*b*) Positive

69. (*a*) $-6000\ \text{V/m}$ (*b*) $(A/x^2)+B$, where $A = 2000\ \text{V}\cdot\text{m}$, $B = -1500\ \text{V/m}$ (*c*) $A+Bx$, where $A = -2000\ \text{V/m}$ and $B = 6000\ \text{V/m}^2$ (*d*) 0

71. (*a*) 25 mm (*b*) 1.3×10^2 mm

73. (*a*) $q_{\text{sphere}} = -2q_{\text{shell}}/5$ (*b*) $q_{\text{sphere}} = -q_{\text{shell}}$

75. In order for 92 protons to stay together in nucleus, negative energy from strong interaction must equal positive electric potential energy, 4.8×10^{-10} J for the entire nucleus. Alternatively, each proton must be held inside the nucleus by a force of magnitude of approximately 300 N.

Chapter 26

1. Charges are equal in magnitude and opposite in sign.

3. Very large

5. 34.1 J

7. $\pm 1.35 \times 10^{-6}$ C

9. Greater electric field magnitude with battery connected; $E_{\text{batt connected}}/E_{\text{batt disconnected}} = 2$

11. $q_1 = q_2$

13. Because the potential difference between the plates is maintained at some value by battery, $V_{\text{cap}} \neq 0$ is always true. This potential difference can be written $V_{\text{cap}} = \int_{+}^{-} \vec{E}\cdot d\vec{\ell}$. If the electric field magnitude outside the plates were zero, there would be a path from one plate to the other such that $\int_{+}^{-} \vec{E}\cdot d\vec{\ell} = 0 = V_{\text{cap}}$, which can never be true. Hence the electric field magnitude outside the plates can never be zero.

15. q

17. (*a*) $+q/2$ (*b*) $+q$

19. Many answers are possible. (*a*) The dielectric and the conductor both cause surface charge to accumulate on the slab. At a constant potential difference, both slabs increase the charge on the capacitor. For an isolated capacitor, both slabs decrease V_{cap} and decrease E between the plates. (*b*) With the conductor, E between the plates is zero; with the dielectric, E between the plates is lower than E outside the plates by not zero. The charge that accumulates on the slab is free on the conductor but bound on the dielectric. The dielectric increases the breakdown threshold but the conductor does not.

21. (*a*) $E_1 > E_2$ (*b*) $V_1 > V_2$ (*c*) $U_1^E > U_2^E$

23. $1.3q$

25. (*a*) 1:1 (*b*) 3:2

27. The conducting slab does not help because its presence increases the electric field magnitude in the space not filled by the slab, making the air in that region more likely to break down. Also, charge carriers can travel across the conducting slab, a motion not possible (under normal conditions) in a dielectric.
Increasing the plate separation does not help because this increases both the potential difference between the plates and the distance over which the potential changes. These two effects cancel when determining the electric field magnitude. (This argument is valid only when the plate areas are much greater than the separation distance. If the plate separation is made very large, the electric field magnitude in the region between the plates could decrease.)

29. Stay the same

31. 2.8×10^{-17}

33. $4.0 \times 10^{-8}\ \text{C/m}^2$

35. 2.77×10^{-2} m

37. 9.3 mm

39. (*a*) $d = \dfrac{2R_{\text{inner}}R_{\text{outer}}}{R_{\text{inner}} + R_{\text{outer}}}$ (*b*) $d = \dfrac{2R_{\text{inner}}R_{\text{outer}}}{R_{\text{inner}} + R_{\text{outer}}}$ (*c*) $d = \sqrt{R_{\text{inner}}R_{\text{outer}}}$, $d = \sqrt{R_{\text{inner}}R_{\text{outer}}}$

41. (*a*) a, $\text{N/C}^2\cdot\text{m}^2$; b, m^2 (*b*) $C = \dfrac{1}{a\left(\dfrac{(128\ \text{m}^3)}{3} + (8\ \text{m})b\right)}$

43. 2.97×10^{-5} J

45. $8U_i^E$

47. (*a*) $C_2 > C_1 > C_3$ (*b*) $q_2 > q_1 > q_3$ (*c*) $E_2 = E_1 > E_3$ (*d*) $U_2^E > U_1^E > U_3^E$ (*e*) $u_{E,2} = u_{E,1} > u_{E,3}$

49. (*a*) $\dfrac{3q^2}{448\pi^2\epsilon_0 R^4}$ (*b*) $\dfrac{q^2(\ln 2)}{12\pi^2\epsilon_0\ell^2R^2}$

51. (*a*) $d/4$ (*b*) Not possible, because the isolated plates have no source of charge, regardless of the separation distance. (*c*) $4d$ (*d*) Not possible, because the energy density is independent of the plate separation.

53. (*a*) Generally no, but you could say that the dielectric constant of a conductor approaches infinity as conductivity increases. (*b*) 0 (because any arbitrarily small electric field separates charge carriers)

55. (*a*) Increase the plate area, decrease the plate separation distance, insert the dielectric that has a higher dielectric constant, change the geometry in some cases. (b) No

57. (*a*) $C_2 = \kappa C_1$ (*b*) $q_2 = \kappa q_1$ (*c*) $U_2^E = \kappa U_1^E$ (*d*) $E_2 = E_1$ (*e*) $u_{E2} = \kappa u_{E1}$

59. (*a*) 4/3 (*b*) If the capacitor is isolated, then there is no change to the bound charge. If the capacitor remains connected to a battery, then the bound charge is reduced to 6/7 of its initial value.

61. 1.1×10^5 V/m

63. 18.3 V

65. $F/\kappa_{\text{distilled water}} = F/80.2$

67. (*a*) $9Q/2$ (*b*) 3/2

69. (*a*) The model shows that increasing the separation distance increases the elastic potential energy stored in the electric field between the objects just as stretching the elastic band increases the elastic potential energy stored in the band. (*b*) The analogy suggests that electric field lines run from a positively charged object to a negatively charged object along the shortest possible path (so as to minimize energy), which is not true.

71. (*a*) $V_1 = V_2$ (*b*) $q_1 = 4q_2$.

73. Decreasing the volume occupied by the charge would always lower energy. There is no way to hold positive and negative charge carriers apart using only electrostatic interactions.

75. $\dfrac{q^2}{A\epsilon_0}$

77. With slabs $d/2$, $d/4$, and $d/5$ inserted, 95% of the gap between the plates is filled with a conductor. Because the electric field in the plates is zero, the entire potential difference now occurs over the remaining gap, which is 5% of the original gap width, and the electric field increases by factor of 20.

Chapter 27

1. North

3. Horizontally, with all north poles at one disk flat face and all south poles at opposite disk flat face

5. Either magnet attracts the unmagnetized bar, but neither magnet repels it. Try all possible two-bar pairings, making sure in each pairing to flip one of the bars and check both orientations. When you are holding a pair that repel each other, you are holding the two magnets, making the remaining bar the unmagnetized one.

9. (*a*) 0 (*b*) $-\Phi_{\text{north}}$ (*c*) 0 (*d*) 0

11. The magnet experiences (1) torque that rotates it until the line directed from S to N is parallel to the magnetic field and (2) the force accelerating it in the direction of the magnetic field, toward the region of the highest field line density.

13. No. In order to match everywhere, patterns must match at their sources. Electric field lines begin on positively charged particles and terminate on negatively charged particles, whereas magnetic field lines never begin nor end, with no way for these source differences to be reconciled into one field line pattern.

15. $\tau_{(a)} = \tau_{(b)} < \tau_{(e)} < \tau_{(c)} = \tau_{(d)}$

17. (*a*) To the left (*b*) Into page

19. (*a*) Yes (*b*) Yes; wire P

21. (*a*) Counterclockwise (*b*) Side 2 downward, side 3 to the left, side 4 upward

23. To the observer in the Earth reference frame, no magnetic force is exerted on S. To the observer in the reference frame M′ moving parallel to M's path but at half the speed of M (as measured from the Earth reference frame), both M and S have nonzero velocity in reference frame M′ and there is magnetic force exerted on S.

27. 0.26 T

29. 1.96 A

31. (*a*) 1.6×10^{19} electrons (*b*) In $-x$ direction. (*c*) 0.50 N/m (*d*)

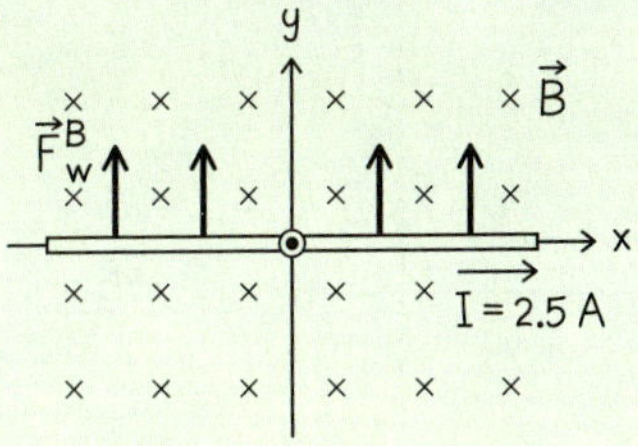

33. 0.52 A

35. (*a*) Out of page ($-y$ direction) (*b*) Into page ($+y$ direction) (*c*) Upward ($+z$ direction) (*d*) To the right ($+x$ direction) (*e*) Not possible

37. (*a*) 14.1 A into page (*b*) $I_{\max} = 42.6$ A

39. $\Phi_{B(a)} = \Phi_{B(b)} = \Phi_{B(e)} < \Phi_{B(c)} = \Phi_{B(d)}$

41. 19°

43. 6.0 Wb

45. (*a*) 0.30 T in the $-y$ direction (*b*) In the $-z$ direction

47. (*a*) $\omega = 3.6 \times 10^7\ \text{s}^{-1}$, $T = 1.7 \times 10^{-7}$ s (*b*) 2.7×10^7 m/s (*c*) 2.4×10^{-12} J

49. (*a*) 2.1×10^{-4} m (*b*) $\omega = 6.2 \times 10^{10}\ \text{s}^{-1}$, $T = 1.0 \times 10^{-10}$ s (*c*) 1.3×10^7 m/s

51. 0.68 kV

53. (*a*) Negative (*b*) 1.1×10^{-4} m/s (*c*) $5.9 \times 10^{28}\ \text{m}^{-3}$

55. (0, 0.023 m, 0.016 m)

57. 18 μV with the left side at the higher potential

59. (*a*) $+x$ (*b*) $-x$

61. $0.23c_0 = 7.0 \times 10^7$ m/s

63. $T_{\text{new},1} = T$, $T_{\text{new},2} = 2T$, $T_{\text{new},3} = T$

65. $B_x = 0.10$ T, $B_y = 0.10$ T, $B_z = -0.15$ T.

67. (*a*) 1.7×10^8 m/s (*b*) 1.6×10^{-4} m downward

69. Label magnets A, B, C. Hold magnet A fixed and mark one of its poles X. Now see which pole of magnet B attracts pole X of magnet A and which pole of magnet C attracts pole X of magnet A. Now you have identified a pole of B and a pole of C that interact with A in the same way, meaning these B and C poles have the same polarity (either both N or both S; you do not know which, but it does not matter). Now bring this pole of B and this pole of C together to see whether like poles attract or repel each other. Seeing them repel each other should convince your colleague.

71. The external magnetic field exerts no force on wire.

Chapter 28

1. There is no magnetic force exerted on the particle because the particle is at rest relative to the magnets.

3. (*a*)–(*d*) All four magnetic fields are directed into the plane of the loop from above.

5. There is a repulsive electrostatic force that obeys Coulomb's law. There is also an attractive magnetic force. Which of these forces is stronger depends on the speed of the electrons. The gravitational force exerted on each electron by Earth is much smaller than the Coulomb force, and the gravitational force exerted on each electron by the other is much smaller still.

7. (*a*) One location (*b*) One location (*c*) Two locations

9. $\vec{F}^B_{12} = 0$, $\vec{F}^B_{21}$ is downward in plane of page

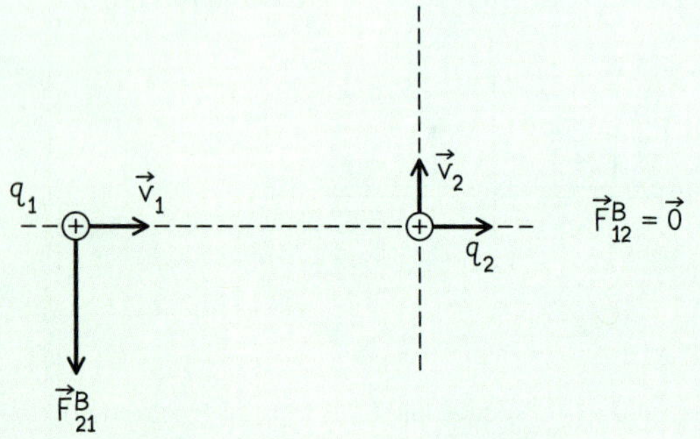

11. At the center of the loop

13. $\vec{B}_1$, $\vec{B}_2$ out of page; $\vec{B}_3$, $\vec{B}_4$ into page

15. If a current loop appears "small" then we are observing it from a distance much greater than the loop size. At this distance, the B field from a square or circular current loop is the same. A sketch of the field lines around each loop would also appear identical (a dipole field). As we approach the square loop, at a distance *r* from a corner, the field would be stronger than at a distance *r* from the side of a circular loop. A more exact analysis would require more information about the loops.

17. The magnetic field of a spinning disk of uniform charge may be thought of as a superposition of the magnetic fields due to many circular current loops with progressively larger radii. At the center of the spinning disk, the magnetic field from all current loops will reinforce each other, so the magnetic field here will be largest. Because all the current in a current loop is a distance *R* from the center, whereas some of the current in a disk is near the center, you expect the magnetic field at the center of the spinning disk to exceed the magnetic field at the center of the comparable current loop. As you move progressively outward from the center of the spinning disk, the magnetic field from the inner current loops will oppose the magnetic field from the outer current loops, decreasing the magnetic field strength with respect to that at the center of the disk. Therefore, in the plane of the disk, you expect the off-axis magnetic field of the spinning disk to decrease more rapidly than the off-axis magnetic field in the plane of the current loop. At the edge of the spinning disk, the magnetic field should be significantly smaller than for the current loop.

19. (*a*) Positive *x* direction (*b*) Negative *x* direction (*c*) Negative *x* direction

21. Because both particles have spin, they both produce magnetic fields, and each particle interacts with the field produced by the other. Because the electron is orbiting the proton, it acts like a tiny current loop, which also produces a magnetic field, and both particles interact with that field. The moving electron is also subject to a magnetic force due to the proton's magnetic field.

23. Clockwise

25. (*a*) Counterclockwise (*b*) Clockwise (*c*) Into page

27. Clockwise when viewed while standing on positive *z* axis and looking toward origin

29. (*a*) Positive *y* direction (*b*) Negative *y* direction (*c*) Negative *x* direction (*d*) Negative *z* direction (*e*) None

31. (*a*) $F^B_{\text{on }1}$ toward top of page; $F^B_{\text{on }2}$ out of page; $F^B_{\text{on }3}$ toward bottom of page; $F^B_{\text{on }4}$ into page (*b*) Into page (*c*) Vertical with side 1 on top

33. (*a*) Yes, it would be different, because the particle at rest would not be subject to a magnetic force if it were not spinning. (Since it is spinning, it experiences a torque that tends to align its magnetic moment with the applied magnetic field.) (*b*) The electromagnetic field produced by the particle as it moves under the influence of the applied electric and magnetic fields would also be different if the particle were not spinning, because it would lack the component due to its magnetic moment.

35. (*a*) $3I$ (*b*) Negative

37. $e < a = b = f < c < d$

39. $|I_1| = |I_2| = |I_3|$; I_1, I_3 out of page, I_2 into page

41. Greater than zero

43. (*a*) $\oint_A = \oint_B$ (*b*) Path A (*c*) Path B is longer than path A but farther from the wire so the magnetic field is smaller and makes a nonzero angle with the path. These differences cancel because the dot product multiplies only the portion of the magnetic field and path length that are parallel. The line integral is independent of the path as long as identical currents are encircled.

45. 2.5 A

47. (*a*) 1.2×10^2 A (*b*) 0.32 mT

49. 2.6 A

51. (*a*) 4.4×10^{-6} T (*b*) 1.9×10^{-6} T (*c*) 1.9×10^{-6} T

(*d*)

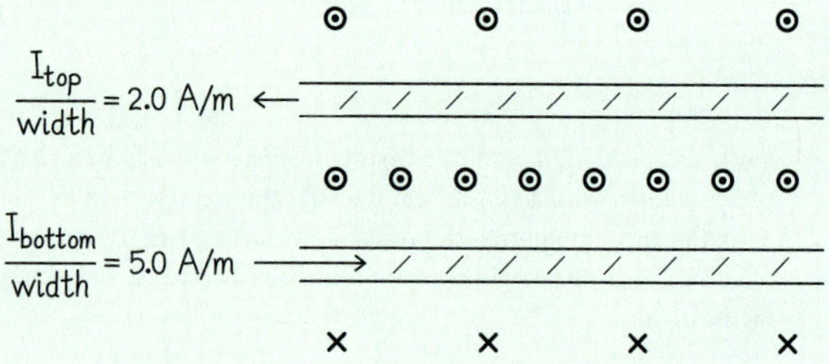

53. (*a*) $B = \begin{cases} 0, & r < R \\ \dfrac{\mu_0 I}{2\pi r}, & r \geq R \end{cases}$

(*b*)

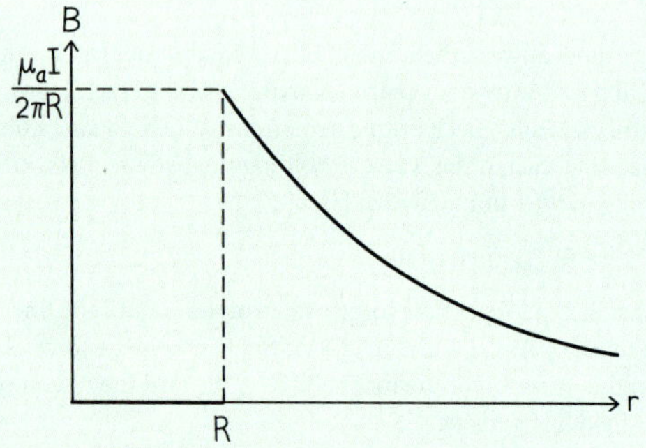

55. 6.28×10^{-3} N/m² downward

57. 1.6×10^{-19} C

59. 2.8×10^3 windings/m

61. In a coordinate system in which the magnetic field generated by the solenoid is in the positive *x* direction and the wire is displaced in the negative *y* direction, the magnetic field at the solenoid center is 5.7×10^{-5} T directed 10° from the positive *x* axis toward the positive *z* axis. It does not matter whether the wire is inside or outside the solenoid.

63. (*a*) 1.0×10^{-6} T (*b*) Zero (*c*) Zero

65. $B = \dfrac{\mu_0 n R_{toroid} I}{r}$

67. Because the circle forming the toroid outer edge is significantly larger than the circle forming the toroid inner edge, the windings are spread over a larger circumference near the outer edge than near the inner

edge. This means that the magnetic field magnitude B_1 at position 1 should be different from the magnetic field magnitude B_2 at position 2. The same argument applies to positions 3 and 4. If the toroid is perfectly symmetric, $B_1 = B_3$ and $B_2 = B_4$. Checking whether or not these equalities hold in this toroid is a good check of the unit's uniformity and symmetry.

69. 1.2×10^{-2} A

71. 2.5×10^{2} A to the right

73. 6.1×10^{-8} T out of page

75. 1.5×10^{-7} T

77. With the velocity direction defined as the positive *x* direction and 15 mm distance below the path being in the negative *y* direction, the magnetic field is 3.6×10^{-15} T in the positive *z* direction.

79. $\vec{B} = \frac{|\vec{E}|}{c^2}\vec{v} \times \hat{r}$

81. $F^B_{12} = \frac{\mu_0 q_{p^+}^2 v_1 v_2}{4\pi r^2}, \quad F^B_{21} = \frac{\mu_0 q_{p^+}^2 v_1 v_2 (\sin 135°)}{4\pi r^2}$

83. 0.53 m

85. (*a*) $\vec{0}$ (*b*) 9.6×10^{-35} N in negative *x* direction

87. (*a*) Yes, in positive *y* direction (*b*) Yes, in negative *x* direction (*c*) No

89. 1.2×10^{-5} N away from wire 2

91. 33 A

93. 531 turns, inner radius 0.020 m, outer radius 0.080 m. The magnetic field magnitude per ampere ranges from 1.3×10^{-3} T at the outer radius to 5.3×10^{-3} T at the inner radius.

Chapter 29

1. (*a*) There is no effect on the charge carriers because the rod moves parallel to the magnetic field. (*b*) The is charge separation because the motion is perpendicular to the magnetic field. If the rod moves in the $+y$ direction, a positive charge accumulates on the side of the rod facing the $+x$ axis, and a negative charge accumulates on the side facing the $-x$ axis. If the rod moves in the $-y$ direction, a positive charge accumulates on the side facing the $-x$ axis, and a negative charge accumulates on the side facing the $+x$ axis.

3. The airplane should fly perpendicular to the magnetic field, with the wings oriented with their width perpendicular to the magnetic field and to the plane's velocity.

7. (*a*) Yes (*b*) Varies with time

9. Circular shape; one winding

11. In the Earth reference frame, you are moving quickly through Earth's magnetic field. Because your motion is not perfectly parallel to the field direction (Avignon is southeast of Paris, and in that region Earth's magnetic field has a component directed toward the planet's center), a magnetic force is exerted on charge carriers in the rod. In an inertial reference attached to the train, the changing magnetic field produces an electric field that causes charge separation in the rod.

13. Concentric circles centered on the long axis of the pipe

15. Hold the magnet above the loop with the south pole facing the loop, move the magnet toward loop. Hold the magnet above the loop with the north pole facing the loop, move the magnet away from the loop. These are two examples; there are other ways.

17. The clockwise induced current occurs whenever the straight-wire current increases: $t = 0$ to $t = \pi/2\omega$, $t = 3\pi/2\omega$ to $t = 5\pi/2\omega, \ldots$. The zero induced current occurs at instants when the straight-wire current is maximum or minimum: $t = \pi/2\omega, 3\pi/2\omega, 5\pi/2\omega \ldots$ The counterclockwise induced current occurs whenever the straight-wire current decreases: $t = \pi/2\omega$ to $t = 3\pi/2\omega$, $t = 5\pi/2\omega$ to $t = 7\pi/2\omega, \ldots$.

19. 3.0 V

21. 4.2×10^{-4} A

23. 1.0×10^{2} windings

25. 9.4×10^{-6} m^2

26. 6.9×10^{-3} V

27. 10 A

29. (*a*) $\Phi(t) = \pi R^2 B_0 e^{-t/\tau}$; decreasing (*b*) $\epsilon(t) = \frac{\pi R^2 B_0}{\tau} e^{-t/\tau}$ (*c*) Clockwise when viewed from the origin along the $+z$ direction

31. 3.6×10^{-2} V

33. (*a*) 0.24 V (*b*) Contact touching disk edge

35. 0.029 s

39. 0.080 T/s

41. (*a*) 3.0×10^{-2} V/m (*b*) 7.5×10^{-2} V/m (*c*) Counterclockwise

43. $B(t) = 2Ct^3$

45. Yes

47. 3.0 H

49. (*a*) $\epsilon_{ind}(t) = -LI_{max}\,\omega \cos(\omega t)$ (*b*) Increasing (*c*) Opposing (*d*) Inductance prevents changes in current from happening instantly. When the current in a circuit containing an inductor tends to increase the emf across the inductor, the inductor acts to oppose the emf increase.

51. (*a*) 5.0×10^{-7} H (*b*) Your friend missed the fact that you cannot have 40 windings with the wire and rod described; the correct value is $N \approx 20$. He then used wire length rather than solenoid length for ℓ in the equation and wire radius rather than solenoid inner radius in calculating solenoid cross-sectional area.

53. 11 J

55. 3.5 J

57. 2.0×10^{5} J, 1.0×10^{4} W

61. -6.7×10^{-4} V, where the minus sign indicates that the induced emf opposes the increase in current.

63. 1.3×10^{2} J

65. (*a*) 0.0075 T (*b*) 0.0020 H (*c*) 0.0089 J (*d*) 0.0089 J

67. (*a*) $2B\pi v^2 t$ (*b*) Clockwise viewed looking into the page.

69. 4.4×10^{-4} V

71. 1.2 m/s

75. 5×10^{4} A

77. The induced emf is around 3 mV. The faster the tape runs, the faster the magnetic field changes direction. This typically corresponds to a higher frequency for the sound waves, although it may also affect their amplitude (because the faster change in flux induces a greater emf).

Chapter 30

1. Increasing

3. There is no magnetic field surrounding the capacitor.

5. (*a*) To the left (*b*) Increasing to the left (*c*) Clockwise when viewed from the position to the right of the right plate

7. (*a*) Yes (*b*) Yes (*c*) No

9. No; the electric field lines would bend but not kink because kinking is a characteristic of a sudden onset of motion.

11. (*a*) No, not in the reference frame in which the positive and negative charge carriers have the same linear charge density. (*b*) Yes (*c*) Yes (*d*) No

15. Upward

17. (*a*) From down to up (*b*) Into page to left of P, out of page to right of P (*c*) In-out of page.

19. Because no radiation is emitted along the long axis. The towers laid horizontally along, say, the north-south line would emit waves detectable east and west of the towers but not north or south of them.

21. Negatively charged

23. 1.9×10^{-5} T

25. 3.2×10^{-5} T

27. (*a*) 5.6×10^{-4} A
(*b*)

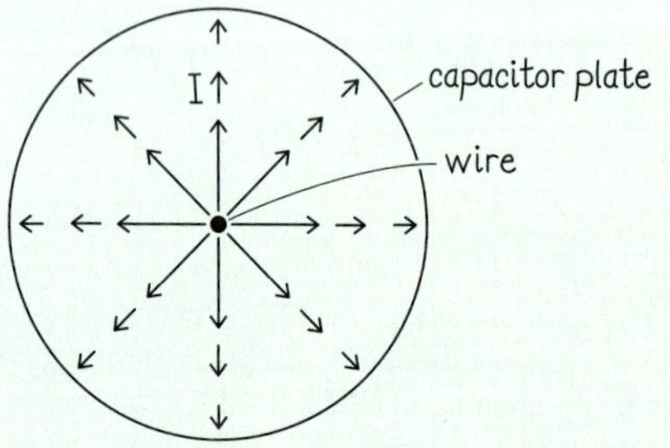

29. (*a*) $E(t) = It/\pi R^2\epsilon_0$ (*b*) 0.22 A (*c*) 0 (*d*) Answer (*c*) is different from answer (*b*) because the flat circular surface in Figure P30.29*b* has charge carriers flowing through it, whereas the flat circular shell surface in Figure P30.29*a* has displacement current only, with no charge carriers moving through it. Answer (*b*) is not 2.0 A because I_{disp} exists everywhere between the plates but the circular surface occupies only a part of this region. Answer (*c*) is not 2.0 A because the open cylindrical shell surface intersects a current-carrying conductor twice: where the wire passes through the closed end and where the cylinder passes through the capacitor plate. So all the charge carriers that pass into the cylinder pass back out again, resulting in zero current.

31. 3.6×10^{-11} T

37. AM wavelengths, 0.3 km to 3.0 km; FM frequencies, 3×10^7 Hz to 3×10^8 Hz.

39. 26 ms

41. For the dipole antenna, the likely frequency is around 1.9 GHz.

43. Around 280 nm, which is UV light

45. 6.3×10^{10} Hz

47. 2.46×10^{-2} N/C

49. The light emitted by an incandescent bulb spreads out over a spherical surface of increasing radius, but the angular spread of a laser beam is extremely small. The result is that the intensity of the laser light 100 m from the source is essentially the same as the intensity 1 m from the source. Over this same distance, the intensity of the incandescent bulb drops by a factor of 10^{-4}.

53. 0.020 s

55. (*a*) $E_{max} = 2.4 \times 10^1$ N/C, $B_{max} = 8.2 \times 10^{-8}$ T (*b*) $E_{max} = 4.9 \times 10^{-2}$ N/C, $B_{max} = 1.6 \times 10^{-10}$ T (*c*) 24 V at 100 m, 49 mV at 50 km.

57. 6.0×10^2 W

59. Assuming the light spreads out spherically, it can be seen 9×10^2 km from the source, a result you know from experience does not make sense.

61. (*a*) $+z$ direction (*b*) 50 W (*c*) $+y$ direction (I) 6.3 mm, 5×10^{10} Hz (I) $\vec{E}(x, y, z, t) = E_{max} \sin^2(kz - \omega t)\hat{i}$, $\vec{B}(x, y, z, t) = B_{max} \sin^2(kz - \omega t)\hat{j}$, where $k = 1000\ \text{m}^{-1}$, $\omega = 3.0 \times 10^{11}\ \text{s}^{-1}$, $E_{max} = 1.9 \times 10^2$ N/C, $B_{max} = 6.5 \times 10^{-7}$ T

63. 177 W/m^2

65. 1.66 m

67. $\lambda_{2.45\ \text{GHz}} = 0.122$ m, antenna length 61.2 mm; $\lambda_{915\ \text{MHz}} = 0.328$ m, antenna length 164 mm.

69. 2.7×10^9 W/m^2

71. $S = 2.2 \times 10^{10}$ W/m^2, $B_{rms} = 9.6 \times 10^{-3}$ T, $E_{rms} = 2.9 \times 10^6$ N/C

73. 50 W/m^2

75. At a distance of 50 from each device, the intensity relationships are $I_{phone} = 3.5I_{oven}$ and $I_{headset} = 0.0080I_{oven}$. With the headset, however, you have to add the intensity contributed by the cell phone at your waist, approximately $I_{waist} = 0.088$ W/m^2, meaning the headset intensity is $I_{headset} + I_{waist} = 0.17$ W/m^2. This is two orders of magnitude smaller than the intensity 50 mm from a microwave oven and 200 times smaller than the intensity 50 mm from a cell phone: a drastic improvement.

Because intensity depends quadratically on the rms value of the magnetic field ($S : B^2_{rms}$), the rms value of the magnetic field you are exposed to using a headset is one order of magnitude smaller than when holding a cell phone to your ear.

The wavelength of the 824.6-MHz radiation from a cell phone is 0.36 m, just a little longer than the head is wide. This tells you that standing waves within the skull are not an issue.

Chapter 31

1. 3×10^{24}

3. $a = b = e = f = j > g = h = c = d$

5.

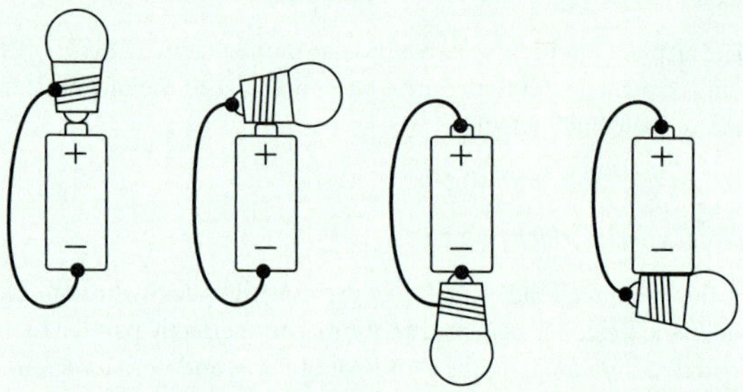

9. Your friend is correct that charge does not flow across the gap, meaning there is no current. There is however a displacement current. The electric field between the plates allows positive and negative charges to influence each other across the gap. Also, we know from our detailed study of capacitors that they can certainly discharge. If the air gap prevented charge from ever flowing from the plates, then no capacitor could ever discharge.

11. (*a*) No, only B, C, and D light up. (*b*) $C > B = D > A$

13. (*a*) No (*b*) Yes

15. $\Delta E_A = 1.5$ J, $\Delta E_B = 3.0$ J, and $\Delta E_C = 4.5$ J

17. A, B, and C are in parallel. E and F are also in parallel.

19.

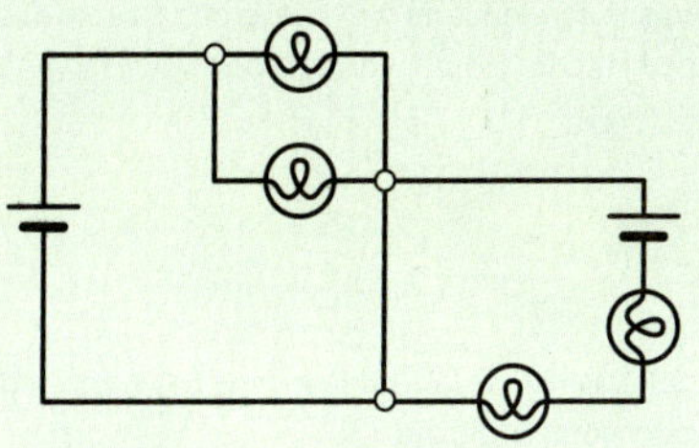

21. (*a*)

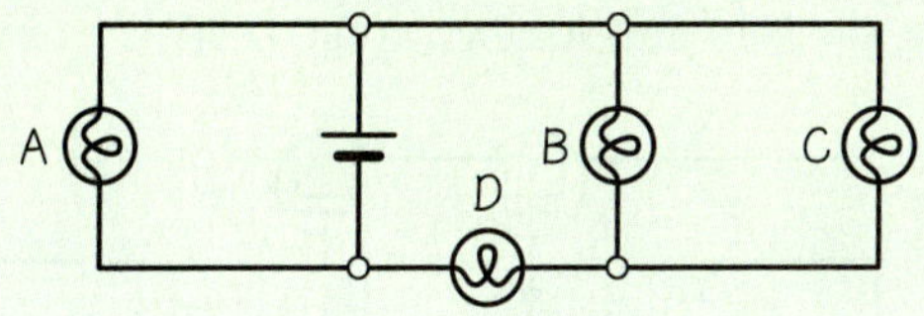

(*b*) Yes, all bulbs light up. (*c*) A is the brightest, B and C are tied for the dimmest. (*d*) B and C are in parallel, and none are wired in series.

23. Lights in a house are wired in parallel with very few exceptions.

25. (*a*) (*b*) (*c*)

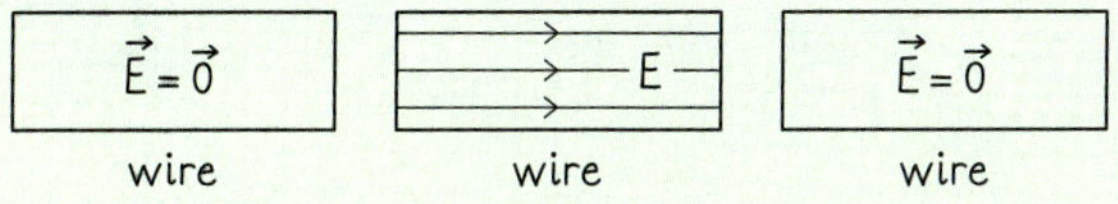

29. 1.0 m when made of nichrome, and 89 m when made from copper

31. 5.7 N/C

33. 1.2×10^3 m for the 4-gauge, and 19 m for the 22-gauge

35. 3.29×10^{-14} s

37. (*a*) Decrease (*b*) increase (*c*) decrease

39. 1.25×10^{10} protons

43. 2.77×10^{13} J

45. 0.90 A clockwise

47. (*a*) 9.0×10^{-2} A clockwise (*b*) 6.1×10^{-3} A counterclockwise (*c*) 1.1×10^{-1} A counterclockwise

49. $\epsilon = 6$ V and $R_{\text{batt}} = 1\ \Omega$

51. 3.0 Ω

53. (*a*) 0.57 A clockwise (*b*) $V_{ab} = 7.1$ V, $V_{bc} = 0$, $V_{cd} = -3.7$ V, $V_{da} = -3.4$ V

55. (*a*) $1.2 \times 10^3\ \Omega$ (*b*) 1.0×10^{-2} A (*c*) $V_a = 12$ V, $V_b = 10$ V, and $V_c = 1$ V

57. 10 Ω

59. 3.1 Ω

61. −1.24 %

63.

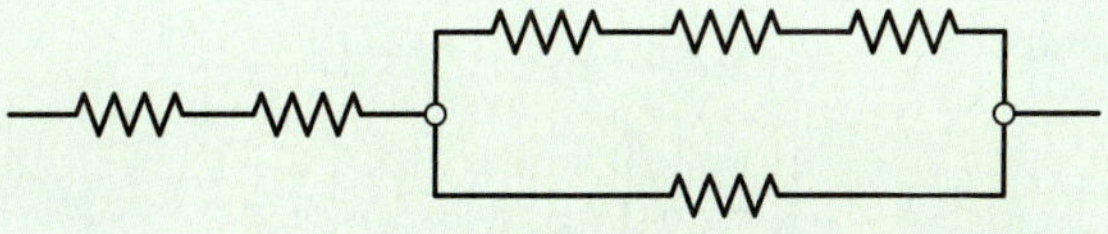

65. (*a*) 750 Ω (*b*) 3.0 V (*c*) The current is 0.020 A down through the 1500 Ω resistor, 0.020 A to the right across the 900 Ω resistor that is along the top wire, 0.010 A down through the 1200 Ω resistor, and 0.010 A downward through both the 900 Ω and the 300 Ω resistors along the far right.

67. $I_1 = 2.0 \times 10^{-2}$ A, $I_2 = 1.5 \times 10^{-2}$ A, $I_3 = 5.0 \times 10^{-3}$ A

69. (*a*) 2.8 Ω (*b*) Let I_n denote the current across resistor number *n*. $I_1 = 5.0$ A, $I_2 = 2.0$ A, $I_3 = 2.0$ A, $I_4 = 1.0$ A, $I_5 = 1.0$ A, and $I_6 = 5.0$ A.

71. 0.085 A

73. The resistance of the entire string is $N\left(\frac{1}{R_b} + \frac{1}{R_a}\right)^{-1}$. If one bulb goes out the remaining bulbs will become dimmer.

75. 17 Ω

77. $I_1 = 0$, $I_2 = 0.67$ A but opposite the direction shown, $I_3 = 1.3$ A, $I_4 = 0.67$ A but opposite the direction shown, and $I_5 = 0.67$ A

79. (*a*) 1.3 A (*b*) 7.0 V

81. (*a*) $P_1 = 16$ W, $P_2 = 11$ W (*b*) $P_{\text{Circuit}} = 27$ W (*c*) $P_1 = 2.6$ W, $P_2 = 3.8$ W, and $P_{\text{Circuit}} = 6.4$ W

83. (*a*) $I_1 = 1.0$ A and $\Delta V = 5.00$ V, $I_2 = I_3 = I_4 = 0.333$ A, and $\Delta V_2 = \Delta V_3 = \Delta V_4 = 1.7$ V (*b*) $P_1 = 5.0$ W, $P_2 = P_3 = P_4 = 0.566$ W (*c*) ϵ_1 supplies a power of 10 W and ϵ_2 uses power at a rate of 3.30 W.

85. The current through all the outer resistors (250 Ω, 100 Ω, 50 Ω, and 200 Ω) is 0.25 A. The current through the center (75 Ω) resistor is zero. $Q_{\text{cap}} = 1.5$ mC

87. The power dissipated is 1.5 kW. Using a higher potential difference means you can deliver the same amount of power to a city at a lower current. Using the lower current means less power is dissipated in the transmission lines leading into the city.

89. Power is delivered by the 12 V battery at a rate of 0.24 W, by the 9 V battery at a rate of 0.14 W, by the two 1.5 V batteries at a rate of 7.5 mW each. The total power delivered by all batteries is 0.39 W. Energy is dissipated in the 300 Ω resistor at a rate of 0.12 W, in the 1000 Ω resistor at a rate of 0.23 W, in the 1200 Ω resistor at a rate of 0.030 W, and in the 600 Ω resistor at a rate of 0.015 W. The total power dissipated by the resistors is 0.39 W. This makes perfect sense, since all the energy provided to the circuit each second by the batteries has to go somewhere. In this case it goes into thermal energy in the resistors.

91. The resistance increases by a factor of 15, or 135 Ω.

93. There may be many correct answers. Examples are electrolytic solutions, solid state ionic conductors, etc.

95. 187 Ω

97. (*a*) 9.0 V (*b*) 18.0 V

99. We would add a resistor in parallel to those already in the circuit. This reduces the overall resistance of the circuit. We would add a resistor of large area like the top resistor.

101. The maximum current you can pull from the battery is 0.10 A. This happens when you fill the gap with a resistor that has such a small resistance that it is practically zero (like adding an ideal conductor). In that case, current would bypass the 100 Ω resistor in parallel with the conductor and the total resistance of the circuit would just be 100 Ω from the resistor that is not in series with anything. The smallest the current could ever be is 0.05 A. This happens when you close the gap with a resistor that has such a huge resistance that current is essentially prohibited from traversing it (or you could just leave the gap there, with nothing closing it). In that case the total resistance of the parallel arrangement would just be 100 Ω, and the total resistance of the circuit would be 200 Ω.

103. Let I_n be the current through resistor R_n. Then $I_{\text{battery}} = I_1 = I_2 = I_7 = 6.1$ A, $I_3 = I_4 = I_5 = 3.0$ A, and $I_6 = 0$. The charge on the 30 μF capacitor is 1.8×10^{-4} C. The charge on the 20 μF capacitor is also 1.8×10^{-4} C.

105. *Principles* equation 31.9 refers to the movement of electrons in a solid. In that case it is an electron that is carrying charge and leading to conduction of a current. In seawater, the particle that carries charge is never a dissociated electron, but rather an entire ion. Even the lightest possible ion (H^+) is about 2000 times heavier than an electron, and the ions in water are typically from salts of much heavier ions. Hence, even if equation 31.9 were valid, it would not be the mass of the electron in the denominator, but the mass of the ion. This leads you to a much lower conductivity.

Chapter 32

1. $B_{rms} = \dfrac{\mu_0 n I_{max}}{\sqrt{2}}$

3. 0.25 s, 0.75 s, 1.25 s, . . .

5. X could certainly contain a resistor, perhaps in series with an inductor or another capacitor. Y could also contain a resistor if there is a source of alternating current maintaining a fixed maximum potential difference.

7. $\dfrac{3}{4}U^E$

9. 4.11 nC

11.

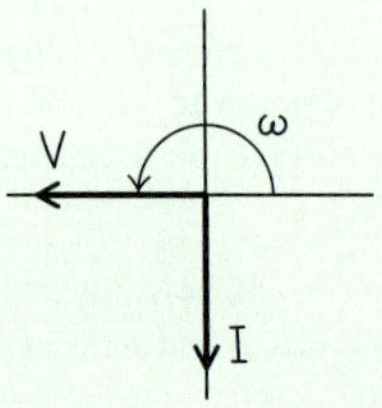

13.

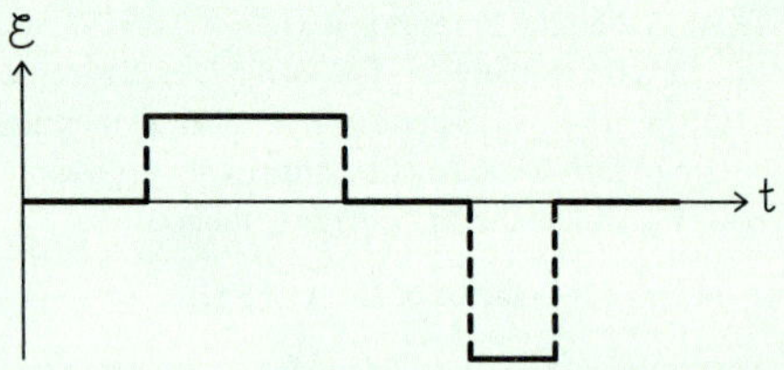

15. The circuit contains only a 9.0 Ω resistor and an AC source operating at a frequency that obeys $f = \left(\frac{1}{8} + n\right)$ Hz, where n is any integer.

17. (*a*) We draw the figure assuming that the capacitor is initially uncharged.

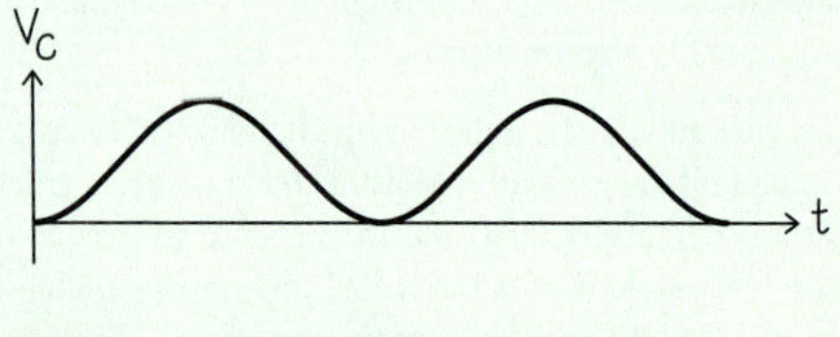

(*b*)

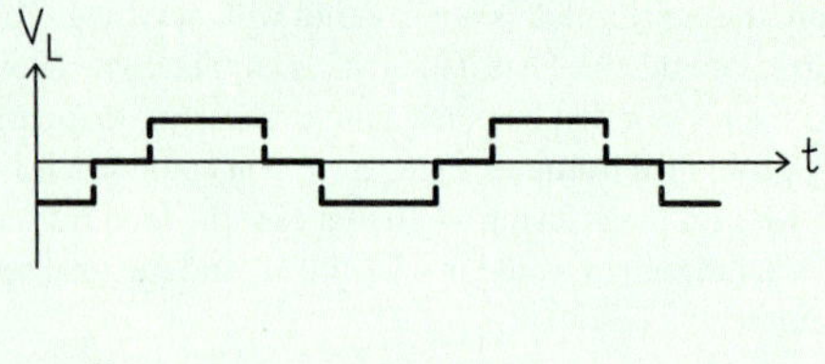

19. 1.2×10^{23}

21. Before doping, there are no free charge carriers in pure silicon (assuming no crystal impurities and very low temperatures). Hence the addition of even a small number of free (conducting) electrons is quite noticeable.

23. (*a*) Either of the doped semiconductors will conduct a current much better than the undoped silicon. (*b*) *n*-type (*c*) None

25. B

27. No

29. No

31. (*a*) B to A (*b*) A to B (*c*) A is *n*-type, and B is *p*-type (*d*) A may contain Phosphorous, and B may contain Boron

33. ABCD, ABC, ABD, ACD, BCD, AC, AD, BC, or BD

35.

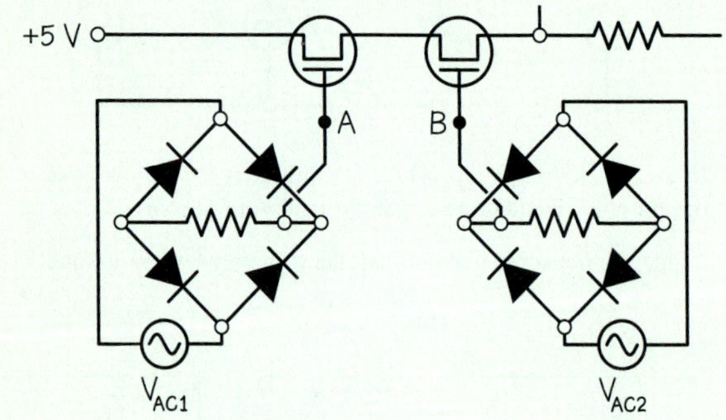

37. 3.3 S^{-1}

39. (*a*) 1.0 A (b) The current amplitude increases linearly with the source frequency.

41. (*a*) 15.2 V (*b*) 3.60 V

43. The device lags behind the source emf (or leading the emf by more than $\pi/2$ radians, but this is less likely).

45. $R = 1.41\ \Omega$ and $\omega = 70.7\ s^{-1}$

47. 4.50 V

49. (*a*) −121 rad, or −69.3° (*b*) $V_C = 2.64$ V, $V_R = 34.9$ V, and $\phi = -0.0756$ rad, or −4.33°

51. 1.56 mH

53. (*a*)

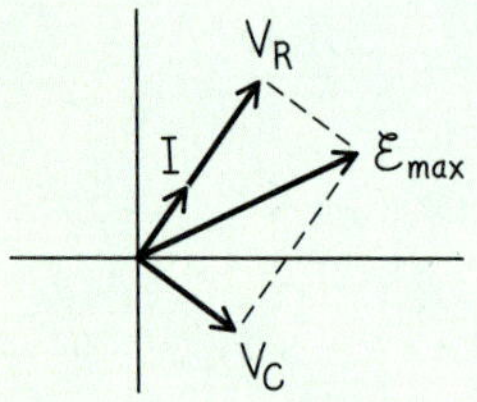

(*b*) −5.95° or −0.104 rad

55. 3.13 H

57. 43 Ω

59. (*a*)

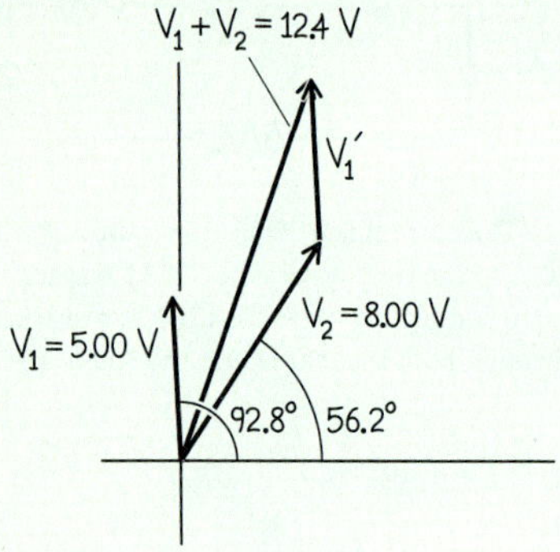

ANSWERS TO QUESTIONS AND PROBLEMS

(*b*) $V = 12.4$ V, $\phi = 41.5°$, $v_{\text{sum}}(t = 0.0500 \text{ s}) = 8.28$ V. These values are in very good agreement with the results from using phasors.

61. $1.0 \times 10^3 \text{ s}^{-1}$

63. 8.7×10^{-6} F

65. $\omega_{0f} = \omega_{0i}$

67. $L = 3.00 \times 10^{-4}$ H and $R = 12.5\ \Omega$

69. (*a*) $5.59 \times 10^3 \text{ s}^{-1}$ (*b*) 6.00 A (c) 4.14 A

71. $C = 2.23 \times 10^{-9}$ F. The radio could be made more selective by lowering the resistance.

73. 50.8 mW

75. 4.00 W

79. $\cos(\phi) = 0.981$, $\phi = -11.3°$, $Z = 102\ \Omega$, $\epsilon_{\text{rms}} = 21.2$ V, $I_{\text{rms}} = 0.208$ A, and $P_{\text{av}} = 4.33$ W

81. (*a*) 6.0 W (*b*) 6.4 W

85.

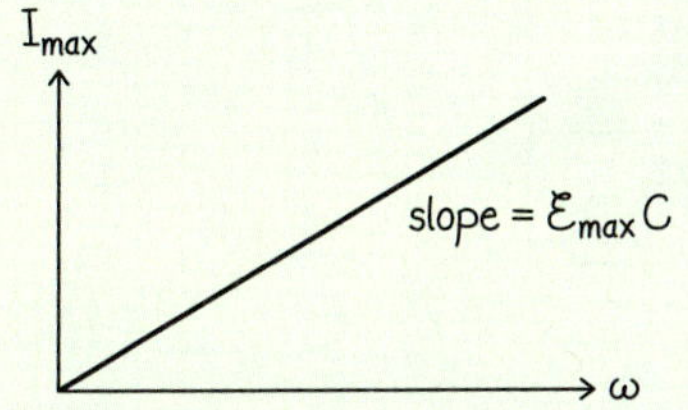

87. (*a*) (A, B) could be (Y, Y), (Y, N), (N, Y), or (N, N). The output is N for all combinations except (Y, Y), for which the output is Y. (b) The possible inputs for (A, B) are the same as in part (a): (Y, Y), (Y, N), (N, Y), or (N, N). Now the output is Y for all combinations except (N, N) for which the output is N.

89. (*a*) $f = 120$ Hz (*b*) $\phi = 85.7°$ or 1.50 radians

91.

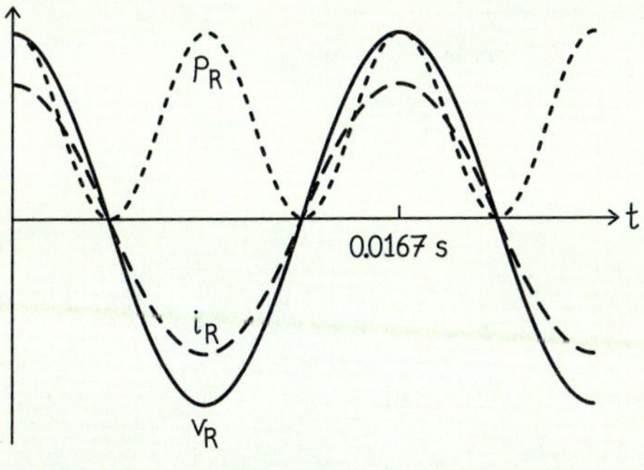

93.

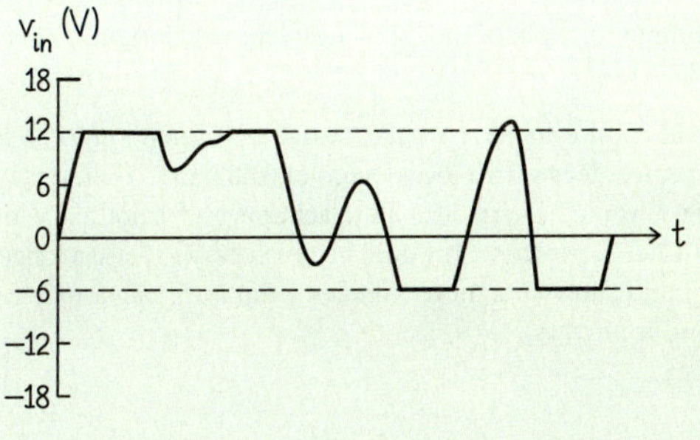

95. You can arrange the diodes and capacitors as shown below. This setup is called a "voltage doubler", or more generally a "voltage multiplier".

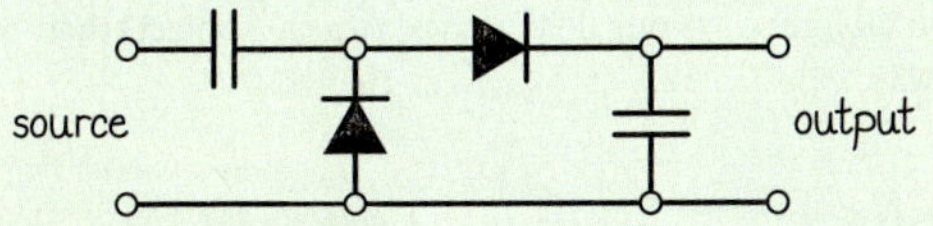

Chapter 33

1. (*a*) Light from all sources (a–h) strikes A. (*b*) Light from six sources (c–h) strikes B.

7. The bright spot would be a circle. The position of the circle may fluctuate as variations in the candle's flame cause the brightest spot to move slightly. The boundary of the circle would not be sharp, as light comes from a 1-3 cm region of flame, rather than a single point source.

9.

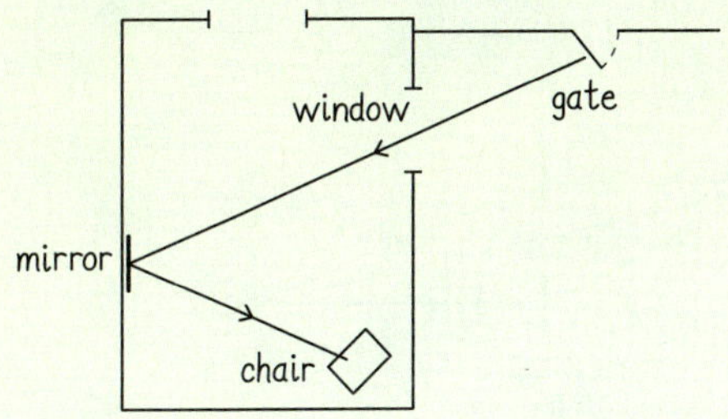

13. Assume you are looking into a mirror at the distant object behind you. Call the distance from you to the distant object d_o, call the distance from you to the mirror d_m, call the height of the distant object h_o, and call the height of the mirror h_m. Then $h_{\text{m,min}} = \dfrac{h_o d_m}{d_m + d_o}$.

15. You could demonstrate the difference between a real image and a virtual image by casting a real image onto a screen. Then look at an object in a mirror and place a screen on the mirror's surface. Note that no visible image appears on the screen. Hence, the image is not being formed at the mirror's surface.

19. The shadow is smaller when the tub is filled with water than when the tub is empty.

21. Shallower

23. Case A: (*a*) Light travels faster in material 2. (*b*) Light originates in material 2. Case B: (*a*) Light travels faster in material 1 (*b*) Light originates in material 2. Case C: (*a*) One cannot tell in which material light moves more quickly from examining a ray that is incident normal to the interface. (*b*) One cannot tell in which material the light originates from examining a ray that is incident normal to the interface.

25.

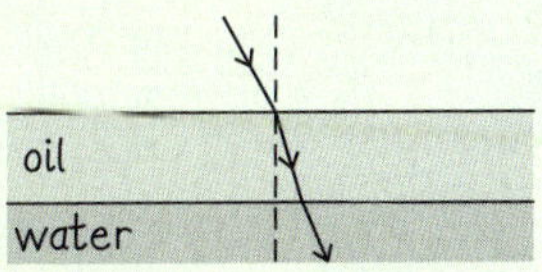

27. The light will pass straight through the vertical edge into the prism. Light cannot undergo total internal reflection when it strikes the diagonal edge. Rather, light will exit the diagonal edge and bend toward the line normal to that diagonal edge. This is shown below.

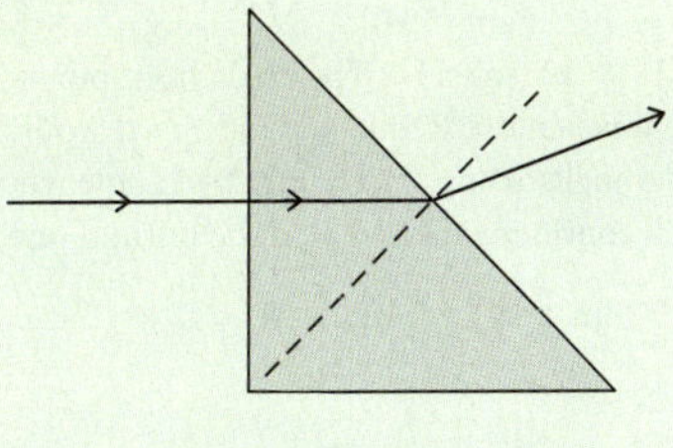

29. Place a second prism next to the first. Invert the second prism, so that its vertex points downward as shown below.

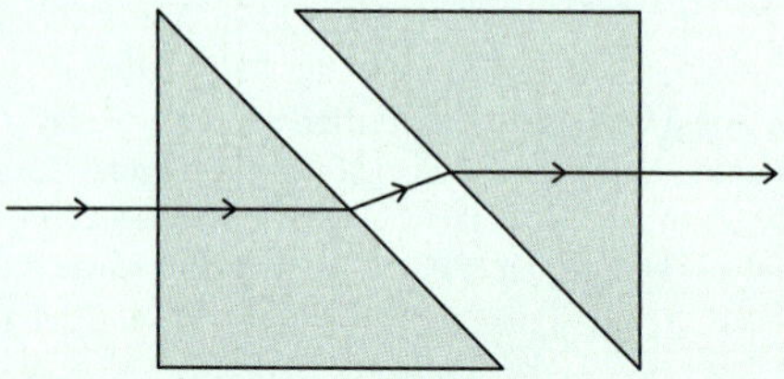

31. (*a*)

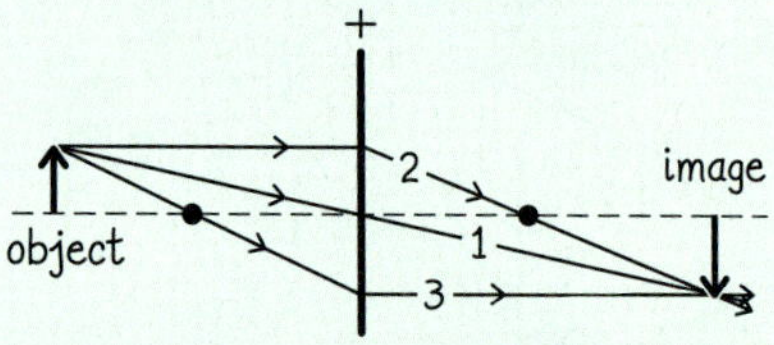

(*b*) Real (*c*) Inverted (*d*) It shrinks.

33. The object is held closer to the lens than the focal point, such that the lens is not able to focus the light down to a single point.

35. The image is on the same side as the object (opposite side from your eyes). If the image is magnified, the lens is converging. If the image is reduced, the lens is diverging.

37. (*a*)

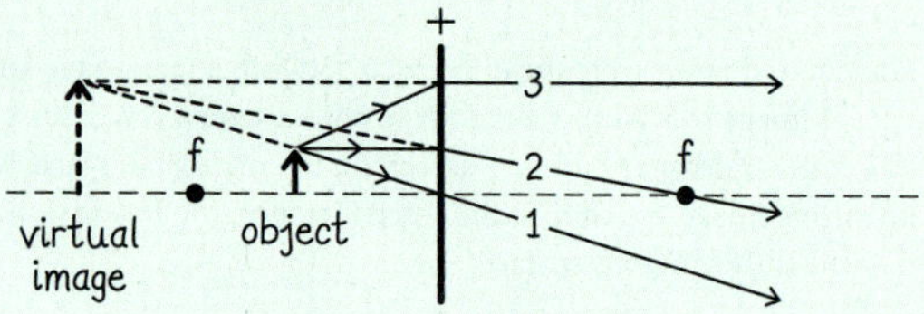

(*b*) Virtual (*c*) Upright (*d*) It becomes larger.

39. (*a*)

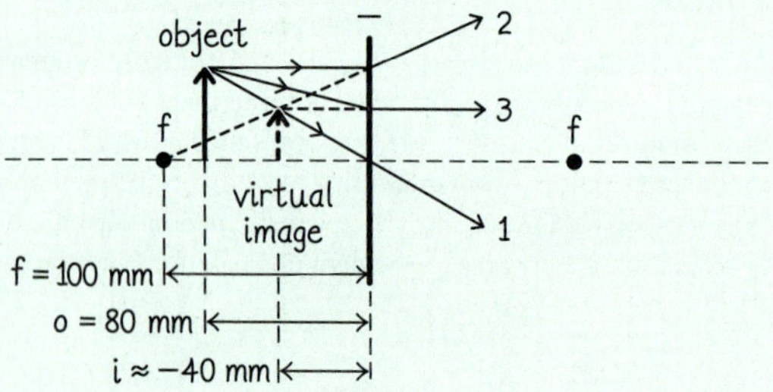

(*b*) Virtual (*c*) Upright (*d*) Smaller than the object

41. $f_{\text{diverging}} = 100$ mm and $f_{\text{converging}} = 200$ mm

43. Diamond

45. $f = 5.66 \times 10^{14}$ Hz and $\lambda = 321$ nm

47. 46.9°

49. (*a*) The wavelength is reduced by 1.333 to $\lambda = 404$ nm. (*b*) The frequency does not change. It remains 5.58×10^{14} Hz. (*c*) The speed is reduced by 1.333 to 2.25×10^8 m/s. (*d*) The angle from normal is reduced to 40.5°. (*e*) The wavelength, frequency, and speed would not be altered by changing the angle of entry. The refracted angle would change to 0°; the light will continue on parallel to the normal line.

51. (*a*) 56.1° (*b*) 53.6° (*c*) 21.7 mm

55. 54°

57. (*a*) $\sin^{-1}(\sqrt{n^2 - 1})$ (*b*) $\sqrt{2}$

59. 3.3 m

61. For a diverging lens, the focal length is negative. Using the lens equation (*Principles* equation 33.16), we can write $\frac{1}{i} = \frac{1}{f} - \frac{1}{o}$. The object distance is always positive. The only way for a real image to be formed is it the image distance is also positive. But clearly both terms on the right hand side of the above equation are negative. Hence $\frac{1}{i} < 0$, from which it immediately follows that $i < 0$. Since the image distance is always negative for a diverging lens, a diverging lens cannot form a real image.

63. 105 mm

65. 50 mm

67. (*a*) −240 mm (*b*) 1.60

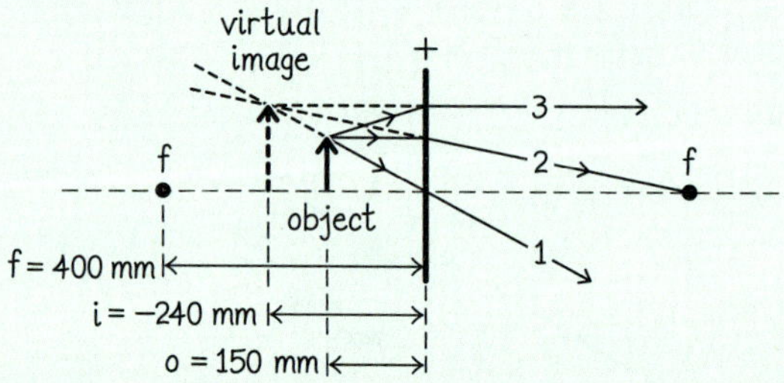

69. (*a*) −143 mm (*b*) 0.714 (*c*)

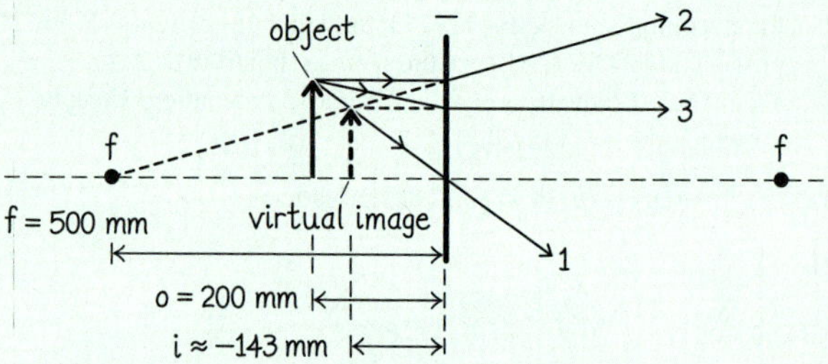

71. 1.5 diopters

73. (*a*) $\frac{dM_\theta}{M_\theta + 1}$ (*b*) $\frac{d}{M_\theta + 1}$

75. (*a*) 0.64 m (*b*) −5.1 (*c*) Inverted

77. The image will be virtual, inverted, and enlarged.

79. (*a*) 181 mm to the right of the right-most lens (*b*) Upright (*c*) Real (*d*) 0.625

81. This would require an objective lens with a focal length of 999.6 mm and an eyepiece lens with a focal length of 0.383 mm. The eyepiece focal length would be very difficult to achieve, and is not likely to be found in a home telescope. It would be much easier to use a longer telescope, and allow for a more complex setup involving multiple lenses and/or mirrors.

83. 333 mm

85. The image appears 392 mm behind mirror. But because the image is reduced, it occupies a much smaller fraction of your field of view than the car itself would. The images occupies roughly the same angular spread in your field of view as a car (object) that is 51 m away.

87. (*a*) 6.09 mm (*b*) Real (*c*) Inverted (*d*)

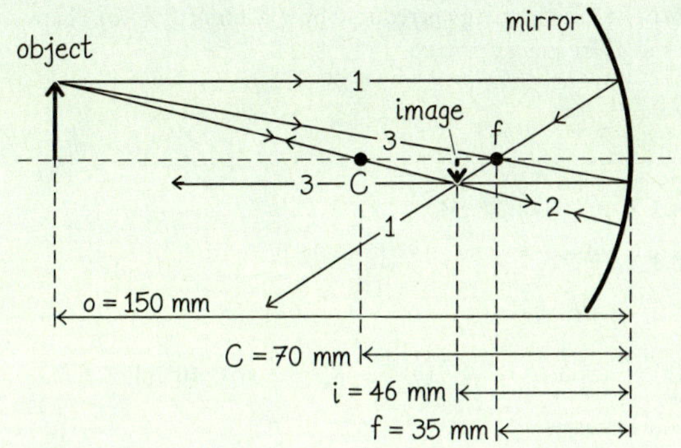

89. 0.40 m

91. 1.00 MM

95.

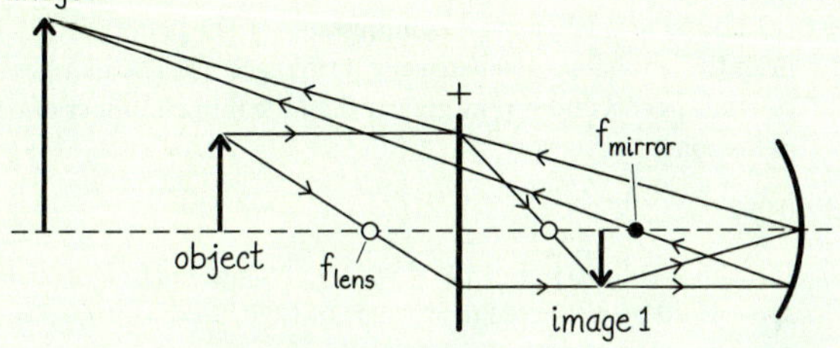

97. $R_2/R_1 = 3$

99. 470 mm

101. 0.10 m

103. 1.2

105. 200 mm

107. (*a*) 80 mm (*b*) 1.4

109. (*a*) Converging (*b*) Neither converging nor diverging (*c*) Diverging

111. You can only see light when it is reflected off of some object. In the air, there is no mechanism by which the laser light can be reflected to your eye. However, if you sprinkle powder into the path of the beam, the particles can scatter/reflect light to your eyes and the beam becomes partly visible.

113. 0.021 s

115. (*a*) This could be used to form a real image that is the same size as the original object. (*b*) This could be used to make light emanating from a points source travel in a straight line without spreading. (*c*) This could be used to focus light down to a single point, such as for heating a small region of space.

117. If the image is upright the object is 33 mm from the lens. If the image is inverted, the object is 67 mm

119. (*a*) Dispersion (*b*) It can be minimized, but not removed completely. (*c*) No

121.

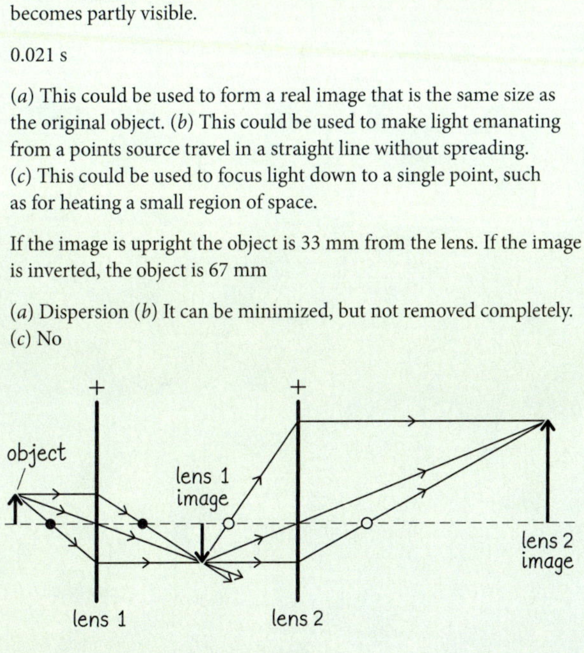

123. (*a*) 43.0° (*b*) 24.4°

125. Use a converging lens with a focal length of 33.48 mm. Place the lens a distance 33.64 mm in front of the film holder. This will cause an image to be cast on the screen 7.316 m in front of the lens, and the image will be three times larger than your initial attempt.

Chapter 34

1. There are many possible answers. Any material consisting of tiny pinholes or gaps is acceptable, such as the fabric of an umbrella. One can also observe diffraction at very sharp edges, such as that of a razor blade.

3. The wave properties of light predict that the center of the pattern should be bright. Since all rays diffracting around the edge of the circular obstacle are equidistant from the center, all the waves should strike the center in phase, and therefore interfere constructively.

5. Sound is also a wave and diffracts around barriers in a fashion similar to light. But the relevant wavelengths of sound waves and light waves are different by many orders of magnitude. Diffraction of a light wave around an object as thick as a tree is negligible, whereas the diffraction of sound around a tree is considerable.

7. 17.1°

9. The criteria to determine the highest order bright fringe visible is $m \leq \frac{w}{\lambda N}$. Then the total number would be $2m_{\max} + 1$.

13. (*a*) 33.0°
(*b*) $\sin^{-1}\left(\frac{\lambda}{d_{\text{orig}} + A\sin(\omega t)}\right)$

$$= \sin^{-1}\left(\frac{546 \times 10^{-9}\text{ m}}{(1.0 \times 10^{-6}) + (0.25 \times 10^{-6})\sin((100\text{ s}^{-1})t)}\right)$$

(*c*) $\frac{3\pi}{200}$ s, which is approximately 4.7×10^{-2} s (*d*) $\frac{\pi}{200}$ s, which is approximately 1.6×10^{-2} s (*e*) Only A, λ, and d_{orig} affect the values of the maximum and minimum angles, although ω affects the time at which these maximum values are achieved.

15. Farther apart

17. 8.717×10^{-10} m

19. 10^{-35} m

21. Yes, the electron has a nonzero chance of reaching the detector in all cases. But the chance may be very small if the obstacle is wide.

23. 6.65×10^{-15} m

25. 5.20×10^3 m/s

27. 5.84×10^{20}

29. 1.34×10^{16} photons per second, assuming that all the power refers to the output power as opposed to internal power use from the batteries, and assuming the photons are not scattered or absorbed by any medium on their way to the wall.

33. (*a*) 3 bright fringes (*b*) 0.165 m

35. 423 nm

37. $\Delta y_{1g} = 0.173$ m, $\Delta y_{2g} = 0.434$ m, $\Delta y_{1b} = 0.135$ m, and $\Delta y_{1g} = 0.307$ m

39. (*a*) $\Delta\theta = 0.11°$ (*b*) No

41. 0.154 m

43. 1.04 m

45. 7.942×10^3 slits

49. 608 nm and 434 nm

53. 2.37

55. 9.5×10^{-5} m

57. 6.25 m

59. 0.10 m

61. Many numerical answers are possible depending on the exact wavelength of light, the width of the door, and the distance from the door to the far wall of the cabin. But the crux of the answer is that the pattern will be extremely small, too small to observe with the naked eye, and too small to observe even with instruments if light from other sources is present. One would not even call this a diffraction pattern. As an example, let us assume that the light has a wavelength of 700 nm, that the door is 1.0 m wide, and that the distance from the door to the far wall of your cabin is 10 m. This would result in a first order dark fringe that is 7.0 μm from the central bright spot.

63. 5.3 mm

65. (*a*) 1.39×10^{-5} m (*b*) 78.4°

69. 226 nm

71. 4.03 μm

73. The minimum resolvable angular separation is between $(1.48 \times 10^{-2})°$ and $(2.47 \times 10^{-4})°$, depending on the wavelength being used.

75. 2.59 mm

77. $y_{r,\text{water}} = \dfrac{y_{r,\text{vac}}}{n} = \dfrac{y_{r,\text{vac}}}{1.33}$

81. 5.82 m

83. Yes, the lights are likely to be resolvable.

85. (*a*) The kinetic energy is reduced by a factor of 1/4. (*b*) There is no change; frequency is fixed.

87. 2.5 pm

89. 304 nm

91. 4.5×10^{-19} J or 2.8 eV

93. 8.8×10^{-19} J

95. 1.22×10^{15} Hz

97. (*a*) $\dfrac{\lambda_e}{\lambda_{ph}} = 3.49 \times 10^{-3}$ (*b*) $E_{ph}/K_e = 2.06 \times 10^5$, photon has more energy.

101. 0.0459°

103. 600 nm

107. 5.2×10^{-5} m

109. (*a*) The pattern will appear compressed. (*b*) The pattern will become brighter, but will be geometrically unchanged. (*c*) The number of photons per second is now greater than the initial number of photons per second.

111. 0.097

113. (*a*) 2.65×10^7 m/s (*b*) 2.74×10^{-11} m (*c*) Yes, the first order bright spot would be diffracted to an angle of 12.9°. So the diffraction pattern should be quite easily detected.

117. 3.75×10^{-4} mm

119. No, the width must be much greater than 1 m to get close to utility with the visible spectrum.

Credits

COVER PHOTO Franklin Kappa

CHAPTER 1 **P. 1** Ted Kinsman/Science Source.

CHAPTER 2 **P. 16** Tomohiro Ohsumi/Bloomberg/Getty Images.

CHAPTER 3 **P. 34** Fahad Shadeed/Reuters; **p. 42** Library of Congress.

CHAPTER 4 **P. 51** Astronaut-EVA/NASA.

CHAPTER 5 **P. 69** Gemasolar solar thermal plant, owned by Torresol Energy ©SENER.

CHAPTER 6 **P. 86** Simon McComb/Getty Images.

CHAPTER 7 **P. 105** Todd Taulman/Shutterstock.

CHAPTER 8 **P. 124** Claus Mikosch/Shutterstock.

CHAPTER 9 **P. 145** Jonathan Blair/Corbis.

CHAPTER 10 **P. 165** Patrick Eden/Alamy.

CHAPTER 11 **P. 189** David Samuel Robbins/Corbis.

CHAPTER 12 **P. 209** Jack Fields/Corbis.

CHAPTER 13 **P. 232** NASA/HubbleSite; **p. 243** NASA.

CHAPTER 14 **P. 248** Erich Lessing/Art Resource.

CHAPTER 15 **P. 267** Tom Wang/Shutterstock.

CHAPTER 16 **P. 286** Peo Quick/Matton Collection/Corbis.

CHAPTER 17 **P. 303** Josef Hanus/Shutterstock.

CHAPTER 18 **P. 317** Sharon Day/Shutterstock.

CHAPTER 19 **P. 338** David Hare/Alamy.

CHAPTER 20 **P. 355** CCat82/Shutterstock.

CHAPTER 21 **P. 373** David Gould/Getty Images.

CHAPTER 22 **P. 393** valdezrl/Fotolia.

CHAPTER 23 **P. 409** John W. Belcher.

CHAPTER 24 **P. 427** Fermilab.

CHAPTER 25 **P. 449** Scott Sinklier/Alamy.

CHAPTER 26 **P. 467** Dave Lindblom; **p. 471** Matarese Photos—Used under a Creative Commons license. http://creativecommons.org/licenses/by/3.0/deed.en

CHAPTER 27 **P. 483** Yamada Taro/Getty Images.

CHAPTER 28 **P. 503** Mircea RUBA/Shutterstock.

CHAPTER 29 **P. 526** Bosca78/Getty Images.

CHAPTER 30 **P. 548** ALMA (ESO/NAOJ/NRAO)/L. Calçada (ESO)/H. Heyer (ESO)/H. Zodet (ESO).

CHAPTER 31 **P. 566** Powered by Light/Alan Spencer/Alamy.

CHAPTER 32 **P. 590** kubais/Shutterstock.

CHAPTER 33 **P. 612** Erich Lessing/Art Resource.

CHAPTER 34 **P. 635** David Palau/Shutterstock.

Unit conversion factors

Length

1 in. = 2.54 cm (defined)

1 cm = 0.3937 in.

1 ft = 30.48 cm

1 m = 39.37 in. = 3.281 ft

1 mi = 5280 ft = 1.609 km

1 km = 0.6214 mi

1 nautical mile (U.S.) = 1.151 mi = 6076 ft = 1.852 km

1 fermi = 1 femtometer (fm) = 10^{-15} m

1 angstrom (Å) = 10^{-10} m = 0.1 nm

1 light − year (ly) = 9.461×10^{15} m

1 parsec = 3.26 ly = 3.09×10^{16} m

Volume

1 liter (L) = 1000 mL = 1000 cm^3 = 1.0×10^{-3} m^3
= 1.057 qt (U.S.) = 61.02 $in.^3$

1 gal (U.S.) = 4 qt (U.S.) = 231 $in.^3$ = 3.785 L = 0.8327 gal (British)

1 quart (U.S.) = 2 pints (U.S.) = 946 mL

1 pint (British) = 1.20 pints (U.S.) = 568 mL

1 m^3 = 35.31 ft^3

Speed

1 mi/h = 1.4667 ft/s = 1.6093 km/h = 0.4470 m/s

1 km/h = 0.2778 m/s = 0.6214 mi/h

1 ft/s = 0.3048 m/s = 0.6818 mi/h = 1.0973 km/h

1 m/s = 3.281 ft/s = 3.600 km/h = 2.237 mi/h

1 knot = 1.151 mi/h = 0.5144 m/s

Angle

1 radian (rad) = 57.30° = 57°18'

1° = 0.01745 rad

1 rev/min (rpm) = 0.1047 rad/s

Time

1 day = 8.640×10^4 s

1 year = 365.242 days = 3.156×10^7 s

Mass

1 atomic mass unit (u) = 1.6605×10^{-27} kg

1 kg = 0.06852 slug

1 metric ton = 1000 kg

1 long ton = 2240 lbs = 1016 kg

1 short ton = 2000 lbs = 909.1 kg

1 kg has a weight of 2.20 lb where $g = 9.80\ m/s^2$

Force

1 lb = 4.44822 N

1 N = 10^5 dyne = 0.2248 lb

Energy and work

1 J = 10^7 ergs = 0.7376 ft · lb

1 ft · lb = 1.356 J = 1.29×10^{-3} Btu = 3.24×10^{-4} kcal

1 kcal = 4.19×10^3 J = 3.97 Btu

1 eV = 1.6022×10^{-19} J

1 kWh = 3.600×10^6 J = 860 kcal

1 Btu = 1.056×10^3 J

Power

1 W = 1 J/s = 0.7376 ft · lb/s = 3.41 Btu/h

1 hp = 550 ft · lb/s = 746 W

1 kWh/day = 41.667 W

Pressure

1 atm = 1.01325 bar = 1.01325×10^5 N/m^2 = 14.7 $lb/in.^2$ = 760 torr

1 $lb/in.^2$ = 6.895×10^3 N/m^2

1 Pa = 1 N/m^2 = 1.450×10^{-4} $lb/in.^2$

Periodic Table of the Elements

Number of protons → 29
Symbol for element → Cu
63.546 ← Average atomic mass in g/mol. For elements having no stable isotope, value in parentheses is approximate atomic mass of longest-lived isotope.

Period \ Group	1	2	3	4	5	6	7	8	9	10	11	12	13	14	15	16	17	18
1	1 **H** 1.008																	2 **He** 4.003
2	3 **Li** 6.941	4 **Be** 9.012											5 **B** 10.811	6 **C** 12.011	7 **N** 14.007	8 **O** 15.999	9 **F** 18.998	10 **Ne** 20.180
3	11 **Na** 22.990	12 **Mg** 24.305											13 **Al** 26.982	14 **Si** 28.086	15 **P** 30.974	16 **S** 32.065	17 **Cl** 35.453	18 **Ar** 39.948
4	19 **K** 39.098	20 **Ca** 40.078	21 **Sc** 44.956	22 **Ti** 47.867	23 **V** 50.942	24 **Cr** 51.996	25 **Mn** 54.938	26 **Fe** 55.845	27 **Co** 58.933	28 **Ni** 58.693	29 **Cu** 63.546	30 **Zn** 65.409	31 **Ga** 69.723	32 **Ge** 72.64	33 **As** 74.922	34 **Se** 78.96	35 **Br** 79.904	36 **Kr** 83.798
5	37 **Rb** 85.468	38 **Sr** 87.62	39 **Y** 88.906	40 **Zr** 91.224	41 **Nb** 92.906	42 **Mo** 95.94	43 **Tc** (98)	44 **Ru** 101.07	45 **Rh** 102.906	46 **Pd** 106.42	47 **Ag** 107.868	48 **Cd** 112.411	49 **In** 114.818	50 **Sn** 118.710	51 **Sb** 121.760	52 **Te** 127.60	53 **I** 126.904	54 **Xe** 131.293
6	55 **Cs** 132.905	56 **Ba** 137.327	71 **Lu** 174.967	72 **Hf** 178.49	73 **Ta** 180.948	74 **W** 183.84	75 **Re** 186.207	76 **Os** 190.23	77 **Ir** 192.217	78 **Pt** 195.078	79 **Au** 196.967	80 **Hg** 200.59	81 **Tl** 204.383	82 **Pb** 207.2	83 **Bi** 208.980	84 **Po** (209)	85 **At** (210)	86 **Rn** (222)
7	87 **Fr** (223)	88 **Ra** (226)	103 **Lr** (262)	104 **Rf** (261)	105 **Db** (262)	106 **Sg** (266)	107 **Bh** (264)	108 **Hs** (269)	109 **Mt** (268)	110 **Ds** (271)	111 **Rg** (272)	112 **Uub** (285)	113 **Uut** (284)	114 **Uuq** (289)	115 **Uup** (288)	116 **Uuh** (292)	117 **Uus** (294)	118 **Uuo**

Lanthanoids	57 **La** 138.905	58 **Ce** 140.116	59 **Pr** 140.908	60 **Nd** 144.24	61 **Pm** (145)	62 **Sm** 150.36	63 **Eu** 151.964	64 **Gd** 157.25	65 **Tb** 158.925	66 **Dy** 162.500	67 **Ho** 164.930	68 **Er** 167.259	69 **Tm** 168.934	70 **Yb** 173.04
Actinoids	89 **Ac** (227)	90 **Th** (232)	91 **Pa** (231)	92 **U** (238)	93 **Np** (237)	94 **Pu** (244)	95 **Am** (243)	96 **Cm** (247)	97 **Bk** (247)	98 **Cf** (251)	99 **Es** (252)	100 **Fm** (257)	101 **Md** (258)	102 **No** (259)